DICTIONARY OF MATHEMATICS

Volume 1

DICTIONARY OF MATHEMATICS

IN FOUR LANGUAGES *English*
German
French
Russian

Volume 1

COMPILED BY
PROF. DR. RER. NAT. HABIL. GÜNTHER EISENREICH
Leipzig (German Democratic Republic)
and
DIPL.-MATH. RALF SUBE
Berlin (German Democratic Republic)

ELSEVIER SCIENTIFIC PUBLISHING COMPANY
Amsterdam – Oxford – New York
1982

Expert: Dr. G. Paulin

Published in coedition with VEB Verlag Technik, Berlin
This book is exclusively distributed in all non-socialist countries
with the exception of the Federal Republic of Germany, West-Berlin,
Austria and Switzerland by
Elsevier Scientific Publishing Company
Molenwerf 1
P. O. Box 211, 1000 AE Amsterdam, The Netherlands

Distributors for the United States and Canada
Elsevier North-Holland, Inc.
52 Vanderbilt
New York, NY 10017

Library of Congress Cataloging in Publication Data
Eisenreich, Günther.
Dictionary of mathematics.
Includes index.
1. Mathematics – Dictionaries – Polyglot.
2. Dictionaries, Polyglot. I. Sube, Ralf. II. Title.
QA5.E35 1981 510'.3 81-17269
ISBN 0-444-99706-7 (set) AACR2

Printed in the German Democratic Republic by Grafischer Großbetrieb Völkerfreundschaft Dresden

PREFACE

The unique feature of this four-language dictionary is that every term has been assigned to a subject category. In addition, in many instances the term is followed by an explanatory note. This extra information is necessary because of the complex problem of synonyms and homonyms. An important criterion of whether a technical multilingual dictionary is easy to use is how quickly and reliably the required term can be found. Subject categories prove particularly helpful in this connection. It thereby becomes easier to achieve accurate translation, because the correct term can quickly be selected and the incorrect term avoided.

Subject categories tend to be fairly broad: fundamentals of mathematics, logic, algebra, topology, mathematical analysis, calculus, statistics, geometry. Further subdivisions are used in cases where a large vocabulary exists for a particular subject category, e. g. group theory within algebra, differential equations within mathematical analysis, elementary geometry within geometry. As a rule, the category is only as specific as is necessary. A particular term may have the same meaning in various subject areas. However, we strongly advise against generalizing without making sure that the generalization is correct, because synonyms may differ from one area to another. Synonyms indicated for a given term are real synonyms and are interchangeable. Synonyms given first are in general those most frequently referred to in the literature or those recommended in encyclopaedias; less current, older or obsolete terms are separated from the former by / /. If there are shades of meaning depending on the context, the terms are separated by a semicolon and, if necessary, a pertinent comment is made. Unless they are homonymous in all languages, homonyms in different subject areas are given as separate entries, except that, when the term deviates in only one language, the entries are grouped together to save space, separated by a semicolon in that one language, and the subject category is given. If there are several homonyms within the same subject area, an explanation or short definition is given to avoid ambiguity.

A table of contents is provided on the section dividers preceding each language section. The list of abbreviations used for the subject categories appears in the "Directions for the user of the dictionary" on p. 8.

Synonyms pose an especially delicate problem in mathematics. There is scarcely any standardization of terminology. Mathematicians, with their sense of tradition, usually adhere to the terminology of standard texts (often valid for decades), but new and often superfluous terms are coined in practical applications and even in translations. Mathematical schools sometimes use different expressions for one and the same term, but also the same expression for different terms. The result is a multitude of synonyms and homonyms running parallel with each other which even specialists can scarcely distinguish between. By compiling all traceable synonyms, we have tried to define the terms as clearly as possible.

Mathematics is a very extensive branch of science whose terminology cannot be fully covered in a four-language dictionary of manageable size. We were obliged to make a very careful selection of the terms we had collected. Thus, the subject of computer mathematics and its specific methods have been completely dispensed with, while more specific applications of mathematics in natural sciences and technology have largely been omitted. The emphasis of this dictionary is on "pure" mathematics. Logic, topology and algebra have been covered in particularly great detail. Verbs and adjectives could be included in exceptional cases.

In most cases, however, the respective nouns are recorded. For adjectives, it is scarcely possible to give generally accepted equivalents, since the translation largely depends on the pertaining noun. That is why compound adjectives have always been given priority. Further compounds can, to some extent, be formed analogously, provided that the same subject area is concerned, but here too it is absolutely necessary to make sure in each case that the word formation is correct.

We would like to thank the publisher's staff and all those who gave valuable advice for their assistance, and express our gratitude to the former for their careful technical preparation of the manuscript for printing. Without their aid it would have been impossible to publish this book.

Suggestions for the improvement of subsequent editions will be appreciated and should be addressed to the publisher.

The Authors.

DIRECTIONS FOR THE USER OF THE DICTIONARY

1. Examples of alphabetical arrangements of terms

algebra
algebraic adjunct
algebraically equivalent set
algebraic variety
algebra of logic

point diagram
point-direction equation
pointed object
pointlike set
point mass

Algebra gleichen Typs
algebraische Struktur
Algebraizität
Algebra mit Involution
Algebra ohne Zentrum

System abgeschlossener Mengen
systematische Probe
systematischer Bruch
systematische Stichprobe
System der Restklassen

condition minimale
conditionnel
conditionnelle inverse
conditionnel strict
condition normée

théorèmes de Tauber
théorèmes d'intersection
théorème sémantique
théorèmes limites
théorème spectral

граф без циклов
график
граф интервалов
графическое вычисление
граф сравнимости

функция Гегенбауэра
β-функция Геделя
L-функция Гекке
η-функция Дедекинда
E-функция Зигеля

2. Signs and abbreviations

( ) Jacobian (elliptic) amplitude = Jacobian amplitude *or* elliptic amplitude
[ ] absolute conic [section] = absolute conic *or* absolute conic section
/ deflate/to = to deflate
raison de symétrie / par = par raison de symétrie
// unusual terms are given after this double diagonal stroke
‹ › subject category indication or explanation
s. = see
s. a. = see also

3. Used subject category indications

AB	algebraic, additive, and analytic number theory	IE	integral equations
AG	algebraic geometry	IG	integral geometry
AL	algebra	IN	mathematical instruments
AN	analysis	IT	integral transforms
AP	almost periodic functions	IV	invariant theory
AR	elementary arithmetics	LA	lattice theory
AT	algebraic topology	LI	limitation
AX	approximation theory	LO	mathematical logic
AY	analytical geometry	MD	matrices and determinants
CA	category theory	ME	measure theory
CS	convex sets	MM	metamathematics
CT	combinatorial analysis	NO	nomography
DE	differential equations	NT	number theory
DG	differential geometry	NU	numerical mathematics
DI	differential and integral calculus	PG	mathematical programming (optimization)
DS	descriptive geometry	PJ	projective geometry
EG	elementary geometry	PO	potential theory
ER	theory of errors	RE	theory of representations
FA	functional analysis	RF	real-valued functions
FD	calculus of finite differences	SE	set theory
FO	foundations of mathematics	SG	synthetic geometry
FT	theory of complex functions	SP	stochastic processes
FU	special functions	SS	sequences, series, products
GE	geometry	TA	theory of automata
GN	general	TG	theory of games
GP	graph theory	TO	topology
GR	group theory	UA	universal algebra
GU	geometry of numbers	VA	calculus of variations
HA	homological algebra	VT	calculus of vectors and tensors

ENGLISH

Foundations of Mathematics

metamathematics · axiomatics
mathematical logic
propositional calculus
predicate calculus
non-classical logics
set theory
relations
cardinal and ordinal numbers
combinatorial analysis
category theory

Algebra

binary systems
group theory (general group theory, topological groups, Lie groups)
groupoids, semigroups, etc.
theory of representations
rings, fields, algebras, modules, ideals, valuation theory
linear algebra
matrices and determinants, vector spaces
theory of algebraic forms · invariant theory
lattice theory
universal algebra
algebraic geometry
algebraic curves, surfaces, varieties
theory of schemes
enumerative geometry
homological algebra
K-theory
number theory
elementary arithmetics
algebraic, analytic, additive number theory
prime number theory
diophantine equations
geometry of numbers
continued fractions

Topology

algebraic topology
homology theory, cohomology theory
homotopy theory
knot theory
fibre bundles
theory of sheaves
graph theory
set topology
topological spaces
dimension theory

Analysis

differential and integral calculus
sequences, series, products · limitation
function theory
potential theory
differential equations · boundary value problems · eigenvalue problems
calculus of finite differences
measure theory and theory of integration · real-valued functions
almost periodic functions
functional analysis · integral transforms
integral equations
calculus of variations
special functions
approximation theory
numerical mathematics (methods)
nomography

Stochastics

theory of errors
stochastic processes
applications (basic mathematical terms)

Mathematical Programming · Theory of Games

Geometry

elementary geometry
analytical geometry
synthetic geometry
special geometries
projective geometry
descriptive geometry
differential geometry
calculus of vectors and tensors
Riemannian geometry
integral geometry · convex sets

Mathematical Instruments

Theory of Automata

A

No.	English	German	French	Russian
	abac <IN>	*s.* C 10		
	abac <NO>	*s.* N 299		
	abacus <IN>	*s.* C 10		
A 1	**abbreviated discriminatory analysis** <ST>	verkürzte Diskriminanzanalyse *f*	analyse *f* discriminatoire abrégée	сокращенный дискриминантный анализ
	abbreviated Gauss method <AL, NU, ST>	*s.* D 891		
	abbreviated multiplication <AR, NU>	*s.* A 47		
	abbreviated subtraction <AR, NU>	*s.* A 48		
	Ab-category <CA>	*s.* P 1169		
A 2	**Abel['s] asymptotic method** <IT>	Abelsche Asymptotik *f*, Asymptotik von Abelschem Charakter	méthode *f* asymptotique d'Abel	асимптотика (асимптотический метод) Абеля
	Abel['s] differential equation <DE>	*s.* A 4		
A 3	**Abel-Dini theorem** <SS>	Satz *m* von Abel und Dini, Abel-Dinischer Satz	théorème *m* d'Abel-Dini	теорема Абеля-Дини
A 4	**Abel['s] equation,** Abel['s] differential equation <of the first *or* second kind> <DE>	Abelsche Differentialgleichung (Gleichung) *f* <erster (1.) *oder* zweiter (2.) Art>	équation *f* [différentielle] d'Abel <de première *ou* seconde espèce>	[дифференциальное] уравнение Абеля <первого *или* второго рода>
	Abel['s] equation <IE>	*s.* A 34		
A 5	**Abel-Goncharov interpolation series** <AX, FD, NU>	Abel-Gontscharowsche Interpolationsreihe *f*, Interpolationsreihe von Abel-Gontscharow	série *f* d'interpolation d'Abel-Gontcharov	интерполяционный ряд Абеля-Гончарова
A 6	**abelian algebra** <in Galois theory>	abelsche Algebra *f*	algèbre *f* abélienne	абелева алгебра
A 7	**abelian algebra,** medial algebra <AL>	bisymmetrische Algebra *f*	algèbre *f* bisymétrique	медиальная алгебра
	abelian binary composition <AL>	*s.* C 1257		
A 8	**Abelian differential,** differential <*e. g.:* of the second *or* third kind> <in an algebraic function field> <AL>	[Abelsches] Differential *n*, <*z. B.:* 2., [von] zweiter, von der zweiten *oder* 3., [von] dritter, von der dritten Gattung>	différentielle *f* [abélienne] <*par exemple:* de deuxième *ou* troisième espèce>	дифференциал [Абеля], абелев дифференциал <*например:* второго (II) *или* третьего (III) рода>
A 9	**Abelian differential** <*e. g.:* of the second *or* third kind> <on a Riemannian surface> <FT>	Abelsches (gewöhnliches) Differential *n*, meromorphes Differential ersten (1.) Grades <*z. B.:* 2., [von] zweiter, von der zweiten *oder* 3., [von] dritter, von der dritten Gattung>	différentielle *f* abélienne <*par exemple:* de deuxième *ou* troisième espèce>	дифференциал Абеля, абелев дифференциал <*например:* второго (II) *или* третьего (III) рода>
A 10	**Abelian differential of the first kind,** differential of the first kind <AL>	ganzes Differential *n*, Differential von der ersten (1.) Gattung	différentielle *f* [abélienne] de première espèce	дифференциал [Абеля] первого рода
A 11	**Abelian differential of the first kind,** differential of the first kind, holomorphic (analytical) differential <on a Riemannian surface> <FT>	[Abelsches] Differential *n* erster (1.) Gattung, holomorphes (analytisches) Differential	différentielle *f* [abélienne] de première espèce, différentielle holomorphe (analytique)	дифференциал [Абеля] первого рода, абелев дифференциал первого (I) рода, голоморфный (аналитический) дифференциал
A 12	**Abelian equation** <in Galois' theory> <AL>	abelsche Gleichung *f*	équation *f* abélienne	абелево уравнение
A 13	**abelian extension [field],** abelian field extension <AL>	abelsche Erweiterung (Körpererweiterung) *f*, abelscher Erweiterungskörper *m*	extension *f* abélienne	абелево расширение [поля]
A 14	**abelian extension** <of a group> <GR, NT>	abelsche Erweiterung *f* <GR, NT>; abelsche Aufspaltung *f* <NT>	extension *f* abélienne	абелево расширение
A 15	**abelian field** <AL>	abelscher Körper *m*	corps *m* abélien	абелево поле
	abelian field extension <AL>	*s.* A 13		
A 16	**Abelian function,** abelian function <FT>	Abelsche Funktion (Transzendente) *f*, abelsche Funktion *f*	fonction *f* abélienne	абелева функция
	Abelian function <FT>	*s.* S 1352		
A 17	**Abelian function field** <FT>	Abelscher (abelscher) Funktionenkörper *m*	corps *m* de fonctions abélien	абелево поле функций
A 18	**abelian functor** <CA>	abelscher Funktor *m*	foncteur *m* abélien	абелев функтор
	abelian group <GR>	*s.* C 1259		
A 19	**abelian group of equal rank** <GR>	ranggleiche abelsche Gruppe *f*	groupe *m* abélien d'égal rang	абелева группа одинакового ранга
A 20	**abelian group of finite rank** <GR>	abelsche A_2-Gruppe *f*, abelsche Gruppe *f* endlichen Ranges	groupe *m* abélien de rang fini	абелева A_2-группа, абелева группа конечного ранга
	abelian group of finite type <GR>	*s.* F 285		
A 21	**abelian groupoid,** commutative groupoid <AL>	abelsches (kommutatives) Gruppoid *n*, kommutatives Operativ *n*	groupoïde *m* abélien (commutatif)	абелев (коммутативный) группоид
	abelian groupoid <AL>	*s.* M 352		
	abelian half-algebra <UA>	*s.* C 1260		
	Abelian identity <SS>	*s.* A 32		

A 22	**Abelian integral** <of the first, second *or* third kind> <AL>	Abelsches Integral *n* <erster (1.), zweiter (2.) oder dritter (3.) Gattung *oder* von der ersten, zweiten oder dritten Gattung>	intégrale *f* abélienne <de première, deuxième *ou* troisième espèce>	интеграл Абеля, абелев (алгебраический) интеграл <первого (I), второго (II) *или* третьего (III) рода>
	abelianizing <GR>	*s.* F 477		
A 23	**Abelianizing functor,** factor-commutator functor <CA> ┌<GR>	Funktor *m* „Abelsch-machen", Funktor Kommutator-Faktorgruppe	foncteur *m* abélisation	функтор взятия фактор-группы по коммутанту
	Abelian linear group	*s.* S 2479		
A 24	**abelian polynomial** <in Galois theory> <AL>	abelsches Polynom *n*	polynôme *m* abélien	абелев многочлен
A 25	**abelian quasi[-]group,** medial quasi[-]group<AL>	bisymmetrische (abelsche) Quasigruppe *f*	quasigroupe *m* bisymétrique	медиальная (абелева) квазигруппа
A 26	**Abelian scheme** <AG>	abelsches Schema *n*	[S-]schéma *m* abélien	абелева [S-]схема
A 27	**abelian semigroup,** commutative semigroup, Abelian system <AL>	abelsche (kommutative) Halbgruppe *f*	demi-groupe *m* abélien (commutatif), monoïde *m* abélien (commutatif)	абелева (коммутативная) полугруппа, абелева система, коммутативный моноид
A 28	**Abelian summation** <LI>	Abelsche Summation *f*	sommation *f* abélienne	абелево суммирование
	Abelian system <AL>	*s.* A 27		
A 29	**Abelian theorem** <AB>	Satz *m* vom Abelschen Typus	théorème *m* de type abélien	теорема абелева типа, абелева теорема
	Abelian theorem <FT>	*s.* A 42		
A 30	**abelian tower,** normal series with abelian factors <GR>	Normalreihe *f* mit abelschen Faktoren	suite *f* de composition à facteurs abéliens	абелева башня <подгрупп>, абелев ряд
A 31	**abelian variety,** Abelian variety <AG>	abelsche (Abelsche) Mannigfaltigkeit *f*	variété *f* abélienne	абелево многообразие
A 32	**Abel['s] identity,** Abelian identity, Abel['s] [partial] summation formula; Abel['s] method of summation by parts <SS>	Abelsche partielle Summation *f*, Abelsche Umformung (Transformation, Identität) *f*	transformation *f* d'Abel, transformation *f* abélienne	преобразование Абеля, суммирование по частям
A 33	**Abel['s] inequality** <SS>	Abelsche Ungleichung *f*	inégalité *f* d'Abel	неравенство Абеля
A 34	**Abel['s] integral equation,** Abel['s] equation <IE>	Abelsche Integralgleichung *f*	équation [intégrale] d'Abel	[интегральное] уравнение Абеля
	Abel['s] interpolation series <AX>	*s.* A 39		
A 35	**Abel['s] lemma** <SS>	erster Abelscher Satz *m*	lemme *m* d'Abel	первая теорема Абеля
	Abel-limit <LI>	*s.* A 491		
	Abel-limitable sequence <LI>	*s.* A 492		
A 36	**Abel['s] [limitation] method,** Abel['s] method of limitation, *A* method <for divergent sequences> <LI>	Abelsches Limitierungsverfahren *n*, *A*-Verfahren *n*	méthode *f* de limitation d'Abel, méthode d'Abel	метод [образования обобщенного предела] Абеля-Пуассона, *A*-метод
	Abel['s] method <LI>	*s.* A 40		
	Abel['s] method of limitation <LI>	*s.* A 36		
	Abel['s] method of summation <LI>	*s.* A 40		
	Abel['s] method of summation by parts <SS>	*s.* A 32		
	Abel['s] partial summation formula <SS>	*s.* A 32		
A 37	**Abel-Poisson method, Abel-Poisson summation [method],** Poisson['s] method [of summation], Poisson['s] summation [method] <for Fourier series> <SS>	Poissonsche (Abel-Poissonsche) Summation *f*, Poissonsches Verfahren (Summationsverfahren) *n*	méthode *f* d'Abel-Poisson, méthode [de sommation] de Poisson	метод Абеля-Пуассона (суммирования Абеля-Пуассона, Пуассона, Абеля в применении к рядам Фурье)
A 38	**Abel['s] polynomial,** binomial polynomial <AL>	Abelsches (binomisches) Polynom *n*	polynôme *m* d'Abel, polynôme binôme	многочлен Абеля, биномиальный многочлен
	Abel-Ruffini theorem <AL>	*s.* T 254		
A 39	**Abel['s] series,** Abel['s] interpolation series <AX>	Abelsche Interpolationsreihe *f* (Reihe *f*)	série *f* [d'interpolation] d'Abel	[интерполяционный] ряд Абеля
	Abel-sum <LI>	*s.* A 1126		
	Abel summability <LI>	*s.* A 1127		
	Abel summable series <LI>	*s.* A 1128		
	Abel['s] summation formula <SS>	*s.* A 32		
A 40	**Abel['s] summation method,** Abel['s] method [of summation], *A* method <for divergent series> <LI>	Abelsches Summierungsverfahren *n*, *A*-Verfahren *n*	méthode *f* [de sommation] d'Abel	метод Абеля-Пуассона, метод суммирования [расходящихся рядов] Абеля-Пуассона, метод суммирования Абеля, *A*-метод
A 41	**Abel['s] test** <for convergence> <SS>	Abelsches Kriterium (Konvergenzkriterium) *n*, Abels Kriterium	critère *m* (règle *f*, théorème *m*) d'Abel, critère de convergence d'Abel	признак (критерий) [сходимости] Абеля
A 42	**Abel['s] theorem,** Abelian theorem <on Abelian integrals> <FT>	Abelsches Theorem *n*, Theorem von Abel	théorème *m* d'Abel	теорема Абеля
A 43	**Abel['s] theorem, Abel['s] theorem on power series, Abel['s] theorem on continuity up to the circle of convergence** <SS>	Abelscher Grenzwertsatz (Konvergenzsatz, Stetigkeitssatz) *m*, <erster und zweiter> Satz *m* von Abel, <erstes und zweites> Theorem *n* von Abel, Abelscher	théorème *m* d'Abel	теорема Абеля [о непрерывности], <первая и вторая> теоремы Абеля, // вторая теорема Абеля

		Satz <im Reellen oder Komplexen>; erweiterter Abelscher Grenzwertsatz (Konvergenzsatz, Stetigkeitssatz) <im Komplexen>, // zweiter Satz von Abel, zweites Theorem von Abel		
A 44	**Abel['s] theorem** <on multiplication of series> <SS>	Satz *m* von Abel <über die Multiplikation von Reihen>, Abelscher Satz	théorème *m* d'Abel	теорема Абеля
A 45	**aberration centre** <DG>	Aberrationszentrum *n*	centre *m* d'aberration, centre de l'aberration	центр аберрации
A 46	**abnormal distribution,** non-normal distribution <ST>	nichtnormale Verteilung *f*	distribution *f* non normale	ненормальное (анормальное) распределение, отклоняющееся от нормального распределение
A 47	**abridged multiplication,** abbreviated (short) multiplication <AR, NU>	abgekürzte Multiplikation *f*	multiplication *f* abrégée	сокращенное умножение; умножение чисел с отбрасыванием излишних десятичных знаков
	abridged notation <GN>	*s.* C 2259		
A 48	**abridged subtraction,** abbreviated (short) subtraction <of numbers> <AR, NU>	abgekürzte Subtraktion *f*	soustraction *f* abrégée	сокращенное вычитание
A 49	**abridged symbolic notation** <AL>	Gleichungssymbolik *f*, abgekürzte symbolische Bezeichnung *f* <Plücker>	symbolisation *f* des équations, notation *f* abrégée	сокращенное символическое обозначение
	abs <AN>	*s.* A 131		
A 50	**abscissa of absolute convergence** <IT, SS>	Abszisse *f* der absoluten Konvergenz, Abszisse absoluter Konvergenz, absolute Konvergenzabszisse *f*	abscisse *f* de convergence absolue	абсцисса абсолютной сходимости
A 51	**abscissa of [simple] convergence** <IT, SS>	Konvergenzabszisse *f*, Abszisse *f* der Grenzgeraden	abscisse *f* de convergence	абсцисса [простой] сходимости
A 52	**abscissa of summability** <IT, SS>	Summabilitätsabszisse *f*	abscisse *f* de sommabilité	абсцисса суммируемости
A 53	**abscissa of uniform convergence** <IT, SS>	gleichmäßige Konvergenzabszisse *f*	abscisse *f* de convergence uniforme	абсцисса равномерной сходимости
A 54	**absence of correlation,** non-correlation <ST>	Unkorreliertheit *f*, Nichtkorreliertheit *f*, Nullkorrelation *f*	absence *f* de corrélation, non-corrélation *f*	отсутствие (недостаток) корреляции
A 55	**absence of failures** <ST>	Ausfallfreiheit *f*	absence *f* de défaillances	безотказность
A 56	**absolute** <of an element of a lattice-ordered group> <AL>	Betrag *m*	valeur *f* absolue	абсолютное значение
A 57	**absolute** <in the Π*n*> <PJ>	absolutes Gebilde *n*, Fundamentalgebilde *n*, Absolutgebilde *n*	absolu *m*	абсолют
	absolute additivity <AN, SE>	*s.* C 2556		
A 58	**absolute circle** <PJ>	absoluter Kreis *m*, Fundamentalkreis *m*	cercle *m* absolu	абсолютная окружность
A 59	**absolute class field,** class field in Hilbert's sense, Hilbert['s] class field, maximal unramified abelian extension <AB>	absoluter (Hilbertscher) Klassenkörper *m*, maximale unverzweigte abelsche Erweiterung *f*	corps *m* de classes absolu de Hilbert, extension *f* abélienne non ramifiée maximale, corps de Hilbert	гильбертово поле классов, абсолютное поле классов
A 60	**absolute class group,** absolute ideal class group <AB>	absolute Klassengruppe *f*	groupe *m* de classes absolu	абсолютная группа классов
A 61	**absolute cohomology** <AT>	absolute Kohomologie *f*	cohomologie *f* absolue	абсолютные когомологии
	absolute complement <SE>	*s.* C 1358		
A 62	**absolute completeness** <LO>	Vollständigkeit *f* im Absolutsinn, absolute Vollständigkeit	complétude *f* absolue	абсолютная полнота
A 63	**absolute conic [section],** absolute (infinite) spherical circle, spherical circle <AY, PJ>	absoluter Kegelschnitt *m*, uneigentlicher (unendlich ferner, unendlichferner, imaginärer) Kugelkreis *m*, Kugelkreis, Maßkegelschnitt *m*	absolu *m*, courbe *f* ombilicale, ombilicale *f*, cercle *m* de l'infini, cercle sphérique de (à) l'infini, cercle sphérique, conique *f* absolue, section *f* conique absolue	абсолют, абсолютное коническое сечение, сферическая окружность
A 64	**absolute convergence,** normal convergence <in a Banach space> <FA>	absolute (normale) Konvergenz *f*	convergence *f* absolue (normale)	абсолютная (нормальная) сходимость
A 65	**absolute convergence** <SS>	absolute Konvergenz *f*	convergence *f* absolue	абсолютная сходимость
A 66	**absolute curvature vector** <of a curve *or* Riemannian manifold> <DG>	absoluter Krümmungsvektor *m*	vecteur *m* de courbure absolue	вектор абсолютной кривизны
A 67	**absolute degree** <of a field> <AL>	Absolutgrad *m*	degré *m* absolu	абсолютная степень
A 68	**absolute different** <AL>	Absolutdifferente *f*	différente *f* absolue	абсолютная дифферента
	absolute differential calculus <DG, VT>	*s.* R 979		
	absolute differentiation <DG. VT>	*s.* R 979		

A 69	**absolute dimension** <of a field> <AL>	arithmetische Dimension *f* <Kähler>, Stufe *f*	dimension *f* absolue	абсолютная размерность
A 70	**absolute dimension** <of a field, contrary to relative dimension> <AL>	absolute Dimension *f*	degré *m* absolu de transcendance	абсолютная степень трансцендентности
A 71	**absolute discriminant** <AB>	Absolutdiskriminante *f*	discriminant *m* absolu	абсолютный дискриминант
A 72	**absolute geometry** <according to J. Bolyai, without parallel axiom> <GE>	absolute Geometrie *f* <nach J. Bolyai>	géométrie *f* absolue <dite de J. Bolyai>	абсолютная геометрия <по Я. Больяй, Бойаи>
	absolute geometry <DG>	*s.* I 845		
A 73	**absolute homology group** <AT>	absolute Homologiegruppe *f*	groupe *m* d'homologie absolu	абсолютная группа гомологий
A 74	**absolute homotopy group** <AT>	absolute Homotopiegruppe *f*	groupe *m* d'homotopie absolu	абсолютная гомотопическая группа
A 75	**absolute Hurewicz isomorphism theorem** <AT>	absoluter Hurewiczscher Isomorphiesatz *m*	théorème *m* absolu d'Hurewicz	абсолютная теорема Гуревича об изоморфизме
	absolute ideal class group <AB>	*s.* A 60		
A 76	**absolute idele class group** <AB>	absolute Idelklassengruppe *f*	groupe *m* de classes d'idèles absolu	абсолютная группа классов иделей
A 77	**absolute inequality,** unconditional inequality <AN>	identische (unbedingte, absolute) Ungleichung *f* <bei allen Einsetzungen erfüllt>	inégalité *f* inconditionnelle	безусловное (тождественное, абсолютное) неравенство
A 78	**absolute isomorphism,** isomorphism over the prime field <AL>	absoluter Isomorphismus *m*, Isomorphismus über dem Primkörper	isomorphisme *m* absolu (sur le sous-corps premier)	абсолютный изоморфизм
A 79	**absolute limitability** <SS>	absolute Limitierbarkeit *f*	limitabilité *f* absolue	абсолютная лимитируемость
A 80	**absolutely abelian field** <AL>	absolut-abelscher Körper *m*	corps *m* cyclique (abélien) absolu	абсолютно абелево поле
A 81	**absolutely additive content,** totally additive content <ME>	volladditiver Inhalt *m*	contenu *m* absolument (complètement) additif	вполне аддитивная протяженность
	absolutely additive function <AN>	*s.* C 2566		
A 82	**absolutely additive measure,** σ-additive (sigma-additive) measure, countably (completely) additive measure <ME>	vollständig additives Maß *n*, σ-additives (sigma-additives) Maß	mesure *f* complètement (dénombrablement) additive	вполне аддитивная мера
	absolutely additive set function <AN>	*s.* C 2566		
A 83	**absolutely algebraic field,** algebraic field over the prime field <AL>	absolut algebraischer Körper *m*	corps *m* absolument algébrique, corps algébrique sur le sous-corps premier	абсолютно алгебраическое поле
A 84	**absolutely algebraic field of finite degree** <AL>	endlich-algebraischer (algebraischer, über seinem Primkörper endlich-erzeugbarer algebraischer) Körper *m*	corps *m* algébrique de degré fini	алгебраическое поле конечной степени, конечно порожденное алгебраическое поле
A 85	**absolutely closed Hausdorff space,** H-closed space, Hausdorff-closed space <TO>	absolut abgeschlossener Hausdorffscher Raum *m*, H-abgeschlossener [Hausdorffscher] Raum, T_2-abgeschlossener T_2-Raum *m*	espace *m* séparé absolument fermé	абсолютно замкнутое отделимое пространство, H-замкнутое [топологическое] пространство, вполне замкнутое пространство
A 86	**absolutely compact set** <TO>	absolut (in sich) kompakte Menge *f* <Fréchet>	ensemble *m* compact en soi	компактное в себе множество
A 87	**absolutely complete system** <LO>	deduktiv und syntaktisch vollständiges System *n*	système *m* absolument complet	абсолютно полная система
A 88	**absolutely continuous distribution** <ST>	kontinuierliche (absolut stetige) Verteilung *f*, Wahrscheinlichkeitsverteilung *f* mit Dichtefunktion	distribution *f* absolument continue	абсолютно непрерывное распределение
A 89	**absolutely continuous function,** completely continuous function <RF>	absolut[ ]stetige Funktion *f*, totalstetige Funktion	fonction *f* absolument (complètement) continue	абсолютно (вполне) непрерывная функция
A 90	**absolutely continuous measure** <ME>	absolutstetiges Maß *n*	mesure *f* absolument continue	абсолютно непрерывная мера
A 91	**absolutely continuous part,** completely continuous part <RF>	absolut[ ]stetiger Teil *m*, totalstetiger Teil; regulärer Teil <einer Mengenfunktion>	partie *f* absolument (complètement) continue	абсолютно (вполне) непрерывная часть
A 92	**absolutely continuous transformation** <AN>	totalstetige (absolutstetige) Transformation *f*	transformation *f* absolument continue	абсолютно непрерывное преобразование
	absolutely convergent continued fraction <NT>	*s.* U 61		
	absolutely convergent improper integral <DI>	*s.* A 93		
A 93	**absolutely convergent integral,** absolutely convergent improper integral <DI>	absolut (unbedingt) konvergentes [uneigentliches] Integral *n*	intégrale *f* [impropre] absolument convergente	абсолютно сходящийся [несобственный] интеграл
A 94	**absolutely convergent series** <SS>	absolut konvergente Reihe *f*	série *f* absolument (normalement) convergente	абсолютно сходящийся ряд
A 95	**absolutely convex hull,** convex circled hull <in a linear space> <FA>	absolut[ ]konvexe Hülle *f*, ausgeglichene konvexe Hülle	enveloppe *f* convexe équilibrée (disquée)	абсолютно (закругленная) выпуклая оболочка

No.	English	German	French	Russian
	absolutely convex set <FA>	*s.* C 2385		
A 96	**absolutely discontinuous function,** completely discontinuous function <RF>	total (ganz) unstetige Funktion *f*	fonction *f* totalement discontinue	вполне прерывная функция
A 97	**absolutely existential sentence** <LO>	unbedingte Existenzaussage *f*	proposition *f* existentielle inconditionnée	неусловное частное высказывание
A 98	**absolutely flat ring** <AL>	absolut flacher Ring *m*	anneau *m* absolument plat, anneau régulier	абсолютно плоское кольцо, регулярное кольцо <в смысле фон Неймана>
A 99	**absolutely free algebra,** Peano['s] algebra <UA>	absolut (anarchisch) freie Algebra *f*, [verallgemeinerte] Peano-Algebra *f*, $K(\tau)$-freie Algebra	algèbre *f* péanienne	пеановская алгебра
	absolutely Galois field <AL>	*s.* F 304		
A 100	**absolutely hereditary class** <of algebraic systems> <UA>	absolut erbliche Klasse *f*	classe *f* absolument héréditaire	абсолютно наследственный класс
A 101	**absolutely integrable** <DI>	absolut integrierbar	intégrable en module, absolument intégrable	абсолютно интегрируемый, интегрируемый по модулю
A 102	**absolutely irreducible character** <of a representation> <AL, RE>	[absolut] irreduzibler Charakter *m*	caractère *m* absolument irréductible	абсолютно неприводимый характер
A 103	**absolutely irreducible representation** <of an algebra, group *or* semigroup> <AL, RE>	absolut irreduzible Darstellung *f*	représentation *f* absolument simple (irréductible)	абсолютно неприводимое (простое) представление
A 104	**absolutely irreducible variety** <Zariski>, variety <Weil>, absolute variety <AG>	absolut irreduzible Mannigfaltigkeit *f*, unteilbare Vielfältigkeit *f* <van der Waerden>, absolut irreduzible Varietät *f*, absolute Varietät *f*	variété *f* absolue, variété, variété absolument irréductible, variété indivisible	абсолютное многообразие
A 105	**absolutely limitable sequence** <SS>	absolut limitierbare Folge *f*	suite *f* absolument limitable	абсолютно лимитируемая последовательность
	absolutely locally normal variety <AG>	*s.* N 666		
	absolutely monotone function <RF>	*s.* C 1490/1		
	absolutely monotone sequence <FD, SS>	*s.* C 1492		
	absolutely monotonic function <RF>	*s.* C 1490/1		
	absolutely monotonic sequence <FD, SS>	*s.* C 1492		
A 106	**absolutely normal number** <NT>	absolut normale Zahl *f*	nombre *m* absolument normal	абсолютно нормальное число
	absolutely normal variety <AG>	*s.* N 666		
	absolutely open formula <LO>	*s.* A 108		
A 107	**absolutely prime ideal** <AL>	absolutes Primideal *n*	idéal *m* absolument premier	абсолютный простой идеал
A 108	**absolutely quantifier-free formula,** absolutely open formula <LO>	absolut quantifikatorenfreier Ausdruck *m*	formule *f* absolument ouverte	абсолютно бескванторная формула
	absolutely semi-additive [set] function <AN>	*s.* C 2569		
A 109	**absolutely semisimple algebra** <AL>	absolut halbeinfache Algebra *f*	algèbre *f* absolument semi-simple	абсолютно полупростая алгебра
A 110	**absolutely semisimple representation** <RE>	absolut vollständig reduzible Darstellung *f*	représentation *f* absolument semi-simple	абсолютно полупростое представление
A 111	**absolutely simple group** <AG>	absolut einfache Gruppe *f*	groupe *m* algébrique absolument simple	абсолютно простая группа
A 112	**absolutely summable sequence** <SS>	absolut summierbare Folge *f*	suite *f* absolument sommable	абсолютно суммируемая последовательность
A 113	**absolutely unbiased estimator** <ST>	absolut erwartungstreue (unverzerrte, unverfälschte, biasfreie) Schätzfunktion (Schätzung, Punktschätzung) *f*	estimateur *m* absolument sans biais	абсолютно несмещенная функция оценки, абсолютно несмещенная оценка
A 114	**absolutely unramified extension** <AL>	absolut[ ]unverzweigte Erweiterung *f*	extension *f* absolument non ramifiée	абсолютно неразветвленное расширение
A 115	**absolute maximum,** maximum in the large, [global] maximum, maximum (largest) value <of a function> <DI>	globales Maximum *n*, Maximum im Großen, [absolutes] Maximum, absoluter Maximalwert *m*, größter Wert *m*	maximum *m* absolu (au sens large, global), maximum	абсолютный максимум, максимум в большом (целом), [глобальный] максимум
A 116	**absolute minimal model** <AG>	absolutes minimales Modell *n*	modèle *m* minimal absolu	абсолютная (абсолютно) минимальная модель
A 117	**absolute minimum,** minimum in the large, [global] minimum, minimum (lowest, least, smallest) value <of a function> <DI>	globales Minimum *n*, Minimum im Großen, [absolutes] Minimum, absoluter Minimalwert *m*, kleinster Wert *m*	minimum *m* absolu (au sens large), minimum [global]	абсолютный минимум, минимум в большом (целом), [глобальный] минимум
A 118	**absolute moment** <of order *k*, *k*-th> <ST>	absolutes Moment *n* <der Ordnung *k*, *k*-tes>	moment *m* absolu <d'ordre *k*, *k*-ième>	абсолютный момент <порядка *k*, *k*-й>
	absolute monotonicity <RF>	*s.* C 1525		
	absolute monotony <RF>	*s.* C 1525		

	absolute *n*-circuit <AT>	*s.* N 63		
A 119	**absolute neighbourhood** <TO>	absolute Umgebung *f*	partie *f* ouverte contenant le point donné	абсолютная окрестность
A 120	**absolute neighbourhood retract** <TO>	absoluter Umgebungsretrakt *m*, *R*-Menge *f*	rétracte *m* absolu de voisinage	абсолютный окрестностный ретракт
A 121	**absolute norm** <AL>	Absolutnorm *f*, absolute Norm *f*	norme *f* absolue	абсолютная норма
A 122	**absolute number** <AL>	konkrete Zahl *f* <wie 2,π usw., kein Buchstabe>	nombre *m* absolu	конкретное число <выраженное цифрами и арифметическими знаками, в отличие от буквенных алгебраических обозначений>
A 123	**absolute number** <the sign being omitted> <AR>	absolute Zahl *f*	nombre *m* absolu (arithmétique)	арифметическое число
	absolute number <AR, NU>	*s.* A 154		
A 124	**absolute oriented homology group** <AT>	orientierte absolute Homologiegruppe *f*	groupe *m* d'homologie absolue orientée	абсолютная группа ориентированных гомологий
	absolute parallelism <DG>	*s.* T 120		
A 125	**absolute permutation** <CT>	absolute Permutation *f*	permutation *f* absolue (discordante, sans rencontre)	абсолютная перестановка
	absolute property <DG>	*s.* I 849		
A 126	**absolute quadric** <PJ>	absolute Quadrik *f*	ombilicale *f*, quadrique *f* absolue	абсолютная квадрика (поверхность второго порядка)
A 127	**absolute ramification index** <of a prime divisor *or* prime ideal> <AB>	Absolutordnung *f* <Primdivisor *oder* Primideal>; Absolutverzweigungsordnung *f* <Primideal>	indice *m* absolu de ramification, ordre *m* de ramification absolu	абсолютный индекс ветвления, абсолютный порядок
	absolute semi-additivity <AN>	*s.* C 2560		
A 128	**absolute singular homology group** <AT>	singuläre absolute Homologiegruppe *f*	groupe *m* d'homologie singulier absolu	абсолютная группа сингулярных гомологий
	absolute spherical circle <AY, PJ>	*s.* A 63		
A 129	**absolute system of neighbourhoods** <TO>	absolutes Umgebungssystem *n*	système *m* de voisinages absolu	абсолютная система окрестностей
	absolute term <AL>	*s.* C 2113		
	absolute term <AL, AN, SS>	*s.* C 2114		
A 130	**absolute value** <AL>	[multiplikative] Bewertung *f*	valeur *f* absolue	абсолютное значение, норма, мультипликативное нормирование
A 131	**absolute value,** modulus, module, abs <of a real *or* complex number>; magnitude, numerical value <of a real number> <AN>	Betrag *m*, Absolutbetrag *m*, absoluter Betrag, Absolutwert *m* <einer reellen *oder* komplexen Zahl>; Modul *m*, Norm *f* <einer komplexen Zahl>	valeur *f* absolue, abs, module *m* <d'un nombre réel *ou* complexe>; norme *f* <d'un nombre complexe>; valeur arithmétique <d'un nombre réel>	абсолютная величина, модуль, абсолютное значение <действительного *или* комплексного числа>
A 132	**absolute value,** modulus <of an element in a partially ordered vector space> <FA>	Absolutbetrag *m*	module *m*	модуль
	absolute value <VT>	*s.* M 24		
	absolute value / in <AL, AN>	*s.* T 25		
A 133	**absolute value sign, |** <GN>	Betragsstrich *m*, Absolutstrich *m*, |	signe *m* de valeur absolue, |	знак модуля, |
	absolute variation <AN>	*s.* T 701		
	absolute variety <AG>	*s.* A 104		
A 134	**absolute zero-divisor, absolute zero divisor** <AL>	Totalnullteiler *m*	diviseur *m* de zéro total	полный делитель нуля
	absorbant set <GP>	*s.* D 887		
	absorbent set <FA>	*s.* A 136		
A 135	**absorbing barrier** <ST>	Absorptionsschirm *m*	barrière *f* absorbante	поглощающий экран
A 136	**absorbing set,** absorbent set <FA>	absorbierende Menge *f*	ensemble *m* absorbant, partie *f* absorbante	поглощающее множество
A 137	**absorbing state** <of a Markov chain> <SP>	absorbierender Zustand *m*	état *m* absorbant	поглощающее состояние, особое состояние
A 138	**absorption law,** law of absorption <LA>	Verschmelzungsgesetz *n*, Absorptionsgesetz *n*	loi *f* (axiome *m*) d'absorption, absorption *f*, identité *f* d'absorption	закон поглощения (абсорбции, абсорбирования)
A 139	**absorption law,** elimination law <LO>	Absorptionsgesetz *n*	loi *f* d'absorption, simplification *f*, absorption *f*	закон поглощения (элиминации)
A 140	**absorption of a set** <by a set> <FA>	Absorbieren *n* einer Menge <durch eine Menge>	absorption *f* d'un ensemble <par un autre>	поглощение множества <множеством>
A 141	**absorption probability** <ST>	Absorptionswahrscheinlichkeit *f*	probabilité *f* d'absorption	вероятность поглощения
A 142	**abstract** <as a term> <FO>	Abstraktion *f*, Abstraktum *n*	abstrait *m*	абстракция, отвлеченный термин
	abstract algebra <UA>	*s.* U 311		
A 143	**abstract algebraic geometry** <AG>	abstrakte algebraische Geometrie *f*, arithmetische Geometrie	géométrie *f* algébrique abstraite, géométrie arithmétique	абстрактная алгебраическая геометрия, арифметическая геометрия
A 144	**abstract automaton** <TA>	abstrakter Automat *m*	automate *m* abstrait	абстрактный автомат
A 145	**abstract category,** semigroupoid <CA>	abstrakte Kategorie *f*	catégorie *f* abstraite	абстрактная категория

No.	English	German	French	Russian
A 146	**abstract complex** <of a skeleton complex> <AT>	absoluter (abstrakter) Komplex *m*, abstrakter Zellkomplex *m*, Zell[en]komplex *m*	complexe *m* abstrait	абсолютный комплекс, комплекс в широком смысле [слова]
	abstract complex <AT>	*s.* 1. C 1597; 2. S 1157		
	abstract complex <HA>	*s.* C 981		
	abstract coset <AL>	*s.* F 415		
	abstract function <AN, FA>	*s.* M 96		
A 147	**abstract graph,** graph <GP>	abstrakter Graph *m*, Graph	graphe *m* abstrait, graphe	абстрактный граф, граф
A 148	**abstract group** <AL, GR>	abstrakte Gruppe *f*, Klasse *f* isomorpher Gruppen	groupe *m* abstrait	абстрактная группа
A 149	**abstract group-theoretical property** <involving all isomorphic groups> <AL, GR>	abstrakte Gruppeneigenschaft *f*	propriété *f* abstraite de groupe	абстрактное теоретико-групповое свойство
A 150	**abstract interval function,** cell function <FA>	abstrakte (verallgemeinerte) Intervallfunktion *f*, Zellenfunktion *f*	fonction *f* d'intervalle abstraite, fonction de cellule	абстрактная функция интервала, функция клетки
A 151	**abstraction** <process> <FO>	Abstraktion *f*	abstraction *f*	абстракция, отвлечение
	abstraction class <SE>	*s.* E 415		
	abstraction class with respect to the relation R <SE>	*s.* R 862		
A 152	**abstraction operator,** singulary functional abstraction operator, operator λ (lambda), λ-operator, lambda[-]operator <LO>	λ-Operator *m*, Lambda-Operator *m*, Churchsche λ-Funktion *f* (Lambda-Funktion *f*)	opérateur *m* λ (lambda)	ламбда-оператор, λ-оператор, оператор функциональной абстракции, оператор абстракции
A 153	**abstraction operator** <Church> <LO>	„abstraction operator" *m*	abstracteur *m*, opérateur *m* d'abstraction	оператор абстракции
	abstract mathematics <GN>	*s.* P 2057		
A 154	**abstract number,** unnamed (absolute) number <AR, NU>	unbenannte (abstrakte) Zahl *f*	nombre *m* abstrait (nombrant)	отвлеченное (абстрактное, неименованное) число, число
A 155	**abstract ordered simplicial complex** <AT>	geordnetes simpliziales Schema *n*	schéma *m* simplicial ordonné	упорядоченная симплициальная схема
	abstract set theory <SE>	*s.* G 183		
A 156	**abstract simplex,** simplex <AT>	absolutes (abstraktes) Simplex *n*	simplexe *m* squelette	абсолютный (абстрактный) симплекс
	abstract simplex <AT>	*s.* S 1154		
	abstract simplicial complex <AT>	*s.* S 1157		
A 157	**abstract simplicial subcomplex** <AT>	simplizialer abstrakter Unterkomplex *m*	sous-schéma *m* simplicial	симплициальная подсхема
A 158	**abstract space** <TO>	abstrakter [topologischer] Raum *m*	espace *m* abstrait <Fréchet>	абстрактное пространство
	abstract vertex <AT>	*s.* V 148		
A 159	**absurdity** <LO>	Absurdität *f*, intuitionistische Negation *f*	absurde *m*, absurdité *f*	абсурд
A 160	**absurd proposition** <LO>	absurde Aussage *f*	énoncé *m* absurde, absurdité *f*	абсурдное (нелепое) высказывание
A 161	**abundant number,** superfluous (redundant) number <NT>	abundante (überschießende, übervollständige, überflüssige) Zahl *f*, numerus *m* abundans, abundans numerus, numerus plus quam-perfectus	nombre *m* imparfait par excès (surabondance), nombre abondant (excédant)	избыточное число
	A.C.C., a.c.c. <AL>	*s.* A 1030		
A 162	**acceleration curve** <GE>	Accelerationskurve *f*, Akzelerationskurve *f*	courbe *f* d'accélération	кривая ускорения
A 163	**acceleration of convergence** <AX, SS>	Verbesserung (Beschleunigung) *f* der Konvergenz, Konvergenzverbesserung *f*, Konvergenzbeschleunigung *f*	accélération *f* de la convergence	ускорение (улучшение) сходимости
	accent <GN>	*s.* P 1282		
	accented quantity <GN>	*s.* P 1290		
A 164	**acceptable quality level,** AQL <in quality control> <ST>	Gutgrenze *f*, Annahmegrenze *f*, annehmbare Qualitätslage *f*, Gutlage *f*	niveau *m* de qualité acceptable	допустимый уровень качества
A 165	**acceptable situation** <TG>	annehmbare Situation *f*	situation *f* acceptable	приемлемая ситуация
A 166	**acceptance** <ST>	Annahme *f*	acceptation *f*	принятие
	acceptance boundary <ST>	*s.* A 168		
A 167	**acceptance inspection,** inspection by attributes <ST>	Attributprüfung *f*, Annahmeprüfung *f*, Gut-Schlecht-Prüfung *f*	inspection *f* d'acceptation, inspection qualitative, contrôle *m* de réception, contrôle au calibres, échantillonnage *m* d'acceptation	приемочный контроль, приемочный статистический контроль
A 168	**acceptance limit,** acceptance boundary <ST>	Annahmeschwelle *f*, Annahmegrenze *f*	limite *f* d'acceptation	граница приемки
A 169	**acceptance line** <ST>	Annahmelinie *f*	ligne *f* (droite *f* limite) d'acceptation	линия приемки, приемочная линия
A 170	**acceptance number** <ST>	Annahmezahl *f*	nombre *m* [limite] d'acceptation	приемочное число
A 171	**acceptance probability,** chance of acceptance <ST>	Annahmewahrscheinlichkeit *f*, Sicherheitswahrscheinlichkeit *f*, statistische Sicherheit *f*	probabilité *f* d'acceptation	вероятность принятия

A 172	**acceptance region** <ST>	Annahmebereich *m*, Annahmegebiet *n*	région *f* d'acceptation	область принятия [гипотезы]
A 173	**acceptance sampling** <ST>	Annahmestichprobenverfahren *n*	échantillonnage *m* pour inspection d'acceptation, échantillonnage pour le contrôle de réception	приемочный (выборочный) контроль
A 174	**acceptance zone** <ST>	Annahmezone *f*	zone *f* d'acceptation	зона принятия [гипотезы]
A 175	**accessibility** <AT>	„accessibility" *f*, Accessibility *f*	accessibilité *f*	достижимость, достигаемость
A 176	**accessible boundary point** <TO>	erreichbarer Randpunkt *m*	point *m* frontière accessible	достижимая граничная точка, достижимая точка границы
A 177	**accessible ordinal number** <SE>	erreichbare Ordnungszahl *f*	nombre *m* ordinal accessible	достижимое порядковое число
A 178	**accessible point** <TO>	erreichbarer Punkt *m*, // zugänglicher Punkt	point *m* accessible	достижимая точка
	accessible subgroup <GR>	*s.* C 1720		
A 179	**accessible vertex** <from *x*> <GP>	<von *x* aus> durch eine Bahn erreichbarer Knotenpunkt *m*	descendant *m* véritable <d'un sommet *x*>	вершина, достижимая при помощи ориентированного маршрута <исходя из *x*>
A 180	**accessory analytical plane** <PJ>	akzessorische synektische (analytische, charakteristische) Ebene *f*	plan *m* analytique accessoire	присоединенная аналитическая плоскость
	accessory canonical differential equations <DE, VA>	*s.* C 84		
	accessory differential equations <DE, VA>	*s.* V 72		
A 181	**accessory extremal,** secondary extremal <VA>	akzessorische (sekundäre) Extremale *f*	extrémale *f* accessoire (secondaire)	присоединенная (вторичная) экстремаль
A 182	**accessory irrational** <AL>	akzessorische Irrationalität *f*	irrationalité (irrationnelle) *f* accessoire	акцессорная (побочная, присоединенная) иррациональность
A 183	**accessory parameter** <DE>	akzessorischer Parameter *m*	paramètre *m* accessoire	присоединенный параметр
A 184	**accessory point** <PJ>	akzessorischer Punkt *m*	point *m* accessoire	присоединенная точка
A 185	**accessory variational problem,** secondary variational problem <VA>	akzessorisches (sekundäres) Variationsproblem *n*, akzessorisches Minimumproblem *n*	problème *m* variationnel accessoire (secondaire)	присоединенная (вторичная) вариационная задача
	accrete space <TO>	*s.* I 381		
A 186	**accumulate / to** <said of terms of a sequence> <TO>	sich häufen	s'accumuler	накопляться
A 187	**accumulated error** <ER>	akkumulierter Fehler *m*	erreur *f* d'accumulation	накопленная ошибка
	accumulation factor <AR>	*s.* G 529		
A 188	**accumulation point,** cluster point, limit[-] point, point of accumulation, limiting point <of a set>; limit[ing] number, limit[ing] value <of numbers> <TO>	Häufungspunkt *m*, Grenzpunkt *m*, β-Punkt *m*, // Verdichtungspunkt *m*	point *m* d'accumulation, point limite	точка накопления, предельная точка <множества>; предельное значение <чисел>
A 189	**accumulation point from the left** <TO>	linksseitiger Häufungspunkt *m*	point *m* d'accumulation à gauche	левая точка накопления
A 190	**accumulation point from the right** <TO>	rechtsseitiger Häufungspunkt *m*	point *m* d'accumulation à droite	правая точка накопления
A 191	**accumulation point of the α-th order** <TO>	Häufungspunkt *m* α-ter Ordnung, Häufungspunkt für die Mächtigkeit α, α-Häufungspunkt *m*	point *m* d'ordre α	точка порядка α
A 192	**accuracy** <AX, NU>	Genauigkeit *f*	précision *f*, exactitude *f*	точность
A 193	**accuracy,** closeness <ST>	Treffgenauigkeit *f*, Genauigkeit *f*, Zuverlässigkeit *f*	justesse *f*	точность
	accurate to ... <GN>	*s.* U 445		
A 194	**acentral element,** noncentral element <AL>	nichtzentrales Element *n*	élément *m* non central	нецентральный элемент
A 195	**acnodal cubic (curve)** <AG>	aknodale Kurve *f* [dritter Ordnung] <mit einem isolierten Punkt>	courbe *f* acnodale, cubique *f* acnodale	кривая [третьего порядка] с изолированной точкой, кубическая кривая с изолированной точкой
	acnodal point <AG>	*s.* A 196		
A 196	**acnode,** acnodal (isolated, conjugate) point <as a singularity of an algebraic curve> <AG>	isolierter Punkt *m*, Einsiedlerpunkt *m*, konjugierter Punkt, isolierter Kurvenpunkt *m*	acnode *m*, point *m* acnodal (isolé, conjugué)	изолированная точка
	acnode <GE>	*s.* C 2811		
A 197	**act continuously / to,** to operate continuously <said of a group> <GR, TO>	stetig operieren	operer continûment	действовать непрерывно
A 198	**act densely / to** <AL>	dicht operieren	opérer densement	действовать плотно
	act freely / to <TO>	*s.* A 211		
A 199	**action** <TG>	Aktion *f*, Handlungsmöglichkeit *f*, Verhaltensweise *f*	action *f*	действие
A 200	**action field** <LI>	Wirkfeld *n*	champ *m* d'action	поле действия
	action integral <VA>	*s.* P 1421		
A 201	**active redundancy** <ST>	heiße Reserve *f*	élément *m* redondant sous tension, réserve *f* sous tension	нагруженный резерв

A 202	**act on a set / to,** to operate on a set <GR>	operieren auf einer Menge	opérer (agir) sur un ensemble	действовать на множество
A 203	**act on the left / to** <on a space *or* set> <AL, TO>	von links operieren, linksseitig operieren <auf einem Raum *oder* einer Menge>	opérer (agir) à gauche <dans un espace *ou* ensemble>	действовать слева <в пространстве *или* множестве>
A 204	**act on the right / to** <on a space *or* set> <AL, TO>	von rechts operieren, rechtsseitig operieren <auf einem Raum *oder* einer Menge>	opérer (agir) à droite <dans un espace *ou* ensemble>	действовать справа <в пространстве *или* множестве>
A 205	**act primitively / to** <GR>	primitiv operieren	opérer primitivement	действовать примитивно
A 206	**act trivially / to** <on a space> <AL, TO>	trivial operieren	opérer trivialement (banalement)	действовать тривиально (тривиальным образом)
A 207	**actual combination** <ST>	echte Kombination *f*	combinaison *f* vraie	фактическая комбинация
	actual domain <SE>	*s.* D 854		
A 208	**actual infinity,** proper infinity, completed infinity <LO>	aktuelles (aktuales, eigentliches, kategorematisches) Unendlich *n*, Aktualunendlich *n*	infini *m* actuel (proprement dit, réel)	актуальная (завершенная) бесконечность
A 209	**actually infinite set** <LO>	aktual (aktuell) unendliche Menge *f*	ensemble *m* actuellement infini	актуально бесконечное множество
A 210	**actual range,** range <of a correspondence> <SE>	Wertevorrat *m*	ensemble *m* des valeurs	область значений
	actual range <AN>	*s.* C 1015		
	actuarial statistics <ST>	*s.* I 595		
A 211	**act without fixed points / to,** to act freely <on a set> <TO>	fixpunktfrei operieren, frei operieren	opérer sans point fixe, opérer sans points fixes, opérer librement	действовать без неподвижных точек, действовать свободно
A 212	**acute angle** <EG>	spitzer Winkel *m*	angle *m* aigu	острый угол
A 213	**acute triangle** <EG>	spitzwinkliges Dreieck *n*	triangle *m* acutangle (acutangulaire)	остроугольный треугольник
A 214	**acyclic complex** <in the dimension *p*> <AT>	azyklischer Komplex *m* <in der Dimension *p*>	complexe *m* acyclique <en dimension *p*>	ацикличный комплекс <в размерности *p*>
	acyclic continuous curve <TO>	*s.* D 225		
	acyclic graph <GP>	*s.* C 699		
A 215	**acyclicity** <GP, SE, TO>	Azyklizität *f* <SE, TO>; Kreisfreiheit *f* <GP>	acyclicité *f*	ацикличность
A 216	**acyclic [Markov] chain** <SP>	azyklische [Markowsche] Kette *f*	chaîne *f* [markovienne] acyclique	ациклическая цепь [Маркова]
A 217	**acyclic-model theorem** <HA>	Satz *m* von den azyklischen Modellen	théorème *m* des modèles acycliques	теорема об ацикличных моделях
A 218	**acyclic relation** <SE>	azyklische Relation *f*, Unterordnung *f*	relation *f* acyclique, sous-ordre *m*	ациклическое отношение
	acyclic set of cells <PG>	*s.* C 700		
	Adams-Bashforth method <DE, NU>	*s.* A 223		
	Adams-Bashforth process <DE, NU>	*s.* A 223		
A 219	**Adams['s] circle** <of the triangle> <EG>	Adamsscher Kreis *m*	cercle *m* d'Adams	окружность Адамса
	Adams['s] extrapolation <DE, NU>	*s.* A 220		
	Adams['s] extrapolation formula <DE, NU>	*s.* A 221		
A 220	**Adams['s] extrapolation method,** Adams['s] extrapolation <DE, NU>	Adamssches Verfahren (Extrapolationsverfahren) *n*, Adams['] (Adamssche) Extrapolation *f*, Extrapolationsverfahren von Adams	méthode *f* d'Adams, méthode d'extrapolation d'Adams, extrapolation *f* d'Adams	метод Адамса, экстраполяционный метод Адамса
A 221	**Adams['s] formula of extrapolation,** Adams['s] extrapolation formula, predictor formula of the Adams-Moulton method <DE, NU>	Adamssche Extrapolationsformel *f*	formule *f* d'extrapolation d'Adams	экстраполяционная формула Адамса
A 222	**Adams['s] formula of interpolation, Adams['s] interpolation formula,** corrector formula of the Adams-Moulton method <NU>	Adamssche Interpolationsformel (Formel) *f*	formule *f* d'interpolation d'Adams, formule d'Adams	интерполяционная формула Адамса
A 223	**Adams['s] interpolation method, Adams-Moulton method,** Adams-Bashforth method (process) <DE, NU>	Adamssches Interpolationsverfahren *n*	méthode *f* d'interpolation d'Adams, méthode d'Adams	интерполяционный метод Адамса, метод Адамса
A 224	**Adams['s] sphere** <of the tetrahedron> <EG>	Adamssche Kugel *f*	sphère *f* d'Adams	сфера Адамса
	Adams-Störmer method <DE, NU>	*s.* S 1828		
A 225	**adapted basis** <GU>	adaptierte Basis *f*	base *f* adaptée	адаптированный базис
A 226	**add / to** <to> <AR>	addieren, hinzuaddieren, [additiv] hinzufügen <zu>	adder <à>	прибавлять <к сумме>
A 227	**addend,** second term <of a sum> <AL, AR>	Auktor *m*, Auctor *m*, Addend *m*, zweiter Summand *m*	second terme *m* [d'une somme]	второе слагаемое
A 228	**addend,** second term <sum of order types> <SE>	Addendus *m*, zweiter Summand *m*	addendus *m*, second terme *m*	второе слагаемое
	addend <AL, AR>	*s.* S 2279		
A 229	**adding [of] the point at infinity,** adjoining [of] a single point <in compactification> <TO>	Adjunktion *f* eines unendlichfernen Punktes, Adjunktion eines Punktes im Unendlichen	adjonction *f* d'un point à l'infini	присоединение бесконечно удаленной точки

	adding together <AR>	*s.* T 638		
	adding up <AR>	*s.* T 638		
A 230	**addition** <of sets>, ordering[-] addition <in lattices>, ∪ <read: cup, join> <SE>	Addition *f*, Vereinigung *f*, ∪ <lies: vereinigt>	réunion, *f*, ∪ <se lit: union, réunion>	сложение, ∪ <читается: чашка, объединение>
	addition <LO>	*s.* R 1483		
A 231	**additional condition** <GN>	Zusatzbedingung *f*; Zusatzforderung *f*	condition *f* additionnelle	дополнительное условие (требование)
A 232	**additional term** <GN>	Zusatzglied *n*	terme *m* additionnel	дополнительный член
A 233	**addition curve** <NU>	Additionskurve *f*, additionslogarithmische Kurve *f*	courbe *f* d'addition	кривая сложения, график гауссовых логарифмов
	addition formula <GN>	*s.* A 242		
A 234	**addition formulas,** addition theorems <of trigonometry> <EG>	Additionstheoreme *npl* <für die trigonometrischen Funktionen>	formules *fpl* (théorèmes *mpl*) d'addition <des fonctions trigonométriques>	теоремы сложения <в тригонометрии>
	addition logarithm <AL, AN>	*s.* G 93		
A 235/6	**addition method** <of elimination> <AL>	Additionsmethode *f*, Multiplikationsmethode *f*	méthode *f* par addition	метод сложения
A 237	**addition method** <of solving a set of linear equations> <AL>	Additions- und Subtraktionsverfahren *n*, Additions- und Subtraktionsmethode *f*	méthode *f* d'addition et de soustraction, méthode d'addition	метод сложения
A 238	**addition of antecedents** <LO>	vordere Kopplung *f*	disjonction *f* des prémisses	сложение антецедентов
	addition of cardinal numbers <SE>	*s.* C 117		
	addition of ordinal numbers <SE>	*s.* O 370		
A 239	**addition sign,** sign of addition, plus sign, + <GN>	Additionszeichen *n*, Pluszeichen *n*, Summenzeichen *n*, +	signe *m* d'addition, +	знак сложения (плюс), +
A 240	**addition system** <NT>	Additionssystem *n*	système *m* de numération additif	аддитивная система счисления; система счисления, основанная на принципе сложения
A 241	**addition table** <AR>	Additionstabelle *f*, Einsundeins *n*	table *f* d'addition	таблица сложения
	addition term by term <AL, AR>	*s.* T 180		
A 242	**addition theorem,** addition formula <GN>	Additionstheorem *n*	théorème *m* d'addition, théorème de l'addition, formule *f* d'addition	теорема сложения, формула сложения, закон сложения
A 243	**addition theorem** <for a distribution> <ST>	Additionssatz *m*	théorème *m* d'addition	теорема сложения
A 244	**addition theorem of probabilities (probability)** <ST>	Additionssatz *m* der Wahrscheinlichkeiten	théorème *m* d'addition de la théorie des probabilités, théorème des probabilités totales	теорема сложения вероятностей
	addition theorems <EG>	*s.* A 234		
A 245	**additive Borel class,** additive class <SE>	additive Borel-Klasse *f*	classe *f* additive [au sens dénombrable]	аддитивный класс
A 246	**additive category** <CA>	additive (präadditive) Kategorie *f*	catégorie *f* additive	аддитивная категория
A 247	**additive character** <AL>	Additivcharakter *m*	caractère *m* additif	аддитивный характер
	additive class <SE>	*s.* A 245		
A 248	**additive composition** <AL>	additive Verknüpfung (Komposition) *f*	loi (composition) *f* additive, loi d'addition	аддитивная композиция
A 249	**additive composition law** <in a ring> <AL>	additives Kompositionsgesetz *n*	loi *f* additive	аддитивный закон композиции
A 250	**additive congruence** <NT>	additive Kongruenz *f*	congruence *f* additive	аддитивное сравнение
	additive congruence <AL>	*s.* O 383		
	additive Cousin problem <FT>	*s.* C 2594		
	σ-additive family <TO>	*s.* C 2565		
	σ-additive function <AN>	*s.* C 2566		
A 251	**additive functional transformation,** distributive functional transformation <FA>	additive (distributive) Funktionaltransformation *f*	transformation (opération) *f* fonctionnelle additive (distributive), opérateur *m* fonctionnel additif (distributif)	аддитивное (дистрибутивное) функциональное преобразование
A 252	**additive group** <of a ring> <AL>	Additivgruppe *f*, additive Gruppe *f*, Additionsgruppe *f* <eines Rings>	groupe *m* additif <d'un anneau>	аддитивная группа, группа по сложению <кольца>
A 253	**additive group** <GR>	additive Gruppe *f*, Modul *m*	groupe *m* additif	аддитивная группа
	additive ideal <AL>	*s.* I 6		
	additive identity <AL>	*s.* Z 14		
	additive identity element <AL>	*s.* Z 14		
A 254	**additive interval function** <AN>	additive Intervallfunktion *f*	fonction *f* additive de l'intervalle, fonction d'intervalle additive	аддитивная функция интервала
A 255	**additive inverse element** <AL>	entgegengesetztes Element *n*	élément-opposé *m*, élément *m* opposé (symétrique)	противоположный (обратный) элемент
A 256	**additive left inverse element** <AL>	linksentgegengesetztes Element *n*	élément *m* opposé (symétrique) à gauche	левый противоположный (обратный) элемент, симметричный слева элемент
A 257	**additively closed** <AL>	additiv abgeschlossen	additivement clos	аддитивно замкнутый

No.	English	German	French	Russian
A 258	**additively commutative ordinal numbers,** ordinal numbers commutative with respect to addition <SE>	additiv vertauschbare Ordnungszahlen *fpl*	nombres *mpl* ordinaux commutables pour l'addition	аддитивно перестановочные порядковые числа
	σ-additive measure <ME>	*s.* A 82		
A 259	**additive net** <as a partial plane> <AL, PJ>	additives Gewebe *n*	tissu *m* additif	аддитивная сеть
A 260	**additive notation** <AL>	additive Schreibweise *f*	notation (écriture) *f* additive	аддитивная форма записи, аддитивная запись
A 261	**additive number theory** <AB>	additive Zahlentheorie *f*, additive Arithmetik *f*	arithmétique *f* additive	аддитивная теория чисел, аддитивная арифметика
	additive process <SP>	*s.* S 1808		
	additive relation <CA>	*s.* C 2501		
A 262	**additive right inverse element** <AL>	rechtsentgegengesetztes Element *n*	élément *m* opposé (symétrique) à droite	правый противоположный (обратный) элемент, симметричный справа элемент
	σ-additive set function <AN>	*s.* C 2566		
A 263	**additive term** <in a sum> <GN>	additives Glied *n*, additiver Term *m*, Zusatzglied *n*, Zusatzterm *m*	terme *m* additif	добавочный (дополнительный, аддитивный) член
	additive valuation <AL>	*s.* E 748		
	σ-additivity <AN, SE>	*s.* C 2556		
A 264	**adele,** repartition, valuation vector, valuation-vector <AB, AL>	Adel *n*, Repartition *f*, Bewertungsvektor *m*, additives Idel *n*	adèle *m*, répartition *f*	адель
A 265	**adele-class group** <AB>	Adelklassengruppe *f*	groupe *m* de classes d'adèles	группа классов аделей
A 266	**adele group** <AB>	Adelgruppe *f*	groupe *m* des adèles, groupe adélique	группа аделей
A 267	**Adem relations** <Steenrod algebra> <TO>	Ademsche Relationen *fpl*	relations *fpl* d'Adem	соотношения Адема
A 268	**adequate definition** <LO>	adäquate Definition *f*	définition *f* adéquate	адекватное определение
A 269	**adequate [logical] matrix** <LO>	adäquate [logische] Matrix *f*	matrice *f* logique adéquate	логически адекватная матрица
A 270	**adequate ring** <AL>	adäquater Ring *m*	anneau *m* adéquate	адекватное кольцо
A 271	**adherence,** supplement <of a set> <TO>	isolierter Teil *m*, Adhärenz *f*, Menge *f* der isolierten Punkte <Cantor>	adhérence *f*	множество изолированных точек, изолированная часть [множества]
	adherence <TO>	*s.* C 934		
	adherent point <TO>	*s.* P 756		
A 272	**adiametrical hyperbolic hyperbola** <AG>	adiametrale hyperbolische Hyperbel *f*	hyperbole *f* hyperbolique adiamétrale	адиаметральная гиперболическая гипербола
A 273	**adjacency** <GP>	Adjazenz *f*	adjacence *f*	прилегание, примыкание
A 274	**adjacency matrix,** vertex matrix <of a graph> <GP>	Adjazenzmatrix *f*, Knotenmatrix *f*, Matrix *f* benachbarter Knoten	matrice *f* associée	матрица смежности [вершин], матрица смежностей
A 275	**adjacent angle** <EG>	anliegender Winkel *m*	angle *m* adjacent	прилежащий (смежный) угол
	adjacent angles <EG>	*s.* A 282		
A 276	**adjacent arc,** adjacent directed edge <of a graph> <GP>	adjazenter Bogen *m*, benachbarte gerichtete Kante *f*	arc *m* adjacent	смежная дуга
A 277	**adjacent continuous fraction** <NT>	benachbarter Bruch (Kettenbruch) *m*	fraction *f* [continue] adjacente, fraction continue voisine	смежная цепная дробь
	adjacent directed edge <GP>	*s.* A 276		
A 278	**adjacent edge** <of a graph> <GP>	adjazente (benachbarte) Kante *f*	arête *f* adjacente	смежное ребро
A 279	**adjacent face** <GP>	adjazente (benachbarte) Fläche *f*	face *f* adjacente	смежная грань
	adjacent point <DG>	*s.* I 460		
A 280	**adjacent side** <of a triangle> <EG>	anliegende Seite *f*	côté *m* adjacent	прилежащая сторона
A 281	**adjacent side, adjacent small side** <of a rectangular triangle> <EG>	Ankathete *f*	côté *m* adjacent	прилежащий катет
A 282	**adjacent supplementary angles,** adjacent angles <EG>	Nebenwinkel *mpl*	angles *mpl* adjacents supplémentaires	смежные углы
A 283	**adjacent vertex** <of a graph> <GP>	benachbarter (adjazenter) Knotenpunkt *m*, Nachbar *m*, benachbarter Knoten *m*	sommet *m* adjacent, voisin *m*	смежная вершина, смежный узел
	adjoining [of] a single point <TO>	*s.* A 229		
	adjoining [of] the identity <AL>	*s.* A 313		
A 284	**adjoint** <of a homomorphism> <AL>	adjungierter Homomorphismus *m*	homomorphisme *m* adjoint, adjoint *m*	сопряженный гомоморфизм
	adjoint <CA>	*s.* A 295		
	adjoint <DE>	*s.* A 289		
	adjoint <FA, TO>	*s.* A 307		
	adjoint <GP>	*s.* D 285		
	adjoint <MD>	*s.* 1. A 303; 2. H 235		
A 285	**adjoint boundary value problem** <DE>	adjungiertes Randwertproblem *n*, adjungierte Randwertaufgabe *f*	problème *m* aux limites adjoint	сопряженная краевая задача
A 286	**adjoint derivation** <of a Lie algebra> <AL>	adjungierte Derivation *f*	dérivation *f* adjointe	присоединенное дифференцирование

A 287	**adjoint determinant** <MD>	Determinante *f* der Adjunktenmatrix, Determinante des adjungierten Systems, adjungierte (reziproke) Determinante	déterminant *m* adjoint, // déterminant réciproque	определитель присоединенной матрицы
A 288	**adjoint difference equation** <FD>	adjungierte Differenzengleichung *f*	équation *f* aux différences finies adjointe	сопряженное уравнение в конечных разностях
A 289	**adjoint differential equation,** adjoint <of a differential equation> <DE>	adjungierte Differentialgleichung *f*, Adjungierte *f*	équation *f* différentielle adjointe, équation adjointe, adjointe *f*	сопряженное дифференциальное уравнение, сопряженное уравнение
A 290	**adjoint differential expression,** Lagrange['s] adjoint <DE>	adjungierter Differentialausdruck *m*, Lagrangesche (Lagranges) Adjungierte *f*	expression *f* différentielle adjointe, adjointe *f* de Lagrange	сопряженное дифференциальное выражение
A 291	**adjoint eigenvector** <FA>	adjungierter Eigenvektor *m*	vecteur *m* propre adjoint	сопряженный собственный вектор
A 292	**adjoint form** <AG>	adjungierte Form *f*	forme *f* adjointe	присоединенная форма
A 293	**adjoint form** <IV>	adjungierte Form *f* <Hermite>	forme *f* adjointe, adjointe *f*; adjointe de Darboux; adjointe de Gauss	сопряженная форма
A 294	**adjoint function** <AG>	adjungierte Funktion *f*	fonction *f* adjointe	присоединенная функция
A 295	**adjoint functor,** adjoint, left adjoint, left-adjoint <*also:* right *instead of* left> <of a functor> <CA>	adjungierter Funktor *m*, linksadjungierter Funktor *m*, Linksadjungierter *m* <*auch:* rechts *statt* links>	foncteur *m* adjoint, adjoint *m*, foncteur *m* adjoint à gauche, adjoint *m* à gauche <*aussi:* droite *au lieu de* gauche>	сопряженный функтор, сопряженный слева функтор, левый сопряженный функтор <*также:* правый *вместе* левый>
A 296	**adjoint functors,** adjoint pair <of functors> <CA>	adjungierte Funktoren *mpl*, adjungiertes Funktorpaar (Paar) *n*, Paar adjungierter Funktoren	foncteurs *mpl* adjoints	сопряженные функторы, сопряженная пара
A 297	**adjoint functor theorem** <CA>	Hauptsatz *m* für adjungierte Funktoren	théorème *m* des foncteurs adjoints	теорема сопряженных функторов
	adjoint graph <GP>	*s.* D 285		
A 298	**adjoint group** <of a Lie group> <GR>	adjungierte Gruppe *f*	groupe *m* adjoint	присоединенная группа
A 299	**adjoint Hilbert problem,** associate[d] Hilbert problem <FT, IE>	adjungiertes Hilbert-Problem *n*	problème *m* de Hilbert adjoint associé	сопряженная (сопутствующая) задача Гильберта
	adjoint ideal <AL>	*s.* P 1258		
A 300	**adjoint integral equation** <IE>	adjungierte Integralgleichung *f*	équation *f* intégrale adjointe	сопряженное интегральное уравнение
A 301	**adjoint kernel** <IE>	adjungierter Kern *m*	noyau *m* adjoint	сопряженное ядро, эрмитово сопряженное ядро
A 302	**adjoint linear map** <Lie algebra> <AL>	adjungierte lineare Abbildung *f*	application *f* linéaire adjointe <de *x*>, dérivation *f* intérieure <définie par *x*>, opération *f* adjointe	внутреннее дифференцирование <определенное элементом *x*>, присоединенное линейное отображение <к *x*>
A 303	**adjoint matrix,** classical adjoint [matrix], adjugate (compound) matrix, adjoint <of a matrix> <MD>	adjungierte Matrix *f*, Adjunktenmatrix *f*	matrice *f* complémentaire, complémentaire *f* d'une matrice, matrice *f* adjointe, système *m* adjoint	присоединенная (взаимная, адъюнгированная, дополнительная) матрица
	adjoint matrix <MD>	*s.* H 235		
A 304	**adjoint operator,** adjoint transformation <in the Hilbert space> <FA>	adjungierter Operator *m*, adjungierte Transformation (Abbildung) *f*, Adjungierte *f*, Adjungierter *m*	opérateur *m* adjoint (associé, conjugué), transformation *f* adjointe, adjoint *m* [hilbertien]	сопряженный оператор, сопряженное преобразование
	adjoint pair <CA>	*s.* A 296		
A 305	**adjoint process** <SP>	adjungierter Prozeß *m*	processus *m* adjoint	сопряженный процесс
A 306	**adjoint representation,** regular representation <of a Lie algebra or group> <AL>	adjungierte Darstellung *f*	représentation *f* adjointe	присоединенное представление
	adjoint set of differential equations <DE>	*s.* A 309		
A 307	**adjoint space,** adjoint, conjugate [space], dual [space], polar space, continuous linear dual, first adjoint (conjugate) <FA, TO>	Dual *m*, dualer Raum *m*, adjungierter (konjugierter, polarer) Raum, [topologischer] Dualraum *m*, topologischer Dual	espace *m* conjugué (dual, adjoint), conjugué *m*, adjoint *m*, dual *m* [topologique]	сопряженное (двойственное, дуальное, топологическое сопряженное) пространство, топологическое сопряженное
A 308	**adjoint surface** <AG>	adjungierte Fläche *f*, Adjungierte *f*	surface *f* adjointe	сопряженная поверхность
A 309	**adjoint system of** <ordinary homogeneous linear> **differential equations,** adjoint set of differential equations <DE>	adjungiertes System *n* von Differentialgleichungen	système *m* adjoint d'équations différentielles	сопряженная система дифференциальных уравнений
A 310	**adjoint transformation** <in a locally convex space> <FA>	Transponierte *f*, Adjungierte *f*, adjungierte (assoziierte, duale, konjugierte) Abbildung *f*, Konjugierte *f*, transponierte Abbildung	application *f* adjointe (duale), transposée *f*, opération *f* associée (conjuguée)	сопряженное отображение (преобразование), транспонированный [линейный] оператор
	adjoint transformation <FA>	*s.* A 304		
	adjugate matrix <MD>	*s.* 1. A 303; 2. P 2017; 3. R 251		
A 311	**adjunction** <CA>	Adjunktion *f*	adjonction *f*	сопряжение
	adjunction <LO> ┌<CA>	*s.* R 1482		
A 312	**adjunction morphism**	Adjunktionstransformation	morphisme *m* d'adjonction	морфизм сопряжения

No.	English	German	French	Russian
	adjunction morphism <CA>	*s.* U 288		
A 313	**adjunction of an identity element,** adjoining [of] the identity <to a semigroup> <AL>	Adjunktion *f* eines Einselements	adjonction *f* d'un élément-unité	присоединение единицы
	adjunction of circles <FT>	*s.* C 676		
A 314	**adjunction theorem** <IV>	Adjunktionssatz *m*	théorème *m* d'adjonction	теорема расширения (присоединения)
A 315	**adjusted coperiodical group** <GR>	justierte koperiodische Gruppe *f*		урегулированная копериодическая группа
A 316	**adjustment analysis** <ST>	Bereinigungsverfahren *n*	méthode *f* de correction	метод удаления резко выделяющихся значений выборки
A 317	**adjustment by controls** <ST>	Standardausgleich *m*	ajustement *m* par témoins	выравнивание при помощи контроля
A 318	**admissible category** <for homology theory> <AT>	zulässige Kategorie *f*	catégorie *f* admissible	допустимая категория
A 319	**admissible centre** <of a group> <GR>	zulässiges Zentrum *n*	centre *m* permis	допустимый центр
A 320	**admissible chart** <of a manifold> <AG, DG>	zulässige Karte *f*	carte *f* admissible	допустимая карта
A 321	**admissible colouration** <GP>	zulässige Färbung *f*	coloriage *m* admissible	допустимая раскраска
A 322	**admissible control** <SP>	zulässige Steuerung *f*	contrôle *m* admissible	допустимое управление
A 323	**admissible decision function (rule)** <ST>	zulässige Entscheidungsfunktion (Entscheidungsregel) *f*	fonction (règle) *f* de décision admissible	допустимая функция решения, допустимое правило решения
A 324	**admissible deformation** <TO>	zulässige Deformation *f*	déformation *f* admissible	допустимая деформация
A 325	**admissible domain** <FA>	zulässiger Bereich *m*	domaine *m* admissible	допустимая область
A 326	**admissible homomorphism** <AT>	zulässiger Homomorphismus *m*	homomorphisme *m* permis	допустимый гомоморфизм
A 327	**admissible hypothesis** <ST>	zulässige Hypothese *f*	hypothèse *f* admissible	допустимая гипотеза
A 328	**admissible lifting** <of a fibre bundle> <AT>	zulässige Anhebung (Liftung) *f*	relèvement *m* admissible	допустимое поднятие
A 329	**admissible map** <of fibre bundles> <AT>	zulässige Abbildung *f*	application *f* admissible	допустимое отображение
A 330	**admissible module** <AL>	zulässiger Modul *m*	module *m* permis	допустимый (инвариантный) модуль
A 331	**admissible operation** <AL>	zulässige Operation *f*	opération *f* admissible	допустимая операция
A 332	**admissible partial subalgebra** <with respect to an operator domain> <AL>	zulässige partielle Teilalgebra *f*	sous-algèbre *f* partielle distinguée	допустимая частичная подалгебра
	admissible policy <SP>	*s.* A 335		
A 333	**admissible sequence** <AT>	zulässige Sequenz *f*	séquence *f* admissible	допустимая последовательность
A 334	**admissible space** <TO>	zulässiger Raum *m*	espace *m* admissible	допустимое пространство
A 335	**admissible strategy,** admissible policy <SP>	zulässige Strategie (Politik) *f*	stratégie *f* admissible	допустимая стратегия
A 336	**admissible subalgebra** <AL, UA>	zulässige Teilalgebra (Unteralgebra) *f*	sous-algèbre *f* permise	допустимая (инвариантная) подалгебра
A 337	**admissible subgroup,** stable subgroup; *M*-subgroup <operator set *M*> <GR>	zulässige Untergruppe *f*; *M*-Untergruppe *f*	sous-groupe *m* stable (permis) <pour la loi de composition externe, par rapport au domaine d'opérateurs (*M*)>; *M*-sous-groupe *m*	допустимая (устойчивая) подгруппа; *M*-подгруппа
A 338	**Θ-admissible subobject** <CA>	Θ-zulässiges Teilobjekt *n*	sous-objet *m* Θ-admissible	Θ-допустимый подобъект
A 339	**admissible test** <ST>	zulässiger Test *m*	test *m* admissible	допустимый критерий
A 340	**admit a solution / to** <GN>	eine Lösung besitzen	admettre une solution	иметь решение
A 341	**Ado['s] theorem** <for a Lie ring> <AL>	Adosches Theorem *n*	théorème *m* d'Ado	теорема Адо
	a.e. <ME, SE, ST>	*s.* A 515		
A 342	**Aeppli['s] group** <FT>	Aepplische Gruppe *f*	groupe *m* d'Aeppli	группа Эппли
A 343	**affect** <of an equation or polynomial> <AL>	Affekt *m*	affect *m*, affection *f*	аффект
	affected quadratic <AL>	*s.* G 174		
A 344	**affect function** <AL>	Affektfunktion *f*	fonction *f* d'affect, fonction d'affection	функция аффекта
	affectless equation <AL>	*s.* E 354		
	affectless polynomial <AL>	*s.* P 1017		
A 345	**affine algebraic [*k*-] set,** algebraic affine variety <over *k*> <AG>	affine algebraische [*k*-] Mannigfaltigkeit *f*, affine algebraische *k*-Menge *f*, algebraische Mannigfaltigkeit *f* <über *k*>	variété *f* algébrique affine <sur *k*>	аффинное [алгебраическое] *k*-многообразие, аффинное алгебраическое множество <над *k*>
A 346	**affine breadth** <DG>	Affinbreite *f*	largeur *f* affine	аффинная широта
A 347	**affine collineation** <AY>	affine Kollineation *f*	collinéation *f* affine	аффинная коллинеация
A 348	**affine collineation group** <AY>	affine Kollineationsgruppe *f*	groupe *m* des collinéations affines	группа аффинных коллинеаций
	affine-connected manifold <DG>	*s.* A 364		
	affine connected space <DG>	*s.* A 365		
A 349	**affine connection,** affine transfer <DG>	affine Übertragung *f*, affiner Zusammenhang *m*	connexion *f* affine, transfert *m* affine	аффинная связность, аффинное перенесение

No.	English	German	French	Russian
	affine connection component <DG>	*s.* C 1664		
	affine co-ordinate ring <AG>	*s.* C 2427		
A 350	**affine co-ordinates,** parallel co-ordinates, Cartesian co-ordinates <AY, GE>	Parallelkoordinaten *fpl*, affine Koordinaten *fpl*, kartesische (cartesische) Koordinaten	coordonnées *fpl* affines (parallèles, cartésiennes)	аффинные (общие декартовы) координаты, декартовы (параллельные) координаты
	affine correspondence <AY, DS>	*s.* P 511		
A 351/2	**affine curvature** <DG>	Affinkrümmung *f*	courbure *f* affine	аффинная кривизна
A 353	**affine differential geometry** <DG>	affine Differentialgeometrie *f*	géométrie *f* différentielle affine	аффинно-дифференциальная геометрия, аффинная дифференциальная геометрия
A 354	**affine distance** <DG>	Affinabstand *m* <zweier Linienelemente>; Affinentfernung *f* <eines Punktes von einem Punkt einer Fläche>	distance *f* affine	аффинное расстояние
	affine figure <DS>	*s.* P 510		
A 355	**affine function,** linear function (mapping) <not necessarily homogeneous> <GN>	affine (affin-lineare, lineare) Funktion *f*	fonction *f* linéaire affine, fonction affine (linéaire)	аффинно-линейная функция, аффинная (линейная) функция
A 356	**affine-geometric** <GE>	affingeometrisch	de (en, à, par) géométrie affine	аффинно-геометрический
A 357	**affine geometry** <AY>	affine Geometrie *f*, Affingeometrie *f*	géométrie *f* affine (linéaire)	аффинная геометрия
A 358	**affine group** <AL, AY>	affine (volle affine) Gruppe *f*	groupe *m* affine	аффинная группа [преобразований], группа аффинных преобразований
A 359	**affine group scheme** <AG>	affines Gruppenschema *n*	schéma *m* de groupes affine	аффинная групповая схема
A 360	**affine Hjelmslev plane,** AH-plane <GE>	affine Hjelmslev-Ebene *f*	plan *m* de Hjelmslev affine	АН-плоскость, аффинная плоскость Гельмслева
	affine independence of points <GE>	*s.* L 802		
A 361	**affine isothermal net** <GE>	affin-isothermes Netz *n*	réseau *m* isotherme affine	аффинно-изотермическая сеть (сетка)
A 362	**affine length** <DG>	Affinlänge *f*, Affinbogen *m*	longueur *f* affine	аффинная длина [дуги], аффинный параметр
A 363	**affine line** <AY, AG>	affine Gerade *f*	droite *f* affine	аффинная прямая
A 364	**affinely connected manifold,** affine-connected manifold <DG>	affin zusammenhängende Mannigfaltigkeit *f*, Mannigfaltigkeit mit affiner Übertragung	variété *f* à connexion affine	многообразие аффинной связности
A 365	**affinely connected space,** affine connected space <DG>	affin[-] zusammenhängender Raum *m*	espace *m* à connexion affine	пространство аффинной связности
	affinely dependent points <GE>	*s.* L 811		
	affinely dependent set <GE>	*s.* L 811		
	affinely independent points <GE>	*s.* L 813		
	affinely independent subset <GE>	*s.* L 813		
A 366	**affine normal,** axis of aberration (deviation) <DG>	Affinnormale *f*, Aberrationsachse *f*, Deviationsachse *f*, Achse *f* der Abweichung	normale *f* affine, axe *m* d'aberration	аффинная нормаль, ось аберрации, ось девиации
A 367	**affine normal** <of a spatial curve> <DG>	affine Hauptnormale *f*, Affin[haupt]normale *f*	normale *f* affine	аффинная нормаль
A 368	**affine parameter** <AY>	affiner Parameter *m*	paramètre *m* affine	аффинный параметр
A 369	**affine principal curvature** <DG>	affine Hauptkrümmung *f*	courbure *f* principale affine	аффинная главная кривизна
A 370	**affine ratio,** division ratio, ratio of division, inner ratio [of division], internal ratio <of three points> <AY, EG>	Teilverhältnis *n*, Abstandsverhältnis *n*, Teilungsverhältnis *n*, inneres Verhältnis *n*	rapport *m* de section, raison *f* des distances	простое отношение, отношение расстояний
A 371	**affine rational transformation** <AG>	affinrationale Transformation *f*	transformation *f* rationnelle affine	аффинно-рациональное преобразование
	affine relation <AY, DS>	*s.* P 511		
A 372	**affine space** <AY>	affiner Raum *m*	espace *m* affine	аффинное пространство
A 373	**affine sphere** <DG>	Affinsphäre *f*	sphère *f* affine	аффинная сфера
A 374	**affine surface** <DG>	Affinoberfläche *f*	surface *f* affine	аффинная поверхность
	affine transfer <DG>	*s.* A 349		
A 375	**affine transformation,** affinity <AY>	affine Abbildung *f* (Transformation *f*, Bewegung *f*, Verwandtschaft *f*, Verwandlung *f*), Affinität *f*, Affintransformation *f*, Bewegung im affinen Raum, Bewegung der affinen Geometrie	application *f* [linéaire-] affine, transformation *f* [linéaire-] affine, fonction *f* [linéaire-] affine, affinité *f*	аффинное преобразование (отображение), аффинность, линейно-аффинное отображение, аффинитет
	affine transformation <AY>	*s.* R 509		
	affine unimodular group <GE>	*s.* E 359		
A 376/7	**affine variety** <AG>	affine Mannigfaltigkeit *f*	variété *f* affine	аффинное (линейное) многообразие
	affinity <AY>	*s.* A 375		
A 378	**affinity ratio** <of a perspective affinity> <DS>	Affinitätsverhältnis *n*	rapport *m* d'affinité	масштаб аффинного преобразования

No.	English	German	French	Russian
A 379	**affinograph** <GE, IN>	Affinzeichner *m*, Affinograph *m*	affinographe *m*	аффинограф
	affinor <VT>	*s.* T 133		
	affinor differential equation <DE, DG, VT>	*s.* T 141		
A 380	**affirmation** <LO>	Affirmation *f*	affirmation *f*	утверждение
	affirmative particular proposition <LO>	*s.* P 1095		
A 381	**affirmative proposition,** positive proposition <LO>	affirmative (bejahende) Aussage *f*, bejahendes (affirmatives) Urteil *n*	proposition *f* affirmative (positive), énoncé *m* affirmatif (positif)	утвердительное (положительное) суждение
A 382	**affix** <of a complex number>, graphically represented complex number <FT>	komplexe Zahl *f* als Punkt der komplexen Zahlenebene, in der Gaußschen Zahlenebene dargestellte komplexe Zahl, Bild *n* einer komplexen Zahl in der Gaußschen Zahlenebene	affixe *m* <d'un point (a,b) du plan complexe; quantité complexe considérée comme liée à sa représentation géométrique>	аффикс, изображающая точка
A 383	**affix** <prefix, infix *or* suffix> <LO>	Affix *n*	affixe *m*	аффикс
A 384	**aggregate** <ST>	Aggregat *n*	agrégat *m*	агрегат
	aggregate <SE>	*s.* S 637		
	aggregate in braces / to <GN>	*s.* P 2078		
	aggregate in brackets / to <GN>	*s.* P 2079		
	aggregate in parentheses / to <GN>	*s.* P 2080		
	aggregate of points <ST>	*s.* S 102		
	aggregation in braces (brackets, parentheses) <GN>	*s.* B 709		
A 385	**aggregative index** <ST>	Aggregatindex *m*	indice *m* synthétique (d'agrégat)	агрегатный индекс
	Agnesi['s] versiera <GE>	*s.* W 272		
A 386	**agreement** <in a coalitional game> <TG>	Absprache *f*	accord *m*	соглашение
	Ahlfors['s] distortion theorem <FT>	*s.* T 255		
	Ahlfors['s] theorem <FT>	*s.* T 255		
	AH-plane <GE>	*s.* A 360		
A 387	**Airy['s] [differential] equation** <DE>	Airysche Differentialgleichung *f*	équation *f* [différentielle] d'Airy	[дифференциальное] уравнение Эри
A 388	**Airy['s] function** <FU>	Airysche Funktion *f*, Airy-Funktion *f*	fonction *f* d'Airy	функция Эри
A 389	**Airy['s] integral,** Airy['s] rainbow integral, rainbow integral of Airy <FU>	Airysches Integral *n*, Airys[ches] Regenbogenintegral *n*, Regenbogenintegral von Airy	intégrale *f* d'Airy, intégrale de l'arc-en-ciel d'Airy	интеграл Эри
	Airy['s] rainbow integral <FU>	*s.* A 389		
A 390	**Aitken['s] interpolation,** recursive interpolation process due to Aitken <AX, FD, NU>	Aitkensches Interpolationsschema *n*, Aitkenscher Interpolationsprozeß *m*, Interpolationsschema (Interpolationsprozeß) von Aitken	procédé (schéma) *m* d'interpolation d'Aitken, interpolation *f* d'Aitken	интерполяционная схема Айткена, интерполяционный процесс Айткена
A 391	**Aitken['s] interpolation formula** <AX, FD, NU>	Interpolationsformel *f* von Aitken, Aitkensche Interpolationsformel	formule *f* d'interpolation d'Aitken	интерполяционная формула Айткена
A 392	**A-kernel** <of a complex sequence> <LI>	*A*-Kern *m*	*A*-noyau *m*	*A*-ядро
A 393	**Alaoglu-Bourbaki theorem** <FA>	Satz *m* von Alaoglu-Bourbaki, Alaoglu-Bourbakischer Satz	théorème *m* d'Alaoglu-Bourbaki	теорема Алаоглу-Бурбаки
A 394	**Albanese['s] variety,** variety of Albanese <AG>	Albanesesche Mannigfaltigkeit *f*, Picardsche Mannigfaltigkeit im Sinne von Severi	variété *f* d'Albanese	многообразие Альбанезе
	Albert['s] theorem <AL>	*s.* T 256		
	aleatory variable <ST>	*s.* V 67		
A 395	**aleph,** aleph number, $\aleph$ <cardinal of a well-ordered set> <SE>	Aleph *n*, Alef *n*, $\aleph$	aleph *m*, nombre *m* aleph, $\aleph$	алеф, $\aleph$
	aleph <SE>	*s.* I 440		
A 396	**aleph nought, aleph null, aleph-null,** aleph-zero, aleph zero, $\aleph_0$ <SE>	Aleph-Null *n*, Aleph *n* null, $\aleph_0$	aleph *m* zéro, $\aleph_0$	алефнуль, алеф-нуль, $\aleph_0$
	aleph number <SE>	*s.* A 395		
	aleph zero, aleph-zero <SE>	*s.* A 396		
A 397	**Alexander cohomology module** <of degree *q* with coefficients in *G*> <AT>	Alexanderscher Kohomologiemodul *m* <vom Grade *q* mit Koeffizienten in *G*>	module *m* de cohomologie d'Alexander <de degré *q* à coefficients dans *G*>	модуль когомологий Александера <*q*-й, с коэффициентами в *G*>
A 398	**Alexander['s] cohomology theory,** Alexander-Spanier cohomology theory <AT>	Alexander-Spaniersche Kohomologietheorie *f*	théorie *f* de cohomologie d'Alexander-Spanier	теория когомологий Александера (Александера-Спеньера)
A 399	**Alexander['s] cohomology with compact supports** <AT>	Alexandersche Kohomologie *f* mit kompakten Trägern	cohomologie *f* d'Alexander-Spanier à support compact	когомологии Александера с компактными носителями

A 400	**Alexander['s] duality theorem** <AT>	Alexanderscher Dualitätssatz *m*	théorème *m* de dualité d'Alexander	закон двойственности Александера, теорема Александера
	Alexander['s] horned sphere <TO>	*s.* H 569		
A 401	**Alexander matrix** <of a knot> <AL, AT>	Alexandersche Matrix *f*	matrice *f* d'Alexander	матрица Александера
A 402	**Alexander['s] polynomial** <of a knot> <AT>	Alexandersches Polynom *n*	polynôme *m* d'Alexander	полином (многочлен) Александера, полином узлов
A 403	**Alexander-Spanier cochain with compact support** <AT>	Alexander-Spaniersche Kokette *f* mit kompaktem Träger	cochaîne *f* d'Alexander-Spanier à support compact	коцепь Александера-Спеньера с компактным носителем
	Alexander-Spanier cohomology theory <AT>	*s.* A 398		
A 404	**Alexander-Whitney diagonal approximation** <AT>	Alexander-Whitneysche Diagonalapproximation *f*, Diagonalapproximation von Alexander-Whitney	approximation *f* diagonale d'Alexander-Whitney	диагональная аппроксимация Александера-Уитни
	Alexandroff['s] compactification <TO>	*s.* O 99		
A 405	**Alexandroff['s] half-line** <TO>	Alexandroffsche Halbgerade *f*	semi-droite *f* d'Alexandroff	полупрямая Александрова
	Alexandroff['s] one-point compactification <TO>	*s.* O 99		
	Alexandroff['s] theorem <TO>	*s.* T 257		
A 406	**algebra,** [linear] associative algebra, hypercomplex system <over *R*>, *R*-algebra <AL>	[assoziative] Algebra *f*, hyperkomplexes System *n*, System komplexer Größen (Zahlen) <über *R*>, *R*-Algebra *f*, assoziative *R*-Algebra	algèbre [associative], système *m* hyper-complexe, système de nombres complexes à multiplication associative <sur *R*>, *R*-algèbre *f*	алгебра, ассоциативная алгебра, гиперкомплексная система, кольцо <над *R*>, *R*-алгебра, ассоциативная *R*-алгебра
A 407	**algebra** <Peirce>, hypercomplex number system over the field of complex numbers <AL>	hyperkomplexes Zahlensystem *n* über dem Körper der komplexen Zahlen	système *m* [de nombres complexes] à coordonnées complexes ordinaires, algèbre *f* [de dimension finie sur le corps des nombres complexes]	система гиперкомплексных чисел над полем комплексных чисел
A 408/9	***-algebra,** self-adjoint [operator] algebra, algebra with an involution *, star algebra <FA>	*-Algebra *f*, Algebra *f* mit Involution *	algèbre *f* stellaire	инволютивная алгебра; алгебра над ℭ, снабженная инволюцией; кольцо с инволюцией; симметричное кольцо
	algebra <AL>	*s.* L 773		
	algebra <AR>	*s.* A 425		
	algebra <UA>	*s.* U 311		
	σ-algebra <AL>	*s.* S 815		
	σ-algebra <ME, SE, TO>	*s.* S 810		
	algebra belonging to the same similarity class <UA>	*s.* U 312		
	algebraic adjunct <MD>	*s.* C 1045		
A 410	**algebraic adjunction** <AL>	algebraische Adjunktion *f*	adjonction *f* algébrique	алгебраическое присоединение, присоединение алгебраического элемента
	algebraic affine variety <AG>	*s.* A 345		
A 411	**algebraic algebra** <AL>	algebraische Algebra *f*	algèbre *f* algébrique	алгебраическая алгебра
A 412	**algebraically closed abelian group,** divisible (complete) abelian group <GR>	divisionsvollständige (vollständige, volle, teilbare, dividierbare) abelsche Gruppe *f*	groupe *m* abélien divisible	полная (делимая) абелева группа, абелева группа с неограниченным делением
A 413	**algebraically closed extension** <UA>	algebraisch abgeschlossene Erweiterung *f*	extension *f* algébriquement fermée	алгебраически замкнутое расширение
A 414	**algebraically closed field,** algebraically complete field <AL>	algebraisch[ ]abgeschlossener Körper *m*, // geschlossener Größenbereich *m*	corps *m* algébriquement clos, domaine *m* clos <Kronecker>	алгебраически замкнутое поле
A 415	**algebraically closed field extension** <AL>	algebraisch abgeschlossene Körpererweiterung *f*	extension *f* algébriquement close	алгебраически замкнутое расширение [поля]
A 416	**algebraically closed field of characteristic zero** <AL>	algebraisch abgeschlossener Körper *m* der Charakteristik Null	corps *m* algébriquement fermé de caractéristique zéro, domaine *m* clos	алгебраически замкнутое поле нулевой характеристики
A 417	**algebraically closed group** <GR>	algebraisch abgeschlossene Gruppe *f*	groupe *m* algébriquement fermé	алгебраически замкнутая группа
A 418	**algebraically compact group** <GR>	algebraisch kompakte Gruppe *f*	groupe *m* algébriquement compact	алгебраически компактная группа
	algebraically complementary vector subspaces <AL, GE>	*s.* C 1403		
	algebraically complete field <AL>	*s.* A 414		
A 419	**algebraically dense subset** <of a vector space> <AL>	algebraisch dichte Untermenge *f*	partie *f* algébriquement dense, partie épaisse, ensemble *m* épais	алгебраически плотное подмножество
A 420	**algebraically dependent elements** <AL>	algebraisch abhängige Elemente *npl*, algebraisch abhängige Menge *f* von Elementen	éléments *mpl* algébriquement dépendants (liés), famille *f* d'éléments algébriquement liée	алгебраически зависимые элементы, алгебраически связанное семейство элементов
A 421	**algebraically equivalent algebraic manifold** <AG>	algebraisch äquivalente [algebraische] Mannigfaltigkeit *f*	variété *f* algébriquement équivalente	алгебраически эквивалентное алгебраическое многообразие

No.	English	German	French	Russian
A 422	**algebraically equivalent set** <AL>	algebraisch äquivalente (gleichwertige) Menge *f*	ensemble *m* algébriquement équivalent	алгебраически равноценное (эквивалентное, равносильное, равнозначное) множество
A 423	**algebraically independent elements,** algebraically independent set of elements <AL>	algebraisch unabhängige Elemente *npl*, algebraisch-unabhängige Menge *f* von Elementen, irreduzibles System *n*	éléments *mpl* algébriquement indépendants, famille *f* d'éléments algébriquement libre	алгебраически независимые элементы, алгебраически независимая система элементов, алгебраически свободное семейство элементов
	algebraically independent elements over *k* <AL>	*s.* T 728		
	algebraically independent generating set <AL>	*s.* T 726		
	algebraically independent set of elements <AL>	*s.* A 423		
	algebraic basis <FA>	*s.* H 58		
A 424	**algebraic branch point, algebraic branch-point,** algebraic singularity (singular point) <FT>	algebraische singuläre Stelle *f*, algebraische Singularität *f*, algebraischer Verzweigungspunkt (Windungspunkt) *m*	singularité *f* (point *m* critique) algébrique	алгебраическая точка ветвления (разветвления), алгебраическая [особая] точка, алгебраическая особенность (критическая точка)
	algebraic branch-point (branch point) of order *k*—1 <FT>	*s.* B 735		
A 425	**algebraic calculus,** operating with letters, algebra <AR>	Buchstabenrechnen *n*, Buchstabenrechnung *f*, elementare Arithmetik (Algebra) *f*	arithmétique *f* élémentaire, algèbre *f* spécieuse, calcul *m* algébrique (littéral)	буквенное исчисление
A 426	**algebraic closure** <of a field> <AL>	algebraischer Abschluß *m*, algebraisch[-]abgeschlossene Hülle *f*, absolute algebraische Hülle	clôture *f* algébrique	алгебраическое замыкание
A 427	**algebraic closure** <in *L*> <of a field> <SE>	[relative] algebraische Hülle *f*, relativ algebraisch-abgeschlossene Hülle, relativer algebraischer Abschluß *m* <in *L*>	fermeture *f* algébrique, clôture *f* algébrique relative <dans *L*>	относительная алгебраическая оболочка <в *L*>
A 428	**algebraic closure operator** <AL, UA>	algebraische Hüllenoperation *f*	fermeture *f* algébrique	оператор алгебраического замыкания
A 429	**algebraic complement** <of a subspace> <AL, FA>	[algebraischer] Komplementärraum *m*, algebraisch komplementärer Teilraum *m*	supplémentaire *m* algébrique	алгебраическое дополнение
A 430	**algebraic complement** <of a topological group> <GR>	algebraisches Komplement *n*	supplémentaire *m* algébrique	алгебраическое дополнение
A 431	**algebraic completion** <AL>	algebraische Abschließung *f*	fermeture *f* algébrique	алгебраическое замыкание
A 432	**algebraic cone** <of *n*-th class> <AG>	algebraischer Kegel *m* <*n*-ter Klasse>	cône *m* algébrique <de classe *n*>	алгебраический конус <класса *n*>
	algebraic conjugate <AB>	*s.* C 1994		
	algebraic curve of [the] second degree (order) <AG, AY>	*s.* C 1944		
	algebraic curve of the fifth degree (order) <AG>	*s.* Q 301		
	algebraic curve of the fourth degree (order) <AG>	*s.* Q 87		
	algebraic curve of the sixth degree (order) <AG>	*s.* S 727		
	algebraic curve of the third degree (order) <AG>	*s.* C 2738		
	algebraic distance <GE>	*s.* S 839		
	algebraic divisor <AB>	*s.* M 788		
A 433	**algebraic equation,** polynomial equation <AL>	algebraische Gleichung *f*, Polynomgleichung *f*	équation *f* algébrique (polynomiale, entière)	алгебраическое (полиномиальное) уравнение
	algebraic equation of [the] fifth degree <AL>	*s.* Q 302		
	algebraic equation of [the] fourth degree <AL>	*s.* Q 88		
	algebraic equation of [the] sixth degree <AL>	*s.* S 728		
	algebraic equation soluble by radicals <AL>	*s.* E 352		
A 434	**algebraic expression,** expression <AL>	[algebraischer] Ausdruck *m*	expression (formule) *f* algébrique, expression	[алгебраическое] выражение
A 435	**algebraic extension** <of a field, over a field>, algebraic field extension <AL>	algebraische Körpererweiterung (Erweiterung) *f*; algebraischer Oberkörper (Erweiterungskörper) *m*, algebraischer Körper *m* über einem Körper	extension *f* algébrique [d'un corps]	алгебраическое расширение поля, алгебраическое расширение
A 436	**algebraic field** <AL>	algebraischer Körper *m* <nicht notwendig endlichen Grades>	corps *m* algébrique	алгебраическое поле

No.	English	Deutsch	Français	Русский
	algebraic field extension <AL>	*s.* A 435		
	algebraic field over the prime field <AL>	*s.* A 83		
A 437	**algebraic form,** rectangular form, $a+ib$ form <of a complex number> <AL, AN>	algebraische Form *f*, komplexe Zahl *f* in der Form $a+bi$	forme *f* algébrique	алгебраическая форма, декартова форма
A 438	**algebraic fraction** <AL>	algebraischer Bruch *m*, Quotient *m* algebraischer Ausdrücke, Buchstabenbruch *m*, litteraler Bruch	fraction *f* algébrique, // fraction littérale	алгебраическая дробь
	algebraic function field <AL>	*s.* F 181		
	algebraic function of the fifth degree <AL>	*s.* Q 300		
A 439	**algebraic group** <defined over *k*> <AG, AL>	algebraische Gruppe *f*, Gruppenmannigfaltigkeit *f* <über *k* definierte>	[*k*-]groupe *m* algébrique	алгебраическая группа <определенная над *k*>
A 440	**algebraic hull** <of a Lie algebra> <AL>	algebraische Hülle *f*	enveloppe *f* algébrique	алгебраическая оболочка
A 441	**algebraic hypersurface of the second order,** second-order algebraic hypersurface <AG>	algebraische Hyperfläche *f* zweiter Ordnung	hypersurface *f* algébrique de deuxième ordre	алгебраическая гиперповерхность второго порядка
A 442	**algebraic integer,** whole [algebraic] number <NT>	ganze algebraische Zahl *f*, ganz-algebraische Zahl, ganzalgebraische (ganze) Zahl	entier *m* algébrique	целое алгебраическое число
A 443	**algebraic irrational [number]** <NT>	algebraische Irrationalität *f*, algebraische irrationale Zahl *f*	irrationalité (irrationnelle) *f* algébrique, nombre *m* irrationnel algébrique	алгебраическая иррациональность, алгебраическое иррациональное число, иррациональное алгебраическое число
A 444	**algebraicity** <AL, NT>	Algebraizität *f*	algébricité *f*	алгебраичность
	algebraic k-set <AG>	*s.* K 185		
A 445	**algebraic lattice,** compactly generated lattice <LA>	algebraischer Verband *m*	treillis *m* algébrique	алгебраическая (компактно порожденная) решетка
A 446	**algebraic Lie algebra** <AL>	algebraischer Liescher Teilring (Ring) *m*	algèbre *f* de Lie algébrique	алгебраическая алгебра Ли
	algebraic manifold <AG>	*s.* A 464		
	algebraic manifold free from singularities <AG>	*s.* A 467		
	algebraic manifold without singularities <AG>	*s.* A 467		
A 447	**algebraic multiplication** <of signed numbers> <AL, AR>	Multiplikation *f* unter Berücksichtigung des Vorzeichens	multiplication *f* algébrique	алгебраическое умножение
A 448	**algebraic multiplicity** <of image cell in an algebraic mapping> <AT>	algebraische Vielfachheit *f*	multiplicité *f* algébrique	алгебраическая кратность
	algebraic multiplicity <AL, MD>	*s.* M 1059		
A 449	**algebraic norm** <of a complex number> <AL>	Norm *f*, Betragsquadrat *n*	norme *f*, norme algébrique	норма, алгебраическая норма
A 450	**algebraic number** <of degree *n*> <NT>	algebraische Zahl *f* <*n*-ten Grades>	nombre *m* algébrique <de degré *n*, d'ordre *n*>	алгебраическое число, иррациональность <*n*-ой степени, степени *n*>
	algebraic number <AR>	*s.* R 763		
A 451	**algebraic number field,** number field <NT>	algebraischer (endlich-algebraischer) Zahlkörper *m*, endlicher Körper *m*	corps *m* de nombres algébriques	алгебраическое числовое поле, поле алгебраических чисел
A 452	**algebraic number of fixed points,** number of signed fixed points <AT>	algebraische Fixpunktzahl *f* (Anzahl *f* der Fixpunkte), Fixpunktzahl	nombre *m* algébrique des points invariants	алгебраическое число неподвижных точек, число неподвижных точек
A 453	**algebraic number of fixed simplexes** <of a mapping> <AT>	algebraische Fixsimplexzahl *f*, Fixsimplexzahl	nombre *m* algébrique des simplexes invariants	число неподвижных симплексов
A 454	**algebraic number theory,** algebraic theory of numbers <AB>	algebraische Zahlentheorie *f*	théorie *f* algébrique des nombres, arithmétique *f* des corps algébriques	алгебраическая теория чисел
A 455	**algebraic operation,** operation <*n*-ary> <UA>	algebraische Operation (Verknüpfung) *f*, Komposition *f*, Verknüpfung *f*, Verknüpfungsoperation *f*, Operation <*n*-stellige>	opération *f* algébrique, opération <*n*-aire>	алгебраическая операция, операция <*n*-арная>
A 456	**algebraic over a field** <AL>	algebraisch über einem Körper	algébrique relatif (par rapport) à un corps	алгебраический относительно поля
	algebraic plane curve of higher degree (order) <AG>	*s.* H 307		
	algebraic plane curve of the fifth degree (order) <AG>	*s.* Q 299		
	algebraic plane curve of the fourth degree (order) <AG>	*s.* Q 86		
	algebraic plane curve of the sixth degree (order) <AG>	*s.* S 726		

No.	English	German	French	Russian
	algebraic plane curve of the third degree (order) <AG>	*s.* C 2726		
A 457	**algebraic root** <of real *or* complex numbers> <AL>	algebraischer Wert *m* der Wurzel, Wurzel *f* mit Vorzeichen	racine *f* algébrique	алгебраический корень, алгебраическое значение корня
A 458	**algebraic set,** bunch of varieties <Weil>, variety <Zariski>, algebraic variety <Hodge-Pedoe> <AG>	algebraische Menge (Mannigfaltigkeit) *f*, Vielfältigkeit *f* <van der Waerden>	ensemble *m* (partie *f*) algébrique, bouquet *m* de variétés	алгебраическое множество
	algebraic set over k <AG>	*s.* K 185		
	algebraic sign <AL, AR>	*s.* S 837		
	algebraic singularity <FT>	*s.* A 424		
	algebraic singular point <FT>	*s.* A 424		
A 459	**algebraic space** <AG>	algebraischer Raum *m*, Etalschema *n*	espace *m* algébrique, schéma *m* étale	алгебраическое пространство, этальное многообразие, этальная схема, минисхема
A 460	**algebraic spiral** <GE>	algebraische Spirale *f*	spirale *f* algébrique	алгебраическая спираль
A 461	**algebraic structure** <AL>	algebraische Struktur *f*	structure *f* algébrique	алгебраическая структура
	algebraic surface of the first order <AG, GE>	*s.* P 638		
	algebraic surface of the second order <AG>	*s.* T 1081		
	algebraic surface without singularities <AG>	*s.* S 2361		
A 462	**algebraic system,** continuous system <of algebraic varieties> <AG>	algebraisches System *n* [von algebraischen Mannigfaltigkeiten], kontinuierliches (stetiges) System *n*	système *m* algébrique	альгебраическая система
	algebraic system <UA>	*s.* U 311		
A 463	**algebraic system with two compositions,** system of double composition <AL>	System *n* mit doppelter Komposition, algebraische Struktur *f* mit zwei zweistelligen inneren Verknüpfungen	ensemble *m* muni de deux lois de composition internes, système *m* ayant deux lois de composition, ensemble possédant deux lois de composition, système à deux compositions	система с двойным законом композиции
	algebraic theory of numbers <AB>	*s.* A 454		
A 464	**algebraic variety,** algebraic manifold <AG>	algebraische Mannigfaltigkeit *f*	variété *f* algébrique, // multiplicité *f* algébrique	алгебраическое многообразие
	algebraic variety <AG>	*s.* A 458		
	algebraic variety <FT>	*s.* P 1665		
A 465	**algebraic variety embedded without singularities** <AG>	singularitätenfrei eingebettete algebraische Mannigfaltigkeit *f*	variété *f* algébrique plongée sans singularités	неособо вложенное алгебраическое многообразие
	algebraic variety free from singularities <AG>	*s.* A 467		
A 466	**algebraic variety locally normal along W** <Zariski>, algebraic variety relatively normal along *W* with reference to *k* <Weil> <AG>	*k*-normale algebraische Mannigfaltigkeit *f* längs *W*	variété *f* algébrique *k*-normale en *W*	*k*-нормальное вдоль *W* алгебраическое многообразие
	algebraic variety over k <AG>	*s.* K 185		
	algebraic variety relatively normal along W with reference to k <AG>	*s.* A 466		
A 467	**algebraic variety without singularities,** algebraic manifold without singularities, algebraic variety (manifold) free from singularities <AG>	singularitätenfreie algebraische Mannigfaltigkeit *f*	variété *f* algébrique dépourvue de singularités, variété algébrique sans singularités	свободное от особенностей алгебраическое многообразие, алгебраическое многообразие без особенностей
A 468	**algebra integrally dependent on R,** algebra integral over *R* <AL>	ganze Algebra *f* über *R*	algèbre *f* entière sur *R*	целая над *R* алгебра
	algebra integral over R <AL>	*s.* A 468		
	algebra inversely isomorphic <AL>	*s.* O 208		
A 469	**algebraist,** algebrist <GN>	Algebraiker *m*	algébriste *m*	алгебраист
A 470	**algebraizable** <AL>	algebraisierbar	algébrisable	алгебраизируемый
A 471	**algebraization** <AL>	Algebraisierung *f*	algébrisation *f*	алгебраизация
A 472	**algebra module** <AL>	Modul *m* über einer Algebra	module *m* sur une algèbre	модуль над алгеброй
	algebra of a group <AL>	*s.* G 452		
	algebra of Borel subsets <TO>	*s.* B 582		
	algebra of Cayley numbers <AL>	*s.* C 281		
A 472a	**algebra of Clifford numbers** <AL>	Algebra *f* der Cliffordschen Zahlen	algèbre *f* des nombres de Clifford	алгебра чисел Клиффорда
A 473	**algebra of constants** <with respect to a derivation> <AL>	Konstantenalgebra *f* <bezüglich einer Derivation>	sous-algèbre *f* des constantes <par rapport à une dérivation>	алгебра констант <относительно дифференцирования>

No.	English	German	French	Russian
	algebra of definition <FA>	*s.* D 123		
	algebra of events <ST>	*s.* F 188		
A 474	**algebra of finite order,** hypercomplex number system <over *R*>, linear associative algebra of finite order, *R*-algebra of finite order <of order *n*> <AL>	hyperkomplexes Zahlensystem *n* (System *n*, System im engeren Sinne), assoziative *R*-Algebra *f* mit endlicher Basis, [*R*-] Algebra *f* endlichen Ranges, endliche Algebra <vom Rang *n*>	algèbre *f* de dimension finie, algèbre finie <sur *R*>, *R*-algèbre *f* de dimension finie	[ассоциативная] алгебра конечного ранга, алгебра конечной размерности, конечная алгебра, система гиперкомплексных чисел <над *R*>, *R*-алгебра конечного типа
A 475	**algebra of logic,** logical algebra <LO>	Algebra *f* der Logik	algèbre *f* de la logique, calcul *m* propositionnel (des propositions), logique *f*; corps *m* logique	алгебра логики, логическая алгебра
	algebra of octaves <AL>	*s.* C 281		
	algebra of octonions <AL>	*s.* C 281		
	algebra of operators <FA>	*s.* W 4		
	algebra of quaternions <AL>	*s.* Q 275		
	algebra of relations <AL>	*s.* R 671		
	algebra of sets <SE>	*s.* S 638		
	σ-algebra of sets <ME, SE, TO>	*s.* S 810		
A 476	**algebra of tensors,** tensor algebra <as a subfield of tensor calculus> <VT>	Tensoralgebra *f*	algèbre *f* de tenseurs	алгебра тензоров
	algebra of the same type <UA>	*s.* U 312		
	algebra of type I <FA>	*s.* W 5		
	algebra of words <UA>	*s.* P 977		
A 477	**algebra over [a field] *K*,** *K*-algebra <AL>	Algebra *f* über [einem Körper] *K*, *K*-Algebra *f*	algèbre *f* sur [un corps] *K*, *K*-algèbre *f*	алгебра над [полем] *K*, *K*-алгебра
	algebra with an involution * <FA>	*s.* A 408/9		
A 478	**algebra with identity [element],** algebra with unit element <AL>	Algebra *f* mit Einselement	algèbre *f* unitaire	алгебра с единицей, унитарная алгебра
	algebra with operators <UA>	*s.* O 182		
	algebra with unit element <AL>	*s.* A 478		
	algebrist <GN>	*s.* A 469		
A 479	**algebro-geometric** <AG>	algebraisch-geometrisch	algébro-géométrique	алгебро-геометрический
A 480	**algebroid function** <FT>	algebroide Funktion *f*, Algebroide *f*	fonction *f* algébroïde	алгеброидная функция
	algebroid set [of differential equations] <DE>	*s.* A 482		
A 481	**algebroid singularity** <AG, FT>	algebroide Singularität *f*	singularité *f* algébroïde	алгеброидная особенность
A 482	**algebroid system [of differential equations],** algebroid set [of differential equations] <DE>	algebroides System *n* [von Differentialgleichungen], algebroides Differentialgleichungssystem *n*	système *m* algébroïde, système d'équations différentielles algébroïde	алгеброидная система [дифференциальных уравнений]
A 483	**algebro-logarithmic branch point, algebro-logarithmic branch-point (singularity, singular point)** <FT>	algebro-logarithmische singuläre Stelle *f*, algebrologarithmischer Verzweigungspunkt (Windungspunkt) *m*, algebrologarithmische Singularität *f*	point *m* critique algébro-logarithmique, singularité *f* algébro-logarithmique	алгебро-логарифмическая точка ветвления, алгебро-логарифмическая точка [разветвления], алгебро-логарифмическая (алгебраически-логарифмическая) критическая (особая) точка
	algorism <MM>	*s.* A 484		
A 484	**algorithm,** algorism, effective process <MM>	Algorithmus *m*	algorithme *m*	алгоритм, // алгорифм
	algorithm <GN>	*s.* C 12		
A 485	**algorithmic insolubility** <FO>	algorithmische Unlösbarkeit *f*	insolubilité *f* algorithmique	алгоритмическая неразрешаемость
A 486	**algorithmization** <FO, NU>	Algorithmisierung *f*	algorithmisation *f*	алгоритмизация
	algorithm of division <AL, NU>	*s.* D 805		
A 487	**algorithm of Euclid,** Euclid['s] algorithm, Euclidean algorithm, continued division <AL>	euklidischer (Euklidischer) Algorithmus *m* [des größten gemeinsamen Teilers], Kettendivision *f*, Euklidisches Schema [des größten gemeinsamen Teilers], // Wechselwegnahme *f*	division *f* euclidienne, algorithme *m* d'Euclide [pour la recherche du p. g. c. d.], procédé *m* d'Euclide [pour la recherche du p. g. c. d.], algorithme *m* du plus grand commun diviseur, algorithme *m* euclidien	алгоритм Евклида, евклидово деление
	algorithm of Martos <PG>	*s.* M 152		
A 488	**algorithm theory,** theory of algorithms <FO, NU>	Algorithmentheorie *f*, Theorie *f* der Algorithmen	théorie *f* des algorithmes	теория алгоритмов
A 489	**aligned [systematic] sampling** <ST>	gezieltes [systematisches] Stichprobenverfahren *n*	échantillonnage (sondage) *m* [systématique] aligné	выровненная [систематическая] выборка
	alignment <NO>	*s.* A 490		
A 490	**alignment chart (graph, map, nomogram, nomograph),**	Fluchtlinientafel *f*, Fluchtliniennomogramm *n*, Fluchtentafel *f*, kollineare	abaque *m* par (à) alignement, abaque à points alignés, nomogramme *m* à (par)	номограмма из выравненных (соединяемых) точек, прямолинейная

No.	English	German	French	Russian
	alignment, collineation nomograph (nomogram, chart), selfcomputing chart, nomogram with points in a line <NO>	Rechentafel *f*, Leitertafel *f*	alignement, nomogramme à points alignés	номограмма
A 491	**A-lim[it],** Abel-limit, limit by Abel's method <LI>	*A*-Limes *m*, Limes *m* nach dem *A*-Verfahren, *A*-lim	*A*-limite *f*, limite *f* par la méthode d'Abel, *A*-lim	*A*-предел, [обобщенный] предел по Абелю[-Пуассону], [обобщенный] предел по методу Абеля[-Пуассона], *A*-lim
A 492	**A-limitable sequence,** Abel-limitable sequence, sequence limitable by Abel's method <LI>	*A*-limitierbare (nach dem *A*-Verfahren limitierbare) Folge *f*	suite *f* *A*-limitable (limitable par la méthode d'Abel)	*A*-лимитируемая последовательность; последовательность, лимитируемая методом Абеля[-Пуассона]
A 493	**aliotransitive relation** <SE>	aliotransitive (schwach transitive) Relation *f*	relation *f* aliotransitive	слабо транзитивное отношение
A 494	**aliotransitivity** <of a relation> <SE>	Aliotransitivität *f*, schwache Transitivität *f*	aliotransitivité *f*	слабая транзитивность
A 495	**aliquot divisor (part),** proper (exact) divisor <of a number> <NT>	aliquoter (aufgehender, ganzer) Teil *m*, echter Teiler *m*	partie *f* aliquote, diviseur *m* propre	аликвотная часть, собственный дивизор
	aliquot part <NT>	*s.* D 823		
	all element <SE>	*s.* G 409		
A 496	**alligation,** rule of alligation <NU>	Mischungsrechnen *n*, Mischungsrechnung *f*, Mischungsregel *f*, Alligationsregel *f*, Vermischungsrechnung *f*, Regel *f* der Beschickung	calcul *m* de mélange (mélanges), règle *f* (calcul) d'alliage, règle de mélanges	расчет по правилу смещения, правило смещения (товарищества)
A 497	**allocation matrix** <ST>	Allokationsmatrix *f*, Aufteilungsmatrix *f*	matrice *f* de répartition de l'échantillon	матрица распределения
A 498	**allocation of sample** <ST>	Stichprobenaufteilung *f*, Aufteilung *f* der Stichprobe	répartition *f* de l'échantillon	распределение объектов в выборке
A 499	**allocation probability** <ST>	Aufteilungswahrscheinlichkeit *f*	probabilité *f* de répartition	вероятность распределения
	allocation problem <PG>	*s.* A 1056		
A 500	**allokurtic distribution** <ST>	allokurtische Verteilung *f*, Verteilung mit verschiedenem Exzeß	distribution *f* allokurtique	разноэксцессное распределение
	all or none <ST>	*s.* Q 73		
A 501	**allowable co-ordinates** <of a manifold> <AG, DG>	zulässige (zugelassene) Koordinaten *fpl*	coordonnées *fpl* admissibles	допустимые координаты
A 502	**allowable defects** <ST>	zulässiger Ausschuß *m*	défauts *mpl* admissibles (tolérables)	допустимое число дефектных изделий в выборке
A 503	**allowable morphism** <CA>	zulässiger Morphismus *m*	morphisme *m* admissible	допустимый морфизм
A 504	**allowable subfunctor** <CA>	zulässiger Subfunktor *m*	sous-foncteur *m* admissible	допустимый подфунктор
	all relation <SE>	*s.* T 687		
	all relation <UA>	*s.* U 323		
	all symbol <LO>	*s.* U 356		
A 505	**almost algebraic operator, almost-algebraic operator** <in a linear space> <AL, FA>	fastalgebraischer Operator *m*	opérateur *m* presque algébrique	почти алгебраический оператор
	almost all / for <ME, SE, ST>	*s.* A 515		
A 506	**almost bounded function,** [μ-]essentially bounded function <AN>	fast überall beschränkte Funktion *f*, wesentlich beschränkte Funktion	fonction *f* bornée presque partout, fonction bornée essentiellement	функция, ограниченная почти всюду; ограниченная почти всюду функция, существенно ограниченная функция
A 507	**almost certain convergence,** almost sure convergence, convergence almost certain (sure), convergence with probability one <of a sequence of random variables> <ST>	Konvergenz *f* fast sicher, fast sichere Konvergenz, Konvergenz mit der Wahrscheinlichkeit Eins, starke Konvergenz	convergence *f* presque sûre, convergence à probabilité un	сходимость почти наверное, почти достоверная сходимость, сходимость с вероятностью единицы
A 508	**almost-closed set** <TO>	fast-abgeschlossene Menge *f*	ensemble *m* presque fermé	почти замкнутое множество
A 509	**almost complex manifold** <DG, FT>	fast-komplexe Mannigfaltigkeit *f*	variété *f* presque[-]complexe, variété munie d'une structure presque complexe	почти комплексное многообразие
A 510	**almost convergent sequence** <SS>	fastkonvergente Folge *f*	suite *f* presque convergente	почти сходящаяся последовательность
A 511	**almost convex subset** <of a metric space> <TO>	fast konvexe Teilmenge *f*	partie *f* (sous-ensemple *m*) presque convexe	почти выпуклое подмножество
	almost-Cross variety <UA>	*s.* J 122		
A 512	**almost cyclic group** <AL>	fast-zyklische Gruppe *f*	groupe *m* presque cyclique	почти циклическая группа
A 513	**almost disjoint sets** <SE>	Mengen *fpl*, die höchstens endlich viele Elemente gemein haben	ensembles *mpl* orthogonaux	множества, которые пересекаются в не более чем конечном числе точек
A 514	**almost equivalent** <ST>	fast äquivalent	presque équivalent	почти эквивалентный
A 515	**almost everywhere,** a.e.; for almost all <ME, SE, ST>	fast überall <μ-fast überall>; für fast alle	presque partout, p. p.; pour presque tous	почти всюду; почти для всех
A 516	**almost hamiltonian group** <GR>	fasthamiltonsche (fast-Hamiltonsche) Gruppe *f*	groupe *m* presque hamiltonien	почти гамильтонова группа

	English	German	French	Russian
A 517	**almost Hermitian metric** <DG>	fasthermitesche (fast-hermitesche) Metrik *f*	métrique *f* presque hermitienne	почти эрмитова метрика
A 518	**almost impossible event** <ST>	fast unmögliches Ereignis *n*	événement *m* presque impossible	почти невозможное событие
A 519	**almost inner automorphism** <GR>	fast innerer Automorphismus *m*	automorphisme *m* presque intérieur	почти внутренний автоморфизм
A 520	**almost integrally dependent element** <of *R*> <AL>	fast ganz-abhängiges Element *n* <von *R*>	élément *m* x du corps des fractions K de R tel que toutes les puissances x^n <$n \geq 0$> soient contenus dans un sous-R-module de type fini de K	элемент x поля частных K от R со свойством, что все степени x^n ($n \geq 0$) содержатся в R-подмодуле конечного типа
A 521	**almost invariant set** <relative to a measurable transformation> <ME, ST>	fast invariante Menge *f*, invariante Menge	partie *f* presque invariante, ensemble *m* presque invariant	почти инвариантное множество
A 522	**almost isomorphic group** <GR>	fast isomorphe Gruppe *f*	groupe *m* presque isomorphe	почти изоморфная группа
	almost-metric <TO>	*s.* P 1955		
A 523	**almost metric space** <TO>	fastmetrischer Raum *m*	espace *m* presque distancié	почти метрическое пространство
A 524	**almost nilpotent endomorphism** <AL>	fast nilpotenter Endomorphismus *m*	endomorphisme *m* presque nilpotent	почти нильпотентный эндоморфизм
A 525	**almost-normal subgroup** <GR>	Fastnormalteiler *m*	sous-groupe *m* presque invariant	почти нормальный делитель
A 526	**almost-open mapping** <TO>	fastoffene Abbildung *f*	application *f* presque ouverte	почти открытое отображение
	almost open set, almost-open set <RF, TO>	*s.* B 23		
A 527	**almost periodic compactification** <of a topological semigroup> <AL>	fastperiodische Kompaktifizierung (Kompaktifikation) *f*	compactifié *m* presque périodique	почти периодическая компактификация
A 528	**almost periodic function, almost-periodic function** <AP>	fastperiodische Funktion *f*	fonction *f* presque périodique, fonction presque-périodique	почти периодическая функция
A 529	**almost periodic function in the sense of Bohr,** Bohr['s] almost periodic function <AP>	Bohrsche fastperiodische Funktion *f*	fonction *f* presque-périodique au sens de Bohr	боровская (равномерная) почти периодическая функция, почти периодическая функция бора
	almost-periodic function in the sense of Levitan <AP>	*s.* L 605		
A 530	**almost-periodic function [in the sense] of [H.] Weyl,** generalized almost-periodic function in the sense of Weyl <on a topological group> <AL>	W-fastperiodische Funktion *f*, Weyl-fastperiodische Funktion	fonction *f* presque-périodique de [H.] Weyl	почти периодическая функция в смысле Г. Вейля
A 531	**almost periodic function [in the sense] of [H.] Weyl,** generalized almost periodic function in the sense of [H.] Weyl, Weyl['s] almost periodic function, W_p (W^p) almost-periodic function <of a real variable> <AP>	W^p-fastperiodische Funktion *f*, Weyl-fastperiodische Funktion	fonction *f* presque-périodique [généralisée] de [H.] Weyl	[обобщенная] почти периодическая функция в смысле Г. Вейля
A 532	**almost periodicity, almost-periodicity** <of a function> <AP>	Fastperiodizität *f*	presque-périodicité *f*	почти-периодичность
A 533	**almost-poly-minimax group** <AL>	Fast-Polyminimaxgruppe *f*	groupe *m* presque poly-minimax	почти полиминимаксная группа
A 534	**almost prime** <NT>	Fastprimzahl *f*	nombre *m* presque premier	почти простое число
A 535	**almost significant** <ST>	fast signifikant	presque significatif	почти значимый
A 536	**almost solvable group** <GR>	fast-auflösbare Gruppe *f*	groupe *m* presque résoluble	почти-разрешимая группа
	almost sure convergence <ST>	*s.* A 507		
	almost uniform convergence <FA>	*s.* Q 261		
	almost uniformly convergent sequence <FA>	*s.* Q 263		
	alphabetical order <SE>	*s.* L 619		
	alpha-error <ST>	*s.* E 477		
	alpha-risk <ST>	*s.* R 1342		
	alpha-sequence <SE>	*s.* A 537		
A 537	**alpha-termed sequence,** α-termed sequence, alpha-sequence, α-sequence, transfinite sequence of type α (alpha) <SE>	Alpha-Folge *f*, α-Folge *f*	alpha-suite *f*, α-suite *f*, suite *f* transfinie de type α (alpha)	альфа-последовательность, α-последовательность, трансфинитная последовательность типа α (альфа)
	Al series <FU>	*s.* W 151		
A 538	**Alt['s] curvature** <of a metric space> <AN>	Altsche Krümmung *f*	courbure *f* d'Alt	кривизна Альта
A 539	**alternant** <a polynomial in n indeterminates *or* a determinant of f_i (r_j) type *or* an operator of the type $AB-BA$ in cumulant theory *or* a quaternary alternating bilinear form> <AL, AN, GE, ST>	Alternante *f*	alternant *m*	альтернант
	alternant <MD>	*s.* V 40		

No.	English	German	French	Russian
A 540	**alternant of degree *n*** <a Lie algebra> <AL>	Alternante *f* vom Grade *n*	alternant *m* de degré *n*	одночлен (коммутатор, альтернант) степени *n*
A 541	**alternate angles** <EG>	Wechselwinkel *mpl*	angles *mpl* alternes	накрестлежащие углы, накрест лежащие углы
	alternate denial <AL, LO>	*s.* S 763		
	alternate exterior angles <EG>	*s.* E 825		
A 542	**alternate form of binomial formula** <AR>	binomischer Satz *m* für $(a-b)^n$	formule *f* du binôme pour $(a-b)^n$	формула бинома для $(a-b)^n$
	alternate interior angles <EG>	*s.* I 717		
	alternate *p*-linear function <AL, GE, VT>	*s.* M 1091		
	alternating bilinear form <AL>	*s.* S 2477		
A 543	**alternating chain** <AT, GP>	alternierende Kette *f*	chaîne *f* alternée	альтернирующая (знакопеременная) цепь <AT>; чередующаяся цепь <GP>
A 544	**alternating continued fraction** <NT>	alternierender Kettenbruch *m*	fraction *f* continue alternée	знакопеременная цепная дробь
A 545	**alternating cross sum** <NT>	alternierende Quersumme *f*	excès *m* de la somme des chiffres de rangs impaires à partir de la droite sur celle des chiffres de rangs pairs	сумма цифр числа с альтернацией
	alternating differential form <DE>	*s.* E 836		
A 546	**alternating form,** skew-symmetric form <AL>	alternierende (schiefsymmetrische) Form *f*	forme *f* alternée (anti[-]symétrique), // forme alternante	знакопеременная (кососимметрическая) форма
	alternating function <AN>	*s.* A 774		
A 547	**alternating group** <on *n* letters> <GR>	alternierende Gruppe (Permutationsgruppe) *f* <von *n* Elementen, *n*-ten Grades>	groupe *m* alterné <de degré *n*, des substitutions de *n* objets>	знакопеременная группа <степени *n*, *n*-ой степени>
	alternating harmonic series <SS>	*s.* L 547		
	alternating inner product <AL>	*s.* S 2481		
A 548	**alternating kernel,** antisymmetric (skew-symmetrical) kernel <IE>	schiefsymmetrischer (alternierender, antisymmetrischer) Kern *m*	noyau *m* symétrique gauche, noyau anti[-]symétrique (alterné)	антисимметричное (кососимметрическое, знакопеременное) ядро
A 549	**alternating knot** <AT>	alternierender Knoten *m*	nœud *m* alterné	альтернирующий узел
A 550	**alternating matrix** <antisymmetric matrix with zero principal diagonal elements> <MD>	alternierende Matrix *f*	matrice *f* alternée	знакопеременная матрица
	alternating matrix <MD>	*s.* S 1184		
A 551	**alternating method,** Schwarz['s] alternating method, "alternierendes Verfahren" <DE, PO>	alternierendes Verfahren *n* [von [H. A.] Schwarz], Schwarzsches alternierendes Verfahren	méthode *f* alternante [de Schwarz], procédé *m* alterné, méthode alternée de Schwarz	альтернирующий метод [Шварца]
A 552	**alternating multilinear form** <AL>	alternierende Multilinearform *f*	forme *f* multilinéaire alternée	полилинейная знакопеременная форма
	alternating part <AL, VT>	*s.* A 560		
A 553	**alternating path method [of Petersen]** <GP>	Petersensche Methode *f*	méthode *f* de Petersen	метод Петерсена
A 554	**alternating permutation** <CT>	alternierende Permutation *f*	permutation *f* alternée <André>	
	alternating product <AL>	*s.* O 550		
	alternating product <VT>	*s.* V 121		
A 555	**alternating renewal process** <ST>	alternierender Erneuerungsprozeß *m*	processus *m* du renouvellement alternatif	альтернирующий процесс восстановления
	alternating second-order tensor <VT>	*s.* A 566		
A 556	**alternating sequence** <GP>	alternierende Folge *f*	séquence *f* alternée <relativement à un ensemble stable>	чередующаяся последовательность
A 557	**alternating sequence** <SS>	alternierende Folge *f*	suite *f* alternée	знакопеременная последовательность
A 558	**alternating series** <SS>	alternierende Reihe *f*, Wechselreihe *f*	série *f* alternée, série de première espèce	знакочередующийся ряд; знакопеременный ряд <имеет члены как положительного так отрицательного знака, а не необходимо поочередно>
A 559	**alternating series test [for convergence],** alternating signs test (rule), Leibniz['s] alternating series test, Leibniz['s] rule (test, theorem), // Leibnitz['s] rule (test, theorem) <SS>	Leibnizsche Regel *f*, Leibnizsches Konvergenzkriterium (Kriterium) *n*	règle *f* de Leibniz, règle des séries alternées, // règle *f* de Leibnitz	теорема (правило, признак) Лейбница
A 560	**alternating share,** alternating part <AL, VT>	alternierender (schiefsymmetrischer) Anteil *m*	partie *f* anti[-]symétrique (symétrique gauche)	кососимметрическая часть
	alternating signs rule <SS>	*s.* A 559		

No.	English	German	French	Russian
	alternating signs test <SS>	*s.* A 559		
A 561	**alternating sum** <SS,TO>	alternierende Summe *f*, Wechselsumme *f*	somme *f* alternante, somme alternée	знакочередующаяся (знакопеременная, альтернированная) сумма
A 562	**alternating tensor** <AL>	alternierender Tensor *m*	tenseur *m* alterné	альтернирующий тензор
A 563	**alternating tensor,** epsilon-system, epsilon-tensor, ε-tensor, Levi-Civita['s] tensor, Levi-Civita symbol, tensor identity of Levi-Civita, generalized Kronecker delta <DG, VT>	Levi-Cività-Tensor *m*, Epsilontensor, ε-Tensor *m*, Levi-Cività-Symbol *n*, Levi-Civitàsches Symbol *n*, total (vollständig) antisymmetrischer Einheitstensor *m*, Levi-Cività-scher Fundamentaltensor *m*, Fundamentaltensor von [Ricci und] Levi-Cività	epsilon-tenseur *m*, ε-tenseur *m*, tenseur (symbole) *m* de Levi-Cività	полностью антисимметричный единичный тензор, единичный антисимметричный псевдотензор, символ Леви-Чивита, эпсилон-тензор, ε-тензор
A 564	**alternating tensor,** antisymmetric[al] (skew-symmetrical, antimetric) tensor <VT>	alternierender (schiefsymmetrischer, antisymmetrischer, antimetrischer) Tensor *m*, Antitensor *m*	tenseur *m* anti[-]symétrique (symétrique gauche)	антисимметрический (антисимметричный, кососимметрический, кососимметричный, знакопеременный) тензор, аксиатор
A 565	**alternating tensor density,** skew-symmetric[al] tensor density, antisymmetric (antimetric) tensor density <VT>	alternierende (antimetrische, antisymmetrische, schiefsymmetrische) Tensordichte *f*	densité *f* tensorielle gauche (anti[-]symétrique)	кососимметрическая (антисимметрическая, альтернирующая) тензорная плотность
	alternating tensor of rank ***p*** <AL, GE, VT>	*s.* M 1091		
A 566	**alternating tensor of second order,** anticonjugate dyadic, alternating (skew-symmetric) second-order tensor <VT>	alternierender Tensor *m* zweiter Stufe, antikonjugierte Dyade *f*, schiefsymmetrischer Tensor zweiter Stufe	tenseur *m* symétrique gauche de second ordre, dyade *f* anticonjuguée, tenseur antisymétrique de second ordre	антисимметричный тензор второй валентности, антисопряженная диада, двухвалентный кососимметрический тензор
A 567	**alternating tree** <SP>	alternierender Baum *m*	arbre *m* alterné	чередующееся дерево
A 568	**alternation,** antisymmetrization <of a tensor, also of a function> <VT>	Alternation *f*, Alternieren *n*, Alternierung *f*, Schiefsymmetrischmachen *n*, Schiefsymmetrisieren *n*, Antisymmetrisierung *f*, Antisymmetrisieren *n*	alternation *f*, antisymétrisation *f*	альтернирование, кососимметрирование, антисимметрирование, альтернация, антисимметризация
	alternation <LO>	*s.* 1. D 705; 2. E 687		
A 569	**alternative** <a special collective> <ST>	Alternative *f*	alternative *f*	альтернатива
	alternative <LO>	*s.* E 687		
A 570	**alternative algebra** <AL>	alternative Algebra *f*	algèbre *f* alternative	альтернативная алгебра
A 571	**alternative character** <ST>	alternatives Merkmal *n*, Attribut *n*	caractère *m* alternatif	альтернативный признак
	alternative denial <AL, LO>	*s.* S 763		
	alternative disjunction <LO>	*s.* D 705		
	alternative division ring <AL>	*s.* A 572		
A 572	**alternative field,** alternative division ring <AL>	Alternativkörper *m*	corps *m* alternatif	альтернативное тело
A 573	**alternative hypothesis** <ST>	Alternativhypothese *f*, Alternative *f*, Gegenhypothese *f*	hypothèse *f* alternative	альтернативная гипотеза
A 574	**alternative law** <AL, GN>	Alternativgesetz *n*, alternatives Gesetz *n*	loi *f* alternative	альтернативный закон
	alternative normal form <AL, TO>	*s.* D 709		
	alternative of Fredholm <IE>	*s.* F 589		
	alternative proposition <LO>	*s.* D 711		
A 575	**alternative ring** <AL>	alternativer Ring *m*, Alternativring *m*	anneau *m* alternatif	альтернативное кольцо
	alternative theorem <AL, FA, GU>	*s.* T 258		
A 576	**alternative variability,** dichotomy, discontinuous (qualitative) variability <ST>	alternative (diskontinuierliche, qualitative) Variabilität *f*, Alternativvariabilität *f*, Dichotomie *f*	variabilité *f* alternative (discontinue, qualitative), dichotomie *f*	альтернативная (качественная, прерывная) изменчивость, дихотомия
A 577	**alternator,** permutation symbol, epsilon-system, epsilon-symbol, ε-system, ε-symbol <DG, VT>	Levi-Cività-Dichte *f*, Levi-Civitàsche Tensordichte *f*, Tensordichte von Levi-Cività	densité *f* (indicateur *m*) de Levi-Cività, tenseur *m* d'orientation	тензорная плотность Леви-Чивита, оператор перестановок
	"alternierendes Verfahren" <DE, PO>	*s.* A 551		
A 578	**altitude** <of a triangle *or* trapezoid *or* tetrahedron> <EG>	Höhe *f*	hauteur *f*	высота
A 579	**altitude,** axis <of a circular cone> <EG>	Höhe *f*	hauteur *f*, axe *m*	высота
	altitude <AY>	*s.* A 815		
A 580	**altitude theorem** <of the rectangular triangle> <EG>	Höhensatz *m*	théorème *m* de la hauteur	теорема о высоте <в прямоугольных треугольниках>
	always true sentence <LO>	*s.* U 349		

	am <FT, FU>	*s.* A 605		
	Δ am <FU>	*s.* A 608		
A 581	**amalgam** <AL>	Amalgam *n*	amalgame *m*	амальгама
A 582	**amalgamated product** <AL>	amalgamiertes Produkt *n*	produit *m* amalgamé	амальгамированное произведение
A 583	**amalgamated subalgebra** <AL>	amalgamierte Unteralgebra *f*	sous-algèbre *f* amalgamée	амальгамированная подальгебра
A 584	**amalgamated subcategory** <CA>	amalgamierte Teilkategorie *f*	sous-catégorie *f* amalgamée	амальгамированная подкатегория
A 585	**amalgamated subgroup** <GR>	vereinigte Untergruppe *f*	sous-groupe *m* amalgamé	объединенная подгруппа
	amalgamated sum <CA>	*s.* 1. F 155; 2. P 2076		
A 586	**amalgamation** <UA>	Amalgamierung *f*	amalgamation *f*	амальгамирование
	amalgamized sum <CA>	*s.* 1. F 155; 2. P 2076		
A 587	**ambient space** <for a point> <TO>	umgebender Raum *m*	espace *m* ambiant	окружающее пространство
A 588	**ambiguous Borel set** <of class α> <SE>	ambige (zweiseitige) Borelsche Menge *f* <der Klasse α>	ensemble *m* borélien ambigu <de classe α>	двустороннее борелевское множество <класса α>
A 589	**ambiguous class** <NT>	ambige (benachbarte) Klasse *f*	classe *f* ambiguë	двусторонний класс
A 590	**ambiguous class** <of forms> <NT>	ambige (zweiseitige) Klasse *f*, Ambige *f*	classe *f* ambiguë	двусторонний класс
A 591	**ambiguous form** <NT>	ambige (zweiseitige) Form *f*, forma *f* anceps <Gauß>	forme *f* ambiguë	двусторонняя [квадратическая] форма
A 592	**ambiguous ideal** <AB>	ambiges (stark ambiges, invariantes) Ideal *n*	idéal *m* ambigu	двусторонний идеал
A 593	**ambiguous number** <of a field> <AB>	Ambige *f*, ambige Zahl *f*	ambigu *m*, nombre *m* ambigu	двустороннее число
A 594	**ambiguous point,** point of indeterminacy <FT>	Unbestimmtheitsstelle *f*	point *m* d'indétermination	точка неопределенности
A 595	**amenability** <AL>	Amenabilität *f*	moyennabilité *f*, amenabilité *f*	аменабельность, усредняемость
A 596	**amenable group** <GR>	amenable (mittelbare) Gruppe *f*	groupe *m* amenable (moyennable)	аменабельная (усредняемая) группа
	A method <LI>	*s.* 1. A 36; 2. A 40		
A 597	**amicable numbers,** friendly numbers <NT>	befreundete (verwandte) Zahlen *fpl*, // numeri *mpl* amicabiles	nombres *mpl* amiables, numeri *mpl* amicabiles	содружественные (дружественные, дружеские) числа
A 598	**𝔄-module of locally finite type** <a sheaf> <AT>	𝔄-Modul *m* lokal endlichen Typs	𝔄-module *m* localement finitiste	𝔄-модуль локально конечного типа
	amount of information <ST>	*s.* I 506		
A 599	**amphicheiral knot** <AT>	amphicheiraler Knoten *m*	nœud *m* isotope à son symétrique	обоюдоручный узел
A 600	**amphidromic curve** <TO>	amphidrome Kurve *f*	courbe *f* amphidromique	амфидромная кривая
A 601	**ample divisor** <AG>	ampler Divisor *m*	diviseur *m* ample	обильный дивизор
A 602	**ample linear system** <AG>	amples lineares System *n*	système *m* linéaire ample, série *f* linéaire ample	обильная линейная система
A 603	**amplitude,** phase, polar angle, angle argument, arg <of a complex number> <AN>	Argument *n*, Arcus *m*, Amplitude *f*, Winkel *m*, Phase *f*, Abweichung *f*, Anomalie *f*, Azimut *n*, arg, arc	argument *m*, amplitude *f*, phase *f*, anomalie *f*, azimut *m*, arg	полярный угол, аргумент, амплитуда
A 604	**amplitude,** azimuth, azimuth (azimuthal, polar, vectorial) angle, argument, phase, anomaly <as a plane polar co-ordinate> <AY>	Richtungswinkel *m*, Amplitude *f*, Polarwinkel *m*	amplitude *f*, azimut *m*, angle *m* d'azimut, angle polaire, anomalie *f*, abscisse *f* circulaire	полярный угол, амплитуда, фаза
A 605	**amplitude,** Jacobian (elliptic) amplitude, am <FT, FU>	Amplitude *f*, Jacobische (elliptische) Amplitude, am	fonction *f* amplitude, amplitude *f* [elliptique], am	амплитуда [эллиптического интеграла], эллиптическая амплитуда, am
A 606	**amplitude cosine,** elliptic sine, cn, cos am <FU>	Cosinus *m* amplitudinis, elliptischer Kosinus *m*, cn, cos am	cosinus *m* d'amplitude, cosinus elliptique, cn, cos am	косинус амплитуды, эллиптический косинус, cn, cos am
A 607	**amplitude cotangent,** elliptic cotangent, cs, cot am, // ctg am <FU>	Cotangens *m* amplitudinis, elliptischer Kotangens *m*, cs, cot am, // ctg am	cotangente *f* d'amplitude, cotangente elliptique, cs, cot am, // ctg am	котангенс амплитуды, эллиптический котангенс, cs, cot am, // ctg am
A 608	**amplitude delta,** dn, Δ am <FU>	Delta *n* amplitudinis, dn, Δ am	delta *m* d'amplitude, dn, Δ am	дельта амплитуды, dn, Δ am
A 609	**amplitude sine,** elliptic sine, sn, sin am <FU>	Sinus *m* amplitudinis, elliptischer Sinus, sn, sin am	sinus *m* d'amplitude, sinus elliptique, sn, sin am	синус амплитуды, эллиптический синус, sn, sin am
A 610	**amplitude tangent,** sc, t am, tan am, // tg am <FU>	Tangens *m* amplitudinis, sc, t am, tan am, // tg am	tangente *f* d'amplitude, sc, t am, tan am, // tg am	тангенс амплитуды, sc, t am, tan am, // tg am
A 611	**Amsler['s] planimeter,** planimeter of Amsler <GE, IN>	Amslersches Planimeter *n*, Planimeter von Amsler	planimètre *m* d'Amsler	планиметр Амслера
A 612	**anacamptic curve,** reflecting curve <GE>	anakamptische (reflektierende) Kurve *f*	courbe *f* réfléchissante (anacamptique, réflectoire)	отражательная (зеркальная) линия
A 613	**anaclastic curve,** refracting curve <GE>	anaklastische (brechende) Kurve *f*	courbe *f* réfractante (anaclastique)	преломляющая (анакластическая) кривая
A 614	**anallagmatic curve** <GE>	anallagmatische Kurve *f*	courbe *f* anallagmatique	аналлагматическая кривая
A 615	**anallagmatic figure** <GE>	anallagmatische Figur *f*	figure *f* anallagmatique, anallagmatique *f*	аналлагматическая фигура
	analysis <AN>	*s.* M 164		
	analysis of a function <DI>	*s.* D 694		

	analysis of covariance <ST>	*s.* C 2598		
	analysis of dispersion <ST>	*s.* M 1087		
A 616	**analysis of time series,** time series analysis <SP>	Zeitreihenanalyse *f*	analyse *f* des séries chronologiques	анализ временных рядов
	analysis of variance <ST>	*s.* V 63		
	analysis situs <AT>	*s.* T 561		
	Analysis Situs invariant <TO>	*s.* T 521		
A 617	**analyst** <NT>	Analytiker *m*	analyste *m*	аналитик
	analytical arc <AN>	*s.* A 627		
	analytical differential <FT>	*s.* A 11		
A 618	**analytical function** <having sets for its arguments and for its values> <FA>	analytische Mengenfunktion *f*	fonction *f* analytique <d'une suite infinie d'ensembles>	аналитическая функция множеств
A 619	**analytical geometry,** analytic (cartesian) geometry <AY>	analytische Geometrie *f*	géométrie *f* analytique	аналитическая геометрия
A 620	**analytical hierarchy** <MM>	analytische Hierarchie *f*	hiérarchie *f* analytique	аналитическая иерархия
	analytical index <DE>	*s.* I 336		
	analytical local Lie group <GR>	*s.* L 939		
A 621	**analytically continuable** <FT, SS>	analytisch fortsetzbar	analytiquement prolongeable	аналитически продолжаемый
A 622	**analytically independent element** <of an algebra> <AL>	analytisch unabhängiges Element *n*	élément *m* analytiquement indépendant	аналитически независимый элемент
A 623	**analytically irreducible k-variety** <along a k-subvariety> <AG>	analytisch irreduzible Mannigfaltigkeit *f*	variété *f* analytiquement irréductible	аналитически неприводимое многообразие
A 624	**analytically representable function** <AN>	analytisch darstellbare Funktion *f*	fonction *f* représentable analytiquement	функция, представимая аналитически
	analytically representable function <RF, TO>	*s.* B 18		
A 625	**analytically representable function of [Baire's] class α** <RF, TO>	Funktion *f* α-ter (alpha-ter) Klasse	fonction *f* représentable analytiquement de classe α	аналитически представимая функция класса α
	analytical mapping <FT>	*s.* H 407		
A 626	**analytical plane,** characteristic plane, synectic plane <PJ>	synektische (analytische, charakteristische) Ebene *f*	plan *m* analytique (caractéristique, synectique)	аналитическая (характеристическая, синэктическая) плоскость
	analytical transformation <FT>	*s.* H 407		
A 627	**analytic arc,** analytic curve, analytical arc <AN>	analytischer Bogen *m*, analytisches Kurvenstück *n*	arc *m* [de courbe] analytique	аналитическая дуга (кривая), аналитический кусок кривой
A 628	**analytic completion (continuation)** <FT>	analytische Fortsetzung *f*	continuation (complétion) *f* analytique	аналитическое продолжение
A 629	**analytic continuation along a curve (path)** <FT>	analytische Fortsetzung *f* längs einer Kurve; analytische Fortsetzung längs eines Weges	continuation *f* analytique le long d'une courbe	аналитическое продолжение вдоль кривой (пути)
A 630	**analytic continuation along a sequence of domains** <especially: circles>, indirect analytic continuation <FT>	analytische Fortsetzung *f* längs (mittels) einer Kette von Gebieten <speziell: mittels einer Kreiskette>, mittelbare analytische Fortsetzung	continuation *f* analytique le long d'une chaîne (séquence) de domaines <en particulier: cercles>, continuation analytique indirecte	аналитическое продолжение посредством (при помощи) цепи (цепочки) областей <особенно: кругов>, косвенное аналитическое продолжение
	analytic curve <AN>	*s.* A 627		
A 631	**analytic factorial** <AN, FU>	analytische Fakultät *f*	faculté *f* analytique	аналитический факториал
	analytic form <AN, GN>	*s.* R 835		
A 632	**analytic function** <FT, RF>	analytische Funktion *f*	fonction *f* analytique	аналитическая функция
	analytic function <DG>	*s.* H 404		
A 633	**analytic function in the Fréchet sense** <FT>	Fréchet-analytische Funktion *f*	fonction *f* analytique au sens de Fréchet	аналитическая функция в смысле Фреше
	analytic function in the sense of Gâteaux <FT>	*s.* G 51		
	analytic geometry <AY>	*s.* A 619		
A 634	**analytic grill** <SE>	analytisches Sieb *n*	crible *m* analytique	аналитическое решето
A 635	**analytic group,** connected Lie group <GR>	analytische (zusammenhängende Liesche) Gruppe *f*	groupe *m* analytique (de Lie connexe)	аналитическая группа, связная группа Ли
A 636	**analytic hypercomplex function,** bilaterally analytic hypercomplex function <FT>	[beidseitig] analytische hyperkomplexe Funktion	fonction *f* hypercomplexe [bilatéralement] analytique	[двусторонняя] аналитическая гиперкомплексная функция
A 637	**analyticity-preserving function** <FA>	analytizitätserhaltende Funktion *f*	fonction *f* conservant l'analyticité	сохраняющая аналитичность функция
A 638	**analytic metric,** Carathéodory['s] metric <FT>	Carathéodorysche Metrik *f*, analytische Metrik	métrique *f* analytique, métrique de Carathéodory	аналитическая метрика, метрика Каратеодори
A 639	**analytic non-continuability** <FT, SS>	[analytische] Nichtfortsetzbarkeit *f*	non-prolongeabilité *f* analytique	аналитическая непродолжимость
A 640	**analytic prime number theory** <NT>	analytische Primzahltheorie *f*	théorie *f* analytique des nombres premiers	аналитическая теория простых чисел

A 641	**analytic proof,** proof by analysis <GN>	analytischer Beweis *m*	démonstration *f* analytique	аналитическое доказательство
A 642	**analytic proposition,** necessary truth <LO>	analytische Aussage *f*, analytisches Urteil *n*	proposition *f* (jugement *m*) analytique	аналитическое суждение
A 643	**analytic quaternion function** <FT>	analytische (reguläre) Quaternionenfunktion *f*	fonction *f* quaternionienne analytique	аналитическая кватернионная функция
A 644	**analytic set** <FT>	analytische Menge *f*	ensemble *m* analytique	аналитическое множество
A 645	**analytic set,** A-set, Souslin set (subset), projective set of class 1 <TO>	analytische Menge *f*, *A*-Menge *f*, Suslinsche Menge, Kern *m* des Suslinschen Schemas	ensemble *m* analytique, ensemble *m* (*A*), ensemble souslinien (de Souslin, A projectif de classe 1)	аналитическое (суслинское) множество, A-множество
A 646	**analytic thread** <GE>	analytischer Faden *m*, eindimensionaler Punktkomplex *m*	fil *m* analytique	аналитическая цепь, одномерный точечный комплекс
A 647	**anamorphosis** <NO>	Verstreckung *f*, Verzerrung *f*, Anamorphose *f*	anamorphose *f*	анаморфоз
	anchor ring <EG>	*s.* T 613		
A 648	**ancillary information,** concomitant information; supplemental information, supplementary information <ST>	zusätzliche Information *f*, Hilfsinformation *f*; ergänzende Information	information *f* ancillaire; information supplémentaire	дополнительная [к основной] информация
A 649	**ancillary statistic** <ST>	Hilfsmaßzahl *f*	fonction *f* ancillaire des observations, statistique *f* ancillaire	статистика, подчиненная основной
A 650	**AND-operator,** ∧ <*read:* and> <LO>	UND-Operator *m*, logisches UND *n*, ∧ <*lies:* und>	opérateur *m* ET, ∧ <*se lit:* et>	И-оператор, ∧ <*читается:* и>
A 651	**André['s] permutation** <CT>	Andrésche Permutation *f*	permutation *f* d'André	перестановка Андре
A 652	**André['s] polynomial** <CT>	Andrésches Polynom *n*	polynôme *m* d'André	многочлен (полином) Андре
A 653	**Andronov-Witt method** <DE, NU>	Methode *f* von Andronow und Witt, Andronow-Wittsche Methode	méthode *f* d'Andronov et Witt	метод Андронова-Витта
A 654	**Anger['s] function** <FU>	Angersche Funktion *f*, Anger-Funktion *f*	fonction *f* d'Anger	функция Ангера, ангерова функция
	angle <AN>	*s.* A 603		
	angle <AY, EG>	*s.* A 673		
	angle <EG>	*s.* P 945		
	angle at centre <EG>	*s.* C 343		
A 655	**angle at circumference,** inscribed angle <of a circle> <EG>	Umfangswinkel *m*, Peripheriewinkel *m*	angle *m* inscrit	вписанный угол
A 656	**angle between a chord and a tangent** <of a circle> <EG>	Sehnentangentenwinkel *m*, Tangentensehnenwinkel *m*	angle *m* entre tangente et corde	угол между хордой и касательной
A 657	**angle between a secant and a tangent** <of a circle> <EG>	Sekantentangentenwinkel *m*	angle *m* entre sécante et tangente	угол между секущей и касательной
A 658	**angle between two curves** <AN, AY>	Winkel *m* zwischen zwei Kurven	angle *m* curviligne (de deux courbes)	криволинейный угол
	angle between two edges <EG>	*s.* E 14		
	angle bracket <GN>	*s.* P 733		
A 659	**angle constant** <PJ>	Winkelkonstante *f*	constante *f* de l'angle	постоянная угла
A 660	**angle function,** turning function <of a continuous mapping> <TO>	Winkelfunktion *f*	fonction *f* angulaire	угловая функция
A 661	**angle-hook** <DS, IN>	Winkelhaken *m*	équerre *f*	наугольник
	angle of 360° <EG>	*s.* P 440		
A 662	**angle of contingence** <of a curve> <DG>	Kontingenzwinkel *m*	angle *m* de contingence	угол смежности
A 663	**angle of contingence** <of two curves> <GE>	Berührungswinkel *m*	angle *m* de contact (contingence)	угол касания (соприкасания, смежности)
A 664	**angle of dip fall, gradient, inclination,** dip angle, angle of slope, inclination, angle of steepest slope, fall (slope) angle <of a plane> <in one-plane projection> <DS>	Böschungswinkel *m*, Neigungswinkel *m*, Fallwinkel *m*	angle *m* d'inclinaison, angle de talus, inclinaison *f* du talus, inclinaison [de la pente], angle de [plus grande] pente	угол наклона (откоса, падения)
A 665	**angle of inclination,** inclination <first, second *or* third> <of a plane to the corresponding plane of projection> <DS>	Tafelneigung *f* <erste, zweite *oder* dritte>	angle *m* d'inclinaison, inclinaison *f* <premier (première), deuxième *ou* troisième> <par rapport au plan horizontal, vertical *ou* de profil>	угол наклона <относительно горизонтальной, вертикальной *или* профильной плоскости>
A 666	**angle of intersection,** intersection angle <EG>	Schnittwinkel *m*	angle *m* d'intersection	угол пересечения
	angle of second curvature <DG>	*s.* A 668		
	angle of [steepest] slope <DS>	*s.* A 664		
A 667	**angle of strike** <DS>	Streichwinkel *m*, Streichen *n*	azimut *m* de la direction	угол простирания
A 668	**angle of torsion,** angle of second curvature <of a space curve> <DG>	Windungswinkel *m*, Schmiegungswinkel *m*, Torsionswinkel *m*	angle *m* de torsion (deuxième courbure)	угол кручения (второй кривизны)
A 669	**angle-preserving mapping,** conformal mapping (transformation), isogonal (isogonic) mapping, equiangular mapping (transformation), angle-pre-	winkeltreue (konforme) Abbildung *f*, isogonale (isogonische, isogone) Abbildung, winkelgleiche Abbildung, konforme (winkeltreue, isogonale, iso-	représentation (application) *f* isogonale (conforme, équiangle, conservant les angles, isogonique)	конформное отображение, сохраняющее углы отображение, изогональное (равноугольное, сохраняющее углы) преобразование

and still: A 669	serving transformation, isogonal (isogonic) transformation <AY, GE>	gonische, isogone) Transformation *f*, orthomorphe Transformation		
	angle-preserving mapping <FT>	*s.* C 1901		
	angle-preserving projection <DS>	*s.* C 1903		
	angle-preserving transformation <AY, GE>	*s.* A 669		
	angle space <AY, EG>	*s.* A 673		
	angle subtended at the centre <EG>	*s.* C 343		
A 670	**angular coefficient,** slope <of a straight line> <AY>	Richtungskoeffizient *m*, Richtungsfaktor *m*, Richtungskonstante *f*, Richtungszahl *f*, Steigungskoeffizient *m*, Steigung *f*, Anstieg *m*	coefficient *m* angulaire, coefficient de direction, pente *f*	угловой коэффициент, наклон
	angular defect <GE>	*s.* D 107		
	angular degree <GE>	*s.* D 174		
A 671	**angular derivative** <FT>	Winkelableitung *f*, Winkelderivierte *f*	dérivée *f* angulaire	угловая производная
A 672	**angular distance,** angular separation <EG>	Winkelabstand *m*, Winkeldistanz *f*, Winkelentfernung *f*	distance *f* (écart *m*) angulaire	угловое расстояние
A 673	**angular domain,** angle [space] <AY, EG>	Winkelraum *m*, Winkelbereich *m*	secteur *m* angulaire, angle *m*	угловой сектор, угловая область, область угла
A 674	**angular domain** <FT>	Winkelraum *m*	domaine *m* angulaire	угловая область
	angular excess <GE>	*s.* E 673		
A 675	**angular metric** <TO>	Winkelmetrik *f*	métrique *f* angulaire	угловая метрика
	angular minute <GE>	*s.* M 659		
A 676	**angular neighbourhood** <VA>	Winkelnachbarschaft *f*	voisinage *m* angulaire	угловая окрестность
	angular point <GE>	*s.* S 12		
	angular second <GE	*s.* S 192		
	angular separation <EG>	*s.* A 672		
A 677	**angular transformation** <ST>	Winkeltransformation *f*	transformation *f* angulaire	тригонометрическое преобразование
A 678	**anharmonic curve** <PJ>	anharmonische Kurve *f*	courbe *f* anharmonique	ангармоническая кривая
	anharmonic ratio <AY>	*s.* C 2710		
A 679	**anholonomic connection,** anholonomic transfer <DG>	anholonome Übertragung *f*	connexion *f* (transfert *m*) anholonome	неголономная связность, неголономное перенесение
A 680	**anholonomic reference system** <DG>	anholonomes Bezugssystem *n*	repère *m* anholonome, repère non holonome	неголономный репер, неголономная система отсчета
	anholonomic transfer <DG>	*s.* A 679		
	anisometric projection <DS>	*s.* T 959		
A 681	**anisotropic geodesic [line]** <GE>	anisotrope Geodätische *f*	ligne *f* géodésique anisotrope (non isotrope), géodésique *f* anisotrope (non isotrope)	анизотропная (неизотропная) геодезическая [линия]
A 682	**anisotropic line,** non-isotropic line <PJ>	anisotrope (nichtisotrope) Gerade *f*	droite *f* anisotrope (non isotrope)	анизотропная (неизотропная) прямая
A 683	**anisotropic plane,** non-isotropic plane <PJ>	anisotrope (nichtisotrope) Ebene *f*	plan *m* anisotrope (non isotrope)	анизотропная (неизотропная) плоскость
A 684	**anisotropic submodule** <AL>	nichtisotroper (anisotroper) Untermodul *m*	sous-module *m* non isotrope	неизотропный подмодуль
	annihilating ideal <AL>	*s.* A 689		
A 685	**annihilation** <AL>	Annullierung *f*	annulation *f*	аннулирование, сведение к нулю
A 686	**annihilator,** order, order ideal, annulet <of a subset of an *R*-module> <AL>	Annullator *m* einer Menge	annulateur *m* d'un ensemble	аннулятор (аннигилятор) множества
A 687	**annihilator** <CA>	Annullator *m*	annulateur *m*	аннулятор
A 688	**annihilator** <IV>	Annihilator *m*	annihilateur *m*	аннигилятор
	annihilator <AL>	*s.* 1. O 334; 2. O 437		
	annihilator <AL, FA>	*s.* O 447		
A 689	**annihilator ideal,** annihilating ideal <AL>	Annullator *m* eines Ideals, annullierendes Ideal *n*	annulateur *m* d'un idéal	аннулирующий идеал
A 690	**annular surface** <common name of hyperboloid of one sheet and hyperbolic paraboloid> <AY, EG>	ringförmige Fläche *f*	surface *f* annulaire	кольцеобразная поверхность
	annulet <AL>	*s.* A 686		
A 691	**annulus,** circular ring <EG>	Kreisring *m*, ebener Kreisring	anneau *m* (couronne *f*) circulaire	[плоское] круговое кольцо
A 692	**anomalous arc** <of a curve> <VA>	anomaler Kurvenbogen (Bogen) *m*, anomales Kurvenstück *n*	arc *m* anomal	аномальная дуга кривой
A 693	**anomalous variational problem** <VA>	anomales Variationsproblem *n*	problème *m* variationnel anomal	аномальная вариационная задача
	anomaly <AY>	*s.* A 604		
	ANOVA <ST>	*s.* V 63		
	ansatz <GN>	*s.* S 706		
A 694	**antecedent** <of a proportion> <AR>	Vorderglied *n*, vorangehendes Glied *n*, Antezedent *m*	antécédent *m*	предыдущий член отношения, антецедент
A 695	**antecedent,** first component, premisse, premise, hypothesis <of an implication> <LO>	Antezedens *m*, Implikationsvorderglied *n*, Vorderglied *n*	prémisse *f*, antécédent *m*, hypothèse *f*	предыдущий член отношения, антецедент, предшествующий (первый) член, посылка

No.	English	German	French	Russian
A 696	**antecedent** <of a sequence> <LO>	Antezedens *n*, Antecedens *n*	antécédent *m*	антецедент
	antecedent <AN>	*s.* I 912		
	antecedent <FO, NT>	*s.* P 1179		
	antecedent <LO>	*s.* P 1222		
A 697	**anterior defect** <of a kernel> <IE>	vorderer Defekt *m*	défaut *m* antérieur	передний дефект
A 698	**anterior null solution** <IE>	vordere Nullösung *f*	solution *f* nulle antérieure	переднее нулевое решение
	antevolute <EG>	*s.* A 721		
A 699	**antianalytic function** <FT>	antianalytische Funktion *f*	fonction *f* anti-analytique	антианалитическая функция
	anti[-]atom <LA>	*s.* C 965		
A 700	**anti-automorphism, antiautomorphism** <of the first *or* second kind> <AL>	Antiautomorphismus *m* <erster (1.) *oder* zweiter (2.) Art>	anti-automorphisme *m*, antiautomorphisme *m* <de première *ou* seconde espèce>	антиавтоморфизм, антиавтоморфизм, инверсивный автоморфизм <первого *или* второго рода>
A 701	**anticentre** <of a group> <GR>	Antizentrum *n*	anticentre *m*	антицентр
A 702	**antichain** <AL, SE>	Antikette *f*, total (voll) antigeordnete Menge *f*, Menge ohne ungleiche vergleichbare Elemente	antichaîne *f*	антицепь
	anticlockwise direction <GE, GN>	*s.* C 2575		
A 703	**anticlockwise revolution (rotation)** <AN, GE>	Umlauf *m* entgegen dem Uhrzeigersinn, positiver Umlauf	rotation *f* dans le sens contraire des aiguilles d'une montre, parcours *m* positif	обход против часовой стрелки, обход в положительном направлении
	anticlockwise sense <GE, GN>	*s.* C 2575		
A 704	**anticollineation** <DS, PJ>	Antikollineation *f*	anticollinéation *f*	антиколлинеация
A 705/6	**anticommutation** <AL>	Antikommutieren *n*	anticommutation *f*	антикоммутирование
A 707	**anticommutation relation** <$AB + BA$> <AL, FA>	[mit dem Antikommutator gebildete] Vertauschungsrelation *f*	relation *f* d'anticommutation	соотношение антикоммутирования, антикоммутационное соотношение
A 708	**anticommutative algebra** <AL>	antikommutative Algebra *f*	algèbre *f* anti-commutative	антикоммутативная алгебра, (—)-алгебра
A 709	**anticommutative diagram** <HA>	antikommutatives Diagramm *n*	diagramme *m* anti-commutatif	антикоммутативная диаграмма
A 710	**anticommutative multiplication** <AL>	antikommutative Multiplikation *f*	multiplication *f* gauche	антикоммутативное умножение
A 711	**anticommutative ring** <AL>	antikommutativer (schiefkommutativer) Ring *m*	anneau *m* anti-commutatif	антикоммутативное (кососкоммутативное) кольцо
A 712	**anticommutativity,** anticommutativity <AL>	Antikommutativität *f*, Schiefkommutativität *f*	anticommutativité *f*	антикоммутативность, косая коммутативность
A 713	**anticommutator** <AL>	Antikommutator *m*	anti-commutateur *m*	антикоммутатор
A 714	**anticompact Lie algebra** <AL>	antikompakte Liesche Algebra *f*	algèbre *f* de Lie anticompacte	антикомпактная алгебра Ли
A 715	**anticomplementary triangle** <GE>	antikomplementäres Dreieck *n*	triangle *m* anticomplémentaire	антидополнительный треугольник
	anticonjugate dyadic <VT>	*s.* A 566		
A 716	**anticorrelation,** antireciprocity <PJ>	Antikorrelation *f*, Antireziprozität *f*	anticorrélation *f*, antiréciprocité *f*	антикорреляция
	anticosecant <FU>	*s.* I 898		
	anticosine <FU>	*s.* I 899		
	anticotangent <FU>	*s.* I 900		
A 717	**antiderivation** <AL>	Antiderivation *f*	antidérivation *f*	антидифференцирование
A 718	**antiderivation,** integration as the inverse of differentiation <DI>	Bildung *f* des unbestimmten Integrals, unbestimmte Integration *f*	primitivation *f*	образование первообразной функции
	antiderivative <DI>	*s.* P 1344		
A 719	**antidifference** <of the function $\varphi(x)$> <FD>	Summe *f* <der Funktion $\varphi(x)$>; Hauptlösung *f* <der Differenzengleichung>	somme *f* <de la fonction $\varphi(x)$>	сумма <функции $\varphi(x)$>
A 720	**antidromic curve** <GE>	antidromische Kurve *f*	courbe *f* antidromique	антидромная кривая
A 721	**anti-evolute,** antevolute <EG>	Antevolute *f*, Antievolute *f*	antévolute *f*, anti-évolute *f*, antidéveloppée *f*	антиэволюта
A 722	**antifilter** <TO>	Antifilter *m*	antifiltre *m*	антифильтр
	antigenus <GE>	*s.* A 756		
A 723	**anti-Hermitian form** <AL>	schiefhermitesche Form *f*	forme *f* antihermitienne	антиэрмитова форма
	antihermitian (anti-Hermitian) kernel <IE>	*s.* S 1166		
	antihermitian part <AL, IE>	*s.* S 1168		
A 724	**antiholomorphic function** <FT>	antiholomorphe Funktion *f*	fonction *f* antiholomorphe	антиголоморфная функция
	anti-homography <FT>	*s.* I 376		
A 725	**antihomomorphism, anti-homomorphism** <AL>	Antihomomorphismus *m*, reziprok homomorphe Abbildung *f*	anti-homomorphisme *m*	антигомоморфизм, инверсный гомоморфизм
	antihyperbolic cosine <FU>	*s.* A 922		
	antihyperbolic cotangent <FU>	*s.* A 923		
	antihyperbolic function <AN>	*s.* I 911		
	antihyperbolic sine <FU>	*s.* A 924		
	antihyperbolic tangent <FU>	*s.* A 925		

No.	English	German	French	Russian
A 726	**anti-inversion** <with respect to a circle> <GE>	Antiinversion *f*, elliptische Inversion *f* <an einem Kreis>	anti-inversion *f* <par rapport à un cercle>	анти-инверсия, эллиптическая инверсия <относительно окружности>
A 727	**anti-involution** <PJ>	Antiinvolution *f*, involutorische Antikollineation *f*	anti-involution *f*, antiinvolution *f*	антиинволюция
A 728	**anti-involutory points,** pair of anti-involutory points <PJ>	antiinvolutorische Punkte *mpl*, antiinvolutorisches Punktepaar *n*	points *mpl* anti-involutifs, paire *f* de points anti-involutifs	анти-инволютивные точки, пара анти-инволютивных точек
A 729	**anti-isogonal conformal mapping,** indirect[ly] conformal mapping (transformation), inversely conformal transformation <FT>	indirekt[e] konforme Abbildung *f*, konforme Abbildung mit Winkelumlegung, konforme Abbildung zweiter Art	application (représentation) *f* conforme indirecte (de deuxième espèce)	конформное отображение второго рода, антиконформное отображение
A 730	**anti-isomorphic,** inversely isomorphic, inverse-isomorphic <AL>	antiisomorph, reziprok isomorph, invers-isomorph	anti-isomorphe	антиизоморфный, инверсно изоморфный
A 731	**anti-isomorphic lattice** <LA>	dual isomorpher Verband *m*	treillis *m* dual	дуально изоморфная структура
A 732	**anti-isomorphism** <of a ring, group, etc.> <AL>	Antiisomorphismus *m*, antiisomorphe Abbildung *f*	anti[-]isomorphisme *m*	антиизоморфизм, инверсный изоморфизм
A 733	**anti-isomorphism** <of partially ordered sets> <SE>	Antiisomorphismus *m*	antimorphisme *m*, anti-isomorphisme *m*, bijection *f* monotone décroissante	дуальный изоморфизм, антиизоморфизм
A 734	**anti-isomorphism [functor]** <CA>	Antiisomorphismus *m*	anti-isomorphisme *m*	антиизоморфизм
A 735	**anti-lexicographic order,** order by last differences, order according to the principle of last differences <SE>	antilexikographische Ordnung *f*, Ordnung nach letzten Differenzstellen	ordre *m* lexicographique en commençant par la droite, ordre d'après le principe des dernières différences	антилексикографическое упорядочение
A 736	**anti-lexicographic [partial] ordering,** partial ordering according to the principle of last differences, partial order by last differences <SE>	antilexikographische Halbordnung *f*, Halbordnung nach letzten Differenzstellen	ordre *m* partiel d'après le principe des dernières différences, ordre [partiel] lexicographique en commençant par la droite	антилексикографическое полуупорядочение
A 737	**antilinear application** <of a linear space> <AL>	konjugiert lineare Abbildung *f*, antilineare Abbildung (Transformation) *f*	application *f* antilinéaire	антилинейное отображение (преобразование), // антигомография
A 738	**antilinear form** <AL>	Antilinearform *f*	forme *f* antilinéaire	антилинейная форма
A 739	**antilinear involution** <PJ>	antilineare Involution *f*	involution *f* antilinéaire	антилинейная инволюция
	antilinear mapping <FA>	*s.* A 740		
	antilinear operator <FA>	*s.* A 740		
A 740	**antilinear transformation,** antilinear mapping (operator) <FA>	antilineare Abbildung (Transformation) *f*, antilinearer Operator *m*	transformation (application) *f*, antilinéaire, opérateur *m* antilinéaire	антилинейное преобразование (отображение), антилинейный оператор
A 741	**antilog[arithm],** inverse logarithm, antlog <AR>	Numerus *m*, Antilogarithmus *m*, Gegenlogarithmus *m*, antlog	antilogarithme *m*, antlog	антилогарифм, обращенный логарифм, antlog, логарифмируемое число
A 742	**antilogism** <LO>	Antilogismus *m*	antilogisme *m*	антилогизм
A 743	**antimagic square** <CT>	antimagisches Quadrat *n*	carré *m* antimagique	антимагический квадрат
	antimetric tensor <VT>	*s.* A 564		
	antimetric tensor density <VT>	*s.* A 565		
A 744	**antimodal distribution** <ST>	antimodale Verteilung *f*	distribution *f* antimodale	антимодальное распределение
A 745	**antimode** <ST>	Antimodalwert *m*, Antimode *m*, wenigst dichter Wert *m*, Minimum *n* der Verteilungsdichte	antimode *m*	антимода, точка минимума плотности распределения
A 746	**antimodule** <AL>	Antimodul *m*	antimodule *m*	антимодуль
A 747	**anti-node** <GP>	Antiknotenpunkt *m*	anti-nœud *m*	антиузел
A 748	**antinomy,** paradox <MM>	Antinomie *f*, Paradoxie *f*	antinomie *f*, paradoxe *m*, paralogisme *m*	антиномия, парадокс
	antinomy of Burali-Forti <LO>	*s.* B 809		
	antinomy of Russell <MM, SE>	*s.* P 84		
	antinomy of the name relation <LO>	*s.* B 218		
	antinomy of the semantical type <FO, LO>	*s.* S 312		
	antinomy of the set of all ordinals <LO>	*s.* B 809		
	antinomy of the set of all sets <LO, SE>	*s.* C 95		
A 749	**anti-ordered set,** inversely ordered set <SE>	invers (konvers) geordnete Menge *f*	ensemble *m* ordonné inversement	антиупорядоченное множество
A 750	**antiparallel** <GE>	Antiparallele *f*	antiparallèle *f*	антипараллель
	antiparallel <GE>	*s.* O 207		
A 751	**antiparallelogram** <GE>	Antiparallelogramm *n*	antiparallélogramme *m*	антипараллелограмм, контрпараллелограмм
A 752	**antipedal [curve], antipedal locus line,** negative pedal <GE>	antipodäre Kurve *f*, Antipodäre *f*	antipodaire *f*, courbe *f* antipodaire	антиподера, антиподерная (антиподэрная) кривая, антиподэра
A 753	**antipedal tetrahedron** <GE>	antipodäres Tetraeder *n*	tétraèdre *m* antipodaire	антиподерный (антиподэрный) четырехгранник (тетраэдр)
A 754	**antipedal triangle** <GE>	antipodäres Dreieck *n*	triangle *m* antipodaire	антиподерный (антиподэрный) треугольник
A 755	**antipodal map,** antipodal transformation <TO>	Antipodenabbildung *f*	application *f* antipodale	антиподальное отображение

A 756	**antipodal point,** antipode, antigenus, diametrically opposed (opposite) point <e.g. of a point of the sphere> <GE>	diametraler Gegenpunkt (Punkt) *m*, Gegenpunkt *m*, diametral gegenüberliegender Punkt *m*, Diametralpunkt *m*, Antipodenpunkt *m*, Antipode *m*	point *m* [diamétralement] opposé, point diamétral (antipodal), antipode *m*	[диаметрально] противоположная точка, диаметральная точка, антипод, антиподальная точка
A 757	**antipodal points** <GE>	Antipodenpaar *n*	points *mpl* diamétralement opposés	пара антиподов
A 758	**antipodal set** <TO>	Antipodenmenge *f*	ensemble *m* antipodal	антиподное множество
	antipodal space <GE>	*s.* S 1490		
	antipodal transformation <TO>	*s.* A 755		
	antipode <GE>	*s.* A 756		
A 759	**antipoints** <GE>	Antipunkte *mpl*	antipoints *mpl*	антиточки
A 760	**antipolar** <GE>	Antipolare *f*	antipolaire *f*	нулевая линия, противополюсная
A 761	**antipolar hyperplane** <PJ>	antipolare Hyperebene *f*	hyperplan *m* antipolaire	антиполярная гиперплоскость
A 762	**antipolarity** <PJ>	Antipolarität *f*, involutorische Antireziprozität *f*	antipolarité *f*	антиполярность
A 763	**antipole** <PJ>	Antipol *m*	antipôle *m*	антиполюс
A 764	**antiprojection** <GE>	Antiprojektion *f*, Gegenprojektion *f*	antiprojection *f*, contreprojection *f*	антипроекция
	antiprojective transformation <PJ>	*s.* A 765		
A 765	**antiprojectivity,** antiprojective transformation <PJ>	Antiprojektivität *f*, antiprojektive Abbildung (Transformation, Umformung) *f*	antiprojectivité *f*, transformation *f* antiprojective	антипроективность, антипроективное преобразование
A 766	**antiradical** <AL>	Antiradikal *n*	antiradical *m*	антирадикал
A 767	**antireciprocity** <AL>	Antireziprozität *f*	antiréciprocité *f*	антивзаимность
	antireciprocity <PJ>	*s.* A 716		
	antireflexively ordered set <SE>	*s.* O 318		
	anti-reflexiveness <SE>	*s.* I 1057		
	antireflexive ordering relation <SE>	*s.* S 1909		
	antireflexive relation <SE>	*s.* I 1056		
A 768	**anti[-]representation** <AL, RE>	Antidarstellung *f*, reziproke Darstellung *f*	antireprésentation *f*	антипредставление, дуальное представление
A 769	**anti[-]representation module** <AL, RE>	Antidarstellungsmodul *m*, Anti-Darstellungsmodul *m*, reziproker Darstellungsmodul *m*	module *m* d[e l]'antireprésentation	модуль антипредставления
	antisecant <FU>	*s.* I 944		
A 770	**anti-self-adjoint linear differential operator** <DE>	antiselbstadjungierter linearer Differentialoperator *m*	opérateur *m* différentiel linéaire anti-autoadjoint	антисамосопряженный линейный дифференциальный оператор
A 771	**anti-semiinvariant** <IV>	Antisemiinvariante *f*	anti-semi-invariant *m*	антиполуинвариант, антисемиинвариант
	antisimilitude circle <GE>	*s.* C 683		
	antisine <FU>	*s.* I 948		
	antisymmetrical matrix <MD>	*s.* S 1184		
	antisymmetrical relation <SE>	*s.* A 1129/32		
	antisymmetrical tensor <VT>	*s.* A 564		
A 772	**antisymmetric bilinear mapping,** skew-symmetric bilinear mapping <AL>	schiefsymmetrische bilineare Abbildung *f*	application *f* bilinéaire antisymétrique (anti-symétrique)	кососимметрическое (антисимметрическое) билинейное отображение
A 773	**antisymmetric dyad** <VT>	antisymmetrische Dyade *f*	dyade *f* antisymétrique	антисимметричная диада
A 774	**antisymmetric function,** alternating function <AN>	schiefsymmetrische (antisymmetrische, alternierende) Funktion *f*	fonction *f* antisymétrique (alternée), alternant *m*	кососимметрическая (антисимметрическая, знакопеременная) функция
A 775	**antisymmetric graph,** asymmetric[al] graph <has not simultaneously edges (ν_1, ν_2) and (ν_1, ν_2)> <GP>	antisymmetrischer Graph *m*, asymmetrischer Graph	graphe *m* antisymétrique, graphe asymétrique	антисимметричный граф, антисимметрический граф
	antisymmetric kernel <IE>	*s.* A 548		
A 776	**antisymmetric linear mapping** <AL>	antisymmetrische lineare Abbildung *f*	application *f* linéaire antisymétrique	антисимметричное линейное отображение
	antisymmetric matrix <MD>	*s.* S 1184		
A 777	**antisymmetric operator,** skew-symmetric[al] operator <FA>	schiefsymmetrischer Operator *m*	opérateur *m* symétrique gauche, opérateur anti[-]symétrique	кососимметрический оператор
A 778	**antisymmetric relation** <SE>	antisymmetrische (identitive) Relation *f*	relation *f* antisymétrique (propre)	антисимметричное (кососимметричное) отношение
	antisymmetric relation <SE>	*s.* A 1129/32		
A 779	**antisymmetric square** <CT>	antisymmetrisches Quadrat *n*	carré *m* antisymétrique	антисимметричный квадрат
A 780	**antisymmetric tensor** <to be distinguished from alternating tensor in the case char = 2> <AL>	antisymmetrischer (schiefsymmetrischer) Tensor *m*	tenseur *m* anti[-]symétrique (symétrique gauche)	кососимметрический тензор

	antisymmetric tensor <VT>	*s.* A 564		
	antisymmetric tensor density <VT>	*s.* A 565		
	antisymmetric tensor of rank two (2) <VT>	*s.* S 1146		
	antisymmetrization <VT>	*s.* A 568		
A 781	**antisymmetrized** <of a tensor> <VT>	Antisymmetrisierte *f*	antisymétrisé *m*	результат альтернирования
A 782	**antisymmetry** <of a relation> <SE>	[schwache] Antisymmetrie *f*	antisymétrie *f*	антисимметричность
A 783	**antisymmetry,** skew symmetry <AL, AN>	Schiefsymmetrie *f*, Antisymmetrie *f*	symétrie *f* gauche, antisymétrie *f*	антисимметрия, косая симметрия, кососимметричность
	antitangent <FU>	*s.* I 953		
A 784	**antitensor,** axiator <VT>	Antitensor *m*, Axiator *m*	antitenseur *m*, axiateur *m*	антитензор, аксиатор
A 785	**antithesis** <LO>	Antithese *f*	antithèse *f*	антитеза, противоположение
	antithetic correlation <ST>	*s.* N 88		
	antithetic events <ST>	*s.* M 1101		
	antitone function <RF>	*s.* D 80		
	antitone many-one correspondence <SE>	*s.* A 786		
A 786	**antitone mapping,** antitone many-one correspondence <of an ordered set> <SE>	antitone Abbildung *f*	application *f* antitone, application [monotone] décroissante	антимонотонное (убывающее, антитонное) отображение
	antitone sequence <SS>	*s.* M 868		
	antitonic function <RF>	*s.* D 80		
A 787	**antitonicity,** antitony <RF, SE>	Antitonie *f*	antitonie *f*	антитонность
	antitonic sequence <SS>	*s.* M 868		
	antitony <RF, SE>	*s.* A 787		
	antitrigonometrical function <AN>	*s.* I 957		
	antitrigonometric function <AN>	*s.* I 957		
A 788	**antiunitary operator** <FA>	antiunitärer Operator *m*	opérateur *m* anti-unitaire	антиунитарный оператор
A 789	**antiweight,** second weight <of an Hermitian quantity> <DG, VT>	Antigewicht *n*, zweites Gewicht *n*	antipoids *m*, second poids *m*	антивес, второй вес
A 790	**anti-well-ordered,** well ordered downward, inversely well-ordered <SE>	gegenwohlgeordnet, konvers wohlgeordnet	bien ordonné inversement, bien ordonné dual	вполне упорядоченный по убыванию, двойственно вполне упорядоченный
	antlog <FU>	*s.* A 741		
A 791	**A-number** <in Mahler's classification of the complex numbers> <NT>	*A*-Zahl *f*	*A*-nombre *m*	*A*-число
A 792	**A-operation** <SE>	*A*-Operation *f*, Suslinsche Operation *f*	opération *f* ($\mathcal{A}$)	($\mathcal{A}$)-операция, *A*-операция
	AOQ <ST>	*s.* A 1256		
	AOQL <ST>	*s.* A 1257		
	AOQ level <ST>	*s.* A 1256		
	AOQ limit <ST>	*s.* A 1257		
	apart from . . . <GN>	*s.* U 445		
A 793	**apart from the order,** except for the order <GN>	bis auf die Reihenfolge	à l'ordre près	с точностью до чередования
A 794	**apart from the sign** <GN>	bis auf das Vorzeichen	au signe près	с точностью до знака
	aperiodic group <GR>	*s.* G 524		
A 795	**aperiodic state** <of a Markov chain> <SP>	aperiodischer Zustand *m*, A-Zustand *m*	état *m* apériodique	непериодическое состояние
	apex <EG>	*s.* 1. V 153; 2. V 155		
A 796	**apex angle,** vertex angle <of the cone> <EG>	Öffnungswinkel *m*	angle *m* d'ouverture	угол раствора [при вершине]
	apex angle <EG>	*s.* V 158		
	apical angle <EG>	*s.* V 158		
A 797	***a*-point** <FT>	*a*-Stelle *f*	*a*-point *m*	*A*-точка
A 798	**apolar conic** <AY>	Kegelschnitt *m* in konjugierter Lage, konjugierter Kegelschnitt, apolare Kurve *f* <die Kurve 2. Ordnung *f* stützt (*oder* trägt) die Kurve 2. Klasse φ, φ stützt sich auf *f*, φ ruht auf *f*>	conique *f* conjuguée, conique apolaire [par rapport à l'autre] <*f* support φ, φ s'appuie sur *f*, φ repose sur *f*>	сопряженное коническое сечение
A 799	**apolar curve** <AG>	apolare Kurve *f*	courbe *f* apolaire	аполярная кривая
A 800	**apolar form** <IV>	apolare (konjugierte) Form *f* <Rosanes>	forme *f* apolaire (conjuguée)	аполярная форма
A 801	**apolarity** <IV, PJ>	Apolarität *f*	apolarité *f*	аполярность
A 802	**apolar triangle** <with respect to a cubic> <PJ>	apolares Dreieck *n* <bezüglich einer Kubik>	triangle *m* apolaire <par rapport à une courbe cubique>	аполярный треугольник <по отношению к кривой K_3>
	Apollonius['] circle <EG>	*s.* C 684		
	Apollonius['s] circles <EG>	*s.* C 695		
A 803	**Apollonius['] diameter** <GE>	Apollonischer (apollonischer) Durchmesser *m*	diamètre *m* d'Apollonius	аполлониев диаметр
	Apollonius['s] hyperbola <GE>	*s.* H 618		

A 804	**Apollonius['] numbers** <NT>	Apollonische Zahlen *fpl*	nombres *mpl* d'Apollonius	числа Аполлония
	Apollonius['s] problem <EG>	*s.* P 1557		
A 805	**Apollonius['] theorem** <EG>	Satz *m* des Apollonius (Apollonios), Apollonischer Satz	théorème *m* d'Apollonius	теорема Аполлония
A 806	**aporia** <FO, LO>	Aporie *f*, Aporisma *n*, Aporon *n*	aporie *f*, aporisme *m*, apore *m*	апория
	a posteriori distribution <ST>	*s.* P 1105		
	a posteriori probability <ST>	*s.* P 1107		
A 807	**apothem** <of a cone> <EG>	Länge *f* der Mantellinie, Mantellinie *f*	apothème *m*	апофема
A 808	**apothem,** slant height <of a regular pyramid *or* of a frustum of a regular pyramid> <EG>	Höhe *f* der Seitenfläche	apothème *m*	апофема
A 809	**apothem,** short radius, radius of the inscribed circle <of a regular polygon> <EG>	Radius *m* des Inkreises, Inkreisradius *m*, Apothema *n*	apothème *m*	апофема
A 810	**apparent contour** <DS>	scheinbarer Umriß *m*	contour *m* apparent	видимый контур
	apparent error <ER>	*s.* R 886a		
A 811	**apparent singularity** <DE>	scheinbar singuläre Stelle *f*, scheinbare Singularität *f*	singularité *f* apparente, point *m* singulier apparent	кажущаяся особенность (особая точка)
	apparent variable <GN, LO>	*s.* B 699		
A 812	**Appell['s] cosine** <FU>	Appellscher Kosinus *m*	cosinus *m* d'Appell	косинус Аппеля
A 813	**Appell['s] function** <F_1, F_2, F_3 *or* F_4> <FU>	Appellsche Funktion *f*	fonction *f* d'Appell	функция Аппеля
	Appell-Humbert theorem <AG>	*s.* T 259		
A 814	**Appell['s] polynomial** <FU>	Appellsches Polynom *n*	polynôme *m* d'Appell	многочлен (полином) Аппеля
	applicable surface <DG>	*s.* I 1111		
A 815	**applicate,** *z* co-ordinate, height, altitude <of a point in R_3> <AY>	Applikate *f*, Kote *f*, *z*-Koordinate *f*	cote *f*, coordonné *f z*, appliquée *f*, ordonnée *f*	аппликата, аппликата, третья координата, *z*-координата
A 816	**applicate axis,** *z*-axis <GN>	Applikatenachse *f*, *z*-Achse *f*	axe *m* de cotes, axe d'appliquées, axe *m* des cotes (appliquées), axe des [coordonnées] *z*	ось аппликат, *z*-ось
	application <AN, FA>	*s.* M 96		
A 817	**approach** <GN>	Vorgehen *n*, Herangehen *n*, Herangehensweise *f*, Angehen *n*	approche *f*	подход
	approach <AX>	*s.* A 859		
	approach <GN>	*s.* S 706		
A 818	**approach infinity / to,** to become infinite; to tend to infinity <DI>	unendlich groß werden, sich Unendlich nähern, ins Unendliche [an]wachsen; sich dem Grenzwert Unendlich nähern, gegen (nach) Unendlich streben	devenir infini; tendre vers l'infini	становиться бесконечным; стремиться к бесконечности
A 819	**approach zero of lower order / to** <AN>	von niedrigerer Ordnung 0 (Null) werden	tendre vers zéro d'ordre inférieur	стремиться к нулю низшего порядка
A 820	**approach zero of the same order / to,** to tend to zero of the same order <AN, SS>	von gleicher Ordnung Null werden, von gleicher Ordnung gegen Null gehen	tendre vers zéro de même ordre	стремиться к нулю одинакового (того же) порядка
A 821	**approximability** <AX, FA>	Approximierbarkeit *f*	approximabilité *f*	аппроксимируемость
A 822	**approximable mapping** <TO>	approximierbare Abbildung *f*	application *f* approchable (approximable)	приближаемое отображение
	approximable set <RF, TO>	*s.* B 23		
	approximant <NT>	*s.* C 2354		
A 823	**approximate construction** <EG>	Näherungskonstruktion *f*, // mechanische Konstruktion *f*	construction *f* approximative (mécanique)	механическое построение
A 824	**approximate continuity** <RF>	approximative Stetigkeit *f*	continuité *f* approximative	аппроксимативная непрерывность
	approximate cubature <AX, DI, NU>	*s.* N 879		
A 825	**approximate derivative** <at a point x_0> <RF>	approximative Ableitung (Derivierte) *f*, approximativer Differentialquotient *m*	dérivée *f* approximative <dans le point x_0>, nombre *m* dérivé approximatif	асимптотическая (аппроксимативная) производная <в точке x_0>, аппроксимативное производное число
A 825a	**approximate derivative (derived function)** <RF>	approximative Derivierten-funktion *f*	dérivée *f* (fonction *f* dérivée) approximative	асимптотическая (аппроксимативная) производная
A 826	**approximate differentiability** <RF>	approximative Differenzierbarkeit *f*	dérivabilité *f* approximative	асимптотическая (аппроксимативная) дифференцируемость
	approximate differentiability <RF>	*s.* A 851		
	approximate differential <RF>	*s.* A 852		
A 827	**approximate differential** <RF>	approximatives Differential *n*	différentielle *f* approximative	аппроксимативный (асимптотический) дифференциал

No.	English	German	French	Russian
A 828	**approximate formula** <AX, NU>	Näherungsformel *f*	formule *f* approximative (approchée)	приближенная (оценочная) формула
A 829	**approximate from above / to** <AX, NU>	von oben approximieren	approcher par excès	приближать с избытком
A 830	**approximate from below / to** <AX, NU>	von unten approximieren	approcher par défaut	приближать с недостатком
A 831	**approximate limit,** lim ap <RF>	approximativer Limes (Grenzwert) *m*, lim ap	limite *f* approximative, lim ap	аппроксимативный (асимптотический) предел, lim ap
A 832	**approximate lower right-hand derivative (derived function)** <RF>	approximative untere rechtsseitige Deriviertenfunktion *f*	dérivée *f* (fonction dérivée) approximative inférieure à droite	аппроксимативная нижняя правосторонняя (правая) производная
A 833	**approximate lower semi-continuity** <RF>	approximative Halbstetigkeit *f* nach unten	semi-continuité *f* approximative inférieurement	аппроксимативная непрерывность снизу
A 834	**approximately equal** **<to>**, ≈ <AX, NU>	angenähert (näherungsweise, etwa) gleich, ≈	approximativement (sensiblement) égal, égal environ, ≈	приближенно равный, ≈
A 835	**approximately everywhere** <PO, SE>	annähernd überall	approximativement partout	приблизительно всюду, с точностью до множества внутренней меры нуль, // почти всюду
A 836	**approximately left-hand lower [semi-]continuous** <RF>	approximativ linksseitig unterhalb[ ]stetig, approximativ linksseitig nach unten [halb]stetig, approximativ linksseitig abwärts [halb]stetig	approximativement [semi-] continu inférieurement à gauche	слева аппроксимативно [полу]непрерывный снизу
A 837	**approximately left-hand upper [semi-]continuous** <RF>	approximativ linksseitig oberhalb[ ]stetig, approximativ linksseitig nach oben [halb]stetig, approximativ linksseitig aufwärts [halb]stetig	approximativement [semi-] continu supérieurement à gauche	слева аппроксимативно [полу]непрерывный сверху
A 838	**approximately lower [semi-]continuous** <RF>	approximativ unterhalb[ ] stetig, approximativ nach unten [halb]stetig, approximativ abwärts [halb-] stetig	approximativement [semi-] continu inférieurement	аппроксимативно [полу]-непрерывный снизу
A 839	**approximately one-sided lower [semi-]continuous** <RF>	approximativ einseitig unterhalb[ ]stetig, approximativ einseitig nach unten [halb]stetig, approximativ einseitig abwärts [halb]stetig	approximativement [semi-] continu inférieurement à un seul côté	аппроксимативно односторонний [полу]непрерывный снизу
A 840	**approximately one-sided upper [semi-]continuous** <RF>	approximativ einseitig oberhalb[ ]stetig, approximativ einseitig nach oben [halb]stetig, approximativ einseitig aufwärts [halb]stetig	approximativement [semi-] continu supérieurement à un seul côté	аппроксимативно односторонний [полу]непрерывный сверху
A 841	**approximately right-hand continuous,** approximately right-hand semi-continuous <RF>	approximativ rechtsseitig [halb]stetig	approximativement [semi-] continu à droite	справа аппроксимативно [полу]непрерывный
A 842	**approximately right-hand lower [semi-] continuous** <RF>	approximativ rechtsseitig unterhalb[ ]stetig, approximativ rechtsseitig nach unten [halb]stetig, approximativ rechtsseitig abwärts [halb]stetig	approximativement [semi-] continu inférieurement à droite	справа аппроксимативно [полу]непрерывный снизу
	approximately right-hand semi-continuous <RF>	*s.* A 841		
A 843	**approximately right-hand upper [semi-] continuous** <RF>	approximativ rechtsseitig oberhalb[ ]stetig, approximativ rechtsseitig nach oben [halb]stetig, approximativ rechtsseitig aufwärts [halb]stetig	approximativement [semi-] continu supérieurement à droite	справа аппроксимативно [полу]непрерывный сверху
A 844	**approximately semi-continuous** <RF>	approximativ halbstetig	approximativement semi-continu	аппроксимативно полунепрерывный
A 845	**approximately upper [semi-]continuous** <RF>	approximativ oberhalb[ ] stetig, approximativ nach oben [halb]stetig, approximativ aufwärts [halb-] stetig	approximativement [semi-] continu supérieurement	аппроксимативно [полу-] непрерывный сверху
	approximate method <AX, NU>	*s.* A 866		
	approximateness <AY>	*s.* D 180		
A 846	**approximate partial derivative (derived function)** <RF>	approximative partielle Deriviertenfunktion *f*	dérivée *f* (fonction *f* dérivée) approximative partielle	асимптотическая (аппроксимативная) частная производная
A 847	**approximate partial differential** <RF>	approximatives partielles Differential *n*	différentielle *f* approximative partielle	аппроксимативный (асимптотический) частный дифференциал
A 848	**approximate point spectrum** <FA>	approximatives Punktspektrum *n*	spectre *m* ponctuel approximatif	аппроксимативный точечный спектр
A 849	**approximate solution,** approximative solution <AX, DE, NU>	Näherungslösung *f*, genäherte (approximierte, approximative, angenäherte) Lösung *f*	solution *f* approchée (approximative)	приближенное решение
A 850	**approximate test** <ST>	Näherungstest *m*, approximativer Test *m*	test *m* approché	приближенный критерий

No.	English	German	French	Russian
A 851	**approximate total differentiability,** approximate differentiability <RF>	approximative [totale] Differenzierbarkeit *f*	dérivabilité *f* [totale] approximative	асимптотическая (аппроксимативная) [полная] дифференцируемость
A 852	**approximate total differential,** approximate differential <RF>	approximatives [totales] Differential *n*	différentielle *f* [totale] approximative	аппроксимативный (асимптотический) [полный] дифференциал
A 853	**approximate *t*-test,** Cochran-Cox method <ST>	approximativer *t*-Test *m*, Näherungsverfahren *n* von Cochran-Cox, Cochran-Coxsches Näherungsverfahren	test *m t* approché, méthode *f* de Cochran-Cox, méthode approchée de Cochran-Cox	приближенный *t*-критерий, метод Кочрэна-Кокса
A 854	**approximate upper left-hand derivative (derived function)** <RF>	approximative obere linksseitige Deriviertenfunktion *f*	dérivée *f* approximative supérieure à gauche	асимптотическая (аппроксимативная) верхняя левосторонняя (левая) производная
A 855	**approximate upper right-hand derivative** <RF>	approximative obere rechtsseitige Derivierte (Ableitung) *f*	dérivée *f* (fonction *f* dérivée) approximative supérieure à droite	асимптотическая (аппроксимативная) верхняя правосторонняя (правая) производная
A 856	**approximate upper semi-continuity** <RF>	approximative Halbstetigkeit *f* nach oben	semi-continuité *f* approximative supérieurement	аппроксимативная непрерывность сверху
A 857	**approximate value by defect** <AX, NU>	Näherungswert *m* mit negativem Fehler	valeur *f* approchée par défaut	приближенное значение с недостатком
A 858	**approximate value by excess** <AX, NU>	Näherungswert *m* mit positivem Fehler	valeur *f* approchée par excès	приближенное значение с избытком
	approximating function <AX, NU>	*s.* A 864		
A 859	**approximation;** approach <AX>	Approximation *f*; Näherung *f*; Annäherung *f*	approximation *f*	аппроксимация, приближение
	ε-approximation <TO>	*s.* E 306		
A 860	**approximation by defect** <AX, NU>	Näherung (Annäherung, Approximation) *f* von unten	approximation *f* par défaut	приближение с недостатком
A 861	**approximation by excess** <AX, NU>	Näherung (Annäherung, Approximation) *f* von oben	approximation *f* par excès	приближение с избытком
	approximation by least squares [method] <AX>	*s.* L 249		
	approximation by polynomials <AX>	*s.* P 978		
A 862	**approximation by series** <AX>	Approximation *f* durch (mittels) Reihen	approximation *f* par séries	аппроксимация (приближение) рядами
	approximation calculus <AX, NU>	*s.* C 18		
A 863	**approximation error** <AX, NU>	Näherungsfehler *m*, Approximationsfehler *m*	erreur *f* d'approximation	ошибка аппроксимации (приближения), погрешность аппроксимации (приближения)
A 864	**approximation function,** approximating function <AX, NU>	Approximationsfunktion *f*, approximierende Funktion *f*, Näherungsfunktion *f*	fonction *f* d'approximation, fonction approximative	аппроксимирующая (приближающая) функция
A 865	**approximation in the quadratic mean** <AX>	Approximation *f* im quadratischen Mittel	approximation *f* en moyenne quadratique	аппроксимация (приближение) в среднем квадратическом
A 866	**approximation method,** approximate method <AX, NU>	Näherungsverfahren *n*, Näherungsmethode *f*, Approximationsverfahren *n*	méthode *f* d'approximation	метод приближения, приближенный метод
A 867	**approximation problem** <AX>	Approximationsproblem *n*	problème *m* d'approximation	задача аппроксимации (приближения)
A 868	**approximation theorem** <for valuations> <AL>	Annäherungssatz *m*, Approximationssatz *m* für Bewertungen	théorème *m* d'approximation [pour les valuations], théorème d'indépendance [des valuations]	аппроксимационная теорема [Артина-Уэплза], теорема об аппроксимации, теорема аппроксимации [для нормирований]
A 869	**approximation theorem** <AX>	Approximationssatz *m*	théorème *m* d'approximation	теорема аппроксимации (о приближении), аппроксимационная теорема
A 870	**approximation theorem of Hurwitz** <in Diophantine approximation> <NT>	Hurwitzscher Approximationssatz *m*, Satz *m* von Hurwitz	théorème *m* de Hurwitz	аппроксимационная теорема Гурвица
	approximation theorems of Jackson <AN, AX>	*s.* J 3		
A 871	**approximation theory** <AX>	Approximationstheorie *f*	théorie *f* d'approximation	теория приближений [функций], теория аппроксимации [функций], конструктивная теория функций
A 872	**approximative functional equation** <for Riemann's zeta function> <FT, NT>	approximative Funktionalgleichung *f*	équation *f* fonctionnelle approximative	аппроксимативное функциональное уравнение
	approximative solution <AX, DE, NU>	*s.* A 849		
A 873	**a priori bound** <DE>	A-priori-Schranke *f*, Apriorischranke *f*	borne *f* a priori; limitation *f* a priori	априорная грань
	a priori distribution <ST>	*s.* P 1523		
	a priori probability <ST>	*s.* P 1525		
	A-proposition <AL>	*s.* G 173		

No.	English	German	French	Russian
	A-proposition <LO>	*s.* U 310		
	apse <AN>	*s.* B 186		
	AQL <ST>	*s.* A 164		
A 874	**arbelos,** cobbler's knife <EG>	Arbelos *m*, Schustermesser *n*, Schusterkneif *m*, scalprum *n* sutorium	arbelos *m* d'Archimède, arbélos *m*, tranchet *m*	арбелон
A 875	**arbitrarily great** <GN>	beliebig groß	arbitrairement grand, aussi grand que l'on veut	произвольно (сколь угодно) большой
A 876	**arbitrarily small** <GN>	beliebig klein	arbitrairement petit, aussi petit qu'on veut	произвольно (сколь угодно) малый
A 877	**arbitrary constant** <AN, DI>	willkürliche (beliebige) Konstante *f*	constante *f* arbitraire	произвольная постоянная
A 878	**arbitrary element** <AL, AN>	beliebiges (irgendein) Element *n*	élément *m* générique	произвольный элемент
A 879	**arbitrary element,** typical element <AL, SE>	allgemeines Element *n*	élément *m* arbitraire (générique), variable *f*	произвольный элемент
A 880	**arbitrary mean** <ST>	willkürliches Mittel *n*	moyenne *f* arbitraire	произвольное среднее [значение]
A 881	**arborescence,** rooted tree, tree <Sylvester>, directed tree; subtree <of a digraph> <GP>	Wurzelbaum *m*, gerichteter Wurzelbaum, Büschel *n*, Arboreszenzgraph *m*, Arboreszenz *f*, // Setzbaum *m*	arborescence *f*	дерево, растущее из корня; продерево, корневое дерево, выходящее дерево
A 882	**arc** <of a curve>, curve arc <GE>	Kurvenbogen *m*, Bogen *m* <einer Kurve>	arc *m* <d'une courbe>	дуга <кривой>
A 883	**arc,** directed line, oriented element, directed segment (branch), // directed edge <of a graph> <GP>	Bogen *m*, gerichtete Kante *f*, Kante, Pfeil *m*	arc *m*	дуга, ориентированное ребро
	arc <AY, GE>	*s.* R 12		
	arc <EG>	*s.* C 704		
	3-arc <TO>	*s.* T 442		
A 884	**arc-component, arc component** <of a space> <TO>	Bogenkomponente *f*	composante *f* connexe par arcs	жорданово-связная компонента
	arc-connected set <TO>	*s.* A 918		
	arc-connected space <TO>	*s.* A 919		
A 885	**arc convex cup (up), arc convex** ◡ <GE>	nach oben konvexer Kurvenbogen *m*	voûte *f*	дуга выпуклостью вверх
	Arc cos, arc cos <FU>	*s.* I 899		
	Arc cosec, arc cosec, arc cosecant <FU>	*s.* I 898		
	arc cosine <FU>	*s.* I 899		
	Arc cot, arc cot <FU>	*s.* I 900		
	arc cotangent <FU>	*s.* I 900		
	arc csc <FU>	*s.* I 898		
	Arc ctg, arc ctg <FU>	*s.* I 900		
	arch <FU>	*s.* A 922		
A 886	**archimedean absolute value,** archimedean valuation <AL>	archimedische Bewertung *f*	valuation *f* archimédienne	архимедово нормирование, архимедова норма (нормировка)
	Archimedean axiom <GE>	*s.* A 897		
A 887	**Archimedean body,** Archimedean solid, semiregular solid (body) <GE>	Archimedischer (halbregelmäßiger) Körper *m*, Archimedisches Polyeder *n*	corps (solide) *m* archimédien, corps (solide) semirégulier	полуправильный многогранник, тело Архимеда, архимедово тело, архимедов многогранник
A 888	**Archimedean group** <AL>	archimedisch geordnete Gruppe *f*	groupe *m* archimédien	архимедова группа
A 889	**Archimedean l-group** <AL>	archimedische Verbandsgruppe *f*	groupe *m* réticulé archimédien	архимедова l-группа
	Archimedean ordered field <AL>	*s.* A 900		
	Archimedean ordered group <AL>	*s.* A 895		
	Archimedean ordered ring <AL>	*s.* A 902		
A 890	**Archimedean partial ordering** <AL>	archimedische Halbordnung *f*	ordre *m* partiel archimédien	архимедово полуупорядочение
A 891	**Archimedean property** <GE>	Archimedische Eigenschaft *f*; Eigenschaft, archimedisch zu sein	propriété *f* d'être archimédien	архимедовость
A 892	**Archimedean ring** <AL>	archimedisch geordneter Ring *m*	anneau *m* archimédien	архимедовски упорядоченное кольцо
	Archimedean screw <GE>	*s.* A 898		
A 893	**Archimedean semigroup** <AL>	archimedisch geordnete Halbgruppe *f*	demi-groupe *m* archimédien	архимедова полугруппа
	Archimedean solid <GE>	*s.* A 887		
A 894	**archimedean space** <FA>	archimedischer [linearer] halbgeordneter Raum *m*	espace *m* archimédien	архимедово пространство
	Archimedean spiral <GE>	*s.* A 898		
A 895	**Archimedean totally ordered group,** Archimedean ordered group <AL>	archimedisch angeordnete Gruppe *f*, archimedische totalgeordnete Gruppe	groupe *m* totalement ordonné archimédien	архимедова [линейно упорядоченная] группа
A 896	**archimedean total order** <AL>	archimedische Anordnung *f*	ordre *m* total archimédien	архимедово [линейное упорядочение
	archimedean valuation <AL>	*s.* A 886		

No.	English	German	French	Russian
A 897	**Archimedes['] axiom,** Eudoxus['] (Eodoxos[']) theorem, axiom of Archimedes (Eudoxus), Archimedean axiom <GE>	Archimedisches Axiom *n*, Axiom von Eudoxus (Eudoxos), Axiom des Messens (Archimedes), Axiom der Meßbarkeit	axiome *m* d'Archimède, axiome d'Eudoxe[-Archimède]	аксиома Архимеда (Евдокса)
A 898	**Archimedes['] spiral,** Archimedean spiral, spiral of Archimedes, Archimedean screw <GE>	Archimedische Spirale *f*, *f*, Conons Spirale	spirale *f* d'Archimède, spirale archimédienne, spirale de Conon	архимедова спираль, спираль Архимеда
A 899	**Archimedes['] theorem** <EG>	Satz *m* des Archimedes	théorème *m* d'Archimède	теорема Архимеда
A 900	**archimedically ordered field,** ordered Archimedean field, ordered field having an Archimedean order, Archimedean ordered field <AL>	archimedisch-angeordneter Körper *m*	corps *m* [ordonné] archimédien	архимедово поле
A 901	**archimedically ordered number field,** ordered Archimedean number field, number field with Archimedean ordering <AL>	archimedisch angeordneter Zahlkörper *m*	corps *m* de nombres ordonné archimédien	архимедово поле чисел
A 902	**archimedically ordered ring,** Archimedean ordered ring <AL>	archimedisch angeordneter Ring *m*	anneau *m* archimédien	архимедово кольцо
	arc-hyperbolic function <AN>	*s.* I 911		
A 903	**Archytas['] curve** <GE>	Kurve *f* von Archytas, Archytas' Kurve	courbe *f* d'Archytas	кривая Архита [Тарентского]
	arc incident <GP>	*s.* E 258		
	arc incident out <GP>	*s.* O 552		
A 904	**arc length,** oriented arc length function <of a point on a curve> <AN, GE>	krummlinige Abszisse *f*, Bogenlänge *f*	abscisse *f* curviligne, longueur *f* de l'arc	длина дуги
	arc length <DG>	*s.* L 570		
	arc-like continuum <TO>	*s.* C 464		
A 905	**arc of an algebraic curve** <AG>	algebraischer Bogen *m*, Bogen *m* einer algebraischen Kurve	arc *m* algébrique	дуга алгебраической кривой
	arc of circle <EG>	*s.* C 704		
A 906	**arc of cycloid** <GE>	Zykloidenbogen *m*, Bogen *m* der Zykloide	arc *m* de cycloïde	арка циклоиды
	Arcosh, arcosh <FU>	*s.* A 922		
	Arcoth, arcoth <FU>	*s.* A 923		
A 907	**arc polygon,** circular polygon, curvilinear polygon <EG>	Kreisbogenpolygon *n*, Kreisbogenvieleck *n*	polygone *m* circulaire, polygone d'arcs circulaire	круговой (дуговой) многоугольник; многоугольник [, состоящий] из дуг окружностей; многоугольник (полигон), составленный дугами окружностей
	arc progression <GP>	*s.* D 544		
A 908	**arc quadrangle,** circular quadrangle, curvilinear quadrangle <EG>	Kreisbogenviereck *n*	quadrangle *m* circulaire, quadrangle d'arcs circulaire	круговой (дуговой) четырехугольник; четырехугольник [, состоящий] из дуг окружностей; четырехугольник, составленный дугами окружностей
	Arc sec, arc sec <FU>	*s.* I 944		
	arc secant <FU>	*s.* I 944		
A 909	**arc-set** <TO>	vollständig bogenverknüpfte Menge *f*	ensemble *m* complètement connexe par arcs	вполне дугообразно связное множество
	Arc sin, arc sin <FU>	*s.* I 948		
	arc sine <FU>	*s.* I 948		
A 910	**arc sine distribution** <ST>	Arkussinusverteilung *f*, arc sin-Verteilung *f*	distribution *f* de l'arc sinus	арксинус-распределение, распределение арксинуса
A 911	**arc sine law** <ST>	Arkussinusgesetz *n*, Arkussinusregel *f*, arc sin-Gesetz *n*	loi *f* de l'arc sinus	закон арксинуса, арксинус-закон
A 912	**arc sine transformation** <ST>	Arkussinustransformation *f*, arc sin-Transformation *f*	transformation *f* arc (de l'arc) sinus	арксинус-преобразование
A 913	**arc-subset,** completely arc-connected subset <TO>	vollständig bogenverknüpfte Teilmenge *f*	partie *f* (sous-ensemble *m*) complètement connexe par arcs	вполне дугообразно связное подмножество, вполне жорданово-связное подмножество
	Arc tan, arc tan <FU>	*s.* I 953		
	arc tangent <FU>	*s.* I 953		
	Arc tg, arc tg <FU>	*s.* I 953		
	arcth <FU>	*s.* A 923		
	Arcth <FU>	*s.* A 923		
A 914	**arc triangle,** circular triangle, curvilinear triangle <EG>	Kreisbogendreieck *n*	triangle *m* circulaire, triangle d'arcs circulaires	круговой (дуговой) треугольник; треугольник [, состоящий] из дуг окружностей, треугольник, составленный дугами окружностей
	arc-trigonometric[al] function <AN>	*s.* I 957		
A 915	**arcufication** <of a segment> <GE>	Arkufikation *f*	arcufication *f*	аркуфикация
A 916	**arcuid** <of a curve> <GE>	Arkuide *f*	arcuide *f*	аркуида
A 917	**arcwise connectedness** <TO>	bogenweiser Zusammenhang *m*, Bogenverknüpftheit *f*	connexité *f* par arcs	связность с помощью дуг

A 918	**arcwise connected set,** arc-connected set <TO>	bogenverknüpfte Menge *f*, bogenweise zusammenhängende Menge *f*	ensemble *m* [intégralement] connexe par arcs	дугообразно связное множество, жорданово-связное множество
A 919	**arcwise connected space,** arc-connected space <TO>	bogenverknüpfter Raum *m*, bogenweise zusammenhängender Raum, bogenzusammenhängender Raum	espace *m* connexe par arcs, espace *m* intégralement connexe par arcs	дугообразно связное пространство, жорданово-связное пространство
A 920	**area,** area of surface, surface area <EG>	Flächeninhalt *m*, Inhalt *m*, Fläche *f*	aire *f*, aire de surface	площадь, площадь поверхности
	area <IG>	*s.* I 627		
A 921	**area function** <in a Minkowski space> <GE>	flächenbestimmende Funktion *f*	fonction *f* déterminant l'aire	функция, определяющая площади
	area histogram <ST>	*s.* H 373		
A 922	**area-hyperbolic cosine,** inverse hyperbolic cosine, antihyperbolic cosine, Arccsh, arcosh, arch, arg ch <principal value: arcosh> <FU>	Areakosinus *m*, Areacosinus *m* hyperbolicus, Arch, Ar Cos, arch, ar cos <Hauptwert: arch, ar cos, veraltet und selten: Arch>, // 𝔄𝔯 ℭ𝔬𝔰	argument *m* [du] cosinus hyperbolique, cosinus *m* hyperbolique inverse, Arcosh, Arch, Argch, arcosh, arch, argch <détermination principale: arcosh, argch>	ареа-косинус гиперболический, обратный гиперболический косинус, Arch, arch <главное значение: arch>
A 923	**area-hyperbolic cotangent,** inverse hyperbolic cotangent, antihyperbolic cotangent, Arcoth, arcoth, arg coth, arcth <principal value: arcth> <FU>	Areakotangens *m*, Areacotangens *m* hyperbolicus, Arcth, Ar Cot, arcth, ar cot <Hauptwert: arcth, ar cot, veraltet und selten: Arcth>, // 𝔄𝔯 ℭ𝔱𝔤	argument *m* [de la] cotangente hyperbolique, cotangente *f* hyperbolique inverse, Arcoth, Argcoth, arcoth, argcoth, arcth <détermination principale: arcoth, argcoth>	ареа-котангенс гиперболический, обратный гиперболический котангенс, Arcth, arcth <главное значение: arcth>
	area-hyperbolic function <AN>	*s.* I 911		
A 924	**area-hyperbolic sine,** inverse hyperbolic sine, antihyperbolic sine, Arsinh, Arsh, arsinh, arsh, arg sh <principal value: arsinh> <FU>	Areasinus *m* [hyperbolicus], Arsh, Ar Sin, arsh, ar sin <Hauptwert: arsh, ar sin, selten und veraltet: Arsh>, // 𝔄𝔯 𝔖𝔦𝔫	argument *m* [du] sinus hyperbolique, sinus *m* hyperbolique inverse, Arsinh, Arsh, Argsh, arsinh, arsh, argsh <détermination principale: arsinh, argsh>	ареа-синус гиперболический, обратный гиперболический синус, Arsh, arsh <главное значение: arsh>
A 925	**area-hyperbolic tangent,** inverse hyperbolic tangent, antihyperbolic tangent, Arctanh, Arth, artanh, arth, argth <principal value: artanh> <FU>	Areatangens *m* [hyperbolicus], Arth, Ar Tan, arth, ar tan <Hauptwert: arth, ar tan, selten und veraltet: Arth>, // 𝔄𝔯 𝔗𝔤	argument *m* [de la] tangente hyperbolique, tangente *f* hyperbolique inverse, Artanh, Arth, Argth, arth, argth <détermination principale: artanh, arg th>	ареа-тангенс гиперболический, обратный гиперболический тангенс, Arth, artanh, arth <главное значение: arth>
	areal curl <VT>	*s.* C 2759		
A 926	**areal derivative,** areolar (surface) derivative <FT>	Flächenableitung *f*, Flächenderivierte *f*	dérivée *f* aréolaire	ареоларная (поверхностная) производная
	areal divergence <VT>	*s.* D 785		
	areal element <DG, DI>	*s.* E 131		
	areal gradient <VT>	*s.* G 363		
A 927	**areal metric,** surface metric <GE, TO>	Flächenmetrik *f*	métrique *f* aréolaire	метрика площадей, ареальная метрика
	area of surface <EG>	*s.* A 920		
A 928	**area of the circle** <EG>	Kreisinhalt *m*, Kreisfläche *f*, Flächeninhalt *m* des Kreises	aire *f* du cercle	площадь круга
A 929	**area of the sphere** <EG>	Oberflächeninhalt (Flächeninhalt) *m* der Kugel, Oberfläche *f* der Kugel, Kugeloberfläche *f*	aire *f* de la sphère	площадь поверхности шара
A 930	**area-preserving map[ping],** equi[-]areal map[ping], equivalent map[ping] <AY>	flächentreue (inhaltstreue, äquivalente, flächengleiche) Abbildung *f*	application (représentation) *f* équivalente (avec conservation des aires, conservant les aires)	сохраняющее площади отображение; отображение, сохраняющее площадь; отображение с сохранением площадей, эквиареальное отображение
	area-principle <FT>	*s.* B 307		
A 931	**area sampling** <ST>	Flächenstichprobenverfahren *n*	sondage *m* aréolaire	пространственный выбор
A 932	**Arens['s] product** <FA>	Arens-Produkt *n*	produit *m* d'Arens	произведение Аренса
A 933	**Arens['s] topology** <FA>	Arens-Topologie *f*	topologie *f* d'Arens	топология Аренса
	areolar derivative <FT>	*s.* A 926		
A 934	**areolar monogenic function** <FT>	areolare monogene Funktion *f*	fonction *f* monogène aréolaire	ареоларная моногенная функция
A 935	**Arf['s] invariant** <AL>	Arfsche Invariante *f*	invariant *m* d'Arf	инфариант Арфа, Arf-инвариант
A 936	**Arf['s] space** <AL>	Arfscher Raum *m*	espace *m* d'Arf	пространство Арфа
	ar function <AN>	*s.* I 911		
	arg <AN>	*s.* A 603		
	Argand diagram <FT>	*s.* A 937		
A 937	**Argand plane,** complex [number] plane, number (finite) plane, plane of complex numbers, Gauss [number] plane, Gaussian plane; Argand diagram <FT>	komplexe Zahlenebene *f*, Gaußsche (konforme, Argand-Gaußsche) Zahlenebene, konforme Ebene *f*, Zahlenebene, Argand-Gaußsche Ebene, komplexe Ebene, *z*-Ebene *f*, [Gaußsche] Ebene der komplexen Zahlen, Argumentebene *f*	plan *m* d'Argand-Cauchy, plan complexe (de Gauss), plan numérique	комплексная плоскость, плоскость Гаусса, гауссова плоскость [чисел], плоскость [комплексных] чисел, числовая плоскость, плоскость комплексной переменной
	arg ch <FU>	*s.* A 922		
	arg coth <FU>	*s.* A 923		
	arg sh <FU>	*s.* A 924		
	arg th <FU>	*s.* A 925		
	Arguesian lattice <LA>	*s.* D 299		

A 938	**argument** <FO, LO>	Beweisgrund *m*	argument *m*	довод, аргумент, основание доказательства
A 939	**argument** <conclusion> <LO>	Argument *n*	argument *m*	аргумент, посылка, основание, довод <доказательства>; доказательство в целом
	argument <AN>	*s.* 1. A 603; 2. I 320		
	argument <AY>	*s.* A 604		
	argument <FO>	*s.* P 1751		
	argumentation <FO>	*s.* P 1751		
	argument domain <SE>	*s.* D 854		
	argument form <LO>	*s.* S 497		
A 940	**argument function** <VA>	Argumentfunktion *f*	fonction *f* d'argument	аргументная функция
	argument place <AL, AN, SE, TO>	*s.* L 279		
A 941	**argument principle,** principle of [the] argument <FT>	Prinzip *n* vom Argument, Argumentprinzip *n*, Argumentenprinzip *n*, Satz *m* vom logarithmischen Residuum	principe *m* d'argument, théorème *m* du résidu logarithmique	принцип аргумента
A 942	**Aristotelian logic** <LO>	Aristotelische (chrysippinische) Logik *f*	logique *f* d'Aristote (aristotélicienne, chrysippienne)	аристотелевская логика
	arithlog diagram <NU>	*s.* S 407		
	arithlog paper <IN, NU>	*s.* S 408		
	arithmetic <NT>	*s.* N 849		
	arithmetic[al] check[ing] <AR, NU>	*s.* C 618		
	arithmetical continuum <AN, SE>	*s.* N 872		
	arithmetical formula <LO, NT>	*s.* N 847		
A 943	**arithmetical function** <of *n* arguments> <NT>	zahlentheoretische Funktion *f* <*n*-stellige>	fonction *f* arithmétique (énumérative, numérique) <*n*-adique>	арифметическая (теоретико-числовая) функция <*n*-местная>
A 944	**arithmetical hierarchy** <MM>	arithmetische Hierarchie *f*	hiérarchie *f* arithmétique	арифметическая иерархия
A 945	**arithmetically effective curve** <AG>	arithmetisch effektive Kurve *f*	courbe *f* arithmétiquement effective	арифметически эффективная кривая
A 946	**arithmetically equivalent variety** <AG>	arithmetisch äquivalente Mannigfaltigkeit *f*	variété *f* arithmétiquement équivalente	арифметически эквивалентное многообразие
A 947	**arithmetically normal *k*-variety** <Zariski>, projectively normal *k*-variety <Hodge-Pedoe>, *k*-normal projective *k*-variety, [projective] *k*-variety projectively normal over *k* <AG>	projektiv normale *k*-Mannigfaltigkeit *f*	*k*-variété *f* projectivement normale	проективно нормальное *k*-многообразие
A 948	**arithmetically normal variety** <AG>	arithmetisch normale Mannigfaltigkeit *f*	variété *f* arithmétiquement normale	арифметически нормальное многообразие
A 949	**arithmetical operation,** arithmetic operation, basic arithmetic[al] operation, fundamental (basic) operation <of the first, second, *or* third kind> <AR>	Grundrechenart *f*, Rechenart *f*, Rechnungsart *f*, Grundrechnungsart *f*, Grund[rechen]operation *f*, Rechenoperation *f*, Fundamentaloperation *f*, Operation *f* <erster (1.) zweiter (2.) *oder* dritter (3.) Stufe>	opération *f* fondamentale, opération arithmétique, règle *f* arithmétique, opération <de rang un, du premier rang *ou* de rang deux, du second rang *ou* de rang trois, du troisième rang>	арифметическое действие, основное действие <первой, второй *или* третьей ступени>
A 950	**arithmetical operation** <NT>	zahlentheoretische Operation *f*	opération *f* arithmétique	арифметическое действие
A 951	**arithmetical predicate** <LO>	zahlentheoretisches (arithmetisches) Prädikat *n*	prédicat *m* arithmétique	арифметический (теоретико-числовой) предикат
A 952	**arithmetical progression,** arithmetic progression, arithmetic sequence of the first order, // arithmetic series <AL, FD>	arithmetische Progression *f*, arithmetische Folge *f* erster Ordnung, // arithmetische Reihe *f*	progression *f* arithmétique (par différence), suite *f* arithmétique de premier ordre, // série *f* arithmétique	арифметическая (разностная) прогрессия, арифметический ряд первого порядка, // арифметический ряд
	arithmetical triangle <AR, CT>	*s.* P 293		
	arithmetic average <AL, ER, ST>	*s.* A 961		
	arithmetic book <AR, GN>	*s.* S 2258		
	arithmetic check[ing] <AR, NU>	*s.* C 618		
	arithmetic class in the wider sense <UA>	*s.* A 1270		
A 953	**arithmetic difference** <AR>	arithmetische Differenz *f*	différence *f* arithmétique	арифметическая разность
A 954	**arithmetic distribution** <ST>	arithmetische Verteilung *f*	distribution *f* arithmétique	арифметическое распределение
	arithmetic distribution <ST>	*s.* D 660		
A 955	**arithmetic division** <AR>	arithmetische Division *f*	division *f* arithmétique	арифметическое деление
A 956	**arithmetic form** <NT>	arithmetische Form *f*, quadratische zahlentheoretische Form, zahlentheoretische Form <vom zweiten Grade> <Gauß>	forme *f* arithmétique	арифметическая форма
A 957	**arithmetic genus** <AG, FT>	arithmetisches (numerisches) Geschlecht *n*	genre *m* arithmétique	арифметический род (жанр)

No.	English	German	French	Russian
A 958	**arithmetic-geometric mean,** arithmetico-geometric mean <AL, ST>	arithmetisch-geometrisches Mittel *n*, arithmetisch-geometrischer Mittelwert *m*	moyenne *f* arithmético-géométrique (arithmétique-géométrique)	арифметико-геометрическое среднее [значение], среднее арифметико-геометрическое
A 959	**arithmetic-geometric progression (sequence),** arithmetico-geometric progression (sequence) <AL>	arithmetisch-geometrische Folge (Progression) *f*	progression *f* arithmético-géométrique (arithmétique-géométrique), suite *f* arithmético-géométrique (arithmétique-géométrique)	арифметико-геометрическая прогрессия
A 960	**arithmetic-geometric series,** arithmetico-geometric series <AL>	arithmetisch-geometrische Reihe *f*	série *f* arithmétique-géométrique (arithmético-géométrique)	арифметико-геометрический ряд
A 961	**arithmetic mean,** arithmetic average, ordinary arithmetic mean <AL, ER, ST>	arithmetisches Mittel *n*, arithmetischer Mittelwert *m*, Durchschnitt *m*, Durchschnittswert *m*, gewöhnliches arithmetisches Mittel, gewöhnlicher arithmetischer Mittelwert	moyenne *f* arithmétique, moyenne arithmétique ordinaire	среднее арифметическое, арифметическое среднее, арифметическая средняя [величина], обыкновенное арифметическое среднее
	arithmetic *n*-space <AN, GE>	*s.* C 167		
A 962	**arithmetic number,** positive real number <NT>	positive reelle Zahl *f*	nombre *m* réel positif	положительное вещественное число
	arithmetic of cardinal numbers <SE>	*s.* C 119		
	arithmetic of ordinals <SE>	*s.* O 371		
	arithmetico-geometric mean <AL, ST>	*s.* A 958		
	arithmetico-geometric progression <AL>	*s.* A 959		
	arithmetico-geometric sequence <AL>	*s.* A 959		
	arithmetico-geometric series <AL>	*s.* A 960		
	arithmetic operation <AR>	*s.* A 949		
A 963	**arithmetic problem;** sum <AR>	arithmetische Aufgabe *f*, Rechenaufgabe *f*; Rechenexempel *n*	problème (calcul) *m* [d']arithmétique, devoir *m* de calcul	арифметическая задача
	arithmetic progression <AL, FD>	*s.* A 952		
A 964	**arithmetic proof;** number-theoretical proof <NT>	arithmetischer Beweis *m*; zahlentheoretischer Beweis	démonstration *f* arithmétique	арифметическое доказательство; теоретико-числовое доказательство
A 965	**arithmetic proportion** <AR>	arithmetische Proportion *f*	proportion *f* arithmétique	арифметическая (разностная) пропорция
A 966	**arithmetic quotient** <AR>	arithmetischer Quotient *m*	quotient *m* arithmétique	арифметическое частное
A 967	**arithmetic root,** root of the absolute value, non[-]negative root <AL, FO>	Wurzel *f* mit positivem Vorzeichen, arithmetische (positiv ausgezogene, nichtnegativ ausgezogene) Wurzel	valeur *f* arithmétique (absolue) du radical, racine *f* arithmétique, radical *m* pris au sens arithmétique, racine non négative	арифметический корень, арифметическое значение корня
A 968	**arithmetics** <AR>	Arithmetik *f*, Zahlenlehre *f*	arithmétique *f*	арифметика
A 969	**arithmetic sequence** <of *k*-th order or of order *k*, of higher order> <AL, FD>	arithmetische Folge *f* <*k*-ter Ordnung, höherer Ordnung>	suite *f* arithmétique <de *k*-ième ordre, d'ordre supérieur>	арифметический ряд <*k*-го порядка, высшего порядка>
	arithmetic sequence of the first order <AL, FD>	*s.* A 952		
A 970	**arithmetic series** <of the first, second, . . ., *m*-th order or order *m*, of higher order> <AL, FD>	arithmetische Reihe *f* <erster, zweiter, . . ., *m*-ter Ordnung, höherer Ordnung>	série (suite) *f* arithmétique <de premier, deuxième, . . ., *m*-e ordre ou d'ordre *m*, d'ordre supérieur>	арифметический (числовой) ряд, арифметическая прогрессия <первого, второго, . . ., *m*-го порядка, высшего порядка>
	arithmetic series <AL, FD>	*s.* A 952		
	arithmetic space <AN, AY>	*s.* E 569		
	arithmetic structure <LA>	*s.* D 772		
A 971	**arithmetic subtraction** <AR>	arithmetische Subtraktion *f*	soustraction *f* arithmétique	арифметическое вычитание
	arithmetic triangle <AR, CT>	*s.* P 293		
A 972	**arithmetization** <AG, MM>	Arithmetisierung *f*	arithmétisation *f*	арифметизация
A 973	**arity,** rank, type, weight <of a relation, operation, or predicate> <LO, UA>	Stellenzahl *f*, Arität *f*, Stelligkeit *f*, Stellenindex *m*	degré *m*, poids *m*	арность
	arm <EG>	*s.* S 784		
	Aronhold['s] differential equations <IV>	*s.* A 974		
A 974	**Aronhold['s] equations,** Aronhold['s] differential equations <IV>	Aronholdsche Differentialgleichungen *fpl*	équations *fpl* [différentielles] d'Aronhold	дифференциальные уравнения Аронгольда
A 975	**Aronhold['s] fraction** <IV>	Aronholdscher Bruch *m*	fraction *f* d'Aronhold	дробь Аронгольда
A 976	**Aronhold['s] invariant** <AG>	Aronholdsche Invariante *f*	invariant *m* d'Aronhold	инвариант Аронгольда

No.	English	German	French	Russian
A 977	**Aronhold['s] process** <IV>	Aronholdscher Prozeß *m*, Deltaprozeß *m*, Delta-Prozeß *m*, Aronholds Prozeß	procédé *m* d'Aronhold	процесс Аронгольда
	Aronhold['s] symbolic <IV>	*s.* S 2420		
A 978	**Aronhold['s] symbolic method,** symbolic method of Aronhold <IV>	Aronholdsche symbolische Methode *f*	méthode *f* symbolique d'Aronhold	символический метод Аронгольда
A 979	**Aronhold['s] theorem** <GE>	Aronholds Satz *m*, Satz von Aronhold	théorème *m* d'Aronhold	теорема Аронгольда
	around P <TO>	*s.* N 130		
A 980	**arrange / to** <a polynomial> <AL>	ordnen	ordonner	упорядочивать
A 981	**arrange in ascending order / to** <AL>	nach wachsender Ordnung ordnen	ranger par ordre croissant (de grandeur croissante)	упорядочивать по возрастающим порядкам
A 982	**arrange** <e.g. a polynomial> **in ascending powers / to** <AL, AN>	nach wachsenden (steigenden) Potenzen ordnen	ordonner suivant les puissances croissantes, ordonner par rapport aux puissances croissantes	упорядочивать по возрастающим степеням
A 983	**arrangement,** ordering, order, permutation, ordered arrangement, reordering <result of arranging a set of things> <CT>	Anordnung *f*, Permutation *f*, Komplexion *f*	permutation *f*, arrangement *m*, rangement *m*, complexion *f*	расстановка
A 984	**arrangement** <of *n* things (elements, objects) [taken] *k* at a time, of *k* out of *n* elements, of *k* elements selected from *n* elements>, *k*-arrangement of *n* elements, // permutation <of *n* things taken *k* at a time> <CT>	Variation *f*, Kombination *f* mit Berücksichtigung der Reihenfolge <von *n* Elementen (Gegenständen) zur *k*-ten Klasse, von *n* Elementen in *k*-ter Klasse>	arrangement *m* <de *n* éléments (lettres, objets) *k* à *k*, de *n* éléments pris *k* à *k*, de *k* éléments pris parmi *n*>, // variation *f*	размещение <из *n* элементов по *k* [элементам], по *k* элементам из *n*>, *k*-перестановка из *n* элементов, // вариация
A 985	**arrangement;** ordering <process> <GN>	Anordnen *n*, Anordnung *f*; Ordnen *n*, Ordnung *f*	arrangement *m*, disposition *f*; rangement *m* [par ordre]	расположение, размещение; расположение (размещение) в [определенном] порядке, упорядочение
	arrangement <GN>	*s.* 1. A 992; 2. S 706		
A 986	**arrangement according to their magnitude** <GN>	Anordnung *f* der Größe nach	arrangement *m* par grandeur croissante	упорядочение по величине
A 987	**arrangement in ascending powers** <AL, GN>	Anordnung *f* nach aufsteigenden (zunehmenden, wachsenden) Potenzen	arrangement *m* suivant les puissances croissantes	упорядочение по восходящим степеням
A 988	**arrangement in descending powers** <AL, GN>	Anordnung *f* nach abnehmenden (absteigenden, fallenden) Potenzen	arrangement *m* suivant les puissances décroissantes	упорядочение по убывающим степеням
A 989	**arrangement into blocks;** arrangement of blocks <ST>	Blockanordnung *f*, Blockeinteilung *f* <Prozeß oder dessen Ergebnis>	arrangement *m* (disposition *f*) en blocs; arrangement (disposition) des blocs	размещение в блоках; размещение блоков
	arrangement of blocks <ST>	*s.* A 989		
A 990	**arrangement without repetitions** <CT>	Variation *f* ohne Wiederholung (Wiederholungen)	arrangement *m* sans répétition[s], arrangement (permutation *f*) simple	размещение без повторений, размещение, соединение
A 991	**arrangement with repetitions** <CT>	Variation *f* mit Wiederholung (Wiederholungen)	arrangement *m* avec répétition[s], arrangement complet, permutation *f* avec répétition	размещение с повторениями
A 992	**array,** arrangement; ordered arrangement, order <result> <GN>	Anordnung *f*; Ordnung *f*	arrangement *m*, disposition *f*; ordre *m*	расположение (размещение) в [определенном] порядке; порядок
	array <AL>	*s.* M 180		
A 993	**array by diagonals** <of a double series> <SS>	Anordnung *f* nach Schräglinien (Diagonalen)	arrangement *m* par diagonales	упорядочение по диагоналям
A 994	**array by squares** <of a double series> <SS>	Anordnung *f* nach Quadraten	arrangement *m* par carrées	упорядочение по квадратам
A 995	**arrow** <AL, HA>	Pfeil *m*	flèche *f*	стрела
A 996	**arrow** <of a diagram scheme> <CA>	Pfeil *m*, gerichtete Kante *f*	flèche *f*	стрелка, стрела, морфизм
	arrow <CA>	*s.* M 899		
	arrow function <CA>	*s.* M 101		
A 997	**arrow head,** arrow-head, end-point, tip <of an arrow> <AL, CA, GN>	Endpunkt *m*, Spitze *f*	extrémité *f* terminale	концевая точка
A 998	**arrows-only axiom** <CA>	objektfreies Axiom *n*	axiome *m* sans objets	безобъектная аксиома
A 999	**arrows-only metacategory** <CA>	objektfreie Metakategorie *f*	métacatégorie *f* sans objets	метакатегория без объектов
	Arsh, arsh <FU>	*s.* A 924		
A 1000	**arsh transformation** <ST>	Areasinustransformation *f*, arsh-Transformation *f*	transformation *f* argsh (arsh), transformation du sinus hyperbolique inverse	ареасинус-преобразование
	Arsinh, arsinh <FU>	*s.* A 924		
	Artanh, artanh, Arth, arth <FU>	*s.* A 925		
	arth distribution <ST>	*s.* Z 11		
	arth transformation <ST>	*s.* Z 88		
	articulation point <GP>	*s.* C 2828		
A 1001	**articulation set,** cut-set, separating set <GP>	trennende Knotenpunktmenge (Eckenmenge) *f*, zerfällende Menge *f*, Artikulation *f*	ensemble *m* d'articulation	множество сочленения

No.	English	German	French	Russian
	articulation vertex <GP>	*s.* C 2828		
A 1002	**artificial constraint** <PG>	künstliche Beschränkung (Bedingung) *f*	contrainte *f* artificielle	искусственная связь, искусственное ограничение
A 1003	**artificial sample** <ST>	künstliche Stichprobe *f*	échantillon *m* artificiel	искусственная (детерминированная) выборка
A 1004	**artificial variable** <PG>	künstliche Variable *f*, Störvariable *f*	variable *f* artificielle	искусственная переменная
A 1005	**artificial variable method,** method of artificial variable <PG>	Methode *f* der künstlichen Variablen, Störvariablenmethode *f*	méthode *f* des variables artificielles	метод искусственных переменных
A 1006	**Artin['s] automorphism** <AB>	Artin-Automorphismus *m*	automorphisme *m* d'Artin	автоморфизм Артина
	Artin['s] braid group <AT>	*s.* B 713		
	Artin-Chevalley symbol <AB>	*s.* C 629		
A 1007	**Artin['s] conductor** <of a character of a Galois group> <AB>	Artinscher Führer *m*	conducteur *m* d'Artin	кондуктор Артина
A 1008	**Artin['s] conjecture** <NT>	Artinsche Vermutung *f*	conjecture *f* d'Artin, hypothèse *f* de M. Artin	гипотеза Артина
A 1009	**Artin['s] group** <AB>	Artin-Gruppe *f*	groupe *m* d'Artin	группа Артина
A 1010	**Artinian algebra** <AL>	artinsche Algebra *f*	algèbre *f* artinienne	артинова алгебра
A 1011	**Artinian category** <CA>	artinsche Kategorie *f*	catégorie *f* artinienne	артинова категория
	Artinian Gorenstein ring <AL>	*s.* Q 160		
A 1012	**Artinian group** <GR>	artinsche Gruppe *f*, Gruppe mit Minimalbedingung	groupe *m* artinien	артинова группа, группа с условием минимальности <для подгруппы>
A 1013	**Artinian module** <AL>	artinscher Modul *m*	module *m* artinien	артинов модуль
A 1014	**Artinian object** <CA>	artinsches Objekt *n*	objet *m* artinien	артинов объект
A 1015	**Artinian ring,** Artin['s] ring <AL>	artinscher Ring *m*	anneau *m* artinien (d'Artin)	артиново кольцо
A 1016	**Artinian scheme** <AG>	artinsches Schema *n*	schéma *m* artinien	артинова схема
A 1017	**Artin['s] *L*-function** <AB>	Artinsche *L*-Funktion *f*	fonction *f L* d'Artin	*L*-функция Артина
A 1018	**Artin['s] *L*-series** <AB>	Artinsche *L*-Reihe *f*	série *f L* d'Artin	[неабелев] *L*-ряд Артина
A 1019	**Artin['s] map[ping]** <AB>	Artinsche Abbildung *f*, Artin-Abbildung *f*	application *f* d'Artin, application de réciprocité	отображение Артина (взаимности)
A 1020	**Artin['s] reciprocity law** <AB>	Artinsches Reziprozitätsgesetz *n*	loi *f* de réciprocité d'Artin	закон взаимности Артина
	Artin-Rees condition <AL>	*s.* C 1831		
	Artin-Rees lemma <AL>	*s.* L 551		
A 1021	**Artin['s] representation** <AB>	Artinsche Darstellung *f*	représentation *f* d'Artin	представление Артина
	Artin['s] ring <AL>	*s.* A 1015		
A 1022	**Artin-Schreier group** <AB>	Artin-Schreiersche Gruppe *f*	groupe *m* d'Artin-Schreier	группа Артина-Шрейера
A 1023	**Artin-Schreier theorem** <AL>	Satz *m* von Artin-Schreier <über formal reelle Körper>, Artin-Schreierscher Satz	théorème *m* d'Artin-Schreier	теорема Артина-Шрейера
A 1024	**Artin['s] symbol** <AB>	Artin-Symbol *n*, Artinsches Symbol *n*	symbole *m* d'Artin	символ Артина
A 1025	**Artzt['s] parabola** <of the first *or* second kind> <GE>	Artztsche Parabel *f* <erster (1.) *oder* zweiter (2.) Art>	parabole *f* d'Artzt	парабола Арцта
	2-ary . . .	*s.* binary . . .		
	3-ary . . .	*s.* ternary . . .		
	4-ary . . . ⌐<FA>	*s.* quaternary . . .		
	Arzelà-Ascoli theorem	*s.* A 1027		
A 1026	**Arzelà['s] limit theorem** <DI>	Arzeläscher Grenzwertsatz *m*	théorème *m* limite d'Arzelà	предельная теорема Арцела
A 1027	**Arzelà['s] theorem,** Arzelà-Ascoli (Ascoli['s], Ascoli-Arzelà) theorem, theorem of Arzelà-Ascoli, theorem of choice [for sequences of functions] <FA>	Satz *m* von Arzelà-Ascoli, Satz von [C.] Arzelà, Arzelà[-Ascoli]scher Satz, Auswahlprinzip *n* (Auswahlsatz *m*, Auswahltheorem *n*) für Funktionenfolgen, Auswahltheorem	théorème *m* d'Arzelà, théorème du choix [sur les suites de fonctions]	теорема Арцела, принцип (теорема) выбора [для последовательностей функций], теорема Арцела-Асколи
A 1028	**ascendant continued fraction,** ascending continued fraction <NT>	aufsteigender Kettenbruch *m*, wachsender (zunehmender) Kettenbruch (Bruch *m*)	fraction *f* continue ascendante, fraction croissante	восходящая цепная дробь
A 1029	**ascending branch,** rising branch <of a curve> <FT, GN>	aufsteigender (ansteigender) Ast *m*	branche *f* ascendante (montante)	восходящая ветвь
A 1030	**ascending chain condition,** A.C.C., a.c.c. <AL>	aufsteigende Kettenbedingung *f*	condition *f* de chaine ascendante, condition des chaines ascendantes	условие обрыва возрастающей цепочки
A 1031	**ascending chain condition (property),** divisor chain condition, chain-condition <for modules *or* ideals> <AL>	Teilerkettensatz *m* <für Moduln>; Teilerkettensatz *m*, *O*-Kettensatz *m*, *O*-Satz *m*, Maximalbedingung *f*, Teilerkettenbedingung *f* <für Ideale>	condition *f* de chaine ascendante	условие обрыва возрастающих цепей, условие обрыва цепочки делителей, условие обрыва цепей
A 1032	**ascending chain condition for invariant subgroups,** maximum condition for invariant subgroups <GR>	Maximalbedingung *f* für Normalteiler	condition *f* des chaines ascendantes de sous-groupes distingués, condition maximale pour les sous-groupes invariants	условие обрыва возрастающей последовательности нормальных подгрупп

A 1033	**ascending chain of ideals** <AL>	aufsteigende Kette *f* von Idealen, O-Kette *f*	suite *f* croissante d'idéaux	возрастающая цепь идеалов
A 1034	**ascending chain of prime ideals** <AL>	aufsteigende Primidealkette *f*	chaîne *f* d'idéaux premiers ascendante	возрастающая цепь простых идеалов
	ascending continued fraction <NT>	*s.* A 1028		
A 1035	**ascending difference,** backward difference <FD>	aufsteigende (rückwärts genommene) Differenz *f*	différence *f* ascendante (latérale ascendante)	взятая назад разность; разность, взятая назад; конечная разность «назад», левая разность; разность для интерполирования назад
	ascending induction <FO>	*s.* U 447		
A 1036	**ascending Loewy series,** standard Loewy series, upper Loewy series <GR>	aufsteigende (obere) Loewy-Reihe *f*, vordere Loewysche Kompositionsreihe *f*	série *f* de Loewy ascendante	возрастающий ряд Лови
A 1037	**ascending Löwenheim-Skolem theorem** <MM>	aufsteigender Satz *m* von Löwenheim-Skolem	théorème *m* de Löwenheim-Skolem ascendant	восходящая теорема Левенгейма-Сколема
A 1038	**ascending normal series,** ascending series <GR>	aufsteigende Normalreihe (Normalkette) *f*	série (chaîne, suite) *f* normale ascendante	возрастающий нормальный ряд, возрастающая нормальная цепь
A 1039	**ascending order / in** <GN>	aufsteigend geordnet, in aufsteigender Anordnung	dans l'ordre croissant	упорядоченный по возрастанию, в возрастающем порядке
A 1040	**ascending powers** <SS>	aufsteigende (steigende, wachsende, zunehmende) Potenzen *fpl*	puissances *fpl* croissantes (ascendantes)	возрастающие степени
A 1041	**ascending power series** <SS>	aufsteigende (steigende, wachsende) Potenzreihe *f*	série *f* croissante	возрастающий степенной ряд
	ascending power series <SS>	*s.* P 1150		
A 1042	**ascending sequence** <of sets> <SE>	aufsteigende Folge (Mengenfolge, Kette) *f*	suite *f* d'ensembles croissante, suite croissante [de parties]	возрастающая последовательность
A 1043	**ascending sequence** <of events> <ST>	aufsteigende (wachsende) Folge *f*	suite *f* croissante	возрастающая последовательность
	ascending series <GR>	*s.* A 1038		
	Ascoli-Arzelà theorem <FA>	*s.* A 1027		
	Ascoli['s] theorem <FA>	*s.* A 1027		
	ascribing <GN>	*s.* A 1055		
	A-set <TO>	*s.* A 645		
	ASN <ST>	*s.* A 1259		
A 1044	**ASN curve,** curve of average sample numbers <ST>	ASN-Kurve *f*	courbe *f* ASN	кривая среднего объема выборки
	ASN function <ST>	*s.* A 1259		
A 1045	**aspherical space** <TO>	asphärischer Raum *m* <Hurewicz>	espace *m* asphérique	асферичное пространство
A 1046	**aspherical surface** <GE>	asphärische (nichtkuglige, deformierte) Fläche *f*	surface *f* asphérique	асферическая поверхность
A 1047	**asphericity** <TO>	Asphärischsein *n*	asphéricité *f*	асферичность
	assemblage of curves <AY>	*s.* F 81		
	assemblage of numbers <NT>	*s.* S 670		
	assemblage of points <SE, TO>	*s.* P 785		
	assemblage-theoretic <SE>	*s.* S 695		
	assembling of boundaries <TO>	*s.* P 297		
A 1048	**assertion,** proposition <GN>	Behauptung *f*; Aussage *f*	assertion *f*, proposition *f*	утверждение, положение [, требующее доказательства]
A 1049	**assertion sign,** ⊢ <*read:* yields> <LO>	Konsequenzzeichen *n*, Ergibt-Symbol *n*, „ergibt"-Zeichen, ⊢ <*lies:* ergibt>	signe (symbole) *m* de déductibilité, ⊢	знак выводимости, знак вывода, турникет, штопор, ⊢ <*читается:* из... выводимо, дает, доказуемо, отсюда, дают>
A 1050	**assertorial judgement, assertoric proposition** <LO>	assertorisches Urteil *n*	jugement *m* assertoire (assertorique, assertif)	ассерторическое суждение, суждение действительности
A 1051	**assessment of rounding errors** <AX, NU>	Näherung *f* von Rundungsfehlern	estimation *f* des erreurs d'arrondi	оценка ошибок округления
A 1052	**assignable cause** <ST>	nichtzufällige (bestimmbare) Ursache *f*	cause *f* assignable	неслучайная (определимая) причина
A 1053	**assigned base point** <of a linear system> <AG>	virtueller Basispunkt *m*	point-base *m* virtuel	виртуальная базисная точка
A 1054	**assigned fixed component** <of a linear system> <AG>	virtueller fester Bestandteil *m*	partie *f* fixe virtuelle	виртуальная неподвижная компонента
	assigned multiplicity <AG>	*s.* V 193		
A 1055	**assignment** <to>, ascribing <to>, attribution <to>, carrying <into> <e.g.: of a value> <GN>	Zuschreiben *n*, Zuordnung *f* <z. B.: eines Wertes>	attribution *f* <par exemple: d'une valeur>	приписывание, отнесение <к>, причисление <например: значения>
	assignment <SE>	*s.* C 2502		
A 1056	**assignment problem,** allocation problem, problem of assignment (allocation) <PG>	Zuteilungsproblem *n*	problème *m* d'affectation	задача о назначениях
	associate <AL>	*s.* A 1102		

No.	English	German	French	Russian
	associate Bertrand curves <DG>	*s.* B 221		
	associate curves <DG>	*s.* B 221		
A 1057	**associated continued fraction** <to a series> <NT>	assoziierter Kettenbruch *m*	fraction *f* continue associée	присоединенная [цепная] дробь, ассоциированная цепная (непрерывная) дробь
A 1058	**associated elementary filter** <TO>	assoziierter Elementarfilter *m*	filtre *m* élémentaire associé	элементарный фильтр, ассоциированный последовательностью; ассоциированный элементарный фильтр
A 1059	**associated fibre bundle** <AT>	assoziiertes (stetig assoziiertes) Faserbündel *n*, assoziiertes Bündel *n*	espace *m* fibré associé	ассоциированное расслоение
A 1060	**associated form** <of an algebraic variety> <AG>	zugeordnete Form *f*, Cayley-Form *f*	forme *f* associée (de Cayley)	ассоциированная форма
A 1061	**associated form** <of a quadratic form> <AL>	assoziierte (beigeordnete) Form *f*	forme *f* associée	ассоциированная форма
A 1062	**associated form** <to a form> <IV>	Schwesterform *f*, assoziierte Form *f*, Gefährtin *f* <einer Form>	forme *f* associée (affiliée), compagne *f* <d'une forme>	ассоциированная форма
A 1063	**associated function** <of an eigenfunction> <IE>	zugeordnete Funktion *f*	fonction *f* associée	присоединенная функция
A 1064	**associated function, associated function in the Borel sense** <LI>	Borelsche Transformierte *f*, assoziierte Funktion *f* [im Borelschen Sinne], Borel-Assoziierte *f*	fonction *f* entière associée, fonction associée [au sens de Borel]	функция, ассоциированная по Борелю <с>; ассоциированная функция
A 1065	**associated graded group** <of a filtered group> <AL>	assoziierte graduierte Gruppe *f* <einer filtrierten Gruppe>	groupe *m* gradué associé <à un groupe filtré>	градуированная группа, ассоциированная с группой, имеющей фильтрацию; ассоциированная градуированная группа
	associated graded ideal <AL>	*s.* L 230		
A 1066	**associated graded module** <of a filtered module> <AL>	assoziierter (zugehöriger) graduierter Modul *m* <eines gefilterten Moduls>	module *m* gradué associé <à un module filtré>	присоединенный (ассоциированный) градуированный модуль <относительно фильтрации>, связанный градуированный модуль <с модулем с фильтрацией>
A 1067	**associated graded ring** <AL>	zugehöriger (zugeordneter) graduierter Ring *m*	anneau *m* gradué associé	ассоциированное градуированное кольцо
A 1068	**associated Hausdorff ring** <AL>	assoziierter separierter Ring *m*	anneau *m* séparé associé	отделимое кольцо, ассоциированное с топологическим кольцом; ассоциированное отделимое кольцо
A 1069	**associated Hausdorff space** <TO>	assoziierter [separierter] Raum *m*	espace *m* séparé associé	ассоциированное отделимое пространство
	associated Hilbert problem <FT, IE>	*s.* A 299		
A 1070	**associated homogeneous [linear differential] equation,** reduced homogeneous equation, corresponding homogeneous equation, auxiliary equation, related homogeneous equation <DE>	zugehörige homogene [lineare] Differentialgleichung *f*, verkürzte (verstümmelte) [lineare] Differentialgleichung	équation *f* [différentielle linéaire] homogène associée, équation sans second membre	соответствующее однородное линейное дифференциальное уравнение, приведенное уравнение
A 1071	**associated homogeneous system,** corresponding homogeneous system <to a system of linear equations> <AL>	zugehöriges homogenes System (Gleichungssystem) *n*	système *m* homogène associé	соответствующая однородная система
A 1072	**associated homogeneous system,** related homogeneous system <DE>	zugeordnetes (zugehöriges) homogenes Differentialgleichungssystem *n*, verkürztes Differentialgleichungssystem, verstümmeltes System *n*	système *m* homogène associé	соответствующая однородная [линейная] дифференциальная система
	associated integer <AL>	*s.* E 452		
A 1073	**associated Koethe space,** associated normed Koethe space <FA>	assoziierter Köthe-Raum *m*	espace *m* de Köthe associé	присоединенное совершенное пространство
A 1074	**associated Laguerre polynomial** <FU>	verallgemeinertes Laguerresches Polynom *n*	polynôme *m* de Laguerre associé (généralisé)	обобщенный многочлен Чебышева-Лагерра, обобщенный полином Лагерра
	associated Legendre equation <DE>	*s.* L 533		
A 1075	**associated Legendre function [of the first kind],** Legendre['s] associated function [of the first kind] <FU>	zugeordnete Legendresche Funktion *f* [erster Art], zugeordnete Kugelfunktion *f* erster Art, Legendresche zugeordnete Funktion [erster Art]	fonction *f* de Legendre associée, fonction associée de Legendre, fonction sphérique fondamentale (associée, associée de première espèce, adjointe)	присоединенная функция Лежандра [первого рода]
A 1076	**associated Legendre function of the second kind,** Legendre['s] associated function of the second kind <FU>	zugeordnete Legendresche Funktion *f* zweiter Art, zugeordnete Kugelfunktion *f* zweiter Art, Legendresche zugeordnete Funktion zweiter Art	fonction *f* de Legendre associée de seconde espèce	присоединенная функция Лежандра второго рода
A 1077	**associated Legendre polynomial** <FU>	zugeordnetes Legendresches Polynom *n*, Legendresches zugeordnetes Polynom	polynôme *m* de Legendre associé, polynôme associé de Legendre	присоединенный многочлен Лежандра

	English	German	French	Russian
A 1078	**associated Mathieu equation** <DE>	zugeordnete Mathieusche Gleichung (Differentialgleichung) *f*	équation *f* de Mathieu associée	присоединенное уравнение Матье
A 1079	**associated Mathieu function of the first kind;** Ce; Se <FU>	zugeordnete Mathieusche Funktion *f* erster Art; Ce; Se	fonction *f* de Mathieu associée de la première espèce; Ce; Se	присоединенная функция Матье первого рода; Ce; Se
	associated matrix <MD>	*s.* E 439		
A 1080	**associated minimal surface** <DG>	assoziierte Minimalfläche *f*	surface *f* minimale associée	присоединенная минимальная поверхность
	associated normed Koethe space <FA>	*s.* A 1073		
A 1081	**associated number** <of a vertex> <GP>	beigeordnete Zahl *f*	nombre *m* associé, écartement *m*	эксцентрицитет
	associated number <NT>	*s.* A 1092		
A 1082	**associated numbers,** associated residues, residuate residuata <NT>	zusammengehörige Zahlen *fpl*	nombres *mpl* homogènes (associés)	ассоциированные числа
A 1083	**associated points** <on a cubic> <PJ>	assoziierte Punkte *mpl*	points *mpl* associés	ассоциированные точки
A 1084	**associated power series** <of a continued fraction> <NT>	assoziierte Potenzreihe *f*	série *f* entière (de puissances) associée	ассоциированный степенной ряд
A 1085	**associated prime element** <AL>	zugehöriges Primelement *n*	élément *m* premier associé	соответствующий простой элемент
A 1086	**associated prime elements** <AL>	assoziierte Primelemente *npl*	éléments *mpl* extrémaux associés	ассоциированные простые элементы
A 1087	**associated prime ideal,** prime ideal <of an ideal> <AL>	zugehöriges Primideal *n*	idéal *m* premier associé (essentiel)	ассоциированный простой идеал
A 1088	**associated prime ideal** <of a module> <AL>	zu einem Modul gehöriges Primideal *n*, assoziiertes (zugehöriges) Primideal	idéal *m* premier associé	ассоциированный простой идеал
A 1089	**associated prime ideal,** relevant prime ideal, primary radical, radical <of a primary ideal> <AL>	zugehöriges Primideal *n*, Radikal *n*, relevantes Primideal	idéal *m* premier associé, racine *f*	соответствующий (ассоциированный) простой идеал <примарному идеалу>
A 1090	**associated quadric** <DG>	assoziierte Quadrik *f*	quadrique *f* associée	присоединенная квадрика
A 1091	**associated radius of convergence** <FT>	assoziierter Konvergenzradius *m*	rayon *m* de convergence associé	сопряженный радиус сходимости
A 1092	**associated residue,** residuum sociatum <*pl*: residua sociata>, associated number <NT>	Socius *m*, socius *m* <Gauß, Euler> <*pl*: Socii>	nombre *m* associé, socius *m* <*pl*: socii>	ассоциированное число <число, обратно по модулю *m*>
	associated residues <NT>	*s.* A 1082		
A 1093	**associated separated group** <AL>	assoziierte separierte Gruppe *f*	groupe *m* séparé associé	отделимая группа, ассоциированная с топологической группой; ассоциированная отделимая группа
A 1094	**associated separated uniform structure** <TO>	assoziierte separierte uniforme Struktur *f*	structure *f* uniforme séparée associée	отделимая равномерная структура, ассоциированная с равномерной структурой; ассоциированная отделимая равномерная структура
A 1095	**associated space,** order dual <of a Riesz space> <AN, TO>	assoziierter Raum *m*	espace *m* associé	присоединенное (ассоциированное) пространство
A 1096	**associated spherical harmonic** <FU>	zugeordnete Kugelfunktion *f*	harmonique *f* sphérique associée	присоединенная гармоническая [функция]
	associated submodule <AL>	*s.* L 231		
A 1097	**associated surface,** relative minimal surface <DG>	assoziierte Fläche *f*, Relativminimalfläche	surface *f* associée (minimale relative)	ассоциированная (относительная минимальная) поверхность
A 1098	**associated system** <of solutions> <VA>	assoziiertes System *n* <von Lösungen>	système *m* associé <de solutions>	присоединенная система <решений>
A 1099	**associated topology** <TO>	assoziierte Topologie *f*	topologie *f* associée	топология, ассоциированная с фильтром; ассоциированная топология
A 1100	**associated undirected graph** <GP>	zugehöriger ungerichteter Graph *m*	graphe *m* non dirigé associé	соответствующий ненаправленный граф
A 1101	**associated valuation ring** <to a place> <AL>	zugehöriger Bewertungsring *m*	anneau *m* de valuation associé	соответствующее кольцо нормирования
A 1102	**associate element,** associate <in a ring> <AL>	assoziiertes Element *n*	élément *m* associé	ассоциированный элемент
A 1103	**associate equation,** associate integral equation <IE>	assoziierte (transponierte, umgestellte) Integralgleichung (Gleichung) *f*	équation *f* associée (intégrale associée)	ассоциированное (союзное) [интегральное] уравнение
	associate σ-function <FT>	*s.* A 1104		
	associate Hilbert problem <FT, IE>	*s.* A 299		
	associate integral equation <IE>	*s.* A 1103		
	associate Lamé function <FU>	*s.* L 60		
	associate matrix <MD>	*s.* H 235		
A 1104	**associate sigma function, associate sigma-function,** associate σ-function <σ_1, σ_2, or σ_3> <FT>	Nebensigmafunktion *f*, Neben-σ-Funktion *f*, Nebensigma *n*, Sigmafunktion (σ-Funktion) *f* mit Index	fonction *f* σ (sigma) associée (avec indice)	сигма-функция (σ-функция) с индексом

No.	English	German	French	Russian
A 1105	**associate tensor** <with respect to the fundamental tensor> <VT>	assoziierter Tensor *m*	tenseur *m* associé	присоединенный тензор
A 1106	**association** <ST>	Assoziation *f*	association *f*	ассоциация, связанность <зависимость между альтернативными признаками в таблице 2×2>
	association <SE>	*s.* C 2502		
	association law for powers <AR>	*s.* F 549		
A 1107	**association to the right** <LO>	Beklammerung *f* von rechts her		правое сочетание скобок
	associative algebra <AL>	*s.* A 406		
A 1108	**associative binary operation,** associative operation <AL>	assoziative [binäre] Operation *f*, assoziative binäre algebraische Verknüpfung *f*	opération *f* [binaire] associative	ассоциативная [бинарная] операция
A 1109	**associative commutative ring,** commutative[-associative] ring <AL>	[assoziativ-]kommutativer Ring *m*	anneau *m* [associatif] commutatif	[ассоциативно-]коммутативное кольцо, коммутативно-ассоциативное кольцо
	associative envelope <AL>	*s.* U 334		
	associative groupoid <AL>	*s.* S 376		
A 1110	**associative lattice,** lattice[-]ordered semigroup, l-semigroup <AL>	verbandsgeordnete Halbgruppe *f*, Verbandshalbgruppe *f*, assoziativer Verband *m*; l-Halbgruppe *f*	demi-groupe (monoïde) *m* réticulé; semi-groupe *m* réticulé	структурно упорядоченная полугруппа, l-полугруппа
A 1111	**associative law,** associativity law <AL>	assoziatives Gesetz (Prinzip) *n*, Assoziativgesetz *n*, Anreihungsregel *f*, Assoziationsgesetz *n*	loi *f* associative (d'association), loi (théorème *m*, formule *f*) d'associativité, principe *m* associatif	ассоциативный (сочетательный) закон, закон (формула) ассоциативности
A 1112	**associative law,** independence of the order of operation of two external laws of composition <for a bimodule> <AL>	durchlaufendes Assoziativgesetz *n*, Operatorvertauschungsregel *f*, Vertauschbarkeit *f* der Operatorwirkungen, gemischte Assoziativität *f*, Vertauschungsregel *f*	permutabilité *f* de deux lois externes, double associativité *f*, associativité mixte, relation *f* exprimant la permutabilité des lois externes <d'un (*A*,*B*)-bimodule>	закон ассоциативности, сочетательный закон, перестановочность двух внешних законов композиции, смешанная ассоциативность
A 1113	**associative law for operator groups** <AL>	Assoziativgesetz *n* für die Multiplikation mit Operatoren, gemischtes Assoziativgesetz	condition *f* d'associativité mixte, associativité *f* mixte	смешанная ассоциативность, ассоциативность умножения
A 1114	**associative law for series** <SS>	Assoziationsgesetz *n* für Reihen	loi *f* associative (d'association) pour les séries	закон ассоциативности рядов
	associativeness <AL>	*s.* A 1116		
	associative operation <AL>	*s.* A 1108		
	associative system <AL>	*s.* S 376		
A 1115	**associative with respect to a partial composition** <in a partial algebraic structure> <AL>	assoziativ bezüglich einer partiellen algebraischen Verknüpfung	associatif par rapport à une loi de composition partielle	ассоциативный относительно частичной бинарной операции
A 1116	**associativity,** associativeness <AL>	Assoziativität *f*	associativité *f*	ассоциативность, сочетательность, сослагательность, свойство ассоциативности
	associativity law <AL>	*s.* A 1111		
A 1117	**associativity law for the conjunction** <LO>	Assoziativgesetz *n* der Konjunktion	loi *f* d'associativité de la conjonction	ассоциативный закон для конъюнкции
A 1118	**associativity law for the disjunction** <LO>	Assoziativgesetz *n* der Alternative (Disjunktion)	loi *f* d'associativité de la disjonction	закон ассоциативности для дизъюнкции
A 1119	**associativity relations** <for the structural constants of an algebra> <AL>	Assoziativitätsrelationen *fpl*	relations *fpl* d'associativité	соотношения ассоциативности
A 1120	**associator** <AL>	Assoziator *m*	associateur *m*	ассоциатор
A 1121	**assosymmetric ring** <AL>	assosymmetrischer Ring *m*	anneau *m* assosymétrique	ассосимметрическое кольцо
	assume/ to<a value><GN>	*s.* A 1199		
	assumed mean <ST>	*s.* W 294		
A 1122	**assumption** <FO, LO>	Annahme *f*	assomption *f*	предположение
A 1122a	**assumption,** premise <of a proof> <GN, LO>	Voraussetzung *f*	prémisse *f*, condition *f*	предположение, посылка, основание, аргумент, довод
A 1123	**assumption formula,** basic formula <LO>	Ausgangsformel *f*, Grundformel *f*	formule *f* initiale	исходная формула
A 1124	**asterisk,** *, ∗ <as a mathematical symbol> <GN>	Stern *m*, Sternchen *n*, *, ∗	astérisque *m*, étoile *f*, *, ∗	звездочка, *, ∗
A 1125	**ast[e]roid,** four-cusped hypocycloid, tetracuspid <GE>	Astroide *f*, Sternkurve *f*, vierspitzige Hypozykloide *f*, Hypozykloide mit vier Rückkehrpunkten, kubische Zykloide *f*, // Asteroide *f*, Astroid *f*	astroïde *f*, hypocycloïde *f* à quatre rebroussements, cubo-cycloïde *f*, as *m* de carreau	астроида, звездовидная кривая
A 1126	**A-sum,** Abel-sum, sum by Abel's method <LI>	*A*-Summe *f*, Summe *f* nach dem *A*-Verfahren	*A*-somme *f*, somme *f* [par la méthode] d'Abel	*A*-сумма, [обобщенная] сумма по методу Абеля[-Пуассона], [обобщенная] сумма по Абелю-Пуассону, [обобщенная] сумма в смысле Абеля-Пуассона
A 1127	**A-summability,** Abel summability, summability by Abel's method <LI>	*A*-Summierbarkeit *f*, Summierbarkeit *f* nach dem *A*-Verfahren	*A*-sommabilité *f*, sommabilité *f* d'Abel, sommabilité par la méthode d'Abel	суммируемость методом (по методу) Абеля[-Пуассона], суммируемость в смысле Абеля-Пуассона

A 1128	***A*-summable series,** Abel summable series, series summable by Abel's method <LI>	*A*-summierbare (nach dem *A*-Verfahren summierbare) Reihe *f*•	série *f* *A*-sommable, série sommable [par la méthode] d'Abel	*A*-суммируемый ряд; ряд, суммируемый методом (по методу) Абеля[-Пуассона]; ряд, суммируемый в смысле Абеля-Пуассона
	asymmetric[al] distribution <ST>	*s.* S 1163		
	asymmetric[al] ellipsoid <AY, EG>	*s.* T 924		
	asymmetric[al] graph <GP>	*s.* 1. A 775; 2. I 64		
A 1129/32	**asymmetric[al] relation,** antisymmetric[al] relation <SE>	asymmetrische Relation *f*	relation *f* asymétrique (strictement antisymétrique)	асимметричное отношение
A 1133	**asymmetric[al] variety** <TO>	asymmetrische Mannigfaltigkeit *f*	variété *f* asymétrique	асимметричное многообразие
A 1134	**asymmetry index** <ST>	Asymmetrieindex *m*	indice *m* de dissymétrie	индекс асимметрии
A 1135	**asymmetry tensor** <DG>	Asymmetrietensor *m*, Torsionstensor *m* <Schouten>	tenseur *m* d'asymétrie	тензор асимметрии
A 1136	**asymptote,** rectilinear (straight-line) asymptote <of an algebraic curve or curve representing a real function> <as the tangent at infinity> <AG, RF>	Asymptote *f*	asymptote *f* [rectiligne], droite *f* asymptote	[прямолинейная] асимптота
A 1137	**asymptote,** principal tangent <of a surface> <DG>	Asymptote *f*, Haupttangente *f*, Schmiegtangente *f*	asymptote *f*, tangente *f* principale	асимптота, главная касательная
	asymptote <RF>	*s.* C 2795		
A 1138	**asymptotically constant random variable** <ST>	asymptotisch konstante Zufallsvariable *f*	variable *f* aléatoire asymptotiquement constante	асимптотически постоянная случайная переменная
	asymptotically convergent <AN>	*s.* C 2358		
A 1139	**asymptotically efficient estimating function, asymptotically efficient estimator** <ST>	asymptotisch wirksame (effektive, wirksamste) Schätzung (Punktschätzung, Schätzfunktion) *f*, wirksame (effektive) Schätzung (Punktschätzung, Schätzfunktion)	estimateur *m* asymptotiquement effectif, fonction *f* d'estimation asymptotiquement effective	асимптотически эффективная оценка
A 1140	**asymptotically equal** <to>, $\simeq$, $\cong$ <obsolete: $\sim$> <AN>	asymptotisch gleich, $\simeq$, $\cong$ <veraltet: $\sim$>	asymptotiquement égal, parallèle <à>, $\simeq$, $\cong$ <vieilli: $\sim$>	асимптотически равный, $\simeq$, $\cong$ <устаревшее: $\sim$>
A 1141	**asymptotically equal sequence** <SS>	asymptotisch gleiche Folge (Zahlenfolge) *f*	suite *f* asymptotiquement égale	асимптотически равная последовательность
A 1142	**asymptotically equivalent function** <with respect to division *or* subtraction> <AN>	asymptotisch äquivalente Funktion *f*	fonction *f* [asymptotiquement] équivalente	[асимптотически] эквивалентная функция
A 1143	**asymptotically equivalent sequence** <of random variables> <ST>	asymptotisch äquivalente Zufallsfolge (Folge) *f*	suite (séquence) *f* asymptotiquement équivalente	асимптотически эквивалентная последовательность
A 1144	**asymptotically normally distributed random variable** <SP>	asymptotisch normalverteilte Zufallsvariable *f*	variable *f* aléatoire distribuée asymptotiquement suivant la loi normale, variable aléatoire à distribution asymptotiquement normale	случайная переменная с асимптотически нормальным распределением
A 1145	**asymptotically normal distribution** <ST>	asymptotische Normalverteilung *f*	distribution *f* normale asymptotique	асимптотически нормальное распределение
A 1146	**asymptotically proportional,** $\sim$ <AN>	asymptotisch proportional, $\sim$	asymptotiquement proportionnel, $\sim$	асимптотически пропорциональный, $\sim$
A 1147	**asymptotically proportional sequence** <SS>	asymptotisch proportionale Folge (Zahlenfolge) *f*	suite *f* asymptotiquement proportionnelle	асимптотически пропорциональная последовательность
A 1148	**asymptotically stable solution,** strongly stable solution <DE>	asymptotisch (stark) stabile Lösung *f*	solution *f* asymptotiquement (fortement) stable	асимптотически (сильно) устойчивое решение
A 1149	**asymptotically unbiased estimator** <ST>	asymptotisch erwartungstreue (unverzerrte, biasfreie) Schätzfunktion (Schätzung, Punktschätzung) *f*	estimateur *m* asymptotiquement sans biais, estimateur asymptotiquement non biaisé	асимптотически несмещенная (вполне корректная) оценка
A 1150	**asymptotically uniformly negligible fluctuation** <ST>	asymptotisch gleichmäßig vernachlässigbare Schwankung *f*	fluctuation *f* asymptotiquement uniformément négligeable	асимптотически равномерно пренебрежимое колебание
A 1151	**asymptotically uniformly negligible random variable** <ST>	asymptotisch gleichmäßig vernachlässigbare Zufallsvariable *f*, Zufallsvariable von asymptotisch gleichmäßig vernachlässigbarer Schwankung	variable *f* aléatoire [de fluctuation] asymptotiquement uniformément négligeable	асимптотически равномерно пренебрежимая случайная величина
A 1152	**asymptotic basis** <of order *h*> <AB>	asymptotische Basis *f*, Basis im Großen <*h*-ter Ordnung>	base *f* asymptotique <d'ordre *h*>	асимптотический базис <порядка *h*>
A 1153	**asymptotic behaviour** <AN, DI>	asymptotisches (infinitäres) Verhalten *n*, Asymptotik *f*	comportement *m* (allure *f*) asymptotique	асимптотическое поведение, асимптотика
A 1154	**asymptotic circle** <of a curve> <DG>	asymptotischer Kreis *m*	cercle *m* asymptote	асимптотическая окружность
A 1155	**asymptotic cone** <AY>	Asymptotenkegel *m*	cône *m* asymptote	асимптотический конус
	asymptotic convergence <AN>	*s.* C 2336		
A 1156	**asymptotic curvature** <DG>	asymptotische Krümmung *f*	courbure *f* asymptote	асимптотическая кривизна

A 1157	**asymptotic curve,** asymptotic line <of a surface> <DG>	Asymptotenlinie *f*, Inflexionskurve *f*, Wendelinie *f*, Haupttangentenlinie *f*, Schmiegtangentenkurve *f*, Asymptotenkurve *f*, asymptotische Kurve *f*, Haupttangentenkurve *f*	ligne *f* asymptotique, ligne asymptote, courbe asymptote, courbe asymptotique, asymptotique *f*	асимптотическая линия
A 1158	**asymptotic density** <of a set of numbers> <AB>	natürliche Dichte *f*, Verteilungsfunktion *f*	densité *f* ordinaire (asymptotique, naturelle)	натуральная (асимптотическая) плотность
A 1159	**asymptotic φ-density,** natural φ-density <of a set of numbers> <AB>	natürliche φ(*x*)-Dichte *f*	φ-densité *f* naturelle	натуральная φ-плотность
A 1160	**asymptotic direction** <of a curve *or* surface> <DG>	Asymptotenrichtung *f*, asymptotische Richtung *f*	direction *f* asymptotique	асимптотическое направление
A 1161	**asymptotic efficiency** <ST>	asymptotische Wirksamkeit (Effizienz) *f*	efficacité (efficience) *f* asymptotique	асимптотическая эффективность
A 1162	**asymptotic egality** <with respect to division> <FT>	asymptotische Gleichheit *f*	égalité *f* asymptotique (infinitaire)	асимптотическое равенство
A 1163	**asymptotic equivalence** <with respect to subtraction *or* division> <FT>	asymptotische Äquivalenz *f* <bezüglich Subtraktion *oder* Division>	équivalence *f* asymptotique <par rapport à la soustraction *ou* division>	асимптотическая эквивалентность <относительно вычитания *или* деления>
A 1164	**asymptotic essential component** <AB>	asymptotische wesentliche Komponente *f*	composante *f* essentielle asymptotique	асимптотическая существенная компонента
A 1165	**asymptotic expansion,** asymptotic representation (power series expansion); asymptotic series (power series), semi-convergent series <Stieltjes> <AX, FT>	asymptotische Entwicklung (Darstellung) *f*; asymptotische (semikonvergente, halbkonvergente) Reihe *f*	développement *m* (représentation *f*) asymptotique; série *f* asymptotique (indéterminée, semi-convergente, semiconvergente)	асимптотическое разложение (представление); асимптотический (полусходящийся, асимптотический степенной) ряд
A 1166	**asymptotic expression,** asymptotic formula (representation) <AX, FT>	asymptotische Darstellung (Formel) *f*, asymptotischer Ausdruck *m*	expression (formule, représentation) *f* asymptotique	асимптотическое выражение (представление), асимптотическая формула (оценка)
	asymptotic formula <AX, FT>	*s.* A 1166		
	asymptotic line <DG>	*s.* A 1157		
A 1167	**asymptotic mean value** <of an arithmetic function> <NT>	asymptotischer Mittelwert *m*, mittlerer Wert *m*	valeur *f* moyenne asymptotique	асимптотическое среднее
A 1168	**asymptotic minimal basis** <of order *h**> <AB>	asymptotische Minimalbasis *f* <der Ordnung *h**>	base *f* minimale asymptotique <d'ordre *h**>	асимптотический минимальный базис <порядка *h**>
A 1169	**asymptotic order,** order <of an asymptotic basis> <AB>	asymptotische Basisordnung *f*, Ordnung *f* einer asymptotischen Basis	ordre *m* asymptotique	асимптотический порядок
A 1170	**asymptotic parameter** <DG>	Asymptotenparameter *m*	paramètre *m* asymptote	асимптотический параметр
A 1171	**asymptotic path** <FT>	Zielweg *m*, asymptotischer Weg *m*, Bestimmtheitsweg *m*, Konvergenzweg *m*	chemin *m* asymptotique	асимптотический (целевой) путь
A 1172	**asymptotic period** <FT>	asymptotische Periode *f*	période *f* asymptotique	асимптотический период
A 1173	**asymptotic plane** <of a space curve *or* ruled surface> <DG>	Asymptotenebene *f*	plan *m* asymptote	асимптотическая плоскость
A 1174	**asymptotic point** <of a curve> <GE>	asymptotischer Punkt *m*	point *m* asymptote	асимптотическая точка
	asymptotic power series [expansion] <AX, FT>	*s.* A 1165		
	asymptotic representation <AX, FT>	*s.* 1. A 1165; 2. A 1166		
	asymptotic series <AX, FT>	*s.* A 1165		
A 1175	**asymptotic stability,** strong stability <DE>	asymptotische (starke) Stabilität *f*	stabilité *f* asymptotique (forte)	асимптотическая (сильная) устойчивость
	asymptotic strip <DG>	*s.* O 530		
A 1176	**asymptotic surface** <DG>	asymptotische Fläche *f*	surface *f* asymptotique (asymptote)	асимптотическая поверхность
A 1177	**asymptotic triangle** <of a cubic> <AG>	Asymptotendreieck *n*	triangle *m* asymptote	асимптотический треугольник
A 1178	**asymptotic value** <FT>	Zielwert *m*, asymptotischer Wert *m*, Konvergenzwert *m*	valeur *f* asymptotique	асимптотическое (целевое) значение
A 1179	**asystatic group** <of transformations> <DE>	asystatische Gruppe *f*	groupe *m* asystatique	асистатическая группа
	asyzygetic form <IV>	*s.* A 1331		
	asyzygetic invariant <IV>	*s.* A 1332		
A 1180	**Atiyah-Singer index theorem** <AN, TO>	Atiyah-Singerscher Indexsatz *m*	théorème *m* d'Atiyah-Singer	теорема Атьи-Зингера об индексе
A 1181	**Atkinson['s] domain** <FA>	Atkinson-Bereich *m*	domaine *m* d'Atkinson	область Эткинсона
A 1182	**Atkinson['s] operator** <FA>	Atkinson-Operator *m*	opérateur *m* d'Atkinson	оператор Эткинсона
A 1183	**atlas** <AT, GE>	Atlas *m* <AT, GE>, Bündelatlas *m* <AT>	atlas *m*, système *m* de cartes	атлас
A 1184	**atom,** atomic (prime) element, point <of a partially ordered set> <LA>	Atom *n*, Atomelement *n*, Punkt *m*, Primelement *n*, unzerlegbares Element *n*	atome *m*, point *m*	атом
A 1185	**atom** <with respect to a measure> <ME>	singuläres Element *n*, Atom *n*, singuläre Menge *f*	atome *m*	атом

	atom <AL>	*s.* I 1032		
	atom <LO>	*s.* 1. A 1189; 2. P 1872		
A 1186	**atomic Boolean algebra** <is extensionally equivalent to atomistic Boolean algebra> <AL>	atomare Boolesche Algebra *f*	algèbre *f* (treillis *m*) de Boole atomique	дискретная (атомическая, атомная) булевая алгебра
A 1187	**atomic decomposition** <LA>	Zerlegung *f* in Atome, atomare Zerlegung	décomposition *f* atomique	разложение на атомы
	atomic element <LA>	*s.* A 1184		
A 1188	**atomic event** <ST>	atomares Ereignis *n*	événement *m* atomique	атомное событие
A 1189	**atomic expression,** [primitive] atomic formula, atom, primitive formula <of the propositional calculus> <LO>	atomarer Ausdruck *m*, A-Atom *n*	formule *f* simple (élémentaire)	атомарная формула
	atomic factorization <AL>	*s.* C 1431		
A 1190	**atomic formula,** molecular formula <of the functional calculus> <LO>	prädikativer Ausdruck *m*	formule *f* simple (élémentaire, atomique) <du calcul des prédicats>	предикативное выражение, атомарная формула <исчисления предикатов>
	atomic formula <LO>	*s.* 1. A 1189; 2. P 1872		
A 1191	**atomicity** <AL, LA>	Atomizität *f*	atomicité *f*	атомность
A 1191a	**atomic lattice** <LA>	atomarer Verband *m*	treillis *m* atomique	атомная решетка, атомная (атомарная, атомическая) структура
	atomic lattice <LA>	*s.* A 1194		
A 1192	**atomic proposition,** simple (elementary) proposition, simple sentence <LO>	atomare Aussage *f*, Elementaraussage *f*, primitive Aussage, Primaussage *f*	proposition *f* simple (atomique), atome *m*, énoncé *m* sans symbole logique, proposition élémentaire	атомарное (элементарное, простое) высказывание
	atomic quasivariety <UA>	*s.* M 571		
	atomic variety <UA>	*s.* M 581		
A 1193	**atomistic Boolean algebra** <AL>	atomistische Boolesche Algebra *f*	algèbre *f* de Boole atomique	атомистическая булева алгебра
A 1194	**atomistic lattice,** // atomic lattice, point lattice, relatively atomic lattice <Maeda> <LA>	atomistischer Verband *m*, atomarer Verband, Punktverband *m*, relativ atomarer Verband	treillis *m* atomique, treillis relativement atomique	атомистическая решетка
A 1195	**atomless Boolean algebra,** non-atomic Boolean algebra <AL>	atomlose (atomfreie) Boolesche Algebra *f*	algèbre *f* de Boole non atomique	непрерывная булева алгебра
A 1196	**atomless measure,** non-atomic measure <ME>	atomfreies Maß *n*	mesure *f* non atomique	неатомическая мера
A 1197	**atriphtaloid** <GE>	Atriphtaloide *f*	atriphtaloïde *f*	атрифталоида
A 1198	**attaching map** <AT>	Verheftungsabbildung *f*	application *f* d'attachement	приклеивающее отображение
A 1199	**attain / to,** to reach, to take, to assume <a value> <GN>	annehmen <einen Wert>	atteindre, prendre <une valeur>, passer <par une valeur>	достигать <значения>, принимать <значение>
A 1200	**attainable accuracy** <NU>	erreichbare (erzielbare) Genauigkeit *f*	précision *f* à atteindre	достижимая точность
A 1201	**attention limit,** warning limit <ST>	Warngrenze *f*	limite *f* d'alarme	предел предостережения
A 1202	**attractor,** point of attraction <NU>	Anziehungspunkt *m*	attracteur *m*, point *m* attractif (d'attraction)	точка притяжения, аттрактор
A 1203	**attribute** <LO>	Attribut *n*	attribut *m*	признак
	attribute <ST>	*s.* Q 72		
	attribution <GN>	*s.* A 1055		
A 1204	**augend,** first term <of a sum *or* a sum of order types> <AL, AR, SE>	erster Summand *m*, Augend[us] *m*	premier terme *m*, augendus *m*	первое слагаемое
A 1205	**augmentation** <AT, HA>	Augmentation *f*, Ergänzung *f*	augmentation *f*	аугментация, дополнение
	augmentation homomorphism <AT, HA>	*s.* A 1207		
A 1206	**augmentation ideal** <AL>	Augmentationsideal *n*	idéal *m* d'augmentation	идеал аугментации
A 1207	**augmentation map[-ping],** augmentation homomorphism <AT, HA>	Augmentationsabbildung *f*, Augmentationshomomorphismus *m*	homomorphisme *m* d'augmentation, augmentation *f*	аугментация, дополнение, дополняющий гомоморфизм
A 1208	**augmentation module** <HA>	Augmentationsmodul *m*	module *m* d'augmentation	модуль аугментации
A 1209	**augmentation-preserving map** <AT>	augmentationstreue Kettentransformation *f*	chaîne-homomorphisme *m* compatible avec l'augmentation	сохраняющее аугментацию цепное отображение
A 1210	**augmented complex** <HA>	augmentierter Komplex *m*	complexe *m* augmenté (muni d'une augmentation)	комплекс с дополнением (аугментацией)
A 1211	**augmented matrix** <of a linear system of equations> <AL>	erweiterte Matrix *f*	matrice *f* complète	расширенная матрица, пополненная матрица
A 1212	**augmented monoid** <AL>	vervollständigtes Monoid *n*		пополненная полугруппа
A 1213	**augmented range** <ST>	vermehrte Spannweite *f*	étendue *f* augmentée	расширенный размах <максимум размаха и максимального элемента выборки>
	Ausdehnungslehre <GE>	*s.* G 254		
	Aussonderungsaxiom <LO, SE>	*s.* A 1293		
A 1214	**authenticity** <ST>	Glaubwürdigkeit *f*, Authentizität *f*	authenticité *f*	достоверность, аутентичность
	autocatalytic function <ST>	*s.* L 1080		
A 1215	**auto[-]collineation,** automorphic collineation <PJ>	Autokollineation *f*, automorphe Kollineation *f*	autocollinéation *f*, collinéation *f* automorphe	автоморфная коллинеация, автоколлинеация

No.	English	Deutsch	Français	Русский
A 1216	**autocorrelation,** serial correlation <ST>	Autokorrelation *f*, Eigenkorrelation *f*, Reihenkorrelation *f*	autocorrélation *f*, corrélation *f* propre (sériale)	автокорреляция, сериальная корреляция
A 1217	**autocorrelation coefficient,** serial correlation coefficient <ST>	Autokorrelationskoeffizient *m*, Reihenkorrelationskoeffizient *m*	coefficient *m* d'autocorrélation	коэффициент автокорреляции
A 1218	**autocorrelation function,** serial correlation function <ST>	Autokorrelationsfunktion *f*, Reihenkorrelationsfunktion *f*	fonction *f* d'autocorrélation	автокорреляционная функция
A 1219	**autocorrelogram** <ST>	Autokorrelogramm *n*	autocorrélogramme *m*	автокоррелограмма
A 1220	**autocovariance** <ST>	Autokovarianz *f*	autocovariance *f*	автоковариация
A 1221	**autocovariance function** <ST>	Autokovarianzfunktion *f*	fonction *f* d'autocovariance	функция автоковариации
A 1222	**autodistributivity;** self-distributive law <AL>	Selbstdistributivität *f*, Autodistributivität *f*	autodistributivité *f*	самодистрибутивность, автодистрибутивность
A 1223	**autoduality** <GE>	selbstduale Abbildung *f*	application *f* auto-duale	автодуальное отображение
	autodual lattice <LA>	*s.* S 284		
A 1224	**autological adjective** <MM>	autologisches Adjektiv *n*	mot *m* autologique	автологическое прилагательное
	automata theory <TA>	*s.* T 373		
	automorph <NT>	*s.* A 1227		
	automorphic collineation <PJ>	*s.* A 1215		
A 1225	**automorphic form of weight *r*** <FT, NT>	automorphe Form *f* zur Dimension *r*	forme *f* automorphe de poids *r*	автоморфная форма веса *r*
A 1226	**automorphic function** <FT>	automorphe Funktion *f*	fonction *f* automorphe	автоморфная функция
	automorphic mapping <GR>	*s.* A 1229		
A 1227	**automorphic transformation,** automorph, transformation into itself <of a form> <NT>	automorphe Transformation (Substitution) *f*	transformation (substitution) *f* automorphe, substitution semblable <Hermite>	автоморфное преобразование
A 1228	**automorphism** <AL, FT>	Automorphismus *m*, automorphe Abbildung *f*	automorphisme *m*, automorphie *f*	автоморфизм
A 1229	**automorphism,** automorphism of groups, group[-] automorphism, automorphic mapping <GR>	Automorphismus *m*, Gruppenautomorphismus *m*, gruppentheoretischer Automorphismus, automorphe Abbildung *f*, // Isomorphismus *m*	automorphisme *m* [de groupes], automorphie *f*, isomorphisme *m* du groupe avec lui-même	автоморфизм [группы], групповой автоморфизм, автоморфное отображение
A 1230	**automorphism group,** group of automorphisms <AL>	Automorphismengruppe *f*	groupe *m* d'automorphismes	группа автоморфизмов
A 1231	**automorphism group** <of a configuration> <GE, TO>	Konfigurationsgruppe *f*	groupe *m* des automorphismes <d'une configuration>	группа автоморфизмов <конфигурации>
A 1232	**automorphism of finite order** <AL>	periodischer Automorphismus *m*	automorphisme *m* périodique	периодический автоморфизм, автоморфизм конечного порядка
	automorphism of groups <GR>	*s.* A 1229		
A 1233	**automorphism over (relative to) *k*,** *k*-automorphism <of *K*> <AL>	Relativautomorphismus *m* über *k*, Automorphismus *m* der Erweiterung *K*/*k*, *k*-Automorphismus *m*, Automorphismus über *k*, Automorphismus der Körpererweiterung *K*/*k*	automorphisme *m* [relatif] sur *k*, *k*-automorphisme <de *K*>	[относительный] автоморфизм над *k*, *k*-автоморфизм <от *K*>
A 1234	**automorphy** <FT>	Automorphie *f*	automorphie *f*	автоморфия
A 1235	**autonomous system [of differential equations],** dynamic system [of differential equations] <DE>	autonomes (stationäres, dynamisches) System *n* [von Differentialgleichungen], autonomes (stationäres, dynamisches) Differentialgleichungssystem *n*	système *m* [d'équations différentielles] autonome, système différentiel autonome	автономная (динамическая, консервативная) система [дифференциальных уравнений]
A 1236	**autoparallel curve** <DG>	autoparallele Kurve (Linie) *f*	courbe *f* autoparallèle	автопараллельная кривая
A 1237	**autoparatopism** <of a quasi-group> <AL>	Autoparatopie *f*	autoparatopie *f*	автопаратопия
	autoprojective mapping <AL, PJ>	*s.* A 1238		
A 1238	**autoprojectivity, auto-projectivity,** autoprojective mapping <of a group> <AL, PJ>	Selbstprojektivität *f*, Autoprojektivität *f*, selbstprojektive Abbildung *f*	autoprojectivité *f*, application (représentation, transformation) *f* autoprojective	автопроективное отображение (преобразование), автопроективитет
	auto[-]projectivity <GR>	*s.* L 161		
A 1239	**autoregression,** serial regression <ST>	Autoregression *f*, Eigenregression *f*, Reihenregression *f*	autorégression *f*, régression *f* propre (sériale)	авторегрессия, сериальная регрессия
A 1240	**autoregression equation** <ST>	Autoregressionsgleichung *f*, Reihenregressionsgleichung *f*	équation *f* d'autorégression	уравнение авторегрессии
A 1241	**autoregressive process** <SP>	autoregressiver Prozeß *m*	processus *m* autorégressif	авторегрессионный процесс
A 1242	**autoregressive transformation** <SP>	autoregressive Transformation *f*	transformation *f* autorégressive	авторегрессионное преобразование
A 1243	**autospectral density** <SP>	Autospektraldichte *f*	densité *f* autospectrale	автоспектральная плотность
A 1244	**autotopism** <of a loop> <AL>	Autotopie *f*	autotopie *m*	автотопия
A 1245	**auxiliary calculation** <AR>	Nebenrechnung *f*, Hilfsrechnung *f*	calcul *m* auxiliaire	вспомогательное вычисление

No.	English	German	French	Russian
A 1246	**auxiliary circle** <of a conic; its radius is the major semi-axis *a*> <AY>	Hauptkreis *m*	cercle *m* principal (homographique, auxiliaire)	основной круг
A 1247	**auxiliary cone,** cone of slope <DS>	Böschungskegel *m*	cône *m* de talus	конус откоса
A 1248	**auxiliary cone with vertex downwards,** cone of slope for cutting <DS>	Böschungskegel *m* für (im) Abtrag		конус откоса при выемке
A 1249	**auxiliary cone with vertex upwards,** cone of [slope for] embankment <DS>	Böschungskegel *m* für Auftrag		вспомогательный конус, конус откоса при насыпи
A 1250	**auxiliary equation,** characteristic (secular, frequency) equation <of a linear differential equation> <DE>	charakteristische Gleichung *f*, Säkulargleichung *f*, säkulare Gleichung, Frequenzgleichung *f*	équation *f* caractéristique (séculaire)	характеристическое (вековое, секулярное, частотное) уравнение
	auxiliary equation <AL>	*s.* C 2511		
	auxiliary equation <DE>	*s.* A 1070		
A 1251	**auxiliary line** <DS, EG>	Hilfslinie *f*	ligne *f* auxiliaire (artificielle)	вспомогательная линия
	auxiliary mean <ST>	*s.* W 294		
A 1252	**auxiliary variable,** subsidiary variable <GN>	Hilfsvariable *f*, Hilfsveränderliche *f*, Hilfsgröße *f*	variable *f* auxiliaire, variable subsidiaire	вспомогательная переменная
	average <ST>	*s.* M 298		
A 1253	**average absolute value;** rectified value <of a periodic quantity> <ER, NU>	arithmetischer Mittelwert *m* der Absolutbeträge, mittlerer Absolutwert *m*; Gleichrichtwert *m* <einer periodischen Größe>	valeur *f* moyenne absolue; valeur redressée <d'une grandeur périodique>	среднее значение абсолютных величин, абсолютное среднее [значение], среднее абсолютное
	average determination <GN>	*s.* A 1260		
A 1254	**average deviation,** mean deviation <ST>	durchschnittliche (mittlere) Abweichung *f*	écart *m* moyen [absolu], écart arithmétique (à la médiane)	среднее отклонение
A 1255	**average error,** mean error <ER, ST>	durchschnittlicher (einfacher mittlerer) Fehler *m*	erreur *f* moyenne	средняя погрешность, средняя ошибка
	average information content <ST>	*s.* E 267		
	average loss <ST>	*s.* E 718		
A 1256	**average outgoing quality [level],** AOQ [level] <ST>	Durchschlupf *m*	qualité *f* (niveau *m* de qualité) moyenne à la sortie	среднее выходное качество, уровень среднего выходного качества
A 1257	**average outgoing quality limit,** AOQ limit, AOQL <ST>	Durchschlupfgrenze *f*	limite *f* de qualité moyenne à la sortie	граница (предел) среднего выходного качества
	average overall subsampling value <ST>	*s.* G 376		
A 1258	**average quality protection** <ST>	Durchschnittsqualitätsschutz *m*	protection *f* de la qualité moyenne	гарантия среднего качества
A 1259	**average sample number,** ASN function, ASN <ST>	durchschnittlicher (mittlerer) Stichprobenumfang *m*, ASN-Funktion *f*, ASN	effectif *m* moyen de l'échantillon, taille *f* moyenne de l'échantillon, fonction *f* ASN	средний объем выборки (инспекции)
	average value <ST>	*s.* M 298		
A 1260	**averaging,** taking of the mean, average determination, determination of average <GN>	Mittelung *f*, Mitteln *n*, Mittelwertbildung *f*, Mittelbildung *f*; Mittelungsprozeß *m*	établissement *m* (formation *f*, processus *m*) de moyennes, prise *f* de moyenne, centrage *m*, médiation *f*	усреднение, осреднение, образование (определение, получение) среднего значения
A 1261	**averaging method** <*e.g.*: of W. Ritz> <AX, DE>	Mittelungsmethode *f*, Mittelungsverfahren *n*; „averaging method" *f* <von W. Ritz>	méthode *f* des moyennes	метод (способ) усреднения
A 1262	**averaging operator** <FA>	Mittelungsoperator *m*, Operator *m* der Mittelwertbildung	opérateur *m* de moyenne	усредняющий оператор, оператор усреднения
A 1263	**axial collineation** <PJ>	axiale Kollineation *f*	collinéation *f* axiale	аксиальная коллинеация
	axial collineation <DS>	*s.* P 514		
A 1264	**axial complex** <PJ>	Achsenkomplex *m*	complexe *m* axial, complexe des axes	осевой комплекс
A 1265	**axial co-ordinates** <of a line> <AY>	Achsenkoordinaten *fpl*	coordonnées *fpl* axiales	осевые (аксиальные) координаты
	axial group <GR>	*s.* K 90		
	axially symmetric <EG>	*s.* A 1322		
	axial pencil <AY>	*s.* P 382		
A 1266	**axial point** <GE>	axialer Punkt *m*	point *m* axial	аксиальная точка
A 1267	**axial symmetry,** symmetry with respect to an axis, symmetry with respect to a line <EG>	Axialsymmetrie *f*, Achsensymmetrie *f*, Symmetrie *f* bezüglich einer Achse, Klappsymmetrie *f*, Spiegelung *f* <an einer Geraden>	axisymétrie *f*, symétrie *f* axiale (de révolution, d'axes, par rapport à une droite, par rapport à un axe)	осевая (аксиальная) симметрия, симметрия относительно оси (прямой)
	axial symmetry / in <EG>	*s.* A 1322		
A 1268	**axial tensor** <VT>	axialer Tensor *m*	tenseur *m* axial	осевой (аксиальный)тензор
A 1269	**axial vector,** pseudovector <VT>	axialer (rotatorischer) Vektor *m*, Pseudovektor *m*, Drehvektor *m*, Achsenvektor *m*	vecteur *m* axial, pseudovecteur *m*	осевой (аксиальный) вектор, псевдовектор
	axiator <VT>	*s.* A 784		
A 1270	**axiomatic class** <Grätzer>, arithmetic class in the wider sense <Tarski>, // elementary class <of structures> <UA>	axiomatische Klasse *f*	classe *f* axiomatique	аксиоматизируемый класс

A 1271	**axiomatic foundation of set theory** <SE>	axiomatischer Aufbau *m* der Mengenlehre, axiomatische Begründung *f* der Mengenlehre	fondation *f* axiomatique de la théorie des ensembles	аксиоматическое обоснование теории множеств
A 1272	**axiomatic method,** postulational method, method of postulation <MM>	axiomatische Methode *f*	méthode *f* axiomatique	аксиоматический метод, метод постулатов
	axiomatic rank <UA>	*s.* R 139		
A 1273	**axiomatics** <MM>	Axiomatik *f*	axiomatique *f*	аксиоматика
A 1274	**axiomatic set theory** <SE>	axiomatische Mengenlehre *f*	théorie *f* axiomatique des ensembles	аксиоматическая теория множеств
A 1275	**axiomatic system,** system of axioms, axiom system <MM>	Axiomensystem *n*	système *m* d'axiomes	система (набор) аксиом
A 1276	**axiomatizability** <MM>	Axiomatisierbarkeit *f*	propriété *f* d'être axiomatisable, axiomatisabilité *f*	аксиоматизируемость
A 1277	**axiomatized theory** <FO>	rekursiv axiomatisierte Theorie *f*	théorie *f* récursivement axiomatisée	рекурсивно аксиоматизированная теория
	axiom for inaccessible sets <SE>	*s.* T 81		
A 1278	**axiom of abstraction,** axiom scheme of abstraction <LO, SE>	Abstraktionsaxiom *n* <Frege>	axiome *m* de partage <Lusin>	принцип свертывания
A 1279	**axiom of accessibility** <SE>	Erreichbarkeitsaxiom *n*	axiome *m* des alephs accessibles	аксиома о достижимых кардиналах
	axiom of amalgamation <SE>	*s.* A 1295		
	axiom of Archimedes <GE>	*s.* A 897		
A 1280	**axiom of choice,** choice axiom, Zermelo['s] axiom, principle of choice, Zermelo['s] choice principle; multiplicative axiom, multiplicative principle <SE>	Auswahlaxiom *n*, Axiom *n* der Auswahl, Auswahlprinzip *n*, Zermelosches Prinzip *n*	axiome *m* du (de) choix, axiome de [E.] Zermelo, axiome de sélection, postulat *m* de [E.] Zermelo	аксиома выбора (Цермело), постулат (принцип, аксиома произвольного) выбора; теорема выбора; мультипликативная аксиома, аксиома мультипликативности
A 1281	**axiom of complete induction,** induction axiom <FO, LO>	Axiom *n* der vollständigen Induktion, Induktionsaxiom *n*	axiome *m* d'induction, axiome de l'induction complète, axiome de récurrence	аксиома математической (полной, возвратной) индукции, аксиома индукции
A 1282	**axiom of completeness,** Hilbert['s] postulate of completeness, [Hilbert['s]] strong axiom of continuity <GE>	Vollständigkeitsaxiom *n*, Axiom *n* der linearen Vollständigkeit, Axiom der Vollständigkeit	axiome *m* de complétion	аксиома полноты
A 1283	**axiom of comprehension,** comprehension principle; axioms of comprehension, axioms of set construction, scheme of comprehension <SE>	Komprehensionsaxiom *n*, Komprehensionsprinzip *n*; Komprehensionsaxiomenschema *n*	axiome *m* de compréhension; schéma *m* d'axiomes de compréhension, schéma de compréhension	аксиома выделения; аксиомы свертывания
A 1284	**axiom of constructibility (constructivity),** Gödel['s] axiom of constructibility <SE>	Konstruktibilitätsaxiom *n*	axiome *m* de constructibilité	аксиома конструктивности
A 1285	**axiom of continuity** <of the probability measure> <ST>	Stetigkeitsaxiom *n* des Wahrscheinlichkeitsmaßes, Stetigkeitssaxiom für Wahrscheinlichkeiten	axiome *f* de continuité de la mesure de probabilité	аксиома непрерывности вероятностной меры
	axiom of countability <TO>	*s.* S 202		
	axiom of coupling <SE>	*s.* A 1288		
	axiom of Dedekind-Cantor <GE>	*s.* C 89		
	axiom of determination <SE>	*s.* A 1286		
	axiom of elementary sets <SE>	*s.* A 1288		
	axiom of Eudoxus <GE>	*s.* A 897		
A 1286	**axiom of extensionality [for sets],** principle of extensionality, extensionality axiom, axiom of determination (extent) <SE>	Extensionalitätsaxiom *n*, Axiom *n* der Umfangsbestimmtheit (Bestimmtheit)	axiome *m* d'extension[alité], axiome relationnel, premier axiome de Zermelo-Fraenkel, postulat *m* de l'extension[alité], axiome de l'égalité des ensembles	аксиома экстенсиональности (объемности, определенности)
	axiom of extent <SE>	*s.* A 1286		
	axiom of foundation <SE>	*s.* A 1291		
	axiom of Fundierung <SE>	*s.* A 1291		
	axiom of identity <TO>	*s.* C 1835		
	axiom of inaccessibility <SE>	*s.* T 81		
	axiom of inaccessible cardinals <SE>	*s.* T 81		
A 1287	**axiom of infinity,** principle of infinity <SE>	Unendlichkeitsaxiom *n*, Axiom *n* des Unendlichen	axiome *m* de l'infini	аксиома бесконечности (существования бесконечного множества)
	axiom of infinity <GE>	*s.* P 1120		
A 1288	**axiom of pairing (pairs),** principle of pairing, pairing axiom, axiom of elementary sets, axiom of coupling (the pair) <SE>	Axiom *n* der Elementarmengen (Paarung), Paarbildungsaxiom *n*	axiome *m* des paires, axiome de l'ensemble à deux éléments, axiome de l'ensemble binaire	аксиома пары (неупорядоченных пар, существования пары любых множеств)

No.	English	German	French	Russian
	axiom of parallelism <GE>	*s.* 1. E 572; 2. P 93		
	axiom of Pasch <GE>	*s.* P 294		
A 1289	**axiom of power-set,** principle of power-set, power[-set] axiom, axiom of the power set, axiom of [the family of] subsets <SE>	Axiom *n* der Potenzmenge, Potenzmengenaxiom *n*	axiome *m* de l'ensemble des parties	аксиома степени (множества частей, множества всех подмножеств, существования множества всех частей произвольного множества)
A 1290	**axiom of reducibility,** reducibility axiom, Russell['s] axiom of reducibility <LO>	Axiom *n* der Reduzibilität, Reduzibilitätsaxiom *n*, Reduzibilitätsprinzip *n*	axiome *m* de réductibilité	аксиома сводимости
A 1291	**axiom of regularity,** axiom of foundation (restriction, Fundierung), regularity (restrictive) axiom, "Fundierungsaxiom" <SE>	Fundierungsaxiom *n*, Axiom *n* der Fundierung	axiome *m* de régularité (fondation), « Axiom *m* der Fundierung »	аксиома основания (регулярности, фундирования, ограничения)
	axiom of replacement <LO>	*s.* A 1294		
A 1292	**axiom of restriction** <SE>	Beschränktheitsaxiom *n*	axiome *m* de restriction	аксиома ограничения
	axiom of restriction <SE>	*s.* A 1291		
	axiom of separation <LO, SE>	*s.* A 1293		
A 1293	**axiom of subsets,** subset axiom, principle of subsets, axiom of separation, limited abstraction principle, separation principle, Zermelo['s] separation principle, Aussonderungsaxiom <for the formula φ>; axiom scheme of separation, Zermelo['s] axiom scheme of separation, separation scheme <LO, SE>	Aussonderungsaxiom *n*, Axiom *n* der Aussonderung (Teilmengen), Aussonderungsprinzip *n*	axiome *m* de séparation; schéma *m* de la séparation	аксиома подмножеств, аксиома выделения [для высказывательной функции]
	axiom of subsets <SE>	*s.* A 1289		
A 1294	**axiom of substitution,** axiom of replacement, replacement axiom, axiom scheme of replacement, axiom scheme of substitution <LO>	Ersetzungsaxiom *n*	axiome *m* de remplacement	аксиома подстановки; аксиома замены, аксиома замены для высказывательной функции
A 1295	**axiom of sum-set,** principle of sum-set, axiom of union[s] (amalgamation), sum-set (sum, union) axiom <SE>	Axiom *n* der Vereinigung, Vereinigungsmengenaxiom *n*, Vereinigungsaxiom *n*, Summenaxiom *n*	axiome *m* de réunion	аксиома суммы (объединения, существования объединения) <всех элементов произвольного множества в новое множество>
	axiom of symmetry <TO>	*s.* C 1838		
A 1296	**axiom of the empty set** <SE>	Axiom *n* der Nullmenge	deuxième axiome *m* de Zermelo-Fraenkel	аксиома нулевого (существования пустого) множества
	axiom of the family of subsets <SE>	*s.* A 1289		
	axiom of the pair <SE>	*s.* A 1288		
	axiom of the power set <SE>	*s.* A 1289		
A 1297	**axiom of union,** union axiom <SE>	Axiom *n* der Vereinigung von zwei Mengen	axiome *m* de réunion de deux ensembles	аксиома объединения двух множеств
	axiom of union[s] <SE>	*s.* A 1295		
A 1298	**axiom scheme, axiom-scheme, axiom schema** <MM>	Axiomenschema *n*	schéma *m* d'axiomes	схема аксиом, аксиомная схема
	axiom scheme of abstraction <LO, SE>	*s.* A 1278		
	axiom scheme of replacement <LO>	*s.* A 1294		
	axiom scheme of separation <LO, SE>	*s.* A 1293		
	axiom scheme of substitution <LO>	*s.* A 1294		
	axioms of betweenness <GE>	*s.* A 1305		
	axioms of comprehension <SE>	*s.* A 1283		
A 1299	**axioms of congruence** <GE>	Axiome *npl* der Kongruenz, Kongruenzaxiome *npl*	axiomes *mpl* de congruence	аксиомы конгруэнтности
	axioms of connection <GE>	*s.* A 1303		
A 1300	**axioms of continuity,** principles of continuity <GE>	Axiome *npl* der Stetigkeit, Stetigkeitsaxiome *npl*	axiomes *mpl* de continuité, postulats *mpl* de la continuité	аксиомы непрерывности
	axioms of Dedekind-Peano <FO>	*s.* P 340		
A 1301	**axioms of equality** <FO>	Axiome *npl* der Gleichheit	axiomes *mpl* de l'égalité	аксиомы равенства
	axioms of equality <LO>	*s.* A 1302		
A 1302	**axioms of identity,** axioms of equality <LO>	Gleichheitsaxiome *npl*	axiomes *mpl* pour l'égalité	аксиомы тождества, правила равенства
A 1303	**axioms of incidence,** axioms of connection <GE>	Axiome *npl* der Verknüpfung (Inzidenz), Inzidenzaxiome *npl*, Verknüpfungsaxiome *npl*	axiomes *mpl* d'incidence	аксиомы связи (сочетания, инцидентности, принадлежности)

A 1304	**axioms of incidence of (in) projective geometry,** projective axioms of incidence <PJ>	projektive Verknüpfungsaxiome *npl*, Verknüpfungsaxiome in der projektiven Geometrie	axiomes *mpl* d'incidence de (dans) la géométrie projective, axiomes d'incidence projectifs	аксиомы связи (сочетания, инцидентности) [в] проективной геометрии, проективные аксиомы связи (сочетания, инцидентности)
A 1305	**axioms of order,** axioms of betweenness <GE>	Axiome *npl* der Anordnung, Anordnungsaxiome *npl*	axiomes *mpl* d'ordre	аксиомы порядка (упорядочения)
A 1306	**axioms of position** <GE>	Axiome (Postulate) *npl* der Lage	postulats *mpl* de situation	аксиомы положения
	axioms of set construction <SE>	*s.* A 1283		
	axiom system <MM>	*s.* A 1275		
	axiom system free from contradiction <FO>	*s.* C 2090		
	axis <AY>	*s.* 1. C 2420; 2. P 840		
	axis <EG>	*s.* 1. A 579; 2. A 1319; 3. A 1321		
	axis <GE>	*s.* C 344		
	axis <PJ>	*s.* C 402		
	axis of aberration <DG>	*s.* A 366		
A 1307	**axis of abscissae;** x-axis <GN>	Abszissenachse *f*; x-Achse *f*, // Abszisse *f*	axe *m* des abscisses, axe d'abscisses; axe des x	ось абсцисс
A 1308	**axis of absolute convergence** <of a Dirichlet series> <SS>	Achse (Grenzgerade) *f* absoluter Konvergenz	axe *m* de convergence absolue	ось (прямая) абсолютной сходимости
A 1309	**axis of affinity** <GE>	Affinitätsachse *f*	axe *m* d'affinité	ось аффинности (аффинного преобразования)
	axis of central collineation <AY, DS>	*s.* A 1316		
A 1310	**axis of collineation,** axis of projectivity (homography) <AY>	Achse *f* der Kollineation (Projektivität, Homographie), Kollineationsachse *f*, Projektivitätsachse *f*, Homographieachse *f*	axe *m* de collinéation (projectivité), axe d'homographie, axe projectif (de projection)	ось коллинеации (гомографии)
	axis of collineation <AY, DS>	*s.* A 1316		
A 1311	**axis of convergence** <FT>	Konvergenzachse *f*, Konvergenzgerade *f*	axe *m* de convergence	прямая сходимости
	axis of co-ordinates <AY>	*s.* C 2420		
A 1312	**axis of curvature,** polar line <of a curve> <DG>	Krümmungsachse *f*, Polargerade *f*	axe *m* de courbure, droite *f* polaire	ось кривизны, полярная прямая
	axis of curvature <DG>	*s.* C 2767		
	axis of deviation <DG>	*s.* A 366		
	axis of figure <EG>	*s.* A 1321		
A 1313	**axis of holomorphy** <of a Dirichlet series> <FT, SS>	Holomorphieachse *f*	axe *m* d'holomorphie	ось голоморфности, прямая голоморфности
	axis of homography <AY>	*s.* A 1310		
	axis of homology <AY, DS>	*s.* A 1316		
	axis of imaginaries <FT>	*s.* I 90		
A 1314	**axis of involution** <AY>	Involutionsachse *f*	axe *m* de l'involution	ось инволюции
A 1315	**axis of ordinates;** y-axis <GN>	Ordinatenachse *f*; y-Achse *f*, // Ordinate *f*	axe *m* des ordonnées, axe d'ordonnées; axe des y	ось ординат
A 1316	**axis of perspective (perspectivity),** axis of homology ([central] collineation, relation) <AY, DS>	Perspektivitätsachse *f*, Achse *f* der Perspektive (Perspektivität), Kollineationsachse *f*, Homologieachse *f*	axe *m* d'homologie, axe perspectif (de perspectivité)	ось гомологии (перспективы)
A 1317	**axis of projection** <DS>	Projektionsachse *f*	axe *m* de projection	ось проектирования
	axis of projectivity <AY>	*s.* A 1310		
A 1318	**axis of reals,** real axis <FT>	reelle Achse *f*	axe *m* réel	вещественная ось
	axis of reflection <EG>	*s.* A 1321		
	axis of relation <AY, DS>	*s.* A 1316		
	axis of revolution <EG>	*s.* A 1319		
A 1319	**axis of rotation,** rotation[al] axis, axis [of revolution] <EG>	Drehachse *f*, Drehungsachse *f*, Rotationsachse *f*, Umdrehungsachse *f*, Achse *f*	axe *m* de rotation (révolution), axe représentatif de la rotation, ligne *f* des pôles, axe	ось вращения (поворота), поворотная ось, ось
A 1320	**axis of similarity,** similarity axis <GE>	Ähnlichkeitsachse *f*	axe *m* de similitude	ось подобия
A 1321	**axis of symmetry,** axis of reflection (figure), axis <EG>	Symmetrieachse *f*, Spiegelungsachse *f*, Figurenachse *f*, Achse *f*	axe *m* de symétrie (réflexion, figure), axe	ось симметрии (отражения, фигуры), ось
A 1322	**axisymmetric,** axially symmetric, in axial symmetry, symmetric about (with respect to) an axis, symmetric about (with respect to) a line <EG>	axialsymmetrisch, achsensymmetrisch, klappsymmetrisch	axisymétrique, symétrique à l'égard d'un axe, symétrique par rapport à un axe, symétrique par rapport à une droite, de symétrie de révolution	аксиально-симметричный, осесимметричный, осевой симметрии, симметричный относительно оси (прямой)
	axode <GE>	*s.* A 1324		
A 1323	**axoid** <GE>	Axoide *f*	axoïde *f*	аксоида
A 1324	**axoid[al surface],** axode <GE>	Achsenfläche *f*, Axoid *n*	surface *f* axoïde, axoïde *m*	аксоидальная поверхность, аксоид
A 1325	**axonometric chart** <ST>	axonometrisches Diagramm *n*	diagramme *m* axonométrique	стереограмма
A 1326	**axonometric image** <DS>	axonometrisches Bild *n*	image *f* axonométrique	аксонометрическое изображение
A 1327	**axonometric mapping** <a parallel projection> <DS>	Axonometrie *f*	axonométrie *f*	аксонометрическая проекция

No.	English	German	French	Russian
A 1328	**axonometric perspective (projection)** <a central projection> <DS>	axonometrische Perspektive *f*	perspective (projection) *f* axonométrique	аксонометрическая проекция
A 1329	**axonometry** <as a method> <GE>	Axonometrie *f*, Methode *f* der Axonometrie	axonométrie *f*	аксонометрия
	azimuth <AY>	*s.* A 604		
	azimuthal angle <AY>	*s.* A 604		
	azimuthal orthomorphic projection <DS>	*s.* S 1753		
	azimuth angle <AY>	*s.* A 604		
	Azpeita-Dickinson method <PG>	*s.* C 1200		
A 1330	**Azumaya['s] algebra** <AL>	Azumaya-Algebra *f*	algèbre *f* d'Azumaya	алгебра Адзумайя
A 1331	**azygetic form,** asyzygetic form <IV>	azygetische (asyzygetische, aszygetische) Form *f*	forme *f* azygétique (asyzygétique)	азигетическая форма
A 1332	**azygetic invariant,** asyzygetic invariant <IV>	azygetische (asyzygetische, aszygetische) Invariante *f*	invariant *m* azygétique (asyzygétique)	азигетическая форма
A 1333	**azygetic series** <FU>	azygetische Reihe *f*	série *f* azygétique	азигетический ряд

B

No.	English	German	French	Russian
B 1	**Bachet['s] problem [of the weights]** <CT>	Bachetsches (Bachets) Gewichtsproblem *n*, Gewichtsproblem von Bachet	problème *m* [des poids] de Bachet	задача [весов] Баше
B 2	**Bachet['s] theorem** <for decomposing a number into four squares> <NT>	Bachets Satz *m*	théorème *m* de Bachet	теорема Баше
	back adjunction <CA>	*s.* C 2552		
	back derivative <DI>	*s.* L 367		
	back derivative function <RF>	*s.* L 368		
	back Dini derivative <RF>	*s.* L 370		
	back differentiability <DI>	*s.* L 334		
B 3	**Bäcklund['s] transform[ation]** <DG>	Bäcklund-Transformation *f*, Bäcklundsche Transmation *f*	transformation *f* de Bäcklund	преобразование Беклунда
B 4	**Backman['s] formula, Backman['s] law** <ST>	Backmans[che] Formel *f*, Backmansches Gesetz (Wachstumsgesetz) *n*	formule (loi) *f* de Backman	формула (закон) Бэкмана
	back substitution <NU>	*s.* I 896		
	backward derivative <DI>	*s.* L 367		
	backward derivative function <RF>	*s.* L 368		
	backward difference <FD>	*s.* A 1035		
B 5	**backward difference operator** <FD, NU>	Operator *m* für absteigende Differenzen, Differenzenoperator *m* Δ	opérateur *m* des différences descendantes	оператор взятых вперед [конечных] разностей
B 6	**backward difference quotient** <FD>	rückwärtiger Differenzenquotient *m*	quotient *m* des différences en arrière	разностное отношение назад («назад»)
	backward differentiability <DI>	*s.* L 334		
	backward differential equation[s] <SP>	*s.* K 117a		
	backward Dini derivative <RF>	*s.* L 370		
	backward equation[s], backward system <SP>	*s.* K 117a		
B 7	***b*-adic expansion** <of a number> <NT>	*b*-adische Entwicklung *f*	développement *m* *b*-adique	*b*-адическое разложение
B 8	**Baer['s] condition** <for a module> <AL>	Baersche Bedingung *f*	condition *f* de Baer	условие Бэра
B 9	**Baer['s] group** <GR>	Baersche Gruppe *f*	groupe *m* de Baer	бэровская группа
B 10	**Baer['s] multiplication** <GR>	Baersche Multiplikation *f*	multiplication *f* de Baer	умножение Бэра
B 11	**Baer-nilpotent group** <GR>	nilpotente Gruppe *f* <im Sinne von Baer>	groupe *m* nilpotent au sens de Baer	нильпотентная группа в смысле Бэра
B 12	**Baer['s] radical** <AL>	Baersches Radikal *n*	radical *m* de Baer	радикал Бэра, нижний нильрадикал Бэра
B 13	**Baer['s] ring** <AL>	Baer-Ring *m*, B-Ring *m*	anneau *m* de Baer	бэровское кольцо, кольцо Бэра
B 14	**Baire['s] category theorem,** Baire['s] theorem, theorem of Baire on category, category theorem of Baire <TO>	Bairescher Kategoriesatz *m*	théorème *m* de Baire	теорема Бэра [о категории полного пространства]
B 15	**Baire['s] class** <RF>	Bairesche Klasse *f*	classe *f* de Baire	класс Бэра
	Baire['s] classification <RF>	*s.* C 782		
B 16	**Baire['s] continuity,** continuity in the Baire sense <RF>	Bairesche Stetigkeit *f*, Stetigkeit im Sinne von Baire	continuité *f* de Baire, continuité au sens de Baire	непрерывность Бэра, непрерывность в смысле Бэра
B 17	**Baire['s] direct theorem** <RF>	direkter Bairescher Satz *m*	théorème *m* direct de Baire	прямая теорема Бэра
B 18	**Baire['s] function,** analytically representable	Borelsche Funktion *f*, Bairesche Funktion	fonction *f* borélienne (de Baire, représentable	функция Бореля (Бэра), беровская функция,

and still:	function <RF, TO>		analytiquement)	В-функция, аналитически представимая функция
B 18	**Baire 1 function** <RF, TO>	*s.* F 771		
B 19	**Baire measurable mapping** <TO>	Baire-meßbare Abbildung *f*	application *f* jouissant de la propriété de Baire	функция, обладающая свойством Бэра
B 20	**Baire['s] measure** <ME>	Bairesches Maß *n*	mesure *f* de Baire	мера Бэра
B 21	**Baire['s] null space** <RF, TO>	Bairescher Nullraum *m*	espace *m* nul de Baire	нулевое пространство Бэра
	Baire['s] property <TO>	*s.* C 1832		
B 22	**Baire property in the restricted sense** <TO>	Bairesche Eigenschaft *f* im engeren Sinne	propriété *f* de Baire au sens restreint	свойство Бэра в узком смысле
B 23	**Baire['s] set,** almost open set, almost-open set, approximable set, set satisfying the condition of Baire, subset having the property of Baire <RF, TO>	Bairesche Menge *f*; offene Menge bis auf eine Menge erster Kategorie; Menge, die die Bairesche Eigenschaft besitzt	ensemble *m* [à propriété] de Baire, ensemble jouissant de la propriété de Baire, ensemble *Z* <Lebesgue>, ensemble approchable	открытое множество по модулю идеала всех множеств первой категории; множество, открытое относительно множеств первой категории; множество Бэра (*Z*); приближаемое множество
B 24	**Baire['s] space** <RF, TO>	Bairescher Raum *m*	espace *m* de Baire	пространство Бэра, бэровское пространство
B 25	**Baire['s] theorem** <on real-valued functions> <RF>	Satz *m* von Baire, Bairescher Satz	théorème *m* de Baire	теорема Бэра
B 26	**Baire['s] theorem** <on complete metric spaces> <TO>	Dichtigkeitssatz *m* von Baire, Bairescher Dichtigkeitssatz (Dichtesatz) *m*	théorème *m* de Baire	теорема Бэра [о полных пространствах]
	Baire['s] theorem <TO>	*s.* B 14		
B 27	**Bairstow['s] method** <for finding complex roots of an algebraic equation> <AL, NU>	Bairstow-Verfahren *n*	méthode *f* de Bairstow	метод Бэрстоу
	Baker-Campbell-Hausdorff formula <GR>	*s.* C 38		
	Baker-Hausdorff formula <GR>	*s.* C 38		
B 28	**balanced category** <CA>	ausgeglichene (balancierte) Kategorie *f*	catégorie *f* balancée	сбалансированная категория
B 29	**balanced difference** <ST>	balancierte Differenz *f*	différence *f* compensée	сбалансированная разность
B 30	**balanced functor** <CA>	ausgeglichener Funktor *m*	foncteur *m* balancé	сбалансированный функтор
B 31	**balanced hull** <in a vector space> <FA>	ausgeglichene Hülle *f*	enveloppe *f* équilibrée (disquée)	уравновешенная (закругленная) оболочка
B 32	**balanced hypergraph** <GP>	Hypergraph *m* im Gleichgewicht	hypergraphe *m* balancé	уравновешенный граф
B 33	**balanced module** <AL>	ausgeglichener Modul *m*	module *m* balancé	сбалансированный модуль
B 34	**balanced neighbourhood,** circled neighbourhood <FA>	ausgeglichene Umgebung *f*	voisinage *m* équilibré	уравновешенная (нормальная) окрестность
B 35	**balanced sample** <ST>	balancierte (balanzierte) Stichprobe *f*	échantillon *m* compensé (équilibré)	уравновешенная (сбалансированная) выборка
B 36	**balanced set,** circled set <of a linear space> <FA>	ausgeglichene Menge *f*, „équilibrée"-Teilmenge *f*, ausgeglichene Teilmenge *f*; „disquée"-Teilmenge *f*	ensemble *m* équilibré, partie *f* équilibrée, partie disquée, ensemble disqué	уравновешенное множество, диск
	balancing calculation <ER, NU>	*s.* C 26		
B 37	**balayage,** sweep[ing] out, sweep[ing] <PO>	Balayage *f*, Ausfegen *n*, Ausfegung *f*, Auskehren *n*, Auskehrung *f*	balayage *m*	выметание
	B-algebra <FA>	*s.* B 40		
	B*-algebra <FA>	*s.* C 34		
B 38	**ball,** solid sphere, closed spherical region, full sphere <as a solid> <DI, GE, TO>	Kugel *f*, Vollkugel *f*	boule *f*, sphère *f* massive	шар, полная сфера
B 39	**Banach-adjoint transform[ation]** <FA>	Banach-adjungierte Transformation *f*	opération *f* conjuguée (associée)	сопряженное преобразование по Банаху
B 40	**Banach['s] algebra,** complete normed algebra, B-algebra <FA>	Banach-Algebra *f*, B-Algebra *f*, vollständige normierte Algebra *f*	algèbre *f* de Banach, algèbre B (normée complète)	банахова алгебра, В-алгебра
	Banach*-algebra <FA>	*s.* S 261		
	Banach algebra with an involution <FA>	*s.* S 261		
B 41	**Banach-Cacciopoli theorem,** Banach['s] fixed point theorem, Banach['s] theorem <FA>	Banachscher Fixpunktsatz *m*, Satz *m* von der kontrahierenden Abbildung	principe (théorème) *m* de Banach[-Cacciopoli] <du point fixe>, principe (théorème) de l'application contractante	теорема (принцип) Банаха [о неподвижной точке]
	Banach completion <TO>	*s.* C 1591		
	Banach['s] co-ordinate space <FA>	*s.* B 489		
	Banach['s] fixed point theorem <FA>	*s.* B 41		
	Banachiewicz['s] method <AL, NU>	*s.* M 447		
B 42	**Banachiewicz['s] scheme** <AL, NU>	Banachiewicz-Schema *n*	schème *m* de Banachiewicz	схема Банахевича
B 43	**Banach['s] Lie group** <GR>	Banachsche Lie-Gruppe *f*	groupe *m* de Lie banachique	банахова группа Ли
B 44	**Banach['s] mean** <FA>	Banachsches Mittel *n*	moyenne *f* de Banach	банахово среднее

B 45	**Banach module** <FA>	Banach-Modul *m*, Banachmodul *m*	module *m* de Banach	банахов модуль
B 46	**Banach['s] problem** <ST>	Banachsches Problem *n*	problème *m* de Banach	задача Банаха
B 47	**Banach-Saks theorem** <FA>	Banach-Saksscher Satz *m*, Satz von Banach-Saks	théorème *m* de Banach-Saks (Banach et Saks)	теорема Банаха-Сакса
	Banach['s] sequence space <FA>	*s.* B 489		
B 48	**Banach['s] space,** B-space, complete normed space <FA>	Banach-Raum *m*, Banachraum *m*, Banachscher Raum *m*, vollständiger (linearer) normierter Raum	espace *m* de Banach (type B), espace [rectoriel] normé complet, espace banachique	банахово пространство, B-пространство, пространство Банаха, полное нормированное векторное пространство
B 49	**Banach space with a base,** B-space having a base <FA>	Banach-Raum *m* mit Basis	espace *m* de Banach à base	B-пространство (банахово пространство), обладающее базисом
B 50	**Banach-Steinhaus theorem,** uniform-boundedness principle <AN>	Satz *m* von Banach-Steinhaus (Banach und Steinhaus), Banach-Steinhausscher Satz *m*, Prinzip *n* der gleichmäßigen Beschränktheit	théorème *m* de Banach-Steinhaus (S. Banach — A. Steinhaus), principe *m* de la borne uniforme	теорема Банаха-Штейнхауса, принцип равномерной ограниченности
B 51	**Banach-Steinhaus theorems** <AN, FA>	Sätze *mpl* von Banach und Steinhaus, Banach-Steinhaussche Sätze	théorèmes *mpl* de Banach-Steinhaus (S. Banach — A. Steinhaus)	теоремы Банаха-Штейнхауса
B 52	**Banach-Tarski paradox** <ME>	Banach-Tarskisches Paradoxon *n*, paradoxe Kugelzerlegung *f*	paradoxe *m* de Banach-Tarski	парадокс Банаха-Тарского
	Banach['s] theorem <FA>	*s.* B 41		
B 53	**Banach-Ulam theorem** <SE>	Satz *m* von Banach und Ulam, Banach-Ulamscher Satz	théorème *m* de Banach-Ulam	теорема Банаха-Улама
B 54	**band** <e.g. of binary relations of a group *or* of semigroups> <AL>	Band *n* <z. B. der binären Relationen *oder* von Halbgruppen>	bande *f* <p. e. des relations binaires *ou* de demi-groupes>	связка <н. п. бинарных отношений *или* полугрупп>
B 55	**band,** closed lattice ideal <of a K-space> <TO>	Band *n*	bande *f*	компонента
	band <AL>	*s.* I 36		
B 56	**band chart** <NU, ST>	Profildarstellung *f*	graphique *f* à bandes	график для изображения функциональной зависимости нескольких величин от одинаковой величины
B 57	**band matrix;** striped matrix <MD>	Bandmatrix *f*	matrice *f* bande	многодиагональная матрица <$a_{ij} = 0$ для $\lvert i-j \rvert > n$>
	band of striction <GE>	*s.* S 1866		
	bank <FT, TO>	*s.* B 567		
B 58	**bar,** cross bar <as a sign, e.g.: $\bar{a}$> <GN>	Querstrich *m*	barre *f*	поперечная черта
	bar <GN>	*s.* 1. O 567; 2. V 187		
	bar chart <GN>	*s.* B 60		
B 59	**bar construction** <AT>	„bar"-Konstruktion *f*	« bar construction » *f*	бар-конструкция, B-конструкция
B 60	**bar diagram (graph),** bar chart, column diagram (graph, chart), histogram, block diagram <two-dimensional> <GN>	Streifendiagramm *n*, Säulendiagramm *n* <Gesamtdarstellung>; Staffelbild *n* <Gesamtdarstellung, übereinanderliegende Streifen>; Histogramm *n* <Gesamtdarstellung, nebeneinanderliegende Streifen>; Treppenpolygon *n*, Rechteckstufenkurve *f*, Rechteckdarstellung *f*, Rechteckzug *m*, Histogramm <obere Begrenzung>	diagramme *m* à colonnes, histogramme *m*	столбчатая диаграмма, диаграмма в виде столбцов, гистограмма <полный график>; ступенчатая кривая прямоугольной формы <верхняя ограничивающая кривая>
B 61	**bargaining problem** <TG>	Vertragsschema *n*		арбитражная схема, задача о сделке, задача торга
B 62	**bargaining set** <TG>	Vertragsmenge *f*		множество договорок, множество следок
B 63	**Barnes['] integral [equation], Barnes['] representation** <FU>	Barnessche Integraldarstellung *f* [der Zylinderfunktionen]	intégrale *f* de Barnes	интеграл Барнеса
B 64	**Barratt['s] exact sequence** <AT>	Barratts[che] exakte Sequenz *f*	suite *f* exacte de Barratt	последовательность Баррата
B 65	**barrel** <EG, FA, TO>	Tonnenkörper *m* <EG>; Tonne *f* <im tonnelierten Raum> <FA, TO>	tonneau *m*	бочка
B 66	**barrel[l]edness** <FA, TO>	Tonneliertheit *f*	propriété *f* d'être tonnelé	бочечность
B 67	**barrelled space,** tunneled space, kegly space <FA, TO>	tonnelierter Raum *m*	espace *m* tonnelé	бочечное пространство
B 68	**Barsotti-Tate group,** B.T.-group, *p* divisible group <GR>	Barsotti-Tate-Gruppe *f*, *p*-teilbare Gruppe *f*	groupe *m* de Barsotti-Tate, groupe *p*-divisible	группа Барсотти-Тейта, *p*-делимая группа [Тейта]
B 69	**Bartlett['s] test** <ST>	Bartlett-Test *m*	test *m* de [M.S.] Bartlett	критерий Бартлетта
B 70	**barycentre,** centroid <of a simplex> <AT>	Schwerpunkt *m*	barycentre *m*	барицентр, центр
B 71	**barycentric calculus** <GE>	baryzentrischer Kalkül *m*	calcul *m* barycentrique	барицентрическое исчисление

	English	German	French	Russian
B 72	**barycentric complex,** dual (reciprocal) complex <AT>	baryzentrischer (dualer) Komplex *m*	complexe *m* barycentrique	барицентрический комплекс
B 73	**barycentric co-ordinates;** barycentric system [of co-ordinates] <GE>	baryzentrische Koordinaten *fpl*, Schwerpunktkoordinaten *fpl*; baryzentrisches Koordinatensystem (System) *n*	coordonnées *fpl* barycentriques; système *m* de coordonnées barycentriques, système barycentrique	барицентрические координаты, координаты Мебиуса; барицентрическая система [координат]
B 74	**barycentric co-ordinates in [3-]space,** barycentric tetrahedral co-ordinates <GE>	baryzentrische Tetraederkoordinaten *fpl*	coordonnées *fpl* barycentriques dans la géométrie d'espace, coordonnées tétraédriques barycentriques	барицентрические координаты в пространстве, барицентрические тетраэдрические координаты
B 75	**barycentric co-ordinates in the plane,** barycentric triangular co-ordinates <GE>	baryzentrische Dreieckskoordinaten *fpl*	coordonnées *fpl* barycentriques en géométrie plane, coordonnées triangulaires barycentriques	барицентрические координаты на плоскости
	barycentric derived <AT>	*s.* B 79		
	barycentric first derived <AT>	*s.* B 79		
B 76	**barycentric mapping** <AT>	baryzentrische (Kuratowskische) Abbildung *f*	application *f* barycentrique	барицентрическое отображение
B 77	**barycentric star dual to a simplex T_i,** dual of a simplex T_i <AT>	baryzentrischer Stern *m*, Barystern *m*, Stern *m* eines Simplexes T_i	étoile *f* barycentrique duale au simplexe T_i	барицентрическая звезда, сопряженная элементу T_i
	barycentric star dual to a vertex <AT>	*s.* M 52		
B 78	**barycentric subdivision,** regular subdivision <method> <AT>	baryzentrische (reguläre) Unterteilung *f*	subdivision *f* barycentrique (regulière)	барицентрическое подразделение (разбиение)
B 79	**barycentric subdivision,** regular subdivision, derived [complex], regular complex, barycentric derived <*n*-fold or *n*-th>; barycentric first derived <of a complex> <AT>	baryzentrische (reguläre) Unterteilung *f*, Normalunterteilung *f*, abgeleiteter (baryzentrisch unterteilter) Komplex *m* <*n*-fach oder vom Grade *n*>	subdivision *f* barycentrique (régulière) <*n*-uple>	барицентрическое подразделение (разбиение) <*n*-кратное>
	barycentric system <GE>	*s.* B 73		
	barycentric system of co-ordinates <GE>	*s.* B 73		
	barycentric tetrahedral co-ordinates <GE>	*s.* B 74		
	barycentric triangular co-ordinates <GE>	*s.* B 75		
	basal element <AL>	*s.* E 858		
B 80	**basal quaternion element,** unit <of a quaternion algebra> <AL>	Grundeinheit *f*, Basiselement *n*	unité *f* de base	базисная единица
B 81	**base** <of the ring, of a linear system, of an algebra, a field extension, *or* a lattice, of an almost periodic function, of a set of real numbers, of a filter> <AB, AG, AL, AP, IV, LA, NT, TO>	Basis *f*	base *f*	базис
B 82	**base** <of a conchoid> <AG>	Grundkurve *f*, Basis *f*, Basiskurve *f*	directrice *f*, base *f*, courbe *f* de base, courbe directrice	базисная кривая
B 83	**base,** radix <of a power> <AL>	Basis *f*, Grundzahl *f*, // Wurzel *f*	base *f*	базис, основание
B 84	**base** <of an isosceles triangle, also of a plane figure> <EG>	Basis *f*, Grundlinie *f*	base *f*	основание
B 85	**base,** lower base <of a pyramid *or* cone *or* cylinder> <EG>	Grundfläche *f*, Basis *f*	base *f*	основание, нижнее основание
B 86	**base** <of a *K*-space> <FA>	Strukturverband *m* <eines *K*-Raumes>	base *f* <d'un *K*-espace>	база <*K*-пространства>
B 87	**base** <of a finitely generated abelian group> <GR>	Basis *f* <einer endlich erzeugten abelschen Gruppe>	base *f* monogène, base <d'un groupe abélien de type fini>	базис, база <конечно порожденной абелевой группы>
B 88	**base,** radix <of a number system> <NT>	Basis *f*, Grundzahl *f*	base *f*	основание, базис
B 89	**base** <of a range of points> <PJ>	Träger *m*	support *m*	носитель
B 90	**base** <for a uniformity> <TO>	Basis *f* <einer uniformen Struktur>	système *m* fondamental d'entourages	фундаментальная система окружений, база <равномерной структуры>, базис равномерности
	base <AL>	*s.* M 774		
	base <AR>	*s.* R 43		
	base <DE>	*s.* F 845		
	base <EG>	*s.* L 1168		
	base <FA>	*s.* B 130		
	base <GE>	*s.* B 99		
	base <SE>	*s.* F 224		
	base <TO>	*s.* 1. B 134; 2. M 497		
	base <VT>	*s.* I 535		
B 91	**base angle** <of an isosceles triangle> <EG>	Basiswinkel *m*	angle *m* adjacent à la base	угол при основании
B 92	**base at a point,** local basis [at a point], local base [at a point], basis, base for (of) the neighbourhood system of a	Fundamentalsystem *n* von Umgebungen eines Punktes, Umgebungsbasis *f* (Umgebungssystem *n*) eines Punktes, Basis *f* für	système *m* [fondamental] de voisinages d'un point	фундаментальная] система окрестностей точки, локальная база [в точке]; фундаментальная система открытых

No.	English	German	French	Russian
	point, local base of neighbourhoods of a point <TO>	das Umgebungssystem eines Punktes		окрестностей точки, локальная открытая база [в точке]
B 93	**base circle** <of a circular cone> <EG>	Grundkreis *m*	cercle *m* de base	направляющая [окружность]
	base condition <AL>	*s.* H 320		
B 94	**base curve,** fixed path <of a roulette> <GE>	Polbahn *f*, Basis *f*, Basiskurve *f*, Grundkurve *f*	base *f*, courbe *f* immobile	базисная (неподвижная) кривая
B 95	**base degree** <of a fibre bundle> <AT>	Basisgrad *m*	degré-base *m*	степень по базе
B 96	**based homeomorphism** <of punctured topological spaces> <TO>	punktierter (basispunkttreuer) Homöomorphismus *m*	homéomorphisme *m* avec point-base	гомеоморфизм с отмеченной точкой
	based homotopy <TO>	*s.* H 552		
B 97	**based homotopy type** <of pointed spaces> <TO>	Homotopietyp *m* punktierter Räume	type *m* d'homotopie d'espaces [topologiques] pointés	гомотопический тип [топологических] пространств с отмеченной точкой
	based map <SE, TO>	*s.* B 106		
	based set <SE>	*s.* P 740		
	based space <TO>	*s.* T 547		
B 98	**base edge** <of a pyramid> <EG>	Grundkante *f*, Basiskante *f*	arête *f* de base	ребро (сторона) основания
	base field <AG, AL>	*s.* G 440		
	base for the neighbourhood system of a point <TO>	*s.* B 92		
B 99	**base line,** base <of a cycloid> <GE>	Polbahn *f*, Basisgerade *f*, Basis *f*	base *f* <une droite>	базисная прямая
B 100	**base number** <of an abelian variety> <AG>	Basiszahl *f*	nombre *m* de base	базисное число
	base of natural logarithms <AN>	*s.* E 1		
B 101	**base of order *h*** <AB>	Basis *f* *h*-ter Ordnung	base *f* d'ordre *h*	базис порядка *h*
	base of the auxiliary cone <DS>	*s.* C 692		
	base of the natural system of logarithms <AN>	*s.* E 1		
	base of the neighbourhood system of a point <TO>	*s.* B 92		
	base period <ST>	*s.* R 454		
B 102	**base point** <*s*-fold> <of a linear *or* algebraic system> <AG>	Basispunkt *m*, Fundamentalpunkt *m* <*s*-facher>	point *m* fixe (de base), point base, point-base *m* <d'ordre *s*>	базисная точка <порядка *s*>
B 103	**base point,** indexed point <of a pointed groupoid> <CA>	ausgezeichneter Grundpunkt *m*	objet *m* distingué	отмеченный объект
B 104	**base point** <of a system of curves> <GE>	Basispunkt *m* <einer Kurvenschar>; Basis *f* <eines Büschels>	point *m* fondamental (de base), base *f*	базисная точка
B 105	**base[-]point,** designated base point, distinguished element <of a set *or* topological space> <SE, TO>	ausgezeichneter Grundpunkt *m*, Grundpunkt	point *m* base, point-base *m*	отмеченная точка
	base point <AG>	*s.* F 840		
	base point <AT>	*s.* B 120		
B 106	**base point-preserving map,** based map <SE, TO>	Abbildung *f* mit Grundpunkt, grundpunkterhaltende (basispunkttreue, punktierte) Abbildung; Abbildung, die die Grundpunkte respektiert	application *f* pointée (à points-bases, préservant les points-bases)	отображение, сохраняющее отмеченные точки; пунктированное отображение
B 107	**base set, base-set** <of a linear system> <AG>	Basismenge *f*	ensemble-base *m*	базисное множество
B 108	**base set,** support <of a universal algebra *or* relational system> <UA>	Träger *m*, Feld *n*	champ *m*	носитель, основное множество
B 109	**base space** <of a fibre bundle *or* a sheaf> <AL, AT>	Basisraum *m*	espace *m* de base <AT>; base *f* <AL, AT>	база
B 110	**base[-]surface** <of a linear system> <AG>	Basisfläche *f*	surface-base *f*	базисная поверхность
	base surface <EG>	*s.* L 1168		
B 111	**base variety, base-variety** <of a linear system> <AG>	Basismannigfaltigkeit *f*	variété-base *f*	базисное многообразие
B 112	**base vector** <AL>	Basisvektor *m*	vecteur *m* de base	базисный (основной) вектор
	base vertex <AT>	*s.* D 744		
	basic arithmetic[al] operation <AR>	*s.* A 949		
B 113	**basic block** <PG>	Basisblock *m*	bloc *m* de base	базисный блок
B 114	**basic cell** <PG>	Basiszelle *f*	cellule *f* de base	базисная ячейка
	basic concept <FO>	*s.* F 804		
B 115	**basic cycle** <PG>	Basiszyklus *m*	cycle *m* de base	базисный цикл
B 116	**basic element,** basis element <AL>	Basiselement *n*	élément *m* basique	базисный элемент
	basic element <PJ>	*s.* B 118		
B 117	**basic feasible program[me] (solution)** feasible basic solution <PG>	zulässige (ausführbare) Basislösung *f*, zulässiges (ausführbares) Basisprogramm *n*, Basisprogramm	solution *f* (programme *m*) de base réalisable	допустимое (исходное) базисное решение, допустимая базисная программа, исходный опорный план
	basic field <AG, AL>	*s.* G 440		
	basic form <PJ>	*s.* B 118		
	basic formula <LO>	*s.* A 1123		

No.	English	German	French	Russian
B 118	**basic geometrical element,** basic element (form) <of the first, second, *or* third degree and of the first order *or* of the second order> <PJ>	geometrisches Grundgebilde *n*, Grundgebilde <erster, zweiter *oder* dritter Stufe und erster Ordnung *oder* zweiter Ordnung>	élément *m* [géométrique] fondamental <de premier, second (deuxième) *ou* troisième degré et de premier ordre *ou* de second (deuxième) ordre>	основная [геометрическая] форма, образ <первой, второй *или* третьей ступени и первого порядка *или* второго порядка>
B 119	**basic index [number]** <ST>	Meßziffer *f*, einfacher Index *m*	indice *m* simple	базисный индекс, индекс с постоянной базой
	basic mathematical sign <LO, MM>	*s.* B 127		
	basic operation <AR>	*s.* A 949		
B 120	**basic point,** base point <in homotopy> <AT>	Basispunkt *m*	point-base *m*	отмеченная точка
B 121	**basic point,** fundamental point <PJ>	Grundpunkt *m*, Eckpunkt *m* des Fundamental- und Koordinatensimplex	point *m* fondamental	основная точка
B 122	**basic representation** <PG>	Basisdarstellung *f*	représentation *f* de base	базисное представление
B 123	**basic ring,** ring of scalars <of an algebra *or* *R*-module> <AL>	Grundring *m*, Skalarenbereich *m*, Skalarbereich *m*	anneau *m* de base, anneau des scalaires	основное кольцо, кольцо скаляров
	basic semiinvariant <DG>	*s.* F 843		
B 124	**basic solution** <PG>	Basislösung *f*	solution *f* de base	базисное решение
B 125	**basic structure** <AL, TO>	Mutterstruktur *f*, Grundstruktur *f*	structure *f*	основная структура
B 126	**basic subgroup** <GR>	Basisuntergruppe *f*	sous-groupe *m* de base	базисная подгруппа
B 127	**basic symbol,** basic mathematical sign <of a calculus> <LO, MM>	Grundzeichen *n*, Atomzeichen *n*	symbole *m* fondamental	основной знак
B 128	**basic variable,** dependent variable <PG>	Basisvariable *f*, abhängige Variable *f*	variable *f* de base, variable dépendante	базисная (зависимая) переменная
B 129	**basis** <of the entire quantities of a field> <AB>	Fundamentalsystem *n*, Basis *f* <des Körpers>, Zahlbasis *f*	base *f*, système *m* fondamental	базис
B 130	**basis,** base <of a linear topological space> <FA>	Basis *f*	base *f*	базис
B 131	**basis** <of a graph *or* matroid> <GP>	Basis *f*	base *f*	базис
B 132	**basis** <of a group> <GR>	Basis *f* <einer Gruppe>; Fundamentalsystem *n* <einer abelschen Gruppe>	base *f*	базис, множество свободных образующих
B 133	**basis** <of a Hausdorff operation> <SE>	Basis *f*	base *f*	база
B 134	**basis,** base, basis of open sets, open base <of a topological space, for a topology> <TO>	Basis *f*, Fundamentalsystem *n* von Umgebungen, offene Basis <eines topologischen Raumes, einer Topologie>	base *f*, système *m* de générateurs, base ouverte <d'un espace topologique, d'une topologie>	база, базис, система образующих, открытая база, база открытых множеств <топологического пространства, топологии>
	basis <AL>	*s.* 1. I 11; 2. V 97		
	basis <DE>	*s.* F 845		
	basis <FA>	*s.* H 58		
	basis <GP>	*s.* C 1001		
	basis <TO>	*s.* B 92		
	basis associated with the spanning tree <GP>	*s.* F 800		
	basis condition <AL>	*s.* H 320		
	basis element <AL>	*s.* B 116		
B 135	**basis for cohomology** <AT>	Kohomologiebasis *f*	base *f* de cohomologie	∇-база, когомологический базис, базис когомологий
B 136	**basis for homology** <AT>	Homologiebasis *f*	base *f* d'homologie	гомологическая база, база гомологии, гомологический базис, базис гомологий
	basis for the neighbourhoods <TO>	*s.* N 126		
	basis for the neighbourhoods of the origin <AL, FA>	*s.* B 137		
	basis of closed sets <TO>	*s.* C 844		
	basis of cycles <GP>	*s.* C 2836		
	basis of Hamel <FA>	*s.* H 58		
B 137	**basis of neighbourhoods of zero,** basis for the neighbourhoods of the origin <AL, FA>	Umgebungsbasis *f* der Null <AL>; Nullumgebungsbasis *f*, Umgebungsbasis des Nullpunktes <FA>	base *f* de voisinage de zéro	базис окрестностей нуля
B 138	**basis of open sets,** open base <as opposed to closed base> <TO>	offene Basis *f*	base *f* ouverte	открытая база, база открытых множеств
	basis of open sets <TO>	*s.* B 134		
B 139	**basis of the induction,** zero step of the induction, initial condition <FO, LO>	Induktionsanfang *m*	base *f* de l'induction	базис индукции
B 140	**basis quasirank** <UA>	Basisquasirang *m*	quasi-rang *m* de base	базисный квазиранг
B 141	**basis rank** <of an algebraic system> <UA>	Basisrang *m*	rang *m* de base	базисный ранг
	basis theorem of Hilbert <AL>	*s.* H 321		
B 142	**basis vector** <of the coordinate system> <AY, VT>	Koordinateneinheitsvektor *m*, Grundvektor *m*, Einheitsvektor *m* <des Koordinatensystems>	vecteur *m* de base	основной вектор, орт
	Basset['s] function <FU>	*s.* M 4		
	batch <ST>	*s.* L 1116		
B 143	**batch variation,** intragroup variation <ST>	Innergruppenvariation *f*, Variation *f* innerhalb der Gruppe	variation *f* à l'intérieur du groupe, variation intragroupe	варьирование внутри группы

No.	English	German	French	Russian
B 144	**Bateman conic** <AG>	Batemanscher Kegelschnitt *m*	conique (section *f* conique) de Bateman	коническое сечение Бейтмена
B 145	**Bateman-Dirichlet principle** <VA>	Bateman-Dirichletsches Prinzip *n*	principe *m* de Bateman-Dirichlet	принцип Бейтмена-Дирихле
B 146	**Bateman['s] function;** <especially:> Bateman['s] *K*-function <FU>	Bateman-Funktion *f*; <speziell:> Batemans *K*-Funktion *f*, Batemansche *K*-Funktion	fonction *f* de Bateman; <en particulier:> fonction *K* de Bateman	функция Бейтмена; <в частности:> *K*-функция Бейтмена, *k*-функция
B 147	**Bateman-Kelvin['s] principle,** Bateman['s] principle, Bateman['s] variational principle <VA>	Bateman-Kelvinsches Prinzip *n*	principe *m* de Bateman-Kelvin	принцип Бейтмена
	Bateman['s] K-function <FU>	*s.* B 146		
	Bateman['s] principle <VA>	*s.* B 147		
B 148	**Bateman['s] *T*-function** <FU>	Batemans[che] *T*-Funktion *f*	fonction *f* *T* de Bateman	*T*-функция Бейтмена
	Bateman['s] variational principle <VA>	*s.* B 147		
	Battaglini['s] complex <PJ>	*s.* H 91		
B 149	**Battaglini['s] conic** <AG>	Battaglini-Kegelschnitt *m*, Kegelschnitt *m* der 14 Elemente	conique *f* (section *f* conique) de Battaglini	коническое сечение Баттальини
B 150	**Bayes['s] approach,** method of inverse probability <ST, TG>	Bayessches Vorgehen *n*, Methode *f* der inversen Wahrscheinlichkeit	procédé *m* de Bayes, approche *f* bayesienne, méthode *f* de probabilité inverse	метод обратной вероятности, бейесов[ский] подход
B 151	**Bayes['] decision function** <ST>	Bayessche Entscheidungsfunktion *f*	fonction *f* de décision de Bayes	решающая функция Бейеса, бейесовская решающая функция
	Bayes['] formula <ST>	*s.* B 156		
	Bayesian risk <ST>	*s.* B 153		
	Bayesian solution <ST>	*s.* B 154		
B 152	**Bayes['] postulate** <ST>	Bayessches Postulat *n*	postulat *m* de Bayes	постулат Бейеса
B 153	**Bayes['] risk,** Bayesian risk <ST>	Bayessches Risiko *n*	risque *m* de Bayes, risque bayesien	бейесов[ский] риск
B 154	**Bayes['] solution,** Bayesian (minimum) solution <ST>	Bayessche Lösung *f*, minimale Lösung	solution *f* de Bayes, solution bayesienne (minimale)	решение Бейеса, бейесово (минимальное) решение
B 155	**Bayes['] strategy** <ST>	Bayessche Strategie *f*	stratégie *f* bayesienne (de Bayes)	бейесовская стратегия
B 156	**Bayes['] theorem,** inverse probability theorem; Bayes['] formula <ST>	Bayesscher Satz *m*, Bayes' Satz (Theorem *n*), Theorem von Bayes; Bayessche Formel *f*, Formel von Bayes, Formel für die Wahrscheinlichkeit a posteriori, Bayessche Regel *f*	théorème *m* (de Bayes; formule *f* (loi *f*) de Bayes	теорема Бейеса (Байеса); формула Бейеса (Байеса)
	BCD system <NT>	*s.* B 359		
	BD class <FA>	*s.* B 210		
	bead <AR, IN>	*s.* C 2573		
B 157	**Beale['s] method** <PG>	Bealesche Methode *f*	méthode *f* de Beale	метод ведущих переменных [Била]
B 158	**beam compas** <GE, IN>	Stangenzirkel *m*	compas *m* à verge	штангенциркуль
B 159	**be an element / to** <of>, to be contained <in>, to belong <to>, to be comprisable, ∈ <SE>	Element sein <von>, als Element enthalten sein <in>, als Element angehören, ∈	être élément <de>, faire partie <de>, appartenir <à>, être agrégé <à>, ∈	быть элементом, ∈
	be a subset / to <of> <SE>	*s.* B 170		
	be between . . . / to <TO>	*s.* B 181		
B 159a	**be cancellable / to** <AL, AR>	sich kürzen lassen	être simplifiable	быть сократимым
B 160	**Beck['s] theorem,** precise tripleability theorem <CA>	Satz *m* von Beck, Beckscher Satz	théorème *m* de Beck	теорема Бека
	be closed with respect to an operation / to <AL>	*s.* C 923		
	become infinite / to <DI>	*s.* A 818		
B 161	**be compatible / to** <with> <AL>	verträglich sein <mit>, respektieren	être compatible <avec>, respecter	быть совместным <с>
	be comprisable / to <SE>	*s.* B 159		
	be contained / to <SE>	*s.* 1. B 159; 2. B 170; 3. P 1171		
B 162	**be contained without remainder / to,** to divide without remainder, to divide [exactly], to go into ... without [a] remainder, to leave no remainder <as referring to an integer> <NT>	aufgehen <in>, ohne Rest enthalten sein <in>, ohne Rest teilen, exakt teilen, teilen	être contenu, ne pas laisser de reste, diviser exactement	делить без остатка, разделять без остатка
B 163	**be divisible [without remainder] / to** <by> <AR, NT>	[ohne Rest] teilbar sein <durch>	être [exactement] divisible <par>	делиться без остатка, делиться точно (нацело) <на>
	be equal / to <AL, AR, GN>	*s.* E 321		
B 164	**be eventually in a set *A* / to** <said of a net> <TO>	gegen einen Punkt der Menge *A* konvergieren <Moore-Smith-Folge	converger vers un point de l'ensemble *A* <suite généralisée>	сходиться к точке в множестве *A* <сеть>
	be finite / to <GR>	*s.* T 174		
	be greater / to <NT, SE>	*s.* S 2227		
	be greater / to <SE>	*s.* F 451		

	English	German	French	Russian
B 165	**behavioural strategy** <TG>	Verhaltensstrategie *f*	stratégie *f* de comportement	стратегия поведения
	behaviour at the boundary <FT>	*s.* B 636		
	behaviour of convergence <SS>	*s.* C 2324		
B 166	**Behrens['] factor** <ST>	Behrens-Faktor *m*	facteur *m* de Behrens	коэффициент Беренса
B 167	**Behrens-Fisher problem** <ST>	Behrens-Fisher-Problem *n*	problème *m* de Behrens-Fisher	проблема Беренса-Фишера
B 168	**Behrens[-Fisher] test,** Fisher-Behrens test <ST>	Behrens-Test *m*, Behrens-Fisher-Test *m*, Fisher-Behrens-Test *m*	test *m* de Behrens, test de Behrens-Fisher, test de Fisher-Behrens	критерий Беренса, критерий Беренса-Фишера, критерий Фишера-Беренса
	bei <FU>	*s.* K 37		
	bei function <FU>	*s.* K 37		
B 169	**be incident / to** <with> <GE>	inzident sein, inzidieren <mit>	être incident <à>	быть инцидентным <с>
	be included / to <SE>	*s.* P 1171		
B 170	**be included / to** <in>, to be a subset <of>, to be contained <in> <a set>, $\leq$ <said of a subset> <SE>	<als Untermenge> enthalten sein <in>, $\leq$	être inclus <dans>, être contenu <dans>, faire partie <de>, être une partie <de>	быть включенным <в>, есть подмножество
B 171	**be infinitely small of higher order / to,** to be infinitesimal of higher order <AN>	von höherer Ordnung unendlich klein sein	être infiniment petit supérieur	быть бесконечно малым высшего порядка
	be infinitesimal of higher order / to <AN>	*s.* B 171		
	being abelian <AL, GR>	*s.* C 1275		
B 172	**being imaginary** <AL, AN>	Imaginärsein *n*	imaginarité *f*	свойство быть имагинарным
	being relatively prime <AL>	*s.* C 2445		
B 173	**being zero** <GN>	Verschwinden *n*, Nullsein *n*	nullité *f*	свойство быть нулем
	be interlaced (intertwined) / to <TO>	*s.* I 742		
	be less / to <SE>	*s.* P 1171		
	belief line <ST>	*s.* C 1861		
B 174	**Bellman['s] equation** <PG>	Bellmansche Gleichung *f*	équation (formule) *f* de Bellman	уравнение Беллмана
B 175	**Bellman['s] principle [of optimality],** principle of optimality, optimality principle <in dynamic programming> <PG>	Bellmansches Prinzip (Optimalitätsprinzip) *n*, Optimalitätsprinzip	principe *m* de Bellman, principe d'optimalité	принцип Беллмана, принцип оптимальности
	bell-shaped curve <ST>	*s.* E 471		
	belong / to <SE>	*s.* B 159		
	Beltrami['s] differential equation <DE>	*s.* B 177		
	Beltrami['s] differential parameter <DG,VT>	*s.* D 467		
B 176	**Beltrami-Enneper theorem,** Enneper['s] theorem <DG>	Satz *m* von [Beltrami-]Enneper, [Beltrami-]Enneperscher Satz	théorème *m* de Beltrami-Enneper, théorème d'Enneper	теорема [Бельтрами-] Эннепера
B 177	**Beltrami['s] equation,** Beltrami['s] differential equation <DE>	Beltramische Differentialgleichung *f*	équation *f* [différentielle] de Beltrami	[дифференциальное] уравнение Бельтрами
B 178	**Beltrami['s] equation** <DG>	Beltramische Gleichung *f*	équation *f* de Beltrami	уравнение Бельтрами
	Beltrami['s] first differential parameter <DG, VT>	*s.* D 468		
B 179	**Beltrami['s] formula** <for geodesic curvature> <DG>	Beltramische Formel *f*	formule *f* de Beltrami	формула Бельтрами
	Beltrami['s] mapping <DG>	*s.* G 244		
	Beltrami['s] point <EG>	*s.* I 1077		
B 180	**Beltrami['s] theorem** <DG>	Satz *m* von Beltrami, Beltramischer Satz	théorème *m* de Beltrami	теорема Бельтрами
B 181	**be metrically between . . . / to,** to be between . . . <in a metric space> <TO>	zwischen . . . liegen, metrisch zwischen . . . liegen	être métriquement entre . . .	лежать метрически между. . .
	be mutually perpendicular / to <EG>	*s.* M 1106		
	bending <DG, GE>	*s.* D 144		
B 182	**bending covariant** <DG>	Biegungskovariante *f*	covariant *m* de déformation	ковариант изгибания
B 183	**bending invariant** <DG>	Biegungsinvariante *f*, Inflektante *f* <Weingarten>	invariant *m* de déformation, inflectant *m*	инвариант изгибания
B 184	**bending line** <DG>	Biegungslinie *f*	ligne *f* de déformation (flexion)	линия изгибания
B 185	**bending parameter** <DG>	Biegungsparameter *m*	paramètre *m* de déformation	параметр изгибания
B 186	**bending point,** turning (bend) point <of a curve in cartesian co-ordinates>; apse <of a curve in polar co-ordinates> <AN>	Extrempunkt *m*, Extremalpunkt *m*	point *m* extrémal	точка экстремума, экстремальная точка
B 187	**bending surface** <DG>	Biegungsfläche *f*	surface *f* de déformation	поверхность, полученная изгибанием
	bend point <AN>	*s.* B 186		
B 188	**benign group** <AL>	gute Gruppe *f*	groupe *m* bénin <Higman>	мягкая группа
	be non-disjoint / to <SE>	*s.* I 792		

No.	English	German	French	Russian
B 189	**be of higher order / to** <than> <said of a number sequence relative to another> <SS>	infinitär größer sein <als>, von höherer Ordnung unendlich werden <als>, stärker (schneller) unendlich werden <als>	devenir infini plus vite <que> <aussi : l'infini vers lequel tend l'une suite est plus grand que l'infini vers lequel tend l'autre, la croissance de l'une série est supérieure à la croissance de l'autre>	иметь бо́льший порядок роста <чем>
B 190	**be of lower order / to** <than> <said of a number sequence relative to another> <SS>	infinitär kleiner sein <als>, von niederer Ordnung unendlich werden <als>, schwächer (langsamer) unendlich werden <als>	devenir infini plus lentement <que> <aussi : l'infini vers lequel tend l'une suite est plus petit que l'infini vers lequel tend l'autre, la croissance de l'une série est inférieure à la croissance de l'autre>	иметь меньший порядок роста <чем>
B 191	**be of the same order / to** <said of two number sequences> <SS>	infinitär gleich sein, von derselben Ordnung unendlich werden <wie>, ebenso unendlich werden <wie>	devenir infini de la même façon <aussi : les infinis vers lesquels tendent les deux suites sont égaux, la croissance des deux suites est la même>	иметь одинаковый порядок роста
	be over / to <SE>	*s.* F 451		
	be permutable / to <AL>	*s.* C 1284		
B 192	**Beppo Levi['s] inequality** <FA>	Beppo Levische Ungleichung *f*, Ungleichung von Beppo Levi	inégalité *f* de Beppo Levi	неравенство Беппо Леви
B 193	**Beppo Levi['s] space,** [B.] Levi['s] space <FA>	Beppo-Levischer Raum *m*, [Beppo-]Levi-Raum *m*	espace *m* [du type] de Beppo Levi	пространство [типа] Беппо Леви
	Beppo Levi['s] theorem <FA>	*s.* B 495		
	be properly contained in / to <SE>	*s.* P 1797		
	ber <FU>	*s.* K 38		
B 194	**be reversed / to** <said of the sense of an inequality > <GN>	sich umkehren <Sinn einer Ungleichung>	se renverser <sens d'une inégalité>	обращаться <смысл неравенства>
	ber function <FU>	*s.* K 38		
	Bergman['s] hermitian metric <FT>	*s.* B 196		
B 195	**Bergman['s] kernel function,** kernel function <FT>	Bergmansche Kernfunktion *f*, Kernfunktion	fonction *f* noyau [de Bergman]	керн[-]функция [Бергмана]
B 196	**Bergman['s] metric,** Bergman['s] hermitian metric <FT>	Bergmansche Metrik *f*	métrique *f* de Bergman	метрика Бергмана
	Bergman-Šilov boundary <PO>	*s.* S 767		
B 197	**bergstrich** <in one-plane projection> <DS>	Bergstrich *m*	bergstrich *m*	бергштрих
B 198	**Bernoullian polynomial,** Bernoulli['s] polynomial <FU>	Bernoullisches (Bernoullis) Polynom *n*, Polynom von Bernoulli	polynôme *m* (fonction *f*) de Bernoulli, fonction bernoullienne	многочлен Бернулли
	Bernoulli['s] binomial distribution <ST>	*s.* B 393		
	Bernoulli-De l'Hospital['s] rule <DI>	*s.* D 208		
	Bernoulli['s] differential equation <DE>	*s.* B 199		
	Bernoulli['s] distribution <ST>	*s.* B 393		
B 199	**Bernoulli['s] equation,** Bernoulli['s] differential equation <DE>	Bernoullische Differentialgleichung *f*	équation *f* [différentielle] de Bernoulli, équation différentielle bernoullienne	уравнение Бернулли [в математике], дифференциальное уравнение Бернулли
B 200	**Bernoulli['s] formula** <ST>	Bernoullische Formel *f* <Wahrscheinlichkeitsfunktion der Binomialverteilung>	formule *f* de Bernoulli	формула Бернулли
B 201	**Bernoulli['s] inequality** <SS>	Bernoullische Ungleichung *f*	inégalité *f* de Bernoulli	неравенство Бернулли
	Bernoulli['s] law of large numbers <ST>	*s.* B 206		
	Bernoulli['s] lemniscate <AG>	*s.* L 560		
	Bernoulli-l'Hospital['s] rule <DI>	*s.* D 208		
B 202	**Bernoulli['s] method** <AL, AX>	Bernoullische Näherungsmethode *f*, Bernoullis Verfahren *n*	méthode *f* de Bernoulli	метод [Д.] Бернулли, метод приближения Бернулли
B 203	**Bernoulli['s] number** <FD, FU>	Bernoullische Zahl *f*, Bernoulli-Zahl *f*	nombre *m* de Bernoulli, nombre bernoullien (tangent)	число Бернулли, бернуллиево число
	Bernoulli['s] polynomial <FU>	*s.* B 198		
B 204	**Bernoulli['s] solution** <DE>	Bernoullische Lösung *f*	solution *f* de Bernoulli	решение Бернулли
B 205	**Bernoulli['s] statistic** <ST>	Bernoullische Stichprobenfunktion (Statistik) *f*, Bernoulli-Stochastik *f*	statistique *f* de Bernoulli	статистика Бернулли
B 206	**Bernoulli['s] theorem,** Bernoulli['s] law of large numbers <ST>	Bernoullischer Grenzwertsatz (Satz) *m*, Bernoullisches Theorem *n*,	théorème *m* de Bernoulli, loi *f* de Jacques Bernoulli, loi des grands	теорема (закон) Бернулли, закон больших чисел Бернулли

and still: B 206		Bernoullis[ches] Gesetz *n* [der großen Zahlen], Satz von Bernoulli	nombres de Bernoulli	
B 207	**Bernoulli trials** <ST>	Bernoulli-Schema *n*, Bernoullisches Versuchsschema (Schema) *n*, Bernoullische Versuchsfolge *f*	schéma *m* de Bernoulli	схема Бернулли, схема испытаний Бернулли
	Bernoulli['s] variable <ST> ┌<ST>	*s.* I 364		
B 208	**Bernoulli['s] variation**	Bernoullische Variation *f*	variation *f* de Bernoulli	дисперсия Бернулли
B 209	**Bernstein['s] condition for convergence, Bernstein['s] convergence theorem** <SS>	Konvergenzkriterium *n* von Bernstein, Bernsteinsches Konvergenzkriterium	critère *m* de convergence de Bernstein, critère de Bernstein	признак сходимости Бернштейна
B 210	**Bernstein-Denjoy class,** BD class <FA>	Bernstein-Denjoysche Klasse *f*, BD-Klasse *f*, quasianalytische Differentialklasse *f* im Denjoyschen Sinne	classe *f* de Bernstein-Denjoy, classe BD	класс Бернштейна-Данжуа
	Bernstein['s] equivalence theorem <SE>	*s.* E 425		
B 211	**Bernstein['s] inequalities** <AX, NU>	Bernsteinsche Ungleichungen *fpl*	inégalités *fpl* de Bernstein	неравенства Бернштейна
B 212	**Bernstein['s] inequality** <AX, ST>	Bernsteinsche Ungleichung *f*	inégalité *f* de Bernstein	неравенство Бернштейна
B 213	**Bernstein['s] polynomial** <FU>	Bernsteinsches Polynom *n*, Bernstein-Polynom *n*	polynôme *m* de Bernstein	многочлен (полином) Бернштейна
	Bernstein-Rogosinski sum <SS>	*s.* R 1363		
B 214	**Bernstein-Rogosinski summation method, Bernstein-Rogosinski method [of summation],** Rogosinski['s] summation method, Rogosinski['s] method [of summation] <for Fourier series> <SS>	Bernstein-Rogosinskisches (Rogosinskisches) Summierungsverfahren *n*, Bernstein-Rogosinskisches Verfahren *n*	méthode *f* de sommation de [Bernstein-]Rogosinski, méthode de [Bernstein-]Rogosinski	метод суммирования Бернштейна-Рогозинского
B 215	**Bernstein-Szegö [asymptotic] formula** <FT>	asymptotische Formel *f* von Bernstein-Szegö, Bernstein-Szegösche asymptotische Formel	formule *f* asymptotique de Bernstein-Szegö	асимптотическая формула Бернштейна-Сеге
B 216	**Bernstein-Szegö polynomial** <FU>	Polynom *n* von Bernstein-Szegö, Bernstein-Szegösches Polynom	polynôme *m* de Bernstein-Szegö	многочлен (полином) Бернштейна-Сеге
B 217	**Bernstein['s] theorem** <for best approximation> <AX, FD>	Satz *m* von [S.N.] Bernstein [über die beste Approximation], Bernsteinscher Satz	théorème *m* de [S.N.] Bernstein	теорема [С.Н.] Бернштейна
B 218	**Berry['s] contradiction (paradox),** paradox of Berry (denotation) <Russell>, antinomy of the name relation <LO>	Berrysche Antinomie *f*, Antinomie von Berry, Antinomie des Denotationsbegriffes	paradoxe *m* de Berry (la désignation des nombres)	парадокс Берри
	Bertalanffy['s] formula <ST>	*s.* V 215		
B 219	**Bertini['s] theorem** <AG>	Satz *m* von Bertini, Bertinischer Satz	théorème *m* de Bertini	теорема Бертини
B 220	**Bertrand['s] criterion,** Bertrand['s] test <SS>	Bertrandsches Kriterium (Konvergenzkriterium) *n*	critère *m* de Bertrand	признак (критерий) Бертрана <сходимости числовых рядов с положительными членами>
B 221	**Bertrand curves,** associate (conjugate) [Bertrand] curves <DG>	Bertrandsches Kurvenpaar *n*, Bertrandsche Kurven *fpl*	courbes *fpl* de Bertrand	кривые Бертрана, пара Бертрана
B 222	**Bertrand['s] paradox** <ST>	Bertrandsches Paradoxon *n*	paradoxe *m* de Bertrand	парадокс Бертрана, бертранов парадокс
B 223	**Bertrand['s] postulate,** postulate of Bertrand <for prime numbers> <NT>	Bertrandsches Postulat *n*, Postulat von J. Bertrand	postulat *m* de Bertrand	постулат Бертрана
	Bertrand['s] test <SS>	*s.* B 220		
B 224	**besace** <GE>	Besace *f*, Quersackkurve *f* <Cramer>	besace *f*	кривая, имеющая уравнение $(x^2 - by)^2 = a^2 (x^2 - y^2)$
	beschränktartig function <FT>	*s.* B 674		
	beschränktartig surface <AN>	*s.* B 675		
	Besicovich['s] almost periodic function <AP>	*s.* G 132		
B 225	**Besicovich['s] sum** <AB>	Besicovitch-Summe *f*	somme *f* de Besicovitch	сумма по Безиковичу
	be smaller / to <SE>	*s.* P 1172		
B 226	**Bessel['s] coefficient** <FU>	Bessel-Koeffizient *m*	coefficient *m* de Bessel	коэффициент Бесселя
B 227	**Bessel['s] [differential] equation** <DE>	Besselsche Differentialgleichung (Gleichung) *f*	équation *f* [différentielle] de Bessel	бесселево уравнение, [дифференциальное] уравнение Бесселя
	Bessel['s] equation <AX, FA>	*s.* B 235		
B 228	**Bessel['s] formula,** Bessel['s] formula of interpolation, Bessel['s] interpolation formula <AX, FD, NU>	Besselsche Interpolationsformel (Formel) *f*, Interpolationsformel (Formel) von Bessel	formule *f* de Bessel, formule d'interpolation de Bessel	формула Бесселя, формула интерполяции Бесселя

No.	English	German	French	Russian
B 229	**Bessel['s] formula [of integration]** <DI, NU>	Besselsche Integrationsformel *f*	formule *f* [d'intégration] de Bessel	формула [интегрирования] Бесселя
	Bessel['s] formula of interpolation <AX, FD, NU>	*s.* B 228		
B 230	**Bessel['s] function,** Bessel['s] function of the first kind, cylindrical Bessel function [of the first kind] <FU>	Bessel-Funktion *f*, Bessel-Funktion (Zylinderfunktion *f*) erster Art, [gewöhnliche] Besselsche Funktion *f*, Besselsche Funktion erster Art	fonction *f* de Bessel (Bessel cylindrique [de première espèce], Bessel de première expèce, Fourier-Bessel, Bourier-Bessel de première espèce)	бесселева функция первого рода, функция Бесселя первого рода, цилиндрическая функция первого рода, бесселева функция, функция Бесселя
B 231	**Bessel['s] function,** cylindrical function, Fourier-Bessel function, cylinder function, cylindrical harmonic <of order, parameter, index ν>, // Fourier function <FU>	Zylinderfunktion *f*, Bessel-Funktion *f*, Besselsche (Fourier-Besselsche) Funktion *f* <der Ordnung ν, mit dem Parameter ν, mit dem Index ν>	fonction *f* de Bessel (Fourier-Bessel), fonction (harmonique *f*) cylindrique, // fonction *f* de Fourier <d'indice ν>	бесселева (цилиндрическая) функция, функция Бесселя (Фурье-Бесселя) <порядка, индекса ν>
	Bessel function of half-odd order <FU>	*s.* S 1444		
B 232	**Bessel['s] function of imaginary argument** <FU>	Zylinderfunktion *f* mit rein imaginärem Argument	fonction *f* de Bessel d'argument imaginaire	функция Бесселя [чисто] мнимого аргумента
	Bessel['s] function of the first kind <FU>	*s.* B 230		
B 233	**Bessel function of the second kind,** cylindrical Bessel function of the second kind, cylindrical Neumann function, Neumann['s] Bessel function, Neumann['s] function, Weber['s] function, Weber['s] Bessel function of the second kind, Neumann['s] Bessel function of the second kind, Nielson-Hankel function; Hankel['s] type of Bessel function of the second kind <FU>	Neumann-Funktion *f*, Neumannsche Funktion *f*, Zylinderfunktion *f* (Bessel-Funktion *f*, Besselsche Funktion) zweiter Art, Webersche Funktion, Weber-Funktion *f*	fonction *f* de Bessel [cylindrique] de deuxième espèce, fonction de Neumann cylindrique, fonction de Weber (Neumann)	бесселева (цилиндрическая) функция второго рода, функция Бесселя второго рода, функция Неймана (Вебера)
B 234	**Bessel function of the third kind,** cylindrical Bessel function of the third kind, cylindrical Hankel function, Hankel['s] function, Hankel['s] Bessel function, Hankel['s] Bessel function of the third kind <first *or* second Hankel function> <FU>	Hankel-Funktion *f*, Hankelsche Funktion *f* (Zylinderfunktion *f*) <erster *oder* zweiter Art>, Zylinderfunktion (Bessel-Funktion *f*, Besselsche Funktion) dritter Art	fonction *f* de Hankel cylindrique, fonction de Bessel [cylindrique] de troisième espèce, fonction de Hankel (Hankel-Bessel) <première *ou* seconde>	бесселева (цилиндрическая) функция третьего рода, функция Бесселя третьего рода, функция Ганкеля (Ханкеля)
B 235	**Bessel['s] identity,** Bessel['s] equation <in a unitary space> <AX, FA>	Besselsche Identität (Gleichung) *f*, Parsevalsche Gleichung	identité *f* de Bessel	равенство Бесселя
B 236	**Bessel['s] inequality** <for orthonormal systems in a unitary space> <AX, FA>	Besselsche Ungleichung *f*, Bessel-Ungleichung *f*	inégalité de Bessel, inégalité de Bessel-Parseval	неравенство Бесселя
B 237	**Bessel['s] inequality** <for eigenvalue problems of differential equations> <DE>	Besselsche Ungleichung *f*, Bessel-Ungleichung *f*	inégalité *f* de Bessel	неравенство Бесселя
B 238	**Bessel['s] integral [equation]** <FU>	Besselsche Integraldarstellung *f* [der Zylinderfunktionen]	intégrale *f* de Bessel	интеграл Бесселя
	Bessel['s] interpolation formula <AX, FD, NU>	*s.* B 228		
B 239	**Bessel['s] polynomial** <FU>	Besselsches Polynom *n*	polynôme *m* de Bessel	многочлен (полином) Бесселя
B 240	**best approximation** <to *f*> <AX, NT>	Bestapproximation *f* <an *f*>, Proximum *n* <von *f*> <AX>; beste Annäherung *f* <Vorgang> <AX>; beste Näherung *f* <NT>	la meilleure approximation *f* <à *f*>	наилучшее приближение <к *f*>
B 240a	**best approximation,** least deviation <deviation of the element of best approximation> <AX>	Defekt *m*, Minimalabweichung *f*, kleinste Abweichung *f*, beste Approximation *f*	la meilleure approximation *f*, déviation *f* minimale	дефект, наименьшее уклонение, наилучшее приближение
B 241	**best approximation in the mean** <AX>	beste Approximation *f* im Mittel, beste mittlere Approximation	la meilleure approximation *f* en moyenne	наилучшее приближение в среднем
B 242	**best asymptotically normal estimate (estimator)** <ST>	asymptotisch beste normale Schätzfunktion (Schätzung, Punktschätzung) *f*	le meilleur estimateur *m* asymptotiquement normal	наилучшая асимптотически нормальная оценка
	BE statistics <ST>	*s.* B 619		
B 243	**best conditioned matrix** <AL, NU>	Matrix *f* bester Kondition		наилучше обусловленная матрица
B 244	**best estimator,** best unbiased linear estimator, Gauss-Markov estimator	beste lineare erwartungstreue Schätzung (Schätzfunktion) *f*, beste	le meilleur estimateur *m* [linéaire sans biais], estimateur de Gauss-	наилучшая [линейная несмешенная] оценка, оценка Гаусса-Маркова

No.	English	German	French	Russian
and still: B 244	<ST>	Schätzung (Schätzfunktion), Gauß-Markov-Schätzung *f*	Markov	
	be strictly contained / to ⌐<SE>	*s.* P 1797		
B 245	**best test** <ST>	bester Test *m*	le meilleur test *m*	наилучший критерий
	best unbiased linear estimator <ST>	*s.* B 244		
	be subelement / to <SE>	*s.* P 1171		
	bet <TG>	*s.* S 1601		
B 246	**beta distribution** <of the first *or* second kind> <ST>	Beta-Verteilung *f* <erster (1.) *oder* zweiter (2.) Art>	distribution *f* bêta <de première *ou* seconde espèce>	бета-распределение <первого *или* второго рода>
	beta-error <ST>	*s.* E 479		
B 247	**beta function,** beta-function, B-function, Eulerian integral of the first kind, Euler['s] beta-function <FU>	Beta-Funktion *f*, B-Funktion *f*, Eulersches Integral *n* erster Art, Euler-Integral *n* erster Art, vollständige (Eulersche) Beta-Funktion	fonction *f* bêta (B), intégrale *f* (fonction) eulérienne de première espèce, première intégrale eulérienne	бета-функция, бета-функция Эйлера, B-функция [Эйлера], эйлеров интеграл первого рода
	beta-risk <ST>	*s.* R 1343		
B 248	**beth [number]** <a cardinal> <SE>	Beth *n*	bêt *m*	бет
B 249	**be topologically embeddable into a space / to** <said of a space> <TO>	von einem Raum umfaßt werden, sich in einen Raum topologisch einbetten lassen	être topologiquement plongeable dans un espace	быть топологически вложимым в пространстве
	be transformed contragrediently / to <AL>	*s.* T 786		
B 250	**better approximation** <AX, PG>	bessere Näherung *f*	approximation *f* améliorée	улучшенное приближение
B 251	**Betti['s] group** <AT>	Bettische Gruppe *f*, reduzierte Homologiegruppe *f* <modulo Torsion>	groupe *m* de Betti	группа Бетти
B 252	**Betti['s] number,** connectivity, index of connection <*n*-th> <AT>	Bettische Zahl *f* <*n*-te>	nombre *m* de Betti <*n*-e>	число Бетти <*n*-мерное или *n*-е>
B 253	**Betti['s] number mod. 2** <of a complex> <AT>	Zusammenhangszahl *f*, Bettische Zahl *f* modulo 2	nombre *m* de connexité (Betti modulo 2)	коэффициент (число) связности, число Бетти по модулю 2
B 254	**Betti['s] number over I_m** <AL>	Bettische Zahl *f* modulo *m*	nombre *m* de Betti modulo *m*	число Бетти по модулю *m*
	between-class correlation <ST>	*s.* I 703		
	between-class variance <ST>	*s.* I 704		
	between-group correlation <ST>	*s.* I 703		
	between-group deviance <ST>	*s.* I 713		
	between-group sum of squares <ST>	*s.* I 713		
	between-group variance <ST>	*s.* I 704		
	betweenness <GE, SE>	*s.* R 678		
B 255	**betweenness group** <with betweenness relation> <GR>	„zwischen"-Gruppe *f*	groupe *m* d'intermédiarité	промежуточная группа
	betweenness relation <GE, SE>	*s.* R 678		
B 256	**betweenness semigroup** <with betweenness relation> <AL>	„zwischen"-Halbgruppe *f*	demi-groupe *m* d'intermédiarité	промежуточная полугруппа
	between relation <GE, SE>	*s.* R 678		
	be under / to <SE>	*s.* P 1171		
B 257	**be weaker / to,** to dominate <rules of punctuation> <GN, LO>	schwächer binden, übergeordnet sein, stärker trennen, herrschen <Klammereinsparungsregeln>	établir une liaison moins forte <règles de parenthèses>	связывать слабее <правила скобок>
	"Beweistheorie" <MM>	*s.* P 1761		
B 258	**be zero / to** <GN>	verschwinden, Null sein	être nul	быть нулем
B 259	**Bézout['s] domain** <AL>	Bézoutscher Ring *m*	anneau *m* de Bézout	кольцо Безу
B 260	**Bézout['s] eliminant** <AL, IV>	Bézoutiante *f*	bézoutien *m*, bézoutiant *m*, résultant *m* de Bézout	результант Безу
B 261	**Bézout['s] identity** <AL>	Bézoutsche Identität *f*	identité (relation, égalité) *f* de Bézout	тождество Безу
B 262	**Bézout['s] theorem** <AG>	Bézoutscher Satz *m*, Bézouts Theorem *n*	théorème *m* de Bézout	теорема Безу <о делении многочлена на линейный двухчлен
	B-function <FU>	*s.* B 247		
B 263	**bi-additive map** <AL>	biadditive Abbildung *f*	application *f* biadditive (**Z**-bilinéaire)	биаддитивное отображение
B 264	**biaffine space** <GE>	biaffiner Raum *m*	espace *m* biaffine	биаффинное пространство
B 265	**bi-alternant** <AL>	Bialternante *f*	bi-alternant *m*	биальтернанта
B 266	**Bianchi['s] identity** <DG, VT>	Bianchische (Padova-Bianchische, Ricci-Bianchische) Identität *f*, Identität von Bianchi-Padova (Ricci-Bianchi)	identité *f* de Bianchi	тождество Бианки
B 267	**Bianchi['s] system** <of surfaces> <DG>	Bianchisches Flächensystem *n*	système *f* de surfaces de Bianchi	система поверхностей Бианки
B 268	**Bianchi['s] transform[ation]** <DG>	Bianchische Transformation *f*	transformation *f* de Bianchi	преобразование Бианки
	biangle <EG>	*s.* L 1188		

B 269	**bias,** systematic error, fixed error, regular error <of a point estimation> <ST>	systematischer (regelmäßiger, methodischer) Fehler *m*, Verzerrung *f*, Verfälschung *f*, Bias *m*, erwartungsmäßige Abweichung *f*	erreur *f* systématique (biaisée, fixe, régulière), biais *m*	систематическая ошибка (погрешность), постоянная (регулярная) ошибка, смещение
B 270	**biased estimator (estimating function)** <ST>	verzerrende (verfälschende, verzerrte, verfälschte, nicht erwartungstreue) Schätzfunktion (Schätzung) *f*	estimateur *m* (fonction *f* estimatrice) avec biais (erreur systématique), estimateur biaisé, fonction estimatrice biaisée	смещенная оценка
B 271	**biased sample** <ST>	verzerrte (verfälschte) Stichprobe *f*	échantillon *m* biaisé (avec biais, avec erreur systématique)	смещенная выборка
B 272	**biased test** <ST>	verzerrter (verfälschter) Test *m*	test *m* biaisé (avec biais, avec erreur systématique)	смещенный критерий
B 273	**biaxial collineation** <PJ>	biaxiale (windschiefe, gescharte) Kollineation *f*	collinéation *f* biaxe (gauche)	биаксиальная коллинеация
B 274	**biaxial involution** <PJ>	windschiefe (biaxiale) Involution, projektive Spiegelung *f* an zwei Geraden (Achsen)	involution *f* biaxe	биаксиальная инволюция, биаксиальное инволюционное преобразование
B 275	**biaxial spherical harmonic [function]** <FU>	zweiachsige Kugelfunktion *f*	fonction *f* harmonique sphérique biaxe, harmonique *f* sphérique biaxe	двуосная сферическая гармоника
B 276	**bicartesian square,** pushme-pull-you <CA>	bikartesisches (bicartesisches) Quadrat *n*, Doolittle-Quadrat *n*	carré *m* bicartésien	бидекартов квадрат
B 277	**bicategory** <MacLane>, 2-category <CA>	Bikategorie *f*	bi-catégorie *f*; catégorie *f* avec multiplication <Benabou>	бикатегория
B 278	**bicentres [of magnitude], bicentres of number,** bicentroid <formed by two half-centres> <of a tree> <GP>	Massenbizentren *npl*	sommets *mpl* du centre de l'assemblage <si le centre est une arête>	центроид <дерева> <состоящий из двух смежных вершин>
B 279	**bicentric polygon** <EG>	bizentrisches Vieleck *n*	polygone *m* bicentrique	бицентрический многоугольник
	bicentroid <GP>	*s.* B 278		
B 280	**bichain** <CA>	Bikette *f*	bichaîne *f*	двойная цепь
B 281	**bicharacteristic** <DE>	Bicharakteristik *f*, Strahl *m*	bicaractéristique *f*, courbe *f* bicaractéristique	бихарактеристика, луч
B 282	**bicircular curve** <GE>	bizirkulare Kurve *f*	courbe *f* bi[-]circulaire	бициркулярная кривая
B 283	**bicolouring** <GP>	Zweifärbung *f*	bicoloration *f*	раскраска двумя цветами
B 284	**bicommutant** <AL>	Bikommutant *m*	bicommutant *m*	бицентрализатор
B 285	**bicompact,** bicompactum, compact Hausdorff space <TO>	Bikompaktum *n*	bicompact *m*	бикомпакт, хаусдорфово бикомпактное пространство
B 286	**bicompactification** <TO>	Bikompaktifizierung *f*	bicompactification *f*	бикомпактификация, бикомпактное расширение
	bicompactification <TO>	*s.* C 1293		
B 287	**bicompact set** <TO>	bikompakte Menge (Punktmenge) *f*	ensemble *m* bicompact	бикомпактное [точечное] множество
	bicompact space <TO>	*s.* Q 114		
B 288/9	**bicompact transformation group** <TO>	bikompakte Transformationsgruppe *f*	groupe *m* de transformations bicompact	бикомпактная группа преобразований
	bicompactum <TO>	*s.* B 285		
	bicomplex <HA>	*s.* D 902		
B 290	**bicomplex function** <AN>	bikomplexe Funktion *f*	fonction *f* bicomplexe	бикомплексная функция
B 291	**bicomplex number** <GE>	bikomplexe Zahl *f*	nombre *m* bicomplexe	бикомплексное число
B 292	**bicomplex quantity** <AN>	bikomplexe Größe *f* <*n*-ter Ordnung, Weierstraß>	quantité *f* bicomplexe	бикомплексная величина
B 293	**biconditional** <as an operation>, ⟷ <LO>	Äquivalenz *f*, aeq, ⟷	biconditionnel *m*, opérateur *m* biconditionnel, équivalence *f* simple, connecteur *m* équivalence, ⟷	эквиваленция, эквивалентность, двойная импликация, функция равнозначности, равнозначность, ⟷
	biconditional <LO>	*s.* 1. M 160; 2. S 2438		
	biconditional — conditional <LO>	*s.* R 1495		
	bicone <EG>	*s.* D 904		
	bi-connected graph <GP>	*s.* N 475		
B 294	**biconnected space** <TO>	bikonnexer topologischer Raum *m*	espace *m* biconnexe	бисвязное пространство
	biconnected space <TO>	*s.* D 955		
B 295	**bicontinuity** <of a mapping> <TO>	beid[er]seitige Stetigkeit *f*	bicontinuité *f*	взаимная непрерывность
B 296	**bicontinuous function** <DI, TO>	beidseitig (beiderseitig, beiderseits, zweiseitig) stetige Funktion *f*	fonction *f* bicontinue	взаимно непрерывная функция
B 297/8	**bicontinuous isomorphism** <AL>	beiderseits stetiger Isomorphismus *m*	isomorphisme *m* bicontinu	непрерывный в обе стороны изоморфизм
B 299	**bicontinuously differentiable** <TO>	beiderseits stetig differenzierbar	bicontinûment dérivable	взаимно непрерывно дифференцируемый
	bi[-]continuous mapping <TO>	*s.* T 519		
B 300	**bicorn [curve],** cocked[-]hat <AG>	Zweihorn *n*, Zweihornkurve *f*, Kremphutkurve *f*	bicorne *f*, courbe *f* bicorne, chapeau *m* à cornes	двурогая кривая
B 301	**bicovector** <VT>	Bikovektor *m*	bicovecteur *m*	биковектор
B 302	**bicubic equation** <AG, AL>	bikubische Gleichung *f*	équation *f* bicubique	бикубическое уравнение
B 303	**bicursal curve** <AG, NO>	bikursale (doppelläufige) Kurve *f* <vom Geschlecht 1>	courbe *f* bicursale	бикурсальная кривая
	bicursal curve <AG>	*s.* E 170		

B 304	**bicylinder** <FT>	Dizylinder *m*	bicylindre *m*	бицилиндр, бикруг
B 305	**bidegree** <of an element in a bigraded module *or* of a differential form> <AL>	Bigrad *m*	bidegré *m*	бистепень
	bidimensional irregularity <AG>	*s.* S 2323		
B 306	**bidimensionality,** two-dimensionality <AL, GE>	Zweidimensionalität *f*	bidimensionnalité *f*	двумерность
B 307	**Bieberbach['s] area theorem,** area-principle <FT>	Bieberbachscher (Bieberbachs) Flächensatz *m*, Flächensatz [von Bieberbach]	théorème *m* de Bieberbach	теорема Бибербаха <о площадях>, принцип площадей
B 308	**Bieberbach['s] coefficient theorem,** coefficient theorem of Bieberbach <FT, SS>	Koeffizientensatz *m* von Bieberbach [und Löwner], Bieberbachscher Koeffizientensatz	théorème *m* des coefficients de Bieberbach	теорема коэффициентов Бибербаха
B 309	**Bieberbach['s] conjecture** <FT>	Bieberbachsche Vermutung *f*, Bieberbachsches Koeffizientenproblem *n*	hypothèse *f* de Bieberbach	гипотеза Бибербаха
B 310	**Bieberbach['s] inequality** <FT>	Bieberbachsche Ungleichung *f*	inégalité *f* de Bieberbach	неравенство Бибербаха
	Bienaymé-Chebyshev['s] inequality <ST>	*s.* C 608		
B 311	**biequivalent points** <TO>	biäquivalente Punkte *mpl*	points *mpl* bi-équivalents	биэквивалентные точки
B 312	**bifactorial model** <ST>	Bifaktormodell *n*	modèle *m* bi[-]factoriel	бифакторная модель
	bifolium <AG>	*s.* D 915		
B 313	**bifunctor,** functor of two variables, two variable functor <CA>	Bifunktor *m*, zweistelliger Funktor *m*, Funktor mit zwei Argumenten	bifoncteur *m*, foncteur *m* de deux variables, foncteur double	двуместный функтор, бифунктор
	bifunctor <CA>	*s.* C 2606		
B 314	**bifunctor contravariant in the first variable and covariant in the second** <CA>	kontra-ko-varianter Funktor *m*	foncteur *m* contra-covariant	контра-ковариантный функтор
B 315	**bifunctorial isomorphism** <CA>	Bifunktorisomorphismus *m*	isomorphisme *m* bifonctoriel	бифункторный изоморфизм
	bifunctor in both variables <CA>	*s.* C 2606		
	bifurcation <GN>	*s.* B 725		
B 316	**bifurcation theory** <AN, DE>	Verzweigungstheorie *f*, Bifurkationstheorie *f*	théorie *f* de bifurcation	теория ветвления
B 317	**big abelian group** <GR, SE>	große abelsche Gruppe *f*	groupe *m* abélien large	большая абелева группа
B 318	**big category,** large category <CA>	große Kategorie *f*	catégorie *f* large	большая категория
B 319	**bigenus** <*pl.* bigenera> <AG>	Bigeschlecht *n*	bigenre *m*	двойной род
	bigit <NT>	*s.* B 361		
B 320	**bigraded group,** double graded group <GR>	bigraduierte (doppelt graduierte) Gruppe *f*	groupe *m* bigradué	дважды градуированная группа, биградуированная группа
B 321	**bigraded module** <AL>	bigraduierter Modul *m*	module *m* bigradué	биградуированный модуль
B 322	**bigrade equation** <NT>	bigrade (zweigradige) Gleichung *f*	équation *f* bigrade	двустепенное уравнение
B 323	**bigraduation** <AL>	Bigraduierung *f*	bigraduation *f*	биградуировка
B 324	**biharmonic equation** <DE, PO>	Bipotentialgleichung *f*, biharmonische Differentialgleichung (Gleichung) *f*	équation *f* biharmonique	бигармоническое уравнение
B 325	**biharmonic function** <PO>	biharmonische Funktion *f*, Bipotentialfunktion *f*	fonction *f* biharmonique	бигармоническая функция
B 326	**biholomorphic function** <FT>	biholomorphe Funktion *f*	fonction *f* biholomorphe (holomorphe inversible)	биголоморфная (бирегулярная) функция
	biholomorphic map <AN>	*s.* P 1918		
B 327	**bihomogeneous set** <TO>	bihomogene Menge *f*	ensemble *m* bihomogène	биоднородное множество
B 328	**bihomomorphism** <AL>	Bihomomorphismus *m*	bi-homomorphisme *m*	бигомоморфизм
B 329	**bi-invariant measure** <on a group> <GR, ME>	biinvariantes Maß *n*	mesure *f* bi-invariante	биинвариантная мера
	bijection <SE>	*s.* B 330		
	bijection <UA>	*s.* I 1132		
	bijective function <SE>	*s.* B 330		
B 330	**bijective mapping,** bijection, one-to-one mapping onto, one-to-one and onto mapping, (1-1)-mapping onto, bi-unique mapping onto, one-to-one correspondence, biunique correspondence, (1-1)-correspondence, bijective function, (1-1)-function onto <SE>	bijektive Abbildung *f*, Bijektion *f*, eineindeutige Abbildung auf, isomorphe Abbildung, Isomorphismus *m*	application *f* bijective, bijection *f*, application biunivoque sur, correspondance *f* bijective <entre>, correspondance biunivoque <entre>, fonction *f* bijective, // bifonction *f*	биективное отображение, биекция, взаимно однозначное отображение, взаимно однозначное соответствие, одно-однозначное соответствие, (1-1)-соответствие
	bijective mapping of a set onto itself <SE>	*s.* O 122		
B 331	**bijectivity** <SE>	Bijektivität *f*	bijectivité *f*	биективность
B 332	**bilateral cancellability,** cancellability <AL>	[zweiseitige] Kürzbarkeit *f*	simplifiabilité *f* bilatérale	двусторонняя сокращаемость
B 333	**bilateral derivative** <DI>	zweiseitige Ableitung (Derivierte) *f*, beid[er]seitige Ableitung (Derivierte)	dérivée *f* bilatérale	двусторонняя производная
	bilateral Dini['s] derivative <RF>	*s.* T 1112		

No.	English	German	French	Russian
B 334	**bilateral extreme approximate limit** <RF>	zweiseitiger extremer approximativer Limes (Hauptlimes) *m*	limite *f* approximative extrême bilatérale	двусторонний экстремальный аппроксимативный предел
B 335	**bilateral Laplace transform[ation],** two-sided Laplace transform[ation] <IT>	zweiseitige (bilaterale) Laplace-Transformation *f*	transformation *f* bilatérale de Laplace	двустороннее преобразование Лапласа
	bilaterally analytic hypercomplex function <FT>	*s.* A 636		
B 336	**bilaterally bounded sequence** <SS>	beiderseits beschränkte Folge *f*	séquence *f* bilatéralement bornée	ограниченная в обе стороны последовательность
B 337	**bilaterally symmetric** <GE>	zweiseitig symmetrisch	bilatéralement symétrique, symétrique vers les deux côtés	двусторонне симметричный
	bilateral ruler <GE, IN>	*s.* R 1519		
B 338	**bilinear covariant** <result> <DG, IV>	bilineare Kovariante *f*, Überschiebung *f*	covariant *m* bilinéaire	билинейный ковариант
B 339	**bilinear equation** <AL, AN>	bilineare Gleichung *f*	équation *f* bilinéaire	билинейное уравнение
B 340	**bilinear form,** bilinear functional <AL, FA>	Bilinearform *f*, bilineares Funktional *n*	forme (fonctionnelle) *f* bilinéaire	билинейная форма, билинейный функционал, билинейное отображение
B 341	**bilinear form module** <AL>	Bilinearformmodul *m*	module *m* des formes bilinéaires	модуль билинейных форм
	bilinear functional <AL, FA>	*s.* B 340		
B 342	**bilinear integral form** <IE>	bilineare Integralform *f*	forme *f* intégrale bilinéaire	билинейная интегральная форма
B 343	**bilinearity** <AL>	Bilinearität *f*	bilinéarité *f*	билинейность
B 344	**bilinear mapping** <AL>	bilineare Abbildung *f*	application *f* bilinéaire	билинейное отображение, билинейная финкция
B 345	**bilinear mapping,** pairing <of groups> <GR>	Paarung *f*, bilineare Abbildung *f*	couplage *m*	билинейное отображение, спаривание
	bilinear moment <ST>	*s.* P 1620		
B 346	**bilinear relation** <AL>	Bilinearrelation *f*, bilineare Relation *f*	relation *f* bilinéaire	билинейное отношение
B 347	**bilinear system** <FA>	Bilinearsystem *n*	système *m* bilinéaire	билинейная система
B 348	**bilinear transformation,** Möbius['s] (fractional linear, linear fractional, linear) transformation, linear (homographic) mapping, homography; direct bilinear (Möbius) transformation <FT>	lineare (allgemeine lineare, gebrochene lineare, gebrochen-lineare) Transformation (Abbildung, Substitution) *f*, Möbiussche Ttransformation (Kreisverwandtschaft, Substitution, Kreistransformation) *f*, Möbius-Transformation *f*, Homographie *f*; lineare (allgemeine lineare, gebrochene lineare, gebrochen-lineare) Transformation (Abbildung, Substitution) erster (1.) Art, gleichsinnige (direkte, eigentliche) Möbiussche Transformation (Kreisverwandtschaft, Kreistransformation) *f*	transformation *f* homographique, homographie *f*; transformation homographique directe, homographie directe, transformation circulaire directe	дробно-линейное преобразование (отображение), преобразование Мебиуса, круговое преобразование; прямое дробно-линейное преобразование (отображение), прямое преобразование Мебиуса, прямое круговое преобразование
B 349	**bimagic square** <CT>	satanisches (bimagisches) Quadrat *n*, Bimagie *f*, zu den beiden ersten Graden magisches Quadrat	carré *m* satanique (magique aux deux premiers degrés)	бимагический квадрат
B 350	**bimatrix game** <TG>	Bimatrixspiel *n*	jeu *m* bimatriciel	биматричная игра
B 351	**bimodal distribution [function],** double-peaked distribution [function] <ST>	bimodale Verteilung[sfunktion] *f*, zweigipflige Verteilung[sfunktion]	distribution *f* bimodale, fonction *f* de distribution bimodale	двухвершинное (бимодальное) распределение, двухвершинная (бимодальная) функция распределения
B 352	**bimodule,** double module <AL>	Bimodul *m*, Doppelmodul *m*	bimodule *m*, double module *m*	бимодуль, двойной модуль
B 353	**bimorphism,** morphism which is both a monomorphism and an epimorphism <CA>	Bimorphismus *m*, bimorpher Morphismus *m*	bimorphisme *m*	биморфизм, биективный морфизм
P 354	**binariant** <of algebraic forms> <AL>	Binariante *f* <der *k*-ten Art>	binariant *m*	бинариант
	binary <CT>	*s.* T 1077		
B 355	**binary analysis** <GE>	Binäranalyse *f*	analyse *f* binaire	бинарный анализ
B 356	**binary arithmetic** <NT>	binäre Arithmetik *f*, Dyadik *f*	arithmétique *f* binaire (dyadique)	бинарная арифметика
	binary chopping <AN, NU>	*s.* M 463		
B 357	**binary code** <NU>	Binärkode *m*, binärer Kode *m*, Dualkode *m*, Dualcode *m*	code *m* binaire	двоичный код
B 358	**binary-coded decimal [number] notation** <NU>	binär verschlüsselte dezimale Zahlendarstellung *f*, binär verschlüsselte Dezimalzahlendarstellung *f*	notation *f* décimale en code binaire, notation décimale codifiée binaire, notation de nombres décimaux codés sous une forme binaire, notation décimale codée sous une forme binaire	представление чисел в двоично-десятичной системе, представление десятичных чисел в двоичном коде, двоично-кодированное представление десятичных чисел

No.	English	German	French	Russian
B 359	**binary coded decimal system,** BCD system <NU>	binär verschlüsseltes Dezimalsystem *n*	code *m* DCB, code du type « décimal codé binaire »	двоично кодированная десятичная система счисления
B 360	**binary connective,** functor of two arguments; binary propositional connective <LO>	binärer (zweistelliger) Junktor *m*	connecteur (opérateur) *m* binaire; opérateur propositionnel binaire	бинарная связка, бинарный функтор; бинарная сентенциональная связка
B 361	**binary digit,** bigit, bit <NT>	binäre Ziffer *f*, Binärziffer *f*, Dualziffer *f*, duale Ziffer, Bit *n*	chiffre (digit) *m* binaire, digit, bit *m*, top *m*, binit *m*, unité *f* binaire	двоичная цифра, двоичный знак (разряд), бит
	binary digit <ST>	*s.* B 470		
B 362	**binary domain** <GE>	binäres Gebiet *n*, Gebiet zweiter Stufe	domaine *m* binaire	бинарная область
B 363	**binary dual projective transformation, binary dual projectivity** <PJ>	binäre duale Projektivität *f*, duale binäre Projektivität	projectivité *f* duale binaire, transformation (application) *f* projective duale binaire	бинарное двойственное (дуальное) проективное преобразование, бинарная двойственная (дуальная) проективность
B 364	**binary field** <NO>	Binärfeld *n*	champ *m* binaire	бинарное поле
B 365	**binary form,** binary (2-ary) quantic <AL>	binäre (2-äre) Form *f*, Binärform *f*, Form von zwei Variablen	forme *f* binaire (2-aire), forme de deux variables, forme algébrique binaire	бинарная (2-арная) форма, двоичная форма, форма от двух переменных
B 366	**binary function** <AL>	binäre (zweistellige) Funktion *f*	fonction *f* binaire	бинарная (двуместная) функция
	binary function <LO>	*s.* F 772		
B 367	**binary functional calculus of first order** <LO>	zweistelliger Prädikatenkalkül *m* erster Stufe	calcul *m* des prédicats dyadiques restreint	исчисление двуместных предикатов первого порядка
B 368	**binary icosahedral group,** compound perfect group of lowest possible order <GR>	binäre Ikosaedergruppe *f*	groupe *m* icosaédrique binaire	бинарная икозаэдрическая группа
	binary internal composition <AL>	*s.* I 760		
B 369	**binary involution** <PJ>	binäre Involution *f*	involution *f* binaire	бинарная инволюция, бинарное инволюционное преобразование
B 369a	**binary logarithm,** lb, log$_2$ <AR, NU>	binärer (dualer) Logarithmus *m*, Logarithmus zur Basis 2, lb, ld, log$_2$	logarithme *m* binaire, lb, log$_2$	бинарный логарифм, lb, log$_2$
	binary notation <NT>	*s.* B 378		
B 370	**binary number,** dual (dyadic) number <NT>	Binärzahl *f*, Dualzahl *f*, dyadische Zahl *f*	nombre *m* binaire (écrit dans le système binaire, dyadique)	двоичное число, бинарное число
	binary number notation <NT>	*s.* B 378		
B 371	**binary number system,** binary system, dyadic [number] system <NT>	Binärsystem *n*, Dualsystem *n*, dyadisches System (Zahlensystem) *n*, Zweiersystem *n*, binäres System (Zahlensystem)	système *m* binaire de numération, système de numération binaire, système (numération *f*) binaire, système dyadique	двоичная система чисел, двоичная система [счисления], бинарная (диадическая) система [счисления]
B 372	**binary operation,** operation of two arguments <AL>	binäre (zweistellige) Operation (Verknüpfung) *f*, binäre algebraische Operation (Verknüpfung)	opération *f* binaire (à deux termes, interne binaire)	бинарная (бинарная алгебраическая) операция
B 373	**binary place,** binary position <NT>	Dualstelle *f*, Binärstelle *f*	place (position) *f* binaire	двоичный разряд, бинарное (двоичное) место
B 374	**binary point** <NT>	Binärkomma *n*, Komma *n* <einer Binärzahl>	virgule *f* binaire	[двоичная] запятая <в двоичном числе>
B 375	**binary polyhedral group** <GR>	binäre Polyedergruppe *f*, homogene Gruppe *f* <zu endlicher Drehgruppe gehörig>	groupe *m* polyédral binaire	бинарная полиэдрическая группа
	binary position <NT>	*s.* B 373		
	binary predicate <LO>	*s.* T 1096		
	binary predicate parameter <LO>	*s.* T 1097		
B 376	**binary projective transformation** <PJ>	binäre projektive Transformation *f*, binäre Projektivität *f*	transformation *f* projective binaire	бинарное проективное преобразование
	binary propositional connective <LO>	*s.* B 360		
	binary quantic <AL>	*s.* B 365		
B 377	**binary relation,** dyadic relation, two-place relation <SE, UA>	binäre (zweistellige) Relation *f*, binäre Beziehung *f*, binäres Relativ *n*	relation (correspondance) *f* binaire	бинарное (двухмерное, двуместное) отношение, бинарное соотношение, соответствие
B 378	**binary representation,** binary number notation, binary notation <of a number> <NT>	binäre Zahlendarstellung (Darstellung) *f*, Binärdarstellung *f*, Dualzahlendarstellung *f*, dyadische Darstellung, binäre Schreibweise *f*, Dualschreibweise *f*, dyadische Schreibweise; binäre Numeration *f*	notation *f* binaire, écriture *f* binaire, représentation *f* binaire, écriture dyadique; numération *f* binaire	двоичное представление, представление <числа> в двоичной системе, двоичная запись; двоичное счисление
B 379	**binary scale** <NO>	Paarleiter *f*, binäre Skala *f*, Verbindungsskala *f*, Übergangsskala *f* <Werkmeister>	échelle *f* binaire (de deux)	бинарная (двоичная) шкала
	binary system <NT>	*s.* B 371		
B 380	**binary-to-decimal conversion, binary to decimal conversion** <NT>	Binär-Dezimal-Konvertierung *f*, Dual-Dezimal-Umwandlung *f*, Binär-Dezimal-Umsetzung *f*	conversion *f* binaire-décimal	преобразование из двоичной системы в десятичную

No.	English	German	French	Russian
	binary vector <PG>	*s.* B 563		
B 381	**bind / to** <a variable; said of a quantifier> <LO>	binden	lier	связывать
	binding quantity <VT>	*s.* C 2054		
B 382	**bind more strongly / to** <rules of punctuation> <GN, LO>	stärker binden, schwächer trennen <Klammereinsparungsregeln>	établir une liaison plus forte <règles de parenthèses>	связывать сильнее (теснее), предшествовать <правила скобок>
B 383	**Binet['s] function** <DI, FU>	Binetsche (Binets) Funktion *f*	fonction *f* de Binet	функция Бине
	binion <CT>	*s.* T 1077		
B 384	**binodal curve** <AG>	binodale Kurve *f*, Doppelknotenkurve *f*	courbe (quartique) *f* binodale	бинодальная кривая, кривая с двумя узловыми (двойными) точками
B 385	**binode,** biplanar double point, biplanar node <of a surface> <AG>	biplanarer Doppelpunkt (Punkt, Knoten) *m*, Biplanarpunkt *m*, Biknoten *m*, Doppelknoten *m*	point *m* double biplanaire, double point biplanaire, nœud *m* biplanaire, binode *m*	бипланарная двойная точка, двойной узел
B 386/7	**binomial,** binomial (two-term[ed]) expression <AL>	Binom *n*, binomischer (zweigliedriger) Ausdruck *m*	binôme *m*, expression *f* binôme (à deux termes)	двучлен, двухчлен, бином, двучленное выражение
	binomial array <AR, CT>	*s.* P 293		
B 388	**binomial character** <of an expression> <AL>	Zweigliedrigkeit *f*	caractère *m* binomial	двучленность
B 389	**binomial chart,** binomial [probability] paper <IN, ST>	Binomialnetz *n*, Binomialpapier *n*	diagramme (papier) *m* à échelles fonctionnelles en $\sqrt{x}$	биномиальная сетка (вероятностная бумага)
B 390	**binomial coefficient,** binomial number < $\binom{m}{n}$, C_n^m, read: binomial *m n* or *m* choose *n* > <AR>	Binomialkoeffizient *m*, Binomialzahl *f* <lies: *m* über *n*>	coefficient *m* du binôme, coefficient (symbole *m*) binomial	биномиальный коэффициент, коэффициент бинома Ньютона
	binomial curve <PJ>	*s.* W 33		
B 391	**binomial differential** <DI>	binomisches Differential *n*	différentielle *f* binôme	дифференциальный бином, биномиальный (биномный) дифференциал
B 392	**binomial differential equation** <DE>	binomische Differentialgleichung *f*	équation *f* différentielle binomiale	биномиальное дифференциальное уравнение
B 393	**binomial distribution [of Bernoulli],** binomial frequency distribution, Bernoulli['s] [binomial] distribution, binomial law <ST>	[Bernoullische] Binomialverteilung *f*, Bernoullische (binomiale) Verteilung *f*, Bernoulli-Verteilung *f*, Binomialgesetz *n*	loi *f* (distribution, répartition) *f* binomiale, loi de Bernoulli, distribution bernoullienne (de Bernoulli)	биномиальное распределение [вероятностей], биномиальный закон распределения, распределение Бернулли
B 394	**binomial equation,** pure equation <AL>	reine (binomische) Gleichung *f*	équation *f* binôme (pure)	чистое (двучленное) уравнение
B 395	**binomial expansion** <AN>	Binomialentwicklung *f*, Entwicklung *f* in eine binomische Reihe, binomische Entwicklung	développement *m* du binôme, développement binomial, formule *f* du binôme	разложение бинома, биномиальное разложение, разложение по формуле бинома
	binomial expression <AL>	*s.* B 386/7		
	binomial formula <AR>	*s.* B 403		
	binomial frequency distribution <ST>	*s.* B 393		
B 396	**binomial integral** <AN>	binomisches Integral *n*, Integral des binomischen Differentials	intégrale *f* de la différentielle binôme, intégrale binôme	интеграл от биномиального дифференциала, биномиальный интеграл
	binomial law <ST>	*s.* B 393		
	binomial number <AR>	*s.* B 390		
	binomial paper <ST>	*s.* B 389		
B 397	**binomial Poisson distribution** <ST>	binomiale Poisson-Verteilung *f*, Poisson-Binomial-Verteilung *f*	distribution *f* de Poisson binomiale	биномиальное распределение Пуассона
	binomial polynomial <AL>	*s.* A 38		
	binomial probability paper <ST>	*s.* B 389		
B 398	**binomial quadratic surd** <AL>	binomische quadratische Irrationalität *f*	binôme *m* quadratique sourd	двучленное квадратичное иррациональное выражение
B 399	**binomial series** <SS>	Binomialreihe *f*, binomische Reihe *f*	série *f* du binôme, série binomiale	биномиальный ряд
B 400	**binomial surd** <AL>	Binomiale *f*, irrationales Binom *n*, binomische Irrationalität *f*	binôme *m* irrationnel	двучленная иррациональность
B 401	**binomial surd** <sum or difference of two roots> <AL>	surdisches (imaginäres) Binom *n*	binôme *m* sourd	двучленное иррациональное выражение
B 402	**binomial test** <ST>	Binomialtest *m*	test *m* binomial	биномиальный критерий
B 403	**binomial theorem,** binomial formula <AR>	binomischer Satz (Lehrsatz) *m*, Binomialsatz *m*, binomische Formel *f*, [Newtonsche] Binomialformel *f*	formule *f* du binôme [de Newton], binôme *m* de Newton, théorème *m* du binôme, formule binomiale [de Newton], théorème binomial	бином Ньютона, формула бинома [Ньютона], биномиальная формула
B 404	**binormal,** second normal <DG>	Binormale *f*	binormale *f*	бинормаль
	binormal <DG>	*s.* B 407		
	binormal distribution <ST>	*s.* B 483		

	English	German	French	Russian
B 405	**binormal space** <TO>	binormaler Raum *m*	espace *m* binormal	бинормальное пространство
B 406	**binormal surface** <DG>	Binormalenfläche *f*	surface *f* de binormales	поверхность бинормалей
B 407	**binormal [unit] vector,** unit binormal [vector], second normal [unit] vector, unit second normal [vector], [unit] vector of binormal (second normal), binormal <DG>	Binormalenvektor *m*, Binormaleneinheitsvektor *m*, Binormalvektor *m*, Binormale *f*	vecteur *m* de la binormale, vecteur unitaire (unité) de la binormale, vecteur [unitaire] binormal, binormale *f*	[единичный] вектор бинормали, бинормаль
B 408	**biorthogonal sequence** <FA>	biorthogonale Folge *f*, Biorthogonalfolge *f*	suite *f* biorthogonale	биортогональная последовательность
B 409	**biorthogonal system** <of functions, vectors, etc.> <AN, FA>	Biorthogonalsystem *n*, biorthogonales System *n*	système *m* biorthogonal	биортогональная система
B 410	**biorthonormal expansion** <FA>	Biorthonormalentwicklung *f*	développement *m* biorthonormal	биортонормальное разложение
B 411	**biorthonormalization** <AN. FA>	Biorthonormalisierung *f*	biorthonormalisation *f*	биортонормализация
B 412	**biorthonormal system** <AN, FA>	Biorthonormalsystem *n*, normiertes Biorthogonalsystem *n*	système *m* biorthonormal (biorthogonal normé)	биортонормированная (нормированная биортогональная) система
B 413	**biparatingent** <DG, TO>	[reduziertes] Biparatingent *n*	biparatingent *m*	бипаратингенция
B 414/5	**bipartite cubic** <AG>	zweiteilige kubische Kurve *f*, elliptische Kurve *f* dritter Ordnung	cubique *f* bipartie, cubique *f* elliptique	двудольная кубическая кривая <кривая $y^2 = x(x-a)(x-b)$, $0 < a < b$>
B 416	**bipartite curve** <AY>	zweiteilige (zweigeteilte) Kurve *f*	courbe *f* bipartite, courbe ayant (possédant) deux branches distinctes	двудольная кривая
B 417	**bipartite graph** <GP>	paarer (zweifach teilbarer, bipartiter) Graph *m*, // bichromatischer Graph	graphe *m* à circuits pairs, graphe-bipartie *m*, graphe de rang 2, graphe simple (biparti, bichromatique)	парный (двудольный, бихроматический) граф, биграф, простой (четный) граф, граф паросочетаний
B 418	**bipartite number** <AB>	„bipartite number" *f*	« bipartite number » *m*	двудольное число
B 419	**bipartite transportation network** <GP, PG>	paares Transportnetz *n*	réseau *m* [de transport] biparti	двудольная транспортная сеть
B 420	**bipartition,** division in two [parts] <GE, GN>	Zweiteilung *f*	bipartition *f*, partage *m* en deux	разделение надвое (на две части), деление на две части, деление на два
	biplanar double point <AG>	*s.* B 385		
	biplanar node <AG>	*s.* B 385		
	biplane <AL, AY, PJ>	*s.* D 932		
B 421	**bipolar** <FA>	bipolare Menge *f*, Bipolare *f*	bipolaire *f*	биполяра
B 422	**bipolar co-ordinates** <GE>	Bipolarkoordinaten *fpl*, bipolare Koordinaten *fpl*	coordonnées *fpl* bipolaires	биполярные координаты
B 423	**bipolar model** <ST>	Bipolarmodell *n*	modèle *m* bipolaire	биполярная (двуполюсная) модель
B 424	**bipolar theorem** <FA>	Bipolarensatz *m*	théorème *m* de la bipolaire	теорема о биполяре
B 425	**biprism,** double prism <EG>	Doppelprisma *n*	biprisme *m*, double prisme *m*	двойная (сложная) призма, бипризма
B 426	**biprojective variety over k** <AG>	biprojektive *k*-Varietät (*k*-Mannigfaltigkeit) *f*	*k*-variété *f* biprojective, *k*-ensemble *m* biprojectif irréductible	бипроективное [неприводимое] *k*-многообразие (многообразие над *k*)
B 427	**bipyramid,** double pyramid <EG>	Doppelpyramide *f*, Dipyramide *f*, Bipyramide *f*	pyramide *f* jumelée, double pyramide, pyramide double, dipyramide *f*	двойная пирамида, дипирамида, бипирамида
	biquadratic [equation] <AL>	*s.* Q 88		
B 428/9	**biquadratic equation** <quartic equation in the form $ax^4 + bx^2 + c = 0$> <AL>	biquadratische Gleichung *f*	équation *f* biquadratique	биквадратное уравнение
B 430	**biquadratic number** <AR>	Biquadratzahl *f*; Biquadrat *n* <vierte Potenz einer Zahl>	nombre *m* biquadratique (bicarré)	биквадратное число
B 431	**biquadratic parabola** <GE>	biquadratische Parabel *f*	parabole *f* biquadratique	парабола четвертого порядка
B 432	**biquadratic residue** <AB>	biquadratischer Rest *m*	résidu *m* biquadratique	биквадратический вычет
B 433	**biquadratic trinomial** <AL>	biquadratisches Trinom *n*	trinôme *m* bicarré	биквадратный трехчлен
B 434	**biquartic curve,** curve of the eighth degree <AG>	Kurve *f* achten Grades	courbe *f* biquartique	кривая восьмой степени
B 435	**biquaternion** <AL>	Biquaternion *f*	biquaternion *m*	бикватернион, дуальный кватернион
B 436	**biquinary [number] notation (representation)** <NT>	biquinäre Zahlendarstellung (Schreibweise) *f*	notation *f* biquinaire [de nombres]	двупятеричное представление [чисел], представление чисел в двоично[-]пятеричной системе
B 437	**birational group** <AG>	birationale Gruppe *f*	groupe *m* birationnel	бирациональная группа, группа бирациональных автоморфизмов
	birational image <AG>	*s.* B 442		
B 438	**birationally equivalent curve** <AG>	birational äquivalente Kurve *f*	courbe *f* birationnellement équivalente	бирационально эквивалентная кривая, эквивалентная линия
B 439	**birationally invariant** <AG>	birational invariant	birationnellement invariant	бирационально инвариантный

B 440	**birationally isomorphic** <AG>	birational isomorph	birationnellement isomorphe	бирационально изоморфный
B 441	**birational map** <AG>	birationale Abbildung *f*	application *f* birationnelle	бирациональное отображение
B 442	**birational model,** birational image <AG>	birationales Modell *n*	modèle *m* birationnel	бирациональная модель
B 443	**birational transformation** <*e.g.*: of higher order, or higher-order> <AG>	birationale Transformation *f* <*z. B.*: höherer Ordnung>	transformation *f* birationnelle <*par exemple*: d'ordre supérieur>	бирациональное преобразование, бирациональное отображение в себя, бирациональный автоморфизм <*например*: высшего порядка>
B 444	**bird's eye perspective (view),** military perspective <DS>	Vogelperspektive *f*, Militärperspektive *f*	vue *f* à vol d'oiseau, perspective *f* militaire	перспектива (вид) с птичьего полета, военная перспектива
B 445	**biregular isomorphism** <AG>	biregulärer Isomorphismus *m*	isomorphisme *m* birégulier	бирегулярный изоморфизм
B 446	**biregular ring** <AL>	biregulärer Ring *m* [im Sinne von Arens und Kaplansky]	anneau *m* birégulier	бирегулярное кольцо
	Birkhoff['s] ergodic theorem <SP>	*s.* I 383		
B 447	**Birkhoff['s] lattice,** semimodular lattice, upper semi-modular lattice <LA>	Birkhoffscher (nach oben semimodularer, ∪-semimodularer ,(∪)-semimodularer, halbdedekindscher, semimodularer) Verband *m*; beschränkt längenendlicher semimodularer Verband	treillis *m* de Birkhoff, treillis B-modulaire (semimodulaire, semi-modulaire supérieurement, semi-mesurable), structure *f* semi-modulaire	полумодулярная (полумодулярная сверху, полудедекиндова) структура, структура Биркгофа
B 448	**Birkhoff['s] theorem** <UA>	Satz *m* von Birkhoff, Birkhoffscher Satz	théorème *m* de Birkhoff	теорема Биркгофа
B 449	**Birkhoff-Witt algebra** <AL>	Birkhoff-Wittsche Algebra *f*	algèbre *f* de Birkhoff-Witt	алгебра Биркгофа-Витта
B 450	**Birkhoff-Witt ring** <AL>	Birkhoff-Wittscher Ring *m*	anneau *m* de Birkhoff-Witt	кольцо Биркгофа-Витта
B 451	**Birkhoff-Witt theorem,** Poincaré-Witt theorem, Poincaré-Birkhoff-Witt theorem, P-B-W theorem <for Lie algebras> <AL>	Satz *m* von Birkhoff-Witt, Birkhoff-Wittscher Satz	théorème *m* de Poincaré-Birkhoff-Witt (Birkhoff-Witt)	теорема Биркгофа-Витта (Пуанкаре-Биркгофа-Витта)
B 452	**birth-and-death process, birth and death process** <SP>	Geburts- und Todesprozeß *m*, Geburten- und Todesprozeß *m*, Geburt-und-Tod-Prozeß *m*, GuT-Prozeß *m*, Zu- und Abgangsprozeß *m*	processus *m* de naissance et [de] mort	процесс гибели и размножения, процесс рождения и гибели
B 453	**birth process** <SP>	Geburtsprozeß *m*, Geburtenprozeß *m*, Geburtprozeß *m*, Zugangsprozeß *m*	processus *m* de naissance, processus d'accroissement	процесс рождения (прироста)
B 454	**birth rate** <ST>	Geburtenrate *f*, Geburtenzahl *f*	taux *m* de natalité	уровень (норма) рождаемости
B 455	**biscalar** <VT>	Biskalar *m*	biscalaire *m*	бискаляр
B 456	**bisecant** <of a space curve *or* manifold> <DG>	Sehne *f*, Bisekante *f*, Doppelsekante *f*, Sekante *f*	bisécante *f*, corde *f*	хорда
	bisecting line <EG, GE>	*s.* B 462		
B 457	**bisecting plane** <EG, GE>	Halbierungsebene *f*	bissecteur *m*, plan *m* bissecteur	биссектральная плоскость
B 458	**bisecting plane** <of a dihedron> <EG>	winkelhalbierende Ebene *f*	plan *m* bissecteur	биссектральная плоскость, плоскость-биссектриса, биссектар[ная] плоскость
B 459	**bisecting point,** midpoint <of a line segment> <EG>	Halbierungspunkt *m*, Mittelpunkt *m*	milieu *m*	середина
B 460	**bisection,** halving, division in half (two equal parts) <EG, GN>	Halbierung *f*	bissection *f*, partage *m* en deux parties égales	деление на две равные части, деление (рассечение) пополам
B 461	**bisector** <EG, IN>	Winkelhalbierer *m*	bissecteur *m*	биссектор
	bisector <EG>	*s.* B 463		
	bisector <EG, GE>	*s.* B 462		
	bisector of triangle <EG>	*s.* B 464		
B 462	**bisectrix,** bisector, bisecting line <EG, GE>	Halbierende *f*, Halbierungslinie *f*	bissectrice *f*	биссектриса, биссектор, равноделящая
B 463	**bisectrix,** bisector <of an angle> <EG>	Winkelhalbierende *f*	bissectrice *f*, ligne *f* bissectrice <d'un angle>	биссектриса, биссектор <угла>
B 464	**bisectrix of triangle,** bissectrix, bisector of triangle, bissector <EG>	Winkelhalbierende *f* [im Dreieck]	bissectrice *f* [du triangle]	биссектриса [треугольника], биссектор [треугольника]
B 465	**biserial correlation** <ST>	Zweireihenkorrelation *f*	corrélation *f* bisériale	бисериальная корреляция
B 466	**bishop problem** <in chess> <CT>	Läuferproblem *n*	problème *m* du fou	задача слона
B 467	**bispherical co-ordinates** <AY>	räumliche Bipolarkoordinaten *fpl*	coordonnées *fpl* bisphériques	бисферические координаты, биполярные координаты в пространстве
B 468	**bispinor** <VT>	Bispinor *m*	bispineur *m*	биспинор
B 469	**bispinor distribution** <VT>	Bispinordistribution *f*	bispineur-distribution *m*	биспинорное распределение
	bissector <EG>	*s.* B 464		
	bissectrix <EG>	*s.* B 464		
	bistochastic matrix <MD, ST>	*s.* D 960		
	bisymmetry <AL>	*s.* E 266		
B 470	**bit,** binary digit <ST>	Bit *n*, bit	bit *m*	бит, двоичная единица информации, двоичный разряд
	bit <NT>	*s.* B 361		

B 471/3	**bitangent,** double tangent with distinct points of contact <of a curve> <AG, DG>	Doppeltangente *f*, Tangente *f* in zwei verschiedenen Punkten einer Kurve	droite *f* bitangente, bitangente *f*	[общая] касательная в двух различных точках
B 474	**bitangent curve** <GE>	in zwei Punkten berührende Kurve, zweipunktig tangierende Kurve *f*	courbe *f* bitangente <à une courbe>	дважды касательная кривая
B 475	**bitangential curve** <of an algebraic curve> <AG>	Bitangentialkurve *f* <geht durch die Berührungspunkte der Doppeltangente>	courbe *f* bitangentielle <Cayley>	битангенциальная кривая <по отношению к алгебраичесской кривой>
B 476	**bitangent plane** <GE>	Tangentialebene *f* in zwei verschiedenen Punkten	plan *m* bitangent	[общая] касательная плоскость в двух различных точках
B 477	**biternary form** <AL>	biternäre Form *f*	forme *f* biternaire	битернарная форма
	biunique correspondence <SE>	*s.* B 330		
	bi-unique mapping <SE>	*s.* I 548		
	bi-unique mapping onto <SE>	*s.* B 330		
B 478	**bivalence** <LO>	Zweiwertigkeit *f*	bivalence *f*	дву[х]значность
B 479	**bivariate density function,** two-dimensional density function <ST>	zweidimensionale (bivariate) Dichtefunktion *f*	fonction *f* de densité à deux variables (dimensions), fonction de densité bidimensionnelle	двумерная плотность распределения
B 480	**bivariate distribution,** two-dimensional distribution, joint distribution <ST>	zweidimensionale (bivariate, bivariable) Verteilung *f*	distribution *f* à deux variables (dimensions), distribution bidimensionnelle	двумерное распределение
B 481	**bivariate distribution function,** two-dimensional distribution function <ST>	zweidimensionale (bivariate) Verteilungsfunktion *f*	fonction *f* de distribution à deux variables (dimensions), fonction de distribution bidimensionnelle	двумерная функция распределения
B 482	**bivariate frequency function,** two-dimensional frequency function <ST>	zweidimensionale (bivariate) Häufigkeitsfunktion *f*	fonction *f* de fréquence à deux variables (dimensions), fonction de fréquence bidimensionnelle	двумерная функция частот
B 483	**bivariate normal distribution,** binormal distribution, two-dimensional normal distribution <ST>	zweidimensionale (bivariate) Normalverteilung *f*, binormale Verteilung *f*	distribution *f* normale à deux variables (dimensions), distribution binormale (normale bidimensionnelle)	двумерное нормальное распределение
	bivariate point distribution <ST>	*s.* S 102		
B 484	**bivariate population,** bivariate universe, two-dimensional population (universe) <ST>	bivariate (zweidimensionale) Grundgesamtheit *f*	population *f* (univers *m*) à deux variables (dimensions), population bidimensionnelle, univers bidimensionnel	двумерная [генеральная] совокупность, двумерная популяция
B 485	**bivariate probability function,** two-dimensional probability function <ST>	zweidimensionale (bivariate) Wahrscheinlichkeitsfunktion *f*	fonction *f* de probabilité à deux variables (dimensions), fonction de probabilité bidimensionnelle	двумерная функция распределения вероятностей
	bivariate universe <ST>	*s.* B 484		
B 486	**bivector,** divector <in the three-dimensional Euclidean space> <DG, VT>	Bivektor *m*, 2-Vektor *m*, Plangröße *f*, Ebenengröße *f*, Ausdehnungsgröße *f* (schiefsymmetrischer Tensor *m*) zweiter Stufe	bivecteur *m*, grandeur *f* planaire, parallélogramme *m* lié	бивектор, двойной вектор
B 487	**bivector space** <bimodule over a field> <AL>	Doppelvektorraum *m*, Bivektorraum *m*	biespace *m* [vectoriel]	бивекторное пространство
B 488	**Björling['s] problem** <GE>	Björlingsches Problem *n*, Problem von E. G. Björling	problème *m* de Björling	задача Бьерлинга
B 489	**BK-space,** Banach['s] coordinate space, Banach['s] sequence space <FA>	BK-Raum *m*, Banachscher Koordinatenraum (Folgenraum) *m*	espace *m* [de type] BK, espace des coordonnées (suites) de Banach, espace des coordonnées (suites) banachien	координатное пространство Банаха, банахово координатное пространство, пространство последовательностей Банаха, банахово пространство последовательностей, пространство типа BK, BK-пространство
B 490	**Blackwell['s] theorem** <ST>	Theorem *n* (Satz *m*) von Blackwell, Blackwell-Theorem *n*	théorème *m* de Blackwell	теорема Блэквелла
B 491	**Blaess['] method** <DE, NU>	Verfahren *n* von Blaess, Blaesssches Verfahren	méthode *f* de Blaess	метод Блесса
B 492	**blank** <of a Turing machine> <TA>	Leerzeichen *n*	vide *m*	пустой символ
	blank <AL, AN, SE, TO>	*s.* L 279		
B 493	**Blaschke['s] function (product)** <FT>	Blaschke-Produkt *n*, Blaschke-Funktion *f*	produit *m* (fonction *f*) de Blaschke	произведение (функция) Бляшке
	Blaschke['s] selection theorem <GE>	*s.* S 257		
B 494	**Blaschke['s] symmetrization** <CS>	Blaschkesche Symmetrisierung *f*	symétrisation *f* de Blaschke	симметрирование (симметризация) Бляшке
	B-lattice <LA>	*s.* M 759		
	B. Levi['s] space <FA>	*s.* B 193		

No.	English	German	French	Russian
B 495	**B. Levi['s] theorem,** Beppo Levi['s] theorem, Levi['s] theorem, theorem of Beppo (B.) Levi <FA>	Satz *m* von Beppo (B.) Levi, Satz von Levi, [Beppo] Levischer Satz	théorème *m* de Beppo (B.) Levi	теорема Беппо (Б.) Леви, теорема Леви
	Blichfeldt['s] theorem <CS>	*s.* T 261		
	B-lim <LI>	*s.* B 589		
	B-limit <LI> ⌐<LI>	*s.* B 589		
	B-limitable sequence	*s.* B 590		
B 496	**Bliss['] condition** <VA>	Blisssche Bedingung *f*	condition *f* de Bliss	условие Блисса
B 497	**Bloch['s] constant** <FT>	Blochsche Konstante *f*	constante *f* de Bloch	константа Блоха
B 498	**Bloch['s] theorem** <FT>	Blochscher Satz *m*	théorème *m* de Bloch	теорема Блоха
B 499	**block** <GP>	Block *m*	bloc *m*	блок
B 500	**block** <of a permutation group *or* a representation> <GR>	Block *m*	bloc *m*	блок
	block <GR>	*s.* S 2520		
B 501	**block** <of a matrix> <MD>	Kästchen *n*, Block *m*	bloc *m*	блок, клетка, ящик
	block <EG>	*s.* R 280		
	block <GR>	*s.* S 2520		
B 502	**block design** <CT, ST>	Blockanlage *f*, Blockplan *m*	plan *m* en blocs	блочный план, блок-схема
	block diagram <GN>	*s.* B 60		
	blocked diagonal matrix <MD>	*s.* M 187		
B 503	**blocked lower triangular matrix** <MD>	untere halbzerfallende Matrix *f*	matrice *f* triangulaire inférieure de matrices	нижняя полураспавшаяся (клеточно-треугольная) матрица
B 504	**blocked triangular matrix,** block triangular matrix <MD>	halbzerfallende Matrix *f*, Quasidreiecksmatrix *f*, verallgemeinerte Dreiecksmatrix *f*	matrice *f* triangulaire de matrices, matrice quasi triangulaire	квазитреугольная (полураспавшаяся, клеточно-треугольная, приведенная, обобщенная треугольная) матрица
B 505	**blocked upper triangular matrix,** block upper triangular matrix <MD>	obere halbzerfallende Matrix *f*	matrice *f* triangulaire supérieure de matrices	верхняя полураспавшаяся матрица, верхняя клеточно-треугольная матрица
B 506	**block form,** partitioned form <of a matrix> <MD>	Blockform *f*, Kästchenform *f*	forme *f* partitionnée	клеточный вид
	block multiplication <MD>	*s.* D 583		
B 507	**block of number,** number group <NT>	Zahlenblock *m*, Zahlengruppe *f*	block (groupe) *m* de nombres	числовой блок, группа чисел
B 508	**block product** <of matrices> <MD>	Übermatrixprodukt *n*, Produkt *n* <von Übermatrizen>	produit *m* <de matrices> par blocs	блочное произведение <матриц>
	block triangular matrix <MD>	*s.* B 504		
	block upper triangular matrix <MD>	*s.* B 505		
B 509	**Blotto game, Blotto-game** <TG>	Blottospiel *n*	jeu *m* de Blotto	игра Блотто
B 510	**blowing-up,** σ-process, sigma-process, monoidal transformation with non-singular centre <AG>	Aufblasen *n*, Aufblasung *f*, σ-Prozeß *m*, Sigma-Prozeß *m*, monoidale Transformation *f* mit nichtsingulärem Zentrum	éclatement *m*, σ-procédé *m*, sigma-procédé *m*, transformation *f* monoïdale à centre non singulier	раздувание, σ-процесс, сигма-процесс, моноидальное преобразование с неособым центром
B 511	**bluffing** <TG>	Bluff *m*	bluff *m*	блеф
	blunder <ER>	*s.* G 434		
	blunted cone <CS, FA, PG>	*s.* U 374		
B 512	**B-measurability,** measurability in Borel's sense, measurability in the sense of Borel <ME>	B-Meßbarkeit *f*, Borel-Meßbarkeit *f*, Meßbarkeit *f* im Borelschen Sinne	B-mesurabilité *f*, mesurabilité *f* au sens de Borel, mesurabilité borélienne	измеримость по Борелю, измеримость в смысле Бореля
	(B)-measurable <ME>	*s.* B 592		
B 513	**B-measurable function,** Borel measurable function, measurable function in the sense of Borel, Borel function <ME> ⌐<TO>	B-meßbare Funktion *f*, Borel-meßbare Funktion, im Borelschen Sinne meßbare Funktion, meßbare Funktion im Sinne von Borel, bezüglich des Borelschen Maßes meßbare Funktion, B-Funktion *f*	fonction B-mesurable, fonction *f* mesurable au sens de Borel, fonction mesurable de Borel	измеримая по Борелю функция, измеримая в смысле Бореля функция, борелевская функция, B-функция
	B-measurable function	*s.* B 593		
	(B) measure B-measure <ME>	*s.* B 594		
	B-method <LI>	*s.* 1. B 595; 2. B 596		
B 514	**B-*N* pair,** Tits['] system <of a group> <AL>	*BN*-Paar *n*	*BN*-paire *f*	(*B*,*N*) пара
B 515	**Bobillier['s] point** <of a quadrangle> <GE>	Bobilliersсher Punkt *m*	point *m* de Bobillier	точка Бобийе
B 516	**Bochner['s] Fejér kernel** <AP>	Bochner-Fejér-Kern *m*, Bochnerscher Fejér-Kern	noyau *m* de Fejér bochnérien	бохнерово ядро Фейера
B 517	**Bochner['s] Fejér polynomial** <AP>	Bochner-Fejér-Polynom *n*, Bochnersches Fejér-Polynom *n*	polynôme *m* de Fejér bochnérien	бохнеров многочлен (полином) Фейера
B 518	**Bochner['s] integral** <AN>	Integral *n* nach Bochner	intégrale *f* de Bochner	интеграл Бохнера
B 519	**Bochner['s] theorem** <FA>	Satz *m* von Bochner, Bochnerscher Satz	théorème *m* de Bochner	теорема Бохнера
	Bockstein['s] boundary homomorphism <AT>	*s.* B 523		

B 520	**Bockstein['s] cohomology homomorphism,** Bockstein['s] homomorphism in cohomology <HA>	Bocksteinscher Kohomologiehomomorphismus *m*	homomorphisme *m* de Bockstein en cohomologie	когомологический гомоморфизм Бокштейна
B 521	**Bockstein cohomology operation** <AT>	Bocksteinsche Kohomologieoperation *f*	opérateur *m* de Bockstein, Bockstein *m*	когомологическая операция Бокштейна
B 522	**Bockstein['s] homology homomorphism,** Bockstein['s] homomorphism in homology <HA>	Bocksteinscher Homologiehomomorphismus *m*	homomorphisme *m* de Bockstein en homologie	гомологический гомоморфизм Бокштейна
B 523	**Bockstein['s] homomorphism,** Bockstein['s] boundary homomorphism <AT>	Bockstein-Homomorphismus *m*	homomorphisme *m* de Bockstein	гомоморфизм Бокштейна
	Bockstein['s] homomorphism in cohomology <HA>	*s.* B 520		
	Bockstein['s] homomorphism in homology <HA>	*s.* B 522		
B 524	**Bodenmiller['s] theorem** <PJ>	Bodenmillerscher Satz *m*	théorème *m* de Bodenmiller	теорема Боденмиллера
B 525	**body** <of a chain> <AT>	Träger *m*, Trägerkomplex *m*	support *m*	тело
B 526	**body,** domain <as a set with interior points contained in the closure of its open kernel> <TO>	Körper *m*	corps *m*	тело
	body <AT>	*s.* S 1304		
	body <EG>	*s.* S 1250		
B 527	**body diagonal** <EG>	Körperdiagonale *f*, Raumdiagonale *f*	diagonale *f* du corps	пространственная диагональ
	body-fixed system [of co-ordinates] <DG, GE>	*s.* B 530		
B 528	**body of constant width** <CS, GE>	Körper *m* konstanter Breite	corps *m* de largeur constante	тело постоянной ширины
B 529	**body of revolution (rotation),** solid of revolution (rotation), revolution solid, rotationally symmetric body (solid), rotation-symmetric body (solid) <EG>	Drehkörper *m*, Rotationskörper *m*, Umdrehungskörper *m*, rotationssymmetrischer Körper *m*	corps (solide) *m* de révolution, révoloïde *m*, solide (corps) à symétrie de révolution	тело вращения (вращательной симметрии), вращательно-симметричное тело, // круглое тело
B 530	**body system [of co-ordinates],** body-fixed system [of co-ordinates] <DG, GE>	körperfestes (fest mit dem Körper verbundenes) Koordinatensystem *n*	système *m* de coordonnées invariablement liées au corps, système d'axes liés au corps	система координат, связанная с телом
B 531	**Bogoliubov['s] integral equation** <IE>	Bogoljubowsche Integralgleichung *f*	équation *f* intégrale de Bogolioubov	интегральное уравнение Боголюбова
B 532	**Bogoliubov['s] theorem** <FT>	Bogoljubowscher Satz *m*, Satz von Bogoljubow	théorème *m* de Bogolioubov	теорема Боголюбова
	Bohr['s] almost periodic function <AP>	*s.* A 529		
B 533	**Bohr['s] compactification** <AP, GR, TO>	Bohr-Kompaktifizierung *f*, Kompaktifizierung *f* einer topologischen Gruppe mittels fastperiodischer Funktionen	compactifié *m* de Bohr	уплотнение Бора
B 534	**Bohr-Favard inequality** <AP> ⌐<NU>	Bohr-Favardsche Ungleichung *f*	inégalité *f* de Bohr-Favard	неравенство Бора-Фавара
	Bohr-Landau theorem	*s.* T 262		
B 535	**Bohr['s] theorem** <AP>	Satz *m* von Bohr, Bohrscher Satz	théorème *m* de Bohr	теорема Бора
	Boltzmann statistics <ST>	*s.* M 278		
B 536	**Boltz['s] method** <ER>	Boltzsches Entwicklungsverfahren *n*	méthode *f* de Boltz	метод Больца
B 537	**Bolzano-Cauchy condition** <AN>	Bolzano-Cauchysche Bedingung *f*	condition *f* de Bolzano-Cauchy	условие Больцано-Коши
	Bolzano['s] theorem <RF>	*s.* L 1017		
B 538	**Bolzano-Weierstrass theorem** <in a metric space> <TO>	Satz *m* von Bolzano-Weierstraß, Bolzano-Weierstraßscher Satz	principe *m* de Bolzano-Weierstrass, théorème *m* de Weierstrass-Bolzano (Bolzano-Weierstrass), lemme *m* de Weierstrass-Bolzano (Bolzano-Weierstrass)	теорема (принцип) Больцано-Вейерштраса <для последовательностей *или* множеств>
	Bolza['s] problem <VA>	*s.* P 1558		
B 539	**Bompiani['s] normal** <DG>	Normale *f* von Bompiani, Bompianische Normale	normale *f* de Bompiani	нормаль Бомпиани
B 540	**bond** <LA>	Komplement *n* eines Antiatoms	complément *m* d'un antiatome	дополнение антиатома
B 541	**Bonnet['s] formula** <for geodesic curvature> <DG>	Bonnetsche Formel *f*, Formel von Bonnet	formule *f* de Bonnet	формула Бонне
B 542	**Bonnet['s] mean value theorem,** second theorem (law) of the mean <for integrals> <DI>	zweiter Mittelwertsatz *m* der Integralrechnung	second théorème *m* de la moyenne, deuxième formule *f* (théorème) de la moyenne	вторая теорема о среднем, теорема Бонне о среднем значении <для интегралов>
B 543	**Bonnet['s] plane co-ordinates** <AY>	Bonnetsche Ebenenkoordinaten *fpl*	coordonnées *fpl* tangentielles du plan de Bonnet	тангенциальные координаты плоскости Бонне

B 544	**Bonnet['s] surface** <DG>	Bonnetsche Fläche *f*	surface *f* de Bonnet	поверхность Бонне
B 545/6	**Bonnet['s] theorem** <DG>	Bonnetscher Satz *m*, Satz von Bonnet	théorème *m* de Bonnet	теорема Бонне
B 547	**Boolean addition** <AL>	Boolesche Addition *f*	addition *f* booléienne (booléenne)	булево сложение
B 548	**Boolean algebra;** Boolean lattice, Boolean tribe, tribe <AL>	Boolesche Algebra *f*, Algebra *f* von Boole; Boolescher Verband *m*, Boole-Verband *m*	algèbre *f* de Boole, algèbre (booléienne, booléenne, boolienne); treillis *m* (réseau *m*, lattice *f*, ensemble *m* réticulé) de Boole, réseau booléien, réseau booléen, treillis *m* booléien	булева алгебра, алгебра Буля; решетка Буля, булева решетка
B 549	**Boolean σ-algebra,** Boolean sigma-algebra <AL, SE>	Boolesche σ-Algebra (Sigma-Algebra) *f*	σ-algèbre (sigma-algèbre) *f* booléienne (booléenne)	булева σ-алгебра (сигма-алгебра)
	Boolean algebra of sets <SE>	*s.* S 638		
B 550	**Boolean form** <AL>	Boolescher Ausdruck *m*	expression (forme) *f* booléienne (booléenne), forme de Boole	форма Буля
B 551	**Boolean function** <AL>	Boolesche Funktion *f*	fonction *f* booléienne (booléenne, binaire, de commutation, de Boole)	функция Буля, булева (булевская) функция; функция алгебры логики
	Boolean join <LA>	*s.* J 59		
	Boolean lattice	*s.* B 548		
	Boolean m-algebra <AL>	*s.* M 290		
B 552	**Boolean matrix** <in a Boolean algebra> <AL>	Boolesche Matrix *f*	matrice *f* booléienne (booléenne)	булева матрица
	Boolean matrix <GP>	*s.* T 797		
	Boolean meet <LA>	*s.* M 362		
B 553	**Boolean multiplication** <AL>	Boolesche Multiplikation *f*	multiplication *f* booléienne (booléenne)	булево умножение
B 554	**Boolean operation** <AL, LO>	Boolesche Operation *f*	opération *f* booléienne (booléenne)	булева операция
B 555	**Boolean polynomial** <AL>	Boolesches Polynom *n*	polynôme *m* booléien (booléen)	[булев] полином
B 556	**Boolean product,** product <of a set of Boolean algebras *or* Boolean matrices> <AL>	Boolesches Produkt *n*	produit *m* booléien (booléen)	булево произведение
B 557	**Boolean ring** <AL>	Boolescher Ring *m*	anneau *m* de Boole, anneau booléien (booléen, commutatif idempotent avec élément-unité)	булево кольцо, кольцо Буля
	Boolean ring of sets <SE>	*s.* F 200		
B 558	**Boolean semigroup** <AL>	Boolesche Halbgruppe *f*	demi-groupe *m* de Boole	булева полугруппа
	Boolean sigma-algebra <AL, SE>	*s.* B 549		
B 559	**Boolean space** <TO>	Boolescher Raum *m*	espace booléien (booléen, de Boole)	булево пространство
B 560	**Boolean subalgebra, Boolean sub[-]lattice,** subalgebra <of a Boolean algebra> <AL>	Boolesche Unteralgebra *f*	sous--algèbre *f* [de Boole], sous-treillis *m* booléien (booléen)	булева подалгебра
B 561	**Boolean sum** <AL>	Boolesche Summe *f*	somme *f* booléienne (booléenne)	булева сумма
	Boolean tribe <AL>	*s.* B 548		
B 562	**Boolean variable** <LO>	Boolesche Variable *f*	variable *f* booléienne (booléenne), variable *f* de commutation (Boole), variable binaire	переменная Буля, булевское переменное
B 563	**Boolean vector,** binary vector <PG>	Boolescher (binärer) Vektor *m*	vecteur *m* booléien (booléen, binaire)	вектор Буля, булев (бинарный) вектор
B 564	**Booth['s] lemniscate,** lemniscate of Booth <AG>	Boothsche Lemniskate *f*	lemniscate *f* de Booth	лемниската Бута
B 565	**Borchardt['s] modulus** <IV>	Borchardtscher Modul *m*	module *m* de Borchardt	модуль Борхардта
B 566	**border / to** <said of a determinant *or* matrix> <MD>	rändern, säumen	border	окаймлять
B 567	**border,** bank, edge <of a cut> <FT, TO>	Schnittufer *n*, Ufer *n*	lèvre *f*, bord *m* <d'une coupure>	край, край (берег) разреза, берег
B 568	**border** <of a set> <TO>	Rand *m*	intersection *f* de l'ensemble avec sa frontière	край, пересечение множества с его границей
B 569	**bordered matrix** <MD>	geränderte Matrix *f*	matrice *f* obtenue en bordant une matrice, matrice *f* bordée	окаймленная матрица
B 570	**border element** <of a set, is contained in this set> <TO>	Randpunkt *m*	point *m* frontière appartenant à l'ensemble lui-même	краевая точка; граничная точка множества, принадлежащая этому множеству
B 571	**bordering,** edging, bounding <GE>	Beranden *n*, Berandung *f*	bordage *m*, bordure *f*	окаймление, ограничение
B 572	**bordering** <of a matrix *or* determinant> <MD>	Rändern *n*, Ränderung *f*	bordage *m*	окаймление
B 573	**border-line case,** limit[ing] case; extreme case <GN>	Grenzfall *m*; Extremfall *m*	cas *m* limite; cas extrême	крайний (предельный) случай
B 574	**border of the domain** <TO>	Gebietsgrenze *f*, Grenze *f* des Gebiets	frontière *f* du domaine	граница области

No.	English	German	French	Russian
B 575	**border set** <TO>	Randmenge *f*	ensemble *m* frontière (linéaire)	граничное множество; множество, составляющее границу
B 576	**bordism** <AT>	Bordismus *m*	bordisme *m*	бордизм, бордантность
B 577	**bordism theory** <TO>	Bordismentheorie *f*	théorie *f* de cobordisme	теория бордизмов
B 578	**Borel-Cantelli['s]** lemma <ST>	Borel-Cantellisches Lemma *n*, Lemma von Borel-Cantelli	lemme *m* de Borel-Cantelli	лемма Бореля-Кантелли
B 579	**Borel-Carathéodory theorem** <FT>	Satz *m* von Borel und Carathéodory, Borel-Carathéodoryscher Satz	théorème *m* de Borel-Carathéodory (Borel et Carathéodory)	теорема Бореля-Каратеодори
B 580	**Borel['s] class** <TO>	Borel-Klasse *f*, Borelklasse *f*	classe *f* borélienne	борелевский класс
	Borel['s] direction <FT>	*s.* D 571		
B 581	**Borel['s] exceptional value,** Borel['s] lacunary value <FT>	Borelscher Ausnahmewert *m*	lacune (valeur *f* lacunaire) de Borel	борелевское исключительное значение
	Borel['s] exponential method <LI>	*s.* 1. B 595; 2. B 596		
	Borel['s] exponential method of limitation <LI>	*s.* B 596		
	Borel['s] exponential method of order *r* <LI>	*s.* 1. B 763; 2. B 764		
	Borel['s] exponential method of summation	*s.* B 595		
	Borel family <TO>	*s.* B 582		
B 582	**Borel['s] field,** field of Borel set, Borel family, family (σ-field, sigma-field) of Borel sets, algebra of Borel subsets <of a space> <generated by all open sets> <TO>	Borelscher Körper *m*, Borel-Körper *m*, Borelsches System *n*, Borelscher Mengenkörper *m*, System aller Borelschen Mengen	tribu *m*, corps *m* de Borel, corps borélien [d'ensembles], tribu borélien, famille *f* des ensembles boréliens	борелевское (борелев) поле [множеств], борелевское тело множеств
	Borel field <ME, SE, TO>	*s.* S 810		
B 583	**Borel field of events** <ST>	Borelsches Ereignisfeld *n*, Borelscher Ereigniskörper *m*	champ *m* d'événements de Borel	борелево (борелевское) поле событий, поле событий Бореля, σ-поле (сигма-поле, борелевская алгебра, σ-алгебра, сигма-алгебра) событий
	Borel function <ME>	*s.* B 513		
B 584	**Borel['s] group** <GR>	Borelsche Gruppe *f*	groupe *m* de Borel	группа Бореля
	Borelian set <SE, TO>	*s.* B 600		
B 585	**Borel['s] integral** <LI>	Borelsches Integral *n*	intégrale *f* de Borel	интеграл Бореля
	Borel['s] lacunary value <FT>	*s.* B 581		
B 586	**Borel['s] law [of large numbers]** <ST>	Borelsches Gesetz *n* [der großen Zahlen]	loi *f* [des grands nombres] de Borel	закон [больших чисел] Бореля, усиленный закон больших чисел Бореля
B 587	**Borel-Lebesgue axiom** <TO>	Borel-Lebesguesches Axiom *n*	axiome *m* de Borel-Lebesgue	аксиома (условие) Бореля-Лебега
B 588	**Borel-Lebesgue covering theorem,** theorem of Heine-Borel-Lebesgue <TO>	Borel-Lebesguescher Überdeckungssatz *m*, Überdeckungssatz von Borel-Lebesgue	théorème *m* de Borel-Lebesgue (Borel)	теорема Бореля-Лебега [о покрытии]
	Borel-Lebesgue measure <ME>	*s.* B 594		
B 589	**Borel-limit,** *B*-limit, limit by Borel's method, *B*-lim <LI>	*B*-Limes *m*, Borel-Limes *m*, Limes *m* nach dem *B*-Verfahren, *B*-lim	limite *f* [par la méthode] de Borel, *B*-limite *f*, *B*-lim	[обобщенный] предел по методу Бореля, [обобщенный] предел по Борелю, *B*-предел, *B*-lim
B 590	**Borel-limitable sequence,** *B*-limitable sequence, sequence limitable by Borel's method <LI>	*B*-limitierbare (Borel-limitierbare, nach dem *B*-Verfahren limitierbare) Folge *f*	suite *f* limitable par la méthode de Borel, suite *B*-limitable	последовательность, лимитируемая методом Бореля; *B*-лимитируемая последовательность
	Borel['s] limitation method <LI>	*s.* B 596		
	Borel['s] limitation method of *r*-th order <LI>	*s.* B 763		
B 591	**Borel['s] matrix** <FA, MD>	Borelsche Matrix *f*	matrice *f* de Borel, matrice borélienne	борелева матрица, матрица Бореля
B 592	**Borel-measurable,** measurable (B), (B)-measurable, B-measurable <ME>	Borel-meßbar, B-meßbar, (B)-meßbar	mesurable (B), mesurable B-mesurable au sens de Borel, mesurable de Borel	B-измеримый, измеримый по Борелю, измеримый в смысле Бореля
B 593	**Borel-measurable function,** B-measurable function, Borel measurable mapping <of class α>, function of class α <TO>	B-meßbare Funktion *f*, Borel-meßbare Funktion *f* <der Klasse α>	fonction *f* mesurable B <de classe α>, fonction de classe α	B-измеримая функция, борелевская функция, B-функция, B-измеримое отображение <класса α>, отображение класса α, функция класса α
	Borel measurable function <ME>	*s.* B 513		
	Borel measurable mapping <TO>	*s.* B 593		
B 594	**Borel['s] measure,** (B) measure, B-measure, Borel-Lebesgue measure <ME>	Borelsches Maß *n*, B-Maß *n*, (B)-Maß *n*	mesure *f* borélienne (de Borel), mesure (B)	мера Бореля, борелева мера

B 595	**Borel['s] method,** Borel['s] method of summation, B-method, Borel['s] exponential method [of summation], Borel['s] summation method <for divergent series> <LI>	Borelsches Summierungsverfahren (Summationsverfahren, Verfahren) *n*, B-Verfahren *n*	méthode *f* de sommation exponentielle (de Borel), méthode de Borel	метод Бореля, метод суммирования [расходящихся рядов] Бореля
B 596	**Borel['s] method [of limitation],** B-method, Borel['s] exponential method [of limitation], Borel['s] limitation method <for divergent sequences> <LI>	Borelsches Limitierungsverfahren (Verfahren) *n*, B-Verfahren *n*	méthode *f* de limitation exponentielle (de Borel), méthode de Borel	метод [образования обобщенного предела] Бореля
	Borel['s] method of r-th order <LI>	*s.* 1. B 763; 2. B 764		
	Borel['s] method of summation <LI>	*s.* B 595		
B 597	**Borel['s] polygon [of summability** <LI>	Borelsches Summationspolygon *n*	polygone *m* de sommabilité [de Borel], polygone de Borel	многогранник (полигон) [суммируемости] Бореля
B 598	**Borel['s] property** <TO>	Borelsche Überdeckungseigenschaft *f*	propriété *f* de Borel	свойство Бореля
B 599	**Borel['s] relation** <MM>	Borelsche Relation *f*	relation *f* borélienne	борелевское отношение
B 600	**Borel set,** Borelian set, Borel subset <SE, TO>	Borel-Menge *f*, Borelsche Menge *f*, B-Menge *f*, B-meßbare Menge *f*, im Borelschen Sinne meßbare Menge *f*, Borelmenge *f*	ensemble *m* borélien (de Borel), partie *f* borélienne, ensemble *m* mesurable B, ensemble *m* mesurable, ensemble *m* bien défini; ensemble *m* projectif de classe 0	множество Бореля, борелевское [множество], борелево множество, В-измеримое множество, В-множество; множество, измеримое В (по Борелю)
B 601	**Borel set of type** α <SE>	Menge *f F* der Klasse α, Menge F_α <Lebesgue>	ensemble *m* de Borel de classe α	борелевское множество порядка α
B 602	**Borel['s] sieve** <TO>	Borelsches Sieb *n*	crible *m* borélien	борелевское решето
	Borel-Stieltjes measure <ME>	*s.* R 516		
B 603	**Borel['s] structure** <TO>	Borelsche Struktur *f*	structure *f* borélienne	борелевская структура
B 604	**Borel['s] subgroup** <AL>	Borelsche Untergruppe *f*	sous-groupe *m* de Borel	борелевская подгруппа, подгруппа Бореля
	Borel subset <SE, TO>	*s.* B 600		
B 605	**Borel sum, Borel-sum,** *B*-sum, sum by Borel's method <LI>	*B*-Summe *f*, Borel-Summe *f*, Summe *f* nach dem *B*-Verfahren	somme *f* [par la méthode] de Borel, *B*-somme *f*	[обобщенная] сумма по методу Бореля, [обобщенная] сумма по Борелю, *B*-сумма
B 606	**Borel summable series,** *B*-summable series, series summable by Borel's method <LI>	*B*-summierbare (Borel-summierbare, nach dem *B*-Verfahren summierbare) Reihe *f*	série *f* sommable [par la méthode] de Borel, série *B*-sommable	ряд, суммируемый методом Бореля; *B*-суммируемый ряд
	Borel['s] summation method <LI>	*s.* B 595		
	Borel['s] summation method of r-th order <LI>	*s.* B 764		
B 607	**Borel['s] system** <generated (determined) by a system of sets> <SE>	Borelsches System *n* <von einem Mengensystem erzeugtes>, Borelsche Erweiterung *f* <eines Mengensystems>	système *m* borélien <engendré par un système d'ensembles>	борелевская система множеств, В-система <порожденная системой множеств>
	Borel['s] theorem <NT>	*s.* T 263		
B 608	**Borel['s] transformation** <LI>	Borel-Transformation *f*	transformation *f* de Borel	преобразование Бореля
B 609	**bornological dual** <TO>	bornologischer Dual *m*	dual *m* bornologique	борнологическое двойственное пространство
B 610	**bornological reflexivity** <TO>	bornologische Reflexivität *f*	réflexivité *f* bornologique	борнологическая рефлективность
B 611	**bornological set** <TO>	bornologische Menge *f*	ensemble *m* bornologique	борнологическое множество
B 612	**bornological space** <FA>	bornologischer Raum *m*	espace *m* bornologique	борнологическое пространство
B 613	**bornological topology** <FA, TO>	bornologische Topologie *f*	topologie *f* bornologique	борнологическая топология
B 614	**bornology** <FA, TO>	Bornologie *f*	bornologie *f*	борнологичность
B 615	**borrow / to** <in subtraction> <AR>	borgen	retenir, emprunter	занимать
	Borsuk['] antipodal point theorem <TO>	*s.* B 617		
	Borsuk['s] antipode theorem <TO>	*s.* B 617		
	Borsuk['s] cohomotopy group <AT>	*s.* C 1107		
B 616	**Borsuk['s] homotopy extension theorem** <AT>	Borsukscher Homotopiefortsetzungssatz *m*	théorème *m* de Borsuk <sur l'extension d'homotopie>	теорема Борсука о продолжении гомотопии
B 617	**Borsuk['s] theorem on antipodes, Borsuk-Ulam theorem,** Borsuk['s] antipode (antipodal point) theorem, fixed-point theorem of Borsuk <TO>	Satz *m* von Borsuk-Ulam (Borsuk), Borsukscher Satz über antipodentreue Abbildungen, Borsukscher Antipodensatz *m*	théorème *m* de Borsuk-Ulam, théorème sur les antipodes de Borsuk-Ulam	теорема Борсука[-Улама]

	Bortkiewicz['s] law <ST>	*s.* P 833		
B 618	**Boscovich['s] circle** <GE>	Boscovichscher Kreis *m*	cercle *m* de Boscovich	окружность Босковича
B 619	**Bose-Einstein statistics,** BE statistics <ST>	Bose-[Einstein-]Statistik *f*, Bose-Einsteinsche Statistik *f*, BE-Statistik *f*	statistique *f* de Bose-Einstein, statistique de Bose	статистика Бозе-Эйнштейна, статистика Бозе
	B_0-space <FA, TO>	*s.* F 585		
B 620	**Boss Puzzle,** 15 (Fifteen) Puzzle, Jeu de Taquin, "Chinese Fifteen" puzzle <CT>	Boss-Puzzle *n*, Fünfzehnerspiel *n*, Boss-Puzzle-spiel *n*	jeu *m* de Taquin, jeu de boss-puzzle	игра «15»
	both open and closed set <TO>	*s.* C 838		
B 621	**both right and left Artinian ring** <AL>	zweiseitig (beiderseits) artinscher Ring *m*, rechts- und links-artinscher Ring	anneau *m* artinien bilatère	артиново справа-слева кольцо
B 622	**both right and left Artinian semigroup** <AL>	zweiseitig (beiderseits) artinsche Halbgruppe *f*, rechts- und links-artinsche Halbgruppe	demi-groupe *m* artinien bilatère	артинова справа и слева полугруппа
B 623	**both right and left noetherian ring** <AL>	zweiseitig (beiderseits) noetherscher Ring *m*, rechts- und links-noetherscher Ring	anneau *m* nœthérien bilatère	нетерово справа и слева кольцо
B 624	**both right and left noetherian semigroup** <AL>	zweiseitig (beiderseits) noethersche Halbgruppe *f*, rechts- und links-noethersche Halbgruppe	demi-groupe *m* nœthérien bilatère	нетерова справа и слева полугруппа
	bottom view <DS>	*s.* W 296		
B 625	**Bott['s] periodicity** <AT>	Bottsche Periodizität *f*	périodicité *f* de Bott	периодичность Ботта
B 626	**Bott['s] periodicity theorem** <AT>	Bottscher Periodizitätssatz *m*	théorème *m* de périodicité de Bott	теорема периодичности Ботта
B 627	**bound** <of a set, sequence, *or* matrix> <DI, MD, SS>	Schranke *f*	borne *f*, limite *f*	грань, граница
	bound <FA>	*s.* O 197		
B 628	**boundary,** chain-boundary <of a chain> <AT>	Rand *m*	bord *m*	[нижняя] граница, Δ-граница
B 629	**boundary** <of a pseudo-manifold> <AT>	Rand *m*	bord *m*	край
B 630	**boundary** <of a star body> <CS, GE>	Rand *m*	coque *f*	скорлупа
B 631	**boundary** <in a boundary-value problem> <DE>	Rand *m*	frontière *f*	носитель <краевых данных>
B 632	**boundary** <of a surface> <GE, TO>	Rand *m*	bord *m*	край, граница
B 633	**boundary** <of a face> <GP>	Rand *m*	frontière *f*	граница
B 634	**boundary** <of a domain> <TO>	Rand *m*, rand	frontière *f*	граница
	boundary <TO>	*s.* F 677		
B 635	**boundary arc** <of a Riemann surface> <FT, TO>	Randbogen *m*	arc *m* frontière	дуга границы
B 636	**boundary behaviour,** behaviour at the boundary <FT>	Randverhalten *n*	allure *f* à la frontière	поведение на границе
B 637	**boundary cell** <of a cell> <AT>	Randzelle *f*, Seite *f*	cellule *f* frontière	граничная клетка (ячейка)
	boundary collocation <DE>	*s.* C 1151		
B 638	**boundary component** <FT>	Randkomponente *f*	composante *f* frontière	компонента границы
B 639	**boundary condition** <AN>	Grenzbedingung *f*	condition *f* à la frontière, condition limite (aux limites)	условие на границе, граничное (предельное) условие
B 639 a	**boundary condition** <DE, VA>	Randbedingung *f*	condition *f* aux limites	краевое условие, граничное условие
	boundary condition of the first kind <DE, PO>	*s.* D 613		
	boundary condition of the second kind <DE, PO>	*s.* N 176		
	boundary condition of the third kind <DE, PO>	*s.* T 420		
B 640	**boundary correspondence** <FT, TO>	Zuordnung *f* der Ränder, Ränderzuordnung *f*	correspondance *f* des frontières	соответствие (соотнесенность) границ
B 641	**boundary curve** <GE, TO>	Randkurve *f*, Randlinie *f*	courbe (ligne) *f* frontière	граничная кривая (линия), граница
	boundary extreme <AN>	*s.* E 897		
B 642	**boundary form** <DE>	Randform *f*	forme *f* frontière	форма, лежащая на границе фундаментальной области, граничная (краевая) форма
B 643	**boundary homomorphism** <AT>	Randhomomorphismus *m*	homomorphisme *m* bord	граничный гомоморфизм
B 644	**boundary interval** <TO>	Randstrecke *f*	segment *m* frontière	граничный отрезок
B 645	**boundary line** <of a plane figure> <EG>	Begrenzungslinie *f*	périmètre *m*	ограничивающая линия

B 646	**boundary line** <GE>	Randgerade *f*	droite *f* frontière	граничная прямая
	boundary mod. $\mathfrak{U}$ <AT>	*s.* R 689		
B 647	**boundary of the simplex** <as a point set> <TO> ┌<AT>	Simplexrand *m*	frontière *f* du simplexe	граница симплекса
	boundary of the simplex	*s.* C 1188		
B 648	**boundary operator** <AT>	Randoperator *m*; unterer Randoperator	opérateur *m* bord, opérateur de bord	граничный оператор, оператор грани, краевой оператор, оператор Δ, гомоморфизм Δ, нижний граничный оператор, оператор взятия границы
B 649	**boundary operator** <DE>	Randwertoperator *m*	opérateur *m* frontière	граничный (краевой) оператор
B 650	**boundary operator,** differential <HA>	Randoperator *m*	opérateur *m* [de] bord, différentielle *f*	граничный оператор, оператор грани, краевой оператор, дифференциал
B 651	**boundary patch** <of an open surface> <TO>	Randstück *n*		кусок (часть) границы
B 652	**boundary point** <of a convex body> <CS, GE>	Randpunkt *m*	point *m* frontière	граничная точка
B 653	**boundary point** <of a Riemannian surface> <FT>	Randpunkt *m*, Randstelle *f*	point *m* frontière	граничная точка
	boundary point <AN>	*s.* E 217		
	boundary point <TO>	*s.* F 678		
	boundary problem <DE, PO>	*s.* B 659		
	boundary problem of the first kind <DE, PO>	*s.* D 629		
	boundary problem of the third kind <DE, PO>	*s.* T 421		
B 654	**boundary relation** <AT>	Randrelation *f*	relation *f* bord	отношение границы
B 655	**boundary sesquilinear form** <DE>	Randsemibilinearform *f*	forme *f* sesquilinéaire frontière	граничная (краевая) полубилинейная форма
B 656	**boundary simplex** <AT>	Randsimplex *n*	simplexe *m* frontière	граничный симплекс
B 657	**boundary strip** <DE>	Randstreifen *m*	bande *f* de bord	граничная полоса (полоска)
B 658	**boundary value** <of a function> <DE, FT, PO>	Randwert *m*	valeur *f* au bord, valeur frontière	краевое (граничное) значение
B 659	**boundary value problem,** boundary problem <DE, PO>	Randwertproblem *n*; Randwertaufgabe *f* <besonders PO>	problème *m* aux limites, problème à la frontière	краевая задача, граничная задача
	boundary value problem of the first kind <DE, PO>	*s.* D 629		
	boundary value problem of the second kind <DE, PO>	*s.* N 180		
	boundary value problem of the third kind <DE, PO>	*s.* T 421		
B 660	**bound decision variable,** bound variable <PG, SP>	vorzeichengebundene (gebundene) Entscheidungsvariable (Steuervariable) *f*, gebundene Variable *f*		связанная переменная решения, связанная [решающая] переменная
B 661	**bound differentiability** <RF>	gebundene Differenzierbarkeit *f*	dérivabilité *f* liée	связанная дифференцируемость
B 662	**bounded above,** semi-bounded (half-bounded) above, semi-bounded (half-bounded) from above <FA>	nach (von) oben halbbeschränkt, oberhalbbeschränkt	semi[-]borné supérieurement	полуограниченный сверху
B 663	**bounded above filtration** <AL>	nach oben beschränkte Filtration *f*	filtration *f* bornée supérieurement	ограниченное сверху фильтрование
B 664	**bounded above ordered set,** bounded from above ordered set, majorized (right-bounded) ordered set, ordered set bounded on the right <SE>	nach oben beschränkte (ordnungsbeschränkte) halbgeordnete Menge *f*, nach rechts beschränkte halbgeordnete Menge	ensemble *m* ordonné majoré (borné supérieurement, borné en haut)	ограниченное сверху полуупорядоченное множество
B 665	**bounded above sequence,** majorized sequence, sequence bounded from above <SS>	nach (von) oben beschränkte Folge *f*, nach rechts beschränkte Folge	suite *f* majorée (bornée supérieurement, bornée en haut)	ограниченная сверху последовательность
	bounded below graduation <AL> ┌<FA>	*s.* G 368		
	bounded below operator	*s.* O 184		
B 666	**bounded below sequence,** minorized sequence, sequence bounded from below <SS>	nach (von) unten beschränkte Folge *f*, nach links beschränkte Folge	suite *f* minorée (bornée inférieurement, bornée en bas)	ограниченная снизу последовательность
B 667	**bounded bilinear form** <FA>	beschränkte [unendliche] Bilinearform *f*	forme *f* bilinéaire bornée	ограниченная билинейная форма
B 668	**bounded chain** <in a partially ordered set> <SE>	beschränkte Kette *f*	chaîne *f* bornée	ограниченная цепь
B 669	**bounded closed set** <TO>	beschränkte abgeschlossene Menge *f*	ensemble *m* fermé borné (à distance fini)	ограниченное замкнутое множество
B 670	**bounded domain** <PG>	beschränkter Bereich *m*; beschränktes Gebiet *n*	domaine *m* borné	ограниченная область

No.	English	German	French	Russian
B 671	**bounded existential quantifier** <LO>	eingeschränkter Partikularisator *m*, Existenzquantifikator *m* mit begrenztem Bereich	quantificateur *m* existentiel relativisé (limité)	ограниченный квантор существования
	bounded from above ordered set <SE>	*s.* B 664		
B 672	**bounded from above set,** bounded on the right set, right-bounded set <SE>	nach oben beschränkte Menge *f*	ensemble *m* majoré (borné supérieurement)	ограниченное сверху множество, мажорированное множество
	bounded from below set <SE>	*s.* S 639		
	bounded from below subset <SE>	*s.* S 2179		
B 673	**bounded function** <AN>	beschränkte Funktion *f*	fonction *f* bornée	ограниченная функция
	bounded left Engel element <GR>	*s.* L 438		
B 674	**bounded-like function,** beschränktartig function <FT>	beschränktartige Funktion *f*	fonction *f* quasi (de type) bornée	функция типа ограниченной; функция, подобная ограниченной
B 675	**bounded-like surface,** beschränktartig surface <AN>	beschränktartige Fläche *f*	surface *f* de type borné, surface quasi bornée	поверхность, подобная ограниченной; поверхность типа ограниченной
B 676	**boundedly convergent series,** restrictedly convergent series <SS>	beschränkt konvergente Reihe *f*	série *f* convergente dans un sens restreint	ограниченно сходящийся ряд
B 677	**bounded matrix** <AN>	beschränkte [unendliche] Matrix *f*	matrice *f* bornée	ограниченная матрица
	σ-bounded measurable set <ME>	*s.* S 811		
B 678	**bounded minimization** <LO>	beschränkte Minimierung *f*	minimisation *f* limitée	ограниченная минимизация
B 679	**boundedness** <AN, SS>	Beschränktheit *f*	propriété *f* d'être borné	ограниченность
	boundedness from one side <FA>	*s.* S 334		
B 680	**boundedness theorem** <MM>	Beschränktheitssatz *m*		теорема ограниченности
	bounded on the left set <SE>	*s.* S 639		
	bounded on the right set <SE>	*s.* B 672		
B 681	**bounded quantification** <LO>	eingeschränkte Quantifizierung *f*	quantification *f* limitée	ограниченная квантификация
B 682	**bounded quantifier,** quantifier with a limited range <LO>	eingeschränkter Quantor *m*, Quantifikator *m* mit begrenztem Bereich	quantificateur *m* relativisé (limité)	ограниченный квантор
	bounded right Engel element <GR>	*s.* R 1215		
B 683	**bounded sequence,** limited sequence <SS>	beschränkte Folge; beschränkte Zahlenfolge *f*	suite *f* bornée	ограниченная последовательность (варианта)
B 684	**bounded set** <TO>	beschränkte Menge (Punktmenge) *f*	ensemble *m* borné	ограниченное [точечное] множество
	bounded set <SE>	*s.* O 288		
B 685	**bounded topology** <AL>	beschränkte Topologie (Ringtopologie) *f*	topologie *f* bornée	ограниченная топология
B 686	**bounded universal quantifier** <LO>	eingeschränkter Generalisator *m*, Allquantifikator *m* mit begrenztem Bereich	quantificateur *m* universel relativisé (limité)	ограниченный квантор всеобщности
B 687	**bounded variation,** limited variation <of a <function> <AN>	beschränkte Variation (Schwankung, Gesamtschwankung) *f*	variation *f* [totale] bornée, oscillation *f* [totale] limitée	ограниченная вариация, ограниченное колебание, // ограниченное изменение
B 688/9	**bounded variation,** finite variation <RF>	beschränkte Variation *f*, endliche Variation (Schwankung *f*)	variation *f* bornée, variation finie	ограниченная (конечная) вариация, конечное колебание
B 690	**bound homotopy** <TO>	gebundene Homotopie *f*	homotopie *f* liée	связанная гомотопия
	bounding <GE>	*s.* B 571		
	bounding chain <AT>	*s.* C 465		
B 691	**bounding cycle** <AT>	berandender Zyklus *m*	cycle *m* bordant	ограничивающий цикл
B 692	**bounding manifold** <AT>	berandende Mannigfaltigkeit *f*	variété *f* bordante	окаймляющее многообразие
B 693	**bounding parallel** <of a hyperbolic plane> <GE>	randparallele (parallele) Gerade *f*	parallèle *f*	параллельная прямая
B 694	**bounding polyhedral surface** <GE>	polyedrische Randfläche *f*	surface *f* polyédrique frontière	граничная многогранная поверхность
B 695	**bounding surface** <GE, TO>	Randfläche *f*	surface *f* frontière	граничная поверхность
B 696	**bound occurrence** <of a variable> <LO>	gebundenes Vorkommen *n*	occurrence *f* liée	связанное вхождение
B 697	**bound osculating space** <DG>	gebundener Schmiegraum *m*, Schmiegraum im engeren Sinne	espace *m* osculateur lié	связанное соприкасающееся пространство
B 698	**bound term** <LO>	gebundener Term *m*	terme *m* lié	связанный терм
B 699	**bound variable,** apparent (dummy) variable <GN, LO>	gebundene Variable (Veränderliche) *f*	variable *f* liée	связанная (мнимая, кажущаяся, фиктивная) переменная
	bound variable <PG, SP>	*s.* B 660		
B 700	**bound vector,** fixed vector, localized vector, field vector <VT>	gebundener Vektor *m*, an einen Punkt gebundener Vektor, Ortsvektor *m*	vecteur *m* appliqué (fixe, lié), vecteur lié à un point, vecteur localisé [en un point], bipoint *m*	связанный (приложенный) вектор
B 701	**Bouniakowski['s] conjecture, Buniakowsky['s] conjecture**<NT>	Bunjakowskische Vermutung *f*	hypothèse *f* de Bouniakowsky	гипотеза (предположение) Буняковского

	Bouniakowski-Schwarz (Bouniakowsky-Schwarz) inequality <AN>	*s.* S 167		
	Bourbaki['s] filter <SE>	*s.* F 223		
B 702	**Bour['s] problem** <DG>	Boursches Problem *n* [isometrischer Flächen]	problème *m* de Bour	задача Бура
B 703	**Boutin['s] point** <EG>	Boutinscher Punkt *m*	point *m* de Boutin	точка Бутэна
	bow compass <GE, IN>	*s.* 1. C 1332; 2. D 791		
	bow divider <GE, IN>	*s.* D 791		
	bowl model <ST>	*s.* U 450		
B 704	**box** <of the paper band of a Turing machine> <FO, IN>	Abschnitt *m*	champ *m*	клетка
B 705	**box argument,** box principle, Dirichlet['s] [box] principle, Dirichlet['s] principle of boxes, chest of drawers argument, kitchen drawer principle, drawer principle of Dirichlet, Dedekind['s] pigeon-hole principle, pigeon-hole principle, shoe box principle <CT>	Dirichletscher Schubkastensatz *m*, [Dirichletsches] Schubkastenprinzip *n*, Schubkastenprinzip von Dirichlet, Schubfachprinzip *n*, [Dirichletscher] Schubfachschluß *m*	principe *m* de Dirichlet-Schläfli, principe des boîtes (tiroirs), méthode *f* des tiroirs de Dirichlet	принцип ящиков (Дирихле), метод выдвижных ящиков Дирихле, принцип ящиков Дирихле
	box[ed] head, box-head <GN>	*s.* T 3		
	box heading <GN>	*s.* T 3		
	box principle <CT>	*s.* B 705		
	B_p almost-periodic function <AP>	*s.* G 132		
	B_p almost-periodic space <AP>	*s.* S 1329		
	brace / to <GN>	*s.* P 2078		
B 706	**brace,** curly bracket, bracket {...} <GN>	geschweifte Klammer *f*, // geschwungene (zusammenfassende) Klammer {...}	accolade *f* {...}	фигурная скобка, парантез {...}
B 707	**brachistochrone,** curve of shortest descent <VA>	Brachistochrone *f*, // Brachystochrone *f*	brachistochrone *f*, courbe *f* brachistochrone, // brachystochrone *f*	брахистохрона. кривая наикратчайшего (наискорейшего, быстрейшего, кратчайшего) спуска
B 708	**brachistochrone problem** <VA>	Problem *n* der Brachistochrone	problème *m* de la brachistochrone	задача о брахистохроне
	bracket / to <GN>	*s.* P 2079		
	bracket <GN>	*s.* 1. B 706; 2. P 162; 3. S 1551		
B 709	**bracketed expression,** expression (aggregation) in brackets <(...) *or* [...]>; expression (aggregation) in parentheses <(...)>; expression (aggregation) in braces <{...}> <GN>	Klammerausdruck *m*	expression *f* en parenthèses	взятое в скобки
B 710	**bracket operation,** Lie['s] multiplication, commutation, Lie['s] bracket, derivative <in a Lie algebra> <AL>	Klammeroperation *f*, Kommutatorbildung *f*, Liesche Multiplikation *f*	opération *f* « crochet », opération de crochet, crochet *m* de Lie, crochet	скобочная операция, умножение Ли
	brackets closed <LO>	*s.* R 1165		
B 711	**Brahmagupta['s] formula** <for the inscribed tetragon> <EG>	Brahmaguptasche Formel *f*	formule *f* de Brahmagupta	формула Бра[х]магупты
B 712	**braid** <TO>	Zopf *m*	tresse *f*	коса
B 713	**braid group,** Artin['s] braid group <AT>	Zopfgruppe *f*	groupe *m* de tresses	группа кос
B 714	**braid invariant** <AT>	Zopfinvariante *f*	invariant *m* de tresses	инвариант кос
B 715	**branch** <of order *n*> <of an algebraic curve> <AG>	Zweig *m* <*n*-ter Ordnung>	branche *f* <d'ordre *n*>	ветвь <*n*-го порядка>
B 716	**branch** <of a curve> <AN, GE>	Kurvenzweig *m*, Zweig *m*, Kurvenast *m*, Ast *m*, Kurvenzug *m*, Zug *m*, Zyklus *m* <Halphen>	branche *f* <d'une courbe>	ветвь кривой, ветвь
B 717	**branch,** regular branch <of a monogenic function> <FT>	Zweig *m*, regulärer Zweig	branche *f*, branche régulière	ветвь, регулярная ветвь
	branch <GP>	*s.* 1. E 12; 2. M 33		
B 718	**branch and bound method** <PG>	Verzweigungsmethode *f*, Verzweigungsverfahren *n*, Methode *f* „branch and bound", „branch-and-bound"-Methode *f*	méthode *f* « branch and bound »	метод ветвления и ограничения
B 719	**branch curve** <AG>	Verzweigungskurve *f*	courbe *f* de ramification	кривая разветвления
B 720	**branch cut,** branch line <of a Riemann surface> <FT>	Verzweigungsschnitt *m*, Schnitt *m*	coupure *f*, ligne *f* de passage	разрез
B 721	**branch divisor** <of a linear series> <AG>	Verzweigungsdivisor *m*	diviseur *m* de ramification	дивизор ветвления
	branched function <FT>	*s.* M 1083		
B 722	**branched solution** <FT>	verzweigte Lösung *f*	solution *f* ramifiée	разветвленное решение

No.	English	German	French	Russian
B 723	**branched value,** ramified value <FT>	verzweigter Wert *m*	valeur *f* ramifiée	разветвленное значение
B 724	**branch element** <of a cover complex> <AT>	Verzweigungselement *n*	élément *m* de ramification	элемент разветвления
B 725	**branching;** ramification; furcation; forking; bifurcation <GN>	Verzweigung *f*; Verästelung *f*; Aufzweigung *f*; Aufspaltung *f*; Gabelung *f*; Gabelteilung *f*; Bifurkation *f*	ramification *f*; embranchement *m*; branchement *m*; dérivation *f*; bifurcation *f*; dédoublement *m*	ветвление; разветвление; вилка; раздваивание, раздвоение, бифуркация
	branching <FT>	*s.* R 63		
B 726	**branching law** <for a Lie group> <GR>	Verzweigungsgesetz *n*	loi *f* de ramification	правило ветвления
	branching point <FT>	*s.* B 733		
B 727	**branching process, branching stochastic process** <SP>	Verzweigungsprozeß *m*, Vervielfachungsprozeß *m*, verzweigter [stochastischer] Prozeß *m*	processus *m* à ramification[s], processus [stochastique] ramifié (de ramification), processus d'embranchement, processus aléatoire branchu (branché)	ветвящийся процесс, ветвящийся случайный (стохастический) процесс
B 728	**branch line** <FT>	Verzweigungslinie *f*	ligne *f* de branchement	линия ветвления (разветвления)
	branch line <FT>	*s.* B 720		
B 729	**branch of hyperbola** <AY>	Hyperbelzweig *m*, Hyperbelast *m*, Zweig (Ast) *m* der Hyperbel	branche *f* de l'hyperbole	ветвь гиперболы
B 730	**branch of mathematics** <GN>	Zweig *m* der Mathematik	branche *f* des mathématiques	раздел математики
B 731	**branch place** <AL>	Verzweigungsstelle *f*	point *m* de ramification	точка разветвления
B 732	**branch point,** ramification point <e.g. of a curve> <AG, TO>	Verzweigungspunkt *m*	point *m* de ramification	точка ветвления
B 733	**branch point, branch-point,** point of ramification, ramification (branching) point <of a many-valued analytic function, Riemannian surface> <FT>	Verzweigungspunkt *m*, Windungspunkt *m*, Verzweigungsstelle *f*	point *m* de branchement (ramification), point critique	точка разветвления (ветвления); точка многозначного характера
B 734	**branch point,** ramification point <in the sense of Menger> <of a curve> <TO>	Verzweigungspunkt *m*, Punkt *m* von mindestens dritter Ordnung	point *m* de ramification	точка ветвления
B 735	**branch point of order *k*—1,** algebraic branch point of order *k*—1, ramification point of order *k*—1 <in the case of finite number of sheets> <FT>	[algebraischer] Verzweigungspunkt *m* der Ordnung *k*—1, [algebraische] Verzweigungsstelle *f* der Ordnung *k*—1	point *m* de ramification d'ordre *k*—1	точка разветвления порядка *k*—1
	branch point of the essential singular type <FT>	*s.* E 518		
B 736	**branch surface** <AG>	Verzweigungsfläche *f*	surface *f* de ramification	поверхность разветвления
B 737	**Brandt['s] groupoid,** connected groupoid <AL>	Brandtsches Gruppoid *n*, Brandtsche Kategorie *f*, zusammenhängendes Gruppoid <Gruppoid im Sinne von Ehresmann, das aus genau einer Komponente besteht>	groupoïde *m* au sens de Brandt, groupoïde transitif de Brandt	группоид Брандта, брандтова категория, связный группоид
B 738	**Brandt semigroup** <AL>	Brandtsches Gruppoid *n* mit Null	demi-groupe *m* de Brandt	полугруппа Брандта
B 739	**Brandt-Snedecor formula** <ST>	Brandt-Snedecorsche Formel *f*, Brandt-Snedecor-Formel *f*	formule *f* de Brandt-Snedecor	формула Брандта-Снедекора
B 740	**Brassine['s] theorem** <EG>	Brassinescher Satz *m*	théorème *m* de Brassine	теорема Брасина
B 741	**Brauer['s] construction** <NO>	Brauersche Konstruktion *f*	construction *f* de Brauer	построение Брауэра
B 742	**Brauer['s] group,** group of classes of algebras <AL>	Brauersche Gruppe (Algebrenklassengruppe) *f*, Algebrenklassengruppe *f*	groupe *m* de Brauer	группа Брауэра
B 743	**Brauer-Siegel theorem** <AB>	Brauer-Siegelscher Satz *m*	théorème *m* de Brauer-Siegel	теорема Брауэра-Сигеля
B 744	**Braun['s] method** <of numerical integration> <DE, NU>	Methode *f* von [E.] Braun, Braunsche Methode <zur numerischen Integration>	méthode *f* de Braun	метод Брауна
	Bravais['s] coefficient [of correlation] <ST>	*s.* P 348		
	Bravais['s] correlation coefficient <ST>	*s.* P 348		
B 745	**breadth,** width <of a plane figure> <EG>	Breite *f*	largeur *f*	ширина
B 746	**breadth** <of a convex body> <GE>	Breite *f*, eindimensionales Quermaß *n*	largeur *f*	ширина
B 747	**break,** break point; knee <of a curve> <NU>	Knick *m*, Knickstelle *f*, Knickpunkt *m*; Abknikken *n*; Knie *n*	coude *m*, pli *m*; genou *m*	излом, точка излома; изгиб, загиб; зубчик
	break[ing]-off <SS>	*s.* T 1033		
	break point <NU>	*s.* B 747		
B 748	**Brelot-Cartan['s] theorem** <PO>	Satz *m* von Brelot-Cartan, Brelot-Cartanscher Satz	théorème *m* de Brelot-Cartan	теорема Брело-Картана

No.	English	German	French	Russian
	Brelot['s] method <PO>	*s.* P 508		
B 749	**Brianchon['s] hexagon** <GE>	Brianchonsches Sechseck (Sechsseit) *n*	hexagone *m* de Brianchon	шестисторонник Брианшона
B 750	**Brianchon['s] point,** point of Brianchon <AY>	Brianchonscher Punkt *m*, Brianchon-Punkt *m*	point *m* de Brianchon	точка Брианшона
B 751	**Brianchon['s] theorem** <for a conic *or* a pair of points> <AY> ⌐<GP>	Satz *m* von (des) Brianchon, Brianchonscher Satz	théorème *m* de Brianchon	теорема Брианшона
B 752	**bridge,** piece, component	Gespinst *n*, Glied *n*, Blatt *n*	pièce *f*	кусок
	bridge <GP>	*s.* S 545		
B 753	**bridging** <in addition> <AR>	Dekadensprung *m* <Fall, daß bei der Addition einer einstelligen Zahl zu einer anderen die Summe eine Stelle mehr hat>	cas *m*, que l'addition d'un nombre à *n* chiffres à un autre à *n* ou moins chiffres donne un nombre de *n* + 1 chiffres	случай при сложении однозначного числа с другим, когда сумма лежит в следующем десятке
	bridging <AR, NU>	*s.* C 150		
B 754	**Briggsian (Briggs['s]) logarithm,** common (decimal, vulgar) logarithm, logarithm to [the] base 10, lg, $\log_{10}$, // log <AR, NU>	Briggsscher (gemeiner, dekadischer) Logarithmus *m*, Zehnerlogarithmus *m*, Logarithmus zur Basis 10, Dezimallogarithmus *m*, dezimaler Logarithmus, lg, $\log_{10}$, // Briggscher Logarithmus, log	logarithme *m* décimal (briggsien, de Briggs), logarithme vulgaire, logarithme à base 10, lg, $\log_{10}$, // log	бриггов (десятичный, обыкновенный) логарифм, логарифм по основанию 10, lg, $\log_{10}$, // log
	Brill and Noether theorem <AG>	*s.* R 937		
B 755/6	**brilliant point** <GE>	Glanzpunkt *m*	point *m* brillant (radiant)	зеркальная точка
B 757	**Brill-Noether theory of algebraic functions** <AL, FT>	Brill-Noethersche Theorie *f* der algebraischen Funktionen	théorie *f* des fonctions algébriques d'A. Brill et M. Noether	теория Брилля-Нетера об алгебраических функциях
B 758	**Bring-Jerrard normal form** <of the quintic equation> <AL>	Bring-Jerrardsche Normalform (Gleichung) *f*	équation *f* de Bring-Jerrard	нормальная форма Бринга-Жеррара
B 759	**Brinkley['s] theorem** <EG>	Brinkleyscher Satz *m* [vom schiefen Kreiszylinder]	théorème *m* de Brinkley	теорема Бринкли
B 760	**Briot-Bouquet [differential] equation** <DE>	Briot-Bouquetsche Differentialgleichung *f*	équation *f* [différentielle] de Briot-Bouquet	[дифференциальное] уравнение Брио-Буке
	(B,r)lim, B_r-lim <LI>	*s.* B 761		
B 761	**(B,r) limit, B_r-limit,** limit by Borel's method of order *r*, (*B*,*r*) lim, B_r-lim <LI>	B_r-Limes *m*, (*B*,*r*)-Limes *m*, Limes *m* nach dem B_r-Verfahren, B_r-lim	limite *f* [par la méthode] de Borel d'ordre *r*, (*B*,*r*)-limite *f*, B_r-limite *f*, B_r-lim	[обобщенный] предел по методу Бореля *r*-го порядка, [обобщенный] предел по Борелю *r*-го порядка
B 762	**(B,r) limitable sequence, B_r-limitable sequence,** sequence limitable by Borel's method of order *r* <LI>	B_r-limitierbare ((*B*,*r*)-limitierbare, nach dem B_r-Verfahren limitierbare) Folge *f*	suite *f* limitable par la méthode de Borel d'ordre *r*, suite (*B*,*r*)-limitable, suite B_r-limitable	последовательность, лимитируемая методом Бореля *r*-го порядка; (*B*,*r*)-лимитируемая последовательность
B 763	**(B,r) method, B_r-method,** Borel['s] method of *r*-th order, Borel['s] exponential method of order *r*, Borel['s] limitation method of *r*-th order <for divergent sequences> <LI>	B_r-Verfahren *n*, (*B*,*r*)-Verfahren *n*, Borelsches Limitierungsverfahren *n* der Ordnung *r*	méthode *f* [de limitation] de Borel d'ordre *r*, méthode de limitation exponentielle d'ordre *r*, méthode (*B*,*r*), méthode B_r	метод [образования обобщенного предела] Бореля *r*-го порядка
B 764	**(B,r) method, B_r-method,** Borel['s] method of *r*-th order, Borel['s] exponential method of order *r*, Borel['s] summation method of *r*-th order <for divergent series> <LI>	B_r-Verfahren *n*, (*B*,*r*)-Verfahren *n*, Borelsches Summierungsverfahren *n* der Ordnung *r*	méthode *f* de sommation exponentielle (de Borel) d'ordre *r*, méthode de Borel d'ordre *r*, méthode (*B*,*r*), méthode B_r	метод Бореля *r*-го порядка, метод суммирования [расходящихся рядов] Бореля *r*-го порядка
B 765	**Brocard['s] angle** <EG>	Brocardscher Winkel *m*	angle *m* de Brocard	угол Брокара
B 766	**Brocard['s] circle** <EG>	Brocardscher Kreis *m*	cercle *m* de Brocard	окружность Брокара
B 767	**Brocard['s] diameter** <EG>	Brocardscher Durchmesser *m*	diamètre *m* de Brocard	диаметр Брокара
B 768	**Brocard['s] ellipse** <EG>	Brocardsche Ellipse *f*	ellipse *f* de Brocard	эллипс Брокара
B 769	**Brocard['s] point** <EG>	Brocardscher Punkt *m*	point *m* de Brocard, point brocardien	точка Брокара
B 770	**Brocard['s] triangle** <first *or* second> <EG>	Brocardsches Dreieck *n* <erstes *oder* zweites>	triangle *m* de Brocard <premier *ou* deuxième>	треугольник Брокара <первый *или* второй>
B 771	**Brody['s] formula (law)** <ST>	Brodysches Wachstumsgesetz (Gesetz) *n*, Brodysche (Brodys) Formel *f*	loi (formule) *f* de Brody	закон [роста] Броди, формула Броди
	Brody['s] growth function <ST>	*s.* V 139		
	broken bracket <GN>	*s.* P 733		
B 772	**broken diagonal** <of a magic square> <CT>	gebrochene Diagonale *f*, Sparrenkoppel *f*	diagonale *f* brisée	ломаная диагональ
B 773	**broken extremal** <VA>	gebrochene (geknickte) Extremale *f*	extrémale *f* brisée	ломаная экстремаль
B 774	**broken focal distance** <of a quadric> <AG>	gebrochene Fokaldistanz *f* <Staudt>	distance *f* focale brisée	ломаное фокальное расстояние
B 775	**broken line,** [open] polygon <GE>	Streckenzug *m*, Polygonzug *m*, Polygon *n*	ligne *f* polygonale (brisée), cheminement *m* polygonal, polygone *m*	ломаная, ломаная (полигональная) линия
B 776	**Bronwin['s] formulas** <for approximate integration> <AX, DI, NU>	Bronwinsche Formeln *fpl*	formules *fpl* de Bronwin	формулы Бронвина
	Brouwer-Čech dimension <TO>	*s.* S 1957		
	Brouwer degree <AT>	*s.* D 185		

B 777	**Brouwer['s] fixed point theorem, Brouwer['s] fixed-point theorem,** Brouwer['s] theorem <TO>	Brouwerscher Fixpunktsatz *m*	théorème *m* de Brouwer, théorème *m* du point fixe de Brouwer	принцип (теорема) Брауэра о неподвижной точке, принцип (теорема) Боля-Брауэра, теорема Брауэра о неподвижных точках [[n-мерного] элемента]
	Brouwer['s] generalization of the Jordan curve theorem <TO>	*s.* J 84		
B 778	**Brouwerian algebra, Brouwerian lattice** <AL>	Brouwersche Algebra *f*, subjunktiver (Brouwerscher) Verband *m*	treillis *m* de Brouwer	решетка (структура, алгебра) Брауэра, брауэровская алгебра, субъюнктивная решетка
	Brouwerian logic <LO>	*s.* I 855		
B 779	**Brouwerian semigroup** <AL>	Brouwer-Halbgruppe *f*	demi-groupe *m* de Brouwer	полугруппа Брауэра
	Brouwer['s] invariance of domain <TO>	*s.* I 859		
B 780	**Brouwer['s] reduction theorem** <TO>	Reduktionssatz *m* von Brouwer, Brouwerscher Reduktionssatz *m*	théorème *m* de réduction de Brouwer	теорема редукции Брауэра
	Brouwer['s] theorem <TO>	*s.* B 777		
B 781	**Brouwer['s] theorem on the invariance of domain,** invariance of domain theorem <TO>	Satz *m* von der Gebietsinvarianz	théorème *m* de l'invariance de domaine	теорема Брауэра об инвариантности области, теорема об инвариантности внутренних точек
	Brownian movement <SP>	*s.* W 253		
	Brownian process <SP>	*s.* W 253		
B 782	**Brown-McCoy radical** <AL>	Radikal *n* im Sinne von [Brown-]McCoy, Brown-McCoy-Radikal *n*	radical *m* de Baer et McCoy, radical *m* de Brown-McCoy	радикал Брауна-Маккоя
B 783	**(B,r) sum, B_r-sum,** sum by Borel's method of r-th order <LI>	B_r-Summe *f*, (B,r)-Summe *f*, Summe *f* nach dem B_r-Verfahren	somme *f* [par la méthode] de Borel d'ordre r, B_r-somme *f*	[обобщенная] сумма по методу Бореля r-го порядка, [обобщенная] сумма по Борелю r-го порядка
B 784	**(B,r) summable series, B_r-summable series,** series summable by Borel's method of r-th order <LI>	B_r-summierbare ((B,r)-summierbare, nach dem B_r-Verfahren summierbare) Reihe *f*	série *f* sommable par la méthode de Borel d'ordre r, série (B,r)-sommable, série B_r-sommable	ряд, суммируемый методом Бореля r-го порядка; (B,r)-суммируемый ряд, B_r-суммируемый ряд
B 785	**Bruhat['s] decomposition** <AL>	Bruhatsche Zerlegung *f*	décomposition *f* de Bruhat	разложение Брюа
B 786	**Bruhat['s] function** <AL>	Bruhat-Funktion *f*	fonction *f* de Bruhat	функция Брюа
	Brun['s] method <AB>	*s.* V 186		
	Brunn-Minkowski theorem <CS>	*s.* T 264		
B 787	**Brunn['s] theorem** <FT>	Brunnscher Satz *m*	théorème *m* de Brunn	теорема Брунна
	Bruns['] expansion <ST>	*s.* B 788		
B 788	**Bruns['] series,** Bruns['] expansion <ST>	Brunssche Reihe (Entwicklung) *f*	série *f* (développement *m*) de Bruns	ряд (разложение) Брунса
	Brun['s] sieve method <AB>	*s.* V 186		
B 789	**Brun['s] theorem on prime twins** <NT>	Brunscher Satz *m* über Primzahlzwillinge	théorème *m* de Brun sur les nombres premiers jumeaux	теорема Бруна о простых близнецах
	B-space <FA>	*s.* B 48		
	B-space having a base <FA>	*s.* B 49		
	B-sum <LI>	*s.* B 605		
	B_α-sum <LI>	*s.* M 675		
	B-summable series <LI>	*s.* B 606		
	B.T.-group <AL>	*s.* B 68		
B 790	**Budan['s] theorem,** theorem of Fourier-Budan <for zeros of polynomials> <AL>	Budan-Fouriersche Regel *f*, Budan-Fouriers Satz *m*, Theorem *n* (Zeichenregel *f*) von Budan-Fourier	théorème *m* (règle *f*) de Budan-Fourier	теорема (правило) Бюдана-Фурье
B 791	**Buffon['s] experiment** <ST>	Buffonsches Experiment *n*, Experiment von Buffon	expérience *f* de Buffon	опыт (эксперимент) Бюффона
B 792	**Buffon['s] needle problem, Buffon['s] problem [of the needle],** needle problem <ST>	[Buffonsches] Nadelproblem *n*, Aufgabe *f* von Buffon, Buffonsche Aufgabe	problème *m* de l'aiguille [de Buffon], problème de Buffon, problème des aiguilles	задача Бюффона об игле, задача о бросании иглы, задача Бюффона
B 793	**bulk sampling** <ST>	Stichprobennahme *f* aus der Masse, Stichprobennahme aus dem Gesamten (Haufen)	échantillonnage *m* global (sur l'ensemble)	выбор из кучи (массы), изъятие выборки из массы
B 794	**bullet nose curve** <GE>	Kohlenspitzenkurve *f*	kohlenspitzencurve *f*	кривая, имеющая уравнение $x^2y^2 = a^2y^2 - b^2x^2$
	bunch <AG, AY>	*s.* L 831		
	bunch <AY>	*s.* B 796		
	bunch chart <NO>	*s.* N 164		
	bunch graph <NO>	*s.* N 164		
	bunch map <NO>	*s.* N 164		
B 795	**bunch of varieties** <AG>	Bund *m* <Vereinigung irreduzibler projektiver Mannigfaltigkeiten>	bouquet *m* de variétés	связка многообразий
	bunch of varieties <AG>	*s.* A 458		
	bunch of varieties normally algebraic over *k* <AG>	*s.* K 185		

	English	German	French	Russian
B 796	**bundle,** connective, sheaf, star, bunch <AY>	Bündel *n*	réseau *m*, étoile *f*, gerbe *f*, famille *f* [biparamétrique]	связка
	bundle <AT>	*s.* 1. F 160; 2. T 692; 3. V 98		
	bundle equivalent to the product bundle <AT>	*s.* T 993		
B 797	**bundle map,** mapping of bundles, fibre preserving map, morphism of bundles <TO>	Bündelabbildung *f*	morphisme *m* d'espaces fibrés	отображение произведений; отображение, сохраняющее связки; отображение с сохранением связок
B 798	**bundle of circles,** sheaf (star) of circles <AY>	Kreisbündel *n*	réseau *m* (étoile *f*, gerbe *f*) de cercles	связка окружностей
B 799	**bundle of coefficients,** system of local coefficients <for homology or cohomology groups> <AT>	Bündel *n* von Koeffizienten	système *m* de coefficients locaux	система локальных коэффициентов
B 800	**bundle of complexes,** sheaf (star) of complexes <PJ>	Komplexbündel *n*	étoile (gerbe) *f* de complexes	связка комплексов
B 801	**bundle of curves,** sheaf (net) of curves <AY>	Kurvenbündel *n*	gerbe *f* de courbes	связка кривых
	bundle of linear spaces <AT>	*s.* V 98		
B 802	**bundle of lines,** bundle of rays, sheaf (star) of lines (rays) <AY, DS>	Strahlenbündel *n*, Geradenbündel *n*	gerbe *f* (étoile *f*, pinceau *m*) de droites (rayons)	связка прямых (лучей)
B 803	**bundle of parallel lines,** sheaf of parallel lines <EG>	Parallelstrahlenbündel *n*	gerbe *f* (pinceau *m*) de droites parallèles	связка параллельных прямых
B 804	**bundle of *p*-forms** <AT>	Vektorraumbündel *n* der *p*-Formen	fibré *m* vectoriel des *p*-formes	расслоение *p*-форм
B 805	**bundle of planes,** sheaf (star) of planes <AY>	Ebenenbündel *n*	gerbe *f* (réseau *m*, étoile *f*) de plans	связка плоскостей
B 806	**bundle of *p*-vectors** <AT>	Vektorraumbündel *n* der *p*-Vektoren	fibré *m* vectoriel des *p*-vecteurs	расслоение *p*-векторов
	bundle of rays <AY, DS>	*s.* B 802		
B 807	**bundle of spheres,** sheaf (star) of spheres <AY>	Kugelbündel *n*, lineare Kugelkongruenz *f* im engeren Sinne	réseau *m* de sphères, congruence *f* de sphères au sens restreint, étoile (famille) *f* de sphères	связка сфер
	bundle projection <AT>	*s.* P 1649		
	bundle space <AT>	*s.* T 692		
B 808	**bundle structure theorem** <AT>	Bündelstruktursatz *m*	théorème *m* structural des fibrés	структурная теорема расслоенных пространств
	Buniakowski-Schwarz inequality <AN>	*s.* S 167		
	Buniakowsky['s] conjecture <NT>	*s.* B 701		
	Burali-Forti['s] antinomy <LO>	*s.* B 809		
B 809	**Burali-Forti['s] contradiction, Burali-Forti['s] paradox,** Burali-Forti['s] antinomy, antinomy of Burali-Forti, antinomy of the set of all ordinals, paradox of the greatest ordinal <LO>	Antinomie *f* von Burali-Forti, Burali-Fortische Antinomie, Paradoxie *f* von Burali-Forti, Antinomie der Menge aller Ordnungszahlen (Ordinalzahlen)	paradoxe *m* (antinomie *f*) de Burali-Forti	парадокс Бурали-Форти
B 810	**Burkill['s] integral** <of φ over J with respect to ≪ > <AN>	Burkillsches Integral *n* <von φ über J hinsichtlich ≪ >	intégrale *f* de Burkill <de φ sur J à l'égard de ≪ >	интеграл Беркиля <φ по J относительно ≪ >
B 811	**Burkill['s] norm integral** <AN>	Burkillsches Normintegral *n*, [Burkillsches] ν-Normintegral *n*, Normintegral, Integral *n* nach der Feinheit der Norm <ν>		
	Bürmann[-Lagrange] series <FT>	*s.* L 33		
B 812	**Burmester['s] point** <GE>	Burmesterscher Punkt *m*	point *m* de Burmester	точка Бурместера
B 813	**Burnside['s] class** <of groups> <GR>	Burnsidesche Klasse *f*	classe *f* de Burnside	бернсайдов класс
	Burnside['s] conjecture <GR>	*s.* B 816		
B 814	**Burnside['s] formula [for mechanical cubature]** <DI, NU>	Burnsidesche Formel (Kubaturformel) *f*	formule *f* [de cubature mécanique] de Burnside	формула [численного интегрирования двойных интегралов] Бернсайда
B 815	**Burnside['s] group** <GR>	„Burnsidesche" Gruppe *f*, Burnside-Gruppe *f*	groupe *m* de Burnside	«бернсайдова» группа, группа Бернсайда
B 816	**Burnside['s] problem,** Burnside['s] conjecture <GR>	Burnsidesches Problem *n*, Burnsidesche Vermutung *f*	problème *m* de Burnside	проблема Бернсайда
B 817	**Burnside['s] theorem** <RE>	Satz *m* von Burnside, Burnsidescher Satz	théorème *m* de Burnside	теорема Бернсайда
	Bush['s] differential analyzer <AN, IN>	*s.* D 448		
B 818	**business arithmetic,** commercial (mercantile) arithmetic <AR>	kaufmännische Arithmetik *f*, kaufmännisches Rechnen *n*	arithmétique *f* mercantile (commerciale), calcul *m* mercantile	коммерческие (торговые) расчеты

B 819	**butterfly-shaped game** <TG>	schmetterlingsförmiges Spiel *n*		бабочкообразная игра
	Bydžovský['s] configuration <SG>	*s.* C 1870		
	1-by-*n* matrix <MD>	*s.* N 59a		

C

	c <GE>	*s.* C 340		
	C_3 <AY, DG>	*s.* S 1309		
C 1	**cactoid** <TO>	Kaktoid *n*	cactoïde *m*	кактоид
C 2	**cactus,** Husimi['s] tree <GP>	Husimi-Baum *m*, Kaktus *m*	cactus *m*	кактус, дерево Хусими
C 3	**Cagnoli['s] formulae** <EG>	Cagnolische Formeln *fpl*	formules *fpl* de Cagnoli	формулы Каньоли
C 4	**Cahen['s] theorem** <SS>	Satz *m* von Cahen, Cahenscher Satz	théorème *m* de Cahen	теорема Каэна
C 5	**calculable mapping** <MM>	berechenbare Abbildung *f*	application *f* calculable	вычислимое отображение
C 6	**calculable relation** <MM>	berechenbare Relation *f*	relation *f* calculable	вычислимое отношение
C 7	**calculable sequence** <MM>	berechenbare Folge *f*	suite *f* calculable	вычислимая последовательность
C 8	**calculating cylinder** <IN, NU>	Rechenwalze *f*	cylindre *m* à calculer	счетные вальцы
C 9	**calculating disk,** circular slide rule <IN, NU>	Rechenscheibe *f*, Kreisrechenschieber *m*, Kreisrechenstab *m*, Rechenrad *n*	disque *m* à calculer, règle *f* à calcul circulaire	круговая логарифмическая (счетная) линейка, вычислительный диск
C 10	**calculating frame,** counting frame; abacus, abac <*pl.*: abaci, abacussi *or* abacuses> <Western Europe>; schety <Russian abacus>; suan-pan <Chinese abacus>; saroban, soroban <Japanese abacus> <IN>	Rechenbrett *n*, Kugelbrett *n*; Abakus *m*; Stschoty *pl*; Suan-pan *m*, Swanpan *m*, Kugelrechenmaschine *f*, Rechentisch *m*; Soroban *m*, Saroban *m*	table *f* à calculer, boulier *m*, boulier-compteur *m*; abaque *m*; stchety *pl*; souwanpan *m*, suan-pan *m*, Souan-pan *m*, Swanpan *m*; soroban *m*	счетная доска; абак; счеты, дощаной счет, досчаный счет; суанпан, счетный стол; соробан, саробан
C 11	**calculating machine,** computing machine, calculator <IN>	Rechenmaschine *f*	calculatrice *f*, machine *f* à calculer	арифмометр
	calculating method <NU>	*s.* M 451		
C 12	**calculating rule,** computing rule, rule of calculation (arithmetic), algorithm <GN>	Rechenregel *f*, Rechnungsregel *f*, Formalgesetz *n*, Rechenvorschrift *f*	règle *f* de calcul (calculs)	правило вычисления
	calculating rule <AR>	*s.* R 1498		
C 13	**calculation;** computation; figuring out <GN>	Berechnung *f*; Rechnung *f*; Errechnung *f*; Ausrechnung *f*	calcul *m*; computation *f*	расчет; вычисление; подсчет; счет
	calculational formula <NU>	*s.* F 495		
	calculation by Monte Carlo method <NU, ST>	*s.* C 1758		
	calculation for adjust for errors <ER, NU>	*s.* C 26		
	calculation of most probable values <ER, NU>	*s.* C 26		
C 14	**calculation with limits** <AN>	Rechnen *n* mit Grenzwerten	calcul *m* des limites	исчисление с пределами
	calculation with logarithms <AR>	*s.* L 1032		
C 15	**calculation with powers** <AR>	Potenzrechnung *f* <Stifel>	calcul *m* des puissances, calcul exponentiel	действие с показателями
C 16	**calculation with roots** <AR>	Wurzelrechnen *n*	calcul *m* des racines	действие с корнями
	calculator <IN>	*s.* C 11		
C 17	**calculus** <LO>	Kalkül *m*, System *n*, // Calcül *m*	calcul *m*	исчисление
	calculus <DI>	*s.* D 449		
	calculus <MM>	*s.* F 465		
C 18	**calculus of approximations,** approximation calculus <AX, NU>	Näherungsrechnung *f*	calcul *m* approximatif (par approximations, approché)	приближенное вычисление, метод приближенного расчета
C 19	**calculus of classes,** class calculus, monadic (singulary) predicate calculus of first order <LO>	Klassenkalkül *m*, einstelliger Prädikatenkalkül *m*	calcul *m* (logique *f*) des classes	исчисление классов, узкое исчисление одноместных предикатов, логика (теория) классов
C 20	**calculus of complexes** <in groups> <GR>	Komplexrechnen *n*, Rechnen *n* mit Komplexen	calcul *m* des parties	счет с комплексами
	calculus of differences <FD>	*s.* C 21		
	calculus of enlargement <FD>	*s.* C 21		
	calculus of equivalent statements <LO>	*s.* P 1868		
	calculus of errors <ER>	*s.* T 382		

No.	English	German	French	Russian
C 21	**calculus of finite differences,** calculus of differences (enlargement) <FD>	Differenzenrechnung *f*	calcul *m* des différences [finies]	исчисление конечных разностей, разностное исчисление
C 22	**calculus of fractions** <CA>	Kalkül *m* von Brüchen	calcul *m* des fractions	исчисление частных
C 23	**calculus of hyperdeterminants** <IV>	Hyperdeterminantenkalkül *m*, Hyperdeterminantenrechnung *f*	calcul *m* des hyperdéterminants	исчисление гипердетерминантов
C 24	**calculus of interpolation** <AX, FD, NU>	Interpolationsrechnung *f*	calcul *m* d'interpolation	интерполяционное вычисление, интерполяционный расчет <в конкретном случае>; интерполяционное исчисление <область математики>
C 25	**calculus of natural deduction** <LO>	Kalkül *m* des natürlichen Schließens <Gentzen>	calcul *m* de la déduction naturelle	натуральное исчисление [математической логики], исчисление естественного вывода, натуральная дедукция
C 26	**calculus of observations,** calculation for adjust for errors, computation (theory) of adjustment, compensation computation (theory), calculation of most probable values, balancing calculation <ER, NU>	Ausgleichungsrechnung *f*, Ausgleichsrechnung *f*	calcul *m* de l'ajustement (compensation)	конфлюентный анализ, исчисление выравнивания, уравнительное вычисление
C 27	**calculus of operations** <AL>	Operationskalkül *m*	calcul *m* des opérations	исчисление операций
	calculus of probabilities <ST>	*s.* P 1547		
	calculus of probability <ST>	*s.* P 1547		
	calculus of quantifiers <LO>	*s.* P 1183		
C 28	**calculus of relations,** many-place predicate calculus <LO>	mehrstelliger Prädikatenkalkül *m*, mehrstellige Prädikatenlogik *f*, Logik *f* der Relationen, Relationenkalkül *m*	calcul *m* des prédicats avec prédicats à plus d'une place, logique *f* des prédicats relatifs, logique (calcul) des relations	логика многоместных предикатов, исчисление (теория, логика) отношений
C 29	**calculus of residues** <FT>	Residuenrechnung *f*, Residuenkalkül *m*, Residuenmethode *f*	calcul *m* (méthode *f*) des résidus	исчисление (метод) вычетов
C 30	**calculus of segments** <GE>	Streckenrechnung *f*, Punktrechnung *f* <Hilbert>	méthode *f* des équipollences <Bellavitis>	исчисление отрезков
C 31	**calculus of sequents** <LO>	Sequenzenlogik *f*	logique *f* des conséquences	секвенциальное исчисление, исчисление секвенций (способов заключений)
C 32	**calculus of variations,** variational calculus <VA>	Variationsrechnung *f*	calcul *m* des variations	вариационное исчисление
C 33	**Calderon-Zygmund operator** <FA>	Calderon-Zygmundscher Operator *m*	opérateur *m* de Calderon-Zygmund	оператор Кальдерона-Зигмунда
C 34	**C^*-algebra,** B^*-algebra, completely regular Banach algebra <FA>	C^*-Algebra *f*, B^*-Algebra *f*	C^*-algèbre *f*, algèbre *f* C^*, B^*-algèbre *f*, algèbre *f* B^* (complètement régulière)	C^*-алгебра, B^*-алгебра, вполне регулярное кольцо
C 35	**Calkin['s] algebra** <FA>	Calkin-Algebra *f*	algèbre *f* de Calkin	алгебра Калкина
C 36	**Calkin['s] theorem** <FA>	Calkinscher Satz *m*, Satz von Calkin	théorème *m* de Calkin	теорема Калкина
	call-back <ST>	*s.* R 820		
C 37	**cam** <GE>	Kurvenkörper *m*	came *f*	кулачок, копир, шаблон
C 38	**Campbell-Hausdorff formula,** Baker-[Campbell-]Hausdorff formula <GR>	Campbell-Hausdorffsche Formel *f*, Campbell-Hausdorff-Formel *f*, symbolische Exponentialformel *f*	formule *f* de Campbell-Hausdorff	формула Кампбелла-Хаусдорфа, формула Бейкера-Хаусдорфа
C 39	**Camp-Meidell['s] inequality** <ST>	Camp-Meidell-Ungleichung *f*	inégalité *f* de Camp-Meidell	неравенство Кампа-Мейделла
C 40	**canal surface** <DG>	Kanalfläche *f*	surface *f* canal	каналовая поверхность, поверхность канала
C 41/2	**cancellability** <AL, AR>	Kürzbarkeit *f*; Regularität *f* <Halbgruppe>	simplifiabilité *f*	сократимость, сокращаемость
	cancellability <AL>	*s.* B 332		
	cancellable element <AL>	*s.* R 539		
	cancellable fraction <AL, AR>	*s.* F 574		
C 43	**cancellation** <out of>, cancelling [out], simplification <of>, reduction <of terms in a quotient> <AR, GN>	Kürzen *n* <mit, durch>; Herauskürzen *n* <aus>; Wegkürzen *n* <aus>; Wegheben *n*, Heben *n* <in>; Reduzieren *n*, Reduktion *f* <von>	simplification *f*, annulation *f*, réduction *f*	сокращение <на>; отмена
C 44	**cancellation,** cancelling [out] <of terms in a sum> <AR, GN>	[gegenseitiges] Wegheben *n*, Heben *n*, [gegenseitiges] Herausheben *n*, Herausfallen *n*, Aufheben *n*, [gegenseitiges] Wegkürzen *n*	annulation *f*, compensation *f*, neutralisation *f*	взаимное уничтожение

	cancellation <AR>	*s.* S 992		
	cancellation groupoid <AL>	*s.* C 50		
	cancellation half-groupoid <AL>	*s.* H 36		
C 45	**cancellation law** <AL>	Kürzungsregel *f*	règle *f* de simplification	закон (правило) сокращения
C 46	**cancellation law** <bilateral> <AL>	[zweiseitige] Kürzungsregel *f*	règle *f* de simplification des deux côtés	закон (правило) двустороннего сокращения
C 47	**cancellation property** <of an operation> <AL>	Kürzungseigenschaft *f*	propriété *f* de simplification	свойство сокращения
C 48	**cancellation semigroup,** cancellative semigroup, semi-group with cancellation, // semigroup <AL>	Semigruppe *f*, reguläre Halbgruppe *f*, Halbgruppe mit regulärer Verknüpfung, Halbgruppe mit Kürzungsregel	semi-groupe *m*, demi-groupe *m* simplifiable (vérifiant la règle de simplification)	регулярная полугруппа, полугруппа с сокращением
C 49	**cancellation subsemigroup** <AL>	Untersemigruppe *f*	sous-semi-groupe *m*	подполугруппа с сокращением
C 50	**cancellative groupoid,** cancellation groupoid <AL>	Gruppoid *n* mit Kürzungsregeln	groupoïde *m* vérifiant la règle de simplification	группоид с двусторонним сокращением, группоид с сокращениями, группоид с двусторонним законом сокращения
	cancellative semigroup <AL>	*s.* C 48		
	cancelling [out] <AR, GN>	*s.* 1. C 43; 2. C 44		
C 51	**cannibals and missionaries puzzle** <GP>	Problem *n* der Missionare und Kannibalen, Problem der Überfahrt	problème *m* des missionnaires et cannibales	задача о миссионерах и людоедах, задача о переправе
C 52	**canonical algorithm** <MM>	kombinatorisches System *n*, kanonischer Algorithmus *m* <Post>	algorithme *m* canonique <dans le sens de Post>	канонический алгоритм
	canonical average <ST>	*s.* C 78		
C 53	**canonical base of the algebra of quaternions** <AL>	kanonische Basis *f* der Quaternionen	base *f* canonique de l'algèbre des quaternions	канонический базис алгебры кватернионов
C 54	**canonical basis** <AT>	kanonische Basis *f*	base *f* canonique	канонический базис; каноническая гомологическая база
C 55	**canonical chart** <of the first *or* second kind> <of a Lie group> <GR>	kanonische Karte *f* <erster *oder* zweiter Art>	carte *f* canonique <de première *ou* deuxième espèce>	каноническая карта <первого *или* второго рода>
C 56	**canonical class** <of divisors> <AG>	kanonische Klasse *f*, Differentialklasse *f*	classe *f* canonique (différentielle)	канонический класс
	canonical class of Eger-Todd <AT>	*s.* T 486		
C 57	**canonical co-ordinate,** canonical variable <VA>	kanonische (allgemeine) Koordinate *f*, kanonische Veränderliche (Variable) *f*	coordonnée *f* canonique [d'Hamilton], variable *f* canonique [d'Hamilton]	каноническая координата, координата Гамильтона, каноническая переменная, переменная Гамильтона
C 58	**canonical co-ordinates;** system of canonical co-ordinates <of the first *or* second kind> <of a Lie group> <GR>	kanonische Koordinaten *fpl*; kanonisches Koordinatensytem *n* <erster *oder* zweiter Art>	coordonnées *fpl* canoniques; système *m* de coordonnées canoniques <de première *ou* deuxième espèce>	канонические координаты; система канонических координат <первого *или* второго рода>
C 59	**canonical correlation coefficient** <ST>	kanonischer Korrelationskoeffizient *m*	coefficient *m* de corrélation canonique	канонический коэффициент корреляции
C 60	**canonical curve** <of an algebraic surface> <AG>	[effektive] kanonische Kurve *f*	courbe *f* canonique [effective]	[эффективная] каноническая кривая
C 61	**canonical decomposition,** canonical reduction <of a spectral operator> <FA>	kanonische Zerlegung *f*	décomposition *f* canonique	каноническое представление
C 62	**canonical equation,** normal equation, equation of centre <*e.g.:* of circle *or* ellipse *or* hyperbola> <AY>	Mittelpunktsgleichung *f*, Gleichung *f*, Normalform *f* der Gleichung <*z. B.:* des Kreises *oder* der Ellipse *oder* Hyperbel>	équation *f* canonique (normale, du centre) <*par exemple:* du cercle *ou* de l'ellipse *ou* de l'yperbole>	каноническое (простейшее) уравнение, нормальный вид уравнения; уравнение, отнесенное к центру <*например:* окружности *или* эллипса *или* гиперболы>
	canonical equation <AY>	*s.* V 162		
C 63	**canonical factorization** <of a closed operator> <FA>	kanonische Zerlegung *f*	décomposition *f* canonique	каноническая факторизация
C 64	**canonical flabby resolution** <of a sheaf> <AL, TO>	kanonische welke Auflösung *f*	résolution *f* [flasque] canonique	каноническая [вялая] резольвента
C 65	**canonical form** <of a class of quadratic forms> <AB>	kanonische Form *f* <Smith>, charakteristische Form <Minkowski>	forme *f* canonique (caractéristique)	каноническая форма
C 66	**canonical form** <e.g. of a binary expression, an equation, a group, a matrix> <AL, MD>	kanonische Form *f*	forme *f* canonique	канонический вид, каноническая форма
C 67	**canonical form** <AY, DE, NO, VA>	kanonische Form; kanonische Gestalt *f* <insbesondere bei Formen und VA>	forme *f* canonique	каноническая форма, канонический вид
	canonical form <MD>	*s.* N 578		
C 68	**canonical form of the accessory boundary-value problem,** Morse['s] normal form <VA>	kanonische Gestalt *f* des akzessorischen Eigenwertproblems, Normalform *f* von Morse, Morsesche Normalform	forme *f* canonique du problème aux limites accessoire, forme normale de Morse	канонический вид присоединенной предельной задачи

No.	English	German	French	Russian
C 69	**canonical fundamental system [of integrals],** canonical system of solutions <DE>	kanonisches Fundamentalsystem *n* [von Lösungen], kanonisches Lösungssystem *n*	système *m* fondamental canonique [d'intégrales], système canonique de solutions	каноническая фундаментальная система [решений (интегралов)], каноническая система решений
C 70	**canonical homomorphism,** natural homomorphism, projection <on a quotient structure> <AL>	kanonischer (natürlicher) Homomorphismus *m*	homomorphisme *m* canonique	канонический (естественный) гомоморфизм
C 71	**canonical homomorphism** <on the factor group> <GR>	Restklassenhomomorphismus *m*, kanonischer Homomorphismus *m*	homomorphisme *m* canonique	канонический гомоморфизм
C 72	**canonical hyperbolic system** <of partial differential equations> <DE>	kanonisch-hyperbolisches System *n*	système *m* hyperbolique canonique	каноническая гиперболическая система
C 73	**canonical image,** natural image <AL, SE>	kanonisches (natürliches) Bild *n*	image *f* canonique	канонический образ
	canonical injection <CA>	*s.* I 544		
	canonical integral <DE>	*s.* C 81		
C 74	**canonically associated bundle** <AT>	kanonisch assoziiertes Bündel (Faserbündel) *n*	fibré *m* canoniquement associé	канонически ассоциированное расслоение
C 75	**canonically conjugate co-ordinate; canonically conjugate quantity; canonically conjugate variable** <DE>	kanonisch konjugierte Koordinate *f*; [kanonisch] konjugierte Größe *f*; [kanonisch] konjugierte Variable *f*	coordonnée *f* canonique [d'Hamilton], conjuguée, coordonnée conjuguée; grandeur *f* canonique [d'Hamilton], conjuguée, grandeur conjuguée; variable *f* canonique [d'Hamilton], conjuguée, variable conjuguée	[канонически] сопряженная координата; [канонически] сопряженная величина; [канонически] сопряженная переменная
C 76	**canonically ordered factor-group (factor group),** naturally ordered factor-group (factor group) <GR>	natürlich (kanonisch) geordnete Faktorgruppe *f*	groupe *m* quotient canoniquement ordonné	естественно (канонически) упорядоченная фактор-группа
C 77	**canonical mapping,** natural mapping <AL>	kanonische (natürliche) Abbildung *f*	application *f* canonique	каноническое (естественное) отображение
	canonical mapping <SE>	*s.* N 32		
C 78	**canonical mean,** canonical average <ST>	kanonisches Mittel *n*, kanonischer Mittelwert *m*	moyenne *f* canonique	среднее каноническое, каноническое среднее [значение]
	canonical projection	*s.* P 1659		
	canonical reduction <FA>	*s.* C 61		
C 79	**canonical sequence** <of transfinite functions> <SE>	Hauptfolge *f*, kanonische (ausgezeichnete) Folge *f*	suite *f* canonique	каноническая последовательность
C 80	**canonical series** <of curves> <AG>	kanonisches Kurvensystem *n*	système *m* canonique de courbes	каноническая система кривых
C 81	**canonical solution,** canonical integral <DE>	kanonische Lösung *f*, kanonisches Integral *n*	solution (intégrale) *f* canonique	каноническое решение
C 82	**canonical system, canonical system of differential equations,** characteristic system of the Hamilton-Jacobi equation, Hamilton['s] equations, Hamiltonian system <DE>	kanonisches Differentialgleichungssystem *n*, charakteristisches Differentialgleichungssystem der Hamilton-Jacobischen Differentialgleichung, Hamiltonsche Gleichungen *fpl*	système *m* canonique, système canonique des équations différentielles, système caractéristique de l'équation de Jacobi, équations *fpl* d'Hamilton, système hamiltonien	каноническая система, каноническая система дифференциальных уравнений, характеристическая система уравнения Гамильтона-Якоби, уравнения Гамильтона, гамильтонова система
	canonical system of solutions <DE>	*s.* C 69		
C 83	**canonical transformation** <DE, ST, VA>	kanonische Transformation *f*	transformation *f* (changement *m*) canonique	каноническое преобразование, каноническая замена переменных
	canonical transformation of Mathieu <DE, VA>	*s.* M 177		
	canonical variable <VA>	*s.* C 57		
C 84	**canonical variational equations,** accessory canonical differential equations <DE, VA>	akzessorische kanonische Differentialgleichungen *fpl*	équations *fpl* variationnelles canoniques, équations différentielles canoniques accessoires	канонические вариационные уравнения, присоединенные канонические дифференциальные уравнения
C 85	**canonical variational problem** <VA>	kanonisches Variationsproblem *n*, Variationsproblem in kanonischer Gestalt	problème *m* variationnel canonique	каноническая вариационная задача
C 86	**canonizant** <of a form> <IV>	Kanonizante *f*, Kanonisante *f* <Sylvester>	canonisant *m*	канонизант
C 87	**Cantelli['s] inequalities** <ST>	Cantellische Ungleichungen *fpl*	inégalités *fpl* de Cantelli	неравенства Кантелли
C 88	**Cantor['s] algebra** <AL>	Cantor-Algebra *f*	algèbre *f* de Cantor	алгебра Кантора
	Cantor-Bendixson theorem <TO>	*s.* T 265		
	Cantor-Bernstein theorem [on cardinals] <SE>	*s.* E 425		
C 89	**Cantor['s] continuity axiom,** axiom of Dedekind-Cantor, Dedekind-Cantor axiom, strong axiom of continuity of Cantor <GE>	Cantorsches (Cantor-Dedekindsches) Axiom *n*, Cantorsches Stetigkeitsaxiom *n*, Invervallschachtelungsaxiom *n*, Vollständigkeitsaxiom *n*	axiome *m* de Cantor-Dedekind (continuité), postulat *m* de Cantor-Dedekind	аксиома (условие) Кантора
	Cantor['s] continuum hypothesis <SE>	*s.* C 2247		
	Cantor['s] continuum problem <SE>	*s.* C 2249		

C 90	**Cantor['s] curve** <TO>	Cantorsche Kurve *f*	ligne *f* cantorienne	канторова кривая, кривая Кантора
	Cantor['s] diagonal method <SE>	*s.* D 397		
	Cantor['s] diagonal procedure <SE>	*s.* D 397		
	Cantor['s] diagonal process <SE>	*s.* D 397		
C 91	**Cantor['s] discontinuum,** middle third set, Cantor['s] set, Cantor['s] ternary (perfect) set <TO>	Cantorsche Menge *f*, Cantorsches Diskontinuum *n*, Cantorsche Wischmenge (Punktmenge) *f*	ensemble *m* de Cantor, ensemble triadique (parfait) de Cantor, discontinu *m* de Cantor, échelle *f* ternaire (triadique) de Cantor	канторовское (канторово) множество, множество Кантора, канторово совершенное (точечное) множество, триадическое множество Кантора, канторов дисконтинуум
C 92	**Cantor['s] fundamental sequence,** fundamental sequence <in completion of Q> <AN>	Cantorsche Fundamentalfolge *f*	suite *f* fondamentale [de Cantor]	[фундаментальная] последовательность Кантора
C 93	**Cantor['s] hypothesis on alephs** <SE>	Alephhypothese *f*	hypothèse *f* de Cantor sur les alephs	гипотеза об алефах
	Cantorian manifold <TO>	*s.* S 1968		
	Cantorian set theory <SE>	*s.* C 779		
C 94	**Cantorian universe** <SE>	Cantorsches Universum *n*	univers *m* de Cantor	универсум Кантора
	Cantor-Lebesgue theorem <AN>	*s.* T 266		
C 95	**Cantor['s] paradox,** antinomy of the set of all sets <LO, SE>	Cantorsche Antinomie *f*, Antinomie der Menge aller Mengen	paradoxe *m* de Cantor	парадокс Кантора
C 96	**Cantor['s] paradox of the greatest cardinal number** <LO, SE>	Cantorsches Paradoxon *n* [von der Menge aller Kardinalzahlen], Antinomie *f* der Menge aller Kardinalzahlen	paradoxe *m* de Cantor	парадокс Кантора
	Cantor['s] perfect set <TO>	*s.* C 91		
C 97	**Cantor['s] product** <SS>	Cantorsches Produkt *n*	produit *m* de Cantor	произведение Кантора
C 98	**Cantor['s] product theorem,** theorem of Cantor, Cantor['s] theorem <TO>	Cantorscher Durchschnittssatz *m*, Durchschnittssatz von Cantor[-Bendixson]	théorème *m* de Cantor	теорема Кантора
C 99	**Cantor['s] series** <SS>	Cantorsche Reihe *f*	série *f* de Cantor	ряд Кантора
	Cantor['s] set <TO>	*s.* C 91		
C 100	**Cantor['s] space** <TO>	Cantorscher Raum *m*	espace *m* de Cantor	канторово пространство
	Cantor['s] ternary set <TO>	*s.* C 91		
C 101	**Cantor['s] theorem,** theorem of Cantor, Cantor['s] theorem on the set of all subsets of a given set <SE>	Satz *m* von Cantor, Cantorscher Satz, Teilmengensatz *m*	théorème *m* de Cantor	теорема Кантора
	Cantor['s] theorem <TO>	*s.* C 98		
	Cantor['s] theorem on the set of all subsets of a given set <SE>	*s.* C 101		
C 101 a	**caoutchouc geometry,** elastic geometry <TO>	Gummigeometrie *f*, Kautschukgeometrie *f*	géométrie *f* élastique	упругая геометрия
	cap <EG>	*s.* S 1448		
	cap <LA>	*s.* M 362		
C 102	**capacity** <AL, PO, TO>	Kapazität *f*	capacité *f*	емкость
C 103	**capacity** <FT>	Kapazität *f*, Kapazitätskonstante *f*	capacité *f*	емкость, емкостная постоянная
C 104	**capacity** <of a transportation network> <GP, PG>	Kapazität *f*, Flußkapazität *f*	capacité *f*	пропускная способность
	capacity <ST>	*s.* C 504		
C 105	**cap body,** 1-tangential body <GE>	Kappenkörper *m*, 1-Tangentialkörper *m*	corps *m* de capuchon, corps tangentiel d'ordre *n*—1	шапочка
C 106	**cap product,** Whitney['s] product, ⌢ product <AT>	⌢-Produkt *n*, [Whitneysches] Cap-Produkt *n*	cap-produit *m* [de Whitney]	⌢-произведение, произведение Уитни
C 107	**caption** <of a nomogram> <NO>	Paß *m*	description *f* de l'emploi	схема пользования, ключ [пользования], паспорт, легенда
	caption <GN>	*s.* T 3		
C 108	**Carathéodory['s] domain** <FT>	Carathéodorysches Gebiet *n*	domaine *m* de Carathéodory	область Каратеодори
	Carathéodory['s] existence theorem <DE>	*s.* C 112		
C 109	**Carathéodory-Koebe method** <FT>	Carathéodory-Koebesches Schmiegungsverfahren *n*	méthode *f* de Carathéodory-Koebe	метод Каратеодори-Кебе
C 110	**Carathéodory['s] measure [of area]** <ME>	Carathéodorysches Flächenmaß (Überdeckungsmaß, Maß) *n*	mesure *f* [d'aire] de Carathéodory	мера площади Каратеодори
C 111	**Carathéodory['s] method** <VA>	Methode *f* von Carathéodory, Carathéodorysche Methode	méthode *f* de Carathéodory	метод Каратеодори
	Carathéodory['s] metric <FT>	*s.* A 638		
C 112	**Carathéodory['s] theorem,** Carathéodory['s] existence theorem <DE>	Carathéodoryscher Existenzsatz *m*, Existenzsatz von Carathéodory	théorème *m* [d'existence] de Carathéodory	теорема [существования] Каратеодори

No.	English	German	French	Russian
C 113	**Carathéodory['s] theorem** <sharpening of Landau's theorem> <FT>	Satz *m* von Carathéodory zum Picardschen Satz, Carathéodorysche Verschärfung *f* des Landauschen Satzes	théorème *m* de Carathéodory	теорема Каратеодори
C 114	**Carathéodory['s] theorem** <on conform mapping of unit circle *or* on a normalized sequence of functions> <FT>	Satz *m* von Carathéodory, Carathéodoryscher Satz	théorème *m* de Carathéodory	теорема Каратеодори
C 115	**Carathéodory['s] theory of measure** <ME>	Carathéodorysche Maßtheorie *f*	théorie *f* des mesures de Carathéodory	теория меры Каратеодори
C 116	**Cardan['s] solution of the cubic** <AL>	Cardanosche Formel *f* (Formeln *fpl*), Cardanische Formel *f*	formule *f* de Cardan	формула Кардано
	cardinal <SE>	*s.* C 123		
C 117	**cardinal addition,** addition of cardinal numbers <SE>	Addition *f* von Kardinalzahlen	addition *f* cardinale (des nombres cardinaux)	сложение кардинальных чисел, кардинальное сложение
C 118	**cardinal algebra** <AL>	Kardinalalgebra *f*	algèbre *f* cardinale	кардинальная алгебра
C 119	**cardinal arithmetic,** arithmetic of cardinal numbers <SE>	Arithmetik *f* der Kardinalzahlen, Kardinalzahlarithmetik *f*	arithmétique *f* cardinale (des nombres cardinaux)	арифметика мощностей
C 120	**cardinality,** order <of an algebraic system> <UA>	Mächtigkeit *f*, Ordnung *f*	puissance *f*, ordre *m*	мощность, порядок
	cardinality <SE>	*s.* C 123		
C 121	**cardinality function** <TO>	Kardinalitätsfunktion *f*	fonction *f* de cardinalité	функция кардинальности
	cardinally equivalent set <SE>	*s.* E 404		
C 121 a	**cardinal multiplication,** multiplication of cardinal numbers <SE>	Multiplikation *f* von Kardinalzahlen	multiplication *f* cardinale (des nombres cardinaux)	умножение кардинальных чисел, кардинальное умножение
C 122	**cardinal number** <AR>	Grundzahl *f*, Kardinalzahl *f*	nombre *m* cardinal	количественное числительное, первоначальное число
C 123	**cardinal number,** cardinal; cardinality, power, potency, order, // manyness <SE>	Kardinalzahl *f*; Mächtigkeit *f*	nombre *m* cardinal, cardinal *m*; cardinalité *f*, puissance *f*; quotité *f* <nombre naturel>	кардинальное число, кардинал, количественное число, мощность по Кантору; кардинальность, мощность
	cardinal number <SE>	*s.* F 260		
C 124	**cardinal number class,** number class, number-class <SE>	Zahl[en]klasse *f*, kardinale (Cantorsche) Zahlklasse *f*	classe *f* [cardinale] de nombres, classe	[кардинальный] класс чисел, числовой класс
	cardinal number inaccessible from below <SE>	*s.* I 209		
	cardinal number inaccessible in the narrower sense <SE>	*s.* S 1976		
C 125	**cardinal number inaccessible in the wider sense,** weakly inaccessible cardinal <SE>	Kuratowskische (im weiteren Sinne) unerreichbare Kardinalzahl *f*, Kuratowskische Zahl *f*, unerreichbare Kardinalzahl im weiteren Sinne, unerreichbarer Aleph *m* im weiteren Sinne, Zahl *f* von exorbitanter Größe *f*, exorbitante Kardinalzahl	cardinal *m* faiblement inaccessible	слабо недостижимый кардинал
	cardinal of the continuum <SE>	*s.* P 1145		
C 126/7	**cardinal product** <of lattices> <LA>	Produktverband *m*	treillis-produit *m*	прямое произведение <структур>
C 128	**cardinal product,** product <of cardinal numbers> <SE>	Produkt *n* <von Kardinalzahlen>	produit *m* [cardinal] <de nombres cardinaux>	[кардинальное] произведение <кардинальных чисел>
	cardinal product <SE>	*s.* C 173		
	cardinal sum <SE>	*s* S 2255		
C 129	**cardioid, cardioid curve (line),** heart contour (shape, line) <AG>	Kardioide *f*, Herzkurve *f*, Herzlinie *f*	cardioïde *f*	кардиода, сердцевидная кривая
C 130	**Carleman['s] kernel,** Carleman-type kernel <of class I *or* II> <IE>	Carlemanscher Kern *m*, Kern vom Carlemanschen Typ <der Klasse I *oder* II>	noyau *m* de [type de] Carleman <de la classe I *ou* II>	ядро [типа] Карлемана <класса I *или* II>
C 131	**Carleman['s] method,** Carleman['s] theory <IE> ⌐<FA>	Carlemansche Methode (Theorie) *f* <der Integralgleichungen>, Methode von Carleman	méthode (théorie) *f* de Carleman	метод (теория) Карлемана
C 132	**Carleman['s] operator**	Carlemanscher Operator *m*	opérateur *m* de Carleman	оператор Карлемана
C 133	**Carleman['s] [orthogonal] polynomials** <FU>	Orthogonalpolynome *npl* von Carleman, Carlemansche Orthogonalpolynome	polynômes *mpl* orthogonaux de Carleman	[ортогональные] многочлены (полиномы) Карлемана
C 134	**Carleman['s] principle [of domain extension],** principle of domain extension <FT>	Carlemansches Prinzip *n* [der Gebietserweiterung], Prinzip der Gebietserweiterung <von Carleman>	principe *f* de l'extension de domaine [de Carleman], principe de Carleman	принцип расширения области [Карлемана], принцип Карлемана
	Carleman['s] theory <IE>	*s.* C 131		
C 135	**Carleman['s] transform** <AN>	Carlemansche Transformierte *f*, Carleman-Transformierte *f*	transformée *f* de [Fourier-]Carleman	изображение (трансформанта) Карлемана

No.	English	German	French	Russian
	Carleman-type kernel <IE>	*s.* C 130		
C 136	**Carleman-Vekua['s] method** <IE>	Methode *f* von Carleman-Vekua, Carleman-Vekuasche Methode	méthode *f* de Carleman-Vekua	метод Карлемана-Векуа
C 137	**Carnot['s] relation** <for the cosines> <EG>	Carnotsche Beziehung *f*	relation *f* de Carnot	соотношение Карно
C 138	**Carnot['s] theorem** <for the inscribed polygon> <EG>	Carnotscher Satz *m*	théorème *m* de Carnot	теорема Карно
C 139	**Carnot['s] theorem** <for the triangle> <EG>	Carnotsches Theorem *n*, Theorem von Carnot, Carnotscher Satz *m*	théorème *m* de Carnot	теорема Карно
C 140	**Carnot['s] theorem** <for the tetrahedron> <EG>	Carnotscher Tetraedersatz *m*	théorème *m* de Carnot	теорема Карно
C 141	**carrier,** underlying set <of an algebraic structure> <AL>	Träger *m*, unterliegende Menge *f*	ensemble *m* sous-jacent	носитель, основное множество
C 142	**carrier,** support <of a distribution> <AN>	Träger *m*	support *m*	носитель
C 143	**carrier** <of a point of the body of a complex> <AT>	Träger *m*, Trägerelement *n*, Trägersimplex *n*	support *m*	носитель, симплекс-носитель
C 144	**carrier** <of a cochain, a form, or a Radon measure> <AT, DG, ME, TG>	Träger *m*	support *m*	носитель
C 145	**carrier,** support <of a function> <FA, RF, TO>	Träger *m*	support *m*, supp	носитель, несущее множество
C 146	**carrier** <TO>	Träger *m*	support *m*	носитель, несущее множество
	carrier <AG, AL, AT>	*s.* S 2342		
	carrier <NO>	*s.* S 90		
C 147	**carrier curve** <DG>	Trägerkurve *f*, Träger *m*	courbe *f* support	кривая-носитель
	carrier space <AL, RE>	*s.* R 844		
C 148	**carry,** carry-over <AR, NU>	Übertrag *m*	retenue *f*	цифры переноса в следующий разряд
C 149	**carry digit** <AR, NU>	übertragene Ziffer *f*	chiffre *m* reporté	цифра переноса
	carrying <AR, NU>	*s.* C 150		
	carrying <GN>	*s.* A 1055		
C 150	**carrying over,** bridging, carrying <in addition *or* subtraction> <AR, NU>	Stellenübertragung *f*, Übertragung *f* <in die nächste Stelle>	report *m* des retenues, report *m*	перенос, перенесение <в следующий разряд>
	carry-over <AR, NU>	*s.* C 148		
	Cartan['s] calculus <DG>	*s.* E 834		
C 151	**Cartan['s] decomposition** <of a Lie algebra> <AL>	Cartansche Zerlegung *f*	décomposition *f* de Cartan	картановское разложение, разложение Картана
C 152	**Cartan['s] domain** <FT>	Cartanscher Körper *m*	domaine *m* de Cartan	(*p*,*q*)-круговая область, область Картана, картанова область
C 153	**Cartan['s] form** <DI>	Cartansche Form *f*	forme *f* de Cartan	картанова форма
C 154	**Cartan formula** <for Steenrod squares> <AT>	Cartansche Formel *f*	formule *f* de Cartan	формула Картана
	Cartan inner product <AL>	*s.* K 72		
C 155	**Cartan['s] integer** <of an ordered pair of roots of a Lie algebra> <AL>	Cartansche Zahl *f*	entier *m* de Cartan	число Картана, целое Картана
	Cartan-Killing form <AL>	*s.* K 72		
C 156	**Cartan['s] subalgebra** <of a Lie algebra> <AL>	Cartansche Unteralgebra *f*, Cartanscher Teilring *m*	algèbre *f* de Cartan	подалгебра Картана, картановская подалгебра
C 157	**Cartan['s] subgroup** <of a Lie group> <AL>	Cartansche Untergruppe *f*	[sous-]groupe *m* de Cartan	подгруппа Картана
C 158	**Cartan['s] theorem,** integral theorem of Cartan, general Stokes theorem <DI>	Cartanscher Integralsatz (Satz) *m*, Integralsatz von Cartan, Cartansche Integralformel (Formel) *f*, allgemeiner Stokesscher Satz (Integralsatz)	formule *f* (théorème *m*) de Cartan, formule de Stokes générale, théorème de Stokes général	формула Картана, общая формула Стокса
C 159	**Carter['s] subgroup** <GR>	Cartersche Untergruppe *f*	sous-groupe *m* de Carter	подгруппа Картера
C 160	**Cartesian chart,** Cartesian graph, Cartesian map <NO>	Cartesische (kartesische) Rechentafel *f*	abaque *m* cartésien	декартова [сетчатая] номограмма
C 161	**Cartesian co-ordinates,** rectangular (orthogonal) Cartesian co-ordinates, orthonormal (rectangular) co-ordinates <AY>	[rechtwinklige] kartesische (cartesische) Koordinaten *fpl*, orthonormierte Koordinaten, rechtwinklige (gewöhnliche, kartesische rechtwinklige) Koordinaten	coordonnées *fpl* cartésiennes [en axes rectangulaires], coordonnées cartésiennes orthogonales, coordonnées orthonormales (rectangulaires)	[прямоугольные] декартовы координаты, декартовы прямоугольные координаты, ортонормированные (прямоугольные) координаты
	Cartesian co-ordinates <AY, GE>	*s.* A 350		
C 162	**Cartesian cyclide** <GE>	Cartesische Zyklide *f*, Zyklide von Descartes	cyclide *f* cartésienne (de Descartes)	декартова циклида
C 163	**Cartesian equation,** rectangular equation <AG, AY>	kartesische Gleichung *f*, Gleichung in kartesischen Koordinaten	équation *f* en coordonnées cartésiennes	уравнение в системе декартовых координат
C 164	**Cartesian folium,** Descartes['] folium, folium of Descartes <AG>	Cartesisches (kartesisches, Descartessches) Blatt *n*, Blatt des Descartes, folium *n* Cartesii, // Jasminkurve *f*	folium *m* de Decartes, feuille *f* cartésienne (de Descartes), // galand *m*, nœud *m* de ruban, fleur *f* de jasmin	декартов лист, лист Декарта

	English	German	French	Russian
	cartesian geometry <AY>	*s.* A 619		
	Cartesian graph <NO>	*s.* C 160		
	Cartesian map <NO>	*s.* C 160		
C 165	**Cartesian multiplication** <of sets> <SE>	kartesische (cartesische) Multiplikation *f*, Bildung *f* des kartesischen Produkts	multiplication *f* directe	образование декартова произведения
C 166	**Cartesian multiplication** <of spaces> <TO>	Bildung *f* des topologischen Produkts	multiplication *f* cartésienne	построение топологического произведения
	Cartesian normal form <AY>	*s.* S 1206		
C 167	**Cartesian *n*-space,** Euclidean *n*-space, *n*-dimensional continuum, arithmetic *n*-space, cartesian space R^n, R^n <AN, GE>	*n*-dimensionaler euklidischer (Euklidischer) Raum *m*, *n*-dimensionaler Cartesischer Zahlenraum *m*, *n*-dimensionaler Zahlenraum (Raum) *m*, euklidischer Raum der Dimension *n*, R^n	espace *m* cartésien à *n* dimensions, espace cartésien *n*-dimensionnel, espace numérique (arithmétique) à *n* dimensions, R^n	числовое *n*-мерное пространство, *n*-мерное числовое пространство, *n*-мерный континуум, *n*-мерное арифметическое (координатное) пространство, эвклидово *n*-мерное пространство, R^n
C 168	**Cartesian oval** <AG>	Cartesisches (Kartesisches) Oval *n*, Cartesische (Kartesische) Kurve *f*, Descartessches Oval, Oval von Descartes	ovale *m* de Descartes, ligne *f* aplanétique, quartique *f* bicirculaire cartésienne, ovale cartésien	декартов овал, овал Декарта
	Cartesian parabola <AG>	*s.* T 933		
C 169	**Cartesian power** <*n*-th> <of a set> <SE>	kartesische (cartesische) Potenz *f*, Mengenpotenz *f* <*n*-te>	puissance *f* directe <d'exposant *n*>	декартова степень <*n*-я>
C 170	**Cartesian product** <of simplicial complexes> <AT>	kartesisches Produkt *n* <von simplizialen Komplexen>	produit *m* cartésien <de complexes simpliciaux>	декартово произведение <симплициальных комплексов>
C 171	**Cartesian product** <of measures *or* measure spaces> <ME>	kartesisches Produkt *n*	produit *m* cartésien	декартово произведение
C 172	**Cartesian product** <of mappings> <SE>	kartesisches (cartesisches) Produkt *n* <von Abbildungen>	produit *m* direct <d'applications>	отображение-произведение
C 173	**Cartesian product, cartesian product,** direct (cross, set, outer, combinatorial, cardinal) product, combination set, product[-aggregate] <of sets>; pair-product <of two sets> <SE>	Mengenprodukt *n*, Verbindungsmenge *f*, kartesisches (cartesisches, äußeres, geordnetes) Produkt *n*, Produkt	produit *m* direct [d'ensembles], produit d'ensembles, produit cartésien (combinatoire, ensembliste), produit, ensemble-produit *m*, ensemble *m* produit	внешнее (прямое, декартово, картезианское, теоретико-множественное) произведение, произведение множеств, упорядоченное (полное прямое) произведение
	Cartesian product <TO>	*s.* T 539		
	Cartesian product <SE>	*s.* R 670		
C 174	**Cartesian product operation** <SE>	Operation *f* der Bildung des kartesischen Produkts	multiplication *f* cartésienne	операция декартового произведения
	Cartesian space <AN, AY>	*s.* E 569		
	cartesian space R^n <AN, GE>	*s.* C 167		
	cartesian square <CA>	*s.* 1. P 2027; 2. P 2029		
	cartesian square <SE>	*s.* C 1207		
C 175	**Cartesian subgroup** <of a free product> <GR>	kartesische (cartesische) Untergruppe *f*	sous-groupe *m* cartésien	декартова подгруппа
C 176	**cartesian sum** <of graphs> <GP>	kartesische Summe *f*	somme *f* cartésienne	произведение
	Cartesian system <AY, GE>	*s.* C 177		
C 177	**Cartesian system of co-ordinates,** Cartesian system <AY, GE>	kartesisches (cartesisches) Koordinatensystem *n*, Parallelkoordinatensystem *n*, affines Koordinatensystem	système *m* de coordonnées cartésiennes, repère *m* cartésien	декартова (общая декартова) система координат, декартова система, аффинная (косоугольная декартова) система координат
C 178	**Cartesian vector** <GE, VT>	kartesischer (cartesischer) Vektor *m*, Vektor im kartesischen Koordinatensystem	vecteur *m* cartésien	декартов вектор, вектор в декартовой системе координат
C 179	**Cartier['s] divisor** <AG>	Cartier-Divisor *m*, Cartierdivisor *m*	diviseur *m* [au sens] de Cartier, diviseur localement principal	дивизор Картье, локальный главный дивизор
C 180	**Cartwright-Littlewood['s] [differential] equation** <DE>	Cartwright-Littlewoodsche Differentialgleichung *f*	équation *f* [différentielle] de Cartwright-Littlewood	[дифференциальное] уравнение Картрайта-Литтльвуда
	cascade method <DE>	*s.* L 72		
C 181	**cascade process** <SP>	Kaskadenprozeß *m*	processus *m* en cascade	каскадный процесс
	case-by-case proof <FO, LO>	*s.* P 1753		
	case distinction <GN, LO>	*s.* D 743		
C 182	**case of a Cramer system** <AL>	Cramerscher Fall *m* <lineares Gleichungssystem>	cas *m* de Cramer	случай крамеровской системы линейных уравнений
C 183	**case of unequal characteristics,** non-equicharacteristic case <AL>	charakteristikungleicher Fall *m*	cas *m* d'inégale caractéristique	случай неравной характеристики
	CA-set <TO>	*s.* C 959		
C 184	**Casimir['s] operator** <AL>	Casimir-Operator *m*	opérateur (élément) *m* de Casimir, Casimir *m*	оператор (элемент) Казимира

C 185	**Casorati['s] determinant** <FD>	Differenzendeterminante *f*	déterminant *m* de Casorati	разностный определитель
C 186	**Casorati-Weierstrass theorem,** Weierstrass['] theorem <FT>	Satz *m* von Casorati-Weierstraß, Weierstraßscher Näherungssatz *m*, Casorati-Weierstraßscher Satz, Satz von Sochotzki	théorème *m* de Casorati-Weierstrass	теорема Сохоцкого, теорема Вейерштрасса, теорема Сохоцкого-Вейерштрасса, теорема Казорати-Вейерштрасса
C 187	**Cassinian [curve]** <GE>	Cassinische Kurve *f*	cassinienne *f*	кассиниана
	Cassinian curve <AG>	*s.* O 563		
	Cassinian ellipse <AG>	*s.* O 563		
	Cassinian oval <AG>	*s.* O 563		
	Cassini['s] oval <AG>	*s.* O 563		
	cast <ST>	*s.* T 469		
	Castelnuovo-Enriques invariant <AG>	*s.* V 192		
C 188	**Castillon['s] problem** <EG>	Castillonsche Aufgabe *f*, Castillons Problem *n*	problème *m* de Castillon	задача Кастильона
C 189	**casting out** <NT>	Kontrolle *f* <einer Multiplikation *oder* Addition> durch Übergang zu Kongruenzen	preuve *f* <d'une multiplication *ou* addition> par réduction modulo *m*	метод проверки <умножения *или* сложения>, основанный на переходе к сравнениям
C 190	**casting out 1001s** <AR>	1001er-Probe *f*, Tausendundein[s]erprobe *f*	preuve *f* par 1001	метод сравнения по модулю 1001
C 191	**casting out eights** <divisibility> <AR>	Achterprobe *f*	preuve *f* par huit	проверка восьмеркой
C 192	**casting out elevens,** eleven test <AR>	Elferprobe *f*	preuve *f* par onze	проверка одиннадцатью, проверка [арифметического вычисления] с помощью числа 11
C 193	**casting out nines,** nine test <AR>	Neunerprobe *f*, 9er-Probe *f*, indische Probe *f*	preuve *f* par neuf, preuve indienne	проверка с помощью девятки, проверка девяткой, метод сравнения по модулю 9
C 194	**casting out sevens** <in the octal system> <NT>	Siebenerprobe *f*	preuve *f* par sept	проверка с помощью семерки
C 195	**Catalan['s] constant** <FU>	Catalansche Konstante *f*	nombre *m* (constante *f*) de Catalan	постоянная Каталана
C 196	**Catalan['s] trisectrix,** trisectrix of Catalan <AG>	Catalansche Trisektrix *f*, Trisektrix von Catalan	trisectrice *f* de Catalan	трисектриса Каталана
C 197	**catalecticant** <IV>	Katalektikante *f*	catalecticant *m*	каталектикант
C 198	**categoric[al];** monomorphic <MM>	kategorisch, monomorph	catégorique	категорический, категоричный
	categorical axiom system <MM>	*s.* C 202		
C 199	**categorical duality** <CA>	kategorientheoretische (kategorielle) Dualität *f*	dualité *f* catégorique	теоретико-категорная (категорийная) двойственность
C 200	**categorical judgement (proposition),** subject-predicate proposition <LO>	kategorisches Urteil *n*	jugement *m* catégorique	категорическое суждение
C 201	**categorical syllogism** <LO>	kategorischer Syllogismus *m*	syllogisme *m* catégorique	категорический силлогизм
C 202	**categorical system of axioms,** categorical axiom system <MM>	kategorisches Axiomensystem *n*	système *m* d'axiomes catégorique (complet)	категоричная система аксиом
C 203	**categorical theory** <MM>	kategorische (monomorphe) Theorie *f*	théorie *f* catégorique	категоричная (категорическая) теория
C 204	**categoricity,** monomorphy <MM>	Kategorizität *f*, Monomorphie *f*	catégoricité *f*	категоричность
C 205	**category,** L[y]usternik-Schnirelman[n] category <of a space> <TO>	Kategorie *f*, Kategorie im Sinne von Lusternik-Schnirelmann (Ljusternik-Schnirelman)	catégorie *f*, catégorie au sens de Lusternik-Schnirelmann	категория [в смысле] Люстерника-Шнирельмана, категория [Шнирельмана-Люстерника]
C 206	**2-category,** two-dimensional category <CA>	2-Kategorie *f*, zweidimensionale Kategorie *f*	2-catégorie *f*	2-категория
	2-category <CA>	*s.* B 277		
C 207	**category concept** <CA>	kategorientheoretischer Begriff *m*	notion *f* catégorique	категорийное понятие
	category locally of finite type <CA>	*s.* L 966		
	category of all categories <CA>	*s.* C 208		
	category of arrows <CA>	*s.* C 212		
	category of based sets <CA, SE>	*s.* C 215		
C 208	**category of categories,** category of all categories <CA>	Kategorie *f* der (aller) Kategorien	catégorie *f* des catégories	категория категорий
	category of diagrams <CA>	*s.* F 788		
	category of functors <CA>	*s.* F 788		
C 209	**category of groups [and homomorphisms]** <CA>	Kategorie *f* der Gruppen	catégorie *f* des groupes	категория групп [и гомоморфизмов]
C 210	**category of left modules** <CA>	Linksmodulkategorie *f*, Kategorie *f* der Linksmoduln	catégorie *f* des modules à gauche	категория левых модулей
C 211	**category of modules** <CA>	Modulkategorie *f*	catégorie *f* des modules	категория модулей

No.	English	German	French	Russian
C 212	**category of morphisms,** category of arrows <of a category> <CA>	Morphismenkategorie *f*, Kategorie *f* der Pfeile	catégorie *f* des morphismes	категория морфизмов
	category of path classes <TO>	*s.* F 827		
	category of pointed sets <CA, SE>	*s.* C 215		
C 213	**category of right modules** <CA>	Rechtsmodulkategorie *f*, Kategorie *f* der Rechtsmoduln	catégorie *f* des modules à droite	категория правых модулей
C 214	**category of sets [and functions]** <CA>	Kategorie *f* der Mengen, Mengenkategorie *f*	catégorie *f* des ensembles	категория множеств [и функций]
C 215	**category of sets with base point,** category of pointed (based) sets <CA, SE>	Kategorie *f* der punktierten Mengen, Kategorie der Mengen mit ausgezeichnetem Grundpunkt	catégorie *f* des ensembles pointés	категория множеств с отмеченной точкой, категория пунктированных множеств
	category of spaces <CA, TO>	*s.* C 216		
C 216	**category of topological spaces [and continuous maps],** category of spaces <CA, TO>	Kategorie *f* der topologischen Räume	catégorie *f* des espaces topologiques	категория топологических пространств [и непрерывных отображений], категория пространств
	category of topological spaces modulo homotopy <CA, TO>	*s.* H 525		
	category theorem of Baire <TO>	*s.* B 14		
C 217	**category with direct limits** <CA>	Kategorie *f* mit Kolimiten (induktiven Limiten)	catégorie *f* à colimites, catégorie avec limites inductives	категория, допускающая прямые пределы; категория с прямыми пределами
C 218	**category with finite coproducts** <CA>	Kategorie *f* mit endlichen Koprodukten	catégorie *f* à coproduits finis	категория, допускающая конечные прямые суммы; категория с конечными суммами
C 219	**category with finite products** <CA>	Kategorie *f* mit endlichen Produkten	catégorie *f* à produits finis	категория с конечными произведениями; категория, допускающая конечные прямые произведения
C 220	**category with inverse limits,** category with limits <CA>	Kategorie *f* mit Limiten (inversen Limiten)	catégorie *f* avec limites [projectives]	категория с обратными пределами; категория, допускающая обратные пределы
C 221	**category with involution** <CA>	Kategorie *f* mit Involution	catégorie *f* avec involution	категория с инволюцией, I-категория
	category with limits <CA>	*s.* C 220		
C 222	**category with multiplication** <MacLane>, monoidal category <CA>	Kategorie *f* mit Multiplikation, monoidale Kategorie	catégorie *f* p_m-structurée, catégorie avec multiplication	категория с умножением
C 223	**category with products,** product-complete category <CA>	Kategorie *f* mit Produkten	catégorie *f* où les produits existent, catégorie avec produits	категория с произведениями; категория, замкнутая относительно прямых произведений
C 224	**category with pullbacks** <CA>	Kategorie *f* mit Pullbacks	catégorie *f* où tous les produits fibrés existent, catégorie à produits fibrés	категория с расслоенными произведениями
C 225	**category with pushouts** <CA>	Kategorie *f* mit Pushouts	catégorie *f* à sommes amalgamées	категория с коуниверсальными квадратами
	category with zero morphisms <CA>	*s.* P 734		
C 226	**catenarian ring** <AL>	katenarischer Ring *m*	anneau *m* caténaire	
C 227	**catenary [curve],** funicular curve (line), chainette <GE>	Kettenlinie *f*, Seilkurve *f*, Katenoide *f*, Segelkurve *f*, Velaria *f*	chainette *f*, arc *m* de chainette, courbe *f* de la chainette, courbe (ligne *f*) funiculaire, caténaire *f*, vélaire *f*	цепная линия, веревочная кривая (линия)
C 228	**catenograph** <IN>	Katenograph *m*, Kettenlinienzeichner *m*	caténographe *m*	катенограф
C 229	**catenoid** <GE>	Kettenfläche *f*, Katenoid *n*, Catenoid *n*	caténoïde *f*, Alysséide *f*	катеноид, поверхность вращения цепной линии
C 230	**caterer problem** <ST>	Lieferantenproblem *n*	problème *m* du fournisseur	задача о поставщике
C 231/2	**cattle problem of Archimedes** <NT>	Ochsenproblem *n*, Rinderproblem *n* <des Archimedes>	problème *m* des bœufs	
C 233	**Cauchy['s] condensation test [for convergence]** <SS>	Cauchyscher Verdichtungssatz (Konvergenzsatz) *m*, Verdichtungssatz für Reihen, Verdichtungssatz [von Cauchy für unendliche Reihen]	théorème *m* de convergence de Cauchy	теорема сходимости Коши
C 234	**Cauchy['s] condition, Cauchy['s] condition for convergence,** Cauchy['s] [convergence] theorem, Cauchy['s] test [for convergence], theorem of Cauchy, Cauchy['s] necessary and sufficient conditions for	Cauchysches Konvergenzkriterium *n*, allgemeines Cauchysches Konvergenzkriterium (Kriterium *n*), Cauchy-Kriterium *n*, Cauchysche Bedingung (Konvergenzbedingung) *f*, Cauchy-Bedingung *f*, Cauchy-	critère *m* de Cauchy [de convergence], critère de convergence de Cauchy, théorème *m* (condition *f*) de Cauchy	критерий (признак) Коши сходимости, критерий Коши, общий признак сходимости <последовательности *или* ряда>

and still: C 234	convergence, general convergence principle, General Principle of Convergence <for number sequences *or* series> <SS>	sches (allgemeines) Konvergenzprinzip *n*, zweites (2.) Hauptkriterium *n*, Fundamentalsatz *m* der Analysis		
	Cauchy['s] conditions <DE>	*s.* I 522		
	Cauchy['s] convergence criterion <SS>	*s.* C 259		
	Cauchy['s] convergence test <SS>	*s.* C 259		
	Cauchy['s] convergence test of the second kind <SS>	*s.* D 4		
	Cauchy['s] convergence theorem <SS>	*s.* C 234		
	Cauchy-convergent sequence <SS, TO>	*s.* C 268		
	Cauchy-convergent series <FA>	*s.* C 269		
	Cauchy-convergent series <SS, TO>	*s.* C 268		
C 235	**Cauchy['s] criterion [for convergence]** <for a function> <DI>	Cauchysches Konvergenzkriterium *n*, Cauchysches Kriterium *n* [für die Existenz des Grenzwertes], Konvergenzkriterium von Cauchy, [Cauchysches] Grenzwertkriterium *n*	critère *m* de Cauchy	критерий (признак) Коши существования предела [функции]
C 236	**Cauchy['s] definition** <of continuity> <TO>	Cauchysche Stetigkeitsbedingung *f*, Cauchysches Kriterium *n* <für Stetigkeit>	définition *f* de Cauchy	определение Коши
	Cauchy['s] diagonal method <SE>	*s.* D 393a		
C 237	**Cauchy['s] distribution.** Cauchy['s] frequency distribution <ST>	Cauchy-Verteilung *f*, Cauchysche Verteilung *f*, Cauchyscher Verteilungstyp *m*	distribution *f* de Cauchy, loi *f* de Cauchy	распределение Коши
	Cauchy-Euler equation <VA>	*s.* E 596		
C 238	**Cauchy['s] filter** <TO>	Cauchy-Filter *m*, Cauchyfilter *m*	filtre *m* de Cauchy	фильтр Коши
C 239	**Cauchy filter base** <TO>	Cauchy-Filter-Basis *f*, Cauchyfilterbasis *f*	base *f* de filtre de Cauchy	базис фильтра Коши
	Cauchy['s] form <DI>	*s.* C 265		
	Cauchy['s] form of the remainder <DI>	*s.* C 265		
C 240	**Cauchy['s] formula,** Cauchy['s] mean value formula, Cauchy['s] theorem, double law of the mean, second (generalized, extended) mean value theorem <of the differential calculus> <DI>	zweiter (erweiterter, verallgemeinerter) Mittelwertsatz *m* der Differentialrechnung, Cauchysche Formel *f*, Formel von Cauchy, Mittelwert *m* von Cauchy	théorème *m* de Cauchy, théorème du rapport des accroissements [de deux fonctions]	теорема (формула) Коши, теорема об отношении приращений двух функций, вторая теорема о среднем [дифференциального исчисления]
	Cauchy['s] frequency distribution <ST>	*s.* C 237		
C 241	**Cauchy-Goursat theorem** <FT>	Cauchy-Goursatscher Satz *m*, Satz von Cauchy-Goursat	théorème *m* de Cauchv-Goursat	теорема Коши-Гурса
C 242	**Cauchy-Hadamard['s] formula**; Cauchy-Hadamard['s] theorem <for the radius of convergence> <FT>	Cauchy-Hadamardsche (Hadamardsche) Formel *f*; Cauchy-Hadamardscher Satz *m*, Satz von Cauchy-Hadamard, Hadamardscher (Hadamards) Satz	formule *f* de Cauchy-Hadamard; théorème *m* de Cauchy-Hadamard (Hadamard), théorème d'Hadamard	формула Коши-Адамара; теорема Коши-Адамара
C 243	**Cauchy-Hadamard['s] inequality** <FT>	Cauchy-Hadamardsche Ungleichung *f*	inégalité *f* de Cauchy-Hadamard	неравенство Коши-Адамара
	Cauchy-Hadamard['s] theorem <FT>	*s.* C 242		
C 244	**Cauchy['s] inequalities** <for the coefficients of a power series> <FT>	Cauchysche Abschätzungsformel *f*, Cauchyscher Koeffizientensatz *m*	inégalités *fpl* de Cauchy	неравенства Коши для коэффициентов степенного ряда
C 245	**Cauchy['s] inequality** <for real and complex numbers>; Cauchy-Schwarz inequality <for complex numbers> <for sums> <AN>	Cauchysche (Lagrangesche, Lagrange-Cauchysche) Ungleichung *f* <für reelle *oder* komplexe Zahlen>; Cauchy-Schwarzsche (Schwarzsche) Ungleichung, Ungleichung von Schwarz, Schwarzsche Ungleichheit *f* <für reelle Zahlen>	inégalité *f* de Cauchy (Cauchy-Schwarz)	неравенство Коши
	Cauchy['s] initial conditions <DE>	*s.* I 522		
	Cauchy['s] initial values <DE>	*s.* I 522		
C 246	**Cauchy['s] integral,** Cauchy type integral, integral of Cauchy type <AN>	Cauchysches Integral *n*, Cauchy-Integral *n*, Integral vom Cauchyschen Typ	intégrale *f* [singulière] de Cauchy	интеграл [типа] Коши

	Cauchy['s] integral convergence test <SS>	*s.* C 248		
C 247	**Cauchy['s] integral formula** <FT>	Cauchysche Integralformel *f*, Integralformel von Cauchy, Cauchysche Formel *f*	formule *f* intégrale de Cauchy, intégrale *f* de Cauchy	формула Коши, интегральная формула Коши, интеграл Коши
C 248	**Cauchy['s] integral test [for convergence],** integral convergence test, Maclaurin-Cauchy test, Cauchy['s] integral convergence test, Cauchy['s] test [for convergence] <SS>	Integralkriterium *n* [von Cauchy], Integralkriterium für Konvergenz	critère *m* [de convergence] de Cauchy-Maclaurin, théorème *m* de Cauchy	интегральный признак (критерий) [сходимости] Коши
	Cauchy['s] integral theorem <FT>	*s.* C 273		
C 249	**Cauchy['s] interpolation formula** <NU>	Cauchysche Interpolationsformel *f*	formule *f* d'interpolation de Cauchy	интерполяционная формула Коши
C 250	**Cauchy['s] kernel** <IE>	Cauchyscher Kern *m*	noyau *m* de Cauchy	ядро Коши
C 251	**Cauchy-Kovalevskaya['s] [existence] theorem,** theorem of Cauchy-Kowalewskaya (Cauchy-Kowalewski) <DE>	Existenzsatz (Satz) *m* von Cauchy-Kowalewskaja ([Cauchy-] Kowalewski), Cauchy-Kowalewskajascher (Cauchy-Kowalewskischer) Existenzsatz, Satz von S. Kowalewski, Kowalewskischer Satz	théorème *m* de Cauchy-Kovalevskaya, théorème d'existence de Cauchy-Kovalevskaya, théorème de Cauchy-Kowalewski	теорема Коши-Ковалевской, теорема С. В. Ковалевской
C 252	**Cauchy['s] limit theorem** <SS>	Cauchyscher Grenzwertsatz *m*	théorème *m* limite de Cauchy	предельная теорема Коши
	Cauchy-Liouville theorem <FT>	*s.* L 889		
C 253	**Cauchy['s] mean** <SS>	Cauchysches Mittel *n*, Cauchy-Mittel *n*	moyenne *f* de Cauchy	среднее Коши
	Cauchy['s] mean value formula <DI>	*s.* C 240		
C 254	**Cauchy['s] method** <for calculating convergence-generating terms> <FT>	Cauchysche Methode *f*, Methode von Cauchy	méthode *f* de Cauchy	метод Коши
C 255	**Cauchy['s] method [of finite differences]** <AX, DE, NU>	Cauchysche Differenzenmethode *f*	méthode *f* [des différences finies] de Cauchy	метод [конечных разностей] Коши
C 256	**Cauchy['s] method [of integration]** <DE>	Cauchysche Integrationsmethode *f*, Integrationsmethode von Cauchy, Cauchysche Methode *f*	méthode *f* [d'intégration] de Cauchy	метод [интегрирования] Коши
C 257	**Cauchy['s] multiplication** <of series> <SS>	Cauchysche Multiplikation *f*	multiplication *f* de Cauchy, multiplication par paquets	умножение Коши
	Cauchy['s] necessary and sufficient condition for convergence <SS>	*s.* C 234		
C 258	**Cauchy['s] net,** generalized Cauchy sequence, fundamental net <TO>	verallgemeinerte Cauchy-Folge *f*, Cauchy-Netz *n*, Cauchy-Moore-Smith-Folge *f*, gerichtete Cauchy-Familie *f*	suite *f* généralisée de Cauchy	сеть Коши, фундаментальная сеть
C 259	**Cauchy['s] *n*-th root test,** root test, Cauchy['s] convergence test, Cauchy['s] radical test [for convergence], Cauchy['s] test for convergence, Cauchy['s] convergence criterion <for series>; Maclaurin-Cauchy test, limit form of Cauchy's root test <SS>	Wurzelkriterium *n*, Cauchysches Wurzelkriterium, zweites [spezielles] Cauchysches Konvergenzkriterium *n*, [Cauchysches] Fundamentalkriterium *n* erster Art; Limesform *f* des Wurzelkriteriums	critère *m* de Cauchy [de première espèce], critère de convergence de Cauchy, critère fondamental de première espèce de Cauchy, règle *f* de Cauchy, théorème *m* de Cauchy	признак Коши, признак сходимости Коши, критерий Коши, критерий сходимости Коши
C 260	**Cauchy['s] principal value,** principal value, main value <of an integral>, singular integral in the Cauchy sense <AN>	Cauchyscher Hauptwert *m*, Hauptwert	valeur *f* principale de (d'après) Cauchy, valeur principale	главное значение по Коши, главное значение [Коши]
C 261	**Cauchy['s] problem,** initial-value problem <DE>	Anfangswertproblem *n*, Anfangswertaufgabe *f*, Cauchysches Anfangswertproblem *n*, Cauchysches Problem *n*	problème *m* de Cauchy, problème aux (des) valeurs initiales, problème des conditions initiales	задача Коши, начальная задача, задача с начальным условием
C 262	**Cauchy['s] process** <SP>	Cauchy-Prozeß *m*, Cauchyscher Prozeß *m*	processus *m* de Cauchy	процесс Коши
C 263	**Cauchy['s] product [series]** <of two series> <SS>	Cauchy-Produkt *n*, Cauchysches Produkt *n*, Cauchysche Produktreihe *f*, Produktreihe	série *f* produit [de Cauchy], série-produit *f* [de Cauchy], série-produit par paquets	произведение Коши <двух рядов>
C 264	**Cauchy['s] projection formula** <IG>	Cauchysche Projektionsformel *f*	formule *f* de projection de Cauchy	формула Коши
	Cauchy['s] radical test [for convergence] <SS>	*s.* C 259		
	Cauchy['s] ratio test <SS>	*s.* D 4		

No.	English	German	French	Russian
C 265	**Cauchy['s] remainder,** Cauchy['s] form [of the remainder] <in Taylor's formula> <DI>	Cauchysches Restglied *n*, Restglied der Taylorschen Formel in der Form von Cauchy	reste *m* (terme *m* résiduel) de Cauchy	остаточный член Коши, остаток Коши, остаточный член [формулы Тейлора] в форме Коши
C 266	**Cauchy['s] residue theorem,** theorem of residues, residue theorem <FT>	Residuensatz *m*	théorème *m* (formule *f*) des résidus, formule du résidu	теорема вычетов (о вычетах, Коши о вычетах)
C 267	**Cauchy-Riemann conditions (differential equations, equations)** <FT>	Cauchy-Riemannsche [partielle] Differentialgleichungen *fpl*, Cauchy-Riemannsche Gleichungen (Bedingungen) *fpl*	relations *fpl* de Cauchy, conditions *fpl* de monogénéité, système *m* homogène de Cauchy-Riemann, conditions de Cauchy-Riemann, équations *fpl* différentielles de Cauchy[-Riemann]	условия (уравнения, система) Даламбера-Эйлера (Д'Аламбера-Эйлера, Коши-Римана)
	Cauchy-Schwarz inequality <AN>	*s.* C 245		
C 268	**Cauchy['s] sequence,** fundamental (convergent, regular, Cauchy-convergent) sequence <of points or numbers>, // Cauchy-convergent series <SS, TO>	Cauchy-Folge *f*, Cauchysche Folge *f*, Fundamentalfolge *f*, konzentrierte Folge, in sich konvergente Folge, im Sinne von Cauchy konvergente Folge, // Fundamentalreihe *f*	suite *f* de Cauchy, suite fondamentale, suite régulière (concentrée), variante *f* fondamentale, // variante *f* convergente <Méray>	фундаментальная последовательность, сходящаяся в себе последовательность, последовательность Коши, // регулярная последовательность
C 269	**Cauchy['s] series,** Cauchy-convergent series, fundamental series <FA>	Cauchy-Reihe *f*, Cauchyreihe *f*, Fundamentalreihe *f*	série *f* de Cauchy, série fondamentale	ряд Коши, фундаментальный ряд
C 270	**Cauchy['s] solution** <DE>	Cauchysche Lösung *f*	solution *f* de Cauchy	решение Коши
C 271	**Cauchy-Stolz limit theorem, Cauchy-Stolz theorem** <SS>	Grenzwertsatz *m* von Cauchy-Stolz, Cauchy-Stolzscher Grenzwertsatz, Stolz-Cauchyscher Grenzwertsatz	théorème *m* [limite] de Cauchy-Stolz	[предельная] теорема Коши-Штольца
	Cauchy sum <SS>	*s.* S 2262		
C 272	**Cauchy-Taylor['s] theorem** <AX>	Cauchy-Taylorscher Satz *m*	théorème *m* de Cauchy-Taylor	теорема Коши-Тейлора
	Cauchy['s] test [for convergence] <SS>	*s.* 1. C 234; 2. C 248; 3. C 259		
C 273	**Cauchy['s] theorem,** Cauchy['s] integral theorem <FT>	Cauchyscher Integralsatz *m*, Integralsatz von Cauchy, Hauptsatz *m* der Funktionentheorie	théorème *m* fondamental de Cauchy, théorème de Cauchy	интегральная теорема Коши, теорема Коши
C 274	**Cauchy['s] theorem** <on analytical functions> <FT>	Cauchyscher Reihensatz *m*, Cauchy-Taylorscher Reihensatz	théorème *m* de Cauchy	теорема Коши о разложимости (разложении) аналитической функции в степенной ряд
	Cauchy['s] theorem <DI>	*s.* C 240		
	Cauchy['s] theorem <GR>	*s.* T 267		
	Cauchy['s] theorem <SS>	*s.* C 234		
C 275	**Cauchy['s] theorem for double series,** major rearrangement theorem <SS>	großer Umordnungssatz *m*, Cauchyscher Doppelreihensatz *m*	théorème *m* de Cauchy pour les séries doubles	теорема Коши для двойных рядов
	Cauchy type integral <AN>	*s.* C 246		
C 276	**causal relation** <ST>	kausaler Zusammenhang *m*	relation *f* causale	причинная связь
C 277	**cause variable,** explanatory variable <ST>	Kausalvariable *f*	variable *f* causale	каузальная переменная, аргумент причинной зависимости
C 278	**cause variable,** explanatory variable <in regression analysis> <ST>	Einflußgröße *f*	variable *f* explicative	каузальная переменная, аргумент причинной зависимости
C 279	**Cavalieri['s] principle (theorem)** <GE>	Cavalieri-Prinzip *n*, Cavalierisches Prinzip *n*	principe *m* de Cavalieri	принцип Кавальери
C 280	**cavalier perspective** <DS>	Kavalierperspektive *f*, freiisometrische Perspektive (Parallelenperspektive) *f*, Militärperspektive *f*	perspective *f* cavalière, axonométrie *f* en vue cavalière	военная перспектива, косоаксонометрическая проекция
C 281	**Cayley['s] algebra,** algebra of octonions, algebra of Cayley numbers, algebra of octaves, Cayley['s] numbers <AL>	Cayleysche Algebra *f*, Cayleysche Algebra achter Ordnung, Cayley-Algebra *f*, Oktavenalgebra *f*	algèbre *f* de Cayley, algèbre d'octaves	алгебра Кэли (Кейли, октав)
C 282	**Cayleyan;** pippian <Cayley> <of a net of curves> <AG>	Cayleysche (Hermitesche) Kurve *f*, Cayleyana *f*	courbe *f* de Cayley, courbe d'Hermite, courbe hermitienne (cayleyenne)	кривая Кэли
C 283	**Cayleyan conic** <of a cubic> <AG>	Cayleyscher Kegelschnitt *m*	conique *f* cayleyenne (de Cayley)	коническое сечение Кэли
	Cayley-Brill formula <AG>	*s.* F 386		
	Cayley['s] colour graph <GR>	*s.* C 287		
	Cayley['s] colour group <GR>	*s.* C 287		
C 284	**Cayley['s] conoid** <AG>	Cayleysches Konoid *n*	conoïde *m* de Cayley	коноид Кэли

No.	English	German	French	Russian
C 285	**Cayley['s] cubic surface** <AG>	Cayleys[che] kubische Fläche *f*	surface *f* cubique de Cayley	кубическая поверхность Кэли
C 286	**Cayley['s] curve** <of a curve of *m*-th order> <AG>	Cayleysche Kurve *f*	cayleyenne *f*, steiner-hessienne *f*, courbe *f* cayleyenne	кэлиана
C 287	**Cayley['s] diagram,** Cayley['s] graph, Cayley['s] colour group, Dehnsche Gruppenbild, Cayley['s] colour graph <of a group> <GR>	Dehnsches Gruppenbild *n*, Cayleysches Diagramm (Gruppendiagramm) *n*, Cayleysche „colour-group" *f*	diagramme *m* de Cayley, Colour-Diagramm *m*	граф группы, групповая диаграмма, диаграмма Кэли, цветная группа, цветной граф
C 288	**Cayley-Dickson algebra** <AL>	Cayley-Dickson-Algebra *f*, verallgemeinerte Cayleysche Algebra *f*	algèbre *f* de Cayley-Dickson	алгебра Кэли-Диксона
C 289	**Cayley['s] elimination method** <AL>	Cayleysche Eliminationsmethode *f*	méthode *f* d'élimination de Cayley	метод исключения Кэли
C 290	**Cayley['s] equations** <AY>	Cayleysche Gleichungen *fpl*, Gleichungen von Cayley	équations *fpl* de Cayley	уравнения Кэли
C 291	**Cayley['s] formulas** <MD>	Cayleysche Formeln *fpl*	formules *fpl* de Cayley	формулы Кэли
	Cayley['s] graph <GR>	*s.* C 287		
	Cayley-Hamilton polynomial <MD>	*s.* P 1003		
C 292	**Cayley-Hamilton theorem,** Hamilton-Cayley theorem <MD>	Satz *m* von Cayley-Hamilton, Cayley-Hamiltonscher Satz, Satz von Hamilton und Cayley	théorème *m* de Hamilton-Cayley (Cayley-Hamilton), théorème d'Hamilton-Cayley	теорема Гамильтона-Кэли (Кэли-Гамильтона)
C 293	**Cayley['s] identity** <FT, IV>	Cayleysche Identität *f* <FT, IV>; Syzygante *f* (Identität) von Cayley <IV>	identité *f* de Cayley	тождество Кэли (Кейли)
	Cayley-Klein metric <PJ>	*s.* P 1708		
C 294	**Cayley-Menger determinant** <in a semi-metric space> <TO>	Cayley-Mengersche Determinante *f*	déterminant *m* de Cayley-Menger	определитель Кэли-Менгера
	Cayley metric <PJ>	*s.* P 1708		
C 295	**Cayley['s] multiplication table,** Cayley['s] table, multiplication table <for an algebraic composition> <AL>	Multiplikationstafel *f*, Kompositionstafel *f*, Multiplikationstabelle *f*	table *f* de multiplication, table d'opération	таблица умножения, таблица Кэли, таблица произведений
C 296	**Cayley['s] number,** Cayley['s] octave <AL>	Cayley-Zahl *f*, Cayleysche Oktave *f*, Oktave	nombre *m* (octave *f*) de Cayley, octonion *m*, octave *f*, octave de Graves et de Cayley, octant *m* <Brioschi>	число Кэли, октава Кэли (Кейли), октава
	Cayley['s] numbers <AL>	*s.* C 281		
	Cayley['s] octave <AL>	*s.* C 296		
C 297	**Cayley['s] parameter** <GE>	Cayleyscher Parameter *m*, Parameter von Cayley-Euler-Gauß	paramètre *m* de Cayley	параметр Кэли
C 298	**Cayley['s] resultant** <of equations> <AL>	Cayleys Resultante *f*	résultant *m* de Cayley	результант Кэли
C 299	**Cayley-Salmon line** <GE>	Cayley-Salmonsche Gerade *f*, Cayleysche Gerade, Cayley-Gerade *f*	droite *f* de Cayley-Salmon, droite *f* de Cayley, droite cayleyenne	прямая Кэли (Кейли)
C 300	**Cayley['s] sextic** <AG>	Cayleysche Sextik *f*	sextique *f* de Cayley	секстика Кэли (Кейли)
C 301	**Cayley['s] surface** <GE>	Cayleysche Regelfläche (Fläche, Oberfläche) *f*	surface *f* de Cayley	поверхность Кэли
	Cayley['s] symbolic <IV>	*s.* S 2421		
	Cayley['s] symmetroid <AG>	*s.* S 2470		
	Cayley['s] syzygy <IV>	*s.* S 2554		
C 302	**Cayley['s] table** <of a unary or binary relation> <AL>	Cayleysche Tafel *f*	table *f* de Cayley	таблица Кэли
C 303	**Cayley['s] table,** group table <GR>	Cayleysche Gruppentafel (Tafel) *f*, Gruppentafel	table *f* de [A.] Cayley, tableau *m* de Cayley, table de groupe (Pythagore)	групповая таблица, таблица Кэли
	Cayley['s] table <AL>	*s.* C 295		
	Cayley['s] tetrahedroid <AG>	*s.* T 239		
C 304	**Cayley['s] theorem** <GP, GR>	Satz *m* von Cayley, Cayleyscher Satz	théorème *m* de Cayley	теорема Кэли
C 305	**Cayley['s] transform** <result> <FA>	Cayley-Transformierte *f*, Cayleysche Transformierte *f*	transformée *f* cayleyenne, transformée de Cayley	изображение (образ) Кэли (Кейли)
C 306	**Cayley['s] transform[ation]** <operation> <FA>	Cayley-Transformation *f*, Cayleysche Transformation *f*	transformation *f* de Cayley, transformation cayleyenne	преобразование Кэли (Кейли)
	cc <GE>	*s.* C 341		
C 307	**𝔈-closed object** <CA>	𝔈-abgeschlossenes Objekt *n*	objet *m* 𝔈-fermé	𝔈-замкнутый объект
C 308	**CCR algebra** <FA>	CCR-Algebra *f*	CCR-algèbre *f*, algèbre de Kaplansky	CCR-алгебра, CCR-C*-алгебра
	c.c. uniformity <TO>	*s.* U 182		
C 309	**c-discriminant equation** <DE>	*c*-Diskriminantengleichung *f*	équation *f* *c*-discriminante	*c*-дискриминантное уравнение
	ce <FU>	*s.* P 455		
	Ce <FU>	*s.* A 1079		

No.	English	German	French	Russian
	Čech['s] axis <DG>	*s.* D 13		
	Čech bicompactification <TO>	*s.* S 1817		
C 310	**Čech['s] co-chain** <AT>	Čechsche Kokette *f*	cochaîne *f* de Čech	чеховская коцепь, коцепь Чеха
C 311	**Čech['s] cohomology** <*e.g.*: with compact supports> <AT>	Čechsche Kohomologie *f* <*z. B.*: mit kompakten Trägern>	cohomologie *f* de Čech, cohomologie *f* au sens de Čech <*par exemple*: à supports compacts>	когомологии [Александрова-] Чеха, спектральные когомологии <*например*: с компактными носителями>
C 312	**Čech['s] cohomology group** <AT>	Čechsche Kohomologiegruppe *f*	groupe *m* [de cohomologie] de Čech	группа [когомологий] Чеха, группа когомологий Александрова-Чеха
	Čech['s] cohomology theory <AT>	*s.* C 1102		
	Čech['s] dimension <TO>	*s.* S 1957		
C 313	**Čech['s] homology** <AT>	Čechsche Homologie *f*	homologie *f* de Čech	гомологии [Александрова-] Чеха, спектральные гомологии
C 314	**Čech['s] homology group** <AT>	Čechsche Homologiegruppe *f*	groupe *m* d'homologie de Čech	группа гомологий Чеха группа гомологий Александрова-Чеха
	Čech-Stone compactification <TO>	*s.* S 1817		
	ceiling <NU>	*s.* R 1422		
C 315	**cell** <as an abstract complex> <AT>	Zelle *f*, abstrakte Zelle	cellule *f*	клетка, ячейка
C 316	**cell,** homology cell <*q*-dimensional> <AT>	Zelle *f*, Homologiezelle *f* <*q*-dimensionale>	cellule *f* [homologique] <à *q* dimensions>	[гомологическая] клетка <*q*-мерная>
C 317	**cell** <GE, GP, TO>	Zelle *f*	cellule *f*	клетка
C 318	**cell** <of a magic square> <CT>	Feld *n*, Zelle *f*	case *f*	клетка
C 319	**cell** <of a matrix> <MD, PG>	Zelle *f*	cellule *f*	ячейка
	cell <GN, ST>	*s.* T 1		
	cell <GP>	*s.* E 84		
	cell <ST>	*s.* 1. C 764; 2. C 792		
C 320	**cell boundary** <AT>	Zellenrand *m*	bord *m* de la cellule	граница ячейки
	cell boundary <ST>	*s.* C 765		
	cell complex <AT>	*s.* P 947		
	cell frequency <ST>	*s.* C 773		
	cell function <FA>	*s.* A 150		
	cell interval <ST>	*s.* 1. C 792; 2. C 794		
	cell length <ST>	*s.* C 794		
	cell limit <ST>	*s.* C 765		
	cell mark <ST>	*s.* C 795		
	cell mean <ST>	*s.* C 796		
	cell of Peaucellier <GE, IN>	*s.* P 358		
	cell range <ST>	*s.* C 794		
C 321	**cellular approximation** <AT>	zellenmäßige Approximation *f*	approximation *f* cellulaire	клеточная аппроксимация
C 322	**cellular approximation theorem** <AT>	zellenmäßiger Approximationssatz *m*	théorème *m* d'approximation cellulaire	теорема о клеточной аппроксимации
C 323	**cellular automaton** <TA>	zellularer Automat *m*	automate *m* cellulaire	клеточный автомат
C 324	**cellular chain** <AT>	Zellenkette *f*	chaîne *f* cellulaire	клеточная цепь
C 325	**cellular chain group** <AT>	Zellenkettengruppe *f*	groupe *m* de chaînes cellulaires	группа клеточных цепей
C 326	**cellular cohomology** <AT>	Zellenkohomologie *f*	cohomologie *f* cellulaire	клеточные когомологии
C 327	**cellular cohomology group** <AT>	zellenmäßige Kohomologiegruppe *f*	groupe *m* de cohomologie cellulaire	клеточная группа когомологий
C 328	**cellular compactum** <TO>	zellulares Kompaktum *n*	compact *m* cellulaire	клеточный компакт
C 329	**cellular cycle** <AT>	Zellenzyklus *m*	cycle *m* cellulaire	клеточный цикл
C 330	**cellular decomposition** <AT>	Zellenzerlegung *f*, Zellzerlegung *f*	décomposition *f* cellulaire	клеточное разбиение, разбивка на ячейки
C 331	**cellular homotopy** <AT>	zellenmäßige Homotopie *f*	homotopie *f* cellulaire	клеточная гомотопия
C 332	**cellularity** <TO>	Zellularität *f*	cellularité *f*	клеточность
C 333	**cellular map** <AT>	zellenmäßige Abbildung *f*	application *f* cellulaire	клеточное отображение
C 334	**cellular space** <AT>	zellularer Raum *m*	espace *m* cellulaire	клеточное пространство
C 335	**cellular subcomplex** <AT>	Zellenunterkomplex *m*	sous-complexe *m* cellulaire	клеточный подкомплекс
C 336	**censoration,** censoring <ST>	Zensorierung *f*, Zensierung *f*	censuration *f*	цензурирование, цензуризация
C 337	**censored distribution** <ST>	zensorierte (zensierte) Verteilung *f*	distribution *f* censurée	цензурированное распределение
	censoring <ST>	*s.* C 336		
C 338	**census** <ST>	Vollerhebung *f*	recensement *m*	полный набор характеристик, ценз, перепись
	center	*s.* centre		
	centesimal angular minute <GE>	*s.* C 340		
	centesimal angular second <GE>	*s.* C 341		
C 339	**centesimal fraction** <NT>	Zentesimalbruch *m*	fraction *f* centésimale	сотенная дробь
C 340	**centesimal minute [of angle],** centesimal angular minute, ^{c}, min <GE>	Neuminute *f*, ^{c}	minute *f* centésimale (d'arc centésimale), ^{c}, min	десятичная [угловая] минута, метрическая минута, ^{c}, мин
C 341	**centesimal second [of angle],** centesimal angular second, ^{cc}, sec <GE>	Neusekunde *f*, ^{cc}	seconde *f* centésimale (d'arc centésimale), ^{cc}, sec	десятичная [угловая] секунда, метрическая секунда, ^{cc}, сек
	centile <ST>	*s.* P 402		

No.	English	German	French	Russian
	central <GR>	*s.* C 401		
C 342	**central algebra,** normal algebra <AL>	zentrale (normale) Algebra <über *K*>	algèbre *f* centrale	центральная алгебра, нормальная алгебра
C 343	**central angle** <US>, angle at centre, angle subtended at the centre <EG>	Mittelpunktswinkel *m*, Zentriwinkel *m*, Mittenwinkel *m*	angle *m* au centre	центральный угол
C 344	**central axis,** axis <of a vector system> <GE>	Zentralachse *f*, Schraubenachse *f*, Achse *f*	axe *m* central	центральная ось
	central collineation <PJ>	*s.* P 522		
C 345	**central confidence interval** <ST>	zentrales Konfidenzintervall *n*	intervalle *m* de confiance centré	центрированный доверительный интервал
C 346	**central conic [section]** <AY> ⌐<DG>	Mittelpunktskegelschnitt *m*	conique *f* à centre, section *f* conique à centre	центральное коническое сечение
	central co-ordinates	*s.* G 233		
C 347	**central curve** <GE>	Mittelpunktskurve *f*, zentrische Kurve *f*, Zentralkurve *f*	courbe *f* à centre, courbe centrale	центральная кривая
C 348	**central derivative** <DI>	zentrale Ableitung *f*	dérivée *f* centrale	центральная производная
C 349	**central difference** <of a function> <FD>	zentrale Differenz *f*	différence *f* centrale	центральная разность
C 350	**central difference operator** <FD, NU>	Operator *m* für zentrale Differenzen, Differenzenoperator *m* δ	opérateur *m* des différences centrales	оператор центральных разностей
	central difference quotient <DI, FD>	*s.* C 352		
C 351	**central** <χ^2-, *F- or t-*> **distribution** <ST>	zentrale <χ^2-, *F- oder t-*> Verteilung *f*	distribution *f* <de χ^2, *F ou t*> centrale	центральное <χ^2-, *F- или t-*> распределение
C 352	**central divided difference,** central difference quotient <of a function> <DI, FD>	zentraler Differenzenquotient *m*, zentrale dividierte (geteilte) Differenz *f*	différence *f* divisée centrale, quotient *m* des différences centrales	центральная (симметричная) разделенная разность, центральное (симметричное) разностное отношение
C 353	**central division algebra** <AL>	zentrale (normale) Divisionsalgebra *f*	algèbre *f* centrale à division	центральная алгебра с делением
C 354	**central edge** <of a tree> <GP>	Achse *f* der linearen Ausdehnung, Achse	arête *f* centrale	ось
C 355	**central element,** element of the centre <with respect to a composition> <AL>	zentrales (invariantes) Element *n*, Element des Zentrums, Zentrumselement *n*	élément *m* central (conjugué de lui-même, invariant, du centre, normal)	центральный элемент
	central element <GR>	*s.* I 1098		
C 356	**central endomorphism** <of a group> <GR>	zentraler Endomorphismus *m* <Zassenhaus>, Zentrumsendomorphismus *m* <Fitting>	endomorphisme *m* central	центральный эндоморфизм
	central envelope <FA>	*s.* C 385		
C 357	**central extension** <of a group> <GR>	zentrale Erweiterung *f*	extension *f* centrale	центральное расширение
	central extension <AL>	*s.* C 358		
C 358	**central extension field,** central extension <of a field> <AL>	zentrale Erweiterung *f*, zentraler Erweiterungskörper *m*	extension *f* centrale	центральное расширение <поля>
C 359	**central field** <of extremals> <VA>	Zentralfeld *n* <von Extremalen>	champ *m* central <d'extrémales>	центральное поле <экстремалей>
	central field <VT>	*s.* C 391		
C 360	**central idempotent** <AL>	Zentrumsidempotent *n*	idempotent *m* central	центральный идемпотент
C 361	**central index** <FT, SS>	Zentralindex *m*	indice *m* central	центральный индекс
C 362	**central invariant subgroup,** central subgroup <GR>	zentraler Normalteiler *m*	sous-groupe *m* invariant central	центральный нормальный делитель
	centralized random variable <ST>	*s.* C 413		
	centralized variate <ST>	*s.* C 413		
C 363	**centralizer** <of a module>, commuting ring <of a ring *or* a module> <AL>	Zentralisator *m* <eines Moduls>	commutant *m* des homothéties <de l'anneau des homothéties d'un module>, commutant *m* <d'un module>	централизатор <модуля>
C 364	**centralizer,** commutant <of a group ><GR>	Zentralisator *m*, Kommutant *m*	centralisateur *m*, commutant *m*	централизатор, коммутант
C 365	**central limit theorem** <ST>	zentraler Grenzwertsatz (Grenzverteilungssatz) *m*	théorème *m* limite central	центральная предельная теорема
C 366	**centrally biased estimator** <ST>	zentral verzerrte (verfälschte) Schätzfunktion (Schätzung, Punktschätzung) *f*	estimateur *m* centralement biaisé	центрально смещённая оценка
C 367	**centrally isomorphic subgroup** <GR>	zentral isomorphe Untergruppe *f*	sous-groupe *m* centralement isomorphe	центрально изоморфная подгруппа
C 368	**centrally located sample,** centred sample <ST> ⌐<GE>	zentral gelagerte Stichprobe *f*, zentrierte Stichprobe	échantillon *m* centré	центрированная выборка
	centrally symmetric[al]	*s.* C 440		
C 369	**central moment** <ST>	zentrales Moment *n*	moment *m* central	центральный момент
C 370	**central oval** <CS, GE>	Mittelpunktseilinie *f*, Oval *n* mit Mittelpunkt	courbe *f* convexe fermée à centre	центральный овал
C 371	**central perspective** <DS>	Zentralperspektive *f*, Perspektive *f* mit Fluchtpunkt	perspective *f* centrale	центральная перспектива
C 372	**central point,** centre <of a line in a complex of lines> <GE>	Zentralpunkt *m*, Mittelpunkt *m*	point *m* central, centre *m*	центральная точка, центр
C 373	**central point** <on a generator of a ruled surface> <DG>	Kehlpunkt *m*, Zwickpunkt *m*, Zentralpunkt *m*, Hauptpunkt *m*, // Kuspidalpunkt *m*	point *m* central	центр образующей, центральная точка, точка перехвата, горловая точка

No.	English	German	French	Russian
	central point <AY>	*s.* C 421		
C 374	**central polynomial** <AL>	zentrales Polynom *n*	polynôme *m* central	центральный многочлен
	central program <PG>	*s.* C 382		
C 375	**central projection,** conic (perspective) projection, perspective <mapping> <DS>	Zentralprojektion *f*, Kegelprojektion, Perspektive *f*, Perspektivität *f*	projection *f* centrale (conique, perspective), perspective *f* conique (linéaire), perspective	центральная (коническая, перспективная) проекция, перспектива
C 376	**central projection** <FA>	Zentralprojektion *f*	projection *f* centrale	центральная проекция
	central projection <DS>	*s.* P 518		
C 377	**central quadric** <AY>	Mittelpunktsquadrik *f*	quadrique *f* à centre, surface *f* à centre du second degré	центральная квадрика (поверхность второго порядка)
C 378	**central quotient group** <GR>	Faktorgruppe *f* nach dem Zentrum	cogrédient *m*, groupe *m* quotient du centre	фактор-группа по центру
C 379	**central section** <of a quadric> <AY>	Zentralschnitt *m*, Mittelpunktsschnitt *m*	section *f* centrale	центральное сечение
C 380	**central sequence of order statistics** <ST>	zentrale Positionsfunktionenfolge *f*	suite *f* centrale de statistiques d'ordre	центральная последовательность порядковых статистик
C 381	**central series** <of a group> <GR>	Zentralreihe *f*, Zentrenreihe *f*	suite *f* centrale	центральный ряд
C 382	**central solution,** central program <in the simplex method> <PG>	zentrales Programm *n*, zentrale Lösung *f*	solution *f* centrale, programme *m* central	центральное решение, центральный план, центральная программа
C 383	**central sphere** <DG>	Zentralkugel *f*	sphère *f* centrale	центральная сфера
C 384	**central subdivision** <relative to a given subdivision of K^{n-1}> <AT>	Zentralunterteilung *f*, Zentralzerlegung *f* <in bezug auf eine gegebene Unterteilung von K^{n-1}>	subdivision *f* centrale <par rapport à une subdivision de K^{n-1} donnée>	центральное подразделение <относительно данного подразделения комплекса K^{n-1}>
	central subgroup <GR>	*s.* C 362		
C 385	**central support,** central envelope <of projection of a *W**-algebra> <FA>	zentraler Träger *m*	support *m* central	центральный носитель
C 386	**central surface** <GE>	Mittelpunktsfläche *f*, zentrische (zentrale) Fläche *f*, Fläche mit Mittelpunkt	surface *f* à centre, surface centrale (centrée)	центральная поверхность
C 387	**central surface** <of a complex of lines> <GE>	Zentralfläche *f*	surface *f* centrale	центральная поверхность
	central surface <DG>	*s.* E 645		
	central-symmetric <GE>	*s.* C 440		
C 388	**central symmetrization** <CS, GE>	Zentralsymmetrisierung *f*	symétrisation *f* centrale	центральное симметрирование
C 389	**central symmetry** <as a property> <EG>	Zentralsymmetrie *f*, Punktsymmetrie *f*, zentrische Symmetrie *f*	symétrie *f* centrale	центральная симметрия, симметрия относительно точки (центра), инверсия
C 390	**central tangent,** ray of striction, striction ray <DG>	Striktionsstrahl *m*, Zentraltangente *f*	tangente *f* centrale, rayon *m* de striction	центральная касательная, стрикционный луч, луч сжатия, горловой луч
C 391	**central vector field,** central field <VT>	zentrales Vektorfeld *n*, Zentralfeld *n*	champ *m* [vectoriel] central	центральное [векторное] поле
C 392	**centre,** center <US> <for an algebraic curve, especially a quadric, *or* surface> <AG, AY>	Mittelpunkt *m* <einer algebraischen Kurve *oder* Fläche>	centre *m* <d'une courbe *ou* surface algébrique>	центр <алгебраической кривой *или* поверхности>
C 393	**centre** <of a local scheme, monoidal transformation, groupoid, Lie algebra, place, quasifield, ring, cell, category, projection, star, lattice *or* projectivity> <AG, AL, AT, CA, DS, GP, LA, PJ>	Zentrum *n*	centre *m*	центр
C 394	**centre** <of a [barycentric] star>; midpoint <of a simplex> <AT>	Mittelpunkt *m*	centre *m*	центр
C 395	**centre,** vortex point <DE>	Wirbelpunkt *m*, Zentrum *n*	centre *m*, sommet *m*	центр
C 396	**centre** <of a Mittag-Leffler star> <FT>	Mittelpunkt *m*, Pol *m*	centre *m*	центр
C 397	**centre** <of a stereographic projection> <FT, PJ>	Zentrum *n*	point *m* de vue	центр
C 398	**centre** <of a function element *or* of a set *or* of a vector system> <FT, SE, VT>	Mittelpunkt *m*	centre *m*	центр
C 399	**centre** <of a pencil, e.g. of conics> <GE>	Grundpunkt *m*, Basispunkt *m*	point *m* fondamental	базисная точка
C 400	**centre** <of a graph> <GP>	Zentrum *n*	centre *m* [de l'assemblage]	центр
C 401	**centre,** central, centrum <of a group> <GR>	Zentrum *n*	centre *m*, central *m*, sous-groupe *m* cogrédient, premier centre	центр
C 402	**centre,** vertex, axis <of a pencil of planes> <PJ>	Träger *m*, Achse *f*	support *m*, axe *m*	носитель, ось
C 403	**centre,** vertex <of a pencil *or* sheaf of lines *or* of a bundle of planes> <PJ>	Scheitel *m*, Träger *m*, Mittelpunkt *m*, Grundpunkt *m* <eines Strahlenbüschels, Strahlenbündels *oder* Ebenenbündels>	centre *m*, sommet *m*, support *m*, point *m* fondamental <d'un faisceau *ou* pinceau de droites *ou* d'une gerbe de plans>	центр, носитель <пучка прямых, связки прямых *или* связки плоскостей>
	centre <AN, SS>	*s.* C 417		
	centre <GE>	*s.* C 429		
	centre <GE>	*s.* C 372		
	centre <GP>	*s.* C 416		
	centre <PJ>	*s.* C 423		
C 404	**centred affine geometry** <GE>	zentro[-]affine Geometrie *f*	géométrie *f* affine centrée	центро[-]аффинная геометрия

No.	English	German	French	Russian
C 405	**centred affine group** <AL, AY>	zentro[-]affine (zentrierte affine) Gruppe *f*	groupe *m* affine centré	центро[-]аффинная группа
C 406	**centred affine map[ping],** centred affine transformation <GE>	zentro[-]affine Abbildung (Transformation) *f*	application (transformation) *f* affine centrée	центро[-]аффинное отображение (преобразование)
C 407	**centred affine space** <DG, GE>	zentro[-]affiner Raum *m*	espace *m* affine centré	центро[-]аффинное пространство
	centred affine transformation <GE>	*s.* C 406		
	centred and normed distribution <ST>	*s.* S 1621		
	centred and normed frequency function <ST>	*s.* S 1622		
	centred and normed normal distribution <ST>	*s.* S 1623		
	centred and normed normal variate <ST>	*s.* S 1624		
	centred and normed random variable <ST>	*s.* S 1626		
	centred and normed realization <ST>	*s.* S 1625		
	centred and normed regression coefficient <ST>	*s.* S 1631		
	centred and normed sample value <ST>	*s.* S 1625		
	centred and normed variable <ST>	*s.* S 1626		
	centred and normed variate <ST>	*s.* S 1626		
	centred collinear transformation <AY>	*s.* C 409		
C 408	**centred euclidean space** <DG>	zentro[-]euklidischer Raum *m*	espace *m* euclidien centré	центро-евклидово пространство
C 409	**centred homographic transformation,** centred collinear transformation, centred transformation <AY>	zentrierte kollineare Abbildung (Transformation) *f*, zentrierte Abbildung (Transformation)	transformation (application) *f* homographique (collinéaire) centrée, transformation (application) centrée	центрированное гомографическое (коллинеарное) преобразование (отображение), центрированное преобразование (отображение)
C 410	**centred process** <SP>	zentrierter Prozeß *m*	processus *m* centré	центрированный процесс
	centred random variable <ST>	*s.* C 413		
	centred sample <ST>	*s.* C 368		
C 411	**centred sequence** <SE, TO>	zentrierte Folge *f*	suite *f* centrée	центрированная последовательность
C 412	**centred system of sets,** system (collection) of sets having the finite intersection property <SE>	zentriertes Mengensystem (System) *n*	système *m* centré [de parties]	система образующих фильтра, центрированное семейство множеств
	centred transformation <AY>	*s.* C 409		
C 413	**centred variate,** centred random variable, centralized variate (random variable) <ST>	zentrierte Zufallsgröße (Zufallsvariable) *f*	variable *f* aléatoire centrée	центрированная случайная величина
C 414	**centreless algebra** <AL>	Algebra *f* ohne Zentrum	algèbre *f* à centre nul	алгебра с нулевым центром
	centre line <DS, EG>	*s.* L 866		
	centre method of Huard <PG>	*s.* H 595		
	centre of area <EG>	*s.* C 434		
C 415	**centre of curvature** <of a curve> <DG>	Krümmungsmittelpunkt *m*	centre *m* de courbure	центр кривизны
	centre of curvature <DG>	*s.* C 425		
	centre of curvature surface <DG>	*s.* E 645		
C 416	**centre of distance,** centre <of a tree> <GP>	Zentrum *n* der linearen Ausdehnung, Zentrum	centre *m*	центр
C 417	**centre of expansion,** centre <of a power series> <AN, SS>	Mittelpunkt *m* der Entwicklung, Mittelpunkt, Entwicklungsmittelpunkt *m*, Entwicklungspunkt *m* <einer Potenzreihe>	centre *m* de développement, centre <d'une série entière>	центр разложения, центр <степенного ряда>
C 418	**centre of gravity,** median point, centroid <of a triangle> <EG>	Schwerpunkt *m*, Schnittpunkt *m* der Seitenhalbierenden	centre *m* de gravité, centroïde *f*	центр тяжести, точка пересечения медиан
	centre of gravity <EG>	*s.* C 434		
	centre of gravity line <EG>	*s.* L 867		
C 419	**centre of gravity of the vertices** <of a polygon> <EG>	Eckenschwerpunkt *m*	centre *m* de gravité (pesanteur) des sommets	центр тяжести одномерного многоугольника, центр тяжести вершин
	centre of homology <PJ>	*s.* C 423		
C 420	**centre of inversion** <GE>	Mittelpunkt *m* (Zentrum *n*) der Inversion, Inversionszentrum *n*	pôle *m* de l'inversion, centre *m* d'inversion	центр (полюс) инверсии
C 421	**centre of involution,** central point <of an involution> <AY>	Involutionszentrum *n*, Zentrum *n* (Zentralpunkt *m*) der Involution	centre *m* (point *m* central) de l'involution	центр (центральная точка) инволюции

No.	English	German	French	Russian
	centre of magnitude (number) <GP>	*s.* C 435a		
C 422	**centre of perspective (perspectivity),** eye position, centre of projection (vision), point of sight <DS>	Perspektivitätszentrum *n*, Zentrum *n* der Perspektive, Kollineationszentrum *n*, Auge *n*, Aug[en]punkt *m*, Blickzentrum *n*, Projektionszentrum *n*, Zentrum der Projektion, Mittelpunkt *m* (Zentrum) der Kollineation, Hauptpunkt *m*	centre *m* de perspective, centre perspectif, point *m* principal (de vue), position *f* de l'œil, œil *m*, centre de projection (collinéation), sommet *m*, pôle *m*	центр проекций (проектирования, проекции, перспективы), глаз, положение глаза, главная точка
C 423	**centre of perspectivity,** centre of homology, ray centre, centre, vertex <PJ>	Perspektivitätszentrum *n*, Homologiezentrum *n*, Zentrum *n* der Perspektivität	centre *m* d'homologie, centre de perspective, centre perspectif	центр гомологии (перспективы)
C 424	**centre of polarity** <PJ>	Mittelpunkt *m* eines Polarsystems	centre *m* d'un système polaire	центр полярной системы
C 425	**centre of principal curvature,** centre of curvature <of a surface> <DG>	Hauptkrümmungsmittelpunkt *m*, Krümmungsmittelpunkt *m*	centre *f* de courbure [principale]	центр [главной] кривизны
C 426	**centre of projection** <AG>	Projektionszentrum *n*	centre *m* de la projection	центр проектирования
	centre of projection <DS>	*s.* C 422		
C 427	**centre of purity** <of a group> <GR>	Servanzzentrum *n*	centre *m* de pureté	центр сервантности
C 428	**centre of range** <ST>	Mitte *f* (Mittenwert *m*) des Änderungsbereichs	centre *m* d'étendue	середина области изменения <ограниченной случайной величины>
	centre of similarity <GE>	*s.* C 429		
C 429	**centre of similitude,** homothetic centre, ray centre, centre of similarity, similarity centre, centre <GE>	Ähnlichkeitspunkt *m* <homothetischer Figuren>; Ähnlichkeitszentrum *n*, Streckungszentrum *n*, Homothetiezentrum *n*, Zentrum *n* der Homothetie, Zentrum, Mittelpunkt *m* der homothetischen Beziehung	centre *m* d'homothétie, centre de similitude, centre, pôle *m*	центр подобия (гомотетии), центр
C 430	**centre of symmetry,** symmetry centre <EG, ST>	Symmetriezentrum *n*, Zentrum *n* der Symmetrie, Symmetriemittelpunkt *m*	centre *m* de symétrie	центр симметрии
	centre of the circumscribed circle <EG>	*s.* C 735		
	centre of the escribed circle <EG>	*s.* E 661		
	centre of the escribed sphere <EG>	*s.* E 662		
	centre of the inscribed circle <EG>	*s.* I 216		
	centre of the inscribed sphere <EG>	*s.* I 217		
	centre of vision <DS>	*s.* C 422		
	centre of volume <EG>	*s.* C 439		
C 431	**centre-to-centre distance, centre-to-centre spacing** <EG>	Mittenabstand *m*, Mittelpunktabstand *m*	distance *f* entre [les] centres	расстояние между центрами
C 432	**centricity** <CS, GE>	Zentrizität *f*	centricité *f*	центричность
	centrobaric rule <DI, EG>	*s.* P 38		
C 433	**centroid** <of a ring *or* group> <AL, GR>	Zentroid *n*	centroïde *m*	центроид
C 434	**centroid,** centre of area, centre of gravity <of a triangle, quadrangle, *or* another figure> <EG>	Schwerpunkt *m*, Flächenschwerpunkt *m*, Flächenmittelpunkt *m*	centroïde *f*, centre *m* de gravité (pesanteur, surface), centre d'aire	центр тяжести, центроид, центр поверхности <двумерного треугольника, четырехугольника и других фигур>
C 435	**centroid** <of *n* points> <GE>	Zentrum *n* (Punkt *m*) der mittleren Entfernungen, Schwerpunkt *m* <von *n* Punkten>	centre *m* des moyennes distances, centre de gravité, barycentre *m* <de *n* points>	центроид, центр средних расстояний, центр тяжести <*n* точек>
C 435a	**centroid,** centre of number (magnitude) <of a tree> <GP>	Massenzentrum *n*	centre *m* de l'assemblage	центроид <состоящий из одной вершины>
	centroid <AT>	*s.* B 70		
	centroid <EG>	*s.* C 418		
C 436	**centroid factor** <ST>	Schwerpunktfaktor *m*	facteur *m* centroïde	центроидный фактор
C 437	**centroid method** <ST>	Schwerpunktmethode *f*, Schwerpunktverfahren *n*	méthode *f* centroïde	центроидный метод
C 438	**centroid of points having the masses** $\lambda_1, \ldots, \lambda_n$ <EG>	Schwerpunkt *m* der mit den Gewichten $\lambda_1, \ldots, \lambda_n$ versehenen Punkte	mélange *m* des points dans les proportions $\lambda_1, \ldots, \lambda_n$	центр тяжести точек, имеющих массы $\lambda_1, \ldots, \lambda_n$
C 439	**centroid of volume,** centre of volume <EG>	Volum[en]schwerpunkt *m*, Volum[en]mittelpunkt *m*	centroïde *f* (centre *m*) de volume	центр тяжести объема, центр объема
	centrosurface <DG>	*s.* E 645		
C 440	**centrosymmetric[al],** centrally symmetric[al], central-symmetric <GE>	zentralsymmetrisch, punktsymmetrisch, zentrischsymmetrisch	centro-symétrique *f*, symétrique *f* central, à (de, par) symétrie centrale	центрально[-]симметричный, центросимметричный, с центральной симметрией
C 441	**centrosymmetric convex body** <CS, GE>	Mittelpunktseikörper *m*, zentralsymmetrischer konvexer Körper *m*	corps *m* convexe centro-symétrique	центрально-симметричное выпуклое тело

No.	English	German	French	Russian
C 442	**centrosymmetric determinant** <MD>	zentrosymmetrische Determinante *f*	déterminant *m* centrosymétrique	центросимметрический определитель
	centrum <GR>	*s.* C 401		
C 443	**Černikov['s] group** <GR>	Tschernikowsche (Černikovsche) Gruppe *f*	groupe *m* de Tchernikov	группа Черникова
C 444	**Černikov['s] *p*-group** <GR>	Tschernikowsche *p*-Gruppe *f*	*p*-groupe *m* de Tchernikov	*p*-группа Черникова
C 445	**certain event,** certainty <ST>	sicheres Ereignis *n*	événement *m* certain (référentiel)	достоверное событие
C 446	**certainty** <ST>	Sicherheit *f*, Gewißheit *f*	certitude *f*	уверенность,(достоверность
	certainty <ST>	*s.* C 445		
C 447	**Cesàro['s] curve [in the plane],** Cesàro['s] plane curve <GE>	Cesàrosche Kurve *f*, Cesàrosche ebene Kurve	courbe *f* de Cesàro, courbe plane de Cesàro	кривая Чезаро, плоская кривая Чезаро
C 448	**Cesàro['s] function** <FT>	Cesàrosche Funktion *f*	fonction *f* de Cesàro	функция Чезаро
C 449	**Cesàro['s] limitation method,** Cesàro['s] method [of limitation], *C*-method <for divergent sequences> <LI>	Cesàrosches Limitierungsverfahren *n*, *C*-Verfahren *n*, Cesàro-Verfahren *n*	méthode *f* de limitation de Cesàro, méthode de Cesàro, *C*-méthode *f*	метод [образования обобщенного предела] Чезаро
	Cesàro['s] limitation method of *k*-th order <LI>	*s.* C 754		
C 450	**Cesàro['s] mean** <of *k*-th order> <LI>	Cesàrosches Mittel *n* <*k*-ter Ordnung>	moyenne *f* de Cesàro <d'ordre *k*>	среднее [арифметическое] Чезаро, среднее <*k*-го порядка>
C 451	**Cesàro['s] method,** Cesàro['s] method of summation, Cesàro['s] summation method, *C*-method <for divergent series> <LI>	Cesàrosches Summierungsverfahren *n*, *C*-Verfahren *n*, Cesàrosche Summabilitätsmethode *f*	méthode *f* de sommation de Cesàro, méthode de Cesàro	метод Чезаро, метод суммирования [расходящихся рядов] Чезаро, метод средних арифметических Чезаро
	Cesàro['s] method <LI>	*s.* C 449		
	Cesàro['s] method of *k*-th order <LI>	*s.* 1. C 753; 2. C 754		
	Cesàro['s] method of limitation <LI>	*s.* C 449		
	Cesàro['s] method of summation <LI>	*s.* C 451		
	Cesàro['s] method of summation of *k*-th order <LI>	*s.* C 753		
	Cesàro['s] plane curve <GE>	*s.* C 447		
C 452	**Cesàro['s] summability,** convergence in the mean <LI>	Cesàrosche Summierbarkeit *f*, Cesàro-Summierbarkeit *f*	convergence *f* au sens de Cesàro, convergence en moyenne	суммируемость средними арифметическими Чезаро, суммируемость в смысле Чезаро
C 453	**Cesàro summable series,** series summable by Cesàro's method [of summation], *C*-summable series, series convergent in the mean <LI>	*C*-summierbare (nach dem *C*-Verfahren summierbare) Reihe *f*	série *f* sommable par la méthode de Cesàro, série sommable (convergente) au sens de Cesàro, série convergente en moyenne	ряд, суммуруемый методом Чезаро
C 454	**Cesàro['s] summation** <LI>	Cesàrosche Summation *f*	sommation *f* de Cesàro	суммирование Чезаро (средними арифметическими Чезаро)
	Cesàro['s] summation method <LI>	*s.* C 451		
	Cesàro['s] summation method of *k*-th order <LI>	*s.* C 753		
C 455	**Cesàro['s] theorem** <LI, SS>	Satz *m* von Cesàro, Cesàroscher Satz	théorème *m* de Cesàro	теорема Чезаро
C 456	**Ceva['s] line** <EG>	Ceva-Gerade *f*, Cevasche Gerade *f*	droite *f* de Ceva	прямая Чевы, чевиана
C 457	**Ceva['s] theorem** <EG>	Satz *m* von (des) Ceva, Cevascher Satz	théorème *m* de Ceva	теорема Чевы
	cf <FU>	*s.* H 53		
	cfα <FU>	*s.* C 2530		
	cg <FU>	*s.* H 54		
	ch <FU>	*s.* H 623		
	CH <SE>	*s.* C 2247		
C 458	**chain** <AT>	Kette *f*, algebraischer Komplex *m*	chaîne *f*	цепь
C 459	**chain** <of simplexes> <AT>	Kette *f* <von Simplexen>	chaîne *f* <de simplexes>	цепочка <симплексов, связывающая симплексы>
C 460	**chain** <of an oriented graph> <GP>	Kantenfolge *f*	chaîne *f*	полумаршрут
C 461	**chain** <as a set of edges> <GP>	Kette *f*	ensembles *m* des arêtes d'une chaîne	неупорядоченная цепь
C 462	**chain** <of substitutions> <LO>	Kette *f* <von Substitutionen>	chaîne *f* <de substitutions>	цепь <подстановок>
C 463	**chain** <of domains> <TO>	Kette *f* <von Gebieten>	chaîne *f* <de domaines>	цепь <областей>
	chain <AL>	*s.* E 798		
	chain <GP>	*s.* E 27		
	chain <SE>	*s.* 1. L 822; 2. M 874		
	ε-chain <TO>	*s.* E 307		
C 464	**chainable continuum,** snakelike continuum, arc-like continuum <TO>	0-verkettetes (nullverkettetes) Kontinuum *n* <für jedes ε gibt es eine überdeckende ε-Kette>	continu *m* serpentin	змеевидный континуум
C 465	**chain-boundary,** bounding chain <AT>	Randkette *f*, berandende Kette *f*	chaîne *f* bordante	ограничивающая цепь

	English	German	French	Russian
	chain-boundary <AT>	*s.* B 628		
C 466	**chain complex,** Mayer['s] complex <AT, HA>	Kettenkomplex *m*, Mayerscher Komplex *m*, Mayersches Gruppensystem *n*	complexe *m* de chaînes	цепной комплекс, комплекс Майера
	chain complex <HA>	*s.* N 87		
C 467	**chain condition** <AL>	Kettenbedingung *f*	condition *f* de chaîne[s]	условие обрыва цепочки (цепей), условие обрыва
	chain-condition <AL>	*s.* A 1031		
C 468	**chain contractible,** contractible <HA>	kettenkontrahierbar	chaîne-contractile	цепно стягиваемый
C 469	**chain contraction** <HA>	Kettenkontraktion *f*	chaîne-contraction *f*	цепное стягивание
C 470	**chained system of sets** <TO>	verkettetes Mengensystem *n*, verkettete Familie *f*	famille *f* d'ensembles enchaînée	сцепленная система множеств
C 471	**chain equivalence** <HA>	Kettenäquivalenz *f*	chaîne-équivalence *f*	цепная эквивалентность
C 472	**chain equivalent** <HA>	kettenäquivalent	chaîne-équivalent	цепно-эквивалентный, цепно эквивалентный
	chainette <GE>	*s.* C 227		
C 473	**chain group,** group of chains <AT, HA>	Kettengruppe *f*	groupe *m* des chaînes	группа цепей
	chain homomorphism <HA>	*s.* C 492		
C 474	**chain homotopic, chain-homotopic** <HA>	kettenhomotop	chaîne-homotope	цепно-гомотопный
C 475	**chain homotopy** <HA>	Kettenhomotopie *f*	chaîne-homotopie *f*	цепная гомотопия
C 476	**chain homotopy class** <HA>	Kettenhomotopieklasse *f*	classe *f* de chaîne-homotopie	цепно гомотопичный класс
C 477	**chain index** <ST>	Kettenindex *m*	indice *m* en chaîne	цепной индекс, индекс с переменной базой
	chain inference <LO>	*s.* S 1289		
C 478	**chain isomorphism** <AT, HA>	Kettenisomorphismus *m*	chaîne-isomorphisme *m*	цепной изоморфизм
	chain map[ping] <HA>	*s.* C 492		
	chain method <AR>	*s.* C 1744		
C 479	**chain mod** ***m*****,** chain over I_m <AT>	Kette *f* mod *m*, $\mathfrak{g}_m$-Kette *f*	chaîne *f* mod. *m*	цепь по модулю *m*
C 480	**chain of abstract simplexes** <AT>	abstrakte Kette *f*, Kette abstrakter Simplizes	chaîne-squelette *f*	цепь абстрактных симплексов
C 481	**chain of equations** <AL>	Gleichungskette *f*	chaîne *f* d'équations	цепочка равенств, цепь уравнений; последовательность равенств
C 482	**chain of ideals** <in a ring> <AL>	Idealkette *f*	chaîne *f* d'idéaux	цепочка идеалов
C 483	**chain of inferences** <LO>	Schlußkette *f*	chaîne *f* (chemin *m*) logique, chaîne d'inférences	цепочка заключений, цепочка (цепь) умозаключений
C 484	**chain of paths** <AT>	Wegekette *f*	chaîne *f* de chemins	цепь путей
C 485	**chain of points** <connecting p_1 to p_n> <TO>	Punktkette *f*, Kette *f* <von Punkten> <die p_1 mit p_n verbindet>	chaîne *f* de points <unissant p_1 et p_n>	цепь точек <связывающая p_1 с p_n>
C 486	**chain of primary ideals** <AL>	Primäridealkette *f*	chaîne *f* d'idéaux primaires	цепь примарных идеалов
C 487	**chain of prime ideals** <AL>	Primidealkette *f*	chaîne *f* d'idéaux premiers	цепь простых идеалов
C 488	**chain of sets** <connecting A_1 to A_s> <TO>	Mengenkette *f*, Kette *f* <von Mengen> <A_1 mit A_s verbindend>	chaîne *f* d'ensembles <unissant A_1 et A_s, entre A_1 et A_s>	цепь множеств <связывающая A_1 с A_s>
C 489	**chain of sets having a void intersection** <SE>	Mengenkette *f* mit leerem Durchschnitt	chaîne *f* d'ensembles ayant une intersection vide	направление
C 490	**chain of syzygies,** syzygy chain <AL, IV>	Syzygienkette *f*	chaîne *f* de syzygies, suite *f* des syzygies	цепь сизигий
	chain over ***I*** <AT>	*s.* I 611		
	chain over I_m <AT>	*s.* C 479		
	chain over $\mathfrak{R}$ <AT>	*s.* R 164		
	chain progression <GP>	*s.* E 29		
C 491	**chain rule** <DI>	Kettenregel *f*	règle *f* de dérivation d'une fonction composée	цепное правило, правило дифференцирования сложной функции, правило дифференцирования функции от функции
	chain-rule interference <LO>	*s.* S 1289		
C 492	**chain transformation,** chain map, chain mapping, chain homomorphism <HA>	Kettentransformation *f*, Kettenhomomorphismus *m*	chaîne-homomorphisme *m*, homomorphisme *m* <d'un complexe de chaînes>, applicadion *f* de chaînes	цепное преобразование, цепное отображение, гомоморфизм <цепного комплекса>
C 493	**chain with complete connections** <SP>	Kette *f* mit vollständigen Bindungen	chaîne *f* à liaisons complètes	цепь с полными связями
C 494	**chamber complex** <AL>	Weylscher Komplex *m*	complexe *m* de Weyl	комплекс Вейля
C 495	**chance** <ST, TG>	Zufall *m*	hasard *m*, chance *f*	случай, шанс
C 496	**chance decision** <ST>	Zufallsentscheidung *f*, zufällige Entscheidung *f*	décision *f* au hasard	случайное решение
	chance event <ST>	*s.* R 99		
C 497	**chance move** <TG>	zufälliger Zug *m*, Zufallszug *m*	coup *m* au hasard	случайный ход
	chance of acceptance <ST>	*s.* A 171		
	chance variable <ST>	*s.* V 67		
C 498	**change in sign,** change of sign, variation of sign, variation in sign, reversal of sign, sign reversal <GN>	Vorzeichenänderung *f*, Vorzeichenwechsel *m*, Vorzeichenumkehr *f*, Umkehrung *f* des Vorzeichens	inversion *f* du signe, changement de signe	изменение (обращение, перемена) знака
	change of a common fraction into a decimal fraction <NT>	*s.* T 774		
C 499	**change of base functor** <AL, CA>	Funktor *m* Basiswechsel	foncteur *m* changement de base	функтор замены базы

No.	English	German	French	Russian
C 500	**change of base in logarithms** <AN>	Übergang *m* zu einer neuen Basis des Logarithmensystems	passage *m* aux logarithmes d'une nouvelle base	переход от одной системы логарифмов к другой
	change of basis matrix <AL>	*s.* M 203		
	change of co-ordinates <AY, GE, GN>	*s.* T 777		
C 501	**change of metrics** <TO>	Ummetrisieren *n*, Ummetrisierung *f*	changement *m* de métrisation	изменение метрики
	change of sign <GN>	*s.* C 498		
C 502	**change of the base** <AL, AN, GE, PG>	Basistransformation *f*, Übergang *m* zu einer anderen Basis, Basiswechsel *m*, Basisänderung *f*, Übergangssubstitution *f* <von einer Basis zu einer anderen>	changement *m* de base	замена (преобразование) базиса
C 503	**change of the variable,** substitution of the variable, transformation of the variable, variable transformation <DI>	Substitution *f* der Variablen, Einführung *f* einer neuen Variablen (Veränderlichen), Variablensubstitution *f*, Transformation *f* der Variablen, Variablentransformation *f*	changement *m* (substitution *f*, transformation *f*) de la variable	замена (замещение, введение новой, преобразование) переменной
	channel <ST>	*s.* C 1246		
C 504	**channel capacity,** capacity <of the channel> <ST>	Kanalkapazität *f*, Kapazität *f*, Übertragungsfähigkeit *f*, Informationskapazität *f* <des Kanals>	capacité *f* d'information <du canal>, capacité <du canal, de la voie>	емкость, информационная емкость, пропускная способность <канала [связи]>
	chaotic topology <TO>	*s.* I 382		
C 505	**Chaplygin['s] [hypergeometric] function** <FU>	Tschaplyginsche Funktion *f*, Tschaplygin-Funktion *f*	fonction *f* de Tchapliguine	функция Чаплыгина
C 506	**Chaplygin['s] inequalities** <DE>	Tschaplyginsche Ungleichungen *fpl*	inégalités *fpl* de Tchapliguine	неравенства Чаплыгина
C 507	**Chaplygin['s] method** <DE, NU>	Tschaplyginsche Methode *f*	méthode *f* de Tchapliguine	метод Чаплыгина [приближенного решения дифференциального уравнения]
C 508	**Chaplygin['s] theorem** <DE>	Satz *m* von Tschaplygin, Tschaplyginscher Satz	théorème *m* de Tchaplyguine	теорема Чаплыгина
C 509	**Chapman-Kolmogoroff equation** <ST>	Chapman-Kolmogorovsche Gleichung *f*	équation *f* de Chapman-Kolmogoroff	уравнение Чепмена-Колмогорова
C 510	**character** <of a system of Pfaff differential equations> <DE>	Charakter *m*	caractère *m*	характер
C 511	**character,** group character <of a representation of a group> <RE>	Charakter *m*, Gruppencharakter *m*, klassischer Charakter	caractère *m*	характер, групповой характер
C 512	**character,** characteristic <ST>	Merkmal *n*	caractère *m*	признак
	character <SE>	*s.* G 45		
C 513	**character group,** dual group <GR>	Charaktergruppe *f*, duale Gruppe *f*, Dualgruppe *f*	groupe *m* des caractères, groupe dual, dual *m* [au sens de Pontrjagin]	группа характеров, дуальная группа
C 514	**characteristic** <of a field *or* ring> <AL>	Charakteristik *f*	caractéristique *f*	характеристика
C 515	**characteristic** <of logarithm> <AR>	Kennziffer *f*, Charakteristik *f*	caractéristique *f*, partie *f* entière, partie caractéristique	характеристика
C 516	**characteristic** <of a system of functions> <AT>	Kroneckersche Charakteristik *f*, Charakteristik	caractéristique *f* de Kronecker, caractéristique	характеристика Кронекера
C 517	**characteristic** <of a vector field> <AT>	Charakteristik *f*	caractéristique *f*	характеристика
C 518	**characteristic,** path <of an autonomous system of differential equations> <DE>	Charakteristik *f*	caractéristique *f*	характеристика
C 519	**characteristic** <of a point with respect to a real curve> <DG>	Charakteristik *f*	caractéristique *f*	характеристика
C 520	**characteristic** <of a quasiconformal mapping> <FT>	Charakteristik *f*	caractéristique *f*	характеристика
C 521	**characteristic** <of a theta function> <FT, FU>	Charakteristik *f*, Periodencharakteristik *f* der Größen der Matrix	caractéristique *f*	характеристика
C 522	**characteristic** <GE>	Charakteristik *f*, charakteristische Zahl *f* <Chasles>	caractéristique *f*, nombre *m* caractéristique	характеристика
C 523	**characteristic** <of a scale> <NO>	Charakteristik *f*	caractéristique *f*	характеристика
C 524	**characteristic** <in semilogarithmic representation of numbers> <NU>	Charakteristik *f*	caractéristique *f*	характеристика
	characteristic <AL>	*s.* 1. F 175; 2. G 442		
	characteristic <AT>	*s.* E 608		
	characteristic <AT, GE>	*s.* E 575		
	characteristic <DE>	*s.* 1. C 530; 2. C 581		
	characteristic <DG>	*s.* C 532		
	characteristic <FT>	*s.* C 552		
	characteristic <GE>	*s.* C 575		

	characteristic <ST>	*s.* C 512		
	characteristically simple group <GR>	*s.* E 109		
C 525	**characteristic boundary value problem** <DE>	charakteristisches Randwertproblem *n*, charakteristische Randwertaufgabe *f*, Charakteristiken-Randwertproblem *n*	problème *m* aux limites caractéristique	характеристическая краевая задача
	characteristic Cauchy problem <DE>	*s.* C 560		
C 526	**characteristic class,** characteristic cohomology class <AT>	charakteristische Kohomologieklasse *f*	classe *f* caractéristique	характеристический класс
	characteristic class in the sense of Chern <AT>	*s.* C 623		
	characteristic class in the sense of Whitney <AT>	*s.* W 239		
	characteristic cohomology class <AT>	*s.* C 526		
	characteristic condition <GN>	*s.* N 74		
C 527	**characteristic cone** <DE>	charakteristischer Kegel *m*	cône *m* caractéristique	характеристический конус
C 528	**characteristic congruence** <AL>	charakteristische Kongruenz *f*	congruence *f* fondamentale, congruence caractéristique <mod. *p*>	характеристическое сравнение
C 529	**characteristic conoid** <DE>	charakteristisches Konoid *n*; Strahlenkonoid *n* <einer total-hyperbolischen Differentialgleichung>	conoïde *m* caractéristique	характеристический коноид
C 530	**characteristic curve,** characteristic <of a partial differential equation> <DE>	charakteristische Kurve *f*, Charakteristik *f*	courbe *f* caractéristique, caractéristique *f*	характеристическая кривая, характеристика
C 531	**characteristic curve** <DG>	charakteristische Linie *f*	courbe *f* caractéristique	характеристическая линия
C 532	**characteristic curve,** characteristic <of a one-parameter family of surfaces> <DG>	Charakteristik *f*	caractéristique *f*	характеристика
C 533	**characteristic derivation** <DE>	charakteristische Ableitung *f*, Ableitung in Richtung einer charakteristischen Kurve	dérivée *f* caractéristique	характеристическая производная, производная по направлению характеристической кривой
C 534	**characteristic determinant** <DE>	charakteristische Determinante *f*; Alternativdeterminante *f* <beim Eigenwertproblem>	déterminant *m* caractéristique	характеристический определитель
	characteristic determinant <MD>	*s.* S 236		
C 535	**characteristic differential equation** <of a partial differential equation> <DE>	charakteristische Differentialgleichung *f*	équation *f* différentielle caractéristique	характеристическое дифференциальное уравнение
C 536	**characteristic direction** <DE>	charakteristische Richtung *f*	direction *f* caractéristique	характеристическое направление
	characteristic direction <AL, GE>	*s.* P 1776		
	characteristic element <FA>	*s.* E 58		
C 537	**characteristic equation** <of an algebra> <AL>	charakteristische Gleichung *f*, Ranggleichung *f*	équation *f* caractéristique, équation *f* au rang	характеристическое уравнение
C 538	**characteristic equation** <of an element of an algebra> <AL>	charakteristische Gleichung *f*	équation *f* propre	характеристическое уравнение
C 539	**characteristic equation** <for simultaneous diagonalization of quadratic forms> <AL>	Cauchysche charakteristische Gleichung *f*, charakteristische Gleichung [von Cauchy]	équation *f* caractéristique de Cauchy	характеристическое уравнение Коши
C 540	**characteristic equation,** secular equation, latent equation <of a matrix *or* form> <AL, MD>	charakteristische Gleichung *f*, Säkulargleichung *f*, säkulare Gleichung <einer Matrix>; Fundamentalgleichung *f* <einer Form>	équation *f* caractéristique (séculaire) <d'une matrice>, // équation latente; équation fondamentale <d'une forme>	характеристическое (вековое, секулярное) уравнение
C 541	**characteristic equation** <of a plane collineation> <AY, PJ>	charakteristische Gleichung *f*	équation *f* caractéristique	характеристическое уравнение
C 542	**characteristic equation,** fundamental equation <of a singularity> <for differential equations in the complex domain> <DE>	Fundamentalgleichung *f*, charakteristische Gleichung *f*	équation *f* caractéristique	характеристическое уравнение
C 543	**characteristic equation** <of partial differential equations *or* a difference equation> <DE, FD>	charakteristische Gleichung *f*	équation *f* caractéristique	характеристическое уравнение
C 544	**characteristic equation,** secular equation <of a matrix eigenvalue problem> <MD>	charakteristische Gleichung *f*, Säkulargleichung *f*, säkulare Gleichung	équation *f* caractéristique (séculaire)	характеристическое (вековое, секулярное) уравнение
	characteristic equation <DE>	*s.* A 1250		

C 545	**characteristic equation, characteristic determinant and characteristic matrix** <AL>	charakteristische Gleichung *f*, charakteristische Determinante *f* und charakteristische Matrix *f*	caractéristiques *fpl* matricielles	характеристическое уравнение, характеристический определитель и характеристическая матрица
C 546	**characteristic equation of the eigenvalue problem** <DE>	Eigenwertgleichung *f*, charakteristische Gleichung *f* des Eigenwertproblems	équation *f* caractéristique du problème aux valeurs propres	характеристическое уравнение задачи на собственные значения
C 547	**characteristic exponent** <of a field> <AL>	charakteristischer Exponent *m*	exposant *m* caractéristique	характеристическая экспонента, характеристический показатель
C 548	**characteristic exponent** <of an integral of a system of ordinary differential equations> <DE>	charakteristischer Exponent *m*	exposant *m* caractéristique	характеристический показатель
C 549	**characteristic exponent** <of a stable type of distribution> <ST>	charakteristischer Exponent *m*	exposant *m* caractéristique	характеристический показатель
	characteristic formula <AG, AL>	*s.* C 550		
C 550	**characteristic function,** Hilbert['s] characteristic function, characteristic Hilbert function, Hilbert['s] function, postulation formula, characteristic formula <of an ideal> <AG, AL>	Hilberts (Hilbertsche) charakteristische Funktion *f*, Hilberts Funktion, Postulationsformel *f*, Hilbert-Funktion *f*, charakteristische Funktion [von Hilbert]	fonction *f* caractéristique de Hilbert, fonction caractéristique, formule *f* de postulation, formule de postulation de Hilbert	характеристическая функция Гильберта, постулационная формула
C 551	**characteristic function,** first characteristic function <of an element of an algebra> <AL>	charakteristisches Polynom *n*, erstes charakteristisches Polynom	polynôme *m* caractéristique	характеристический многочлен
C 552	**characteristic function,** characteristic <of a meromorphic function> <FT>	Charakteristik *f*, charakteristische Funktion *f*	fonction *f* de croissance, fonction caractéristique, caractéristique *f*	характеристическая функция, характеристика
C 553	**characteristic function** <of a linear homogeneous difference equation, in Fourier transformation, *or* of a predicate> <FD, IT, LO>	charakteristische Funktion *f*	fonction *f* caractéristique	характеристическая функция
C 554	**characteristic function** <of a set> <SE>	charakteristische Funktion *f*, Indikatorfunktion *f*	fonction *f* caractéristique, fonction indicatrice, caractéristique *f*	характеристическая функция, индикатор
C 555	**characteristic function** <of a one-dimensional random variable *or* distribution *or* a game> <ST, TG>	charakteristische Funktion *f*	fonction *f* caractéristique	характеристическая функция
	characteristic function <DE, IE>	*s.* E 57		
	characteristic function <DE, VA>	*s.* 1. H 64; 2. L 653		
	characteristic function <DG>	*s.* W 198		
	characteristic function <FA>	*s.* E 58		
	characteristic function <MD>	*s.* C 573		
C 556	**characteristic functional** <SP>	charakteristisches Funktional *n* [von Kolmogorov]	fonctionnelle *f* caractéristique	характеристический функционал [Колмогорова]
C 557	**characteristic group** <of points> <AG, PJ>	charakteristische Punktgruppe *f*, charakteristische Gruppe *f*	groupe *m* <de points> caractéristique	характеристическая группа <точек>
	characteristic Hilbert function <AG, AL>	*s.* C 550		
C 558	**characteristic homology class** <AT>	charakteristische Homologieklasse *f*	classe *f* caractéristique d'homologie	характеристический класс гомологий
C 559	**characteristic index** <in the theory of Mathieu's functions> <FU>	charakteristischer Exponent *m*	indice *m* caractéristique	характеристический показатель
	characteristic index <DE>	*s.* C 761		
C 560	**characteristic initial value problem,** characteristic Cauchy problem <DE>	charakteristisches Anfangswertproblem *n*, charakteristische Anfangswertaufgabe *f*, charakteristisches Cauchysches Problem *n*	problème *m* de Cauchy caractéristique, problème aux valeurs initiales caractéristique	характеристическая задача Коши, характеристическая задача с начальными значениями
C 561	**characteristic linear system** <PJ>	charakteristische Schar *f*	système *m* linéaire caractéristique	характеристическое семейство точек
C 562	**characteristic manifold** <of a partial differential equation> <DE>	charakteristische Mannigfaltigkeit *f*	variété *f* caractéristique	характеристическое многообразие
C 563	**characteristic manifold,** characteristic subspace, characteristic space, eigenraum <associated with *or* belonging to an eigenvalue> <of a linear operator> <FA>	<zu einem Eigenwert gehöriger> Eigenraum *m*	sous-espace *m* propre, espace *m* propre <associé à une valeur propre>	собственное пространство (подпространство) <соответствующее собственному значению>
C 564	**characteristic matrix** <DE, MD>	charakteristische Matrix *f*	matrice *f* caractéristique	характеристическая матрица

No.	English	German	French	Russian
C 565	**characteristic number,** eigenvalue <of a linear operator or transformation <AL, FA>	Eigenwert *m*, charakteristische Zahl *f*	nombre *m* caractéristique, valeur *f* propre	собственное значение, характеристическое число
C 566	**characteristic number** <VA>	Eigenwert *m*	nombre *m* caractéristique	характеристическое число
	characteristic number <DE>	*s.* L 638		
	characteristic number <MD>	*s.* E 61		
C 567	**characteristic of the residue field** <AL>	Restklassenkörpercharakteristik *f*	caractéristique *f* résiduelle	характеристика поля вычетов
C 568	**characteristic parameter** <DE>	charakteristischer Parameter *m*; Eigenwertparameter <beim Randwertproblem>	paramètre *m* caractéristique	характеристический параметр
C 569	**characteristic plane,** eigenplane <VT>	Eigenebene *f*	plan *m* propre	собственная плоскость
	characteristic plane <PJ>	*s.* A 626		
C 570	**characteristic point** <of a one-parameter family of curves *or* a two-parameter family of surfaces> <DG>	Grenzpunkt *m*, charakteristischer Punkt *m*	point *m* caractéristique	характеристическая точка
C 571	**characteristic polynomial** <of an ideal> <AG, AL>	Hilbertsches charakteristisches Polynom *n*, Hilbert-Polynom *n*	polynôme *m* caractéristique de Hilbert, polynôme de Hilbert	характеристический многочлен Гильберта, многочлен Гильберта
C 572	**characteristic polynomial** <of ordinary differential equations> <DE>	charakteristisches Polynom *n*	polynôme *m* caractéristique	характеристический многочлен
C 573	**characteristic polynomial,** characteristic function <of a matrix *or* form> <MD>	charakteristisches Polynom *n*	polynôme *m* caractéristique, fonction *f* caractéristique <d'une forme *ou* matrice>; déterminant *m* caractéristique <d'une forme>	характеристический многочлен
	characteristic polynomial <AL>	*s.* F 201		
C 574	**characteristic Pontrjagin number** <AT>	charakteristische Pontrjaginsche Zahl *f*	nombre *m* caractéristique de Pontrjagin	характеристическое число Понтрягина
	characteristic root <MD>	*s.* E 61		
C 575	**characteristic ruled surface,** characteristic <of a complex of lines> <GE>	charakteristische Regelfläche *f*, Charakteristik *f*	surface *f* réglée caractéristique, caractéristique *f*	характеристическая линейчатая поверхность, характеристика
C 576	**characteristic series** <of a group> <GR>	charakteristische Reihe *f*	suite *f* caractéristique	характеристический ряд
	characteristic set [of differential equations] <DE>	*s.* C 582		
C 577	**characteristic singularity** <DE>	charakteristische Singularität *f*	singularité *f* caractéristique	характеристическая особенность
	characteristic solution <DE, IE>	*s.* E 57		
	characteristic solution <FA>	*s.* E 58		
	characteristic space <FA>	*s.* C 563		
C 578	**characteristic state,** eigenstate, proper state <FA>	Eigenzustand *m*	état *m* propre	собственное состояние
C 579	**characteristic strip** <of *n*-th order> <DE>	charakteristischer Streifen *m*, Charakteristik *f* <*n*-ter Ordnung>	bande *f* caractéristique, caractéristique *f* <d'ordre *n*>	характеристическая полоса <*n*-го порядка>
C 580	**characteristic subgroup** <GR>	charakteristische Untergruppe *f*, charakteristischer Teiler *m*	sous-groupe *m* caractéristique, diviseur *m* caractéristique	характеристическая подгруппа
	characteristic subspace <FA>	*s.* C 563		
C 581	**characteristic surface,** characteristic <of a partial differential equation> <DE>	charakteristische Fläche *f*, Charakteristik *f*	surface *f* caractéristique, caractéristique *f*	характеристическая поверхность, характеристика
C 582	**characteristic system,** characteristic set [of differential equations] <of a partial differential equation> <DE>	charakteristisches Differentialgleichungssystem *n*, charakteristisches System *n* [der <partiellen> Differentialgleichung]	système *m* caractéristique [d'équations différentielles]	характеристическая система [дифференциальных уравнений]
	characteristic system of the Hamilton-Jacobi equation <DE>	*s.* C 82		
C 583	**characteristic value** <of a matrix> <AL>	charakteristische Zahl *f*, charakteristische Wurzel *f*, charakteristischer Wert *m*, // Eigenwert *m*	racine *f* caractéristique, nombre *m* caractéristique, valeur *f* caractéristique, // valeur propre	характеристическое число
	characteristic value <DE>	*s.* E 59		
	characteristic value <MD>	*s.* E 61		
	characteristic vector <FA>	*s.* E 58		
	characteristic vector <MD>	*s.* E 65		
C 584	**characterization theorem** <LO>	Charakterisierungssatz *m*	théorème *m* de caractérisation	теорема характеризации
C 585	**character of being even-numbered,** even-numberedness <GN>	Geradzahligkeit *f*	propriété *f* d'être pair	четность

C 586	**character of discontinuity** <DI>	Unstetigkeitsverhalten *n*	caractère *m* de discontinuité	характер разрыва
C 587	**character ring** <AL, GR>	Charakterenring *m* <AL>; Charakterring *m* <GR>	anneau *m* de caractères	кольцо характеров
C 588	**character semigroup** <of a semigroup> <AL>	Charakterhalbgruppe *f*	demi-groupe *m* des caractères	полугруппа характеров
C 589	**character space** <ST>	Merkmalsraum *m*	espace *m* des caractères	пространство признаков
C 590	**character transformation** <ST>	Merkmaltransformation *f*	transformation *f* d'un caractère	преобразование признака
	charge <ME>	*s.* C 2157		
C 591	**Charlier['s] expansion** <ST>	Charliersche Entwicklung *f*	expansion *f* de Charlier	разложение Шарлье
C 592	**Charlier['s] polynomial,** Poisson-Charlier polynomial <FU, ST>	Charliersches (Poisson-Charliersches) Polynom *n*	polynôme *m* de Charlier (Poisson-Charlier)	многочлен Шарлье (Пуассона-Шарлье)
C 593	**Charlier['s] series** <ST>	Charliersche Reihe *f*	série *f* de Charlier	ряд Шарлье
C 594	**Charnes['] epsilon-method (ε-method)** <PG>	Charnessche ε-Methode (Epsilon-Methode) *f*, ε-Methode (Epsilon-Methode) von Charnes	ε-méthode (epsilon-méthode) *f* de Charnes	ε-метод (эпсилон-метод) Чарнса
C 595	**chart,** local co-ordinate system <AG, DG>	Karte *f*, euklidische Karte, lokales Koordinatensystem *n*	carte *f*, carte locale, système *m* de coordonnées locales	локальная карта, система локальных координат, локальная система координат
C 596	**chart** <of a fibre bundle> <AT>	Bündelkarte *f*, Koordinatensystem *n*, lokale Karte *f* <eines Faserraums>; stetige Bündelkarte *f* <eines Faserbündels>	carte *f* locale	локальная карта
	chart <AN, NU>	*s.* D 408		
	chart <NO>	*s.* N 299		
	chase about the diagram <AL, GN>	*s.* D 409		
	Chasles-Cayley-Brill correspondence formula <AG>	*s.* F 386		
	Chasles-Cayley-Brill formula <AG>	*s.* F 386		
C 597	**Chasles['] theorem** <EG>	Satz *m* von Chasles, Chaslesscher Satz	théorème *m* de Chasles	теорема Шаля
C 598	**Chebotarev['s] density theorem,** density theorem of Chebotarev <AB>	Dichtigkeitssatz *m* von Čebotarev, Čebotarevscher (Tschebotarewscher) Dichtigkeitssatz	théorème *m* de densité de Tchebotarev	теорема Чеботарёва о плотности, теорема плотности Чеботарева
C 599	**Chebyshev['s] alternant,** Chebyshev['s] alternation <AX, NU>	Tschebyscheffsche Alternante (Abwechslung) *f*, Tschebyscheff-Alternante *f*	alternance *f* de Tchebychev	альтернант (чередование) Чебышева, чебышевский альтернанс
	Chebyshev['s] alternation <AX, NU>	*s.* C 599		
C 600	**Chebyshev['s] approach,** Chebyshev['s] approximation, min-max (minimax) technique <of a function> <AX, NU>	Tschebyscheffsche Annäherung (Approximation) *f*	approximation *f* de Tchebychev	приближение Чебышева
	Chebyshev['s] approximation <AX, NU>	*s.* C 600		
C 601	**Chebyshev['s] array,** Dolph-Chebyshev array, Chebyshev['s] net, equidistant system (net) <of parametric curves on a surface>, // Tchebycheff['s] net <DG>	Tschebyscheffsches (äquidistantes) Kurvensystem *n*, Tschebyscheff-Netz *n*	réseau *m* de Dolph-Tchebychev	сеть Чебышева, эквидистантная система кривых, решетка Дольфа-Чебышева
C 602	**Chebyshev['s] constant** <FT, FU>	Tschebyscheffsche Konstante *f*, Tschebyscheff-Konstante *f*	constante *f* de Tchebychev	постоянная Чебышева
	Chebyshev['s] differential equation <DE>	*s.* C 603		
C 603	**Chebyshev['s] equation,** Chebyshev['s] differential equation <DE>	Tschebyscheffsche Differentialgleichung (Gleichung) *f*	équation *f* de Tchebychev, équation différentielle de Tchebychev	уравнение Чебышева, дифференциальное уравнение Чебышева
C 604	**Chebyshev['s] formulas** <AX, DI, NU>	Tschebyscheffsche (Čebyshevsche) Formeln (Quadraturformeln) *fpl*, Tschebyscheff-Formeln *fpl*, Formeln [der numerischen Integration] von Tschebyscheff	formules *fpl* de Tchebychev	формулы [численного интегрирования] Чебышева
C 605	**Chebyshev['s] function** <of the first *or* second kind> <FU>	Tschebyscheffsche Funktion *f*, Tschebyscheff-Funktion *f* <erster (I.) *oder* zweiter (II.) Art>	fonction *f* de Tchebychev <de première *ou* deuxième espèce>	функция Чебышева <первого *или* второго рода>
C 606	**Chebyshev['s] function** <sum of the logarithms of prime numbers> <NT>	Tschebyscheffsche Funktion *f*	fonction *f* de Tchebychev (Tschébychef)	функция Чебышева
C 607	**Chebyshev['s] inequality** <SS>	Tschebyscheffsche Ungleichung *f*	inégalité *f* de Tchebychev	неравенство Чебышева
C 608	**Chebyshev['s] inequality,** Bienaymé-Chebyshev['s] inequality,	Tschebyscheffsche (Bienaymé-Tschebyscheffsche) Ungleichung *f*,	inégalité *f* de Bienaymé (Tchebyshev), théorème (lemme) *m* de Tcheby-	неравенство (теорема, лемма) Чебышева

No.	English	German	French	Russian
and still: C 608	Chebyshev['s] lemma <ST>	Ungleichung von Tschebyscheff[-Bienaymé], Tschebyscheffsches Lemma *n*	shev	
C 609	**Chebyshev['s] interpolation** <AX, NU>	Tschebyscheffsche Interpolation *f*	interpolation *f* de Tchebychev	интерполяция Чебышева
	Chebyshev['s] interpolation node <AX, NU>	*s.* C 612		
C 610	**Chebyshev['s] law of large numbers** <ST>	Tschebyscheffsches Gesetz *n* [der großen Zahlen]	loi *f* des grands nombres de Tchebyshev	закон [больших чисел] Чебышева
	Chebyshev['s] lemma <ST>	*s.* C 608		
C 611	**Chebyshev['s] method** <of fitting> <ER, NU>	Ausgleichsmethode *f* von Tschebyscheff, Tschebyscheffsche Ausgleichsmethode (Methode *f*)	méthode *f* de Tchebycheff	способ Чебышева
	Chebyshev['s] net <DG>	*s.* C 601		
C 612	**Chebyshev['s] node,** Chebyshev['s] interpolation node <of the first *or* second kind> <AX, NU>	Tschebyscheff-Knoten *m*, Tschebyscheffscher Interpolationsknoten *m* <erster *oder* zweiter Art>	nœud *m* de Tchebychev, nœud d'interpolation de Tchebychev <de première *ou* deuxième espèce>	узел Чебышева, узел интерполяции Чебышева <первого *или* второго рода>
C 613	**Chebyshev['s] polynomial** <of the first *or* second kind>, // Tchebycheff['s] polynomial <FU>	Tschebyscheffsches Polynom *n*, Tschebyscheff-Polynom *n* <erster (I.) *oder* zweiter (II.) Art>	polynôme *m* de Tchebychev (Tchebycheff, Tchebyshev, Tchebichef, Tschebyscheff) <de première *ou* deuxième espèce>	многочлен Чебышева <первого *или* второго рода>
C 614	**Chebyshev['s] problem** <AX, NU>	Tschebyscheffsche Approximationsaufgabe *f*, Tschebyscheffsches Problem *n*	problème *m* de Tchebychev	задача (проблема) Чебышева
C 615	**Chebyshev['s] problem** <DG>	Tschebyscheffsches Bekleidungsproblem *n*	problème *m* de Tchebychev	задача Чебышева
C 616	**Chebyshev['s] system [of functions]** <with respect to the interval [*a*, *b*]> <AX, NU>	Tschebyscheff-System *n*, Tschebyscheffsches Funktionensystem *n*	système *m* [de fonctions] de Tchebychev	система [функций] Чебышева
C 617	**Chebyshev['s] theorem** <on a sequence of random variables> <ST>	Satz *m* von Tschebyscheff, Tschebyscheffscher Satz	théorème *m* de Tchebyshev	теорема Чебышева
	Chebyshev['s] theorem <AX, NU>	*s.* T 268		
C 618	**check,** checking, arithmetic[al] check, arithmetic[al] checking, computing test, computing check, numerical check <on [the correctness of] a solution of an equation> <AR, NU>	Probe *f*, Rechenprobe *f*, Rechenkontrolle *f*, Rechnungsprobe *f*	preuve *f*, épreuve *f*, essai *m* de calcul, contrôle *m* de calcul, vérification *f* numérique, vérification arithmétique	проверка вычисления, испытание вычисления, контроль вычисления, арифметическая проверка, числовая проверка
	check a calculation / to <AR>	*s.* R 239		
C 619	**check a calculation (computation) / to** <NU>	die Probe auf eine Rechnung machen	faire l'épreuve	сделать проверку задачи
C 620	**check by resubstitution,** checking by resubstitution <into the original equation> <NU>	Probe *f* durch Einsetzen	preuve *f* par substitution	проверка подстановкой
	checking <AR, NU>	*s.* C 618		
	checking by resubstitution <NU>	*s.* C 620		
C 621	**Chenevier['s] chart (graph)** <NO>	Chenevierscher Tafel *f*	nomogramme (diagramme) *m* de Chenevier	номограмма Шеневье
C 622	**Chern character** <AT>	Chernscher Charakter *m*	caractère *m* de Chern	характер Чженя
	Chern['s] characteristic class <AT>	*s.* C 623		
C 623	**Chern['s] class,** Chern['s] characteristic class, characteristic class in the sense of Chern <AT>	Chernsche Klasse *f*, Chernsche Kohomologieklasse *f*	classe *f* de Chern	класс Чженя
C 624	**Chern['s] number** <AT>	Chernsche Zahl *f*	nombre *m* de Chern	число Чженя
C 625	**Chern['s] polynomial** <AT>	Chernsches Polynom *n*	polynôme *m* de Chern	многочлен Чженя
	chest of drawers argument <CT>	*s.* B 705		
C 626	**Chevalley['s] algebra** <AL>	Chevalleysche Algebra *f*	algèbre *f* de Chevalley	алгебра Шевалле
C 627	**Chevalley['s] basis** <for a Lie algebra> <AL>	Chevalleysche Basis *f*	base *f* de Chevalley	базис Шевалле
C 628	**Chevalley['s] group** <AL>	Chevalleysche Gruppe *f*	groupe *m* de Chevalley	группа Шевалле
	Chevalley-Jacobson density theorem <AL>	*s.* D 250		
	Chevalley['s] norm residue symbol <AB>	*s.* C 629		
C 629	**Chevalley['s] symbol,** Chevalley['s] norm residue symbol, Artin-Chevalley symbol, generalized Artin symbol> <AB>	Chevalley-Symbol *n*, Artin-Chevalley-Symbol *n*, verallgemeinertes Artin-Symbol *n*, verallgemeinerter Artin-Automorphismus *m*	symbole *m* de Chevalley	символ Шевалле
	chevron <GN>	*s.* P 733		

No.	English	German	French	Russian
C 630	**chi-distribution,** χ-distribution <ST>	χ-Verteilung *f*, Chi-Verteilung *f*	distribution *f* χ, distribution chi	χ-распределение, хи-распределение
	chief-composition series <GR>	*s.* P 1472		
	chief factor <GR>	*s.* F 17		
	chief minor <MD>	*s.* M 646		
	chief series <GR>	*s.* P 1472		
C 631	**chief system,** principal system <of subgroups> <GR>	Hauptsystem *n*	système *m* principal	главная система
	"Chinese Fifteen" puzzle <CT>	*s.* B 620		
C 632	**Chinese Remainder Theorem,** CRT <AL>	chinesischer Restesatz (Restsatz) *m*, Hauptsatz *m* über simultane Kongruenzen	théorème *m* chinois, théorème des restes chinois	китайская теорема об остатках, китайская лемма
C 633	**chironomy,** dactylonomy <AR>	Fingerrechnen *n*, Rechnen *n* mit den Fingern, Chironomie *f*, Daktylonomie *f*, Daktylonomia *f*, Chironomia *f*	chironomie *f*, dactylonomie *f*, calcul *m* digital, calcul sur les doigts	хирономия, дактилономия
C 634	**chi-square[d] distribution,** χ^2(-)distribution, chi-two type distribution; Helmert-Pearson distribution, Helmert['s] distribution <ST>	χ^2-Verteilung *f*, Chi-Quadrat-Verteilung *f*; Helmert-Pearson-Verteilung *f*, Helmert-Verteilung *f*	distrubution *f* [de] χ^2, distribution de (du) chi carré, répartition *f* χ^2 (de χ^2, chi carré, de chi carré, du chi carré), loi *f* χ^2, loi de χ^2 (chi carré), loi de distribution χ^2; distribution de Helmert-Pearson, distribution de Helmert	χ^2-распределение, распределение χ^2, распределение хи-квадрат, хи-квадрат-распределение; распределение Хелмерта-Пирсона, распределение Хелмерта
	chi-squared omnibus test <ST>	*s.* O 73		
	chi-squared overall test <ST>	*s.* O 73		
C 635	**chi-squared statistic,** χ^2-statistic, statistic χ^2, statistic chi-square <ST>	χ^2-Prüfzahl *f*, χ^2-Wert *m*, Stichprobenfunktion *f* χ^2, Chi-Quadrat-Prüfzahl *f*, Chi-Quadrat-Wert *m*, Stichprobenfunktion Chi-Quadrat, Chi-Quadrat *n*, Chiquadrat *n*, χ^2 *n*	critère *m* χ^2, statistique *f* χ^2, valeur *f* de χ^2, critère chi carré, statistique chi carré, valeur de chi carré	χ^2-статистика, χ^2-значение, статистика хи-квадрат, значение хи-квадрат
C 636	**chi-squared statistic,** χ^2-statistic, χ^2 <ST>	χ^2-Maßzahl *f*, Chi-Quadrat-Maßzahl *f*, Chi-Quadrat *n*, Chi-quadrat *n*, χ^2 *n*	statistique *f* χ^2, statistique chi carré, χ^2	χ^2-статистика, статистика хи-квадрат, хи-квадрат, χ^2
C 637	**chi-squared test,** χ^2-test, chi-square test <ST>	χ^2-Test *m*, Chi-Quadrat-Test *m*, Chi-Quadrat *n*, Chiquadrat *n*	test [du] χ^2, test du (de) chi carré, test chi carré, test χ^2 de Pearson, critérium *m* χ^2 (chi carré) [de Pearson]	χ^2-критерий, критерий χ^2, критерий соответствия χ^2, критерий хи-квадрат
C 638	**chi-squared test of goodness of fit,** χ^2-test of goodness of fit <ST>	χ^2-Anpassungstest *m*, Chi-Quadrat-Anpassungstest *m*	test *m* χ^2 (chi carré) de validité de l'ajustement	χ^2-критерий согласия, критерий хи-квадрат согласия
C 639	**chi-squared test of homogeneity,** χ^2-Test of homogeneity <ST>	χ^2-Homogenitätstest *m*, Chi-Quadrat-Homogenitätstest *m*	test *m* χ^2 d'homogénéité, test chi carré d'homogénéité	χ^2-критерий однородности, критерий хи-квадрат однородности
C 640	**chi-squared test of independence,** χ^2-test of independence <ST>	χ^2-Unabhängigkeitstest *m*, Chi-Quadrat-Unabhängigkeitstest *m*	test *m* χ^2 d'indépendance, test chi carré d'indépendance	χ^2-критерий независимости, критерий хи-квадрат независимости
C 641	**chi-squared test of variances,** χ^2-test of variances <ST>	χ^2-Streuungstest *m*, Chi-Quadrat-Streuungstest *m*	test *m* χ^2 de dispersion, test chi carré de dispersion	χ^2-критерий для дисперсии, критерий хи-квадрат для дисперсии
C 642	**chi square partition,** χ^2 partition, partition of χ^2 (chi square) <ST>	χ^2-Zerlegung *f*, Chi-Quadrat-Zerlegung *f*	décomposition *f* χ^2 (chi carré), partition *f* χ^2 (chi-carré)	χ^2-разложение, χ^2-разбиение, разложение (разбиение) хи-квадрат
	chi-square test <ST>	*s.* C 637		
C 643	**chi-statistic,** χ-statistic <ST>	χ-Maßzahl *f*, Chi-Maßzahl *f*, χ *n*	statistique *f* χ, statistique chi	χ-статистика, хи-статистика
	chi-two type distribution <ST>	*s.* C 634		
	choice <MM>	*s.* O 245		
	choice axiom <SE>	*s.* A 1280		
C 644	**choice function** <in axiom of choice> <SE>	Auswahlfunktion *f*	fonction *f* de choix	выборочная (выбирающая) функция, функция выбора
C 645	**choice of base** <AL>	Basiswahl *f*	choix *f* de la base	выбор базиса
	choice sequence <MM>	*s.* I 473		
C 646	**Cholesky['s] method, Choleski['s] method,** method of Cholesky, square-root method <AL, NU>	Cholesky-Methode *f*, Verfahren *n* von Cholesky, Choleskysches Verfahren, Quadratwurzelmethode *f*	procédé *m* du commandant Cholesky (Choleski), méthode *f* de Cholesky (racine carrée)	метод квадратного корня, метод Холеского
C 647	**chord** <of a circle *or* sphere, *also* of a curve> <EG>	Sehne *f*	corde *f*	хорда
C 648	**chord** <GP>	Sehne *f*, Kante *f* des Komplements eines Baumes	corde *f*	хорда <остова>
C 649	**chord,** diagonal <of an elementary cycle> <GP>	Sehne *f*	corde *f*, diagonale *f*	хорда
C 650	**chordal continuity,** spherical continuity <FT>	chordale Stetigkeit *f*, Kugelstetigkeit *f*	continuité *f* sphérique (cordale)	хордальная (сферическая) непрерывность

C 650a	**chordal convergence** <FT, SS>	chordale Konvergenz *f*	convergence *f* cordale	хордальная сходимочть
	chordal convergent sequence <FT>	*s.* U 154		
C 651	**chordal distance,** spherical distance <FT>	chordaler Abstand *m*, Kugelabstand *m*	distance *f* sphérique, distance cordale	хордальное (сферическое) расстояние
C 652	**chordally continuous function,** spherically continuous function <FT>	chordal stetige Funktion *f* kugelstetige Funktion	fonction *f* sphériquement continue	хордально (сферически) непрерывная функция
C 653	**chordally convergent sequence,** spherically convergent sequence <FT>	chordal konvergente Folge *f*, kugelkonvergente Folge	suite *f* sphériquement (cordalement) convergente	хордально (сферически) сходящаяся последовательность
C 654	**chordal metric,** spherical metric <FT>	chordale Metrik *f*, Kugelmetrik *f*	métrique *f* sphérique, métrique cordale	хордальная метрика, сферическая метрика
	chordal uniform convergence <FT, SS>	*s.* U 122		
C 655	**chord length,** length of the chord <EG>	Sehnenlänge *f*	longueur *f* de la corde	длина хорды
C 656	**chord of contact** <GE>	Berührungssehne *f*	corde *f* de contact	хорда, проходящая через точки касания касательных, проведенных из общей точки <к коническому сечению>
C 656a	**chord of curvature** <DG>	Krümmungssehne *f*	corde *f* de courbure	хорда кривизны
C 657	**chord theorem,** theorem on the chords <of a circle> <EG>	Sehnensatz *m*	théorème *m* sur les cordes	теорема о хордах
C 658	**Chow['s] co-ordinates** <AG>	Chow-Koordinaten *fpl*	coordonnées *fpl* de Chow	координаты Чжоу (Чао)
C 659	**Chow['s] lemma** <AG>	Chowsches Lemma *n*	lemme *m* de Chow	лемма Чжоу
C 660	**Chow['s] point** <AG>	Chow-Punkt *m*	point *m* de Chow, point associé <d'un cycle>	точка Чжоу (Чао)
C 661	**Chow-ring, Chow['s] ring** <AG>	Chow-Ring *m*	anneau *m* de Chow	кольцо Чжоу
C 662	**Chow['s] theorem** <AG>	Satz *m* von Chow, Chowscher Satz	théorème de Chow	теорема Чжоу
C 663	**Christoffel['s] coefficient** <DI, NU>	Christoffelsche Zahl (Konstante) *f*	coefficient (nombre) *m* de Christoffel	число (коэффициент) Кристоффеля
C 664	**Christoffel-Darboux formula,** Christoffel-Darboux identity <for orthonormal polynomials> <AN, NU>	Christoffel-Darbouxsche Identität (Formel) *f*, Identität (Formel) von Christoffel-Darboux	formule (identité) *f* de Christoffel-Darboux	тождество Кристоффеля-Дарбу
C 665	**Christoffel-Darboux formula** <for a Fourier series> <SS>	Christoffel-Darbouxsche Formel *f*, Formel von Christoffel-Darboux	formule *f* de Christoffel-Darboux	формула Кристоффеля-Дарбу
	Christoffel-Darboux identity <AN, NU>	*s.* C 664		
C 666	**Christoffel['s] formula** <for conformal mappings> <FT>	Christoffelsche Formel *f*	formule *f* de Christoffel	формула Кристоффеля
C 667	**Christoffel['s] symbol,** [Riemann-Christoffel] three-index symbol, 3-index symbol <of the first kind> <DG>	Christoffelsches Dreiindizessymbol (Symbol) *n*, Dreiindizessymbol, [Christoffelsches] Dreizeigersymbol *n*, Christoffel-Symbol *n*, Christoffelsymbol *n*, Christoffelsche Affinität *f*, Christoffel-Affinität *f*, g-Klammer *f*, Koeffizient *m* des affinen Zusammenhangs, Drei-Index-Symbol *n* <erster (I.) *oder* zweiter (II.) Art>	symbole *m* de Christoffel <de première *ou* deuxième espèce>	символ Кристоффеля, трехиндексный символ Кристоффеля <первого *или* второго рода>
C 668	**Christoffel['s] theorem** <DG>	Christoffelscher Satz *m*, Satz *m* von Christoffel	théorème *m* de Christoffel	теорема Кристоффеля
C 669	**chromatic index,** edge colouration number, line-chromatic number <GP>	chromatische Klasse *f*	indice *m* (classe *f*) chromatique	хроматический класс, реберно-хроматическое число, хроматический индекс
C 670	**chromatic number** <GP>	chromatische (chrome) Zahl *f*	nombre *m* chromatique	хроматическое число
C 671	**chromatic polynomial** <GP>	chromatisches (chromes) Polynom *n*	polynôme *m* chromatique	хроматический полином
	chromosome <AL>	*s.* D 1079		
C 672	**chunk sample** <ST>	Raffprobe *f*		
C 673	**Church['s] theorem** <LO>	Satz *m* von Church, Churchscher Satz	théorème *m* de Church	теорема Черча
C 674	**Church['s] thesis** <MM>	Churchsche Hypothese *f*	thèse *f* de Church[-Turing]	тезис Черча
	Ci <FU>	*s.* C 2531		
	Cih <FU>	*s.* H 624		
	cipher <NT>	*s.* F 215		
C 675	**circle,** circumference, periphery of the circle <EG>	Kreis *m*, Kreislinie *f*, Kreisrand *m*, Kreisperipherie *f*	cercle *m*, circonférence *f*, périphérie *f* <du cercle>, frontière *f* du disque	окружность
	circle <EG>	*s.* D 714		
C 676	**circle adjunction,** adjunction of circles <FT>	Kreisscheibenadjunktion *f*	adjonction *f* de cercles	присоединение кругов
	circle circumscribed <EG>	*s.* C 737		
C 677	**circled closure** <FA>	kreisförmige Hülle *f*	enveloppe *f* cerclée	закругленная оболочка

	English	Deutsch	Français	Русский
C 678	**circle diagram,** circle vector diagram <AN, NU>	Kreisdiagramm *n*	diagramme *m* circulaire	круговая [векторная] диаграмма
C 679	**circled kernel** <FA>	kreisförmiger Kern *m*	noyau *m* cerclé	закругленное ядро
	circled neighbourhood <FA>	*s.* B 34		
C 680	**circled set** <of a linear space> <FA>	kreisförmige Menge *f*, „ensemble cerclé" *n*	ensemble *m* cerclé	закругленное множество
	circled set <FA>	*s.* B 36		
C 681	**circle group** <GR>	Gruppe *f* der Kreisdrehungen, Kreisdrehungsgruppe *f*, Kreisgruppe *f*	groupe *m* circulaire	группа вращений окружности
C 682	**circle method** <NT>	Kreismethode *f*	méthode *f* de cercle	круговой метод
C 683	**circle of antisimilitude,** antisimilitude circle <GE>	„circle of antisimilitude" *m*, Antiähnlichkeitskreis *m*	cercle *m* d'antisimilitude	окружность антиподобия
C 684	**circle of Apollonius,** Apollonius['] circle <EG>	Apollonischer (apollonischer) Kreis *m*	cercle *m* apollonien (d'Apollonius)	окружность Аполлония [Пергского]
C 685	**circle of contact** <of a triangle> <EG>	Berührungskreis *m*	cercle *m* de contact (tangence)	окружность касания
C 686	**circle of convergence,** disk of convergence <SS>	Konvergenzkreis *m*, wahrer Konvergenzkreis	cercle (disque) *m* de convergence	круг сходимости
C 687	**circle of curvature,** osculating circle <of a curve> <DG>	Krümmungskreis *m*, Schmiegkreis *m*, Schmiegungskreis *m*, Oskulationskreis *m*	cercle *m* de courbure, cercle osculateur	соприкасающаяся окружность, окружность кривизны, соприкасающийся круг, круг кривизны, окружность соприкасания
C 688	**circle of curvature at the vertex** <AY>	Scheitelkrümmungskreis *m*	cercle *m* de courbure au sommet	окружность кривизны в вершине
C 689	**circle of geodesic curvature,** geodesic [curvature] circle <of the second kind> <on a surface> <DG>	Krümmungskreis *m*, geodätischer Kreis *m* <zweiter Art>, geodätischer Krümmungskreis <nach Lie und Darboux>	cercle *m* [de courbure] géodésique <de deuxième espèce>	окружность [геодезической] кривизны, геодезическая окружность <второго рода>
	circle of geodesic distance <DG>	*s.* G 238		
C 690	**circle of inversion,** circle of the inversion <GE>	Grundkreis *m* [der Inversion], Inversionskreis *m*	cercle *m* d'inversion	окружность инверсии
	circle of Longchamps <EG>	*s.* L 1092		
C 691	**circle of similarity,** similarity circle <GE>	Ähnlichkeitskreis *m*, Isogonalkreis *m*	cercle *m* de similitude	окружность подобия
C 692	**circle of the base of the auxiliary cone,** base of the auxiliary cone <DS>	Böschungskreis *m*	cercle *m* de base du cône de talus, base *f* du cône de talus	окружность основания конуса откоса, основание конуса откоса
	circle of the inversion <GE>	*s.* C 690		
	circle polynomial <FU>	*s.* Z 13		
C 693	**circle problem** <NT>	Kreisproblem *n*	problème *m* du cercle	проблема круга
C 694	**circles cutting at right angles, circles cutting orthogonally,** orthogonal circles <GE>	orthogonale Kreise *mpl*	cercles *mpl* orthogonaux	ортогональные окружности
C 695	**circles of Apollonius,** Apollonius['] circles <of the triangle> <EG>	Apollonische Kreise *mpl*	cercles *mpl* apolloniens (d'Apollonius)	окружности Аполлония, аполлониевы окружности
	circle vector diagram <AN, NU>	*s.* C 678		
C 696	**circuit** <of an algebraic curve> <AG>	Kurvenzug *m*, Zug *m*, reeller Zug	trait *m*	поток
C 697	**circuit** <set of edges in an unoriented graph> <GP>	geschlossener Kantenzug *m* <Menge von Kanten, die bei entsprechender Anordnung eine geschlossene Kantenzugprogression bilden>	ensemble *m* des arêtes d'un cycle simple	неупорядоченный цикл
	circuit <AN>	*s.* C 2252		
	circuit <AT>	*s.* C 2831		
	circuit <GP>	*s.* 1. C 854; 2. E 98; 3. S 1774; 4. S 892 a		
	0-circuit <AT>	*s.* D 513		
	circuit edge <GP>	*s.* E 21		
C 698	**circuit element** <of a graph> <GP>	Kante *f* eines Graphen, die in einem Kreis enthalten ist	arête *f* qui est contenue dans un circuit	ребро, включенное в простой цикл
C 699	**circuit-free graph,** acyclic graph, graph free of circuits <GP>	kreisfreier (kreisloser, azyklischer, antizyklischer) Graph *m*	graphe *m* sans circuit[s], graphe acyclique	граф без контуров (циклов), ациклический (бесконтурный) граф
C 700	**circuit-free set of cells,** acyclic set of cells <PG>	kreisfreie Menge *f* von Zellen	ensemble *m* de cellules acyclique	ациклическое множество ячеек, множество ячеек без циклов
C 701	**circuit matrix** <of a linear oriented graph> <GP>	Kanten-Zyklen-Matrix *f*		матрица контуров
	circuit progression <GP>	*s.* C 860		
	circuit rank <GP>	*s.* C 2891		
C 702	**circulant [determinant],** cyclic determinant <MD>	Zirkulante *f*, zyklische (negativ-orthosymmetrische) Determinante *f*, Zirkulardeterminante *f*, // Cirkulante *f*	déterminant *m* circulaire (à circulation, circulant), circulant *m*, déterminant cyclique (négativement orthosymétrique, doublement orthosymétrique)	циркулянт, циклический определитель (детерминант)
C 703	**circulant matrix** <MD>	zyklische Matrix *f*	circulante *f*, matrice *f* cyclique (circulante)	циклическая матрица, циркулянт, циркулянтная матрица

No.	English	German	French	Russian
C 704	**circular arc,** arc of circle, arc <of circle, circumference> <EG>	Kreisbogen *m*, Kreisbogenabschnitt *m*, Kreisbogenstück *n*, Bogen *m* <des Kreises>	arc *m* circulaire, arc de cercle, arc <du cercle, de la circonférence>	дуга окружности
C 705	**circular barrel** <GE>	Kreistonnenkörper *m*	tonneau *m* circulaire	круговая (круглая) бочка
C 706	**circular body,** circular solid <common name of sphere, right circular cone and right circular cylinder> <EG>	Kreiskörper *m*	corps *m* circulaire	круглое тело
C 707	**circular chart,** circular graph (nomogram) <NO>	Kreisnomogramm *n*, Kreistafel *f*	abaque (nomogramme) *m* circulaire	круговая номограмма
C 708	**circular chart** <ST>	Kreisdiagramm *n*	diagramme *m* circulaire (à secteurs)	круговая диаграмма
C 709	**circular cone** <EG>	Kreiskegel *m*	cône *m* [à base] circulaire	круглый (кругловой) конус, конус
C 710	**circular conoid,** Wallis['] conic wedge <GE>	Kreiskonoid *n*, Kegelkeil *m* von Wallis, Wallisscher Kegelkeil, Wallis' Keilfläche *f*, Konokuneus *m*	conoïde *m* circulaire, coin *m* conique de Wallis, conocuneus *m*	круговой коноид
C 711	**circular co-ordinates** <Cayley> <DG, GE>	isotrope Koordinaten *fpl*, Minimalkoordinaten *fpl* <Klein>	coordonnées *fpl* isotropes <Laguerre>	изотропные координаты
C 712	**circular correlation** <ST>	Kreiskorrelation *f*	corrélation *f* circulaire	круговая корреляция
	circular correlation <GE>	*s.* C 729		
	circular curvature <DG>	*s.* M 302		
C 713	**circular curve** <having two isotropic asymptotes> <AG>	zirkulare Kurve *f*, Kreiskurve *f*	courbe *f* circulaire	циркулярная кривая
C 714	**circular cylinder,** cylinder of revolution <EG>	Kreiszylinder *m*, Drehzylinder *m*	cylindre *m* [à base] circulaire, cylindre de révolution	круговой (круглый) цилиндр, цилиндр вращения
	circular cylindrical co-ordinates <AY>	*s.* C 2909		
	circular disk <EG>	*s.* D 714		
C 715	**circular distribution** <ST>	Kreisverteilung *f*	distribution *f* circulaire	распределение на окружности
	circular division <NU>	*s.* C 2902		
C 716	**circular domain** <several complex variables> <FT>	Kreiskörper *m*, Kreisbereich *m*, // Kreisgebiet *n*	domaine *m* cerclé	круговая область
C 717	**circular elliptic integral of the third kind** <FT, FU>	zirkuläres elliptisches Integral *n* dritter (3.) Gattung	intégrale *f* elliptique circulaire de troisième espèce	круговой эллиптический интеграл третьего рода
	circular field <VT>	*s.* C 732		
	circular function <AN>	*s.* T 944		
	circular geometry <DG>	*s.* G 273		
	circular graduation <NU>	*s.* C 2902		
	circular graph <NO>	*s.* C 707		
C 718	**circular helix,** cylindrical helix, helix <GE>	gemeine Schraubenlinie *f*, Schraubenlinie	hélice *f* circulaire (cylindrique), hélice	цилиндрическая винтовая линия, винтовая линия [на круговом цилиндре]
	circular hyperconic <DG>	*s.* H 664		
	circularity <LO>	*s.* V 176		
C 719	**circular lune** <EG>	Kreisbogenzweieck *n*, Bogenzweieck *n*	fuseau *m* circulaire	круговой двуугольник, круговая луночка
	circular measure <AY, GE>	*s.* R 12		
C 720	**circular neighbourhood** <TO>	Kreisumgebung *f*	voisinage *m* circulaire	круговая окрестность
	circular nomogram <NO>	*s.* C 707		
	circular permutation <AL>	*s.* C 2868		
	circular permutation <CT>	*s.* C 2863		
	circular permutation <GN>	*s.* C 2869		
	circular point <DG>	*s.* U 29		
	circular points [at infinity] <AY, PJ>	*s.* C 2873		
	circular polygon <EG>	*s.* A 907		
	circular quadrangle <EG>	*s.* A 908		
	circular ring <EG>	*s.* A 691		
C 721	**circular ring of minimal breadth** <containing given points> <CS, GE>	Minimalkreisring *m*	couronne *f* circulaire d'épaisseur minimale <qui renferme un système de points donnés>	круговое кольцо наименьшей ширины <содержащее данные точки>
C 722	**circular section** <of a surface> <GE>	Kreisschnitt *m*	section *f* circulaire	круговое сечение
C 723	**circular segment,** segment <of the circle> <EG>	Kreisabschnitt *m*, Kreissegment *n*, Abschnitt *m*, Segment *n* <des Kreises>	segment *m* circulaire, segment <du cercle>	круговой сегмент, сегмент <круга>
	circular slide rule <IN, NU>	*s.* C 9		
C 724/5	**circular slit domain** <FT>	Kreisschlitzbereich *m*, Kreisbogenschlitzgebiet *n* <Mittelpunkte im Ursprung>	domaine *m* muni de fentes circulaires	область кругового разреза

	circular solid <EG>	*s.* C 706		
C 726	**circular symmetry,** cyclic symmetry <of variables> <GN>	zyklische Vertauschbarkeit *f*	symétrie *f* circulaire (cyclique)	круговая (кругообразная) симметрия
	circular symmetry <EG>	*s.* R 10		
C 727	**circular torus** <EG>	Kreistorus *m*	tore *m* de révolution, tore circulaire	тор вращения, круговой тор
C 728	**circular tractrix** <GE>	zirkuläre Traktrix *f*, Kreistraktrix *f*	tractrice *f* circulaire	круговая трактриса
C 729	**circular transformation,** transformation carrying (taking) circles into circles, correspondence mapping circles into circles, circular correlation <GE>	kreisverwandte Abbildung *f*, Kreisverwandtschaft *f*, Kreistransformation *f*, zirkulare Transformation *f*	transformation (corrélation, substitution) *f* circulaire, transformation homographique	круговое преобразование, круговая корреляция, круговое родство
C 730	**circular triad** <ST>	zirkuläre Triade *f*	triade *f* circulaire	циркуляционная триада
	circular triangle <EG>	*s.* A 914		
C 731	**circular unicursal cubic** <AG>	zirkulare unikursale Kubik *f*	cubique *f* circulaire unicursale	циркулярная уникурсальная кривая третьего порядка
C 732	**circular vector field,** circular field <VT>	zirkulares Vektorfeld *n*, Kreisfeld *n*, zirkulares Feld *n*	champ *m* vectoriel circulaire, champ circulaire	круговое векторное поле, круговое поле
	circulating decimal <NT>	*s.* P 446		
C 733	**circulating function** <Herschel> <AB>	„circulating function" *f*	« circulating function » *f*, circulator *m*	циркулятор
C 734	**circulation,** tangential line integral <of **F** along the closed curve *C*> <of a vector field> <VT>	Zirkulation *f*, Randintegral *n* <eines Vektorfeldes>	circulation *f* <d'un champ vecteur>	циркуляция <векторного поля>
C 734a	**circulatory integral,** line (curvilinear) integral along a closed curve (path, line, contour), line (curvilinear) integral along a contour, contour integral, φ <AN>	geschlossenes Kurvenintegral (Linienintegral) *n*, Kurvenintegral (Linienintegral) längs einer geschlossenen Kurve, Kurvenintegral (Linienintegral) längs eines geschlossenen Weges, φ; Randintegral *n*	intégrale *f* circulatoire, intégrale curviligne le long d'un contour [fermé], intégrale curviligne le long d'une courbe (ligne, route) fermée, intégrale de contour, φ	[криволинейный] интеграл[, взятый] по замкнутой кривой, [криволинейный] интеграл [, взятый] по [замкнутому] контуру, контурный интеграл, φ
	circules <AY, PJ>	*s.* C 2873		
C 735	**circumcentre,** centre of the circumscribed circle <EG>	Mittelpunkt *m* des Umkreises, Umkreismittelpunkt *m*	centre *m* du cercle circonscrit	центр описанной окружности
C 736	**circumcentre** <EG>	Mittelpunkt *m* der Umkugel, Umkugelmittelpunkt *m*	centre *m* de la sphère circonscrite	центр описанной сферы
C 737	**circumcircle,** circle circumscribed <*e.g.*: of a triangle>, circumscribed circle <*e.g.*: about a triangle> <EG>	Umkreis *m*, umschriebener (umbeschriebener) Kreis *m* <*z. B.*: eines Dreiecks>	cercle *m* circonscrit, circonférence *f* circonscrite <*par exemple:* à un triangle>	описанная окружность, описанный круг <*например:* треугольника>; окружность, описанная <*например:* вокруг, около треугольника>
	circumference <EG>	*s.* C 675		
C 738	**circumradius,** radius of the circumscribed circle <of a triangle>; long radius, radius of the circumscribed circle <of a regular polygon> <EG>	Radius *m* des Umkreises, Umkreisradius *m*	rayon *m* du cercle circonscrit	радиус описанной окружности
C 739	**circumradius,** radius of the circumsphere <e.g. of a tetrahedron> <EG>	Radius *m* der Umkugel, Umkugelradius *m*	rayon *m* de la sphère circonscrite	радиус описанной сферы
	circumscribed circle <EG>	*s.* C 737		
C 740	**circumscribed figure** <of, about> <EG>	umbeschriebene Figur *f*	figure *f* circonscrite <à>	описанная фигура <вокруг>
C 741	**circumscribed hyperbola** <of a triangle> <EG>	Umhyperbel *f*	hyperbole *f* circonscrite	описанная гипербола
C 742	**circumscribed quadrangle** <EG>	umbeschriebenes Viereck *n*	quadrilatère *m* circonscrit	описанный четырехугольник
	circumscribed sphere <EG>	*s.* C 745		
C 743	**circumscribed Steiner ellipse** <about a triangle> <EG>	umbeschriebene Steinersche Ellipse *f*	ellipse *f* steinérienne circonscrite	описанный эллипс Штейнера
C 744	**circumscribed triangle** <EG>	umbeschriebenes Dreieck *n*	circonscrite *f*, triangle *m* circonscrit	описанный треугольник
C 745	**circumsphere,** circumscribed sphere <e.g. of a tetrahedron> <EG>	Umkugel *f*, umbeschriebene (umschriebene) Kugel *f*	sphère *f* circonscrite	описанная сфера
C 746	**Cisotti['s] differential-difference equation** <DE, FD>	Cisottische Differential-Differenzen-Gleichung *f*	équation *f* [différentio-différentielle] de Cisotti	[дифференциально-разностное] уравнение Чизотти
C 747	**cissoid,** cissoid of Diocles, Diokles['s] cissoid <AG>	Zissoide (Kissoide) *f* [des Diokles], Dioklea *f*, gerade Kissoide, Efeublattkurve *f*, Efeulinie *f*	cissoïde *f*, cissoïde de Dioclès (Diocle), diocléa *f*, cissoïde droite (cuspidale), courbe *f* de Diocle	циссоида, циссоида Диоклеса, прямая циссоида
	cissoid <GE>	*s.* C 749		
C 748	**cissoidal** <of a cubic> <GE>	begleitende Kissoide *f*	cissoïdale *f*	визиера Пеано, сопровождающая циссоида, визиера
C 749	**cissoidal curve,** cissoid <GE>	Zissoide *f*, Kissoide *f*, Kissoidale *f*, zissoidale (kissoidale) Kurve *f*, Zissoidalkurve *f*, Kissoidalkurve *f*, Cissoidalkurve *f*, // Cissoide *f*	cissoïdale *f*, courbe *f* cissoïdale, cissoïde *f*	циссоидаль, циссоидальная кривая, циссоида

C 750	**cissoidal function** <FT>	Funktion *f* $e^{i\omega t}$	fonction *f* cissoïdale	циссоидальная функция
	cissoid of Diocles <AG>	*s.* C 747		
C 751	**cissoid of Zahradnic** <GE>	Zahradnicsche Kissoide *f*	cissoïde *f* de Zahradnic	циссоидальная кривая, циссоидаль, циссоида Заградника
	C_k-lim[it], (C,k) limit <LI>	*s.* L 712		
C 752	**C_k-limitable ((C,k) limitable) sequence,** sequence limitable (*C*,*k*), sequence limitable by Cesàro's method [of limitation] of order *k*, sequence limitable (C_k), sequence limitable by Cesàro's *k*-th mean <LI>	C_k-limitierbare ((*C*,*k*)-limitierbare) Folge *f*, nach dem C_k-Verfahren limitierbare Folge	suite *f* limitable d'ordre *k*, suite limitable par la méthode de Cesàro d'ordre *k*, suite *k* fois indéterminée	последовательность, лимитируемая порядка *k* в смысле Чезаро; последовательность, лимитируемая методом Чезаро *k*-го порядка; (*C*,*k*)-лимитируемая последовательность
C 753	**C_k-method, (C,k) method,** Cesàro['s] method [of summation] of *k*-th order, Cesàro['s] summation method of *k*-th order <for divergent series> <LI>	C_k-Verfahren *n*, (*C*,*k*)-Verfahren *n*, Cesàrosches Summierungsverfahren *n* der Ordnung *k*	méthode *f* de sommation de Cesàro d'ordre *k*, méthode de Cesàro d'ordre *k*, méthode C_k, méthode (*C*,*k*)	метод Чезаро *k*-го порядка, метод суммирования [расходящихся рядов] Чезаро *k*-го порядка
C 754	**C_k-method, (C,k) method,** Cesàro['s] method of *k*-th order, Cesàro['s] limitation method of *k*-th order <for divergent sequences> <LI>	C_k-Verfahren *n*, (*C*,*k*)-Verfahren *n*, Cesàrosches Limitierungsverfahren *n* der Ordnung *k*	méthode *f* [de limitation] de Cesàro d'ordre *k*, méthode (*C*,*k*)	метод [образования обобщенного предела] Чезаро *k*-го порядка
	C_k-sum, (C,k) sum <LI>	*s.* S 2260		
C 755	**C_k-summability, (C,k) summability** <LI>	C_k-Summierbarkeit *f*, (*C*,*k*)-Summierbarkeit *f*	sommabilité *f* [au sens de Cesàro] d'ordre *k*	суммируемость порядка *k* методом (в смысле) Чезаро
C 756	**C_k-summable series,** series summable C_k, series summable (*C*,*k*), series summable by Cesàro's method [of summation] of order *k*, series summable by Cesàro's *k*-th mean <LI>	C_k-summierbare ((*C*,*k*)-summierbare, nach dem C_k-Verfahren summierbare) Reihe *f*	série *f* sommable par la méthode de Cesàro d'ordre *k*, série sommable d'ordre *k*, série *k* fois indéterminée	ряд, суммируемый методом Чезаро *k*-го порядка; ряд, суммируемый порядка *k* в смысле Чезаро; (*C*,*k*)-суммируемый ряд
	Clairaut['s] curve <GE>	*s.* C 2783		
C 757	**Clairaut['s] [differential] equation,** [differential] equation of Clairaut <DE>	Clairautsche Differentialgleichung *f*, Clairautsche Gleichung *f*	équation *f* de Clairaut, équation différentielle de Clairaut	уравнение Клеро, дифференциальное уравнение Клеро
C 758	**Clairaut['s] partial differential equation** <DE>	Clairautsche partielle Differentialgleichung *f*	équation *f* différentielle de Clairaut aux dérivées partielles, équation de Clairaut généralisée	дифференциальное уравнение Клеро в частных производных
C 759	**Clairaut['s] theorem** <for geodesic lines> <DG>	Clairautscher Satz *m* [über geodätische Linien auf Rotationsflächen]	théorème *m* de Clairaut	теорема Клеро
C 760	**clan** <AL>	kompakte zusammenhängende Hausdorffsche Halbgruppe *f*	clan *m*	клан, компактная связная хаусдорфова полугруппа
C 761	**class,** characteristic index <of a singularity> <DE>	Klasse *f*, charakteristischer Index *m*	classe *f*, indice *m* caractéristique	класс, характеристический показатель
C 762	**class** <of a differentiable variety> <DG>	Klasse *f* <einer differenzierbaren Mannigfaltigkeit>	classe *f* de différentiation	класс <дифференцируемого многообразия>
C 763	**class,** stratum <of a partition> <SE>	Klasse *f* <bei der Zerlegung einer Menge>	classe *f* <d'une partition>	смежный класс, слой <разбиения>
C 764	**class,** cell <ST>	Klasse *f*	classe *f*	класс
	class <AL>	*s.* N 243		
	class <GR>	*s.* 1. C 799; 2. M 555		
	class <ST>	*s.* 1. C 792; 2. G 446		
C 765	**class bound[ary],** cell boundary, class (cell) limit <ST>	Klassengrenze *f*; Wechselpunkt *m* <Argumentwert der Klassengrenze>	limite *f* de classe	граница интервала группировки, предел (граница) класса
	class calculus <LO>	*s.* C 19		
C 766	**class equation** <GR>	Klassengleichung *f*, Klassengleichung für konjugierte Elemente	équation *f* des classes	формула (уравнение) классов
C 767	**classes of ordinal numbers cofinal with each other** <SE>	zusammengehörige Klassen *fpl* von Ordnungszahlen	classes *fpl* de nombres ordinaux cofinales l'une avec l'autre	конфинальные классы порядковых чисел
C 768	**class field** <AB>	Klassenkörper *m*	corps *m* de (des) classes	поле классов
	class field in Hilbert's sense <AB>	*s.* A 59		
C 769	**class field theory** <AB>	Klassenkörpertheorie *f*	théorie *f* du corps de classe	теория полей классов
C 770	**class field tower,** tower of class fields, class tower <AB>	Klassenkörperturm *m*	tour *f* de corps de classes	башня полей классов
C 771	**class formation** <in class field theory> <AB>	Klassenformation *f*	formation *f* de classes	формация классов
C 772	**class formation** <SE>	Klassenbildung *f*	formation *f* de classes	образование классов
C 773	**class frequency,** cell frequency <ST>	Klassenhäufigkeit *f*, Klassenbesetzung *f*	effectif *m* de classe, fréquence *f* de classe	частота попадания в класс, групповая частота
C 774	**class function** <AL>	Klassenfunktion *f*	fonction *f* de classes	функция классов
	classical adjoint [matrix] <MD>	*s.* A 303		
	classical Boltzmann statistics <ST>	*s.* M 278		
	classical canonical form <MD>	*s.* J 99		

	classical hypergeometric series <SS>	*s.* H 694		
C 775	**classical Lie algebras** <of simple Lie rings> <AL>	Hauptklassen *fpl* <einfacher Liescher Ringe>, klassische Liesche Algebren *fpl*	algèbres *fpl* de Lie classiques	классические алгебры Ли
	classical Poisson bracket[s] <DE>	*s.* P 815		
C 776	**classical propositional logic** <LO>	klassische Aussagenlogik (Junktorenlogik) *f*, chrysippinische Logik *f*	logique *f* chrysippienne	классическая логика высказываний
C 777	**classical ruin problem,** discontinuous ruin problem <TG>	klassisches (unstetiges) Ruinproblem *n*	problème *m* de la ruine classique (discontinu)	классическая (прерывная) задача о разорении [игрока]
C 778	**classical sentential calculus,** two-valued sentential calculus <LO>	klassischer (zweiwertiger) Aussagenkalkül *m*	calcul *m* classique des propositions	классическое (двузначное) исчисление высказываний
C 779	**classical set theory,** Cantorian set theory <SE>	Cantorsche Mengentheorie *f*, klassische Mengenlehre *f*	théorie *f* classique des ensembles	канторовская теория множеств
	classical statistics <ST>	*s.* M 278		
C 780	**classification** <ST>	Klassifikation *f*	classification *f*	классификация
	classification <ST>	*s.* C 788		
C 781	**classification factor,** factor <ST>	Klassifikationsfaktor *m*, Faktor *m*	facteur *m* de classification, facteur	фактор [классификации], параметр
C 782	**classification of Baire,** Baire['s] classification <RF>	Bairesche Klassifikation *f*	classification *f* de [M.] Baire	классификация Бэра
C 783	**classification of transcendental numbers by Koksma** <NT>	Koksmasche Klassifikation *f* transzendenter Zahlen	classification *f* des nombres transcendants par Koksma	классификация Коксма трансцендентных чисел
C 784	**classification statistic** <ST>	Stichprobenfunktion *f* für die Klassifikation	statistique *f* de classification	статистика, по значениям которой производится классификация
C 785	**classification theorem** <of class field theory> <AB>	Anordnungssatz *m*	loi *f* d'ordination	теорема вложения
C 786	**classification theorem,** ordering theorem <for fibre bundles> <AT>	Klassifikationssatz *m*, Klassifizierungssatz *m*	théorème *m* de classification	теорема о классификации
C 787	**classifier,** set builder <LO, SE>	Abstraktionsoperator *m*	classificateur *m*	оператор абстракции
C 788	**classifying,** classification <as an operation> <ST>	Klassifizierung *f*	classement *m*	классифицирование
C 789	**classifying map** <TO>	klassifizierende Abbildung *f*	application *f* classifiante	классифицирующее отображение
C 790	**classifying space** <AT>	klassifizierender Raum *m*	espace *m* classifiant (classificateur)	классифицирующее пространство
C 791	**class index** <of a curve *or* surface> <DG>	Klassenindex *m*	indice *m* de classe	индекс класса
C 792	**class interval,** cell interval, class, cell <ST>	Klassenintervall *n*, Klasse *f*	intervalle *m* de classe, classe *f*	интервал группировки, группа, класс
	class interval [length] <ST>	*s.* C 794		
C 793	**class invariant** <FU>	Klasseninvariante *f*	invariant *m* de classe	инвариант класса
C 794	**class length,** class interval length, length of class interval, class interval (range), cell length (interval, range) <ST>	Klassenbreite *f*, Klassenintervallänge *f*, Klassenintervall *n*, Klassengröße *f*	longueur *f* de l'intervalle de classe, intervalle *m* de classe	длина (величина, размер) интервала группировки, интервал группировки, ширина интервала [группирования]
	class limit <ST>	*s.* C 765		
C 795	**class mark,** class mid value, cell mark <ST>	Klassenmitte *f*	centre *m* (valeur *f* centrale) de classe	середина интервала группировки
C 796	**class mean,** cell mean <ST>	Klassenmittel *n*	moyenne *f* de (sur la) classe	среднее внутри класса
	class mid value <ST>	*s.* C 795		
C 797	**class number** <ST>	Klassennummer *f*	valeur *f* type (caractéristique) de classe	номер класса
C 798	**class number, class-number** <of an algebraic number field or a group> <AB, GR>	Klassenzahl *f*	nombre *m* des classes	число классов
	class number <ST>	*s.* N 817		
	class of all subsets <SE>	*s.* P 1122		
C 799	**class of conjugate elements,** conjugacy (conjugate, conjugation) class, class, conjugate set, complete sequence <of a group> <GR>	Klasse *f* konjugierter Elemente, Konjugationsklasse *f*	classe *f*, classe de conjugaison, classe conjuguée (d'éléments semblables), suite *f* complète d'éléments conjugués, système *m* complet	класс сопряженных элементов, сопряженный класс
	class of divisors <AL>	*s.* D 826		
C 800	**class of equivalent matrix representations** <of a ring> <AL, RE>	Matrizendarstellungsklasse *f*, Darstellungsklasse *f*	classe *f* de représentations matricielles équivalentes	класс эквивалентных матричных представлений
	class of homotopic mappings <TO>	*s.* H 527		
	class of indices <SE>	*s.* D 854		
	class of [mutually] isomorphic [algebraic] systems <UA>	*s.* I 1074		
C 801	**class of *p*-conjugate elements,** *p*-class <of a group> <GR>	Klasse *f p*-konjugierter Elemente, *p*-Klasse *f*	classe *f* d'éléments *p*-conjugués, *p*-classe *f*	класс *p*-сопряженных элементов, *p*-класс
C 802	**class of simple Lie algebras** <AL>	Killing-Cartansche Klasse *f* <Liescher Ringe>	classe *f* d'algèbres de Lie simples	класс Киллинга-Картана <алгебр Ли>

No.	English	German	French	Russian
C 803	**class of the zero element** <AL>	Nullklasse *f*; Klasse *f*, die das Nullelement enthält; Nullrestklasse *f*	classe-zéro *m*	класс нулевого элемента
	class range <ST>	*s.* C 794		
C 804	**class satisfying the finite intersection property** <SE>	zentrierte Klasse *f*	classe *f* centrée	центрированный класс
C 805	**class sum,** sum over the classes <AL, ST>	Klassensumme *f*	somme *f* sur les classes	сумма по классам
	class tower <AB>	*s.* C 770		
C 806	**class tower problem** <AB>	Klassenkörperturmproblem *n*	problème *m* de la tour de corps de classes	проблема башни полей классов
	C-lattice <LA>	*s.* D 772		
C 807	**Clausen['s] series** <SS>	Clausensche Reihe *f*	série *f* de Clausen	ряд Клаузена
	Clavius['] law <LO>	*s.* F 331		
C 808	**clear a fraction / to** <AR>	den Nenner beseitigen	chasser le dénominateur	освобождаться от знаменателя
C 809	**clearing of fractions** <AL>	Beseitigung *f* des Nenners, Beseitigung der Brüche	suppression *f* du dénominateur	освобождение от знаменателя
C 810	**Clebsch['s] condition** <VA>	Clebschsche Bedingung *f*, Clebsch-Bedingung *f*	condition *f* de Clebsch	условие Клебша
C 811	**Clebsch-Gordan coefficient,** vector addition coefficient <AL>	Clebsch-Gordan-Koeffizient *m*, Vektoradditionskoeffizient *m*	coefficient *m* de Clebsch-Gordan (l'addition vectorielle)	коэффициент Клебша-Гордана (векторного сложения), // коэффициент Клебша-Жордана
C 812	**Clebsch-Gordan expansion** <IV>	Clebsch-Gordan-Zerlegung *f*	développement *m* de Clebsch-Gordan	разложение Клебша-Гордана
C 813	**Clebsch-Gordan rule** <IV>	Clebsch-Gordansche Regel *f*, Clebsch-Gordan-Regel *f*	règle *f* de Clebsch-Gordan, loi *f* de Clebsch-Gordan	правило Клебша-Гордана
C 814	**Clebsch-Gordan series** <IV>	Clebsch-Gordan-Reihe *f*, Gordansche Reihenentwicklung *f*, Clebsch-Gordansche Reihe *f*	série *f* de Clebsch-Gordan	ряд Клебша-Гордана
C 815	**Clebsch['s] map[ping]** <AG>	Clebsch-Abbildung *f*, Clebschabbildung *f*	application *f* de Clebsch	отображение Клебша
C 816	**Clebsch['s] principle [of transference],** principle of Clebsch <AG>	Übertragungsprinzip *n* von Clebsch, Clebschsches Übertragungsprinzip	principe *m* de transfert de Clebsch, principe de Clebsch	принцип перенесения Клебша
C 817	**Clebsch['s] sufficient condition,** sufficient condition <VA>	Clebschsche hinreichende Bedingung *f*, Clebschsche S-Bedingung *f*, S-Bedingung von Clebsch	condition *f* suffisante de Clebsch, condition suffisante	достаточное условие Клебша
C 818	**Clebsch['s] transformation,** transformation of Clebsch <IV>	Clebsch-Transformation *f*, Clebschsche Transformation *f*	transformation *f* de Clebsch	преобразование Клебша
C 819	**clélie** <GE>	Claelie *f* von Grandi, Cleliakurve *f*, Clelie *f* <erster *oder* zweiter Art>	courbe *f* clélie, clélie *f*	клелия
C 820	**Clifford['s] algebra** <AL>	Cliffordsche Algebra *f*, Clifford-Algebra *f*	algèbre *f* de Clifford	алгебра Клиффорда, клиффордова алгебра
C 821	**Clifford['s] group** <AL>	Cliffordsche Gruppe *f*	groupe *m* de Clifford, groupe spinoriel, spin *m*, spinn *m*	группа Клиффорда
	Clifford['s] group of translations <GE>	*s.* C 830		
C 822	**Clifford-Klein form,** space form <GE>	Clifford-Kleinsche Raumform *f*, Raumform *f*	forme *f* de Clifford-Klein, forme de l'espace, forme géométrique, forme spatiale	форма Клиффорда-Клейна, пространственная форма Клиффорда-Клейна
C 823	**Clifford-Klein['s] [form] problem** <GE>	Clifford-Kleinsches Raumformenproblem (Problem) *n*	problème *m* [des formes spatiales] de Clifford-Klein	задача [пространственных форм] Клиффорда-Клейна
C 824	**Clifford['s] module** <AL>	Cliffordscher Modul *m*	module *m* de Clifford	модуль Клиффорда
C 825	**Clifford['s] number** <AL>	Cliffordsche Zahl *f*	nombre *m* de Clifford	число Клиффорда, число Клиффорда-Липшица
C 826	**Clifford['s] parallel** <GE>	Cliffordsche Parallele *f*	parallèle *f* [au sens] de Clifford	параллель [в смысле] Клиффорда
	Clifford['s] semigroup <AL>	*s.* C 1509		
C 827	**Clifford['s] surface** <GE>	Cliffordsche Fläche *f*	surface *f* de Clifford	поверхность Клиффорда
C 828	**Clifford['s] theorem** <AG>	Satz *m* von Clifford, Cliffordscher Satz	théorème *m* de Clifford	теорема Клиффорда
C 829	**Clifford['s] translation** <GE>	Cliffordsche Schiebung *f*	translation *f* de Clifford	перенос Клиффорда
C 830	**Clifford['s] translation[al] group,** Clifford['s] group of translations <GE>	Cliffordsche Schiebungsgruppe *f*	groupe *m* de Clifford [des translations], groupe des translations de Clifford	группа Клиффорда [переносов], группа переносов Клиффорда
	C-lim[it] <LI>	*s.* L 711		
C 831	**C_1-limit, (*C*,1) limit, C_1 lim, (*C*,1) lim,** limit by arithmetic means <LI>	*M*-Limes *m*, Limes *m* nach dem *M*-Verfahren, *M*-lim, (*C*,1)-Limes *m*, C_1-Limes *m*, (*C*,1)-lim, C_1-lim	limite *f* par moyennes arithmétiques, (*C*,1)-limite *f*, (*C*,1)-lim	[обобщенный] предел по методу средних арифметических
	C-limitable sequence <LI>	*s.* S 578		
C 832	**C_1-limitable sequence, (C,1) limitable sequence,** sequence limitable by arithmetic means <LI>	*M*-limitierbare (nach dem *M*-Verfahren limitierbare, (*C*,1)-limitierbare, C_1-limitierbare) Folge *f*	suite *f* limitable par moyennes arithmétiques, suite simplement indéterminée	последовательность, лимитируемая средними арифметическими
C 833	**clique** <GP>	Clique *f*, Sippe *f*	clique *f*, préordre *m* complet symétrique	клика

No.	English	German	French	Russian
C 834	**clockwise** <GE, GN>	im Uhrzeigersinn, in mathematisch negativem Sinn, in mathematisch negativer Richtung, in negativer Richtung, mathematisch negativ	en (dans le) sens direct, en (dans le) sens négatif, en (dans le) sens d'horloge, en (dans le) sens des aiguilles d'une montre, en (dans le) sens du soleil, dextrorsum	по часовой стрелке, по ходу часовой стрелки
C 835	**clockwise direction,** negative direction; clockwise sense, negative sense <GE, GN>	Uhrzeigerrichtung *f*, negative (mathematisch negative) Richtung *f*; Uhrzeigersinn *m*, negativer (mathematisch negativer) Sinn *m*, Drehsinn *m* in Uhrzeigerrichtung	direction *f* des aiguilles d'une montre, direction du soleil, direction négative; sens *m* des aiguilles d'une montre, sens du soleil, sens direct (négatif)	направление [вращения] по часовой стрелке, отрицательное направление
	clockwise revolution <AN, GE>	*s.* C 836		
C 836	**clockwise rotation,** clockwise revolution <AN, GE>	negativer Umlaufsinn *m*, Umlauf *m* im Uhrzeigersinn	rotation *f* dans le sens des aiguilles d'une montre, parcours *m* négatif	обход в отрицательном направлении
	clockwise rotation <EG>	*s.* R 1157		
	clockwise sense <GE, GN>	*s.* C 835		
C 837	**clone** <of an algebra> <UA>	Klon *m*	clone *m*	клон, замкнутое множество операций
C 838	**clopen set,** closed-and-open set, [both] open and closed set, closed-and-open subset, open-and-closed subset <TO>	zugleich offene und abgeschlossene Menge *f*, abgeschlossene offene Menge, offen-abgeschlossene Menge	ensemble *m* [à la fois] ouvert et fermé, ensemble fermé-ouvert (ouvert-et-fermé), ouvert-et-fermé *m*	открыто-замкнутое множество
C 839	**closable linear operator,** pre-closed linear operator <FA>	abschließbarer linearer Operator *m*	opérateur *m* linéaire fermable, transformation (application) *f* linéaire fermable	линейный оператор, допускающий замкнутое расширение
	close <TO>	*s.* P 1883		
C 840	**close a parenthesis / to;** to close the bracket <GN, LO>	die Klammer schließen	fermer la parenthèse	закрыть скобку
	close approximation <AX, NT>	*s.* G 340		
	closed-and-open [sub]set <TO>	*s.* C 838		
C 841	**closed arc progression,** closed directed-edge sequence <of an oriented graph> <GP>	geschlossene gerichtete Kantenprogression *f*, geschlossene kontinuierlich gerichtete Kantenfolge *f* <Wiederholung von Bögen und Ecken möglich>	circuit *m*, suite *f* circulaire d'arcs	замкнутый ориентированный маршрут
C 842	**closed ball,** closed sphere <TO>	abgeschlossene Kugel *f*, abgeschlossene Vollkugel *f*	boule *f* achevée (fermée, de première espèce), sphère *f* généralisée fermée, sphéroïde *f*	замкнутый шар, замкнутая сфера
	closed ball <DI, GE, TO>	*s.* C 901		
C 843	**closed barycentric star** <dual to a vertex> <AT>	abgeschlossener baryzentrischer Stern *m*	étoile *f* barycentrique fermée	замкнутая барицентрическая звезда <сопряженная вершине>
C 844	**closed base** <for a topological space>, basis of closed sets <of a topological space> <TO>	abgeschlossene Basis *f*, Basis abgeschlossener Mengen	base *f* fermée	замкнутая база, база замкнутых множеств
	closed bounded o-symmetric convex body <GU>	*s.* S 1603		
C 845	**closed broken line** <GE>	geschlossener Polygonzug *m*	ligne *f* brisée fermée	замкнутая ломаная
C 846	**closed category** <CA>	abgeschlossene Kategorie *f*	catégorie *f* fermée	замкнутая категория
C 847	**closed chain** <of sets> <TO>	geschlossene Mengenkette *f*	chaîne *f* d'ensembles fermée	замкнутая цепь <множеств>
	closed chain <AT>	*s.* C 2831		
C 848	**closed class** <SE>	abgeschlossene Klasse *f* <in *A*>	classe *f* close	замкнутый класс
C 849	**closed combinatorial surface** <AT>	geschlossene [kombinatorische] Fläche *f*	surface *f* combinatoire fermée	замкнутая комбинаторная поверхность
C 850	**closed complex** <AT>	[ab]geschlossener Komplex *m*	complexe *m* fermé	замкнутый комплекс
	closed complex plane <FT>	*s.* E 762		
	closed contour <AN>	*s.* C 2252		
	closed convex curve <GE>	*s.* O 562		
C 851	**closed convex hull,** convex cover <CS, GE> ⌐<CS, GE>	abgeschlossene konvexe Hülle *f*	enveloppe *f* fermée convexe, enveloppe convexe fermée	замкнутая выпуклая оболочка
	closed convex surface	*s.* C 2407		
C 852	**closed cover[ing]** <TO>	abgeschlossene Überdeckung *f*	recouvrement *m* fermé	замкнутое покрытие
C 853	**closed current** <DG>	geschlossener Strom *m*	courant *m* fermé	замкнутый ток
	closed curve <AN>	*s.* C 2252		
	closed directed-edge sequence <GP>	*s.* C 841		
C 854	**closed directed-edge train,** circuit, directed circuit <of a digraph> <GP>	geschlossener kontinuierlich gerichteter Kantenzug *m*, Zyklusprogression *f*, geschlossene Bogenfolge *f* <ohne Wiederholung von Bögen>	circuit *m* simple, circuit	контур, ориентированный цикл

C 855	**closed disk** <AN, TO>	abgeschlossener Kreis *m*, abgeschlossene Kreisscheibe *f*, Kreisscheibe mit Rand	disque *m* fermé, cercle *m* circonférencié	замкнутый круг
C 856	**closed domain,** closed region <a connected set of points> <AN, FT>	Bereich *m*, abgeschlossenes Gebiet *n*, Bereich im engeren Sinne, abgeschlossener Bereich	domaine *m* fermé	замкнутая (закрытая) область
C 857	**closed domain** <TO>	Bereich *m*, abgeschlossener Bereich, Stück *n*, topologischer Bereich	domaine *m* fermé	замкнутая область
C 858	**closed egde path,** edge-loop <AT>	geschlossener Kantenzug (Kantenweg) *m*	chemin *m* fermé, formé par des arrêtes d'un complexe	замкнутая ломаная <комплекса>
C 859	**closed edge sequence,** cyclic sequence <of edges of an unoriented graph> <GP>	geschlossene Kantenfolge (Kantenprogression) *f*	pseudo-cycle *m*, cycle *m*	замкнутый маршрут
C 860	**closed edge train,** circuit progression <of an unoriented graph> <GP>	geschlossener Kantenzug *m*, geschlossene Kantenzugprogression *f* <alle Kanten verschieden>	cycle *m* simple, cycle	цикл
C 861	**closed equivalence relation** <TO>	abgeschlossene Äquivalenzrelation *f*	relation *f* d'équivalence fermée, équivalence *f* fermée	замкнутое отношение эквивалентности
C 862	**closed extension** <of an operator> <FA>	abgeschlossene Fortsetzung (Erweiterung) *f*	prolongement *m* fermé	замкнутое продолжение
C 863	**closed family of sets** <TO>	System *n* (Familie *f*) abgeschlossener Mengen	famille *f* d'ensembles fermés	семейство замкнутых множеств
C 864	**closed filter** <LA>	abgeschlossener Filter *m*	filtre *m* fermé	замкнутый фильтр
C 865	**closed form** <AN, DG>	geschlossene Form *f*	forme *f* fermée	замкнутая форма
	closed form <AN, GN>	*s.* R 835		
C 866	**closed formula** <LO>	abgeschlossener Ausdruck *m*, [ab]geschlossene Aussageform *f*, geschlossene Formel *f*	formule *f* close	замкнутая (закрытая) формула, замкнутое выражение, замкнутая форма высказывания
	closed function <TO>	*s.* C 883		
C 867	**closed geodesic** <DG>	geschlossene Geodätische *f*	géodésique *f* fermée, lacet géodésique	замкнутая геодезическая
C 868	**closed graph** <FA>	abgeschlossener Graph *m*	graphique (graphe) *m* fermé	замкнутый граф[ик]
	closed graph <GP>	*s.* U 112		
	closed-graph mapping <FA>	*s.* C 882		
C 869	**closed-graph theorem** <FA>	Satz *m* vom abgeschlossenen Graph (Graphen), Graphensatz *m*	théorème *m* du graphe fermé	теорема о замкнутом графике
C 870	**closed grill** <SE>	abgeschlossenes Sieb *n*	crible *m* fermé	замкнутое решето
C 871	**closed group** <GR>	geschlossene [kontinuierliche] Gruppe *f*	groupe *m* clos	замкнутая группа
	closed half-line <GE>	*s.* R 198		
C 872	**closed half-plane** <FT, GE>	abgeschlossene Halbebene *f*	demi-plan *m* fermé	замкнутая полуплоскость
C 873	**closed half space, closed half-space** <FT, GE>	abgeschlossener Halbraum *m*	demi-espace *m* fermé	замкнутое полупространство
C 874	**closed ideal** <AL>	abgeschlossenes Ideal *n*	idéal *m* fermé	замкнутый идеал
	closed interior two-sided cut <AT>	*s.* C 911		
C 875	**closed interval,** segment <[*a*,*b*] *or* <*a*,*b*>> <TO>	abgeschlossenes Intervall *n*, Segment *n* <mit den Endpunkten *a*, b>	intervalle *m* fermé, segment *m*, segment fermé <d'extrémités *a*,*b*>	отрезок, сегмент, замкнутый отрезок (интервал) <с концами *a*,*b*>; числовой отрезок
	closed interval <LA>	*s.* I 825		
C 876	**closed in the operator norm** <FA>	normabgeschlossen	fermé pour la norme (topologie uniforme)	замкнутый в смысле нормы операторов
	closed join of O and *K* <AT>	*s.* C 1847		
	closed Jordan curve <TO>	*s.* S 894		
C 877	**closed kernel** <IE>	abgeschlossener Kern *m*	noyau *m* fermé	замкнутое ядро
	closed lattice <LA>	*s.* C 1449		
	closed lattice ideal <TO>	*s.* B 55		
	closed line <AN>	*s.* C 2252		
C 878	**closed linear manifold** <of a topological linear space> <FA, TO>	Unterraum *m*, Teilraum *m*, abgeschlossene lineare Mannigfaltigkeit *f*	variété *f* linéaire fermée	замкнутое линейное многообразие
C 879	**closed linear operator** a <FA>	bgeschlossener linearer Operator *m*	opérateur *m* linéaire fermé	замкнутый линейный оператор
C 880	**closed line segment** <FA, GE>	abgeschlossene Strecke *f*	segment *m* linéaire fermé	замкнутый отрезок
	closed loop <AN>	*s.* C 2252		
C 881	**closed manifold** <TO>	geschlossene Mannigfaltigkeit *f*	variété *f* fermée (close)	замкнутое многообразие
	closed manifold <AT>	*s.* C 894		
C 882	**closed map[ping],** closed transformation, closed-graph mapping <FA>	abgeschlossene Abbildung *f*, Abbildung mit abgeschlossenem Graphen, abgeschlossene Transformation *f*	application *f* fermée, transformation *f* fermée, application à graphique (graphe) fermé	замкнутое преобразование, замкнутое отображение, преобразование с замкнутым графиком
C 883	**closed map[ping],** closed transformation (function) <TO>	abgeschlossene Abbildung *f*	application *f* fermée, morphisme *m* fermé	замкнутое отображение
C 884	**closed morphism** <CA>	abgeschlossener Morphismus *m*	morphisme *m* fermé	замкнутый морфизм
C 885	**closed multidimensional interval** <TO>	mehrdimensionales abgeschlossenes Intervall *n*	segment *m*	многомерный промежуток
	closed *n*-ball <GE>	*s.* C 900		

C 886	**closed n-cell,** solid n-sphere, n-disk <homeomorphic image of the closed n-ball> <TO>	abgeschlossene n-dimensionale Zelle *f*, n-dimensionale abgeschlossene Zelle	n-cellule *f* fermée	n-мерный элемент; пространство, гомеоморфное замкнутому шару
C 887	**closed n-dimensional interval (rectangular parallelepiped),** n-dimensional closed interval <GE, RF>	n-dimensionales [achsenparalleles] abgeschlossenes Intervall *n*, abgeschlossenes achsenparalleles Intervall, abgeschlossener n-dimensionaler Quader *m*	pavé *m* fermé [à n dimensions]	полисегмент, замкнутый полиинтервал, замкнутый [n-мерный] кирпич
C 888	**closed neighbourhood** <TO>	abgeschlossene Umgebung *f*	entourage (voisinage) *m* fermé	замкнутая окрестность
C 889	**closed normal form** <LO>	abgeschlossene Normalform *f*, abgeschlossener Ausdruck *m*	forme *f* normale close	замкнутая нормальная форма
C 890	**closed object** <CA>	abgeschlossenes Objekt *n*	objet *m* fermé	замкнутый объект
C 891	**closed one-sided cut [line]** <AT, TO>	einufriger Rückkehrschnitt *m*	rétrosection *f* à une lèvre	линия замкнутого однобережного разреза, замкнутый однобережный разрез
	closed orthogonal sequence <AN>	*s.* C 1540		
	closed orthogonal system <AN>	*s.* C 1541		
	closed orthonormal system <AN, FA>	*s.* C 1543		
C 892	**closed path,** loop <based at x_0> <TO>	geschlossener Weg *m*	lacet *m*, chemin *m* fermé <d'origine x_0, au point x_0>	замкнутый путь, петля <в точке x_0>
	closed path <AN>	*s.* C 2252		
	closed plane <FT>	*s.* E 762		
C 893	**closed point** <TO>	abgeschlossener Punkt *m*	point *m* fermé	замкнутая точка
	closed point set <TO>	*s.* C 897		
C 894	**closed polyhedral manifold,** closed manifold <AT>	geschlossene Polyedermannigfaltigkeit (Mannigfaltigkeit) *f*	variété *f* polyédrale close	замкнутое [полиэдральное] многообразие
	closed region <AN, FT>	*s.* C 856		
C 895	**closed Riemann surface** <FT>	geschlossene (kompakte) Riemannsche Fläche *f*	surface *f* de Riemann close	замкнутая риманова поверхность
C 896	**closed sequential scheme** <ST>	geschlossenes Sequentialschema *n*	schéma *m* séquentiel fermé, schéma progressif limité	замкнутая последовательная схема
C 897	**closed set,** closed point set <TO>	abgeschlossene Menge (Punktmenge) *f*	ensemble *m* fermé, fermé *m*, partie *f* fermée	замкнутое [точечное] множество
	closed set of functions <AN>	*s.* C 1577		
C 898	**closed set of identities** <UA>	abgeschlossenes System *n* von Identitäten	système *m* d'identités clos	замкнутое множество тождеств
	closed simple curve <TO>	*s.* S 894		
C 899	**closed simplex** <AT>	abgeschlossenes Simplex *n*	simplexe *m* fermé	замкнутый симплекс
C 900	**closed solid n-sphere,** [closed] n-ball, solid n-sphere, n-dimensional solid sphere <GE>	abgeschlossene n-dimensionale Kugel *f*, n-dimensionale Vollkugel *f*	boule *f* fermée à n dimensions, boule [euclidienne] fermée n-dimensionnelle	n-мерный замкнутый [евклидов] шар, n-мерный шар
C 901	**closed solid sphere,** closed ball <in R_n> <DI, GE, TO>	abgeschlossene Kugel (Vollkugel) *f*, Vollkugel *f*	boule *f* [euclidienne] fermée	замкнутый [евклидов] шар, замкнутая сфера
	closed sphere <TO>	*s.* C 842		
	closed spherical region <DI, GE, TO>	*s.* B 38		
C 902	**closed star** <AT>	abgeschlossener Stern *m*, kombinatorische Umgebung *f*	étoile *f* fermée	замкнутая звезда
	closed statement <LO>	*s.* P 1865		
C 903	**closed sub-base,** sub-basis of closed sets <of a topological space> <TO>	abgeschlossene Subbasis *f*	sous-base *f* fermée	замкнутая подбаза
C 904	**closed subgroup** <of a topological group> <GR>	abgeschlossene Untergruppe *f*	sous-groupe *m* fermé	замкнутая подгруппа
C 905	**closed subscheme** <AG>	abgeschlossenes Unterschema *n*	sous-schéma *m* fermé	замкнутая подсхема
	closed subset <AL>	*s.* S 438		
C 906	**closed subset with respect to an operation,** subset stable under an operation <AL>	gegenüber einer Operation abgeschlossene Untermenge *f*	sous-ensemble *m* [fermé] pour une opération, partie *f* stable (fermée) par une loi de composition	подмножество, замкнутое относительно операции; подмножество, допускающее операцию
C 907	**closed surface** <GE, TO>	geschlossene Fläche *f*	surface *f* fermée	замкнутая поверхность, компактная поверхность без края
	closed surface integral <AN>	*s.* I 644		
C 908	**closed system** <DE, NT>	geschlossenes System *n*	système *m* fermé	замкнутая система
C 909	**closed system** <in the theory of exterior differential forms> <DI, DG, VT>	abgeschlossenes System *n*	système *m* fermé	замкнутая система
	closed system of functions <AN>	*s.* C 1577		
C 910	**closed term** <LO>	abgeschlossener Term *m*	terme *m* clos	замкнутый терм
	closed transformation <FA>	*s.* C 882		
	closed transformation <TO>	*s.* C 883		
C 911	**closed two-sided cut [line],** closed interior two-sided cut, two-sided cut <of the first or second kind> <AT>	zweiufriger Rückkehrschnitt *m* <erster *oder* zweiter Art>	rétrosection *f* à deux lèvres <de première *ou* seconde espèce>	линия замкнутого двубережного разреза, замкнутый внутренний двубережный разрез <первого *или* второго рода>

No.	English	German	French	Russian
C 912	**closed-type quadrature formula** <AX, DI, NU>	Quadraturformel (Formel) *f* vom geschlossenen Typ	formule *f* [pour l'intégration numérique] de type fermé	квадратурная формула замкнутого типа
C 913	**closed under a closure operation** <SE>	abgeschlossen bezüglich (gegenüber) einer Hüllenbildung, abgeschlossen in bezug auf eine Hüllenbildung	stable pour une opération de fermeture	замкнутый относительно операции замыкания
	closed under a law of composition <AL>	*s.* C 922		
	closed under an operation <AL>	*s.* C 922		
C 914	**closed under a partial operation** <subset> <AL>	abgeschlossen bezüglich (gegenüber) einer partiellen algebraischen Verknüpfung, abgeschlossen in bezug auf eine partielle algebraische Verknüpfung	stable pour une opération partielle	замкнутый относительно частичной операции
	closed under a relation <SE>	*s.* C 925		
	closed under intersection <SE>	*s.* M 374		
C 915	**closed under limits** <CA>	abgeschlossen gegenüber Limiten	stable pour les limites	замкнутый относительно пределов
C 916	**closed under multiplication** <AL>	abgeschlossen gegenüber Multiplikation, multiplikativ abgeschlossen	multiplicativement fermé (stable)	замкнутый относительно умножения, мультипликативно замкнутый
C 917	**closed under multiplication with ring elements** <AL>	abgeschlossen gegenüber Multiplikation mit Ringelementen	multiplicativement permis	замкнутый относительно умножения с элементами кольца
C 918	**closed under operation by the endomorphisms of the algebraic structure** <AL>	stabil (abgeschlossen) gegenüber den Endomorphismen	endostable	замкнутый относительно эндоморфизмов
C 919	**closed under the formation of homomorphic images** <AL>	abgeschlossen gegenüber homomorphen Bildern	stable pour les images homomorphes	замкнутый относительно гомоморфных образов
C 920	**closed under the formation of subalgebras** <AL>	abgeschlossen gegenüber Unteralgebren	fermé par sous-algèbres	замкнутый относительно подалгебр
C 921	**closed under the formation of ultraproducts,** closed with respect to ultraproducts, ultraclosed <UA>	abgeschlossen gegenüber Ultraproduktbildung	stable pour les ultraproduits	замкнутый относительно ультрапроизведений, ультразамкнутый
	closed under the union operation <SE>	*s.* J 74		
C 922	**closed with respect to a law of composition,** closed (stable) under a law of composition, closed (stable) under an operation, stable with respect to a law of composition <AL>	abgeschlossen gegenüber einem Verknüpfungsgesetz, abgeschlossen bezüglich einer Verknüpfung	stable (fermé, clos) pour (par) une loi de composition, stable (fermé, clos) par rapport à une opération	замкнутый относительно закона композиции, замкнутый относительно алгебраической операции
C 923	**closed with respect to an operation / to be** <AL>	gegenüber einer Operation abgeschlossen sein, eine Operation gestatten	être stable par une opération, être fermé par (pour) une opération	быть замкнутым относительно операции, допускать операцию
C 924	**closed with respect to an operator** <AL, SE>	abgeschlossen gegenüber einem Operator	stable pour un opérateur	замкнутый относительно [некоторого] оператора
C 925	**closed with respect to a relation,** closed (saturated) under a relation <subset> <SE>	abgeschlossen gegenüber einer Relation	saturé à gauche pour une relation	замкнутый относительно [некоторого] отношения
	closed with respect to ultraproducts <UA>	*s.* C 921		
	closeness <ST>	*s.* A 193		
C 926/7	**close-point** <of an algebraic surface> <Cayley> <AG>	Close-point *m*, singulärer Einzelpunkt *m*	point-clos *m*, point *m* solide singulier	замыкающая точка
	close-point <GE>	*s.* T 19		
	close the bracket / to <GN, LO>	*s.* C 840		
C 928	**closure** <of a map> <AL, TO>	Hülle *f* <einer Abbildung>	fermeture *f* <d'application>	замыкание <отображения>
C 929	**closure** <AT>	Hülle *f*, abgeschlossene Hülle	fermeture *f*	замыкание
C 930	**closure** <of an operator> <FA>	Abschließung *f*	fermeture *f*	замыкание
C 931	**closure** <of a Riemannian surface> <FT>	Abschließung *f*, uneigentliche Fortsetzung *f*	fermeture *f*	замыкание
C 932	**closure** <of a formula *or* an expression containing free variables> <LO>	Abschließung *f* <einer Formel> <Bindung aller freien Variablen durch Quantoren>	clôture *f* <d'une formule>	навешивание кванторов, замыкание <формулы>
C 933	**closure** <TO>	Abgeschlossenheit *f*	fermeture *f*	замкнутость
C 934	**closure,** adherence <of a set> <TO>	abgeschlossene Hülle *f*, Abschluß *m*, Abschließung *f*, Hülle *f*, Adhärenz *f* <Bourbaki>	adhérence *f*, fermeture *f*, fermeture topologique	замыкание
	closure <AL, LO, TO>	*s.* C 940		
	closure <SE>	*s.* T 802		
C 935	**closure algebra** <AL>	Hüllenalgebra *f*	algèbre *f* de fermeture	алгебра с замыканием
	closure algebra <AL>	*s.* T 502		

	English	German	French	Russian
C 936	**closure condition** <AL, GE>	Schließungsbedingung *f*	condition *f* de fermeture	условие замыкания
C 937	**closure condition of Reidemeister** <in geometry of webs> <GE, TO>	Reidemeistersche Schließungsbedingung *f*	condition *f* de fermeture de Reidemeister	условие замыкания Рейдемейстера
C 938	**closure criterion** <FA>	Abgeschlossenheitskriterium *n*	critère *m* de fermeture	критерий замкнутости
C 939	**closure operation** <TO>	Abschließung *f* <Übergang zur abgeschlossenen Hülle>	opération *f* de fermeture, fermeture *f*	операция замыкания, замыкание
	closure operation <AL, LO, TO>	*s.* C 940		
C 940	**closure operator,** closure operation, closure, Moore closure <AL, LO, TO>	Hüllenoperator *m*, Hüllenoperation *f*, Hüllenbildung *f*	opération *f* de [la] fermeture, application *f* de fermeture [de Moore]; fermeture *f* [de Moore]	оператор (операция) замыкания
C 941	**closure problem** <AG>	Schließungsproblem *n* <Poncelet>	problème *m* de fermeture (clôture)	проблема замыкания
C 942	**closure property** <AL, LO, TO>	Hülleneigenschaft *f*	propriété *f* de fermeture	свойство замыкания
C 943	**closure system** <SE>	Hüllensystem *n*	système *m* de fermeture	система замыканий
C 944	**closure theorem** <GE>	Schließungssatz *m*	théorème *m* de fermeture, théorème dit « de fermeture »	теорема замыкания
C 945	**closure theorem** <LO>	Abschließungssatz *m*	théorème *m* de clôture	теорема замыкания
C 946	**clothing** <of a surface> <GE>	Bekleidung *f*	revêtement *m*	оснащение
	clothoid [curve] <GE>	*s.* C 2471		
C 947	**clustering** <ST>	Aufteilung *f* in Klumpen	répartition *f* en grappes	разбиение совокупности на гнезда
C 948	**cluster point** <of a net> <TO>	Berührungspunkt *m*, Häufungspunkt *m*	point *m* adhérent	предельная точка
	cluster point <TO>	*s.* A 188		
C 949	**cluster sample,** nested sample <ST>	Klumpenstichprobe *f*, Klumpenprobe *f*	échantillon *m* en grappes	гнездовая выборка, выборка гнездами (по гнездам)
C 950	**cluster sampling** <ST>	Klumpenauswahlverfahren *n*, Klumpenstichprobenverfahren *n*, Nestprobenverfahren *n*	échantillonnage *m* en grappes, sondage *m* en grappes	выборка гнездами, выбор по гнездам, гнездовой выбор
	cluster set <TO>	*s.* D 292		
	cluster spectrum <FA>	*s.* L 752		
	C-method <LI>	*s.* 1. C 449; 2. C 451		
	C_1-method, (C,1) method <LI>	*s.* M 443		
	cn <FU>	*s.* A 606		
	coadjoint <CA>	*s.* C 951		
C 951	**co[-]adjoint functor,** coadjoint, right[-] adjoint <of a functor> <*also:* left instead of right> <CA>	koadjungierter (coadjungierter) Funktor *m*, rechtsadjungierter Funktor, Rechtsadjungierter *m* <*auch:* links statt rechts>	foncteur *m* co-adjoint, coadjoint *m*, foncteur adjoint à droite, adjoint *m* à droite <*aussi:* gauche au lieu de droite>	сопряженный справа функтор, правый сопряженный функтор <*также:* «левый» вместе «правый»>
C 952	**coadjunction** <CA>	Koadjunktion *f*, Coadjunktion *f*	coadjonction *f*	косопряжение
C 953	**coalgebra** <AL>	Koalgebra *f*, Coalgebra *f*	cogèbre *f*	коалгебра
C 954	**coalition** <TG>	Koalition *f*, Bündnis *n*	coalition *f*, alliance *f*	коалиция, союз
	coalitional game <TG>	*s.* C 2417		
C 955	**coalitionally rational payoff configuration** <TG>	koalitionsrationale Konfiguration *f*		коалиционно рациональная конфигурация
C 956	**coalition of action** <TG>	Handlungskoalition *f*	coalition *f* d'action	коалиция действия
C 957	**coalition of interests** <TG>	Interessenkoalition *f*	coalition *f* d'intérêts	коалиция интересов
C 958	**co-altitude** <of an ideal> <AL>	Kohöhe *f*, Cohöhe *f*	cohauteur *f*	ковысота
C 959	**coanalytic set,** *CA*-set <TO>	komplementär-analytische Menge *f*, *CA*-Menge *f*	ensemble *m* complémentaire analytique, ensemble complémentaire aux ensembles (*A*), ensemble *CA*, ensemble projectif de classe 2	аналитическое дополнение, *CA*-множество; множество, дополнительное к *A*-множеству; проективное множество класса 2
	coarse estimate <ST>	*s.* R 196		
C 960	**coarser covering** <TO>	gröbere Überdeckung *f*	recouvrement *m* moins fin	более грубое покрытие
C 961	**coarser partition** <SE>	gröbere Zerlegung *f*, Vergröberung *f* <einer Zerlegung>	surpartition *f*	более грубое разбиение
C 962	**coarser topology,** stronger topology, <sometimes also:> weaker topology <TO>	gröbere (stärkere) Topologie *f*, <manchmal auch:> schwächere Topologie	topologie *f* moins fine, topologie plus faible	мажорируемая топология
C 963	**coarser uniform structure** <TO>	gröbere uniforme Struktur *f*	structure *f* uniforme moins fine	более грубая униформная структура, мажорируемая равномерная структура
	coarsest topology <TO>	*s.* S 1221		
C 964	**coassociative law** <LO>	koassoziatives (coassociatives) Gesetz *n*	loi *f* co[-]associative	коассоциативный закон
C 965	**coatom,** anti[-]atom, dual atom, copoint; hyperplane <LA>	duales Atom *n*, Antiatom *n*, Kopunkt *m*, Copunkt *m*	coatome *m*, anti-atome *m*, copoint *m*; hyperplan *m* <treillis géométrique>	антиатом, коатом
C 966	**coaxial planes** <EG>	Ebenen *fpl*, die sich in einer Geraden schneiden	plans *mpl* coaxiaux	плоскости, имеющие одну общую прямую
C 967	**co-base,** dual base <SE>	Kobasis *f*, Cobasis *f*	cobase *f*	кобазис

	English	Deutsch	Français	Русский
C 968	**Cobb-Douglas function** <ST>	Cobb-Douglas-Funktion *f*	fonction *f* de Cobb-Douglas	функция Кобба-Дугласа
	cobbler's knife <EG>	*s.* A 874		
C 969	**cobordant manifolds** <AT>	cobordante Mannigfaltigkeiten *fpl*, „cobordantes" *fpl*	variétés *fpl* cobordantes	внутренне гомологичные многообразия, кобордантные многообразия, бордантные многообразия <многообразия · соограничивают>
C 970	**cobordism** <AT>	Kobordismus *m*, Cobordismus *m*	cobordisme *m*	кобордизм
C 971	**cobordism class** <AT>	Kobordismusklasse *f*, Cobordismusklasse *f*	classe *f* de cobordisme, classe des variétés-bords	класс кобордизмов, класс внутренних гомологий
C 972	**cobordism group** <AT>	Kobordismusgruppe *f*, Cobordismusgruppe *f*	groupe *m* de cobordisme	группа кобордизмов, группа внутренних гомологий
C 973	**cobordism ring** <AT>	Thomsche Algebra *f*, Kobordismusalgebra *f*, Cobordismusalgebra *f*, Kobordismusring *m*, Cobordismusring *m*	algèbre *f* de cobordisme (Thom), anneau *m* de cobordisme	кольцо кобордизмов
C 974	**coboundary** <of a chain> <AT>	Korand *m*, Corand *m*, Ableitung *f*	cobord *m*	кограница
C 975	**coboundary** <of a cochain> <AT, GR, HA>	Korand *m*, Corand *m*	cobord *m*	ко[-]граница, ∇-граница, верхняя граница, кокрай <AT, HA>; граница <GR>
	coboundary <GP>	*s.* C 1000		
C 976	**coboundary homomorphism** <AT, HA>	Korandhomomorphismus *m*, Corand-Homomorphismus *m*	homomorphisme *m* cobord	кограничный гомоморфизм
C 977	**coboundary operator** <AT>	Korandoperator *m*, Corand-Operator *m*, oberer Randoperator *m*	opérateur *m* cobord, opérateur de cobord	кограничный оператор
C 978	**cobounded subset** <of a topological space> <TO>	Komplementärmenge *f* einer beschränkten Menge	sous-ensemble *m* co-borné	коограниченное подмножество
	cocartesian square <CA>	*s.* 1. F 155; 2. P 2076; 3. P 2077		
C 979	**co-category, cocategory** <TO>	Kokategorie *f*, Cokategorie *f*	co-catégorie *f*	кокатегория
C 980	**cochain** <AT, HA>	Kokette *f*, Cokette *f*	cochaîne *f*	коцепь; цепь <в теории групп>
C 981	**cochain complex,** abstract complex <HA>	Kokettenkomplex *m*, Cokettenkomplex *m*, formaler Komplex *m*	complexe *m* de cochaînes	коцепной комплекс
	cochain complex <HA>	*s.* P 1063		
C 982	**cochain homotopy** <HA>	Kokettenhomotopie *f*, Cokettenhomotopie *f*	homotopie *f* de cochaînes	коцепная гомотопия
C 983	**cochain map** <HA>	Kokettentransformation *f*, Cokettentransformation *f*	homomorphisme *m* <d'un complexe de cochaînes>	коцепное отображение, гомоморфизм <коцепного комплекса>
C 984	**cochleoid** <GE>	Kochleoide *f*, Schneckenlinie *f*, Schneckenhauslinie *f*, Schraubenkurve *f*	cochléoïde *f*	кохлеоида
	Cochran-Cox method <ST>	*s.* A 853		
C 985	**Cochran['s] test** <ST>	Cochran-Test *m*	test *m* de Cochran	критерий Кочрэна
C 986	**Cochran['s] theorem** <ST>	Satz *m* von Cochran, Cochranscher Satz	théorème *m* de Cochran	теорема Кочрэна
C 987	**cocircuit** <GP> ⌐<AG>	Kokreis *m*, Cokreis *m*, Cocircuit *m*, Cozirkuit *m*	cocircuit *m*	коцикл, все дуги которого имеют одинаковое направление
	cocked hat, cocked-hat	*s.* B 300		
C 988	**coclosed current** <DG>	kogeschlossener (cogeschlossener) Strom *m*	courant *m* cofermé	козамкнутый поток
C 989	**cocommutative** <AL, CA>	kokommutativ, cokommutativ	cocommutatif	кокоммутативный
C 990	**cocompactification** <TO>	Kokompaktifizierung *f*, Cokompaktifizierung *f*	co-compactification *f*	кокомпактификация
C 991	**cocompact space** <TO>	kokompakter (cokompakter) Raum *m*	espace *m* cocompact	кокомпактное пространство
C 992	**cocomplete category,** right complete category, right-complete category <CA>	kovollständige (covollständige, rechtsvollständige) Kategorie *f*	catégorie *f* cocomplète	полная справа категория, кополная категория
C 993	**cocompleteness** <CA>	Kovollständigkeit *f*, Covollständigkeit *f*	co-complétude *f*	кополнота
	co-cone <CA>	*s.* L 726		
C 994	**co-connectedness** <TO>	Kozusammenhang *m*, Co-Zusammenhang *m*	co-connexion *f*	косвязность
C 995	**co[-]connected variety** <TO>	kozusammenhängende (cozusammenhängende) Mannigfaltigkeit *f*	variété *f* co-connexe	косвязное множество
C 996	**co-continuous mapping** <TO>	kostetige (costetige) Abbildung *f*	application *f* co-continue	конепрерывное отображение
C 997	**co-contravariant functor** <CA>	ko-kontra-varianter Funktor *m*	foncteur *m* co-contravariant	ко-контравариантный функтор
C 998	**co-contravariant hom-functor** <as a bifunctor> <CA, HA>	Hom-Funktor *m*, kontra-ko-varianter Hom-Funktor *m*	bifoncteur *m* Hom	основной двуместный функтор
	cocontravariant tensor <VT> ⌐<CA>	*s.* M 700		
	co-covariant functor	*s.* C 2606		
C 999	**cocycle** <AT, GR, HA>	Kozyklus *m*, Cozyklus *m*, Kozykel *m*, Cozykel *m*	cocycle *m*	коцикл, ∇-цикл, верхний цикл <AT, HA>; цикл <GR>

No.	English	German	French	Russian
C 1000	**cocycle,** coboundary <generated by the set *A*> <GP>	Kozyklus *m*, Cozyklus *m* <von der Menge *A* erzeugter>	cocycle *m* <engendré par *A*>	коцикл <порожденный множеством *A*>
C 1001	**cocycle basis,** basis <of cocycles> <GP>	Kozyklenbasis *f*, Cozyklenbasis *f*, Basis *f*	base *f* de cocycles	базис коциклов
C 1002	**cocyclomatic number** <GP>	kozyklomatische (cozyklomatische) Zahl *f*	nombre *m* cocyclomatique	коцикломатическое число, коциклический ранг
C 1003	**Codazzi['s] equations [of the surface], Codazzi-Gauss equations [of the surface],** Mainardi-Codazzi equations, Mainardi-Codazzi relations, Mainardi['s] equations, Gauss-Codazzi equations [of the surface], equations of Gauss [, Mainardi] and Codazzi <DG>	Mainardi-Codazzische Gleichungen *fpl*, Codazzi-Mainardische Differentialgleichungen *fpl* (Gleichungen), Mainardische (Codazzische) Gleichungen, Codazzi-Gaußsche Gleichungen, Gleichungen von Mainardi-Codazzi	équations *fpl* de Codazzi, équations de Mainardi-Codazzi, relations *fpl* de Mainardi-Codazzi, équations de Mainardi, relations de Mainardi	уравнения Петерсона-Кодацци, уравнения Майнарди-Кодацци
	code <MM>	*s.* G 325		
C 1004	**codenumerable set** <SE>	Komplementärmenge *f* einer abzählbaren Untermenge	sous-ensemble *m* codénombrable	косчетное множество
C 1005	**coderived functor** <CA>	koabgeleiteter (coabgeleiteter) Funktor *m*	foncteur *m* co-dérivé	копроизводный функтор
C 1006	**codiagonal element** <MD>	Kodiagonalelement *n*	élément *m* codiagonal	кодиагональный элемент
C 1007	**codiagonal morphism** <CA>	Kodiagonalabbildung *f*, Kodiagonale *f*, Codiagonalabbildung *f*, Codiagonale *f*	morphisme *m* codiagonal, application *f* codiagonale	кодиагональ
C 1008	**codifferent** <AL>	Kodifferente *f*, Codifferente *f*, inverse Differente *f*	codifférente *f*, différente *f* inverse	кодифферент
C 1009	**codifferential** <AN>	Kodifferential *n*, Codifferential *n*	codifférentielle *f*	кодифференциал
C 1010	**codification** <of a theory> <MM>	Kodifikation *f*	codification *f*	кодификация
	codification <ST>	*s.* C 1012		
	codim <AL, TO>	*s.* C 1011		
C 1011	**codimension,** codim <AL, TO>	Kodimension *f*, Codimension *f*, codim	codimension *f*, co-dimension *f*, codim	коразмерность
	codimension <AL>	*s.* D 262		
C 1012	**coding,** codification <ST>	Kodierung *f*, Codierung *f*	codification *f*, codage *m*	кодирование, шифрование
C 1013	**coding of data** <ST>	Verschlüsseln *n* von Daten	codification *f* (codage *m*) de données	кодирование данных
C 1014	**coding theorem** <ST>	Kodierungssatz *m*, Codierungssatz *m*	théorème *m* de codification	теорема кодирования
	coding theory <ST>	*s.* I 512		
C 1015	**codomain,** range (set) of values, actual range, range <of a function, mapping, operator, etc.> <AN>	Wertebereich *m*, Nachbereich *m*, Bildbereich *m*, Gegenbereich *m*, Wertevorrat *m*, Zielmenge *f*, Bildraum *m*	ensemble *m* d'arrivée, ensemble (domaine *m*) des valeurs, contre[-]domaine *m*	область (совокупность, множество, запас, пространство) значений, область (множество) изменения
	codomain <CA>	*s.* 1. R 120; 2. R 240		
	codomain <SE, TO>	*s.* R 123		
	codomain category <CA>	*s.* R 240		
C 1016	**coefficient** <of a Dirichlet series>; Dirichlet['s] coefficient <of an almost periodic function> <AP, SS>	Dirichlet-Koeffizient *m*, Dirichletscher Koeffizient *m*	coefficient *m*; coefficient de Dirichlet	коэффициент в ряде Дирихле; коэффициент Дирихле
	coefficient <MD>	*s.* E 85		
	coefficient <SS>	*s.* C 1032		
	coefficient comparison <GN>	*s.* M 450		
C 1017	**coefficient domain** <AL, SS>	Koeffizientenbereich *m*	domaine *m* des coefficients	область коэффициентов
	coefficient domain <AL, AT>	*s.* C 1038		
C 1018	**coefficient function** <of a power series> <SS>	Koeffizientenfunktion *f*	fonction *f* des coefficients	функция коэффициентов
C 1019	**coefficient functional** <FA>	Koeffizientenfunktional *n*	fonctionnelle *f* des coefficients	функционал коэффициентов
	coefficient group <AT, TO>	*s.* G 476		
	coefficient in the expansion <SS>	*s.* C 1032		
C 1020	**coefficient in the** <first *or* second> **fundamental form** <in surface theory> <DG>	Fundamentalgröße *f* <erster *oder* zweiter Ordnung>	coefficient *m* de la <première *ou* deuxième> forme fondamentale	коэффициент в <первой *или* второй> основной квадратичной форме
C 1021	**coefficient of agreement** <ST>	Übereinstimmungskoeffizient *m*	coefficient *m* d'agrément	коэффициент согласования
C 1022	**coefficient of alienation** <ST>	Alienationskoeffizient *m*, Zweideutigkeitsmaß *n*	coefficient *m* d'aliénation	коэффициент алиенации (расхождения), мера двузначности
C 1023	**coefficient of association** <ST>	Assoziationskoeffizient *m*; Gebundenheitskoeffizient *m*	coefficient *m* d'association	коэффициент ассоциации; коэффициент связанности
	coefficient of concordance <ST>	*s.* K 41		
C 1024	**coefficient of consistency** <ST>	Konsistenzkoeffizient *m*	coefficient *m* de consistance	коэффициент состоятельности

C 1025	**coefficient of contingency** <ST>	Kontingenzkoeffizient *m*	coefficient *m* de contingence	коэффициент сопряженности признаков
C 1026	**coefficient of contraction** <of a transformation> <GE>	Kontraktionskoeffizient *m*	coefficient *m* de contraction	коэффициент сжатия
C 1027	**coefficient of covariation,** covariation coefficient <ST>	Kovariationskoeffizient *m*	coefficient *m* de covariation	коэффициент совместного изменения
C 1028	**coefficient of determination** <ST>	Bestimmtheitsmaß *n*; einfaches Bestimmtheitsmaß <im Unterschied zum multiplen Bestimmtheitsmaß>	coefficient *m* de détermination	квадрат коэффициента корреляции, коэффициент (квадрат) смешанной корреляции, мера определенности
C 1029	**coefficient of dilatation** <of a transformation> <GE>	Dilatationskoeffizient *m*, Streckungsverhältnis *n*	coefficient *m* de dilatation	коэффициент растяжения
	coefficient of divergence <ST>	*s.* D 716		
	coefficient of excess <ST>	*s.* E 674		
	coefficient of multiple correlation <ST>	*s.* M 993		
C 1030	**coefficient of non-determination,** non-determination <ST>	Unbestimmtheitsmaß *n*	coefficient *m* de non-détermination, non-détermination *f*	коэффициент неопределенности, неопределенность
	coefficient of proportionality <GN>	*s.* F 51		
	coefficient of rank correlation <ST>	*s.* 1. R 143; 2. S 1350		
C 1031	**coefficient of relationship** <ST>	Verwandtschaftskoeffizient *m* [nach Wright]	coefficient *m* de parenté	коэффициент взаимосвязи (родства)
	coefficient of repeatability <ST>	*s.* R 817		
	coefficient of rotation <DG>	*s.* R 1403		
	coefficient of standard variation <ST>	*s.* S 1606		
C 1032	**coefficient of the expansion [in a series];** expansion coefficient, coefficient [of the variables] in the expansion; coefficient of the series; coefficient <SS>	Entwicklungskoeffizient *m*, Koeffizient *m* der Entwicklung; Koeffizient der Reihe; Koeffizient	coefficient *m* de développement [en série]; coefficient de la série; coefficient	коэффициент разложения [в ряд]; коэффициент ряда, коэффициент
	coefficient of the series <SS>	*s.* C 1032		
C 1033	**coefficient of the substitution** <AL>	Substitutionskoeffizient *m*	coefficient *m* d'une substitution	коэффициент подстановки
	coefficient of the variables in the expansion <SS>	*s.* C 1032		
	coefficient of torsion <AT>	*s.* T 589		
C 1034	**coefficient of trend** <ST>	Trendkoeffizient *m*	coefficient *m* de tendance	коэффициент тренда
C 1035	**coefficient of variation,** variation coefficient <of Pearson> <ST>	Variationskoeffizient *m* [nach Pearson], Variabilitätskoeffizient *m*, Variationsbeiwert *m*	coefficient *m* de variation (variabilité, dispersion)	коэффициент вариации [Карла Пирсона], коэффициент изменчивости (однородности), вариационный коэффициент
C 1036	**coefficient of variation** <in %> <ST>	Variationskoeffizient *m*, relative Standardabweichung *f* <in %>	coefficient *m* de variation <en %>	коэффициент вариации <в %>
C 1037	**coefficient problem** <FT>	Koeffizientenproblem *n*	problème *m* des coefficients	проблема коэффициентов
C 1038	**coefficient ring,** coefficient domain <AL, AT>	Koeffizientenbereich *m*, Koeffizientenring *m*	anneau *m* de coefficients, domaine *m* de coefficients	кольцо коэффициентов, область коэффициентов
C 1039	**coefficients** <of a linear recurring sequence> <NT>	Skala *f*	échelle *f* de relation	постоянные величины
	coefficient theorem of Bieberbach <FT, SS>	*s.* B 308		
	coefficient theorem of Loewner <SS>	*s.* L 1019		
C 1040	**co[-]equalizer,** cokernel, difference cokernel <CA>	Differenzkokern *m*, Differenzcokern *m*, Koegalisator *m*, Coegalisator *m*, „coequalizer" *m*	conoyau *m*	правый уравнитель, коядро
C 1041	**coercivity** <DE>	Koerzitivität *f*	coercitivité *f*	коэрцитивность
C 1042	**coexact sequence** <AT>	koexakte (coexakte) Sequenz *f*	suite *f* coexacte	коточная последовательность
C 1043	**coextensive,** extensionally equal, $\doteq$ <LO, SE>	umfangsgleich, $\doteq$	coextensif, $\doteq$	равнообъемный, $\doteq$
C 1044	**coextensivity** <LO>	Umfangsgleichheit *f*	coextensivité *f*	равнообъемность
C 1045	**cofactor,** signed minor, algebraic adjunct <of a determinant> <MD>	Adjunkte *f*, algebraisches Komplement *n*, algebraische Adjungierte *f*, Kofaktor *m*, adjungierte Unterdeterminante *f*	cofacteur *m*, complément *m* algébrique, mineur *m* avec son signe	алгебраическое дополнение, кофактор, адъюнкт, минор <элемента, к элементу>
C 1046	**cofaithful module** <AL>	kotreuer (cotreuer) Modul *m*	module *m* cofidèle	коточный модуль
	co-fibering <TO>	*s.* C 1047		
C 1047	**cofibration,** co-fibration <AL, TO>; cofibre map, co-fib[e]ring <TO>	Kofaserung *f*, Cofaserung *f*	cofibration *f*	корасслоение
C 1048	**co-fibre, cofibre** <TO>	Kofaser *f*, Cofaser *f*	co-fibre *m*, cofibre *m*	кослой
	cofibred sum <CA>	*s.* 1. F 155; 2. P 2076		

No.	English	German	French	Russian
	cofibre map <TO>	*s.* C 1047		
	co-fibring <TO>	*s.* C 1047		
C 1049	**cofilter, co-filter** <SE>	Kofilter *m*, Cofilter *m*	cofiltre *m*	кофильтр
C 1050	**cofinal family of mappings,** inductive (coterminal) family of mappings <CA, SE, TO>	koterminale Familie *f* von Abbildungen	famille *f* d'applications coterminales	коконцевое семейство отображений
	co[-]finality <SE>	*s.* C 1880		
C 1051	**cofinal ordinal** <SE>	konfinale Ordnungszahl *f*	ordinal *m* cofinal	конфинальное ординальное число
C 1052	**co[-]final set,** confinal (right-cofinal) set, set cofinal from the right <to> <SE>	konfinale Menge *f* <zu>	ensemble *m* cofinal <à>	конфинальное (сопредельное) множество <к>
	co[-]final set <SE>	*s.* C 1121		
C 1053	**cofinal subset,** right-cofinal subset, subset cofinal from the right <SE>	konfinale Untermenge *f*, konfinaler Teil *m*	partie *f* cofinale	конфинальная часть, конфинальное подмножество
C 1054	**cofine open covering** <TO>	gleichfeine [offene] Überdeckung *f*	recouvrement *m* équivalent	эквивалентное покрытие
C 1055	**cofinite module** <AL>	koendlicher (coendlicher) Modul *m*	module *m* cofini	коконечный модуль
C 1056	**cofinite subset** <SE>	Komplementärmenge *f* einer endlichen Menge	sous-ensemble *m* cofini	коконечное подмножество
C 1057	**cofree object,** right free object <on an object> <CA>	kofreies (cofreies) Objekt *n*	objet *m* co-libre	косвободный объект, свободный справа объект <над объектом>
C 1058	**cofunction,** complementary trigonometric function <AN>	Kofunktion *f*, trigonometrische Kofunktion *f*, Cofunktion *f*	cofonction *f*	кофункция, ко-функция
	cogenerating set <CA>	*s.* F 80		
C 1059	**cogenerator** <AL>	Koerzeugende *f*, Coerzeugende *f*	cogénérateur *m*	кообразующая
C 1060	**cogenerator** <of an object> <CA>	Kogenerator *m*, Cogenerator *m*	cogénérateur *m*	кообразующая
C 1061	**cogeodesic hypersurface** <DG>	kogeodätische Hyperfläche *f*	hypersurface *f* cogéodésique	когеодезическая гиперповерхность
	cogradient set <IV>	*s.* C 1062		
	cogredient automorphism <GR>	*s.* I 551		
C 1062	**cogredient set, cogredient system** <of variables or symbols>, // cogradient set <IV>	kogrediente Reihe *f*, kogredientes System *n*	suite *f* cogrédiente, système *m* cogrédient	когредиентная (одинаково преобразующаяся, ковариантная) система
C 1063	**cogredient variable** <AL>	kogrediente Variable *f*	variable *f* cogrédiente	когредиентная (ковариантная) переменная
C 1064	**cogroup** <AL>	Kogruppe *f*, Cogruppe *f*	co-groupe *m*	когруппа
	coheight <AL>	*s.* D 503		
C 1065	**Cohen-Macaulay module** <AL>	Cohen-Macaulay-Modul *m*	module *m* de Cohen-Macaulay	модуль Коэна-Маколея
	Cohen-Macaulay ring <AL>	*s.* M 1		
C 1066	**Cohen-Seidenberg theorem** <AL>	Satz *m* von Cohen-Seidenberg, Cohen-Seidenbergscher Satz	théorème *m* de Cohen-Seidenberg	теорема Коэна-Сейденберга
C 1067	**coherence** <AL, CA>	Kohärenz *f*	cohérence *f*	когерентность
C 1068	**coherence** <intersection of a set and its derivation> <TO>	Kohärenz *f*	cohérence *f*	совокупность предельных точек множества, принадлежащих этому множеству
C 1069	**coherence condition** <AG>	Kohärenzbedingung *f*	condition *f* de cohérence	условие когерентности
C 1070	**coherently oriented simplex,** concordantly oriented simplex <TO>	kohärent orientiertes Simplex *n*	simplexe *m* d'orientation cohérente	когерентно ориентированный симплекс
C 1071	**coherent module** <AG>	kohärenter Modul *m*	module *m* cohérent	когерентный модуль
C 1072	**coherent ring** <AL>	kohärenter Ring *m*	anneau *m* cohérent	когерентное кольцо
C 1073	**coherent set** <CA>	kohärente Menge *f*	ensemble *m* cohérent	когерентное множество
C 1074	**coherent sheaf (stack)** <AL, TO>	kohärente Garbe *f*	faisceau *m* cohérent	когерентный пучок
C 1075	**coherent topology,** weak topology <on the space of a complex> <AT>	schwache Topologie *f*	topologie *f* faible (cohérente)	когерентная (слабая) топология
C 1076	**cohesive group** <GR>	kohäsive Gruppe *f*	groupe *m* cohésif	связанная группа
C 1077	**Cohn['s] ring** <AL>	Cohnscher Ring *m*	anneau *m* de Cohn	коновское кольцо
C 1078	**cohomological dimension,** cohomology dimension <AT, HA>	kohomologische (cohomologische) Dimension *f*	dimension *f* cohomologique	когомологическая размерность
C 1079	**cohomological invariant** <AT>	Kohomologieinvariante *f*	invariant *m* cohomologique	когомологический инвариант
C 1080	**cohomologically trivial module** <HA>	kohomologisch (cohomologisch) trivialer Modul *m*	module *m* cohomologiquement trivial	когомологически тривиальный модуль
C 1081	**cohomological resolution** <HA>	kohomologische (cohomologische) Auflösung *f*	résolution *f* cohomologique	когомологическая резольвента
C 1082	**cohomological semipurity theorem** <HA>	kohomologischer (cohomologischer) Semireinheitssatz *m*	théorème *m* de semi-pureté cohomologique	
C 1083	**cohomologous cochain** <AT, HA>	kohomologe (cohomologe) Kokette (Cokette) *f*	cochaîne *f* cohomologue	когомологическая коцепь
C 1084	**cohomologous to zero** <AT>	nullkohomolog	cohomologique à zéro	∇-гомологический нулю
C 1085	**cohomology** <AT, HA>; ∇-homology, upper homology <AT>	Kohomologie *f*, Cohomologie *f*	cohomologie *f*	когомология <AT, HA>; ∇-гомология, верхняя гомология <AT>

C 1086	**cohomology algebra** <AT>	Kohomologiealgebra *f*	algèbre *f* de cohomologie	алгебра когомологий
C 1087	**cohomology class** <AT, HA>	Kohomologie klasse *f*	classe *f* de cohomologie	класс когомологий
	cohomology dimension <AT, HA>	*s.* C 1078		
C 1088	**cohomology extension** <of a functor> <HA>	kohomologische (cohomologische) Erweiterung *f*	extension *f* cohomologique	когомологическое расширение
C 1089	**cohomology functor** <AT>	Kohomologiefunktor *m*	foncteur *m* cohomologique	когомологический функтор, функтор когомологии
C 1090	**cohomology group** <AT>	Kohomologiegruppe *f*, ∇-Gruppe *f*, obere Bettische Gruppe *f*	groupe *m* de cohomologie	группа когомологий, ∇-группа, верхняя группа Бетти
C 1091	**cohomology group** <HA>	Kohomologiegruppe *f*	groupe *m* de cohomologie	группа верхних гомологий, группа ∇-гомологий, группа когомологий (гомологий)
C 1092	**cohomology group with coefficients G** <AT, HA>	Kohomologiegruppe *f* mit Koeffizienten in *G*, Kohomologiegruppe bezüglich des Koeffizientenbereichs *G*	groupe *m* de cohomologie à coefficients dans *G*	группа когомологий с коэффициентами в *G*
	cohomology homomorphism <AT>	*s.* I 392		
C 1093	**cohomology manifold** <AT>	Kohomologiemannigfaltigkeit *f*	variété *f* cohomologique	когомологическое многообразие
	cohomology Mayer-Vietoris sequence <AT>	*s.* M 282		
C 1094	**cohomology module** <HA>	Kohomologiemodul *m*	module *m* de cohomologie	модуль когомологий
C 1095	**cohomology obstruction** <AT>	Hinderniskohomologieklasse *f*	classe *f* cohomologique d'obstruction	когомологическое препятствие
C 1096	**cohomology operation** <of type (p,q; G,G')> <AT>	Kohomologieoperation *f*	opération *f* cohomologique	когомологическая операция <типа (p,q; G,G')>
C 1097	**cohomology ring** <AT>	Kohomologiering *m*	anneau *m* de cohomologie	кольцо когомологий
C 1098	**cohomology sequence** <AT, HA>	Kohomologiesequenz *f*	suite *f* de cohomologie	последовательность когомологий, когомологическая последовательность
C 1099	**cohomology set with a distinguished element** <HA>	Kohomologiemenge *f* mit ausgezeichnetem Element	ensemble *m* de cohomologie à élément distingué	множество когомологий с отмеченным элементом, когомологическое множество с отмеченным элементом
C 1100	**cohomology space** <of a Lie algebra> <HA>	Kohomologieraum *m*	espace *m* de cohomologie	пространство когомологий
C 1101	**cohomology spectral sequence** <AT>	Spektralsequenz *f* der Kohomologie	suite *f* spectrale de cohomologie	когомологическая спектральная последовательность, спектральная последовательность когомологий
C 1102	**cohomology theory of Čech,** Čech['s] cohomology theory <AT, HA>	Čechsche Kohomologietheorie *f*	théorie *f* cohomologique de Čech	теория когомологий [Александрова-] Чеха
C 1103	**cohomology theory with coefficients G** <AT>	Kohomologietheorie *f* mit Koeffizienten in *G*, Kohomologietheorie bezüglich des Koeffizientenbereichs *G*	théorie *f* cohomologique à coefficients dans *G*	теория когомологий с коэффициентами в *G*
C 1104	**cohomology with coefficients G** <AT, HA>	Kohomologie *f* mit Koeffizienten in *G*	cohomologie *f* à coefficients (valeurs) dans *G*	когомологии со значениями в *G*
C 1105	**cohomotopic** <AT>	kohomotop, cohomotop	cohomotopique	когомотопический
C 1106	**cohomotopy** <AT>	Kohomotopie *f*, Cohomotopie *f*	cohomotopie *f*	когомотопия
C 1107	**cohomotopy group,** Borsuk['s] cohomotopy group <AT>	Kohomotopiegruppe *f*	groupe *m* de cohomotopie [de Borsuk]	когомотопическая группа
C 1108	**co-ideal, coideal** <CA>	Koideal *n*, Coideal *n*	co-idéal *m*, coidéal *m*	коидеал
C 1109	**coimage** <AL, CA>	Kobild *n*, Cobild *n*	co-image *f*	кообраз
C 1110	**coincide in extension / to** <said of properties> <LO>	extensional gleich sein	être extensionalement égal	быть экстенсионально равный
C 1111	**coincidence** <AG, AT, PJ>	Koinzidenz *f*	coïncidence *f*	совпадение <AG, PJ>; коинцидентность <преобразований> <AT>
C 1112	**coincidence,** superposition, superimposition <AY, EG>	Deckung *f*	coïncidence *f*, concordance *f* parfaite, superposition *f*	совпадение, коинцидентность, совмещение
C 1113	**coincidence curve** <AG, DG>	Koinzidenzkurve *f*	courbe *f* de coïncidence	прилегающая кривая
C 1114	**coincidence number** <AT>	Koinzidenzzahl *f*	nombre *m* des points de coïncidence	индекс коинцидентности, число точек совпадения
C 1115	**coincidence[-]point,** pertacticle point <of algebraic curves> <AG>	Koinzidenzpunkt *m*	point *m* de coïncidence	точка совпадения, пертактическая точка
C 1116	**coincidence point** <of a mapping> <TO>	Koinzidenzpunkt *m*	point *m* de coïncidence	точка совпадения
	coincidence surface <DG>	*s.* S 2366		
C 1117	**coincident roots** <AL>	zusammenfallende Wurzeln *fpl*	racines *fpl* confondues	совпадающие корни
	coincident roots <AL>	*s.* D 940		
	coincident set <SE>	*s.* E 332		
C 1118	**coinduced topology** <TO>	koinduzierte (coinduzierte) Topologie *f*	topologie *f* co-induite	коиндуцированная топология

No.	English	German	French	Russian
	coinitial family of mappings <TO>	s. C 1120		
C 1119	**coinitiality,** left cofinality <SE>	Koinitialität *f*	coinitialité *f*	коинициальность
C 1120	**coinitial maps,** coinitial (projective) family of mappings <TO>	koinitiale (coinitiale) Abbildungen *fpl*	applications *fpl* co-initiales	коинициальные отображения
C 1121	**co-initial set,** coinitial set, left-cofinal set, set cofinal from the left, co[-]final set <SE>	koinitiale Menge *f*	ensemble *m* co-initial	коинициальное множество
C 1122	**cointegral object** <of a category> <CA>	koganzes (coganzes) Objekt *n*	objet *m* cointégral	коинтегральный объект
C 1123	**cointersection,** comeet <CA>	Kodurchschnitt *m*, Codurchschnitt *m*	co-intersection *f*	правое пересечение
C 1124	**coin tossing,** tossing of coin, toss <ST>	Münzwurf *m*, Wurf *m* einer Münze	jeu *m* de pile ou face, lancement *m* de pièce de monnaie	подбрасывание монеты, жеребьевка
C 1125	**co-irreducible object** <CA>	koirreduzibles (coirreduzibles) Objekt *n*	objet *m* coirréductible	конеприводимый объект
C 1126	**cokernel** <AL, CA>	Kokern *m*, Cokern *m*	conoyau *m*, co-noyau *m*	коядро
	cokernel <CA>	s. C 1040		
C 1127	**cokernel preserving functor** <CA>	Funktor *m*, der Kokerne respektiert	foncteur *m* préservant les conoyaux	функтор, сохраняющий коядра
	col <DG>	s. H 640		
C 1128	**colength** <of an ideal, 𝔄-module> <AL>	Kolänge *f*, Colänge *f*	colongueur *f*	кодлина
C 1129	**coliberty morphism,** right liberty, universal arrow from, couniversal arrow <over an object> <CA>	universeller Pfeil *m* von, kouniversaler (couniversaler) Pfeil	flèche *f* couniverselle	коосвобождающий (освобождающий справа) морфизм
C 1130	**colimit,** direct limit, right root, supremum, output, inductive limit <CA>	Kolimes *m*, Colimes *m*, direkter (induktiver) Limes *m*, Supremum *n*, Rechtswurzel *f*	limite *f* inductive, colimite *f*	индуктивный предел, прямой предел, копредел
C 1131	**colimiting cone,** initial cone <CA>	Kolimeskegel *m*, Colimeskegel *m*	cône *m* initial	инициальный конус
C 1132	**colimit preserving functor** <CA>	Kolimiten (Colimiten) respektierender Funktor *m*	foncteur *m* préservant les limites	функтор, сохраняющий индуктивные пределы
	colimit preserving functor <CA>	s. R 1107		
C 1133	**collapsed strata** <ST>	zusammengefaßte Schichten *fpl*	strates *fpl* unies par paires	попарно соединенные слои
	collapsibility <TO>	s. C 2261		
	collapsible [topological] space <TO>	s. C 2265		
C 1134	**collapsing [to one point]** <TO>	Identifizierung *f* zu einem Punkt	identification *f* en un point	стягивание в одну точку
C 1135	**collect / to** <terms> <GN>	ähnliche Glieder <z. B. eines Polynoms> zusammenfassen, sammeln <z. B. reelle und imaginäre Glieder>	réduire les termes semblables <p. e. dans un polynôme entier>, rassembler les termes	собирать члены, приводить подобные члены
	collect in braces / to <GN>	s. P 2078		
	collect in brackets / to <GN>	s. P 2079		
C 1136	**collecting terms** <GN>	Zusammenfassen (Sammeln) *n* ähnlicher Glieder	réduction *f* des termes semblables	приведение подобных членов
	collect in parentheses / to <GN>	s. P 2080		
	collection of formulas <GN>	s. F 499		
	collection of nested intervals <AN>	s. N 158		
	collection of points <ST>	s. S 102		
	collection of sets having the finite intersection property <SE>	s. C 412		
C 1137	**collectionwise normal space** <TO>	kollektiv normaler Raum *m*	espace *m* collectivement normal	коллективно нормальное пространство
C 1138	**collective** <a special universe> <ST>	Kollektiv *n*	collectif *m*	коллектив
C 1139	**collectivization axiom** <SE>	Kollektivisierungsaxiom *n*	axiome *m* de collectivisation	коллективизирующая аксиома
C 1140	**collectivizing relation** <SE>	kollektivisierende Relation *f*	relation *f* collectivisante	коллективизирующее отношение
C 1141	**Collignon['s] chart (diagram, graph)** <NO>	Collignons[che] Tafel *f*	nomogramme (diagramme) *m* de Collignon	номограмма Коллиньона
C 1142	**Collignon['s] theorem** <for a pseudo-square> <EG>	Satz *m* von Collignon, Collignonscher Satz	théorème *m* de Collignon	теорема Коллиньона
C 1143	**collinearity** <PJ, ST>	Kollinearität *f*	collinéarité *f*	коллинеарность
C 1144	**collinear lines** <GE>	kollineare Gerade *fpl*	droites *fpl* collinéaires	коллинеарные прямые
C 1145	**collinear points** <GE>	kollineare Punkte *mpl*	points *mpl* alignés (en ligne droite, collinéaires)	точки, лежащие на одной прямой; коллинеарные точки
C 1146	**collinear vectors** <VT>	kollineare Vektoren *mpl*	vecteurs *mpl* collinéaires	коллинеарные векторы
C 1147	**collineation,** collineatory transformation, linear projectivity, linear projective	Kollineation *f*, kollineare Abbildung *f*, lineare Projektivität *f*, lineare pro-	collinéation *f*, projectivité *f* linéaire, transformation *f* projective linéaire, appli-	коллинеация, коллинеарное соответствие, линейная проективность, ли-

and still: C 1147	mapping, projectivity, projective mapping, projective transformation, projective relation, linear homogeneous transformation, homography <AY, PJ>	jektive Abbildung (Verwandtschaft) *f*, Projektivität, projektive Abbildung (Verwandtschaft, Transformation *f*), lineare homogene Transformation, Bewegung *f* im projektiven Raum, Bewegung der projektiven Geometrie, Homographie *f*	cation *f* linéaire projective, application projective linéaire, projectivité, transformation (application, relation *f*) projective, homographie *f*, transformation (application, relation) homographique, transformation linéaire homogène	нейное проективное преобразование (отображение), проективность, проективное преобразование (отображение, соответствие), однородное линейное преобразование, гомография
	collineation chart <NO>	*s.* A 490		
C 1148	**collineation group** <AL, AY>	Kollineationsgruppe *f*, inhomogene Gruppe *f* <zu einer Gruppe gehörige>	groupe *m* de collinéation	группа коллинеаций
	collineation nomogram <NO>	*s.* A 490		
	collineation nomograph <NO>	*s.* A 490		
	collineatory transformation <AY, PJ>	*s.* 1. C 1147; 2. N 356		
C 1149	**collision of variables** <LO>	Kollision *f* der Variablen, Variablenkollision *f*	collision *f* des variables liées	коллизия переменных
	collocation <AX, DE, NU>	*s.* C 1150		
C 1150	**collocation method,** collocation <AX, DE, NU>	Kollokationsmethode *f*, Kollokation *f*	méthode *f* de collocation, collocation *f*	метод коллокаций (коллокации), коллокация, метод расположения (совпадения), интерлокационный метод
C 1151	**collocation of boundary,** boundary collocation <DE>	Randkollokation *f*	collocation *f* de bord	коллокация границы, граничная коллокация
C 1152	**collocation of domain,** domain collocation <DE>	Gebietskollokation *f*	collocation *f* de domaine	коллокация области
C 1153	**collocation point** <AX, DE, NU>	Kollokationspunkt *m*, Kollokationsstelle *f*	point *m* de collocation	точка коллокации
	co-locally finite group <GR>	*s.* U 424		
C 1154	**colocally small category,** co-well-powered category <CA>	kolokal (colokal) kleine Kategorie *f*, lokal kokleine (cokleine) Kategorie	catégorie *f* colocalement petite	локально малая справа категория
C 1155	**cologarithm, colog** <colog $N = \log 1/N$> <AR>	negativer Logarithmus *m*, logarithmische Ergänzung *f*, Kologarithmus *m*, Co-Logarithmus *m* <Logarithmus des Inversen>	logarithme *m* négatif, cologarithme *m*, complément *m* logarithmique, colog	кологарифм, дополнительный логарифм, colog
C 1156	**colourable** <TO>	färbbar	colorable	раскрашиваемый
	colouration of the edges <GP>	*s.* E 15		
C 1157	**colouring** <TO>	Färbung *f*	coloriage *m*, coloration *f*	раскрашивание
C 1158	**colouring of the nodes;** vertex colouration <GP>	Knotenpunktfärbung *f*	coloration *f* des sommets	раскраска вершин графа
C 1159	**colour problem** <GP, TO>	Färbungsproblem *n*	problème *m* de coloration	задача раскраски
C 1160	**column,** vertical row <of a matrix, double sequence *or* double series, table> <GN, MD, SS>	Spalte *f*, Kolonne *f*, Vertikalreihe *f*	colonne *f*, rangée (ligne) *f* verticale	столбец, колонка, вертикальный ряд
	1-column array <MD>	*s.* C 1164		
	column average <ST>	*s.* M 313		
	column chart <GN>	*s.* 1. B 60; 2. C 1161		
C 1161	**column diagram,** column graph, column chart <three-dimensional><GN>	Säulendiagramm *n*	diagramme *m* à colonnes (tuyaux d'orgue)	столбчатая диаграмма, диаграмма в виде столбцов
	column diagram <GN>	*s.* B 60		
C 1162	**column-finite matrix** <MD>	spaltenfinite Matrix *f*	matrice *f* dont les colonnes ne contiennent qu'un nombre fini d'éléments non nuls	конечно-столбцевая матрица
	column graph <GN>	*s.* 1. B 60; 2. C 1161		
C 1163	**column index,** vertical row index <MD>	Spaltenindex *m*, Kolonnenindex *m*	indice *m* de la colonne, indice (rang *m*) de colonne	столбцевой индекс, индекс столбца
	column limit <SS>	*s.* L 713		
C 1164	**column matrix,** 1-column matrix, single-column matrix, one-column matrix (array), column vector <MD>	Spaltenmatrix *f*, einspaltige Matrix *f*, Spaltenvektor *m*	matrice *f* colonne, matrice-colonne *f*, matrice unicolonne (à une colonne), vecteur *m* colonne, vecteur-colonne *m*	матрица-столбец, одностолбцовая матрица, вектор-столбец
	column mean <ST>	*s.* M 313		
C 1165	**column-monomial matrix** <MD>	spaltenmonomiale Matrix *f*	matrice *f* monomiale par rapport aux colonnes	мономиальная по столбцам матрица
C 1166	**column nullity, column-nullity** <of a matrix> <MD>	Spaltenrangdefekt *m*	nullité *f* pour les colonnes	столбцевой дефект
C 1167	**column of tens** <AR>	Zehnerkolonne *f*	colonne *f* des dizaines	колонка десятков
C 1168	**column of the co-ordinates** <GE>	Koordinatenspalte *f*	colonne *f* des coordonnées	столбец координат
C 1169	**column rank** <of a matrix> <MD>	Spaltenrang *m*	rang *m* des vecteurs colonnes, rang à droite pour les colonnes	столбцевой ранг, ранг по столбцам
C 1170	**column space,** column vector space <of a matrix> <AL>	Spaltenraum *m* <von den Spalten einer Matrix aufgespannter Vektorraum>	espace *m* vectoriel engendré par les colonnes	пространство столбцов

No.	English	German	French	Russian
	column sum <MD, SS>	*s.* S 2261		
C 1171	**column total** <ST>	Spaltensumme *f*	total *m* de la colonne	сумма по столбцу
	column vector <MD>	*s.* C 1164		
	column vector space <AL>	*s.* C 1170		
C 1172	**column-wise addition** <MD, SS>	spaltenweise Addition *f*	addition *f* par colonnes	постолбцевое сложение
C 1173	**comaximal elements** <AL>	stark teilerfremde Elemente *npl*	éléments *mpl* fortement étrangers	сильно взаимно простые элементы
C 1174	**comaximal ideals,** relatively prime ideals, mutually prime ideals <AL>	teilerfremde Ideale *npl*	idéaux *mpl* étrangers	комаксимальные идеалы, взаимно-простые (взаимно простые) идеалы
C 1175	**comaximal polynomials** <AL>	stark teilerfremde Polynome *npl*	polynômes *mpl* étrangers	сильно взаимно простые многочлены
	Combescure['s] transform[ation] <DG>	*s.* T 776		
C 1176	**combinant** <IV>	Kombinante *f* <Sylvester>	combinant *m*	комбинант
C 1177	**combination** <of *n* things [taken] *k* at a time, of *k* out of *n* objects, of *k* elements selected from *n* elements> <CT>	Kombination *f*, Kombination ohne Berücksichtigung der Reihenfolge, Komplexion *f* <Hindenburg> <von *n* Elementen zur *k*-ten Klasse>	combinaison *f* <de *n* éléments *k* à *k*, de *n* objets pris *k* à *k*, de *n* éléments pris *k* à *k*>	сочетание, сочетание без повторений <из *n* элементов по *k* [элементам]>
C 1178	**combination** <of tests *or* probabilities *or* events> <ST>	Kombination *f*	combinaison *f*	комбинация
	combination <AL>	*s.* C 1691		
	2-combination <CT>	*s.* T 1077		
	3-combination <CT>	*s.* T 445		
	4-combination <CT>	*s.* F 508		
	combination analysis <CT>	*s.* C 1187		
	combination law <AL>	*s.* M 1028		
	combination matrix <AL>	*s.* C 1714		
C 1179	**combination method** <of solving systems of linear equations> <AL, NU>	Kombinationsmethode *f*	méthode *f* de (par) combinaison	метод комбинаций
	combination of *k* elements taken from *n* elements without repetition <CT>	*s.* C 1181		
C 1180	**combination of *n* elements taken *k* at a time with repetition; combination of *n* things, *k* at a time, [when] repetitions [are] allowed** <CT>	Kombination *f* von *n* Elementen zur *k*-ten Klasse [ohne Berücksichtigung der Reihenfolge] mit Wiederholung	combinaison *f* complète de *n* objets pris *k* à *k*, combinaison avec répétition de *n* objets pris *k* à *k*, combinaison complète de *n* éléments distincts pris *k* à *k*	сочетание из *n* элементов по *k* с повторением
C 1181	**combination of *n* things, *k* at a time, repetitions not allowed;** combination of *k* elements taken from *n* elements without repetition <CT>	Kombination *f* von *n* Elementen zur *k*-ten Klasse [ohne Berücksichtigung der Reihenfolge] ohne Wiederholung	combinaison *f* simple de *n* objets pris *k* à *k*, combinaison simple de *n* éléments distincts pris *k* à *k*	сочетание из *n* элементов по *k* без повторений
	combination of sentences <LO>	*s.* C 1745		
C 1182	**combination of signs** <AL>	Vorzeichenkombination *f*	combinaison *f* des signes	комбинация знаков
	combination of the *k*-th class (order) <CT>	*s.* K 29		
	combination, repetition[s] allowed <CT>	*s.* 1. C 1184; 2. C 1622		
	combination, repetitions not allowed <CT>	*s.* 1 C 1183; 2. C 1621		
	combination set <SE>	*s.* C 173		
	combination theory <CT>	*s.* C 1187		
	combination, when repetitions are allowed <CT>	*s.* C 1184		
	combination, when repetitions are not allowed <CT>	*s.* C 1183		
C 1183	**combination without repetition[s];** combination, repetitions not allowed; combination, when repetitions are not allowed; simple combination <CT>	Kombination *f* ohne Wiederholung[en], einfache Kombination, Kombination ohne Berücksichtigung der Reihenfolge ohne Wiederholung[en]	combinaison *f* sans répétition[s], combinaison simple	сочетание без повторений
	combination without repetition[s] <CT>	*s.* C 1621		
C 1184	**combination with repetitions [allowed];** combination, repetitions allowed; combination, when repetitions are allowed; complete combination <CT>	Kombination *f* mit Wiederholung[en], vollständige Kombination, Kombination ohne Berücksichtigung der Reihenfolge mit Wiederholung[en]	combinaison *f* avec répétitions (répétition), combinaison complète	сочетание с повторениями
	combination with repetition[s] [allowed] <CT>	*s.* C 1622		

No.	English	German	French	Russian
C 1185	**combination with restricted positions** <CT>	Kombination *f* mit beschränkter Stellenbesetzung	combinaison *f* soumis à des conditions restrictives	сочетание с ограниченными позициями
C 1186	**combinatorial absolute two-manifold** <TO>	unberandete kombinatorische zweidimensionale Mannigfaltigkeit *f*, unberandete kombinatorische Fläche *f*	surface *f* combinatoire sans bord	комбинаторная поверхность без края
C 1187	**combinatorial analysis,** combinatorics, combinatorial theory, combinatory analysis, combination theory, theory of combinations, combination analysis <CT>	Kombinatorik *f*, Kombinationslehre *f*, kombinatorische Analysis *f*	analyse *f* combinatoire, théorie *f* des combinaisons, combinatorique *f*	комбинаторика, комбинаторный анализ, теория соединений
	combinatorial Analysis Situs <AT>	*s.* C 1212		
C 1188	**combinatorial boundary of the simplex,** boundary of the simplex <as a complex> <AT>	Simplexrand *m*	bord *m* combinatoire du simplexe	край симплекса
C 1189	**combinatorial cell** <AT>	kombinatorische Zelle *f*	cellule *f* combinatoire	комбинаторная клетка
	combinatorial characteristic <AT>	*s.* E 608		
C 1190	**combinatorial closure** <of an element of a partially ordered set> <SE>	kombinatorische Hülle *f*	adhérence *f* combinatoire	комбинаторное замыкание
C 1191	**combinatorial closure of the simplex** <AT>	Simplexhülle *f*	fermeture *f* combinatoire du simplexe	комбинаторное замыкание симплекса, симплициальная оболочка
C 1192	**combinatorial dimension** <of a Noetherian space> <TO>	kombinatorische Dimension *f*	dimension *f* combinatoire	комбинаторная размерность
	combinatorial dimension <AT>	*s.* D 516		
C 1193	**combinatorial game** <TG>	kombinatorisches Spiel *n*	jeu *m* combinatoire	комбинаторная игра
C 1194	**combinatorial geometry** <GE>	kombinatorische Geometrie *f*	géométrie *f* combinatoire	комбинаторная геометрия
C 1195	**combinatorially definable function** <MM>	kombinatorisch definierbare Funktion *f*	fonction *f* combinatoirement définissable	комбинаторно определимая функция
C 1196	**combinatorially distinct complex** <AT>	kombinatorisch inäquivalenter Komplex *m*	complexe *m* combinatoirement distinct	комбинаторно неэквивалентный комплекс
C 1197	**combinatorially equivalent chain** <AT>	isomorphe (kombinatorisch äquivalente) Kette *f*	chaîne *f* combinatoirement équivalente, chaîne équivalente du point de vue combinatoire	комбинаторно эквивалентная цепь
C 1198	**combinatorially equivalent complex** <AT>	elementarverwandter (kombinatorisch äquivalenter) Komplex *m*	complexe *m* combinatoirement équivalent	комбинаторно эквивалентный комплекс
	combinatorially equivalent complex <AT>	*s.* I 1116		
C 1199	**combinatorially equivalent tableau** <PG>	kombinatorisch äquivalentes Tableau *n*	tableau *m* combivalent (équivalent du point de vue combinatoire)	комбинаторно эквивалентная таблица
C 1200	**combinatorial method** <of Azpeita-Dickinson>, Azpeita-Dickinson method <PG>	kombinatorische Methode *f* <von Azpeita-Dickinson>, Azpeita-Dickinsonsche kombinatorische Methode	méthode *f* combinatoire <d'Azpeita-Dickinson>	комбинаторный метод <Ацпейта-Дикинсона>
	combinatorial optimization <PG>	*s.* C 1204		
	combinatorial optimization problem <PG>	*s.* C 1205		
C 1201	**combinatorial path** <AT>	Weg *m*, kombinatorischer Weg *m*	chemin *m* combinatoire	комбинаторный путь
C 1202	**combinatorial power mean** <ST>	kombinatorisches Potenzmittel *n*	moyenne *f* puissance combinatoire	комбинаторное степенное среднее, комбинаторное среднее степенное
	combinatorial pregeometry <LA>	*s.* E 677		
	combinatorial problem <PG>	*s.* C 1205		
C 1203	**combinatorial product** <Grassmann> <GE>	kombinatorisches Produkt *n*	produit *m* combinatoire	комбинаторное произведение
	combinatorial product <SE>	*s.* C 173		
C 1204	**combinatorial programming,** combinatorial optimization <PG>	kombinatorische Optimierung (Programmoptimierung, Programmierung) *f*	programmation (optimisation) *f* combinatoire	комбинаторное программирование, комбинаторная оптимизация
C 1205	**combinatorial programming problem,** combinatorial [optimization] problem <PG>	kombinatorisches Optimierungsproblem *n*	problème *m* [de programmation] combinatoire	комбинаторная задача программирования, задача комбинаторного программирования
C 1206	**combinatorial sphere** <AT>	kombinatorische Sphäre *f*, Sphäre	sphère *f* combinatoire	комбинаторная сфера
C 1207	**combinatorial square,** cartesian square <of a set> <SE>	kartesisches (cartesisches) Quadrat *n*	carré *m* combinatoire (direct)	декартов квадрат
C 1208	**combinatorial sum** <of simplexes> <AT>	kombinatorische Summe *f*	somme *f* combinatoire	комбинаторная сумма
	combinatorial surface <TO> <CT>	*s.* C 1210		
	combinatorial theory	*s.* C 1187		

C 1209	**combinatorial theory of probabilities** <ST>	kombinatorische Wahrscheinlichkeitsrechnung *f*	théorie *f* combinatoire des probabilités	комбинаторная теория вероятностей
	combinatorial topology <AT>	*s.* C 1212		
C 1210	**combinatorial two-manifold,** combinatorial surface <TO>	kombinatorische Fläche *f*, zweidimensionale kombinatorische Mannigfaltigkeit *f*	surface *f* combinatoire	комбинаторная поверхность
	combinatorics <CT>	*s.* C 1187		
	combinatory analysis <CT>	*s.* C 1187		
C 1211	**combinatory logic** <LO>	kombinatorische Logik *f*	logique *f* combinatoire	комбинаторная логика
C 1212	**combinatory topology,** combinatorial Analysis Situs, combinatorial topology, piece-wise linear topology <AT>	kombinatorische Topologie *f*	topologie *f* combinatoire	комбинаторная топология
C 1213	**combined alignment chart (graph, map, nomogram, nomograph)** <NO>	kombinierte Fluchtlinientafel *f*, kombiniertes Fluchtliniennomogramm *n*, kombinierte Fluchtentafel (Fluchtlinien-Netztafel) *f*, vereinigte Netz- und Leitertafel *f*	abaque *m* par alignement combiné, nomogramme *m* à (par) alignement combiné	комбинированная номограмма из выравненных (соединяемых) точек, комбинированная прямолинейная номограмма
C 1214	**combined matrix** <PG>	Kombinationsmatrix *f*	matrice *f* de combinaison	комбинированная матрица
C 1215	**combined ratio estimate** <ST>	kombinierte Verhältnisschätzung *f*	estimation *f* par quotient combinée	комбинированная оценка в виде отношения
C 1216	**combined regression estimate** <ST>	kombinierte Regressionsschätzung *f*	estimation *f* par régression combinée	комбинированная оценка [по уравнению] регрессии
C 1217	**combined sample** <ST>	vereinigte (kombinierte) Stichprobe *f*	échantillon *m* combiné	объединенная выборка
C 1218	**co-meager set,** residual set <TO>	Komplementärmenge *f* einer Menge erster Kategorie	ensemble *m* résiduel, complémentaire *m* d'un ensemble de première (I[e]) catégorie	остаточное множество; множество второй (II) категории, дополнительное к множеству первой (I) категории; дополнение к тощему множеству
	comeet <CA>	*s.* 1. C 1123; 2. P 2027		
C 1219	**comitant** <IV>	Komitante *f*, Invariante *f* im weiteren Sinn	comitant *m*	комитант
C 1220	**comma category** <CA>	Kommakategorie *f*	catégorie *f* comma	
C 1221	**commensurability** <GE, NT>	Kommensurabilität *f*, Gleichmeßbarkeit *f*	commensurabilité *f*	соизмеримость
C 1222	**commensurable $\mathfrak{A}$-module** <AL>	kommensurabler $\mathfrak{A}$-Modul	$\mathfrak{A}$-module *m* commensurable	соизмеримый $\mathfrak{A}$-модуль
	commensurable fraction <AR>	*s.* R 170		
C 1223	**commensurable quantities** <GE, NT>	kommensurable Größen *fpl*, // ermeßliche Größen	grandeurs (quantités) *fpl* commensurables	соизмеримые величины
C 1224	**commensurable segments** <GE>	kommensurable Strecken *fpl*	segments *mpl* commensurables	соизмеримые отрезки
C 1225	**commensurable subgroups** <GR>	kommensurable Untergruppen *fpl*	sous-groupes *mpl* commensurables	соизмеримые подгруппы
C 1226	**commensuration** <GE>	Bestimmung *f* des gemeinsamen Maßes	commensuration *f*	нахождение общей меры
	commercial arithmetic <AR>	*s.* B 818		
C 1227	**common conchoid** <GE>	gewöhnliche Konchoide *f*	conchoïde *f* commune	обычная (обыкновенная) конхоида
	common cycloid <GE>	*s.* C 2888		
C 1228	**common denominator** <AL, AR>	gemeinsamer (gemeinschaftlicher) Nenner *m*, Generalnenner *m*	dénominateur *m* commun	общий (одинаковый) знаменатель
	common denominator <AL, NT>	*s.* L 238		
C 1229	**common difference,** difference <of an arithmetic progression> <AR>	Differenz *f*	raison *f*, raison arithmétique, rapport *m* arithmétique	разность арифметической прогрессии, модуль
C 1230	**common divisor,** common measure <of numbers> <NT>	gemeinsamer Teiler *m*	diviseur *m* commun, commun diviseur	общий делитель
C 1231	**common evolvent of circle** <GE>	gemeine Kreisevolvente *f*	développante *f* du cercle commun	обыкновенная эвольвента (развертка) окружности
C 1232	**common factor** <in factorial analysis> <ST>	gemeinsamer Faktor *m*	facteur *m* commun	простой фактор
C 1233	**common-factor theory** <ST>	Theorie *f* der gemeinsamen Faktoren	théorie *f* des facteurs communs	теория общих факторов
C 1234	**common fraction,** vulgar (ordinary, simple) fraction <AR>	gewöhnlicher Bruch *m*, Bruch, gemeiner Bruch	fraction *f* ordinaire (vulgaire, simple)	арифметическая (обыкновенная, простая) дробь, дробь в арифметике, дробное число
C 1235	**common fraction yielding a recurring decimal** <NT>	erzeugender Bruch *m* <gewöhnlicher Bruch, der einen periodischen Dezimalbruch ergibt>	fraction *f* génératrice	простая дробь, которая определяет периодическую десятичную дробь
C 1236	**common left multiple** <of ordinals> <AL>	gemeinsames linksseitiges Vielfaches *n*	multiple *m* à gauche commun	общее левое кратное
	common logarithm <AR, NU>	*s.* B 754		
C 1237	**common measure** <GE, NT>	gemeinsames Maß *n*	commune mesure *f*	общая мера
	common measure <NT>	*s.* C 1230		
C 1238	**common multiple** <AL, AR, NT>	gemeinsames (gemeinschaftliches) Vielfaches *n*	multiple *m* commun, comultiple *m*	общее кратное

No.	English	German	French	Russian
	common part <SE>	*s.* I 802		
C 1239	**common perpendicular** <EG>	Gemeinlot *n*, gemeinsames Lot *n*	perpendiculaire *f* commune	общий перпендикуляр
C 1240	**common point** <of a three-parameter linear system> <AY>	Grundpunkt *m*	point *m* commun	общая точка
C 1241	**common ratio,** ratio, step <of a geometric progression> <AR>	Quotient *m* <einer geometrischen Progression>	raison *f* <d'une progression géométrique>	знаменатель <геометрической прогрессии>
C 1242	**common refinement** <AL>	gemeinsame Verfeinerung *f*	raffinement *m* commun	общее подразделение; общее продолжение
C 1243	**common refinement** <of coverings> <TO>	gemeinsame Verfeinerung *f*	raffinement *m* commun	общее измельчение
C 1244	**communality** <ST>	Kommunalität *f*	communalité *f*	относительная дисперсия простых факторов
C 1245	**communicated states** <SP>	verbundene Zustände *mpl*	états *mpl* liés	сообщающиеся состояния
C 1246	**communication channel,** channel <ST>	Nachrichtenübertragungskanal *m*, Kanal *m*	canal *m* d'information, canal de liaisons, canal	канал связи (информации), канал
	commutability <AL, AN>	*s.* C 1273		
	commutable operators <FA>	*s.* P 482		
C 1247	**commutable substitutions** <AL>	vertauschbare (permutable) Substitutionen *fpl*	substitutions *fpl* permutables (échangeables)	перестановочные подстановки
C 1248	**commutant** <as a determinant> <MD>	Kommutante *f*	commutant *m*	коммутант
	commutant <GR>	*s.* 1. C 364; 2. C 1281		
C 1249	**commutating subalgebras** <AL>	kommutierende Teilalgebren *fpl*	sous-algèbres *fpl* commutantes	коммутирующие подалгебры
C 1250	**commutation,** commutator operation <AL>	Kommutatorbildung *f*	opération *f* « commutateur »	операция коммутирования, коммутирование
C 1251	**commutation** <of two elements> <operation> <GN>	Vertauschung *f*, Kommutieren *n*	commutation *f*, interversion *f*	перестановка, коммутирование
	commutation <AL>	*s.* B 710		
C 1252	**commutation law,** law of commutation <for a series *or* an infinite product> <SS>	Kommutationsgesetz *n*	loi *f* de commutation	закон коммутативности
	commutation law <AL, LO>	*s.* C 1262		
C 1253	**commutation law for the conjunction,** principle of permutation for the conjunction <LO>	Gesetz *n* der Kommutativität der Konjunktion	loi *f* de permutation des facteurs d'une conjonction, loi de commutativité de la disjonction; règle *f* de symétrie	переместительный закон для конъюнкции, закон коммутативности для конъюнкции
C 1254	**commutation property** <AL>	Vertauschungseigenschaft *f*, Vertauschbarkeitseigenschaft *f*	propriété *f* de commutativité	переместительное (коммутативное) свойство
C 1255	**commutation relation** <$AB-BA$> <AL, FA>	Vertauschungsrelation *f*	relation *f* de commutation	перестановочное (коммутационное) соотношение, соотношение коммутирования
	commutative-associative ring <AL>	*s.* A 1109		
C 1256	**commutative band** <AL>	kommutative idempotente Halbgruppe *f*	demi-groupe *m* idempotent commutatif	коммутативная связка
C 1257	**commutative binary composition,** abelian binary composition <AL>	kommutative (abelsche) binäre algebraische Verknüpfung *f*	composition *f* binaire commutative	коммутативная (абелева) [бинарная] композиция
	commutative convergence <SS>	*s.* U 59		
C 1258	**commutative diagram,** consistent diagram <AL, CA, SE, TO>	kommutatives Diagramm *n*	diagramme *m* commutatif	коммутативная диаграмма
	commutative elements <AL>	*s.* P 481		
	commutative field <AL>	*s.* F 170		
	commutative 2-fir ring <AL>	*s.* G 102		
C 1259	**commutative group,** abelian group, Abelian group <GR>	kommutative (abelsche) Gruppe *f*	groupe *m* commutatif (abélien), abélien *m*, // groupe eulérien	коммутативная (абелева) группа
	commutative groupoid <AL>	*s.* A 21		
C 1260	**commutative half-algebra,** abelian half-algebra <UA>	kommutative (abelsche) Halbalgebra (partielle algebraische Struktur) *f*	algèbre *f* partielle commutative (abélienne)	коммутативная (абелева) полуалгебра
C 1261	**commutative lattice** <LA>	kommutativer [multiplikativer] Verband *m*	treillis *m* commutatif	структура с коммутативным умножением
C 1262	**commutative law,** commutation law, law of commutation, law of commutativity <AL, LO>	Kommutativgesetz *n*, kommutatives Gesetz *n*, Vertauschungsregel *f*, Vertauschungsgesetz *n*, // Kommutationsgesetz *n*, kommutatives Prinzip *n*, Umkehrungsprinzip *n*, Vertauschungsprinzip *n*	loi *f* commutative (de commutativité, de commutation), principe *m* de commutation, principe commutatif	закон коммутативности (переместительности), переместительный закон
	commutative law <LO>	*s.* P 1513		
C 1263	**commutative law of identity** <LO>	Kommutativgesetz *n* der Gleichheit, Gesetz *n* der Symmetrie der Identität	loi *f* de commutativité d'égalité	[неполный] закон коммутативности равенства
C 1264	**commutative Lie ring** <AL>	abelscher (kommutativer) Liescher Ring *m*	anneau *m* de Lie commutatif	коммутативное кольцо Ли
	commutatively convergent series <SS>	*s.* U 62		

C 1265	**commutative operation** <AL, AN>	kommutative Operation *f*	opération *f* commutative	коммутативная операция, перестановочное действие
	commutative operators <FA>	*s.* P 482		
C 1266	**commutative ordinal numbers** <SE>	vertauschbare Ordnungszahlen *fpl*	nombres *mpl* ordinaux commutables	перестановочные порядковые числа
C 1267	**commutative property** <AL>	kommutative Eigenschaft *f*	propriété *f* commutative	переместительное (коммутативное) свойство
C 1268	**commutative R-algebra** <AL>	kommutative *R*-Algebra *f*	*R*-algèbre *f* commutative	коммутативная *R*-алгебра
C 1269	**commutative ring** <AL>	kommutativer Ring *m*	anneau *m* commutatif (abélien)	коммутативное (абелево) кольцо
	commutative ring <AL>	*s.* A 1109		
C 1270	**commutative ringed space** <AG>	kommutativ geringter Raum *m*	espace *m* commutativement annelé	коммутативно кольцованное пространство
	commutative semigroup <AL>	*s.* A 27		
	commutative semihereditary domain (entire ring) <AL>	*s.* P 1893		
C 1271	**commutative topological group** <AL>	kommutative topologische Gruppe *f*	groupe *m* topologique commutatif	коммутативная топологическая группа
C 1272	**commutative valuation** <AL>	kommutative allgemeine Bewertung *f*	valuation *f* [de Krull] commutative	коммутативное нормирование
	commutative weak Bézout domain <AL>	*s.* G 102		
C 1273	**commutativity,** commutability <of two elements> <AL, AN>	Kommutativität *f*, Vertauschbarkeit *f*, Kommutierbarkeit *f*	commutativité *f*, commutabilité *f*, permutabilité *f*	коммутативность, переместительность, перестановочность, коммутируемость
C 1274	**commutativity** <of a diagram> <AL, CA, SE, TO>	Kommutativität *f*	commutativité *f*	коммутативность
C 1275	**commutativity,** being abelian <AL, GR>	Kommutativität *f*, Abelschsein *n*	commutativité *f*	коммутативность, абелевость
C 1276	**commutativity condition** <for a diagram scheme> <CA>	Kommutativitätsbedingung *f*	condition *f* de commutativité	условие коммутирования
C 1277	**commutativity relation** <CA>	Kommutativitätsrelation *f*	relation *f* de commutativité	соотношение коммутирования
C 1278	**commutator** <of a group *or* ring> <AL, GR>	Kommutator *m*	commutateur *m*	коммутатор
	commutator <AL>	*s.* L 672		
C 1279	**commutator calculus** <GR>	Kommutatorkalkül *m*	calcul *m* des commutateurs	коммутаторное исчисление
C 1280	**commutator closed group** <GR>	kommutatorgeschlossene Gruppe *f*		коммутаторно замкнутая группа
	commutator-factor group <GR>	*s.* F 25		
C 1281	**commutator group,** commutator subgroup, commutant, derived group <of a group> <GR>	Kommutatorgruppe *f*, abgeleitete Gruppe *f*, Ableitung *f*, Kommutatoruntergruppe *f*, Kommutant *m*	sous-groupe *m* dérivé, groupe *m* dérivé (des commutateurs), commutant *m*, groupe commutateur, premier dérivé *m*, dérivée *f* première, dérivée *f*, groupe de commutateur, groupe commutant	коммутант, производная (коммутаторная) группа, второй член нижнего центрального ряда
C 1282	**commutator identities** <GR>	Kommutatoridentitäten *fpl*	identités *fpl* pour les commutateurs	коммутаторные тождества
	commutator operation <AL>	*s.* C 1250		
	commutator quotient group <GR>	*s.* F 25		
	commutator subgroup <GR>	*s.* C 1281		
C 1283	**commutatrix** <GR>	Kommutatrix *f*	commutatrice *f*	коммутатриса
C 1284	**commute / to,** to be permutable <AL>	kommutieren, vertauschbar (kommutativ) sein	commuter, être commutable	коммутировать
C 1285	**commuting matrices** <MD>	vertauschbare Matrizen *fpl*	matrices *fpl* commutables	перестановочные (коммутирующие) матрицы
	commuting operators <FA>	*s.* P 482		
	commuting ring <AL>	*s.* C 363		
C 1286	**commuting ring of endomorphisms** <of an ideal> <AL>	Kommutant *m* <eines Ideals>	anneau *m* des endomorphismes <d'un idéal>, commutant *m*	коммутант <идеала>
C 1287	**commuting transformations** <AL>	vertauschbare (permutable) Transformationen *fpl*	transformations *fpl* échangeables	перестановочные преобразования
C 1288	**comonad, comonoid,** standard construction, cotriple <CA>	Komonade *f*, Comonade *f*, Standardkonstruktion *f*, Kotripel *n*, Cotripel *n*, Komonoid *n*, Comonoid *n*	cotriple *m*	стандартная конструкция, котройка
C 1289	**comorphism** <AL, CA>	Komorphismus *m*, Comorphismus *m*	comorphisme *m*	коморфизм
	compact <TO>	*s.* C 1304		
C 1290	**compact connected component** <TO>	kompakte Zusammenhangskomponente *f*	composante *f* connexe compacte	компактная компонента связности
C 1291	**compact convergence** <TO>	kompakte Konvergenz *f*	convergence *f* compacte	компактная сходимость
C 1292	**compact group** <GR>	kompakte Gruppe *f*	groupe *m* compact (de type compact)	компактная группа
	compact Hausdorff space <TO>	*s.* 1. B 285; 2. C 1305		

No.	English	German	French	Russian
C 1293	**compactification,** bicompactification <TO>	Kompaktifizierung *f*, Kompaktifikation *f*, Bikompaktifizierung *f*	compactifié *m*, compactification *f*, bicompactification *f*	компактификация, компактное пополнение (замыкание, расширение), бикомпактное расширение (пополнение), бикомпактификация
	β-compactification <TO>	*s.* S 1817		
C 1294	**compactification of Satake,** Satake['s] compactification <TO>	Satakesche Kompaktifizierung *f*	compactification *f* de Satake	компактификация Сатаке
C 1295	**compactification theorem** <TO>	Kompaktifizierungssatz *m*	théorème *m* de compactification	теорема о компактификации
C 1296	**compact Lie group** <GR>	kompakte (geschlossene) Liesche Gruppe *f*	groupe *m* de Lie compact (clos)	компактная группа Ли
	compact linear operator <FA>	*s.* C 1462		
	compactly generated Hausdorff space <TO>	*s.* K 35		
	compactly generated lattice <LA>	*s.* A 445		
C 1297	**compactly generated l-group** <AL>	kompakt erzeugte Verbandsgruppe (l-Gruppe) *f*	groupe *m* réticulé compactement généré	компактно-порожденная l-группа
	compactly generated space <TO>	*s.* K 35		
	compact mapping <FA>	*s.* 1. C 1302; 2. C 1464		
	compact mapping <TO>	*s.* C 1463		
C 1298	**compactness** <TO>	Kompaktheit *f*	compacité *f*	компактность
C 1299	**compactness** <of a space> **in itself** <TO>	Kompaktheit *f* in sich	compacité *f* en soi	компактность в себе
	σ-compactness <TO>	*s.* S 812		
C 1300	**compactness theorem,** localization principle <LO>	Kompaktheitstheorem *n*	théorème *m* de compacité, principe *m* de localisation	теорема компактности, принцип локализации
C 1301	**compact-open subgroup** <AL> ⌈<TO>	kompakt-offene Untergruppe *f*	sous-groupe *m* compact-ouvert	компактно-открытая подгруппа
	compact-open topology	*s.* T 566		
C 1302	**compact operator,** compact transformation (mapping) <not necessarily continuous> <FA>	kompakter Operator *m*, kompakte Transformation (Abbildung) *f* <beschränkte Mengen werden in kompakte übergeführt>	opérateur *m* compact, transformation (application) *f* compacte	компактный оператор, компактное отображение (преобразование)
	compact operator <FA>	*s.* 1. C 1462; 2. C 1464		
C 1303	**compact real form** <of a complex Lie algebra> <AL>	kompakte Form *f*	forme *f* compacte	компактная форма
C 1304	**compact set,** compact <TO>	kompakte Menge (Punktmenge) *f*, in sich kompakte Menge (Punktmenge), Kompaktum *n*	ensemble *m* compact, compact *m*	компактное (компактное точечное) множество, компакт
	σ-compact set <TO>	*s.* S 813		
C 1305	**compact space** <Bourbaki>, compact Hausdorff space <TO>	kompakter Raum *m* <Bourbaki>, bikompakter Hausdorffscher Raum	espace *m* compact <Bourbaki>, espace de Hausdorff parfaitement compact en soi <Fréchet>	компактное пространство <Бурбаки>, бикомпактное хаусдорфово пространство
C 1306	**compact space, 1-compact space, ℵ-compact space** <TO>	kompakter Raum *m* <nach Fréchet>, $\aleph_0$-kompakter („russisch-kompakter", BW-kompakter, Bolzano-Weierstraß-kompakter) Raum	espace *m* compact au sens de Fréchet	пространство, компактное в смысле Фреше
C 1307	**compact space,** countably compact space, sequentially compact space <TO>	kompakter Raum *m* <nach Fréchet>, folgenkompakter (abzählbar kompakter, in sich kompakter) Raum	espace *m* compact (semi-compact, compact au sens de Fréchet), espace dénombrablement (séquentiellement) compact	секвенциально компактное пространство, компактное (полукомпактное) пространство; пространство, компактное в себе (смысле Фреше); счетно компактное пространство
	compact space <TO>	*s.* Q 114		
	σ-compact space <TO>	*s.* S 814		
C 1308	**compact support** <AT, FT>	kompakter Träger *m*	support *m* compact	компактный носитель
	σ-compact topological space <TO>	*s.* S 814		
	compact transformation <FA>	*s.* 1. C 1302; 2. C 1464		
C 1309	**compactum** <*e.g.:* of finite category> <as a metrizable compact space> <TO>	Kompaktum *n* <*z. B.:* von endlicher Kategorie>	compactum *m* <*par exemple:* de catégorie finie>	компакт <*например:* конечной категории>
C 1310	**companion knot** <TO>	Begleitknoten *m*		сопровождающий узел
C 1311	**companion matrix** <of a polynomial> <AL>	Begleitmatrix *f*	matrice *f* associée	сопровождающая (сопутствующая, вспомогательная) матрица
C 1312	**comparability graph** <GP>	Vergleichsgraph *m*	graphe *m* de comparabilité, transitivitable *m*	граф сравнимости
C 1313	**comparability of cardinals** <SE>	Vergleichbarkeit *f* der Kardinalzahlen	comparabilité *f* des nombres cardinaux	сравнимость кардинальных чисел
C 1314	**comparability relation** <SE>	Vergleichbarkeitsrelation *f*	relation *f* de comparabilité	отношение сравнимости
C 1315	**comparable curve;** comparable function <VA>	Vergleichskurve *f*; Vergleichsfunktion *f*	courbe *f* de comparaison; fonction *f* de comparaison	кривая сравнения; функция сравнения
C 1316	**comparable function,** comparison function <of an eigenvalue problem> <DE>	Vergleichsfunktion *f*, zulässige Funktion *f*	fonction *f* de comparaison	функция сравнения, сравнительная функция

No.	English	German	French	Russian
C 1317	**comparable function,** strongly comparable function <RF>	vergleichbare (stark vergleichbare) Funktion *f*	fonction *f* comparable (fortement comparable)	сравнимая (сильно сравнимая) функция
	comparable function <VA>	*s.* C 1315		
C 1318	**comparable relation[-] type** <SE>	vergleichbarer Relationstyp *m*	type *m* relationnel comparable	сравнимый реляционный тип
	comparable series<SS>	*s.* C 1326		
C 1319	**comparable topology** <TO>	vergleichbare Topologie *f*	topologie *f* comparable	сравнимая топология
C 1320	**comparable uniformity** <TO>	vergleichbare uniforme Struktur *f*	structure *f* uniforme comparable	сравнимая равномерная структура
C 1321	**comparative statistics** <ST>	vergleichende Statistik *f*	statistique *f* comparative	сравнительная статистика
	comparing rule <GE, IN>	*s.* M 348		
C 1322	**comparison element** <IV>	Vergleichselement *n*	élément *m* de comparaison	элемент сравнения, сравнивающий элемент
C 1323	**comparison function** <NT>	Vergleichsfunktion *f*	fonction *f* de comparaison	функция сравнения, сравнительная функция
	comparison function <DE>	*s.* C 1316		
C 1324	**comparison method** <for ordinary differential equations> <DE>	Majorantenmethode *f*, Majorantenverfahren *n*	calcul *m* des limites (fonctions majorantes), méthode *f* de comparaison	метод мажорант, теорема сравнения
	comparison of coefficients [method] <GN>	*s.* M 450		
C 1325	**comparison of series** <SS>	Reihenvergleichung *f*, Reihenvergleich *m*	comparaison *f* des séries	сравнение рядов
	comparison relation <RF>	*s.* R 679		
C 1326	**comparison series,** comparable series <SS>	Vergleichsreihe *f*	série *f* de comparaison (référence), série étalon	ряд сравнения
C 1327	**comparison test,** majorant criterion <for absolute convergence of series with complex terms> <FT, SS>	Majorantenkriterium *n*, Vergleichskriterium *n*	règle *f* de comparaison	сравнительный признак (критерий сходимости), мажорантный признак (критерий сходимости)
C 1328	**comparison test** <for convergence> <in a general sense> <SS>	Vergleichskriterium *n*	règle *f* (critère *m*, théorème *m*) de comparaison	признак (критерий) сравнения, сравнительный признак (критерий)
	comparison test of the first kind <SS>	*s.* F 332		
	comparison test of the second kind <SS>	*s.* S 205		
C 1329	**comparison theorem** <for eigenvalue problems *or* for oscillatory integrals> <DE, MD, NU>	Vergleichssatz *m*, Vergleichungssatz *m*	théorème *m* de comparaison	теорема сравнения
C 1330	**compass** <GE, IN>	Zirkel *m*	compas *m*	циркуль
C 1331	**compass construction** <EG>	Zirkelkonstruktion *f*	construction *f* par le compas, construction au moyen d'un compas	построение с помощью циркуля, построение циркулем
C 1332	**compass[es] with jointed legs,** bow compass, extension divider <GE, IN>	Einsatzzirkel *m*	compas *m* à dessin	циркуль [со вставной ножкой]
C 1333	**compatibility** <AL, SE>	Kompatibilität *f*, Vereinbarkeit *f*	compatibilité *f*	совместимость, совместность
C 1334	**compatibility,** consistency <of equations> <GN>	Verträglichkeit *f*, Widerspruchsfreiheit *f*, Lösbarkeit *f*	compatibilité *f*	совместность
	compatibility <GN, LO>	*s.* C 2082		
C 1335	**compatibility condition** <AL>	Verträglichkeitsbedingung *f*	condition *f* de compatibilité	условие совместности
C 1336	**compatibility condition** <DE>	Kompatibilitätsbedingung *f*	condition *f* de compatibilité	условие совместности
C 1337	**compatibility relation** <AL>	Kompatibilitätsrelation *f*	relation *f* de compatibilité	соотношение согласования
	comparability theorem <SE>	*s.* T 926		
C 1338	**compatible** <AL, SE>	kompatibel, [miteinander] vereinbar, verträglich	compatible	совместимый, совместный
C 1339	**compatible** <with> <said of an order> <SE>	verträglich <mit>	compatible <avec>, inclus <dans>	совместный <с>
	compatible axioms <FO>	*s.* C 2090		
C 1340	**compatible collection of halfgroupoids** <AL>	verträgliche Halbgruppoide *npl*, verträgliches System *n* von Halbgruppoiden	famille *f* de groupoïdes partiels compatible	совместная совокупность частичных группоидов
C 1341	**compatible collection of orientations** <in a pseudo-manifold> <AT>	kompatible Familie *f* von Orientierungen	famille *f* d'orientations compatible	согласованное семейство ориентаций
C 1342	**compatible conditions** <LO>	verträgliche Bedingungen *fpl*	conditions *fpl* compatibles	совместные условия
	compatible equations <GN>	*s.* C 2098		
C 1343	**compatible formula** <LO>	vergleichbarer Ausdruck *m*	formule *f* comparable	сравнимая формула
C 1344	**compatible metric** <with a uniformity> <TO>	verträgliche Metrik *f*	distance *f* compatible	расстояние, согласующееся <с равномерной структурой>
C 1345	**compatible norm** <with the norm of an algebra> <AL>	verträgliche Norm *f*	norme *f* compatible	норма, согласующаяся <со структурой алгебры>
C 1346	**compatible operation** <with an operator> <AL>	verträgliche Verknüpfung *f*	opération *f* compatible	совместная операция

No.	English	German	French	Russian
C 1347	**compatible system of algebraic equations** <AL>	kompatibles algebraisches System *n*, kompatibles System algebraischer Gleichungen	système *m* d'équations algébriques compatible	совместная система алгебраических уравнений
C 1348	**compatible system of equations** <GR>	verträgliches Gleichungssystem *n*	système *m* d'équations compatible	совместная система уравнений
C 1349	**compatible theories** <MM>	verträgliche Theorien *fpl*	théories *fpl* compatibles	совместные теории
C 1350	**compatible topology** <with the algebraic structure> <AL, TO>	verträgliche Topologie *f* <mit der algebraischen Struktur>	topologie *f* compatible <avec la structure algébrique>	топология, согласующая <с алгебраической структурой>
C 1351	**compatible uniformity** <with the topology> <TO>	verträgliche uniforme Struktur *f* <mit der Topologie>	structure *f* uniforme compatible <avec la topologie>	равномерная структура, согласующая <с топологией>
	compensation computation <ER, NU>	*s.* C 26		
C 1352	**compensation planimeter** <GE, IN>	Kompensationsplanimeter *n*	planimètre *m* à compensation	компенсационный планиметр
	compensation theory <ER, NU>	*s.* C 26		
	competitive optimization <PG>	*s.* C 1639		
	competitive programming <PG>	*s.* C 1639		
	complanarity <GE>	*s.* C 2441		
	complanar line <GE>	*s.* C 2442		
	complanar vector <VT>	*s.* C 2443		
	complanation <DI, DG>	*s.* Q 50		
C 1353	**complement,** direct complement, complementary direct factor <of an *R*-module> <AL>	direktes Komplement *n*, Ergänzungsmodul *m*	sous-module *m* supplémentaire	дополнительный подмодуль, дополнение, прямое дополнение <подмодуля>
C 1354	**complement,** complementary subspace (space) <of a vector space> <AL>	Supplementärraum *m* <eines Unterraums>, supplementärer Raum *m* <zu einem Unterraum>, komplementärer Raum, Komplementärraum *m*	supplémentaire *m*, sous-espace *m* supplémentaire, sous-espace [vectoriel] complémentaire, espace *m* complémentaire	дополнительное подпространство
C 1355	**complement** <of a subobject> <CA>	Komplement *n*	complément *m*	дополнение
C 1356	**complement,** complementary graph <of a graph> <GP>	Komplement *n*, Negation *f*, komplementärer Graph *m*	graphe *m* complémentaire	дополнение графа, дополнительный граф
C 1357	**complement,** complementary element <LA>	Komplement *n*, komplementäres Element *n*	complément *m*	дополнение, дополнительный элемент
C 1358	**complement,** complementary set, negate, set-theoretic[al] complement, absolute complement <of a set> <SE>	Komplementärmenge *f*, komplementäre Menge *f*, Komplement *n*, Ergänzungsmenge *f*, absolutes Komplement	complémentaire *m*, ensemble *m* complémentaire, complément *m*	дополнение, дополнительное множество, абсолютное дополнение
C 1359	**complement** <of an event>, complementary event <ST>	komplementäres Ereignis *n*, Komplementereignis *n*, Komplement *n*	événement *m* contraire (complémentaire)	дополнение <события>, дополнительное событие
	complement <FA, TO>	*s.* T 507		
	complement <LO>	*s.* N 79		
	complement <NT>	*s.* C 1382		
	complement <SE>	*s.* R 697		
C 1360	**complementary angle** <EG>	Komplementwinkel *m*, Komplement *n*	angle *m* complémentaire, complément *m*	дополнительный угол
C 1361	**complementary base** <of an algebra> <AL>	komplementäre Basis *f*	base *f* complémentaire	дополнительный базис
C 1362	**complementary class** <of divisors> <AL>	Ergänzungsklasse *f*	classe *f* complémentaire	дополнительный класс, класс дополнительности
C 1363	**complementary class** <LO, SE>	komplementäre Klasse *f*, Komplementärklasse *f*	classe *f* complémentaire	дополнительный класс
C 1364	**complementary degree** <of a filtration> <AL>	komplementärer Grad *m*	degré *m* complémentaire	дополнительная степень
	complementary direct factor <AL>	*s.* C 1353		
C 1365	**complementary divisor** <AG, AL>	komplementärer Divisor *m*	diviseur *m* complémentaire	дополнительный дивизор
C 1366	**complementary divisor** <of a number *or* order type> <AL, NT, SE>	komplementärer Teiler *m*, Komplementärteiler *m*	facteur (diviseur) *m* complémentaire	дополнительный делитель
C 1367	**complementary domain** <TO>	Komplementärgebiet *n*	domaine *m* complémentaire	дополнительная область
	complementary element <LA>	*s.* C 1357		
	complementary event <ST>	*s.* C 1359		
C 1368	**complementary factor** <of a least common demoninator> <AL, AR>	Erweiterungsfaktor *m*	facteur *m* complémentaire	дополнительный множитель
C 1369	**complementary function** <DE>	Lösung *f* der zugehörigen homogenen Differentialgleichung	solution *f* de l'équation [differentielle] homogène associée	решение соответствующего однородного дифференциального уравнения
C 1370	**complementary function** <in an Orlicz space> <FA>	komplementäre Funktion *f*	fonction *f* complémentaire	дополнительная функция
	complementary function <DE>	*s.* G 128		
C 1371	**complementary game** <TG>	komplementäres Spiel *n*	jeu *m* complémentaire	дополнительная игра

No.	English	German	French	Russian
C 1372	**complementary graph** <of a subgraph>, subgraph complement <GP>	komplementärer Teilgraph *m*	sous-graphe *m* complémentaire	дополнительный подграф
	complementary graph <GP>	*s.* C 1356		
C 1373	**complementary group** <in a group> <GR>	komplementäre Gruppe *f*	groupe *m* complémentaire	дополнительная группа
	complementary group <GR>	*s.* F 26		
C 1374	**complementary homology class** <AT>	komplementäre Homologieklasse *f*	classe *f* d'homologie complémentaire	двойственный класс гомологий
C 1375	**complementary ideal** <of an ideal> <AB>	komplementäres (relativkomplementäres) Ideal *n*	idéal *m* complémentaire	дополнительный идеал
C 1376	**complementary interval** <SE, TO>	Komplementärintervall *n*	intervalle *m* complémentaire	дополнительный интервал
C 1377	**complementary laws,** complementary theorems, supplements <to the quadratic reciprocity law> <NT>	Ergänzungssätze *mpl*	relations *fpl* complémentaires	дополнительные теоремы
C 1378	**complementary minor** <MD>	komplementärer Minor *m*, komplementäre Unterdeterminante (Subdeterminante) *f*, supplementäre (adjungierte) Unterdeterminante, adjungierte Subdeterminante, Ergänzungsminor *m*	mineur *m* complémentaire, sous[-]déterminant *m* complémentaire, sous[-]déterminant adjoint, sous[-]déterminant supplémentaire, complémentaire *m*	дополнительный минор
C 1379	**complementary module** <of an integral extension> <AL>	Komplementärmodul *m*	module *m* complémentaire	дополнительный модуль
C 1380	**complementary modulus** <of an elliptic integral> <FU>	komplementärer Modul *m*, Komplement *n*, Komplementärmodul *m*	module *m* complémentaire	дополнительный модуль
C 1381	**complementary number** <AR, NT>	dekadische Ergänzung *f*	nombre *m* complémentaire	логарифмическое дополнение
C 1382	**complementary number,** complement <of a number> <NT>	arithmetisches Komplement *n*, Ergänzungszahl *f*, arithmetische Ergänzung *f*, Komplementärzahl *f*	complément *m* arithmétique, nombre *m* complémentaire	арифметическое дополнение <к данному числу>, дополнительное число
C 1383	**complementary point** <on a cubic> <AG>	komplementärer Punkt *m*	point *m* complémentaire	дополняющая точка
C 1384	**complementary polygon,** polygon formed by the mid-points <of a polygon> <EG>	Mittenvieleck *n*, komplementäres Vieleck *n*	polygone *m* complémentaire, polygone ayant pour sommets les milieux des côtés	срединный многоугольник, антимедиальный многоугольник
C 1385	**complementary power series** <SS>	komplementäre Potenzreihe *f*	série *f* entière complémentaire	дополнительный степенной ряд
C 1386	**complementary probability** <ST>	komplementäre (entgegengesetzte) Wahrscheinlichkeit *f*	probabilité *f* contraire (complémentaire)	дополнительная вероятность
C 1387	**complementary relation,** negation <of a relation> <SE>	komplementäre Relation *f*	complémentaire *f*, complémentaire *m*	отрицание отношения
	complementary set <SE>	*s.* C 1358		
	complementary space <FA, TO> ┌<AL>	*s.* T 507		
	complementary space	*s.* C 1354		
C 1388	**complementary submodules** <AL>	supplementäre Untermoduln *mpl*	sous-modules *mpl* supplémentaires	подмодули, прямая сумма которых дает весь модуль
C 1389	**complementary subproduct** <of a cartesian product> <SE, UA>	komplementäres Teilprodukt *n*	sous-produit *m* complémentaire	дополнительное подпроизведение
C 1390	**complementary subset** <SE> ┌**space** <AL>	komplementäre Untermenge *f*	partie *f* complémentaire	дополнительное подмножество
	complementary sub-	*s.* C 1354		
	complementary subspace <FA, TO>	*s.* T 507		
C 1391	**complementary system** <of a set system> <SE>	komplementäres System *n* <bezüglich einer Obermenge>	système *m* complémentaire	дополнительная система
C 1392	**complementary tetrahedron** <EG>	komplementäres Tetraeder *n*	tétraèdre *m* complémentaire	дополнительный четырехгранник (тетраэдр)
	complementary theorems <NT>	*s.* C 1377		
C 1393	**complementary transformation** <DG>	Komplementärtransformation *f*	transformation *f* complémentaire	дополнительное преобразование
C 1394	**complementary triangle,** triangle formed by the mid-points <of a triangle> <EG>	Mittendreieck *n*, komplementäres Dreieck *n*	triangle *m* fondamental complémentaire, triangle ayant pour sommets les milieux des côtés	антимедиальный треугольник <относительно треугольника>, срединный треугольник
	complementary trigonometric function <AN>	*s.* C 1058		
	complementary vector spaces <AL, GE>	*s.* C 1403		
C 1395	**complementation** <in a Boolean algebra> <LA>	Komplementbildung *f*	complémentation *f*	переход к дополнению
C 1396	**complementation** <SE>	Komplementärmengenbildung *f*, Komplementbildung *f*, Komplementierung *f*, Übergang *m* zur Komplementärmenge	passage *m* au complémentaire, complémentation *f*	переход к дополнению

No.	English	Deutsch	Français	Русский
C 1397	**complementation rule** <SE>	Komplementierungsregel *f*	règle *f* de complémentation	правило дополнения
C 1398	**complemented lattice** <LA>	komplementärer Verband *m*	treillis *m* complémenté, structure *f* complémentée, lattice *m* complémenté	структура (решетка) с дополнениями
	complement of a knot <TO>	*s.* K 107		
C 1399	**complement on *b*** <in a representation of numbers to base *b*> <NT>	*b*-Komplement *n* <arithmetisches Komplement zur Basis *b*>	complément *m* juste	дополнение до *b*
C 1400/1	**complement on *b* — 1** <in a representation of numbers to base *b*> <NT>	(*b* — 1)-Komplement *n*; Neunerkomplement *n*	complément *m* faux	дополнение до (*b* — 1)
C 1402	**complement relation** <functional equation $\Gamma(z)\,\Gamma(1-z)=\pi/\sin(\pi z)$ for the Γ-function> <FU>	Funktionalgleichung *f* für die Komplemente der Γ-Funktion, Funktionalgleichung von Euler, Eulersche Funktionalgleichung	relation *f* des compléments, formule *f* des compléments	формула дополнения, отношение дополнения
C 1403	**complements** <in a vector space>, complementary vector spaces, algebraically complementary vector subspaces <AL, GE>	supplementäre Unterräume *mpl*, komplementäre Teilräume *mpl*	sous-espaces *mpl* supplémentaires	подпространства, прямая сумма которых дает все пространство
C 1404	**complement** <of a number> **with respect to 10** <NT>	Zehnerkomplement *n*	complément *m* à 10	дополнение до 10
	complete abelian group <GR>	*s.* A 412		
C 1405	**complete Abelian variety** <AG>	vollständige abelsche Mannigfaltigkeit *f*	variété *f* abélienne complète	полное абелево многообразие
C 1406	**complete accumulation point** <TO>	vollständiger (maximaler) Häufungspunkt *m*	point *m* totalement adhérent <à>, point d'accumulation maximée	точка полного накопления, максимальная предельная точка
C 1407	**complete algebraic curve** <AG>	vollständige algebraische Kurve *f*	courbe *f* [algébrique] complète	полная [алгебраическая] кривая
C 1408	**complete algebraic system,** complete continuous system <of algebraic varieties> <AG>	algebraisches Vollsystem *n*, komplettes (vollständiges) algebraisches System *n*	système *m* algébrique complet	полная алгебраическая система
	complete $\mathfrak{A}$-module <AL>	*s.* D 798		
	complete analytic function <FT>	*s.* M 841		
C 1409	**complete and cocomplete category** <CA>	zugleich rechts- und linksvollständige Kategorie *f*, vollständige Kategorie	catégorie *f* complète et cocomplète	биполная (полная) категория
C 1410	**complete axiom system,** logically complete axiom system <FO>	vollständiges Axiomensystem, vollständiges System *n* <von Axiomen>	système *m* complet <d'axiomes>	полная система аксиом, полная система <аксиом>
C 1411	**complete binary quadratic form** <NT>	vollständige binäre quadratische Form *f*	forme *f* quadratique binaire complète	полная бинарная квадратичная форма
C 1412	**complete bipartite graph, complete-bipartite graph** <GP>	vollständig-paarer (vollständiger paarer) Graph *m*	graphe *m* biparti-complet	полный двудольный граф
C 1413	**complete Boolean algebra** <AL>	vollständige Boolesche Algebra *f*	algèbre *f* de Boole complète	полная булева (по Дедекинду) алгебра
	σ-complete Boolean algebra <AL>	*s.* S 815		
C 1414	**complete branch** <of an algebraic curve> <AG>	vollständiger Zweig *m*	cycle *m*	полная ветвь
C 1415	**complete cardinal product** <of ordered sets> <SE>	uneingeschränktes Kardinalprodukt *n*	produit *m* cardinal général	полное кардинальное произведение
C 1416	**complete category,** left complete category, left-complete category <CA>	vollständige (linksvollständige) Kategorie *f*	catégorie *f* complète	полная (полная слева) категория
C 1417	**complete class** <ST>	vollständige Klasse *f*	classe *f* complète	полный класс
	complete class <SE>	*s.* T 801		
	complete combination <CT>	*s.* C 1184		
C 1418	**complete commutative law of equivalence** <LO>	vollständiges Kommutativgesetz *n* der Äquivalenz	loi *f* de symétrie de l'équivalence, loi de commutativité d'équivalence complète	полный закон коммутативности равенства
C 1419	**complete continuity** <FA, TO>	Vollstetigkeit *f*	continuité *f* complète, complète continuité	полная (вполне) непрерывность
	complete continuous system <AG>	*s.* C 1408		
C 1420/1	**complete correlation matrix** <with the variances equal to unity> <ST>	vollständige Korrelationsmatrix *f*	matrice *f* de corrélation complète	полная корреляционная матрица
C 1422	**complete cross classification** <ST>	vollständige Kreuzklassifikation *f*	classification *f* croisée complète	полная обратная классификация
C 1423	**complete definiteness** <DE>	Volldefinitheit *f*	propriété *f* d'être complètement défini	полная определенность
C 1424	**complete diagram** <of an algebra> <UA>	vollständiges Diagramm *n*	diagramme *m* complet	полная диаграмма
	complete differential <DI>	*s.* T 624		
	completed infinity <LO>	*s.* A 208		
C 1425	**complete direct product,** unrestricted direct product, direct product <GR>	uneingeschränktes (vollständiges, abgeschlossenes, kartesisches, cartesisches) direktes Produkt *n*	produit *m* direct général (complet, cartésien)	полное прямое произведение, прямое произведение

C 1426	**complete direct sum** <GR>	uneingeschränkte (vollständig) direkte Summe *f*	somme *f* directe complète (générale)	полная прямая сумма
	complete direct sum <UA> ┌<LO>	*s.* D 596		
C 1427	**complete disjunction**	vollständige Disjunktion *f*	disjonction *f* complète	полная дизъюнкция
	complete distributive law of conjunction over disjunction <LO>	*s.* D 774		
C 1428	**complete elliptic integral** <of the first, second, *or* third kind> <FU>	vollständiges elliptisches Integral *n* <erster, zweiter *oder* dritter Gattung>	intégrale *f* elliptique complète <de première, deuxième *ou* troisième espèce>	полный эллиптический интеграл <первого, второго *или* третьего рода>
C 1429	**complete equation** <of the *n*-th degree> <with all coefficients ≠ 0> <AL>	vollständige Gleichung *f* <*n*-ten Grades>	équation *f* complète <du *n*-e degré>	полное уравнение <*n*-ой степени>
C 1430	**complete extension** <of a Boolean algebra> <AL>	vollständige Erweiterung *f*	extension *f* complète	пополнение
C 1431	**complete factorization,** atomic factorization <of a ring element> <AL>	vollständige Zerlegung *f*	factorisation *f* complète	полное (атомное) разложение
C 1432	**complete family of congruences** <of an algebraic system> <UA>	vollständiges Kongruenzensystem *n*	famille *f* complète de congruences	полная система (совокупность) конгруэнций
C 1433	**complete family of homomorphisms** <of an algebraic system> <UA>	vollständiges System *n* von Homomorphismen	famille *f* complète d'homomorphismes	полная система гомоморфизмов
C 1434	**complete field** <with respect to a valuation> <AL>	perfekter (vollständiger, kompletter) Körper *m* <bezüglich einer Bewertung>	corps *m* complet	полное поле
C 1435	**complete field of sets** <AL, SE>	vollständige Mengenalgebra *f*, vollständiger Mengenkörper *m*	corps *m* d'ensembles complet, corps complet	полная алгебра множеств, полное поле множеств
C 1436	**complete figure of Pappus' theorem** <AY, SG>	Pascalsche Konfiguration *f*, Konfiguration von Pascal	figure *f* de Pascal	конфигурация Паппа
	σ-complete filter <AL, SE>	*s.* S 816		
	complete function <FT>	*s.* M 841		
C 1437	**complete graph,** complete linear complex <GP>	vollständiger Graph *m*	graphe *m* (complexe *m* linéaire) complet	полный граф (линейный комплекс)
C 1438	**complete group;** divisible group <additive>; radicable group <multiplicative> <GR>	divisionsvollständige (vollständige, volle, teilbare, dividierbare) Gruppe *f*	groupe *m* divisible	группа с неограниченным делением, полная (делимая) группа
C 1439	**complete group** <as a group without centre having inner automorphisms only> <GR>	vollständige (abgeschlossene, vollkommene) Gruppe	groupe *m* complet	совершенная группа
	complete group <GR>	*s.* C 1583		
	π-complete group <GR>	*s.* R 14		
	Π-complete group <GR>	*s.* P 582		
C 1440	**complete group variety** <AG>	vollständige Gruppenmannigfaltigkeit *f*	variété *f* de groupe complète	полное групповое многообразие
C 1441	**complete homogeneous Boolean algebra** <AL>	vollhomogene Algebra *f*	algèbre *f* de Boole complètement homogène	вполне однородная алгебра
C 1442	**complete homomorphism** <of a Boolean algebra> <AL>	vollständiger Homomorphismus *m*	homomorphisme (morphisme) *m* complet	полный гомоморфизм
	σ-complete ideal <AL, SE>	*s.* S 826		
C 1443	**complete independent system of units** <AB>	volles unabhängiges Einheitensystem *n*	système *m* des unités indépendant complet	полная независимая система единиц
	complete induction <FO>	*s.* M 165		
	complete information <TG>	*s.* P 414		
C 1444	**complete integral,** Jacobi['s] complete integral, complete solution <of a partial differential equation> <DE>	vollständiges (Jacobis vollständiges) Integral *n*, vollständige Lösung *f*	intégrale *f* complète [de Jacobi], solution *f* complète	полное решение, полный интеграл [Якоби]
C 1445	**complete intersection** <AG>	vollständiger Durchschnitt (Schnitt) *m*	intersection *f* complète	полное пересечение
C 1446	**complete intersection point system** <of algebraic curves> <AG>	vollständiges Schnittpunktsystem *n*	système *m* complet de points d'intersection	полная система точек пересечений
C 1447	**complete intersection system** <AG>	vollständiges Schnittsystem *n*	système *m* complet d'intersection	полная система пересечений
C 1448	**complete in the sense of Post** <MM>	vollständig im Sinne von Post	complet au sens de Post	полный в смысле Поста
C 1449	**complete lattice,** closed lattice, continuous lattice <LA>	vollständiger Verband *m*	treillis (lattice) *m* complet, réseau *m* achevé, structure *f* complète	полная структура (решетка)
C 1450	**complete law of contraposition,** contraposition principle, law of contraposition <LO>	vollständiges Kontrapositionsgesetz *n*, Gesetz *n* der vollständigen Kontraposition, Prinzip *n* der Kontraposition	loi *f* de contraposition [complète]	полный закон контрапозиции, закон простой контрапозиции, принцип контрапозиции
	complete law of double negation <LO>	*s.* L 182		
C 1451	**complete l-group** <AL>	vollständige l-Gruppe *f*	groupe *m* complètement réticulé	полная l-группа

No.	English	German	French	Russian
	complete limit <SE>	*s.* L 753		
	complete linear complex <GP>	*s.* C 1437		
	complete linear group <GR>	*s.* F 716		
C 1452	**complete linear series,** complete series <of divisors> <AG>	vollständige Divisorenschar (Schar) *f*, vollständiges System *n*	série *f* [linéaire] complète, système *m* complet de diviseurs, système complet	полное семейство дивизоров
C 1453	**complete linear system,** complete system, complete series <*e.g.*: of algebraic curves> <AG, PJ>	vollständiges lineares System *n*, vollständiges System (Linearsystem *n*), vollständige Linearschar *f*, lineare Vollschar *f*, Vollschar	série *f* [linéaire] complète, système *m* linéaire complet	полная линейная система
C 1454	**complete local ring** <AL>	kompletter (vollständiger, perfekter) lokaler Ring *m*	anneau *m* local complet	полное локальное кольцо
C 1455	**complete lower semilattice** <AL>	vollständiger Durchschnittshalbverband ($\cap$-Halbverband) *m*	inf-demi-treillis (inf demi-treillis) *m* complet	полная нижняя полурешетка
	σ-complete lower semilattice <AL>	*s.* S 817		
C 1456	**completely additive family of sets** <SE>	vollständig additive Mengenfamilie *f*, vollständig additives Mengensystem	famille *f* complètement additive d'ensembles	вполне аддитивное семейство множеств
	completely additive measure <ME>	*s.* A 82		
C 1457	**completely antisymmetric tensor density** <VT>	vollständig alternierende Tensordichte *f*	densité *f* tensorielle complètement antisymétrique	вполне антисимметричная тензорная плотность
	completely arc-connected subset <TO>	*s.* A 913		
C 1458	**completely asymptotic subspace** <of a Hilbert space> <FA>	vollständig asymptotischer Teilraum *m*	sous-espace *m* complètement asymptotique	вполне асимптотическое подпространство
C 1459	**completely characteristic ideal** <CA>	vollständig charakteristisches Ideal *n*	idéal *m* complètement caractéristique	вполне характеристический идеал
C 1460	**completely compact set** <TO>	vollständig kompakte Menge *f*	ensemble *m* complètement compact	вполне компактное множество
C 1461	**completely continuous function** <of infinitely many variables> <RF>	vollstetige Funktion *f*	fonction *f* complètement continue	вполне непрерывная функция
	completely continuous function <RF>	*s.* A 89		
C 1462	**completely continuous linear operator,** completely continuous operator, compact [linear] operator <FA>	vollstetiger [linearer] Operator *m*, kompakter [linearer] Operator, kompakte (vollstetige) [lineare] Abbildung (Transformation) *f*	opérateur *m* [linéaire] complètement continu, opérateur [linéaire] totalement continu, opérateur [linéaire] compact, application (transformation) *f* [linéaire] compacte (complètement continue)	вполне непрерывный [линейный] оператор, компактный [линейный] оператор
C 1463	**completely continuous mapping,** compact mapping <TO>	vollstetige Abbildung *f*	application *f* complètement continue, application compacte	вполне непрерывное отображение
C 1464	**completely continuous mapping (operator),** completely continuous transformation, compact operator (transformation, mapping) <FA>	vollstetiger (kompakter) Operator *m*, vollstetige (kompakte) Abbildung (Transformation) *f*	opérateur *m* complètement (totalement) continu, opérateur compact, application (transformation) *f* complètement (totalement) continue, application (transformation) compacte	вполне непрерывный оператор, компактный оператор, вполне непрерывное преобразование (отображение), компактное преобразование (отображение)
	completely continuous operator <FA>	*s.* C 1462		
	completely continuous part <RF>	*s.* A 91		
	completely continuous transformation <FA>	*s.* C 1464		
	completely convex set <FA>	*s.* C 2385		
C 1465	**completely decomposable matrix** <MD>	vollständig zerlegbare (reduzible) Matrix *f*	matrice *f* complètement décomposable	вполне разложимая матрица
C 1466	**completely decomposable module** <AL>	vollständig zerlegbarer Modul *m*	module *m* complètement décomposable	вполне разложимый модуль
C 1467	**completely defined correspondence** <SE>	überall definierte Korrespondenz *f*	correspondance *f* partout définie	всюду (полностью) определенное соответствие
	completely defined mapping <AL, SE>	*s.* T 676		
C 1468	**completely definite eigenvalue problem** <DE>	volldefinites Eigenwertproblem *n*, volldefinite Eigenwertaufgabe *f*, volldefinites Problem *n*	problème *m* aux valeurs propres complètement défini	вполне определенная задача на собственные значения
	completely discontinuous function <RA>	*s.* A 96		
C 1469	**completely distributive lattice,** infinitely distributive lattice <LA>	vollständig distributiver Verband *m*	treillis *m* complètement distributif général	вполне дистрибутивная структура
C 1470	**completely equivalent matrix method** <LI>	volläquivalentes Matrixverfahren (*A*-Verfahren) *n*	méthode *f* matricielle complètement équivalente	вполне эквивалентный матричный метод
C 1471/2	**completely faithful module** <AL>	völlig treuer Modul *m*	module *m* pleinement fidèle	вполне точный модуль

C 1473	**completely homologous map[ping]s** <of complexes> <AT>	vollständig homologe Abbildungen *fpl*	applications *fpl* complètement homologiques	вполне гомологичные между собою отображения
C 1474	**completely homology-equivalent complex** <AT>	vollständig homologieäquivalenter Komplex *m*	complexe *m* complètement homologiquement équivalent	вполне гомологично эквивалентный комплекс
C 1475	**completely indecomposable group** <GR>	vollständig unzerlegbare Gruppe *f*	groupe *m* complètement indécomposable	вполне неразложимая группа
C 1476	**completely independent system of axioms** <FO>	vollständig unabhängiges Axiomensystem *n*	système *m* d'axiomes complètement indépendant	вполне независимая система аксиом
C 1477	**completely integrable system** <of Pfaffian equations> <DE>	vollständig integrierbares System *n*	système *m* complètement intégrable	вполне интегрируемая система
C 1478	**completely integrable system,** totally integrable system, involutory system <of partial differential equations> <DE>	Involutionssystem *n*, vollständig integrierbares System *n*	système *m* complètement intégrable, système en involution	вполне интегрируемая система, инволюционная система
C 1479	**completely integrally closed domain** <AL>	vollständig ganz[-] abgeschlossener Integritätsbereich *m*	anneau *m* complètement intégralement clos	вполне целозамкнутое кольцо
C 1480	**completely integrally closed ring** <AL>	vollständig ganz[-] abgeschlossener Ring *m*	anneau *m* complètement entier-fermé	вполне целозамкнутое кольцо
C 1481	**completely irreducible between two points** <TO>	vollständig irreduzibel zwischen zwei Punkten	complètement irréductible entre deux points	вполне неприводимый между двумя точками
C 1482	**completely join-stable** <SE>	abgeschlossen gegenüber beliebigen Vereinigungen	stable pour les réunions infinies	замкнутый относительно бесконечных объединений
C 1483	**completely lattice-ordered semigroup** <AL>	vollständig verbandsgeordnete Halbgruppe *f*	monoïde *m* complètement réticulé	вполне решеточно-упорядоченная полугруппа
C 1484	**completely lattice-preserving mapping** <of a quasi-ordered class> <SE>	vollständiger Verbandshomomorphismus *m*	homomorphisme *m* complètement réticulé	вполне решетчатый гомоморфизм
C 1485	**completely lattice-stable** <SE>	abgeschlossen gegenüber beliebigen Durchschnitten und Vereinigungen	stable pour les intersections et les réunions infinies	замкнутый относительно бесконечных пересечений и объединений
C 1486	**completely meet-irreducible submodule** <AL>	vollständig durchschnittsunzerlegbarer Untermodul *m*	sous-module *m* complètement $\cap$-irréductible, sous-module super-irréductible	вполне $\cap$-неразложимый подмодуль
C 1487	**completely meet-stable** <SE>	abgeschlossen gegenüber beliebigen Durchschnitten	stable pour les intersections infinies	замкнутый относительно бесконечных пересечений
C 1488	**completely mixed game** <TG>	vollständig gemischtes Spiel *n*	jeu *m* complètement mixte	вполне смешанная игра
C 1489	**completely mixed strategy** <TG>	völlig gemischte Strategie *f*	stratégie *f* complètement mixte	вполне смешанная стратегия
	completely monotone function <RF>	*s.* C 1490/1		
	completely monotone sequence <FD, SS>	*s.* C 1492		
C 1490/1	**completely monotonic function,** completely monotone function, absolutely monotonic (monotone) function <RF>	vollmonotone (totalmonotone) Funktion *f*	fonction *f* complètement (absolument) monotone	вполне (абсолютно) монотонная функция
C 1492	**completely monotonic sequence,** completely monotone sequence, totally (absolutely) monotonic (monotone) sequence <FD, SS>	vollmonotone (totalmonotone) Folge *f*	suite *f* complètement (totalement) monotone	вполне (абсолютно) монотонная последовательность
C 1493	**completely multiplicative class** <of sets> <SE>	vollständig multiplikatives Mengensystem *n*	famille *f* complètement multiplicative <d'ensembles>	вполне мультипликативное семейство <множеств>
C 1494	**completely multiplicative function** <NT>	stark (distributive) multiplikative zahlentheoretische Funktion *f*, stark multiplikative Funktion, distributive Funktion	fonction *f* strictement multiplicative	вполне мультипликативная функция
	completely ordered set <SE>	*s.* L 822		
C 1495	**completely parallelizable manifold** <DG>	vollständig parallelisierbare Mannigfaltigkeit *f*	variété *f* complètement parallélisable	вполне параллелизируемое многообразие
C 1496	**completely primary ring** <Artinian ring whose quotient modulo its Jacobson radical is a division ring> <AL>	vollständig primärer Ring *m*	anneau *m* complètement primaire, anneau complète-primaire	вполне примарное кольцо
C 1497	**completely prime ideal** <AL>	vollständiges Primideal *n*	idéal *m* complètement premier	вполне простой идеал
C 1498	**completely ramified extension** <of a field> <AL>	vollständig verzweigte Erweiterung *f*	extension *f* totalement (complètement) ramifiée	вполне разветвленное расширение
C 1499	**completely ramified prime [number],** totally ramified prime [number] <NT>	vollständig verzweigte Primzahl *f*	nombre *m* premier complètement ramifié	вполне разветвленное простое число
C 1500	**completely ramified valuation** <AL>	vollständig verzweigte Bewertung *f*	valuation *f* totalement ramifiée	полностью разветвленное нормирование
C 1501	**completely ramified value** <FT>	vollständig verzweigter Wert *m*	valeur *f* totalement ramifiée	совершенно разветвленное значение

No.	English	German	French	Russian
C 1502	**completely recursively enumerable subclass** <FO>	vollständig rekursiv aufzählbare Unterklasse *f*	sous-classe *f* complètement récursivement énumérable	вполне рекурсивно перечислимый подкласс
C 1503	**completely reduced form** <of a matrix representation> <RE>	vollständig reduzierte Form *f*	forme *f* complètement réduite	вполне приводимый вид
C 1504	**completely reduced game** <TG>	vollständig reduziertes Spiel *n*	jeu *m* complètement réduit	полностью приведенная (редуцированная) игра
C 1505	**completely reducible group** <GR>	vollständig reduzible Gruppe *f*	groupe *m* complètement réductible	вполне приводимая группа
	completely reducible representation <AL>	*s.* F 726		
C 1506	**completely reducible ring** <AL>	vollständig reduzibler Ring *m*, vollreduzibler Ring	anneau *m* complètement réductible, anneau semi-simple	вполне приводимое кольцо, полупростое (классически полупростое) кольцо
C 1507	**completely reducible system of matrices** <AL>	vollständig reduzibles Matrixsystem *n*, vollreduzibles System *n*	système *m* de matrices complètement réductible	вполне приводимая система матриц
	completely regular Banach algebra <FA>	*s.* C 34		
C 1508	**completely regular filter** <TO>	vollständig regulärer Filter *m*	filtre *m* complètement régulier	вполне регулярный фильтр
C 1509	**completely regular semigroup,** union of groups, Clifford['s] semigroup <AL>	vollständig reguläre Halbgruppe *f*	demi-groupe *m* complètement régulier	вполне регулярная полугруппа, клиффордова полугруппа
C 1510	**completely regular [topological] space, completely regular T_1 space,** Tychonoff['s] space, uniformizable space, separated uniformizable space, $T_{3\frac{1}{2}}$-space, // Tichonov['s] space <TO>	vollständig regulärer (regulärer topologischer) Raum *m*, uniformisierbarer Hausdorffscher Raum, Tychonoffscher Raum	espace *m* complètement régulier, espace topologique complètement régulier	пространство Тихонова, тихоновское (вполне регулярное, вполне регулярное топологическое) пространство, вполне регулярное T_1-пространство, равномеризуемое пространство
C 1511	**completely regular topology** <TO>	vollständig reguläre Topologie *f*	topologie *f* complètement régulière	вполне регулярная топология
C 1512	**completely separable space,** space satisfying the [second] axiom of countability, second countable space, second countable topological space, [topological] space having a countable basis, space with a countable base, space of countable weight, separable space, perfectly separable space <TO>	Raum *m* mit abzählbarer Basis, topologischer Raum mit abzählbarer Basis, vollständig separabler [topologischer] Raum, rationaler [topologischer] Raum; Raum, der dem zweiten Abzählbarkeitsaxiom genügt	espace *m* à base dénombrable, espace topologique à base dénombrable, espace parfaitement séparable, espace contenant une base	пространство, имеющее счетный базис; пространство со счетной [открытой] базой, пространство счетного веса, топологическое пространство со счетным базисом, пространство веса $\aleph_0$
C 1513	**completely separated sets** <TO>	funktional trennbare Teilmengen *fpl*	ensembles *mpl* normalement séparés	нормально отделимые множества
C 1514	**completely splitted ideal** <AB>	vollständig zerlegtes Ideal *n*	idéal *m* totalement décomposé	полностью разложенный идеал
C 1515	**completely splitted place** <AL>	vollständig zerlegte Stelle *f*	place *f* complètement décomposée	полностью разложенное место
C 1516	**completely splitted prime ideal** <AB>	vollständig zerlegtes Primideal *n*, vollzerlegtes Primideal	idéal *m* premier complètement décomposé	полностью разложенный простой идеал
C 1517	**completely symmetric endomorphism** <FA>	vollsymmetrischer (vollständig symmetrischer, vollkommen symmetrischer) Endomorphismus *m*	endomorphisme *m* complètement symétrique	вполне симметричный эндоморфизм
C 1518	**completely symmetrizable endomorphism** <FA>	vollsymmetrisierbarer Endomorphismus *m*	endomorphisme *m* complètement symétrisable	вполне симметризуемый эндоморфизм
C 1519	**completely totalizable function** <in *J*>, D_*-integrable function <RF>	vollständig totalisierbare Funktion *f*, D_*-integrierbare Funktion	fonction *f* complètement totalisable, fonction intégrable au sens de Denjoy-Perron	вполне тотализуемая функция, интегрируемая в смысле Данжуа-Перрона функция
	completely transitive group <AL>	*s.* F 728		
C 1520	**completely unordered set** <SE>	vollständig ungeordnete Menge *f*	ensemble *m* totalement non ordonné	вполне неупорядоченное множество
	complete matrix ring <AL>	*s.* T 677		
C 1521	**complete measure** <ME>	vollständiges Maß *n*	mesure *f* complète	полная мера
C 1522	**complete measure space** <ME, ST>	vollständiger Maßraum *m*	espace *m* mesuré complet	пространство с полной мерой
C 1523	**complete metric space** <TO>	[metrisch] vollständiger Raum *m*, metrischer Raum *m*	espace *m* métrique complet	полное метрическое пространство
C 1524	**complete module** <AL>	vollständiger Modul *m*	module *m* complet	полный модуль
	complete monomial group <GR>	*s.* G 154		
C 1525	**complete monoton[icit]y,** absolute monotonicity (monotony) <of a function> <RF>	Vollmonotonie *f*	monotonie *f* complète (absolue)	полная (абсолютная) монотонность
C 1525 a	**complete monoton[icit]y,** total monotonicity (monotony) <of a sequence> <SS>	Vollmonotonie *f*, Totalmonotonie *f*, totale Monotonie *f*	monotonie *f* complète (totale)	полная монотонность

No.	English	German	French	Russian
C 1526	**complete multilateral,** complete polylateral <DS, PJ>	vollständiges Vielseit *n*	multilatère (polylatère) *m* complet	полный многосторонник
C 1527	**completeness** <of a system of functions> <AN>	Vollständigkeit *f*, L^2-Vollständigkeit *f*	complété *f*, complet *m*	полнота
C 1528	**completeness** <LO>	Vollständigkeit *f*	complétude *f*, suffisance *f*	полнота
C 1529	**completeness** <of a space> <TO>	Vollständigkeit *f*	fait *m* d'être complet	полнота
	completeness <LO>	*s.* S 307		
	σ-completeness <AL, SE>	*s.* S 818		
	ω-completeness <MM>	*s.* O 65		
C 1530	**completeness axiom** <MM>	Vollständigkeitsaxiom *n*	axiome *m* de la complétude	аксиома полноты
C 1531	**completeness condition** <LO>	Vollständigkeitsvoraussetzung *f*, Vollständigkeitsbedingung *f*	condition *f* de complétude	условие полноты
C 1532	**completeness degree** <TO>	Vollständigkeitsgrad *m*	degré *m* de complétude	степень полноты
C 1533	**completeness proof** <LO>	Vollständigkeitsbeweis *m*	démonstration *f* de la complétude	доказательство полноты
C 1534	**completeness property** <LO>	Vollständigkeitseigenschaft *f*	propriété *f* de complétude	свойство полноты
	completeness relation <FA>	*s.* P 173		
	completeness relation <SS>	*s.* P 175		
C 1535	**completeness theorem** <DE, LO>	Vollständigkeitssatz *m* <DE, LO>; Vollständigkeitsaussage *f* <LO>	théorème *m* de complétude	теорема о полноте, теорема полноты
C 1536	**completeness theorem** <GE>	Satz *m* der Vollständigkeit	théorème *m* de complétude	теорема полноты
	completeness theorem of Gödel <MM>	*s.* G 322		
C 1537	**complete normality axiom,** T_5-separation axiom <TO>	verschärftes Tietzesches Trennungsaxiom *n*, fünftes Trennungsaxiom, T_5-Axiom *n*	second axiome *m* de Tietze, axiome T_5	вторая аксиома Титце, аксиома (T_5)
	complete normed algebra <FA>	*s.* B 40		
	complete normed space <FA>	*s.* B 48		
C 1538	**complete number scale,** number scale <NT>	Zahlenreihe *f*, Reihe *f* der ganzen Zahlen	suite *f* des nombres entiers	числовой ряд, ряд целых чисел
C 1539	**complete ordered field** <AL>	vollständiger geordneter Körper *m*	corps *m* ordonné complet	полное упорядоченное поле
	complete ordering <SE>	*s.* 1. L 830; 2. W 211		
C 1540	**complete orthogonal sequence;** closed orthogonal sequence <AN>	vollständige Orthogonalfolge *f*; abgeschlossene Orthogonalfolge	suite *f* orthogonale complète; suite orthogonale fermée	полная ортогональная последовательность; замкнутая ортогональная система
	complete orthogonal set <AN>	*s.* C 1541		
C 1541	**complete orthogonal system,** complete orthogonal set; closed orthogonal system <AN>	vollständiges Orthogonalsystem *n*; abgeschlossenes Orthogonalsystem	système *m* orthogonal complet; système orthogonal fermé	полная ортогональная система; замкнутая ортогональная система
C 1542	**complete orthonormal sequence** <AN>	vollständige Orthonormalfolge *f*	suite *f* orthonormale complète, système *m* orthonormal complet dénombrablement infini	полная ортонормированная последовательность
C 1543	**complete orthonormal system,** orthonormal base; closed orthonormal system <AN, FA>	vollständiges Orthonormalsystem *n*, Orthonormalbasis *f*; abgeschlossenes Orthonormalsystem	système *m* orthonormal (orthonormé) complet, famille *f* orthonormale et totale, base *f* orthonormale (orthonormée); système orthonormal (orthonormé) fermé	полная ортонормированная (ортонормальная) система, ортонормированный базис; замкнутая ортонормированная (ортонормальная) система
	complete oscillatory set <TO>	*s.* P 1326		
	complete path <GP>	*s.* H 70		
C 1544	**complete polygon** <DS, PJ>	vollständiges Vieleck *n*	polygone *m* complet	полный многовершинник (многоугольник)
	complete polylateral <DS, PJ>	*s.* C 1526		
C 1545	**complete polynomial** <with all coefficients $\neq 0$> <AL>	vollständiges Polynom *n*	fonction *f* rationnelle entière complète	полный многочлен
	complete primitive <DE>	*s.* G 127		
C 1546	**complete probability space** <ST>	vollständiger Wahrscheinlichkeitsraum *m*	espace *m* de probabilité complet, espace probabilisé complet	полное вероятностное пространство
C 1547	**complete product** <of groups> <GR>	vollständiges Produkt *n*	produit *m* complet	полное произведение
C 1548	**complete projective system** <AT>	vollständiges projektives System *n*	système *m* projectif complet	полный проекционный спектр
C 1549	**complete quadrangle** <DS, PJ>	vollständiges Viereck *n*	quadrangle *m* complet	полный четырехвершинник (четырехугольник)
C 1550	**complete quadrilateral** <DS, PJ>	vollständiges Vierseit *n*	quadrilatère *m* complet	полный четырехсторонник
C 1551	**complete quasi-ordered class,** order-complete quasi-ordered class <SE>	vollständige Klasse *f*	classe *f* complète	полный класс

No.	English	German	French	Russian
C 1552	**complete quotient** <of numbers> <AL, NT>	vollständiger Quotient *m*	quotient *m* complet (exact)	полное частное, точное значение частного; частное <при делении без остатка>
C 1553	**complete reducibility theorem** <AG>	Satz *m* von der vollständigen Reduzibilität	théorème *m* de la réducibilité complète	теорема о полной приводимости
C 1554	**complete regularity separation axiom,** $T_{3,5}$-separation axiom <TO>	Tychonoffsches Trennungsaxiom *n*, Trennungsaxiom von Tychonoff, Tychonowsches Trennungsaxiom, Axiom *n* FT_3	axiome *m* de Tychonoff	аксиома Тихонова (O_{IV})
C 1555	**complete regular product** <of algebraic systems> <UA>	vollständiges reguläres Produkt *n*	produit *m* régulier complet	полное регулярное произведение
C 1556	**complete Reinhardt domain** <FT>	vollkommener Reinhardtscher Körper *m*	domaine *m* multicirculaire complet	полная кратнокруговая (*n*-круговая) область
	complete relation <SE>	*s.* T 687		
C 1557	**complete residue system modulo *m*,** complete set of incongruent numbers modulo *m* <NT>	vollständiges Restsystem *n* modulo *m*	système *m* complet de restes (mod. *m*), système complet des résidus (mod. *m*)	полная система вычетов по модулю *m*
C 1558	**complete Riemannian space** <DG>	vollständiger Riemannscher Raum *m*	espace *m* de Riemann complet (normal)	полное (нормальное) риманово пространство
C 1559	**complete Riesz space** <FA, TO>	vollständiger Rieszcher Raum *m*	espace *m* de Riesz complètement réticulé	полное пространство Риса
C 1560	**complete ring** <AL>	perfekter (vollständiger, kompletter) Ring *m*	anneau *m* complet	полное кольцо
C 1561	**complete ring of quotients,** total quotient ring <AL>	voller Quotientenring *m*, Gesamtquotientenring *m*	anneau *m* total de fractions	полное кольцо частных
C 1562	**complete ring of right quotients** <AL> ┌<AL>	voller Rechtsquotientenring *m*	anneau *m* total de fractions à droite	полное правое кольцо частных
	σ-complete semi-lattice	*s.* S 819		
	complete sequence <GR>	*s.* C 799		
	complete series <AG>	*s.* C 1452		
	complete series <PJ>	*s.* C 1453		
C 1563	**complete set** <FO>	vollständige Menge *f*	ensemble *m* complet	полное множество
	complete set <SE>	*s.* T 809		
C 1564	**complete set of conjugates** <AL>	vollständiges Konjugiertensystem *n*	système *m* complet de conjugués	полная система сопряженных элементов
C 1565	**complete set of events,** complete system of events <ST> ┌<AN>	vollständiges Ereignissystem *n*	système *m* complet d'événements	полная система событий
	complete set of functions	*s.* C 1577		
	complete set of incongruent numbers modulo *m* <NT>	*s.* C 1557		
C 1566	**complete set of nonassociates** <of a ring> <AL>	vollständiges System *n* nichtassoziierter Elemente	système *m* complet d'éléments non associés	полная система неассоциированных элементов
C 1567	**complete set of nonbounding 1-circuits** <AT>	Bettische Basis *f*, eindimensionale Zyklenbasis *f*	base *f* de cycles unidimensionnels	базис одномерных циклов
C 1568	**complete set of relations** <GR>	vollständiges Relationensystem *n*	système *m* de relations complet	полная система соотношений
C 1569	**complete set of representations** <of a topological group> <RE>	vollständiges System *n* von Darstellungen	système *m* complet de représentations	полная система представлений
C 1570	**complete set of representatives,** complete system of representatives <AL>	vollständiges (volles) Repräsentantensystem (Vertretersystem) *n*	système *m* de représentants [complet]	полная система представителей
	complete set of residues <NT>	*s.* R 375		
C 1571	**complete simplex method** <PG>	vollständiges Simplexverfahren *n*	méthode *f* simpliciale (de simplexes) complète	полный симплексный метод, полный симплекс-метод
C 1572	**complete solution** <of a system of linear equations> <AL>	vollständige Lösung *f*	solution *f* complète	полное решение
	complete solution <DE>	*s.* C 1444		
C 1573	**complete space** <FA, TO>	vollständiger Raum *m*	espace *m* complet	полное пространство
C 1574	**complete straight line** <GE>	vollständige Gerade *f*	droite *f* complète	полная прямая
	complete subcategory <CA>	*s.* F 721		
C 1575	**complete symmetry** <EG, FA>	Vollsymmetrie *f*, vollständige (vollkommene) Symmetrie *f*	symétrie *f* complète	полная симметрия
	complete system <AG>	*s.* C 1453		
	complete system of events <ST>	*s.* C 1565		
C 1576	**complete system of fractions** <NT>	vollständiges System *n* echter Brüche	système *m* complet de fractions	полная система дробей
C 1577	**complete system of functions,** complete set of functions; closed system (set) of functions <AN>	vollständiges Funktionensystem *n*; abgeschlossenes Funktionensystem	système *m* complet de fonctions; système fermé de fonctions	полная система функций; замкнутая система функций
C 1578	**complete system of invariants** <DG, GR, IV>	vollständiges Invariantensystem <DG, GR, IV>; volles Invariantensystem (System *n* von Komitanten) <IV>	système *m* complet d'invariants	полная система инвариантов

	complete system of representatives <AL>	*s.* C 1570		
C 1579	**complete tangent,** tangent <to a set> <GE>	Volltangente *f*, Tangente *f* <an eine Menge>	tangente *f* <à un ensemble>	касательная <к множеству>
C 1580	**complete tensor product** <of sheaves> <AL, TO>	vollständiges Tensorprodukt *n*	produit *m* tensoriel total	полное тензорное произведение
C 1581	**complete theory** <MM>	vollständige Theorie *f*	théorie *f* saturée (complète)	полная теория
C 1582	**complete theory** <MM>	deduktiv vollständige Theorie *f*	théorie *f* complète	дедуктивно полная теория
C 1583	**complete topological group,** complete group <with respect to topology> <GR>	vollständige topologische Gruppe *f*, vollständige Gruppe	groupe *m* [topologique] complet	полная [топологическая] группа
C 1584	**complete upper semilattice** <AL>	vollständiger ∪-Halbverband (Vereinigungshalbverband) *m*	sup-demi-treillis (sup demi-treillis) *m* complet	полная верхняя полурешетка
	σ-complete upper semilattice <AL>	*s.* S 820		
C 1585	**complete wreath product,** wreath product <GR>	uneingeschränktes (vollständiges) Kranzprodukt *n*, Kranzprodukt	couronne *f* complète, couronne	полное сплетение, сплетение
	completing of the square <AL>	*s.* C 1595		
C 1586	**completion** <of a field *or* ring> <AL>	Komplettierung *f*, Vervollständigung *f*, vollständige (perfekte) Hülle *f*	complété *m*	пополнение
C 1587	**completion** <of a local ring> <AL>	Komplettierung *f*, Vervollständigung *f*, komplette Hülle *f*, vervollständigter (komplettierter) lokaler Ring *m*	complété *m*, anneau *m* local complété	пополнение, полная оболочка
C 1588	**completion** <of a topological group *or* ring> <AL, CA>	Vervollständigung *f*, vollständige Hülle *f*	complété *m*	пополнение, полная оболочка
C 1589	**completion** <as an operation> <AL, CA, TO>	Vervollständigung *f*	complétion *f*	пополнение
C 1590	**completion** <of a presheaf> <AL, TO>	Vervollständigung *f*	complété *m*	пополнение
C 1591	**completion** <of a metric, normed, *or* proximity space>; Banach completion <of a normed space> <TO>	Vervollständigung *f*, vollständige Hülle *f*, vervollständigter Raum *m*	espace *m* complété, complété *m*	пополненное пространство, пополнение
C 1592	**completion** <of a uniform space> <TO>	vollständige Hülle *f*, Vervollständigung *f*, Komplettierung *f*, komplette Hülle	complété *m*	пополнение, полная оболочка
	ω-completion <MM>	*s.* O 65		
	completion by cuts <SE>	*s.* D 83		
C 1593	**completion of a field with respect to a metric** <AL>	Komplettierung *f* eines Körpers für eine Metrik, Vervollständigung *f* eines Körpers bezüglich einer Metrik	complété *m* d'un corps pour une métrique	пополнение поля по метрике
C 1594	**completion of a valued field** <AL>	perfekte Hülle *f* eines Körpers mit Bewertung, Komplettierung *f* eines Körpers für eine Bewertung, Vervollständigung *f* eines bewerteten Körpers	complété *m* d'un corps pour une valuation	пополнение поля по показателю
C 1595	**completion of the square,** quadratic supplement; completing of the square <AL>	quadratische Ergänzung *f*, Ergänzung zum vollständigen Quadrat	complément *m* au carré total	дополнение до полного квадрата, дополнение до квадрата
	completion theorem of Lindenbaum <LO>	*s.* L 770		
C 1596	**complex** <of a group *or* groupoid> <AL, GR>	Komplex *m*	partie *f* [non vide], complexe *m*	комплекс
C 1597	**complex,** abstract complex <AT>	orientierter Komplex *m* <Tucker>	complexe *m* orienté	d-комплекс, клеточный (ориентированный) комплекс
C 1598	**complex,** sequence of order two <*e.g.*: of degree *s*> <CA, HA>	Komplex *m*, Sequenz *f* der Ordnung 2 <*z. B.*: vom Grade *s*>	complexe *m* <*par exemple*: de degré *s*>	комплекс <*например*: степени *s*>
C 1599	**complex,** complex of elements <SE>	[mengentheoretischer] Komplex *m*, Elementekomplex *m*, Elementkomplex *m*	complexe *m* [d'éléments]	комплекс [элементов]
	complex <GE>	*s.* 1. C 1633; 2. C 1635		
	1-complex <AT, GP>	*s.* T 517		
	complex analysis <FT>	*s.* F 782		
C 1600	**complex analytic fibre bundle** <AT>	holomorphes (komplexanalytisches) Faserbündel *n*	espace *m* fibré analytique	комплексно-аналитическое расслоение
	complex analytic function <DG>	*s.* H 404		
	complex analytic line bundle <AT>	*s.* C 1627		
	complex analytic manifold <DG>	*s.* H 406		
	complex analytic mapping <FT>	*s.* H 407		
C 1601	**complex analytic structure** <in a Hausdorff space> <TO>	komplex-analytische Struktur *f*	structure *f* analytique[-] complexe	комплексно-аналитическая структура

No.	English	German	French	Russian
	complex analytic transformation <FT>	*s.* H 407		
C 1602	**complex binary domain** <PJ>	binäres komplexes Gebiet *n*, komplex-binäres Gebiet, eindimensionales komplexes Gebiet	domaine *m* binaire complexe	комплексная бинарная область
C 1603	**complex cone,** cone of the complex <GE>	Komplexkegel *m*, Kegel *m* <des Strahlenkomplexes>	cône *m* du complexe	конус комплекса
C 1604	**complex conjugate,** conjugate [complex], conjugate imaginary <AL, FT>	konjugiert-komplex, konjugiert komplex, konjugiertkomplex, [komplex] konjugiert, konj. kom.	complexe conjugué, imaginaire conjugué, conjugué complexe, conjugué	комплексно сопряженный, мнимо сопряженный, сопряженный
C 1605	**complex conjugate** <of a matrix>, [complex] conjugate matrix <MD>	konjugiert[]komplexe Matrix *f*, [komplex] konjugierte Matrix *f*	matrice *f* [imaginaire] conjuguée, conjuguée *f*	сопряженная матрица
C 1606	**complex conjugate character** <NT>	konjugiert[]komplexer Charakter *m*	caractère *m* complexe et conjugué, caractère *m* imaginaire conjugué, caractère opposé	комплексно сопряженный характер
	complex conjugate matrix <MD>	*s.* C 1605		
	complex conjugate transpose <MD>	*s.* H 235		
	complex conjugation <FT>	*s.* C 1961		
C 1607	**complex constructive dilemma;** law of compound constructive dilemma <LO>	zusammengesetztes konstruktives Dilemma *n*	dilemme *m* constructif composé	сложная конструктивная дилемма; формула сложной конструктивной дилеммы
	complex co-ordinates <DG>	*s.* C 2429		
C 1608	**complex curve** <GE>	Komplexkurve *f*	courbe *f* du complexe	кривая комплекса
C 1609	**complex curvilinear integral** <FT>	komplexes Kurvenintegral *n*, Integral *n* einer komplexen Funktion	intégrale *f* curviligne complexe	интеграл комплексной функции
C 1610	**complex destructive dilemma** <LO>	zusammengesetztes destruktives Dilemma *n*	dilemme *m* destructif composé	сложная деструктивная дилемма
	complex domain <AL>	*s.* C 1614		
C 1611	**complex domain / in the** <GN>	im Komplexen	dans le complexe	в комплексной области
	complex experiment <ST>	*s.* F 34		
C 1612	**complex extension** <of a Lie group> <GR>	Komplexifizierung *f*	complexification *f*	комплексная оболочка, комплексификация
C 1613	**complex extension [algebra]** <of a Lie algebra> <AL>	Komplexifizierung *f*	complexification *f*	комплексная оболочка, комплексификация
C 1614	**complex field,** complex domain, field of complex numbers <AL>	Körper *m* der komplexen Zahlen	corps *m* des [nombres] complexes, corps complexe	поле комплексных чисел
C 1615	**complex fraction,** compound fraction <numerator and denominator of which are fractions> <AL, AR>	zusammengesetzter Bruch *m*, Bruch von Brüchen, Doppelbruch *m*, Bruchbruch *m*	fraction *f* de fraction, fraction complexe (double)	сложная («многоэтажная», составная, «четырехэтажная») дробь
	complex function <FT>	*s.* C 1650		
	complex geometry <GE>	*s.* G 279		
	complex group <GR>	*s.* S 2479		
	complex having the same combinatorial type <AT>	*s.* I 1116		
	complex hull <AL, FA>	*s.* C 1618		
C 1616	**complexification** <of a bundle> <AT>	komplexe Erweiterung *f*, Komplexifizierung *f*	complexification *f*	комплексификация, комплексное расширение
C 1617	**complexification** <of a variety> <TO>	Komplexifizierung *f*	complexifié *m*	комплексификация
C 1618	**complexification,** complex hull <of a vector space> <AL, FA>	Komplexifikation *f*, Komplexifizierung *f*	complexification *f*, complexifié *m*	комплексификация, комплексная оболочка
C 1619	**complexified vector space** <AL, FA>	komplexifizierter (komplex erweiterter) Vektorraum *m*	espace *m* vectoriel complexifié	комплексифицированное (полученное комплексификацией) векторное пространство
	complex integer <NT>	*s.* G 75		
C 1620	**complexion** <common name of permutation, arrangement and combination> <CT>	Komplexion *f*	complexion *f*	соединение
	complexion, repetition[s] allowed <CT>	*s.* C 1622		
	complexion, repetition[s] not allowed <CT>	*s.* C 1621		
C 1621	**complexion without repetition[s];** complexion, repetition[s] not allowed; combination without repetition[s]; combination, repetition[s] not allowed <*in the general sense:* combination, arrangement, *or* permutation> <CT>	Komplexion (Kombination) *f* ohne Wiederholung	complexion *f* sans répétitions	соединение без повторений
C 1622	**complexion with repe-**	Komplexion (Kombination)	complexion *f* avec répé-	соединение с повторе-

No.	English	German	French	Russian
	tition[s] [allowed]; complexion, repetition[s] allowed; combination with repetition[s] [allowed]; combination, repetition[s] allowed <*in the general sense:* combination, arrangement, *or* permutation> <CT>	*f* mit Wiederholung	titions	ниями
C 1623	**complexity** <MM>	Komplexität *f*	complexité *f*	сложность
C 1624	**complex line,** complex ray <AY, DG>	Komplexstrahl *m*, Komplexgerade *f*	droite *f* (rayon *m*) du complexe	прямая (луч) комплекса
C 1625	**complex-linearly dependent** <AL, AN>	komplex-linear abhängig, komplexlinear abhängig, linear abhängig über dem Körper der komplexen Zahlen	linéairement dépendant sur le corps complexe	комплексно-линейно зависимый
C 1626	**complex linearly independent** <AL>	komplex-linear unabhängig, komplexlinear unabhängig, linear unabhängig über dem Körper der komplexen Zahlen	linéairement indépendant sur le corps complexe	комплексно-линейно независимый
C 1627	**complex line bundle,** complex analytic line bundle <AT>	komplex-analytisches Geradenbündel *n*, komplexes Geradenbündel	fibré *m* (espace *m* fibré) analytique complexe <de fibre *C* associé à un espace fibré analytique complexe principal de fibre *C**, le groupe *C** opérant dans *C* au moyen de la multiplication>	комплексно-аналитическое векторное расслоение на прямые, одномерное комплексно-аналитическое векторное расслоение
C 1628	**complex logic** <LO>	komplexe Logik *f*	logique *f* complexe	комплексная логика
C 1629	**complex multiplication** <of an Abelian *or* elliptic function> <AB, AL, FT>	komplexe Multiplikation *f*	multiplication *f* complexe	комплексное умножение
C 1630	**complex multiplication** <AL>	Komplexmultiplikation *f*	multiplication *f* de complexes	умножение комплексов
C 1631	**complex *n*-plane bundle,** complex vector bundle <AT>	komplexes Vektorraumbündel *n*	espace *m* fibré à fibre vectorielle complexe	комплексное *n*-мерное векторное расслоение
C 1632	**complex number,** imaginary number <AL>	komplexe Zahl *f*, gemeine komplexe Zahl (Größe *f*), [gewöhnliche] komplexe Größe, imaginäre Größe (Zahl)	nombre *m* (quantité *f*) complexe, nombre complexe ordinaire, complexe *m*, nombre (quantité) imaginaire, nombre (quantité) mixte, nombre (quantité) intermédiane	комплексное (мнимое) число, комплексное число гиперболического типа
	complex number plane <FT>	*s.* A 937		
C 1633	**complex of curves,** complex <GE>	Kurvenkomplex *m*, Komplex *m*	complexe *m* de courbes, complexe	комплекс кривых, комплекс
C 1634	**complex of elements,** variety of elements <DE, GE>	Elementverein *m*, Streifenmannigfaltigkeit *f*, Elementmannigfaltigkeit *f*	association *f* d'éléments, variété *f* d'éléments	многообразие полос[ок], комплекс элементов
	complex of elements <SE>	*s.* C 1599		
C 1635	**complex of lines,** complex of rays, rectilinear complex, complex <GE>	Strahlenkomplex *m*, Geradenkomplex *m*, Komplex *m*	complexe *m* de droites, complexe linéaire, complexe	комплекс прямых (лучей), комплекс
	complex of principal normals <DG>	*s.* P 1451		
	complex of rays <GE>	*s.* C 1635		
C 1636	**complex of segments** <TO>	Streckenkomplex *m*	complexe *m* de segments	отрезочный комплекс, комплекс отрезков, линейный комплекс
	complex optimization <PG>	*s.* C 1639		
	complex plane <FT>	*s.* A 937		
C 1637	**complex plane except *k* points,** complex plane with exclusion of *k* points, plane [of complex numbers] with exclusion of *k* points <FT>	*k*-fach punktierte Ebene *f*, *k*-fach punktierte [komplexe] Zahlenebene *f*	plan *m* [complexe] privé de *k* points, plan des nombres [complexes] troué *k* fois, plan des nombres [complexes] privé de *k* points	комплексная плоскость с *k* выколотыми точками, [комплексная] плоскость без *k* точек, [комплексная] плоскость с *k* дырками
C 1638	**complex plane except one point,** complex plane with exclusion of one point, plane [of complex numbers] with exclusion of one point, punctured [complex] plane <FT>	punktierte Ebene *f*, punktierte [komplexe] Zahlenebene *f*	plan [complexe] privé d'un point, plan des nombres [complexes] troué (privé d'un point)	комплексная плоскость с выколотой точкой, [комплексная] плоскость без одной точки, [комплексная] плоскость с дыркой
	complex plane with exclusion of *k* points <FT>	*s.* C 1637		
	complex plane with exclusion of one point <FT>	*s.* C 1638		
	complex process <SP>	*s.* C 1641		
C 1639	**complex programming,** complex optimization; competitive programming (optimization) <PG>	komplexe Optimierung (Programmoptimierung, Programmierung) *f*; konkurrierende Optimierung (Programmoptimierung, Programmierung)	programmation (optimisation) *f* complexe; programmation (optimisation) compétitive	сложное программирование; конкурирующее программирование
C 1640	**complex quantity** <FT>	komplexe Größe *f*	quantité *f* complexe (imaginaire)	комплексная величина

C 1641	**complex random process,** complex [stochastic] process <SP>	komplexer stochastischer Prozeß *m*, komplexer Prozeß	processus *m* aléatoire complexe	комплексный стохастический процесс
	complex rational number <AL>	*s.* G 79		
	complex ray <AY, DG>	*s.* C 1624		
C 1642	**complex rotation group** <GR>	komplexe Drehgruppe *f*	groupe *m* des rotations complexe, groupe orthogonal unimodulaire	комплексная группа вращений
C 1643	**complex sphere** <AY, DG>	Komplexkugel *f*	sphère *f* du complexe	сфера комплекса
	complex sphere <FT>	*s.* R 1030		
C 1644	**complex sphere except *k* points,** complex sphere with exclusion of *k* points, sphere of complex numbers with exclusion of *k* points <FT>	*k*-fach punktierte Kugel (Zahlenkugel) *f*, *k*-fach punktierte Riemannsche (komplexe) Zahlenkugel	sphère *f* de Riemann privée de *k* points, sphère des nombres [complexes] trouée *k* fois, sphère des nombres [complexes] privée de *k* points	числовая сфера с *k* выколотыми точками, числовая сфера без *k* точек, числовая точка с *k* дырками
C 1645	**complex sphere except one point,** complex sphere with exclusion of one point, sphere of complex numbers with exclusion of one point, punctured sphere <FT>	punktierte Kugel *f*, punktierte [Riemannsche] Zahlenkugel *f*, punktierte komplexe Zahlenkugel	sphère *f* de Riemann privée d'un point, sphère des nombres [complexes] trouée (privée d'un point)	числовая сфера с выколотой точкой, числовая сфера без одной точки, числовая сфера с дыркой
	complex sphere with exclusion of *k* points <FT>	*s.* C 1644		
	complex sphere with exclusion of one point <FT>	*s.* C 1645		
	complex stochastic process <SP>	*s.* C 1641		
C 1646	**complex surface** <DG>	Komplexfläche *f*	surface *f* du complexe	поверхность комплекса
C 1647	**complex symbol** <IV>	Komplexsymbol *n*, antikommutatives Symbol *n*	symbole *m* complexe	комплексный символ
C 1648	**complex unit** <FT>	unimodulare Zahl *f*, komplexe Einheit *f*	unité *f* complexe	унимодулярное число
C 1649	**complex unitary group** <U_n (**C**)> <GR>	komplexe unitäre Gruppe *f*	groupe *m* unitaire	комплексная унитарная группа
C 1650	**complex valued function,** complex function <FT>	komplexwertige (komplexe) Funktion *f*	fonction *f* à valeurs complexes, fonction complexe	комплекснозначная (комплексная) функция
	complex vector bundle <AT>	*s.* C 1631		
C 1651	**component,** connected component <of a groupoid> <AL>	Zusammenhangskomponente *f*, Komponente *f*	composante *f* connexe	компонента, связная компонента
C 1652	**component** <of a quaternion> <AL>	Koeffizient *m*, Komponente *f*	composante *f*	коэффициент
C 1653	**component,** connected component <of a topological group> <AL>	Komponente *f*	composante *f* connexe	связная компонента
C 1654	**component** <of a complex> <AT>	Komponente *f*, Zusammenhangskomponente *f*, Bestandteil *m*	composante *f* connexe	компонента
C 1655	**component** <of an element in a direct product> <GR>	Komponente *f*, Konstituent *m*	composante *f*	компонента
C 1656	**component,** element <of a logical connective> <LO>	Glied *n*	terme *m*	член
C 1657	**component** <of a relation> <SE>	zusammenhängende Komponente *f* <einer Relation>	composante *f* connexe <d'une relation>	связная компонента <отношения>
C 1658	**component,** connected component <of a topological space> <TO>	Komponente *f*, Zusammenhangskomponente *f*, Bestandteil *m*	composante *f* connexe, composante	связная компонента, компонента, композанта
C 1659	**component,** component vector <of a vector, being itself a vector> <VT>	Komponente *f*	composante *f* vectorielle	компонента, составляющая
C 1660	**component,** co-ordinate <of a tensor with respect to a co-ordinate system> <VT>	Komponente *f*, Koordinate *f*, Bestimmungszahl *f* <eines Tensors bezüglich einer Basis>	composante *f*, coordonnée *f* <d'un tenseur par rapport à une base>	компонента, координата <тензора в данном базисе>
	component <AN, NU>	*s.* H 89		
	component <DG>	*s.* C 2056		
	component <FA, VT>	*s.* C 2419		
	component <GP>	*s.* 1. B 752; 2. M 229		
	component <LO>	*s.* 1. M 381; 2. M 382; 3. P 186		
C 1661	**component analysis** <ST>	Komponentenanalyse *f*	analyse *f* des composantes	компонентный анализ
	component analysis <ST>	*s.* F 23		
	component of a disjunction <LO>	*s.* P 205		
C 1662	**component of error** <ST>	Komponente *f* des Fehlers	composante *f* de l'erreur	компонента ошибки
C 1663	**component of *n*-th degree (order)** <of regression> <ST>	Komponente *f* *n*-ter Ordnung, Komponente *n*-ten Grades <der Regression>	composante *f* d'ordre *n*, composante de l'ordre *n* <de la régression>	компонента *n*-го порядка <регрессии>
C 1664	**component of the affine connection,** affine connection component <DG>	Komponente *f* des affinen Zusammenhangs	composante *f* de la connexion affine	компонента аффинной связности
	component of the first degree (order) <ST>	*s.* L 778		
C 1665	**component of the identity** <of a topological group> <GR>	zusammenhängende Komponente *f* des Einselements, Komponente des Einselements	composante *f* neutre	нейтральная компонента, компонента единицы, связная компонента единицы

C 1666	**component of the projective connection,** projective connection component <DG>	Komponente *f* des projektiven Zusammenhangs	composante *f* de la connexion projective	компонента проективной связности
	component of the second degree (order) <ST>	*s.* Q 20		
C 1667	**component of variance,** variance component <ST>	Varianzkomponente *f*	composante *f* de variance	компонента дисперсии
C 1668	**component projector** <FA>	Komponentenprojektor *m*, Komponentenprojektion	projecteur *m* de composante	оператор проектирования компоненты
	component vector <VT>	*s.* C 1659		
C 1669	**componentwise convergence,** convergence by components, convergence component by component, co-ordinatewise (pointwise) convergence <FA, TO>	komponentenweise Konvergenz *f*, koordinatenweise Konvergenz	convergence *f* par composantes (coordonnées)	сходимость по компонентам, покомпонентная сходимость, сходимость по координатам, покоординатная сходимость
C 1670	**componentwise multiplication** <AL>	komponentenweise Multiplikation *f*	multiplication *f* composante par composante	покомпонентное умножение
C 1671	**composable arrows,** composable pair of arrows <CA>	zusammensetzbare Morphismen *mpl*, zusammensetzbares Paar *n* von Pfeilen	morphismes *mpl* composables	компонируемые морфизмы
	composable pair of arrows <CA>	*s.* C 1671		
C 1672	**composable sequence** <of length *n*> <AT, CA>	komponierbare Sequenz *f* <der Länge *n*>	suite *f* composable <de longueur *n*>	компонируемая последовательность <длины *n*>
C 1673	**composite,** product, composition <of morphisms *or* arrows> <CA>	Produkt *n*, Kompositum *n*, Produktmorphismus *m*	composé *m*, morphisme *m* composé, composition *f*, application-composition *f*	композиция, произведение [морфизмов]
C 1674	**composite** <of graphs> <GP>	relatives Produkt *n* <von Graphen>	produit *m* simple, composé *m* <de graphes>	композиция <графов>
	composite <AL>	*s.* 1. C 1724; 2. C 1725		
	composite <SE, UA>	*s.* R 767		
	composite <AN, SE, TO>	*s.* P 1595		
C 1675	**composite arrow** <in a diagram scheme> <CA>	Weg *m*	chemin *m*	путь
	composite chain <SP>	*s.* C 1682		
	composite distribution <ST>	*s.* C 1729		
C 1676	**composite divisor** <of a number> <NT>	zusammengesetzter Divisor (Teiler) *m*	diviseur *m* composé	составной делитель
C 1677	**composite equation** <AL>	zusammengesetzte Gleichung *f*	équation *f* composée	сложное уравнение
C 1678	**composite function,** function of a function, product function <AN>	mittelbare (zusammengesetzte, verkettete) Funktion *f*, Funktion einer Funktion, Funktionenfunktion, Funktionsfunktion *f*	fonction *f* composée (de fonction, superposée, produit), composé *m* <de fonctions>	сложная функция, функция от функции, композиция функций
	composite function <AN, SE, TO>	*s.* P 1595		
C 1679	**composite functor** <CA>	zusammengesetzter Funktor *m*, Produktfunktor *m*	foncteur *m* composé	сложный (составной) функтор
C 1680	**composite group** <GR>	zusammengesetzte (nichteinfache) Gruppe *f*	groupe *m* composé	составная группа
C 1681	**composite hypothesis** <ST>	zusammengesetzte Hypothese *f*	hypothèse *f* composée	сложная (составная) гипотеза
	composite mapping <AN, SE, TO>	*s.* P 1595		
C 1682	**composite Markov chain,** composite chain <SP>	zusammengesetzte [Markovsche] Kette *f*	chaîne *f* [markovienne] composée	сложная (составная) цепь [Маркова]
C 1683	**composite matrix** <AL>	in ein Produkt zerlegbare Matrix *f*	matrice *f* factorisable	составная матрица
C 1684	**composite nomogram (nomograph)** <NO>	zusammengesetztes Nomogramm *n*	nomogramme *m* composé	составная номограмма
C 1685	**composite number** <NT>	zusammengesetzte Zahl *f*, Nichtprimzahl *f*, zerlegbare Zahl, // geometrische Zahl	nombre *m* composé (non premier, décomposable), // nombre géométrique	составное число
C 1686	**composite polynomial** <AL, AN>	zusammengesetztes Polynom *n*	polynôme *m* composé	композиция многочленов
C 1687	**composite probability** <ST>	zusammengesetzte Wahrscheinlichkeit *f*	probabilité *f* composée	полная вероятность
	composite process <SP>	*s.* C 1688		
	composite statement <LO>	*s.* C 1745		
C 1688	**composite stochastic process,** composite process <SP>	zusammengesetzter [stochastischer] Prozeß *m*	processus *m* [aléatoire] composé	сложный (составной) [случайный] процесс
C 1689	**composition** <of a nonnegative integer> <AB>	Komposition *f*, Zergliederung *f*, Zerfällung *f*	composition *f*	композиция
C 1690	**composition** <of specializations, covariants, substitutions, *or* games> <AG, AL, TG>	Zusammensetzung *f*	composition *f*	композиция
C 1691	**composition,** combination <AL>	Verknüpfung *f*, Komposition *f*, Zusammensetzung *f*	composition *f*	композиция
C 1692	**composition,** product <of an algebraic composition> <AL>	Kompositum *n*, Produkt *n*	composé *m* <pour une loi de composition>	составной элемент <полученный в результате алгебраической операции>

C 1693	**composition** <of fields *or* quadratic forms> <AL>	Komposition *f*	composition *f*	композиция
C 1694	**composition,** product <of words> <AL>	Produkt *n*	produit *m*	композиция, произведение
C 1695	**composition,** multiplication <of permutations> <AL, CT>	Zusammensetzung *f*, Multiplikation *f* <von Permutationen>	composition *f* <de permutations>	умножение <перестановок>
C 1696	**composition** <in a proportion>, corresponding addition <AR>	korrespondierende Addition *f*	transition *f* <de la proportion $a : b = c : d$ > à la proportion $(a + b) : b = (c + d) : d$	переход <от пропорции $a : b = c : d$> к производной пропорции $(a + b) : b = (c + d) : d$
C 1697	**composition** <of arrows *or* morphisms> <CA>	Verknüpfung *f*, Komposition *f*	composition *f*, application *f* de composition	композиция
C 1698	**composition** <of functors> <CA>	Produkt *n* <von Funktoren>	foncteur *m* composé	композиция <функторов>
C 1699	**composition** <of graphs> <GP>	relative Multiplikation *f* <von Graphen>	composition *f* <de graphes>	образование композиции <графов>
C 1700	**composition** <of classes of quadratic forms> <NT>	Zusammensetzung *f*, Komposition *f*	composition *f*	композиция
C 1701	**composition** <of applications> <SE>	Hintereinanderausführung *f*, Verkettung *f*, Nacheinanderausführung *f*, Hintereinanderschaltung *f*, Zusammensetzung *f* <von Abbildungen>	composition *f* <d'applications>	последовательное выполнение, композиция, последовательное применение <отображений>
C 1702	**composition,** relative multiplication <of binary relations> <SE>	Multiplikation *f*	composition *f*	операция композиции
	composition <AN, SE, TO>	*s.* P 1595		
	composition <CA>	*s.* C 1673		
	composition <GR>	*s.* W 297		
	composition <SE, UA>	*s.* R 767		
	composition <TO>	*s.* P 1627		
	composition <VT>	*s.* I 557		
C 1703	**composition algebra** <of quadratic forms> <AL>	Kompositionsalgebra *f*	algèbre *f* des compositions	композиционная алгебра
C 1704	**composition and division** <in a proportion>, corresponding addition and subtraction <AR>	korrespondierende Addition *f* und Subtraktion *f*	transition *f* <de la proportion $a : b = c : d$ > à la proportion $(a + b) : (a - b) = (c + d) : (c - d)$	переход <от пропорции $a : b = c : d$> к производной пропорции $(a + b) : (a - b) = (c + d) : (c - d)$
C 1705/6	**composition chain** <of a group> <GR>	Kompositionskette *f*, Normalreihe *f* <Zassenhaus>, Kompositionssystem *n* <von Untergruppen>	suite *f* de composition	композиционная система, цепь композиций
	┌<GR> **composition difference**	*s.* C 1707		
C 1707	**composition[-] factor** <in the case of groups>; composition difference <in the case of modules> <of a composition series> <GR>	Kompositionsfaktor *m*, Primfaktor *m*, Primfaktorgruppe *f*, Faktor *m*, // Faktor der Zusammensetzung	quotient *m* de Jordan-Hölder, quotient d'une suite de composition, facteur *m* premier, groupe *m* facteur premier	композиционный фактор
C 1708	**composition function** <AB>	Kompositionsfunktion *f*, Kompositionsanzahlfunktion *f*, Zerfällungsfunktion *f*	fonction *f* de composition	функция композиции
C 1709	**composition homomorphism** <AL>	Produkthomomorphismus *m*, Produkt *n* <von Homomorphismen>	homomorphisme *m* composé, composé *m* d'homomorphismes	композиция (произведение) гомоморфизмов, сквозной гомоморфизм
C 1710	**composition homomorphism** <UA>	Kompositionshomomorphismus *m*	homomorphisme *m* de composition	композиционный гомоморфизм
C 1711	**composition law admitting left cancellation** <AL>	linksreguläre Verknüpfung *f*	loi *f* de composition admettant simplification à gauche	операция, допускающая сокращение слева
C 1712	**composition law admitting right cancellation** <AL>	rechtsreguläre Verknüpfung *f*	loi *f* de composition admettant simplification à droite	операция, допускающая сокращение справа
C 1713	**composition law compatible with an equivalence relation** <AL>	mit einer Äquivalenzrelation verträgliches Kompositionsgesetz *n*	loi *f* stable pour une équivalence	операция, совместная с отношением эквивалентности
	composition mapping <AN, SE, TO>	*s.* P 1595		
C 1714	**composition matrix,** combination matrix <AL>	Verknüpfungsmatrix *f*	matrice *f* de composition (combinaison)	матрица связи (композиции), связывающая матрица
C 1715	**composition of natural transformations** <CA>	Produkt *n* natürlicher Transformationen	morphisme *m* fonctoriel composé	произведение естественных преобразований
C 1716	**composition operator** <RF>	Kompositionsoperator *m*	opérateur *m* de composition	оператор композиции
C 1717	**composition product** <of graphs> <GP>	Kompositionsprodukt *n*	produit *m* direct	композиция
	composition product <AN, SE, TO>	*s.* P 1595		
C 1718	**composition ring** <AL>	Kompositionsring *m*	anneau *m* de composition	композиционное кольцо
C 1719	**composition[-] series** <AL>	Kompositionsreihe *f*, Jordansche Kompositionsreihe, // Reihe *f* der Zusammensetzung	suite *f* de composition au sens de C. Jordan, suite de Jordan (Jordan-Hölder, composition), série *f* de composition (composition sans répétition), chaine *f* de composition	композиционный ряд, ряд композиций (Жордана-Гельдера)
C 1720	**composition subgroup,** accessible subgroup <GR>	nachinvariante (erreichbare, subnormale, nach-	sous-groupe *m* sous-normal, sous-groupe sous-	достижимая (субнормальная, субинвариантная)

		normale) Untergruppe *f*, Subnormalteiler *m*, subinvariante Untergruppe	invariant	подгруппа
C 1721	**composition symbol** <AL>	Verknüpfungssymbol *n*, Kompositionssymbol *n*	symbole *m* de composition	символ композиции
C 1722	**composition with *g* on the right** <for a hom functor> <CA>	rechtsseitige Komposition *f* mit *g*	composition *f* avec *g* à droite	композиция с *g* справа
C 1723	**composition with *k* on the left,** map induced by *k* <for a hom functor> <CA>	linksseitige Komposition *f* mit *k*, durch *k* induzierte Abbildung *f*	composition *f* avec *k* à gauche	композиция с *k* слева
C 1724	**compositum,** composite <of fields> <AL>	Kompositum *n*, Körperkompositum *n*	borne *f* supérieure, corps *m* engendré par des corps, corps composé, le plus petit commun multiple *m*	составное поле, композит
C 1725	**compositum,** composite <of [field] extensions> <AL>	Kompositum *n* <von Erweiterungen, Körpererweiterungen>	extension *f* composée, composé *m* <d'extensions>	композиция <расширений [поля]>
	compound <NT>	*s.* C 1732		
C 1726/7	**compound addition** <AR>	Addition *f* benannter Zahlen	addition *f* de nombres concrets	сложение именованных чисел
	compound alignment chart (graph) <NO>	*s.* I 698		
	compound bunch [nomo]graph <NO>	*s.* C 1740		
C 1728	**compound determinant** <whose elements themselves are determinants> <MD>	zusammengesetzte Determinante *f*	déterminant *m* composé	определитель определителей
C 1729	**compound distribution,** composite (mixed) distribution, superposition of distributions <ST>	zusammengesetzte Verteilung *f*, Mischverteilung *f*, gemischte Verteilung	distribution *f* composée (complexe)	сложное (составное, смешанное) распределение
	compounded form <NT>	*s.* C 1732		
C 1730	**compounded genus** <of quadratic forms> <NT>	zusammengesetztes Geschlecht *n*	genre *m* composé	составной род
C 1731	**compounded linear system,** compounded system <AG>	zusammengesetztes [lineares] System *n*	système *m* [linéaire] composé	составная [линейная] система
C 1732	**compounded quadratic form,** compounded form, compound <NT>	zusammengesetzte [quadratische] Form *f*, komponierte quadratische Form	forme *f* [quadratique] composée	составная [квадратичная] форма, компонированная крадратичная форма
	compounded system <AG>	*s.* C 1731		
C 1733	**compound event** <ST>	zusammengesetztes Ereignis *n*	événement *m* composé	сложное (составное) событие
C 1734	**compound field extension** <AL>	zusammengesetzte (nichteinfache) Körpererweiterung *f*	extension *f* composée	составное расширение поля
C 1735	**compound form** <of a field> <AB>	zusammengesetzte Form *f*	forme *f* composée	составная форма
	compound fraction <AL, AR>	*s.* C 1615		
C 1736	**compound index** <GN>	zusammengesetzter Index *m*	indice *m* composé (synthétique)	сложный (составной) индекс
C 1737	**compound interest** <AR>	Zinseszins *m*	intérêt *m* composé (des intérêts)	сложный процент
C 1738	**compound interest account** <AR>	Zinseszinsrechnung *f*	calcul *m* des intérêts composés	исчисление сложных процентов
C 1739	**compound interest formula** <AR>	Zinseszinsformel *f*	formule *f* des intérêts composés	формула сложных процентов
	compound matrix <MD>	*s.* A 303		
C 1740	**compound nomogram [with radial lines],** compound bunch [nomo]graph <NO>	mehrteilige Netztafel *f*, Verbundnomogramm *n*, Verbundtafel *f*	abaque *m* [à radiantes] composé	составная [сетчатая] номограмма, сложная сетчатая номограмма
	compound nomogram [with points in a line] <NO>	*s.* I 698		
C 1741	**compound number** <NU>	mehrfach (zusammengesetzte) benannte Zahl *f*	nombre *m* complexe	составное именованное число; число, составленное из различных наименований
	compound perfect group of lowest possible order <GR>	*s.* B 368		
C 1742	**compound proportion** <AR>	zusammengesetzte Proportion *f*	proportion *f* composée	составная пропорция
	compound proposition <LO>	*s.* C 1745		
C 1743	**compound rule of detachment** <LO>	zusammengesetzte Abtrennungsregel *f*	règle *f* de conclusion composée	сложное правило заключения
C 1744	**compound rule of three,** conjoined rule of three, chain method <AR>	zusammengesetzte Regeldetri *f*, zusammengesetzter Dreisatz *m*, zusammengesetzte Regel *f* de tri, Kettensatzrechnung *f*, Kettenrechnung *f*, Kettenregel *f*, Kettensatz *m*, Kettenschlußregel *f*	règle *f* de trois composée, règle conjointe	сложное тройное правило, цепное правило
C 1745	**compound sentence,** compound (molecular) proposition, composite statement; sentential combination, combination of sentences <LO>	zusammengesetzte Aussage *f*, Aussagenverbindung *f*, Aussagenverknüpfung *f*	proposition *f* composée, composition *f* complexe, proposition moléculaire	сложное (молекулярное, составное) высказывание, сложное предложение

No.	English	German	French	Russian
C 1746	**compound substitution rule,** extended rule of substitution <LO>	zusammengesetzte Einsetzungsregel *f*	règle *f* de substitution composée	сложное правило подстановки
	comprehending set <SE>	*s.* I 241		
	comprehension principle <SE>	*s.* A 1283		
C 1747	**compressibility** <of a measurable transformation> <ME>	Kompressibilität *f*	compressibilité *f*	сжимаемость
C 1748	**compressible extension** <of a universal algebra> <UA>	kompressible Erweiterung *f*	extension *f* compressible	сжимаемое расширение
C 1749	**compressible measurable transformation** <ME>	kompressible meßbare Transformation *f*	transformation *f* mesurable compressible	сжимаемое измеримое преобразование
C 1750	**compression,** shrinking <GE>	Stauchung *f*, Stauchen *n*	compression *f*	сжатие
C 1751	**compression** <of a mapping> <UA>	Kompression *f*	compression *f*	сжатие
	computability theory <FO>	*s.* R 322		
C 1752	**computable decimal fraction** <FO>	berechenbarer (rekursiver) Dezimalbruch *m*	fraction *f* décimale calculable	вычислимая десятичная дробь
C 1753	**computable function,** reckonable function <MM>	berechenbare Funktion *f*	fonction *f* calculable	вычислимая (изобразимая) функция
C 1754	**computable number** <MM>	berechenbare Zahl *f*	nombre *m* calculable	вычислимое число
	computation <GN>	*s.* C 13		
C 1755	**computational** <GN>	rechnerisch	par voie de calcul	счетный
C 1756	**computational error,** computing error, computational mistake, miscalculation <ER, NU>	Rechenfehler *m*	erreur *m* (faute *f*) de calcul, erreur du calcul	ошибка в подсчете, арифметическая ошибка
	computational formula <NU>	*s.* F 495		
	computational mistake <ER, NU>	*s.* C 1756		
C 1757	**computation** <of limits etc.> **argument by argument** <CA>	argumentweise Berechnung *f*	calcul *m* argument par argument	поаргументное вычисление
C 1758	**computation by Monte Carlo method,** calculation by Monte Carlo method, Monte Carlo computation <NU, ST>	Monte-Carlo-Rechnung *f*; Monte-Carlo-Berechnung *f*	calcul *m* par la méthode de Monte-Carlo	расчет (вычисление) методом Монте Карло
	computation of adjustment <ER, NU>	*s.* C 26		
C 1759	**computer** <IN, NU>	Rechner *m*, Computer *m*, Elektronenrechner *m*, elektronische Rechenmaschine *f*, Rechenautomat *m*	calculatrice *f* [électronique], ordinateur *m*, calculateur *m* [électronique], machine *f* calculatrice électronique	электронная вычислительная машина, ЭВМ
	computer program <NU>	*s.* C 1763		
	computing check <AR, NU>	*s.* C 618		
	computing error <ER, NU>	*s.* C 1756		
	computing law <AR>	*s.* R 1498		
	computing machine <IN>	*s.* C 11		
	computing of the root <AL, AR>	*s.* T 29		
C 1760	**computing operation,** operation <NU>	Rechenoperation *f*, Operation *f*	opération *f* de calcul, opération	вычислительная операция, операция [счета]
C 1761	**computing plan** <NU>	Rechenschema *n*, Rechenplan *m*	plan *m* de calcul	план вычислений, схема вычисления
	computing program <NU>	*s.* C 1763		
C 1762	**computing result** <NU>	Rechenergebnis *n*	résultat *m* de calcul	результат вычислений
C 1763	**computing routine,** computing program, computer program <NU>	Rechenprogramm *n*	programme *m* de calcul, routine *f* de calcul	вычислительная (расчетная) программа, программа вычислений
	computing rule <GN>	*s.* C 12		
C 1764	**computing table** <NU>	Rechentafel *f*, Rechentabelle *f*	tableau *m* de calcul, table *f* à calculer	счетная (вычислительная расчетная) таблица
	computing test <AR, NU>	*s.* C 618		
	computing with logarithms <AR>	*s.* L 1032		
C 1765	**comultiplication** <AL, CA>	Komultiplikation *f*, Comultiplikation *f*	comultiplication *f*	коумножение
C 1766	**concatenation** <*e.g.:* of words> <AL, LO>	Verkettung *f*, Hintereinanderschreiben *n* <*z. B.:* von Wörtern>	concaténation *f* <*par exemple:* des mots>	сочленение, сцепление <*например:* слов>
C 1767	**concave angle** <EG>	konkaver Winkel *m*, hohler Winkel	angle *m* concave, angle saillant	вогнутый угол; угол, меньший развернутого
C 1768	**concave-convex game** <TG>	konkav-konvexes Spiel *n*	jeu *m* concave-convexe	вогнуто-выпуклая игра
C 1769	**concave [down] curve,** convex up curve, convex cap curve, convex ⌒ curve <AN, GE>	konkave Kurve *f*, konvexe Kurve aufwärts (nach oben), konkave Kurve abwärts (nach unten), von unten hohle Kurve	courbe *f* concave, courbe convexe vers le haut, courbe concave vers le bas	вогнутая кривая, выпуклая кверху кривая, вогнутая книзу кривая

No.	English	German	French	Russian
C 1770	**concave function,** convex cap function, convex ⌢ functinn <AN>	konkave Funktion *f*, von oben konvexe Funktion	fonction *f* concave	вогнутая функция
C 1771	**concave *n*-gon (polygon)** <GE>	konkaves Vieleck *n*, konkaves *n*-Eck *n*	polygone *m* concave, *n*-gone *m* concave	невыпуклый многоугольник, невыпуклый *n*-угольник
	concave programming <PG>	*s.* C 2401		
	concave up curve <AN, GE>	*s.* C 2388		
C 1772	**concavity,** convexity upward, concavity downward <AN, GE>	Konkavität *f*, Konvexität *f* von oben, Konkavität von unten	concavité *f*, convexité *f* dirigée vers le haut, concavité dirigée vers le bas	вогнутость, выпуклость кверху, вогнутость книзу
C 1773	**concavity coefficient** <of a gauge body> <GU>	Konkavitätskoeffizient *m*	coefficient *m* de concavité	коэффициент вогнутости
	concavity downward <AN, GE>	*s.* C 1772		
	concavity upward <AN, GE>	*s.* C 2395		
	concentrated mass <ME>	*s.* P 753		
C 1774	**concentrated space** <in the neighbourhood of a subset> <TO>	konzentrierter Raum *m* <auf Umgebung einer Untermenge>	espace *m* concentré <autour d'un ensemble>	сосредоточенное пространство <вокруг подмножества>
C 1775	**concentration ellipse** <ST>	Konzentrationsellipse *f*	ellipse *f* de concentration	эллипс кучности, эллипс рассеяния для $c^2 = 4$
C 1776	**concentration interval** <ST>	Konzentrationsintervall *n*	intervalle *m* de concentration	интервал кучности
	concentration measure <ST>	*s.* M 338		
C 1777	**concentric conics (conic sections)** <AY>	konzentrische Kegelschnitte *mpl*	coniques *fpl* (sections *fpl* coniques) concentriques	концентрические конические сечения
C 1778	**concept of infinity (the infinite),** notion of the infinite <GN>	Begriff *m* des Unendlichen	concept *m* (notion *f*) de l'infini	понятие бесконечности
C 1779	**conchoid** <GE>	Konchoide *f*, Muschellinie *f*	conchoïde *f*	конхоида
C 1780	**conchoidal branch** <of a cubic> <AG>	konchoidaler Zweig *m*	branche *f* conchoïdale	конхоидальная ветвь
C 1781	**conchoidal motion (movement)** <GE>	konchoidale Bewegung *f*	mouvement *m* conchoïdal	конхоидальное движение
C 1782	**conchoid of a circle** <AG>	Kreiskonchoide *f*	conchoïde *f* du (de) cercle	конхоида окружности
	conchoid of De Sluse <GE>	*s.* D 338		
C 1783	**conchoid of Dürer,** Dürer['s] conchoid <conchoid of the line with $\varphi = \pi/4$> <GE>	Muschellinie *f* von A. Dürer	conchoïde *f* de Dürer	конхоида Дюрера
C 1784	**conchoid of Nicomedes,** Nicomedes['] conchoid, Nicomedean conchoid, conchoid of the line <GE>	Konchoide *f* des (von) Nikomedes, Konchoide der Geraden, Muschellinie *f* des Nikomedes	conchoïde *f* de Nicomède (Nikomedes), conchoïde de [la] droite, conchoïde première	конхоида Никомеда, конхоида прямой
	conchoid of the circle <GE>	*s.* P 290		
	conchoid of the line <GE>	*s.* C 1784		
C 1785	**conchospiral** <GE>	Konchospirale *f*, Muschelspirale *f* <Naumann>	conchospirale *f*	конхоспираль
C 1786	**conclusion,** consequent <LO>	Conclusio *f*, Konklusion *f*, Behauptung *f*	conclusion *f*	[умо]заключение, вывод, логическое следствие, следствие
C 1786 a	**conclusion** <LO>	Schlußfolgerung *f*	conclusion *f*	вывод
C 1787	**conclusion ex absurdo** <LO>	indirekter Schluß *m*	raisonnement *m* apagogique	заключение от противного
C 1788	**concomitant** <μ-th> <of a bilinear *or* quadratic form> <AL>	Konkomitante *f*, begleitende Form *f* <Sylvester>, Begleitform *f*, Adjungierte <μ-te>	concomitant *m*, adjointe *f*, forme *f* satellite <μ-me>	конкомитант, совместный комитант, сателлит формы <μ-й>
C 1789	**concomitant** <IV>	Konkomitante *f*, Concomitante *f* <Sylvester>, Komitante *f*, Comitante *f* <Reuschle>	concomitant *m*	конкомитант
C 1790	**concomitant factor** <ST>	konkomitanter Faktor *m*	facteur *m* concomitant	сопутствующий фактор
	concomitant information <ST>	*s.* A 648		
C 1791	**concomitant variable** <ST>	konkomitante Variable *f*	variable *f* concomitante	сопутствующая переменная
C 1792	**concordant [binary quadratic] forms** <NT>	konkordante [binäre quadratische] Formen *fpl*, einige [binäre quadratische] Formen	formes *fpl* [binaires quadratiques] concordantes	согласованные [бинарные квадратичные] формы
	concordantly oriented <GE, TO>	*s.* S 876		
	concordantly oriented simplex <TO>	*s.* C 1070		
C 1793	**concrete category** <CA>	konkrete Kategorie *f*	catégorie *f* concrète	конкретная категория
	concrete estimate <ST>	*s.* E 544		
	concrete estimation region <ST>	*s.* E 549		
C 1794	**concrete number;** denominate number <AR>	benannte Zahl *f*	nombre *m* concret (nombré, dénommé)	именованное число
	concrete sample <ST>	*s.* S 16		
	concurrence <LO>	*s.* S 314		
C 1795	**concurrent,** copunctal <GE>	durch denselben (einen) Punkt [gehend], mit einem gemeinsamen Punkt	concourant, ayant un point commun	имеющий общую точку, сходящийся

C 1796	**concurrent form,** semantically equivalent form <LO>	wertverlaufsgleicher [aussagenlogischer] Ausdruck *m*, semantisch äquivalenter [aussagenlogischer] Ausdruck *m*	formule *f* sémantiquement équivalente	семантически эквивалентная формула
	concurrent [straight] lines <EG>	*s.* I 793		
C 1797	**concurrent planes,** copunctal planes <EG>	Ebenen *fpl* durch einen gemeinsamen Punkt	plans *mpl* concourants	плоскости, имеющие только одну общую точку
C 1798	**concyclic points** <GE>	konzyklische Punkte *mpl*	points *mpl* concycliques (cocycliques)	точки, лежащие на одной окружности
C 1799	**concyclic quadrics** <AY>	konzyklische Flächen *fpl* zweiter Ordnung	quadriques *fpl* concycliques	конциклические поверхности второго порядка
C 1800	**condensated set** <TO>	verdichtete Menge *f*, // verdichtete Mannigfaltigkeit *f*	ensemble *m* condensé	уплотненное множество
C 1801	**condensation continuum,** non-dense continuum containing more than one point <TO>	Kondensationskontinuum *n*, nichtdichtes Kontinuum *n* mit mehr als einem Punkt	continu *m* de condensation, continu non dense contenant plus d'un point	континуум конденсации
C 1802	**condensation of singularities** <AN>	Kondensation *f* der (von) Singularitäten <Hankel>, Verdichtung *f* der Singularitäten	condensation *f* des singularités	конденсация особенностей
	condensation point <TO>	*s.* P 757		
C 1803	**condensation point from the left** <of a sequence> <AN>	linksseitiger Verdichtungspunkt *m*	valeur *f* de condensation à gauche	левая точка сгущения
C 1804	**condensation point from the right** <of a sequence> <AN>	rechtsseitiger Verdichtungspunkt *m*	valeur *f* de condensation à droite	правая точка сгущения
C 1805	**condensation principle** <of singularities> <AN>	Kondensationsprinzip *n* <der Singularitäten>	principe *m* de condensation <des singularités>	принцип конденсации <особенностей>
	condition <DI, VA>	*s.* S 788		
	conditional <LO>	*s.* 1. M 161; 2. S 852		
	conditional — biconditional <LO>	*s.* R 1484		
C 1806	**conditional convergence** <SS>	bedingte Konvergenz *f*	convergence *f* simple (conditionnée, limitée), semi-convergence *f*	условная (обусловленная, относительная) сходимость
C 1807	**conditional definition; conditional defining** <LO>	bedingte Definition *f*	définition *f* conditionnelle	условное определение
C 1808	**conditional density [function],** conditional probability density <ST>	bedingte Wahrscheinlichkeitsdichte (Dichte, Dichtefunktion) *f*	densité *f* [de probabilité] conditionnelle, fonction *f* de densité conditionnelle	условная плотность [вероятности], условная функция плотности
C 1809	**conditional distribution [function]** <ST>	bedingte Verteilung (Wahrscheinlichkeitsverteilung, Verteilungsfunktion, Wahrscheinlichkeitsfunktion) *f*	distribution *f* conditionnelle, fonction *f* de distribution (probabilité) conditionnelle, fonction de répartition conditionnée	условное распределение, условная функция распределения
C 1810	**conditional entropy** <ST>	bedingte Entropie *f*, Kontextentropie *f*	entropie *f* conditionnelle	условная энтропия
C 1811	**conditional equation,** equation [of condition] <GN> ⌐<ER>	Bestimmungsgleichung *f*	équation *f* déterminative, égalité *f* conditionnelle	условное равенство
	conditional equation	*s.* C 1829		
C 1812	**conditional event** <ST>	bedingtes Ereignis *n*	événement *m* conditionnel	условное событие
C 1813	**conditional expectation,** projection <ST>	bedingter Erwartungswert *m*; bedingte Erwartung *f*	espérance *f* [mathématique] conditionnelle	условное математическое ожидание
C 1814	**conditional inequality** <AL, AN>	bedingte Ungleichung *f* <nur für gewisse Werte>	inégalité *f* conditionnelle	условное неравенство
C 1815	**conditionally compact set** <TO>	bedingt kompakte Menge *f*	ensemble *m* conditionnellement compact	условно (относительно) компактное множество, предкомпактное подпространство метрического пространства
	conditionally compact set <TO>	*s.* R 731		
C 1816	**conditionally complete lattice** <LA>	bedingt vollständiger Verband *m*	treillis *m* conditionnellement complet	условно полная структура
	conditionally complete set <SE>	*s.* O 290		
C 1817	**conditionally convergent continued fraction** <NT>	bedingt konvergenter Kettenbruch *m*	fraction *f* continue infinie imparfaitement convergente	условно сходящаяся цепная дробь
C 1818	**conditionally convergent series,** relatively convergent series <SS>	bedingt konvergente Reihe *f*	série *f* [simplement] convergente, série semi-convergente	условно сходящийся ряд
C 1819	**conditionally divergent continued fraction** <NT>	bedingt divergenter Kettenbruch *m*	fraction *f* continue infinie imparfaitement divergente	условно расходящаяся цепная дробь
C 1820	**conditionally stable solution** <DE>	bedingt stabile Lösung *f*	solution *f* conditionnellement stable	условно устойчивое решение
	conditional measure <ST>	*s.* C 1822		
C 1821	**conditional probability** <ST>	bedingte Wahrscheinlichkeit *f* [bezüglich *B*], Wahrscheinlichkeit unter einer Bedingung (Hypothese) *B*	probabilité *f* conditionnelle (liée, subordonnée, conditionnée)	условная вероятность
	conditional probability density <ST>	*s.* C 1808		
C 1822	**conditional probability measure,** conditional measure <ST>	bedingtes Wahrscheinlichkeitsmaß (Maß) *n*	mesure *f* [de probabilité] conditionnelle	условная [вероятностная] мера

C 1823	**conditional proposition (sentence),** hypothetical proposition, conditional statement, implication <LO>	bedingte Aussage *f*, hypothetisches Urteil *n*, Bedingungssatz *m*	jugement *m* hypothétique, proposition *f* conditionnelle	условное (импликативное) высказывание, импликативное суждение
C 1824	**conditional stability** <DE>	bedingte Stabilität *f*	stabilité *f* conditionnelle	условная устойчивость
	conditional $\supset$-symbol <LO>	*s.* S 852		
C 1825	**conditional test** <ST>	bedingter Test *m*	test *m* conditionnel	условный критерий
C 1826	**conditional variation** <VA>	Variation *f* unter Nebenbedingungen	variation *f* conditionnelle	условная вариация
C 1827	**conditioned equivalence** <LO>	bedingte Äquivalenz *f*	équivalence *f* conditionnée	условная эквивалентность
C 1828	**conditioned observation** <ER>	bedingte Beobachtung *f*	observation *f* conditionnée	обусловленное наблюдение
C 1829	**condition equation,** conditional equation <US>, equation <ER>	Bedingungsgleichung *f*	equation *f* conditionnelle (de condition)	условное уравнение; условие
C 1830	**condition for continuity** <AN>	Stetigkeitsbedingung *f*	condition *f* de continuité	условие непрерывности
C 1831	**condition of Artin-Rees,** Artin-Rees condition <AL>	Artin-Rees-Bedingung *f*	condition *f* d'Artin-Rees	условие (свойство) Артина-Риса
C 1832	**condition of Baire,** Baire['s] property, property of Baire <of a set> <TO>	Bairesche Eigenschaft *f*	propriété *f* de Baire [au sens large]	свойство Бэра [в широком смысле]
C 1833	**condition of connectedness** <TO>	Zusammenhangsbedingung *f*	condition *f* de connexion	условие связности
C 1834	**condition of effectivity** <AG, AL>	Ganzheitsbedingung *f*	condition *f* de positivité	условие эффективности
	condition of Hölder <AN>	*s.* H 385		
C 1835	**condition of identity,** axiom of identity <in a metrical space> <TO>	Identitätsaxiom *n*, Koinzidenzaxiom *n*	axiome *m* de coïncidence, condition *f* d'identité, séparation *f*	аксиома тождества
	condition of involution <DE>	*s.* I 992		
	condition of Lipschitz <DE, FA>	*s.* L 892		
C 1836	**condition of orthogonality (perpendicularity)** <AL, GE>	Orthogonalitätsbedingung *f*, Orthogonalitätsvoraussetzung *f*	condition *f* d'orthogonalité, condition de perpendicularité	условие ортогональности
C 1837	**condition of positivity** <for a metric> <TO>	Positivitätsbedingung *f*	condition *f* de positivité	условие положительности
C 1838	**condition of symmetry,** axiom of symmetry <for a metric> <TO>	Symmetrieaxiom *n*	axiome *m* (condition *f*) de symétrie, symétrie *f*	аксиома симметрии
	condition of transversality <VA>	*s.* T 869		
	conditions of integrability <AN, DG>	*s.* I 604		
	condition which ensures their conformability <MD>	*s.* C 1891		
C 1839	**conductor** <of a character mod. *m* *or* in class field theory> <AB>	Führer *m*	conducteur *m*	кондуктор, ведущий модуль
C 1840	**conductor** <in the sense of Fueter, Dedekind> <AB>	Führer *m*	conducteur *m*, guide *m*	кондуктор
C 1841	**conductor** <of a multiplicative character of a ring> <AL, NT>	Führer *m*	conducteur *m*	кондуктор, ведущий идеал
	conductor <AL>	*s.* N 282		
C 1842	**conductor-discriminant theorem** <in class field theory> <AB>	Führer-Diskriminanten-Satz *m*, Führer-Diskriminanten-Formel *f*, Führer-Diskriminanten-Produktformel *f*, Führer-Diskriminantenformel *f*, Führerdiskriminantenproduktformel *f*	Führer-Diskriminantenformel *f*, Führerdiskriminantenproduktformel *f* d'Artin	теорема о дискриминанте и ведущем модуле, формула произведения главных дискриминантов <Артина и Хассе>
C 1843	**conductor-ramification theorem** <in class field theory> <AB>	Führer-Verzweigungssatz *m*	loi *f* de conducteur	теорема кондуктора
C 1844	**cone** <of the *n*-th degree *or* of the *n*-th class> <AG>	Kegel *m* <von der *n*-ten Ordnung, *n*-ten Grades *oder* von der *n*-ten Klasse>	cône *m* <du *n*-e degré *ou* de la *n*-e classe>	конус <*n*-го порядка *или* *n*-го класса>
C 1845	**cone** <as a solid> <EG>	Kegel *m*, Kegelkörper *m*	cône *m*	конус
C 1846	**cone** <in a linear space> <FA>	Kegel *m*, Konus *m*	cône *m*	конус
	cone <AX, DG>	*s.* C 1948		
	cone <EG>	*s.* R 1093		
C 1847	**cone-complex with vertex O and base K,** cone with vertex *O* and base *K*, closed join of *O* and *K*, cone over *K* with vertex *O*, cone over *K* with cone-point *O* <AT>	Kegel *m* über dem Grundkomplex *K* mit der Spitze *O*, Stern *m* über dem Grundkomplex *K* mit dem Zentrum *O*, Simplexstern *m* mit dem Außenrand *K* und Mittelpunkt *O*	cône *m* sur le complexe *K* à sommet *O*	пирамида с вершиной *O* над комплексом *K*
	cone from a functor <CA>	*s.* L 726		

No.	English	German	French	Russian
C 1848	**co-neighbourhood** <TO>	Koumgebung *f*, Co-Umgebung *f*	co-voisinage *m*	ко-окрестность
C 1849	**cone of a complex,** join of a complex with a point <AT>	Kegel *m* über einem Komplex	cône *m* sur un complexe	пирамида над комплексом
C 1850	**cone of a simplex,** join of a point and a simplex <AT>	Kegel *m* über einem Simplex, Simplexstern *m*	cône *m* sur un simplexe	пирамида над симплексом
C 1851	**cone of curvature,** curvature cone <DG>	Krümmungskegel *m*	cône *m* de courbure	конус кривизны
	cone of dual numbers <PJ>	*s.* G 535		
	cone of embankment <DS>	*s.* A 1249		
C 1852	**cone of revolution (rotation)** <EG>	Drehkegel *m*, Rotationskegel *m*, Umdrehungskegel *m*	cône *m* de révolution	конус вращения; коническая поверхность вращения
	cone of slope <DS>	*s.* A 1247		
	cone of slope for cutting <DS>	*s.* A 1248		
	cone of slope for embankment <DS>	*s.* A 1249		
C 1853	**cone of support** <CS, GE>	Stützkegel *m*	cône *m* d'appui	опорный конус
	cone of the complex <GE>	*s.* C 1603		
	cone of the first order <DE>	*s.* M 820		
	cone of the second order <DE>	*s.* P 73		
	cone over *K* with cone-point (vertex) O <AT>	*s.* C 1847		
	cone semi-angle <EG>	*s.* S 327		
C 1854	**co-net, conet** <TO>	Konetz *n*, Co-Netz *n*	co-réseau *m*	косеть
	cone with vertex O and base *K* <AT>	*s.* C 1847		
C 1855	**confidence belt** <ST>	Konfidenzgürtel *m*	zone *f* de confiance	доверительный пояс
C 1856	**confidence coefficient** <$= \min K(\gamma,\gamma)$, $\gamma \in \Gamma$> <ST>	Konfidenzkoeffizient *m*	coefficient *m* de confiance	доверительный коэффициент
	confidence coefficient <ST>	*s.* C 1861		
	confidence domain estimate (estimation) <ST>	*s.* C 1865		
C 1857	**confidence ellipse** <ST>	Konfidenzellipse *f*, Vertrauensellipse *f*	ellipse *f* de confiance	доверительный эллипс
C 1858	**confidence ellipsoid** <ST>	Konfidenzellipsoid *n*, Vertrauensellipsoid *n*	ellipsoïde *m* de confiance	доверительный эллипсоид
	confidence estimate <ST>	*s.* 1. C 1860; 2. C 1865		
	confidence estimation <ST>	*s.* 1. C 1860; 2. C 1865		
C 1859	**confidence interval** <ST>	Konfidenzintervall *n*, Vertrauensintervall *n*	intervalle *m* de confiance	доверительный интервал, доверительные границы
C 1860	**confidence interval estimate (estimation),** confidence estimation (estimate), interval estimation (estimate) <one-dimensional> <ST>	Konfidenzintervallschätzung *f*, Konfidenzschätzung *f*, Intervallschätzung *f*	estimation *f* par intervalle de confiance, estimation de confiance, estimation par intervalle	оценивание (оценка) с помощью доверительных границ (интервалов), доверительное оценивание, доверительная оценка
C 1861	**confidence level,** confidence coefficient (probability), belief line <ϵ, $1 - \alpha$> <ST>	Konfidenzniveau *n*, Konfidenzkoeffizient *m*, Konfidenzwahrscheinlichkeit *f*, Vertrauenskoeffizient *m*	niveau *m* (coefficient *m*, probabilité *f*) de confiance	коэффициент доверия, доверительный коэффициент (уровень), доверительная вероятность
C 1862	**confidence limit** <ST>	Konfidenzgrenze *f*, Vertrauensgrenze *f*, Mutungsgrenze *f*	limite *f* de confiance	доверительная граница, доверительный предел
C 1863	**confidence probability** <ST>	Sicherheitswahrscheinlichkeit *f*, statistische Sicherheit *f*, Grenzwahrscheinlichkeit *f*	probabilité *f* de confiance, probabilité de sécurité, coefficient *m* de sécurité	статистическая достоверность
	confidence probability <ST>	*s.* C 1861		
C 1864	**confidence region** <ST>	Konfidenzbereich *m*, Vertrauensbereich *m*	région *f* (domaine *m*) de confiance	доверительная область
C 1865	**confidence region estimate (estimation),** confidence domain estimation (estimate), confidence (region, domain) estimation (estimate) <multidimensional> <ST>	Konfidenzbereichsschätzung *f*, Konfidenzschätzung *f*, Bereichsschätzung *f*	estimation *f* par région (domaine) de confiance, estimation de confiance, estimation par région (domaine)	оценивание (оценка) с помощью доверительных областей, доверительное оценивание, доверительная оценка
C 1866	**confidence set** <ST>	Konfidenzmenge *f*	ensemble *m* de confiance	доверительное множество
C 1867	**confidence statement** <ST>	Konfidenzbehauptung *f*	jugement *m* de confiance	указание доверительной области, утверждение доверия
C 1868	**configuration** <GE, TG, TO>	Konfiguration *f*	configuration *f*	конфигурация
C 1869	**configuration in space,** spatial configuration, point-line-plane-con-	räumliche Konfiguration *f*, Punkt-Geraden-Ebenen-Konfiguration *f*, Kon-	configuration *f* de (dans) l'espace, configuration spatiale; configuration de	конфигурация в пространстве, пространственная конфигурация, конфи-

	figuration <of type $(p_{\gamma\varepsilon'}, g_{\pi\varepsilon'}, e_{\pi'\gamma'})$, also written (n_a^b, m_c^d, r_e^f)> <SG>	figuration im Raum	points, droites et plans	гурация точек, прямых и плоскостей
	configuration in the plane <SG>	*s.* P 641		
C 1870	**configuration of Bydžovský,** Bydžovský['s] configuration <SG>	Konfiguration *f* von Bydžovský, Bydžovskýsche Konfiguration	configuration *f* de Bydžovský	конфигурация Быджовского
C 1871	**configuration of De Vries,** De Vries['s] configuration <SG>	Konfiguration *f* von de Vries, de Vriessche Konfiguration	configuration *f* de de Vries	конфигурация де Фриза (Фриса)
C 1872	**configuration of Hesse,** Hesse['s] configuration <AG, SG>	Hessesche Konfiguration *f*, Wendepunktskonfiguration *f*, Konfiguration *f* von O. Hesse	configuration *f* hessienne	конфигурация Гессе
C 1873	**configuration of Klein,** Klein['s] configuration <SG>	Konfiguration *f* von Klein, Kleinsche Konfiguration	configuration *f* de Klein	конфигурация Клейна
C 1874	**configuration of Kummer,** Kummer['s] configuration <SG>	Kummersche Konfiguration *f*	configuration *f* de Kummer	конфигурация Куммера
C 1875	**configuration of Metelka,** Metelka['s] configuration <SG>	Konfiguration *f* von Metelka, Metelkasche Konfiguration	configuration *f* de Metelka	конфигурация Метелки
C 1876	**configuration of Petersen and Morley,** Petersen-Morley['s] configuration <SG>	Konfiguration (Figur) *f* von Petersen und Morley, Petersen-Morleysche Konfiguration	configuration *f* de Petersen et Morley	конфигурация Петерсена-Морли
C 1877	**configuration of Zacharias,** Zacharias['s] configuration <SG>	Zachariassche Konfiguration *f*, Konfiguration von Zacharias	configuration *f* de Zacharias	конфигурация Цахариаса
C 1878	**configuration problem,** Reye['s] configuration problem <SG>	Problem *n* der Konfiguration, Reyesches Problem [der Konfiguration]	problème *m* de la configuration [de Reye]	задача конфигурации [Рейе]
C 1879	**configuration series** <CT>	Konfigurationsreihe *f*		ряд подсчета, перечисляющий конфигурации
C 1880	**confinality,** co[-]finality, right cofinality <SE>	Konfinalität *f*	confinalité *f*	конфинальность, сопредельность
	confinal set <SE>	*s.* C 1052		
	confinement of the relation to X <SE>	*s.* R 677		
C 1881	**conflict** <TG>	Konflikt *m*	conflit *m*	конфликт
C 1882	**confluence of singular points** <DE>	Konfluenz *f* singulärer Punkte	confluence *f* des points singuliers	слияние особых точек
C 1883	**confluent divided difference** <FD>	Steigung *f* mit wiederholtem Argument	différence *f* divisée à argument répété	разделенная разность с совпадающими (кратными) точками
C 1884	**confluent hypergeometric equation [of Kummer],** Kummer['s] [differential] equation, Pochhammer-Barnes equation <DE>	konfluente hypergeometrische Differentialgleichung *f*, Kummersche Differentialgleichung	équation *f* hypergéométrique confluente, équation différentielle de Kummer	конфлюентное гипергеометрическое уравнение, дифференциальное уравнение Куммера
C 1885	**confluent hypergeometric function,** Kummer['s] function <FU>	konfluente hypergeometrische Funktion *f*, Kummersche Funktion, [Kummer-]Pochhammersche Funktion, Funktion des Drehparaboloids	fonction *f* hypergéométrique confluente, fonction de Kummer	конфлюентная (вырожденная) гипергеометрическая функция, функция Куммера
C 1885 a	**confluent hypergeometric series,** Kummer['s] series <FU>	konfluente hypergeometrische Reihe *f*, Kummersche Reihe *f*, Pochhammersche Reihe	série *f* hypergéométrique confluente, série de Kummer	конфлюентный гипергеометрический ряд, ряд Куммера
C 1886	**confluent interpolation polynomial** <AN, NU>	Interpolationspolynom *n* mit mehrfachen Stützstellen	polynôme *m* d'interpolation à nœuds multiples	интерполяционный многочлен с совпадающими (кратными) узлами
C 1887	**confocal central surfaces [of second order]** <AY>	konfokale (homofokale) Mittelpunktsflächen *fpl* [zweiter Ordnung]	surfaces *fpl* [de deuxième ordre] centrales homofocales	софокусные (конфокальные) центральные поверхности [второго порядка]
C 1888	**confocal conics (conic sections), confocal curves [of the second order]** <AY>	konfokale (homofokale) Kegelschnitte *mpl*, konfokale (homofokale) Kurven *fpl* [zweiter Ordnung]	coniques *fpl* (sections *fpl* coniques) homofocales, courbes *fpl* homofocales [de deuxième ordre]	софокусные (конфокальные) кривые [второго порядка], софокусные (конфокальные) конические сечения
	confocal ellipsoidal co-ordinates <AY>	*s.* E 160		
	confocal hypersurfaces of second order <AY>	*s.* C 1890		
	confocal paraboloidal co-ordinates <AY>	*s.* P 71		
C 1889	**confocal pencil** <of conics> <AY>	konfokale (homofokale) Schar *f*, monofokale Schar *f*	faisceau *m* monofocal (homofocal)	семейство софокусных (конфокальных) кривых, софокусное (конфокальное) семейство
C 1890	**confocal quadrics,** confocal hypersurfaces of second order <AY>	konfokale (homofokale) Quadriken *fpl*, konfokale (homofokale) Hyperflächen *fpl* zweiter Ordnung	quadriques *fpl* homofocales, hypersurfaces *fpl* de deuxième ordre homofocales	софокусные (конфокальные) квадрики, софокусные (конфокальные) гиперповерхности второго порядка

C 1891	**conformability condition** <for matrices>, condition <placed on the sizes of two matrices> which ensures their conformability <MD>	Verkettungsbedingung *f*	condition *f* d'enchainement	условие согласования формы
C 1892	**conformable matrices** <*B* is conformable with respect to *A*> <MD>	verkettete Matrizen *fpl*	couple *m* composable <de matrices>, matrices *fpl* conformes	матрицы согласованной формы
C 1893	**conformal curvature** <DG>	konforme Krümmung *f*	courbure *f* conforme	конформная кривизна
	conformal curvature tensor <DG>	*s.* W 232		
C 1894	**conformal differential geometry** <DG>	konforme Differentialgeometrie *f*	géométrie *f* différentielle conforme	геометрия конформной связности, конформная дифференциальная геометрия, конформно-дифференциальная геометрия
C 1895	**conformal geometry** <GE>	äquiforme Geometrie *f*, Ähnlichkeitsgeometrie *f*	géométrie *f* anallagmatique (conforme)	конформная геометрия, геометрия подобия (подобных фигур)
	conformal geometry in the plane <GE>	*s.* M 712		
	conformal geometry in the space <GE>	*s.* M 711		
C 1896	**conformal group** <GE>	konforme Gruppe *f*	groupe *m* conforme (anallagmatique)	конформная группа
C 1897	**conformal hypergraph,** // hypergraph with a faithful graph representation <GP>	konformer Hypergraph *m*	hypergraphe *m* conforme	конформный гиперграф
C 1898	**conformally connected manifold,** conformal manifold <DG>	konform-zusammenhängende (konform zusammenhängende) Mannigfaltigkeit *f*, konforme Mannigfaltigkeit	variété *f* à connexion conforme, variété conforme	многообразие конформной связности, конформное многообразие
C 1899	**conformally Euclidean (flat) space** <DG>	konform-euklidischer (konform euklidischer) Raum *m*, konform-ebener Raum	espace *m* conformément euclidien	конформно евклидово (плоское) пространство
C 1900	**conformally geodesic lines** <DG>	natürliches Bahnsystem *n*, konform geodätische Linien *fpl*	lignes *fpl* conformément géodésiques	конформно геодезические линии, конформно-геодезическая сеть
	conformal manifold <DG>	*s.* C 1898		
C 1901	**conformal map[ping],** conformal representation, angle-preserving mapping, equiangular (isogonal) mapping, conformal transformation <FT>	konforme (winkeltreue) Abbildung *f*, in den kleinsten Teilen ähnliche Abbildung, konforme Transformation *f*, Ähnlichkeitstransformation *f* im Kleinen	application (représentation, correspondance, transformation) *f* conforme	конформное отображение (преобразование), сохраняющее углы отображение
	conformal mapping <AY, GE>	*s.* A 669		
C 1902	**conformal mapping onto itself** <FT>	konforme Selbstabbildung *f*	application *f* conforme sur lui-même	конформное отображение на себя
	conformal mapping theorem <FT>	*s.* R 1043		
C 1903	**conformal projection,** equiangular (angle-preserving, orthomorphic) projection <DS>	winkeltreue (konforme) Projektion *f*, winkeltreuer (konformer) Entwurf *m*, Winkeltreuentwurf *m*, orthomorphe Projektion	projection *f* conforme (équiangle, orthomorphique)	равноугольная (конформная, ортоморфная) проекция
C 1904	**conformal radius,** mapping radius <FT>	konformer Radius *m*	rayon *m* conforme	конформный радиус
	conformal representation <FT>	*s.* C 1901		
	conformal transformation <AY, GE>	*s.* A 669		
	conformal transformation <FT>	*s.* C 1901		
	conformity <FT, GE>	*s.* P 1240		
C 1905	**conformity condition** <FT>	Konformitätsbedingung *f*	condition *f* de conformité	условие конформности
	conform tensor <DG>	*s.* W 232		
C 1906	**confounding** <ST>	Vermengen *n*, Verquickung *f*	confusion *f*, « confounding » *m*	смешение, смешивание
C 1907	**confusion** <of free and bound variables> <LO>	Konfusion *f*	fausse homonymie *f*, confusion *f*	смешение
C 1908	**congruence** <on a groupoid> <AL>	Kongruenz *f* <in einem Gruppoid>	congruence *f* <dans un groupoïde>	отношение конгруэнтности, конгруэнция, двусторонняя стабильная эквивалентность <в группоиде>
C 1909	**congruence** <AL, GR>	Kongruenz *f*	congruence *f*	сравнение
C 1910	**congruence** <of forms *or* matrices> <AL, MD>	Kongruenz *f*	congruence *f*	конгруэнтность
C 1911	**congruence** <of categories, curves, lines> <CA, DG>	Kongruenz *f*	congruence *f*	конгруэнция
C 1912	**congruence,** identity <of geometrical figures> <EG>	Kongruenz *f*, Gleichheit *f*, Deckungsgleichheit *f*, Form[en]gleichheit *f*	coïncidence *f*, congruence *f*, isométrie *f*, égalité *f*	конгруэнтность, равенство, тождество
C 1913	**congruence** <of numbers> <NT>	Kongruenz *f* <von Zahlen>, Zahlenkongruenz *f*	congruence *f* arithmétique (numérique), congruence <de nombres>	сравнение <чисел>

No.	English	German	French	Russian
C 1914	**congruence,** congruence relation <UA>	Kongruenz *f*, Kongruenzrelation *f*, relationentreue Äquivalenzrelation *f*, kompatible Klasseneinteilung *f*	congruence *f*, relation *f* de congruence, équivalence *f* régulière, relation d'équivalence régulière	конгруэнция, отношение сравнения (конгруэнтности), соотношение конгруэнтности, конгруэнтность, правильное разбиение
	congruence <AY, DG>	*s.* C 1923		
C 1915	**congruence axiom of triangles** <GE>	Kongruenzaxiom *n* der Dreiecke	axiome *m* de congruence des triangles	аксиома конгруэнтности треугольников
C 1916	**congruence ζ-function,** congruence zeta-function <AL>	Kongruenzzetafunktion *f*, Kongruenz-ζ-Funktion *f*, Artin-F. K. Schmidtsche Zetafunktion (ζ-Funktion) *f*, Zetafunktion (ζ-Funktion) eines algebraischen Funktionenkörpers	fonction *f* zêta (ζ) d'Artin-Schmidt	ζ-функция (дзета-функция) поля алгебраических функций
C 1917	**congruence group** <NT>	Kongruenzgruppe *f*	groupe *m* de congruence	конгруэнц-группа
	congruence kernel <AL>	*s.* C 1929		
	congruence lattice <LA>	*s.* L 127		
C 1918	**congruence method [of Greenberger],** Greenberger['s] method <ST>	Kongruenzmethode *f* [von Greenberger]	méthode *f* de la congruence [de Greenberger], méthode de Greenberger	метод сравнимости [Гринбергера], метод конгруэнтности [Гринбергера]
C 1919	**congruence modulo a double module** <AL>	Kongruenz *f* nach einem Doppelmodul	congruence *f* par rapport à un double module	сравнение по двойному модулю
C 1920	**congruence of angles** <GE>	Winkelkongruenz *f*	congruence *f* d'angles	конгруэнтность углов
C 1921	**congruence of curves,** curvilinear congruence, curve congruence <DG>	Kurvenkongruenz *f*, Kongruenz *f* von Kurven	congruence *f* de courbes, congruence curvilinéaire	криволинейная конгруэнция, конгруэнция кривых
	congruence of geodesic lines <DG>	*s.* G 232		
C 1922	**congruence of higher degree** <AL>	höhere Kongruenz *f*, Bestimmungskongruenz *f*	congruence *f* de degré supérieur <> 1>, congruence supérieure, // équivalence *f* <Cauchy>	высшее сравнение, определяющая конгруэнция
C 1923	**congruence of lines,** congruence of rays (straight lines), rectilinear (line, ray) congruence, congruence, system of lines (rays), line (ray) system <AY, DG>	Strahlenkongruenz *f*, Strahlensystem *n*, Linienkongruenz *f*, Geradenkongruenz *f*, Kongruenz *f* von Geraden, Kongruenz	congruence *f* de droites, congruence, système *f* de droites	прямолинейная конгруэнция, конгруэнция лучей, конгруэнция прямых, конгруэнция, система прямых (лучей)
	congruence of line segments <GE>	*s.* C 1924		
	congruence of normals <DG>	*s.* N 546		
	congruence of rays <AY, DG>	*s.* C 1923		
C 1924	**congruence of segments,** congruence of line segments, segment congruence <GE>	Streckenkongruenz *f*, Streckensystem *n*	congruence *f* de segments	конгруэнция сегментов (отрезков)
	congruence of straight lines <AY, DG>	*s.* C 1923		
C 1925	**congruence of tangents** <DG>	Tangentenkongruenz *f*	congruence *f* de tangentes	конгруэнция касательных
C 1926	**congruence of the *n*-th degree** <AL>	Kongruenz *f* *n*-ten Grades	congruence *f* de degré *n*	сравнение *n*-го порядка
C 1927	**congruence relation** <with respect to a composition law> <AL>	Kongruenzrelation *f*, relationentreue Äquivalenzrelation *f* <bezüglich eines Kompositionsgesetzes>	équivalence *f* régulière <par rapport à une loi de composition, pour une loi de composition>, équivalence compatible <avec une loi de composition>, relation *f* d'équivalence permise (compatible) <avec une loi de composition>; Ω-équivalence *f*, relation d'équivalence compatible avec la loi externe <dans un domaine d'opérateurs Ω>	стабильная эквивалентность, конгруэнция <относительно операции>
C 1928	**congruence relation** <EG>	Beziehung *f* kongruent, Kongruenzbeziehung *f*	relation *f* de congruence	отношение конгруэнтности
	congruence relation <UA>	*s.* C 1914		
C 1929	**congruence relation [naturally] induced by a homomorphism,** kernel congruence, congruence kernel <of a homomorphism> <AL>	durch einen Homomorphismus induzierte Kongruenzrelation *f*	congruence *f* nucléaire [associée à l'homomorphisme], congruence (équivalence *f*) d'homomorphisme	ядерная конгруэнция <гомоморфизма>; отношение конгруэнтности, естественно индуцированное гомоморфизмом; конгруэнтность, естественно индуцированная гомоморфизмом; ядро гомоморфизма
C 1930	**congruence subgroup** <of level *n*> <AB>	Kongruenzuntergruppe *f*	sous-groupe *m* de congruence	конгруэнц-подгруппа
C 1931	**congruence subgroup problem** <AB>	Kongruenzproblem *n*	problème *m* des groupes de congruence	конгруэнц-проблема
C 1932	**congruence theorem,** theorem on congruence <of triangles> <EG>	Kongruenzsatz *m* <für Dreiecke>	théorème *m* de congruence <des triangles>	теорема равенства <треугольников>
	congruence transformation <AL, MD>	*s.* C 1943		
	congruence zeta-function <AL>	*s.* C 1916		

C 1933	**congruent** <modulo an ideal $\mathfrak{a}$> <in a ring> <AL>	kongruent <nach einem Ideal $\mathfrak{a}$, mod $\mathfrak{a}$, modulo $\mathfrak{a}$>	congru <modulo $\mathfrak{a}$>	сравнимый <по модулю $\mathfrak{a}$, mod. $\mathfrak{a}$>
C 1934	**congruent,** congruous, equiresidual, ≡ <modulo> <AL, NT>	kongruent, ≡ <nach [dem Modul], modulo>, // gleichrestig	congruent, congru, ≡ <modulo, suivant le module>	сравнимый, конгруэнтный, равновычетный, равноостаточный, ≡ <по модулю>
C 1935	**congruent,** superposable, identical, ≡, ≅, // congruous <EG>	kongruent, gleich, deckungsgleich, form[en]gleich, übereinstimmend, ≡, ≅	coïncident, congru, égal, isométrique, superposable, ≡, ≅, // congruent	конгруэнтный, равный, тождественный, ≡, ≅
C 1936	**congruent** <modulo *N*> <GR>	kongruent <modulo *N*>	congru <par rapport à *N*, selon le module *N*>, équivalent <selon le module *N*>	сравнимый <по модулю *N*>
	congruent and conformal <EG>	*s.* D 578		
	congruent and indirectly conformal <EG>	*s.* I 922		
C 1937	**congruent form** <quadratic *or* bilinear> <AL>	kongruente Form *f*	forme *f* congruente	конгруэнтная форма
C 1938	**congruent mapping,** congruent transformation <AY, EG, TO>	kongruente Abbildung (Transformation) *f*, Kongruenzabbildung *f*, Kongruenztransformation *f*, Bewegung *f* <eines metrischen oder Kleinschen Raumes>	application (transformation, représentation) *f* coïncidente (congrue)	конгруэнтное отображение (преобразование)
C 1939	**congruent matrix** <MD>	kongruente Matrix *f*	matrice *f* congruente	конгруэнтная матрица
C 1940	**congruent matrix by an orthogonal transformation,** orthogonal similar matrix <MD>	orthogonal ähnliche Matrix *f*	matrice *f* semblable par une transformation orthogonale	ортогонально подобная матрица
C 1941	**congruent number,** congruous number, equiresidual numbers <modulo *m*, modulus *m*> <NT>	kongruente Zahl *f* <mod *m*, modulo *m*, nach [dem Modul] *m*>, // gleichrestige Zahl	nombre *m* congru (congruent, de même résidu) <suivant le module *m*, modulo *m*, mod. *m*>	сравнимое (конгруэнтное, равновычетное, равноостаточное) число <по модулю *m*>
	congruent polynomial <NT>	*s.* I 39		
C 1942	**congruent subspace** <in a linear topological space> <TO>	kongruenter Teilraum *m*	sous-espace *m* congruent	конгруэнтное подпространство
C 1943	**congruent transformation,** congruence transformation <of forms *or* matrices> <AL, MD>	Kongruenztransformation *f*, kongruente Transformation *f*	transformation *f* congruente (congrue)	преобразование конгруэнтности
	congruent transformation <AY, EG, TO>	*s.* C 1938		
	congruous <AL, NT>	*s.* C 1934		
	congruous <EG>	*s.* C 1935		
	congruous number <NT>	*s.* C 1941		
C 1944	**conic,** conic section, [algebraic] curve of [the] second degree (order), plane [algebraic] curve of [the] second degree (order), point conic, point-conic, one-dimensional quadric, quadric curve, quadratic curve <AG, AY>	Kegelschnitt *m*, Kurve *f* zweiter (2.) Ordnung, [ebene] algebraische Kurve zweiter (2.) Ordnung, [algebraische] ebene Kurve zweiter (2.) Ordnung, eindimensionale Quadrik *f*, Punktkegelschnitt *m*	conique *f*, section *f* conique, courbe *f* [algébrique] de (du) deuxième (2-me) ordre (degré), courbe [algébrique] plane de deuxième (second, 2-me) ordre (degré), quadrique *f* unidimensionnelle	коническое сечение, [плоская] алгебраическая кривая второго (2-го) порядка, [алгебраическая] кривая (линия) второго (2-го) порядка, одномерная квадрика, коника
	conic <AY>	*s.* N 357		
C 1945	**conical curve** <of a surface> <GE>	konische Kurve *f*	courbe *f* conique	коническая кривая
	conical frustum <EG>	*s.* F 681		
	conical function <FU>	*s.* C 1950		
C 1946	**conical helix** <GE>	zylindrokonische Schraubenlinie (Böschungslinie, Schneckenlinie) *f*, Loxodrome *f* des Kreiskegels	hélice *f* conique	коническая винтовая линия, коническая кривая постоянного склона
C 1947	**conical rotation of [the quaternion] *p*,** transform of *p* <by *q*> <AL>	Transformation *f* der Quaternion *p* <durch *q*>	conjugaison *f* du quaternion *p* <par *q*>	преобразование кватерниона *p* <элементом *q*>
C 1948	**conical surface,** cone <AY, DG>	Kegelfläche *f*, Kegel *m*	surface *f* conique, cône *m*	коническая поверхность, конус
	conical ungula <EG>	*s.* U 101		
C 1949	**conic construction** <AT>	Kegelkonstruktion *f*	construction *f* conique	построение пирамиды над комплексом
	conic envelope <AY>	*s.* L 854		
C 1950	**conic function,** conical function <FU>	Kegelfunktion *f*	fonction *f* conique	коническая функция
C 1951	**conic in affine geometry** <GE>	affiner Kegelschnitt *m*	conique *f* affine	аффинное коническое сечение, аффинная коника
	conic node, conicnode <AG>	*s.* C 1956		
C 1952/3	**conico-cylindric surface** <GE>	konisch-zylindrische Fläche *f*	surface *f* conico-cylindrique	конико-цилиндрическая поверхность
C 1954	**conic of centres** <of a pencil> <PJ>	Mittelpunktskegelschnitt *m*, Zentralkegelschnitt *m*, Zentrakegelschnitt *m*	conique *f* des centres	коническое сечение центров
	conicoid <AY>	*s.* P 1821		
C 1955	**conic operator** <in conic construction> <AT>	Kegeloperator *m*	opérateur *m* conique <de sommet *a*>	конический оператор <вершиной *a*>
C 1956	**conic point,** conic node, conicnode <of a surface> <AG>	konischer (kegelförmiger) Doppelpunkt *m*, konischer Punkt (Knoten) *m*	point *m* conique (double conique), nœud *m* conique	коническая двойная точка, коническая точка, двойная коническая точка
	conic projection <DS>	*s.* C 375		

C 1957	**conics** <AY>	Theorie *f* der Kegelschnitte	théorie *f* des [sections] coniques	теория конических сечений
	conic section <AG, AY>	*s.* C 1944		
	conic section <AY>	*s.* N 357		
	conic section in projective geometry <PJ>	*s.* P 1674		
C 1958	**conic spiral** <GE>	konische Spirale (Schraubenlinie) *f*, Kegelschraubenlinie *f*	spirale *f* conique	коническая винтовая линия
C 1959	**conjective point ranges,** [projective] point ranges on (having) the same base <PJ>	konjektive Punktreihen *fpl*, [projektive] Punktreihen auf demselben Träger	ponctuelles *fpl* conjectives, ponctuelles [projectives] sur le même support	конъективные ряды точек, [проективные] ряди точек на одном и том же носителе
	conjoined rule of three <AR>	*s.* C 1744		
C 1960	**conjugacy** <AL>	Konjugiertheit *f*, Konjugiertsein *n*	propriété *f* d'être conjugué	сопряженность
C 1961	**conjugacy,** complex conjugation <FT>	Übergang *m* zum Konjugiertkomplexen, komplexe Konjugation *f*	conjugaison *f* complexe	комплексное сопряжение
C 1962/3	**conjugacy** <GE>	Konjugium *n*	conjugaison *f* complexe	сопряженное преобразование
	conjugacy class <GR>	*s.* C 799		
	conjugacy problem <GR>	*s.* C 2016		
	conjugate <AB>	*s.* C 1994		
	conjugate <AB, AL>	*s.* C 1982		
	conjugate <AG>	*s.* C 1999		
	conjugate <AL>	*s.* C 2004		
	conjugate <AL, FT>	*s.* C 1604		
	conjugate <FA>	*s.* C 1995		
	conjugate <FA, TO>	*s.* A 307		
	conjugate <GP>	*s.* C 2008		
C 1964	**conjugate algebraic form** <of a field> <AL>	konjugierte [algebraische] Form *f* <Kronecker>	forme *f* conjuguée, conjuguée *f*	сопряженная форма
	conjugate algebraic number <AB>	*s.* C 1994		
	conjugate angle <EG>	*s.* E 723		
C 1965	**conjugate axis** <of a hyperbola> <AY>	Nebenachse *f*, imaginäre (konjugierte) Achse *f*, Querachse *f*	axe *m* secondaire, second axe, axe conjugué (imaginaire, non transverse), // axe transverse	мнимая ось
	conjugate Bertrand curves <DG>	*s.* B 221		
C 1966	**conjugate bilinear form** <AL, FA>	konjugierte Form (Bilinearform) *f*	forme *f* bilinéaire conjuguée	сопряженная билинейная форма
C 1967	**conjugate binary form** <NT>	konjugierte (apolare, harmonische) binäre Form *f*	forme *f* binaire conjuguée	сопряженная бинарная форма
C 1968	**conjugate binomial surd,** conjugate radical <AL>	konjugierter binomischer irrationaler Ausdruck *m*	binôme *m* conjugué	сопряженное двучленное иррациональное выражение, сопряженный двучлен
C 1969	**conjugate character** <RE>	konjugierter Charakter *m*	caractère *m* conjugué	сопряженный характер
	conjugate class <GR>	*s.* C 799		
C 1970	**conjugate complex** <of a group> <GR>	konjugierter (ähnlicher) Komplex *m*	complexe *m* conjugué	подобный комплекс
	conjugate complex <AL, FT>	*s.* C 1604		
C 1971	**conjugate complex number;** conjugate imaginary [number] <non-real> <AL, FT>	konjugiert[e] komplexe Zahl *f*; konjugiert[-] komplexe Zahl, konjugiert-imaginäre Zahl	nombre *m* [complexe] conjugué; imaginaire *m* conjugué, nombre imaginaire conjugué	сопряженное [комплексное] число; сопряженное мнимое число
	conjugate congruence [of lines] <DG>	*s.* C 2006		
	conjugate congruence of rays <DG>	*s.* C 2006		
C 1972	**conjugate convex function,** polar (conjugate) function <AN>	konjugierte konvexe Funktion *f*	fonction *f* convexe conjuguée	сопряженная [выпуклая] функция
C 1973	**conjugate curve** <AY>	konjugierte Kurve *f*, Nebenkurve *f*	courbe *f* conjuguée	сопряженная кривая
C 1974	**conjugate curve of the second order** <AY>	supplementärer Kegelschnitt *m* <Poncelet>, konjugierte Kurve *f* zweiter Ordnung <Steiner>	conique *f* supplémentaire	сопряженная кривая второго порядка
	conjugate curves <DG>	*s.* B 221		
C 1975	**conjugate cycle** <AG>	konjugierter Zyklus *m*	transformé *m* conjugué <d'un cycle>	сопряженный цикл
C 1976	**conjugate diameter** <of a conic *or* quadric> <AY>	konjugierter Durchmesser *m*	diamètre *m* conjugué (rectiligne conjugué)	сопряженный диаметр
C 1977	**conjugate diameter** <of a given "principal" diameter of a hyperbola> <AY>	Nebendurchmesser *m*	diamètre *m* conjugué	сопряженный диаметр
C 1978	**conjugate diametral (diametric[al]) hyperplane** <GE>	konjugierte Durchmesserhyperebene (Diametralhyperebene) *f*	hyperplan *m* diamétral conjugué	сопряженная диаметральная гиперплоскость
C 1979	**conjugate dual number** <AL>	konjugiert[e] duale Zahl *f*, konjugiert-duale Zahl	nombre *m* dual conjugué	сопряженное дуальное число
C 1980	**conjugate dual point** <PJ>	konjugierter (konjugiert) dualer Punkt *m*	point *m* dual conjugué	сопряженная двойственная точка
C 1981	**conjugate dyad,** // **conjugate dyadic** <VT>	konjugierte Dyade *f*	dyade *f* conjuguée	сопряженная диада
C 1982	**conjugate element,** conjugate <over *k*> <AB, AL>	konjugiertes Element *n* <über *k*>	conjugué *m*, élément *m* conjugué <sur *k*>	сопряженный элемент <над *k*>

C 1983	**conjugate element** <of a group> <GR>	konjugiertes (gleichberechtigtes, ähnliches) Element *n*	élément *m* conjugué (homologue, semblable, canoniquement équivalent)	сопряженный (подобный) элемент
C 1984	**conjugate elements** <of a matrix> <MD>	symmetrisch zur Hauptdiagonale gelegene Elemente *npl* <a_{ij} und a_{ji}>	éléments *mpl* symétriques par rapport à la diagonale principale	элементы, симметричные относительно главной диагонали
C 1985	**conjugate exponent** <in Hölder's inequality> <AN>	konjugierter Exponent *m*	exposant *m* conjugué	сопряженный показатель
	conjugate extension <AL>	*s.* C 1986		
	conjugate family of curves <DG>	*s.* C 2010		
C 1986	**conjugate field,** conjugate extension; conjugate subfield <AL>	konjugierter Körper *m*, Konjugierte *f*, konjugierte Erweiterung *f*	conjugué *m*, corps *m* conjugué, isomorphe *m*, corps algébrique conjugué; sous-extension *f* conjuguée	сопряженное поле
C 1987	**conjugate function** <in field theory> <AL>	konjugierte Funktion *f*	fonction *f* conjuguée	сопряженная функция
C 1988	**conjugate function,** conjugate harmonic function, conjugate potential function <FT, PO>	konjugierte (harmonische konjugierte, konjugierte harmonische) Funktion *f*, konjugierte Potentialfunktion *f*	fonction *f* conjuguée (harmonique conjuguée, harmonique associée)	сопряженная (сопряженная гармоническая) функция
	conjugate function <AN>	*s.* C 1972		
C 1989	**conjugate group,** conjugate subgroup, equivalent group <Kirkman> <GR>	konjugierte Untergruppe *f*, konjugierte Gruppe *f*, gleichberechtigte Gruppe *f* <Klein>, gleichberechtigte Untergruppe *f*	sous-groupe *m* conjugué, groupe *m* équivalent <Kirkman>, groupe *m* conjugué, conjugué *m* <de sous-groupes>	сопряженная подгруппа
	conjugate harmonic function <FT, PO>	*s.* C 1988		
C 1990	**conjugate hyperbola** <AY>	konjugierte Hyperbel *f*	hyperbole *f* conjuguée	сопряженная гипербола
	conjugate imaginary <AL, FT>	*s.* C 1604		
	conjugate imaginary [number] <AL, FT>	*s.* C 1971		
C 1991	**conjugate Latin square** <CT, ST>	konjugiertes lateinisches Quadrat *n*	carré *m* latin conjugué	сопряженный (транспонированный) латинский квадрат
C 1992	**conjugate line,** conjugate ray <of a conic *or* quadric> <AY>	konjugierte Gerade *f*, konjugierter Strahl *m*	droite *f* conjuguée, rayon *m* conjugué	сопряженная прямая, сопряженный луч
	conjugate matrix <MD>	*s.* 1. C 1605; 2. T 848		
C 1993	**conjugate net [of curves]** <PJ>	konjugiertes Netz *n*, konjugiertes Kurvennetz *n*	réseau *m* conjugué [de courbes]	сопряженная [криволинейная] сеть
C 1994	**conjugate number,** conjugate algebraic number, [algebraic] conjugate; field conjugate <of a number with respect to a fixed field> <AB>	konjugierte Zahl *f*, konjugierte algebraische Zahl *f*	nombre *m* conjugué, nombre *m* algébrique conjugué	сопряженное число, сопряженное алгебраическое число
C 1995	**conjugate operator,** conjugate <of an operator> <FA>	konjugierter Operator *m*, Konjugierte *f*	opérateur *m* conjugué	сопряженный оператор
	conjugate partition <NT>	*s.* D 1020		
C 1996	**conjugate permutation,** similar permutation <CT>	ähnliche (konjugierte) Permutation *f*, ähnliche Substitution *f*	permutation *f* semblable, substitution *f*, permutation conjuguée, conjuguée *f* <d'une substitution>, substitution semblable	сопряженная подстановка
C 1997	**conjugate permutations** <CT>	verwandte (reziproke, konjugierte) Permutationen *fpl* <Stellenelement und Stellenordnung gegeneinander vertauscht>	permutations *fpl* réciproques (en affinité, conjuguées)	двойственные перестановки
C 1998	**conjugate place** <of a field> <AL>	konjugierte Stelle *f*	place *f* conjuguée	сопряженная точка
C 1999	**conjugate point,** conjugate, tangential <of a point> <AG>	äquivalenter (konjugierter) Punkt *m*	point *m* conjugué	сопряженная точка
C 2000	**conjugate point** <of a cubic> <AY>	konjugierter Punkt *m*	point *m* conjugué	сопряженная (соответственная) точка
C 2001	**conjugate point** <of a point relative to a conic *or* quadric> <AY>	konjugierter Punkt *m*	point *m* conjugué	сопряженная точка
C 2002	**conjugate point** <on an extremal> <VA>	konjugierter Punkt *m*	point *m* conjugué [de Jacobi]	сопряженная точка
	conjugate point <AG>	*s.* A 196		
C 2003	**conjugate points** <with respect to a net> <AY>	zugeordnete Pole *mpl*, konjugierte Punkte *mpl* <bezüglich eines Bündels zweiter Ordnung>	points *mpl* conjugués <par rapport à un réseau>	сопряженные точки
	conjugate potential function <FT, PO>	*s.* C 1988		
C 2004	**conjugate quaternion,** conjugate <of a quaternion> <AL>	konjugierte Quaternion *f*	quaternion *m* conjugué, conjugué *m* <d'un quaternion>	сопряженный кватернион
	conjugate radical <AL>	*s.* C 1968		
C 2005	**conjugate ranking** <ST>	konjugierte Rangordnung *f*	rangement *m* conjugué	сопряженное ранжирование
	conjugate ray <AY>	*s.* C 1992		

C 2006	**conjugate rectilinear congruence,** conjugate congruence [of lines (rays)] <DG>	konjugierte Strahlenkongruenz (Linienkongruenz, Geradenkongruenz, Kongruenz) *f*, konjugiertes Strahlensystem *n*	congruence *f* rectiligne conjuguée, congruence [de droites] conjuguée	сопряженная прямолинейная конгруэнция, сопряженная конгруэнция [прямых (лучей)]
C 2007	**conjugate ruled surface** <of a ruled surface> <GE>	konjugierte Fläche *f*	surface *f* conjuguée	сопряженная поверхность
C 2008	**conjugate sequence,** conjugate <in the Ferrers diagram> <GP>	konjugierte Folge *f*	séquence *f* conjuguée	сопряженная последовательность
C 2009	**conjugate series** <of a trigonometric series> <SS>	konjugierte Reihe *f*	série *f* conjuguée	сопряженный ряд
	conjugate set <GR>	*s.* C 799		
	conjugate space <FA, TO>	*s.* A 307		
	conjugate subfield <AL>	*s.* C 1986		
	conjugate subgroup <GR>	*s.* C 1989		
C 2010	**conjugate system of curves,** conjugate family of curves <on a surface> <DG>	konjugiertes Netz *n* (Kurvensystem *n*, System *n*)	système *m* de courbes conjugué	сопряженная система линий
C 2011	**conjugate tensor** >VT>	konjugierter Tensor *m*	tenseur *m* conjugué	сопряженный тензор
	conjugate transpose[d matrix] <MD>	*s.* H 235		
C 2012	**conjugate variety** <AG>	konjugierte Mannigfaltigkeit *f*, konjugierte Varietät *f*	variété *f* conjuguée	сопряженное многообразие
C 2013	**conjugation,** conjugation operator <in a Hilbert space> <FA>	Konjugation *f*, Konjugationsoperator *m*	conjugaison *f*, opération *f* de conjugaison	оператор сопряжения
C 2014	**conjugation,** transformation <by a group element> <GR>	Konjugation *f*, Transformation *f* <durch ein Gruppenelement, mit einem Gruppenelement>	conjugaison *f* <par un élément>	сопряжение, трансформирование <элементом>
	conjugation <AL>	*s.* K 82		
	conjugation class <GR>	*s.* C 799		
C 2015	**conjugation map** <GR>	Konjugationsabbildung *f*	conjugaison *f*	операция сопряжения
	conjugation operator <FA>	*s.* C 2013		
C 2016	**conjugation problem,** conjugacy problem <as a word problem> <GR>	Transformationsproblem *n*, Problem *n* des Konjugiertseins	problème *m* de conjugaison	проблема преобразования слов, проблема сопряженности (трансформирования)
	conjunct <LO>	*s.* P 186		
C 2017	**conjunction,** logical conjunction, logic[al] product <LO>	Konjunktion *f*, logische Konjunktion *f*, logisches Produkt *n*	conjonction *f* [logique], produit *m* logique, intersection *f*	конъюнкция, логическое произведение
C 2018	**conjunction,** logical multiplication <operation> <LO>	Konjunktion *f*, logische Multiplikation *f*, „und"-Operation *f*, logische Produktbildung *f*	multiplication *f* logique, détermination *f*, multiplication, opération *f* ET, conjonction *f*, coïncidence *f*, intersection *f*, produit *m* logique	логическое умножение, операция И, булево умножение, конъюнкция, логический «И», функция совпадения, логическое произведение, // определение <Ламберт>
C 2019	**conjunction** <of several propositions> <LO>	Konjunktion *f*, logisches Produkt *n* <mehrerer Aussagen>	produit *m* logique, conjonction *f* continue <de plusieurs propositions>	конъюнкция <некоторых высказываний>
C 2020	**conjunction of relations** <LO>	Konjunktion *f* von Relationen	relation-conjonction *f*, produit *m* logique de deux relations	конъюнкция отношений
	conjunction sign (symbol) <LO>	*s.* S 2437		
	conjunctive-disjunctive normal form <AL, LO>	*s.* C 2022		
C 2021	**conjunctive mapping** <DG>	konjunktive Abbildung *f*	application *f* conjonctive	конъюнктивное отображение
	conjunctive matrix <MD>	*s.* M 186		
	conjunctive matrix by a unitary transformation <MD>	*s.* U 259		
C 2022	**conjunctive normal form,** conjunctive-disjunctive normal form <AL, LO>	konjunktive Normalform *f*	forme *f* normale conjonctive, deuxième forme *f* normale	конъюнктивная нормальная форма, кнф
C 2023	**conjunctive proposition** <LO>	konjunktive Aussage *f*, Konjunktion *f* von Aussagen	proposition *f* conjonctive, conjonction *f*	конъюнктивное высказывание, соединительное (конъюнктивное) суждение
	conjunctivity by a unitary transformation <MD>	*s.* U 258		
	connected algebraic group <AL, TO>	*s.* G 518		
C 2024	**connected asymptotic paths** <FT>	verbundene Zielwege *mpl*	chemins *mpl* asymptotiques liés	связанные асимптотические пути
C 2025	**connected category** <CA>	verbundene (zusammenhängende) Kategorie *f*	catégorie *f* connexe	связанная категория
C 2026	**connected chain,** maximal chain <in a lattice> <LA>	Hauptreihe *f*	suite *f* normale	главный ряд
	connected chain <SE>	*s.* M 227		
C 2027	**connected closed set** <TO>	Kontinuum *n* im weiteren Sinne, zusammenhängende abgeschlossene Teilmenge *f*	ensemble *m* fermé connexe	связное замкнутое множество
C 2028	**connected complex** <AT>	zusammenhängender Komplex *m*	complexe *m* connexe	связный комплекс

C 2029	**connected component** <of a category> <CA>	Zusammenhangskomponente *f*, zusammenhängende Komponente *f*	composante *f* connexe	компонента связности, связная компонента
	connected component <AL>	*s.* 1. C 1651; 2. C 1653		
	connected component <GP>	*s.* M 229		
	connected component <TO>	*s.* C 1658		
C 2030	**connected curve** <GE>	zusammenhängende Kurve *f*	courbe *f* connexe	связная кривая
C 2031	**connected domain** <TO>	zusammenhängendes Gebiet *n*	domaine *m* connexe	связная область
C 2032	**connected doublet,** Sierpiński space <TO>	zusammenhängendes Punktepaar *n*, Sierpiński-Raum *m*	paire *f* de points connexe	связное двоеточие
C 2033	**connected form,** connected quadratic form <AL, GU>	nicht in die Summe zweier Formen in disjunkten Mengen von Variablen zerlegbare quadratische Form *f*	forme *f* indécomposable <en somme de deux formes à systèmes disjoints de variables>	квадратичная форма, не разложимая в сумму двух форм в дизъюнктных множествах переменных
C 2034	**connected graph** <GP>	zusammenhängender Graph *m*	graphe *m* connexe (simplement connexe, s-connexe)	связный граф
C 2035	**connected group** <GR, TO>	zusammenhängende Gruppe *f*	groupe *m* connexe	связная группа
	connected groupoid <AL>	*s.* B 737		
C 2036	**connected homomorphism,** homomorphism, contraction <of a graph> <GP>	Homomorphismus *m*, Kontraktion *f*, Zusammenzug *m*	contraction *f*	гомоморфизм
C 2037	**connected Hopf algebra** <AL>	zusammenhängende Hopfsche Algebra *f*	algèbre *f* de Hopf connexe	связная алгебра Хопфа
	connected im kleinen point set <TO>	*s.* L 954		
	connected Lie group <GR>	*s.* A 635		
C 2038	**connected neighbourhood** <TO>	zusammenhängende Umgebung *f*	voisinage *m* connexe	связная окрестность
C 2039	**connected pair of functors** <CA>	verbundenes Paar *n* von Funktoren	« connected pair of functors » *m*	связанная пара функторов
	connected point set <TO>	*s.* C 2043		
C 2040	**connected polyhedron** <GE>	zusammenhängendes Polyeder *n*	polyèdre *m* connexe	связный многогранник
	connected quadratic form <AL, GU>	*s.* C 2033		
C 2041	**connected relation,** connective (determinate) relation <SE>	konnexe (zusammenhängende) Relation *f*	relation *f* connexe (strictement totale, connective)	связное отношение
C 2042	**connected sequence of functors** <CA>	verbundene Folge *f* von Funktoren	« connected sequence of functors » *m*	связанная (связывающая) последовательность функторов
C 2043	**connected set,** connected point set <TO>	zusammenhängende Menge (Punktmenge) *f*, Bereich *m*	ensemble *m* connexe (d'un seul tenant), domaine *m*	связное (связное точечное) множество
C 2044	**connected space,** connected topological space <TO>	zusammenhängender (zusammenhängender topologischer) Raum *m*	espace *m* connexe (topologique connexe)	связное (связное топологическое) пространство
	1-connected space <TO>	*s.* S 997		
C 2045	**connected space in dimension r** <TO>	in der Dimension *r* zusammenhängender Raum *m*, zusammenhängender Raum in der Dimension *r*	espace *m* connexe en dimension *r*	связное в размерности *r* пространство
C 2046	**connected sum** <of manifolds> <AT>	zusammenhängende Summe *f*	somme *f* connexe	связная сумма
	connected topological space <TO>	*s.* C 2044		
C 2047	**connecting homomorphism,** connecting morphism <HA>	Verbindungshomomorphismus *m*, verbindender Homomorphismus *m*	homomorphisme *m* de connexion	связывающий (граничный) гомоморфизм
C 2048	**connecting line** <of two points> <EG>	Verbindungsgerade *f*	droite *f* de jonction	соединяющая прямая
C 2049	**connecting line segment** <of two points> <EG>	Verbindungsstrecke *f*	segment *m* rectiligne unissant	соединяющий отрезок
C 2050	**connecting morphism** <CA>	Verbindungsmorphismus *m*	« connecting homomorphism » *m*	связывающий морфизм, связывающее отображение
	connecting morphism <HA>	*s.* C 2047		
C 2051	**connecting object,** connecting quantity <of a connection> <DG>	Zusammenhangsgröße *f*	objet *m* de connexion	объект связности
C 2052	**connecting path** <ST>	Verbindungspfad *m*	voie *f* de connexion	линия связи
C 2053	**connecting plane** <of three points> <EG>	Verbindungsebene *f*	plan *m* de jonction	соединяющая плоскость
C 2054	**connecting quantity,** binding quantity <in a vector space> <AL>	Verbindungsgröße *f*	grandeur *f* de connexion	величина, определенная на произведении пространств
	connecting quantity <DG>	*s.* C 2051		
C 2055	**connection,** transfer, // connexion <DG>	Übertragung *f*, Zusammenhang *m*	connexion *f*, transfert *m*	связность, перенесение
C 2056	**connection component,** component <of a connection> <DG>	Zusammenhangskomponente *f*, Komponente *f* <eines Zusammenhangs>	composante *f* connexe, composante <d'une connexion>	компонента [связности]
	connection number <GP>	*s.* V 159		

No.	English	German	French	Russian
	connective <AY>	*s.* B 796		
	connective <LO>	*s.* S 498		
	connective relation <SE>	*s.* C 2041		
	connective symbol <LO>	*s.* S 498		
C 2057	**connectivity** <of a triangulation> <AT>	Zusammenhangszahl *f*	connectivité *f*	порядок связности
C 2058	**connectivity,** connexivity, connexity <of a relation> <SE>	Konnexität *f*	totalité *f* stricte, complétude *f*	связность
C 2059	**connectivity,** one-dimensional Betti number, linear connectivity <of a curve> <TO>	Zusammenhangszahl *f*, eindimensionale Betti-Zahl *f*	connectivité *f*	порядок связности, одномерное число Бетти
C 2060	**connectivity** <property> <TO>	Zusammenhang *m*	connexion *f*	связность
	connectivity <AT>	*s.* B 252		
	connectivity <GP>	*s.* 1. C 2891; 2. V 159		
	connectivity <TO>	*s.* O 344		
C 2061	**connex** <PJ>	Konnex *m*	connexe *m*, connexe algébrique	коннекс
	connexion <DG>	*s.* C 2055		
	connexi[vi]ty <SE>	*s.* C 2058		
	connotation <MM>	*s.* I 691		
C 2062	**conoid** <GE>	Konoid *n*, Konoidfläche *f*, // Afterkegel *m*	conoïde *m*, surface *f* conoïde	коноид
C 2063	**conorm** <of a divisor> <AB, AL>	Konorm *f*, Conorm *f*	conorme *f*	ко-норма, конорма
C 2064	**co-normal** <DE>	Konormale *f*	conormale *f*	конормаль
C 2065	**conormal category** <CA>	konormale (conormale) Kategorie *f*	catégorie *f* conormale	конормальная категория
C 2066	**conormal epimorphism** <CA>	konormaler (conormaler) Epimorphismus *m*	épimorphisme *m* conormal	конормальный эпиморфизм
C 2067/8	**conormal image** <DG>	Konormalenbild *n*	image *f* conormale	конормальный образ
	consecutive mean <ST>	*s.* M 930		
	consecutive member <SE>	*s.* N 121		
	consecutive numbering <GN>	*s.* C 2229		
	consecutive prime numbers <NT>	*s.* N 141		
C 2069	**consequence** <LO>	Folgerung *f*; Folge *f*	conséquence *f*	вывод, следствие
	consequence <LO>	*s.* L 1059		
C 2070	**consequent** <of a proportion *or* ratio> <AR>	Hinterglied *n*	conséquent *m*, deuxième membre *m*, second membre	последующий член, второй член
C 2071	**consequent** <of an implication> <LO>	Hinterglied *n*	conséquent *m*	консеквент, последующий член, второй член
	consequent <LO>	*s.* 1. C 1786; 2. S 2226		
	consequent <NT, SE>	*s.* S 2237		
C 2072	**conservation of the number** <of an algebraic surface> <AG>	Erhaltung *f* der Anzahlen, Erhaltung des Geschlechts	conservation *f* des nombres, conservation du genre	сохранение количества
C 2073	**conservative extension** <of a theory> <LO>	konservative Erweiterung *f*	extension *f* conservative	консервативное расширение
C 2074	**conservative functor** <CA>	konservativer Funktor *m*	foncteur *m* conservatif	консервативный функтор
C 2075	**conservative genus** <of a function field> <AL>	konservatives Geschlecht *n*	genre *m* conservatif	консервативный род
C 2076	**conservative Markov process** <SP>	konservativer Markovscher Prozeß *m*	processus *m* de Markov conservatif	консервативный процесс Маркова
C 2077	**conservative measurable transformation** <ME>	konservative meßbare Transformation *f*	transformation *f* measurable conservative	консервативное измеримое преобразование
C 2078	**conservative test** <ST>	konservativer Test *m*	test *m* conservatif	консервативный критерий
C 2079	**consideration of analogy** <GN>	Analogiebetrachtung *f*	raisonnement *m* similaire	аналогичное рассуждение
C 2080	**consideration of continuity** <DI, TO>	Stetigkeitsbetrachtung *f*, Kontinuitätsbetrachtung *f*; Stetigkeitsverfahren *n*	considération *f* de continuité	рассмотрение (заключение) по непрерывности; способ рассуждения по непрерывности
C 2081	**consideration of the limit cases** <GN>	Grenzbetrachtung *f*, Betrachtung *f* der Grenzfälle	considération *f* des cas limites	предельное рассмотрение
	consistence <MM, ST>	*s.* C 2083		
C 2082	**consistency,** freedom of contradiction, compatibility <GN, LO>	Widerspruchsfreiheit *f*	non-contradiction *f*, consistance *f*, cohérence *f*	непротиворечивость, совместность, консистенция
C 2083	**consistency,** consistence <MM, ST>	Konsistenz *f*	consistance *f*	состоятельность
	consistency <GN>	*s.* C 1334		
	consistency <LO>	*s.* 1. L 1060; 2. N 81		
	ω-consistency <LO, MM>	*s.* O 66		
C 2084	**consistency conditions** <for linear equations> <AL>	Lösbarkeitsbedingungen *fpl*	conditions *fpl* de compatibilité	условия (требования) разрешимости
C 2085	**consistency problem** <MM>	Problem *n* der Widerspruchsfreiheit	problème *m* de la non-contradiction	проблема непротиворечивости
C 2086	**consistency[-]proof** <FO>	Widerspruchsfreiheitsbeweis *m*	démonstration *f* de non-contradiction	доказательство непротиворечивости
C 2087	**consistency theorem** <Bernays> <LO>	Widerspruchsfreiheitssatz *m*	théorème *m* de non-contradiction	теорема непротиворечивости
C 2088	**consistent** <MM>	konsistent	consistant	консистентный
C 2089	**consistent algebraic theory** <CA>	konsistente algebraische Theorie *f*	théorie *f* algébrique consistante	совместная алгебраическая теория

No.	English	German	French	Russian
C 2090	**consistent axiom system,** axiom system free from contradiction, compatible axioms <FO>	widerspruchsfreies (konsistentes) Axiomensystem *n*	système *m* consistant (non contradictoire), axiomes *mpl* compatibles	внутренне непротиворечивая система аксиом, непротиворечивая (совместная, консистентная) система аксиом
C 2091	**consistent definition** <FO>	widerspruchsfreie (verträgliche) Definition *f*	définition *f* non contradictoire	совместное (непротиворечащее) определение
	consistent diagram <AL, CA, SE, TO>	*s.* C 1258		
C 2092	**consistent equation** <GN>	widerspruchsfreie (lösbare) Gleichung *f*	équation *f* compatible	разрешимое (непротиворечивое) уравнение
	consistent equations ⌐<GN>	*s.* C 2098		
C 2093	**consistent estimate (estimator),** weakly consistent estimator (estimate) <ST>	[schwach] konsistente Schätzfunktion (Punktschätzung, Schätzung) *f*, passende Schätzfunktion (Punktschätzung, Schätzung)	estimateur *m* convergent (consistant, faiblement convergent, faiblement consistant)	состоятельная (слабо состоятельная) оценка
	consistent method <LI>	*s.* R 595		
	consistent method of limitation <LI>	*s.* R 596		
	consistent method of summation <LI>	*s.* R 595		
C 2094	**consistent methods of limitation** <LI>	verträgliche (konsistente) Limitierungsverfahren *npl*	méthodes *fpl* de limitation consistantes	совместные методы образования обобщенного предела
C 2095	**consistent methods of summation** <LI>	verträgliche (konsistente) Summierungsverfahren *npl*	méthodes *fpl* de sommation consistantes	совместные методы суммирования
C 2096	**consistent proposition** <LO>	widerspruchsfreie Aussage *f*	proposition *f* non contradictoire	непротиворечивое высказывание
C 2097	**consistent sequence,** weakly consistent sequence <of estimators *or* tests> <ST>	konsistente (schwach konsistente) Folge *f*	suite *f* consistante (faiblement consistante)	состоятельная (слабо состоятельная) последовательность
	consistent system <LO>	*s.* S 2509		
C 2098	**consistent system of equations,** consistent equations, compatible equations <GN>	lösbares (verträgliches) Gleichungssystem *n*, lösbares System *n* [von Gleichungen], lösbare (verträgliche) Gleichungen *fpl*	système *m* compatible [d'équations], équations *fpl* compatibles	совместная система [уравнений], совместные уравнения
C 2099	**consistent test** <ST>	konsistenter (passender) Test *m*	test *m* convergent (consistant)	состоятельный критерий
C 2100	**consistent theory,** noncontradictory theory <FO>	widerspruchsfreie Theorie *f*	théorie *f* non contradictoire, théorie consistante (cohérente)	непротиворечивая теория
C 2101	**constancy of sign** <GN>	Vorzeichenkonstanz *f*	permanence *f* de signe	знакопостоянство
C 2102	**constant** <of a ring> <AL>	Konstante *f*	constante *f*	константа
C 2103	**constant,** constant quantity <AN>	Konstante *f*, konstante Größe *f*	constante *f*, grandeur (quantité) *f* constante	постоянная, постоянная величина, константа
	constant <GN>	*s.* C 2116		
	constant <LO>	*s.* L 1061		
C 2104	**constant atomic proposition** <LO>	konstante Elementaraussage *f*	proposition *f* élémentaire constante	постоянное элементарное высказывание
	constant field <AL>	*s.* F 186		
	constant field extension <AL>	*s.* E 806		
	constant function <SE>	*s.* C 2107		
C 2105	**constant in the condition of Hölder,** Hölder['s] constant <AN>	Hölder-Koeffizient *m*, Hölderscher Koeffizient *m*, Koeffizient (Konstante *f*) in der Hölder-Bedingung, Hölder-Konstante *f*, Höldersche Konstante	constante *f* dans la condition de Hölder (Lipschitz)	постоянная условия (в условии) Гельдера, постоянная Гельдера, гельдеровская постоянная, коэффициент Гельдера; константа Липшица <для числовых функций одного действительного переменного>
C 2106	**constant in the condition of Lipschitz,** Lipschitz['s] constant <DE>	Lipschitz-Konstante *f*, Lipschitzsche Konstante *f*, Lipschitz-Koeffizient *m*, Lipschitzscher Koeffizient *m*, Koeffizient (Konstante *f*) in der Lipschitz-Bedingung	constante *f* dans la condition de Lipschitz	постоянная условия (в условии) Липшица, постоянная Липшица
C 2107	**constant mapping,** trivial map, constant function <SE>	konstante Abbildung *f*	application *f* constante	постоянное отображение, тривиальное отображение
	constant of multiplication <AL>	*s.* C 2108		
	constant of proportionality <GN>	*s.* F 51		
C 2108	**constant of structure,** structure constant, constant of multiplication, multiplication constant <of an algebra> <AL>	Strukturkonstante *f*, Produktkonstante *f*, Multiplikationszahl *f*, Multiplikationskonstante *f*, Zusammensetzungskonstante *f*	constante *f* de structure	структурная константа (постоянная)
C 2109	**constant path,** point curve <TO>	konstanter Weg *m*, Punktweg *m*	chemin *m* réduit à un point	постоянный (точечный) путь
	constant quantity <AN>	*s.* C 2103		
C 2110	**constant sheaf,** simple sheaf <AL, TO>	konstante Garbe *f*	faisceau *m* constant, faisceau *m* simple	постоянный пучок, простой пучок

No.	English	German	French	Russian
C 2111	**constant-sum game** <TG>	Konstantsummenspiel *n*	jeu *m* de somme constante	игра с постоянной суммой
C 2112	**constant symbol** <LO>	Konstantensymbol *n*	symbole *m* de constantes, symbole fonctionnel à 0 place	символ [для] постоянной
C 2113	**constant term,** absolute term <of an equation> <AL>	konstantes Glied *n*, Absolutglied *n*, // homogeneum *n* comparationis, Epanophora *f*	terme *m* absolu, // épanophore *m*	постоянный член
C 2114	**constant term,** absolute term <of a polynomial *or* power series> <AL, AN, SS>	Absolutglied *n*, konstantes Glied *n*, absolutes Glied *n*, freies Glied	terme *m* constant, terme *m* absolu, terme indépendant	свободный член, постоянный член
C 2115	**constant term** <of a translation> <GE>	Betrag *m*	amplitude *f*	постоянный член
	constant transition probability <SP>	*s.* S 1684		
C 2116	**constant value,** constant <GN>	konstanter Wert *m*, Festwert *m*, Konstante *f*	valeur *f* constante	постоянное значение, постоянная величина
C 2117	**constituent** <LO>	Konstituente *f*, Elementaralternative *f*, disjunktive Konstituente *f*	somme *f* élémentaire, constituante *f*	конституэнт, конституанта, конституента, элементарный многочлен
C 2118	**constituent** <relative to a Lusin sieve> <TO>	Konstituente *f* <bezüglich eines Lusinschen Siebes>	constituante *f* <déterminée par un crible>	составляющая, конституанта <определяемая решетом>
C 2119	**constrained game** <TG>	Spiel *n* mit Beschränkungen	jeu *m* borné	игра с побочными платежами, ограниченная игра, игра с ограничениями
C 2120	**constrained maximization,** constraint maximization <PG>	Maximierung *f* mit (unter) Nebenbedingungen	maximisation *f* à contraintes, maximisation contrainte	максимизация с ограничениями, условная максимизация
C 2121	**constrained minimization,** constraint minimization <PG>	Minimierung *f* mit (unter) Nebenbedingungen	minimisation *f* à contraintes, minimisation contrainte	минимизация с ограничениями, условная минимизация
C 2122	**constrained optimization** <PG>	Optimierung *f* mit (unter) Nebenbedingungen	optimisation *f* à contraintes, optimisation contrainte	оптимизация с ограничениями, условная оптимизация
C 2123	**constraint,** restriction, side condition <PG>	Nebenbedingung *f*, Bedingung *f*, Restriktion *f*, Einschränkung *f*, Zusatzbedingung *f*	contrainte *f*, restriction *f*	условие, ограничение
	constraint <DI, VA>	*s.* S 788		
	constraint extremum <DI, PG, VA>	*s.* E 898		
	constraint maximization <PG>	*s.* C 2120		
	constraint maximum <DI, PG, VA>	*s.* M 276		
	constraint minimization <PG>	*s.* C 2121		
	constraint minimum <DI, PG, VA>	*s.* M 621		
C 2124	**constructed example,** fictitious example <GN>	fiktives Beispiel *n*	exemple *m* fictif	искусственный (фиктивный) пример
	constructed experiment <ST>	*s.* I 110		
C 2125	**constructibility,** constructivity <SE>	Konstruierbarkeit *f*	constructibilité *f*	конструктивность
C 2126	**constructible map** <TO>	konstruierbare Abbildung *f*	application (fonction) *f* constructible	конструируемое отображение
C 2127	**constructible set** <SE>	konstruierbare Menge *f*	ensemble *m* constructible	конструктивное множество
C 2128	**constructible subspace** <TO>	konstruierbarer Unterraum *m*	sous-espace *m* constructible	конструируемое подпространство
	construction by compass alone <EG>	*s.* M 803		
	construction by ruler and compass <EG>	*s.* S 1833		
	construction by transfinite induction <LO>	*s.* D 141		
C 2129	**construction of a circle whose area is equal to that of a given square** <EG>	Zirkulatur *f* des Quadrats, Verwandlung *f* des Quadrats in einen Kreis	circulature (cerclure) *f* du carré	циркулятура квадрата
C 2130	**construction of Kochansky,** Kochansky['s] approximate construction <for the circumference of a circle> <GE>	Kochanskische Rektifikation *f* des Kreises	construction *f* de Kochanski <pour la circonférence d'un cercle>	[приближенное] построение Коханского окружности
C 2131	**construction of shadows** <DS>	Schattenkonstruktion *f*	construction *f* des ombres	построение теней
C 2132	**construction of the prism over a complex** <AT>	Prismenkonstruktion *f*	construction *f* du prisme sur un complexe	построение призмы над комплексом
C 2133	**construction problem** <EG>	Konstruktionsaufgabe *f*	problème *m* de construction	задача на построение
	construction with compass alone <EG>	*s.* M 803		
	construction with compass and ruler <EG>	*s.* S 1833		
C 2134	**constructive analysis** <MM>	konstruktive (berechenbare) Analysis *f*	analyse *f* constructive	конструктивный анализ
C 2135	**constructive dilemma** <LO>	konstruktives Dilemma *n*	dilemme *m* constructif	конструктивная дилемма, утверждающая форма дилеммы, modus ponens дилеммы

No.	English	German	French	Russian
C 2136	**constructive existence proof,** constructive proof of existence <GN>	konstruktiver Existenzbeweis *m*	démonstration *f* constructive d'existence	конструктивное доказательство существования
	constructive infinity <FO, SE>	*s.* P 1124		
C 2137	**constructive mathematics** <MM>	konstruktive Mathematik *f*	théorie *f* du constructif	конструктивная математика
C 2138	**constructiveness** <MM>	Konstruktivität *f*	constructivité *f*	конструктивность
C 2139	**constructive nondenumerability** <MM>	konstruktive Nichtaufzählbarkeit *f*	innumérabilité *f* constructive	конструктивная неперечислимость
	constructive proof of existence <GN>	*s.* C 2136		
	constructivity <SE>	*s.* C 2125		
C 2140	**construct recursively / to** <FO, GN>	rekursiv konstruieren	construire par récurrence	строить по индукции
C 2141	**consumer's risk** <ST>	Konsumentenrisiko *n*, Risiko *n* des Konsumenten	risque *m* du consommateur	риск покупателя (потребителя)
C 2142	**contact** <of the *m*-th order or of order *m*>; tangency; contingence <GE>	Berührung *f* <[von] *m*-ter Ordnung>	contact *m* <d'ordre *m* ou du *m*-ème ordre>; tangence *f*; attouchement *m*	касание <порядка *m* или *m*-го порядка>; соприкосновение
C 2143	**contact curve** <of two surfaces> <GE>	Berührungslinie *f*	courbe (ligne) *f* de raccordement, ligne de tangence	линия касания
C 2144	**contact transformation, contact-transformation** <AN, DE, DG>	Berührungstransformation *f*	transformation *f* de contact	преобразование прикосновения, касательное (контактное) преобразование
	contagious distribution <ST>	*s.* P 920		
C 2145	**contain / to** <subobjects> <CA>	majorisieren, größer sein <als> <Unterobjekte>	majorer <des sous-objets>	мажорировать <подобъекты>
C 2146	**contain / to** <elements> <SE>	enthalten <Elemente>	contenir, enfermer <ses éléments>	содержать <элементы>
	contain / to <SE>	*s.* F 451		
C 2147	**contained class field** <AB>	Teilklassenkörper *m*, Teil-Klassenkörper *m*	corps *m* de classes contenu	подполе классов
C 2148	**contained filter** <TO>	feinerer Filter *m* <*F* ist feiner als *F'*, *F'* ist gröber als *F*>	filtre *m* plus fin <que>	мажорирующий фильтр <*F* мажорирует *F'*>
C 2149	**contained prime ideal** <AL>	Primunterideal *n*	sous-idéal *m* premier	простой подыдеал
C 2150	**containing field extension** <AL>	umfassendere Körpererweiterung *f*	surextension *f*	надрасширение поля
C 2151	**containing filter** <TO>	gröberer Filter *m*	filtre *m* moins fin <que>	минорирующий (мажорируемый) фильтр
C 2152	**containing prime ideal** <AL>	Primoberideal *n*	suridéal *m* premier	простой надыдеал
C 2153	**containing universal domain** <AG>	universaler Oberkörper *m*	surcorps *m* universel	универсальное надполе
C 2154	**contain properly / to,** to include properly <as a subset> <SE>	echt (strikt) enthalten	contenir strictement	строго содержать внутри
C 2155	**content** <of a polynomial> <AL>	Inhalt *m* <Zahl *oder* Ideal>	contenu *m*, contenance *f*	содержание
C 2156	**content** <of a concept> <LO>	Inhalt *m*	contenu *m*, compréhension *f*	содержание
C 2157	**content,** content function, finitely additive measure, charge <ME>	Inhaltsfunktion *f*, Inhalt *m*	contenu *m*	протяженность
C 2158	**content,** Jordan['s] content, Jordan['s] measure <of a set> <ME>	Inhalt *m*, Peano-Jordanscher (Jordanscher) Inhalt	étendue *f*	жорданова мера
	content function <ME>	*s.* C 2157		
C 2159	**content-preserving connection (transfer)** <DG>	inhaltstreue Übertragung *f*	connexion *f* (transfert *m*) avec conservation de l'étendue	сохраняющая меру связность, сохраняющее меру перенесение
C 2160	**context-insensitive grammar** <TA>	kontextfreie Grammatik *f*	grammaire *f* « context-free »	бесконтекстная грамматика, контекстно-свободная грамматика, кс-грамматика
C 2161	**context-sensitive grammar** <TA>	kontextempfindliche Grammatik *f*	grammaire *f* « context-sensitive »	грамматика [непосредственно] составляющих, НС-грамматика, контекстная грамматика
C 2162	**contiguity** <of simplicial maps> <AT>	Benachbartsein *n*	contiguïté *f*	смежность, сопряженность
C 2163	**contiguity** <TO>	Benachbartheit *f*	contiguïté *f*	смежность, соприкосновение
C 2164	**contiguity class** <of simplicial mappings> <AT>	Nachbarschaftsklasse *f*	classe *f* de contiguïté	класс сопряженности
C 2165	**contiguous confluent hypergeometric function** <FU>	verwandte konfluente hypergeometrische Funktion *f*	fonction *f* hypergéométrique confluente contiguë	смежная конфлюентная гипергеометрическая функция
C 2166	**contiguous country** <GP>	benachbartes (adjazentes) Land *n*	pays *m* contigu	смежная область
C 2167	**contiguous hypergeometric function** <FU>	benachbarte [hypergeometrische] Funktion *f*	fonction *f* contiguë	смежная гипергеометрическая функция
C 2168	**contiguous intervals** <GN>	aneinandergrenzende (angrenzende) Intervalle *npl*	intervalles *mpl* contigus	смежные интервалы
C 2169	**contiguous map** <AT>	benachbarte Abbildung *f*	application *f* contiguë	смежное отображение
C 2169 a	**contiguous simplicial map** <AT>	[kombinatorisch] benachbarte simpliziale Abbildung *f*	application *f* simpliciale contiguë	сопряженное симплициальное отображение
C 2170	**contingence** <DG>	Kontingenz *f*	contingence *f*	касание

	contingence <GE>	*s.* C 2142		
C 2171	**contingency** <ST>	Kontingenz *f*	contingence *f*	сопряженность признаков, контингенция
C 2172	**contingency table** <ST>	Kontingenztafel *f*	tableau *m* de contingence, table *f* de contingence	таблица сопряженности признаков, таблица контингенции
C 2173	**contingent** <of a point set> <GE>	Kontingent *n*, Contingent *n*	contingent *m*	контэнжан
C 2174	**contingent compound** <expression neither universally valid nor a contradiction> <LO>	Neutralität *f*	expression (proposition, formule) *f* neutre, formule amphotère, neutralité *f*	нейтральность
C 2175	**continuability** <of an integral curve> <DE>	Fortsetzbarkeit *f*	prolongeabilité *f*	продолжаемость
	continuability <TO>	*s.* E 769		
C 2176	**continual reduction** <NT>	kontinuierliche Reduktion *f*	réduction *f* continue	
C 2177	**continuant** <AL>	Kontinuante *f*, Kettenbruchdeterminante *f*	continuant *m*	континуанта, определитель цепной (непрерывной) дроби
C 2178	**continuation** <of an isomorphism> <AL>	Fortsetzung *f*, Erweiterung *f*	prolongement *m*	продолжение
	continuation <AL, TO>	*s.* E 779		
C 2179	**continue by continuity / to** <AN, TO>	stetig fortsetzen	prolonger par continuité, continuer indéfiniment	продолжать непрерывно, продолжать по непрерывности
	continued division <AL, NT>	*s.* A 487		
C 2180	**continued equality** <AL>	fortlaufende Gleichung *f*	suite *f* d'égalités, chaîne *f* d'équations	цепь уравнений, цепь равенств; последовательность равенств
C 2181	**continued fraction** <*e.g.:* of *n*-th order, of order *n* *or* of higher order> <NT>	Kettenbruch *m*, kontinuierlicher Bruch *m* <*z. B.:* *n*-ter Ordnung, *n*-gliedriger *oder* höherer Ordnung>	fraction *f* continue <*par exemple:* de l'ordre *n* *ou* d'ordre supérieur>	цепная дробь, непрерывная дробь <*например:* порядка *n* *или* высшего порядка>
	continued fraction <NT>	*s.* G 137		
C 2182	**continued fraction algorithm** <AX>	Kettenbruchalgorithmus *m*, Kettenbruchmethode *f*	algorithme *m* des fractions continues	алгоритм цепных дробей
	continued fraction expansion <AN, AX, NT>	*s.* E 711		
C 2183	**continued fraction expansion of Laguerre** <NT>	Laguerrescher Kettenbruch *m*	développement *m* en fraction continue de Laguerre	лагерровское разложение в цепную дробь
C 2184	**continued fraction expansion of Lambert** <NT>	Lambertscher Kettenbruch *m*	fraction *f* continue de J. H. Lambert	непрерывная дробь Ламберта
C 2185	**continued fraction periodic in the limit** <NT>	limitär[ ]periodischer Kettenbruch *m*	fraction *f* continue limite périodique	предельно-периодическая цепная дробь
	continued fraction representation <AN, AX, NT>	*s.* E 711		
C 2186	**continued isomorphism** <AL>	fortgesetzter Isomorphismus *m*	isomorphisme *m* prolongé	продолженный изоморфизм
	continued product <SS>	*s.* I 469		
C 2187	**continued proportion** <$a:b:c:\ldots = d:e:f:\ldots$> <AR>	fortlaufende Proportion *f*, Kettenproportion *f*, stetige Proportion *f*	proportion *f* continue	кратная пропорция, цепь пропорций, ряд отношений
	continuing without end <AN>	*s.* I 492		
	μ-continuity <AN>	*s.* M 943		
C 2188	**continuity axiom** <intuitionism, Brouwer> <MM>	Stetigkeitsaxiom *n*	axiome *m* de continuité	аксиома непрерывности
C 2189	**continuity domain** <AN, TO>	Stetigkeitsgebiet *n*	domaine *m* de continuité	область непрерывности
C 2190	**continuity interval** <AN, ST>	Stetigkeitsintervall *n*	intervalle *m* de continuité	интервал непрерывности
	continuity in the Baire sense <RF>	*s.* B 16		
C 2191	**continuity in the mean** <FA>	Stetigkeit *f* im Mittel	continuité *f* en moyenne	непрерывность в среднем
C 2192	**continuity method** <AN, FT>	Kontinuitätsmethode *f*	méthode *f* de continuité	метод непрерывности
C 2193	**continuity on both sides,** two-sided continuity <DI>	zweiseitige Stetigkeit *f*	continuité *f* vers (à) deux côtés	двусторонняя непрерывность
	continuity on one side <AN>	*s.* O 103		
C 2194	**continuity on the left** ┌<AN>	linksseitige Stetigkeit *f*	continuité *f* à gauche	непрерывность слева
C 2195	**continuity on the right** <AN>	rechtsseitige Stetigkeit *f*	continuité *f* à droite	непрерывность справа
C 2196	**continuity principle of Poncelet,** Poncelet['s] principle of continuity <GE>	Kontinuitätsprinzip *n* von Poncelet, Ponceletsches Kontinuitätsprinzip	principe *m* de continuité [de Poncelet]	принцип непрерывности Понселе
C 2197	**continuity statement** <AN, TO>	Stetigkeitsaussage *f*	énoncé *m* de continuité	утверждение [о] непрерывности
C 2198	**continuity theorem** <for singularities> <FT>	Kontinuitätssatz *m*	théorème *m* de continuité	теорема непрерывности
	continuity with respect to μ <AN>	*s.* M 943		
C 2199	**continuous boundary** <AT>	stetiger Rand *m*	bord *m* continu	непрерывная граница

C 2200	**continuous cell** <AT>	stetige (singuläre) Zelle *f*	cellule *f* continue	непрерывная клетка
C 2201	**continuous continuation** <TO>	stetige Fortsetzung *f*, stetige Erweiterung *f*	prolongement *m* par continuité	продолжение (расширение) <отображения> по непрерывности
C 2202	**continuous convergence in the restricted sense** <TO>	stetige Konvergenz *f* im engeren Sinne	convergence *f* continue au sens étroit	непрерывная сходимость в узком смысле
	continuous correspondence <TO>	*s.* C 2227		
C 2203	**continuous curve,** Peano['s] continuum <TO>	stetige Kurve *f*, stetiges Streckenbild *n*, Jordansche (Peanosche) Kurve, Peanosche (stetig durchlaufbare) Menge *f*	courbe *f* continue, ligne *f* de Jordan, ensemble *m* péanien (Peanien)	непрерывная кривая, жорданова кривая, кривая Жордана, пеановский континуум
C 2204	**continuous cut** <of ordered sets> <SE>	stetiger Schnitt *m*	coupe *f* continue	непрерывное сечение
	"continuous" cycle <AT>	*s.* S 1060		
C 2205/6	**continuous decomposition** <of a space> <TO>	stetige Zerlegung *f*	décomposition *f* continue	непрерывное разбиение
	continuous deformation <TO>	*s.* D 145		
C 2207	**continuous differentiability** <DI>	stetige Differenzierbarkeit *f*	dérivabilité (différentiabilité) *f* continue, dérivabilité de classe C^1	непрерывная дифференцируемость
C 2208	**continuous diffusion** <ME>	stetige Diffusion *f*	diffusion *f* continue	непрерывная диффузия
C 2209	**continuous distribution,** geometric distribution <ST>	stetige (kontinuierliche) Verteilung *f*, geometrische Verteilung	distribution *f* continue, distribution géométrique	непрерывное распределение, геометрическое распределение
C 2210	**continuous distribution function** <ST>	stetige Verteilungsfunktion *f*, Verteilungsfunktion vom stetigen Typ	fonction *f* de distribution continue	непрерывная функция распределения
C 2211	**continuous flow** <SP>	kontinuierliche Strömung *f*	courant *m* continu	непрерывный поток
	continuous from one side <AN>	*s.* C 2230		
	continuous function <TO>	*s.* C 2227		
	μ-continuous function <AN>	*s.* M 944		
C 2212	**continuous function in the extended sense,** function continuous in the extended sense <AN>	im weiteren Sinne stetige Funktion *f*, stetige Funktion im weiteren Sinne	fonction *f* continue au sens général	обобщенно непрерывная функция
C 2213	**continuous function in the mean** <FA>	stetige Funktion *f* im Mittel, im Mittel stetige Funktion	fonction *f* continue en moyenne	непрерывная в среднем функция
	continuous functor <CA>	*s.* L 324		
C 2214	**continuous game** <TG>	kontinuierliches (stetiges) Spiel *n*	jeu *m* continu	непрерывная игра
C 2215	**continuous geometry** <GE, LA>	kontinuierlich[dimensional]e Geometrie *f*, stetige Geometrie	géométrie *f* continue	непрерывная геометрия
	continuous group <GR>	*s.* T 518		
C 2216	**continuous homology** <AT>	stetige Homologie *f*	homologie *f* continue	непрерывные гомологии
C 2217	**continuous homology group** <AT>	stetige Homologiegruppe *f*	groupe *m* d'homologie continue	группа непрерывных гомологий
C 2218	**continuous image** <TO>	stetiges Bild *n*	image *f* continue	непрерывный образ
C 2219	**continuous in the Mackey topology** <TO>	stetig in der Mackey-Topologie	M-continu	непрерывный в смысле Макки
C 2220	**continuous in x** <DI>	stetig in *x*	continu en *x*	непрерывный по *x*
	continuous lattice <LA>	*s.* C 1449		
C 2221	**continous limit** <of a filter> <TO>	stetiger Limes *m*	limite *f* continue	непрерывный предел
	continuous linear dual <FA, TO>	*s.* A 307		
C 2222	**continuously convergent sequence of functions** <AN>	stetig konvergente Funktionenfolge *f*	suite *f* de fonctions continûment (localement uniformément) convergente	непрерывно (локально равномерно) сходящаяся последовательность функций
C 2223	**continuously convergent sequence of functions in the narrower sense** <AN>	stetig konvergente Funktionenfolge *f* im engeren Sinne	suite *f* de fonctions convergente de façon continue au sens étroit	непрерывно сходящаяся в узком смысле последовательность функций
C 2224	**continuously differentiable function** <DI>	stetig differenzierbare Funktion *f*	fonction *f* continûment différentiable (dérivable), fonction *f* différentiable (dérivable) de classe C^1	непрерывно дифференцируемая функция
C 2225	**continuously embedded space** <TO>	stetig eingebetteter Raum *m*	espace *m* continûment plongé	непрерывно вложенное пространство
C 2226	**continuously homologous chains** <AT>	stetig homologe Ketten *fpl*	chaînes *fpl* continûment homologues	непрерывно гомологические цепи
	continuously ordered set (system) <SE>	*s.* C 2232		
C 2227	**continuous map[ping],** continuous correspondence (transformation, function), map, mapping <TO>	stetige Abbildung *f*	application *f* continue	непрерывное отображение
C 2228	**continuous method [of limitation]** <LI>	stetiges Limitierungsverfahren (V-Verfahren,	méthode *f* continue [de limitation]	непрерывный метод [образования обобщенного

No.	English	German	French	Russian
		Verfahren) *n*, Matrixverfahren *n* mit stetigem Parameter		предела]
C 2229	**continuous numbering,** (consecutive) numbering <GN>	fortlaufende Numerierung *f*, Durchnumerierung *f*	numération *f* en continu, numérotage *m*, numérotation *f*	непрерывная нумерация, перенумерование, снабжение сквозной нумерацией
C 2230	**continuous on one side,** continuous from one side, unilaterally continuous <AN>	einseitig stetig	continu vers (à) un seul côté	непрерывный с одной стороны
C 2231	**continuous on the left,** left-hand continuous, left-continuous <AN>	linksseitig (rückwärts) stetig, linksstetig	continu vers le gauche, continu à gauche	непрерывный слева
C 2232	**continuous ordered set,** continuous set, continuously ordered set (system) <SE>	stetige Menge *f*	ensemble *m* continu, ensemble *m* totalement ordonné continu	непрерывное множество
C 2233	**continuous part** <of a function of bounded variation> <RF, FA>	stetiger Anteil (Teil) *m*	partie *f* continue	непрерывная часть
C 2234	**continuous process,** continuous stochastic process <SP>	stetiger (kontinuierlicher) Prozeß *m*, stetiger (kontinuierlicher) stochastischer Prozeß	processus *m* continu, processus stochastique continu	непрерывный процесс, непрерывный случайный процесс
C 2235	**continuous progression** <AR>	stetige Progression *f*	progression *f* continue	непрерывная прогрессия
C 2236	**continuous random variable,** continuous variate <ST>	stetige Zufallsgröße *f* (Zufallsvariable *f*), stetige (kontinuierliche) zufällige Variable *f*	variable *f* aléatoire continue	непрерывная случайная величина (переменная), непрерывно распределенная случайная величина
C 2237	**continuous representation** <of a topological group in a topological group> <GR>	stetige Darstellung *f* <einer topologischen Gruppe in einer topologischen Gruppe>	représentation *f* continue <d'un groupe topologique dans un groupe topologique>, morphisme *m* <d'un groupe topologique dans un groupe topologique pour les structures de groupe topologique>	непрерывное представление <топологической группы в топологическую группу>, морфизм <топологической группы в топологическую группу для структур топологических групп>
C 2238	**continuous ruin problem** <TG>	Ruinproblem *n* bei stetigem Spiel, stetiges Ruinproblem	problème *m* de la ruine continu	непрерывная задача о разорении [игрока]
C 2239	**continuous section** <of a fibre bundle> <AT>	stetiger Schnitt *m*	section *f* continue	непрерывное сечение
	continuous set <SE>	*s.* C 2232		
C 2240	**continuous set function with respect to a measure** <AN, ME>	stetige Mengenfunktion *f* in bezug auf ein Maß	fonction *f* d'ensemble continue par rapport à une mesure	функция множества, непрерывная по мере
C 2241/2	**continuous spectrum** <FA, IE>	kontinuierliches Spektrum *n*, Streckenspektrum *n*	spectre *m* continu	непрерывный спектр
C 2243	**continuous stationary process [in the broader sense]** <SP>	stationärer stetiger Prozeß *m* im weiteren Sinne, im weiteren Sinne stationärer stetiger Prozeß *m*	processus *m* continu stationnaire au sens large	стационарный в широком смысле непрерывный процесс
	continuous stochastic process <SP>	*s.* C 2234		
	continuous system <AG>	*s.* A 462		
	continuous transformation <TO>	*s.* C 2227		
C 2244	**continuous type** <of distribution functions> <ST>	stetiger Typ *m*	type *m* continu	непрерывный тип
C 2245	**continuous uniform distribution,** uniform distribution, rectangular distribution, rectangular partition <ST>	stetige gleichmäßige Verteilung *f*, gleichmäßige Verteilung *f*, Gleichverteilung *f*, Rechteckverteilung *f*, rechteckige Verteilung *f*, Rechtecksverteilung *f*	distribution *f* uniforme continue, distribution uniforme, répartition *f* uniforme continue, répartition uniforme, loi *f* uniforme continue, loi uniforme, distribution (répartition, loi) rectangulaire	непрерывное равномерное распределение, равномерное распределение, прямоугольное распределение
	continuous variate <ST>	*s.* C 2236		
C 2246	**continuum** <*e.g.*: of bounded order> <TO>	Kontinuum *n*, topologisches Kontinuum <*z. B.*: beschränkter Ordnung>	continu *m*, espace *m* continu <*par exemple*: d'ordre borné>	континуум <*например*: ограниченного порядка>
	continuum <AN, SE>	*s.* N 872		
C 2247	**continuum hypothesis, continuum-hypothesis,** Cantor['s] continuum hypothesis, hypothesis of the continuum, CH <SE>	Kontinuumhypothese *f*, Kontinuumshypothese *f*	hypothèse *f* du continu	гипотеза континуума, континуум-гипотеза, континуум-гипотеза Кантора
	continuum infinite set <SE>	*s.* S 657		
C 2248	**continuum of convergence** <TO>	Konvergenzkontinuum *n*	continu *m* de convergence	континуум сходимости
	continuum of numbers <AN, SE>	*s.* N 872		
	continuum of real numbers <AN, SE>	*s.* N 872		
	continuum power <SE>	*s.* P 1145		

C 2249	**continuum problem [of Cantor]**, Cantor['s] continuum problem <SE>	Kontinuumproblem *n*, Kontinuumsproblem *n*	problème *m* du continu	проблема континуума
C 2250	**contour** <of a combinatorial surface> <AT>	Rand *m*	contour *m*	контур
C 2251	**contour** <DS>	Umriß *m*, Bildgrenze *f*, Kontur *f*	contour *m*	контур [проекции], очертание
C 2252	**contour,** closed contour (curve, line, loop), loop, circuit; closed path <AN>	geschlossene Kurve (Linie) *f*, Kontur *f*; geschlossener Weg *m*	contour *m* [fermé], courbe (ligne) *f* fermée, circuit *m*; chemin *m* fermé, route *f* fermée, lacet *m*	[замкнутый] контур, замкнутая кривая (линия); замкнутый путь
C 2253	**contour** <of a face> <GP>	Kontur *f* <eines Gebiets>	contour *m* <d'une face>	грань <области>
C 2254	**contour** <of a surface> <TO>	[geschlossene] Randkurve *f*, geschlossener Rand *m*	contour *m*	контур
	contour circle <DS>	*s.* H 171		
	contour ellipse <ST>	*s.* E 157		
	contour ellipsoid <ST>	*s.* E 162		
C 2255	**contour integral,** $\oint$ <FT>	Umlaufintegral *n*, $\oint$, // Umlaufsintegral *n*	intégrale *f* de contour, $\oint$	контурный интеграл, $\oint$
	contour integral <AN>	*s.* C 734a		
C 2256	**contour line** <DS>	Konturlinie *f*	ligne *f* du contour	контурная линия
	contour line <DS>	*s.* L 598		
	contour plane <DS>	*s.* L 600		
	contour surface <DG, RF, ST>	*s.* L 601		
C 2257	**contract / to** <tensors>, to form the inner product <of tensors> <VT>	überschieben <Tensoren>	multiplier et contracter <des tenseurs>	свернуть <тензоры>
C 2258	**contracted ideal,** contraction <of an ideal> <AL>	Verengungsideal *n*	idéal *m* contracté	сжатый идеал
C 2259	**contracted notation,** abridged notation <GN>	abgekürzte Bezeichnung (Schreibung) *f*, Kurzbezeichnung *f*, Kurzschreibweise *f*	notation *f* abrégée	сокращенное обозначение
	contracted product <TO>	*s.* S 1229		
C 2260	**contracted tensor** <VT>	verjüngter Tensor *m*	tenseur *m* contracté	свернутый тензор
C 2261	**contractibility,** collapsibility <relatively to a space> <TO>	Zusammenziehbarkeit *f* <relativ zu einem Raum>	contractilité *f* <relativement à un espace>	стягиваемость <относительно пространства>
	contractible <HA>	*s.* C 468		
C 2262	**contractible graph** <AT, GP>	zusammenziehbarer Graph *m*	graphe *m* contractile	стягиваемый граф
C 2263	**contractible parallel pair** <of morphisms> <CA>	zusammenziehbares (zusammenziehbares paralleles) Paar *n* <von Morphismen>	paire *f* <de morphismes> contractile	стягиваемая пара <морфизмов>
	contractible space <TO>	*s.* C 2265		
C 2264	**contractible to a set** <TO>	zu einer Menge zusammenziehbar	contractile en un ensemble	стягиваемый в множество
C 2265	**contractible topological space,** collapsible (reducible) topological space, contractible (collapsible, reducible) space, space deformable into a point, space contractible into itself <TO>	kontrahierbarer (auf einen Punkt zusammenziehbarer, in einen Punkt deformierbarer) Raum *m*, [in sich] zusammenziehbarer [topologischer] Raum	espace *m* contractile (topologique contractile, intégralement contractile), espace [intégralement] contractile en soi, espace déformable en un seul point	стягиваемое пространство, деформируемое в точку (себе) пространство, стягиваемое топологическое пространство
C 2266	**contracting function** <AN> ┌<HA>	kontrahierende Funktion *f*	fonction *f* contractante	сжимающая функция
C 2267	**contracting homotopy**	kontrahierende Homotopie *f*	homotopie *f* contractante	стягивающая гомотопия
	contracting mapping <FA, TO>	*s.* C 2271		
C 2268	**contracting mapping principle** <DE, FA, IE>	Prinzip *n* der kontrahierenden Abbildung	principe *m* de l'application contractante	принцип сжатых отображений
	contracting mapping principle <AN, DE, TO>	*s.* M 488		
C 2269	**contracting operator** <FA>	kontrahierender Operator *m*, Kontraktionsoperator *m*	opérateur *m* contractant, opérateur *m* de contraction	сжимающий оператор, оператор сжатия
C 2270	**contraction** <of a continued fraction, a Lie algebra, *or* a matroid> <AB, AL, CT>	Kontraktion *f*	contraction *f*	сжатие
C 2271	**contraction,** contracting mapping, contractive transformation, contraction mapping (map) <FA, TO>	kontrahierende Abbildung (Transformation) *f*, Kontraktion *f*	contraction *f*, application *f* contractante, transformation *f* contractante	сжатое отображение, сжимающее отображение (преобразование), преобразование сжатия, стягивающее отображение (преобразование)
C 2272	**contraction,** shrinkage <of vertices> <GP>	Kontraktion *f*	contraction *f*, rétrécissement *m*	сжатие
C 2273	**contraction** <*e.g.:* in the antecedent, in the succedent> <LO>	Zusammenziehung *f*, Verschmelzung *f* <*z. B.:* im Antezedens, im Sukzedenz>	contraction *f* <*par exemple:* dans l'antécédent, dans le conséquent>	сокращение <*например:* в антецеденте, в сукцеденте>
C 2274	**contraction** <of a tensor>, strangling <of an index> <VT>	Verjüngung, Faltung *f*, Kontraktion *f*, Zusammenziehung *f*, Tensorverjüngung <bezüglich eines Index>	contraction *f*, saturation *f* <d'un indice>	свертывание <индексов>

No.	English	German	French	Russian
	contraction <AL>	*s.* C 2258		
	contraction <GP>	*s.* C 2036		
	contraction <VT>	*s.* I 557		
	contraction map[ping] <FA, TO>	*s.* C 2271		
C 2275	**contraction rule** <LO>	Verschmelzungsregel *f*, Kürzungsregel *f*	règle *f* de contraction (tautologie)	правило сокращения, разрешение опускать одну из совпадающих посылок
	contractive transformation <FA, TO>	*s.* C 2271		
C 2276	**contradiction** <LO>	Widerspruch *m*	contradiction *f*	противоречие
C 2277	**contradiction,** identically false formula, false formula, non satisfiable formula <LO>	Falschform *f*, Kontradiktion *f*, unerfüllbare (kontradiktorische, falsche) Formel *f*, logische Kontradiktion; unerfüllbarer A-Ausdruck *m* <im Aussagenkalkül>	contradiction *f*, antilogie *f*, formule *f* toujours (identiquement, logiquement) fausse, formule irréalisable (insatisfiable, non satisfiable, fausse)	всегда-ложное высказывание, невыполнимая (тождественно[-]ложная) формула, противоречие, ложная формула
	contradictoriness <LO>	*s.* I 279		
C 2278	**contradictory proposition** <LO>	widerspruchsvolle Aussage *f*	proposition *f* contradictoire	противоречивое высказывание
C 2279	**contradictory propositions** <LO>	kontradiktorische (sich widersprechende) Aussagen *fpl*	propositions *fpl* contradictoires	противоречащие (контрадикторные, противоречивые) предложения
	contradictory system of axioms <FO>	*s.* I 284		
C 2280	**contragradient composition,** opposite composition <AL>	entgegengesetzte Verknüpfung *f*	composition *f* opposée	противоположная композиция
	contragradient set <IV>	*s.* C 2284		
C 2281	**contragredience** <AL,GE>	Kontragredienz *f*	contragrédience *f*	контрагредиентность
	contragredient <AL>	*s.* C 2283		
C 2282	**contragredient automorphism** <GR>	kontragredienter Automorphismus *m*	automorphisme *m* contragrédient	контрагредиентный автоморфизм
	contragredient automorphism <GR>	*s.a.* O 543		
C 2283	**contragredient isomorphism (mapping),** contragredient transformation, contragredient <AL>	kontragrediente Abbildung (Transformation) *f*, Kontragrediente *f*	isomorphisme *m* contragrédient, contragrédient *m*, application (transformation) *f* contragrédiente, contragrédiente *f*	контрагредиентное отображение (преобразование)
	contragredient representation <RE>	*s.* S 1656		
C 2284	**contragredient set (system)** <of variables *or* symbols>, // contragradient set <IV>	kontragrediente Reihe *f*, kontragredientes System *n*	suite *f* contragrédiente, système *m* contragrédient	контрагредиентная система, контравариантная система, противоположно преобразующаяся система
	contragredient transformation <AL>	*s.* C 2283		
C 2285	**contraharmonic mean [value]** <ST>	kontraharmonisches Mittel *n*, kontraharmonischer Mittelwert *m*	moyenne *f* contra[-]harmonique	контрагармоническое среднее, среднее контрагармоническое
	contraposition <LO>	*s.* 1. C 2287; 2. T 858		
	contraposition principle <LO>	*s.* C 1450		
	contrapositive <LO>	*s.* C 2287		
C 2286	**contrapositive of the implication** <LO>	Kontraposition *f* der Implikation	contraposition *f* du conditionnel	контрапозитивная импликация
C 2287	**contrapositive sentence,** contrapositive <of a theorem>, contraposition <of a proposition> <LO>	Kontraposition *f* <einer Aussage>, Umkehrung *f* <einer Aussage *oder* eines Urteils>	contraposition *f* <d'un jugement>	контрапозитивное высказывание, контрапозиция <высказывания>, противопоставление <высказывания>
C 2288	**contrariant** <form invariable in reciprocal substitutions> <IV>	Kontrariante *f* <Sylvester>	contrariant *m*	контрариант
C 2289	**contrariness** <LO>	Konträrsein *n*	contrariété *f*	противоположность
C 2290	**contrary** <GN>	entgegengesetzte Behauptung *f*	assertion *f* contraire	противное утверждение
C 2291	**contrary propositions** <LO>	konträre Aussagen *fpl*, entgegengesetzte Aussagen	jugements *mpl* (propositions *fpl*) contraires, paire *f* de contraires	контрарные суждения, контрарные (противные, противоположные) предложения
C 2292	**contrary theorem** <GN>	entgegengesetzter Satz *m*	théorème *m* contraire	противоположная теорема
C 2293	**contrast,** linear contrast <ST>	Kontrast *m*, linearer Kontrast <*pl.:* Kontrasts>	contraste *m*, contraste linéaire	контраст, линейный контраст
C 2294	**contravariance** <AL, VT>	Kontravarianz *f*	contravariance *f*, contrevariance *f*	контравариантность, контрагредиентность
C 2295	**contravariant** <IV>	Kontravariante *f*, zugehörige Form *f*, Zwischenform *f*	contrevariant *m*, contravariant *m*	контравариант
C 2296	**contravariant coordinate (component)** <AL, VT>	kontravariante Koordinate (Komponente) *f*	coordonnée (composante) *f* contravariante	контравариантная координата (компонента, составляющая)
C 2297	**contravariant density** <VT>	kontravariante Dichte *f*, relative Invariante *f* vom Gewicht —1	densité *f* contravariante	относительный инвариант веса —1, контравариантная плотность
C 2298	**contravariant derivative** <DG, VT>	kontravariante Ableitung *f*	dérivée *f* contravariante	контравариантная производная
C 2299	**contravariant functor adjoint on the right** <CA>	rechtsseitig adjungierter kontravarianter Funktor *m*	foncteur *m* contravariant adjoint à droite	сопряженный справа контравариантный функтор
	contravariant homfunctor <CA, HA>	*s.* C 2301		
C 2300	**contravariant index** <of a tensor> <VT>	kontravarianter Index *m*	indice *m* contravariant	контравариантный индекс

C 2301	**contravariant morphism functor,** contravariant hom-functor <CA, HA>	kontravarianter Hom-Funktor *m*	foncteur *m* Hom contravariant	основной [одноместный] контравариантный функтор
	contravariant order <VT>	*s.* C 2306		
C 2302	**contravariant set system** <of variables> <IV>	kontravariante Größenreihe, (Symbolreihe, Reihe) *f*	système *m* contravariant	контравариантная система
C 2303	**contravariant tangent bundle,** vector bundle of contravariant tangent vectors <AT>	Vektorraumbündel *n* der kontravarianten Tangentialvektoren, kontravariantes tangentielles Vektorraumbündel	fibré *m* tangent contravariant	векторное расслоение контравариантных касательных векторов, контравариантное касательное расслоение
C 2304	**contravariant tensor of order *p*,** contravariant tensor of valence *p*, *p*-times contravariant tensor <AL, VT>	*p*-stufig kontravarianter Tensor *m*, [rein] kontravarianter Tensor der Stufe *p*	tenseur *m* *p* fois contravariant, tenseur contravariant d'ordre (de valence) *p*	*p* раз контравариантный тензор, контравариантный тензор ранга (валентности) *p*
C 2305	**contravariant tensor of the second order,** diatensor <VT>	Diatensor *m* <Budde>, kontravarianter Tensor *m* zweiter (2.) Stufe	tenseur *m* deux fois contravariant	контравариантный тензор валентности 2
	contravariant tensor of valence *p* <AL, VT>	*s.* C 2304		
C 2306	**contravariant valence,** contravariant order <VT>	kontravariante Valenz (Stufe) *f*	valence *f* contravariante, ordre *m* contravariant	контравариантная валентность, контравариантный ранг
C 2307	**control cart** <ST>	Kontrollkarte *f*	carte *f* de contrôle	контрольная (поверочная) карта
C 2308	**control chart method (technique)** <ST>	Kontrollkartentechnik *f*	méthode *f* des cartes de contrôle	метод контрольных карт
	control device <PG>	*s.* C 2313		
	control function <ST>	*s.* S 1688		
C 2309	**controllable stochastic process** <SP>	steuerbarer stochastischer Prozeß *m*	processus *m* stochastique contrôlable	управляемый случайный процесс
	controlled member <PG>	*s.* C 2311		
C 2310	**controlled stochastic process** <SP>	gesteuerter stochastischer Prozeß *m*	processus *m* stochastique contrôlé	управленный случайный процесс
C 2311	**controlled system,** system to be controlled, controlled member <PG>	gesteuertes Teilsystem *n*, Steuerstrecke *f*, Regelstrecke *f*, Prozeßsystem *n*	système *m* réglé (commandé, à régler), installation *f* réglée	управляемая (регулируемая) система
	controller <PG>	*s.* C 2313		
C 2312	**control limit** <ST>	Kontrollgrenze *f*	limite *f* de contrôle	контрольная граница, контрольный предел
C 2313	**controlling system,** control device, controller <PG>	steuerndes Teilsystem *n*, Steuereinrichtung *f*, Regler *m*, Leitungssystem *n*	contrôleur *m*, régulateur *m*	управляющая система, регулятор
C 2314	**control parameter,** decision <SP>	Steuerparameter *m*, Entscheidung *f*	paramètre *m* de contrôle, décision *f*	параметр управления, решение
C 2315	**control treatment,** control variant <ST>	Kontrollprüfglied *n*, Kontrollbehandlung *f*, Kontrollvariante *f*, Bezugsvariante *f*, Bezugsprüfglied *n*, Standard *m*	traitement *m* témoin	контрольная обработка, контрольный вариант, контрольное испытание
	control variable <PG, SP>	*s.* D 46		
	control variant <ST>	*s.* C 2315		
C 2316	**conull object,** initial object, coterminal object <CA>	initiales Objekt *n*, Kopunkt *m*, Copunkt *m*, Anfangsobjekt *n*, Kopunktobjekt *n*, Copunktobjekt *n*, Anfang *m*	∅-somme *f*, objet *m* initial	инициальный объект, левый нуль, начальный объект
C 2317	**co-null set,** set which is complement of a null set <ME>	Menge *f*, die Komplement einer Menge vom Maß Null ist	épaisseur *f* pleine, plénitude *f*	множество, дополнение которого имеет меру нуль
C 2318	**converge / to,** to tend <to *or* towards a limit> <AN, SS>	konvergieren, streben, gehen <gegen einen *oder* nach einem Grenzwert>	converger, tendre <vers une limite>	сходиться, сойтись, стремиться <к пределу>
C 2319	**converge continuously / to** <AN, TO>	stetig konvergieren	converger de façon continue	непрерывно сходиться
C 2320	**converge more slowly / to** <AN, NU>	schlechter (langsamer) konvergieren	converger plus lentement	сходиться более медленно
C 2321	**convergence,** convergence by rectangles <of a double series> <SS>	Konvergenz *f*, Konvergenz nach Rechtecken	convergence *f*, convergence par rectangles	сходимость, сходимость по четырехугольникам
C 2322	**(*)-convergence** <in a partially ordered linear space> <FA>	(*)-Konvergenz *f*	(*)-convergence *f*	(*)-сходимость
	convergence <FA, TO>	*s.* S 1935		
	convergence <ST>	*s.* C 2332		
	convergence almost certain <ST>	*s.* A 507		
C 2323	**convergence almost everywhere** <AN>	Konvergenz *f* fast überall	convergence *f* presque partout	сходимость почти всюду
	convergence almost sure <ST>	*s.* A 507		
C 2324	**convergence behaviour,** behaviour of convergence <of a sequence *or* series> <SS>	Konvergenzverhalten *n*	comportement *m* de convergence	характер сходимости
C 2325	**convergence by columns** <of a double series> <SS>	Spaltenkonvergenz *f*, Kolonnenkonvergenz *f*	convergence *f* par colonnes	сходимость по столбцам
	convergence by components <FA, TO>	*s.* C 1669		

C 2326	**convergence by diagonals** <of a double series> <SS>	Konvergenz *f* nach Schräglinien (Diagonalen)	convergence *f* par diagonales	сходимость по диагоналям
C 2327	**convergence by hyperbolas,** Dirichlet['s] convergence <of a double series> <SS>	Konvergenz *f* nach Hyperbeln, Dirichletsche Konvergenz	convergence *f* par hyperboles, convergence de Dirichlet	сходимость по гиперболам, сходимость Дирихле
	convergence by rectangles <SS>	*s.* C 2321		
C 2328	**convergence by rows** <of a double series> <SS>	Zeilenkonvergenz *f*	convergence *f* par lignes	сходимость по строкам, построчная сходимость
	convergence by segments <FA>	*s.* S 247		
C 2329	**convergence by squares** <of a double series> <SS>	Konvergenz *f* nach Quadraten	convergence *f* par carrées	сходимость по квадратам
C 2330	**convergence class** <of nets> <TO>	Konvergenzklasse *f*	classe *f* de convergence	класс сходимости
	convergence component by component <FA, TO>	*s.* C 1669		
	convergence criterion <SS>	*s.* C 2670		
	convergence domain <FT>	*s.* D 863		
C 2331	**convergence everywhere,** permanent convergence <SS>	beständige Konvergenz *f*, Konvergenz überall	convergence *f* partout	сходимость всюду
C 2332	**convergence everywhere,** ordinary convergence, convergence <ST>	Konvergenz *f* im gewöhnlichen Sinne, Konvergenz überall, [gewöhnliche] Konvergenz	convergence *f* partout, convergence ordinaire, convergence	сходимость всюду, обыкновенная сходимость, сходимость
	convergence exponent <FT>	*s.* E 750		
C 2333	**convergence factor** <SS>	Konvergenzfaktor *m*	facteur *m* de convergence	коэффициент (множитель) сходимости
C 2334	**convergence factors** <SS>	Konvergenzfaktorenfolge *f*, Folge *f* von Konvergenzfaktoren, Faktorenfolge *f*	suite *f* de facteurs de convergence	последовательность коэффициентов сходимости
C 2335	**convergence-free sequence (co-ordinate) space** <FA>	konvergenzfreier Koordinatenraum (Folgenraum) *m*	espace *m* des coordonnées (suites) sans convergence	пространство последовательностей без сходимости, координатное пространство без сходимости
	convergence in mean <ST>	*s.* C 2342		
	convergence in mean <FA, RF>	*s.* 1. C 2341; 2. S 1934		
C 2336	**convergence in measure,** asymptotic convergence <AN>	Konvergenz *f* dem Maße nach, Konvergenz nach [dem] Maß, asymptotische Konvergenz	convergence *f* en mesure, convergence asymptotique	сходимость по мере, асимптотическая сходимость
C 2337	**convergence in norm,** convergence in the norm, uniform convergence <of a sequence of operators> <FA>	Konvergenz *f* bezüglich (nach) der Norm, Konvergenz nach Norm, Normkonvergenz *f*, Konvergenz der Norm nach, gleichmäßige Konvergenz	convergence *f* en norme, convergence uniforme	сходимость по норме, равномерная сходимость
C 2338	**convergence in probability,** probability convergence, stochastic convergence, weak convergence <ST>	Konvergenz *f* in [der] Wahrscheinlichkeit, Konvergenz nach Wahrscheinlichkeit, stochastische (schwache) Konvergenz	convergence *f* en probabilité, convergence stochastique (faible)	сходимость по вероятности, стохастическая (слабая) вероятность
	convergence in *p*-th mean <FA, RF>	*s.* S 1934		
	convergence in *p*-th mean <ST>	*s.* C 2343		
	convergence in quadratic (square) mean <FA, RF>	*s.* C 2341		
C 2339	**convergence in square (quadratic) mean** <e.g. in a normed space> <FA, ST>	Konvergenz *f* im quadratischen Mittel	convergence *f* en moyenne quadratique	сходимость в среднем квадратичном, среднеквадратичная сходимость
C 2340	**convergence in the Mackey topology** <in a linear topological space> <TO>	Mackeysche (totale) Konvergenz *f*, Konvergenz im Sinne von Mackey, Konvergenz in der Mackey-Topologie	Mackey-convergence *f*, M-convergence *f*, convergence *f* bornologique	сходимость в смысле Макки
C 2341	**convergence in the mean,** convergence in mean, mean convergence, strong convergence, convergence in square (quadratic) mean <in the space L_2> <FA, RF>	Konvergenz *f* im Mittel, starke (mittlere) Konvergenz, Konvergenz im quadratischen Mittel	convergence *f* en moyenne, convergence forte (en moyenne quadratique)	сходимость в среднем, сильная (среднеквадратичная) сходимость
C 2342	**convergence in the mean,** convergence in mean, mean convergence <ST>	Konvergenz *f* im Mittel	convergence *f* en moyenne	сходимость в среднем
	convergence in the mean <FA, RF>	*s.* S 1934		
	convergence in the mean <LO>	*s.* C 452		
	convergence in the Moore-Smith sense <FA, TO>	*s.* M 886		

	convergence in the norm <FA>	*s.* C 2337		
C 2343	**convergence in the p-th mean,** convergence in p-th mean <ST>	Konvergenz *f* im p-ten Mittel	convergence *f* [en moyenne] d'ordre p	сходимость [в среднем] p-го порядка
	convergence in the topology <TO>	*s.* T 510		
C 2344	**convergence in variation** <ST>	Konvergenz *f* in Variation	convergence *f* en variation	схождение по вариации
C 2345	**convergence line** <of a Dirichlet series> <SS>	Konvergenzgerade *f*, Grenzgerade *f* [der Konvergenz]	droite *f* de convergence	прямая сходимости
C 2346	**convergence preserving matrix** <LI>	konvergenztreue Matrix *f*	matrice *f* conservant la convergence	матрица, сохраняющая сходимость
C 2347	**convergence preserving method,** convergence preserving method of summation <LI>	konvergenztreues Summierungsverfahren *n*	méthode *f* (procédé *m*) [de sommation] conservant la convergence	метод суммирования, сохраняющий сходимость
C 2348	**convergence preserving method of limitation** <LI>	konvergenztreues Limitierungsverfahren (*V*-Verfahren) *n*	méthode *f* (procédé *m*) de limitation conservant la convergence	метод образования обобщенного предела, сохраняющий сходимость
	convergence preserving method of summation <LI>	*s.* C 2347		
	convergence region <FT, SS>	*s.* D 864		
	convergence set <FT>	*s.* S 658		
C 2349	**convergence space** <TO>	Konvergenzraum *m*	espace *m* de convergence	пространство сходимости
C 2350	**convergence statement** <SS>	Konvergenzaussage *f*, Konvergenzsatz *m*	énoncé *m* de convergence	утверждение о сходимости, теорема сходимости
C 2351	**convergence strip** <AN>	Konvergenzstreifen *m*	bande *f* de convergence	полоса сходимости
	convergence test <SS>	*s.* C 2670		
C 2352	**convergence theorem** <FA, FT>	Konvergenzsatz *m*	théorème *m* de convergence	теорема сходимости
	convergence with probability one <ST>	*s.* A 507		
C 2353	**convergence with respect to a valuation** <AL>	Konvergenz *f* bezüglich einer Bewertung	convergence *f* par rapport à une valuation	сходимость относительно нормирования
C 2354	**convergent,** approximant <n-th> <of a continued fraction> <NT>	Näherungsbruch *m* <n-ter, n-ter Ordnung>	réduite *f*, fraction *f* approchée <n-e, de rang n, d'ordre n>	подходящая дробь, отрезок <порядка n>
C 2355	**convergent almost everywhere** <AN>	fast überall konvergent, konvergent fast überall	convergent presque partout	сходящийся почти всюду
	convergent by segments <FA>	*s.* S 248		
C 2356	**convergent continued fraction** <NT>	konvergenter Kettenbruch (Bruch, unendlicher Kettenbruch) *m*	fraction *f* [continue] convergente, fraction continue infinie convergente	сходящаяся непрерывная дробь
C 2357	**convergent infinite product,** convergent product <SS>	konvergentes [unendliches] Produkt *n*	produit *m* [infini] convergent	сходящееся [бесконечное] произведение
C 2358	**convergent in measure,** asymptotically convergent <AN>	konvergent dem Maße nach, konvergent nach [dem] Maß, asymptotisch konvergent, maßkonvergent	convergent en mesure, asymptotiquement convergent	сходящийся по мере, асимптотически сходящийся
	convergent in quadratic mean <ST>	*s.* C 2359		
C 2359	**convergent in square mean,** convergent in quadratic mean <ST>	konvergent im quadratischen Mittel, im quadratischen Mittel konvergent	convergent en moyenne quadratique	сходящийся в среднем квадратичном
C 2360	**convergent integral** <DI>	bedingt konvergentes [uneigentliches] Integral *n*	intégrale *f* convergente	сходящийся [несобственный] интеграл, несобственный сходящийся интеграл
C 2361	**convergent iteration** <AX, NU>	konvergente Iteration *f*	itération *f* convergente	сходящаяся итерация
	convergent product <SS>	*s.* C 2357		
C 2362	**convergent sequence,** regular sequence <SS, TO>	konvergente Folge *f*	suite *f* convergente	сходящаяся последовательность
	convergent sequence <SS, TO>	*s.* C 268		
C 2363	**(*)-convergent sequence** <in a partially ordered linear space> <FA>	(*)-konvergente ((t)-konvergente) Folge *f*	suite *f* (*)-convergente	(*)-сходящаяся последовательность
	φ-convergent sequence <AL>	*s.* P 561		
C 2364	**convergent sequence of sets** <SE>	[algebraisch] konvergente Mengenfolge *f*	suite *f* d'ensembles convergente	сходящаяся последовательность множеств
C 2365	**convergent series** <SS>	konvergente Reihe *f*	série *f* convergente	сходящийся ряд
C 2366	**converge pointwise / to** <said of a function sequence> <AN>	punktweise konvergieren	converger simplement	поточечно сходиться
C 2367	**converge quasi[-]uniformly / to** <said of a sequence of measurable functions in a measure space> <FA>	nahezu gleichmäßig konvergieren, quasigleichmäßig konvergieren, wesentlich gleichmäßig konvergieren	converger quasi-uniformément (quasi uniformément)	квазиравномерно сходиться
C 2368	**converge quasi[-]uniformly / to** <said of a sequence of real functions on an interval> <RF>	quasigleichmäßig (streckenweise gleichmäßig) konvergieren	converger quasi-uniformément (quasi uniformément)	квазиравномерно сходиться
C 2369	**converge regularly / to** <TO>	regulär konvergieren	tendre régulièrement	регулярно сходиться

	converse <GN>	*s.* I 954		
	converse <LO>	*s.* 1. C 2372; 2. C 2375		
	converse <SE>	*s.* I 941		
C 2370	**converse automorphism,** dual automorphism <LA>	dualer Automorphismus *m*	automorphisme *m* dual	двойственный автоморфизм
	converse domain <SE>	*s.* R 122		
C 2371	**converse graph,** directional dual <of a graph> <GP>	Konversion *f*, entgegengesetzter Graph *m*, Dualgraph *m*	graphe *m* converse	противонаправленный граф
C 2372	**converse implication,** converse <of an implication> <LO>	umgekehrte Implikation *f*, Gegenimplikation *f*, konverse Implikation	implication *f* réciproque (inverse, converse), conditionnel *m* inverse, converse *f* du conditionnel	обратное следование, обратная импликация, конверсное следование
C 2373	**converse law of contraposition** <LO>	inverses Gesetz *n* der Wendung, Gesetz der inversen Kontraposition	loi *f* de contraposition inverse	обратный закон контрапозиции
	converse of Poincaré's theorem <DG>	*s.* P 710		
	converse ordering relation <SE>	*s.* D 1019		
C 2374	**converse order type,** type ordered inversely, inverse order type <SE>	entgegengesetzter (inverser, konverser, reziproker, dualer) Ordnungstyp *m*	type *m* d'ordre converse	обратный порядковый тип, обратный тип
	converse ordinal number <SE>	*s.* I 932		
	converse partial ordering <SE>	*s.* D 1019		
	converse relation <SE>	*s.* I 941		
C 2375	**converse sentence,** converse <of the given sentence> <LO>	konverses Urteil *n*	conversion *f* <d'une proposition>, proposition *f* réciproque	конверсное суждение
C 2376	**conversion** <of a number> <NT>	Konvertierung *f*, Transformation (Überführung) *f* der Darstellung	conversion *f*	обращение, перевод <из одной системы счисления в другую>
C 2377	**conversion** <e.g. to another unit of measurement> <NU>	Umrechnung *f*	conversion *f*	перевод <одной величины в другую>; пересчет
C 2378	**conversion** <of a relation> <SE>	Umkehrung *f* <einer Relation>	conversion *f*, inversion *f* <d'une relation>	обращение <отношения>
	conversion <GN>	*s.* T 761		
	λ-conversion <LO>	*s.* L 48		
C 2379	**conversion calculus** <LO>	Churchscher λ-Kalkül *m*, λ-Kalkül, Lambda-Kalkül *m*	calcul *m* de conversion [λ], calcul de conversion lambda	исчисление Черча, исчисление λ-конверсии (ламбда-конверсии)
C 2380	**conversion formula** <NU>	Umrechnungsformel *f*	formule *f* de conversion	формула перевода; формула пересчета
	conversion formula <GN>	*s.* I 963		
C 2381	**conversion table** <NU>	Umrechnungstabelle *f*	table *f* de conversion	таблица перевода
C 2382	**convex** <in a surface> <GE>	konvexes Gebiet *n*	domaine *m* convexe	выпуклая область
	convex <CS>	*s.* C 2392		
C 2383	**convex angle,** reflex angle <EG>	überstumpfer (konvexer, erhabener) Winkel *m*	angle *m* convexe (rentrant)	выпуклый угол; угол, больший развернутого
C 2384	**convex body [in the sense of Minkowski],** egg-shaped body, convex solid, ovoid body, ovoid <CS, GE>	konvexer Körper *m*, Eikörper *m*), nirgends konkaver Körper	corps *m* convexe, figure *f* convexe <en R_n>, corps nulle part concave	выпуклое тело
	convex cap curve <AN, GE>	*s.* C 1769		
	convex cap function <AN>	*s.* C 1770		
	convex circled hull <FA>	*s.* A 95		
C 2385	**convex circled set,** absolutely convex set, completely convex set <FA>	absolut[ ]konvexe Menge *f*, kreiskonvexe Menge	ensemble *m* absolument convexe	абсолютно выпуклое множество
	convex closure <CS>	*s.* C 2392		
C 2386	**convex combination,** convex linear combination <of points> <CS, FA, PG>	konvexe Kombination *f*, Konvexkombination *f*, konvexe Linearkombination *f*	combinaison *f* linéaire convexe	выпуклая линейная комбинация
C 2387	**convex cone** <CS, FA, GE, PG>	konvexer Kegel *m*	cône *m* convexe	выпуклый конус
	convex cover <TO>	*s.* C 851		
	convex cup curve <AN, GE>	*s.* C 2388		
	convex cup function <AN>	*s.* C 2391		
C 2388	**convex curve,** convex cup curve, convex $\cup$ curve, convex down curve, concave up curve< AN, GE>	konvexe Kurve *f*, konvexe Kurve abwärts (nach unten), konkave Kurve aufwärts (nach oben), von oben hohle Kurve	courbe *f* convexe, courbe convexe vers le bas, courbe concave vers le haut	выпуклая кривая, выпуклая книзу кривая, вогнутая кверху кривая
	convex $\cap$ curve <AN, GE>	*s.* C 1769		
	convex $\cup$ curve <AN, GE>	*s.* C 2388		
C 2389	**convex domain** <PG>	konvexer Bereich *m*	domaine *m* convexe	выпуклая область
	convex down curve <AN, GE>	*s.* C 2388		
C 2390	**convex equivalence relation** <SE>	konvexe Äquivalenzrelation *f*	relation *f* d'équivalence convexe	выпуклое отношение эквивалентности
	convex extension <CS>	*s.* C 2392		
C 2391	**convex function, convex $\cup$ function,** convex cup function <AN>	konvexe (von unten konvexe) Funktion *f*	fonction *f* convexe	выпуклая функция

	convex ⌒ function <AN>	*s.* C 1770		
C 2392	**convex hull,** convex closure (linear hull, extension), convex <CS>	konvexe Hülle *f*	enveloppe *f* convexe, fermeture *f* convexe	выпуклая оболочка, выпуклое замыкание
C 2393	**convexifiable topological space** <TO>	konvexifizierbarer topologischer Raum *m*	espace *m* topologique convexifiable	конвексируемое топологическое пространство
C 2394	**convexity** <CS, GE>; Minkowski['s] convexity <GE>	Konvexität *f*	convexité *f*	выпуклость
C 2395	**convexity,** convexity downward, concavity upward <AN, GE>	Konvexität *f*, Konvexität von unten, Konkavität *f* von oben	convexité *f*, convexité *f* dirigée vers le bas, concavité *f* dirigée vers le haut	выпуклость, выпуклость книзу, вогнутость кверху
C 2396	**convexity constraint** <PG>	Konvexitätsbedingung *f*	contrainte *f* de convexité	условие выпуклости
	convexity downward <AN, GE>	*s.* C 2395		
	convexity theorem of M. Riesz <FA>	*s.* R 1048		
	convexity upward <AN, GE>	*s.* C 1772		
	convex linear combination <CS, FA, PG>	*s.* C 2386		
	convex linear hull <CS>	*s.* C 2392		
	convex linear space <FA, TO>	*s.* L 960		
C 2397	**convex neighbourhood** <FA, TO>	konvexe Umgebung *f*	voisinage *m* convexe	выпуклая окрестность
	convex *n*-gon <CS, PG>	*s.* C 2398		
	convex optimization <PG>	*s.* C 2401		
	convex parallelohedron <EG>	*s.* F 117		
	convex point set <CS>	*s.* C 2404		
C 2398	**convex polygon,** convex *n*-gon <CS, PG>	konvexes Polygon (Vieleck, *n*-Eck) *n*, polygonaler Bereich *m*	polygone (*n*-gone) *m* convexe	выпуклый многоугольник (полигон, *n*-угольник)
C 2399	**convex polyhedral domain** <CS, GE, TO>	konvexe Zelle *f*	domaine *m* polyédral convexe	выпуклый многогранник, выпуклая клетка
C 2400	**convex polyhedron,** Euler['s] polyhedron <CS, GE, PG>	konvexes Polyeder *n*, Eipolyeder *n*, Eulersches (eigentliches) Polyeder, Polyeder	polyèdre *m* convexe (eulérien, propre); tronçon *m* <pas nécessairement borné>	выпуклый многогранник (полиэдр), эйлеров многогранник
C 2401	**convex programming,** convex optimization; concave programming <PG>	konvexe Optimierung (Programmoptimierung, Programmierung) *f*, konvexes Programmieren *n*; konkave Optimierung (Programmoptimierung, Programmierung) *f*, konkaves Programmieren *n*	programmation (optimisation) *f* convexe; programmation concave	выпуклое программирование; вогнутое программирование
C 2402	**convex region [in the sense of Minkowski]** <GE>	konvexer Bereich *m*, Eibereich *m*	domaine *m* convexe	выпуклая область
C 2403	**convex sequence** <SS>	konvexe Folge (Zahlenfolge) *f*	suite *f* convexe	выпуклая последовательность
C 2404	**convex set,** convex point set <CS>	konvexe Menge (Punktmenge) *f*	ensemble *m* [de points] convexe	выпуклое [точечное] множество
	convex solid <CS, GE>	*s.* C 2384		
	convex subgroup <GR>	*s.* I 1102		
C 2405	**convex sublattice** <LA>	konvexer Teilverband *m*	sous-treillis *m* convexe, sous-lattice *f* convexe (quotient)	выпуклая подструктура
C 2406	**convex subset** <of an ordered set> <SE>	konvexe (isolierte) Untermenge *f*	partie *f* convexe	выпуклое подмножество
	convex subset <CS, TO>	*s.* M 494		
C 2407	**convex surface,** closed convex surface <CS, GE>	Eifläche *f*, geschlossene konvexe Fläche *f*, Oval *n*	surface *f* ovoïde, surface convexe [fermée]	овальная поверхность, [замкнутая] выпуклая поверхность
C 2408	**convex tube** <FT>	konvexer Zylinderbereich *m*	domaine *m* cylindrique convexe	выпуклая цилиндрическая область
	convex up curve <AN, GE>	*s.* C 1769		
C 2409	**convolution,** folding, faltung <with>, resultant <of integrable functions> <AN>	Faltung *f* <mit>	convolution *f* <avec>, transformation *f* de convolution, produit *m* de composition	свертка, свертывание, конволюция, композиция, преобразование свертки, операция свертывания
	convolution <AN, ME>	*s.* C 2411		
C 2410	**convolution equation** <FA>	Faltungsgleichung *f*	équation *f* de convolution	уравнение свертывания
C 2411	**convolution product,** convolution <of functions *or* measures> <AN, ME>	Faltungsprodukt *n*	produit *m* de convolution, convolée *f*, convolution *f*	свернутое произведение, свертка, произведение типа свертки
C 2412	**convolution product** <of distributions> <FA>	Faltungsprodukt *n*, Kompositionsprodukt *n*	produit *m* de convolution	произведение типа свертки, произведение композиции
C 2413	**convolution theorem,** faltung theorem <for functions> <AN>	Faltungssatz *m*	théorème *m* de composition, théorème de Duhamel	теорема о свертке, теорема свертки, теорема свертывания
C 2414	**convolution theorem** <of Laplace transform> <IT>	Faltungssatz *m*	règle *f* sur le produit de composition	теорема умножения

C 2415	**Conway['s] game,** population game, life game, life <TG>	Conway-Spiel *n*, Populationsspiel *n*, Lebensspiel *n*, Leben *n*	jeu *m* de Conway (vie), vie *f*	игра Конвея
C 2416	**co-operation** <CA>	Kooperation *f*, Cooperation *f*	co-opération *f*	кооперация
C 2417	**co[-]operative game,** coalitional game <TG>	kooperatives Spiel *n*, Kooperationsspiel *n*, Koalitionsspiel *n*	jeu *m* coopératif, jeu avec alliances	кооперативная игра, игра с возможностью кооперирования, коалиционная игра
C 2418	**co-ordinate,** coordinate <AY, GN>	Koordinate *f*, Zeiger *m*	coordonnée *f*	координата
C 2419	**co-ordinate,** component, projection <of a vector, also in a sequence space> <as a scalar> <FA, VT>	Koordinate *f*, Komponente *f*, Projektion *f*	coordonnée *f*, valeur *f* algébrique (relative), composante *f*, projection *f*	координата, компонента, составляющая, компонент, проекция
	co-ordinate <VT>	*s.* C 1660		
C 2420	**co-ordinate axis,** axis of co-ordinates, axis <AY>	Koordinatenachse *f*, Achse *f* des Koordinatensystems, Achse	axe *m* de coordonnées, axe	координатная ось, ось [координат], нулевая координатная линия
	co-ordinate curve <AN, AY>	*s.* C 2423		
	co-ordinate domain <AG>	*s.* C 2427		
C 2421	**co-ordinate-free** <GE>	koordinatenfrei	sans coordonnées	бескоординатный
C 2422	**co-ordinate function** <AT>	Koordinatenfunktion *f*	fonction *f* coordonnée	координатная функция
	co-ordinate function <AL, SE>	*s.* P 1648		
	co-ordinate hyperplane <PJ>	*s.* H 710		
C 2423	**co-ordinate line,** // co-ordinate curve <AN, AY>	Koordinatenlinie *f*, // Koordinatenkurve *f*	ligne *f* de coordonnées, // courbe *f* de coordonnées	координатная линия, // координатная кривая
C 2424	**co-ordinate method** <AY>	Koordinatenmethode *f*	méthode *f* des coordonnées	метод координат
C 2425	**co-ordinate neighbourhood** <in a manifold> <DG, TO>	Koordinatenumgebung *f*	voisinage *m* de coordonnées	координатная окрестность
C 2426	**co-ordinate *n*-frame** <GE>	Koordinaten-*n*-Bein *n*	repère *m* des coordonnées	координатный репер, репер (базис) *n*-мерного [евклидового] пространства, репер
	co-ordinate origin <AY>	*s.* O 421		
	co-ordinate plane <AY>	*s.* P 650		
C 2427	**co-ordinate ring,** co-ordinate domain, affine co-ordinate ring, ring of the affine co-ordinates, ring of the polynomials <on *V*> <AG>	Koordinatenring *m*, affiner Ring *m* <von *V*>	anneau *m* de[s] coordonnées <de *V*>, anneau de coordonnées affines <de *V*>, anneau des polynômes <sur *V*>, anneau de la variété <*V*>	координатное кольцо, аффинное координатное кольцо <многообразия *V*>
C 2428	**co-ordinate simplex** <PJ>	Koordinatensimplex *n*	simplexe *m* de base des coordonnées	координатный симплекс
	co-ordinates in the plane <AY>	*s.* P 644		
	co-ordinates of the asymmetric ellipsoid <AY>	*s.* E 160		
	co-ordinates of the asymmetric paraboloid <AY>	*s.* P 71		
C 2429	**co-ordinates of the linear complex,** complex co-ordinates <DG>	Koordinaten *fpl* des linearen Strahlenkomplexes, Komplexkoordinaten *fpl*	coordonnées *fpl* du complexe linéaire	координаты линейного комплекса
C 2430	**co-ordinates of the parabolic cylinder,** parabolic cylindrical co-ordinates <GE>	Koordinaten *fpl* des parabolischen Zylinders, parabolische Zylinderkoordinaten *fpl*	coordonnées *fpl* du cylindre parabolique	координаты параболического цилиндра, параболические цилиндрические координаты
C 2431	**co-ordinates of the paraboloid of revolution,** parabolic co-ordinates <GE>	rotationsparabolische (spezielle parabolische) Koordinaten *fpl*, Koordinaten des Rotationsparaboloids	coordonnées *fpl* du paraboloïde de révolution	параболоидальные координаты, координаты параболоида вращения
	co-ordinate space <FA, TO>	*s.* S 589		
C 2432	**co-ordinate surface** <AY, GE>	Koordinatenfläche *f*	surface *f* coordonnée, surface de coordonnées	координатная поверхность
C 2433	**co-ordinate system,** system of co-ordinates <AN, AY>	Koordinatensystem *n*	système *m* de coordonnées	система координат, координатная система
	co-ordinate system <AL>	*s.* V 97		
	co-ordinate tetrahedron <AY>	*s.* T 242		
C 2434	**co-ordinate transformation** <of the bundle> <AT>	Koordinatentransformation *f*	transformation *f* des coordonnées	координатное преобразование
C 2435	**co-ordinate transformation** <in a manifold> <DG, TO>	Übergang *m* zu einer anderen Karte, Koordinatentransformation *f*	changement *m* de cartes	координатное преобразование
	co-ordinate transformation <AN, AY>	*s.* T 777		
C 2436	**co-ordinate triangle** <PJ>	Koordinatendreieck *n*, Fundamentalsimplex *n* in der projektiven Ebene	triangle *m* de base	основной треугольник
	co-ordinate triangle <AY>	*s.* T 903		

No.	English	German	French	Russian
C 2437	**co-ordinate trihedral** <AY>	Koordinatendreiflach *n*, Koordinatendreibein *n*	trièdre *m* des axes, trièdre des coordonnées	координатный трехгранник, трехгранник координат
	co-ordinatewise convergence <FA, TO>	*s.* C 1669		
	coordination <SE>	*s.* C 2502		
C 2438	**coordination problem,** problem of coordination <PG>	Zuordnungsproblem *n*, Koordinierungsproblem *n*	problème *m* de coordination	проблема соответствия, задача координирования
C 2439	**co[-]ordinatograph** <IN, NU>	Koordinatograph *m*	coordinatographe *m*	координатограф
C 2440	**coparallelism** <GE>	Koparallelismus *m*, Co-Parallelismus *m*	co-parallèlisme *m*	копараллелизм
C 2441	**coplanarity,** complanarity <GE>	Komplanarität *f*, Koplanarität *f*	coplanarité *f*, complanarité *f*	компланарность, копланарность
C 2442	**coplanar line,** complanar line <GE>	komplanare Gerade *f*, koplanare Gerade	droite *f* coplanaire (complanaire)	компланарная прямая, копланарная прямая
C 2443	**coplanar vector,** complanar vector <VT>	komplanarer Vektor *m*, koplanarer Vektor	vecteur *m* coplanaire (complanaire)	компланарный вектор, копланарный вектор
	copoint <LA>	*s.* C 965		
C 2444	**copower** <CA>	Kopotenz *f*, Copotenz *f*	co-puissance *f*	костепень
C 2445	**coprimality,** being relatively prime <AL>	Teilerfremdheit *f*	propriété *f* d'être relativement premier	отсутствие общих делителей, копростота
C 2446	**coprimary module** <AL>	koprimärer (coprimärer) Modul *m*	module *m* coprimaire	копримарный модуль
	coprime elements <AL>	*s.* R 751		
C 2447	**coprime numbers,** relatively prime numbers, numbers prime to each other <NT>	relativ prime Zahlen *fpl*, teilerfremde Zahlen, relative Primzahlen *fpl*	nombres *mpl* premiers entre eux [dans leur ensemble], nombres sans diviseur commun, nombres sans commun diviseur	взаимно-простые числа, взаимно простые числа
	coprime numbers <NT>	*s.* N 840		
C 2448	**coproduct** <AL>	Koprodukt *n*, Coprodukt *n*	coproduit *m*	копроизведение
C 2449	**coproduct,** free join, sum <CA>	Koprodukt *n*, Coprodukt *n*, Summe *f*, direkte Summe, inverses Produkt *n*	somme *f* directe, coproduit *m*	копроизведение, сумма, прямая сумма, свободное произведение
C 2450	**coproduct-complete category** <CA>	Kategorie *f* mit Koprodukten	catégorie *f* à coproduits	категория с суммами
	copunctal <GE>	*s.* C 1795		
	copunctal planes <EG>	*s.* C 1797		
C 2451	**copy** <AL>	Exemplar *n*	exemplaire *m*, copie *f*	экземпляр, копия
C 2452	**co-radical** <AL>	Koradikal *n*, Coradikal *n*	coradical *m*	корадикал
	co-rank <FA>	*s.* D 116 a		
C 2453	**co-rational extension** <of a module> <AL>	korationale (corationale) Erweiterung *f*	extension *f* corationnelle	корациональное расширение
C 2454/5	**core** <of a sequence of domains> <FT>	Kern *m* <einer Gebietsfolge>	noyau *m* <d'une suite de domaines>	ядро <последовательности областей>
C 2456	**core,** greatest square-free divisor <of a number> <NT>	Kern *m*, quadratfreier Kern, größter quadratfreier Teiler *m*	noyau *m*	наибольший бесквадратный делитель
C 2457	**coreflective subcategory** <CA>	koreflexive (coreflektive) Unterkategorie *f*	sous-catégorie *f* coréflexive	корефлективная подкатегория
C 2458	**coreflector** <CA>	Koreflektor *m*, Coreflektor	co-réflecteur *m*	корефлектор
C 2459	**corepresentation** <AL>	Kodarstellung *f*, Codarstellung *f*	co-représentation *f*	копредставление
C 2460	**coresidual divisor** <AG>	korresidualer (corresidualer, koresidualer, coresidualer) Divisor *m*	diviseur *m* corésiduel	соостаточный дивизор
C 2461	**coresidual group of points** <on an algebraic curve> <AG>	äquivalente Punktgruppe *f*, korresiduale (corresiduale, koresiduale, coresiduale) Punktgruppe (Gruppe) *f*, beigeordnete Gruppe	groupe *m* corésiduel	соостаточная группа [точек], совычетная группа [точек]
C 2462	**coresidual point** <AG>	korresidualer, corresidualer, koresidualer, coresidualer) Punkt *m*	point *m* corésiduel	корезидюальная точка, противоположная точка
C 2463	**corestriction homomorphism** <HA>	Koeinschränkung *f*, Coeinschränkung *f*	corestriction *f*, morphisme *m* de corestriction	гомоморфизм коограничения
C 2464	**coretraction,** section, left semi-isomorphism <CA>	Koretraktion *f*, Coretraktion *f*, Schnitt *m*	inverse *m* à droite	обратимый справа морфизм, иссечение, инверсия справа, сечение
C 2465	**corner,** vertex <of a polyhedron *or* polygon> <EG>	Eckpunkt *m*, Ecke *f*	sommet *m*, coin *m*	вершина
	corner <EG>	*s.* P 945		
	corner <VA>	*s.* C 2467		
C 2466	**corner condition** <PG>	Eckenbedingung *f*, Eckbedingung *f*	condition *f* aux coins	условие на вершины
C 2467	**corner point,** corner <of a broken extremal> <VA>	Eckpunkt *m*, Knickpunkt *m*	point *m* anguleux	угловая точка
	corner point <GE>	*s.* S 12		
C 2468	**corner solution** <PG>	Ecklösung *f*	solution *f* au sommet	решение на вершине
C 2469	**corner test,** Olmstead-Tukey corner test <ST>	Eckentest *m* <nach Olmstead und Tukey>	test *m* du coin	серединный критерий
C 2470	**Cornish-Fisher expansion** <ST>	Cornish-Fisher-Entwicklung *f*	expansion *f* de Cornish-Fisher	разложение Корниша-Фишера
C 2471	**Cornu['s] spiral,** clothoid, clothoid curve, Euler['s] spiral, spiral of Cornu (Euler) <GE>	Cornusche Spirale *f*, Cornu-Spirale *f*, Klothoide *f*, Spinnlinie *f*, Cornusche Kurve *f*, Cornuspirale *f*	spirale *f* de Fresnel, spirale (courbe *f*) de Cornu, clothoïde *f*, courbe en double spirale	спираль Корню, клотоида, спираль Эйлера
C 2472	**Corolla['s] curve** <a quartic> <AG>	Corolla-Kurve *f*	courbe *f* Corolla	кривая Королла
C 2473	**corollary** <GN>	Korollar *n*, Folgesatz *m*, Folgerung *f*	corollaire *m*, conclusion *f*, conséquence *f*	королларий, следствие
	corpus <AL>	*s.* D 813		

No.	English	German	French	Russian
C 2474	**corrected error** <ST>	bereinigter Fehler *m*	erreur *f* corrigée	скорректированная ошибка
C 2475	**corrected mean,** modified mean <ST>	bereinigter Mittelwert *m*	moyenne *f* corrigée	скорректированное среднее
C 2476	**correction** <AX, NU>	Korrektion *f*, Korrektur *f*	correction *f*	поправка
C 2477	**correction** <as a common name of true or apparent error> <ER>	Verbesserung *f*	correction *f*	поправка
C 2478	**correction factor** <AX, NU, ST>	Korrektionsfaktor *m*, Korrekturfaktor *m*	facteur *m* de correction	поправочный коэффициент
C 2479	**correction for continuity** <ST>	Kontinuitätskorrektur *f*, Stetigkeitskorrektur *f*	correction *f* pour la continuité	поправка на непрерывность
C 2480	**correction for grouping** <ST>	Gruppierungskorrektur *f*	correction *f* pour le groupement	поправка на группировку
C 2481	**correction term,** corrective term <AX, NU, ST>	Korrektionsglied *n*, Korrektionsterm *m*, Korrekturglied *n*, Korrekturterm *m*	terme *m* correctif, terme de correction	поправочный член
C 2482	**correction term** <in the least squares method> <ST>	Korrekturglied *n*, Subtraktionsglied *n*	terme *m* correctif	поправочный член
	corrective term <AX, NU, ST>	*s.* C 2481		
	correct logical formula <LO>	*s.* 1. F 488; 2. S 499		
	correctly constructed formula <LO>	*s.* 1. F 488; 2. M 307		
	corrector formula of the Adams-Moulton method <NU>	*s.* A 222		
	correct to . . . <GN>	*s.* U 445		
C 2483	**correlated causes** <ST>	korrelierte Ursachen (Kausalvariable) *fpl*	causes *fpl* corrélées	коррелированные причины
C 2484	**correlated variables (variates)** <ST>	korrelierte Variable *fpl*	variables *fpl* corrélées	коррелированные переменные
C 2485	**correlation,** reciprocity <AY, PJ>	Korrelation *f*, Reziprozität *f*, reziproke Verwandtschaft *f*	corrélation *f*, réciprocité *f*	корреляция, коррелятивное преобразование
C 2486	**correlation,** intercorrelation <ST>	Korrelation *f*	corrélation *f*	корреляция
C 2487	**correlation analysis** <ST>	Korrelationsanalyse *f*	analyse *f* de corrélation	корреляционный анализ
	correlation between classes (treatments) <ST>	*s.* I 703		
C 2488	**correlation calculus** <ST>	Korrelationsrechnung *f*	calcul *m* des corrélations, calcul de corrélation	исчисление корреляций, корреляционное исчисление
C 2489	**correlation coefficient** <ST>	Korrelationskoeffizient *m*	coefficient *m* de corrélation [linéaire], indice *m* de covariance	коэффициент корреляции; смешанный коэффициент корреляции
C 2490	**correlation determinant** <ST>	Korrelationsdeterminante *f*	déterminant *m* de corrélation	корреляционный определитель, определитель корреляционной матрицы
	correlation diagram <ST>	*s.* S 102		
	correlation ellipse <ST>	*s.* E 157		
	correlation ellipsoid <ST>	*s.* E 162		
C 2491	**correlation function** <ST>	Korrelationsfunktion *f*	fonction *f* de corrélation, fonction corrélative	корреляционная функция
C 2492	**correlation matrix** <ST>	Korrelationsmatrix *f*	matrice *f* de corrélation	корреляционная матрица
C 2493	**correlation measure** <ST>	Korrelationsmaßzahl *f*, Korrelationsmaß *n*	mesure *f* de corrélation	мера корреляции
C 2494	**correlation parameter** <ST>	Korrelationsparameter *m*	paramètre *m* de corrélation	параметр корреляции
C 2495	**correlation pleiad** <ST>	Korrelationsplejade *f*	pléiade *f* de corrélation	корреляционная плеяда
C 2496	**correlation ratio** <ST>	Korrelationsverhältnis *n*	rapport (quotient) *m* de corrélation	корреляционное отношение
C 2497	**correlation table** <ST>	Korrelationstabelle *f*, Korrelationstafel *f*; Korrelationsfeld *n*	tableau *m* de corrélation, table *f* de corrélation	корреляционная таблица; корреляционное поле
	correlative mapping <AY>	*s.* R 260		
	correlative proposition <PJ>	*s.* D 1036		
	correlative transformation <AY>	*s.* R 260		
C 2498	**correlator** <of relations> <SE>	Korrelator *m*	corrélateur *m*, relation *f* corrélatrice	коррелятор
C 2499	**correlogram** <ST>	Korrelogramm *n*	corrélogramme *m*	коррелограмма
C 2499 a	**correspond** <to> / **to,** △ <NU>	entsprechen, △	correspondre <à>, △	соответствовать, △
C 2500	**correspondence** <AG>	Korrespondenz *f*	correspondance *f*; correspondance ensembliste <entre ensembles algébriques>	соответствие
C 2501	**correspondence,** additive (homomorphic) relation <in an Abelian category> <CA>	additive Relation *f*	relation *f* additive	аддитивное отношение
C 2502	**correspondence,** coordination, assignment, association <SE>	Zuordnung *f*	coordination *f*	соответствие, поставление в соответствие, сопоставление
	correspondence <AN, FA>	*s.* M 95		

	(1—1)-correspondence <SE>	*s.* 1. B 330; 2. O 121		
C 2503	**correspondence formula** <AG>	Korrespondenzgleichung *f*	équation *f* de correspondance	уравнение соответствия
C 2504	**correspondence law** <PJ>	Korrespondenzgesetz *n* <Chasles>	loi *f* de correspondance	закон соответствия
	correspondence mapping circles into circles <GE>	*s.* C 729		
C 2505	**correspondence of a set with itself** <SE>	Korrespondenz *f* einer Menge mit sich	autocorrespondance *f* <dans un ensemble>	соответствие множества в себя
C 2506	**correspondence of Zeuthen** <AG>	Zeuthensche Korrespondenz *f*	correspondance *f* de Zeuthen	соответствие Цейтена
C 2507	**correspondence principle of Chasles** <AG>	Chaslessches Korrespondenzprinzip *n*, Korrespondenzprinzip von Chasles	principe *m* de Chasles	принцип соответствия Шаля
C 2508	**correspondence sign,** ○—●, ↄ, ≑ <IT>	Korrespondenzzeichen *n*, ○—●, ↄ, ≑	signe *m* de correspondance, ○—●, ↄ, ≑	знак соответствия, ○—● ↄ, ≑
	corresponding addition <AR>	*s.* C 1696		
	corresponding addition and subtraction <AR>	*s.* C 1704		
C 2509	**corresponding angles** <DS>	entsprechende (korrespondierende) Winkel *mpl*	angles *mpl* correspondants	соответственные углы
C 2510	**corresponding angles,** exterior-interior angles <EG>	Gegenwinkel *mpl*, gleichliegende Winkel *mpl*	angles *mpl* correspondants	соответственные углы
C 2511	**corresponding auxiliary equation,** auxiliary equation <of a linear equation> <AL>	zugehörige homogene (homogene lineare) Gleichung *f*	équation *f* [linéaire] homogène associée, équation sans second membre associée, équation linéaire et homogène associée	соответствующее однородное уравнение
C 2512	**corresponding continued fraction** <to a series> <NT>	korrespondierender Kettenbruch *m* <mit einer Reihe>	fraction *f* continue correspondant[e] <à une série>	соответствующая цепная дробь <ряду>
	corresponding homogeneous equation <DE>	*s.* A 1070		
	corresponding homogeneous system <AL>	*s.* A 1071		
C 2513	**corresponding ideal** <of an algebraic variety> <AG>	zugehöriges (assoziiertes) Ideal *n*	idéal *m* correspondant	соответствующий идеал
C 2514	**corresponding matrix** <MD>	korrespondierende Matrix *f*	matrice *f* correspondante <Gordan>	соответствующая матрица
C 2515	**corresponding points** <AG, AY>	[miteinander] korrespondierende Punkte *mpl*	points *mpl* correspondants	соответствующие точки
C 2516	**corresponding points** <DS>	entsprechende Punkte *mpl*	points *mpl* correspondants	соответствующие точки
C 2517	**corresponding polynomial** <of a variety> <AG>	zugeordnetes Polynom *n*	polynôme *m* correspondant	соответствующий многочлен
C 2518	**corresponding series** <to a continued fraction> <NT>	korrespondierende Reihe *f* <mit einem Kettenbruch>	élément *m* correspondant <à une fraction continue>	соответствующий ряд <цепной дроби>
	corresponding subtraction <AR>	*s.* D 803		
C 2519	**corresponding term** <of a sequence> <SS>	homologes (entsprechendes) Glied *n*	terme *m* homologue	соответствующий член
	cos <DI>	*s.* C 2528		
	cos^{-1} <FU>	*s.* I 899		
	cos am <FU>	*s.* A 606		
	cosec <DI>	*s.* C 2520		
	cosec^{-1} <FU>	*s.* I 898		
C 2520	**cosecant,** cosecant function, cosec, // csc <DI>	Kosekans *m*, Kosekansfunktion *f*, cosec, // Cosecans *m*	cosécante *f*, fonction *f* cosécante, cosec, csc	косеканс, функция косеканс, cosec
C 2521	**cosecant curve,** cosecant line, cosecantoid <DI>	Kosekanskurve *f*, Kosekanslinie *f*, Kosekansoide *f*	cosécantoïde *f*, courbe *f* cosécante, ligne *f* cosécante	косекансоида, график косеканса
	cosecant function <DI>	*s.* C 2520		
	cosecant line <DI>	*s.* C 2521		
	cosecantoid <DI>	*s.* C 2521		
C 2522	**cosecantoidal curve (line)** <DI>	kosekansförmige Kurve *f*, Kosekanskurve *f*	ligne (courbe) *f* cosécantoïdale	косекансоидальная кривая (линия)
	cosech <FU>	*s.* H 622		
C 2523	**coset,** residue class <*e.g.:* relative to *H*> <in a group> <GR>	Restklasse *f*, Nebenklasse *f*, Nebengruppe *f*, Nebenkomplex *m*, Nebenschar *f* <*z. B.:* nach *H*, modulo *H*>	classe *f*, classe latérale, co-groupe *m*, reste *f* <*par exemple:* modulo *H*, suivant *H*>, complexe *m* <*par exemple:* associé à *H* par *a*>, // groupe *m* conjugué (associé)	смежный класс, класс смежности <*например:* по *H*>
	coset <AL>	*s.* R 889		
C 2524	**coset decomposition (expansion),** decomposition into cosets <of a group> <GR>	Restklassenzerlegung *f*, Zerlegung *f* <einer Gruppe> nach einer Untergruppe, Zerlegung in Restklassen	décomposition *f* <d'un groupe> en ses complexes de même espèce, décomposition en classes	разложение <группы> по подгруппе, расщепление <группы> на смежные классы
C 2525	**coset of the same kind** <right *or* left> <GR>	Restklasse *f* gleicher Art	complexe *m* de même espèce (nature)	класс смежности одинакового рода
	coset space <AL>	*s.* F 56		

	English	German	French	Russian
	cosh <FU>	*s.* H 623		
C 2526	**cosimplex** <LA, SE>	Kosimplex *n*, Cosimplex *n*	cosimplexe *m*	косимплекс
C 2527	**co-simplicial object, cosimplicial object** <CA, HA>	kosimpliziales (cosimpliziales) Objekt *n*	objet *m* cosimplicial	косимплициальный объект
C 2528	**cosine,** cosine function, cos <DI>	Kosinus *m*, Kosinusfunktion *f*, cos, // Cosinus *m*	cosinus *m*, fonction *f* cosinus, cos	косинус, функция косинус, cos
C 2529	**cosine curve,** cosine line, cosinusoid <DI>	Kosinuskurve *f*, Kosinuslinie *f*, Kosinusoide *f*	cosinusoïde *f*, courbe *f* cosinus, ligne *f* cosinus	косинусоида, график косинуса
C 2530	**cosine factorial,** cf_{α} <FU>	Kosinusfaktorial *n*, Cosinus-Faktorial *n*, cf_{α}	cosinus-factorielle *f*, cf_{α}	косинус-факториал, cf_{α}
	cosine function <DI>	*s.* C 2528		
C 2531	**cosine integral, cosine-integral function,** integral cosine, Ci <FU>	Integralkosinus *m*, Cosinus *m* integralis, Kosinusintegralfunktion *f*, Ci	cosinus *m* intégral, Ci	интегральный косинус, Ci
	cosine law <EG>	*s.* 1. C 2533; 2. L 176		
C 2532	**cosine law for sides (the side of a spherical triangle)** <EG>	Seitenkosinussatz *m*	théorème *m* des cosinus pour le côté d'un triangle sphérique	теорема косинусов для стороны сферического треугольника, теорема о косинусе стороны сферического треугольника
	cosine line <DI>	*s.* C 2529		
C 2533	**cosine rule,** cosine law <for an angle of a spherical triangle> <EG>	Winkelkosinussatz *m*	théorème *m* des cosinus <pour l'angle d'un triangle sphérique>	теорема косинусов <для угла сферического треугольника>
	cosine rule <EG>	*s.* L 176		
C 2534	**cosine series** <SS>	Kosinusreihe *f*	série *f* du cosinus	ряд косинуса
C 2535	**cosine series** <as a special trigonometric series> <SS>	Kosinusreihe *f*	série *f* en cosinus	ряд косинусов, ряд по косинусам
	cosinusoid <DI>	*s.* C 2529		
C 2536	**cosinusoidal curve (line)** <DI, NU>	kosinusförmige Kurve *f*, Kosinuskurve *f*	ligne (courbe) *f* cosinusoïdale	косинусоидальная кривая (линия)
C 2537	**cost function** <in decision theory> <ST>	Kostenfunktion *f*	fonction *f* coût, fonction de coût	функция стоимости
	cost function <PG>	*s.* O 6		
C 2538	**cost matrix** <in transportation problems> <PG>	Kostenmatrix *f*	matrice *f* coût, matrice de coût	матрица стоимости
	cos vers <DI>	*s.* V 146		
	cot <DI>	*s.* C 2539		
	cot^{-1} <FU>	*s.* I 900		
	cot am <FU>	*s.* A 607		
C 2539	**cotangent,** cotangent function, cot, // ctg <DI>	Kotangens *m*, Kotangensfunktion *f*, cot, // Cotangens *m*, ctg	cotangente *f*, fonction *f* cotangente, cot, // ctg	котангенс, функция котангенс, cot, // ctg
C 2540	**cotangent curve,** cotangent line, cotangentoid <DI>	Kotangenskurve *f*, Kotangenslinie *f*, Kotangensoide *f*	cotangentoïde *f*, courbe *f* cotangente, ligne *f* cotangente	котангенсоида, график котангенса
	cotangent function <DI>	*s.* C 2539		
	cotangent line <DI>	*s.* C 2540		
	cotangentoid <DI>	*s.* C 2540		
C 2541	**cotangentoidal curve (line)** <DI>	kotangensförmige Kurve *f*, Kotangenskurve *f*	ligne (courbe) *f* cotangentoïdale	котангенсоидальная кривая (линия)
	cote <DS>	*s.* H 169		
	coted height <DS>	*s.* P 813		
	coted line <DS>	*s.* L 877		
	coted projection <DS>	*s.* T 501		
	co-terminal family of mappings <CA, SE, TO>	*s.* C 1050		
	coterminal object <CA>	*s.* C 2316		
C 2542	**Cotes['] coefficient** <DI, NU>	Cotessche Zahl *f*	coefficient (nombre) *m* de Cotes	коэффициент Котеса
	Cotes['] [quadrature] formulae <DI, NU>	*s.* N 195		
	Cotes['] rule <DI, NU>	*s.* N 195		
C 2543	**Cotes['] spiral** <GE>	Cotessche Spirale *f*, Ährenkurve *f*	spirale *f* de Cotes	спираль Котеса
C 2544	**Cotes['] theorem** <for binomial equations> <AL>	Cotesscher Lehrsatz *m*, Cotesischer Satz *m*	théorème *m* de Cotes	теорема Котеса
	coth <FU>	*s.* H 625		
C 2545	**co-topology** <TO>	Kotopologie *f*, Cotopologie *f*	co-topologie *f*	котопология
	C-O topology <TO>	*s.* T 566		
C 2546	**cotorsion-free module** <AL>	kotorsionsloser (cotorsionsloser) Modul *m*	module *m* sans co[-]torsion	модуль без кокручения
C 2547	**cotorsion group** <AT, GR> ⌐<AL>	Kotorsionsgruppe *f*, Cotorsionsgruppe *f*	groupe *m* de co-torsion	группа кокручения <AT>; копериодическая группа <GR>
C 2548	**cotrace** <of a repartition>	Kospur *f*, Cospur *f*, Cotrace *f*	cotrace *f*	ко-след
C 2549	**cotree** <GP>	Kobaum *m*, Co-Baum *m*	coarbre *m*	кодерево
	cotriple <CA>	*s.* C 1288		
	Coulomb['s] wave function <FU>	*s.* W 245		
C 2550	**counion** <CA>	Kovereinigung *f*, Covereinigung *f*	co-union *f*	ко-объединение
C 2551	**counit** <of a coalgebra> <AL>	Koeinselement *n*, Coeinselement *n*	co-unité *f*, coünité *f*	коединица
C 2552	**counit of the adjunction,** back adjunction <CA>	Koeinheit (Coeinheit) *f* der Adjunktion	co-unité *f* d'adjonction	коединица сопряжения
	couniversal arrow <CA>	*s.* C 1129		
C 2553	**co-universal functor** <CA>	kouniversaler (couniversaler) Funktor *m*	foncteur *m* co-universel	коуниверсальный функтор
	count <SE>	*s.* E 276		
C 2554	**countability,** denumerability, enumerability <SE>	Abzählbarkeit *f*	dénombrabilité *f*	счетность

No.	English	German	French	Russian
C 2555	**countability axioms,** Hausdorff['s] countability axioms <TO>	Abzählbarkeitsaxiome *npl*	axiomes *mpl* de dénombrabilité	аксиомы счетности
C 2556	**countable additivity,** total additivity, absolute additivity, σ-additivity, sigma-additivity <AN, SE>	abzählbare (totale) Additivität *f*, Volladditivität *f*, σ-Additivität *f*, Sigma-Additivität *f*, vollständige Additivität	additivité *f* dénombrable (complète), σ-additivité *f*, sigma additivité *f*	счетная (полная) аддитивность, σ-аддитивность, сигма-аддитивность
C 2557	**countable base** <TO>	abzählbare Basis *f*	base *f* dénombrable	счетная база
C 2558	**countable distributivity** <AL, SE>	abzählbare Distributivität *f*	distributivité *f* dénombrable	счетная дистрибутивность
C 2559	**countable infinity** <SE>	abzählbare Unendlichkeit *f*	infinité *f* dénombrable	счетная бесконечность
	countable open covering <TO>	*s.* L 257		
C 2560	**countable semi-additivity,** total (absolute) semi-additivity <AN>	abzählbare (absolute, totale) Halbadditivität *f*	semi-additivité *f* dénombrable (complète, au sens dénombrable)	счетная (полная) полуаддитивность
C 2561	**countable set,** enumerable set, at most countable set, denumerable set <finite or infinite> <SE>	abzählbare Menge *f*, höchstens abzählbare Menge	ensemble *m* dénombrable (au plus dénombrable)	не более чем счетное множество
	countable set <SE>	*s.* D 252		
C 2562	**countable subadditivity,** σ-subadditivity, sigma-subadditivity <AN>	abzählbare Unteradditivität *f*	sous-additivité *f* dénombrable	счетная (полная) аддитивность снизу
C 2563	**countable superadditivity** <AN>	abzählbare Oberadditivität *f*	suradditivité *f* dénombrable	счетная аддитивность сверху
C 2564	**countable-valued logic** <LO>	abzählbarwertige Logik *f*	logique *f* à valeurs dénombrables	счетнозначная логика
	countably additive algebra <AL>	*s.* S 815		
	countably additive algebra [of sets] <ME, SE, TO>	*s.* S 810		
C 2565	**countably additive family,** σ-additive family <TO>	abzählbar additive Familie *f*	famille *f* additive au sens dénombrable	счетно-аддитивное семейство
	countably additive measure <ME>	*s.* A 82		
C 2566	**countably additive [set] function,** totally additive [set] function, absolutely additive [set] function, σ-additive [set] function, sigma-additive [set] function <AN>	abzählbar additive Funktion (Mengenfunktion) *f*, abzählbar-additive Funktion (Mengenfunktion), absolut additive Funktion (Mengenfunktion), total[-]additive (volladditive, σ-additive, sigma-additive) Funktion (Mengenfunktion)	fonction *f* (fonction d'ensemble) dénombrablement additive, fonction (fonction d'ensemble) complètement additive, fonction (fonction d'ensemble) additive au sens dénombrable, fonction (fonction d'ensemble) σ-additive, fonction (fonction d'ensemble) sigma-additive	счетно-аддитивная функция [множества], вполне аддитивная функция [множества], σ-аддитивная функция [множества], сигма-аддитивная функция [множества]
	countably compact set <TO>	*s.* S 647		
	countably compact space <TO>	*s.* C 1307		
	countably complete filter <AL, SE>	*s.* S 816		
C 2567	**countably generated module** <AL>	abzählbar erzeugter Modul *m*	module *m* à nombre dénombrable de générateurs	модуль с счетным числом образующих
	countably infinite orthonormal system <FA>	*s.* O 494		
	countably infinite set <SE>	*s.* D 252		
C 2568	**countably multiplicative class** <TO>	abzählbar multiplikative Klasse *f*	classe *f* dénombrablement multiplicative	счетно-мультипликативный класс
C 2569	**countably semi-additive [set] function,** totally (absolutely) semi-additive [set] function <AN>	abzählbar (absolut, total) halbadditive Funktion (Mengenfunktion)	fonction *f* [d'ensemble] dénombrablement (complètement) semi-additive, fonction [d'ensemble] semi-additive au sens dénombrable	вполне полуаддитивная функция [множества]
C 2570	**countably subadditive [set] function,** σ-subadditive [set] function <AN>	abzählbar unteradditive Funktion (Mengenfunktion) *f*, σ-vereinigungsbeschränkte (sigma-vereinigungsbeschränkte) Funktion (Mengenfunktion)	fonction *f* (fonction d'ensemble) dénombrablement sous-additive, fonction [d'ensemble] σ-sous-additive	вполне аддитивная снизу функция [множества]
C 2571	**countably superadditive [set] function** <AN>	abzählbar oberadditive Funktion (Mengenfunktion) *f*	fonction *f* [d'ensemble] dénombrablement suradditive	вполне аддитивная сверху функция [множества]
C 2572	**count by twos / to** <AR>	in Zweierschritten zählen	compter par deux	считать двойками
C 2573	**counter;** bead <of an abacus> <AR, IN>	Rechenstein *m*, Rechenpfennig *m*, Raitpfennig *m*	abaculus *m*, jeton *m*	счетная марка, счетный пфенниг
C 2574	**counterclockwise** <GE, GN>	entgegengesetzt zum Uhrzeigersinn, in mathematisch positivem Sinn, in [mathematisch] positiver Richtung, im Gegen[uhr]zeigersinn, mathematisch positiv	en (dans le) sens inverse [des aiguilles d'une montre], en sens opposé, en (dans le) sens positif	против часовой стрелки
C 2575	**counterclockwise direction,** anticlockwise direction, positive direction; counterclockwise sense, anticlockwise sense,	Gegenuhrzeigerrichtung *f*, [mathematisch] positive Richtung *f*; Gegenuhrzeigersinn *m*, positiver (mathematisch positiver)	direction *f* inverse [des aiguilles d'une montre], direction inverse du soleil, direction positive; sens *m* inverse [des aiguilles d'une	направление [вращения] против часосой стрелки, положительное направление

No.	English	German	French	Russian
	positive sense <of rotation> <GE, GN>	Sinn, Drehsinn *m* entgegengesetzt zum Uhrzeiger	montre], sens inverse du soleil, sens opposé (rétrograde, positif, trigonométrique)	
	counterclockwise rotation <EG>	*s.* L 373		
	counterclockwise sense <GE, GN>	*s.* C 2575		
	counter[-]domain, counter domain <SE>	*s.* R 122		
C 2576	**counter-example** <GN>	Gegenbeispiel *n*	contre-exemple *m*	контрпример, противоречащий пример
C 2577	**counter image** <of a mapping> <SE, TO>	Urbildelement *n*, Originalpunkt *m*, Urbildpunkt *m*	élément *m* de départ, antécédent *m*	точка-прообраз
	counter[-] image <AN>	*s.* I 912		
	counter image <SE, TO>	*s.* F 712		
C 2578	**counter-module** <AL>	Gegenmodul *m*	contremodule *m*	контрмодуль
C 2579	**counter-objection** <TG>	Gegendrohung *f*	contre-menace *f*	контругроза
C 2580	**counterpart** <LO>	Abbild *n*	image *f*	образ
C 2581	**counting** <*e.g.*: by twos> <GN>	Zählen *n* <*z. B.*: in Zweierschritten>	compte *m* <*par exemple:* par deux>	счет <*например:* двойками>
	counting <SE>	*s.* E 276		
C 2582	**counting constants** <AG>	Abzählung *f* der Konstanten, Konstantenzählung *f*	dénombrement *m* (énumération *f*, décompte *m*) des constantes	пересчет констант
	counting frame <IN>	*s.* C 10		
C 2583	**counting off** <GN>	Durchzählen *n*	comptage *m* un à un	пересчет
C 2584	**counting polynomial** <CT, GP>	Ziffernreihe *f*		ряд, перечисляющий фигуры
	couple <SE>	*s.* O 307		
C 2585	**couple of sliding vectors** <GE>	Stäbepaar *n* <Study>	couple *m* de vecteurs glissants, couple de Poinsot	пара скользящих векторов
	couple of vectors <GE, VT>	*s.* V 101		
C 2586	**courant** <DG>	Strom *m*	courant *m*	поток
C 2587	**Courant-Hilbert polynomial** <DE, FU>	Courant-Hilbertsches Polynom *n*	polynôme *m* de Courant-Hilbert	многочлен Куранта-Гильберта
C 2588	**Courant['s] theorem** <DE>	Satz *m* von Courant, Courantscher Satz	théorème *m* de Courant	теорема Куранта
C 2589	**Courant-Weyl [comparison] theorem** <FA>	Vergleichssatz *m* von Courant-Weyl, Courant-Weylscher Vergleichssatz	théorème *m* de Courant-Weyl (comparaison de Courant-Weyl)	теорема Куранта-Вейля (сравнения Куранта-Вейля)
C 2590	**course of value** <AN, FO>	Wertverlauf *m*	développement *m* des valeurs	изменение значений
	course-of-value function <FO>	*s.* G 199		
C 2591	**course-of-values induction (recursion),** strong induction, recursion with respect to a course of values <FO>	Wertverlaufsrekursion *f*	induction *f* sur le développement des valeurs	возвратная рекурсия
C 2592	**Cousin data** <FT>	Cousin-Verteilung *f*	donnée *f* de Cousin	данные Кузена
C 2593	**Cousin['s] problem** <FT>	Cousinsches Problem *n*	problème *m* de Cousin	проблема (задача) Кузена
C 2594	**Cousin I problem, Cousin problem I,** first Cousin problem additive Cousin problem <FT>	erstes Cousinsches Problem *n*, Cousin I-Problem *n*, additives Cousinsches Problem	premier (1-er) problème *m* de Cousin, problème de Cousin additif	первая проблема (задача) Кузена, аддитивная проблема Кузена
C 2595	**Cousin['s] II problem, Cousin['s] problem II,** second Cousin problem, multiplicative Cousin problem <FT>	zweites Cousinsches Problem *n*, Cousin II-Problem *n*, multiplikatives Cousinsches Problem	deuxième problème *m* de Cousin, problème de Cousin additif	вторая проблема (задача) Кузена, мультипликативная проблема Кузена
C 2596	**covariance** <AL, VT>	Kovarianz *f*	covariance *f*	ковариантность, когредиентность
C 2597	**covariance** <ST>	Kovarianz *f*, Covarianz *f*, covar	covariance *f*	ковариация, смешанный второй момент
C 2598	**covariance analysis,** analysis of covariance <ST>	Kovarianzanalyse *f*; Mitstreuungszerlegung *f*	analyse *f* de covariance	ковариационный анализ
C 2599	**covariance function** <ST>	Kovarianzfunktion *f*	fonction *f* des covariances	ковариационная функция
C 2600	**covariance functional** <ST>	Kovarianzfunktional *n*	fonctionnelle *f* des covariances	ковариационный функционал
C 2601	**covariance matrix,** dispersion matrix <ST>	Kovarianzmatrix *f*, Varianz-Kovarianz-Matrix *f*, Streuungsmatrix *f*, Dispersionsmatrix *f*	matrice *f* des covariances (variances et covariances), matrice de covariance (dispersion)	ковариационная матрица
C 2602	**covariant** <*e.g.*: of a form *or* a pencil> <AL, AY, NT>	Kovariante *f* <*z. B.*: einer Form *oder* eines Büschels>	covariant *m* <*par exemple:* d'une forme *ou* d'un faisceau>	ковариант <*например:* формы *или* пучка>
C 2603	**covariant [analytic] continuation** <FT>	[unmittelbare] kovariante [analytische] Fortsetzung *f*	prolongement *m* covariant (analytique covariant)	ковариантное (ковариантное аналитическое) продолжение
	covariant curvature tensor <DG>	*s.* R 1040		
C 2604	**covariant derivative** <VT>	kovariante Ableitung *f*	dérivée *f* covariante	ковариантная производная
C 2605	**covariant differentiation** <of a tensor> <VT>	kovariante Differentiation *f*, Erweiterung *f*	dérivation (différentiation) *f* covariante	ковариантное дифференцирование
C 2606	**covariant functor in both variables,** co-covariant functor, bifunctor [in both variant] <CA>	zweifach kovarianter Bifunktor *m*, ko-kovarianter Funktor *m*, Bifunktor	foncteur *m* co-covariant	ко-ковариантный функтор
C 2607	**covariant index** <VT>	kovarianter Index *m*	indice *m* covariant	ковариантный индекс

No.	English	German	French	Russian
C 2608	**covariant morphism functor** <CA>	kovarianter Hom-Funktor *m*	foncteur *m* Hom covariant	основной одноместный ковариантный функтор
C 2609	**covariant order,** covariant valence <VT>	kovariante Stufe (Ordnung, Valenz) *f*	valence *f* covariante, ordre *m* covariant	ковариантная валентность, ковариантный ранг
C 2610	**covariant set** <of variables> <IV>	kovariante Reihe (Größenreihe, Symbolreihe) *f*	système *m* covariant <de variables>	ковариантная система <переменных>
C 2611	**covariant tangent bundle,** vector bundle of covariant tangent vectors <AT>	Vektorraumbündel *n* der kovarianten Tangentialvektoren, kovariantes tangentielles Vektorraumbündel	fibré *m* tangent covariant	векторное расслоение ковариантных касательных векторов
C 2612	**covariant tensor of order (valence) *p*,** *p*-times covariant tensor <VT>	*p*-stufig kovarianter Tensor *m*, rein kovarianter Tensor der Stufe *p*, kovarianter Tensor der Stufe *p*	tenseur *m p* fois covariant, tenseur covariant d'ordre (de valence) *p*	*p* раз ковариантный тензор, ковариантный тензор ранга (валентности) *p*
	covariant valence <VT>	*s.* C 2609		
C 2613	**covariant vector** <VT>	kovarianter Vektor *m*, kovarianter Tensor *m* erster (1.) Stufe	vecteur *m* covariant	ковариантный вектор
C 2614	**covariation** <ST>	Kovariation *f*, Covariation *f*	covariation *f*	совместное изменение <нескольких переменных или признаков>
	covariation coefficient <ST>	*s.* C 1027		
C 2615	**covector** <VT>	Kovektor *m*	covecteur *m*	ковектор, вектор сопряженного векторного пространства
	cover <DI>	*s.* V 146		
	cover <EG>	*s.* U 440		
	cover <GP>	*s.* C 2618		
	cover <SE>	*s.* F 86		
	cover <SE, TO>	*s.* C 2620		
C 2616	**covering** <of a manifold, groupoid *or* complex> <AT, CA, DG, TO>	Überlagerung *f*	revêtement *m*	наложение
C 2617	**covering** <*n*-fold> <EG>	Überdeckung *f* <*n*-fache>	recouvrement *m* <*n*-uple>	покрытие <*n*-кратное>
C 2618	**covering,** cover <GP>	Überdeckung *f*	recouvrement *m*	реберное разделение
C 2619	**covering** <of a group> <GR>	Überdeckung *f*	recouvrement *m*	покрытие
C 2620	**covering,** cover, // overlapping <SE, TO>	Überdeckung *f*	recouvrement *m*	покрытие, покрышка
C 2621	**covering,** covering map <TO>	Überlagerung *f*, Überlagerungsabbildung *f*	revêtement *m*	наложение
	covering <AX>	*s.* W 188		
	covering <GE, TO>	*s.* P 1652		
	covering base <EG>	*s.* U 440		
C 2622	**covering complex** <AT>	Überlagerungskomplex *m*	complexe *m* de revêtement	комплекс наложения
C 2623	**covering complex** <of a polyhedron> <result> <AT>	Triangulation *f*, trianguliertes Polyeder *n*	polyèdre *m* triangulé	триангулированный полиэдр
C 2624	**covering constant** <GE>	Überdeckungskoeffizient *m*	coefficient *m* de recouvrement	коэффициент покрытия
C 2625	**covering dimension,** Lebesgue['s] dimension <TO>	Überdeckungsdimension *f*, Pflasterdimension *f*	dimension *f* de Lebesgue	размерность <определенная посредством покрытий>
C 2626	**covering group** <GR>	Überlagerungsgruppe *f*	groupe *m* de recouvrement, revêtement *m* <d'un groupe>	накрывающая группа, группа наложения, накрытие <группы>
C 2627	**covering homomorphism** <of a Lie group> <GR>	Überlagerungshomomorphismus *m*	homomorphisme *m* de projection	накрывающий гомоморфизм
C 2628	**covering homotopy theorem** <AT>	Deckhomotopietheorem *n*, Homotopieliftungstheorem *n*	théorème *m* de (du) relèvement des homotopies, lemme *m* de déformation	теорема о накрывающей гомотопии
C 2629	**covering manifold** <DG, TO>	Überlagerungsmannigfaltigkeit *f*	recouvrement *m*, revêtement *m* <d'une variété>, variété *f* de recouvrement	многообразие наложения, накрывающее многообразие
	covering map <TO>	*s.* C 2621		
C 2629 a	**covering number** <AT>	Überdeckungszahl *f*, Bedeckungszahl *f*	nombre *m* de recouvrement	число покрытий, кратность покрытия; кратность, с которой цепь покрывает точку
C 2630	**covering of finite order** <TO>	Überdeckung *f* von endlicher Ordnung	recouvrement *m* d'ordre fini	покрытие конечной кратности
C 2631	**covering of finite type** <TO>	Überdeckung *f* von endlichem Typ (Typus)	recouvrement *m* de type fini	покрытие конечного типа
C 2632	**covering path** <TO>	Überlagerungsweg *m*	chemin *m* revêtant	накрывающий путь
	covering projection <GE, TO>	*s.* P 1652		
	covering projection <TO>	*s.* E 633		
C 2633	**covering space** <DG, TO>	Überlagerungsraum *m*	espace *m* de recouvrement; espace étalé	накрывающее пространство, пространство наложения
C 2634	**covering structure** <TO>	Überdeckungsstruktur *f*	structure *f* de recouvrement	структура покрытия
C 2635	**covering surface** <FT, TO>	Überlagerungsfläche *f*	surface *f* de recouvrement	накрывающая поверхность, поверхность наложения (покрытия)
	covering surface <EG>	*s.* U 440		
C 2636	**covering theorem** <TO>	Überdeckungssatz *m*	théorème *m* de recouvrement	теорема о покрытии, теорема покрытия
	covering theorem of Borel <TO>	*s.* H 174		
C 2637	**covering transformation,** deckbewegung, self-equivalence <of a covering projection> <AT, TO>	Decktransformation *f*, Deckbewegung *f*	opération *f* de recouvrement	накрывающее преобразование, самоэквивалентность, преобразование наложения, накрывающее отображение

No.	English	German	French	Russian
	coversed sine, coversine <DI>	s. V 146		
	co-well-powered category <CA>	s. C 1154		
C 2638	**Coxeter['s] class** <AL>	Coxetersche Klasse *f*	classe *f* de Coxeter	класс Коксетера
C 2639	**Coxeter['s] complex** <AT>	Coxeterscher Komplex *m*	complexe *m* de Coxeter	комплекс Коксетера
C 2640	**Coxeter['s] element** <of a Lie group> <AL>	Coxetersches Element *n*	élément *m* de Coxeter	элемент Коксетера
C 2641	**Coxeter['s] group,** real reflection group <AL>	Coxetersche Gruppe *f*	groupe *m* de Coxeter	группа Коксетера
C 2642	**Coxeter['s] matrix** <AL>	Coxetersche Matrix *f*	matrice *f* de Coxeter	матрица Коксетера
C 2643	**Coxeter['s] system** <AL>	Coxeter-System *n*	système *m* de Coxeter	система Коксетера
C 2644	**cozero-set,** N-set, exact open set, functionally open set <TO>	Komplementärmenge *f* einer Nullstellenmenge	complémentaire *m* d'un ensemble de zéros	дополнение множества нулей
	cp <EG>	s. Q 22		
	CPM <PG>	s. C 2677		
C 2645	**cracovien** <as a matrix> <MD, NU>>	Krakoviane *f*	cracovien *m*	краковян, краковиян
C 2646	**Cramér['s] condition** <ST>	Cramérsche Bedingung *f*	condition *f* de Cramér	условие Крамера
C 2647	**Cramer['s] paradox** <AG>	Cramersches (Cramers) Paradoxon *n*	paradoxe *m* de Cramer	парадокс Крамера
C 2648	**Cramer['s] rule** <MD>	Cramersche Regel *f*, Cramers Regel	formules *fpl* (formule *f*, théorème *m*, règle *f*) de Cramer	правило Крамера, теорема Крамера
C 2649	**Cramér-Smirnov test,** Cramér-von Mises test, ω^2-Test, omega-squared test <ST>	Cramér-Smirnov-Test *m*, Cramér-von-Mises-Test *m*, ω^2-Test *m*, Omega-Quadrat-Test *m*, ω^2-Verfahren *n*, Omega-Quadrat-Verfahren *n*	test *m* de Cramér-Smirnov, test de Cramér-von Mises, test ω^2, test oméga carré	критерий Крамера-Смирнова, критерий Крамера-Мизеса, ω^2-критерий, критерий омега-квадрат
C 2650	**Cramer['s] system,** regular system, non-singular system <AL>	Cramersches Gleichungssystem *n*, reguläres System *n* <lineares System aus *n* Gleichungen für *n* Unbekannte mit nichtverschwindender Determinante>	système *m* de Cramer	крамеровская система линейных уравнений, регулярная система
C 2651	**Cramér['s] theorem** <ST>	Satz *m* von Cramér, Cramérscher Satz	théorème *m* de Cramér	теорема Крамера
	Cramér-von Mises test <ST>	s. C 2649		
C 2652	**Cramér-Wold theorem** <ST>	Satz *m* von Cramér-Wold, Cramér-Woldscher Satz	théorème *m* de Cramér-Wold	теорема Крамера-Вольда
C 2653	**creating function** <MM>	kreative Funktion *f*	fonction *f* créative	креативная функция
C 2654	**creative axiom** <LO>	kreatives Axiom *n*	axiome *m* créatif	креативная аксиома
C 2655	**creative set** <LO>	kreative Menge *f*	ensemble *m* créatif	креативное множество
C 2656	**creativity** <LO>	Kreativität *f*	créativité *f*	креативность
C 2657	**Cremona['s] configuration** <AG>	Cremonasche Konfiguration *f*	configuration *f* de Cremona (Crémona)	конфигурация Кремоны
C 2658	**Cremona['s] curve** <of a net> <AG>	Cremonasche Kurve *f*	courbe *f* crémonienne	кремонова кривая, кривая Кремоны
C 2659	**Cremona['s] group** <AG>	Cremona-Gruppe *f*, Cremonagruppe *f*	groupe *m* de Cremona, groupe *m* Cremona (Crémona), crémonien *m*	группа Кремоны, кремонова группа
C 2660	**Cremona['s] transformation** <AG>	Cremona-Transformation *f*, Cremonatransformation *f*, Cremonasche Transformation *f*	transformation *f* crémonienne, transformation *f* de Cremona (Crémona)	кремоново преобразование, преобразование Кремоны
C 2661	**Cremona transformation in the plane,** plane Cremona transformation <of order *n*> <AG>	ebene Cremona-Transformation *f* <*n*-ter Ordnung>	transformation *f* de Crémona dans le plan <d'ordre *n*>	кремоново преобразование в плоскости <порядка *n*>
C 2662	**Crépin['s] chart (diagram, graph)** <NO>	Crépinsche Tafel *f*	nomogramme (diagramme) *m* de Crépin	номограмма Крепэна
	crescent of Hippokrates	s. H 370		
C 2663	**crest line** <in one-plane projection> < DS>	Kammweg *m*, Rückenlinie *f*	ligne *f* de crête	линия гребня, гребневая линия
C 2664	**C^r function** <AN>	C^r-Funktion *f*, Funktion *f* von der Klasse C^r; C^r-differenzierbare Funktion *f*	fonction *f* de classe C^r, C^r-fonction *f*	функция класса C^r, C^r-функция
	crib of Eratosthenes <NT>	s. S 805		
C 2665	**criterion** <GN>	Kriterium *n*	critère *m*	признак; критерий <необходимый и достаточный>
C 2666	**criterion for divisibility** <of a number> <NT>	Teilbarkeitskriterium *n*, Charakter *m* der Teilbarkeit	caractère *m* de divisibilité	признак делимости
C 2667/8	**criterion for rationality** <AG>	Rationalitätskriterium *n*	critère *m* de rationalité	критерий рациональности
	criterion for tensors <VT>	s. T 138		
C 2669	**criterion for uniform distribution** <NT>	Gleichverteilungskriterium *n*	critère *m* d'équirépartition	признак равномерного распределения
C 2670	**criterion of convergence,** test for (of) convergence, convergence test (criterion) <SS>	Konvergenzkriterium *n*	critère *m* de convergence, caractère *m* de convergence	признак сходимости; критерий сходимости <признак необходимый и достаточный>

No.	English	German	French	Russian
C 2671	**criterion of irrationality** <for a real number> <NT>	Irrationalitätskriterium *n*	critère *m* d'irrationalité	признак иррациональности
	criterion of Kleinmichel <PG>	*s.* K 93		
C 2672	**criterion of non-creativity** <LO>	Kriterium *n* der Nicht-kreativität	critère *m* de non-créativité	критерий некреативности
	criterion of optimality <PG>	*s.* O 236		
C 2673	**critical bound** <PG>	kritische Schranke *f*	borne *f* critique	критическая грань
C 2674	**critical difference,** least significant difference, LSD <ST>	Grenzdifferenz *f*, kritische Differenz *f*, GD	plus petite différence significative	наименьшая значимая разность, критическая разность
	critical function <ST>	*s.* T 207		
	γ-critical graph <GP>	*s.* V 160		
C 2675	**critical level** <in Morse's theory> <VA>	kritischer Wert *m*	niveau *m* (valeur *f*) critique	критическое значение
	critical level <ST>	*s.* C 2680		
C 2676	**critical path** <GP, PG>	kritischer Weg (Pfad) *m*, kritische Bahn *f*	chemin *m* critique	критический путь
C 2677	**critical path method (planning),** CPM <PG>	Methode *f* des kritischen Weges (Pfades), CPM-Methode *f*, CPM-Verfahren *n*, CPM	méthode *f* à chemin critique	метод критического пути
C 2678	**critical point,** singular point, equilibrium point <of a system of differential equations> <DE>	singulärer (kritischer) Punkt *m*	point *m* critique (singulier)	особая (критическая) точка
C 2679	**critical point** <of a function> <PG, RF, VA>	[differentialer] kritischer Punkt *m*, [differentialer] stationärer Punkt *m*, stationäre Stelle *f*	point *m* critique, point *m* stationnaire, point *m* critique de Morse	критическая точка
	critical point <DG>	*s.* S 1110		
C 2680	**critical probability,** critical level <ST>	kritische Wahrscheinlichkeit *f*	probabilité *f* critique, niveau *m* critique [de probabilité]	критическая вероятность, критический уровень [вероятности]
C 2681	**critical region;** rejection region <ST>	kritischer Bereich *m*, kritische Region *f*; Ablehnungsbereich *m*, Ablehnungsgebiet *n*	région *f* (domaine *m*) critique; région de rejet	критическая область; область непринятия [гипотезы]
C 2682	**critical strip** <for the zetafunction> <FT, NT>	kritischer Streifen *m*	bande *f* critique	критическая полоса
	critical value <ST>	*s.* R 661		
C 2683	**C^r manifold,** differentiable manifold of class C^r <DG>	C^r-Mannigfaltigkeit *f*, differenzierbare Mannigfaltigkeit *f* der Klasse C^r	variété *f* [différentiable] de classe C^r	[дифференцируемое] многообразие класса C^r
C 2684	**C^r mapping** <DG>	C^r-Abbildung *f*, Abbildung *f* von der Klasse C^r	C^r-application *f*, application *f* de classe C^r	отображение класса C^r, C^r-отображение
C 2685	**Crofton['s] formula** <IG>	Croftonsche Schnittformel *f*	formule *f* de Crofton	формула Крофтона
C 2686	**Crofton['s] theorem** <IG>	Croftonscher (Croftons) Satz *m*	théorème *m* de Crofton	теорема Крофтона
	cross bar <GN>	*s.* B 58		
C 2687	**cross-cap,** handle of the second kind <TO>	Kreuzhaube *f*, Henkel *m* zweiter Art	anse *f* de deuxième espèce	скрещенный колпак, пленка Мебиуса, «перехлестнутый чепец», ручка второго рода
	cross-checking <AR, NU>	*s.* C 2703		
C 2688	**cross classification** <ST>	Kreuzklassifikation *f*, Überkreuzklassifikation *f*	classification *f* croisée	обратная (многосторонняя) классификация
C 2689	**cross correlation,** intercorrelation <ST>	Kreuzkorrelation *f*, gegenseitige Korrelation *f*	corrélation *f* mutuelle, intercorrélation *f*, corrélation croisée	взаимная корреляция, кросскорреляция
C 2690	**cross correlation analysis,** intercorrelation analysis <ST>	Kreuzkorrelationsanalyse *f*, gegenseitige Korrelationsanalyse *f*	analyse *f* de corrélation mutuelle (croisée), analyse d'intercorrélation	взаимнокорреляционный анализ, кросскорреляционный анализ
C 2691	**cross correlation coefficient,** intercorrelation coefficient <ST>	Kreuzkorrelationskoeffizient *m*, gegenseitiger Korrelationskoeffizient *m*	coefficient *m* de corrélation mutuelle, coefficient d'intercorrélation	коэффициент взаимной корреляции, кросскорреляционный коэффициент
C 2692	**cross correlation function** <ST>	Kreuzkorrelationsfunktion *f*, gegenseitige Korrelationsfunktion *f*, Kreuzkorrelation *f*, gegenseitige Korrelation *f*	fonction *f* de corrélation mutuelle (croisée), fonction d'intercorrélation; fonction de corrélation diaphonique <en téléphoniste>	взаимнокорреляционная функция, кросскорреляционная функция, функция взаимной корреляции, корреляционная функция связи
C 2693	**cross covariance function** <ST>	Kreuzkovarianzfunktion *f*	fonction *f* des covariances mutuelles (croisées)	взаимноковариационная функция, функция взаимной ковариации
C 2694	**cross cut** <AT>	Querschnitt *m*	section *f* transversale	поперечный разрез
	cross[-] cut <FT, TO>	*s.* R 952		
	cross-cut <LA>	*s.* M 362		
C 2695	**crossed automorphism** <AL>	verschränkter Automorphismus *m*	automorphisme *m* croisé	скрещенный автоморфизм
C 2696	**crossed equivalence** <AL>	verschränkte Äquivalenz *f*	équivalence *f* croisée	скрещенная эквивалентность
C 2697	**crossed functor** <CA>	verschränkter Funktor *m*	foncteur *m* croisé	скрещенный функтор
C 2698	**crossed isomorphism** <AL>	verschränkter Isomorphismus *m*	isomorphisme *m* croisé	скрещенный изоморфизм
C 2699	**crossed module** <AL>	verschränkter Modul *m*	module *m* croisé	скрещенный модуль
C 2700	**crossed multiplication** <AL>	verschränkte Multiplikation *f*	multiplication *f* croisée	скрещенное умножение

No.	English	German	French	Russian
C 2701	**crossed product** <of algebras>, **crossed product algebra** <AL>	verschränktes Produkt *n*	produit *m* croisé	скрещенное произведение
C 2702	**cross elevation,** cross projection, profile <orthogonal to elevation> <DS>	Kreuzriß *m*, Seitenriß *m*, dritte Projektion *f*	profil *m*, projection *f* en profil	профильная проекция
C 2703	**crossfooting,** cross-checking <AR, NU>	Querrechnen *n*, Querrechnung *f*	calcul *m* transversal, opération *f* horizontale	поперечное вычисление (исчисление), суммирование по горизонтали
C 2704	**crossing number** <GP>	Schnittpunktzahl *f*, Überkreuzungszahl *f*, Überschneidungszahl *f*	nombre *m* de croisement	число скрещиваний
C 2705	**cross multiplication, cross-multiplication** <AL>	Multiplikation *f* über Kreuz, kreuzweise Multiplikation *f*, Crossmultiplikation *f*	multiplication *f* en croix	умножение крест-накрест, умножение «крест на крест»
C 2706	**cross-multiply / to,** to multiply criss[-]cross, to multiply crosswise <AL>	kreuzweise multiplizieren	multiplier en croix	множить накрест
	cross plane [of projection] <DS>	*s.* C 2709		
C 2707	**cross point** <DS>	Kreuzungspunkt *m*, scheinbarer Schnittpunkt *m*	point *m* de croisement	точка пересечения
C 2708	**cross point** <of a holomorphic function> <FT>	Kreuzungspunkt *m*	point *m* de croisement	критическая точка
	cross point <GP>	*s.* N 275		
	cross product <FA>	*s.* D 595		
	cross product <SE>	*s.* C 173		
	cross product <VT>	*s.* V 121		
	cross projection <DS>	*s.* C 2702		
C 2709	**cross projection plane,** cross plane [of projection] <orthogonal to the vertical plane> <DS>	Kreuzrißebene *f*, Kreuzrißtafel *f*, Seitenrißebene *f*, Seitenrißtafel *f*, dritte Projektionsebene (Tafel) *f*	plan *m* de projection en profil	плоскость профильной проекции
C 2710	**cross ratio, cross-ratio,** double ratio, anharmonic ratio <of four elements, especially points> <AY>	Doppelverhältnis *n*, anharmonisches Verhältnis *n*, Doppelschnittverhältnis *n* <Möbius> <von vier Elementen, insbesondere Punkten>	birapport *m*, rapport *m* anharmonique, rapport de double section, biquotient *m* <de quatre éléments ou d'une quaterne d'éléments, en particulier de points>	сложное отношение, двойное отношение, ангармоническое отношение <четырех элементов, в частности точек>
	cross-ratio of four tangents from a point <AG>	*s.* M 790		
C 2711	**cross-section,** section <of a fibre bundle> <AT>	Schnitt *m* <eines Faserbündels>	section *f* <d'un espace fibré>	сечение <расслоенного пространства>
C 2712	**cross-section** <of a partition of a set> <SE>	Schnitt *m* <einer Zerlegung einer Menge>	section *f* <d'une partition d'un ensemble>	поперечное сечение <разбиения множества>
C 2713	**cross-sectional measure** <of a convex body> <CS, GE>	Quermaß *n*, [äußeres] Quermaß *n*, $(n - 1)$-dimensionales [äußeres] Quermaß <in einer Richtung>	travers *m* extérieur, aire *f* du travers extérieur <dans une direction>	поперечная мера
	CRT <AL>	*s.* C 632		
C 2714	**cruciforme curve** <as a curve of fourth order> <AG>	Kreuzkurve *f*	courbe *f* cruciforme, kreuzcurve *f*	крестообразная кривая, крестовидная кривая
	crude approximation <AX, NU>	*s.* R 1414		
	crunodal curve <GE>	*s.* C 2791		
	crunode <AG>	*s.* N 272		
C 2715	**crystalline cohomology** <AG>	kristalline Kohomologie *f*	cohomologie *f* cristalline	кристальные когомологии
	cs <FU>	*s.* A 607		
	csc <DI>	*s.* C 2520		
	csch <FU>	*s.* H 622		
C 2716	**(C)-set** <of a metric space> <TO>	C-Menge *f*, gesiebte Menge *f*	(C)-ensemble *m*	(C)-множество
	C.S.S. complex <AT, CA>	*s.* S 991		
C 2717	**C_1-sum, (C, 1) sum,** sum by the method of arithmetic means <LI>	*M*-Summe *f*, Summe *f* nach dem *M*-Verfahren, $(C, 1)$-Summe *f*, C_1-Summe *f*	somme *f* par la méthode des moyennes arithmétiques, $(C, 1)$-somme *f*, C_1-somme *f*	[обобщенная] сумма по методу средних арифметических
	C-sum <LI>	*s.* S 2259		
C 2718	**C_1-summable series, (C, 1) summable series,** series summable by arithmetic means <LI>	*M*-summierbare (nach dem *M*-Verfahren summierbare, C_1-summierbare) Reihe *f*	série *f* simplement indéterminée, série sommable par moyennes arithmétiques, série sommable $(C, 1)$, série sommable C_1	ряд, суммируемый средними арифметическими; ряд, суммируемый по [методу] Чезаро средними первого порядка; суммируемый C_1 ряд; суммируемый $(C, 1)$ ряд
	C-summable series <LI>	*s.* C 453		
	ctg <DI>	*s.* C 2539		
	ctg am <FU>	*s.* A 607		
	ctgh <FU>	*s.* H 625		
	cth <FU>	*s.* H 625		
C 2719	**cubable solid,** integrable solid <DI>	kubierbarer (integrierbarer) Körper *m*	corps *m* cubable (intégrable)	кубируемое (интегрируемое) тело
C 2720	**cubage; cubature;** cubing <EG, DI>	Volumenbestimmung *f*, Volum[en]berechnung *f*; Kubatur *f*, Inhaltsberechnung *f*	cubage *m*; cubature *f*	кубатура, нахождение объема
C 2721	**cubature formula,** formula for numerical (mechanical) cubature <DI, NU>	mechanische Kubaturformel *f*, Kubaturformel	formule *f* de cubature, formule de cubature numérique (mécanique)	формула механических кубатур, кубатурная формула

C 2722	**cube** <as a topological product of closed unit intervals> <TO>	Würfel *m*	cube *m*	куб
	cube <EG>	*s.* R 559		
C 2723	**cube domain** <TO>	Würfelgebiet *n*	domaine *m* d'un cube	кубическая область
C 2724	**cube lemma** <CA>	Würfellemma *n*	lemme *m* du cube	лемма о кубе
C 2725	**cubic,** cubic surface, surface of third order <AG>	kubische Fläche *f*, Fläche dritter Ordnung, Fläche dritten Grades	surface *f* cubique (du troisième ordre)	поверхность третьего порядка, кубическая поверхность
C 2726	**cubic,** plane cubic [curve], plane algebraic curve of the third degree (order), algebraic plane curve of the third degree (order) <AG>	algebraische ebene Kurve *f* dritter (3.) Ordnung, ebene [algebraische] Kurve dritter (3.) Ordnung, ebene Kubik *f*	courbe *f* algébrique plane d'ordre trois (3), courbe plane d'ordre trois (3), courbe cubique plane, cubique *f* plane	плоская алгебраическая кривая третьего (3-го) порядка, плоская кривая третьего (3-го) порядка
	cubic <AG>	*s.* C 2738		
	cubic <AL>	*s.* 1. C 2739; 2. C 2743		
C 2727	**cubical circle** <as a space curve> <AG>	windschiefer (kubischer) Kreis *m*, räumliche zirkulare Kurve *f* dritter (3.) Ordnung	cubique *f* circulaire gauche, cercle *m* cubique	кубическая окружность
C 2728	**cubical ellipse** <AG>	kubische Ellipse *f*, Raumellipse *f*	ellipse *f* gauche	кубический эллипс
C 2729	**cubical graph,** cubic (trivalent) graph, regular graph of degree 3, regular graph with the valence 3 at each vertex <GP>	kubischer Graph *m*, regulärer Graph vom Grad 3, dreiwertiger Graph	graphe *m* cubique (régulier de degré 3)	тривалентный (кубический) граф
C 2730	**cubical hyperbola** <AG>	kubische Hyperbel *f*, Raumhyperbel *f*, hyperbolische Kurve *f*	hyperbole *f* gauche (cubique), courbe (cubique) *f* hyperbolique	кубическая гипербола
C 2731	**cubical hyperbolic parabola,** parabolic hyperbola <as a cubic curve in space> <AG>	[kubische] parabolische Hyperbel *f*, hyperbolische (kubisch-hyperbolische) Parabel *f*, parabolische Raumhyperbel	hyperbole *f* parabolique, parabole *f* hyperbolique (hyperbolique cubique), hyperbole gauche parabolique	кубическая гиперболическая парабола, параболическая гипербола
C 2732	**cubical parabola,** parabolic curve of third order, parabola of degree three <as a plane curve> <AG>	kubische Parabel *f*, parabolische Kurve *f* [dritter Ordnung]	courbe (cubique) *f* parabolique	кубическая парабола
	cubical parabola <AG>	*s.* C 2742		
	cubical singular cohomology <AT>	*s.* C 2737		
C 2733	**cubical singular homology** <AT>	kubische singuläre Homologie *f*	homologie *f* singulière cubique, homologie cubique	сингулярные кубические гомологии, кубические гомологии
C 2734	**cubical singular homology group** <AT>	kubische singuläre Homologiegruppe *f*	groupe *m* d'homologie cubique	группа кубических гомологий
C 2735	**cubic array,** cubic matrix <MD>	kubische Matrix *f*	matrice *f* cubique	кубическая матрица
C 2736	**cubic circular [curve]** <AG>	zirkulare Kubik *f*, Kreiskurve *f* dritter (3.) Ordnung	cubique *f* circulaire	циркулярная кривая третьего порядка
C 2737	**cubic cohomology,** cubical singular cohomology <AT>	kubische [singuläre] Kohomologie *f*	cohomologie *f* cubique	кубические когомологии
	cubic conic [section] <AG>	*s.* S 1309		
C 2738	**cubic curve,** cubic, [algebraic] curve of the third degree (order) <AG>	Kurve *f* dritter (3.) Ordnung, Kubik *f*, kubische Kurve, algebraische Kurve dritter (3.) Ordnung, Kurve dritten (3.) Grades	courbe *f* cubique, cubique *f*, courbe [algébrique] du troisième (3-e) ordre	кубическая кривая, [алгебраическая] кривая третьего (3-го) порядка
C 2739	**cubic equation,** cubic, equation of [the] third degree, third-degree polynomial equation <AL>	kubische Gleichung *f*, Gleichung dritten (3.) Grades, algebraische Gleichung dritten (3.) Grades	équation *f* cubique, équation du troisième (3-e) degré (ordre)	кубическое уравнение, кубичное уравнение, уравнение третьей (3-ей) степени
	cubic graph <GP>	*s.* C 2729		
	cubic homogeneous polynomial <AL>	*s.* C 2743		
C 2740	**cubic of Lucas,** Lucas['] cubic <AG>	Lucassche (isodynamische) Kurve *f*	courbe *f* de Lucas (isodynamique), cubique *f* de Lucas	кривая Люка
	cubic matrix <MD>	*s.* C 2735		
C 2741	**cubic of Tschirnhausen** <AG>	Tschirnhausensche Kubik *f*	cubique *f* de Tschirnhausen	кривая Чирнгаузена (Лопиталя)
C 2742	**cubic parabola,** cubical parabola <in space> <AG>	kubische (windschiefe) Parabel *f*	parabole *f* gauche (cubique)	кубическая парабола
C 2743	**cubic quantic,** cubic homogeneous polynomial, cubic, quantic of the third degree, form of the third degree <AL>	kubische Form *f*, Form dritten Grades, Kubik *f*	forme *f* cubique	кубическая форма, форма третьей степени
C 2744	**cubic residue** <NT>	kubischer Rest *m*	résidu *m* cubique	кубический вычет
	cubic resolvent <AL>	*s.* R 913		
C 2744 a	**cubic spline function** <AX, NU>	kubische Spline-Funktion *f*	fonction *f* spline cubique	кубическая сплайн-функция
	cubic surface <AG>	*s.* C 2725		
C 2745	**cubic table** <NT, NU>	Kubiktafel *f*	table *f* (tableau *m*) des cubes	таблица кубов, таблица кубов чисел

C 2746	**cubing,** raising to the third power <AL, AR>	Erhebung *f* in die dritte Potenz, Kubierung *f*	élévation *f* au cube, élévation à la puissance trois, cubage *m*	возведение в куб
	cubing <EG, DI>	*s.* C 2720		
	cuboid <EG>	*s.* R 280		
C 2747	**cuboidal lattice** <ST>	Quadergitter *n*	treillis *m* semi-cubique	кубоидальная решетка
C 2748	**cubo-octahedron** <EG>	Kubooktaeder *n*	cubo-octaèdre *m*	кубооктаэдр
	cumulant <ST>	*s.* S 395		
	cumulant function <ST>	*s.* C 2749		
C 2749	**cumulant generating function,** cumulant function <ST>	kumulant[en]erzeugende Funktion *f*, Kumulant[en]erzeugende *f*, Kumulantenfunktion *f*	fonction *f* génératrice des cumulants, fonction des cumulants	производящая функция семиинвариантов, функция семиинвариантов, функция кумулянтов
C 2750	**cumulant ratio** <ST>	Kumulantenquotient *m*	rapport *m* de cumulants	отношение семиинвариантов
	cumulative distribution function <ST>	*s.* D 758		
C 2751	**cumulative effect** <ST>	kumulative Wirkung *f*	effet *m* cumulatif	накопленный эффект
C 2752	**cumulative frequency** <ST>	Summenhäufigkeit *f*, kumulative Häufigkeit *f*	fréquence *f* cumulée	накопленная частота
C 2753	**cumulative frequency curve** <ST>	Summenkurve *f*, Summenhäufigkeitskurve *f*, kumulative Häufigkeitskurve *f*	courbe *f* de[s] fréquences cumulées	функция накопленных частот
	cumulative frequency function <ST>	*s.* D 758		
	cumulative normal distribution <ST>	*s.* N 559		
	cumulative probability function <ST>	*s.* D 758		
C 2754	**cup product,** Kolmogorov-Alexander product <AT, HA>	[Alexander-Kolmogorowsches] Cup-Produkt *n*	cup-produit *m* [d'Alexander-Kolmogoroff], produit *m* cup	произведение Колмогорова-Александера, ∪-произведение; произведение классов когомологий
	cup-product homomorphism <TO>	*s.* C 2756		
C 2755	**cup product operation** <AT, HA>	Bildung des Cup-Produkts	opération *f* du cup-produit	умножение Колмогорова-Александера, умножение в когомологиях, ∪-умножение
C 2756	**cup product pairing,** cup-product homomorphism <TO>	Paarung *f* durch das Cup-Produkt		умножение в когомологиях, произведение Колмогорова-Александера, ∪-произведение
C 2757	**curl, Curl** <of a tensor> <VT>	tensorielle Rotation *f*, Rotation *f*, Rot, rot <eines Tensors>	rotationnel *m*, Rot <de tenseur>	вихрь, ротор, Rot <тензора>
C 2758	**curl,** rotor, rotation <of a vector field> <VT>	Rotation *f*, Rotor *m*, vektorielle Rotation, Wirbel *m*, rot, // Curl *m*, Quirl *m*	rotationnel *m*, curl *m*, vecteur-curl *m*, tourbillon *m*, vecteur *m* rotationnel, (tourbillon), rotation *f*, rot	вихрь, ротор, ротация, rot, curl
C 2759	**Curl, curl [at a surface] of discontinuity,** surface curl, areal curl, <VT>	Flächenrotation *f*, Flächenwirbel *m*, Flächenrotor *m*, Sprungrotation *f*, Sprungwirbel *m*, Sprungrotor *m*, Rot	rotationnel *m* de (dans une surface de) discontinuité, rotationnel de surface, rotationnel superficiel, Rot	вихрь (ротор) разрыва, вихрь (ротор) на поверхности разрыва, поверхностный вихрь (ротор), Rot
	curly bracket <GN>	*s.* B 706		
C 2760	**cursor,** moving part <US> <of a slide rule> <IN>	Läufer *m*	curseur *m*	бегунок
C 2761	**curtate cissoid** <GE>	verkürzte Kissoide *f*	cissoïde *f* raccourcie	укороченная циссоида
C 2762	**curtate cycloid** <GE>	verkürzte (gestreckte, verkürzte gemeine, gestreckte gemeine) Zykloide *f*	cycloïde *f* raccourcie	укороченная циклоида
C 2763	**curtate epicycloid (epitrochoid)** <GE>	verkürzte (gestreckte) Epizykloide (Epitrochoide) *f*	épicycloïde (épitrochoïde) *f* raccourcie	укороченная эпициклоида (эпитрохоида)
C 2764	**curtate hypocycloid (hypotrochoid)** <GE>	verkürzte (gestreckte) Hypozykloide (Hypotrochoide) *f*	hypocycloïde (hypotrochoïde) *f* raccourcie	укороченная гипоциклоида (гипотрохоида)
C 2765	**curtate trochoid** <common name of curtate epitrochoid and curtate hypotrochoid> <GE>	verkürzte (gestreckte) Trochoide (Rollkurve) *f*	trochoïde *f* raccourcie	укороченная трохоида
C 2766	**curvature,** first curvature <of a curve> <DG>	Krümmung *f*, erste Krümmung, Flexion *f*	courbure *f*, première courbure	кривизна, первая кривизна
C 2767	**curvature axis,** curvature-axis, axis of curvature <of a ruled surface> <DG>	Krümmungsachse *f*	axe *m* de courbure	ось кривизны
	curvature cone <DG>	*s.* C 1851		
C 2768	**curvature field** <DG>	Krümmungsfeld *n*	champ *m* de courbures	поле кривизн
C 2769	**curvature form** <DG>	Krümmungsform *f*	forme *f* de courbure	форма кривизны
C 2770	**curvature of the second kind** <DG>	Streckenkrümmung *f*, Streckenwirbel *m*	courbure *f* segmentaire (d'homothétie), courbure de seconde espèce	кривизна второго рода
C 2771	**curvature of the three points** <of a metric space> <DG>	Krümmung *f* von drei verschiedenen Punkten	courbure *f* des trois points	кривизна трех точек
C 2772	**curvature scalar** <DG>	Krümmungsskalar *m*	scalaire *m* de courbure	скаляр кривизны
C 2773	**curvature tensor** <of rank 3 *or* 4> <DG>	Krümmungstensor *m*	tenseur *m* de courbure	тензор кривизны
C 2774	**curvature tensor** <in a Weyl transfer> <DG>	Vektorkrümmung *f*, Vektorwirbel *m*	tenseur *m* de courbure <d'un transfert de Weyl>	тензор кривизны <при перенесении Вейля>
	curvature tensor <DG>	*s.* R 1040		
C 2775	**curvature vector** <DG>	Krümmungsvektor *m*	vecteur *m* de courbure	вектор кривизны
	curve arc <GE>	*s.* A 882		
	curve congruence <DG>	*s.* C 1921		

C 2776	**curve convex toward a side** <GE>	von einer Seite konvexe Kurve *f*	courbe *f* convexe vers un côté	выпуклая к одной стороне кривая
C 2777	**curved polyhedron,** topological polyhedron <AT>	krummes (topologisches) Polyeder *n*, triangulierbarer Raum *m*	polyèdre *m* topologique	кривой (криволинейный) полиэдр, кривой многогранник
C 2778	**curved ruler** <GE, IN>	Kurvenlineal *n*, Bogenlineal *n*	pistolet *m* [à dessin], règle *f* courbe	лекало, фигурная линейка
C 2779	**curved scale,** scale <NO>	bezifferte Kurve *f*, Skala *f*	échelle *f* curviligne, échelle	криволинейная шкала, шкала
	curved surface <EG>	*s.* L 110		
C 2780	**curve in the sense of Menger and Urysohn** <TO>	Kurve *f* im Sinne von Menger und Urysohn	courbe *f* au sens de Menger et Urysohn	кривая в смысле Менгера и Урысона
C 2781	**curve of a** <linear> **system** <AG>	Systemkurve *f*	courbe *f* d'un système	кривая системы
	curve of average sample numbers <ST>	*s.* A 1044		
C 2782	**curve of bounded rotation** <PO>	Kurve *f* mit beschränkter Drehung	courbe *f* à rotation bornée	кривая с ограниченным вращением
C 2783	**curve of Clairaut,** Clairaut['s] curve <GE>	Clairautsche Kurve *f*, Mediatrixkurve *f* von Clairaut	courbe (multiplicatrice) *f* de Clairaut, courbe des médianes	кривая Клеро
	curve of constant breadth <CS, GE>	*s.* O 247		
	curve of constant slope <GE>	*s.* S 1207		
	curve of double curvature <DG>	*s.* S 1306		
	curve of Eudoxus <AG>	*s.* K 8		
	curve of inflection points <DG, DI>	*s.* I 500		
C 2784	**curve of intersection,** intersection curve <of two surfaces> <AY, DS, EG>	Schnittkurve *f*, Schnittlinie *f*	ligne (courbe) *f* d'intersection	кривая (линия) пересечения
	curve of intersection of two quadrics (general quadric surfaces) <AG>	*s.* E 187		
	curve of normal distribution [of errors] <ST> ⌐<AG>	*s.* E 471		
	curve of pinchpoints	*s.* C 2808		
C 2785	**curve of principal type** <DG>	Haupttypkurve *f*, Kurve *f* vom Haupttyp	courbe *f* de type principal	кривая главного типа
C 2786	**curve of pursuit,** dog curve <DE>	Verfolgungskurve *f*, Hundekurve *f*, Fliehkurve *f*, Fluchtkurve *f*	courbe *f* de poursuite, courbe du chien	кривая погони (преследования)
	curve of second degree (order) <AG, AY>	*s.* C 1944		
	curve of shortest descent <VA>	*s.* B 707		
	curve of slope <VA>	*s.* L 872		
C 2787	**curve of support,** support (supporting) curve <CS, GE>	Stützkurve *f*	courbe *f* d'appui	опорная кривая
	curve of the eighth degree <AG>	*s.* B 434		
	curve of the fifth degree (order) <AG>	*s.* Q 301		
	curve of the fourth degree (order) <AG>	*s.* Q 87		
C 2788	**curve of the *n*-th class** <AG> ⌐<AY>	Kurve *f* *n*-ter Klasse	courbe *f* de la *n*-e classe	кривая *n*-го класса
	curve of the second class	*s.* L 854		
	curve of the second degree (order) <AG, AY>	*s.* C 1944		
	curve of the sixth degree (order) <AG>	*s.* S 727		
	curve of the third degree (order) <AG>	*s.* C 2738		
C 2789	**curve space** <AG>	Kurvenraum *m*	espace *m* des courbes	пространство кривых
C 2790	**curve with boundary** <TO>	berandete Kurve *f*	courbe *f* à bord	кривая с краем
C 2791	**curve with double point,** crunodal curve <GE>	Kurve *f* mit Doppelpunkt	courbe *f* à point double, courbe crunodale	кривая с двойной точкой
C 2792	**curve without boundary** <TO>	unberandete Kurve *f*	courbe *f* sans bord	кривая без края
C 2793	**curve without double points** <GE>	doppelpunktfreie Kurve *f*	courbe *f* privée de points doubles	кривая без двойных точек
C 2794	**curvilinear asymptote** <GE>	krummlinige Asymptote *f*	asymptote *f* curviligne	криволинейная асимптота
C 2795	**curvilinear asymptote,** asymptote <RF>	asymptotische Kurve *f*, Asymptote *f*	asymptote *f* [curviligne]	[криволинейная] асимптота
	curvilinear congruence <DG>	*s.* C 1921		
C 2796	**curvilinear co-ordinates** <AN, AY>	krummlinige Koordinaten	coordonnées *fpl* curvilignes	криволинейные координаты
C 2797	**curvilinear co-ordinates,** Gauss co-ordinates <on a surface *or* manifold> <DG>	krummlinige (Gaußsche) Koordinaten *fpl*, Parameter *mpl*	coordonnées *fpl* curvilignes (gaussiennes)	криволинейные (гауссовы, внутренние) координаты
C 2798	**curvilinear co-ordinate system,** curvilinear system [of co-ordinates] <AN, GE>	krummliniges Koordinatensystem *n*	système *m* de coordonnées curvilignes, système curviligne [de coordonnées]	криволинейная система координат

C 2799	**curvilinear diameter** <of a cubic> <AG>	krummliniger Durchmesser *m*	diamètre *m* curviligne	криволинейный диаметр
	curvilinear generator <GE>	*s.* G 201		
C 2800	**curvilinear integral,** line integral <of the first type, i.e. over length function, *or* of the second type, i.e. over a co-ordinate or over the co-ordinates> <DI, FT>	Kurvenintegral *n*, Linienintegral *n* <erster, zweiter *oder* allgemeiner Art>	intégrale *f* curviligne <de premier *ou* deuxième type>	криволинейный интеграл <первого, второго *или* общего типа>
	curvilinear integral along a closed contour (curve, line, path) <AN>	*s.* C 734 a		
	curvilinear integral along a contour <AN>	*s.* C 734 a		
	curvilinear polygon <EG>	*s.* A 907		
	curvilinear quadrangle <EG>	*s.* A 908		
C 2801	**curvilinear regression** <ST>	kurvilineare (curvilineare) Regression *f*	régression *f* curviligne (curvilinéaire)	криволинейная регрессия
	curvilinear system [of co-ordinates] <AN, GE>	*s.* C 2798		
	curvilinear trend <ST>	*s.* N 413		
C 2802	**curvilinear triangle** <EG>	krummliniges Dreieck *n*	triangle *m* curviligne	криволинейный треугольник
	curvilinear triangle <EG>	*s.* A 914		
C 2803	**curvometer** <GE, IN>	Kurvimeter *n*	curvimètre *m*	курвиметр
C 2804	**Cusanus['] construction** <of corresponding circular arcs> <GE>	Cusanussche Konstruktion *f*, Konstruktion des Nikolaus Cusanus	construction *f* de Cusanus	построение Кузануса
C 2805	**cusp,** cuspidal point, stationary point <of a curve> <GE>	Rückkehrpunkt *m*, Spitze *f*, Kuspidalpunkt *m*, stationärer Punkt *m*, Spitzpunkt *m*, Kehrpunkt *m*, Wiederkehrungspunkt *m*, Stillstandpunkt *m*	point *m* de rebroussement, rebroussement *m*, point « en aiguille », point cuspidal, cuspide *m*, pointe *f*, point spinodal (stationnaire)	точка возврата (заострения), касп, острие
	cusp <GE>	*s.* C 2814		
C 2806	**cusp-form, cusp form** <as a modular form> <FT, NT>	Spitzenform *f*	« Spitzenform » *f*, forme *f* parabolique	параболическая форма
C 2807	**cuspidal asymptote** <GE>	Kuspidalasymptote *f*	asymptote *f* cuspidale	касательная в несобственной (бесконечно удаленной) точке возврата
C 2808	**cuspidal curve,** curve of pinchpoints <of an algebraic surface> <AG>	Kuspidallinie *f*	ligne *f* cuspidale	куспидальная линия
	cuspidal edge <DG>	*s.* E 22		
C 2809	**cuspidal pair** <of groups> <GR>	parabolisches Paar *n*		параболическая пара
C 2810	**cuspidal plane** <GE>	Kuspidalebene *f*, Klemmebene *f*	plan *m* cuspidal	
	cuspidal point <GE>	*s.* C 2805		
	cuspidal point of [the] first kind <GE>	*s.* C 2814		
C 2811	**cuspidal point of [the] second kind,** cusp of [the] second kind, acnode, ramphoid cusp <of a curve> <GE>	Spitze *f* zweiter Art, Schnabelspitze *f*, Rückkehrpunkt (Umkehrpunkt) *m* zweiter Art, Schnabelpunkt *m*, Schnabel *m*, Knotenspitze *f*, Nadelknoten *m*, Nadelpunkt *m*	point *m* de rebroussement de deuxième (2-e) espèce, rebroussement *m* de seconde (deuxième) espèce, rebroussement ramphoïdal, ramphoïde *m*, rebroussement en bec, pointe *f* à bec, bec *m*	точка возврата второго рода, обыкновенная точка возврата, касп
C 2812	**cuspidal tangent** <GE>	Rückkehrtangente *f*, Tangente *f* in einem Rückkehrpunkt, Kuspidaltangente *f*	tangente *f* de rebroussement, tangente cuspidale	касательная в точке возврата
C 2813	**cusp-locus** <GE>	Kuspidalort *m*, Ort *m* der Rückkehrpunkte	lieu *m* des points de rebroussement	место точек возврата
C 2814	**cusp of [the] first kind,** cuspidal point of [the] first kind, simple cusp, ordinary cuspidal point, cusp, spinode <Cayley> <of a curve> <GE>	Spitze *f* (Umkehrpunkt *m*) erster Art, gewöhnliche Spitze, Spitze in engerem Sinne, gewöhnlicher Rückkehrpunkt *m*, Dornknoten *m*, Rückkehrpunkt	point *m* de rebroussement ordinaire (de première espèce), rebroussement *m* de première espèce, rebroussement ordinaire, point cuspidal, cuspide *m*, kératoïde *m*, nœud *m* spinal	точка возврата первого рода, обыкновенная точка возврата, касп
	cusp of [the] second kind <GE>	*s.* C 2811		
C 2815	**cut,** edge cut-set <of a transportation network> <GP, PG>	Schnitt *m* <eines Transportnetzes>	coupe *f* <d'un réseau de transport>	разрез <транспортной сети>
C 2816	**cut** <LO>	Schnitt *m*	section *f*	сечение
C 2817	**cut** <TO>	Schnitt *m* <und Verheftung>	section *f*	разрез
	cut <AN, SE>	*s.* D 84		
	cut <EG>	*s.* S 2369		
C 2818	**cut continuum** <TO>	zerlegbares Kontinuum *n*	continuum *m* décomposable	разрезаемый континуум
	cut[-] edge <GP>	*s.* S 545		
	cut embankment <DS>	*s.* E 195		
C 2819	**cut line** <of a surface> <AT>	Schnittlinie *f*	ligne *f* d'intersection	линия разреза
C 2820	**cut-off** <of sequential sampling> <ST>	Abbrechen *n*, Abbruch *m*	arrêt *m*, tronquage *m*	отсечка, прерывание

	cut off from the x-axis <AY>	*s.* X 1		
	cut off from the y-axis <AY>	*s.* L 875		
C 2821	**cut operation** <AT>	Schnittoperation *f*	opération *f* de section	операция разреза
C 2822	**cut point** <TO>	Zerlegungspunkt *m*; zyklisches Element *n* zweiter Art <eines Kontinuums>	point *m* de décomposition	разрезающая точка
	cut point, cut-point, cutpoint <GP>	*s.* C 2828		
C 2823	**cut set, cut-set** <of a connected graph> <GP>	Schnittmenge *f*	cocircuit *m*	разрез
	cut-set <GP>	*s.* A 1001		
C 2824	**cut-set matrix** <GP>	Matrix *f* der Schnittmenge	matrice *f* des coupes	матрица разрезов
C 2825	**cutting method** <PG>	Schnittverfahren *n*, Schnittmethode *f*	méthode *f* de section	метод (способ) сечения
C 2826	**cutting method of Gomory,** Gomory['s] method <PG>	Verfahren *n* (Schnittmethode *f*) von Gomory, Gomorysches Verfahren	méthode *f* de Gomory	метод Гомори
	cutting plane <EG>	*s.* I 794		
C 2827	**cutting problem** <PG>	Zuschnittproblem *n*	problème *m* de découpage	задача раскроя (об оптимальном раскрое) <материалов>
C 2828	**cut vertex, cut-vertex,** separating vertex, cut[-]point, cut point, articulation point (vertex) <GP>	Zerlegungspunkt *m*, Zerfällungspunkt *m*, Zerfällungsknotenpunkt *m*, trennender Knotenpunkt *m*, Artikulationspunkt *m*, Artikulation *f*	articulation *f*, point *m* d'articulation	точка сочленения
C 2829	**CW approximation** <AT>	CW-Approximation *f*	CW-approximation *f*	CW-аппроксимация
C 2830	**CW complex, CW-complex** <AT>	CW-Komplex *m*	CW-complexe *m*, complexe *m* cellulaire	CW-комплекс, клеточное разбиение
C 2831	**cycle,** circuit, closed chain <AT>	Zyklus *m*, geschlossene Kette *f*	cycle *m*	цикл, Δ-цикл
C 2832	**cycle** <on a Riemann surface> <FT>	[linearer] Kreis *m*, Zyklus *m*, Ringweg *m*	cycle *m*	цикл
C 2833	**cycle** <of an oriented graph> <GP>	Zyklus *m*, geschlossene Kette *f*	cycle *m*	цикл
C 2834	**cycle** <of a set of arcs> <GP>	Zyklus *m*	ensemble *m* des arcs d'un circuit simple	неупорядоченный контур
	cycle <AG>	*s.* D 828		
	cycle <AL>	*s.* C 2868		
	cycle <AY>	*s.* O 409		
	cycle <GP>	*s.* E 98		
	cycle <NU>	*s.* I 1226		
	cycle <SP>	*s.* P 447		
	1-cycle <AL, CT>	*s.* O 76		
C 2835	**2-cycle** <of a permutation> <AL>	Zweierzyklus *m*	cycle *m* binaire	двойной цикл
	3-cycle <AL, CT>	*s.* T 446		
C 2836	**cycle basis,** basis of cycles <GP>	Zyklenbasis *f*	base *f* [fondamentale] de cycles	[основной] базис циклов
	cycle decomposition <AL, CT>	*s.* C 2854		
	cycle edge <GP>	*s.* E 21		
C 2837	**cycle of length** *n* <GP>	*n*-Kreis *m*, Kreis (Zyklus) *m* der Länge *n*, *n*-Eck *n*; *n*-Zyklus *m*	cycle *m* de longueur *n*, circuit *m* de *n* arcs	*n*-угольник, цикл длины *n*
	cycle of length *n* <AL>	*s.* N 58		
	cycle of length 3 <AL, CT>	*s.* T 446		
	cycle of length 3 <GP>	*s.* T 900		
	cycle of length one <AL, CT>	*s.* O 76		
C 2838	**cycle of numbers** <cyclic array of numbers> <NT>	Zahlenkreis *m*	cycle *m* de nombres	цикл чисел
C 2839	**cycle of the cycle decomposition** <of a permutation> <AL>	Zyklus *m* in einer kanonischen Zyklendarstellung	cycle *m* canonique (composant)	циклический подстановка-сомножитель
C 2840	**cycle of the first kind,** trivial cycle <AT>	Zyklus *m* erster Art, trivialer Zyklus	cycle *m* trivial	цикл первого рода
C 2841	**cycle of the second kind,** non-trivial cycle <AT>	Zyklus *m* zweiter Art, nichttrivialer Zyklus	cycle *m* non trivial	цикл второго рода
	cycle rank <GP>	*s.* C 2891		
C 2842	**cyclically connected set** <TO>	zyklisch zusammenhängende Menge *f*	ensemble *m* cycliquement connexe	циклически связное множество
C 2843	**cyclically ordered ring** <AL>	zyklisch geordneter Ring *m*	anneau *m* cycliquement ordonné	циклически упорядоченное кольцо
C 2844	**cyclically reduced word** <for a free product of cyclic groups> <GR>	zyklisch reduziertes Wort *n*	mot *m* cycliquement réduit	циклически приведенное слово
C 2845	**cyclic cell** <PG>	Kreiszelle *f*	cellule *f* cyclique	циклическая ячейка
	cyclic chain <SP>	*s.* C 2860		
	cyclic change <AL>	*s.* C 2868		
C 2846	**cyclic character** <AB>	zyklischer Charakter *m*	caractère *m* cyclique	циклический характер
C 2847	**cyclic complex in the dimension** *p* <AT>	zyklischer Komplex *m* in der Dimension *p*	complexe *m* cyclique en dimension *p*	циклический в размерности *p* комплекс
C 2848	**cyclic congruence [of lines (rays)]** <DG>	zyklische Strahlenkongruenz (Linienkongruenz, Geradenkongruenz, Kongruenz) *f*, zyklisches Strahlensystem *n*	congruence *f* de droites cyclique, congruence cyclique	циклическая конгруэнция [прямых (лучей)]
C 2849	**cyclic constant** <PO>	zyklische Konstante *f*, Periodizitätsmodul *m*	constante *f* cyclique	циклическая постоянная

No.	English	German	French	Russian
	cyclic curve <AG>	*s.* S 1453		
	cyclic determinant <MD>	*s.* C 702		
C 2850	**cyclic equation** <AL>	zyklische Gleichung *f*	équation *f* cyclique	циклическое уравнение
C 2851	**cyclic extension** <AL>	zyklische Erweiterung (Körpererweiterung) *f*	extension *f* cyclique	циклическое расширение (расширение поля)
C 2852	**cyclic field** <AL>	zyklischer Körper (Erweiterungskörper) *m*	corps *m* cyclique	циклическое поле
	cyclic field extension <AL>	*s.* R 740		
C 2853	**cyclic field over the rationals** <AB>	absolut-zyklischer Zahlkörper (Körper) *m*	corps *m* de nombres absolument cyclique	абсолютно циклическое поле чисел
C 2854	**cyclic form,** cycle decomposition, decomposition into cycles; decomposition into disjoint cycles <of a permutation> <AL, CT>	Zyklendarstellung *f*, Zyklenschreibweise *f*, zyklische Darstellung *f*, Zykeldarstellung *f*; kanonische Zyklendarstellung, Darstellung als Produkt elementfremder Zyklen	décomposition *f* en [un] produit de cycles, décomposition en cycle[s], notation *f* cyclique (en cycles, par cycles); expression *f* cyclique canonique, forme *f* cyclique réduite	цикловая (полная цикловая) запись, циклическое представление
C 2855	**cyclic function,** cyclosymmetric function <AL>	zyklische Funktion *f*	fonction *f* cyclique	циклическая функция
C 2856	**cyclic Galois group of a field extension** <AL>	zyklische Relativgruppe *f*	groupe *m* cyclique relatif	циклическая группа Галуа расширения поля
C 2857	**cyclic graph** <GP>	zyklischer Graph *m*	graphe *m* cyclique	контурный (циклический) граф
C 2858	**cyclic group** <GR>	zyklische Gruppe *f*	groupe *m* monogène (cyclique)	циклическая группа
C 2859	**cyclic index** <GN>	zyklischer Index *m*	indicateur *m* de cycles	циклический индекс
	cyclic interchange <AL>	*s.* C 2868		
C 2860	**cyclic Markov chain,** cyclic chain <SP>	zyklische [Markovsche] Kette *f*	chaîne *f* [markovienne] cyclique	циклическая цепь [Маркова]
C 2861	**cyclic method** <for indeterminate equations> <NT>	zyklische Methode *f*	méthode *f* cyclique	циклический метод
C 2862	**cyclic module,** monogenic module, principal module <AL>	zyklischer (monogener, eingliedriger) Modul *m*	module *m* monogène	циклический (моногенный, главный, одночленный) модуль
C 2863	**cyclic order,** circular permutation <CT>	zyklische Anordnung *f*	ordre *m* cyclique (circulaire)	циклический порядок
C 2864	**cyclic order** <of four points> <PJ>	zyklische (projektive) Anordnung *f*	ordre *m* cyclique	циклический порядок
C 2865	**cyclic order** <SE>	zyklische Ordnung *f*	ordre *m* circulaire	циклический порядок
C 2866	**cyclic order / in** <CT>	in zyklischer Reihenfolge	en ordre circulaire	в циклическом порядке
C 2867	**cyclic period** <of an Abelian integral> <FT>	zyklische Periode *f*	période *f* circulaire (cyclique)	циклический период
C 2868	**cyclic permutation,** cycle, circular permutation, cyclic interchange, cyclic change <AL>	zyklische Permutation *f*, Zyklus *m*, zyklische Substitution (Vertauschung) *f*, Ringtausch *m*, Kreispermutation *f*, Zykel *m*	permutation *f* circulaire, cycle *m*, permutation cyclique, substitution *f* circulaire	цикл, циклическая подстановка, круговая (циклическая) перестановка
C 2869	**cyclic permutation,** circular permutation <GN>	zyklische Vertauschung *f*	permutation *f* cyclique (circulaire)	циклическая перестановка (подстановка)
C 2870	**cyclic permutation group** <GR>	zyklische Permutationsgruppe *f*	groupe *m* de permutations cyclique	циклическая группа подстановок
C 2871	**cyclic plane,** cyclic projective plane <PJ>	zyklische Ebene *f*	plan *m* cyclique	циклическая плоскость
C 2872	**cyclic point** <DG>	zyklischer Punkt *m*, Scheitel *m*	point *m* cyclique	циклическая точка
C 2873	**cyclic points,** circular points, circular points at infinity, isotropic points, focoids, circules <of the plane> <AY, PJ>	absolute (uneigentliche, unendlich ferne, unendlichferne, imaginäre) Kreispunkte *mpl*, Kreispunkte, absolute Punkte *mpl*, absolutes Punktepaar *n*, imaginäres Kreispunktepaar *n*	ombilics *mpl*, ombilics imaginaires (du plan), points *mpl* ombilics du plan, points cycliques (circulaires imaginaires, circulaires)	циклические (бесконечные мнимые круговые, бесконечно удаленные мнимые циклические) точки
C 2874	**cyclic polynomial** <in Galois' theory> <AL>	zyklisches Polynom *n*	polynôme *m* cyclique	циклический многочлен
	cyclic projective plane <PJ>	*s.* C 2871		
C 2875	**cyclic *-representation** <of a C*-algebra> <FA>	zyklische *-Darstellung *f*	*-représentation *f* cyclique	циклическое *-представление
	cyclic representation module <AL>	*s.* M 843		
C 2876	**cyclic semigroup** <AL>	zyklische Halbgruppe *f*	demi-groupe *m* cyclique (monogène)	моногенная (циклическая) полугруппа
	cyclic sequence <GP>	*s.* C 859		
C 2877	**cyclic subclass** <of states> <SP>	zyklische Unterklasse *f*	sous-classe *f* (sous-ensemble *m*) cyclique	циклический подкласс
C 2878	**cyclic subgroup** <GR>	zyklische Untergruppe *f*	sous-groupe *m* monogène <engendré par *a*>	циклическая подгруппа
C 2879	**cyclic subgroup generated by a group element** <GR>	Periode *f* eines Gruppenelements, von einem Gruppenelement erzeugte zyklische Untergruppe *f*	période *f* d'un élément d'un groupe, sous-groupe *m* monogène engendré par un élément d'un groupe	циклическая подгруппа, порожденная элементом группы
C 2880	**cyclic sum** <GN>	zyklische Summe *f*	somme *f* cyclique	циклическая сумма
C 2881	**cyclic surface** <GE>	zyklische Fläche *f*	surface *f* cyclique	циклическая поверхность
	cyclic symmetry <AN, DG>	*s.* C 2892		
	cyclic symmetry <GN>	*s.* C 726		
C 2882	**cyclic system of curves** <DG>	zylisches Kurvensystem *n*	système *m* cyclique de courbes	циклическая система кривых

C 2883	**cyclic system of orthogonal surfaces** <DG>	zyklisches Flächensystem *n* (System *n* orthogonaler Flächen)	système *m* cyclique de surfaces orthogonales	циклическая система ортогональных поверхностей
C 2884	**cyclic tower** <GR>	Normalreihe *f* mit zyklischen Faktoren	suite *f* de composition à facteurs cycliques	циклическая башня <подгрупп>
C 2885	**cyclic transformation** <of elements> <AR>	zyklische Transformation *f*	transformation *f* cyclique	циклическое преобразование
C 2886	**cyclic transformation group** <GR>	zyklische (monogene) Transformationsgruppe *f*	groupe *m* de transformations monogène	моногенная (циклическая) группа преобразований
C 2887	**cyclide** <GE>	Zyklide *f*, allgemeine Zyklide, Zyklidenfläche *f*	cyclide *f*, surface *f* cyclide	циклида
C 2888	**cycloid,** common cycloid <base curve: a straight line, moving curve: a circle> <GE>	Zykloide *f*, gemeine (gewöhnliche, gespitzte) Zykloide, Radlinie *f*, Radkurve *f*	cycloïde *f*, cycloïde commune	циклоида, обычная (обыкновенная) циклоида
C 2889	**cycloidal curve** <GE>	zyklische Kurve *f*, Zykloide *f*	courbe *f* cycloïdale, roulette *f* <Pascal>	циклоидальная кривая
C 2890	**cyclomatic matrix** <GP>	zyklomatische Matrix *f*	matrice *f* cyclomatique	цикломатическая матрица
C 2891	**cyclomatic number,** circuit rank, cycle rank, connectivity, nullity, first Betti number <GP>	zyklomatische Zahl (Ordnungszahl) *f*, Zusammenhangszahl *f*, Index *m*, Rang *m* <Listing>, // cyklomatische Zahl (Ordnungszahl)	nombre *m* cyclomatique, degré *m* de continuité — 1 <Jordan>	цикломатическое число, циклический ранг
	cyclometric function <AN>	*s.* I 957		
	cyclosymmetric function <AL>	*s.* C 2855		
C 2892	**cyclosymmetry,** cyclic symmetry <of a function *or* a curvature tensor> <AN, DG>	zyklische Symmetrie *f* <AN, DG>; Symmetrie gegenüber zyklischer Vertauschung <AN>	cyclosymétrie *f*, symétrie *f* cyclique	циклическая симметрия
C 2893	**cyclotomic congruence** <AL>	Kreisteilungskongruenz *f*	congruence *f* cyclotomique	сравнение деления круга
C 2894	**cyclotomic equation** <of order *n*> <AL>	Kreisteilungsgleichung *f* <*n*-te>	équation *f* de la division du cercle <en *n* parties égales>, équation cyclotomique <d'indice *n*>	уравнение деления круга (окружности) <на *n* равных частей>
C 2895	**cyclotomic extension** <AB>	Kreiskörpererweiterung *f*	extension *f* cyclotomique	циклотомическое расширение
C 2896	**cyclotomic field** <AL>	Kreisteilungskörper *m*, Kreiskörper *m*, Einheitswurzelkörper *m*	corps *m* cyclotomique (circulaire, de la division du cercle)	поле деления круга, круговое поле, круговое расширение, циклотомическое поле, поле деления окружности
C 2897	**cyclotomic field of order *n*** <AL>	*n*-ter Kreiskörper (Einheitswurzelkörper, Kreisteilungskörper) *m*, Körper *m* der *n*-ten Einheitswurzeln	corps *m* des racines *n*-èmes de l'unité	поле деления круга на *n* равных частей
C 2898	**cyclotomic function** <AL>	Kreisteilungsfunktion *f*, zyklotomische Funktion *f*	fonction *f* cyclotomique	функция деления круга
C 2899	**cyclotomic integer** <AL>	Produkt *n* von Kreisteilungspolynomen	produit *m* de polynômes cyclotomiques	произведение круговых многочленов
C 2900	**cyclotomic polynomial** <AL>	Kreisteilungspolynom *n*	polynôme *m* cyclotomique, polynôme circulaire	круговой многочлен, многочлен деления круга, круговой полином, полином деления круга, циклотомический многочлен
	cyclotomic polynomial of order *n* <AL>	*s.* N 734		
C 2901	**cyclotomy** <AL, GE>	Kreisteilung *f*	cyclotomie *f*	деление круга, деление окружности
C 2902	**cyclotomy,** graduation of the circle, division of the circle, circular graduation, circular division <NU>	Kreisteilung *f*, Kreiseinteilung *f*	cyclotomie *f*, graduation *f* (divisionnement *m*, division *f*) du cercle	деление круга, деление окружности
C 2903	**cylinder** <as a solid> <CS, EG, GE>	Zylinder *m*	cylindre *m*	цилиндр
	cylinder <AY>	*s.* C 2911		
	cylinder <EG>	*s.* R 1094		
	cylinder co-ordinates <AY>	*s.* C 2909		
	cylinder function <FU>	*s.* B 231		
C 2904	**cylinder functor** <AT>	Zylinderfunktor *m*	foncteur *m* cylindre	функтор цилиндра
	cylinder of revolution <EG>	*s.* C 714		
	cylindrical Bessel function <FU>	*s.* B 230		
	cylindrical Bessel function of the first kind <FU>	*s.* B 230		
	cylindrical Bessel function of the second kind <FU>	*s.* B 233		
	cylindrical Bessel function of the third kind <FU>	*s.* B 234		
C 2905	**cylindrical congruence [of lines (rays)]** <DG>	zylindrische Strahlenkongruenz (Linienkongruenz, Geradenkon-	congruence *f* [de droites] cylindrique	цилиндрическая конгруэнция [прямых (лучей)]

No.	English	German	French	Russian
		gruenz, Kongruenz) *f*, zylindrisches Strahlensystem *n*		
	cylindrical co-ordinates <AY>	*s.* C 2909		
C 2906	**cylindrical curve** <of a surface> <DG>	zylindrische Kurve *f*	courbe *f* cylindrique	цилиндрическая кривая
C 2907	**cylindrical domain** <as a Cartesian product of Riemann surfaces> <FT>	Zylindergebiet *n*; Zylinderbereich *m* <Produkt abgeschlossener Bereiche>	domaine *m* cylindrique	полицилиндрическая область
	cylindrical field <VT>	*s.* C 2912		
	cylindrical function <FU>	*s.* B 231		
C 2908	**cylindric algebra** <LO, UA>	zylindrische Algebra *f*	algèbre *f* cylindrique	цилиндрическая алгебра
	cylindrical Hankel function <FU>	*s.* B 234		
	cylindrical harmonic <FU>	*s.* B 231		
	cylindrical helix <GE>	*s.* 1. C 718; 2. H 185		
	cylindrical Neumann function <FU>	*s.* B 233		
C 2909	**cylindrical polar co-ordinates, cylindrical polars,** cylindrical (cylinder, semi-polar, circular cylindrical) co-ordinates <AY>	Zylinderkoordinaten *fpl*, Kreiszylinderkoordinaten *fpl*	coordonnées *fpl* cylindriques (cylindro-polaires, semi-polaires)	цилиндрические (полу-полярные) координаты
	cylindrical projection <DS>	*s.* P 117		
C 2910	**cylindrical set,** elementary set <RF, SE, TO>	Zylindermenge *f*	ensemble *m* (partie *f*) cylindrique	цилиндрическое множество
C 2911	**cylindrical surface,** cylinder <AY>	Zylinderfläche *f*, zylindrische Fläche *f*, Zylinder *m*	surface *f* cylindrique, cylindre *m*	цилиндрическая поверхность, цилиндр
	cylindrical ungula <EG>	*s.* U 102		
C 2912	**cylindrical vector field,** cylindrical field <VT>	zylindrisches Vektorfeld *n*, Zylinderfeld *n*, zylindrisches Feld *n*	champ *m* vectoriel cylindrique, champ cylindrique	цилиндрическое векторное поле, цилиндрическое поле
C 2913	**cylindroid** <DG>	Zylindroid *n*	cylindroïde *m*	цилиндроид
	cypher <NT>	*s.* F 215		

D

No.	English	German	French	Russian
	dactylonomy <AR>	*s.* C 633		
	d'Alembert['s] differential equation <DE>	*s.* D 450		
D 1	**d'Alembert['s] equations,** d'Alembert['s] system, homogeneous linear system (set) [of differential equations] with constant coefficients <DE>	d'Alembertsches System *n* [von gewöhnlichen Differentialgleichungen], d'Alembertsches Differentialgleichungssystem *n*, [homogenes] lineares Differentialgleichungssystem (System) [in Normalform] mit konstanten Koeffizienten, System mit konstanten Koeffizienten	système *m* (équations *fpl*) de d'Alembert, système linéaire homogène [d'équations différentielles] à coefficients constants	система Д'Аламбера, система дифференциальных уравнений Д'Аламбера, [однородная] линейная система дифференциальных уравнений с постоянными коэффициентами
D 2	**Dalembertian, d'Alembertian [operator],** □ <DE>	d'Alembertscher Operator *m*, D'Alembert-Operator *m*, Viereckoperator *m*, □	dalembertien *m*, opérateur *m* dalembertien (de d'Alembert), □	даламбертиан, оператор Д'Аламбера, оператор Даламбера, волновой оператор, □
D 3	**d'Alembert['s] method,** d'Alembert['s] reduction method <DE>	Reduktionsmethode *f* (Reduktionsverfahren *n*) von d'Alembert, d'Alembertsche Reduktionsmethode, d'Alembertsches Reduktionsverfahren	méthode *f* [de réduction] de d'Alembert	метод Д'Аламбера (Даламбера), метод приведения Д'Аламбера (Даламбера)
D 4	**d'Alembert['s] ratio test,** ratio test, Cauchy['s] ratio test, generalized ratio test, d'Alembert['s] test [for convergence], Cauchy['s] convergence test of the second kind <for series> <SS>	[Cauchysches] Quotientenkriterium *n*, erstes [spezielles] Cauchysches Konvergenzkriterium *n*, d'Alembertsches Konvergenzkriterium (Quotientenkriterium, Kriterium *n*), [Cauchysches] Fundamentalkriterium *n* zweiter Art	critère *m* de d'Alembert, règle *f* de d'Alembert, théorème *m* de d'Alembert	признак [сходимости] Д'Аламбера, признак Даламбера, признак сходимости Даламбера
	d'Alembert['s] reduction method <DE>	*s.* D 3		
D 5	**d'Alembert['s] solution** <DE>	d'Alembertsche Lösung *f*	solution *f* de d'Alembert	решение Д'Аламбера, решение Даламбера
	d'Alembert['s] system <DE>	*s.* D 1		
	d'Alembert['s] test [for convergence] <SS>	*s.* D 4		
	dancing problem <CT>	*s.* M 149		
D 6	**Dandelin['s] sphere** <AY>	Dandelinsche Kugel *f*	sphère *f* de Dandelin	сфера Данделена
D 7	**Daniell['s] integral** <DI>	Daniellsches Integral *n*	intégrale *f* de Daniell	интеграл Даниелля

No.	English	German	French	Russian
D 8	**Dantzig-van de Panne method,** simplex method for quadratic programming <PG>	Methode *f* von Dantzig und van de Panne, Dantzig-van de Pannesche Methode, Simplexmethode *f* für quadratische Optimierung	méthode *f* de Dantzig et van de Panne	симплекс-метод (симплексный метод) для квадратичного программирования, метод Данцига и Ван де Панне
	Dantzig-Wolfe decomposition principle <PG>	*s.* D 75		
D 9	**Darboux['s] cubic** <DG>	Darbouxsche Kurve *f*, Darboux-Kurve *f*	cubique *f* de Darboux	кривая Дарбу
	Darboux['s] curve <DG>	*s.* D 17		
D 10	**Darboux['s] [differential] equation** <DE>	Darbouxsche Differentialgleichung (Gleichung) *f*	équation [différentielle] de Darboux	[дифференциальное] уравнение Дарбу
D 11	**Darboux['s] integral** <DI>	Darbouxsches Integral *n*	intégrale *f* de Darboux	интеграл Дарбу
D 12	**Darboux['s] property,** intermediate value property <of a function> <RF>	Darboux-Eigenschaft *f*, Zwischenwerteigenschaft *f*	propriété *f* de Darboux; condition *f* de Darboux	свойство Дарбу
D 13	**Darboux-Segre normal,** Čech['s] axis <first *or* second> <DG>	Normale *f* von Darboux-Segre, Darboux-Segresche Normale, Čechsche Achse *f*, Achse von Čech <erste *oder* zweite>	normale *f* de Darboux-Segre, axe *m* de Čech <premier *ou* second>	нормаль Дарбу-Сегре, ось Чеха <первая *или* вторая>
D 14	**Darboux['s] tangent** <DG>	Darbouxsche Tangente *f*, Darboux-Tangente *f*	tangente *f* de Darboux	касательная Дарбу
D 15	**Darboux['s] theorem** <DI>	Darbouxscher Satz *m*, Zwischenwertsatz *m* für Ableitungen	théorème *m* de Darboux	теорема Дарбу
D 16	**Darboux['s] theorem** <on existence of upper and lower Darboux integral> <DI>	Satz *m* von Darboux, Darbouxscher Satz	théorème *m* de Darboux	теорема Дарбу
	dash <GN>	*s.* P 1282		
	D.C.C. <AL, SE>	*s.* D 309		
	DC group <HA>	*s.* D 461		
D 17	**D-curve,** Darboux['s] curve <of a surface> <DG>	D-Kurve *f*, Darbouxsche Kurve *f*	D-courbe *f*, courbe *f* de Darboux	D-кривая, кривая Дарбу
D 18	**death process** <SP>	Sterbeprozeß *m*, Todesprozeß *m*	processus *m* de mort	процесс гибели
	death rate <ST>	*s.* M 906		
D 19	**decade** <CT, NT>	Zehnergruppe *f*, Dekade *f*, Zehnzahl *f*	décade *f*	декада
	decadic number <NT>	*s.* D 32		
	decadic [number] system <NT>	*s.* D 38		
D 20	**decagonal number** <as a figurate number> <NT>	Dekagonalzahl *f*, Zehneckszahl *f*	nombre *m* décagone (décagonal)	декагональное число
D 21	**decahedron** <EG>	Zehnflach *n*, Dekaeder *n*, Zehnflächner *m*	décaèdre *m*	десятигранник, декаэдр
D 22	**decidability** <MM>	Entscheidbarkeit *f*.	décidabilité *f*	разрешимость
	decidability problem <MM>	*s.* D 41		
D 23	**decidable elementary theory** <MM>	entscheidbare elementare Theorie *f*	théorie *f* élémentaire décidable	разрешимая элементарная теория
D 24	**decidable property** <MM>	entscheidbare (entscheidungsdefinite) Eigenschaft	propriété *f* décidable	разрешимое свойство
D 25	**decidable set** <MM>	entscheidbare Menge *f*	ensemble *m* décidable	разрешимое множество
D 26	**decile** <ST>	Dezil *n*, Dezentil *n*	décile *m*	дециль
	decimal <AR, NT>	*s.* D 30		
	decimal <NT>	*s.* 1. D 28; 2. D 32		
D 27	**decimal arithmetic,** decimal numeration <AR>	Dezimalbruchrechnung *f*, Dezimalrechnung *f*, dezimale Arithmetik *f*	arithmétique *f* décimale, calcul *m* décimal, numération *f* décimale	счисление десятичных дробей, десятичное счисление
	decimal-binary conversion <NT>	*s.* D 39		
D 28	**decimal digit,** decit, digit occupying a decimal place, decimal [place] <NT>	Dezimale *f*, Dezimalziffer *f*, Dezimalstelle *f* <Ziffer>	décimale *f*, digit (chiffre) *m* décimal, unité *f* décimale, décit *m*	десятичная цифра, десятичный знак
D 29	**decimal expansion** <NT>	Dezimalbruchentwicklung *f*	développement *m* décimal	разложение в десятичную дробь
D 30	**decimal fraction,** decimal [number] <AR, NT>	Dezimalbruch *m*, dekadischer Bruch *m*, Zehnerbruch *m*, zehnteiliger Bruch	fraction (partie) *f* décimale; nombre *m* fractionnaire décimale, fraction systématique à base 10, décimale *f*, nombre décimal	десятичная дробь
D 31	**decimal geometric sequence** <AR>	dezimalgeometrische Folge *f*	progression *f* géométrique à quotient $\sqrt[n]{10}$	геометрическая прогрессия со знаменателем $\sqrt[n]{10}$
	decimal logarithm <AR, NU>	*s.* B 754		
	decimal notation <NT>	*s.* D 37		
D 32	**decimal number,** decimal, decadic number <NT>	Dezimalzahl *f*, Zehnerzahl *f*	nombre *m* décimal	десятичное число; число, записанное в десятичной системе
	decimal number <AR, NT> ┌<NT>	*s.* D 30		
	decimal number system	*s.* D 38		

	English	German	French	Russian
	decimal numeration <AR>	*s.* D 27		
	decimal numeration <NT>	*s.* D 38		
D 33	**decimal of many places** <AR, NT>	vielstellige Dezimalzahl *f*	nombre *m* décimal à nombreux chiffres	многоразрядное десятичное число
D 34	**decimal part** <of a number> <NT>	Dezimalteil *m* <hinter dem Dezimalkomma>	partie *f* décimale	десятичная часть
D 35	**decimal place,** decimal position <NT>	Dezimalstelle *f* <Stelle>	place *f* décimale, position *f* décimale	десятичный разряд, разряд десятичной дроби
	decimal place <NT>	*s.* D 28		
D 36	**decimal point,** separatrix <NT>	Dezimalkomma *n*, Komma *n*	virgule *f* décimale, virgule	десятичная запятая, запятая [в десятичном числе], сепаратриса
	decimal position <NT>	*s.* D 35		
D 37	**decimal representation,** decimal notation <of a number> <NT>	Dezimaldarstellung *f*, dezimale Schreibweise (Zahlendarstellung) *f*, Dezimalschreibung *f*	notation *f* décimale, écriture *f* décimale	представление [чисел] в десятичной системе, десятичная запись
D 38	**decimal system [of numeration],** decimal number system, decimal numeration, decadic [number] system <NT>	Dezimalsystem *n*, dezimales (dekadisches) Zahlensystem *n*, dekadisches Positionssystem (System) *n*, Zehnersystem *n*	système *m* de numération décimal, système décimal, système de (à) base dix, numération *f* décimale	десятичная система [счисления], десятичная позиционная система
D 39	**decimal-to-binary conversion,** decimal-binary conversion <NT>	Dezimal-Binär-Konvertierung *f*, Dezimal-Dual-Umwandlung *f*, Dezimal-Binär-Umsetzung *f*, Dezimal-Binär-Umwandlung *f*	conversion *f* décimal-binaire	преобразование из десятичной системы в двоичную, преобразование десятичного счисления в двоичное, переход от десятичной системы счисления к двоичной
D 40	**decision** <MM>	Entscheidung *f*	décision *f*	решение, разрешение
	decision <SP>	*s.* C 2314		
	decision content <ST>	*s.* I 506		
	decision function <ST>	*s.* S 1688		
	decision making problem <ST>	*s.* S 1689		
D 41	**decision problem,** decidability problem <MM>	Entscheidungsproblem *n*	problème *m* de [la] décision	проблема разрешения (разрешимости)
	decision problem <ST>	*s.* S 1689		
	decision problem for validity <LO>	*s.* S 308		
D 42	**decision procedure** <MM>	Entscheidungsalgorithmus *m*, Entscheidungsverfahren *n*	procédé *m* de décision, procédé décisif, méthode *f* de décision	разрешающая процедура, разрешающий метод (алгоритм), алгоритм, способ решения
	decision procedure <ST>	*s.* S 1690		
	decision process <PG, SP>	*s.* S 1691		
	decision rule <ST>	*s.* S 1692		
D 43	**decision space** <ST>	Entscheidungsraum *m*	espace *m* des décisions	пространство решений
D 44	**decision theory,** statistical (stochastic) decision theory, theory of choice (statistical decision[s]) <ST>	Entscheidungstheorie *f*, statistische Entscheidungstheorie *f*, Theorie *f* der [statistischen] Entscheidungsfunktionen	théorie *f* de la décision [statistique], théorie des décisions [statistiques]	теория решений, статистическая теория решений (распознавания)
D 45	**decision tree** <PG>	Entscheidungsbaum *m*	arbre *m* des décisions	дерево решений
D 46	**decision variable,** control variable <PG, SP>	Entscheidungsvariable *f*, Steuervariable *f*, beeinflußbarer Parameter *m*	variable *f* de décision, variable de contrôle	переменная решения, решающая переменная, переменная управления
	decit <NT>	*s.* D 28		
	deckbewegung <AT, TO>	*s.* C 2637		
D 47	**decomposability** <of a game> <TG>	Zerlegbarkeit *f*	décomposabilité *f*	разделимость
D 48	**decomposable bilinear form** <AL>	zerfallende Bilinearform *f*	forme *f* bilinéaire décomposable	распадающаяся билинейная форма
D 49	**decomposable element** <of an exterior power> <AL>	zerlegbares Element *n*	élément *m* décomposable	разложимый элемент
D 50	**decomposable form** <AL>	zerlegbare Form	forme *f* décomposable (réductible)	разложимая форма
D 51	**decomposable ideal,** ideal decomposable into primary ideals <AL>	zerlegbares Ideal *n*, Ideal mit Primärkomponentenzerlegung	idéal *m* décomposable [en idéaux primaires]	разложимый идеал; идеал, разложимый в примарные идеалы
	decomposable into factors <AL>	*s.* F 21		
D 52	**decomposable matrix** <MD>	zerlegbare Matrix *f*	matrice *f* réductible	разложимая (редуцируемая) матрица
D 53	**decomposable module** <AL>	zerlegbarer Modul *m*	module *m* décomposable	разложимый модуль
D 54	**decomposable operator** <in a Hilbert space> <FA>	zerlegbarer Operator *m*	opérateur *m* décomposable	разложимый (разлагаемый) оператор
D 55	**decomposable ordinal number** <with respect to the operation *f*> <SE>	zerlegbare (reduzible) Ordnungszahl *f* <bezüglich der Operation *f*>	nombre *m* ordinal décomposable <par rapport à l'opération *f*>	разложимое порядковое число <относительно операции *f*>
D 56	**decomposable representation** <RE>	zerlegbare (zerfällbare, vollreduzible, ganz reduzible) Darstellung *f*	représentation *f* décomposable	разложимое представление
D 57	**decomposable Riemannian space,** separable Riemannian space <DG>	zerlegbarer Riemannscher Raum *m*	espace *m* de Riemann décomposable	разложимое риманово пространство
	decomposable surface <GE>	*s.* R 410		

D 58	**decompose / to** <said of a curve *or* representation> <AY, RE>	zerfallen <Kurve *oder* Darstellung>	se décomposer <courbe *ou* représentation>	распадаться <кривая> <AY>; разлагаться <представление> <RE>
	decompose / to <TO>	*s.* S 529		
	decomposed curve <GE>	*s.* R 394		
D 59	**decomposed prime ideal** <AB>	zerlegtes Primideal *n*	idéal *m* premier décomposé	разложенный простой идеал
D 60	**decomposed prime number** <AB>	zerlegte Primzahl *f*	nombre *m* premier décomposé	разложенное простое число
D 61	**decompose into prime factors / to,** to factorize <AL, NT>	in Primfaktoren zerlegen	factoriser, décomposer en facteurs premiers	разлагать на простые множители
D 62	**decomposing subspace** <TO>	zerlegender Unterraum *m*	sous-espace *m* séparateur	разбивающее подпространство
D 63	**decomposition** <of a number into factors *or* squares *or* of a prime divisor *or* prime ideal) <AB, NT>	Zerlegung *f*	décomposition *f*, partition *f*	разложение
D 64	**decomposition** <of a polynomial *or* semigroup *or* group> <AL, GR>	Zerlegung *f*	décomposition *f*	разложение
D 65	**decomposition** <of a time series *or* of populations> <SP, ST>	Zerlegung *f* <einer Zeitreihe> <SP>; Entmischung *f* <von Grundgesamtheiten> <ST>	décomposition *f*	разложение
	decomposition <RE>	*s.* U 8		
	decomposition <SE>	*s.* P 276		
	decomposition <VT>	*s.* V 102		
D 66	**decomposition field** <AL, NT>	Zerlegungskörper *m*	corps *m* de décomposition	поле разложения
	decomposition field <AL>	*s.* S 1544		
D 67	**decomposition formula** <TO>	Zerlegungsformel *f*	formule *f* de décomposition	формула разложения
D 68	**decomposition group** <AL, NT>	Zerlegungsgruppe *f*	groupe *m* de décomposition	группа разложения
D 69	**decomposition homomorphism** <AL>	Zerlegungshomomorphismus *m*	homomorphisme *m* de décomposition	гомоморфизм разложения
D 70	**decomposition in a direct sum** <of an algebra> <AL>	direkte additive Zerlegung *f*	décomposition *f* en somme directe	разложение в прямую сумму
	decomposition into cosets <GR>	*s.* C 2524		
D 71	**decomposition into cubes** <AT>	Würfelzerlegung *f*, Würfeleinteilung *f*	décomposition *f* en cubes	разложение (разбиение) на кубы
	decomposition into cycles <AL, CT>	*s.* C 2854		
D 72	**decomposition** <of a group> **into cyclic groups** <GR>	Zerlegung *f* <einer Gruppe> in zyklische Gruppen	décomposition *f* <d'un groupe> en groupes cycliques	циклическое разложение <группы>
	decomposition into disjoint cycles <AL, CT>	*s.* C 2854		
	decomposition into factors <GN>	*s.* F 47		
D 73	**decomposition** <of an algebraic manifold> **into its components** <AG>	Komponentenzerlegung *f*	décomposition *f* en composantes	разложение в компоненты
	decomposition into left cosets <AL, GR>	*s.* L 327		
	decomposition into partial fractions <AL, FT>	*s.* P 208		
	decomposition into right cosets <AL, GR>	*s.* R 1110		
	decomposition of a fraction <AL>	*s.* P 208		
	decomposition of unity <TO>	*s.* P 281		
D 74	**decomposition operator** <AL>	Zerlegungsoperator *m*	opérateur *m* de décomposition	оператор разложения
D 75	**decomposition principle,** Dantzig-Wolfe decomposition principle <PG>	Dekompositionsprinzip *n* [von Dantzig und Wolfe], Dantzig-Wolfesches Dekompositionsprinzip	principe *m* de décomposition [de Dantzig et Wolfe]	принцип разложения
D 76	**decomposition ring** <AL>	Zerlegungsring *m*	anneau *m* de décomposition	кольцо разложения
	decomposition space <TO>	*s.* Q 347		
D 77	**decomposition theorem** <e.g. for rings *or* in a subspace of L^2> <AL, AT, DG, FA>	Zerlegungssatz *m* <AL, AT, DG, FA>; Zerlegungstheorem *n* <FA>	théorème *m* de décomposition	теорема разложения
D 78	**decomposition theory** <CA>	Zerlegungstheorie *f*	théorie *f* de décompositions	теория разложения
D 79	**decreasing filtration,** descending filtration <of a module> <AL>	absteigende Filtration *f*	filtration *f* décroissante	убывающая фильтрация
D 80	**decreasing function,** nonincreasing (antitonic, antitone) function, monotone (monotonic, monotonically) decreasing (nonincreasing) function <RF>	[monoton] fallende (abnehmende, nicht zunehmende, nicht wachsende) Funktion [im weiteren Sinne], antitone Funktion	fonction *f* décroissante (non croissante, antitone), fonction monotone (monotoniquement) décroissante (non croissante)	убывающая (монотонно убывающая, монотонная убывающая, [монотонно] невозрастающая, монотонная невозрастающая, антитонная) функция
	decreasing geometric sequence <AR>	*s.* M 867		

No.	English	German	French	Russian
D 81	**decreasing progression** <AR>	fallende (abnehmende, absteigende) Progression *f*	progression *f* décroissante (descendante)	убывающая прогрессия
	decreasing semi-martingale <ST>	*s.* S 2324		
	decreasing sequence <SS>	*s.* M 868		
D 82	**Dedekind['s] axiom,** Dedekind['s] cut axiom (postulate), Dedekind['s] axiom of Lückenlosigkeit, strong axiom of continuity of Dedekind <GE>	Dedekindsches Axiom (Schnittaxiom) *n*, Axiom vom Dedekindschen Schnitt, Schnittprinzip *n*	axiome *m* [de continuité] de Dedekind, condition *f* de Dedekind	аксиома Дедекинда [непрерывности числовой прямой], аксиома непрерывности Дедекинда; теорема Дедекинда о непрерывности числовой прямой; принцип Дедекинда непрерывности числовой прямой
	Dedekind['s] axiom <LA>	*s.* M 755		
	Dedekind['s] axiom of Lückenlosigkeit <GE>	*s.* D 82		
	Dedekind-Cantor axiom <GE>	*s.* C 89		
	Dedekind complete set <SE>	*s.* O 290		
D 83	**Dedekind['s] completion,** MacNeille['s] completion, completion by cuts <SE>	Dedekindsche (Dedekind-MacNeillesche) Vervollständigung *f*, Vervollständigung durch Schnitte	complétion *f* de MacNeille; complété *m* de MacNeille	пополнение методом сечений, пополнение по Дедекинду
D 84	**Dedekind['s] cut,** section, cut, separation <of ordered numbers> <AN, SE>	Dedekindscher Schnitt *m*, Klassenschnitt *m*, Schnitt *m*	coupure *f* de Dedekind, coupure, section *f* en classes	дедекиндово сечение, сечение [Дедекинда]
	Dedekind['s] cut axiom (postulate) <GE>	*s.* D 82		
D 85	**Dedekind['s] domain,** Dedekind['s] ring, Dedekindian ring <AL>	Dedekindscher Ring *m*	anneau *m* de Dedekind, anneau dédékindien	дедекиндово кольцо, дедекиндова область
D 86	**Dedekind['s] eta-function,** Dedekind['s] η-function <FU>	Dedekindsche η-Funktion (Eta-Funktion) *f*	fonction *f* η (êta) de Dedekind	η-функция (эта-функция) Дедекинда
D 87	**Dedekind['s] finiteness** <of a set> <SE>	D-Endlichkeit *f*, Endlichkeit *f* im Dedekindschen Sinne	finitude *f* au sens de Dedekind	конечность в смысле Дедекинда
D 88	**Dedekind['s] finite set,** non-reflexive set, set finite in the sense of Dedekind <SE>	D-endliche Menge *f*, im Dedekindschen Sinne endliche Menge	ensemble *m* fini au sens de Dedekind	конечное множество в смысле Дедекинда, конечное по Дедекинду множество
	Dedekind['s] ζ-function <AB>	*s.* D 94		
	Dedekind['s] η-function <FU>	*s.* D 86		
D 89	**Dedekind['s] ideal theory** <AB, AL>	Dedekindsche Idealtheorie *f*	théorie *f* des idéaux de Dedekind	теория идеалов Дедекинда
	Dedekindian ring <AL>	*s.* D 85		
D 90	**Dedekind['s] infinite set,** infinite set in Dedekind['s] sense, reflexive set, set infinite in the sense of Dedekind <SE>	D-unendliche Menge *f*, im Dedekindschen Sinne unendliche Menge	ensemble *m* infini au sens de Dedekind	бесконечное множество в смысле Дедекинда
	Dedekind['s] lattice <LA>	*s.* M 759		
	Dedekind['s] law <LA>	*s.* M 755		
	Dedekind-Noether isomorphism theorems <AL, CA>	*s.* I 1141		
	Dedekind['s] pigeon-hole principle <CT>	*s.* B 705		
	Dedekind['s] ring <AL>	*s.* 1. D 85; 2. Z 84		
D 91	**Dedekind['s] set** <SE>	Dedekindsche Menge *f*	ensemble *m* de Dedekind	дедекиндово множество
	Dedekind['s] structure <LA>	*s.* M 758		
D 92	**Dedekind['s] sum** <FT, FU, NT>	Dedekindsche Summe *f*	somme *f* de Dedekind	сумма Дедекинда
D 93	**Dedekind['s] theorem** <for Dedekind's cut> <NT, SE>	Satz *m* von Dedekind, Dedekindscher Satz	théorème *m* de Dedekind	принцип Дедекинда
D 94	**Dedekind['s] zeta function,** Dedekind['s] ζ-function <AB>	Dedekindsche Zetafunktion (ζ-Funktion) *f*, Zetafunktion (ζ-Funktion) <eines endlich-algebraischen Zahlkörpers>	fonction *f* zêta (ζ) de Dedekind	дзета-функция (ζ-функция) Дедекинда
D 95	**deducibility by natural deduction** <LO>	Ableitbarkeit (Beweisbarkeit) *f* durch natürliches Schließen	déductibilité *f* par déduction naturelle	выводимость при помощи натурального вывода
D 96	**deducibility in the stronger sense** <LO>	Ableitbarkeit *f* im engeren Sinne, unbeschränkte Ableitbarkeit	déductibilité *f* au sens étroit	выводимость в узком смысле
D 97	**deducibility theorem** <LO>	Ableitbarkeitssatz *m*	théorème *m* sur la déductibilité	теорема о выводимости
	deducible <LO>	*s.* D 265		
D 98	**deducible formula** <in a system> <LO>	ableitbare Formel *f*	formule *f* dérivable (déductible, déduite)	выводимая формула
D 99	**deduction** <LO>	Deduktion *f*	déduction *f*, raisonnement *m* déductif	выведение, вывод, умозаключение, дедукция
	deduction <LO>	*s.* L 1062		
	deduction law (theorem) <LO>	*s.* L 178		
D 100	**deductive completeness** <of an axiom system> <MM>	deduktive Vollständigkeit *f*, Entscheidungsdefinitheit *f*	complétude *f* au sens faible (large)	дедуктивная полнота

No.	English	German	French	Russian
D 101	**deductive conclusion** <ST>	deduktiver Schluß *m*, deduktive Rechtfertigung *f* des Induktionsschlusses, Inklusionsschluß *m*, Schluß vom Ganzen auf einen Teil	conclusion *f* déductive	дедуктивное заключение, заключение путем включения
D 102	**deductively complete system** <LO>	klassisch (deduktiv) vollständiges System *n*, entscheidungsdefinites System	système *m* complet au sens large (faible)	дедуктивно полная система
D 103	**deductive proof** <FO, LO>	deduktiver Beweis *m*	démonstration *f* déductive, raisonnement *m* déductif	дедуктивное доказательство, доказательство по выводу, дедуктивное рассуждение
	deductive rule <LO>	*s.* D 278		
	def <VT>	*s.* D 146		
D 104	**defeated coalition** <TG>	Verlustkoalition *f*		проигрывающая коалиция
D 105	**defect** <of a quadratic form *or* of a kernel> <AL, IE>	Defekt *m*	défaut *m*	дефект
D 106	**defect,** deficiency <in the sense of Nevanlinna> <of an analytic function> <FT>	Defekt *m*, Nevanlinnascher Defekt	défaut *m* [au sens de M. Nevanlinna]	дефект, неванлинновский дефект
D 107	**defect,** angular defect <of a polygon, especially triangle, in hyperbolic geometry> <GE>	Defekt *m*, Winkeldefekt *m*	déficience *f*, défaut *m*, défaut angulaire	дефект, недостаток, угловой дефект, угловой недостаток
D 108	**defective equation,** depressed equation <AL>	Gleichung *f* mit weniger Wurzeln, als die vorgegebene Gleichung hat	équation *f* déficiente	уравнение с меньшим числом корней, чем исходное; уравнение, имеющее меньше корней, чем заданное
D 109	**defective hyperbola,** deficiens hyperbola <Newton> <as a cubic> <AG>	mangelhafte Hyperbel *f*	hyperbole *f* déficiente (défective)	дефективная (недостаточная) гипербола
	defective item <ST>	*s.* D 111 a		
D 110	**defective number,** deficient number, diminute number <NT>	defiziente (mangelhafte, unvollkommene, unvollständige) Zahl *f*, numerus *m* deficiens, deficiens numerus	nombre *m* imparfait par défaut, nombre déficient (défaillant, défectif)	дефектное (недостаточное) число
D 111	**defective sample** <ST>	unvollständige Stichprobe *f*	échantillon *m* défectueux	дефектная (некачественная) выборка
D 111 a	**defective unit,** defective item <ST>	fehlerhafte Einheit *f*	unité *f* défectueuse	дефектный (некачественный) элемент
D 112	**defective value** <FT>	defekter Wert *m*, Nevanlinnascher Ausnahmewert *m*	valeur *f* déficiente	дефектное значение
D 113	**defect relation** <FT>	Defektrelation *f*	relation *f* de défaut	[со]отношение дефектов
D 114	**deferent** <of an anallagmatic curve> <GE>	Deferente *f*	déférente *f*	деферент
D 115	**deficiency** <of a linear system> <AG>	Defekt *m*	déficience *f*	дефект
D 116	**deficiency** <of a graph> <GP>	Fehlmenge *f*	déficience *f*	дефицит
	deficiency <AG>	*s.* 1. G 220; 2. G 221		
	deficiency <FT>	*s.* D 106		
D 116 a	**deficiency [-index],** co-rank <of a linear operator> <FA>	Bilddefekt *m*, Kodimension *f* des Bildraumes, Defekt *m*	indice *m* de défaut	дефект
D 117	**deficiency index** <of an operator> <FA>	Defektindex *m*, Defektzahl *f*	indice *m* de défaut	дефектное число, индекс дефекта, дефект
D 118	**deficiency space** <of an operator> <FA>	Defektraum *m*, defekter Unterraum *m*	sous-espace *m* de défaut	дефектное подпространство, подпространство дефекта
	deficiens hyperbola <AG>	*s.* D 109		
	deficient number <NT>	*s.* D 110		
D 119	**definability** <LO, MM>	Definierbarkeit *f*	définissabilité *f*	определимость
D 120	**definability theorem** <MM>	Definierbarkeitssatz *m*	théorème *m* de définissabilité	теорема определимости
	λ-definable function <FO>	*s.* L 49		
D 121	**definiendum** <LO>	Definiendum *n*, zu definierender Ausdruck *m*	ce qui est à définir, definiendum *m*, défini *m*	определяемое [выражение], дефиниендум
D 122	**definiens** <LO>	Definiens *n*, definierender Ausdruck *m*	définissant *m*, expression *f* définissante, definiens *m*	дефиниенс, определяющее [выражение]
D 123	**defining algebra,** algebra of definition <FA>	Definitionsalgebra *f*	algèbre *f* de définition	алгебра определения
D 124	**defining contrast** <ST>	bestimmender Vergleich *m*	contraste *m* déterminant (définissant)	определяющий контраст
D 125	**defining equation** <of a field extension> <AL>	definierende (erzeugende) Gleichung *f*	équation *f* génératrice	определяющее равенство (уравнение, отношение)
D 126	**defining equation** <GN>	Definitionsgleichung *f*	équation *f* de définition, équation à définir	определяющая формула, определяющее уравнение
	defining field <AG>	*s.* F 187		
D 127	**defining ideal,** ideal of definition <AL, FA>	Definitionsideal *n*	idéal *m* de définition	идеал определения
D 128	**defining relations** <of a relative *or* a primitive class> <UA>	definierende Relationen *fpl*	relations *fpl* de définition	определяющие отношения, определяющая совокупность
	defining relations <AL, GR>	*s.* G 202		
	defining relator <AL, GR>	*s.* G 202		
D 129	**definite description** <LO>	bestimmte Deskription *f*	description *f* définie	определенная дескрипция
	definite description operator <LO>	*s.* D 325		
	definite divergence <SS>	*s.* P 1777		

D 130	**definite eigenvalue problem** <DE>	definite Eigenwertaufgabe *f*, definites Eigenwertproblem *n*	problème *m* défini aux valeurs singulières (caractéristiques, critiques, propres)	определенная задача на собственные значения
D 131	**definite integral** <DI>	bestimmtes Integral *n*	intégrale *f* <d'une fonction réglée dans un intervalle compact>, intégrale définie	определенный интеграл
	definitely divergent sequence <SS>	*s.* P 1804		
D 132	**definitely self-adjoint problem** <DE>	definit-selbstadjungiertes Eigenwertproblem *n*, definit-selbstadjungierte Eigenwertaufgabe *f*	problème *m* auto-adjoint défini aux valeurs singulières (caractéristiques, critiques, propres)	определенно-самосопряженная задача на собственные значения
D 133	**definiteness** <AL, AN>	Definitheit *f*	propriété *f* d'être défini	знакоопределенность, определенность
	definiteness in Kamke's sense <DE>	*s.* K 31		
D 134	**definite operator** <FA>	[eigentlich] definiter Operator *m*	opérateur *m* défini	определенный оператор
D 135	**definition / by** <GN>	definitionsgemäß, per definitionem, nach Definition	par définition	по определению
D 136	**definitional identity** <GN, LO>	definitorische Gleichheit *f*	identité *f* par définition	равенство по определению
D 137	**definitionally equal** <to>, by definition equal <to> <LO>	definitionsgleich <mit>	par définition égal <à>, égal par définition <à>	по определению равный
D 138	**definition by abstraction** <LO>	Definition *f* durch Abstraktion	définition *f* par abstraction, définition en compréhension	определение через абстракцию
D 139	**definition by cases** <LO>	Definition *f* durch Fallunterscheidung	définition *f* par cas	определение разбором случаев
D 140	**definition by induction,** inductive (recursive, recursion) definition, definition by recursion <FO>	rekursive (induktive) Definition *f*, Definition durch Induktion	définition *f* par récurrence, définition récursive (inductive, par induction)	индуктивное (рекурсивное) определение, определение по (с помощью) индукции
	definition by recursion <FO>	*s.* D 140		
D 141	**definition by transfinite induction (recursion),** construction by transfinite induction <LO>	Definition *f* durch transfinite Induktion	définition *f* par induction transfinie	определение трансфинитной индукцией
	definition equal / by <LO>	*s.* D 137		
D 142	**deflate / to** <a matrix> <MD>	die Ordnung <einer Matrix> erniedrigen	abaisser l'ordre <d'une matrice>	понижать порядок, уменьшать размеры <матрицы>
	deflation <MD>	*s.* R 430		
D 143	**deformable surface** <DG>	verbiegbare Fläche *f*	surface *f* déformable (flexible)	изгибаемая поверхность
D 144	**deformation,** bending <of a surface> <DG, GE>	Verbiegung *f*, Biegung *f*	déformation *f*	изгибание
D 145	**deformation,** continuous deformation <TO>	Deformation *f*, stetige Deformation *f*	déformation *f*, déformation *f* continue	деформация, непрерывная деформация
D 146	**deformation,** def <of a vector> <VT>	Deformation *f*, def, grad	déformation *f*, def	деформация, def
D 147	**deformation retract** <TO>	Deformationsretrakt *m*	rétracte *m* de (par) déformation	деформационный ретракт, ретракт посредством деформации
D 148	**deformation retraction** <TO>	Deformationsretraktion *f*	rétraction *f* par déformation	деформационная ретракция, ретракция посредством деформации
D 149	**deform continuously to a point / to** <TO>	zu einem Punkt zusammenziehen, [stetig] in einen Punkt deformieren	déformer en un point	стягивать в одну точку
	deg <GE>	*s.* D 174		
D 150	**degeneracy** <AN, GE>	Ausartung *f*	dégénérescence *f*	вырождение
	degeneracy <AT>	*s.* D 151		
D 151	**degeneracy operator,** degeneracy <AT>	Ausartungsoperator *m*	opérateur *m* [de] dégénérescence	оператор вырождения (вырождений)
D 152	**degenerate bilinear mapping** <AL>	ausgeartete bilineare Abbildung *f*	application *f* bilinéaire dégénérée	вырожденное билинейное отображение
D 153	**degenerate case** <e.g. of simplex method> <GN, PG>	Ausartungsfall *m*, Entartungsfall *m*, ausgearteter Fall *m*	cas *m* de dégénérescence	вырожденный случай, случай вырождения
D 154	**degenerate collineation,** projection <PJ>	ausgeartete Kollineation *f*, Projektion *f*	collinéation *f* dégénérée, projection *f*	вырожденная коллинеация, проекция
	degenerate conic [section] <AY>	*s.* S 1055		
D 155	**degenerate distribution,** singular distribution <ST>	entartete Verteilung *f*, Einpunktverteilung *f*, uneigentliche (ausgeartete, singuläre, degenerierte) Verteilung, Delta-Verteilung *f*	distribution *f* dégénérée (singulière), répartition *f* dégénérée (singulière)	вырожденное (сингулярное) распределение
D 156	**degenerate eigenvalue** <of a matrix> <MD>	mehrfacher Eigenwert *m*, mehrfache charakteristische Zahl *f*	valeur *f* propre multiple	кратное собственное значение
D 157	**degenerate kernel,** kernel of finite rank <IE>	ausgearteter Kern *m*, entarteter Kern	noyau *m* de rang fini, noyau dégénéré (d'ordre fini)	вырожденное ядро, ядро конечного ранга
D 158	**degenerate linear problem** <PG>	degeneriertes (entartetes, ausgeartetes) lineares Problem *n*	problème *m* linéaire dégénéré	вырожденная линейная задача
	degenerate mapping <GE>	*s.* S 1093		

	English	German	French	Russian
D 159	**degenerate parabolic equation, degenerate parabolic [partial] differential equation** <DE>	parabolisch ausgeartete Differentialgleichung (Gleichung, partielle Differentialgleichung) *f*	équation *f* parabolique dégénérée, équation aux dérivées partielles parabolique dégénérée	вырожденное параболическое уравнение, вырожденное параболическое дифференциальное уравнение [в частных производных]
D 160	**degenerate polyhedron** <GE>	ausgeartetes (singuläres) Polyeder *n*	polyèdre *m* dégénéré	вырожденный многогранник
D 161	**degenerate quadric,** improper quadric <AG>	ausgeartete Fläche *f* zweiter (2.) Ordnung, ausgeartete Quadrik *f* <der Dimension 2>	quadrique *f* impropre	вырожденная квадрика
D 162	**degenerate set,** one-point set <SE>	einpunktige Menge *f*, Einpunktmenge *f*	partie *f* réduite à un seul point	одноточечное множество
D 163	**degenerate simplex** <AT>	ausgeartetes Simplex *n*	simplexe *m* dégénéré (singulier)	вырожденный (вырождающийся) симплекс
D 164	**degenerate singular simplex** <AT>	ausgeartetes singuläres Simplex *n*	simplexe *m* singulier dégénéré	вырожденный сингулярный симплекс
D 165	**degenerate solution** <PG>	degenerierte (entartete, ausgeartete) Lösung *f*	solution *f* dégénérée	вырожденное решение
D 166	**degenerate type of distribution** <ST>	uneigentlicher Verteilungstyp *m*	type *m* de distribution dégénéré	вырожденный тип распределения
D 167	**degeneration** <of a conic> **into a pair of lines** <AY>	Zerfall *m* (Zerfallen *n*) in ein Linienpaar (Geradenpaar)	dégénérescence *f* dans une paire de droites	вырождение (распадение) в пару прямых
	degeneration principle [of Enriques-Zariski] <AG>	*s.* E 255		
D 168	**deg-order** <Cayley> <degree of the coefficients and order of the variables of a binary form> <AL>	Gradordnung *f*	ordre *m* des degrés	
D 169	**degree,** order <of a linear *or* algebraic system> <AG>	Grad *m*, Ordnung *f*	degré *m*	степень
D 170	**degree,** order <of an algebraic curve *or* surface *or* variety> <AG>	Ordnung *f*, Grad *m*; Punktgrad *m* <einer Kurve *oder* Fläche>	ordre *m*, degré *m*	порядок, степень
D 171	**degree** <of a divisor *or* divisor class> <AG, AL>	Grad *m*	degré *m*, ordre *m*	степень
D 172	**degree,** linear rank <of a finite field extension> <AL>	Grad *m*, linearer Rang *m*, Erweiterungsgrad *m*	degré *m*	степень [расширения]
D 173	**degree,** order <of a polynomial> <AL>	Grad *m*	degré *m* <d'un polynôme>; dimension *f*, poids *m* <d'un polynôme homogène>	степень, измерение
D 174	**degree,** degree of angle (arc), angular (sexagesimal) degree, °, deg <unit angle> <GE>	Grad *m*, Winkelgrad *m*, Bogengrad *m*, Altgrad *m*, °	degré *m*, degré de l'angle, degré d'arc, degré angulaire (sexagésimal), °	градус, градус угла (дуги), угловой (старый) градус, °
D 175	**degree,** upper (maximal) valency, maximal degree <of a graph> <GP>	Maximalvalenz *f*	degré *m* maximum	максимальная степень
D 176	**degree,** valency, local degree <of a vertex, at a vertex>, vertex degree <GP>	Valenz *f*, Grad *m*, Eckengrad *m* <eines Knotenpunkts>	degré *m* <d'un sommet>	степень, валентность, локальная степень <вершины>
D 177	**degree,** dimension <of a character> <RE>	Grad *m*	degré *m*, dimension *f*	степень, размерность
	degree <AL>	*s.* 1. F 176; 2. L 566		
	degree <AL, VT>	*s.* R 133		
	degree <AT>	*s.* D 185		
	degree <FU>	*s.* O 269		
D 178	**degree matrix** <of a graph> <GP>	Valenzmatrix *f*	matrice *f* des valences	матрица валентностей
D 179	**degree mod. 2** <AT>	Abbildungsgrad (Grad) *m* mod 2	degré *n*. mod. 2	четность отображения, степень по модулю два <отображения>
	degree of angle <GE>	*s.* D 174		
D 180	**degree of approximation,** approximateness <AX>	Annäherungsgrad *m*, Grad *m* der Approximation, Approximationsgrad *m*	degré *m* d'approximation	степень приближения (аппроксимации), приблизительность
	degree of arc <GE>	*s.* D 174		
D 181	**degree of a representation,** dimension (dimensionality) of a representation <of a semigroup, group, *or* algebra> <AL, GR, RE>	Grad *m* (Dimension *f*) der Darstellung, Darstellungsgrad *m*; R-Rang *m* des Darstellungsmoduls, Zeilenzahl *f* der Darstellungsmatrizen <Matrizendarstellung einer Algebra>	degré *m* (dimension *f*) de la représentation	размерность (степень) представления
D 182	**degree of freedom** <ST>	Freiheitsgrad *m*	degré *m* de liberté	степень свободы
D 183	**degree of homogeneity** <of a homogeneous function> <AL, AN>	Dimension *f*, Grad *m*, Ordnung *f*, Homogenitätsgrad *m*	degré *m* d'homogénéité, dimension *f*	измерение, измерение (степень, показатель) однородности
D 184	**degree of inseparability,** inseparable [factor of the] degree <of a field extension> <AL>	Inseparabilitätsgrad *m*, Grad *m*	partie *f* (facteur *m*) inséparable du degré	несепарабельная степень, степень несепарабельности
	degree of *K* over *k* <AL>	*s.* D 187		

D 185	**degree of mapping,** degree [of topological mapping], Brouwer degree <of map> <AT>	[Brouwerscher] Abbildungsgrad *m*, Abbildungsgrad (Grad *m*) im Großen	degré *m* d'application, degré, degré [d'une application] topologique, degré des applications	степень отображения, степень [в целом], степень топологического отображения
D 186	**degree of response,** response degree <ST>	Wirkungsgrad *m*	degré *m* de réponse	степень эффективности
	degree of separability <AL>	*s.* 1. R 352; 2. R 353		
D 187	**degree of the field extension *K/k*, degree of the field *K* over *k*,** degree of *K* over *k* <AL>	Relativgrad *m* des Körpers *K* über *k*, Grad *m* von *K* über *k*, Grad von *K/k*	degré *m* de l'extension *K* de *k*, degré du surcorps *K* par rapport au corps *k*	степень [поля] *K* над *k*, степень расширения *K/k*
	degree of topological mapping <AT>	*s.* D 185		
	degree of truth <LO>	*s.* T 1046		
D 188	**degree relation** <AB>	Gradrelation *f*	relation *f* des degrés	соотношение для степеней
D 189	**degree theory** <AT>	Theorie *f* des Abbildungsgrades	théorie *f* du degré [topologique]	теория степени отображения
D 190	**degree with respect to the base space** <in a fibre space> <AT>	Grad *m* bezüglich des Basisraums	degré-base *m*	степень по отношению к базе
	degree with respect to the fibre <AT>	*s.* F 153		
D 191/2	**Dehn['s] lemma** <AT>	Dehnsches Lemma *n*	lemme *m* de Dehn	лемма Дена
	Dehnsche Gruppenbild <GR>	*s.* C 287		
D 193	**Dehn['s] theorem** <on polyhedrons> <GE>	Dehnscher Satz *m*, Satz von Dehn	théorème *m* de Dehn	теорема Дена
D 194	**Deinostratos['] quadratrix,** Dinostratus['] quadratrix <GE>	Quadratrix *f* von (des) Deinostratos (Dinostratus, Hippias)	quadratrice (courbe) *f* de Dinostrate	квадратриса Динострата
	de Jonquières['] group <AG>	*s.* J 80		
	de Jonquières['] transformation <AG>	*s.* J 81		
D 195	**del,** del (nabla) operator, nabla vector, nabla, Hamilton['s] partial differential operator, Hamiltonian, ∇, ∇ <VT>	Nablaoperator *m*, Nabla *n*, Nablavektor *m*, Gradient[en]vektor *m*, Gradientoperator *m*, Operator *m* der räumlichen Differentiation, Hamiltonscher Operator, ∇, ∇	nabla *m*, opérateur *m* nabla (hamiltonien), vecteur *m* nabla, opérateur vectoriel gradient, hamiltonien *m*, ∇, ∇	набла, набла-оператор, оператор «набла» (Гамильтона), ∇-оператор, гамильтониан, ∇, ∇
	Delambre['s] analogies <EG>	*s.* G 71		
D 196	**Delaunay['s] curve** <GE>	Delaunaysche Kurve *f*	courbe *f* de Delaunay	кривая Делоне
D 197	**Delaunay['s] problem** <VA>	Delaunaysches Problem *n*	problème *m* de Delaunay	задача Делоне
D 198	**de la Vallée Poussin['s] decomposition** <of an interval function> <AN>	de la Vallée Poussinsche Zerlegung *f*	décomposition *f* de de la Vallée Poussin	разложение Ла Валле Пуссена
D 199	**de la Vallée Poussin['s] inequality** <AX>	Ungleichung *f* von de Vallée Poussin, de la Vallée Poussinsche Ungleichung	inégalité *f* de de la Vallée Poussin	неравенство Ла Валле Пуссена
	de la Vallée Poussin['s] mean <AX, SS>	*s.* D 201		
D 200	**de la Vallée Poussin['s] singular integral** <AX, RF>	de la Vallée Poussinsches singuläres Integral *n*, singuläres Integral von de la Vallée Poussin	intégrale *f* singulière de de la Vallée Poussin	особый (сингулярный) интеграл Ла Валле Пуссена
D 201	**de la Vallée Poussin['s] sum,** de la Vallée Poussin['s] mean <AX, SS>	Mittel *n* (Summe *f*) von de la Vallée Poussin	moyenne (somme) *f* de de la Vallée Poussin	сумма (среднее) Ла Валле Пуссена
D 202	**de la Vallée Poussin['s] test [for convergence]** <of Fourier series> <SS>	de la Vallée Poussinsches Kriterium *n*	critère *m* de de la Vallée Poussin	признак сходимости Ла Валле Пуссена
D 203	**de la Vallée Poussin['s] theorem** <AX, SS>	Satz *m* von de la Vallée Poussin, de la Vallée Poussinscher Satz	théorème *m* de de la Vallée Poussin	теорема Ла Валле Пуссена, теорема Валле[-] Пуссена
D 204	**delay [differential] equation,** differential equation with delayed argument, differential equation with delays, differential equation with lagging (retarded) argument, differential equation with lag <DE>	Differentialgleichung *f* mit nacheilendem (verzögertem) Argument, Hysterodifferentialgleichung *f*, Hystero-Differentialgleichung *f*	équation *f* différentielle à argument retardé, équation différentielle à retardement	дифференциальное уравнение с запаздывающим аргументом
D 205	**delete / to** <lines of a matrix> <MD>	streichen <Zeilen einer Matrix>	supprimer, barrer <des lignes d'une matrice>	вычеркивать <строки матрицы>
D 206	**deleted neighbourhood** <TO>	reduzierte Umgebung *f*	voisinage *m* pointé	проколотая окрестность, окрестность выколотой точкой
D 207	**deletion** <of an edge> <GP>	Streichen *n*, Löschen *n*, Dialyse *f* <einer Kante>	suppression *f* <d'une arête>	вычеркивание <ребра>
D 208	**[De] l'Hospital['s] rule,** [L']Hospital['s] rule, Bernoulli-l'Hospital['s] rule, Bernoulli-De l'Hospital['s] rule, l'Hôpital['s] rule <DI>	[de] l'Hospitalsche Regel *f*, Bernoulli-[de-]l'Hospitalsche Regel, Regel von [de] l'Hospital, Regel von Bernoulli-[de-]L'Hospital	règle *f* de l'Hôpital, règle de L'Hospital, règle de de l'Hospital (L'Hospital), règle de Bernoulli-de l'Hospital	правило Лопиталя, правило [Бернулли-]Делопиталя, правило Бернулли-Лопиталя

No.	English	German	French	Russian
D 209	**Delian problem,** Delic problem, duplication of the cube <EG>	Delisches Problem *n*, Problem der Würfelverdopplung	problème *m* déliaque (délique, de la duplication du cube, de Délos, de Délios)	делосская задача, задача удвоения (об удвоении) куба, делийская задача
	Delic problem <EG>	*s.* D 209		
	del operator <VT>	*s.* D 195		
	delta <DE, DG, DI, PO>	*s.* L 91		
D 210	**delta-field,** δ-field <SE>	δ-Körper *m*, Deltakörper *m*	δ-corps *m*, delta-corps *m*	δ-поле, дельта-поле
D 211	**delta function [of Dirac],** Dirac['s] delta function, [Dirac['s]] δ-function, Dirac['s] function, Dirac['s] delta distribution, Dirac['s] distribution (functional), Dirac['s] measure, unit impulse function [of order one], spike function, delta operator <FA>	Delta-Funktion *f* von Dirac, Delta-Distribution *f*, [Diracsche] Delta-Funktion (δ-Funktion *f*), Dirac-Funktion *f*, Diracsche Funktion *f*, Diracsches Funktional (Maß) *n*, Dirac-Impuls *m*, Nadelimpuls *m*, [normierte] Zackenfunktion *f*, Einheitsimpuls *m*; Verschiebungsoperator *m* <im Heaviside-Kalkül>	distribution *f* [delta] de Dirac, delta *m* (δ) de Dirac, fonction (fonctionnelle, mesure, masse) *f* de Dirac, mesure définie par la masse unité placée à un point, fonction impulsion[nelle] unité de Dirac, fonction aiguille	дельта-функция, δ-функция, [обобщенная] функция Дирака, функционал Дирака, импульсная функция нулевого порядка, зубцевидная функция, острый импульс, бесконечный всплеск
D 212	**delta-number,** δ-number, principal number of multiplication, principal ordinal of (for) multiplication <SE>	multiplikative Hauptzahl *f*, δ-Zahl *f*, Delta-Zahl *f*, Hauptzahl der Multiplikation	nombre *m* principal multiplicatif, nombre-δ *m*, nombre delta	дельта-число, δ-число
	delta operator <DE, DG, DI, PO>	*s.* L 91		
	delta operator <FA>	*s.* D 211		
D 213	**delta-ring,** δ-ring <SE>	δ-Ring *m*, Delta-Ring *m*	δ-anneau *m*, delta-anneau *m*	δ-кольцо, дельта-кольцо
D 214	**delta-system,** δ-system <in a proximity space *or* as a set system> <SE, TO>	δ-System *n*, Delta-System *n*, Deltasystem *n*	δ-système *m*, delta-système *m*	δ-система, дельта-система
D 215	**deltoid** <a non-convex figure> <EG>	Deltoid *n*	deltoïde *m*	дельтоид
	deltoid <EG>	*s.* K 84		
	deltoid <GE>	*s.* T 931		
	demension <TO>	*s.* D 518		
D 216	**de Méré['s] problem** <ST>	Aufgabe *f* des Chevalier de Méré, de Mérés Aufgabe	problème *m* du Chevalier de Méré	задача де Мере
D 217	**demidegree** <GP>	Ausgangs- oder Eingangsgrad *m*, Ausgangs- oder Eingangsvalenz *f*	demi-degré *m*	полустепень
	demi-degree inward <GP> ┌<GP>	*s.* I 305		
	demi-degree outward	*s.* O 542		
	demigroup <AL>	*s.* S 376		
	de Moivre['s] formula <AN>	*s.* M 805		
	de Moivre-Laplace['s] [limit] theorem <ST>	*s.* M 806		
	de Moivre-Laplace['s] local limit theorem <ST>	*s.* M 807		
	de Moivre['s] theorem <AN>	*s.* M 808		
	demonstrability <LO>	*s.* P 1879		
	demonstrable <LO>	*s.* P 1880		
	demonstrate / to <FO, LO>	*s.* P 1882		
D 218	**De (de) Morgan['s] formulae (laws),** De (de) Morgan['s] rules <AL, SE>	[de] Morgansche Regeln *fpl*, Formeln *fpl* von [de] Morgan, [de] Morgansche Formeln	lois *fpl* de De (de) Morgan, formules *fpl* de A. de Morgan, formule *f* de De (de) Morgan	формулы де Моргана
D 219	**De (de) Morgan['s] laws** <LO>	Verneinungsgesetze *npl*, [de] Morgansche Sätze *mpl* (Gesetze *npl*, Regeln *fpl*), Sätze des Petrus hispanus, Prinzipien *npl* der Verneinung von zusammengesetzten Aussagen	lois *fpl* de De (de) Morgan, lois de Morgan (dualité)	законы (формулы) де Моргана, законы Моргана
D 220	**De (de) Morgan['s] laws in the functional calculus, De (de) Morgan['s] law for quantifiers,** laws of negating the quantifiers <LO>	[de] Morgansche Gesetze *npl* des Prädikatenkalküls	formules *fpl* de De Morgan généralisées	законы отрицания кванторов, обобщенные формулы Моргана
	De (de) Morgan['s] rules <AL, SE>	*s.* D 218		
D 221	**De (de) Morgan rules for infinite joins and meets** <AL>	verallgemeinerte de Morgansche Regeln *fpl*	formules *fpl* de de Morgan généralisées	обобщенные формулы де Моргана
D 222	**Demoulin['s] quadrilateral** <DG>	Vierseit *n* von Demoulin, Demoulinsches Vierseit	quadrilatère *m* de Demoulin	четырехсторонник Демулена
D 223	**Demoulin['s] surface** <DG>	Fläche *f* von Demoulin, Demoulinsche Fläche	surface *f* de Demoulin	поверхность Демулена
D 224	**Demoulin['s] tetrahedron** <DG>	Demoulinsches Tetraeder *n*	tétraèdre *m* de Demoulin	тетраэдр (четырехгранник) Демулена
D 225	**dendrite,** acyclic continuous curve, tree-like continuum, locally connected dendroid <TO>	Baum *m*, Baumkurve *f* <Kontinuum>	dendrite *f*	дендрит, древовидный континуум

D 226	**Denjoy-Carleman-Ahlfors theorem,** theorem of Denjoy-Carleman-Ahlfors <FT>	Satz *m* von Denjoy-Carleman-Ahlfors, Denjoy-Carleman-Ahlforsscher Satz	théorème *m* de Denjoy-Carleman-Ahlfors	теорема Данжуа-Карлемана-Альфорса
D 227	**Denjoy-Carleman['s] theorem** <FT>	Denjoy-Carlemanscher Satz *m*, Satz von Denjoy-Carleman	théorème *m* de Denjoy-Carleman	теорема Данжуа-Карлемана
D 228	**Denjoy-integrable function** <DI>	Denjoy-integrierbare Funktion *f*	fonction *f* intégrable au sens de Denjoy	функция, интегрируемая в смысле Данжуа
D 229	**Denjoy['s] integral** <DI>	Denjoysches Integral *n*	intégrale *f* [au sens] de Denjoy	интеграл [в смысле] Данжуа
	Denjoy-Khinchine integral <RF>	*s.* D 528		
D 230	**Denjoy-Khinchine theorem** <RF>	Denjoy-Chintschinscher (Denjoy-Khintchinescher) Satz *m*, Satz von Denjoy-Chintschin (Denjoy-Khintchine)	théorème *m* de Denjoy-Khintchine	теорема Данжуа-Хинчина
	Denjoy-Perron integral <RF>	*s.* D 529		
D 231	**Denjoy-Young-Saks theorem** <FA>	Satz *m* von Denjoy-Young-Saks, Denjoy-Young-Saksscher Satz	théorème *m* de Denjoy-Young-Saks	теорема Данжуа-Янга-Сакса
	denominate number <AR>	*s.* C 1794		
D 232	**denominator** <of a convergent of a continued fraction> <NT>	Näherungsnenner *m*	dénominateur *m* d'une réduite	знаменатель подходящей дроби
D 233	**denominator** <of a fraction> <AL, AR, NT>	Nenner *m*	dénominateur *m*, nominateur *m* <Stevin>, // note *f* inférieure <Girard>	знаменатель
D 234	**denominator determinant** <AL>	Nennerdeterminante *f*	déterminant *m* dénominateur	определитель-знаменатель
D 235	**denominator divisor** <AL>	Nennerdivisor *m*	dénominateur *m* <d'un diviseur>	дивизор-знаменатель
	denominator of the n-th convergent <AB>	*s.* N 735		
D 236	**denominator parameter** <of the generalized hypergeometric series> <FU>	Nennerparameter *m*	paramètre *m* du dénominateur	параметр знаменателя
D 237	**denotation** <LO>	Denotat *n* <Church>, Nominatum *n* <Frege>		денотат <Черч>, номинат <Фреге>
	denotation <MM>	*s.* I 691		
D 238	**dense chain** <in a partially ordered set> <SE>	dichte Kette *f*	chaîne *f* dense	плотно (плотное линейно) упорядоченное множество, в себе плотное [линейно] упорядоченное множество
D 239	**dense-in-itself set, dense in itself set** <TO>	insichdichte Menge *f*, in sich dichte Punktmenge *f*	ensemble *m* dense en soi, ensemble dense en lui-même	плотное в себе [точечное] множество; множество, плотное в себе
	densely ordered set (system) <SE>	*s.* D 242		
D 240	**denseness** <of a set> <TO>	Dichtheit *f*	densité *f*	свойство быть плотным, плотность
D 241	**dense ordering** <SE>	dichte Ordnung *f*	ordre *m* dense (sans trou, dense en soi, partout dense en soi, indéfiniment divisible)	плотное упорядочение
D 242	**dense set,** densely ordered set (system), everywhere dense set <as an ordered set> <SE>	dichte (dichte geordnete, überall dichte, dichtgeordnete) Menge *f*	ensemble *m* dense (partout dense)	плотно упорядоченное множество
D 243	**dense set,** everywhere dense set <TO>	dichte Menge (Punktmenge) *f*, überall dichte Punktmenge, // pantachische Menge	ensemble *m* dense (partout dense), // ensemble pantachique	[всюду] плотное множество, плотное (всюду плотное) точечное множество
D 244	**dense set** <with respect to another set> <TO>	dichte Menge *f* <zu>	ensemble *m* dense <par rapport à>	плотное множество <относительно>
D 245	**dense subset** <on> <TO>	dichte (überall dichte, dichtliegende) Teilmenge <in>	partie *f* (sous-ensemble *m*) dense <en>	плотное подмножество <в>
D 246	**density** <of prime ideals *or* prime numbers *or* of a graph> <AB, GP, NT>	Dichte *f*	densité *f* <AB, GP, NT>, pourcentage *m* <AB, NT>	плотность
	density <GE>	*s.* P 3		
	density <ST>	*s.* P 1534		
	density <VT>	*s.* R 721		
	density function <ST>	*s.* P 1534		
	density function of the marginal distribution <ST>	*s.* M 117		
D 247	**density of death** <ST>	Sterbensdichte *f*	densité *f* de mort	плотность смерти (смертности)
	density of packing <GE>	*s.* P 3		
	density of probability <ST>	*s.* P 1534		
D 248	**density of weight —1** <VT>	Dichte *f* vom Gewicht —1	capacité *f*	плотность веса —1
D 249	**density theorem** <AL>	Dichtigkeitssatz *m*	théorème *m* de densité; lemme *m* de densité	теорема [о] плотности
	density theorem of Chebotarev <AB>	*s.* C 598		
D 250	**density theorem of Chevalley-Jacobson,** Chevalley-Jacobson density theorem <AL>	Dichtigkeitssatz *m* von Chevalley-Jacobson, Chevalley-Jacobsonscher Dichtigkeitssatz	théorème *m* de densité de Chevalley-Jacobson	теорема плотности Шевалле-Джекобсона, теорема плотности Джекобсона

No.	English	German	French	Russian
	denumerability <SE>	*s.* C 2554		
D 251	**denumerable number of branches / with a** <TO>	abzählbar-verzweigt	avec un nombre dénombrable de ramifications	счетно[-]ветвящийся
D 252	**denumerable set,** countable (enumerable) set, denumerably (countably, enumerably) infinite set <SE>	abzählbar unendliche Menge *f*, abzählbare Menge	ensemble *m* dénombrable [infini], ensemble infini dénombrable; infinité *f* dénombrable	счетное множество, счетно[е] бесконечное множество
	denumerable set <SE>	*s.* C 2561		
	denumerably infinite set <SE>	*s.* D 252		
D 253	**denumerably many elements** <SE>	abzählbar viel[e] Elemente *npl*	éléments *mpl* à une infinité dénombrable; une infinité *f* dénombrable d'éléments	счетное количество элементов
D 254	**denumerant** <Sylvester> <CT>	Denumerante *f*	dénumérant *m*	денумерант
	denumeration <SE>	*s.* E 276		
	dependence <ST>	*s.* S 1788		
D 255	**dependence relation** <AL>	Abhängigkeitsbeziehung *f*	relation *f* de dépendance	отношение зависимости
	dependence theorem <DE>	*s.* T 272		
D 256	**∪-dependent** <LA>	vereinigungsabhängig	∪-dépendant, ∨-dépendant	∪-зависимый
D 257	**dependent elements** <AL>	abhängige Elemente *npl*	famille *f* non libre, éléments *mpl* dépendants	зависимые элементы
	dependent event <ST>	*s.* S 1780		
D 258	**dependent probability** <ST>	abhängige Wahrscheinlichkeit *f*	probabilité *f* dépendante	зависимая вероятность
D 259	**dependent sampling** <ST>	abhängige Stichprobenauswahl (Stichprobennahme) *f*, abhängiges Stichprobenerhebungsschema *n*	échantillonnage *m* dépendant, sondage *m* dépendant	зависящий выбор
	dependent variable <PG>	*s.* B 128		
D 260	**dependent variate** <ST>	abhängige Zufallsvariable *f*; Zielgröße *f* <in der Regressionsanalyse>	variable *f* [aléatoire] dépendante	зависимая случайная переменная (величина), зависимая переменная
	depressed equation <AL>	*s.* D 108		
	depression of the order of an equation <DE>	*s.* L 1150		
D 261	**depth** <of an element> <AL>	Tiefe *f*	profondeur *f*	высота
D 262	**depth,** homological codimension, codimension, grade <of a module, ideal *or* ring> <AL>	Tiefe *f*, homologische Kodimension *f*	profondeur *f*, codimension *f* homologique	глубина, гомологическая коразмерность
	depth <AL>	*s.* D 503		
	depth contour [line] <DS>	*s.* L 598		
D 263	**depth line** <in central perspective> <DS>	Tiefenlinie *f*	ligne *f* de profondeur	линия глубины
D 264	**de Rham['s] group** <of a variety> <DG>	Gruppe *f* von de Rham, de Rhamsche Gruppe	groupe *m* de de Rham	группа де Рама
	deranging parameter <ST>	*s.* N 759		
	derivability <DI>	*s.* D 443		
D 265	**derivable** <from>, entailed <by>, deducible <from> <LO>	ableitbar <aus>, beweisbar <aus>	déductible, dérivable <de>	выводимый <из>
D 266	**derivable expression, derivable sequence of symbols** <LO>	herleitbare Zeichenreihe *f*	assemblage *m* de signes déducible	выводимая последовательность символов
D 267/8	**derivation** <of a Lie ring> <AL>	Derivation *f*, infinitesimaler Automorphismus *m*	dérivation *f*, automorphisme *m* infinitésimal	дифференцирование
D 269	**derivation,** differentiation, deriving <of a function, process> <DI>	Differenzieren *n*, Differentiation *f*, Ableiten *n*, Ableitung *f*	dérivation *f*, différentiation *f*	дифференцирование, нахождение производной
D 270	**derivation,** deriving <e.g. of a formula> <GN>	Herleiten *n*, Herleitung *f*, Ableiten *n*, Ableitung *f*	déduction *f*, dérivation *f*	вывод, выведение
	derivation <TO>	*s.* D 292		
	derivation filament <LO>	*s.* P 1757		
D 271	**derivation module** <AL>	Derivationsmodul *m*	module *m* des dérivations	модуль дифференцирований
D 272	**derivation trivial on R,** *R*-derivation <AL>	Derivation *f* über *R*	*R*-dérivation *f*	дифференцирование, тривиальное на *R*
D 273	**derivative,** derived function <first *or* 1st *or* first-order *or* of order 1, second *or* 2nd *or* second-order *or* of order 2, . . . , *n*-th *or* *n*-th order *or* of order *n*> <as a function, resulting from differentiation>, // fluxion <Newton> <DI>	Ableitung *f*, Differentialquotient *m*, Derivierte *f*, <erste *oder* 1. *oder* erster Ordnung, zweite *oder* 2. *oder* zweiter Ordnung, . . . *n*-te *oder* *n*-ter Ordnung>, // Fluxion *f* <Newton>	dérivée *f*, fonction *f* dérivée <premier, première *ou* 1-r, 1-e *ou* d'ordre 1, second, seconde *ou* deuxième *ou* 2-e *ou* 2-ème *ou* d'ordre 2, . . . , *n*-ème *ou* *n*-e *ou* d'ordre *n*>, // fluxion *f* <Newton>	производная, производная функция <первая *или* 1-я, вторая *или* 2-я, . . . , *n*-я *или* порядка *n* *или* *n*-го порядка>, // флюксия <Ньютон>
	derivative <AL>	*s.* B 710		
	derivative <AN>	*s.* D 274		
	derivative <TO>	*s.* D 292		

No.	English	German	French	Russian
D 274	**derivative at a point,** differential coefficient, // differential quotient <DI>	Differentialquotient *m*, Ableitung *f* <in einem Punkt>	dérivée *f* <dans un point>, coefficient *m* différentiel, nombre *m* dérivé, // quotient différentiel	производная <в точке>
D 275	**derivative function** <RF>	Deriviertenfunktion *f*	fonction *f* dérivée	[обобщенная] производная функция
	derivative function on the left <RF>	*s.* L 368		
	derivative function on the right <RF>	*s.* R 1151		
	derivative in a direction <DI>	*s.* D 561		
D 275 a	**derivative of a vector** <with respect to a parameter> <VT>	Ableitung *f* eines Vektors <nach einem Parameter>	vecteur *m* dérivé, dérivée *f* vectorielle (d'une fonction vectorielle) <par rapport à un paramètre>	производная вектор-функции, векторная производная <по параметру>
D 276	**derivative of higher order,** higher (higher-order) derivative <DI>	höhere Ableitung *f*, Ableitung höherer Ordnung	dérivée *f* d'ordre supérieur, dérivée supérieure	производная высшего порядка, высшая производная
D 277	**derivative of the Dirac function** <FA>	Ableitung *f* der δ-Funktion, Ableitung der Dirac-Funktion	dérivée *f* de la fonction de Dirac	импульсная функция первого порядка
	derivative on one side <AN>	*s.* O 104		
	derivative on the left <DI>	*s.* L 367		
	derivative on the right <DI>	*s.* R 1150		
D 278	**derivative rule,** rule of derivation, deductive rule <LO>	Ableitungsregel *f*	règle *f* de déduction	правило вывода
	derivative set <TO>	*s.* D 292		
	derived <AT>	*s.* B 79		
D 279	**derived algebra** <of a Lie algebra> <AL>	derivierter Ring *m*, Kommutatorideal *n*	algèbre *f* dérivée, idéal *m* dérivé	идеал коммутатора, коммутаторный идеал
D 280	**derived category** <CA>	abgeleitete Kategorie *f*	catégorie *f* dérivée	производная категория, производная <от категории>
	derived complex <AT>	*s.* B 79		
D 281	**derived dyad** <VT>	Ableitungsdyade *f*, derivierte Dyade *f*, Nabladyade *f*, Nablaaffinor *m*	dyade *f* dérivée	производная диада
D 282	**derived equation** <by algebraic operations> <AL>	abgeleitete Gleichung *f*	équation *f* dérivée	производное уравнение
D 283	**derived form,** derived quadratic form <from a primitive form> <NT>	abgeleitete (derivierte) [quadratische] Form *f*	forme *f* dérivée	производная форма
	derived function <AN>	*s.* D 274		
	derived function <DI>	*s.* D 273		
D 284	**derived functor** <CA>	abgeleiteter Funktor *m*	foncteur *m* dérivé, dérivé *m* <d'un foncteur>	производный функтор, производное <функтора>
D 285	**derived graph,** adjoint [graph] <GP>	Bogenmittengraph *m*, adjungierter Graph *m*, Kantenmittengraph *m*	graphe *m* adjoint, adjoint *m*	сопряженный граф
	derived graph <GP>	*s.* L 860		
	derived group <GR>	*s.* C 1281		
	derived matrix <MD>	*s.* P 2017		
D 286	**derived module** <AL>	abgeleiteter Modul *m*	module *m* dérivé	производный модуль
	derived number <AN>	*s.* D 524		
D 287	**derived operation** <UA>	derivierte (abgeleitete, algebraische) Operation *f*	opération *f* dérivée	производная операция
D 288	**derived operator** <UA>	derivierter Operator *m*	opérateur *m* dérivé	производный оператор
	derived quadratic form <NT>	*s.* D 283		
D 289	**derived relation** <of a relation> <AL>	Folgerelation *f*	relation *f* dérivée	следствие [отношения]
D 290	**derived rule of inference** <LO>	abgeleitete Regel *f* des Schließens, abgeleitete Schlußregel *f*	règle *f* de conclusion dérivée	производное правило заключения
D 291	**derived series,** descending derived series <of a group> <GR>	Kommutatorreihe *f*, Folge *f* der höheren Kommutatorgruppen (Ableitungen), absteigende Kommutatorkette *f*, abgeleitete Reihe (Kette) *f*	série *f* dérivée	цепь коммутантов, убывающая цепь коммутантов, последовательность (ряд) коммутантов
D 292	**derived set,** derivation, derivative [set], cluster set <α-th *or* of order α> <of a set> <TO>	Ableitung *f*, abgeleitete Menge (Punktmenge) *f*, Derivierte *f*, derivierte Menge <α-te *oder* der Ordnung α>	ensemble *m* dérivé, dérivé *m* <d'ordre α>	производное [точечное] множество, производная <порядка α>
D 293	**derived sheaf,** homology sheaf <AT>	abgeleitete Garbe *f*	faisceau *m* dérivé	производный пучок
D 294	**derived surface** <of a function> <FT>	Ableitungsfläche *f*	surface *f* dérivée	производная поверхность
D 295	**derived vector,** tractor <of a covariant tensor of rank 2> <VT>	[erster] derivierter Vektor *m*, Traktor *m*, ∇, div <Voigt>, grad <Weber>, tr <Emde>	vecteur *m* dérivé, tracteur *m*	производный вектор, трактор
	deriving <DI>	*s.* D 269		
	deriving <GN>	*s.* D 270		
D 296	**derogatory matrix** <MD>	derogatorische Matrix *f*	matrice *f* privilégiée (dérogatoire)	непростая матрица

D 297	**Desargues['s] (Desarguesian) configuration** <PJ>	Desarguessche Konfiguration *f* [zweier perspektiver Dreiecke], Desargues-Konfiguration *f*	configuration *f* de Desargues	конфигурация Дезарга
D 298	**Desarguesian geometry** <AL, PJ>	Desarguessche Geometrie *f*	géométrie *f* arguésienne <AL, PJ>; treillis *m* projectif arguésien <AL>	дезаргова геометрия <AL, PJ>; геометрия дезаргова пространства <PJ>
D 299	**Desarguesian lattice,** Arguesian lattice <LA>	Desarguesscher Verband *m*	treillis *m* arguésien	дезаргова структура
	Desarguesian plane <PJ>	*s.* D 301		
D 300	**Desarguesian space,** Desargues['s] space <PJ>	Desarguesscher Raum *m*	espace *m* arguésien	дезаргово пространство
D 301	**Desargues['s] plane,** Desarguesian plane <PJ>	Desarguessche Ebene *f*	plan *m* arguésien	плоскость Дезарга, дезаргова плоскость
	Desargues['s] space <PJ>	*s.* D 300		
D 302	**Desargues-Sturm theorem** <AY>	Desargues-Sturmscher Satz *m*, Desarguesscher Involutionssatz *m*, Involutionssatz von Desargues	théorème *m* de Desargues-Sturm	теорема Дезарга-Штурма
D 303	**Desargues['s] theorem,** theorem of Desargues <on perspective triangles> <PJ>	Desarguesscher Satz *m*, Satz von Desargues <über perspektive Dreiecke>	théorème *m* de Desargues, involution *f* de six points	теорема Дезарга, предложение Дезарга <о гомологичных треугольниках>
	Descartes['] folium <AG>	*s.* C 164		
	Descartes['s] parabola <AG>	*s.* T 933		
D 304	**Descartes['] rule of signs,** rule of signs (Descartes), Harriot-Descartes rule <AL>	kartesische (Cartesische, Descartessche, Descartes', Harriotsche, Harriots) Zeichenregel *f*, Descartes' (Harriots) Satz *m*	règle *f* [des signes] de Descartes, méthode *f* des variations de Descartes, règle des signes de Harriot, théorème *m* de Descartes (Harriot)	правило знаков Декарта, правило Декарта, декартово правило, теорема Декарта
D 305	**descendant** <SP>	Nachfolger *m*, Nachkomme *m*	descendant *m*	потомок
D 306	**descending chain** <of ideals, groups, *or* modules> <AL>	Vielfachenkette *f*, U-Kette *f*, absteigende Kette *f*	chaîne *f* descendante	убывающая цепь
D 307	**descending chain** <of sets> <AL, SE, TO>	absteigende Kette *f*	chaîne *f* descendante	убывающая цепь
D 308	**descending chain condition** <for ideals, groups, modules> <AL>	Vielfach[en]kettensatz *m*, U-Satz *m*, U-Kettensatz *m*, Minimalbedingung *f*, absteigende Kettenbedingung *f*	condition *f* minimale (des chaînes descendantes)	условие обрыва убывающих цепей
D 309	**descending chain condition,** D.C.C. <AL, SE>	absteigende Kettenbedingung *f*	condition *f* de chaîne descendante [finie], condition des chaînes descendantes	условие обрыва убывающих цепей, условие обрыва убывающей цепочки
D 310	**descending chain condition for the powers of a principal ideal** <AL>	Potenzkettensatz *m* <für Ideale>	condition *f* des chaînes descendantes de puissances d'un idéal principal	условие обрыва убывающих цепей степеней главных идеалов
D 311	**descending composition series** <GR>	absteigende Kompositionsreihe *f*	série *f* de composition descendante	убывающий композиционный ряд
D 312	**descending continued fraction** <NT>	absteigender Kettenbruch *m*	fraction *f* continue descendante	нисходящая цепная дробь
	descending derived series <GR>	*s.* D 291		
D 313	**descending difference,** forward difference <of order *n*> <FD>	absteigende (vorwärts genommene) Differenz *f* <*n*-ter Ordnung>	différence *f* descendante (latérale descendante, latérale) <d'ordre *n*>	взятая вперед разность; разность, взятая вперед; конечная разность «вперед», правая разность, разность для интерполирования вперед <порядка *n*>
	descending filtration <AL>	*s.* D 79		
D 314	**descending induction,** downward[s] induction <on> <FO>	absteigende Induktion *f* <nach>	récurrence *f* descendante	индукция по убывающим значениям, индукция спуска
D 315	**descending Loewy series** <AL>	untere Loewy-Reihe *f*, hintere Loewysche Kompositionsreihe *f*	série *f* de Loewy descendante	нижний ряд Лови
D 316	**descending Löwenheim-Skolem theorem** <MM>	absteigender Satz *m* von Löwenheim-Skolem	théorème *m* de Löwenheim-Skolem descendant	нисходящая теорема Левенгейма-Сколема
D 317	**descending order / in** <GN>	in absteigender Anordnung, fallend geordnet	dans l'ordre décroissant	в нисходящем порядке
D 318	**descending power series** <SS>	fallende (absteigende) Potenzreihe (Reihe) *f*, Potenzreihe (Reihe) nach fallenden Potenzen	série *f* descendante	ряд по убывающим степеням
D 319	**descending sequence of events** <ST>	absteigende (abnehmende) Folge *f* von Ereignissen	suite *f* décroissante (descendante) d'événements	убывающая последовательность событий
D 320	**descending series of subgroups,** tower of subgroups <AL>	absteigende Reihe *f* von Untergruppen	série *f* descendante de sous-groupes	ряд подгрупп, башня подгрупп
D 321	**descent** <PG>	Abstieg *m*	descente *f*	спуск
D 322	**described angle** <EG>	überstrichener Winkel *m*	angle *m* balayé	описываемый угол
D 323	**description** <LO>	Deskription *f*	description *f*	дескрипция, описание

	English	German	French	Russian
	descriptional operator	*s.* D 325		
D 324	**description of a curve** <GN>	Durchlaufung (Beschreibung) *f* einer Kurve	parcours *m* d'une courbe	описывание кривой
D 325	**description operator,** iota operator, ι operator, definite description operator, descriptional operator <LO>	bestimmter Artikel *m* ι, Funktor *m* ι (iota), ι-Funktor *m*, Iota-Funktor *m*, Unifikator *m*, deskriptiver Operator *m*, Kennzeichnungsoperator *m*, Kennzeichnungsterm	iota *m* renversé, opérateur *m* iota (ι), symbole *m* iota (ι)	оператор дескрипции, йота-оператор, оператор описания, ι
D 326	**description term** <LO>	Kennzeichnungsterm *m*, ι-Term *m*, Iota-Term *m*	terme *m* descriptif	дескриптивный термин
D 327	**descriptive connection** <DG>	deskriptive Übertragung *f*, deskriptiver Zusammenhang *m*	connexion *f* descriptive	дескриптивная (описательная) связность
D 328	**descriptive derivative** <DG>	deskriptive Ableitung *f*	dérivée *f* descriptive	дескриптивная (описательная) производная
D 329	**descriptive form (function),** designatory function <LO>	deskriptive Funktion *f*	fonction *f* descriptive	дескриптивная функция, дескриптивный термин
D 330	**descriptive function theory** <RF>	deskriptive Funktionentheorie *f*	théorie *f* descriptive des fonctions	дескриптивная теория функций
D 331	**descriptive geometry** <DG>	deskriptive Geometrie *f*	géométrie *f* descriptive	описательная (дескриптивная) геометрия
D 332	**descriptive geometry** <DS>	darstellende Geometrie *f*	géométrie *f* descriptive	начертательная геометрия
D 333	**descriptive set theory** <SE>	deskriptive Mengenlehre (Punktmengenlehre) *f*	théorie *f* descriptive des ensembles	дескриптивная (описательная) теория множеств
D 334	**descriptive statistics** <ST>	beschreibende Statistik *f*	statistique *f* descriptive	описательная статистика
D 335	**design,** design of experiment, experimental design <ST>	Versuchsanlage *f*, Anlage *f*	plan *m* [d'expérience], plan expérimental, dispositif *m* [d'expérience], dispositif expérimental	план, план эксперимента (опыта)
	designated base point <SE, TO>	*s.* B 105		
D 336	**designation** <LO>	Bezeichnung *f*	désignation *f*	обозначение
	designatory function <LO>	*s.* D 329		
	design of experiment <ST>	*s.* D 335		
D 337	**design of experiments,** experimental design, planning of experiments <ST>	statistische Versuchsplanung *f*, Versuchsplanung	planification *f* des expériences	планирование эксперимента
D 338	**De Sluse['s] conchoid,** Sluse['s] conchoid, conchoid of De Sluse <GE>	[De] Sluses Konchoide *f*	conchoïde *f* slusienne	конхоида Слюза
D 339	**desmic surface** <PJ>	desmische Fläche *f*	surface *f* desmique	десмическая поверхность
D 340	**desmic tetrahedrons** <PJ>	desmische (verbundene) Tetraeder *npl*	tétraèdres *mpl* desmiques (liés)	связанные (десмические) четырехгранники
D 341	**destructive dilemma** <LO>	destruktives Dilemma *n*	dilemme *m* destructif	деструктивная (диструктивная) дилемма, отрицающая форма дилеммы, modus tollens дилеммы
	det <MD>	*s.* D 343		
D 342	**determinant** <of a quadratic form> <AL>	Determinante *f*	déterminant *m*, réalisant *m*, invariant *m* <d'une forme algébrique>	детерминант, определитель
D 343	**determinant,** det (a_{ik}), $\lvert a_{ik} \rvert$ <of the first, ..., *n*-th order *or* of order 1, ..., *n*; of higher order *or* higher-order determinant> <MD>	Determinante *f*, det (a_{ik}), $\lvert a_{ik} \rvert$ <1-, ..., *n*-reihige *oder* [von] erster, ..., *n*-ter Ordnung *oder* der Ordnung 1, ..., *n* oder ersten, ..., *n*-ten Grades *oder* vom Grade 1, ..., *n* *oder* von 1^2, ..., n^2 Elementen; höherer Ordnung>, // alternierende Funktion *f* <Cauchy>	déterminant *m*, det (a_{ik}), $\lvert a_{ik} \rvert$ <de premier, ..., *n*-e ordre *ou* d[e l]'ordre 1, ..., *n* *ou* du degré 1, ..., *n*; d'ordre supérieur>, // fonction *f* alternée <Cauchy>	определитель, детерминант <1-ой, ..., *n*-ой степени или 1-го, ..., *n*-го порядка *или* порядка 1, ..., *n*; высшего порядка>
	determinant <AL>	*s.* D 685		
	determinant <AL, AY>	*s.* D 354		
D 344	**determinantal divisor** <of a matrix> <AL>	Determinantenteiler *m*	diviseur *m* déterminantiel	детерминантный дивизор
D 345	**determinantal equation** <AL, MD>	Gleichung *f*, die man durch Nullsetzen einer Determinante erhält	équation *f* se résultant par l'annulation d'un déterminant	уравнение, которое получается сводя определитель к нулю
D 346	**determinantal equation** <GN>	Determinantengleichung *f*	équation *f* déterminantielle	уравнение, содержащее определитель (определители)
D 347	**determinantal ideal** <AL>	Determinantenideal *n*	idéal *m* déterminantiel, idéal-déterminant *m*	детерминантный идеал
	determinantal polynomial <MD>	*s.* S 236		
D 348	**determinantal representation** <AL>	Determinantendarstellung *f*	représentation *f* par un déterminant	представление детерминантом
	determinant inequality of Minkowski <MD>	*s.* M 629		
D 349	**determinant of a square submatrix with highest rank** <MD>	Hauptunterdeterminante *f*, nichtverschwindende Unterdeterminante *f* höchster Ordnung	déterminant *m* principal	отличный от нуля минор наивысшего порядка

No.	English	German	French	Russian
	determinant of higher dimension <MD>	*s.* M 956		
D 350	**determinant of infinite order,** infinite determinant <MD>	unendliche Determinante *f*, Determinante von unendlicher Ordnung	déterminant *m* infini (d'ordre infini)	определитель бесконечного порядка
D 351	**determinant of substitution** <AL>	Substitutionsdeterminante *f*, Modul *m* <der Substitution>	détermination *f* de substitution, déterminant (module) *m* de la substitution	определитель подстановки
D 352	**determinant of the coefficients** <of a system of equations> <GN>	Koeffizientendeterminante *f*	déterminant *m* de la matrice du système	определитель (детерминант) коэффициентов
D 353	**determinant of the coefficients of a linear form** <AL>	Koeffizientendeterminante *f* einer Linearform, Eliminante *f*	déterminant *m* des coefficients d'une forme linéaire	определитель коэффициентов линейной формы
D 354	**determinant of the transformation coefficients (matrix),** determinant <of a transformation> <AL, AY>	Transformationsdeterminante *f*, Koeffizientendeterminante *f*	déterminant *m* de transformation	определитель преобразования
	determinant rank <MD>	*s.* R 136		
D 355	**determinate automaton** <TA>	determinierter Automat *m*	automate *m* déterminé	детерминированный автомат
	determinate relation <SE>	*s.* C 2041		
D 356	**determinate system of partial differential equations,** determined system of partial differential equations <DE>	bestimmtes System *n* von partiellen Differentialgleichungen	système *m* déterminé d'équations [différentielles] aux dérivées partielles	определенная система дифференциальных уравнений в частных производных
	determination of average <GN>	*s.* A 1260		
	determined system of partial differential equations <DE>	*s.* D 356		
D 357	**determining equation** <of a homogeneous linear differential equation at a point of determinacy> <DE>	determinierende Gleichung (Fundamentalgleichung) *f*	équation *f* déterminante	определяющее уравнение
D 358	**determining factor** <DE>	determinierender Faktor *m*	facteur *m* déterminant	определяющий фактор
	determining function <AN>	*s.* O 426		
D 359	**determining set** <in a Stein manifold> <FT>	bestimmende Menge *f*	ensemble *m* déterminant	определяющее множество
	determining variable <ST>	*s.* R 506		
D 360	**deterministic optimization (programming)** <PG>	deterministische Optimierung (Programmoptimierung, Programmierung) *f*	programmation (optimisation) *f* déterministe	детерминированное (детерминистское) математическое программирование
	deterministic process <SP>	*s.* S 1121		
	dev <VT>	*s.* D 367		
D 361	**developable,** developable surface, torse, single-curved surface <DG>	[auf die Ebene] abwickelbare Regelfläche (Fläche) *f*, Torse *f*, developpable (aufrollbare) Fläche, Developpable *f*	développable *f*, surface *f* développable, torse *f*	развертывающаяся поверхность, развертывающаяся [на плоскость] линейчатая поверхность, торс
D 362	**developable function** <AN>	entwickelbare Funktion *f*	fonction *f* développable	разложимая функция, поддающаяся разложению функция
	developable surface <DG>	*s.* D 361		
	developable tangent surface <DG>	*s.* T 46		
D 363	**development** <of a solid *or* polyhedron> <GE>	Netz *n* <eines Körpers *oder* Polyeders>	développement *m*, réseau *m* <d'un solide *ou* polyèdre>	развертка <тела *или* многогранника>
	development <MD>	*s.* E 705		
	development in a series <AN>	*s.* E 709		
	development into a continued fraction <AN, AX, NT>	*s.* E 711		
	development theorem <MD>	*s.* E 715		
D 364	**deviance,** squariance, [pooled] sum of squares <ST>	Summe *f* der Abweichungsquadrate (Quadrate), Quadratsumme *f*	somme *f* des carrés [des écarts]	сумма квадратов [отклонений от среднего значения]
	deviate <ST>	*s.* R 95		
D 365	**deviation** <of an approximating function> <AX>	Abweichung *f*	écart *m*, déviation *f*	отклонение, уклонение
D 366	**deviation** <of two point sets> <TO>	Abweichung *f*, Entfernung *f* <Hausdorff>, Nachbarschaftsmaß *n*	distance *f*	отклонение, расстояние
D 367	**deviation,** dev <of a vector> <VT>	Deviation *f*, dev	déviation *f*, dev	девиация, уклонение, dev
D 368	**deviation from regression,** residual, remainder <ST>	Abweichung *f* von der Regression, Rest *m* der geschätzten Regression, Schätzwert *m* des Anpassungsfehlers	écart *m* à la régression, résidu *m*	отклонение от регрессии, остаток
D 369	**deviation from the mean** <AX>	Abweichung *f* vom Mittelwert	écart *m* à la moyenne	отклонение от среднего значения
D 370	**deviator** <VT>	Deviator *m*	déviateur *m*	девиатор

No.	English	German	French	Russian
D 371	**devil's curve** <a special quartic> <GE>	Teufelskurve *f*	courbe *f* du diable	кривая, имеющая уравнение $y^4 - x^4 + ay^2 + bx^2 = 0$
	De Vries['s] configuration <SG>	*s.* C 1871		
	dextrorse curve <GE>	*s.* R 1156		
D 372	**dextrorse helix,** right-hand[ed] helix, right-twisted helix <GE>	rechtsgängige (rechtswendige) Schraubenlinie *f*	hélice *f* rétrograde (dextrorsum, à droite, à torsion droite, à torsion dextre)	винтовая линия правого вращения, завитая вправо винтовая линия, вправо завитая винтовая линия, правовинтовая линия, правая винтовая линия
D 373	**dextrorse ruled surface,** right-hand[ed] ruled surface <GE>	positiv gewundene Regelfläche *f*, rechtsgewundene Regelfläche	surface *f* réglée dextrorsum	линейчатая поверхность правого вращения, завитая вправо линейчатая поверхность
	dextrorse screw <GE>	*s.* R 1261		
	dextrorsum curve <GE>	*s.* R 1156		
D 374	**D-group** <GR>	D-Gruppe *f*, dividierbare R-Gruppe *f*	D-groupe *m*	D-группа, полная R-группа
	diabolic magic square <CT, NT>	*s.* P 416		
	diagonability <AL>	*s.* D 385		
	diagonable matrix <MD>	*s.* D 388		
D 375	**diagonal** <of a polygon or polyhedron, a circuit, a set product, a magic square <CT, EG, GP, SE>	Diagonale *f* <CT, EG, GP, SE>; Sparren *m* <CT>	diagonale *f*	диагональ
D 376	**diagonal** <of a matrix *or* determinant> <MD>	Diagonale *f*, Diagonalreihe *f*, Schrägreihe *f*, Schräglinie *f*	diagonale *f*	диагональ
	diagonal <GP>	*s.* C 649		
	diagonal <MD>	*s.* M 34		
	diagonal <SE>	*s.* E 326		
	diagonal <TO>	*s.* D 401		
D 377	**diagonal approximation** <of a functorial chain map> <AT>	Diagonalapproximation *f*	approximation *f* diagonale	диагональная аппроксимация
D 378	**diagonal block** <of a partitioned matrix> <MD>	Diagonalkästchen *n*	bloc *m* diagonal, cellule *f* diagonale	диагональный блок, диагональная клетка
D 379	**diagonal block form** <of a matrix> <MD>	verallgemeinerte Diagonalform *f*, Form *f* diagonal aneinandergereihter Kästchen	forme *f* quasi diagonale, forme diagonale par blocs	клеточно-диагональный (квазидиагональный) вид
	diagonal coefficient <MD>	*s.* D 381		
D 380	**diagonal continued fraction** <NT>	Diagonalkettenbruch *m*	fraction *f* continue diagonale	диагональная цепная дробь
D 381	**diagonal element,** diagonal coefficient, element whose row and column numbers are equal, element which is its own conjugate element <of a matrix *or* determinant>; leading element <of a determinant> <MD>	Diagonalelement *n*, Diagonalkoeffizient *m*, Diagonalglied *n*, Hauptdiagonalelement *n*	élément *m* diagonal	диагональный элемент, диагональная компонента, элемент главной диагонали
D 382	**diagonal Euler square** <CT>	diagonales Eulersches Quadrat *n*	carré *m* d'Euler diagonal	диагональный эйлеров квадрат
D 383	**diagonal form** <MD>	Diagonalform *f*, Diagonalgestalt *f*	forme *f* diagonale	диагональный вид
D 384	**diagonal group** <AL>	Gruppe *f* der Diagonalmatrizen	groupe *m* des matrices diagonales	группа диагональных матриц
D 385	**diagonalizability,** diagonability <AL>	Diagonalisierbarkeit *f*	diagonalisabilité *f*, diagonabilité *f*	диагонализуемость, приводимость к диагональному виду
D 386	**diagonalizable endomorphism** <AL>	diagonalisierbarer Endomorphismus *m*	endomorphisme *m* diagonalisable (réductible à la forme diagonale)	диагонализуемый эндоморфизм; эндоморфизм, приводимый к диагональному виду
D 387	**diagonalizable linear group** <GR>	diagonalisierbare lineare Gruppe *f*	groupe *m* linéaire diagonalisable	диагонализуемая линейная группа
D 388	**diagonalizable matrix,** diagonable matrix <MD>	diagonalisierbare Matrix *f*, zu einer Diagonalmatrix ähnliche Matrix	matrice *f* diagonalisable (diagonable), matrice de structure simple	диагонализуемая матрица, матрица простой структуры; матрица, подобная диагональной
D 389	**diagonalization** <AL>	Diagonalisierung *f*	diagonalisation *f*	диагонализация, приведение к диагональному виду
	diagonalization <AL>	*s.* T 784		
D 390	**diagonalization theorem,** theorem on diagonalization <SE>	Diagonalisierungssatz *m*, Diagonalprinzip *n*	théorème *m* de la diagonale	теорема о диагонали, принцип диагонали
D 391	**diagonally transformed co-ordinate (sequence) space** <FA, TO>	diagonaltransformierter Koordinatenraum (Folgenraum) *m*	espace *m* des coordonnées (suites) diagonalement transformé	диагонально преобразованное пространство последовательностей, диагонально преобразованное координатное пространство
D 392	**diagonal map** <AL, SE>	Diagonalabbildung *f*	application *f* diagonale	диагональное отображение
	diagonal map <CA>	*s.* D 394		
D 393	**diagonal matrix** <MD>	Diagonalmatrix *f*	matrice *f* diagonale	диагональная матрица
	diagonal method <SE>	*s.* D 397		

D 393 a	**diagonal method of Cauchy,** Cauchy['s] diagonal method, diagonal process, method of diagonals <for rearranging a double sequence> <SE>	Diagonalverfahren *m*	méthode *f* de la diagonale, méthode des diagonales	диагональный метод, диагональный процесс
D 394	**diagonal morphism,** diagonal map <CA>	Diagonalabbildung *f*, Diagonale *f*	morphisme *m* diagonal, application *f* diagonale	диагональ
D 395	**diagonal of the face** <EG>	Flächendiagonale *f*	diagonale *f* de la face	диагональ грани
D 396	**diagonal point** <AY, DS>	Diagonalpunkt *m*	point *m* diagonal	диагональная точка
D 397	**diagonal procedure (process),** diagonal method, Cantor['s] diagonal method (procedure, process) <SE>	Cantorsches Diagonalverfahren *n*, [Cantors] Diagonalverfahren	procédé *m* diagonal, méthode *f* de [diagonale de] Cantor	диагональный процесс [Кантора], канторов диагональный процесс, диагональный метод Кантора
	diagonal process <SE>	*s.* D 393 a		
D 398	**diagonal proof** <FO>	Beweis *m* nach dem Cantorschen Diagonalverfahren	démonstration *f* par la méthode de Cantor	доказательство диагональным методом
D 399	**diagonal quadratic form,** quadratic form without mixed terms <linear combination of squares> <AL>	quadratische Form *f* in Hauptachsenform, diagonale quadratische Form	forme *f* quadratique diagonale	диагональная квадратичная форма
D 400	**diagonal regression** <ST>	Diagonalregression *f*	régression *f* diagonale	диагональная регрессия
D 401	**diagonal sequence,** diagonal <TO>	Diagonalfolge *f*	suite *f* diagonale	диагональная последовательность
D 402	**diagonal square** <ST>	Diagonalquadrat *n*	carré *m* diagonal	диагональный квадрат
	diagonal sum <MD>	*s.* T 712		
	diagonal sum <SS>	*s.* S 2262		
D 403	**diagonal sum rule** <AL, MD>	Diagonalsummengesetz *n*, Invarianz *f* der Spur einer Matrix von der Darstellung	règle *f* de l'addition diagonale	правило инвариантности следа матрицы
D 404	**diagonal surface** <AG>	Diagonalfläche *f* [von Clebsch], Clebschsche Diagonalfläche	surface *f* diagonale	диагональная поверхность
D 405	**diagonal term** <of a quadratic form> <AL>	rein[ ]quadratisches Glied *n*, quadratisches Glied (Glied der Form $a_{ii}x_i^2$)	terme *m* diagonal (« carré »)	диагональный член, член вида $a_{ii}x_i^2$
D 406	**diagonal trilateral** <AY, DS>	Diagonaldreiseit *n*	trilatère *m* diagonal	диагональный трехсторонник
D 407	**diagram,** Hasse['s] diagram <of a partial order> <SE>	Hasse-Diagramm *n*	diagramme *m* [de Hasse], graphe *m*	диаграмма Хассе
D 408	**diagram,** chart, graph, graphic representation, plot, image curve <of a function> <AN, NU>	Diagramm *n*, [graphische] Darstellung *f*, Kurvendarstellung *f*, Kurvenbild *n*, Graph *m*, Bildkurve *f*	diagramme *m*, graphique *m*, représentation *f* graphique, carte *f*, graphe *m*, courbe *f* image, courbe-image *f*	диаграмма, график, графическое изображение (представление)
	diagram category <CA>	*s.* F 788		
D 409	**diagram chase (chasing),** chase about the diagram <AL, GN>	Diagrammjagd *f*	chasse *f* sur les diagrammes, « diagram-chasing » *m*	петляние по диаграммам, диаграммный поиск
D 410	**diagram functor** <CA>	Diagrammfunktor *m*	foncteur *m* diagramme	функтор диаграмм
D 411	**diagram lemma** <CA>	Diagrammlemma *n*	lemme *m* sur le diagramme	лемма о диаграмме
D 412	**diagram scheme,** graph, precategory <CA>	Diagrammschema *n*, [gerichteter] Graph *m*, Präkategorie *f*	schéma *m* de diagrammes, précatégorie *f*	схема [диаграммы], диаграммная схема, предкатегория
D 413	**diagram sub-scheme** <CA>	Unterdiagrammschema *n*	sous-schéma *m* de diagrammes	подсхема
	dialytic method <AL>	*s.* S 2405		
D 414	**diameter** <of a graph> <GP>	Durchmesser *m*, Diameter *m*	diamètre *m*, longueur *f* <Sainte-Laguë>	диаметр
	diametral curve <AG>	*s.* D 417		
	diametral plane <GE>	*s.* D 418		
D 415	**diametric[al] chord** <of a convex body> <GE>	Durchmessersehne *f*	corde *f* diamétrale	диаметральная хорда
D 416	**diametric[al] conic** <of a curve of *n*-th order> <AG>	Diametralkegelschnitt *m*	conique *f* diamétrale, section *f* conique diamétrale	криволинейный диаметр, диаметральное коническое сечение
D 417	**diametric[al] curve,** diametral curve <AG>	diametrale Kurve *f*	courbe *f* diamétrale	диаметральная линия
	diametrically opposed (opposite) point <GE>	*s.* A 756		
D 418	**diametric[al] plane,** diametral plane <GE>	Durchmesserebene *f*, Diametralebene *f*	plan *m* diamétral	диаметральная плоскость
D 419	**diametric[al] surface** <of a space curve> <DG>	Sehnenmittenfläche *f*	surface *f* diamétrale	диаметральная поверхность
	diamond isomorphism theorem <GR>	*s.* F 341		
	diatensor <VT>	*s.* C 2305		
D 420	**dichotomy** <SE>	Dichotomie *f*	dichotomie *f*	дихотомичность, дихотомия
	dichotomy <ST>	*s.* A 576		
D 421	**Dickson['s] method of ascent** <AB>	Dicksonsches Aufstiegsverfahren *n*	méthode *f* de l'ascente de Dickson	метод подъема Диксона
	dictionary order <SE>	*s.* L 619		
D 422	**diet problem** <PG>	Nahrungsmittelproblem *n*, Diätproblem *n*	problème *m* d'alimentation	задача о диете
D 423	**diffeomorphic mapping, diffeomorphism,** differentiable homeomorphism <DG, TO>	diffeomorphe Abbildung *f*, Diffeomorphismus *m*, differenzierbarer Homöomorphismus *m*	difféomorphisme *m*, homéomorphisme *m* différentiable	диффеоморфизм, гладкий гомеоморфизм, дифференцируемый [гомео-]морфизм
D 424	**difference,** remainder <in subtraction> <AL, AR>	Differenz *f*, Rest *m* <bei der Subtraktion>	différence *f*, rapport *m* arithmétique, reste *m*, résidu *m* <de la soustraction>	разность, остаток <при вычитании>

No.	English	Deutsch	Français	Русский
D 425	**difference** <of 1st, …, n-th order, of order 1, …, n, first-order difference, 1st, …, n-th> <of a function> <FD, NU>	Differenz f <1., …, n-te, 1., …, n-ter Ordnung, [von] der 1., …, n-ten Ordnung>	différence f <première, …, n-e, d'ordre 1, …, n, de premier, …, n-e ordre>	разность <первого, …, n-го порядка, порядка 1, … n, первая, …, n-я>
D 426	**difference** <of ordinals> <SE>	[linke] Differenz f	différence f	разность
D 427	**difference,** set[-]theoretic[al] difference <of two sets A and B>, relative complement <of a set B with respect to a set A>, $A \setminus B$, $A - B$ <*read:* A minus B> <SE>	Differenz f, mengentheoretische Differenz <von A und B>, Differenzmenge f, relatives Komplement n <von B in A>	différence f <entre deux ensembles A et B>, complément m <de B relativement *ou* par rapport à A> <*se lit:* A moins B>	разность <множеств A и B>, относительное множество <множества B до множества A>
	difference <AR>	s. C 1229		
D 428	**difference algebra** <of an R-algebra> <AL>	Differenzenalgebra f, Restklassenalgebra f	algèbre f quotient	алгебра классов вычетов, факторалгебра
	difference-algebra <AL>	s. R 897		
D 429	**difference base** <AB>	Differenzbasis f	base f de différence	разностная база
D 430	**difference boundary value problem** <FD>	Differenzenrandwertproblem n, Differenzenrandwertaufgabe f	problème m aux limites aux différences finie	разностная краевая задача
D 431	**difference bundle** <AT>	Differenzbündel n	fibré m différence	разностное расслоение
D 432	**difference cochain** <AT>	Differenzkokette f	cochaîne f distinctive	различающая ∇-цепь
	difference cokernel <CA>	s. C 1040		
D 433	**difference-differential equation** <DE, FD>	Differenzen-Differentialgleichung f, Differential-Differenzengleichung f, // Hystero-Differentialgleichung f, gemischte Differenzengleichung f	équation f aux différences mêlées, équation différentio-différentielle	дифференциально-разностное уравнение
D 434	**difference equation** <of the 1st, …, n-th order *or* of order 1, …, n; of higher order> <FD>	Differenzengleichung f <erster,…, n-ter Ordnung *oder* [von] der ersten, …, n-ten Ordnung; höherer Ordnung>	équation f aux différences finies <de premier, …, n-e ordre *ou* d'ordre 1, …, n; d'ordre supérieur>	конечно-разностное уравнение, [конечно] разностное уравнение, уравнение в конечных разностях <первого, …, n-го порядка *или* порядка 1, …, n; высшего порядка>
	difference field <AL>	s. R 893		
	difference group <GR>	s. F 27		
	difference kernel <CA>	s. E 327		
	difference method <ST>	s. P 20		
	difference module <AL>	s. F 50		
D 435	**difference of partial sums** <of an infinite series> <SS>	Teilstück n, Partialrest m	différence f de sommes partielles	разность частичных сумм
D 436	**difference operator,** finite difference operator <of 1st, …, n-th order *or* of order 1, …, n for the interval h> <FD, NU>	Differenzenoperator m <1., …, n-ter Ordnung *oder* [von] der Ordnung 1, …, n zur Schrittweite h>	opérateur m de différences finies <de premier, …, n-e ordre *ou* d'ordre 1, …, n pour l'intervalle h>	конечно-разностный оператор, [конечно] разностный оператор <первого, …, n-го порядка *или* порядка 1, …, n по интервалу h>
	difference-product <FD>	s. P 1623		
	difference quotient <AN, DI, FD>	s. D 789		
	difference ring <AL>	s. R 897		
D 437	**difference schema,** difference table <FD, NU>	Differenzenschema n, Tafel f der Differenzen	schéma m aux différences [finies]	разностная схема, таблица разностей
D 438	**difference schema method,** finite-difference method <NU>	Differenzenschemaverfahren n	méthode f des schémas aux différences [finies]	метод разностных схем
D 439	**difference sequence** <FD>	Differenzenfolge f, Differenzenkette f, Differenzenreihe f	suite f de différences	ряд разностей, разностный ряд
D 440	**difference set** <CS, CT, NT>	Differenzenmenge f	ensemble m des différences	множество разностей
	difference table <FD, NU>	s. D 437		
D 441	**different,** fundamental ideal <of an algebraic number field> <AB>	Differente f, Grundideal n, // Fundamentalideal n	différente f, idéal m fondamental	дифферента, фундаментальный идеал
D 442	**different** <of an algebraic function field> <AL>	Differente f, Verzweigungsdivisor m	différente f, diviseur m de ramification	дифферента
	different from zero <GN>	s. N 519		
D 443	**differentiability,** derivability <DI>	Differenzierbarkeit f, Ableitbarkeit f	différentiabilité f, dérivabilité f	дифференцируемость
	differentiability on one side <AN>	s. O 105		
	differentiability on the left <DI>	s. L 334		
	differentiability on the right <DI>	s. R 1120		
	differentiable function <DI, RF>	s. T 644		
	differentiable homeomorphism <DG, TO>	s. D 423		
D 444	**differentiable in a point** <RF>	[gebunden] differenzierbar in einem Punkt	dérivable (différentiable) dans un point	дифференцируемый (моногенный) в точке
	differentiable manifold of class C^r <DG>	s. C 2683		
D 445	**differential** <of degree 1, 2, …, n; of higher degree> <of an exterior differential form> <AN>	Differential n <ersten, zweiten, …, n-ten Grades; höheren Grades>	différentielle f <de degré 1, 2, …, n; de degré supérieur>	дифференциал <степени 1, 2, …, n; высшей степени>
D 446	**differential** <first or of the first order, …, n-th or of the n-th order; of higher order> <DI>	Differential n <erstes oder erster Ordnung, …, n-tes oder n-ter Ordnung; höherer Ordnung>	différentielle f <première ou du premier ordre, …, n-e ou d'ordre n ou du n-e ordre; d'ordre supérieur>	дифференциал <первый или первого порядка, …, n-й или n-го порядка; высшего порядка>

	English	German	French	Russian
	differential <AL>	*s.* A 8		
	differential <DI>	*s.* T 624		
	differential <HA>	*s.* B 650		
D 447	**differential algebra** <AL>	Algebra *f* mit Differentiation	algèbre *f* différentielle	дифференциальная алгебра
D 448	**differential analyzer,** Bush['s] differential analyzer <AN, IN>	Integriermaschine *f*, Differential[gleichungs]-analysator *m* <nach Bush>	analyseur *m* différentiel <de Bush>	дифференциальный анализатор <Буша>
D 449	**differential and integral calculus,** infinitesimal calculus, calculus, infinitesimal analysis <DI>	Differential- und Integralrechnung *f*, Infinitesimalrechnung *f*	calcul *m* différentiel et intégral, calcul infinitésimal, analyse *f* infinitésimale	дифференциальное и интегральное исчисления, инфинитезимальное исчисление, исчисление (анализ) бесконечно малых
	differential calculus of Cartan <DG>	*s.* E 834		
	differential coefficient <DI>	*s.* D 274		
	differential equation <DE>	*s.* O 385		
	differential equation of Clairaut <DE>	*s.* C 757		
D 450	**differential equation of d'Alembert-Lagrange,** d'Alembert['s] differential equation, Lagrange['s] differential equation <DE>	d'Alembertsche Differentialgleichung (Gleichung) *f*, Differentialgleichung von d'Alembert-Lagrange, Lagrangesche Differentialgleichung	équation *f* différentielle de d'Alembert, équation différentielle de Lagrange	уравнение Д'Аламбера (Даламбера), дифференциальное уравнение Д'Аламбера (Даламбера), уравнение Лагранжа
	differential equation of Fuchsian type <DE>	*s.* F 699		
	differential equation of Hill type <DE>	*s.* H 367		
D 451	**differential equation of limit circle type;** limit circle type <DE>	Differentialgleichung *f* vom Grenzkreistypus; Grenzkreistypus *m*	équation *f* différentielle de type « Grenzkreis »; type *m* « Grenzkreis »	дифференциальное уравнение типа предельного круга; тип предельного круга
D 452	**differential equation of limit point type;** limit point type <DE>	Differentialgleichung *f* vom Grenzpunkttypus; Grenzpunkttypus *m*	équation *f* différentielle de type « Grenzpunkt »; type *m* « Grenzpunkt »	дифференциальное уравнение типа предельной точки; тип предельной точки
	differential equation of mixed type <DE>	*s.* E 336		
	differential equation of Riccati <DE>	*s.* R 977		
	differential equation of the elliptic[al] type <DE>	*s.* E 172		
	differential equation of the hyperbolic type <DE>	*s.* H 627		
	differential equation of the parabolic type <DE>	*s.* P 53		
	differential equation of the spherical harmonics <DE>	*s.* L 533		
D 453	**differential equation with advanced argument** <DE>	Differentialgleichung *f* mit voreilendem (beschleunigtem) Argument	équation *f* différentielle à argument avancé (accéléré)	дифференциальное уравнение с опережающим аргументом
D 454	**differential equation with deviating argument** <DE>	Differentialgleichung *f* mit abweichendem Argument	équation *f* différentielle à argument dévié	дифференциальное уравнение с отклоняющимся аргументом
	differential equation with delayed argument <DE>	*s.* D 204		
	differential equation with delays (lag[ging argument], retarded argument) <DE>	*s.* D 204		
D 455	**differential expression** <AN>	Differentialausdruck *m*	expression *f* différentielle	дифференциальное выражение
	differential form [of Cartan] <DG>	*s.* E 836		
	differential form of degree (order) 1 <AN>	*s.* P 546		
D 456	**differential form of the first kind** <AN>	Differentialform *f* erster Gattung	forme *f* différentielle de première espèce	дифференциальная форма первого рода
D 457	**differential form without poles** <DG>	Differentialform *f* ohne Pole	forme *f* différentielle dépourvue de pôles	дифференциальная форма без полюсов
D 458	**differential-functional equation** <DE, FA>	Funktional-Differentialgleichung *f*	équation *f* différentielle-fonctionnelle	функционально-дифференциальное уравнение, дифференциально-функциональное уравнение
D 459	**differential game of pursuit** <TG>	Differential-Verfolgungsspiel *n*	jeu *m* des poursuites différentiel	дифференциальная игра преследования
D 460	**differential-geometric** <DG>	differentialgeometrisch	de (en, à) géométrie différentielle, géométrique différentielle	дифференциально-геометрический
	differential geometry in the large <DG>	*s.* G 300		
	differential geometry in the small <DG>	*s.* I 480		
D 461	**differential graded group,** DC group <HA>	graduierte Gruppe *f* mit Differential	groupe *m* différentiel gradué	градуированная дифференциальная группа, DG-группа, комплекс

D 462	**differential group** <AL>	Gruppe *f* mit Differential	groupe *m* différentiel	дифференциальная группа
D 463	**differential ideal** <AL>	Differentialideal *n*	idéal *m* différentiel	дифференциальный идеал
D 464	**differential module,** module with differentiation <AL>	Differentialmodul *m*	module *m* différentiel	дифференциальный модуль, модуль с дифференцированием
D 465	**differential of arc,** element of length, linear (line) element <DG, DI>	Bogenelement *n*, Bogendifferential *n*, Linienelement *n*	élément *m* d'arc, différentielle *f* de l'arc [de courbe], élément de longueur, élément linéaire	дифференциал дуги, элемент длины [дуги], линейный элемент
	differential of area <DG, DI>	*s.* E 131		
	differential of the first kind <AL>	*s.* A 10		
	differential of the first kind <FT>	*s.* A 11		
D 466	**differential operator** <FA>	Differentialoperator *m*; gewöhnlicher Differentialoperator	opérateur *m* différentiel	дифференциальный оператор
D 467	**differential parameter [of Beltrami],** Beltrami['s] differential parameter <DG, VT>	Beltramischer Differentialparameter (Differentiator) *m*, Differentialparameter (Differentiator) von Beltrami	paramètre *m* différentiel [de Beltrami], paramètre de Lamé-Beltrami	дифференциальный параметр [Бельтрами]
D 468	**differential parameter of the first order,** two-parametric gradient, Beltrami['s] first differential parameter, Δ_1 <DG, VT>	erster Beltramischer Differentialparameter (Differentiator) *m*, erster Differentialparameter, Δ_1	paramètre *m* différentiel du premier ordre [de Beltrami], premier paramètre différentiel de Beltrami, Δ_1	дифференциальный параметр [Бельтрами] первого рода, первый дифференциальный параметр Бельтрами, Δ_1
D 469	**differential parameter of the second order** <DG, VT>	zweiter Beltramischer Differentialparameter (Differentiator) *m*, zweiter Differentialoperator *m* von Beltrami, Δ_2	paramètre *m* différentiel du second ordre [de Beltrami]	дифференциальный параметр [Бельтрами] второго рода
	differential parameter of the second order <DE, DG, DI, PO>	*s.* L 91		
	differential process <SP>	*s.* S 1808		
	differential quotient <DI>	*s.* D 274		
D 470	**differential ring** <AL>	Differentialring *m*	anneau *m* différentiel (à dérivations)	дифференциальное кольцо
	differentiation <DI>	*s.* D 269		
	differentiation by terms <DI>	*s.* D 472		
D 471	**differentiation operator** <AN>	Differentiationsoperator *m*	opérateur *m* de dérivation (différentiation)	оператор дифференцирования
D 472	**differentiation term by term,** differentiation by terms, term-by-term differentiation, termwise differentiation <DI>	gliedweise Differentiation *f*	dérivation *f* terme à terme	почленное дифференцирование, дифференцирование по членам
	differentiation under the sign of integration <DI>	*s.* D 474		
D 473	**differentiation with respect to a domain** <AN>	Gebietsdifferentiation *f*	dérivation *f* par rapport à un domaine	дифференцирование по области
D 474	**differentiation** <of an integral> **with respect to a parameter,** differentiation under the sign of integration <DI>	Differentiation (Ableitung) *f* <eines Integrals> nach einem Parameter, Differentiation unter dem Integralzeichen	dérivation *f* <d'une intégrale> par rapport à un paramètre, différentiation sous le signe d'intégration	дифференцирование <интеграла> по параметру, дифференцирование под знаком интеграла
D 475	**differentiation with respect to index** <DI>	Differentiation *f* nach dem Index	dérivation *f* par rapport à l'indice	дифференцирование по индексу
D 476	**differentiator** <IN>	Differentiator *m*, Derivimeter *n*, Derivator *m*	dérivimètre *m*, dérivateur *m*	дифференциатор, деривиметр
D 477	**diffusion coefficient** <SP>	Diffusionskoeffizient *m*	coefficient *m* de diffusion	коэффициент диффузии
D 478	**diffusion process** <SP>	Diffusionsprozeß *m*	processus *m* de diffusion	диффузионный процесс
D 479	**difunctional relation** <SE, UA>	difunktionale Relation *f*	relation *f* di-fonctionnelle	дифункциональное отношение
D 480	**digamma function,** Ψ-function, psi-function, Psi function, Gaussian Ψ-function (psi-function), Gauss['s] Ψ-function (psi-function), double gamma function <FU>	Digammafunktion *f*, Gaußsche Ψ-Funktion (Psi-Funktion) *f*, Ψ-Funktion, Psi-Funktion	fonction *f* digamma, fonction Ψ [de Gauss], fonction psi [de Gauss]	дигамма-функция, Ψ-функция [Гаусса], пси-функция [Гаусса]
D 481	**digit,** place digit <of a number> <NT>	Stelle *f*, Stellenziffer *f*, Stellenwertziffer *f*	place *f*, chiffre *m*	разряд
	digit <NT>	*s.* O 93		
D 482	**digital** <NU>	digital	numérique, // digital	цифровой
	digit in the units place <NT>	*s.* U 286		
	digit occupying a decimal place <NT>	*s.* D 28		
D 483	**digit with like place value** <NT>	Ziffer *f* gleichen Stellenwerts	chiffre *m* de la même valeur de position	цифра одного разряда
D 484	**digon** <circuit of two edges> <GP>	Zweieck *n*	2-gone *m*	двуугольник

	English	German	French	Russian
	digraph <GP>	*s.* D 545		
D 485	**Diguet['s] formula** <DG>	Diguets[che] Formel *f*	formule *f* de Diguet	формула Диге
D 486	**dihedral angle** <EG>	Diederwinkel *m*, Winkel *m* der Kante <Schnittwinkel zweier Ebenen>	rectiligne *m*, angle *m* rectiligne	линейный угол
D 487	**dihedral angle,** dihedron <EG>	Kante *f*, Diederecke *f*, Dieder *n*, Zweiflach *n*	angle *m* dièdre, dièdre *m*	двугранный угол, диэдр, двугранник
D 488	**dihedral form** <of *n*-th order> <AL>	Diederform *f* <*n*-ter Ordnung>	forme *f* dièdre <d'ordre *n*>	диэдрическая форма <*n*-го порядка>
D 489	**dihedral group** <AL, GR>	Diedergruppe *f*	groupe *m* diédral (du dièdre, de dièdre, dièdre)	группа диэдра, диэдральная группа
D 490	**dihedron** <Klein> <GE>	Dieder *n*	dièdre *m*	диэдр
	dihedron <EG>	*s.* D 487		
D 491	**dihomology** <AT>	Dihomologie *f*	dihomologie *f*	дигомология
D 492	**dilatation** <a special transvection> <AG>	Dilatation *f*	dilatation *f*	дилатация
D 493	**dilatation** <of a set of points> <SE>	Dilatation *f*, Streckung *f*	dilatation *f*	растяжение, дилатация
	dilatation <AG>	*s.* M 850		
	dilatation <EG>	*s.* S 1851		
D 494	**dilatation ratio** <in conformal mapping> <AN>	Dilatationsquotient *m*		[относительное] растяжение, характеристика квазиконформного отображения
D 495	**dilated maximum principle** <PO>	erweitertes Maximumprinzip *n*	principe *m* du maximum λ-dilaté	расширенный принцип максимума
D 496	**dilemma,** horned syllogism, syllogismus cornutus <LO>	Dilemma *n*, Alternativschluß *m*, klassisches Dilemma	dilemme *m*	дилемма
D 497	**diluted sequence** <SS>	verdünnte Folge *f*	suite *f* raréfiée	разбавленная последовательность
D 498	**dilution** <of series> <SS>	Verdünnung *f*	raréfaction *f*	разбавление
	dim <FA>	*s.* D 506		
D 499	**dimension,** freedom <of a linear system> <AG>	Stufe *f*, Dimension *f*, Mannigfaltigkeitsstufe *f*	dimension *f*, rang *m*, espèce *f*	размерность
D 500	**dimension** <of a divisor *or* of a quadratic form> <AG, AL>	Dimension *f*	dimension *f*	размерность
D 501	**dimension** <of a semilocal ring> <AL>	Dimension *f*	dimension *f*	размерность
D 502	**dimension** <of the place> <AL>	Dimension *f* <der Stelle>	dimension *f* <de la place>	размерность <точки, места>
D 503	**dimension,** highest dimension <of an ideal>; depth, coheight <of a prime ideal> <AL>	Dimension *f*, Korang *m*, Corang *m*, Dimensionszahl *f* <eines Ideals *oder* Primideals>; Höchstdimension *f* <eines Ideals>	dimension *f*, corang *m*	ко[-]ранг
D 504	**dimension** <of a vector space> <AL>	Dimension *f*, [linearer] Rang *m*	dimension *f*, rang *m*	размерность
D 505	**dimension** <of an integral> <DI>	Vielfachheit *f* <eines Integrals>	multiplicité *f* <d'une intégrale>	кратность <интеграла>
D 506	**dimension,** dim <of a Hilbert space> <FA>	Dimension *f*, dim	dimension *f* hilbertienne	размерность
D 507	**dimension** <of a linear affine variety> <GE>	Dimension *f*	dimension *f*, rang *m* affine	размер
D 508	**dimension,** dimensionality <GE, TO>	Dimension *f*	dimension *f*	размерность, число измерений
D 509	**dimension,** length <of a lattice> <LA>	Dimension *f*	dimension *f*	размер, длина
D 510	**dimension,** height, rank <of an element of a partly ordered set *or* a lattice> <LA, SE>	Dimension *f*, Höhe *f*, verbandstheoretische Dimension	hauteur *f*, rang *m*, niveau *m*	длина
D 511	**dimension,** length <of a partly ordered set> <SE>	Dimension *f*	longueur *f*	размер
D 512	**dimension,** topological dimension <TO>	Dimension *f*, topologische (mengentheoretische) Dimension	dimension *f* [topologique]	[топологическая] размерность
	dimension <AL>	*s.* O 256		
	dimension <AL, GR>	*s.* R 132		
	dimension <AT>	*s.* D 516		
	dimension <RE>	*s.* D 177		
D 513	**0-dimensional circuit,** zero-dimensional circuit (manifold), 0-circuit, zero-circuit, 0-dimensional manifold <AT>	Paar *n* von 0-Zellen (Nullzellen)	couple *m* de 0-cellules (zéro-cellules)	пара 0-клеток (нуль-клеток)
	dimensionality <GE,TO>	*s.* D 508		
	dimensionality of a representation <AL, GR, RE>	*s.* D 181		
D 514	**dimensional kernel** <TO>	dimensioneller Kern *m*	noyau *m* dimensionnel	размерное (размерностное) ядро
D 515	**dimensionally[-]homogeneous [differential] equation,** homogeneous [differential] equation <of the first order> <DE>	homogene [gewöhnliche] Differentialgleichung *f* <erster (1.) Ordnung>	équation *f* [differentielle] homogène <de premier ordre>	однородное [дифференциальное] уравнение <первого порядка>
	0-dimensional manifold <AT>	*s.* D 513		
	∞-dimensional space <AN, GE, TO>	*s.* I 444		

No.	English	German	French	Russian
D 516	**dimension number,** [combinatorial] dimension <of a complex> <AT>	Dimension *f*, Dimensionszahl *f*, kombinatorische (algebraische) Dimension	dimension *f*	число измерений, размерность
	dimension of a representation <AL, GR, RE>	*s.* D 181		
D 517	**dimension of connectivity** <TO>	Zusammenhangsstufe *f*	dimension *f* de la connexité	размерность связности
D 518	**dimension of embedding,** demension <TO>	Einbettungsdimension *f*	dimension *f* de plongement	размерность вложения
D 519	**dimension of the solution space of $(\mathfrak{A}-\lambda_i \mathfrak{E})\, x = 0$** <AL, MD>	[geometrische] Vielfachheit *f* <eines Eigenwerts der Matrix $\mathfrak{A}$>	multiplicité *f* géométrique <d'une valeur propre de la matrice $\mathfrak{A}$>	геометрическая кратность <собственного значения матрицы $\mathfrak{A}$>
D 520	**dimension theory** <AL, TO>	Dimensionstheorie *f*	théorie *f* de la dimension	теория размерности
D 521	**dimetric projection** <DS>	dimetrische (monodimetrische) Projektion *f*	projection *f* dimétrique	диметрическая проекция
D 522	**dimetric skew axonometry,** frontal axonometry <DS>	dimetrische Axonometrie *f*, Frontalperspektive *f*	axonométrie *f* dimétrique, axonométrie frontale	диметрия, диметрическая (фронтальная) аксонометрия
	diminute number <NT>	*s.* D 110		
D 523	**Dini['s] condition,** Dini-Lipschitz condition <AN>	Dini-[Lipschitzsche] Bedingung *f*, Dinische Bedingung	condition *f* de Dini[-Lipschitz]	условие Дини[-Липшица]
D 524	**Dini['s] derivative,** derived number <of a function> <AN>	extreme Derivierte *f*, Hauptderivierte *f*, [Dinische] Derivierte *f*, Ableitungszahl *f*	nombre *m* dérivé [de Dini]	производное число [по Дини]
	Dini['s] derivative from one side <AN>	*s.* O 106		
	Dini['s] derivative on the left <RF>	*s.* L 370		
	Dini['s] derivative on the right <RF>	*s.* R 1154		
	Dini-Lipschitz condition <AN>	*s.* D 523		
	Dini['s] rule <SS>	*s.* D 526		
D 525	**Dini['s] series** <SS>	Dini-Reihe *f*	série *f* de Dini	ряд Дини
D 526	**Dini['s] test,** Dini['s] rule <for Fourier series> <IT>	Dinisches Kriterium *n*, Dinische Regel *f*	règle *f* (théorème *m*, critère *m*) de Dini	признак (критерий) Дини
D 527	**Dini['s] theorem** <DG, SS>	Satz *m* von Dini, Dinischer Satz	théorème *m* de Dini	теорема Дини
	Dinostratus['] quadratrix <GE>	*s.* D 194		
	D-integrable <RF>	*s.* T 636		
	D_*-integrable function <RF>	*s.* C 1519		
D 528	**D-integral,** Denjoy-Khinchine integral, general indefinite Denjoy integral <RF>	D-Integral *n*, Denjoy-Chintschinsches (Denjoy-Khintchinesches) Integral *n*, allgemeines (im weiteren Sinne) unbestimmtes Denjoysches Integral	intégrale *f* D, intégrale de Denjoy-Khintchine, intégrale de Denjoy indéfinie générale	D-интеграл, интеграл Данжуа-Хинчина, общий неопределенный интеграл Данжуа
D 529	**D_*-integral,** Denjoy-Perron integral <special indefinite Denjoy integral> <RF>	D_*-Integral *n*, Denjoy-Perronsches Integral *n*, spezielles (besonderes, im engeren Sinne) unbestimmtes Denjoysches Integral	intégrale *f* D_*, intégrale [au sens] de Denjoy-Perron	D_*-интеграл, интеграл [в смысле] Данжуа-Перрона
	Diokles['s] cissoid <AG>	*s.* C 747		
	Diophantic equation <NT>	*s.* D 532		
D 530	**diophantine (Diophantine) analysis** <NT>	Theorie *f* der diophantischen Gleichungen <und Ungleichungen>, diophantische (unbestimmte) Analysis *f*	analyse *f* diophantine (diophantienne, indéterminée, de Diophante)	диофантов (неопределенный) анализ
D 531	**diophantine (Diophantine) approximation** <NT>	diophantische Approximation *f*	approximation *f* diophantienne	диофантово приближение
D 532	**diophantine (Diophantine) equation,** Diophantic (indeterminate) equation <NT>	diophantische (unbestimmte) Gleichung *f*	équation *f* diophantienne (diophantine, indéterminée, de Diophante)	диофантово (неопределенное) уравнение, уравнение Диофанта
D 533	**diophantine (Diophantine) geometry** <AG>	diophantische Geometrie *f*	géométrie *f* diophantienne	диофантова геометрия
D 534	**diophantine (Diophantine) problem** <NT>	diophantisches Problem *n*, diophantische Aufgabe *f*	problème *m* diophantien (indéterminé, diophantin)	неопределенная (диофантова) проблема
	dip angle <DS>	*s.* A 664		
	Dirac['s] [delta] distribution (function) <FA>	*s.* D 211		
	Dirac['s] δ-function (functional, measure) <FA>	*s.* D 211		
	direct affine transformation <AY>	*s.* P 1061		
D 535	**direct analytic continuation** <FT>	unmittelbare analytische Fortsetzung *f*	prolongement *m* analytique direct	непосредственное аналитическое продолжение

	direct bilinear transformation <FT>	*s.* B 348		
D 536	**direct boundary point** <of a Riemann surface> <FT>	unmittelbare (direkte) Randstelle *f*	point *m* frontière direct	прямая граничная точка
	direct complement <AL>	*s.* C 1353		
	direct cone <CA>	*s.* I 406		
	direct conformal mapping (transformation) <FT>	*s.* I 1085		
	direct correlation <ST>	*s.* P 1066		
D 537	**direct correspondence** <DI, GN>	gleichsinnige Zuordnung *f*	correspondance *f* directe	прямое соответствие
D 538	**direct decomposition** <AL>	direkte (additive) Zerlegung *f*, Zerlegung in eine direkte Summe	décomposition *f* directe	прямое разложение
D 539	**direct decomposition** <CA>	direkte Zerlegung *f*	décomposition *f* directe	прямое разложение
	directed arc <GP>	*s.* D 549		
	directed branch <GP>	*s.* A 883		
D 540	**directed circuit,** elementary (oriented) circuit, simple cycle <of an oriented graph> <GP>	Kreis *m*, kontinuierlich gerichteter Elementarzirkuit *m*, Zyklus *m*, einfache Zyklusprogression *f* <ohne doppelte Knotenpunkte>	circuit *m* élémentaire, polygone *m*, cycle *m* topologique, stigme *m*, ensemble *m* minimal dépendant	элементарный цикл, простой контур
	directed circuit <GP>	*s.* C 854		
D 541	**directed complete graph** <GP>	total gerichteter Graph *m*, Netz *n*	graphe *m* dirigé complet	полный направленный граф
D 542	**directed distance** <of *x* to *y*> <GP>	orientierte Entfernung *f* <vom Punkt *x* zum Punkt *y*>	écart *m* <du sommet *x* au sommet *y*>	расстояние <от вершины *x* до вершины *y*>
	directed distance <GE>	*s.* S 839		
	directed downward partial order <SE>	*s.* L 336		
	directed downward quasi-order <SE>	*s.* L 338		
D 543	**directed downward set,** left-directed set <SE>	absteigend filtrierende Menge *f*, nach links gefilterte Menge, nach unten gerichtete (filtrierende) Menge, konvers gerichtete Menge	ensemble *m* ordonné filtrant décroissant, ensemble filtrant inférieurement (à gauche)	направленное вниз (упорядоченное) множество, фильтрующееся влево множество; множество, фильтрующееся вниз (влево); убывающее направленное семейство
	directed edge <GP>	*s.* A 883		
D 544	**directed-edge sequence,** arc progression <in an oriented graph> <GP>	kontinuierlich gerichtete Kantenfolge *f*, gerichtete Kantenprogression *f*; kontinuierlich gerichteter Weg *m*, in dem jede Kante dieselbe Richtung besitzt wie als Kante des Graphen <Wiederholung von Bögen und Ecken möglich>	chemin *m*	ориентированный маршрут, ормаршрут, маршрут
	directed-edge train <GP>	*s.* S 934		
D 545	**directed graph,** digraph <GP>	gerichteter Graph *m*, Digraph *m*	graphe *m* dirigé, digraphe *m*	направленный граф, диграф, ориентированный граф, орграф
D 546	**directed group** <GR>	gerichtete Gruppe *f*; geordnete Gruppe, die die Moore-Smithsche Eigenschaft besitzt	groupe *m* filtrant (dirigé)	направленная группа, фильтрующая[ся] группа
	directed line <GE>	*s.* O 416		
	directed line <GP>	*s.* A 883		
D 547	**directed line segment,** directed segment <GE>	gerichtete (orientierte) Strecke *f*	segment *m* dirigé (orienté)	направленный отрезок (сегмент)
	directed number <AR>	*s.* R 763		
D 548	**directed path,** simple chain <in an oriented graph, arcs are different> <GP>	Kette *f*, einfache Kette	chemin *m* (chaîne *f*) simple	простая цепь
D 549	**directed path,** elementary path, directed arc, path <in a digraph, vertices are different> <GP>	elementare Bahn *f*, einfache gerichtete Wegprogression *f*	chemin *m* élémentaire	простой (элементарный) путь, путь простая орцепь
	directed preorder[ed set] <SE>	*s.* Q 140		
D 550	**directed quantity,** vectored quantity <GE>	gerichtete Größe *f*, Richtungsgröße *f*	grandeur *f* directive (dirigée)	векторная (направленная) величина
	directed quasi-ordered set <SE>	*s.* Q 140		
	directed segment <GE>	*s.* D 547		
	directed segment <GP>	*s.* A 883		
	directed sequence <GP>	*s.* S 579		
D 551	**directed set** <upward *or* downward> <SE>	gerichtete Menge *f* <gemeinsame Bezeichnung für gerichtete *oder* konvers gerichtete Menge>	ensemble *m* filtrant <à droite *ou* à gauche>	направленное множество <вверх *или* вниз>
D 552	**directed set,** directed system, right[-]directed set, directed upward set, in-creasing directed set,	gerichtete Menge *f*, nach oben gerichtete Menge, nach rechts gefilterte Menge, aufsteigend (nach	ensemble *m* filtrant supérieurement, ensemble filtrant à droite, ensemble filtrant, ensemble filtré,	направленное [вверх] множество, фильтрующееся множество, фильтрующееся возрастаю-

No.	English	German	French	Russian
	filtered set <partially ordered> <SE>	oben) filtrierende Menge	ensemble ordonné filtrant, ensemble dirigé	щее семейство, фильтрующееся вправо множество; множество, фильтрующееся вверх; множество, фильтрующееся вправо, направление, сеть, направленное упорядоченное множество, возрастающее направленное семейство, возрастающее частично упорядоченное множество
	directed set <SE>	*s.* Q 140		
	directed straightline <GE>	*s.* O 416		
D 553	**directed system** <of submodules> <AL>	aufsteigend filtrierende Menge *f*, gerichtetes System *n* <von Untermoduln>	famille *f* filtrante croissante <de sous-modules>	фильтрующееся семейство <подмодулей>
	directed system <AL, CA, SE>	*s.* D 610		
	directed system <SE>	*s.* 1. D 552; 2. M 887; 3. Q 140		
	directed tree <GP>	*s.* A 881		
	directed tree with reference node e <GP>	*s.* T 886		
D 554	**directed union** <SE, UA>	gerichtete Vereinigung *f*	union *f* dirigée	направленное объединение
D 555	**directed upward quasi-ordered class** <SE>	gerichtete Klasse *f*	classe *f* filtrante à droite	направленный класс
	directed upward set <SE>	*s.* 1. D 552; 2. Q 140		
	directed value <GN>	*s.* V 38		
D 556	**direct factor,** direct summand <of groups> <GR>	direkter Summand (Faktor) *m*	facteur *m* direct, sous-module *m* composant	прямое слагаемое
D 557	**direct homothety,** direct similitude, positive similitude (homothety) <GE>	Ähnlichkeitstransformation (Homothetie) *f* mit positivem Ähnlichkeitsverhältnis	homothétie *f* directe (positive)	прямая гомотетия, гомотетия с положительным коэффициентом
D 558	**direct image** <of a sheaf> <AT>	direktes Bild *n*	image *f* directe	прямой образ
D 559	**directing curve** <of a conoid> <GE>	Leitkurve *f*, Leitlinie *f*	courbe *f* directrice	направляющая линия
	directing line <GE>	*s.* D 599		
D 560	**direction** <of an affine subset> <GE>	Richtung *f*, Stellung *f*	direction *f*	направляющая
	direction <GE>	*s.* O 411		
D 561	**directional derivative,** derivative in a direction <DI>	Richtungsableitung *f*, Ableitung *f* in einer Richtung, Richtungsderivierte *f*	dérivée *f* suivant (dans) une direction	производная по направлению
D 562	**directional differentiation** <DI>	Richtungsdifferentiation *f*, Differentiation *f* in einer Richtung (Fortschreitungsrichtung)	dérivation *f* suivant une direction	дифференцирование (дифференциация) по направлению
	directional dual <GP>	*s.* C 2371		
D 563	**directional field,** direction field [of lineal elements], field of tangents <DE>	Richtungsfeld *n*, Feld *n* von Linienelementen	champ *m* de directions	поле направлений (псевдовекторов)
D 564	**directional field,** unit vector field <TO>	Richtungsfeld *n*	champ *m* de directions	поле направлений
D 565	**direction angle** <of a geodesic *or* any other curve on a sphere *or* ellipsoid> <AY>	Richtungswinkel *m*, Amplitude *f*	angle *m* directeur	дирекционный (направляющий) угол
D 566	**direction cosine** <AY>	Richtungskosinus *m*	cosinus *m* directeur (dirigé)	направляющий косинус, косинус направления
D 567	**direction curve** <GE>	Richtungskurve *f*	courbe *f* de direction	направляющая кривая
D 568	**direction density** <IG>	Richtungsdichte *f*	densité *f* de directions	плотность направлений
	direction field [of lineal elements] <DE>	*s.* D 563		
D 569	**direction logarithm** <AN>	Richtungslogarithmus *m*, Direktionslogarithmus *m*	logarithme *m* de direction	логарифм направления
D 570	**direction of affinity** <in perspective affinity> <DS>	Affinitätsrichtung *f*	direction *f* d'affinité	направление сдвига при аффинно-перспективном преобразовании
D 571	**direction of Julia,** Julia['s] (Borel['s]) direction <FT>	Juliasche (Borelsche) Richtung *f*	direction *f* de Borel (Julia)	луч (направление) Жюлия (Бореля)
	direction of principal curvature <DG>	*s.* P 1408		
D 572	**direction of support** <CS, GE>	Stützrichtung *f*	direction *f* d'appui	опорное направление
D 573	**direction parameter** <of a straight line> <AY>	Richtungsparameter *m*	paramètre (coefficient) *m* directeur, paramètre principal	параметр направления
D 574	**direction vector** <of a straight line> <AY>	Richtungsvektor *m*	vecteur *m* directeur	направляющий вектор
	direction vector <VT>	*s.* U 302		
	direct join <CA>	*s.* P 1591		
D 575	**direct limit** <of groups> <GR>	direkter Limes *m* <von Gruppen>	groupe *m* limite direct	предельная группа <для групп>
D 576	**direct limit,** inductive limit <of a directed system> <TO>	induktiver (direkter) Limes *m*	limite *f* inductive (droite)	индуктивный (инъективный) предел, предел <прямого спектра>

	direct limit <CA>	*s.* C 1130		
D 577	**direct limit of a sequence of groups** <GR>	direkte Grenzgruppe *f*	limite *f* inductive d'une séquence de groupes	прямая предельная группа
	directly conformal mapping (transformation) <FT>	*s.* I 1085		
D 578	**directly congruent,** congruent and conformal <EG>	direkt (gleichsinnig) kongruent, kongruent ohne Umlegung	directement coïncident (congru, égal)	конгруэнтный с сохранением направления обхода
D 579	**directly decomposable group,** divisible group <GR>	direkt zerlegbare Gruppe *f*, zerlegbare (zerfallende) Gruppe	groupe *m* décomposable [en produit direct]	разложимая [в прямое произведение] группа
D 580	**directly indecomposable algebraic system** <AL, UA>	direkt unzerlegbare [universelle] Algebra *f*	algèbre *f* indécomposable en produit direct	декартово неразложимая алгебраическая система
D 581	**directly indecomposable group,** indivisible group <GR>	direkt[-]unzerlegbare Gruppe *f*, unzerlegbare Gruppe [in ein direktes Produkt], additiv direkt unzerlegbare Gruppe	groupe *m* indécomposable [en produit direct], groupe directement indécomposable	неразложимая в прямое произведение группа, неразложимая группа
D 582	**directly proportional** <AR>	direkt proportional	directement proportionnel, en raison directe	прямо пропорциональный
	directly proportional <GN>	*s.* P 1853		
	direct Möbius transformation <FT>	*s.* B 348		
D 583	**direct multiplication,** block multiplication <of matrices>, multiplication of partitioned matrices <MD>	Übermatrixmultiplikation *f*, direkte Multiplikation *f* von Matrizen, Multiplikation von Übermatrizen	multiplication *f* <de matrices> par blocs, multiplication directe <de matrices>	блочное (прямое) умножение <матриц>
	director <AY>	*s.* O 498		
D 584	**director circle** <of a conic; its centre is the focus> <AY>	Leitkreis *m*, Richtungskreis *m*	cercle *m* directeur	направляющий круг
	director circle <AY>	*s.* O 498		
D 585	**director cone** <of a curve *or* surface, also a ruled surface> <AY>	Richtkegel *m*, Leitkegel *m*, Richtungskegel *m*	cône *m* directeur	направляющий конус
D 586	**director curve** <of a polarity> <AY>	Ordnungskurve *f*	courbe *f* directrice	
D 587	**direct orientation,** orientation in the same direction <GE, GN>	gleichsinnige (gleichlaufende) Orientierung *f*	orientation *f* directe <de même direction>	прямая (равнонаправленная) ориентация, ориентация одинакового направления
D 588	**director plane,** plane director, directrix plane <of a conoid> <AY>	Leitebene *f*, Richtebene *f*	plan *m* directeur	направляющая плоскость
D 589	**director sphere** <AY>	Direktorkugel *f*, Leitkugel *f*	sphère *f* directrice	направляющая сфера
D 590	**director surface** <of a rectilinear congruence> <DG>	Leitfläche *f*	surface *f* directrice	направляющая поверхность
	direct predecessor <SE>	*s.* I 115		
D 591	**direct product** <of topological groups *or* rings> <AL>	Produkt *n*; direktes Produkt <von Ringen>	anneau *m* topologique produit; anneau(-)produit *m*	произведение <колец>
D 592	**direct product** <of algebras> <AL>	tensorielles (direktes) Produkt *n*, direktes Algebrenprodukt *n*, Kronecker-Produkt *n*, Kronecker-produkt *n*	produit *m* tensoriel	тензорное произведение
D 593	**direct product** <of topological groups> <GR>	[direktes] Produkt *n*	groupe *m* topologique produit	[прямое] произведение
D 594	**direct product,** tensor product <of distributions> <AN>	Tensorprodukt *n*, direktes Produkt *n*	produit *m* direct (tensoriel)	прямое произведение
D 595	**direct product,** cross product, tensor product, Kronecker['s] product <of Hilbert *or* locally convex spaces> <FA>	Tensorprodukt *n*, direktes Produkt *n*; projektives Tensorprodukt <nur von lokal konvexen Räumen>	produit *m* tensoriel, produit de Kronecker; produit tensoriel topologique <d'espaces localement convexes>	прямое произведение
D 596	**direct product,** complete direct sum, direct union <of algebras> <UA>	direktes Produkt *n*, vollständige direkte Summe *f*	somme *f* directe complète, produit *m* direct	прямое произведение
	direct product <AL>	*s.* 1. D 612; 2. T 156		
	direct product <FA>	*s.* D 606		
	direct product <GR>	*s.* 1. C 1425; 2. W 47		
	direct product <MD>	*s.* K 163		
	direct product <RE>	*s.* K 164		
	direct product <SE>	*s.* C 173		
D 597	**direct proportionality** <AR>	direkte Proportionalität *f*, direktes Verhältnis *n*	raison *f* directe	прямая пропорциональность, прямая пропорциональная зависимость
D 598	**directrix** <of a Delaunay curve> <GE>	Leitlinie *f*, Leitgerade *f*, Direktrix *f*	directrice *f*	директриса
D 599	**directrix,** directing line <of a conoid> <GE>	Leitgerade *f*, Achse *f*	directrice *f*, droite *f* directrice	направляющая прямая
D 600	**directrix** <of a ruled surface> <GE>	Leitkurve *f*, Direktrix *f*	courbe *f* directrice	направляющая [линия]
D 601	**directrix** <of a conic *or* a plane algebraic curve *or* a quadric> <GE>	Leitlinie *f*, Direktrix *f*, Leitgerade *f*	directrice *f*	директриса
	directrix <DG>	*s.* W 258		
	directrix plane <AY>	*s.* D 588		

No.	English	German	French	Russian
D 602	**direct rule of inference** <LO>	direkte Schlußregel *f*	règle *f* de conclusion directe	прямое правило вывода
D 603	**direct rule of three** <AR>	direkter Dreisatz *m*	règle *f* de trois directe	прямое тройное правило
D 604	**direct similarity (similitude)** <AL>	direkte ähnlich unitäre Kollineation *f*	similitude *f* directe	прямое подобие
	direct similitude <GE>	*s.* D 557		
	direct spectrum <AL, CA, SE>	*s.* D 610		
	direct successor <SE>	*s.* I 117		
D 605	**direct sum** <of linear spaces>; direct sum vector space <AL, FA>	direkte Summe *f* <von linearen Räumen>	somme *f* directe <d'espaces vectoriels>; espace *m* vectoriel somme directe	прямая сумма <линейных пространств>
D 606	**direct sum,** // direct product <of Hilbert spaces> <FA>	direkte Summe *f*, äußere direkte Summe	somme *f* [directe] hilbertienne, somme directe externe	прямая сумма, произведение
D 607	**direct sum,** vertex direct sum <of graphs> <GP>	Summe *f* <von Graphen>	somme *f* directe <de graphes>	объединение <графов>
D 608	**direct sum** <GR, MD>	direkte Summe *f*	somme *f* directe	прямая сумма
D 609	**direct sum** <of representations> <RE>	direkte Summe *f*, Summe	somme *f* directe	прямая сумма, кронекеровская сумма
	direct sum <AL>	*s.* 1. R 1313; 2. W 49		
	direct summand <GR>	*s.* D 556		
	direct sum vector space <AL, FA>	*s.* D 605		
D 610	**direct system,** directed system, inductive system, // direct spectrum <over a directed set> <AL, CA, SE>	direktes System *n*, induktives System, induktive Familie *f*	système *m* inductif	прямой спектр, направленная система, индуктивная система
D 611	**direct union** <AL>	direkte Vereinigung *f*	union *f* directe	прямое объединение
D 612	**direct union,** direct product <of Boolean algebras> <AL>	Vereinigung *f*, direkte Summe *f*, direktes Produkt *n*	produit *m* direct [algébrique]	соединение, прямая сумма, прямое произведение
	direct union <UA>	*s.* D 596		
D 613	**Dirichlet['s] boundary condition,** first boundary condition <for a partial differential equation>; boundary condition of the first kind <also for an ordinary differential equation of the second order> <DE, PO>	Dirichletsche Randbedingung *f*, erste (1.) Randbedingung; Randbedingung erster (1.) Art	condition *f* aux limites de Dirichlet, première condition aux limites, données *fpl* du type Dirichlet; condition aux limites de première espèce	первое краевое условие, краевое условие Дирихле, условие Дирихле; краевое (граничное) условие первого рода
	Dirichlet['s] boundary [value] problem <DE, PO>	*s.* D 629		
	Dirichlet['s] box principle <CT>	*s.* B 705		
D 614	**Dirichlet['s] character (mod *m*)** <AB>	Dirichletscher Charakter *m* (mod ***m***)	caractère *m* de Dirichlet (mod ***m***)	характер Дирихле (по модулю m)
	Dirichlet['s] coefficient <AP, NT, SS>	*s.* C 1016		
D 615	**Dirichlet['s] conditions** <for a Fourier series> <SS>	Dirichletsche Bedingungen *fpl*	conditions *fpl* de Dirichlet	условия Дирихле
	Dirichlet['s] convergence <SS>	*s.* C 2327		
D 616	**Dirichlet['s] density** <AB>	Dirichlet-Dichte *f*, Dirichletdichte *f*, Dirichletsche Dichte *f*	densité *f* de Dirichlet	плотность Дирихле
D 617	**Dirichlet['s] discontinuity factor** <AN, NT>	Dirichletscher diskontinuierlicher Faktor *m*, Diskontinuitätsfaktor *m*	facteur *m* de discontinuité	интеграл Дирихле, разрывный множитель Дирихле, коэффициент прерывности
D 618	**Dirichlet distribution** <ST>	Dirichlet-Verteilung *f*	distribution *f* de Dirichlet	распределение Дирихле
D 619	**Dirichlet['s] divisor problem,** divisor problem of Dirichlet <NT>	Dirichletsches Teilerproblem *n*, Teilerproblem	problème *m* de partition de Dirichlet	проблема делителей Дирихле
D 620	**Dirichlet['s] domain** <GU>	Dirichletsches Gebiet *n*	domaine *m* de Dirichlet	область Дирихле, область Вороного
D 621	**Dirichlet['s] expansion,** expansion in a Dirichlet series <e.g. of an almost periodic function> <AN>	Dirichlet-Entwicklung *f*	développement *m* en série de Dirichlet	разложение в ряд Дирихле
	Dirichlet['s] exponent <AP, NT, SS>	*s.* E 731		
D 622	**Dirichlet['s] formula,** Dirichlet['s] integral formula, Dirichlet['s] integral theorem <DE>	Dirichletsche Formel *f*, Dirichletsche Integralformel *f*; Dirichletsche Umformung *f*	formule *f* de Dirichlet	формула Дирихле
D 623	**Dirichlet['s] formula** <DI>	Dirichletsche Formel *f*	formule *f* de Dirichlet	формула Дирихле
D 624	**Dirichlet['s] function** <NT>	Dirichletsche Funktion *f*	fonction *f* de Dirichlet	функция Дирихле
D 625	**Dirichlet['s] integral** <of a Fourier series *or* function> <PO, SS, VA>	Dirichletsches Integral *n* <PO, SS, VA>; Dirichletsches singuläres Integral <SS>	intégrale *f* de Dirichlet	интеграл Дирихле
	Dirichlet['s] integral formula (theorem) <DE>	*s.* D 622		
D 626	**Dirichlet-Jordan test,** Jordan-Dirichlet (Dirich-	Dirichlet-Jordansches Kriterium (Konvergenzkrite-	règle *f* (théorème *m*, critère *m*) de Dirichlet-Jordan,	признак (критерий) [сходимости] Дирихле-

and still: D 626	let['s]) test <for convergence of a Fourier series> <SS>	rium) *n*, Jordan [-Dirichlet]sches Kriterium (Konvergenzkriterium)	règle (théorème, critère) de Jordan[-Dirichlet]	Жордана, признак (критерий) [сходимости] Жордана[-Дирихле]
D 627	**Dirichlet['s] *L*-series** <AB>	Dirichletsche *L*-Reihe *f*	série *f L* de Dirichlet	*L*-ряд Дирихле
D 628	**Dirichlet['s] principle** <PO, VA>	Dirichletsches Prinzip *n*, Thomson-Dirichletsches Prinzip	principe *m* de Dirichlet	принцип Дирихле
	Dirichlet['s] principle [of boxes] <CT>	*s.* B 705		
D 629	**Dirichlet['s] problem,** Dirichlet['s] boundary [value] problem, first boundary [value] problem, first problem <for a partial differential equation>; boundary [value] problem of the first kind <also for an ordinary differential equation of the second order> <DE, PO>	Dirichletsches Problem *n*, Dirichletsches Randwertproblem *n*, Dirichlet-Problem *n*, Dirichletsche Randwertaufgabe *f*, erstes Randwertproblem, erste Randwertaufgabe; Randwertproblem (Randwertaufgabe) erster Art	problème *m* de Dirichlet, premier problème aux limites, premier problème; problème aux limites de première espèce	первая краевая задача, краевая задача первого рода <для обыкновенных дифференциальных уравнений второго порядка *или* дифференциальных уравнений в частных производных>; задача Дирихле, краевая задача Дирихле <в теории потенциала>
D 630	**Dirichlet['s] product** <of series> <SS>	Dirichletsches Produkt *n*	produit *m* de Dirichlet	произведение Дирихле
D 631	**Dirichlet['s] series,** ordinary Dirichlet series <SS>	Dirichletsche Reihe *f*, Dirichlet-Reihe *f*, gewöhnliche (spezielle) Dirichletsche Reihe, gewöhnliche Dirichlet-Reihe	série *f* de Dirichlet (Lejeune Dirichlet proprement dite)	ряд Дирихле, ординарный ряд Дирихле
D 632	**Dirichlet['s] space** <FA>	Dirichletscher Raum *m*	espace *m* de Dirichlet	пространство Дирихле
	Dirichlet['s] sum <SS>	*s.* S 2265		
D 633	**Dirichlet['s] test** <for convergence> <SS>	Dirichletsches Kriterium (Konvergenzkriterium) *n*, Dirichlet-Kriterium *n*	critère *m* (règle *f*, théorème *m*) de Dirichlet	признак (критерий) [сходимости] Дирихле
	Dirichlet['s] test <SS>	*s.* D 626		
D 634	**Dirichlet['s] test for uniform convergence,** Hardy['s] test <SS>	Dirichletsches Kriterium *n* für gleichmäßige Konvergenz	critère *m* de Dirichlet pour la convergence uniforme	признак (критерий) равномерной сходимости Дирихле
D 635	**Dirichlet['s] theorem** <for Fourier series> <SS>	Dirichletsche Regel *f*, Satz *m* von Dirichlet, Dirichletscher Satz	théorème *m* (règle *f*) de Dirichlet	теорема Дирихле
D 636	**Dirichlet['s] theorem [on units], Dirichlet['s] unit theorem** <AB>	Dirichletscher Einheitensatz *m*	théorème *m* de Dirichlet sur les unités	теорема Дирихле об алгебраических единицах, теорема о единицах
	Dirichlet['s] theorem on primes <NT>	*s.* T 260		
D 637	**discard / to,** to reject <a figure> <AR, NU>	streichen, wegstreichen, fortnehmen <eine Zahl>	retrancher <un nombre>	вычеркивать <число>
	disconnect / to <TO>	*s.* S 529		
D 638	**disconnected space,** unconnected space <TO>	nichtzusammenhängender (unzusammenhängender) Raum *m*	espace *m* non connexe, espace disconnexe	несвязное пространство
D 639	**discontinuity** <of the first *or* second kind> <DI>	Unstetigkeit *f* <erster (1.) *oder* zweiter (2.) Art>	discontinuité *f* <de première *ou* seconde (deuxième) espèce>	разрыв <первого *или* второго рода>
D 640	**discontinuity** <of a function> <RF>	Diskontinuität *f*	discontinuité *f*	разрывность
D 641	**discontinuity factor** <AN>	Unstetigkeitsfaktor *m*	facteur *m* de discontinuité	разрывный множитель
D 642	**discontinuity interval** <of a function> <DI>	Unstetigkeitsintervall *n*	intervalle *m* de discontinuité	интервал разрывности
D 643	**discontinuity line,** line of discontinuity <DE>	Unstetigkeitslinie *f*, Diskontinuitätslinie *f*	ligne *f* de discontinuité	линия разрыва
D 644	**discontinuity on the left** <DI>	Unstetigkeit *f* von links, linksseitige Unstetigkeit	discontinuité *f* à gauche	разрыв слева
D 645	**discontinuity on the right** <DI>	Unstetigkeit *f* von rechts, rechtsseitige Unstetigkeit	discontinuité *f* à droite	разрыв справа
D 646	**discontinuity surface,** surface of discontinuity <DE>	Unstetigkeitsfläche *f*, Diskontinuitätsfläche *f*, Sprungfläche *f*	surface *f* de discontinuité	поверхность разрывности (разрыва)
D 647	**discontinuous compactum** <TO>	diskontinuierliches Kompaktum *n*	compactum *m* punctiforme	вполне несвязный метризуемый компакт
D 648	**discontinuous function** <DI>	unstetige Funktion *f*	fonction *f* discontinue	разрывная функция
D 649	**discontinuous group** <of linear transformations> <AL, FT>	diskontinuierliche (diskrete, unstetige) Gruppe *f*	groupe *m* discontinu	прерывная группа
D 650	**discontinuous group** <of homeomorphisms> <TO>	diskontinuierliche Gruppe *f*	groupe *m* discontinu	разрывная группа
	discontinuous process <SP>	*s.* D 673		
D 651	**discontinuous proportion** <AR>	unstetige (diskontinuierliche) Proportion *f*	proportion *f* discontinue	прерывная пропорция
	discontinuous random variable <ST>	*s.* D 654		
	discontinuous ruin problem <TG>	*s.* C 777		
D 652	**discontinuous set** <TO>	diskontinuierliche Menge *f*	ensemble *m* punctiforme	разрывное множество <множество, не содержащее ни одного неодноточечного связного компактного множества>

D 653	**discontinuous space** <TO>	diskontinuierlicher Raum *m*	espace *m* punctiforme	[наследственно] разрывное пространство
	discontinuous stochastic process <SP>	*s.* D 673		
	discontinuous variability <ST>	*s.* A 576		
D 654	**discontinuous variate,** discontinuous random variable <ST>	unstetige Zufallsvariable (Zufallsgröße) *f*	variable *f* aléatoire discontinue	разрывная случайная величина
D 655	**discontinuous variational problem** <VA>	diskontinuierliches Variationsproblem *n*	problème *m* variationnel discontinu	прерывная вариационная задача
D 656	**discontinuum** <TO>	Diskontinuum *n*	discontinu *m*	дисконтинуум
D 657	**discount factor** <reciprocal growth factor> <AR>	Diskontierungsfaktor *m*, Abzinsungsfaktor *m*	facteur *m* d'escompte	дисконтный множитель
D 658	**discount rate** <AR>	Diskont *m*, mathematischer Diskont, Diskontsatz *m*	taux *m* d'escompte	учетный процент, дисконт норма учета
	discrete absolute value <AL>	*s.* D 678		
	discrete algebra <FA>	*s.* W 5		
D 659	**discrete category,** set <CA>	diskrete Kategorie *f*	catégorie *f* discrète	дискретная категория
	discrete direct sum <AL>	*s.* W 49		
D 660	**discrete distribution,** arithmetic distribution <ST>	diskrete Verteilung *f*, Verteilung vom diskreten Typ, arithmetische Verteilung	distribution *f* discrète (arithmétique)	дискретное (арифметическое) распределение
D 661	**discrete distribution function** <ST>	diskrete Verteilungsfunktion *f*, Verteilungsfunktion vom diskreten Typ	fonction *f* de distribution discrète	дискретная функция распределения
D 662	**discrete family [of subsets]** <TO>	diskretes Mengensystem *n*, diskretes System *n* von Teilmengen	famille *f* de parties discrète	дискретное семейство <подмножеств>
	σ-discrete family of subsets <TO>	*s.* S 821		
D 663	**discrete flow** <SP>	diskrete Strömung *f*	courant *m* discret	дискретный поток
D 664	**discrete group** <as a topological group> <AL>	diskrete (diskontinuierliche, diskrete topologische) Gruppe *f*	groupe *m* discret	дискретная группа
D 665	**discrete lattice,** lattice satisfying the descending and ascending chain condition <LA>	längenendlicher Verband *m*; Verband, in dem die absteigende und die aufsteigende Kettenbedingung gilt <alle Ketten haben endliche Länge>	treillis *m* vérifiant la condition des chaînes limitées	структура, удовлетворяющая условию обрыва убывающих и возрастающих цепей
D 666	**discreteness** <TO>	Diskretheit *f*	discrètetè *f*, propriété *f* d'être discret	дискретность, прерывность
	discrete optimization <PG>	*s.* D 669		
D 667	**discrete order** <SE>	diskrete Ordnung *f*	ordre *m* discret	дискретное упорядочение
D 668	**discrete ordered group** <AL>	diskrete [einfach geordnete] Gruppe *f*	groupe *m* ordonné discret	дискретная группа
	discrete point set <TO>	*s.* D 672		
	discrete process <SP>	*s.* D 673		
D 669	**discrete programming,** discrete optimization <PG>	diskrete Optimierung (Programmoptimierung, Programmierung) *f*, diskretes Programmieren *n*	programmation *f* discrète, optimisation *f* discrète	дискретное программирование, дискретная оптимизация
D 670	**discrete random variable** <ST>	diskrete Zufallsgröße (Zufallsvariable, zufällige Veränderliche) *f*	variable *f* aléatoire discrète	дискретная случайная величина
D 671	**discrete series** <RE>	diskrete Reihe *f*	série *f* discrète de Bargmann	дискретная серия
D 672	**discrete set [of points],** discrete point set, isolated set <TO>	diskrete Menge (Punktmenge) *f*, isolierte Menge <von Punkten>	ensemble *m* discret (isolé)	дискретное (изолированное, дискретное точечное) множество, множество изолированных элементов
	discrete space <TO>	*s.* D 675		
	discrete spectrum <FA>	*s.* P 791		
D 673	**discrete stochastic process,** discrete process, discontinuous [stochastic] process <SP>	diskreter [stochastischer] Prozeß *m*	processus *m* [aléatoire, stochastique] discret, processus [aléatoire, stochastique] discontinu	дискретный [стохастический] процесс
D 674	**discrete time** <SP>	diskrete (diskontinuierliche) Zeit *f*	temps *m* discret	дискретное время
D 675	**discrete topological space,** discrete space <TO>	diskreter [topologischer] Raum *m*	espace *m* discret, espace topologique discret	дискретное [топологическое] пространство
D 676	**discrete topology** <TO>	diskrete Topologie *f*	topologie *f* discrète	дискретная топология
D 677	**discrete uniform distribution** <ST>	diskrete gleichmäßige Verteilung *f*	distribution *f* uniforme discrète	дискретное равномерное распределение
D 678	**discrete valuation,** discrete absolute value <AL>	diskrete (ganzzahlige) Bewertung *f*	valuation *f* discrète	дискретное нормирование, дискретная оценка (норма, нормировка)
D 679	**discrete valuation ring** <AL>	diskreter Bewertungsring *m*	anneau *m* de valuation discrète, anneau d'une valuation discrète	кольцо дискретного нормирования, кольцо дискретных нормирований
	discrete von Neumann algebra <FA>	*s.* W 5		

No.	English	German	French	Russian
	discrete W*-algebra <FA>	*s.* W 5		
D 680	**discretization** <of a problem> <AN, NU>	Diskretisierung *f*, Diskretisation *f*	discrétisation *f*, discrétion *f*	дискретизация
	discriminance analysis <ST>	*s.* D 692		
D 681	**discriminant** <of an irrational number, *or* a number field, *or* an element> <AB>	Diskriminante *f*; Elementdiskriminante *f*	discriminant *m*	дискриминант
D 682	**discriminant** <of a basis> <AL>	Basisdiskriminante *f*, Diskriminante *f* <einer Basis>	discriminant *m* <d'une base>	дискриминант <базиса>
D 683	**discriminant** <of a divisor, ideal, polynomial, a quadratic form, ring, *or* system> <AL>	Diskriminante *f*	discriminant *m*	дискриминант
D 684	**discriminant** <of a quadratic equation> <AL>	Diskriminante *f*, //alternierende Summe *f* <Cauchy>	discriminant *m*, réalisant *m*, //somme *f* alternée <Cauchy>	дискриминант
D 685	**discriminant,** determinant <of a bilinear form> <AL>	Diskriminante *f*, Determinante *f*	discriminant *m*, déterminant *m*	дискриминант, определитель
	discriminant <AL>	*s.* F 178		
	discriminant analysis <ST>	*s.* D 692		
	discriminant curve <DE>	*s.* P 337		
D 686	**discriminant form** <of the field> <AL>	Diskriminantenform *f* <der Gattung, des Körpers>	forme *f* discriminante <du corps>	дискриминантная форма <поля>
D 687	**discriminant-function, discriminant function** <in a harmonic space> <DG>	Diskriminantenfunktion *f*	fonction *f* discriminante	дискриминантная функция
D 688	**discriminant function,** discriminator <ST>	Diskriminanzfunktion *f*, Trennfunktion *f*, Unterscheidungsfunktion *f*, diskriminierende (diskriminatorische) Funktion *f*, Diskriminator *m*	fonction *f* discriminante (discriminatoire), discriminateur *m*	дискриминантная (классифицирующая) функция, дискриминатор
	discriminant information <ST>	*s.* I 508		
	discriminant score <ST>	*s.* L 787		
D 689	**discriminant surface** <AL, GE>	Diskriminantenfläche *f*, Diskriminantenmannigfaltigkeit *f*	surface-discriminant *f*, surface *f* discriminante, (de discriminant), multiplicité *f* discriminante	дискриминантная поверхность
D 690	**discriminant theorem** <AB>	Diskriminantensatz *m*	théorème *m* du discriminant	теорема о дискриминанте
D 691	**discriminator** <ST>	Diskriminator *m*	discriminateur *m*	дискриминатор
	discriminator <ST>	*s.* D 688		
D 692	**discriminatory analysis,** discriminant (discriminance) analysis <ST>	Diskriminanzanalyse *f*, Trennverfahren *n*, Unterscheidungsanalyse *f*	analyse *f* discriminatoire, analyse discriminante	дискриминантный анализ, метод классификации
D 693	**discriminatory power** <ST>	Diskriminationsfähigkeit *f*	pouvoir *m* discriminatoire	классифицирующая способность
D 694	**discussion of a function,** analysis of a function <with respect to its zeros, extrema, etc.> <DI>	Kurvendiskussion *f*	discussion (analyse, étude) *f* d'une fonction	анализ (обсуждение) функции
	disjoint collection <SE>	*s.* D 700		
	disjoint complement <AL>	*s.* O 437		
D 695	**disjoint cycles** <of permutations> <AL>	elementefremde (elementfremde) Zyklen *mpl*	cycles *mpl* sans éléments communs	циклы без общих элементов
D 696	**disjoint decomposition** <ST>	disjunkte Zerlegung *f*	décomposition *f* disjointe	разложение на несовместимые события
	disjoint decomposition <SE>	*s.* P 276		
D 697	**disjointed set** <LA>	disjunkte Menge *f*	ensemble *m* disjoint	дизъюнктное множество
	disjointed set <SE>	*s.* D 700		
D 698	**disjoint elements** <AL, GR>	disjunkte Elemente *npl*	éléments *mpl* disjoints (étrangers)	дизъюнктные элементы
D 699	**disjoint elements** <of a partially ordered linear space> <TO>	orthogonale Elemente *npl*	éléments *mpl* étrangers	дизъюнктные элементы
D 700	**disjoint family,** disjointed set, family of disjoint sets, disjoint collection <of sets> <SE>	disjunkte Familie *f*, disjunktes System *n*, disjunkter Mengenkomplex *m*	famille *f* d'ensembles sans élément commun	семейство непересекающихся множеств
	0-disjoint ideals <AL>	*s.* Z 26		
D 701	**disjointness** <SE>	Disjunktheit *f*, Durchschnittsfremdheit *f*	propriété *f* d'être disjoint	непересекаемость, неперекрываемость
D 702	**disjoint relations** <LO, SE>	disjunkte Relationen *fpl*	relations *fpl* disjointes	непересекающиеся отношения
D 703	**disjoint sets,** sets without common elements, non-overlapping sets, non-intersecting sets <SE>	disjunkte (durchschnittsfremde, elemente[n]-fremde, elementfremde, punktfremde, fremde, zueinander fremde,	ensembles *mpl* disjoints, ensembles sans élément (point) commun	непересекающиеся (дизъюнктные, неперекрывающиеся, разделенные) множества; множества, не имеющие

No.	English	German	French	Russian
		getrennte) Mengen *fpl*		общих элементов; множества без общих элементов (точек), множества без общей части
	disjoint subgraphs <GP>	*s.* V 161		
D 704	**disjoint sum (union),** set sum <SE>	kartesische (cartesische) Summe *f*, disjunkte Vereinigung *f*	réunion (somme) *f* disjointe	непересекающееся объединение, объединение непересекающихся множеств, дизъюнктное объединение, декартова сумма, сумма
	disjunct <LO>	*s.* P 205		
D 705	**disjunction,** alternative disjunction, disjunction in the inclusive sense, logic[al] sum, inclusive disjunction, alternation, vel [function], ∨ <*read:* or, . . . or . . . or both> <LO>	Alternative *f*, logische Alternative, nichtausschließende Disjunktion *f*, Disjunktion, logische Summe *f*, Adjunktion *f*, Adjunkt *n*, vel, ∨ <*lies:* oder>	disjonction *f*, disjonction (somme *f*) logique, alternative *f*, disjonction inclusive (non exclusive), réunion *f*, trilemme *m*, somme digitale, ∨ <*se lit:* ou, . . . ou . . . ou les deux>	[логическая] дизъюнкция, неразделительная дизъюнкция, дисъюнкция, логическая сумма, соединительно-разделительная дизъюнкция, неисключающая (слабая, нестрогая) дизъюнкция, комбинирование, операция или, дизъюнкция в неисключающем смысле, подразделительная дизъюнкция, ∨ <*читается:* или, клин>
D 706	**disjunction,** logical addition <as an operation> <LO>	Disjunktion *f*, logische Addition (Summenbildung) *f*	disjonction *f*, addition *f* logique, opération *f* OU inclusif, union *f*, somme *f* logique	дизъюнкция, логическое (булево) сложение, логическое «или», функция разделения
D 707	**disjunction** <of several propositions> <LO>	Disjunktion *f*, logische Summe *f* <mehrerer Aussagen>	somme *f* logique, disjonction *f* continue <de plusieurs propositions>	дизъюнкция <нескольких высказываний>
	disjunction in the inclusive sense <LO>	*s.* D 705		
D 708	**disjunction sign (symbol),** symbol of disjunction, symbol of logical sum, ∨ <*to be read:* or, . . . or . . . or both> <LO>	Zeichen *n* der Alternative, Oder-Zeichen *n*, Zeichen der Disjunktion, Disjunktionszeichen *n*, Adjugat *n*, ∨ <*lies:* oder>	symbole *m* de disjonction, ∨ <*se lit:* ou, . . . ou . . . ou les deux>	знак дизъюнкции, знак логического сложения, «или», ∨ <*читается:* или, клин>
	disjunctive canonical (-conjunctive normal) form <AL, LO>	*s.* D 709		
D 709	**disjunctive normal form,** alternative (disjunctive-conjunctive) normal form, disjunctive canonical form <AL, LO>	disjunktive Normalform *f*, alternative Normalform	forme *f* normale disjonctive, première forme *f* normale (canonique), forme canonique disjonctive	дизъюнктивная нормальная форма, альтернативная нормальная форма, ДНФ
D 710	**disjunctive normal form theorem** <LO>	disjunktiver Normalformsatz *m*	théorème *m* de la forme normale disjonctive	теорема о дизъюнктивной нормальной форме
D 711	**disjunctive proposition,** alternative proposition <LO>	alternative Aussage *f*, Alternative *f*, logische Summe *f* <von Aussagen>	proposition *f* disjonctive, disjonction *f*	разделительное суждение, не строго-разделительное высказывание, соединительно-разделительное суждение
D 712	**disjunctive test** <first, of the first kind *or* second, of the second kind> <SS>	disjunktives Kriterium (Doppelkriterium, Konvergenzkriterium) *n* <erster (1.) *oder* zweiter (2.) Art>	critère *m* disjonctif, règle *f* disjonctive, théorème *m* disjonctif <de première *ou* seconde (deuxième) espèce>	дизъюнктивный признак (критерий) <первого *или* второго рода>
D 713	**disjuncture** <for a partial plane> <AL>	Disjunktheitsbedingung *f*	condition *f* de disjonction	условие разъединения
D 714	**disk,** circular disk, circle <as a surface> <EG>	Kreisscheibe *f*, Vollkreis *m*, Kreis *m*	disque *m*, cercle *m*	круг
	disk of convergence <SS>	*s.* C 686		
D 715	**dispersed trial** <ST>	Streulageversuch *m*, Streuversuch *m*	expérience *f* dispersée, essai *m* dispersé	опыт с рассеянием, опыт рассеяния
	dispersion <ST>	*s.* 1. S 101; 2. V 62		
	dispersion analysis <ST>	*s.* M 1087		
	dispersion diagram <ST>	*s.* S 102		
	dispersion ellipse <ST>	*s.* E 157		
	dispersion ellipsoid <ST>	*s.* E 162		
D 716	**dispersion index,** divergence coefficient, coefficient of divergence <ST>	Dispersionskoeffizient *m*, Dispersionsindex *m*, Divergenzkoeffizient *m*	indice *m* de dispersion, coefficient *m* de divergence	индекс рассеяния, коэффициент расхождения
	dispersion matrix <ST>	*s.* C 2601		
D 717	**displacement** <of a connection in a variety> <DG>	Verschiebung *f*	transport *m*	перенос, перенесение
	displacement <AY>	*s.* E 564		
	displacement <GE>	*s.* M 915		
	ε-displacement <TO>	*s.* E 308		
D 718	**displacement-invariant property** <AB>	verschiebungsinvariante Eigenschaft *f*	propriété *f* invariante par déplacement	свойство, инвариантное при смещении
D 719	**displacement operator** <AL>	Verschiebungsoperator *m*	opérateur *m* de déplacement	оператор сдвига
D 720	**displacement vector** <GE>	Verschiebungsvektor *m*, Verrückungsvektor *m*	vecteur *m* déplacement, vecteur-déplacement *m*	вектор сдвига (смещения)
D 721	**disproportionate subclass numbers** <ST>	nichtproportionale Klassenbesetzung *f*	effectifs *mpl* non proportionnels des sous-classes	непропорциональная численность в подклассах

D 722	**dissection** <of a filtration of a chain complex> <HA>	Zerlegung *f*	dissection *f*	разбиение
D 723	**dissection** <of a complex> <TO>	Zerschneidung *f* <eines Komplexes>	dissection *f* <d'un complexe>	рассечение <комплекса>
D 724	**dissimilar matrix** <MD>	nichtähnliche Matrix *f*	matrice *f* non semblable	неподобная матрица
D 725	**dissimilar terms** <AL>	unähnliche (einander nicht entsprechende) Glieder *npl*	termes *mpl* non semblables	неподобные члены; члены <выражения>, не являющиеся подобными
D 726	**dissipative measurable transformation** <ME>	dissipative meßbare Transformation *f*	transformation *f* dissipative mesurable	диссипативное измеримое преобразование
	dissolution of brackets <GN>	*s.* R 802		
D 727	**distance** <first, second *or* third> <from one of the planes of projection> <DS>	Tafelabstand *m* <erster, zweiter *oder* dritter>	distance *f* <première, deuxième *ou* troisième> <du plan de projection>	расстояние <от горизонтальной, вертикальной *или* профильной плоскости>
D 728	**distance,** eye distance <in central perspective> <DS>	Distanz *f*	distance *f*	расстояние
D 729	**distance** <of two points in a metric space> <ME, TO>	Abstand *m*, Distanz *f*, Entfernung *f*	distance *f*	расстояние
D 730	**distance** <from . . . to . . .> <between two subsets> <TO>	Abstand *m*, untere Entfernung *f*, Entfernung	distance *f* mutuelle, écart *m*	расстояние, нижнее расстояние
	distance <TO>	*s.* M 491		
D 731	**distance axioms,** metric axioms <TO>	Axiome *npl* des metrischen Raumes	axiomes *mpl* de distance	аксиомы расстояния (метрического пространства)
D 732	**distance circle** <DS>	Distanzkreis *m*	cercle *m* de distance	окружность расстояния
	distance[-]circle <DG>	*s.* G 238		
D 733	**distance constant** <PJ>	Abstandskonstante *f*	constante *f* de distance	постоянная расстояния
	distance function <CS, GE>	*s.* G 54		
	distance function, distance-function <TO>	*s.* M 491		
D 734	**distance geometry** <GE>	Abstandsgeometrie *f*	géométrie *f* des espaces distanciés, géométrie avec métrique	геометрия пространств с расстоянием, геометрия с метрикой
D 735	**distance in the mean** <ME>	Abstand *m* im Mittel	distance *f* en moyenne	расстояние в среднем
D 736	**distance in the sense of Nikodým,** Nikodým['s] distance <ME>	Nikodýmsche Entfernung *f*, Entfernung	distance *f* au sens de Nikodým	расстояние в смысле Никодима
D 737	**distance matrix** <GP, PG>	Entfernungsmatrix *f*	matrice *f* des distances	матрица расстояний
D 738	**distance of parallelism** <of an angle in hyperbolic geometry> <GE>	Paralleldistanz *f*	distance *f* de parallélisme	расстояние между параллелями
D 739	**distance of support** <CS, GE>	Stützabstand *m*	distance *f* d'appui	опорное расстояние
D 740	**distance point** <DS>	Distanzpunkt *m*	point *m* de distance	точка расстояния
	distance preserving mapping <DG, TO>	*s.* I 1112		
D 741	**distance space** <TO>	Abstandsraum *m*	espace *m* distancié	метризованное пространство, пространство с расстоянием
D 742	**distant,** non-proximal, remote <in a proximity space> <TO>	nicht[ ]benachbart, entfernt	distant	далекий
D 743	**distinction of cases,** case distinction <GN, LO>	Fallunterscheidung *f*	disjonction *f* des cas, distinction *f* des cas	разбор случаев, разделение случаев
D 744	**distinguished base vertex,** base vertex <of a simplicial complex> <AT>	ausgezeichneter Eckpunkt *m*	sommet *m* distingué	отмеченная вершина
	distinguished conjunctive normal form <LO>	*s.* P 1402		
	distinguished disjunctive normal form <LO>	*s.* P 1409		
	distinguished element <SE, TO>	*s.* B 105		
	distinguished ideal <AL>	*s.* R 563		
D 745	**distinguished neighbourhood** <TO>	ausgezeichnete Umgebung *f*	voisinage *m* distingué	отмеченная окрестность
	distinguished normal form <LO>	*s.* P 1452		
D 746	**distinguished polynomial** <of a local ring> <AL>	ausgezeichnetes Polynom *n*	polynôme *m* distingué	отмеченный многочлен
	distinguished subgroup <GR>	*s.* I 883		
D 747	**distinguish points / to,** to separate points <of mappings> <AL, TO>	Punkte trennen	séparer les points	разделять точки
D 748	**distortion** <DG>	Verzerrung *f*	distorsion *f*	искажение
D 749	**distortion** <of a vector> <VT>	Distortion *f*, Distorsion *f*	distorsion *f*	дисторсия

No.	English	German	French	Russian
D 750	**distortion angle** <DS>	Verzerrungswinkel *m*	angle *m* de distorsion	угол искажения
	distortion ellipse <DG>	*s.* T 483		
D 751	**distortion ratio** <DS>	Verzerrungsverhältnis *n*	rapport *m* de distorsion	показатель искажения
D 752	**distortion theorem,** theorem on distortion <FT>	Verzerrungssatz *m*	théorème *m* de (sur la) distorsion	теорема об искажении
	distributing <LO>	*s.* D 754		
D 753	**distribution,** generalized function <different definitions by L. Schwartz; H. König; S. de Silva; J. Mikusinski and R. Sikorski> <AN>	Distribution *f*, verallgemeinerte Funktion *f*	distribution *f*, fonction *f* généralisée	обобщенная функция, дистрибуция, распределение <по Л. Шварцу; Х. Кенигу; С. де Сильва; Й. Микусиньскому и Р. Сикорскому>
D 754	**distribution,** distributing <of quantifiers> <LO>	Distribution *f*	distribution *f*	распределение
	distribution <ST>	*s.* 1. D 758; 2. P 1535		
	0-1 distribution <ST>	*s.* Z 47		
	χ-distribution <ST>	*s.* C 630		
	χ^2-distribution <ST>	*s.* C 634		
	distribution a posteriori <ST>	*s.* P 1105		
D 755	**distribution curve** <ST>	Verteilungskurve *f*, kumulative Verteilungskurve	courbe *f* de distribution (répartition)	кривая распределения
	distribution density <ST>	*s.* P 1534		
D 756	**distribution family,** family of distributions <ST>	Verteilungsfamilie *f*, Familie *f* von Verteilungen	famille *f* de distributions	семейство распределений
	distribution[-] free test <ST>	*s.* N 443		
D 757	**distribution function** <as a real-valued function> <RF>	Verteilungsfunktion *f*	fonction *f* de distribution	функция распределения
D 758	**distribution function,** probability distribution function, distribution, cumulative distribution function, [cumulative] probability function, cumulative frequency function, partition function <ST>	Verteilungsfunktion *f*, Wahrscheinlichkeitsverteilungsfunktion *f*, Verteilung *f*, Summenverteilung *f*, Summenfunktion *f*, kumulative (integrale) Verteilungsfunktion *f*, Summenhäufigkeitsverteilung *f*	fonction *f* de distribution, distribution *f* cumulative (cumulée), fonction de distribution cumulative, distribution, fonction de répartition (probabilité, probabilités totales)	функция распределения, распределение, интегральная функция распределения
D 759	**distribution function to modulus unity** <NT>	Veteilungsfunktion *f* (mod 1)	fonction *f* de répartition modulo un	функция распределения по модулю 1
	distribution law <ST>	*s.* P 1535		
	distribution of *N* into *M* <SE>	*s.* I 589		
D 760	**distribution of prime numbers** <NT>	Primzahlverteilung *f*, Verteilung *f* der Primzahlen	distribution (répartition) *f* des nombres premiers	распределение простых чисел
	distribution of values <FT>	*s.* V 30		
D 761	**distribution parameter** <of a ruled surface> <DG>	Drall *m*, Verteilungsparameter *m*, Distributionsparameter *m*	paramètre *m* de distribution	параметр распределения, «перехват», «сжатие»
D 762	**distribution parameter,** parameter <of a distribution <ST>	Verteilungsparameter *m*, Parameter *m* <einer Verteilung>	paramètre *m* de distribution, paramètre	параметр распределения, параметр
D 763	**distribution rule** <LO>	Regel *f* der gliedweisen Quantifizierung	loi *f* de distributivité	правило дистрибутивности
	distribution solution <DE>	*s.* W 125		
D 764	**distribution space** <FA>	Distributionenraum *m*	espace *m* distributions	пространство обобщенных функций, пространство дистрибуций
D 765	**distribution** <of numbers> **to modulus unity** <NT>	Verteilung *f* (mod 1)	répartition *f* modulo un	распределение по модулю 1
	distribution type <ST>	*s.* T 1149		
D 766	**distribution with negative skewness** <ST>	linksschiefe (rechtssteile) Verteilung *f*	distribution *f* d'asymétrie négative	распределение с отрицательной асимметрией
D 767	**distribution with positive skewness** <ST>	rechtsschiefe (linkssteile) Verteilung *f*	distribution *f* d'asymétrie positive	распределение с положительной асимметрией
D 768	**distributive** <over> <AL>	distributiv <gegenüber, bezüglich>	distributif <par rapport à>, distribué <par>	дистрибутивный, распределительный <относительно>
D 769	**distributive composition law** <AL>	distributives Verknüpfungsgesetz (Kompositionsgesetz) *n* <rechts und links>	loi *f* [de composition] doublement distributive	дистрибутивный закон композиции
	distributive functional transformation <FA>	*s.* A 251		
	distributive ideal <LA>	*s.* N 185		
D 770	**distributive identity** <LA>	distributive Identität *f*	identité *f* de distributivité	тождество дистрибутивности
D 771	**distributive inequality** <LA>	distributive Ungleichung *f*	inégalité *f* distributive (de distributivité)	дистрибутивное неравенство
D 772	**distributive lattice,** // arithmetic structure, C-lattice <LA>	distributiver Verband *m*, // Dualgruppe *f* vom Idealtypus	treillis *m* distributif, ensemble *m* réticulé distributif, treillis médian, réticulé *m* distributif, // logique *f* distributive	дистрибутивная структура, дистрибутивная решетка

D 773	**distributive law** <AL>	Distributivgesetz *n*, distributives Gesetz *n*, Mischungsregel *f*, // Distributionsgesetz *n*, distributives Prinzip *n*, Verteilungsprinzip *n*	loi *f* de distributivité, loi distributive (de distribution), formule *f* de distributivité, principe *m* distributif (de distribution)	дистрибутивный (распределительный) закон, закон дистрибутивности
D 774	**distributive law for conjunction into disjunction, distributive law of conjunction over disjunction;** complete distributive law of conjunction over disjunction <LO>	Distributivgesetz *n* der Konjunktion bezüglich der Alternative	loi *f* de distributivité de la conjonction par rapport à la disjonction	закон дистрибутивности конъюнкции (логического умножения) относительно дизъюнкции, закон дистрибутивности логического умножения относительно логического сложения
D 775	**distributive on the right and on the left** <AL>	rechts- und linksdistributiv	doublement distributif	дистрибутивный справа и слева
	distributive property <AL, LO>	*s.* D 776		
D 776	**distributivity,** distributive property <AL, LO>	Distributivität *f*	distributivité *f*; double distributivité *f*	дистрибутивность, распределительность, распределительное свойство
	distributivity <LO>	*s.* S 365		
D 777	**$\cap$-distributivity** <LA, SE>	Distributivität *f* der Durchschnittsbildung, $\cap$-Distributivität *f*, Gesetz *n* der Distributivität des Durchschnitts bezüglich der Vereinigung	$\cap$-distributivité *f*	$\cap$-дистрибутивность
D 778	**$\cup$-distributivity** <LA, SE>	Distributivität *f* der Vereinigungsoperation, $\cup$-Distributivität *f*, Gesetz *n* der Distributivität der Vereinigung bezüglich des Durchschnitts	$\cup$-distributivité *f*	$\cup$-дистрибутивность
D 779	**distributivity of multiplication over addition** <AL>	Distributivität *f* der Multiplikation mit der Addition	distributivité *f* de la multiplication vis-à-vis de l'addition	дистрибутивность умножения относительно сложения
D 780	**distributivity of the existential quantifier with respect to conjunction,** semi-distributivity of the existential quantifier with respect to conjunction <LO>	Halbdistributivität *f* der Partikularisierung in bezug auf die Konjunktion, Halbdistributivität erster Art	semi-distributivité *f* de première espèce [du quantificateur existentiel par rapport à $\wedge$]	полудистрибутивность квантора существования относительно конъюнкции
D 781	**distributivity of the universal quantifier with respect to disjunction,** semi-distributivity of the universal quantifier with respect to disjunction <LO>	Halbdistributivität *f* der Generalisierung in bezug auf die Alternative, Halbdistributivität zweiter Art	semi-distributivité *f* de deuxième espèce [du quantificateur universel par rapport à $\vee$]	полудистрибутивность квантора общности относительно дизъюнкции
	Div <VT>	*s.* D 785		
	div <VT>	*s.* D 783		
	divector <DG, VT>	*s.* B 486		
D 782	**divergence,** divergency <of a product, sequence, series> <SS>	Divergenz *f*	divergence *f*	расходимость
D 783	**divergence,** div, ∇ <of a vector *or* tensor field> <VT>	Divergenz *f*, Quelldichte *f*, Ergiebigkeit, div, ∇	divergence *f*, div, ∇	дивергенция, расхождение, расходимость, ковариантная расходимость, div, ∇
	divergence at a surface of discontinuity <VT>	*s.* D 785		
D 784	**divergence class** <FT>	Divergenzklasse *f*	classe *f* de divergence	класс расходимости, расходящийся класс
	divergence coefficient <ST>	*s.* D 716		
D 785	**divergence of discontinuity,** divergence at a surface of discontinuity, surface divergence, areal divergence, Div <VT>	Flächendivergenz *f*, Sprungdivergenz *f*, Div	divergence *f* de discontinuité, divergence dans une surface de discontinuité, divergence de surface, divergence superficielle, Div	дивергенция (расходимость) разрыва, дивергенция (расходимость) на поверхности разрыва, поверхностная дивергенция (расходимость), Div
	divergence theorem <DI, VT>	*s.* G 427		
	divergence to $+\infty$ or $-\infty$ <SS>	*s.* P 1777		
	divergency <SS>	*s.* D 782		
D 786	**divergenti teration** <NU>	divergente Iteration *f*	itération *f* divergente	расходящаяся итерация
D 787	**divergent parabola** <a cubic> <AG>	divergierende Parabel *f* <Newton>	parabole *f* divergente	расходящаяся парабола
D 788	**divergent sequence** <SS>	divergente Folge *f*	suite *f* divergente	расходящаяся последовательность
	divide / to <NT>	*s.* B 162		
D 789	**divided difference,** gradient, rate of change, difference quotient, <zero-order, first-order, ..., *n*-th-order, of the zeroth, first, ..., *n*-th order; higher-order, of higher order> <of a function> <AN, DI, FD>	Steigung *f*, Differenzenquotient *m*, dividierte (geteilte) Differenz *f* <nullter (0.), erster (1.), ..., *n*-ter Ordnung; höherer Ordnung>	différence *f* divisée, rapport *m* d'accroissement, taux *m* d'accroissement, fonction *f* interpolaire, // rapport incrémentiel, quotient *m* des différences <d'ordre 0, 1, ..., *n*, de nullième, premier, ..., *n*-e ordre; d'ordre supérieur>	разделенная разность, разностное отношение, отношение приращений, отношение приращения функции к приращению аргумента, // разность, деленная на степени разности <нулевого, первого, ..., *n*-го порядка, порядка 0, 1, ..., *n*; высшего порядка>
	divide exactly / to <NT>	*s.* B 162		
D 790	**dividend** <AR>	Dividend *m*, Dividendus *m*	dividende *m*	делимое

No.	English	German	French	Russian
D 791	**divider compasses, dividers,** bow divider (compass) <GE, IN>	Stechzirkel *m*, Teilzirkel *m*	compas *m* à pointes sèches, compas diviseur (à balustre)	измерительный (делительный) циркуль, измеритель-делитель
	divide without remainder / to <NT>	*s.* B 162		
D 792	**dividing divisor,** divisor <of a divisor> <AL>	Teiler *m*	diviseur *m*	делитель
D 793	**dividing point,** separating point <TO>	trennender Punkt *m*	point *m* de séparation (division)	разделяющая точка
D 794	**divisibility** <of a group> <GR>	Divisionsvollständigkeit *f*, Vollständigkeit *f*, Dividierbarkeit *f*	divisibilité *f*	полнота
D 795	**divisibility of the first** <*or* second> **kind** <by a module system> <AL>	Teilbarkeit *f* erster <*oder* zweiter> Art	divisibilité *f* de première <*ou* seconde> espèce	делимость первого <*или* второго> рода
D 796	**divisibility rule** <NT>	Teilbarkeitsregel *f*	règle *f* de divisibilité	правило делимости
D 797	**divisible,** divisible without remainder <by> <AL, AR, NT>	teilbar, ohne Rest teilbar <durch>	divisible, exactement divisible <par>	делимый, делимый без остатка <на>
	divisible abelian group <GR>	*s.* A 412		
D 798	**divisible $\mathfrak{A}$-module,** complete $\mathfrak{A}$-module <AL>	divisionsvollständiger $\mathfrak{A}$-Modul *m*	$\mathfrak{A}$-module *m* divisible	делимый $\mathfrak{A}$-модуль, полный $\mathfrak{A}$-модуль, $\mathfrak{A}$-модуль с неограниченным делением
D 799	**divisible element,** infinitely divisible element <AL>	unbeschränkt teilbares Element *n*	élément *m* divisible	неограниченно (бесконечно) делимый элемент
	divisible group <GR>	*s.* 1. C 1438; 2. D 579		
	π-divisible group <GR>	*s.* R 14		
D 800	**divisible hull** <of a module> <AL>	teilbare Hülle *f*	enveloppe *f* divisible	делимая оболочка
D 801	**divisible hull,** injective hull <of a group> <GR>	Divisionshülle *f*, dividierbare Hülle *f*	enveloppe *f* divisible	дивизионное замыкание, пополнение
	divisible without remainder <AL, AR, NT>	*s.* D 797		
D 802	**division** <by> <AR>	Division *f*, Teilung *f* <durch>	division *f* <par>	деление <на>
D 803	**division** <in a proportion>, corresponding subtraction <AR>	korrespondierende Subtraktion *f*	transition *f* <de la proportion $a:b=c:d$> à la proportion $(a-b):b=(c-d):d$	переход от пропорции $a:b=c:d$ к производной пропорции $(a-b):b=(c-d):d$
	division <AN>	*s.* S 2093		
	division <NO, NU>	*s.* S 91		
D 804	**division algebra** <AL>	Divisionsalgebra *f*	algèbre *f* à division	алгебра с делением
D 805	**division algorithm,** algorithm of division <AL, NU>	Divisionsalgorithmus *m*	algorithme *m* de la division, algorithme de division avec reste	алгоритм деления
	division comes out even <AL, AR>	*s.* D 808		
D 806	**division equation** <for an elliptic function> <FT, FU>	Teilungsgleichung *f*	équation *f* de la division	уравнение деления
D 807	**division group,** Severi['s] group <on an algebraic variety> <AG>	Severische Gruppe *f*	groupe *m* de Severi	группа Севери
	division in extreme and mean ratio <EG>	*s.* G 331		
	division in half <EG, GN>	*s.* B 460		
	division in two <GE, GN>	*s.* B 420		
	division in two equal parts <EG, GN>	*s.* B 460		
	division in two parts <GE, GN>	*s.* B 420		
D 808	**division** <of *a* by *b*> **is exact, division leaves no remainder,** division comes out even, exact division is reached <AL, AR>	die Division <von *a* durch *b*> geht [ohne Rest] auf, *a* läßt sich exakt (ohne Rest) durch *b* teilen	la division <de *a* par *b*> se fait exactement	*a* делится нацело на *b*, *a* делится на *b* без остатка, деление *a* на *b* не дает остатка
	division neoring <AL>	*s.* N 144		
D 809	**division of a line segment** <in a given ratio> <EG>	Teilung *f* einer Strecke <in einem gegebenen Verhältnis>	partage *m* d'un segment <dans un rapport donné>	деление отрезка <в данном отношении>
D 810	**division of polynomials** <AL>	Division *f* von Polynomen	division *f* algébrique, division de deux polynômes	деление многочленов
D 811	**division of the argument** <of a function> <AN>	Teilung *f* des Arguments	division *f* de l'argument	деление аргумента
	division of the circle <NU>	*s.* C 2902		
D 812	**division problem** <for an elliptic function> <FT, FU>	Teilungsproblem *n*	problème *m* de la division	проблема деления
	division ratio <AY, EG>	*s.* A 370		
D 813	**division ring,** skew field, s-field, corpus <*pl*: corpora>, non-commutative division ring <AL>	Schiefkörper *m*, [nichtkommutativer] Körper *m*, Divisionsring *m*	corps *m*, corps gauche (non commutatif); anneau *m* à division <non nécessairement commutatif>	[некоммутативное] тело, кольцо с делением, поле
D 814	**division ring of quaternions,** quaternion field <AL>	Quaternionenkörper *m*, Quaternionenschiefkörper *m*, Schiefkörper *m* der Quaternionen	corps *m* des (de) quaternions	тело кватернионов
D 815	**division ring of real quaternions** <AL>	reeller Quaternionenkörper *m*	corps *m* des quaternions réels	тело вещественных кватернионов

No.	English	German	French	Russian
	division sign <NU>	*s.* S 569		
D 816	**division theory** <NT>	Teilbarkeitslehre *f*	théorie *f* de la divisibilité	теория делимости
D 817	**division transformation,** division with remainder <AL, NT>	Division *f* mit Rest	division *f* euclidienne, division avec reste	деление с остатком
	division transformation <AL, AR>	*s.* L 1095		
D 818	**division value** <of an elliptic function> <FT, FU> ⌈<AL, NT>	Teilwert *m*	« Teilwert » *m*	значение деления
	division with remainder	*s.* D 817		
D 819	**divisor** <of the first *or* second kind> <AG, AL>	Divisor *m* <erster *oder* zweiter Art>	diviseur *m*, diviseur algébrique <de première *ou* deuxième espèce>	дивизор <первого *или* второго рода>
D 820	**divisor,** factor <AL>	Teiler *m*	diviseur *m*	делитель
D 821	**divisor** <in division> <AR>	Divisor *m*	diviseur *m*	делитель
D 822	**divisor** <of a form *or* the type of a partially ordered set> <NT, SE>	Teiler *m* <einer Form *oder* eines Halbordnungstyps>	diviseur *m* <d'une forme *ou* d'un type d'ordre>	делитель <формы *или* типа полуупорядоченного множества>
D 823	**divisor,** aliquot part <of a number> <NT>	Teiler *m*, Divisor *m*, aliquoter Teil *m*, enthaltene Zahl *f*, exakter Teiler	diviseur *m*, partie *f* aliquote, diviseur exact, nombre *m* contenu	делитель, делитель без остатка
	divisor <AL>	*s.* D 792		
	divisor <NT>	*s.* F 18		
D 824	**divisor algebraically equivalent to zero** <AG>	algebraisch nullāquivalenter Divisor *m*	diviseur *m* algébriquement équivalent à zéro	дивизор, алгебраически эквивалентный нулю
D 825	**divisor chain** <in a groupoid> <AL>	Teilerkette *f*	chaîne *f* de diviseurs	цепочка делителей
	divisor chain condition <AL>	*s.* A 1031		
D 826	**divisor class,** class of divisors <AL>	Divisorenklasse *f*, Divisorklasse *f*	classe *f* de diviseurs	класс [эквивалентности] дивизоров
D 827	**divisor function** <NT>	Teileranzahlfunktion *f*, [nullte] Teilerfunktion *f*	fonction *f* de diviseurs	функция делителей
D 828	**divisorial cycle,** cycle, multiplicative variety <Hodge-Pedoe>, virtual variety <AG>	Zyklus *m*, Kette *f* <van der Waerden>	cycle *m*	цикл
D 829	**divisorial ideal** <AL>	Divisorideal *n*	idéal *m* divisoriel	дивизориальный идеал
D 830	**divisorial module** <AL>	Divisormodul *m*, Divisor-Modul *m*	idéal *m* fractionnaire divisoriel	дивизориальный дробный идеал
D 831	**divisor induction** <AL>	Teilerinduktion *f*	récurrence *f* sur les diviseurs	индукция по делителям
	divisorless ideal <AL, LA>	*s.* M 234		
D 832	**divisor linearly equivalent to zero** <AG>	linear nullāquivalenter Divisor *m*	diviseur *m* linéairement équivalent à zéro	дивизор, линейно эквивалентный нулю
D 833	**divisor of a differential** <of an algebraic function> <AL>	Differentialdivisor *m*, Differentialteiler *m*, Divisor *m* des Differentials	diviseur *m* d'une différentielle	дивизор дифференциала
D 834	**divisor of degree zero** <AL>	Nulldivisor *m*	diviseur *m* de degré zéro	нулевой дивизор, нульдивизор
D 835	**divisor of the discriminant** <AB>	Diskriminantenteiler *m*	facteur *m* du discriminant	множитель дискриминанта
	divisor of zero <AL>	*s.* Z 28		
	divisor of zeros <AL, FT>	*s.* N 766		
D 836	**divisor problem** <NT>	Teilerproblem *n*	problème *m* de partition	проблема делителей
	divisor problem of Dirichlet <NT>	*s.* D 619		
D 837	**divisor sum, divisor-sum function** <of a number> <NT>	Teilersumme *f*, Divisorensumme *f*, Summe *f* der Divisoren (Teiler), erste Teilerfunktion *f*	somme *f* des (de) diviseurs	сумма делителей (натуральных делителей)
D 838	**divisor-sum function** <NT>	Teilerfunktion *f*, Teilersumme *f*	somme *f* des diviseurs	функция-делитель
D 839	**Dixon['s] formula** <FU>	Dixonsche Formel *f*	formule *f* de Dixon	формула Диксона
D 840	**Dixon['s] test** <ST>	Dixon-Test *m*	test *m* de Dixon	критерий Диксона
	DI <RF>	*s.* L 370		
	dn <FU>	*s.* A 608		
D 841	**dodecagon** <EG>	Zwölfeck *n*, Dodekagon *n*, 12-Eck *n*	dodécagone *m*	двенадцатиугольник
D 842	**dodecahedral form** <in representing binary forms on the sphere> <AL>	Dodekaederform *f*	forme *f* du dodécaèdre, forme dodécaédrique	додекаэдрическая форма
	dodecahedral group <AL, GR>	*s.* I 3		
D 843	**dodecahedral number** <a figurate number> <NT>	Dodekagonalzahl *f*, Zwölfeckszahl *f*	nombre *m* dodécagone (dodécagonal)	двенадцатиугольное число
D 844	**dodecahedron** <EG>	Zwölfflach *n*, Dodekaeder *n*, Zwölfflächner *m*	dodécaèdre *m*	двенадцатигранник, додекаэдр
	dodecahedron <EG>	*s.* R 535		
D 845	**Doeblin['s] condition** <ST>	Doeblinsche Bedingung *f*	condition *f* de Doeblin	условие Деблина
	dog curve <DE>	*s.* C 2786		
D 846	**Dolbeault['s] isomorphism** <of a fibre bundle> <AT, FT>	Dolbeault-Isomorphismus *m*	isomorphisme *m* de Dolbeault	изоморфизм Дольбо
D 847	**Dolbeault-Serre theorem** <AT, FT> ⌈<DG>	Satz *m* von Dolbeault-Serre, Dolbeault-Serrescher Satz	théorème *m* de Dolbeault-Serre	теорема Дольбо-Серра
	Dolph-Chebyshev array	*s.* C 601		
D 848	**domain** <common name of ring, domain of integrity, and field> <AL>	[algebraischer] Bereich *m*	domaine *m*	область

No.	English	German	French	Russian
D 849	**domain** <of a partial operation> <AL>	Definitionsbereich *m*, Operationsgebiet *n*	ensemble (domaine) *m* de définition	область определенности
D 850	**domain,** domain (set, range) of definition, range of validity, range of arguments, range <of a map, function, operator, etc.>; range of the independent variable <of a function> <AN>	Definitionsbereich *m*, Vorbereich *m*, Urbildbereich *m*, Argumentbereich *m*, Variabilitätsbereich *m*, Wirkungsbereich *m*, Definitionsgebiet *n*, Definitionsmenge *f*	domaine *m*, domaine de validité (définition, variation), intervalle (champ) *m* de variation, ensemble *m* de définition (départ), ensemble des arguments, ensemble source	область определения (задания), множество определения, область изменения [переменной], множество изменения [переменной]
D 851	**domain,** source, domain[-]object, domain carrier <of a morphism> <CA>	Quelle *f*, Start *m*, Definitionsbereich *m*	source *f*, objet *m* initial	источник, начало, область определения, область, «начальный» объект
D 852	**domain** <GP>	Gebiet *n*	région *f*, face *f*	область
D 853	**domain** <of a propositional function> <LO>	Definitionsbereich *m*	domaine (ensemble) *m* de définition	область определения
D 854	**domain,** argument (relation's, left, actual) domain <of a relation>; set (domain) of indices; class of indices <of a single-valued relation> <SE>	Argumentbereich *m*, Vorbereich *m*, Definitionsbereich *m*, Urbildbereich *m*	domaine *m*, domaine (ensemble *m*) de définition, première projection *f*	область определения (значений аргументов)
D 855	**domain,** region, open connected set <non-empty open connected set> <TO>	Gebiet *n*, offenes Gebiet, offener Bereich *m*	domaine *m*, domaine ouvert	область, открытая область, открытое связное множество
	domain <AL>	*s.* 1. D 869; 2. F 170		
	domain <CA>	*s.* D 857		
	domain <SE>	*s.* I 361		
	domain <TO>	*s.* 1. B 526; 2. O 153		
D 856	**domain carrier,** latent domain <of a correspondence> <SE>	Vorbereich *m* <einer Korrespondenz>	ensemble *m* de départ, ensemble initial <d'une correspondance>	множество отправления <соответствия>
	domain carrier <CA>	*s.* D 851		
D 857	**domain category,** domain <of a functor> <CA>	Quellkategorie *f*	domaine *m* <d'un foncteur>	область определения <функтора>
	domain collocation <DE>	*s.* C 1152		
	domain estimate (estimation) <ST>	*s.* C 1865		
D 858	**domain[-]extension,** extension of domain <FT>	Gebietserweiterung *f*	extension *f* de domaine	расширение области
D 859	**domain[-]extension** <of a mapping> <SE>	Erweiterung *f* des Definitionsbereichs	extension *f* du domaine	расширение области определения
D 860	**domain integral** <DI>	Gebietsintegral *n*	intégrale *f* étendue à un domaine, intégrale de domaine	интеграл по области
D 861	**domain invariance,** invariance of domain (the region) <under holomorphic mapping> <FT>	Gebietstreue *f*	invariance *f* de domaine	свойство сохранения области, сохраняемость (инвариантность) области; сохранение области
	domain object, domain-object <CA>	*s.* D 851		
	domain of a polygon <GE, TO>	*s.* P 934		
D 862	**domain of attraction** <of a distribution function> <ST>	Anziehungsbereich *m*, Einzugsbereich *m* <einer Verteilungsfunktion>	domaine *m* d'attraction <d'une fonction de distribution>	область притяжения <функции распределения>
D 863	**domain of convergence,** convergence domain <*n*-dimensional> <FT>	Konvergenzkörper *m*	domaine *m* de convergence	область сходимости
D 864	**domain of convergence,** region of convergence, convergence region, set of convergence <of a function sequence> <FT, SS>	Konvergenzbereich *m*, Konvergenzgebiet *n*	région *f* de convergence, domaine *m* de convergence, ensemble *m* de convergence	область сходимости, множество сходимости
	domain of definition <AN>	*s.* D 850		
D 865	**domain of determinacy** <DE>	Fortsetzungsbereich *m*, Bestimmtheitsbereich *m*	domaine *m* de détermination	область определенности
D 866	**domain of existence,** existence domain (region) <of an analytic function> <FT>	Existenzbereich *m*, Existenzgebiet *n*	région *f* d'existence, domaine *m* d'existence	область существования, вейерштрассова область
	domain of finite connectivity <TO>	*s.* F 284		
	domain of indexes <SE>	*s.* I 361		
	domain of indices <SE>	*s.* D 854		
D 867	**domain of individuals** <LO>	Gegenstandsbereich *m*, Individuenbereich *m*, Objektbereich *m*	univers *m* du discours	предметная область, область объектов, поле, область предметов (индивидуумов), область, универсум, универсум рассуждения (рассмотрения), универсальное множество
D 868	**domain of integration** <DI>	ntegrationsbereich *m*, Integrationsgebiet *n*	domaine *m* d'intégration	область интегрирования
D 869	**domain of integrity,** domain, integral domain (ring) <AL>	Integritätsbereich *m*, kommutativer Ring *m* ohne Nullteiler, Integritätsring *m*	anneau *m* d'intégrité, anneau intègre, domaine *m* d'intégrité	область целостности, целостное [коммутативное] кольцо, кольцо целостности, область
D 870	**domain of integrity of characteristic *p*,** integral domain of characteristic *p* <AL>	Integritätsbereich *m* der Charakteristik *p*	domaine *m* d'intégrité de caractéristique *p*, domaine pseudoholoïde <König>	область целостности характеристики *p*

D 871	**domain of integrity of characteristic zero,** integral domain of characteristic zero <AL>	Integritätsbereich *m* der Charakteristik Null	domaine *m* d'intégrité de caractéristique zéro, domaine holoïde <König>	область целостности нулевой характеристики
D 872	**domain of meromorphy** <FT>	Meromorphiegebiet *n*	domaine *m* de méromorphie	область мероморфности
	domain of multipliers <AL>	*s.* O 204		
	domain of normality <FT>	*s.* N 596		
	domain of operators <AL>	*s.* O 204		
	domain of rationality <AL>	*s.* F 170		
D 873	**domain of regularity** <of a linear operator> <FA>	Regularitätsgebiet *n*	domaine *m* de régularité	область регулярности
D 874	**domain of transitivity,** minimal fixed block, orbit, set of transitivity, transitivity set, system of transitivity <of a permutation group> <GR>	Transitivitätsgebiet *n*, Transitivitätssystem *n*, minimaler Festblock *m*, Bahn *f*	domaine (système) *m* de transitivité	область (система) транзитивности
D 875	**domain of univalence** <FD, FT, NU>	Eindeutigkeitsbereich *m*	domaine *m* d'univalence	область однозначности (однолистности)
D 876	**domain of unsolvability** <PG>	Nichtlösbarkeitsbereich *m*	domaine *m* d'irrésolubilité	область неразрешимости
D 877	**domain of variability** <of a variable> <DI>	Variabilitätsbereich *m*	domaine *m*	область изменения
D 878	**domain restriction, domain-restriction** <of a mapping> <AN, SE, TO>	Einschränkung *f* des Definitionsbereichs	restriction *f* du domaine	сужение области определения
	domain unit <AL>	*s.* R 1287		
D 879	**domain without singularities** <GE>	singularitätenfreies Gebiet *n*	domaine *m* sans singularités	область без особенностей
	dominance number <GP>	*s.* N 822		
	dominant ergodic theorem <SP>	*s.* W 250		
	dominant main diagonal <MD, NU>	*s.* D 885		
D 880	**dominant module** <AL>	dominanter Modul *m*	module *m* dominant	доминантный модуль
D 881	**dominant weight,** highest weight <for a Lie algebra> <AL>	dominantes Gewicht *n*	poids *m* dominant, poids maximum	доминантный вес, старший вес
D 882	**dominate / to** <AL>	dominieren, beherrschen, Erweiterung sein <von> <Kähler>, ein Zentrum <Maximalideal> haben <in>	dominer	доминировать, лежать <над>
	dominate / to <LO>	*s.* B 257		
	dominate / to <SS>	*s.* M 45		
D 883	**dominated convergence,** normal convergence <of a function series> <SS>	normale (maximale) Konvergenz *f*	convergence *f* dominée (normale)	нормальная сходимость
D 884	**dominated convergence** <SS>	dominierte Konvergenz *f*	convergence *f* majorée	мажорированная сходимость
	dominated series <SS>	*s.* M 48		
D 885	**dominating diagonal,** dominant main diagonal <of a matrix> <MD, NU>	überwiegende (dominierende) Hauptdiagonale *f*	diagonale *f* dominante (principale dominante)	доминирующая [главная] диагональ
D 886	**dominating local ring** <AL>	Erweiterung *f* <eines lokalen Rings>	domination *f* <d'un anneau local>	доминирующее локальное кольцо
D 887	**dominating set,** externally stable set, absorbant set, independent edge family <GP>	äußerlich stabile Menge *f*, dominierende Menge	ensemble *m* absorbant, ensemble stable extérieurement	доминирующее множество, внешнее устойчивое [под]множество, независимое (устойчивое) множество ребер; обратное доминирующее множество <в ориентированном графе>
D 888	**domination** <TG>	Dominierung *f*	domination *f*	доминирование
	domination number <GP>	*s.* N 822		
	domination principle <PO>	*s.* P 1501		
D 889	**domino** <EG>	Domino *n*	domino *m*	домино
D 890	**domino problem** <CT>	Dominoproblem *n*, Dominoaufgabe *f*	problème *m* de domino	задача домино
D 890a	**do not contain / to;** $\not\ni$ <as an element>; $\not\supset$ <as a subset> <SE>	nicht enthalten	ne contenir pas	не содержать
	Don Scotus['] law <LO>	*s.* L 162		
D 891	**Doolittle['s] method,** Gauss-Doolittle method, abbreviated Gauss method, method of Doolittle <AL, NU, ST>	Gauß-Doolittle-Methode *f*, abgekürzte (verkürzte) Gauß-Methode *f*, abgekürztes (verkürztes) Gaußsches Verfahren *n*, Doolittle-Methode *f*, Doolittle-Verfahren *n*	méthode *f* de Gauss-Doolittle (Gauss abrégée, Doolittle)	метод Гаусса-Дулиттля, сокращенный метод Гаусса, метод Дулиттля
D 892	**door space** <TO>	topologischer Raum *m*, in dem jede Unter-	espace *m* topologique dont chaque partie est ouverte	дверное пространство; топологическое про-

		menge offen oder abgeschlossen ist	ou fermée	странство, каждое подмножество которого является открытым или замкнутым
D 893	**dose-response method** <ST>	Dosis-Wirkungs-Verfahren *n*, Toleranzanalyse *f*	méthode *f* dose-réponse	метод зависимости между дозой и эффектом
D 894	**dot chart (diagram),** point diagram <NU, ST>	Punktdiagramm *n*	diagramme *m* ponctuel (en points, par points)	точечная диаграмма
	dot product, dot-product <VT>	*s.* S 86		
D 895	**dot product of a vector with itself** <VT>	Skalarprodukt *n* mit sich selbst	carré *m* scalaire	скалярный квадрат
D 896	**dotted spinor** <AL, VT>	punktierter Spinor *m*	spineur *m* pointé	пунктированный спинор
D 897	**double-angle formulas, double angle formulas, double-angle identities** <in plane trigonometry> <EG>	Doppelwinkelformeln *fpl*	formules *fpl* pour les angles doubles	формулы для [тригонометрических] функций двойного угла
D 898	**double arrow,** ⟷ <LO>	Doppelpfeil *m*, ⟷	double flèche *f*, ⟷	двойная стрелка, ⟷
D 899	**double category** <CA>	Doppelkategorie *f*	catégorie *f* doublée (double)	двойная категория
D 900	**double chain complex** <HA>	Doppelkettenkomplex *m*	double complexe *m* de chaînes	двойной цепной комплекс
D 901	**double character group** <GR>	Charaktergruppe *f* der Charaktergruppe	groupe *m* bidual	бидуальная группа
D 902	**double complex,** bicomplex <HA>	Doppelkomplex *m*, Bikomplex *m*	double complexe *m*, complexe *m* double, bicomplexe *m*	двойной (дважды градуированный) комплекс, бикомплекс
D 903	**double composition** <in a set> <AL>	doppelte Komposition *f*	structure *f* définie par deux lois de composition	двойная композиция
D 904	**double cone,** bicone <EG>	Doppelkegel *m*, Doppelkonus *m*	bicône *m*, double cône *m*	двойной конус, полный конус
D 905	**double connectivity** <TO>	zweifacher Zusammenhang *m*	double connexion *f*	двусвязность, связность порядка два
D 906	**double coset** <of a group G as regards H_1 and H_2> <GR>	Doppelrestklasse *f*	double classe *f*	смежный класс по двойному модулю, двойной смежный класс
D 907	**double coset decompositon** <of a group> <GR>	Zerlegung *f* <einer Gruppe> nach zwei Untergruppen, Zerlegung <einer Gruppe> nach einem Doppelmodul	décomposition *f* <d'un groupe> en double classes	разложение <группы> по двойному модулю
D 908	**double curve** <of a surface> <AG>	Doppelkurve *f*, Doppellinie *f*, Knotenlinie *f*, Doppelpunktlinie *f*	courbe *f* double, ligne *f* double	двойная кривая
D 909	**double-curved surface** <GE>	Nichtregelfläche *f*	surface *f* non réglée	нелинейчатая кривая поверхность
	double cusp <GE>	*s.* T 19		
D 910	**double differential** <of the first *or* second kind> <AL, FT>	Doppeldifferential *n* <[von] erster (1.) *oder* zweiter (2.) Gattung>	différentielle *f* double <de première *ou* deuxième espèce>	двойной дифференциал <первого *или* второго рода>
D 911	**double dual** <of a linear space> <AL>	Bidual m, Bidualraum *m*, bidualer Vektorraum *m*	bidual *m*	бидуальное пространство
D 912	**double element,** fixed element <of an involution> <PJ>	Doppelelement *n*, Fixelement *n*	élément *m* double (fixe)	двойной (неподвижный) элемент
	double-entry table <GN>	*s.* T 12		
D 913	**double exponential distribution** <ST>	doppelte Exponentialverteilung *f*	distribution *f* exponentielle double	двойное показательное распределение
D 914	**double factorial** <FU>	doppelte Fakultät *f*	factorielle *f* double	двойной факториал
D 915	**double folium,** bifolium <AG>	Zweiblatt *n*, Bifolium *n*, doppelte Blattkurve *f*, Doppelblatt *n*	bifolium *m*, folium *m* double	двулистник
D 916	**double Fourier series,** Fourier['s] double series <SS>	Fouriersche Doppelreihe *f*	série *f* de Fourier double	двойной ряд Фурье
D 917	**double Fourier transform[ation],** two-dimensional Fourier transform[ation] <IT>	zweidimensionale (doppelte, zweifache) Fourier-Transformation *f*	double transformation *f* de Fourier, transformation bidimensionnelle de Fourier, transformation de Fourier à deux variables	двойное (двумерное) преобразование Фурье, преобразование Фурье функции двух переменных
	double gamma function <FU>	*s.* D 480		
	double graded group <GR>	*s.* B 320		
D 918	**double grouping,** twofold grouping <ST>	zweifache (doppelte) Gruppierung *f*	groupement *m* double (à double entrée)	двойная (двукратная) группировка
	double indexed sequence <SE, SS>	*s.* D 942		
D 919	**double integral** <of the first *or* second kind> <of a double differential> <AL, FT>	Doppelintegral *n* <[von] erster (1.) *oder* zweiter (2.) Gattung>	intégrale *f* double <de première *ou* deuxième espèce>	двойной интеграл <первого *или* второго рода>
D 920	**double Laplace transform[ation],** two-dimensional Laplace transform[ation] <IT>	zweidimensionale (doppelte, zweifache) Laplace-Transformation *f*	double transformation *f* de Laplace, transformation bidimensionnelle de Laplace, transformation de Laplace à deux variables	двойное (двумерное) преобразование Лапласа, преобразование Лапласа функции двух переменных
	double law of the mean <DI>	*s.* C 240		
D 921	**double layer** <PO>	Doppelbelegung *f*	double couche *f*	двойной слой
D 922	**double-layer potential** <PO>	Doppelbelegungspotential *n*, Potential *n* einer Doppelbelegung	potentiel *m* d'une double couche	потенциал двойного слоя

No.	English	German	French	Russian
D 923	**double limit** <of a double sequence> <SS>	Doppellimes *m* <Grenzwert für unabhängig voneinander nach ∞ strebende *m*, *n*>	double limite *f*	двойной предел, предел предела; двойной переход к пределу
D 924	**double line,** repeated line, doubly straight line <AG, AY>	Doppelgerade *f*	droite *f* double, deux droites *fpl* parallèles confondues	двойная прямая
D 925	**double line,** fixed line <of an involution> <PJ>	Doppelgerade *f*, Fixgerade *f*	droite *f* double (fixe)	двойная (неподвижная) прямая
	double logarithmic paper <IN, NU>	*s.* L 1085		
D 926	**double logarithmic transformation** <ST>	doppelt[ ]logarithmische Transformation *f*	transformation *f* bilogarithmique	двойное логарифмическое преобразование
D 927	**double loop** <DI, FT, TO>	Doppelschleife *f*	boucle *f* double, double lacet *m*	двойная петля
	double module <AL>	*s.* B 352		
D 928	**double negation** <LO>	doppelte Negation *f*	double négation *f*	двойное отрицание, отрицание отрицания
D 929	**double orthogonal system** <AN>	doppelt orthogonales System *n*	système *m* doublement orthogonal	дважды ортогональная система
	double-peaked distribution [function] <ST>	*s.* B 351		
	double periodic function <FT>	*s.* D 958		
D 930	**double periodicity** <FT>	Doppelperiodizität *f*	double périodicité *f*	двупериодичность
D 931	**double permutable operator (transformation)** <FA>	doppelt[ ]vertauschbarer Operator *m*, doppelt[ ] vertauschbare Transformation *f*, doppelvertauschbare Transformation	opérateur *m* doublement permutable, transformation *f* doublement permutable	дважды перестановочный оператор, дважды перестановочное преобразование (отображение)
D 932	**double plane,** biplane <AL, AY, PJ>	Doppelebene *f*	plan *m* double, biplan *m*	двойная плоскость
D 933	**double plane,** fixed plane <of an involution> <PJ>	Doppelebene *f*, Fixebene *f*	plan *m* double, plan fixe	двойная плоскость, неподвижная плоскость
D 934	**double point** <of a curve> <GE>	Doppelpunkt *m*	point *m* double	двойная точка
D 935	**double point,** fixed point, self-corresponding point <of an involution *or* geometric transformation> <AY, PJ>	Doppelpunkt *m*, Fixpunkt *m*	point *m* double, point fixe	двойная точка, неподвижная точка
D 936	**double point divisor** <AG>	Doppelpunktdivisor *m*, Divisor *m* der mehrfachen Punkte	diviseur *m* des points doubles	дивизор двойной точки
D 937	**double Poisson distribution,** Thomas['s] distribution <ST>	doppelte Poisson-Verteilung *f*, Thomas-Verteilung *f*	distribution *f* de Poisson double, distribution de Thomas	двойное распределение Пуассона, распределение Томаса
	double position <AN, NU>	*s.* M 463		
D 938	**double primed quantity** <GN>	zweigestrichene (zweifach gestrichene) Größe *f*	quantité *f* deux fois primée	величина с двумя штрихами
	double prism <EG>	*s.* B 425		
D 939	**double product** <SS>	Doppelprodukt *n*, zweifach (doppelt) unendliches Produkt *n*, Produkt mit doppeltem Eingang	produit *m* double (à double entrée)	двойное произведение
	double pyramid <EG>	*s.* B 427		
	double quotient theorem <GR>	*s.* T 424		
	double ratio <AY>	*s.* C 2710		
D 940	**double root,** repeated root, root of multiplicity two, two-fold root, coincident (equal) roots <AL>	Doppelwurzel *f*	racine *f* double	двойной корень, корень кратности два, двукратный корень
D 941	**double scale** <NO>	Doppelleiter *f*, Doppelskala *f*, doppelte Funktionsskala *f*	double échelle *f*	двойная шкала
D 942	**double sequence,** double indexed sequence; doubly infinite sequence <SE, SS>	Doppelfolge *f*, zweifach-indizierte Folge *f*; zweifach unendliche Folge *f*, unendliche Doppelfolge; zweifach unendliche Zahlenfolge *f*	suite *f* double (à double entrée, à deux indices); suite infinie à double entrée, suite doublement infinie	двойная последовательность; последовательность с двумя индексами
D 943	**double series** <SS>	Doppelreihe *f*, zweifach unendliche Reihe *f*, Reihe mit doppeltem Eingang	série double (à double entrée)	двойной ряд
	double-six of lines <PJ>	*s.* S 126		
D 944	**double subscript** <lower index>; double superscript <upper index> <GN>	Doppelindex *m*, zweifacher Index *m*, Doppelmarke *f*	double indice *m*	двойной индекс
D 945	**double sum** <SS>	Doppelsumme *f*	somme *f* double	двойная сумма
	double sum <SS>	*s.* S 2257		
	double superscript <GN>	*s.* D 944		
D 946	**double surface** <GE>	Doppelfläche *f*	surface *f* double	двойная поверхность
	double system [of quantities] <GN>	*s.* S 2539		
	doublet <TO>	*s.* T 1101		
	double-tailed test <ST>	*s.* T 1124		
D 947	**double tangent** <two coincident lines> <AG>	Doppeltangente *f*	tangente *f* double	двойная касательная

No.	English	German	French	Russian
D 948	**double-tangential knot** <GE>	zweitangentiger Knoten *m*	nœud *m* de deux tangentes	двухтангентный узел
	double tangent with distinct points of contact <AY, DG>	*s.* B 471/3		
D 949	**double tensor,** tensor of order two, second-order tensor <VT>	Tensor *m* zweiter Stufe, zweistufiger Tensor	tenseur *m* d'ordre deux	тензор второй валентности, двухвалентный тензор, //диадик, диада
D 950	**double-valued function** <AN, FT>; two-sheeted function <FT>	zweideutige (zweiwertige) Funktion *f*; zweiblättrige Funktion	fonction *f* bivalente (bivaluée, à deux valeurs); fonction biforme (à deux feuilles, à double couche)	дву[х]значная функция; дву[х]листная функция
D 951	**double-valuedness,** two-valuedness <AL>	Zweiwertigkeit *f*	propriété *f* d'avoir deux valeurs, bivalence *f*	двузначность, двухзначность
D 952	**double-valuedness** <AL, AN>	Zweideutigkeit *f*	bivalence *f*	двузначность, двухзначность
D 953	**double wedge** <EG>	Doppelkeil *m*	coin *m* double	двусторонний клин
	double-well-ordered set	*s.* D 961		
D 954	**doubly binary form** <AL>	doppelt binäre Form *f*	forme *f* doublement binaire	двоякобинарная форма
D 955	**doubly connected space,** biconnected space <TO>	zweifach zusammenhängender Raum *m*	espace *m* doublement connexe	двусвязное пространство
	doubly infinite array <MD>	*s.* I 464		
	doubly infinite sequence <SE, SS>	*s.* D 942		
D 956	**doubly inflected hyperbola** <as a cubic> <AG>	doppelt (zweifach) inflektierte Hyperbel *f* <Salmon>	hyperbole *f* doublement infléchie	
D 957	**doubly ordered set** <Cantor> <SE>	doppelt geordnete Menge *f*	ensemble *m* doublement ordonné	двоякоупорядоченное множество
D 958	**doubly periodic function,** double periodic function <FT>	doppelt[-]periodische Funktion *f*	fonction *f* doublement périodique	двоякопериодическая функция
D 959	**doubly projective variety** <AG, PJ>	doppeltprojektive (zweifach projektive) Mannigfaltigkeit *f*	variété *f* doublement projective	двупроективное многообразие
D 960	**doubly stochastic matrix,** bistochastic matrix <MD, ST>	doppelt stochastische Matrix *f*	matrice *f* bistochastique	дважды стохастическая матрица, бистохастическая матрица
	doubly straight line <AG, AY>	*s.* D 924		
	doubly-transitive group <GR>	*s.* T 1089		
D 961	**doubly well-ordered set,** double-well-ordered set <SE>	doppeltwohlgeordnete Menge *f*	ensemble *m* doublement bien ordonné	двояко вполне упорядоченное множество
	Douglas['] problem ┌<AN>	*s.* P 1561		
D 962	**downcross, down-cross** <SP>	Niveauschnitt *m* nach unten	intersection *f* de niveau vers le bas	пересечение уровня вниз <точка временного ряда, в которой знак отклонения от средней меняется с плюса на минус>
D 963	**downward bias** <ST>	Verzerrung *f* nach unten, [systematische] Abweichung *f* nach unten	biais *m* en (vers le) bas	смещение вниз (в сторону уменьшения)
	downward deviation ┌<AX>	*s.* L 1139		
	downward[s] induction <FO>	*s.* D 314		
D 964	**dragging-along** <the coordinate system> <DG>	Mitschleppen *n*, Mitnahme *f* <des Koordinatensystems>	entraînement *m* <du système des coordonnées>	увлечение <системы координат>
	drawer principle of Dirichlet <CT>	*s.* B 705		
	drawing <ST>	*s.* S 34		
D 965	**drawing without replacement,** sampling without replacement <ST>	Ziehen *n* ohne Zurücklegen, Stichprobennahme *f* ohne Zurücklegen	tirage *m* sans remise (remplacement), tirage exhaustif, échantillonnage *m* sans remplacement, sondage *m* sans remplacement, échantillonnage (sondage) sans remise, échantillonnage (sondage) exhaustif	извлечение (выбор) без возвращения, выбор без повторения, выборка без возвращения (повторения), безвозвратная выборка, бесповторная выборка
D 966	**drawing with replacement,** sampling with replacement <ST>	Ziehen *n* mit Zurücklegen, Stichprobennahme *f* mit Zurücklegen	tirage (échantillonnage, sondage) *m* avec remise (remplacement), tirage (échantillonnage, sondage) *n* non exhaustif, tirage au sort dans l'urne de Bernoulli	извлечение (выбор) с возвращением, выбор с повторением, выборка с возвращением (повторением), возвратная (повторная) выборка
D 967	**draw the parallel / to** <to a line through a point> <EG>	die Parallele ziehen (zeichnen) <zu einer Geraden durch einen Punkt>	tirer (mener) la parallèle <à une droite en (à travers) un point>	проводить (провести) параллель <к прямой через точку>
	draw the perpendicular to a line in a point / to <EG>	*s.* E 457		
D 968	**draw (drop) the perpendicular (normal) to a line from a point / to** <EG>	das Lot fällen von einem Punkt auf eine Gerade	abaisser (mener) la perpendiculaire à partir d'un point sur une droite	опускать перпендикуляр с точки к прямой

D 969	**Droz-Farny theorem** <EG>	Droz-Farnyscher Satz *m*, Satz von Droz-Farny	théorème *m* de Droz-Farny	теорема Дроза-Фарни
D 970	**d-system** <of sets> <SE>	*d*-System *n*	famille *f* [simplement] multiplicative	*d*-система
	dual <AL, FA>	*s.* F 704		
	dual <FA, TO>	*s.* A 307		
	dual <LO>	*s.* D 991		
	dual <SE>	*s.* 1. D 1022; 2. I 941		
D 971	**dual abelian group** <GR>	duale abelsche Gruppe *f*	groupe *m* abélien dual	дуальная абелева группа
D 972	**dual abelian variety** <AG>	duale abelsche Mannigfaltigkeit *f*	variété *f* abélienne duale	двойственное абелево многообразие
D 973	**dual anti-involution** <PJ>	duale Antiinvolution *f*, involutorische duale Antikollineation *f*	antiinvolution *f* duale	двойственная антиинволюция
	dual atom <LA>	*s.* C 965		
	dual automorphism <LA>	*s.* C 2370		
D 974	**dual base** <AB>	duale Basis *f*	base *f* supplémentaire (duale)	дуальный базис
D 975	**dual base,** dual basis <AL>	duale Basis *f*	base *f* duale	сопряженный (дуальный, двойственный) базис
D 976	**dual base** <of a lattice> <AL>	duale Basis *f*	base *f* duale	сопряженная база
	dual base <SE>	*s.* C 967		
D 977	**dual basis** <of a topological space> <TO>	duale Basis *f*	base *f* duale	двойственный базис
	dual basis <AL>	*s.* D 975		
D 978	**dual bundle** <AT>	duales Vektorraumbündel (Bündel) *n*, Dual *n*	fibré *m* vectoriel dual	двойственное расслоение
D 979	**dual category,** opposite category <CA>	duale („entgegengesetzte") Kategorie *f*	catégorie *f* duale (opposée)	двойственная (дуальная) категория
D 980	**dual cell** <AT>	duale Zelle *f*, Komplementärzelle *f*	cellule *f* duale	двойственная клетка
D 981	**dual Chern class** <AT>	duale Chernsche Klasse *f*	classe *f* duale de Chern	дуальный класс Чженя
D 982	**dual collineation** <PJ>	duale Kollineation *f*	collinéation *f* duale	двойственная (дуальная) коллинеация
D 983	**dual complex** <AT>	dualer (konjugierter) Komplex *m*	complexe *m* dual	дуальный комплекс
	dual complex <AT>	*s.* B 72		
D 984	**dual cone** <GE>	Reziprokalkegel *m*	cône *m* réciproque	двойственный конус
D 985	**dual correlation** <PJ>	duale Korrelation *f*	corrélation *f* duale	двойственная (дуальная) корреляция, двойственное (дуальное) коррелятивное преобразование
D 986	**dual couple,** dual vector spaces <FA>	Dualsystem *n*, Linearsystem *n*, duales Paar *n*	couple *m* d'espaces associés	дуальная пара, дуальные (спаренные) векторные пространства
D 987	**dual curve** <AG, AY>	Reziprokalkurve *f*, duale Kurve *f*	courbe *f* réciproque (réciprocale, duale)	двойственная кривая
D 988	**dual diagram scheme** <CA>	duales Diagrammschema *n*	schéma *m* de diagrammes dual	двойственная диаграммная схема, дуальная схема
D 989	**dual figure** <PJ>	duale Figur *f*	figure *f* duale	двойственная (дуальная) фигура
D 990	**dual form** <AL>	duale Form *f*	forme *f* duale	двойственная форма
D 991	**dual formula,** dual <LO>	duale Formel *f*, dualer Ausdruck *m*	formule *f* duale	двойственная формула
D 992	**dual fraction,** dyadic fraction <NT>	Dualbruch *m*, dyadischer (binärer) Bruch *m*, Bruch des Binärsystems	fraction *f* dyadique (binaire), // fraction diadique	двоичная дробь
D 993	**dual functor** <CA>	dualer Funktor *m*	foncteur *m* dual	двойственный функтор
D 994	**dual graph,** medial graph <GP>	dualer Graph *m*	graphe *m* dual	двойственный граф
	dual group <GR>	*s.* C 513		
D 995	**dual ideal,** product ideal, filter <of a lattice> <LA>	$\cap$-Ideal *n*, duales Ideal *n*, Dualideal *n*, Filter *m*	d-idéal *m*, $\cap$-idéal *m*, filtre *m*	дуальный идеал, двойственный идеал, фильтр
D 996	**dual involution** <PJ>	duale Involution *f*	involution *f* duale	двойственная (дуальная) инволюция, двойственное (дуальное) инволюционное преобразование
D 997	**dual isomorphism** <LA>	dualer Isomorphismus *m*	isomorphisme *m* dual	дуальный изоморфизм
D 998	**duality** <AL, DG, LO, NO, PG, PJ, TO>	Dualität *f*	dualité *f*	двойственность
	duality <PJ>	*s.* R 263		
	duality formula <AT>	*s.* W 242		
D 999	**duality functor** <CA>	Dualitätsfunktor *m*	foncteur *m* de dualité	функтор двойственности
D 1000	**duality principle** <AL, CA, LA>	Dualitätsprinzip *n*	principe *m* (loi *f*) de dualité <AL, CA>; principe de réflexivité <LA>	принцип двойственности
D 1001	**duality principle** <LO>	Dualitätstheorem *n*, Prinzip *n* der Dualität, Dualitätsprinzip *n*	principe *m* de dualité	закон двойственности, принцип дуальности
D 1002	**duality principle,** principle of duality <of projective geometry> <PJ>	Dualitätsprinzip *n*, Dualitätsgesetz *n*, Prinzip *n* der Dualität (Reziprozität), Reziprozitätsprinzip *n*	principe *m* de dualité (réciprocité)	принцип двойственности (взаимности), дуальный принцип; малый принцип двойственности <в проективной плоскости>; большой принцип двойственности <в проективном пространстве>

D 1003	**duality principle of predicate calculus** <LO>	erweitertes Dualitätsprinzip *n*, Dualitätsprinzip des Prädikatenkalküls, prädikatenlogisches Dualitätstheorem *n*	principe *m* de dualité du calcul des prédicats	расширенный принцип двойственности
D 1004	**duality principle of set algebras** <AL>	Dualitätsprinzip *n* der Mengenalgebra, mengenalgebraische Dualität *f*	principe *m* de dualité des algèbres d'ensembles	принцип двойственности алгебр множеств
D 1005	**duality relation** <AL, LO, PG, PJ, TO>	Dualitätsrelation *f*, Dualitätsbeziehung *f*	relation *f* de dualité	соотношение двойственности
D 1006	**duality theorem** <for linear programming> <PG>	Dualitätssatz *m*, Dualitätstheorem *n*, Dualitätsprinzip *n*	théorème *m* de dualité	теорема двойственности
	duality theorem <AL>	*s.* P 1032		
	duality theorem of Poincaré <AT>	*s.* P 704		
D 1007	**duality theorem of Tannaka** <for groups> <GR>	Tannakas Dualitätssatz *m*	théorème *m* de dualité de Tannaka	теорема двойственности Таннака
	duality theorem of Wolfe <PG>	*s.* W 287		
D 1007a	**dualizable module** <AL>	dualisierbarer Modul *m*	module *m* dualisable	дуализируемый модуль <модуль, для которого существует двойственный модуль>
	dualization <AL, LO, PG, PJ, TO>	*s.* D 1009		
D 1008	**dualized problem** <PG>	dualisierte Aufgabe *f*, dualisiertes Problem *n*	problème *m* dualisé	двойственная задача
D 1009	**dualizing,** dualization <AL, LO, PG, PJ, TO>	Dualisierung *f*, Dualisieren *n*	dualisation *f*, procédé *m* dual	дуализация, переведение в двойственное
	dualizing <AY, PJ>	*s.* P 889		
	dualizing <AY, PJ>	*s.* P 867		
D 1010	**dualizing functor** <AL, CA>	dualisierender Funktor *m*	foncteur *m* dualisant	дуализирующий функтор
D 1011	**dualizing module** <of a group> <AL>	dualisierender Modul *m*	module *m* dualisant	дуализирующий модуль
D 1012	**dual lattice** <AL>	duales Gitter *n*	réseau *m* dual	сопряженная решетка
D 1013	**dual lattice** <LA>	dualer Verband *m*	treillis *m* dual	дуальная структура
D 1014	**dual mapping** <of dual modules> <AL>	duale Abbildung *f*	application *f* duale	двойственное (дуальное) преобразование
D 1015	**dual module,** linear form module, module of linear forms <of a module> <AL>	dualer Modul *m*, Linearformenmodul *m*, Dualmodul *m*	module *m* dual, dual *m*	модуль линейных форм, дуальный (двойственный) модуль
D 1016	**dual number** <AL>	duale Zahl *f* <Study>; dualer Zahlenwert *m*	nombre *m* dual	дуальное число, комплексное число параболического типа
	dual number <NT>	*s.* B 370		
	dual of a simplex T_i <AT>	*s.* B 77		
D 1017	**dual operation** <LO>	duale Operation *f*	opération *f* duale	двойственная операция
D 1018	**dual operator,** dual transformation <FA>	dualer Operator *m*, duale Transformation *f*	opérateur *m* dual, transformation *f* duale	двойственный оператор, двойственное преобразование
D 1019	**dual partial ordering,** converse partial ordering, converse ordering relation <SE>	konverse Halbordnung *f*, konverse Ordnungsrelation *f*	relation *f* d'ordre duale, structure *f* (relation) d'ordre opposée, ordre *m* inverse (dual, opposé)	двойственный частичный порядок
D 1020	**dual partition,** conjugate partition <NT>	konjugierte Partition *f*	partition *f* conjuguée	двойственное разбиение
D 1021	**dual point** <PJ>	dualer Punkt *m*	point *m* dual	двойственная точка
D 1022	**dual poset,** dual <of a partially ordered set> <SE>	konvers halbgeordnete Menge *f*	ensemble *m* ordonné dual, inverse *m* <d'un ensemble ordonné>	двойственное частично упорядоченное множество
D 1023	**dual principal ideal** <in a lattice> <LA>	duales Hauptideal *n*, ⌒-Hauptideal *n*	idéal *m* principal dual	двойственный главный идеал
	dual principal ideal <AL, SE>	*s.* P 1415		
D 1024	**dual problem** <of programming> <PG>	duales Problem (Optimierungsproblem) *n*, duale Aufgabe *f*	problème *m* dual	двойственная задача [программирования]
D 1025	**dual projective line** <PJ>	duale projektive Gerade *f*	droite *f* projective duale	двойственная (дуальная) проективная прямая
D 1026	**dual proposition** <LO>	duale Aussage *f*	proposition *f* duale, duale *f*	двойственное высказывание
	dual proposition <PJ>	*s.* D 1036		
D 1027	**dual quantifier** <LO>	dualer Quantor *m*	quantificateur *m* dual	двойственный квантор
D 1028	**dual representation** <of a Lie algebra> <AL, RE>	duale Darstellung *f*	représentation *f* duale	дуальное представление
D 1029	**dual Schützenberger group** <AL>	duale Schützenberger-Gruppe *f*	groupe *m* de Schützenberger dual	двойственная группа Шютценберже
D 1030	**dual sentence,** reciprocal sentence <LO>	dualisierte Aussage *f*	énoncé *m* dualisé	двойственное предложение
D 1031	**dual simplex method** <PG>	duale Simplexmethode *f*, duales Simplexverfahren *n*	méthode *f* du simplexe duale, méthode simpliciale duale	двойственный симплекс-метод
D 1032	**dual simplex tableau** <PG>	duales Simplextableau *n*	tableau *m* simplicial dual	двойственная симплексная таблица
	dual space <AL, FA>	*s.* F 704		
	dual space <FA, TO>	*s.* A 307		
D 1033	**dual spaces,** dual vector spaces <with respect to an inner product> <AL>	duale Vektorräume *mpl*	espace *mpl* vectoriels duaux	спаренные векторные пространства, дуальные векторные пространства
	dual standard construction <CA>	*s.* M 815		
D 1034	**dual Stiefel-Whitney class** <AT>	duale Stiefel-Whitneysche Klasse *f*	classe *f* duale de Stiefel-Whitney	двойственный класс Штифеля-Уитни
D 1035	**dual surface** <of an algebraic surface> <AG>	Reziprokalfläche *f*	surface *f* réciproque	двойственная поверхность

	English	German	French	Russian
D 1036	**dual theorem,** reciprocal theorem, dual (reciprocal, correlative) proposition <PJ>	dualer Satz *m*	théorème *m* dual	двойственная теорема
D 1037	**dual transformation** <LO> ┌<FA>	duale Transformation *f*	transformation *f* duale	двойственное преобразование
	dual transformation	*s.* D 1018		
D 1038	**dual vector space** <AL>	dualer Vektorraum *m*	espace *m* vectoriel dual	сопряженное векторное пространство
	dual vector space <AL, FA>	*s.* F 704		
	dual vector spaces <AL>	*s.* D 1033		
	dual vector spaces <FA>	*s.* D 986		
D 1039	**Du Bois-Reymond['s] lemma** <VA>	Lemma *n* von Du Bois-Reymond, Du Bois-Reymondsches Lemma	lemme *m* de Du Bois-Reymond	теорема Дюбуа-Реймона
D 1040	**Du Bois-Reymond['s] test** <for convergence> <SS>	Du Bois-Reymondsches Kriterium *n*, Du Bois-Reymond-Kriterium *n*	critère *m* de [Paul] du Bois-Reymond	признак [сходимости] Дюбуа-Реймона
D 1041	**Du Bois-Reymond['s] theorem** <for trigonometric series> <SS>	Du Bois-Reymondscher Satz *m*	théorème *m* de [Paul] du Bois-Reymond	теорема Дюбуа-Реймона
D 1042	**duel,** game of timing <TG>	Duell *n*	duel *m*	дуэль, игра с выбором момента времени
D 1043	**Duffing['s] [differential] equation** <DE>	Duffingsche Differentialgleichung (Gleichung) *f*	équation *f* (équation différentielle) de Duffing	уравнение (дифференциальное уравнение) Дуффинга
D 1044	**Duhamel['s] integral** <DI>	Duhamelsches Integral *n*, Duhamel-Integral *n*	intégrale *f* de Duhamel	интеграл Дюамеля, // интеграл Дюхамеля
D 1045	**Duhamel['s] test [for convergence]** <SS>	Duhamelsches Konvergenzkriterium *n*	règle *f* de Duhamel	признак Дюамеля
D 1046	**Duhamel['s] theorem** <DI>	Duhamelsche Formel *f*, Duhamelscher Satz *m*	théorème *m* de Duhamel	теорема Дюамеля
D 1047	**dummy** <TG>	Strohmann *m*	mort *m*, homme *m* de paille	болван
	dummy <VT>	*s.* D 1049		
D 1048	**dummy combination,** pseudo-combination <ST>	Scheinkombination *f*	pseudo-combinaison *f*	псевдокомбинация, условная комбинация
D 1049	**dummy index,** dummy, umbral (saturated) index, umbral suffix, summation dummy (index) <of a tensor> <VT>	Summationsindex *m*	indice *m* muet (de sommation)	немой индекс, индекс суммирования
D 1050	**dummy scale** <NO>	Zapfenlinie *f*	ligne *f* de correspondance <entre deux tableaux nomographiques>	немая шкала
D 1051	**dummy subscript** <of a tensor> <VT>	unterer Summationsindex *m*	indice *m* inférieur muet	немой нижний индекс
	dummy suffix notation (summation convention) <VT>	*s.* S 2283		
	dummy variable <GN, LO>	*s.* B 699		
D 1052	**Duncan test** <ST>	Duncan-Test *m*	test *m* de Duncan	критерий Данкена
D 1053	**Dunett test** <ST>	Dunett-Test *m*	test *m* de Dunett	критерий Дунетта
	Dunford['s] spectral mapping theorem <FA>	*s.* S 1405		
D 1054	**Dunkerley-Jeffcott formula, Dunkerley['s] formula** <DE>	Aufspaltungsformel *f* von Dunkerley-Jeffcott, Dunkerleysche Formel *f*	formule *f* de Dunkerley [-Jeffcott]	формула Данкерлея
D 1055	**duodecimal arithmetic** <AR>	duodezimale Arithmetik *f*, Duodezimalrechnung *f*	arithmétique *f* duodécimale	двенадцатеричное счисление
D 1056	**duodecimal fraction** <AR>	Duodezimalbruch *m*, duodekadischer (zwölfteiliger) Bruch *m*	fraction *f* duodécimale	двенадцатеричная дробь
D 1057	**duodecimal notation** <of numbers> <NT>	duodezimale Schreibweise *f*, duodezimale Zahlendarstellung *f*	notation *f* duodécimale	представление [чисел] в двенадцатеричной системе
D 1058	**duodecimal system [of numbers]** <NT>	Duodezimalsystem *n*, duodezimales System (Zahlensystem) *n*, Zwölfersystem *n*	système *m* de numération duodécimal, système duodécimal [de numération]	двенадцатеричная система счисления, двенадцатеричная система
	duo-ring <AL>	*s.* I 878		
D 1059	**duotricenary [number] notation** <NT>	duotrizinäre Schreibweise (Zahlendarstellung) *f*	notation *f* duotricinaire	представление [чисел] в тридцатидвухричной системе
D 1060	**Dupin-Binet theorem** <DG>	Dupin-Binetscher Satz *m*, Satz von Dupin-Binet	théorème *m* de Dupin-Binet	теорема Дюпена-Бине
D 1061	**Dupin['s] cyclide** <DG>	Dupinsche Zyklide *f*, Zyklide von Dupin, Dupins Zyklide	cyclide *f* de [M.] Dupin, cyclide à quatre points coniques	циклида Дюпена
D 1062	**Dupin['s] indicatrix** <DG>	Dupinsche (Dupins) Indikatrix *f*, Dupinscher Kegelschnitt *m*	indicatrice *f* de Dupin, indicatrice de courbure	индикатриса Дюпена
D 1063	**Dupin['s] theorem** <DG>	Satz *m* von Dupin, Dupinscher Satz	théorème *m* de Dupin	теорема Дюпена
D 1064	**duplicate sample** <ST>	doppelt erhobene Stichprobe *f*	échantillon *m* répété, échantillon double	дубликат выборки, повторная (двойная) выборка
D 1065	**duplication formula,** Legendre['s] duplication formula <for the gamma-function> <FU>	Verdopplungsformel *f* <der Gammafunktion>	formule *f* de duplication	формула дополнения
D 1066	**duplication of the cube** <AL, EG>	Würfelverdopp[e]lung *f*, Kubusverdopplung *f*, Verdopplung *f* des Würfels	duplication *f* du cube	удвоение куба

No.	English	German	French	Russian
	duplication of the cube <EG>	*s.* D 209		
D 1067	**duplicatrix** <GE>	Duplikatrix *f*, Verdopplungskurve *f*	duplicatrice *f*, courbe *f* de duplication, cubique *f* duplicatrice	дупликатриса
D 1068	**duplicatrix of de Longchamps** <GE>	[kubische] Duplikatrix *f* von de Longchamps	duplicatrice *f* de de Longchamps	кубическая дупликатриса [Лоншампа], токсоида
	Dürer['s] conchoid <GE>	*s.* C 1783		
D 1069	**dyad,** dyadic product, tensor product <of two vectors> <VT>	Dyade *f*, dyadisches Produkt *n* <Jahnke>, unbestimmtes Produkt <Gibbs, Wilson>	dyade *f*, produit *m* tensoriel	диада, диадное произведение
D 1070	**dyadic** <VT>	Dyadensumme *f*	somme *f* de <deux ou plusieurs> dyades	сумма диад, диадик
D 1071	**dyadic discontinuum** <SE>	dyadisches Diskontinuum *n*	continu *m* dyadique	двоичный дисконтинуум
D 1072	**dyadic expansion** <of a number> <NT>	dyadische Entwicklung (Bruchentwicklung) *f*	développement *m* dyadique (binaire)	диадическое (двоичное) разложение, разложение в двоичную дробь
	dyadic fraction <NT>	*s.* D 992		
	dyadic Green['s] function <DE>	*s.* G 420		
D 1073	**dyadic multiplication** <VT>	dyadische Multiplikation *f*	multiplication *f* dyadique	диадное умножение
	dyadic number <NT>	*s.* B 370		
	dyadic number system <NT>	*s.* B 371		
	dyadic product <VT>	*s.* D 1069		
	dyadic product of two unit base vectors <VT>	*s.* U 273		
D 1074	**dyadic rational, dyadic-rational number** <NT>	dyadische rationale Zahl *f*, dyadisch-rationale Zahl	nombre *m* rationnel-binaire	двоично-рациональное число
	dyadic relation <LO>	*s.* T 1098		
	dyadic relation <SE, UA>	*s.* B 377		
D 1075	**dyadic set** <TO>	dyadische Menge *f*	ensemble *m* dyadique	диадическое множество
D 1076	**dyadic space** <TO>	dyadischer Raum *m*	espace *m* dyadique	диадическое пространство
	dyadic system <NT>	*s.* B 371		
	dynamic boundary condition <DE>	*s.* R 866		
	dynamic optimization <PG>	*s.* D 1077		
D 1077	**dynamic programming,** dynamic optimization <PG>	dynamische Optimierung (Programmoptimierung, Programmierung) *f*	programmation *f* dynamique, optimisation *f* dynamique	динамическое программирование (планирование), динамическая оптимизация
D 1078	**dynamic system** <SP, ST>	dynamisches (gesteuertes) System *n*	système *m* dynamique	динамическая система
	dynamic system [of differential equations] <DE>	*s.* A 1235		
D 1079	**Dynkin['s] diagram,** root diagram, chromosome, Schläfli['s] diagram <of the roots of a Lie algebra> <AL>	Dynkin-Diagramm *n*, Wurzeldiagramm *n*, Diagramm *n*	diagramme (schéma) *m* de Dynkin	диаграмма (схема) Дынкина

E

No.	English	German	French	Russian
E 1	**e,** number *e*, base of natural logarithms, base of the natural system of logarithms <AN>	*e*, Zahl *f e*, Basis *f* der natürlichen Logarithmen	base *f* des logarithmes népériens, nombre *m* de Néper	неперово число, основание натуральных логарифмов
	e, *e* <AN>	*s.* E 740		
	E <LO>	*s.* 1 E 698; 2. E 699		
	E <NT>	*s.* I 645		
	earlier <SE>	*s.* L 585		
E 2	**earlier element,** preceding (smaller) element <with respect to an order relation> <SE>	kleineres Element *n*	élément *m* antérieur (inférieur, plus petit)	элемент меньше <чем>
E 3	**easier Waring problem** <AB>	vereinfachtes Waring-Problem *n*	problème *m* de Waring simplifié	облегченная проблема Варинга
E 4	**Eberlein['s] theorem** <TO>	Satz *m* von Eberlein, Eberleinscher Satz	théorème *m* d'Eberlein	теорема Эберлейна
E 5	**E-calculus,** equivalence calculus <LO>	Äquivalenzenkalkül *m*, E-Kalkül *m*	calcul (système) *m* équivalentiel	исчисление эквивалентностей
E 6	**écart** <TO>	écart *m*	écart *m*	отклонение
	écart <TO>	*s.* P 1955		
E 7	**eccentric angle** <of an ellipse> <AY, EG>	exzentrische Anomalie *f*	anomalie *f* excentrique	эксцентрическая аномалия
E 8	**eccentricity,** numerical eccentricity <of a conic> <AY>	numerische Exzentrizität *f*, Exzentrizität	excentricité *f*, excentricité numérique	эксцентрицитет, числовой эксцентрицитет
E 9	**Eckhardt['s] point** <AG>	Eckhardtscher Punkt *m*	point *m* d'Eckhardt	точка Эккарта
	e-complete space <TO>	*s.* H 284		
E 10	**edge** <of a simplicial set> <AT>	Kante *f*	arête *f*	симплициальный отрезок, стандартный одномерный симплекс
E 11	**edge,** lateral edge <of a polyhedral angle *or* polyhedron> <EG>	Kante *f*	arête *f*	ребро
E 12/3	**edge,** element, line, branch, link <GP>	Kante *f*, Strecke *f*	ligne *f*, arête *f*, chemin *m*, lien *m*, segment *m*	ребро
	edge <AT>	*s.* S 240		

	edge <FT, TO>	*s.* B 567		
E 14	**edge[-]angle,** [plane] angle between two edges <of a solid angle *or* polyhedron> <EG>	Kantenwinkel *m*, // Seite *f*	angle *m* plan (rectiligne, compris entre deux arêtes, d'arêtes)	плоский угол [при вершине]
E 15	**edge colouration,** colouration of the edges <GP>	Kantenfärbung *f*	coloration *f* des arêtes	раскраска ребр
	edge colouration number <GP>	*s.* C 669		
E 16	**edge connectivity,** edge-connectivity <of a graph> <GP>	Kantenzusammenhang *m*	indice *m* de connexité	реберная связность
	edge-critical graph <GP>	*s.* L 857		
E 17	**edge curvature** <DG>	Kantenkrümmung *f*		реберная кривизна [по Я. Штейнеру]
	edge cut-set <GP, PG>	*s.* C 2815		
	edge-group <AT>	*s.* E 25		
E 18	**edge homomorphism** <HA>	Randhomomorphismus *m*	edge-homomorphisme *m*	краевой гомоморфизм
	edge independence number <GP>	*s.* N 822		
	edge issuing <GP>	*s.* O 552		
E 19	**edge length** <of a polyhedron> <EG>	Kantenlänge *f*	côté *m*, longueur *f* du côté	сторона, длина стороны
	edge-loop <AT>	*s.* C 858		
E 20	**edge of a hypergraph** <GP>	Kante *f* eines Hypergraphen	hyperarête *f*	гиперребро
E 21	**edge of an elementary cycle,** circuit edge, cycle edge <GP>	Kreiskante *f*	arête *f* d'un cycle élémentaire	ребро, принадлежащее к элементарному циклу
E 22	**edge of regression,** cuspidal edge <of a torse> <DG>	Rückkehrkante *f*, Kuspidalkante *f*, Gratlinie *f*, Rückkehrkurve *f*, Rebroussementskurve *f*	arête (courbe) *f* de rebroussement, arête, // côté *m* de rebroussement	ребро возврата
E 23	**edge of the wedge theorem** <FA>	„edge-of-the-wedge"-Theorem *n*	théorème *m* « Edge of the Wedge »	теорема об «острии клина»
E 24	**edge path,** edge-path, subpath <of a complex> <AT>	Kantenweg *m*, Kantenzug *m*		ломаная
E 25	**edge-path group** <of a complex *K* with base vertex v_0>, edge-group <of *K*, based at v_0> <AT>	Kantenwegegruppe *f* <eines Komplexes *K*>		группа ломаных <комплекса *K* с отмеченной вершиной v_0>
E 26	**edge-*p*-critical graph** <GP>	kanten-*p*-kritischer Graph *m*	graphe *m* *p*-arête-critique	реберно-*p*-критический граф
	edge progression <GP>	*s.* E 27		
E 27	**edge sequence,** sequence of edges, edge progression, chain, walk <of a nonoriented graph> <GP>	Kantenfolge *f*, Kantenzug *m*, Kantenprogression *f*	chaîne *f*, pseudochaîne *f*	маршрут
	edge starting from a pendant vertex <GP>	*s.* T 168		
E 28	**edge that is no loop** <GP>	echte Kante *f*	arête *f*, qui n'est pas une boucle	ребро, не являющееся петлей
E 29	**edge train,** trail, chain progression <of a nonoriented graph> <GP>	Kantenzug *m*, einfacher Kantenzug, Kettenprogression *f*	chaîne *f* simple, chaine *f*	цепь
E 30	**edge vector** <of a parallelotope> <GE>	Kantenvektor *m*	vecteur *m* de l'arête	вектор ребра
	Edgeworth expansion <ST>	*s.* E 31		
E 31	**Edgeworth series;** Edgeworth expansion <ST>	Edgeworth-Reihe *f*; Edgeworth-Entwicklung *f*	série *f* d'Edgeworth; expansion *f* d'Edgeworth	ряд Эджворта; разложение Эджворта
	edging <GE>	*s.* B 571		
	ef <FU>	*s.* 1. E 737; 2. H 53		
E 32	**effective convergence** <of a series> <SS>	effektive Konvergenz *f*	convergence *f* effective	эффективная сходимость
E 33	**effective cycle,** positive cycle <AG>	effektiver (positiver) Zyklus *m*	cycle *m* effectif (positif)	эффективный цикл
E 34	**effective definition** <MM>	effektive Definition *f*	définition *f* effective	эффективное определение
	effective denumerability <SE>	*s.* E 271		
	effective divisor <AG>	*s.* N 422		
	effective error mean square <ST>	*s.* E 43		
	effective group <AL>	*s.* E 42		
E 35	**effectively computable function** <MM>	effektiv berechenbare Funktion *f*	fonction *f* effectivement (intuitivement, mécaniquement) calculable	эффективно вычислимая функция, интуитивно вычислимая функция
E 36	**effectively decidable theory** <MM>	effektiv entscheidbare Theorie *f*	théorie *f* [effectivement] décidable	эффективно решимая теория
E 37	**effectively denumerable set,** enumerable set <SE>	effektiv abzählbare Menge *f*, aufzählbare Menge	ensemble *m* effectivement énumérable (dénombrable), ensemble énumérable	перечислимое множество
E 38	**effectively equivalent sets** <SE>	einwertig äquivalente Mengen *fpl* <Bernstein>, effektiv äquivalente Mengen	ensembles *mpl* ayant effectivement même puissance	эффективно эквивалентные множества
E 39	**effectively of the power of the continuum** <SE>	effektiv kontinuumsmächtig	effectivement de puissance du continu	имеющий эффективно мощность континуума
E 40	**effective multiplicity** <AG>	effektive Multiplizität *f*	multiplicité *f* effective	эффективная кратность
E 41	**effective number of replications** <ST>	effektive Wiederholungszahl *f*	nombre *m* effectif des répétitions	эффективное число репликаций
	effective process <MM>	*s.* A 484		

	English	German	French	Russian
E 42	**effective transformation group,** effective group <AL>	[effektive] Transformationsgruppe *f*	groupe *m* de transformations effectif	эффективная группа преобразований
E 43	**effective variance of error,** effective error mean square <ST>	effektive Fehlervarianz *f*	variance *f* effective de l'erreur	эффективная дисперсия ошибки
E 44	**effectivity** <of group action; also in logic> <AL, LO>	Effektivität *f*	effectivité *f*	эффективность
E 45	**effect variable** <ST>	Wirkungsvariable *f*	variable *f* dépendante influencée (sous influence)	влияемая зависимая переменная
E 46	**efficiency** <of a point estimation> <ST>	Wirksamkeit *f*, Effizienz *f*, Leistungsfähigkeit *f*	efficacité *f*, efficience *f*	эффективность
E 47	**efficiency factor,** relative efficiency <ST>	Wirksamkeitsfaktor *m*, Effizienzfaktor *m*, Wirksamkeitsgrad *m*, relative Wirksamkeit *f*	facteur *m* d'efficacité, efficacité *f* relative	коэффициент эффективности, относительная эффективность
E 48	**efficient estimating function, efficient estimator** <ST>	wirksame (effiziente, effektive) Schätzung *f*, effektive (wirksame) Schätzfunktion *f*	estimateur *m* efficace (effectif), fonction *f* d'estimation efficace (effective)	эффективная оценка
E 49	**efficient point** <PG>	Effizienzpunkt *m*	point *m* d'efficacité	точка эффективности
E 50	**efficient preference** <TG>	effiziente (wirksame) Präferenz *f*	préférence *f* efficace	эффективный преферанс, эффективное предпочтение
E 51	**efficient test** <ST>	effizienter (wirksamer, effektiver) Test *m*	test *m* efficace (effectif)	эффективный критерий
E 52	**E-function** <NT>	*E*-Funktion *f*	*E*-fonction *f*	*E*-функция [Зигеля]
	e-function <AN>	*s.* E 740		
	E-function of MacRobert <FU>	*s.* M 15		
	$\mathcal{E}$-function of Weierstrass <VA>	*s.* W 159		
	eg <FU>	*s.* H 54		
	Eger-Todd class <AT>	*s.* T 486		
	egg-shaped body <CS, GE>	*s.* C 2384		
	Egoroff['s] system [of surfaces] <DG>	*s.* E 552		
	Egoroff['s] theorem <ME>	*s.* E 53		
	Egorov['s] system [of surfaces] <DG>	*s.* E 552		
E 53	**Egorov['s] theorem,** Yegorov['s] (Egoroff['s]) theorem <ME>	Satz *m* von Egorov (Jegorow, Egorow, Egoroff), Egorovscher (Jegorowscher) Satz	théorème *m* d'Egoroff	теорема Егорова
E 54	**Ehrenfest['s] model** <ST>	Ehrenfestsches Modell *n*, Modell von Ehrenfest	modèle *m* d'Ehrenfest	модель Эренфеста
E 55	**Ehrenfeucht['s] theorem** <LO>	Satz *m* von Ehrenfeucht, Ehrenfeuchtscher Satz	théorème *m* d'Ehrenfeucht	теорема Эренфойхта
E 56	**Ehresmann['s] groupoid,** groupoid <CA>	Gruppoid *n* im Sinne von Ehresmann, Ehresmannsches Gruppoid	groupoïde *m*	группоид
	ei <FU>	*s.* I 624		
	Eichkörper <GU>	*s.* S 1603		
	eif <DE, IE>	*s.* E 57		
	eigenelement <FA>	*s.* E 58		
E 57	**eigenfunction,** eigensolution, characteristic function (solution), proper function (solution), fundamental function, eif <DE, IE>	Eigenfunktion *f*, Eigenlösung *f*	fonction *f* caractéristique, solution *f* caractéristique, fonction propre, solution propre	собственная функция, собственное решение, характеристическая функция, характеристическое решение
	eigenfunction <FA>	*s.* E 58		
	eigenfunction expansion <DE, IE>	*s.* E 710		
	eigenplane <VT>	*s.* C 569		
	eigenraum <FA>	*s.* C 563		
E 58	**eigensolution,** eigenfunction, eigenvector, eigenelement, characteristic solution (function, vector, element) <belonging to [the eigenvalue] λ> <of an operator equation> <FA>	Eigenlösung *f*, Eigenelement *n*, Eigenfunktion *f*, Eigenvektor *m* <zum Eigenwert λ gehörig>	élément *m* (solution *f*, vecteur *m*, fonction *f*) propre (caractéristique) <associé[e] à la valeur propre λ>	собственный элемент (вектор), собственная функция, собственное решение, характеристический элемент (вектор), характеристическая функция, характеристическое решение <соответствующие собственному значению λ>
	eigensolution <DE, IE>	*s.* E 57		
	eigenstate <FA>	*s.* C 578		
E 59	**eigenvalue,** characteristic (proper, principal) value, eit <DE>	Eigenwert *m*, charakteristischer Wert *m*	valeur *f* singulière (caractéristique, critique, propre)	собственное (характеристическое) значение
E 60	**eigenvalue** <of a linear integral equation> <IE>	Eigenwert *m*	valeur *f* propre	собственное значение
E 61	**eigenvalue,** proper value, characteristic value (root, number), proper number, [latent] root <of a matrix> <MD>	Eigenwert *m*, charakteristischer Wert *m*, charakteristische Zahl (Wurzel) *f*	valeur *f* propre (caractéristique), racine *f* caractéristique (latente), // racine lambdaïque <Sylvester>	характеристический корень, собственное (характеристическое) значение, характеристическое (собственное) число, собственный корень
	eigenvalue <AL, FA>	*s.* C 565		
E 62	**eigenvalue problem,** proper value problem <DE>	Eigenwertproblem *n*, Eigenwertaufgabe *f*	problème *m* aux valeurs singulières (caractéristiques, critiques, propres), pro-	задача на собственные значения, задача о собственных значениях,

and still: E 62			blème de valeur singulière (caractéristique, critique, propre)	задача нахождения (на отыскание) собственных значений
E 63	**eigenvalue problem, eigenvalue problem for matrices,** proper value problem <MD>	Eigenwertproblem *n*, Eigenwertaufgabe *f*, Matrizen-Eigenwertaufgabe *f*	problème *m* aux valeurs propres, problème de valeur propre [pour les matrices], problème de valeurs propres	задача о собственных значениях; задача нахождения собственных значений, задача на отыскание собственных значений, задача на собственные значения матрицы, матричная задача на собственные значения
E 64	**eigenvalue problem of an integral equation** <of the second kind> <IE>	Integralgleichungs-Eigenwertaufgabe *f*, Integralgleichungs-Eigenwertproblem *n*	problème *m* aux valeurs propres d'une équation intégrale <de deuxième espèce>	задача на собственные значения интегрального уравнения <второго рода>
E 65	**eigenvector,** proper (latent, characteristic) vector, modal column, proper state, pole <of a matrix> <MD>	Eigenvektor *m*	vecteur *m* propre (caractéristique)	собственный вектор, характеристический вектор
	eigenvector <FA>	*s.* E 58		
E 66	**eigenvector belonging to an eigenvalue** <MD>	zu einem Eigenwert gehöriger (gehörender) Eigenvektor *m*	vecteur *m* propre appartenant à une valeur propre	собственный вектор, принадлежащий к собственному числу
	eight curve <GE>	*s.* F 217		
	eikonal <VA>	*s.* G 237		
	Eilenberg-MacLane group <AT>	*s.* G 478		
E 67	**Eilenberg-MacLane space** <AT>	Eilenberg-MacLanescher Raum *m*	espace *m* d'Eilenberg-MacLane, espace de Eilenberg-MacLane	пространство Эйленберга-Маклейна
E 68	**Eilenberg-Zilber decomposition** <AT>	Eilenberg-Zilbersche Zerlegung *f*	décomposition *f* d'Eilenberg-Zilber	разложение Эйленберга-Зильбера
E 69	**Eilenberg-Zilber lemma (theorem)** <AT>	Satz *m* von Eilenberg-Zilber, Eilenberg-Zilberscher Satz	théorème *m* d'Eilenberg-Zilber	теорема (лемма) Эйленберга-Зильбера
E 70	**einartig ideal,** single-primed ideal <AL>	einartiges Ideal *n*	idéal *m* dont les suridéaux premiers minimaux sont maximaux	идеал с одним простым делителем, единообразный идеал
	Einstein['s] convention <VT>	*s.* S 2283		
E 71	**Einstein['s] space** <DG>	Einsteinsche Mannigfaltigkeit *f*, Einsteinscher Raum *m*, Einstein-Raum *m*	espace *m* d'Einstein, espace einsteinien	пространство Эйнштейна
	Einstein['s] summation convention <VT>	*s.* S 2283		
	Einstein['s] sum-notation <VT>	*s.* S 2283		
	Einstein['s] tensor <DG>	*s.* R 981		
E 72	**einstufig group** <GR>	einstufige Gruppe *f*		одноступенчатая группа
E 73	**Eisenhart['s] classification** <ST>	Eisenhartsche Klassifikation *f*	classification *f* d'Eisenhart	классификация Эйзенхарта
	Eisenstein['s] criterion <AL>	*s.* E 76		
E 74	**Eisenstein['s] equation** <AL>	Eisensteinsche (eisensteinsche) Gleichung *f*	équation *f* d'Eisenstein	уравнение Эйзенштейна
E 75	**Eisenstein extension** <of a field> <AL>	eisensteinsche Erweiterung *f*	extension *f* d'Eisenstein	расширение Эйзенштейна
E 76	**Eisenstein['s] irreducibility criterion,** Eisenstein['s] criterion <AL>	Eisensteinsches Irreduzibilitätskriterium *n*, Eisensteins Satz *m* <über die Irreduzibilität algebraischer Gleichungen>	critère *m* d'irréductibilité d'Eisenstein, théorème *m* d'Eisenstein	критерий Эйзенштейна, критерий неприводимости Эйзенштейна
E 77	**Eisenstein['s] number** <AB>	Eisensteinsche Zahl *f*	nombre *m* d'Eisenstein	число Эйзенштейна
E 78	**Eisenstein['s] polynomial** <AL>	Eisensteinsches Polynom *n*	polynôme *m* d'Eisenstein	многочлен Эйзенштейна
E 79	**Eisenstein['s] series** <AN>	Eisenstein-Reihe *f*, Eisensteinsche Reihe *f*	série *f* d'Eisenstein, suite *f* d'Eisenstein	ряд Эйзенштейна
E 80	**Eisenstein['s] sum** <AB>	Eisensteinsche Summe *f*	somme *f* d'Eisenstein	сумма Эйзенштейна
	eit <DE>	*s.* E 59		
	ejector <GE>	*s.* I 204		
	elastic geometry <TO>	*s.* C 101 a		
E 81	**element** <of a pencil> <AG, AY>	Büschelelement *n*, Element *n*	membre *m*	элемент
E 82	**element,** rudiment <of a theory> <EO>	Element *n*	élément *m*	начало
E 83	**element** <of a family of curves> <GE>	Scharkurve *f*	courbe *m* d'un système de courbes	кривая семейства
E 84	**element,** cell <of a matroid> <GP>	Element *n*	élément *m*	элемент
E 85	**element,** coefficient, entry <of a matrix *or* determinant> <MD>	Element *n*, Koeffizient *m*, Glied *n*	élément *m*, coefficient *m*, terme *m*	элемент, коэффициент, компонента
E 86	**element** <of a partially ordered set> <SE>	Soma *n* <*pl*: Somen>, Element *n* <eines Vereins>	élément *m*	элемент
E 87	**element,** member <of a set> <SE>	Element *n*	élément *m*, membre *m*, point *m*	элемент, член

	element <EG>	*s.* G 249		
	element <FT>	*s.* F 759		
	element <GP>	*s.* E 12		
	element <GR>	*s.* G 459		
	element <LO>	*s.* 1. C 1656; M 381		
E 88	**element algebraically dependent** <on a set over a field> <AL>	algebraisch-abhängiges Element *n* <über einem Körper von einer Menge>	élément *m* algébriquement dépendant <d'un ensemble sur un corps>	элемент, алгебраически зависимый <от множества над полем>
E 89	**element algebraically independent** <of a set over a field> <AL>	algebraisch-unabhängiges Element *n* <über einem Körper von einer Menge>	élément *m* algébriquement indépendant <d'un ensemble sur un corps>	элемент, алгебраически независимый <от множества над полем>
E 90	**elementary arc** <DG>	Elementarbogen *m*	arc *m* élémentaire	элементарная дуга
E 91	**elementary automaton** <TA>	Elementarautomat *m*	automate *m* élémentaire	элементарный автомат
E 92	**elementary chain** <AT>	Elementarkette *f*	chaînon *m*	одночленная цепь
E 93	**elementary chain** <in an oriented graph> <GP>	elementare Kette *f*, kontinuierlich gerichteter Weg *m*	chaîne *f* élémentaire	элементарная цепь
E 94	**elementary characteristic** <of curves, surfaces, conics> <GE>	Elementarcharakteristik *f*, Charakteristik *f* eines Elementarsystems	caractéristique *f* élémentaire	элементарная характеристика
E 95	**elementary circuit** <GP>	Elementarzirkuit *m*	circuit *m* élémentaire	элементарный контур
	elementary circuit <GP>	*s.* D 540		
	elementary class <UA>	*s.* A 1270		
E 96	**elementary column transformation,** elementary operation (transformation) on the columns <of a matrix> <MD>	elementare Transformation *f* der Spalten	transformation *f* élémentaire des colonnes	элементарное преобразование столбцов
E 97	**elementary conjunction** <LO>	Elementarkonjunktion *f*, Elementarprodukt *n*	produit *m* élémentaire	элементарное произведение
E 98	**elementary cycle,** cycle, circuit, loop, simple circuit <in a non-directed graph> <GP>	Elementarzyklus *m*, Kreis *m*, einfache geschlossene Kantenzugprogression *f*	cycle *m* élémentaire	элементарный цикл, простой цикл
	elementary cycle <GP>	*s.* S 892a		
E 99	**elementary disjunction** <LO>	elementare Disjunktion *f*, Elementarsumme *f*	disjonction *f* élémentaire, somme *f* élémentaire	элементарная сумма
E 100	**elementary divisor,** invariant factor <of a matrix> <AL>	Elementarteiler *m*, invarianter Faktor *m*	diviseur *m* élémentaire, produit *m* élémentaire <Drach>	элементарный делитель
E 101	**elementary divisor** <Weierstrass>, simple elementary divisor <of a polynomial matrix *or* module> <AL>	einfacher (Weierstraßscher) Elementarteiler *m*, elementare Invariante *f* <Polynommatrix>; primärer Elementarteiler *m* <Matrix, Modul>	diviseur *m* élémentaire, invariant *m* élémentaire	элементарный делитель, элементарный инвариант
E 102	**elementary divisor theorem** <AL>	Elementarteilersatz *m*, E. T.-Satz *m*	théorème *m* sur les diviseurs élémentaires	теорема об элементарных делителях
E 103	**elementary domain** <of degree *m*> <GE>	Elementarbereich *m*, Elementargebiet *n*, Ausdehnungsgebiet *n* <*m*-ter Stufe>	domaine *m* élémentaire <du degré *m*>	элементарная область, элемент области <*m*-ой степени>
E 104	**elementary embedding** <UA>	elementare Einbettung *f*	plongement *m* élémentaire	элементарное вложение, Е-вложение
E 105	**elementary error** <ER>	Elementarfehler *m*	erreur *f* élémentaire	элементарная погрешность
	elementary event <ST>	*s.* S 908		
	elementary figure <TO>	*s.* E 118		
E 106	**elementary filter** <TO>	Elementarfilter *m*	filtre *m* élémentaire	элементарный фильтр
E 107	**elementary formula,** prime formula <LO>	Elementarformel *f*	formule *f* élémentaire	элементарная формула
	elementary function <AN>	*s.* S 1747		
E 108	**elementary geometry,** Euclidian geometry <EG>	Elementargeometrie *f*, elementare (Euklidische) Geometrie *f*; Schulgeometrie *f*	géométrie *f* élémentaire (euclidienne)	элементарная (евклидова) геометрия; геометрия, изучаемая в средней школе
E 109	**elementary group,** characteristically simple group, characteristically-simple group <GR>	elementare Gruppe *f*, charakteristisch einfache Gruppe, charakteristisch-einfache Gruppe	groupe *m* élémentaire	элементарная группа, характеристически простая группа
E 110	**elementary integral** <of the first, second, *or* third kind> <AL, AN>	Elementarintegral *n* <erster (1.), zweiter (2.) *oder* dritter (3.) Gattung>	intégrale *f* élémentaire <de première, deuxième *ou* troisième espèce>	элементарный интеграл <первого, второго *или* третьего рода>
	elementary Jordan matrix <AL>	*s.* J 94		
	elementary logic [of predicates] <LO>	*s.* F 347		
	elementary logic with equality (identity)	*s.* F 348		
E 111	**elementary logic with identity and function symbols** <LO>	I-Kalkül *m* mit Funktionalen, Funktionalkalkül *m* erster Stufe mit Identität	logique *f* fonctionnelle avec identité	функциональное исчисление первого порядка с равенством
	elementary logic without identity <LO>	*s.* F 349		
E 112	**elementary matrix** <AL>	Elementarmatrix *f*, elementare Matrix *f*	matrice *f* élémentaire, système *m* élémentaire <Kronecker>	элементарная матрица
E 113	**elementary *n*-chain,** *n*-dimensional elementary chain <AT>	*n*-dimensionale Elementarkette *f*	*n*-chaînon *m*, chaînon *m* de dimension *n*	*n*-мерная одночленная цепь
E 114	**elementary notion** <FO>	elementarer Begriff *m*	notion *f* élémentaire, concept *m* élémentaire	начальное понятие, единичное понятие

No.	English	German	French	Russian
E 115	**elementary number theory** <FO, NT>	elementare Zahlentheorie (Arithmetik) *f*, reine Zahlentheorie	arithmétique *f* élémentaire	элементарная теория чисел, элементарная арифметика
E 116	**elementary operation,** equivalent transformation <on a matrix> <MD>	elementare Transformation *f*, elementare Umformung *f*, Elementartransformation *f*	transformation (opération) *f* élémentaire	элементарное преобразование, элементарная операция, простейшее преобразование
	elementary operation on the columns <MD>	*s.* E 96		
E 117	**elementary patch [of surface]** <TO>	elementares Flächenstück *n*, Elementarfläche *f*, Elementarflächenstück *n*, zweidimensionales Element *n*	aire *f* élémentaire	элементарный простой кусок
	elementary path <GP>	*s.* D 549		
	elementary predicate logic <LO> ⌐<LO>	*s.* F 347		
	elementary proposition	*s.* A 1192		
E 118	**elementary set,** elementary figure <in a product space> <TO>	Elementarmenge *f*	ensemble *m* élémentaire	элементарное множество
	elementary set <RF, SE, TO>	*s.* C 2910		
E 119	**elementary subdivision** <AT>	Elementarunterteilung *f*, Elementarzerlegung *f*, elementare Unterteilung *f*	subdivision *f* élémentaire	элементарное подразделение
E 120	**elementary subsystem** <UA>	elementares Untersystem *n*	sous-système *m* élémentaire	элементарная подсистема, Е-подсистема
E 121	**elementary symmetric function** <n-th, of degree n> <AL>	symmetrisches Grundpolynom *n*, elementarsymmetrisches Polynom *n*, elementares symmetrisches Polynom, symmetrische Grundfunktion *f*, elementar[-]symmetrische Funktion *f* <vom Grade n>	fonction *f* (polynôme *m*) symétrique élémentaire <de degré n>	основная симметрическая функция, элементарно-симметрическая функция, симметрическая функция <n-ая, n-ой степени>, элементарный симметрический многочлен <n-й, n-ой степени>
	elementary transformation on the columns <MD>	*s.* E 96		
E 122	**elementary yield** <ST>	Elementarertrag *m*	rendement *m* élémentaire	элементарный выход
E 123	**element at infinity,** infinite (ideal, improper) element <PJ>	unendlich[ ]fernes Element, uneigentliches (ideales) Element, Fernelement *n*	élément *m* à (de) l'infini, élément idéal (impropre), direction *f*	бесконечно удаленный элемент, несобственный элемент
E 124	**element between x and y** <SE>	Element *n* zwischen x und y	élément *m* entre x et y, élément intermédiaire (compris) entre x et y	элемент между x и y
E 125	**element defined by the** <Dedekind> **section** <AN, SE>	Schnittelement *n*	élément *m* défini par la coupure, élément à la coupure	элемент, определяемый сечением
E 126	**element** <of a ring> **divisible on the left** <AL>	linksteilbares Element (Ringelement) *n*	élément *m* <d'un anneau> divisible à gauche	делимый слева элемент <кольца>
E 127	**element** <of a ring> **divisible on the right** <AL>	rechtsteilbares Element (Ringelement) *n*	élément *m* <d'un anneau> divisible à droite	делимый справа элемент <кольца>
	element inaccessible from below <LA>	*s.* I 210		
	element integrally dependent on R <AL>	*s.* I 622		
E 128	**element in the first position in the first column** <of a matrix> <MD>	Element *n* in der linken oberen Ecke, Element links oben, linkes oberes Element, Spitzenelement *n*	élément *m* en position (1, 1)	верхний элемент главной диагонали
	element in the (i, j) position <MD>	*s.* E 130		
E 129	**element locally zero** <AT>	Element *n* lokal Null	élément *m* localement nul	локально нулевой элемент
E 130	**element lying in the i-th row and j-th column,** entry lying in the i-th row and j-th column, element in the (i, j) position, i, j matrix element <of a matrix *or* determinant> <MD>	Element *n* an der Stelle (i, j)	coefficient *m* i-e rangée, j-e colonne	элемент, лежащий в i-й строке и j-м столбце; элемент, стоящий в i-й строке и j-м столбце; элемент на месте (i, j), элемент на (i, j)-месте, (i, j)-й элемент
E 131	**element of area,** differential of area, areal element, surface element <DG, DI>	Flächenelement *n*, Oberflächenelement *n*	élément *m* de surface, élément superficiel (d'aire), surface *f* élémentaire	элемент площади [поверхности], элемент поверхности, площадка
E 131a	**element of best approximation,** minimal (minimum) solution <AX>	Element *n* der besten Approximation, Minimallösung <für f in R>, Projektion *f* <von f auf R>	élément *m* de la meilleure approximation, solution *f* minimale	элемент наилучшего приближения, минимальное решение, проекция
E 132	**element of contact** <DG, GE>	Berührungselement *n*, Element *n*	élément *m* de contact	элемент касания
E 133	**element of contact of dimension n** <DG>	n-dimensionales Element *n* <mit dem Träger z>	n-élément *m*, élément *m* de contact de dimension n <d'origine z>	n-мерный элемент касания
E 134	**element of finite order,** torsion (periodic) element <of a group> <GR>	Element *n* endlicher Ordnung, Element von endlicher Ordnung	élément *m* d'ordre fini	элемент конечного порядка, периодический (нильпотентный) элемент

	element of integration <DI>	*s.* I 670		
	element of length <DG, DI>	*s.* D 465		
	element of one index <GN>	*s.* S 1031		
E 135	**element of order 2** <GR>	Element *n* der Ordnung 2, zweiseitiges Element Involution *f*	élément bilatéral	элемент второго порядка, инволюция группы
E 136	**element of reserve** <ST>	Reserveelement *n*	élément *m* de réserve	резервное оборудование
	element of space <DI>	*s.* S 1310		
	element of the centre <AL>	*s.* C 355		
	element of the centre <GR>	*s.* I 1098		
E 137	**element regular on the left,** left regular (cancellable) element <AL>	links[-]kürzbares Element *n*, links[-]reguläres Element *n*, linksseitig reguläres Element *n*	élément *m* simplifiable (régulier) à gauche	сократимый слева элемент, регулярный слева элемент
E 138/9	**element regular on the right,** right regular (cancellable) element <AL>	rechts[-]kürzbares Element *n*, rechts[-]reguläres Element *n*, rechtsseitig reguläres Element	élément *m* simplifiable à droite, élément régulier à droite	сократимый справа элемент, регулярный справа элемент
E 140/1	**elements** <of a continued fraction> <NT>	Elemente *npl*	quotients *mpl* incomplets	элементы, неполные частные
	elements commuting with each other <AL>	*s.* P 481		
E 142	**elements having the same complement *x*** <LA>	Elemente *npl*, die dasselbe Komplement *x* besitzen	éléments *mpl* qui admettent le même complément *x*	*x*-связанные элементы, связанные элементы
	element-sum <SE>	*s.* U 202		
	element which is its own conjugate element <MD>	*s.* D 381		
	element whose row and column numbers are equal <MD>	*s.* D 381		
	elementwise product <MD>	*s.* K 163		
E 143	**elevation,** vertical projection, second projection <DS>	Aufriß *m*, Vertikalprojektion *f*, zweite Projektion *f*	élévation *f*, projection *f* verticale, seconde (deuxième) projection; coupe *f* verticale	вертикальная (вторая) проекция; вертикальный разрез
E 144	**eleven-point conic** <AY>	Elfpunktekegelschnitt *m*	conique *f* des onze points	коническое сечение одиннадцати точек
	eleven test <AR>	*s.* C 192		
	E-lim <LI>	*s.* E 155		
E 145	**eliminability** <LO>	Eliminierbarkeit *f*	éliminabilité *f*	элиминируемость, устранимость
E 146	**eliminant** <in elimination theory> <AL>	Eliminante *f*, Endgleichung *f*, Eliminationsresultante *f*	éliminant *m*, équation *f* finale	элиминант
	eliminant <AL>	*s.* R 938		
E 147	**elimination** <*e.g.* of quantifiers> <LO>	Elimination *f* <*z. B.* von Quantoren>	élimination *f* <*par exemple*, des quantificateurs>	элиминация, устранение <*например*, кванторов>
	elimination <AL>	*s.* G 72		
E 148	**elimination by comparison** <AL>	Elimination *f* durch Gleichsetzen	élimination *f* par égalisation	исключение способом уравнивания коэффициентов
E 149	**elimination by substitution** <AL>	Elimination *f* durch Substitution (Einsetzen)	élimination *f* par substitution	исключение способом (посредством) подстановки
E 150	**elimination ideal** <AL>	Eliminationsideal *n*	idéal *m* d'élimination	идеал исключения
	elimination law <LO>	*s.* A 139		
	elimination method <AL>	*s.* M 459		
	elimination method of Kronecker <AL>	*s.* K 160		
E 151	**elimination of an operator** <LO>	Beseitigung *f* eines Operators	exclusion *f* d'un opérateur	удаление (устранение, исключение) символов логических операций
E 152	**elimination of unknowns,** removal of unknowns <AL, AN> ⌐<LO>	Elimination *f* (Beseitigung *f*, Ausschaltung *f*, Hinauswerfen *n*) der Unbekannten	élimination *f* des inconnues	исключение (элиминация) неизвестных
E 153	**elimination theorem**	Eliminationstheorem *n*	théorème *m* d'élimination	теорема исключения
E 154	**elimination theory** <AL>	Eliminationstheorie *f*	théorie *f* de l'élimination	теория исключения (элиминации)
E 155	**E-limit,** limit by Euler's method, *E*-lim <LI>	*E*-Limes *m*, Limes *m* nach dem *E*-Verfahren, *E*-lim	limite *f* par la méthode d'Euler, *E*-limite *f*, *E*-lim	[обобщенный] предел по методу Эйлера, [обобщенный] предел по Эйлеру, *E*-lim
E 156	**E-limitable sequence,** Euler-limitable sequence, sequence limitable by Euler's method <LI>	*E*-limitierbare (nach dem *E*-Verfahren limitierbare) Folge *f*	suite *f* limitable par la méthode d'Euler, suite *E*-limitable	последовательность, лимитируемая методом Эйлера; *E*-лимитируемая последовательность
E 157	**ellipse of correlation,** correlation (homothetic, dispersion, contour) ellipse <ST>	Korrelationsellipse *f*, Umrißellipse *f*, Streuungsellipse *f*, homothetische Ellipse *f*	ellipse *f* de corrélation (dispersion, niveau), ellipse homothétique	эллипс рассеяния (корреляции), контурный (гомотетический) эллипс
E 158	**ellipse of deformation** <AY> ⌐<GE>	Deformationsellipse *f*	ellipse *f* de déformation	эллипс деформации
	ellipse of higher order	*s.* E 191		
E 159	**ellipsograph,** elliptic compass, [elliptic] trammel <IN>	Ellipsograph *m*, Ellipsenzirkel *m*	ellipsographe *m*, compas *m* elliptique	эллипсограф, эллиптический циркуль

No.	English	German	French	Russian
E 160	**ellipsoidal co-ordinates,** confocal ellipsoidal co-ordinates, elliptical co-ordinates [of Lamé] [in the [three-dimensional] space], co-ordinates of the asymmetric ellipsoid <AY>	elliptische Koordinaten *fpl* im [dreidimensionalen] Raum, Lamésche [elliptische] Koordinaten, [allgemeine] elliptische Koordinaten, elliptische Raumkoordinaten *fpl*, Koordinaten des dreiachsigen Ellipsoids	coordonnées *fpl* ellipsoïdales, coordonnées elliptiques [dans l'espace [tridimensionnel]], coordonnées de l'ellipsoïde asymétrique (à trois axes inégaux)	эллипсоидальные координаты, эллиптические координаты [в трехмерном] пространстве]
	ellipsoidal function <FU>	*s.* L 58		
E 161	**ellipsoidal harmonic** <PO>	Lamésches Produkt *n*, Lamés Produkt	produit *m* de Lamé	эллипсоидальная гармоническая функция, эллипсоидальная гармоника (функция)
	ellipsoidal wave function <FU>	*s.* L 65		
E 162	**ellipsoid of correlation,** correlation (homothetic, dispersion, contour) ellipsoid <ST>	Korrelationsellipsoid *n*, Umrißellipsoid *n*, Streuungsellipsoid *n*, homothetisches Ellipsoid *n*	ellipsoïde *m* de corrélation (dispersion, niveau), ellipsoïde homothétique	эллипсоид рассеяния (корреляции), контурный (гомотетический) эллипсоид
E 163	**ellipsoid of revolution,** spheroid of revolution, spheroid <EG>	Drehellipsoid *n*, Rotationsellipsoid *n*, Umdrehungsellipsoid *n*, Rotationssphäroid *n*, Sphäroid *n*	ellipsoïde (sphéroïde) *m* de révolution, sphéroïde	эллипсоид (сфероид) вращения, сфероид
	elliptical co-ordinates [in the plane] <AY>	*s.* E 169		
	elliptical co-ordinates [of Lamé] in the [three-dimensional] space <AY>	*s.* E 160		
	elliptical differential equation <DE>	*s.* E 172		
E 164	**elliptically curved oval** <DG>	elliptisch gekrümmte Kurve *f*	ovale *m* elliptiquement courbé	эллиптически искривленный овал
	elliptical motion <GE>	*s.* E 186		
	elliptical partial differential equation <DE>	*s.* E 172		
	elliptic amplitude <FT, FU>	*s.* A 605		
	elliptic automorphism <FT>	*s.* E 189		
E 165	**elliptic barrel** <GE>	elliptischer Tonnenkörper *m*	tonneau *m* elliptique	эллиптическая бочка
E 166	**elliptic boundary value problem** <DE>	elliptisches Randwertproblem *n*	problème *m* aux valeurs limites de type elliptique	эллиптическая краевая задача
E 167	**elliptic case** <in uniformization theory> <FT>	elliptischer Fall *m*	cas *m* elliptique	эллиптический случай
E 168	**elliptic catenary** <GE>	elliptische Kettenlinie *f*	chaînette (caténaire) *f* elliptique, roulette *f* des foyers de l'ellipse	эллиптическая цепная линия
	elliptic compass <IN>	*s.* E 159		
E 169	**elliptic co-ordinates [in the plane],** elliptical co-ordinates [in the plane] <AY>	elliptische Koordinaten *fpl* [in der Ebene]	coordonnées *fpl* elliptiques [dans le plan]	эллиптические координаты [в плоскости]
	elliptic cotangent <FU>	*s.* A 607		
E 170	**elliptic curve,** bicursal curve <Cayley> <AG>	elliptische Kurve *f*	courbe *f* elliptique	эллиптическая кривая
E 171	**elliptic cycloid** <GE>	Elliptozykloide *f*	cycloïde *f* elliptique	эллиптическая циклоида
	elliptic cylinder function	*s.* M 173		
	elliptic differential equation <DE>	*s.* E 172		
E 172	**elliptic equation,** elliptical equation, elliptic[al] differential equation, elliptic[al] partial differential equation, [partial] differential equation of the elliptic[al] type <DE>	elliptische Differentialgleichung (Gleichung, partielle Differentialgleichung) *f*, Differentialgleichung vom elliptischen Typ[us]	équation *f* elliptique, équation de type elliptique, équation aux dérivées partielles elliptique	эллиптическое уравнение, [дифференциальное] уравнение [в частных производных] эллиптического типа, эллиптическое дифференциальное уравнение [в частных производных]
E 173	**elliptic function [in the proper sense], elliptic function of the first kind** <FT, FU>	elliptische Funktion *f*, elliptische Funktion erster (1.) Art, elliptische Funktion im eigentlichen Sinne, eigentliche elliptische Funktion	fonction *f* elliptique, fonction elliptique (doublement périodique) de première espèce, fonction elliptique [dans le sens] propre	эллиптическая функция, эллиптическая функция первого рода, собственная эллиптическая функция, собственно эллиптическая функция
E 174	**elliptic function of the second kind** <FT, FU>	elliptische Funktion *f* zweiter (2.) Art	fonction *f* elliptique (doublement périodique) de deuxième (seconde) espèce, fonction à multiplicateur constant	эллиптическая функция второго рода
E 175	**elliptic function of the third kind** <FT, FU>	elliptische Funktion *f* dritter (3.) Art	fonction *f* elliptique (doublement périodique) de troisième espèce, fonction à multiplicateur exponentiel	эллиптическая функция третьего рода
E 176	**elliptic geometry,** Riemannian geometry <GE>	elliptische (Riemannsche) Geometrie *f*	géométrie *f* elliptique (riemannienne, de Riemann)	геометрия Римана, эллиптическая геометрия (геометрия Римана)
E 177	**elliptic integral** <of the first, second or third kind> <FU>	elliptisches Integral *n* <erster, zweiter *oder* dritter Gattung>	intégrale *f* elliptique <de première, deuxième *ou* troisième espèce>	эллиптический интеграл <первого, второго *или* третьего рода>

No.	English	German	French	Russian
E 178	**elliptic integral** <of the first, second, *or* third kind> **[in Legendre's normal (standard) form],** incomplete elliptic integral, Legendre['s] [standard] form of the elliptic integral <of the first, second, *or* third kind>, Legendre['s] normal form of the elliptic integral <of the first, second, *or* third kind>, normal (standard) elliptic integral <of the first, second, *or* third kind> in Legendre's notation, Legendre['s] [elliptic] integral <of the first, second, *or* third kind>, Legendre['s] standard integral <of the first, second, *or* third kind> <FU>	[elliptisches] Normalintegral *n* <erster, zweiter *oder* dritter Gattung> [in der Legendreschen Normalform], Legendresche Normalform *f* des elliptischen Integrals <erster, zweiter *oder* dritter Gattung>, unvollständiges elliptisches Integral *n* <erster, zweiter *oder* dritter Gattung>, Legendresches Normalintegral <erster, zweiter *oder* dritter Gattung>	intégrale *f* elliptique [incomplète] <de première, deuxième ou seconde, *ou* troisième espèce>, intégrale [normale] de Legendre> de première, deuxième ou seconde, *ou* troisième espèce>	[эллиптический] интеграл <первого, второго *или* третьего рода> [в [нормальном (нормальной)] виде (форме)] Лежандра, стандартный эллиптический интеграл <первого, второго *или* третьего рода>, стандартный (нормальный) вид [Лежандра] эллиптического интеграла <первого, второго *или* третьего рода>, нормальный интеграл Лежандра <первого, второго *или* третьего рода>
E 179	**elliptic inverse [point]** <AY>	elliptisch inverser Punkt *m*	point *m* réciproque elliptique, inverse *m* elliptique	эллиптически инверсная точка
E 180/1	**elliptic involution** <AY>	gleichlaufend projektive Involution *f*, elliptische Involution	involution *f* elliptique	эллиптическая инволюция, эллиптическое инволюционное преобразование
E 182	**ellipticity,** property to be elliptic[al] <DE>	Elliptizität *f*; Eigenschaft *f*, elliptisch zu sein	ellipticité *f*, propriété *f* d'être elliptique	эллиптичность, свойство быть эллиптичным
E 183	**elliptic line,** elliptic ray <of a rectilinear congruence> <AY, DS>	elliptischer Strahl *m*	droite *f* (rayon *m*) elliptique	эллиптическая прямая, эллиптический луч
E 184	**elliptic modular function,** modular function <$\lambda(\tau) = k^2(\tau)$> <FT>	Legendresche Modulfunktion *f*, elliptische Modulfunktion, Modulfunktion	fonction *f* modulaire elliptique, fonction modulaire $k^2(\tau)$, fonction $k^2(\tau)$	эллиптическая модулярная функция, модулярная функция $k^2(\tau)$
E 185	**elliptic modular group** <FT>	elliptische Modulgruppe *f*, weitere elliptische Modulgruppe *f*	groupe *m* modulaire elliptique	эллиптическая модулярная группа
E 186	**elliptic motion,** elliptical motion <GE>	elliptische Bewegung *f*, Bewegung der elliptischen Geometrie, Bewegung im elliptischen Raum	mouvement *m* elliptique	эллиптическое движение
	elliptic partial differential equation <DE>	*s.* E 172		
E 187	**elliptic quartic curve,** curve of intersection of two quadrics, intersection of two quadrics, curve of intersection of two general quadric surfaces <AG>	Raumkurve *f* vierter (4.) Ordnung erster (1.) Spezies (Art), k_4 *f* erster Art, vollständiger Durchschnitt *m* zweier Quadriken, Schnittkurve *f* zweier Quadriken	quartique *f* de première espèce, courbe *f* gauche du quatrième ordre de première espèce, biquadratique *f* gauche, biquadratique	пространственная кривая четвертого (4-го) порядка первого (I-го) рода, полное пересечение двух квадрик
	elliptic ray <AY, DS>	*s.* E 183		
	elliptic sine <FU>	*s.* 1. A 606; A 609		
E 188	**elliptic space,** polar space <PJ>	elliptischer Raum *m*	espace *m* elliptique	эллиптическое пространство
E 189	**elliptic substitution,** elliptic automorphism <FT>	elliptische [lineare] Transformation *f*, elliptische Kreisverwandtschaft (Substitution *f*, lineare Abbildung *f*, Abbildung, Möbius-Transformation *f*)	substitution *f* elliptique	эллиптическое дробно-линейное преобразование
E 190	**elliptic system [of [partial] differential equations]** <DE>	elliptisches System *n* [von partiellen Differentialgleichungen]	système *m* [d'équations aux dérivées partielles] elliptique	эллиптическая система [дифференциальных уравнений в частных производных]
	elliptic theta-function <FU>	*s.* J 36		
	elliptic trammel <IN>	*s.* E 159		
E 191	**elliptoid,** higher-order ellipse, ellipse of higher order <GE>	Elliptoid *n*, Elliptois *n*, Ellipse *f* von höherem Geschlecht, Ellipse höherer Ordnung	elliptoïde *m*, ellipse *f* de genre supérieur, ellipse *f* d'ordre supérieur	эллипс высшего порядка
E 192	**emanant** <of an algebraic form> <IV>	Emanante *f*, *n*-te Polare *f*	émanant *m*	эманант
E 193	**embankment line of cut** <DS>	Böschungslinie *f* im Abtrag		линия откоса при выемке
E 194	**embankment line of fill** <DS>	Böschungslinie *f* im Auftrag		линия откоса при насыпи
	embankment in negative projection <DS>	*s.* E 195		
	embankment in positive projection <DS>	*s.* E 196		
E 195	**embankment of cut[ting],** embankment in negative projection, cut embankment, slope of cutting <DS>	Einschnittböschung *f*, Anschnittböschung *f*, Böschung *f* im Abtrag		откос выемки
E 196	**embankment of fill,** embankment in positive projection, fill embankment, slope of embankment <DS>	Auftragsböschung *f*, Böschung *f* im Auftrag		откос насыпи

	embeddability <AL>	*s.* I 105		
E 197	**embedding** <of a group> <GR>	Einbettung *f*, Einlagerung *f*	plongement *m*	вложение
E 198	**embedding,** imbedding, injection <TO>	Einbettung *f*	plongement *m*	вложение, погружение
E 199	**embedding** <as a mapping> <TO>	Einbettungsabbildung *f*	plongement *m*	вложение, отображение вложения
	embedding <CA>	*s.* F 67		
	embedding <TO>	*s.* T 515		
	embedding <UA>	*s.* E 503		
E 200	**embedding operator** <SE>	Einbettungsoperator *m*	opérateur *m* d'immersion (d'inclusion)	оператор вложения
E 201	**embedding space** <AG>	Einbettungsraum *m*	espace *m* de plongements	пространство вложения
E 202	**embedding theorem,** imbedding theorem <AL, FA, TO, VA>	Einbettungssatz *m*	théorème *m* d'immersion	теорема вложения (включения, о погружении)
E 203	**Emden['s] [differential] equation** <DE>	Emdensche Differentialgleichung (Gleichung) *f*, Emdens Differentialgleichung	équation *f* d'Emden, équation différentielle d'Emden	уравнение Эмдена, дифференциальное уравнение Эмдена
	E-method <LI>	*s.* 1. E 598; 2. E 619		
E 204	**empirical dispersion,** empirical variance <ST>	empirische Streuung (Varianz) *f*	dispersion *f* empirique, variance *f* empirique	эмпирическая дисперсия
E 205	**empirical distribution curve** <ST>	empirische Verteilungskurve *f*	courbe *f* de distribution empirique	график функции эмпирического распределения, вариационная кривая
E 206	**empirical excess** <ST>	empirischer Exzeß *m*	excès *m* empirique	эмпирический эксцесс
E 207	**empirical median** <ST>	empirischer Median *m*	médiane *f* empirique	эмпирическая медиана
E 208	**empirical mode** <ST>	empirischer Modalwert (Mode) *m*	mode *m* empirique	эмпирическая мода
E 209	**empirical quantile** <ST>	empirisches Quantil *n*	quantile *m* empirique	эмпирический квантиль
E 210	**empirical regression coefficient** <ST>	empirischer Regressionskoeffizient *m*	coefficient *m* de régression empirique	эмпирический коэффициент регрессии
	empirical variance <ST>	*s.* E 204		
E 211	**empty attribute** <LO>	Nullattribut *n*, leeres Attribut *n* <*n*-stelliges>	attribut *m* vide	пустой признак
	empty class <LO, SE>	*s.* N 765		
E 212	**empty mapping** <SE>	leere Abbildung *f*	application *f* vide	пустое отображение
E 213	**emptyness** <SE>	Leerheit *f*	vacuité *f*	пустота
E 214	**empty product** <AL>	leeres Produkt *n*	produit *m* vide (de zéro facteur)	пустое произведение
E 215	**empty relation,** null relation <SE>	leere Relation *f*, Nullrelation *f*	relation *f* vide	пустое (нулевое) отношение
	empty set <SE>	*s.* V 204		
E 216	**enchained sets** <TO>	[miteinander] verkettete Mengen *fpl*	ensembles *mpl* enchaînés	сцепленные множества
	enclose in braces / to <GN>	*s.* P 2078		
	enclose in brackets / to <GN>	*s.* P 2079		
	enclose in parentheses / to <GN>	*s.* P 2080		
E 217	**end,** end-point, terminus, terminal point, extremity, boundary point <of an interval> <AN>	Endpunkt *m*, Begrenzungspunkt *m*, Intervallgrenze *f*	extrémité *f*, bout *m*, point *m*, terminus *m*	крайняя точка, конец, граница
E 218	**end** <of an ordered set> <SE>	Randelement *n*	élément *m* minimum ou maximum	наименьший или наибольший элемент
E 219	**end,** terminal point <of a path *or* curve> <TO>	Endpunkt *m*	extrémité *f*	конец, конечная вершина
E 220	**end** <of a space> <TO>	Ende *n*	bout *m*	конец
E 221	**end correction** <ST>	Korrektion (Korrektur) *f* der Extremwerte	correction *f* des queues, correction aux limites	поправка на крайние значения
	Ende <SE>	*s.* R 789		
E 222	**end formula** <LO>	Endformel *f*	formule *f* d'arrivée	концевая (оконечная, конечная) формула
E 223	**end formula** <of a Markov algorithm ><MM>	Schlußformel *f*, Endformel *f*	règle *f* conclusive	заключительная (окончательная) формула
	end-object <CA>	*s.* R 120		
	end of brackets (parentheses) <LO>	*s.* R 1165		
E 224	**endofunctor** <CA>	Endofunktor *m*	endofoncteur *m*	эндофунктор
E 225	**endogenous variable** <ST>	endogene Variable *f*	variable *f* endogène	эндогенная переменная
E 226	**endomorphic image** <AL> <GR>	endomorphes Bild *n*	image *f* endomorphe	эндоморфный образ
	endomorphic mapping	*s.* E 229		
E 227	**endomorphism** <of an Abelian variety> <AG>	Endomorphismus *m*, Multiplikator *m*	endomorphisme *m*	эндоморфизм
E 228	**endomorphism,** linear transformation (operator) into itself <of a vector space> <AL, FA>	Endomorphismus *m*, lineare Selbstabbildung (Transformation in sich) *f*	endomorphisme *m*, opérateur *m* linéaire en soi	эндоморфизм
E 229	**endomorphism,** endomorphic mapping <of a group> <GR>	Endomorphismus *m*, Autohomomorphismus *m*, Endomorphie *f*, // Automorphismus *m*	endomorphisme *m*, endomorphie *f*	эндоморфизм
E 230	**endomorphism group** <AL, GR>	Endomorphismengruppe *f*	groupe *m* des endomorphismes	группа эндоморфизмов
E 231	**endomorphism ring** <of a module> <AL>	Endomorphismenring *m*, voller Endomorphismenring, Homomorphismenring *m*, Endomorphismenbereich *m*	anneau *m* des endomorphismes	кольцо (область) эндоморфизмов

E 232	**end[-] point** <of a path> <AT>	Randpunkt *m*, Endpunkt *m* <Anfangs- oder Endpunkt>	extrémité *f*	граничная точка
E 233	**end point, end-point,** extremity <of a spectrum> <FA>	Randpunkt *m*	extrémité *f*	краевая точка
E 234	**end-point** <of an edge *or* arc> <GP>	Endpunkt *m*	extrémité *f*	граничная точка
E 235	**end-point,** pendant vertex <of a graph> <GP>	Endpunkt *m*, Endknoten *m*, Knotenpunkt *m* vom Grade 1, hängender Knotenpunkt	sommet *m* pendant (terminal)	концевая вершина, висячая вершина
E 236	**end[-]point, end point** <of an elementary curve> <TO>	Endpunkt *m*, Punkt *m* erster Ordnung	point *m* d'arrêt, point d'ordre 1	концевая точка, точка порядка 1
	end-point <AL, CA, GN>	*s.* A 997		
	end-point <AN>	*s.* E 217		
	end-point <VT>	*s.* T 170		
E 237	**end segment** <initial or final segment> <of an ordered set> <SE>	Randstück *n*, Endstück *n* <im Sinne von Anfangs- oder Endstück>	section *f* commençante ou finissante	граничный отрезок
E 238	**energy norm** <PO>	Energienorm *f*	norme-énergie *f*	энергетическая норма
	energy principle <PO>	*s.* P 1502		
E 239	**Eneström-Kakeya theorem,** Kakeya-Eneström theorem <for polynomials> <AL, FT>	Kakeyascher Satz *m*	théorème *m* de Kakeya	
E 240	**enforced curvature** <of a Riemannian variety> <DG>	erzwungene Krümmung *f*		вынужденная кривизна
E 241	**Engel['s] condition** <AL>	Engel-Bedingung *f*, Engelsche Bedingung *f*	condition *f* d'Engel	энгелевость
E 242	**Engel['s] element** <of a group> <AL>	engelsches Element *n*	élément *m* engelien	энгелев элемент
E 243	**Engel['s] group** <AL>	Engel-Gruppe *f*, Engelsche Gruppe *f*, // Nilgruppe *f*	groupe *m* d'Engel	энгелева группа, // нильгруппа
E 244	**Engel['s] module** <AL>	Engel-Modul *m*	module *m* d'Engel	энгелев модуль
E 245	**Engel['s] theorem** <for a Lie ring> <AL>	Engelsches Theorem *n*, Theorem von Engel	théorème *m* d'Engel	теорема Энгеля
	Engesser-Vianello method <DE>	*s.* I 1230		
E 246	**Engset['s] formula** <ST>	Engsetsche Formel *f*	formule *f* d'Engset	формула Энгсета
E 247	**enigmatic problem** <AR>	Rätselaufgabe *f*	problème *m* énigmatique	загадывание загадки
E 248	**enneiamond** <GE>	Enneiamant *m*	ennéiamant *m*	эннеиамант
E 249	**Enneper['s] minimal surface** <DG>	Ennepersche Minimalfläche *f*	surface *f* minimale d'Enneper	минимальная поверхность Эннепера
E 250	**Enneper['s] surface** <GE>	Ennepersche Fläche *f*	surface *f* d'Enneper	поверхность Эннепера
	Enneper['s] theorem <DG>	*s.* B 176		
E 251	**enough allowable projectives** <CA>	genügend viele zulässige projektive Objekte *npl*	assez d'objets *mpl* projectifs permis	достаточное количество допустимых проективных объектов
E 252	**enough injectives** <CA>	genügend viele injektive Objekte *npl*	assez d'objets *mpl* injectifs, assez d'injectifs *mpl*	достаточное (достаточно большое) количество (число) инъективных объектов, достаточно много инъективных объектов
E 253	**enough projectives** <CA>	genügend viele projektive Objekte *npl*	assez d'objets *mpl* projectifs, assez de projectifs *mpl*	достаточное (достаточно большое) количество (число) проективных объектов, достаточно много проективных объектов
E 254	**enquete** <ST>	Enquete *f*	enquête *f*	анкета, опрос
E 255	**Enriques['] principle of degeneration,** degeneration principle [of Enriques-Zariski], principle of degeneration <AG>	Entartungsprinzip *n*	principe *m* de dégénérescence, théorème *m* de connexion, principe *m* de dégénération d'Enriques	принцип вырождения Энриквеса
E 256	**Enriques['] surface** <AG>	Enriquessche Fläche *f*	surface *f* d'Enriques	поверхность Энрик[в]еса
E 257	**Enriques['] system** <AG>	Enriquessches System *n*	système *m* d'Enriques	система Энриквеса
	ensemble <SE>	*s.* S 637		
	ent <NT>	*s.* I 645		
	entailed <LO>	*s.* D 265		
E 258	**entering edge,** incoming edge <to>, arc incident <into> <GP>	nach innen inzidenter Bogen *m* <mit>; gerichtete Kante, mit der der Knoten negativ inzident ist	arc *m* incident vers l'intérieur <de>	дуга, с которой вершина отрицательно инцидентна
	entier <NT>	*s.* I 645		
	entire form <FT>	*s.* E 260		
E 259	**entire function,** integral function <FT>	ganze Funktion *f*	fonction *f* entière	целая функция
E 260	**entire modular form,** entire form <FT>	ganze Modulform *f* <*m*-ten Grades zu Γ und der Dimension -*r*>	forme *f* modulaire entière	целая модулярная форма
E 261	**entire part** <of a rational function> <FT>	ganzer Teil *m*	partie *f* entière (principale à l'infini)	целая часть
E 262	**entire rational function,** integral rational function, rational integral function, polynomial <AN>	ganze rationale Funktion *f*, ganz[-]rationale Funktion, Polynom *n*, ganzes Polynom	fonction *f* rationnelle entière, fonction entière rationnelle, polynôme *m*, polynôme entier	целая рациональная функция, многочлен, полином
	entire ring <AL>	*s.* I 620		

No.	English	German	French	Russian
E 263	**entire series,** permanently (everywhere) convergent [power] series <SS>	beständig (überall) konvergente Potenzreihe *f*	série *f* entière partout convergente	всюду (перманентно) сходящийся степенной ряд
E 264	**entire surd** <AL>	irrationaler Ausdruck *m*, dessen Glieder rein irrational sind		иррациональное выражение, все члены которого чисто иррациональны
E 265	**entire transcendental function,** integral transcendental function <FT>	ganze transzendente Funktion *f*, ganz[-]transzendente Funktion	fonction *f* transcendante entière, fonction entière transcendante	целая трансцендентная функция
	entourage <TO>	*s.* M 383		
E 266	**entropy,** bisymmetry, mediality <of groupoids, quasigroups> <AL>	Bisymmetrie *f*	bisymétrie *f*, échange *m* des moyens, entropie *f*	бисимметрия, энтропия, медиальность
E 267	**entropy,** entropy of information source, average information content, negentropy, negative entropy <ST>	Entropie *f*, Entropie der Informationsquelle, mittlerer Informationsgehalt *m*, Negentropie *f*, negative Entropie	entropie *f*, entropie d'information, entropie informative (négative), néguentropie *f*	энтропия, энтропия множества сообщений, энтропия информации, информационная (отрицательная) энтропия, негэнтропия
	entropy <SP>	*s.* K 128		
	entropy of information source <ST>	*s.* E 267		
E 268	**entry** <of a table> <GN, NU>	Eingang *m*	entrée *f*	вход
	entry <MD>	*s.* E 85		
E 269	**entry column,** initial column <of a table> <GN, NU>	Eingangsspalte *f*, Vorspalte *f*	première colonne *f*, colonne-type *f*, colonne type	начальный (первый) столбец, входная колонка
	entry lying in the *i*-th row and *j*-th column <MD>	*s.* E 130		
E 270	**entry row,** initial row <GN, NU>	Eingangszeile *f*, Vorzeile *f*	première ligne *f*, ligne-type *f*, ligne type	входная (начальная, первая) строка
E 271	**enumerability,** effective denumerability <SE>	Aufzählbarkeit *f*, effektive Abzählbarkeit *f*	énumérabilité *f*, dénombrabilité *f* effective	перечислимость, эффективная счетность
	enumerability <SE>	*s.* C 2554		
	enumerable set <SE>	*s.* 1. C 2561; 2. D 252; 3. E 37		
E 272	**enumerably infinite dimensional space** <TO>	abzählbar unendlichdimensionaler Raum *m*	espace *m* à une infinité dénombrable de dimensions	счетно-бесконечномерное пространство
	enumerably infinite set <SE>	*s.* D 252		
E 273	**enumerating function** <of a set of integers> <NT>	„fonction *f* énumératrice", Abzählungsfunktion *f*	fonction *f* énumératrice	
E 274	**enumerating power series,** generating function <NT>	erzeugende Funktion *f*	fonction *f* génératrice	производящая функция
E 275	**enumeration** <SE>	Aufzählung *f*	énumération *f*	перечисление, пересчет
E 276	**enumeration,** denumeration, counting, count <SE>	Abzählen *n*, Abzählung *f*	dénombrement *m*	нумерация, перечисление, пересчет, счет, подсчет
E 277	**enumeration data** <ST>	Häufigkeitsdaten *pl*, Zählungsdaten *pl*	données *fpl* d'énumération	перенумерованные данные
E 278	**enumeration principle** <for groups> <GR>	Abzählprinzip *n*	principe *m* énumératif	принцип перечислимости
E 279	**enumeration problem** <CT, NT>	Abzählungsproblem *n*, Enumerationsproblem *n*	problème *m* d'énumération	задача перечисления, проблема перечисления
E 280	**enumeration statistics,** statistics of attributes <ST>	Ereignisstatistik *f*	statistique *f* d'attributs, statistique d'énumération	статистика признаков
E 281	**enumerative geometry** <GE>	abzählende Geometrie *f*, Geometrie der Anzahl	géométrie *f* énumérative	исчислительная геометрия
E 282	**enumerative technique** <CT>	Abzählungsverfahren *n*	méthode *f* énumérative	метод перечисления
E 283	**envelope** <in line coordinates> <AG>	Klassenkurve *f*, Geradenort *m*, Hüllkurve *f*, einhüllende Kurve *f*	courbe *f* comme enveloppe d'une droite	кривая, рассмотренная как огибающая прямых
E 284	**envelope** <*n*-dimensional> <AN, GE>	Einhüllende, Enveloppe *f*, Hüllgebilde *n*, Umhüllende *f*	enveloppe *f*	огибающая
E 285	**envelope,** enveloping curve, envelope curve <of a system of curves> <AN, GE>	Einhüllende *f*, Enveloppe *f*, Hüllkurve *f*, Hüllgebilde *n*, eingehüllte Linie *f*, Umhüllende *f*	enveloppe *f*, courbe *f* enveloppe, enveloppe de courbe, courbe enveloppée	огибающая семейства линий, огибающая, огибающая кривая (линия)
E 286	**envelope,** enveloping function <RF>	Hüllfunktion *f*	enveloppe *f*	огибающая [функция]
	envelope <AN, GE>	*s.* E 293		
	envelope curve <AN, GE>	*s.* E 285		
E 287	**envelope equation** <of a surface *or* manifold> <AG>	Tangentialgleichung *f*, Klassengleichung *f*	équation *f* tangentielle	тангенциальное уравнение
	envelope equation <AG>	*s.* T 53		
E 288	**envelope of holomorphy** <FT>	Holomorphiehülle *f*	enveloppe *f* d'holomorphie	оболочка голоморфности
	envelope surface <AN, GE>	*s.* E 293		
E 289	**enveloping algebra** <AL>	Hüllalgebra *f*	algèbre *f* enveloppante	обертывающая алгебра
E 290	**enveloping bialgebra** <of a Lie algebra> <AL>	Hüllbialgebra *f*, Hüllbialgebra *f*	bigèbre *f* enveloppante	обертывающая биалгебра
	enveloping curve <AN, GE>	*s.* E 285		
	enveloping function <RF>	*s.* E 286		

E 291	**enveloping ring** <of a ring> <AL>	Hüllring *m*	anneau *m* enveloppant	обертывающее кольцо
E 292	**enveloping series** <AN>	einhüllende Reihe *f*, Hüllreihe *f*	série *f* enveloppante	обертывающий ряд
E 293	**enveloping surface,** envelope [surface] <of a system of surfaces> <AN, GE>	Einhüllende *f*, Enveloppe *f*, Hüllfläche *f*, Enveloppenfläche *f*, eingehüllte Fläche *f*, Hüllgebilde *n*	enveloppe *f*, surface *f* enveloppe, enveloppe de surfaces, surface enveloppée	огибающая [семейства поверхностей], огибающая поверхность
	Eodoxos['] theorem <GE>	*s.* A 897		
	epi <CA>	*s.* E 297		
	epi [arrow] <CA>	*s.* E 299		
	epic <CA>	*s.* 1. E 297; 2. E 299		
	epic morphism <AL>	*s.* O 127		
	epic morphism <CA>	*s.* E 299		
E 294	**epicycloid** <GE>	Epizykloide *f*	épicycloïde *f*, épicycloïde plane	эпициклоида
E 295	**epi-endomorphism,** surjective endomorphism <AL>	Epiendomorphismus *m*, surjektiver Endomorphismus *m*	endomorphisme *m* surjectif	эпи-эндоморфизм, сюръективный эндоморфизм
E 296	**Epimenides['] contradiction (paradox of the liar),** paradox of the lying Epimenides, liar paradox, paradox of the liar, Eubulides['] Liar Paradox <LO>	Antinomie *f* des Lügners, Paradoxie *f* des Kreters Epimenides, Paradoxon *n* vom lügenden Kreter, Paradoxon des Epimenides	antinomie *f* (paradoxe *m*) du menteur, paradoxe du crétois menteur, paradoxe d'Epiménide	парадокс лжеца (лгущего критянина)
	epimorph <AL, CA>	*s.* E 298		
E 297	**epimorphic,** epic, epi <CA>	epimorph, vorn kürzbar, surjektiv, epic	épimorphe	эпиморфный
E 298	**epimorphic image,** epimorph <AL, CA>	epimorphes Bild *n*	image *f* épimorphe	эпиморфный образ
E 299	**epimorphism,** epic morphism, epic, epi, epi arrow <CA>	Epimorphismus *m*, epimorpher Pfeil *m*	épimorphisme *m*	эпиморфизм, суперъективный морфизм
	epimorphism <AL>	*s.* O 127		
	epistemological paradox <FO, LO>	*s.* S 312		
E 300	**episyllogism** <LO>	Episyllogismus *m*	épisyllogisme *m*	эписиллогизм
E 301	**epitrochoid** <GE>	Epitrochoide *f*	épitrochoïde *f*	эпитрохоида
E 302	**(*E*,*p*) lim[it], E_p-lim[it],** limit by Euler's method of *p*-th order <LI>	E_p-Limes *m*, (*E*, *p*)-Limes *m*, Limes *m* nach dem E_p-Verfahren, E_p-lim	limite *f* par la méthode d'Euler d'ordre *p*, E_p-limite *f*, E_p-lim	[обобщенный] предел по методу Эйлера *p*-го порядка
E 303	**(*E*, *p*) limitable sequence, E_p-limitable sequence,** sequence limitable by Euler's method of *p*-th order <LI>	E_p-limitierbare ((*E*, *p*)-limitierbare, nach dem E_p-Verfahren limitierbare) Folge *f*	suite *f* limitable par la méthode d'Euler d'ordre *p*, suite (*E*,*p*)-sommable	последовательность, лимитируемая методом Эйлера *p*-го порядка; (*E*, *p*)-лимитируемая последовательность
E 304	**(*E*,*p*) method, E_p-method,** Euler['s] [limitation] method of *p*-th order <for divergent sequences> <LI>	E_p-Verfahren *n*, (*E*,*p*)-Verfahren *n*, Euler-Knoppsches Limitierungsverfahren *n* der Ordnung *p*	méthode *f* [de limitation] d'Euler d'ordre *p*, méthode (*E*,*p*)	метод [образования обобщенного предела] Эйлера *p*-го порядка
E 305	**(*E*,*p*) method, E_p-method,** Euler['s] method of *p*-th order, Euler['s] summation method of *p*-th order <for divergent series> <LI>	E_p-Verfahren *n*, (*E*,*p*)-Verfahren *n*, Euler-Knoppsches Summierungsverfahren *n* der Ordnung *p*	méthode *f* [de sommation] d'Euler d'ordre *p*, méthode (*E*,*p*)	метод Эйлера *p*-го порядка, метод суммирования [расходящихся рядов] Эйлера *p*-го порядка
	epsilon <SE>	*s.* S 856		
E 306	**epsilon-approximation,** ε-approximation <of a mapping> <TO>	ε-Approximation *f*, Epsilon-Approximation *f*	ε-approximation *f*, epsilon-approximation *f*	ε-приближение, эпсилон-приближение
E 307	**epsilon-chain,** ε-chain <TO>	ε-Kette *f*, Epsilon-Kette *f*	*V*-chaîne *f*	ε-цепь, эпсилон-цепь, *V*-цепь
E 308	**epsilon-displacement,** ε-displacement <TO>	ε-Verschiebung *f*, Epsilon-Verschiebung *f*, ε-Überführung *f*, Epsilon-Überführung *f*, ε-Abbildung *f*, Epsilon-Abbildung *f*	ε-déplacement *m*	ε-сдвиг, эпсилон-сдвиг
E 309	**epsilon function,** ε-function, Hilbert['s] ε-function <LO>	ε-Funktion *f*, Epsilon-funktion *f*, Hilbertsche (logische) ε-Funktion *f*	fonction *f* ε (epsilon)	ε-функция [Гильберта], эпсилон-функция [Гильберта]
E 310	**epsilon-homologous,** ε-homologous <AT>	ε-homolog, epsilon-homolog	ε-homologue, epsilon-homologue	ε-гомологичный, эпсилон-гомологичный
E 311	**epsilon-homotopy,** ε-homotopy <TO>	ε-Homotopie *f*, Epsilon-Homotopie *f*	ε-homotopie *f*, epsilon-homotopie *f*	ε-гомотопия, эпсилон-гомотопия
E 312	**epsilon-map[ping],** ε-map[ping], ε-transformation, epsilon-transformation <TO>	ε-Abbildung *f*, Epsilon-Abbildung *f*	ε-transformation *f*, epsilon-transformation *f*	ε-отображение, эпсилон-отображение
E 313	**epsilon-neighbourhood,** ε-neighbourhood, spherical neighbourhood of radius ε <TO>	ε-Umgebung *f*, sphärische Umgebung *f* vom Radius ε, Epsilon-Umgebung *f*, Epsilonumgebung *f*, ε-Nachbarschaft (Epsilon-Nachbarschaft) *f* [nullter Ordnung]	ε-voisinage *m*, epsilon-voisinage *m*, voisinage *m* sphérique de rayon ε	ε-окрестность, эпсилон-окрестность, сферическая окрестность радиуса ε
E 314	**epsilon-net,** ε-net <TO>	ε-Netz *n*, Epsilon-Netz *n*, Netz *n*	ε-réseau *m*, epsilon-réseau *m*	ε-сеть, эпсилон-сеть

E 315	**epsilon[-]number,** ε-number, principal number (ordinal) of exponentiation, principal ordinal for exponentiation <SE>	exponentielle Hauptzahl *f*, ε-Zahl *f*, Epsilon-Zahl *f*, Hauptzahl der Potenzierung, Epsilonzahl *f*	nombre *m* principal exponentiel, nombre-ε *m*, nombre epsilonien	эпсилоновое число, ε-число
	epsilon-symbol <DG, VT>	*s.* A 577		
	epsilon-system <DG, VT>	*s.* 1. A 563; 2. A 577		
E 316	**epsilon-technique,** ε-technique <AN>	Epsilontik *f*	technique *f* des ε (epsilons)	язык ε, δ
	epsilon-tensor <DG, VT>	*s.* A 563		
E 317	**epsilon-term,** ε-term <LO>	ε-Term *m*, Epsilon-Term *m*, Hilbertscher ε-Term (Epsilon-Term)	ε-terme *m*, epsilon-terme *m*	ε-терм, эпсилон-терм
	epsilon-transformation <TO>	*s.* E 312		
E 318	**Epstein['s] zeta function, Epstein['s] zeta-function, Epstein['s] *Z*-function (*Z*-series)** <FU>	Epsteinsche Zetafunktion (*Z*-Funktion) *f*, Zetafunktion von Epstein, Epsteinsche Zetareihe *f*	fonction zêta (*Z*) d'Epstein, série *f Z* d'Epstein	дзета-функция (*Z*-функция, дзета-ряд) Эпштейна
E 319	**(*E,p*) sum, E_p-sum,** sum by Euler's method of *p*-th order <LI>	E_p-Summe *f*, (*E,p*)-Summe *f*, Summe *f* nach dem E_p-Verfahren	E_p-somme *f*, somme *f* par la méthode d'Euler d'ordre *p*	[обобщенная] сумма по методу Эйлера *p*-го порядка
E 320	**(*E,p*) summable series, E_p-summable series,** series summable by Euler's method of *p*-th order <LI>	E_p-summierbare ((*E,p*)-summierbare, nach dem E_p-Verfahren summierbare) Reihe *f*	série *f* sommable par la méthode d'Euler d'ordre *p*, série (*E,p*)-sommable	ряд, суммируемый методом Эйлера *p*-го порядка; (*E,p*)-суммируемый ряд
E 321	**equal / to** <to>, to be equal <to> <AL, AR, GN>	gleich sein	être égal <à>, égaler	быть равным, равняться
	equal cardinality <SE>	*s.* E 403		
	equal characteristic case <AL>	*s.* E 365		
E 322	**equal fraction** <AL, NT>	gleicher (gleichwertiger, gleichgültiger) Bruch *m*	fraction *f* équivalente (égale)	равная дробь
	equal in dimension <AL, TO>	*s.* E 377		
E 323/4	**equality constraint** <PG>	Gleichungsnebenbedingung *f*, Nebenbedingung *f* in Gleichungsform	contrainte *f* sous forme d'une équation	условие в виде уравнения
E 325	**equality predicate** <LO>	Gleichheitsprädikat *n*	prédicat *m* d'égalité	предикат равенства
E 326	**equality relation[ship],** identity relation, relation of equality (identity), diagonal, identity <as a binary relation> <SE>	Einheitsrelation *f*, Identitätsbeziehung *f*, identische Relation *f*, Gleichheitsbeziehung *f*, Identitätsrelation *f*, Diagonale *f*, Identität *f*, Gleichheit *f*, Relation der Gleichheit	relation *f* diagonale (d'égalité, d'identité)	отношение равенства (тождества), диагональ, единичное бинарное отношение
	equality symbol <GN>	*s.* S 850		
E 327	**equalizer,** kernel, difference kernel, left equalizer, left root <of a diagram consisting of two coinitial and coterminal morphisms> <CA>	Differenzkern *m*, Egalisator *m*, Kern *m*, „equalizer" *m*, „kernel" *m*	noyau *m*, objet *m* des coïncidences	левый уравнитель, уравнитель, ядро <как семейство морфизмов>
E 328	**equalizer** <of morphisms of sets> <CA>	Differenzkern *m*	noyau *m*, ensemble *m* de coïncidences	ядро
	equalizing <GN>	*s.* E 335/6		
	equal likelihood <ST>	*s.* E 402		
	equally continuous family <AN>	*s.* E 370		
	equally continuous sequence of functions <AN, TO>	*s.* E 369		
	equally continuous set <AN>	*s.* E 370		
E 329	**equally distributed random variable,** random variable having the same distribution<ST>	gleichverteilte Zufallsvariable *f*, Zufallsvariable [mit] gleicher Verteilung	variable *f* aléatoire également distribuée (répartie), variable aléatoire à (de) distribution égale	случайная переменная с одинаковым распределением
	equally distributed random variable <ST>	*s.* U 161		
E 330	**equally oriented curve** <GE, TO>	gleich[ ]orientierte Kurve *f*	courbe *f* ayant la même orientation	одинаково ориентированная кривая
E 331	**equally possible event,** likely possible event <ST>	gleichmögliches Ereignis *n*	événement *m* également possible	равновозможное событие
	equal of magnitude, but opposite of sign <GN>	*s.* O 209		
	equal possibility <ST>	*s.* E 402		
	equal power <SE>	*s.* E 403		
	equal roots <AL>	*s.* D 940		
E 332	**equal set,** coincident set <SE>	gleiche Menge *f*	ensemble *m* égal (identique)	совпадающее множество
	equal sign <GN>	*s.* S 850		
	equals relation <SE>	*s.* E 417		
	equals sign <GN>	*s.* S 850		
E 333	**equal-tails test** <ST>	symmetrischer [zweiseitiger] Test *m*	test *m* bilatéral symétrique	симметрично ограниченный критерий

E 334	**equate to zero / to,** to set equal to zero, to nullify <GN>	Null setzen, gleich Null setzen, zu Null machen	annuler, poser égal à zéro	сводить к нулю, положить равным нулю
E 335/6	**equating,** equation, equalizing, putting equal <to> <GN>	Gleichsetzen *n*, Gleichsetzung *f*	égalisation *f*	приравнивание, уравнивание
	equation <ER>	*s.* C 1829		
	equation <GN>	*s.* 1. C 1811; 2. E 335/6		
E 337	**equational class,** primitive class, equationally defin[iss]able class, lattice variety <of algebras>, variety <UA>	gleichungsdefinierte Klasse *f*, Varietät *f*, primitive Klasse, Mannigfaltigkeit *f*, Variety *f*, durch Gleichungen definierte Klasse, primitive Algebrenklasse *f*	classe *f* équationnelle (primitive), variété *f*	многообразие, эквационально определимый класс, примитивный класс
	equational class of groups <UA>	*s.* V 84		
	equationally complete class <UA>	*s.* M 581		
E 338	**equationally complete extension** <AL>	gleichungsmäßig vollständige Erweiterung *f*		эквационально полное расширение
	equationally definable (definissable) class <UA>	*s.* E 337		
E 339	**equationally equivalent system,** I-equivalent system <UA>	gleichungsäquivalente Algebra *f*, I-äquivalentes algebraisches System *n*	système *m* I-équivalent	эквационально эквивалентная система, I-эквивалентная система
	equation between numerical values <NU>	*s.* N 909		
E 340	**equation for the components** <GN>	Komponentengleichung *f*	équation *f* pour les composantes	уравнение на компоненты
	equation incapable of solution <AL>	*s.* U 396		
E 341	**equation in co-ordinates** <AY>	Koordinatengleichung *f*, Gleichung *f* in Koordinaten	équation *f* en coordonnées	уравнение в координатах
E 342	**equation in monic (normal) form** <AL, AY>	Gleichung *f* in Normalform	équation *f* sous la forme standard	уравнение в стандартной форме
	equation in polar co-ordinates <AY>	*s.* P 859		
	equation in several variables <AL>	*s.* E 355		
	equation in the *p*-form <AL>	*s.* E 344		
E 343	**equation of a circle** <AY>	Kreisgleichung *f*	équation *f* d'un cercle	уравнение окружности
	equation of centre <AY>	*s.* C 62		
	equation of Clairaut <DE> ⌐<GN>	*s.* C 757		
	equation of condition	*s.* C 1811		
	equation of Euler <DG>	*s.* E 621		
	equation of fourth degree <AL>	*s.* Q 88		
E 344	**equation of integral dependence,** *p*-form of an equation, equation in the *p*-form <AL>	Gleichung *f* für die ganze Abhängigkeit <Gleichung der Form $x^n + p_1x^{n-1} + \cdots + p_n = 0$ mit ganzen p_i>	équation *f* de dépendance intégrale	уравнение целой зависимости
E 345	**equation of integral dependence** <satisfied by α> **over *A*** <AL>	algebraische Gleichung *f* mit Koeffizienten aus *A* und höchstem Koeffizienten 1	équation *f* de dépendance intégrale à coefficients dans *A*	целое уравнение <для α> над *A*
E 346	**equation of Jacobi** <AL>	Jacobische Gleichung *f*	équation *f* jacobienne (de Jacobi)	уравнение Якоби
E 346 a	**equation of mixed type,** differential equation of mixed type, mixed [partial] differential equation; mixed type <DE>	Differentialgleichung (Gleichung) *f* von gemischtem Typ, gemischte [partielle] Differentialgleichung; gemischter Typ *m*	équation *f* du (de) type mixte, équation différentielle [de (du) type] mixte; type *m* mixte	[дифференциальное] уравнение смешанного типа, смешанное дифференциальное уравнение [в частных производных]; смешанный тип
E 347	**equation of projectivity** <PJ>	Gleichung *f* der Projektivität	équation *f* de projectivité	уравнение проективности
	equation of telegraphy <DE>	*s.* T 119		
	equation of the first degree <AL>	*s.* L 791		
	equation of the fourth degree <AL>	*s.* Q 88		
	equation of the Fuchsian type <DE>	*s.* F 699		
	equation of the Monge-Ampère type <DE>	*s.* M 818		
E 348	**equation of the polar** <AY, PJ>	Polarengleichung *f*, Gleichung *f* der Polare	équation *f* de la polaire	уравнение поляры
	equation of the second degree <AL>	*s.* Q 25		
E 349	**equation of the straight line** <AY>	Geradengleichung *f*	équation *f* de la droite	уравнение прямой
	equation of [the] third degree <AL>	*s.* C 2739		

	equations of Gauss <DG>	*s.* 1. F 815; 2. G 69		
	equations of Gauss [, Mainardi] and Codazzi <DG>	*s.* C 1003		
E 350/1	**equations of Maurer-Cartan,** Maurer-Cartan equations <for a Lie group> <GR>	Maurer-Cartansche Gleichungen *fpl*	formules (équations) *fpl* de Maurer-Cartan	формулы Маурера-Картана
E 352	**equation soluble by radicals,** algebraic equation soluble by radicals, soluble equation <over *K*> <AL>	primitive Gleichung *f*, durch Radikale [auf-] lösbare Gleichung *f*, durch Wurzeln [auf]lösbare Gleichung, algebraisch auflösbare Gleichung, [auf]lösbare Gleichung <über *K*>	équation *f* primitive, équation résoluble en (par) radicaux, équation résoluble [algébriquement] <sur *K*>	уравнение, разрешимое в радикалах <над *K*>
E 353	**equation with integral coefficients** <AL>	ganzzahlige Gleichung *f*	équation *f* à coefficients entiers	целочисленное уравнение
	equation with multiple roots <AL>	*s.* M 1078		
E 354	**equation without affect,** affectless (unaffected) equation <AL>	affektlose (affektfreie) Gleichung *f*, Gleichung ohne Affekt	équation *f* sans affect	уравнение без аффекта
	equation with regular singular points <DE>	*s.* F 699		
E 355	**equation with several unknowns (variables),** equation in several variables <AL>	Gleichung *f* mit mehreren Unbekannten	équation *f* à plusieurs inconnues	уравнение с несколькими неизвестными, уравнение со многими неизвестными
E 356	**equatorial radius** <of a solid of revolution> <GE>	Äquatorradius *m*	rayon *m* équatorial	экваториальный (осевой) радиус
E 357	**equatorial section** <GE>	Äquatorschnitt *m*	section *f* équatoriale	экваториальное сечение
E 358	**equatorial surface** <PJ>	Äquatorialfläche *f*	surface *f* équatoriale	экваториальная поверхность
E 359	**equiaffine group,** affine unimodular group, special affine group <GE>	äquiaffine (speziell-affine, affine unimodulare) Gruppe *f*, spezielle affine Gruppe	groupe *m* équiaffine (affine spécial, affine unimodulaire)	эквиаффинная (аффинная унимодулярная, унимодулярная аффинная, унимодулярно-аффинная) группа, специальная аффинная группа
E 360	**equiaffine mapping** <GE>	äquiaffine Abbildung *f*	application *f* équiaffine	унимодулярно-аффинное преобразование, эквиаффинное преобразование
E 361	**equi-angled, equi-angular** <EG>	gleichwinklig	équiangle, équiangulaire	равноугольный
	equiangular hyperbola <AY>	*s.* E 389		
	equiangular mapping <AY, GE>	*s.* A 669		
	equiangular mapping <FT> ┌<DS>	*s.* C 1901		
	equiangular projection	*s.* C 1903		
	equiangular spiral <GE>	*s.* L 1053		
	equiangular transformation <AY, GE>	*s.* A 669		
E 362	**equianharmonic cross ratio** <PJ>	äquianharmonisches Doppelverhältnis *n*	rapport *m* équianharmonique	эквиангармоническое отношение
E 363	**equianharmonic cubic, equianharmonic curve [of third order]** <AG>	äquianharmonische Kurve *f* [dritter Ordnung]	courbe *f* équianharmonique [de troisième ordre], cubique *f* équianharmonique	эквиангармоническая кривая [третьего порядка]
	equi[-]areal map[ping] <AY>	*s.* A 930		
E 364	**equi-asymptotic stability** <DE>	äquiasymptotische Stabilität *f*	stabilité *f* équi-asymptotique	эквиасимптотическая устойчивость
E 365	**equicharacteristic case,** equal characteristic case <AL>	charakteristikgleicher Fall *m*	cas *m* d'égale caractéristique	случай одинаковой (равной) характеристики, случай равных характеристик
E 366	**equicharacteristic local ring** <AL>	charakteristikgleicher lokaler Ring *m*	anneau *m* local équicaractéristique	равнохарактеристическое локальное кольцо
E 367	**equiconjugate diameter** <GE>	äquikonjugierter (gleichlanger und konjugierter) Durchmesser *m*	diamètre *m* équi-conjugué, diamètre équiconjugué	равный и сопряженный диаметр
E 368	**equicontinuity** <AN, TO> ┌<AN>	gleichgradige (gleichartige) Stetigkeit *f*, Gleichstetigkeit *f*	équicontinuité *f*	равностепенная непрерывность
	equicontinuous family	*s.* E 370		
E 369	**equicontinuous sequence of functions,** equally continuous sequence of functions <AN, TO>	gleichgradig (gleichartig) stetige Funktionenfolge *f*, gleichstetige Funktionenfolge (Folge *f* von Funktionen)	suite *f* de fonctions équicontinue	равностепенно непрерывная последовательность функций
E 370	**equicontinuous set,** equicontinuous family, equally continuous set (family) <AN>	gleichgradig stetige Menge *f*	ensemble *m* équicontinu, famille *f* également continue	равностепенно непрерывное множество
E 371	**equiconvergence** <of a limitation method> <LI>	Konvergenzgleichheit *f*	équiconvergence *f*	равносходимость

No.	English	German	French	Russian
E 372	**equiconvergence** <SS>	Äquikonvergenz *f*	équiconvergence *f*	равносходимость
E 373	**equiconvergent method,** equiconvergent method of summation, equiconvergent summation method <LI>	konvergenzgleiches Summierungsverfahren *n*	méthode *f* de sommation équiconvergente	равносходящийся метод суммирования
E 374	**equiconvergent method of limitation** <LI>	konvergenzgleiches Limitierungsverfahren (*V*-Verfahren) *n*	méthode *f* de limitation équiconvergente	равносходящийся метод образования обобщенного предела
	equiconvergent method of summation <LI>	*s.* E 373		
E 375	**equiconvergent series** <SS>	äquikonvergente Reihe *f*	série *f* équivalente	равносходящийся ряд
	equiconvergent summation method <LI>	*s.* E 373		
E 376	**equiderivable family of functions** <RF>	gleichgradig differenzierbare Menge (Familie) *f* von Funktionen	famille *f* de fonctions équidérivable	равностепенно дифференцируемое семейство (множество) функций
E 377	**equidimensional,** equal in dimension <AL, TO>	dimensionsgleich	équidimensionnel, à égale dimension	равноразмерный
E 378	**equidimensional ideal,** unmixed ideal <of dimension *d*> <AL>	ungemischtes Ideal *n* <der Dimension *d*>, rein-*d*-dimensionales Ideal	idéal *m* équidimensionnel <de dimension *d*>	несмешанный идеал <размерности *d*>
E 379	**equidimensionality** <AL>	Ungemischtheit *f*	équidimensionalité *f*	чистота, несмешанность
E 380	**equidimensionality condition** <AL>	Ungemischtheitsbedingung *f*	condition *f* d'équidimension	условие чистоты
E 381	**equidimensionality theorem** <AL>	Ungemischtheitssatz *m*	théorème *m* d'équidimensionalité	теорема несмешанности
E 382	**equidimensionality theorem of Macaulay** <AL>	Macaulayscher Ungemischtheitssatz *m*	théorème *m* d'équidimensionalité de [Cohen-] Macaulay	теорема чистоты Маколея
E 383	**equidimensional submodule,** unmixed submodule <AL>	ungemischter Untermodul *m*	sous-module *m* équidimensionnel	несмешанный подмодуль
E 384	**equidistant curve** <DG>	Äquidistanzkurve *f*	équidistante *f*	эквидистантная кривая, эквидистанта
	equidistant net <DG>	*s.* C 601		
E 385	**equidistant surface** <DG>	Äquidistanzfläche *f*	surface *f* équidistante	эквидистантная поверхность
	equidistant system <DG>	*s.* C 601		
	equidistributed random variable <ST>	*s.* U 161		
	equidistribution <ST>	*s.* U 127		
E 386	**equi-isocline** <GE>	Äquiisokline *f*	équi-isocline *f*	экви-изоклина
E 387	**equilateral cone** <AY>	gleichseitiger Kegel *m*	cône *m* équilatère	равносторонний конус
E 388	**equilateral cubical hyperbola** <AG>	gleichseitige kubische Hyperbel *f*	hyperbole *f* gauche équilatère	равносторонняя кубическая гипербола
E 389	**equilateral hyperbola,** equiangular (rectangular) hyperbola <AY>	gleichseitige Hyperbel *f*	hyperbole *f* équilatère	равнобочная (равносторонняя) гипербола
E 390	**equilateral rectangular cubical hyperbola** <AG>	gleichseitige Kurve *f* <Raumkurve 3. Ordnung mit paarweise rechtwinkligen Asymptoten>	courbe *f* équilatère, cubique *f* gauche équilatère	
E 391	**equilateral triangle,** regular triangle <EG>	gleichseitiges (regelmäßiges) Dreieck *n*	triangle *m* équilatéral (équiangle, régulier)	равносторонний (правильный) треугольник
E 392	**equilibrium distribution** <PO>	Gleichgewichtsverteilung *f*	distribution *f* d'équilibre	распределение равновесия
E 393	**equilibrium kernel** <PO>	Gleichgewichtskern *m*; Kern *m*, der dem Gleichgewichtsprinzip genügt	noyau *m* d'équilibre	ядро равновесия
E 394	**equilibrium point,** equilibrium situation <TG>	Gleichgewichtspunkt *m*, Gleichgewichtslage *f*, Gleichgewichtssituation *f*	point *m* (situation *f*) d'équilibre	ситуация (точка) равновесия
	equilibrium point <DE>	*s.* C 2678		
	equilibrium principle <PO>	*s.* P 1503		
E 395	**equilibrium process** <SP>	[stochastischer] Gleichgewichtsprozeß *m*	processus *m* [aléatoire] d'équilibre	равновесный [стохастический] процесс
	equilibrium situation <TG>	*s.* E 394		
E 396	**equimorphic proximity space** <TO>	äquimorpher Nachbarschaftsraum *m*	espace *m* de proximité équimorphe	δ-изоморфное пространство близости, эквиморфное пространство близости
E 397	**equimorphism,** proximal homeomorphism <of a proximity space> <TO>	Äquimorphismus *m*, δ-Homöomorphismus *m*, Delta-Homöomorphismus *m*	équimorphisme *m*	δ-изоморфизм, эквиморфизм
E 398	**equimultiples** <NT>	Gleichvielfache *npl*; Zahlen *fpl*, die sich aus gewissen Zahlen durch Multiplikation mit demselben Faktor ergeben	nombres *mpl* équimultiples, équimultiples *mpl*	числа, получаемые из некоторых чисел умножением на один и тот же множитель
E 399	**equimultiple term** <GN, NT>	mit dem gleichen Faktor multipliziertes Glied *n*	terme *m* équimultiple	член, умноженный на тот же множитель
	equinumerosity <SE>	*s.* E 403		
	equinumerous set <SE>	*s.* E 404		
	equipartition <ST>	*s.* U 127		
	equipartitioned random variable <ST>	*s.* U 161		
	equipollence <SE>	*s.* E 403		

No.	English	German	French	Russian
E 400	**equipollent segment** <GE>	äquipollente Strecke *f* <gleichlang, parallel und gleichgerichtet>	segment *m* équipollent	эквиполлентный отрезок
	equipollent set <SE>	*s.* E 404		
E 401	**equipollent vector,** equivalent vector <GE>	äquipollenter Vektor *m*	vecteur *m* équipollent (équivalent)	эквиполлентный вектор
E 402	**equipossibility,** equal possibility (likelihood) <ST>	Gleichmöglichkeit *f*	égale possibilité *f*, équipossibilité *f*	равновозможность
E 403	**equipotency,** equipollence, equinumerosity, equivalence, set-theoretic[al] equivalence, equal cardinality (power), similarity <of sets> <SE>	Gleichmächtigkeit *f*, Äquivalenz *f*	équipotence *f*, equicardinalité *f*	равномощность, эквивалентность, количественная эквивалентность, подобие
E 404	**equipotent set,** equipollent (equivalent, equinumerous, similar, isomorphic) set, set in (1–1)-correspondence, set having the same cardinality, cardinally equivalent set <SE>	gleichmächtige (äquivalente, isomorphe) Menge *f*, Menge [von] gleicher Mächtigkeit, Mannigfaltigkeit *f* [von] gleicher Mächtigkeit	ensemble *m* équipotent (semblable, de même puissance, ayant la même puissance, d'égale puissance, isomorphe)	равномощное (эквивалентное, подобное, изомерное, равночисленное) множество, множество равной (одинаковой) мощности
E 405	**equiprojective** <PJ>	äquiprojektiv	équiprojectif	эквипроективный
	equiresidual <AL, NT>	*s.* C 1934		
	equiresidual number <NT>	*s.* C 1941		
E 406	**equiresidual semigroup** <AL>	äquiresiduale Halbgruppe *f*	demi-groupe *m* équirésiduel	равновычетная полугруппа
E 407	**equisingular** <AG>	äquisingulär	équisingulier	равноособенный, эквисингулярный
E 408	**equitangential curve** <of a curve> <GE>	Äquitangentialkurve *f*, äquitangentiale Kurve *f*, Kurve gleicher Tangenten	courbe *f* équitangentielle	равнокасательная кривая
E 409	**equivalence** <in the narrow *or* broad sense> <of forms> <AL>	Äquivalenz *f* <im engeren *oder* weiteren Sinne>	équivalence *f* <au sens étroit *ou* large>	эквивалентность <в узком *или* широком смысле>
E 410	**equivalence** <as a functor> <CA>	Äquivalenz *f*	équivalence *f*	эквивалентность; функтор, устанавливающий эквивалентность
E 411	**equivalence,** logical equivalence <of formulae> <LO>	Gleichwertigkeit *f*, Äquivalenz *f*, logische Gleichwertigkeit (Äquivalenz) *f*	équivalence *f*, équivalence tautologique (logique), équipollence *f*, égalité *f* logique	равносильность, равнозначность, эквивалентность, логическая эквивалентность
E 412	**equivalence** <proposition> <LO>	Äquivalenz *f*	équivalence *f*, implication *f* réciproque	эквивалентность, биусловное (эквивалентное, взаимно-условное) высказывание
	equivalence <CA>	*s.* I 1127		
	equivalence <LO>	*s.* M 160		
	equivalence <SE>	*s.* 1. E 403; 2. E 417		
	∞-equivalence <TO>	*s.* W 66		
	equivalence block <SE>	*s.* E 415		
E 413	**equivalence by completion** <GE>	Ergänzungsgleichheit *f*, e, $\overset{e}{=}$	égalité *f* par différence, équivalence *f* par adjonction	равность по дополнительности
E 414	**equivalence by dissection** <GE>	Zerlegungsgleichheit *f*	égalité *f* par somme	равнопоставленность
	equivalence calculus <LO>	*s.* E 5		
E 415	**equivalence class,** abstraction class, equivalence block <determined by the element *x*, containing *x*> <SE>	Äquivalenzklasse *f*, Abstraktionsklasse *f*, Klasse *f*, Restklasse *f* <von *x*>, Faser *f* <über *x*, von *x* erzeugte>	classe *f* d'équivalence, classe <de *x*>	класс эквивалентности (абстракции) <содержащий *x*>
	equivalence class mod $\mathfrak{L}$ <AL>	*s.* L 227		
	equivalence class mod $\mathfrak{R}$ <AL>	*s.* R 206		
	equivalence class modulo *R* <SE>	*s.* R 862		
	equivalence kernel <SE, UA>	*s.* I 393		
	equivalence naturally induced <SE, UA>	*s.* I 393		
E 416	**equivalence problem** <of forms> <AL>	Äquivalenzproblem *n*	problème *m* de l'équivalence	задача (проблема) эквивалентности
E 417	**equivalence relation,** equivalence, equals relation <SE>	Äquivalenzrelation *f*, Äquivalenzbeziehung *f*, Relation *f* der Äquivalenz, Äquivalenz *f*	relation *f* d'équivalence, équivalence *f*, relation classificatoire, préordre *m* symétrique	отношение эквивалентности, эквивалентность, отношения типа равенства, эквивалентное отношение
E 418	**equivalence relation generated by a reflexive relation** <SE, UA>	von einer reflexiven Relation erzeugte Äquivalenzrelation *f*	équivalence *f* de connexité	отношение эквивалентности, порожденное рефлексивным отношением
E 419	**equivalence relation generated by a relation** <AL, SE>	von einer Relation erzeugte Äquivalenzrelation *f*	relation *f* d'équivalence engendrée par une relation	отношение эквивалентности, порожденное отношением
E 420	**equivalence relation induced by a closure operation** <SE>	durch eine Hüllenbildung induzierte Äquivalenzrelation *f*	équivalence *f* de fermeture [de Moore]	отношение эквивалентности, индуцированное операцией замыкания
E 421	**equivalence relation induced by a homomorphism** <AL>	durch einen Homomorphismus induzierte Äquivalenzrelation *f*	équivalence *f* d'homomorphisme	отношение эквивалентности, индуцированное гомоморфизмом

No.	English	German	French	Russian
E 422	**equivalence relation induced by a quasiorder** <SE>	durch die Vorordnung induzierte Äquivalenzrelation *f*	relation *f* d'équivalence associée au préordre, équivalence *f* associée au préordre	ассоциированное отношение эквивалентности
	equivalence sign (symbol) <LO>	*s.* S 2438		
E 423	**equivalence theorem** <for the *C*- and *H*-methods of limitation>, Knopp-Schnee theorem <LI>	Knopp-Schneescher Satz *m*, Äquivalenzsatz *m* der *C*- und *H*-Verfahren	théorème *m* d'équivalence, théorème de Knopp-Schnee	теорема эквивалентности (Кноппа-Шне)
E 424	**equivalence theorem** <LO>	Äquivalenzsatz *m*, Ersetzungstheorem *n* für äquivalente Formeln	théorème *m* d'équivalence	теорема эквивалентности
E 425	**equivalence theorem,** Schröder-Bernstein theorem, Schroeder-Bernstein theorem, theorem of Bernstein-Schröder, Cantor-Bernstein theorem [on cardinals], Bernstein['s] equivalence theorem <SE>	Äquivalenzsatz *m* von Bernstein, Cantor-Bernsteinscher Äquivalenzsatz, Äquivalenzsatz für Mengen, Schröder-Bernsteinscher Satz *m*, Bernsteins[cher] Äquivalenzsatz	théorème *m* de Cantor-Bernstein	теорема Шредера-Бернштейна (Кантора-Бернштейна, эквивалентности, Бернштейна, Кантора
E 426	**equivalent,** $\sim$ <AL>	äquivalent, $\sim$	équivalent, $\sim$	эквивалентный, $\sim$
E 427	**equivalent,** logically equivalent, $\longleftrightarrow$, $\equiv$, $\rightleftarrows$, $\sim$ <*read:* is equivalent to . . ., if and only if> <LO>	äquivalent, logisch äquivalent (gleichwertig), gleichbedeutend <*gelesen:* äquivalent, gleichwertig; genau dann, wenn>	équivalent, logiquement équivalent <*se lit:* équivalent à . . ., entraîne . . . et réciproquement, implique . . . et réciproquement>	эквивалентный, логически эквивалентный, равносильный, равнозначный <*читается:* тогда и только тогда, когда. . .>
E 428	**equivalent écart** <TO>	äquivalenter „écart" *m*, äquivalente Pseudometrik *f*	écart *m* équivalent	эквивалентное отклонение
E 429	**equivalent element** <with respect to an equivalence relation> <SE>	äquivalentes Element *n* <bezüglich einer Äquivalenzrelation>	élément *m* équivalent (congru) <par rapport à une relation d'équivalence, modulo une relation d'équivalence>	эквивалентный элемент <относительно отношению эквивалентности>
E 430	**equivalent equation** <AL>	äquivalente Gleichung *f*	équation *f* équivalente	равносильное (эквивалентное) уравнение
E 431	**equivalent fibre bundle in (over) *G*,** *G*-equivalent fibre bundle <AT>	*G*-äquivalentes Faserbündel *n*	espace *m* fibré *G*-équivalent	*G*-эквивалентное расслоение
E 432	**equivalent figure** <in the Möbius plane> <FT>	kongruente Figur *f*	figure *f* congruente	фигура, получаемая из другой круговым преобразованием
E 433	**equivalent form** <of a field> <AB>	[absolut] äquivalente Form *f*, inhaltsgleiche Form, im engeren Sinne äquivalente algebraische Form	forme *f* équivalente (associée, absolument équivalente, de même contenu, d'égale contenance)	эквивалентная форма
	equivalent form <AL>	*s.* I 1109		
E 434	**equivalent formula** <LO>	äquivalenter Ausdruck *m*, logisch gleichwertige Formel *f*, gleichwertige Formel *f*	formule *f* équivalente	эквивалентная (равносильная, конгруэнтная) формула
E 435	**equivalent formula of the propositional calculus** <LO>	äquivalenter Ausdruck *m* des Aussagenkalküls, junktorenlogisch äquivalente Formel *f*	formule *f* équivalente du calcul propositionnel	эквивалентная формула исчисления высказываний
	equivalent group <GR>	*s.* C 1989		
E 436	**equivalent ideal in the restricted sense** <AB>	im engeren Sinne äquivalentes Ideal *n*	idéal *m* équivalent au sens restreint	в узком смысле эквивалентный идеал
E 437	**equivalent knot** <AT>	isomorpher Knoten *m*	nœud *m* isomorphe	эквивалентный узел, узел одного и того же типа
E 438	**equivalent limitation methods** <LI>	äquivalente (gleichstarke, konsistente) Limitierungsverfahren (*V*-Verfahren) *npl*	méthodes *fpl* équivalentes de limitation	равносильные (эквивалентные) методы образования обобщенного предела
	equivalent map[ping] <AY>	*s.* A 930		
E 439	**equivalent matrix,** associated matrix <MD>	äquivalente Matrix *f*	matrice *f* équivalente	эквивалентная матрица
E 440	**equivalent matrix representation,** similar matrix representation <AL>	äquivalente (ähnliche) Matrizendarstellung *f*	représentation *f* matricielle semblable (équivalente)	эквивалентное матричное представление
E 441	**equivalent methods [of summation],** equivalent summation methods <LI>	äquivalente (gleichstarke, konsistente) Summierungsverfahren *npl*	méthodes *fpl* équivalentes de sommation	равносильные (эквивалентные) методы суммирования
E 442	**equivalent metric** <TO>	äquivalente (topologisch[-] gleichwertige, topologisch äquivalente) Metrik *f*, topologisch äquivalenter Abstand *m*	métrique *f* [topologiquement] équivalente, distance *f* [topologiquement] équivalente	[топологически] эквивалентная метрика, топологически равносильная метрика
E 443	**equivalent neighbourhood system** <TO>	gleichwertiges (topologisch gleichwertiges, äquivalentes) Umgebungssystem *n*	système *m* de voisinages définissant la même topologie	фундаментальная система окрестностей, определяющая одну и ту же топологию
E 444	**equivalent normal series** <AL>	isomorphe Normalreihe *f*	suite *f* de composition équivalente	изоморфный нормальный ряд

No.	English	German	French	Russian
E 445	**equivalent object,** isomorphic object <CA>	isomorphes Objekt *n*	objet *m* isomorphe	эквивалентный объект
	equivalent-perspective affinity <DS>	*s.* S 758		
E 446	**equivalent point** <in the case of a discontinuous group> <GR>	äquivalenter (konjugierter) Punkt *m*	point *m* équivalent	эквивалентная точка
E 447	**equivalent proposition** <LO>	äquivalente Aussage *f*	proposition *f* identique (équivalente), proposition, assertion *f* équivalente	равнозначное высказывание, эквивалентное высказывание
E 448	**equivalent refinement,** isomorphic refinement <of chains> <AL>	isomorphe Verfeinerung *f*	raffinement *m* isomorphe	изоморфное уплотнение
E 449	**equivalent representation,** similar representation, isomorphic representation <RE>	äquivalente (ähnliche) Darstellung *f*; zur gleichen Klasse gehörige Darstellung <einer Algebra>	représentation *f* semblable (isomorphe, équivalente)	эквивалентное (изоморфное) представление
E 450	**equivalent series** <of a continued fraction> <NT>	äquivalente Reihe *f* <eines Kettenbruchs>	série *f* équivalente <à une fraction continue>	равноценный ряд <непрерывной дроби>
	equivalent set <SE>	*s.* E 404		
	equivalent space <DG>	*s.* I 1124		
E 451	**equivalent stochastic process,** stochastic modification <SP>	äquivalenter stochastischer Prozeß *m*, stochastische Modifikation *f*	processus *m* stochastique équivalent, modification *f* stochastique	эквивалентный случайный процесс, стохастическая модификация
	equivalent summation methods <LI>	*s.* E 441		
	equivalent transformation <MD>	*s.* E 116		
	equivalent vector <GE>	*s.* E 401		
E 452	**equivalent whole number [as regards divisibility],** associated integer <AL>	assoziierte ganze Zahl *f*	nombre *m* entier associé	ассоциированное целое число
E 453	**equivariant map** <TO>	äquivariante Abbildung *f*	application *f* équivariante	эквивариантное отображение
E 454	**Erdélyi['s] function** <FU>	Erdélyische Funktion *f*	fonction *f* d'Erdélyi	функция Эрдей[и]
E 455	**Erdélyi['s] polynomial** <FU>	Erdélyisches Polynom *n*	polynôme *m* d'Erdélyi	многочлен Эрдей[и], полином Эрдей[и]
E 456	**Erdmann-Weierstrass corner condition,** Weierstrass-Erdmann corner (vertex) condition <VA>	Weierstraß-Erdmannsche Eckenbedingung *f*, Erdmann-Weierstraßsche Eckenbedingung, Eckenbedingung [von Weierstraß-Erdmann]	condition *f* d'Erdmann	условие [н углы] Вейерштрасса-Эрдмана, угловое условие Вейерштрасса-Эрдмана
E 457	**erect the perpendicular to a line in a point / to,** to draw the perpendicular to a line in a point <EG>	die Senkrechte errichten auf einer Geraden in einem Punkt	élever la perpendiculaire sur une droite en un point	восставлять (восставить, проводить, провести) перпендикуляр к прямой в точке
	erf[i] <ER, ST>	*s.* E 473		
	ergodic chain <SP>	*s.* E 459		
	ergodic flow <ME>	*s.* E 463		
E 458	**ergodicity** <SP>	Ergodizität *f*	ergodicité *f*	эргодичность
E 459	**ergodic Markov chain,** ergodic chain <SP>	ergodische [Markovsche] Kette *f*	chaîne *f* [markovienne] ergodique	эргодическая цепь [Маркова]
E 460	**ergodic state** <of a Markov chain> <SP>	ergodischer Zustand *m*, E-Zustand *m*	état *m* ergodique	эргодическое состояние
	ergodic theorem in the mean <SP>	*s.* S 1693		
E 461	**ergodic theorem of Hopf,** Hopf['s] ergodic theorem <SP>	Ergodensatz *m* von Hopf, Hopfscher Ergodensatz	théorème *m* ergodique de Hopf	эргодическая теорема Хопфа
E 462	**ergodic theory** <SP>	Ergodentheorie *f*	théorie *f* ergodique	эргодическая теория
E 463	**ergodic transformation,** metrically transitive transformation (flow), ergodic flow <ME>	ergodische [maßtreue] Transformation *f*, metrisch transitive [maßtreue] Transformation	transformation *f* ergodique (métriquement transitive)	эргодическое (метрически транзитивное, неразложимое) преобразование
E 464	**Erlang distribution** <ST>	Erlang-Verteilung *f*	distribution *f* d'Erlang	распределение Эрланга
E 465	**"Erlanger Programm",** Klein['s] Erlanger program[m] <GE>	Erlanger Programm *n*	« Erlanger Programm » *m*, programme *m* d'Erlangen [de Klein]	эрлангенская программа, Эрлангенская программа [Ф. Клейна]
E 466	**Erlang['s] formula** <ST>	Erlangsche Formel *f*	formule *f* d'Erlang	формула Эрланга
E 467	**Ermakoff['s] test,** Yermakov['s] test <for convergence> <SS>	Ermakowsches Kriterium (Konvergenzkriterium) *n*	critère *m* (règle *f*) d'Ermakoff	критерий (признак) Ермакова
E 468	**error** <ER, NU>	Fehler *m*, Wert *m* des Fehlers, Fehlerwert *m*	erreur *f*, reste *f*, résidu *m*	погрешность
	α-error <ST>	*s.* E 477		
	β-error <ST>	*s.* E 479		
	γ-error <ST>	*s.* E 481		
E 469	**error band** <ST>	Fehlerbereich *m*, Zufallsbereich *m*	intervalle *m* d'erreur	область (интервал, полоса) ошибок
E 470	**error component** <ST>	Fehlerkomponente *f*	composante *f* de l'erreur	составляющая ошибки, компонента ошибки
E 471	**error curve,** [Gauss] error distribution curve, normal error (frequency, distribution) curve, normal curve, [normal] probability curve,	Gauß-Kurve *f*, Gaußsche Kurve (Fehlerkurve) *f*, Fehlerkurve, Gaußsche Glockenkurve *f*, Wahrscheinlichkeitskurve *f*, Normalverteilungskurve	courbe *f* de Gauss (Laplace, Laplace-Gauss), courbe de distribution d'erreurs [de Gauss], courbe d'erreurs [de Gauss], courbe de pro-	кривая Гаусса (ошибок, ошибок Гаусса), гауссова кривая распределения ошибок, нормальная кривая [распределения], кривая

No.	English	German	French	Russian
	Gaussian curve [of error], Gaussian (Gauss['] error curve, curve of normal distribution [of errors]; bell-shaped curve <ST>	*f*, Normalkurve *f*; Glockenkurve	babilité de Gauss, courbe normale; courbe en cloche	вероятности (плотности нормального распределения, обеспеченности); колоколообразная кривая
	error distribution curve <ST>	*s.* E 471		
E 472	**error equation** <ER>	Verbesserungsgleichung *f*, Fehlergleichung *f*	équation *f* d'erreurs	уравнение ошибок
	error estimation <ER>	*s.* E 548		
	error first kind <ST>	*s.* E 477		
E 473	**error function [integral], error integral,** Gaussian error function, Gauss['] error function, Gaussian transcendental function; erf, erfi; Erf, Erfi <ER, ST>	Fehlerfunktion *f*, Fehlerintegral *n*, Kramp-Laplacesche Transzendente *f*, Krampsche Transzendente (Funktion) *f*, Gaußsche Transzendente (Funktion), ,,error function" *f*; Fehlerwahrscheinlichkeitsfunktion *f*, Gaußsches Fehlerintegral; erf; Erf	fonction *f* erreur, fonction des erreurs, fonction d'erreur, fonction de Kramp, intégrale de Gauss; fonction d'erreurs de Gauss; erf; Erf	интеграл вероятности, функция Лапласа, нормированная функция Лапласа, функция вероятности ошибок, интеграл вероятности ошибок; erf; Erf
E 474	**error in the input data,** input error <ER, NU>	eingangsbedingter Fehler *m*, Eingangsfehler *m*	erreur *f* sur les données [d'entrée]	ошибка [входных] данных
E 475	**error law, error-law distribution,** [normal] law of errors, Gaussian law of error [distribution] <ER>	Gaußsches Fehlergesetz *n*, Fehlergesetz	loi *f* des erreurs [d'observation], loi de Gauss, loi de la distribution normale [des erreurs]	закон ошибок, закон [нормального] распределения ошибок, гауссов закон погрешностей
	error mean square <ST>	*s.* E 486		
	error model <ST>	*s.* N 566		
	error of approximation <ER, NU>	*s.* P 1582		
E 476	**error of estimation** <ST>	Schätzfehler *m*	erreur *f* d'estimation	ошибка (погрешность) оценки
E 477	**error of first kind,** error [of the] first kind, type I error, α-error, alpha-error <ST>	Fehler *m* erster (1.) Art, α-Fehler *m*, Alpha-Fehler *m*	erreur *f* de première catégorie (espèce), erreur du type 1, erreur α, erreur alpha	ошибка первого рода
E 478	**error of fitting** <ST>	Anpassungsfehler *m*	erreur d'ajustement, erreur de lissage	погрешность (ошибка) выравнивания
	error of measurement <ST>	*s.* M 347		
	error of procedure <ER, NU>	*s.* P 1582		
E 479	**error of second kind,** error [of the] second kind, type II error, β-error, beta-error <ST>	Fehler *m* zweiter (2.) Art, β-Fehler *m*, Beta-Fehler *m*	erreur *f* de seconde catégorie (espèce), erreur du type 2, erreur β, erreur bêta	ошибка второго рода
E 480	**error of single observation** <ER>	Einzelfehler *m*	erreur *f* de l'observation [individuelle]	единичная ошибка
	error of the first kind <ST>	*s.* E 477		
	error of the second kind <ST>	*s.* E 479		
E 481	**error of [the] third kind,** error third kind, type III error, γ-error, gamma-error <ST>	Fehler *m* dritter (3.) Art, γ-Fehler *m*, Gamma-Fehler *m*	erreur *f* de troisième catégorie (espèce), erreur du type 3, erreur γ, erreur gamma	ошибка третьего рода
E 482	**error of truncation,** truncation error <ST>	Stutzungsfehler *m*	erreur *f* de troncature	ошибка усечения
	error of truncation <NU>	*s.* T 1035		
E 483	**error probability** <ST>	Fehlerwahrscheinlichkeit *f*	probabilité *f* d'erreur	вероятность ошибки
	error probability <ST>	*s.* 1. L 599; 2. S 842		
	error propagation <ER>	*s.* P 1763		
	error propagation law (theorem) <ER>	*s.* P 1764		
	error rate <ST>	*s.* 1. L 599; 2. S 842		
E 484	**error rate determined by comparison,** type I error rate determined by comparison <ST>	vergleichsbezogene Irrtumswahrscheinlichkeit *f*	probabilité *f* d'erreur déterminée par comparaison	вероятность ошибки, определенная по сравнению
E 485	**error rate determined by experiment,** type I error rate determined by experiment <ST>	versuchsbezogene Irrtumswahrscheinlichkeit *f*	probabilité *f* d'erreur déterminée par expérience	вероятность ошибки, определенная по эксперименту
	error second kind <ST>	*s.* E 479		
	error sum [of squares] <ST>	*s.* R 882		
	error third kind <ST>	*s.* E 481		
	error variable <ST>	*s.* R 98		
E 486	**error variance,** error mean square <ST>	Fehlervarianz *f*, Fehlerkomponente *f*	variance *f* de l'erreur	дисперсия ошибки
E 487	**escribed angle** <of a circle> <EG>	Tangentenwinkel *m*	angle *m* exinscrit	вневписанный угол
	escribed circle <EG>	*s.* E 680		
	escribed sphere <EG>	*s.* E 758		
E 488	**∈-space** <PO>	∈-Raum *m*	espace *m* ∈ <Brelot>	∈-пространство
E 489	**essential boundary condition,** geometric boundary condition <DE>	wesentliche (geometrische) Randbedingung *f*	condition *f* aux limites essentielle (géométrique)	существенное (геометрическое) краевое условие

No.	English	German	French	Russian
E 490	**essential component** <AB>	wesentliche Komponente *f*	composante *f* essentielle	существенная компонента
E 491	**essential constant** <AN>	wesentliche Konstante *f*, wesentlicher Parameter *m*	constante *f* essentielle	существенный параметр
E 492	**essential convergence** <of a sequence of functions> <AN>	wesentliche Konvergenz *f*, Konvergenz *f* im wesentlichen	convergence *f* essentielle	сходимость в основном
E 493	**essential cover** <CA>	wesentliche Bedeckung *f*	revêtement *m* essentiel	собственное (существенное) покрытие
E 494	**essential cycle** <AT>	wesentlicher Zyklus *m*	cycle *m* essentiel	существенный цикл
E 495	**essential divisor** <of a discriminant> <AB> ┌<AT>	wesentlicher Diskriminantenteiler *m* (Teiler *m*) <einer Diskriminante>	facteur (diviseur) *m* essentiel <du discriminant>	существенный делитель <дискриминанта>
E 496	**essential element** <of a cellular decomposition>	wesentliches Element *n*	élément *m* essentiel	существенный элемент
E 497	**essential epimorphism** <CA>	wesentlicher Epimorphismus *m*	épimorphisme *m* essentiel	существенный эпиморфизм
E 498	**essential extension** <of a module> <AL>	wesentliche Erweiterung *f*	extension *f* essentielle	существенное расширение
E 499	**essential extension** <CA>	wesentlicher Monomorphismus *m*	monomorphisme *m* essentiel	существенный мономорфизм
E 500	**essential extension** <of an object> <CA>	wesentliche Erweiterung *f*	extension *f* essentielle	существенное расширение
E 501	**essential game** <TG>	wesentliches Spiel *n*	jeu *m* essentiel	существенная игра
E 502	**essential graded ideal** <AL>	wesentliches graduiertes Ideal *n*	idéal *m* gradué essentiel	существенный градуированный идеал
	μ-essential greatest lower bound <RF>	*s.* E 505		
E 503	**essential homomorphism** <AL>	wesentlicher Homomorphismus *m*	homomorphisme *m* essentiel	существенный гомоморфизм
E 504	**essential inferior limit** <of a net of measurable functions> <RF>	wesentlicher Limes *m* inferior, e lim inf	limite *f* inférieure essentielle	существенный нижний предел
E 505	**[μ-]essential infinimum,** μ-essential greatest lower bound, ess inf <of a function> <RF>	wesentliches Infimum *m*, e inf	infimum *m* essentiel, minimum *m* en mesure	существенная нижняя грань
	μ-essential least upper bound <RF>	*s.* E 537		
E 506	**essential left ideal** <AL>	wesentliches Linksideal *n*	idéal *m* à gauche essentiel	существенный (большой) левый идеал
	[μ]-essentially bounded function <AN>	*s.* A 506	fonction *f* bornée essen-	существенно ограничен-
E 507/8	**essentially convergent sequence** <of measurable functions> <AN>	wesentlich konvergente Folge *f*	suite *f* essentiellement convergente	существенно сходящаяся последовательность
E 509	**essentially different number** <NT>	wesentlich verschiedene Zahl *f*	nombre *m* essentiellement différent	существенно разное число
	essentially divergent [infinite] continued fraction <NT>	*s.* I 172		
E 510	**essentially general position** <TO>	wesentlich allgemeine Lage *f*	position *f* essentiellement générale	существенно общее положение
E 511	**essentially homotopic** <TO>	wesentlich homotop	essentiellement homotope	в существенном гомотопный
E 512	**essentially infinite cover** <TO>	wesentlich unendliche Überdeckung *f*	recouvrement *m* essentiellement infini	существенно бесконечное покрытие
E 513	**essentially infinite join** <in a Boolean algebra> <AL, SE>	wesentlich unendliche Vereinigung *f*	union *f* essentiellement infinie	существенно бесконечное объединение
E 514	**essentially[-]injective module** <AL>	wesentlich[ ]injektiver Modul *m*	module *m* essentiellement injectif	существенно инъективный модуль
E 515	**essentially locally bounded function** <AN>	wesentlich lokal beschränkte Funktion *f*	fonction *f* essentiellement localement bornée	существенно локально ограниченная функция
E 516	**essentially recursively undecidable theory** <MM>	wesentlich rekursiv unentscheidbare Theorie *f*	théorie *f* essentiellement récursivement indécidable	существенно рекурсивно неразрешимая теория
E 517	**essentially self-adjoint operator** <FA>	wesentlich selbstadjungierter Operator *m*	opérateur *m* essentiellement auto-adjoint	существенно самосопряженный оператор
E 518	**essentially singular branch[-]point,** branch point of the essential singular type <of a many-valued analytic function> <FT>	Verzweigungspunkt *m* von wesentlich singulärem Typ, Verzweigungspunkt vom wesentlich singulären Typ, wesentlich singulärer Verzweigungspunkt	point *m* critique (de ramification) essentiellement singulier	критическая существенно особая точка, точка разветвления (ветвления) существенно особого типа
E 519	**essentially singular quaternion function** <FT>	wesentlich singuläre Quaternionenfunktion *f*	fonction *f* quaternionienne essentiellement singulière	существенно особая кватернионная функция
E 520	**essentially undecidable theory** <MM>	wesentlich unentscheidbare Theorie *f*	théorie *f* essentiellement non décidable	существенно неразрешимая теория
	essentially uniform convergence <FA>	*s.* Q 261		
	essentially uniformly convergent sequence <FA>	*s.* Q 263		
E 521	**essential map[ping]** <AT, TO>	wesentliche Abbildung *f*	application *f* essentielle	существенное отображение
E 522	**essential parameter** <of a family of geometrical objects *or* of a transformation group> <AL, GE>	wesentlicher Parameter *m*	paramètre *m* essentiel	существенный параметр
E 523	**essential point** <TO>	wesentlicher Punkt *m*	point *m* essentiel	существенная точка
E 524	**essential polyhedron** <AT>	wesentliches Polyeder *n*	polyèdre *m* essentiel	существенный полиэдр

No.	English	German	French	Russian
E 525	**essential prime ideal** <AL>	wesentliches Primideal *n*	idéal *m* premier essentiel	существенный простой идеал
E 526	**essential right ideal** <AL>	wesentliches Rechtsideal *n*	idéal *m* à droite essentiel	существенный (большой) правый идеал
E 527	**essential singularity,** isolated essential singularity, [isolated] essential singular point <of a single-valued analytic function> <FT>	wesentlich[e] singuläre Stelle *f*, isolierte wesentlich[e] singuläre Stelle, [isolierte] wesentliche Singularität *f*	point *m* singulier essentiel [isolé], singularité *f* essentielle [isolée]	[изолированная] существенно особая точка, существенная особенность, изолированная существенная особенность
E 528	**essential singularity,** essential singular point <not necessarily isolated> <FT>	wesentlich[e] singuläre Stelle *f* zweiter Art, wesentliche singuläre Stelle	singularité *f* essentielle, point *m* singulier essentiel	существенная особенность (особая точка)
	essential singularity <DE>	*s.* I 1069		
E 529	**essential singular kernel,** singular kernel <IE>	stark (wesentlich) singulärer Kern *m*, singulärer Kern	noyau *m* singulier essentiel, noyau singulier	существенно особое ядро
	essential singular point <DE>	*s.* I 1069		
	essential singular point <FT>	*s.* 1. E 527; 2. E 528		
E 530	**essential space** <TO>	wesentlicher Raum *m*	espace *m* essentiel	существенное пространство
E 531	**essential spectrum** <FA>	wesentliches Spektrum *n*	spectre *m* essentiel	существенный спектр
E 532	**essential state** <SP>	wesentlicher Zustand *m*	état *m* essentiel	существенное состояние
E 533	**essential strategy** <TG>	aktive (wesentliche) Strategie *f*	stratégie *f* essentielle	активная (существенная) стратегия
E 534	**essential submodule** <AL>	wesentlicher Untermodul *m*	sous-module *m* essentiel	существенный подмодуль
E 535	**essential subsequence** <of a double sequence> <SS>	wesentliche Teilfolge *f*	suite *f* partielle essentielle	существенная подпоследовательность
E 536	**essential superior limit** <of a net of measurable functions> <RF>	wesentlicher Limes *m* superior, e lim sup	limite *f* supérieure essentielle	существенный верхний предел
E 537	**[μ-]essential supremum,** essential upper bound, μ-essential least upper bound, ess sup <RF>	wesentliches Supremum *n*, e sup	suprémum *m* essentiel, maximum *m* en mesure	существенная верхняя грань
E 538	**essential undecidability** <LO>	wesentliche Unentscheidbarkeit *f*	indécidabilité *f* essentielle	существенная неразрешимость
	essential upper bound <RF>	*s.* E 537		
E 539	**essential valuation** <AL>	wesentliche Bewertung *f*	valuation *f* essentielle	существенное нормирование
E 540	**essential value** <TO>	wesentlicher Wert *m*	valeur *f* essentielle	существенное значение
E 541	**essential zero** <of an ideal> <AL>	wesentliche Nullstelle *f*	zéro *m* essentiel	существенный нуль
	ess inf <RF>	*s.* E 505		
	ess sup <RF>	*s.* E 537		
E 542	**estimable function** <ST>	schätzbare Funktion *f*	fonction *f* estimable	функция, допускающая оценку
E 543	**estimable hypothesis** <ST>	schätzbare Hypothese *f*	hypothèse *f* estimable	проверяемая гипотеза
E 544	**estimate,** statistical estimate, concrete estimate <ST>	[statistischer] Schätzwert *m*, konkrete Punktschätzung (Schätzung) *f*, konkreter Schätzwert	estimation *f*, estimation statistique, estimation concrète, valeur *f* estimée	оценка, статистическая (конкретная) оценка, оценочное значение
	estimate <AN, NU>	*s.* E 545		
	estimating function <ST>	*s.* E 550		
	estimating of the root <AL, AR>	*s.* T 29		
E 545	**estimation** <process>; estimate <value> <AN, NU>	Abschätzung *f*	estimation *f*	оценка
E 546/7	**estimation,** statistical estimation <ST>	Schätzen *n*, [statistische] Schätzung *f*	estimation *f*, estimation statistique	отыскание оценки, [статистическое] оценивание
E 548	**estimation of error,** error estimation <ER>	Fehlerschätzung *f*, Schätzung *f* des Fehlers; Fehlerabschätzung *f*	estimation *f* de l'erreur	оценка ошибки (погрешности)
E 549	**estimation region,** concrete estimation region <ST>	Schätzbereich *m*, konkrete Bereichsschätzung *f*, konkreter Schätzbereich	région *f* d'estimation, région d'estimation concrète	доверительная область, конкретная доверительная область
	estimation theory <ST>	*s.* T 383		
E 550	**estimator,** estimating function <ST>	Schätzfunktion *f*, Punktschätzung *f*, Schätzung *f*, Schätzungsfunktion *f*	estimateur *m*, fonction *f* estimatrice (estimateur, d'estimation)	оценка, статистическая (точечная) оценка; статистика, используемая в качестве оценки
E 551	**E-sum,** sum by Euler's method <LI>	*E*-Summe *f*, Summe *f* nach dem *E*-Verfahren	somme *f* par la méthode d'Euler, *E*-somme *f*	[обобщенная] сумма по методу Эйлера, [обобщенная] сумма по Эйлеру, *E*-сумма
	E-summable series <LI>	*s.* S 625		
E 552	**E-system [of surfaces],** Egorov['s] (Egoroff['s]) system [of surfaces] <DG>	E-System *n* von Flächen, Egorovsches (Jegorowsches, Egorowsches) Flächensystem *n*	E-système de surfaces, système *m* d'Egoroff de surfaces	система поверхностей Егорова
	eta-function of Jacobi <FU>	*s.* H 294		
E 553	**etale (étale) cohomology** <AL, TO>	Etalkohomologie *f*	cohomologie *f* étale	накрывающие (этальные) когомологии

E 554	**etale (étale) covering** <AG>	Etalüberdeckung *f*	revêtement *m* étale	этальное накрытие
E 555	**etale (étale) mapping** <AL, TO>	Etalabbildung *f*	application *f* étale	этальное отображение
E 556	**etale (étale) morphism** <AG, AL>	Etalmorphismus *m*	morphisme *m* étalé, étalement *m*	этальный (накрывающий) морфизм
E 557	**etale neighbourhood** <TO>	Etalumgebung *f*	voisinage *m* étale	этальная окрестность
E 558	**etale space** <AT>	Etalraum *m*, etalierter Raum *m*	espace *m* étalé	накрывающее (этальное) пространство
E 559	**etale (étale) topology** <AG>	Etaltopologie *f*	topologie *f* étale	накрывающая (этальная) топология
	Eubulides['] Liar Paradox <LO>	*s.* E 296		
	Euclid['s] algorithm <AL>	*s.* A 487		
	Euclid['s] axiom [in Ptolemy's form] <GE>	*s.* P 667		
	Euclidean algorithm <AL>	*s.* A 487		
	Euclidean complex <AT>	*s.* G 255		
E 560	**Euclidean displacement,** rigid motion, orientation-preserving isometry <in a metric space> <TO>	Bewegung *f*, euklidische Bewegung	déplacement *m*, isométrie *f* positive, déplacement euclidien	движение
	Euclidean displacement <AY>	*s.* E 564		
E 561	**Euclidean domain,** Euclidean ring <AL>	euklidischer Ring *m*	anneau (domaine) *m* euclidien	евклидово кольцо
E 562	**Euclidean (euclidean) geometry,** Euclidian (euclidian) geometry, parabolic geometry <GE>	euklidische (parabolische) Geometrie *f*	géométrie *f* euclidienne (parabolique)	евклидово (параболическая) геометрия, // эвклидова геометрия
	Euclidean geometry <EG>	*s.* E 108		
E 563	**Euclidean metric,** Pythagorean metric <GE>	euklidische Metrik *f*	métrique *f* euclidienne	евклидова метрика
E 564	**Euclidean movement,** Euclidean displacement, displacement <in the Euclidean space> <AY>	euklidische Bewegung *f*, Bewegung	déplacement *m* euclidien, déplacement	евклидово движение, движение
E 565	**Euclidean norm,** norm <of a matrix> <MD>	euklidische Norm *f*, Norm	norme *f* euclidienne, norme	евклидова норма, норма
	Euclidean norm <VT>	*s.* M 24		
	Euclidean *n*-space <AN, GE>	*s.* C 167		
E 566	**Euclidean plane,** number plane <AN, GE>	Zahlenebene *f*	plan *m* numérique	числовая плоскость
E 567	**Euclidean plane** <AY>	euklidische (Euklidische) Ebene *f*	plan *m* euclidien	евклидова плоскость
E 568	**Euclidean (euclidean) property** <AY, GE>	euklidische Eigenschaft *f*	propriété *f* euclidienne	евклидово свойство
	Euclidean ring <AL>	*s.* F 561		
E 569	**Euclidean space,** Cartesian (arithmetic) space <AN, AY>	euklidischer (Euklidischer) Raum *m*, kartesischer Raum, euklidische Mannigfaltigkeit *f*, Euklidischer Zahlenraum *m*, Zahlenraum, kartesischer Zahlenraum, arithmetischer Raum, arithmetische Mannigfaltigkeit	espace *m* euclidien (cartésien, numérique, arithmétique)	евклидово пространство, пространство Евклида, числовое (арифметическое, координатное) пространство
	Euclidean space <FA>	*s.* R 233		
	Euclidean theorem <EG>	*s.* E 573		
E 570	**Euclid['s] factorization theorem for rational integers,** unique factorization theorem, fundamental theorem of [rational] arithmetic, theorem of unique prime number factorization, unique factorization theorem for integers, fundamental law of arithmetic, fundamental theorem of arithmetic, factorization theorem <NT>	Fundamentalsatz(Hauptsatz) *m* der [elementaren] Zahlentheorie, Satz *m* von der Primfaktorzerlegung	théorème *m* de la factorisation première des entiers, théorème fondamental de l'arithmétique	теорема о единственности разложения числа на простые сомножители, основная теорема арифметики
	Euclid['s] fifth postulate <GE>	*s.* E 572		
	Euclid['s] first theorem <AL, NT>	*s.* E 571		
	Euclidian geometry <EG>	*s.* 1. E 108; 2. E 562		
E 571	**Euclid['s] lemma,** Euclid['s] first theorem <AL, NT>	Euklidischer Fundamentalsatz *m*, erster Euklidischer Satz *m*	lemme *m* d'Euclide, théorème *m* de Gauss	лемма Евклида, теорема Гаусса
	Euclid['s] parallel axiom <GE>	*s.* E 572		
	Euclid['s] parallel, axiom [in Ptolemy's form] <GE>	*s.* P 667		

No.	English	German	French	Russian
E 572	**Euclid['s] parallel postulate,** Euclid['s] parallel axiom, parallel axiom (postulate) [of Euclid], axiom of parallelism, Euclid['s] fifth postulate <GE>	Euklidisches (euklidisches) Parallelenaxiom (Parallelenpostulat) *n*, Parallelenaxiom (Parallelenpostulat) von Euklid, Parallelenaxiom, Parallelenpostulat, Axiom *n* der Parallelen, Euklidisches Axiom [der Parallelen], fünftes Postulat von Euklid, Euklids fünftes (V.) Postulat	postulat *m* d'Euclide, postulat des parallèles d'Euclide, postulat des parallèles, axiome *m* d'Euclide, axiome des parallèles, axiome de parallélisme, postulat euclidien, axiome euclidien	аксиома параллельности (параллельных) Евклида, аксиома параллельности (параллельных), постулат (аксиома) Евклида [о параллельных прямых], пятый постулат Евклида
E 573	**Euclid['s] theorem,** Euclidean theorem, theorem of Euclid <EG>	Euklidischer Lehrsatz *m*, Satz *m* von Euklid, Kathetensatz *m*	théorème *m* d'Euclide	теорема Евклида
E 574	**Eudoxus semigroup** <AL>	eudoxische Halbgruppe *f*	demi-groupe *m* d'Eudoxe	эвдоксова полугруппа
	Eudoxus['] theorem <GE>	*s.* A 897		
	Euler['s] angle <AY>	*s.* E 591		
	Euler['s] beta-function <FU>	*s.* B 247		
	Euler-Cauchy [differential] equation <DE>	*s.* E 582		
E 575	**Euler['s] characteristic,** characteristic <of an elementary curve, or of a complex <AT, GE>	[Eulersche] Charakteristik *f*	caractéristique *f* [d'Euler]	эйлерова характеристика, характеристика <кривой *или* комплекса>; характеристика Эйлера-Пуанкаре <комплекса>
	Euler['s] characteristic <AT>	*s.* E 608		
E 576	**Euler['s] circuit,** Euler['s] line <in an oriented graph> <GP>	geschlossene Eulersche Linie *f*	circuit *m* eulérien	эйлеров контур
E 577	**Euler['s] class** <AT>	Eulersche Klasse *f*	classe *f* d'Euler	класс Эйлера
	Euler coefficient <AN, AP, AX, NU>	*s.* F 520		
E 578	**Euler['s] condition** <VA>	Eulersche [notwendige] Bedingung *f*	condition *f* d'Euler	условие Эйлера
E 579	**Euler['s] constant,** Euler-Mascheroni constant, Mascheroni['s] constant <FU>	Eulersche Konstante *f*, [Euler-]Mascheronische Konstante, Euler[-Mascheroni]-Konstante *f*	constante *f* d'Euler, constante d'Euler-Mascheroni, constante de Mascheroni	постоянная Эйлера, постоянная Эйлера-Маскерони
E 580	**Euler['s] criterion** <NT>	Eulersches Kriterium *n*	critère *m* d'Euler	критерий Эйлера
E 581	**Euler['s] diagram** <LO, SE>	Eulersches Diagramm *n*, Euler-Diagramm *n*	diagramme *m* eulérien	эйлерова диаграмма
	Euler['s] diagram <LO>	*s.* E 626		
E 582	**Euler['s] differential equation,** Euler-Cauchy [differential] equation <DE>	Eulers[che] Differentialgleichung *f*, Eulersche Gleichung *f*	équation *f* différentielle d'Euler, équation d'Euler	[обыкновенное] дифференциальное уравнение Эйлера, уравнение Эйлера
E 583	**Euler['s] differential equation** <with separated variables> <DE>	Eulersche Differentialgleichung *f*	équation *f* différentielle d'Euler	дифференциальное уравнение Эйлера
E 584	**Euler['s] dilogarithm** <FU>	Eulersche dilogarithmische Funktion *f*, [Eulerscher] Dilogarithmus *m*	dilogarithme *m*	дилогарифм Эйлера
	Euler['s] equation <DG>	*s.* E 621		
	Euler['s] equation <VA>	*s.* E 596		
	Euler['s] exactness principle <AT>	*s.* E 657		
E 585	**Euler['s] formula,** Euler['s] relation <for the exponential function> <AN, FT>	Eulersche Formel *f* (Formeln *fpl*), Eulersche Gleichung *f*, Euler-Moivresche Formel	formule *f* d'Euler, identité *f* d'Euler	формулы Эйлера
E 586	**Euler['s] formula** <for the tetrahedron> <EG>	Eulersche Tetraederformel *f*	formule *f* d'Euler	формула Эйлера
	Euler['s] formula <EG>	*s.* E 622		
E 587	**Euler['s] formulas, Euler-Fourier formulas,** Fourier-Euler['s] formulas <AN, NU, SS>	Eulersche Formeln *fpl*, Euler-Fouriersche Formeln, Fouriersche Koeffizientenformeln *fpl*	formules *fpl* d'Euler[-Fourier], formules de Fourier	формулы Эйлера[-Фурье]
E 588	**Euler['s] φ(Φ)-function,** Euler['s] phi function, φ-function, phi[ ]function, Euler['s] totient function, totient, indicator <of an integer> <NT>	Eulersche Funktion *f*, Eulersche φ (*n*)-Funktion *f*	indicateur *m* d'Euler, indicateur, fonction *f* d'Euler, totient *m*, fonction φ eulérienne, fonction eulérienne	функция Эйлера <в теории чисел>, эйлерова фи-функция (φ-функция), φ-функция Эйлера, фи-функция Эйлера, тотиент
E 589	**Euler['s] graph,** Eulerian (eulerian) graph <GP>	Eulerscher Graph *m*	graphe *m* eulérien	эйлеров граф
E 590	**Euler-Grothendieck group** <AL>	Euler-Grothendieck-Gruppe *f*, Grothendieck-Gruppe *f* einer Serreschen Unterkategorie der Kategorie der Moduln	groupe *m* de Grothendieck d'une sous-catégorie de Serre de la catégorie des modules	группа Эйлера-Гротендика
E 591	**Eulerian angle,** Euler['s] angle <AY>	Eulerscher Winkel *m*	angle *m* d'Euler	угол Эйлера, эйлеров угол
E 592	**eulerian chain** <GP>	offene Eulersche Linie *f*, Eulersche Linie	chaine *f* eulérienne, chemin *m* eulérien	эйлерова цепь
	Eulerian cycle <GP>	*s.* E 606		
	Eulerian graph <GP>	*s.* 1. E 589; 2. U 112		
	Eulerian integral of the first kind <FU>	*s.* B 247		
	Eulerian integral of the second kind <FU>	*s.* G 42		

No.	English	German	French	Russian
E 593	**Eulerian parameters,** Euler-Rodrigues parameters, parameters of Rodrigues <GE>	Eulersche symmetrische Parameter *mpl*, Eulersche ([Euler-]Rodriguessche) Parameter, Parameter von Rodrigues	paramètres *mpl* d'Olinde-Rodrigues, paramètres d'Euler-Rodrigues	параметры Родрига
	Eulerian square <CT>	*s.* E 616		
E 594	**Euler['s] identity,** identity of Euler <in Lagrange's theorem> <AL>	Eulersche Identität *f*	identité *f* d'Euler	тождество Эйлера о четырех квадратах
E 595	**Euler['s] identity** <for pentagonal numbers *or* for a Dirichlet series> <NT, SS>	Eulersche Identität *f*	identité *f* d'Euler	тождество Эйлера <о пятиугольных чисел *или* о ряде Дирихле>
	Euler['s] integral of the second kind <FU>	*s.* G 42		
E 596	**Euler-Lagrange equation,** Cauchy-Euler equation, Euler['s] equation <VA>	Eulersche Differentialgleichung *f*, [Euler-]Lagrangesche Differentialgleichung (Gleichung *f*), Euler-Lagrange-Gleichung *f*	équation *f* d'Euler-Lagrange	уравнение Эйлера <вариационного исчисления>, уравнение Эйлера-Лагранжа
E 597	**Euler-Lagrange theorem** <AL> ⌐<LI>	Satz *m* von Euler-Lagrange, Euler-Lagrangescher Satz	théorème *m* d'Euler-Lagrange	теорема Эйлера-Лагранжа
	Euler-limitable sequence	*s.* E 156		
E 598	**Euler['s] limitation method,** Euler['s] method [of limitation], *E*-method <for divergent sequences> <LI>	Euler-Knoppsches Limitierungsverfahren *n*, *E*-Verfahren *n*	méthode *f* de limitation d'Euler, méthode d'Euler	метод [образования обобщенного предела] Эйлера
	Euler['s] limitation method of *p*-th order <LI>	*s.* E 304		
E 599	**Euler['s] line** <EG>	Eulersche Gerade *f*	droite *f* d'Euler	прямая Эйлера
	Euler['s] line <GP>	*s.* E 576		
E 600	**Euler-Maclaurin formula, Euler-Maclaurin['s] sum formula** <NU>	Euler-Maclaurinsche Formel (Summationsformel) *f*, Formel von Euler [-Maclaurin], Euler-Maclaurinsche Summenformel *f*	formule *f* sommatoire (de sommation) d'Euler-Maclaurin, formule (développement *m*, série *f*) d'Euler-Maclaurin, formule sommatoire d'Euler-Maclaurin	формула суммирования Эйлера-Маклорена, формула Эйлера-Маклорена
	Euler-Mascheroni constant <FU>	*s.* E 579		
E 601	**Euler['s] method,** Euler['s] reduction method <DE>	Eulersche Reduktionsmethode *f*, Verfahren *n* der Reduktion in ganzen Zahlen	méthode *f* d'Euler, méthode de réduction d'Euler	метод Эйлера, метод приведения Эйлера
E 602	**Euler['s] method** <DE, NU>	Eulersches Verfahren *n*, Verfahren (Methode *f*) der wiederholten Integration, Trapezverfahren *n*, Seilpolygonverfahren *n*	méthode *f* d'Euler	метод ломаных Эйлера, способ Эйлера, обыкновенный метод Эйлера
	Euler['s] method <DE>	*s.* P 935		
	Euler['s] method <LI>	*s.* E 619		
	Euler['s] method [of limitation] <LI>	*s.* E 598		
	Euler['s] method of *p*-th order <LI>	*s.* 1. E 304; 2. E 305		
	Euler['s] method of summation <LI>	*s.* E 619		
E 603	**Euler-Minding formulas** <for a continued fraction> <NT> ⌐<DE>	Euler-Mindingsche Formeln *fpl*	formules *fpl* d'Euler-Minding	формулы Эйлера-Миндинга
	Euler['s] multiplier	*s.* I 672		
E 604	**Euler['s] number** <of order $l = 1$ and $\alpha_1 = 1$> <AN>	Eulersche Zahl *f*, Sekantenkoeffizient *m*, gewöhnliche Eulersche Zahl	nombre *m* eulérien (d'Euler), coefficient *m* d'Euler, nombre sécant	число Эйлера
E 605	**Euler number** <of a differentiable manifold> <AT>	Eulersche Zahl *f*	nombre *m* d'Euler	эйлерово число
E 606	**Euler['s] path,** Eulerian (eulerian) cycle <in a nonoriented graph> <GP>	[geschlossene] Eulersche Linie *f*, geschlossener Eulerscher Kantenzug *m*	cycle *m* eulérien	эйлеров цикл
	Euler['s] phi function <NT>	*s.* E 588		
E 607	**Euler-Poincaré characteristic** <of a graded module< <AL>	Euler-Poincarésche Charakteristik *f*	caractéristique *f* d'Euler-Poincaré	характеристика Эйлера-Пуанкаре
E 608	**Euler-Poincaré characteristic,** Euler['s] characteristic, [combinatorial] characteristic <of a triangulation> <AT>	Eulersche Charakteristik *f*, [gewöhnliche] Euler-Poincarésche Charakteristik	caractéristique *f* d'Euler-Poincaré	эйлерова характеристика, характеристика Эйлера-Пуанкаре, комбинаторная характеристика
	Euler-Poincaré formula <AT>	*s.* E 609		
E 609	**Euler-Poincaré relation,** Euler-Poincaré formula <AT>	Euler-Poincarésche Formel *f*, Formel von Euler-Poincaré, Eulersche Gleichung *f*	formule *f* d'Euler-Poincaré	формула Эйлера-Пуанкаре
	Euler['s] polyhedron <CS, GE, PG>	*s.* C 2400		
E 610	**Euler polynomial** <*also* of higher and negative order> <FU>	Eulersches Polynom *n* <*auch* höherer und negativer Ordnung>	polynôme *m* d'Euler <*aussi* d'ordre supérieur et négatif>	многочлен Эйлера <*также* высшего и отрицательного порядка>

No.	English	German	French	Russian
E 611	**Euler['s] problem** <CT>	Eulersches (Eulers) Problem *n*	problème *m* d'Euler (eulérien)	задача Эйлера
E 612	**Euler['s] product** <AN>	Eulersches Produkt *n*, Euler-Produkt *n*	produit *m* eulérien	эйлерово (эйлеровское) произведение
E 613	**Euler['s] product [formula]**, <for the ζ-function> <NT>	Eulersche Produktdarstellung *f* <der Zetafunktion>, [spezielle] Eulersche Identität *f*	identité *f* (produit *m*) d'Euler	тождество Эйлера <о простых числах>, произведение Эйлера
	Euler['s] reduction method <DE>	*s.* E 601		
E 614	**Euler['s] relation** <for four points in the plane> <EG>	Eulersche Beziehung *f*	relation *f* d'Euler, formule *f* d'Euler	формула Эйлера
	Euler['s] relation <AN, FT>	*s.* E 585		
	Euler['s] relation <EG>	*s.* E 622		
	Euler-Rodrigues parameters <GE>	*s.* E 593		
E 615	**Euler['s] rotation theorem**, Euler['s] theorem <AY>	Satz *m* von Euler, Eulerscher Satz	théorème *m* d'Euler	теорема Эйлера
	Euler['s] second integral <FU>	*s.* G 42		
	Euler['s] spherical triangle <EG>	*s* E 625		
	Euler['s] spiral <GE>	*s.* C 2471		
E 616	**Euler['s] square**, Graeco-Latin square, Greco-Latin square <US>, Eulerian square <CT>	Eulersches (griechisch-lateinisches) Quadrat *n*	carré *m* d'Euler, carré latin d'Euler, carré gréco-latin	эйлеров (греко-латинский) квадрат
E 617	**Euler['s] substitution** <AN>	Eulersche Substitution *f*	substitution *f* d'Euler	подстановка Эйлера, эйлерова подстановка <первая, вторая *или* третья>
E 618	**Euler['s] summation formula** <AB>	Eulersche Summenformel *f*	formule *f* sommatoire d'Euler	формула суммирования Эйлера
E 619	**Euler['s] summation method**, Euler['s] method [of summation], *E*-method <for divergent series> <LI>	Euler-Knoppsches Summierungsverfahren *n*, *E*-Verfahren *n*	méthode *f* de sommation d'Euler, méthode d'Euler	метод Эйлера, метод суммирования [расходящихся рядов] Эйлера, метод суммирования [Эйлера-] Кноппа
	Euler['s] summation method of p-th order <LI>	*s.* E 305		
E 620	**Euler['s] theorem**, Euler['s] φ-theorem <on congruences> <AL, NT>	Eulerscher Satz *m*, Satz von Euler	théorème *m* d'Euler	теорема Эйлера <в теории сравнений>
E 621	**Euler['s] theorem**, Euler['s] equation, equation of Euler <on curvature> <in surface theory> <DG>	Eulersche Formel (Gleichung) *f* <für die Normalkrümmung>, Eulerscher Satz *m*, Satz von Euler <der Flächentheorie>	théorème *m* (formule *f*) d'Euler	формула Эйлера <о кривизнах>
E 622	**Euler['s] theorem**, Euler['s] formula, Euler['s] relation, theorem of Euler <on (for) polyhedrons> <EG>	Eulerscher Polyedersatz *m*, Descartes-Eulerscher Polyedersatz, Eulersche Polyederformel *f*, Eulerscher Satz *m* <über die Polyeder>	théorème *m* de Lhuilier, théorème de L'Huilier, théorème [de polyèdre] d'Euler, formule *f* d'Euler <pour les polyèdres>, théorème eulérien	теорема Эйлера [о многогранниках], теорема Декарта-Эйлера [о многогранниках], формула [Декарта-] Эйлера [о многогранниках]
E 623	**Euler['s] theorem** <for (on) homogeneous functions>, theorem of Euler <AN>	Eulersche Identität *f* (partielle Differentialgleichung *f*, Homogenitätsrelationen *fpl*), Satz *m* von Euler, Eulerscher Satz <für homogene Funktionen>	identité *f* (théorème *m*) d'Euler, théorème des fonctions homogènes, relation *f* d'homogénéité	теорема Эйлера
E 624	**Euler['s] theorem** <in the isoperimetric problem> <VA>	Eulersche Regel *f*, Satz *m* von Euler, Eulerscher Satz	théorème *m* d'Euler	теорема Эйлера
	Euler['s] theorem <AY>	*s.* E 615		
	Euler['s] theorem <GP>	*s.* T 274		
	Euler['s] φ-theorem <AL, NT>	*s.* E 620		
	Euler['s] totient function <NT>	*s.* E 588		
E 625	**Euler['s] triangle**, Euler['s] spherical triangle <EG>	Eulersches sphärisches Dreieck *n*	triangle *m* [sphérique] d'Euler	сферический треугольник [в смысле] Эйлера
E 626	**Euler-Venn diagram**, Venn['s] diagram, Euler['s] diagram <LO>	Vennsches Diagramm *n*, V-Diagramm *n*	diagramme *m* d'Euler-Venn, diagramme de Venn, diagramme logique	диаграмма Эйлера-Венна (Венна)
E 627	**eutactic positive definite quadratic form** <AL>	eutaktische quadratische Form *f*	forme *f* quadratique eutactique	евтактическая квадратичная форма
	eutactic set <SE>	*s.* W 210		
E 628	**evaluation** <of an expression> <AL, GN, LO>	Auswertung *f*	évaluation *f*	обработка, оценка, подытоживание <AL, GN>; вычисление <выражения> <LO>
	evaluation <AL, SE>	*s.* P 1648		
	evaluation <CA>	*s.* E 629		
	evaluation <MD>	*s.* E 705		
	evaluation at n <AL, SE>	*s.* P 1657		
E 629	**evaluation functor**, evaluation <CA>	Auswertungsfunktor *m*, Wertfunktor *m*	foncteur *m* évaluation	
	evaluation map <AL, SE>	*s.* P 1648		

E 630	**evectant** <IT>	Evektante *f*, Evectante *f*	évectant *m*	эвектант
E 631	**evectant process** <IV>	Evektantenprozeß *m*	processus *m* d'évectant	эвектантный процесс
	even arrangement <CT>	*s.* E 637		
E 632	**even circuit** <of a curve> <AG>	paarer Zug *m*	trait *m* pair	четный поток
E 633	**even covering,** covering projection <TO>	unverzweigte Überlagerung *f*	revêtement *m* non ramifié, recouvrement *m* sans ramification	накрывающее отображение
E 634	**even function** <AN>	gerade Funktion *f*	fonction *f* paire	четная функция
E 635	**evenness** <of a number> <NT>	Geradheit *f*	parité *f*, propriété *f* d'être pair	четность
	even-numberedness <GN>	*s.* C 585		
E 636	**even permutation** <operation> <AL, CT>	gerade Permutation *f*	permutation (substitution) *f* paire, permutation de première classe, permutation positive	четная перестановка (подстановка)
E 637	**even permutation,** even arrangement <CT>	gerade Permutation (Anordnung, Komplexion) *f*, Komplexion erster (der ersten) Klasse	arrangement *m* de première classe, complexion *f* paire	четная перестановка
E 638	**even polar,** second polar <of a point with respect to a cubic> <AG>	gerade (zweite) Polare *f*	polaire *f* droite, deuxième polaire	прямолинейная (вторая) поляра
	event <ST>	*s.* R 99		
E 639	**even-versus-odds rule** <ST>	Vorzeichenregel *f* im 2^k-Versuch	règle *f* des signes dans l'expérience factorielle 2^k	правило «чет-нечет»
E 640	**Everett['s] extension** <of a ring> <AL>	Everettscher Erweiterungsring *m*, Everettsche Erweiterung *f*	extension *f* d'Everett	расширение Эверетта
E 641	**Everett['s] formula of interpolation, Everett['s] interpolation formula,** <AX, FD, NU>	Everettsche Interpolationsformel (Formel) *f*, Interpolationsformel (Formel) von Everett	formule *f* d'interpolation d'Everett	интерполяционная формула Эверетта, формула Эверетта
E 642	**everywhere calculable function** <FO>	überall berechenbare Funktion *f*	fonction *f* partout calculable	всюду вычислимая функция
	everywhere convergent [power] series <SS>	*s.* E 263		
E 643	**everywhere convergent sequence,** sequence convergent everywhere <SS>	konvergente Folge *f* im gewöhnlichen Sinne, überall konvergente Folge	suite *f* partout convergente	всюду сходящаяся последовательность
	everywhere dense set <SE>	*s.* D 242		
	everywhere dense set <TO>	*s.* D 243		
E 644	**evolute,** evolute of curve <DG>	Evolute *f*	développée *f*, lieu *m* des centres de courbure	эволюта
	evolute <DG>	*s.* E 645		
	evolute of curve <DG>	*s.* E 644		
E 645	**evolute [of] surface,** evolute, centre of curvature surface, central surface, surface of centres, centrosurface <of a surface> <DG>	Krümmungsmittelpunktsfläche *f*, Evolutenfläche *f*, Zentralfläche *f*, Zentrafläche *f*	surface *f* centrale, surface des centres de courbure, lieu *m* des centres de courbure	центральная поверхность
	evolution <AL, AR>	*s.* T 29		
	evolution <ST>	*s.* T 127		
E 646	**evolution equation** <AN>	Evolutionsgleichung *f*, Entwicklungsgleichung *f*	équation *f* d'évolution	эволюционное уравнение
E 647	**evolutoid** <DG>	Evolutoide *f*	développoïde *f*	эволютоида
E 648	**evolvent,** involute [of evolute] <of a curve> <DG>	Evolvente *f*, Fadenevolvente *f*, Filarevolvente *f*, Involute *f* [der Evolute]	développante *f*	эвольвента, инволюта [эволюты], развертка
E 649	**exact at . . .** <in a sequence> <HA>	exakt an der Stelle . . .	exact en . . .	точный в члене. . .
	exact chi-square test <ST>	*s.* F 364		
	exact closed set <TO>	*s.* Z 61		
E 650	**exact cohomology sequence** <AT, HA>	exakte Kohomologiesequenz *f*, exakte Sequenz *f* von Kohomologiegruppen	suite *f* exacte de cohomologie	точная когомологическая последовательность, точная последовательность когомологий, когомологическая точная последовательность
E 651	**exact differential** <AL>	exaktes Differential *n*	différentielle *f* exacte	точный дифференциал
	exact differential <DI>	*s.* T 624		
E 652	**exact differential equation,** exact equation, total [differential] equation <of *n*-th order> <DE>	exakte (totale, vollständige) Differentialgleichung *f* <*n*-ter Ordnung>	équation *f* aux différentielles totales, équation différentielle totale <d'ordre *n*>	уравнение в полных дифференциалах, дифференциальное уравнение в полных дифференциалах <*n*-го порядка>, уравнение типа полного дифференциала
E 653	**exact division** <AL>	exakte Division *f*, aufgehende Division *f*, Division *f* ohne Rest	division *f* exacte	деление без остатка
	exact division is reached <AL, AR>	*s.* D 808		
	exact divisor <NT>	*s.* A 495		
	exact equation <DE>	*s.* E 652		

E 654	**exact homology sequence of the triple,** homology sequence of the triple <HA>	exakte Homologiesequenz *f* des Tripels	suite *f* excacte d'homologie du triple	гомологическая точная последовательность триады
E 655	**exact homotopy sequence** <AT>	exakte Homotopiesequenz *f*	suite *f* exacte d'homotopie	точная гомотопическая последовательность
E 656	**exact limit** <CA>	exakter Limes *m*	limite *f* exacte	точный предел
E 657	**exactness axiom, exactness principle [of Euler],** Euler['s] exactness principle <AT>	Exaktheitsaxiom *n*	axiome *m* d'exactitude	аксиома точности
	exact open set <TO>	*s.* C 2644		
E 658	**exact solution** <AX>	exakte (genaue) Lösung *f*	solution *f* exacte (stricte)	точное решение
E 659	**exact square,** smooth square <CA, HA>	exaktes Quadrat *n*	carré *m* exact	бикоммутативная (точная) диаграмма
	exact χ^2-test <ST>	*s.* F 364		
	exceeding probability <ST>	*s.* P 1537		
E 660	**excellent local ring** <AL>	exzellenter lokaler Ring *m*	anneau *m* local excellent	превосходное локальное кольцо
E 661	**excentre,** centre of the escribed circle <EG>	Mittelpunkt *m* des Ankreises, Ankreismittelpunkt *m*	centre *m* du cercle exinscrit	центр вневписанной окружности
E 662	**excentre,** centre of the escribed sphere <EG>	Mittelpunkt *m* der Ankugel, Ankugelmittelpunkt *m*	centre *m* de la sphère exinscrite	центр внекасательной сферы
	except for the order <GN>	*s.* A 793		
E 663	**exceptional character** <AL>	Ausnahmecharakter *m*	caractère *m* exceptionnel (particulier)	исключительный характер
E 664	**exceptional curve** <of the first *or* second kind> <AG>	ausgezeichnete Kurve *f*, exzeptionelle Kurve <[von] erster (1.) *oder* zweiter (2.) Gattung>	courbe *f* exceptionnelle <de première *ou* seconde (deuxième) espèce>	исключительная кривая <первого *или* второго рода>
E 665	**exceptional divisor** <AG>	Ausnahmedivisor *m*	diviseur *m* exceptionnel	исключительный дивизор
	exceptional function in the sense of Julia <FT>	*s.* J 110		
E 666	**exceptional group,** exceptional Lie group <GR>	Ausnahmegruppe *f*	groupe *m* [de Lie] exceptionnel	исключительная группа
E 667	**exceptional Jordan algebra** <AL>	exzeptionelle Jordan-Algebra *f*, Ausnahmealgebra *f*	algèbre *f* de Jordan exceptionnelle	исключительная жорданова алгебра
	exceptional Lie group <GR>	*s.* E 666		
E 668	**exceptional point** <of a cubic> <AG>	Ausnahmepunkt *m*	point *m* exceptionnel	исключительная точка
E 669	**exceptional subvariety of the first kind** <AG>	exzeptionelle Untermannigfaltigkeit *f* erster Art	sous-variété *f* exceptionnelle de première espèce	исключительное подмногообразие первого рода
E 670	**exceptional surface** <of the first *or* second species> <AG>	ausgezeichnete Fläche *f* <[von] erster (1.) *oder* zweiter (2.) Art>	surface *f* exceptionnelle <de première *ou* deuxième espèce>	исключительная поверхность <первого *или* второго рода>
E 671	**exceptional value,** lacunary value <of an analytic function> <FT>	Ausnahmewert *m*	lacune *f*, valeur *f* lacunaire	исключительное значение
E 672	**excess** <of a semi-invariant> <AL>	Exzeß *m* <Sylvester>	excès *m*	избыток
E 673	**excess,** angular excess <of a polygon, especially triangle> <GE>	Exzeß *m*, Winkelexzeß *m*	excès *m*, excès angulaire	избыток, эксцесс, угловой избыток (эксцесс)
E 674	**excess,** coefficient of excess, kurtosis <ST>	Exzeß *m*, Koeffizient *m* des Exzesses, Kurtosis *f*	excès *m*, coefficient *m* d'excès	эксцесс, коэффициент эксцесса
	excess function <VA>	*s.* W 159		
E 675	**excess of elevens** <AR>	Elferrest *m*	reste *f* de la division par 11	остаток при делении на 11
E 676	**excess of nine[s]** <AR>	Neunerrest *m*	reste *f* de la division par 9	остаток при делении на 9, остаток при проверке девяткой
	excess-three-code <NT>	*s.* T 451		
	exchange axiom <AL>	*s.* P 1504		
E 677	**exchange lattice,** matroid [lattice], relatively complemented semi-modular lattice; combinatorial pregeometry, pregeometry <LA>	Austauschverband *m*, relativ komplementärer semimodularer Verband *m*, relativ-komplementärer halbmodularer Verband	treillis *m* échangiste (d'échange), matroïde *m*, treillis supérieurement semi-modulaire relativement complementé, M-structure *f*; prégéométrie *f*	М-структура, полумодулярная структура с относительными дополнениями, структура с заменой
	exchange law <AL>	*s.* S 1733		
	exchange law <AL, LA>	*s.* E 678		
E 678	**exchange theorem,** exchange law, replacement theorem <for dependencies, linear spaces, in lattice theory> <AL, LA>	Austauschsatz *m*	loi *f* (lemme *m*, théorème *m*) d'échange	теорема о замене, лемма о замещении
	exchange theorem <AL>	*s.* S 1733		
E 679	**exchange theorems** <for proportions> <AR>	Vertauschungssätze *mpl*	théorèmes *mpl* de l'échangeabilité <des moyens ou des extrêmes entre eux ou des moyens avec les extrêmes dans une proportion>	перестановочные свойства пропорции
E 680	**excircle,** escribed circle <of a triangle> <EG>	Ankreis *m*, angeschriebener (anbeschriebener) Kreis *m*	cercle *m* exinscrit, circonférence *f* exinscrite	вневписанная окружность; вневписанный круг

No.	English	German	French	Russian
E 681	**excision** <AT>	Exzision *f*, Ausschneidung *f*	excision *f*	вырезание
E 682	**excision isomorphism** <AT>	Exzisionsisomorphismus *m*	isomorphisme *m* d'excision	изоморфизм вырезания
E 683	**excision lemma** <AL, TO>	Exzisionslemma *n*	lemme *m* d'excision	лемма вырезания
E 684	**excision map** <TO>	Exzisionsabbildung *f*, Ausschneidung *f*, Exzision *f*	excision *f*	отображение вырезания
E 685	**excision theorem** <AT>	Exzisionstheorem *n*	théorème *m* d'excision	теорема вырезания
E 686	**exclusion,** NOT-IF-THEN <LO>	Inhibition *f*	exclusion *f*	исключение
E 687	**exclusive disjunction,** alternation, non-equivalence, material non-equivalence, alternative <LO>	Disjunktion *f*, ausschließende Disjunktion *f*, Alternative *f*, ausschließende Alternative, Antivalenz *f*, aut	alternative *f*, disjonction *f* exclusive, exclusion *f*, exclusion réciproque (mutuelle), dilemme *m*, inéquivalence *f*, addition *f* modulo 2, OU *m* exclusif	строго-разделительная дизъюнкция, исключающая (сильная, строгая) дизъюнкция, исключающая альтернатива, дизъюнкция в исключающем смысле, разделительная дизъюнкция, антиэквивалентность, альтернатива, сумма по модулю 2, отрицание эквивалентности; функция неравнозначности
E 688	**exclusive OR (["]or["])** <LO>	ausschließendes Oder (ODER) *n*, exklusives Oder *n*	OU *m* exclusif, OU disjonctif, « ou » étant pris au sens exclusif	исключающее ИЛИ («или»), «или» в исключающем смысле, строго разделительный союз «или», «или» в исключающем значении, «или» в строго разделительном значении, исключающее «или-или»
E 689	**exercise,** problem <AR, GN>	Übungsaufgabe *f*	problème *m*	задача
	exhaustible set <TO>	*s.* M 293		
E 690	**exhaustion principle** <GE>	Exhaustionsprinzip *n*	principe *m* de l'exhaustion, principe d'exhaustion [d'Eudoxe]	принцип исчерпывания
E 691	**exhaustive classification** <SE>	erschöpfende Klasseneinteilung *f*	classification *f* exhaustive	исчерпывающая классификация
E 692	**exhaustive filtration,** filtration convergent above <AL>	erschöpfende Filtration *f*	filtration *f* exhaustive	исчерпывающая фильтрация, сходящаяся сверху фильтрация
E 693	**exhaustive sequence** <AL>	erschöpfende Folge *f*	suite *f* exhaustive	исчерпывающая последовательность
	existence domain <FT>	*s.* D 866		
	existence proof <DE, FO, GN>	*s.* P 1759		
	existence region <FT>	*s.* D 866		
E 694	**existence theorem** <AB, DE, GN>	Existenzsatz *m* <AB, DE, GN>; Existentialtheorem *n* <GN>	théorème *m* d'existence <DE, GN>; loi *f* d'existence <en théorie du corps de classe> <AB>	теорема существования
E 695	**existence theorem for roots** <AL>	Wurzelexistenzsatz *m*	théorème *m* d'existence de racines	теорема о существовании корней
E 696	**existential closure** <of a formula> <LO>	Partikularisierte *f* <eines Ausdrucks>	existentialisée *f*	формула, связанная квантором существования
	existential formula <LO>	*s.* E 697		
	existential generalization <LO>	*s.* 1. P 271; 2. R 1472		
E 697	**existentially quantified formula,** existential formula <LO>	partikularisierte Formel *f*	formule *f* particularisée	формула, связанная квантором существования
E 698	**existential quantifier,** existential symbol, ∃-symbol, ∃, *E*, Σ, V <*to be read*: there exists, there is> <LO>	Zeichen *n* des Partikularisators, Es-gibt-Zeichen *n*, Seinszeichen *n*, ∃, *E*, Σ, V <*gelesen:* es gibt>	symbole *m* de quantification existentielle, symbole « il existe », signe *m* d'existence, ∃, *E*, Σ, V <*se lit:* il existe>	знак существования, ∃, *E*, Σ, V <*читается:* существует [для некоторых *x*]>
E 699	**existential quantifier,** particular quantifier, existential symbol, ∃-symbol, ∃, *E*, Σ, V <LO>	Partikularisator *m*, Existenzquantifikator *m*, Existenzquantor *m*, Existenzoperator *m*, Existentialoperator *m*, Seinszeichen *n*, Es-gibt-Zeichen *n*, Einsquantor *m*, ∃	quantificateur *m* existentiel (spécial, petit, particulier, d'existence), quanteur *m* existentiel, signe *m* d'existence, symbole *m* « il existe», ∃	квантор существования, экзистенциальный квантор, ∃
	existential quantifier introduction <LO>	*s.* R 1472		
E 700	**existential sentence,** sentence of an existential character, particular proposition <LO>	Existentialaussage *f*, partikuläre Aussage *f*, partikuläres Urteil *n*	proposition *f* particulière (existentielle)	частное высказывание (суждение), экзистенциальное суждение (высказывание)
	existential symbol <LO>	*s.* 1. E 698; 2. E 699		
E 701	**existential-universal sentence,** ∃∀ sentence <LO>	∃∀-Aussage *f*	proposition *f* universelle existentialisée	∃∀-высказывание
E 702	**exogenous variable** <ST>	exogene Variable *f*	variable *f* exogène	экзогенная переменная
E 703	**exotic space** <TO>	exotischer Raum *m*	espace *m* exotique	экзотическое пространство
	exp <AN>	*s.* E 740		
	exp <GR>	*s.* E 742		
E 704	**expansion** <of a proposition> <LO>	Entwicklung *f*	expansion *f*	разложение

No.	English	German	French	Russian
E 705	**expansion,** development, evaluation <of a determinant> <MD>	Entwicklung *f*, Zerlegung *f*	développement *m*, décomposition *f*	разложение
	expansion <AR>	*s.* R 440/1		
E 706	**expansion according to the [elements of the] *i*-th column,** expansion <of a determinant> by the *i*-th column, *i*-th column expansion <of a determinant> <MD>	Entwicklung *f* nach der *i*-ten Spalte	développement *m* suivant la *i*-e colonne, développement suivant la colonne d'indice *i*	разложение по *i*-ему столбцу
E 707	**expansion according to the first *m* rows** <of a determinant> <MD>	Entwicklung *f* nach den [Unterdeterminanten aus den] *m* ersten Zeilen	développement *m* suivant les *m* premières lignes	разложение по *m* первым строкам
	expansion by the *i*-th column <MD>	*s.* E 706		
	expansion coefficient <SS>	*s.* C 1032		
	expansion factor <NU, ST>	*s.* E 863		
	expansion in a Dirichlet series <AN>	*s.* D 621		
E 708	**expansion in an infinite product** <AN>	Entwicklung *f* in ein unendliches Produkt, Produktentwicklung *f*	développement *m* en produit infini, développement en produit	разложение в произведение
	expansion in an orthogonal series <AN>	*s.* O 452		
E 709	**expansion in a series,** series expansion, development in a series, expansion into a series <AN>	Entwicklung (Zerlegung) *f* in eine Reihe, Reihenentwicklung *f*	développement *m* en série	разложение в ряд
	expansion in base *n* <NT>	*s.* R 837		
	expansion in continued fractions <AN, AX, NT>	*s.* E 711		
	expansion in orthogonal polynomials <AN>	*s.* O 469		
	expansion in partial fractions <AL, FT>	*s.* P 208		
	expansion in terms of continued fractions <AN, AX, NT>	*s.* E 711		
E 710	**expansion** <of a function> **in terms of eigenfunctions,** series expansion in terms of eigenfunctions, eigenfunction expansion; expansion series <DE, IE>	Entwicklung (Reihenentwicklung) *f* nach [den] Eigenfunktionen, Entwicklung in eine Reihe nach Eigenfunktionen; Eigenfunktionenreihe *f*, Reihe *f* nach Eigenfunktionen	développement *m* [en série] aux (suivant les) fonctions propres; série *f* en fonctions propres	спектральное разложение функции, спектральный анализ функции, разложение <функции> [в ряд] по собственным функциям; ряд по собственным функциям
E 711	**expansion into a continued fraction,** development into a continued fraction, continued fraction expansion, expansion in [terms of] continued fractions, continued fraction representation <of a function *or* number> <AN, AX, NT>	Kettenbruchentwicklung *f*, Kettenbruchdarstellung *f*, Entwicklung *f* in einen Kettenbruch	représentation *f* en fractions continues, développement *m* en fraction[s] continue[s]	представление в цепных дробях, разложение в цепную дробь, разложение в непрерывную дробь
E 712	**expansion** <of a number> **into a regular continued fraction** <NT>	regelmäßige Kettenbruchentwicklung *f*	développement *m* en fraction continue régulière	разложение в правильную цепную дробь
	expansion into a series <AN>	*s.* E 709		
	expansion into partial fractions <AL, FT>	*s.* P 208		
E 713	**expansion of an ordinal number for the base γ** <SE>	Cantorsche Polynomdarstellung *f*, Polynomdarstellung einer Ordnungszahl bezüglich der Ordnungszahl γ	développement *m* d'un nombre ordinal par rapport à γ	разложение порядкового числа по основанию γ
E 714	**expansion rule** <LO>	Regel *f* der Einführung der Alternative	règle *f* de simplification pour ∨	правило расширения
	expansion rule <LO>	*s.* R 1483		
	expansion series <DE, IE>	*s.* E 710		
E 715	**expansion theorem,** development theorem <for determinants> <MD>	Entwicklungssatz *m*	théorème *m* de développement	теорема разложения, теорема о разложении
E 716	**expectancy** <in the periodogram> <ST>	Expektanz *f*	expectance *f*	ожидание, срединная ордината периодограммы
	expectancy <ST>	*s.* E 719		
	expectation <ST>	*s.* E 719		
	expectation function <ST>	*s.* E 720		
	expectation value <ST>	*s.* E 719		
	expectation vector <ST>	*s.* E 721		
E 717	**expected gain,** expected payoff <TG>	Gewinnerwartung *f*, erwarteter Gewinn *m*	espérance *f* de gain, gain *m* espéré	математическое ожидание выигрыша (выплаты), ожидание выигрыша (выплаты), ожидаемый выигрыш, ожидаемая выплата
E 718	**expected loss,** average loss <ST>	erwarteter Verlust *m*, durchschnittlicher Verlust	espérance *f* mathématique des pertes, perte *f* moyenne (espérée)	ожидаемая потеря, средняя потеря

No.	English	German	French	Russian
	expected payoff <TG>	*s.* E 717		
E 719	**expected value,** expectancy, expectation [value], mathematical expectation, mean [value] <of a random variable> <ST>	Erwartungswert *m*, Erwartung *f*, mathematische Erwartung (Hoffnung *f*), mathematischer Erwartungswert, Mittelwert *m* [der Verteilung], Durchschnitt *m*, Mittel *n* [der Verteilung]	espérance *f* mathématique, espérance, moyenne *f*, valeur *f* moyenne, valeur probable	математическое ожидание, ожидание, среднее значение, среднее
E 720	**expected value function,** expectation function <ST>	Erwartungswertfunktion *f*	fonction *f* d'espérance [mathématique]	функция математического ожидания
E 721	**expected value vector,** expectation vector <ST>	Erwartungswertvektor *m*	vecteur *m* d'espérance [mathématique]	вектор математического ожидания
	experimental design <ST>	*s.* 1. D 335; 2. D 337		
E 722	**experimental error** <ER, ST>	Versuchsfehler *m*, experimenteller Fehler *m*	erreur *f* expérimentale	погрешность (ошибка) эксперимента
	experimental plan <ST>	*s.* P 629		
	explanatory variable <ST>	*s.* 1. C 277; 2. C 278		
E 723	**explement, explement of angle, explementary angle,** conjugate angle <EG>	Ergänzungswinkel *m* zu 360°, Komplement *n* (Komplementwinkel *m*) zu 360°	explément *m*, explément de l'angle, angle *m* supplémentaire au 360°	пополнительный угол до 360°, пополнение угла до 360°
E 724	**explicit differential equation,** explicit form of the ordinary differential equation <DE>	explizite (explizite gewöhnliche) Differentialgleichung *f*	équation *f* différentielle explicite	разрешенное дифференциальное уравнение, разрешенный вид обыкновенного дифференциального уравнения
E 725	**explicit differential equation of the first order the right-hand side of which satisfies a Lipschitz condition** <DE>	explizite [gewöhnliche] Differentialgleichung *f* erster Ordnung, deren rechte Seite einer Lipschitz-Bedingung genügt	équation *f* différentielle lipschitzienne	разрешенное дифференциальное уравнение первого порядка, правая сторона которого удовлетворяет условию Липшица
	explicit form of the ordinary differential equation <DE>	*s.* E 724		
E 726	**explicit function** <AN>	explizite Funktion *f*, explizit[e] dargestellte Funktion, entwickelte Funktion	fonction *f* explicite	явная функция
E 727	**explicit occurrence** <LO>	explizites Eingehen *n*	occurrence *f* explicite	явное вхождение
E 728	**explosion** <of a random process> <SP>	Explosion *f*	explosion *f*	взрыв
E 729	**exponent** <of a divisor class *or* a primary ideal <AL>	Exponent *m*	exposant *m*	показатель
E 730	**exponent,** index, power exponent, power <of a power> <AL, AR>	Exponent *m*, Potenzexponent *m*, Potenzindex *m*	exposant *m*, indice *m*	показатель [степени]
E 731	**exponent** <of a Dirichlet series>**;** Dirichlet['s] exponent <of an almost periodic function <AP, NT, SS>	Dirichlet-Exponent *m*, Dirichletscher Exponent *m*	exposant *m*; exposant de Dirichlet	показатель [в общем ряде] Дирихле
E 732	**exponent** <of a group, *or* group element> <GR>	Exponent *m*; Charakteristik *f* <einer additiven Gruppe>	exposant *m*	показатель
E 733	**exponent** <of a group variety> <UA>	Exponent *m*	exposant *m*	экспонента
	exponent <AN>	*s.* E 734		
	exponential <AN>	*s.* 1. E 739; 2. E 740		
	exponential <GR>	*s.* E 742		
	exponential <SE>	*s.* P 1122		
	exponential category <CA>	*s.* F 788		
E 734	**exponential curve,** exponent <AN>	Exponentialkurve *f*, Exponentiallinie *f*	courbe *f* exponentielle, exponentielle *f*	показательная кривая, экспоненциальная кривая, экспонента
E 735	**exponential distribution** <ST>	Exponentialverteilung *f*	distribution *f* exponentielle	показательное (экспоненциальное) распределение, показательный закон распределения
E 736	**exponential equation** <AL, AN>	Exponentialgleichung *f*	équation *f* exponentielle	показательное уравнение
	exponential expression <AN>	*s.* E 739		
E 737	**exponential factorial,** ef <FU>	Exponentialfaktorial *n*, ef	factorielle *f* exponentielle, ef	экспоненциальный факториал, ef
E 738	**exponential family** <ST>	Exponentialfamilie *f*	famille *f* exponentielle	экспонентное семейство
E 739	**exponential function,** exponential [expression] <AN>	Exponentialfunktion *f* [im weiteren Sinne], Exponentialausdruck *m*	fonction (expression) *f* exponentielle, exponentielle *f*	показательная функция, показательное выражение
E 740	**exponential function** <to the base e>, exponential e-function, exp, e, // *e* <AN>	Exponentialfunktion *f* [im engeren Sinne], spezielle Exponentialfunktion, e-Funktion *f*, exp, e, // *e*	fonction *f* exponentielle, exponentielle *f* <de base e>, exp, e, // *e*	экспоненциальная функция, экспонента, показательная функция [с основанием e], e-функция, exp, e, // *e*
	exponential integral [function] <FU>	*s.* I 624		
	exponential law <AL, SE>	*s.* L 185		
E 741	**exponentially asymptotic stability** <DE>	exponentiell asymptotische Stabilität *f*	stabilité *f* exponentiellement asymptotique	экспоненциально асимптотическая устойчивость

E 742	**exponential map[ping],** exponential, exp <in a Lie group> <GR>	Exponentialabbildung *f*, exp	application *f* exponentielle, exponentielle *f*	экспоненциальное отображение, exp
E 743	**exponential *p*-adic valuation** <AL>	*p*-adische Exponentenbewertung *f*	valuation *f* exponentielle *p*-adique	показательная *p*-адическая нормировка; *p*-адический показатель
E 744	**exponential series** <AN, SS>	Exponentialreihe *f*	série *f* exponentielle	показательный (экспоненциальный) ряд
E 745	**exponential sum** <NT>	Exponentialsumme *f*	somme *f* exponentielle	экспоненциальная сумма
	exponential topology <TO>	*s.* V 185		
E 746	**exponential trend** <ST>	Exponentialtrend *m*	tendance *f* exponentielle	экспоненциальный тренд
E 747	**exponential type** <of entire function> <FT>	Exponentialtyp *m*	type *m* exponentiel	показательный тип
E 748	**exponential valuation,** additive valuation <AL>	Exponentenbewertung *f*, Ordnungszahlbewertung *f*, Exponentialbewertung *f*, additive Bewertung *f*	valuation *f* exponentielle	аддитивная норма, аддитивная (показательная) нормировка
	exponentiate to the second power / to <AL>	*s.* S 1550		
	exponentiation <AR>	*s.* R 54		
E 749	**exponent notation** <AL>	Exponentenschreibweise *f*	notation *f* exponentielle	экспоненциальное обозначение
E 750	**exponent of convergence,** convergence exponent <FT>	Konvergenzexponent *m*	exposant *m* de convergence <von Schaper>, ordre *m* réel <Borel>, ordre *m* de densité	показатель сходимости
E 751	**exponent of inseparability** <of an inseparable polynomial *or* field extension> <AL>	Exponent *m*	exposant *m*	показатель несепарабельности
E 752	**exponent of irregularity** <of a quadratic form *or* of a function> <NT>	Irregularitätsexponent *m*	exposant *m* d'irrégularité	показатель иррегулярности
E 753	**exportation** <LO>	Exportation *f*	exportation *f*	вынос, экспортация
	exportation <LO>	*s.* L 186		
	export-import law <LO>	*s.* L 222		
	expressing in partial fractions <AL, FT>	*s.* P 208		
E 754	**expression** <of the object language>, sequence of symbols <LO>	Zeichenreihe *f* <der Mengenlehre, der Mathematik>, Ausdruck *m*	assemblage *m* de signes	последовательность символов
	expression <AL>	*s.* A 434		
	expression <LO>	*s.* F 488		
	expression by a series <AN>	*s.* S 624		
	expression in a closed form <AN, GN>	*s.* R 835		
	expression in an analytic form <AN, GN>	*s.* R 835		
	expression in base *n* <NT>	*s.* R 837		
	expression in braces (brackets, parentheses) <GN>	*s.* B 709		
E 755	**expression in form of a product,** trial solution in form of a product <DE, NU>	Produktansatz *m*	expression *f* en produit	выражение (представление) в виде произведения
	expression of elementary logic <LO>	*s.* M 307		
	expression to be integrated <DI>	*s.* I 670		
E 756	**exradius,** radius of the escribed circle <EG>	Radius *m* des Ankreises, Ankreisradius *m*	rayon *m* du cercle exinscrit	радиус вневписанной окружности
E 757	**exradius,** radius of the escribed sphere <EG>	Radius *m* der Ankugel, Ankugelradius *m*	rayon *m* de la sphère exinscrite	радиус внекасательной сферы
E 758	**exsphere,** escribed sphere <of a tetrahedron> <EG>	Ankugel *f*	sphère *f* exinscrite	внекасательная (вневписанная) сфера
	extendability <TO>	*s.* E 769		
E 759	**extended commutator,** higher commutator <AL>	höherer Kommutator *m*	commutateur *m* étendu	коммутатор высшего порядка, сложный коммутатор
	extended complex plane <FT>	*s.* E 762		
E 760	**extended ideal** <AL>	Erweiterungsideal *n*	extension *f* d'un idéal	расширенный идеал
E 761	**extended linear continuum,** extended real numbers (number system), extended reals <AN, TO>	abgeschlossene Zahlengerade *f*, Raum *m* der durch $\pm\infty$ ergänzten reellen Zahlen, durch $\pm\infty$ vervollständigte Zahlengerade *f*	droite *f* [numérique] achevée	расширенная [числовая] прямая, прямая, пополненная бесконечными точками
	extended mean value theorem <DI>	*s.* C 240		
	extended mean value theorem <DI>	*s.* T 102		
E 762	**extended plane,** extended complex plane, full plane, full function-theoretical plane, closed plane, closed complex plane <FT>	Vollebene *f*, vollständige (abgeschlossene, volle, geschlossene) Zahlenebene (komplexe Zahlenebene, komplexe Ebene, Ebene) *f*	plan *m* fermé (complexe fermé, de Gauss fermé, achevé, complexe achevé, complet, complexe complet)	расширенная (полная, замкнутая) плоскость (комплексная плоскость), расширенная плоскость комплексного переменного
E 763	**extended point transformation** <AN, DE, VA>	erweiterte Punkttransformation *f*	transformation *f* ponctuelle étendue	расширенное точечное преобразование

E 764/5	**extended predicate calculus** <LO>	erweiterter Prädikatenkalkül *m*	calcul *m* des prédicats élargi	расширенное исчисление предикатов
E 765	**extended real numbers** <AN, TO>	*s.* E 761		
	extended real number system <AN, TO>	*s.* E 761		
	extended reals <AN, TO>	*s.* E 761		
E 766	**extended Riemann hypothesis** <FT, NT>	erweiterte Riemannsche Vermutung *f*	hypothèse *f* de Riemann étendue	расширенная гипотеза Римана
	extended rule of substitution <LO>	*s.* C 1746		
E 767	**extended space** <FA>	Erweiterungsraum *m*	espace *m* élargi	расширенное пространство
E 768	**extended unitary group** <GR>	erweiterte unitäre Gruppe *f*	groupe *m* unitaire étendu	расширенная унитарная группа
E 769	**extendibility,** extendability, continuability <of a mapping> <TO>	Fortsetzbarkeit *f*	prolongeabilité *f*	продолжаемость
E 770	**extendible representation** <RE>	fortsetzbare Darstellung *f*	représentation *f* prolongeable	продолжаемое представление
E 771	**extension** <of a specialization> <AG>	Fortsetzung *f*, Spezialisierungsfortsetzung *f*	extension *f*, prolongement *m*	продолжение [специализации]
E 772	**extension** <of a Boolean algebra, a number domain, a ring> <AL>	Erweiterung *f*	extension *f*	расширение
E 773	**extension** <of a derivation> <AL>	Fortsetzung *f*	prolongement *m*	продолжение
E 774	**extension** <of a field>, field extension <AL>	Erweiterung *f* <eines Körpers>, Körpererweiterung *f*	extension *f* [d'un corps]	расширение поля, расширение
E 775	**extension** <of a module by a module> <AL>	Erweiterung *f* <eines Moduls durch einen Modul>	extension *f* <d'un module par un module>	расширение <модуля посредством модуля>
E 776	**extension** <of a place> <AL>	Stellenfortsetzung *f*, Fortsetzung *f* <einer Stelle>	extension *f* <d'une place>	продолжение <точки>
E 777	**extension** <of a representation> <AL>	Fortsetzung *f*	agrandissement *m*, extension *f*	продолжение
E 778	**extension** <of a valuation> <AL>	Bewertungsfortsetzung *f*, Fortsetzung *f*, Fortsetzungsbewertung *f*	prolongement *m* <d'une valuation>	продолжение <нормирования, абсолютного значения>
E 779	**extension,** continuation <of a map *or* homomorphism> <AL, TO>	Fortsetzung *f*, Erweiterung *f*	extension *f*, prolongement *m*	продолжение, распространение
E 780	**extension,** prolongation <of the first *or* second kind> <of a mapping, function, transformation, a functional, *or* an operator> <AN, FA>	Fortsetzung *f*, Erweiterung *f* <erster *oder* zweiter Art>	prolongement *m*, extension *f* <de première *ou* deuxième (seconde) espèce>; opérateur *m* [de] prolongement	продолжение <первого *или* второго рода>
E 781	**extension** <of a sheaf> <AT>	Erweiterung *f*	extension *f*	распространение
E 782	**extension** <CA>	Erweiterung *f*	extension *f*	расширение
E 783/4	**extension** <of a linear form> <FA>	Fortsetzung *f*	prolongement *m*	продолжение
E 785	**extension,** group extension <GR, NT>, // splitting <NT> <of a group G′ by a group G″>	Erweiterung *f*, Gruppenerweiterung *f* <GR, NT>, // Aufspaltung *f* <NT> <einer Gruppe G′ durch eine Gruppe G″, einer Gruppe G′ mit einer Gruppe G″>	extension *f* <d'un groupe G′ par un groupe G″>	расширение, групповое расширение< GR, NT>, // расщепление <NT> <группы G′ посредством группы G″, группы G′ при помощи группы G″>
E 786	**extension** <of a relation> <LO>	Extension *f*	portée *f*	экстенсия
E 787	**extension,** sense <of a concept> <LO, MM>	Ausdehnung *f*, Extension *f*	extension *f*	экстенсия, объем, протяженность
E 788	**extension** <of a measure> <ME>	Fortsetzung *f*	prolongement *m*, extension *f*	продолжение
E 789	**extension** <of a theory> <MM>	Erweiterung *f*	extension *f*	расширение
E 790	**extension** <of a continued fraction> <NT>	Extension *f*	extension *f*	растяжение
E 791	**extension,** extension space <of a topological space> <TO>	Erweiterung *f*; Oberraum *m* <alter Raum nicht notwendig dicht darin>; Erweiterungsraum *m* <alter Raum dicht darin>	extension *f*	расширение
E 792	**extension** <of an algebra> <UA>	Erweiterung *f*; Oberalgebra *f*	extension *f*	расширение
E 793	**extension** <of a structure> <UA>	Oberstruktur *f*	extension *f* d'une structure	расширение структуры
	extension <AR>	*s.* R 440/1		
E 794	**extensionality** <LO, SE>	Extensionalität *f*	extensionalité *f*	экстенсиональность, экстенциональность, экстензиональность
	extensionality axiom <SE>	*s.* A 1286		
E 795	**extensional logic** <LO>	extensionale Logik *f*	logique *f* extensionnelle (extensiviste)	экстенсиональная логика
	extensionally equal <LO, SE>	*s.* C 1043		
E 796	**extensional relation** <SE>	extensionale Relation *f*	relation *f* extensionnelle	экстенсиональное отношение
E 797	**extensional set** <LO, SE>	extensionale Menge *f*	ensemble *m* extensionnel	экстенсиональное множество
E 798	**extension chain,** chain <of extensions> <AL>	Kette *f* <von Erweiterungen>	chaîne *f* <d'extensions>	цепочка <расширений>
	extension divider <GE, IN>	*s.* C 1332		

	extension field <AL>	*s.* O 575		
E 799	**extension finitely generated over *k*,** finite field over *k* <AL>	endliche Körpererweiterung *f* über *k*, endlich-algebraische Körpererweiterung von *k*, endlich-algebraischer Oberkörper *m* von *k*	extension *f* finie sur *k*	конечное расширение поля над *k*
E 800	**extension ideal,** over-ideal <of an ideal> <AL>	Oberideal *n*, Teiler *m*	suridéal *m*, sur-idéal *m*, diviseur *m*	надыдеал, надидеал
E 801	**extension integral domain** <AL>	Erweiterungsintegritätsbereich *m*, Oberintegritätsbereich *m*	sur-domaine *m* d'intégrité	надобласть целостности
E 802	**extension module** <AL>	Erweiterungsmodul *m*	module *m* d'extension	модуль расширения
	extension module <AL>	*s.* O 583		
E 803	**extension obtained by a sequence of successive Galois extensions** <AL>	metagaloissche Erweiterung *f* <erhalten durch eine Folge galoisscher Erweiterungen>	extension *f* métagaloisienne	расширение, полученное посредством последовательности последовательных расширений Галуа
E 804	**extension of a division ring** <AL>	Oberschiefkörper *m*	sur[-]corps *m*	надтело
	extension of domain <FT>	*s.* D 858		
	extension of the base field <AL>	*s.* E 807		
E 805	**extension of the basic ring,** extension of the ring of scalars, extension of the scalar field <in a vector space> <AL>	Grundringerweiterung *f*, Erweiterung *f* des Skalarenbereichs	extension *f* des scalaires, extension de l'anneau des scalaires	расширение скаляров (кольца скаляров, основного кольца)
E 806	**extension of the field of constants,** constant field extension <AL>	Konstantenerweiterung *f*, Konstantenkörpererweiterung *f*, Grundkörpererweiterung *f*	extension *f* du corps des constantes	расширение поля констант
E 807	**extension of the ground field,** extension of the base field <AL>	Grundkörpererweiterung *f*	extension *f* du corps de base	расширение основного поля
E 808	**extension of the positive part** <in an ordered ring> <AL>	Erweiterung *f* des Positivbereichs	extension *f* de la partie positive	расширение области положительных элементов
E 809	**extension of the residue field** <AL>	Restklassenkörpererweiterung *f*	extension *f* résiduelle	расширение поля вычетов
	extension of the ring of scalars <AL>	*s.* E 805		
	extension of the scalar field <AL>	*s.* E 805		
	extension ring <AL>	*s.* O 585		
	extension soluble by radicals <AL>	*s.* F 179		
	extension space <TO>	*s.* E 791		
E 810	**extension that is not Galois;** non-normal extension <of a field> <AL>	nichtgaloissche Erweiterung *f*, nichtnormale Körpererweiterung *f*, nichtnormale Erweiterung <eines Körpers>	extension *f* non galoisienne; extension non normale	ненормальное расширение
E 811	**extension theorem** <for linear forms> <FA>	Fortsetzungssatz *m* <für Linearformen>	théorème *m* de prolongement <pour les formes linéaires>	теорема о продолжении <линейных форм>
E 812	**extension theorem** <for representations> <RE>	Fortsetzungssatz *m*, Fortsetzungstheorem *n*	théorème *m* d'agrandissement	теорема о продолжении
E 813	**extension theorem** <for mappings> <TO>	Erweiterungssatz *m*	théorème *m* d'extension	теорема о продолжении
E 814	**extensive function** <TO>	Abbildung *f*, die die Einbettungseigenschaft hat <Hüllenoperator>	application *f* extensive	экстенсивное отображение
	extensive game <TG>	*s.* P 1051		
E 815	**extensive mean** <ST>	extensiver Mittelwert *m*	moyenne *f* extensive	протяженное среднее [значение]
E 816	**extensive quantity** <GE>	extensive Größe *f*, Ausdehnungsgröße *f* <Graßmann>, geometrische Größe	grandeur *f* extensive (géométrique), quantité *f* extensive	протяженная величина
E 817	**extensive sampling** <ST>	extensives Stichprobenverfahren *n*, extensive Stichprobennahme *f*	échantillonnage *m* extensif, sondage *m* extensif	протяженный выбор, протяженное обследование
E 818	**extensivity** <of a mapping> <SE>	Extensivität *f*	extensivité *f*	экстенсивность
E 819	**extensivity** <for a closure operation> <AL, AN, LO, TO>	Satz *m* der Einbettung, Einbettungssatz *m* <für die Hüllenbildung>	extension *f*, extensivité *f* <de l'opération de fermeture>	экстенсивность <операции замыкания>
E 820	**extensor** <VT>	Extensor *m*	extenseur *m*	экстензор
E 821	**extent** <of a semi-invariant> <AL>	Extent *m*	extente *f*	
E 822	**extent** <also of a notion> <LO, SE>	Umfang *m*	étendue *f*	объем
E 823	**exterior** <of a set> <TO>	Äußeres *n*	extérieur *m*	внешность, множество внешних точек
E 824	**exterior algebra,** Grassmann['s] algebra <AL>	äußere (Graßmannsche) Algebra *f*	algèbre *f* extérieure (alternée)	внешняя (знакопеременная) алгебра, алгебра Грассмана, свободная антикоммутативная алгебра
E 825	**exterior alternate angles,** alternate exterior angles <US> <EG>	äußere Wechselwinkel *mpl*	angles *mpl* alternes externes, angles alternes-externes	внешние накрестлежащие углы

No.	English	German	French	Russian
E 826	**exterior angle** <EG>	Außenwinkel *m*	angle *m* extérieur (externe)	внешний угол
E 827	**exterior angle** <of a circle> <EG>	Sekantenwinkel *m*	angle *m* extérieur au cercle	угол с вершиной вне круга; вневписанный угол, образуемый секущими и с вершиной вне круга
E 828	**exterior bisector (bisectrix)** <EG>	Außenwinkelhalbierende *f*, äußere Winkelhalbierende *f*	bissectrice *f* extérieure (d'un angle extérieur)	биссектриса (биссектор) внешнего угла
E 829	**exterior boundary [value] problem,** exterior problem <DE, PO>	äußeres Randwertproblem *n*, äußere Randwertaufgabe *f*, Randwertproblem (Randwertaufgabe) für das Außengebiet, Außenproblem *n*	problème *m* extérieur, problème aux limites extérieur	внешняя краевая задача, внешняя задача
E 830	**exterior centre of similarity (similitude)** <GE>	äußerer Ähnlichkeitspunkt *m*	centre *m* de similitude extérieur	внешний центр подобия
E 831	**exterior content,** outer (exterior Jordan, outer Jordan) content <of a set> <ME>	äußerer (äußerer Peano-Jordanscher, Cantorscher, Harnackscher) Inhalt *m*	aire *f* extérieure	внешняя жорданова мера
E 832	**exterior derivative** <AN>	äußere Ableitung *f*; herausführende Ableitung	dérivée *f* extérieure	внешняя производная
E 833	**exterior differential** <of a form in the Cartan calculus> <DG>	äußeres Differential *n*, abgeleitete Form *f*	différentielle *f* extérieure	внешний дифференциал
E 834	**exterior differential calculus,** Cartan['s] calculus, differential calculus of Cartan <DG>	Cartanscher Kalkül *m* [der äußeren Differentialformen], äußerer Differentialkalkül *m*, Kalkül der alternierenden Differentialformen	calcul *m* différentiel extérieur, calcul de Cartan	внешнее дифференциальное исчисление
E 835	**exterior differential equation** <DG>	äußere Differentialgleichung *f*	équation *f* aux différentielles extérieures	уравнение во внешних дифференциалах
E 836	**exterior differential form,** alternating differential form, differential form [of Cartan] <of degree *p*> <DG>	äußere (alternierende) Differentialform *f* <vom Grade *p*>	forme *f* différentielle [à multiplication] extérieure <de degré *p*>	внешняя дифференциальная форма <степени *p*>
E 837	**exterior differential geometry** <DG>	äußere Differentialgeometrie *f*	géométrie *f* différentielle extérieure	внешняя дифференциальная геометрия
E 838	**exterior differentiation** <operation> <DG>	äußere Differentiation (Ableitung) *f*	dérivation *f* extérieure	внешнее дифференцирование
E 839	**exterior domain** <DE, GE, TO>	Außengebiet *n*	domaine *m* extérieur	внешняя область
	exterior-interior angles <EG>	*s.* C 2510		
	exterior Jordan content <ME>	*s.* E 831		
	exterior measure <ME>	*s.* O 548		
E 840	**exterior multiplication,** Grassmann multiplication <AL>	äußere Multiplikation *f*	multiplication *f* extérieure	внешнее (знакопеременное) умножение
E 841	**exterior multiplication** <of differential forms> <DI>	äußere Multiplikation *f*	multiplication *f* extérieure	внешнее умножение
E 842	**exterior normal,** outward normal <DG>	äußere Normale *f*	normale *f* extérieure	внешняя нормаль
E 843	**exterior opposite angles** <EG>	äußere entgegengesetzte (entgegengesetzt liegende) Winkel *mpl*	angles *mpl* co-externes, angles extérieurs du même côté de la sécante	внешние односторонние углы
E 844	**exterior Pfaff problem,** exterior problem <DE>	äußeres [Pfaffsches] Problem *n*	problème *m* [de Pfaff] extérieur	внешняя задача [Пфаффа]
E 845	**exterior point** <TO, SE>	äußerer Punkt *m*	point *m* extérieur	внешняя точка
E 846	**exterior power** <AL>	äußere Potenz *f*	puissance *f* extérieure	внешняя (знакопеременная) степень
	exterior problem <DE, PO>	*s.* E 829		
	exterior problem <DE>	*s.* E 844		
	exterior product <AL>	*s.* O 550		
E 847	**exterior surface** <GE>	Außenfläche *f*	surface *f* extérieure	внешняя поверхность
E 848	**external composition** <AL>	äußere Verknüpfung *f*	composition *f* (loi *f* de composition) externe	внешняя композиция
E 849	**external composition law,** external law of composition <AL>	äußeres Kompositionsgesetz (Verknüpfungsgesetz) *n*	loi *f* de composition externe, opération *f* externe	внешний закон композиции, закон внешней композиции, внешняя композиция
	external correlation <ST>	*s.* I 703		
	external direct product group <GR>	*s.* O 546		
E 850/1	**external direct sum** <AL>	äußere (externe) direkte Summe *f*	somme *f* directe [externe]	внешняя прямая сумма
E 852	**external division** <of a line segment> <EG>	äußere Teilung *f* <einer Strecke>	division *f* externe <d'un segment>	деление <отрезка> в крайнем отношении, внешнее деление <отрезка>
	external law of composition <AL>	*s.* E 849		
	externally stable set <GP>	*s.* D 887		
E 853	**externally tangent** <GE>	[sich] von außen berührend, außenberührend	tangent extérieurement	имеющий внешнее касание, касающийся внешним образом

E 854	**external negation** <LO>	externe Verneinung *f*	négation *f* externe	внешнее отрицание
E 855	**external sequence of order statistics** <ST>	äußere Positionsfunktionenfolge *f*	suite *f* externe de statistiques d'ordre	внешняя последовательность порядковых статистик
E 856	**external stability** <GP, TG>	externe (äußere) Stabilität *f*	stabilité *f* externe	внешняя устойчивость
	external variance <ST>	*s.* I 704		
	Ext-module <HA>	*s.* M 778		
	extraction of the root <AL, AR>	*s.* T 29		
	extralogical constant <LO, SE>	*s.* N 415		
E 857	**extraneous root** <of a method of solving an algebraic equation> <AL>	fremde Wurzel *f*	racine *f* étrangère, solution *f* étrangère	посторонний корень, лишний корень, непригодный корень, паразитический корень <уравнения>
E 858	**extraordinary** <Cayley>, vid <Peirce>, unit, basal element <of hypercomplex numbers> <AL>	Einheit *f*, Haupteinheit *f*	unité *f* [de base], unité relative (principale); clef *m* [algébrique] <Cauchy>	базисная единица
E 859	**extraordinary divisor of the discriminant** <AB>	außerwesentlicher Diskriminantenteiler *m* (Teiler *m* der Diskriminante), Index *m*	facteur *m* extraordinaire du discriminant, facteur non essentiel du discriminant	экстраординарный множитель дискриминанта
E 860	**extrapolation; extrapolating** <AX, NU>	Extrapolation *f*; Extrapolieren *n*	extrapolation *f*	экстраполяция; экстраполирование
E 861	**extrapolation** <NU, ST>	Hochrechnung *f*	extrapolation *f*	экстраполяция
E 862	**extrapolation,** stochastic extrapolation, statistical extrapolation <of a stochastic process> <SP>	Extrapolation *f*, statistische (stochastische) Extrapolation	extrapolation *f*, extrapolation stochastique (statistique)	экстраполирование, стохастическое (статистическое) экстраполирование, стохастическая экстраполяция
E 863	**extrapolation factor,** expansion (inflation) factor <NU, ST>	Hochrechnungsfaktor *m*	facteur *m* d'extrapolation	экстраполяционный фактор, фактор роста
E 864	**extremal** <VA>	Extremale *f*	extrémale *f*	экстремаль
	extremal <VA>	*s.* E 878		
E 865	**extremal-convex domain,** geodesically convex domain <VA>	extremal (geodätisch) konvexes Gebiet *n*	domaine *m* géodésiquement convexe	геодезически (экстремально) выпуклая область
E 866	**extremal correlation** <ST>	extremale Korrelation *f*	corrélation *f* extrémale	экстремальная корреляция
E 867	**extremal curvature** <VA>	extremale Krümmung *f*; erste Krümmung <Finsler>	courbure *f* extrémale	экстремальная кривизна
E 868	**extremal element** <VA>	Extremalenelement *n*, vollständiges Linienelement *n*	élément *m* extrémal	экстремальный элемент
	extremal element <AL>	*s.* I 1032		
E 869	**extremal function** <AN>	Extremalfunktion *f*	fonction *f* extrémale	экстремальная функция
E 870	**extremally disconnected space** <TO>	extrem unzusammenhängender Raum *m*	espace *m* extrêmement discontinu	экстремально несвязное пространство
E 871	**extremal monomorphism** <CA>	extremer Monomorphismus *m*	monomorphisme *m* extrémal	экстремальный мономорфизм
E 872	**extremaloid** <VA>	Extremaloide *f*	extrémaloïde *f*	экстремалоида
E 873	**extremal point,** extreme point <of a convex set> <CS>	Extremalpunkt *m*	point *m* extrémal	экстремальная точка, крайняя точка
E 874	**extremal polynomial** <AX>	Extremalpolynom *n*	polynôme *m* extrémal	экстремальный многочлен (полином)
E 875	**extremal property,** extremum property <GN>	Extremaleigenschaft *f*, Extremumeigenschaft *f*	propriété *f* extrémale (d'extrémum)	экстремальное свойство
E 876	**extremal quotient** <ST>	Extremalquotient *m*	quotient *m* extrémal	экстремальное отношение
E 877	**extremal subset** <CS>	extremale Teilmenge *f*	partie *f* extrémale, sous-ensemble *m* extrémal	экстремальное подмножество
E 878	**extremal surface,** extremal <VA>	Extremalfläche *f*, Extremale *f*	surface *f* extrémale, extrémale *f*	экстремальная поверхность, экстремаль
E 879	**extremant** <VA>	Extremante *f*	extrémant *m*	экстреманта
E 880	**extreme,** extreme term <of a proportion> <AR>	äußeres Glied *n*, Außenglied *n*	extrême *m*, terme *m* extrême	крайний (внешний) член
	extreme <DI, PG>	*s.* E 896		
	extreme case <GN>	*s.* B 573		
E 881	**extreme form,** extreme quadratic form <GU>	Extremform *f*, quadratische Extremform, extreme [quadratische] Form *f*, Grenzform *f*	forme *f* extrême, forme quadratique positive extrême	экстремальная форма
E 882	**extreme generator** <of a convex cone> <GE>	extremale Erzeugende *f*	génératrice *f* extrémale	экстремальная образующая
E 883	**extreme half-space** <CS>	extremer Halbraum *m*	demi-espace *m* extrémal	экстремальное полупространство
E 884	**extreme lattice** <GU>	extremes Gitter *n*	réseau *m* extrémal	экстремальная решетка
E 885	**extreme linear form** <in Diophantine approximation> <NT>	extreme Linearform *f*	forme *f* linéaire extrémale	экстремальная линейная форма
	extremely disconnected space <TO>	*s.* S 1821		
E 886	**extreme mean** <ST>	extremer Mittelwert *m*	moyenne *f* extrême	экстремальное среднее
E 887	**extreme parallelogram** <GU>	extremes Parallelogramm *n*	parallélogramme *m* extrémal	экстремальный параллелограмм
E 888	**extreme point** <of a convex body> <GE>	extremer Punkt (Randpunkt) *m*	point *m* extrémal	экстремальная точка
	extreme point <CS>	*s.* E 873		
	extreme quadratic form	*s.* E 881		
E 889	**extreme tac-line** <CS>	extreme Stützgerade *f*	droite *f* d'appui limite	экстремальная опорная прямая

No.	English	German	French	Russian
E 890	**extreme tac-plane** <CS>	extreme Stützebene *f*	plan *m* d'appui limite	экстремальная опорная плоскость
E 891	**extreme tangent** <to a set> <DG>	extreme Tangente *f*	tangente *f* limite	экстремальная касательная
	extreme term <AR>	*s.* E 880		
	extreme value <DI, PG>	*s.* E 896		
E 892	**extreme value distribution** <of type I, II *or* III> <ST>	Extremwertverteilung *f* <vom Typ I, II *oder* III>	distribution *f* des valeurs extrêmes <du type I, II *ou* III>	распределение экстремальных значений <типа I, II *или* III>
E 893	**extreme value problem** <CS, DI, PG, VA>	Extremwertaufgabe *f*, Extremwertproblem *n* <DI, PJ, VA>; Extremumproblem *n* <CS>; Extremalproblem *n* <VA>	probléme *m* d'extrémum, problème d'extrémums	задача на экстремум, экстремальная задача
E 894	**extreme value problem with one-sided constraints** <VA>	Extremalproblem *n* mit einseitigen Bindungen, Extremalproblem mit Gebietseinschränkungen	problème *m* d'extrémum sous contraintes unilatérales	задача на экстремум с односторонними условиями
E 895	**extremity** <of an arrow> <CA>	Ende *n*, Endpunkt *m*, rechter Eckpunkt *m*	but *m*	конец
	extremity <AN>	*s.* E 217		
	extremity <FA>	*s.* E 233		
E 896	**extremum,** extreme value, extreme <of a function> <DI, PG>	Extremum *n*, Extremwert *m*	extrémum *m*, valeur *f* extrême, extrême *m*	экстремум, экстремальное значение, крайнее значение
	extremum <RF, SE>	*s.* L 699		
E 897	**extremum at the boundary,** boundary extreme <of a function> <AN>	Randextremum *n*	extrémum *m* correspondant à un point frontière; extrémum correspondant à une extrémité de l'intervalle	граничный экстремум
	extremum in the narrow sense <DI>	*s.* S 1859		
	extremum in the small <DI> ┌<GN>	*s.* L 930		
	extremum property	*s.* E 875		
E 898	**extremum with a condition (constraint, side condition),** constraint extremum, relative extremum <DI, PG, VA>	Extremum *n* unter (mit) einer Nebenbedingung (Bindung), gebundenes (relatives) Extremum	extrémum (extrême) *m* lié, extrémum sous une condition (contrainte), extrémum contraint (relatif)	экстремум с условием (ограничением), условный (относительный) экстремум
	eye distance <DS>	*s.* D 728		
E 899	**eye-fit** <ST>	Anpassen *n* (Anpassung *f*) nach Augenmaß	ajustement *m* à vue, lissage *m* de points à vue	выравнивание «на глаз»
	eye position <DS>	*s.* C 422		

F

No.	English	German	French	Russian
F 1	**Faber['s] polynomial** <FT>	Fabersches Polynom *n*	polynôme *m* de Faber	многочлен (полином) Фабера
F 2	**Faber['s] series** <FT>	Faber-Reihe *f*	série *f* [en polynômes] de Faber	ряд [по многочленам] Фабера
F 3	**Fabry['s] gap condition** <SS>	Fabrysche Lückenbedingung *f*	condition *f* des lacunes de Fabry	условие лакунарности Фабри
F 4	**Fabry['s] gap theorem,** gap theorem of Fabry <SS>	Fabryscher Lückensatz *m*	théorème *m* des lacunes de Fabry	теорема о лакунах Фабри, теорема Фабри о лакунах
F 5	**Fabry['s] theorem** <FT, SS>	allgemeiner Satz *m* von Fabry, Satz von Fabry, Fabryscher Satz	théorème *m* de Fabry	теорема Фабри
F 6	**face** <of a simplex> <AT>	Seitensimplex *n*, Seite *f* <eines Simplex>	face *f* <d'un simplexe>	грань <симплекса>
F 7	**face,** lateral face, plane surface, side <of a polyhedron *or* polyhedral angle> <EG>	Seite *f*, Seitenfläche *f*, [ebene] Randfläche (Begrenzungsfläche, Grenzfläche) *f*, Fläche *f*	face *f*, face latérale, facette *f* [latérale], surface *f* plane, plan *m*	грань, боковая грань, плоская поверхность
F 8	**face,** // region <GP>	Fläche *f*	face *f*	грань, внутренняя грань
F 9	**face angle, face-angle** <of a solid angle> <EG>	Flächenwinkel *m*, Winkel *m*	angle *m* dièdre	двугранный угол, угол <соседних граней>
	face angle <EG>	*s.* S 786		
F 10	**face operator** <AT>	Seitenoperator *m*	opérateur *m* face (de face)	оператор граней
F 11	**factor** <of the *n*-th degree> <of an algebraic expression> <AL>	Faktor *m* <*n*-ten Grades>	facteur *m* <du degré *n*>	фактор <степени *n*>
F 12	**factor,** multiplier <of a monomial substitution> <AL>	Faktor *m*, Multiplikator *m*	multiplicateur *m*	умножитель
F 13	**factor,** principal factor <of a principal series of semi-groups> <AL>	Faktor *m*	facteur *m*	фактор, главный фактор
F 14	**factor** <of a product> <AL, AR>	Faktor *m*	facteur *m*	сомножитель
F 15	**factor** <of a series of semi-groups, a von Neumann or W^* algebra, a graph, an intersection, *or* in factor analysis> <AL, FA, GP, SE, ST>	Faktor *m*	facteur *m*	фактор
F 16	**factor,** 2-factor <GP>	quadratischer Faktor *m*	facteur *m*, semi-facteur *m*	квадратичный фактор
F 17	**factor,** chief factor <of a principal series of groups> <GR>	Faktor *m*	groupe *m* quotient, groupe *m* facteur premier, facteur *m* premier, facteur	фактор
F 18	**factor,** divisor <of an integer> <NT>	Teiler *m*	diviseur *m*, sous-multiple *m*, facteur *m*	делитель

No.	English	German	French	Russian
F 19	**factor** <of a cartesian product of sets> <SE>	Faktormenge *f*	ensemble *m* facteur	множество-сомножитель
F 20	**factor** <of a topological product> <TO>	Faktor *m*	espace *m* facteur	пространство-сомножитель
	factor <AL>	*s.* D 820		
	factor <LO>	*s.* M 382		
	factor <ST>	*s.* C 781		
	2-factor <GP>	*s.* F 16		
F 21	**factorable,** factorizable, decomposable into factors, factored <AL>	in Faktoren zerlegbar, faktorisierbar	décomposable en facteurs, factorisable	факторизуемый, разложимый на множители
F 22	**factorable method [of limitation]** <LI>	faktorisierbares Limitierungsverfahren *n*	méthode *f* [de limitation] factorisable	факторизуемый метод образования обобщенного предела
	factorable polynomial <AL>	*s.* R 405		
F 23	**factor analysis,** component analysis <ST>	Faktor[en]analyse *f*; Generalfaktorenanalyse *f*	analyse *f* factorielle (des facteurs)	факторный (составной) анализ
F 24	**factor combination** <ST>	Faktorenkombination *f*	combinaison *f* de facteurs	комбинация факторов
	factor-commutator functor <CA>	*s.* A 23		
F 25	**factor-commutator group,** commutator-factor group, commutator quotient group <GR>	Faktorkommutatorgruppe *f*, abelsch gemachte Gruppe *f*, Kommutatorfaktorgruppe *f*	groupe *m* quotient par le groupe des commutateurs	фактор-группа <группы> по коммутанту
	factored <AL>	*s.* F 21		
F 26	**factor group,** complementary group <of a Lie group with respect to a Lie normal divisor> <GR>	Faktorgruppe *f*, Komplementärgruppe *f*, Restklassengruppe *f*	groupe *m* de Lie quotient <de *X* par *G*>	фактор[-]группа
F 27	**factor group, factor-group,** quotient group, difference group, group of cosets <of *G* with respect to *H*> <GR>	Faktorgruppe *f*, Restklassengruppe *f*, Quotientengruppe *f*, Differenzgruppe *f* <von *G* nach *H*>	groupe *m* quotient <de *G* par *H*>, groupe facteur, groupe-facteur *m*, complémentaire *m* <de *H* dans (par rapport à) *G*>, réciproque *m* <de *H* dans *G*>	фактор-группа, факторгруппа <группы *G* по [нормальному делителю] *H*>
F 28	**factor group of a topological group** <GR>	topologische Faktorgruppe *f*, Faktorgruppe einer topologischen Gruppe	groupe *m* topologique quotient	топологическая фактор-группа
F 29	**factor group of the additive group of the real numbers with respect to the group of integers** <GR>	Faktorgruppe *f* der additiven Gruppe der reellen Zahlen nach der Untergruppe der ganzen Zahlen	groupe *m* quotient du groupe additif des réels par le groupe des entiers	группа каппа
F 30	**factor groupoid,** quotient groupoid <AL>	Faktorgruppoid *n*, Faktoroid *n*, Restklassenstruktur *f* eines Gruppoids	groupoïde *m* quotient	фактор-группоид, факторгруппоид
F 31	**factorial,** factorial function <FU>	Fakultät *f*, Fakultätenfunktion *f*	factorielle *f*, fonction *f* factorielle	факториал
	factorial <FU>	*s.* H 52		
F 32	**factorial coefficient,** Stirling['s] number <of the first *or* second kind> <AN>	Stirlingsche Zahl *f* <erster (1.) *oder* zweiter (2.) Art>	nombre *m* de Stirling <de première *ou* deuxième, seconde espèce>	число Стирлинга <первого *или* второго рода>
F 33	**factorial cumulant** <ST>	faktorielle Kumulante *f*	cumulant *m* factoriel	факториальный семиинвариант
F 34	**factorial experiment,** complex experiment <ST>	faktorieller Versuch *m*, Komplexversuch *m*	expérience *f* factorielle (complexe)	факторный (составной) эксперимент
F 35	**factorial function** <$(u, + x)^y$ *or* $(u, - x)^y$> <FU>	faktorielle Funktion *f*, Fakultät *f*	fonction *f* factorielle	факториальная функция
	factorial function <FD, FU>	*s.* F 38		
	factorial function <FU>	*s.* 1. F 31; 2. G 42; 3. H 52		
	factorial function of Halphen <FU>	*s.* H 52		
	factorial model <ST>	*s.* F 49		
	2 factorial model <ST>	*s.* T 1087		
F 36	**factorial moment** <ST>	faktorielles Moment *n*	moment *m* factoriel	факториальный момент
F 37	**factorial moment generating function** <ST>	faktorielle momenterzeugende Funktion *f*, faktorielle Moment-erzeugende *f*	fonction *f* génératrice des moments factoriels	производящая функция факториальных моментов
F 38	**factorial polynomial,** factorial function; generalized factorial, Pochhammer['s] symbol, $x^{(n)}$, $x^{(-n)}$ <FD, FU>	Faktorielle *f*, verallgemeinerte Potenz *f*, Faktorpolynom *n*, arithmetische Faktorielle, numerische Fakultät *f*, Zahlenfakultät *f*	fonction *f* factorielle, factorielle *f*, produit *m* continuel, factorielle arithmétique, faculté *f* numérique	обобщенная степень, факториальный многочлен, обобщенный факториал, факториал
	factorial ring <AL>	*s.* U 216		
F 39	**factorial series** <FT>	Fakultätenreihe *f*	série *f* de factorielles (faculté), série factorielle	факториальный ряд, ряд факториалов
F 40	**factoring** <of a quadratic form> <AL>	Zerlegung *f* <einer quadratischen Form> in Linearfaktoren	décomposition *f* <d'une forme quadratique> en facteurs linéaires	разложение <квадратичной формы> на линейные факторы
	factoring <GN>	*s.* F 47		
	factorizable <AL>	*s.* F 21		
F 41	**factorizable group** <is product of two subgroups> <GR>	zerlegbare (eigentlich zerfallende, zerfallende) Gruppe *f*	groupe *m* décomposable	разложимая группа

F 42	**factorization** <in a ring> <AL>	Faktorzerlegung *f*	factorisation *f*	разложение [на множители]
F 43	**factorization** <of a morphism *or* mapping> <AL, CA, TO>	Faktorisierung *f*, Aufspaltung *f*	factorisation *f*	разложение
F 44	**factorization** <into a [finite] number of prime factors>, prime factorization, prime decomposition <of an element *or* a number> <AL, NT>	Primfaktorzerlegung *f*, Primelementzerlegung *f*	décomposition *f* en facteurs (éléments) premiers; décomposition en facteurs extrémaux <dans un anneau principal>	разложение на простые множители (элементы); разложение на неприводимые элементы; разложение на экстремальные элементы
F 45	**factorization** <of a graph> <GP>	Zerlegung *f* <eines Graphen> in Faktoren, Faktorzerlegung *f*	factorisation *f* <d'un graphe>	факторизация <графа>, рассечение на факторы
F 46	**factorization** <GR>	Restklassenbildung *f*, Faktorisierung *f*	factorisation *f*, passage *m* au quotient	факторизация
	factorization <FT>	*s.* W 155		
	factorization <GN>	*s.* F 47		
	factorization theorem <NT>	*s.* E 570		
	factorize / to <AL, NT>	*s.* D 61		
F 47	**factorizing,** factorization, factoring, decomposition into factors <GN>	Faktorisation *f*, Faktorisierung *f*, Faktorzerlegung *f*, Faktorenzerlegung *f*, Zerlegung *f* [in Faktoren]	factorisation *f*, décomposition *f* en facteurs, décomposition [en produits de facteurs]	факторизация, разложение на множители, представление в виде произведения, разложение [в произведение]
	factor level <ST>	*s.* L 594		
	factor loading <ST>	*s.* L 911		
F 48	**factor matrix** <ST>	Faktormatrix *f*	matrice *f* des facteurs de pondération	матрица факторных коэффициентов
F 49	**factor model**, factorial model <ST>	Faktormodell *n*	modèle *m* factoriel	фактор[-]модель, факторная модель
F 50	**factor module,** quotient (difference, residue class) module <of *M* by *N*, of *M* with respect to *N*> <AL>	Faktormodul *m*, Restklassenmodul *m*, Modulquotient *m*, Quotientenmodul *m* <von *M* nach *N*, von *M* modulo *N*>	module *m* quotient (des résidus) <de *M* par le sous-module *N*>	фактор-модуль, фактор-модуль, модуль вычета <модуля *M* по *N*>
F 51	**factor of proportionality,** proportionality factor (coefficient), coefficient (constant) of proportionality <GN>	Proportionalitätsfaktor *m*, Proportionalitätskoeffizient *m*	facteur *m* (coefficient *m*, constante *f*) de proportionnalité, facteur de proportion	коэффициент (множитель) пропорциональности
F 52	**factor out / to,** to put before the brackets <GN>	vor die Klammer ziehen (setzen) <einen gemeinsamen Faktor>, <einen gemeinsamen Faktor> ausklammern, aus der Klammer herausziehen	mettre en facteur [commun]	вынести <общий множитель> за скобки
	factor[-]ring <AL>	*s.* R 897		
F 53	**factor-ring by the radical** <AL>	Radikalrestklassenring *m*, Restklassenring *m* nach dem Radikal	anneau *m* quotient par le radical	факторкольцо по радикалу
F 54	**factor rotation** <ST>	Faktorrotation *f*	rotation *f* des facteurs	чередование факторов
F 55	**factor set** <AL, FT>	Faktorensystem *n*, Faktorsystem *n*	système *m* des (de) facteurs	система факторов
	factor set <SE>	*s.* Q 343		
F 56	**factor space,** coset (quotient, homogeneous) space, set of cosets, space of right cosets <of a topological group> <AL>	Faktorraum *m*, Restklassenraum *m*, homogener Raum *m*	espace-quotient *m*, espace *m* homogène [topologique]; espace homogène de Lie <d'un groupe de Lie>	фактор-пространство, пространство смежных классов, однородное [топологическое] пространство
	factor space <TO>	*s.* Q 347		
F 57	**factor system** <of an automorphic form> <FT>	Multiplikatorensystem *n*, Multiplikatorsystem *n*	système *m* de multiplicateurs	множители автоморфности
F 58	**factor theorem** <of an algebraic equation> <AL>	Faktorsatz *m* <wenn *r* Wurzel von *P*(*x*) ist, so teilt *x*-*r* *P*(*x*)>	théorème *m* de Bézout	теорема Безу <о делении многочлена на линейный двучлен), теорема о делимости многочлена на выражение *x*-*r*
	factor theorem <GR>	*s.* H 505		
F 59	**Faddeev['s] theorem** <DI>	Satz *m* von Faddeev (Faddejew), Faddeevscher (Faddejewscher) Satz	théorème *m* de Faddeev	теорема Фаддеева
F 60	**Fagnano['s] ellipse** <AY, EG>	Fagnanosche Ellipse *f*	ellipse *f* de Fagnano, ellipse équilatère	эллипс Фаньяно
F 61	**Fagnano['s] theorem** <on rectification of the ellipse> <AY>	Theorem *n* von Fagnano, Fagnanosches Theorem	théorème *m* de Fagnano	теорема Фаньяно
F 62	**Fagnano['s] theorem** <for a triangle> <EG>	Fagnanoscher Schwerpunktsatz *m*	théorème *m* de Fagnano	теорема Фаньяно
F 63	**failure** <ST>	Ausfall *m*, Versagen *n*	défaillance *f*, panne *f*	отказ
	failure intensity <ST>	*s.* R 805		
F 64	**failure rate** <ST>	Ausfallrate *f*, Ausfallsrate *f*, Ausfall[s]häufigkeit *f*, Versagenshäufigkeit *f*	taux *m* (fréquence *f*) de défaillances	интенсивность отказов
F 65	**fair game** <TG>	gerechtes (faires) Spiel *n*	jeu *m* équitable	справедливая (безобидная) игра
F 66	**faithful anti-representation,** true anti-representation <of a groupoid> <RE>	treue Antidarstellung *f*	antireprésentation *f* fidèle	точное антипредставление
F 67	**faithful functor,** embedding <CA>	treuer Funktor *m*, Einbettung *f*	foncteur *m* fidèle	унивалентный (точный) функтор
F 68	**faithful interpretation** <MM>	treue Interpretation *f*	interprétation *f* fidèle	точная интерпретация

F 69	**faithfully flat ring** <AL>	treu flacher Ring *m*	anneau *m* fidèlement plat	строго плоское кольцо
F 70	**faithful module** <AL>	treuer Modul *m*	module *m* fidèle	точный модуль
F 71	**faithfulness** <of a functor> <CA>	Treue *f*	fidélité *f*	унивалентность, точность
F 72	**faithfulness** <of a representation> <RE>	Treue *f* <einer Darstellung>	fidélité *f* <d'une représentation>	точность <представления>
F 73	**faithful representation** <also of a groupoid>; true representation <of a groupoid> <RE>	treue Darstellung *f*	représentation *f* fidèle	точное представление <также группоида>; изоморфное (правильное) представление <группоида>
F 74	**faithful semifinite normal trace** <of a von Neumann algebra> <FA>	treue halbendliche normale Spur *f*	trace *f* normale semi-finie fidèle	точный полуконечный нормальный след
	fallacy <LO>	*s.* P 126		
	fall angle <DS>	*s.* A 664		
F 75	**fall line, fall-line,** steepest line, line of steepest slope <DS>	Fallinie *f*	ligne *f* de pente	линия падения
	fall scale <DS>	*s.* G 366		
F 76	**false conclusion** <LO>	Fehlschluß *m*, falscher Schluß *m*	fausse conclusion *f*	ложный вывод
	false ellipse <GE>	*s.* T 443		
	false formula <LO>	*s.* C 2277		
F 77	**falsehood** <of a proposition> <LO>	Falschheit *f*	fausseté *f*	ложность, ложь
F 78	**falsifiability** <LO>	Falsifizierbarkeit *f*	falsifiabilité *f*	фальсифицируемость
F 79	**falsification** <LO>	Falsifikation *f*, Falsifizierung *f*, Nichterfüllung *f* <eines Ausdrucks>	falsification *f*	фальсификация, невыполнение
	faltung <AN>	*s.* C 2409		
	faltung theorem <AN>	*s.* C 2413		
	family of Borel sets <TO>	*s.* B 582		
F 80	**family of cogenerators,** cogenerating set <for a category> <CA>	Kogeneratormenge *f*, Cogeneratormenge *f*, koerzeugende (coerzeugende) Menge *f*	ensemble *m* cogénérateur	семейство кообразующих
F 81	**family of curves,** group (system, assemblage) of curves <AY>	Kurvenschar *f*, Schar *f* von Kurven, Kurvensystem *n*	famille *f* de courbes (lignes), réseau *m* de courbes	семейство кривых (линий), система кривых
	family of disjoint sets <SE>	*s.* D 700		
	family of distributions <ST>	*s.* D 756		
F 82	**family of elements,** system of elements, indexed set (collection) of elements <of a set> <SE>	Familie *f* von Elementen, Funktion *f*	famille *f* d'éléments	семейство элементов, система элементов, обозначенные элементы
F 83	**family of extremals**< VA>	Extremalenschar *f*	famille *f* d'extrémales	семейство экстремалей
F 84	**family of generators,** generating set <for a category> <CA>	Generatormenge *f*, erzeugende Menge *f*, koseparierende (coseparierende) Menge, Menge von Generatoren	ensemble *m* de générateurs	семейство образующих
F 85	**family of planes** <AY>	Ebenenschar *f*	famille *f* de plans	семейство плоскостей
F 86	**family of sets,** indexed system of sets, cover, system of sets <SE>	Mengenfamilie *f*, indiziertes System (Mengensystem) *n*, Mengensystem, Mengenkomplex *m*	famille *f* d'ensembles	семейство множеств, система занумерованных множеств, комплекс множеств
	family of sets <SE>	*s.* S 961		
F 87	**family of several parameters** <AL, GE>	mehrparametrige Familie *f*	famille *f* à plusieurs paramètres, famille multiparamétrique	многопараметрическое семейство
F 88	**family of solutions** <DE, GN>	Lösungsschar *f*, Lösungsgesamtheit *f*, Lösungsmannigfaltigkeit *f*	famille *f* de solutions	семейство (многообразие, совокупность) решений
F 89	**family of supports** <TO>	Trägerfamilie *f*	famille *f* de supports	семейство носителей
F 90	**family of surfaces,** system of surfaces <AY>	Flächenschar *f*, Flächensystem *n*	famille *f* (système *m*) de surfaces	семейство (система) поверхностей
F 91	**fan** <in a vertex> <GP>	Fächer *m*	éventail *m*	веер <в вершине>
F 92	**Fano['s] configuration** <PJ>	Fanosche Konfiguration *f*	configuration *f* de Fano	конфигурация Фано
F 93	**Fano['s] plane** <CT, GE>	Fano-Ebene *f*	plan *m* de Fano	плоскость Фано
F 94	**Fano['s] variety** <AG>	Fanosche Mannigfaltigkeit *f*	variété *f* de Fano	многообразие Фано
F 95	**Fantappiè['s] indicatrix** <of an analytic functional> <AN>	Fantappièsche (schiefsymmetrische) Indikatrix *f*, Indikatrix	indicatrice *f* de Fantappiè	кососимметрическая индикатриса
F 96	**Farey['s] dissection of the continuum** <NT>	Farey-Zerschneidung *f* des Kontinuums, Farey-Teilung *f*	dissection *f* de Farey	разбиение Фарея
	Farey['s] fraction <NT>	*s.* F 573		
F 97	**Farey['s] number** <NT>	Fareysche Zahl *f*	nombre *m* de Farey	число Фарея
F 98	**Farey['s] series** <of order *n*, *n*-th> <NT>	Farey-Reihe *f*, Fareysche Reihe *f* <*n*-te, *n*-ter Ordnung>	suite *f* de Farey, série *f* de Farey <d'ordre *n*>	последовательность Фарея, ряд Фарея <порядка *n*>
	Farey['s] theorem <NT>	*s.* T 276		
F 99	**Fasenmyer['s] polynomial** <FU>	Fasenmyersches Polynom *n*	polynôme *m* de Fasenmyer	многочлен (полином) Фазенмайера
F 100	**Fatou['s] lemma** <FA>	Fatousches Lemma *n*, Lemma von Fatou	lemme *m* de Fatou	лемма Фату
F 101	**Fatou-Riesz theorem** <FT>	Satz *m* von Fatou-M. Riesz	théorème *m* de Fatou et M. Riesz	теорема Фату-Риса
F 102	**Fatou['s] theorem** <FT>	Satz *m* von Fatou, Fatouscher Satz	théorème *m* de Fatou	теорема Фату

F 103	**Faure['s] theorem** <GE>	Faurescher Satz *m*	théorème *m* de Faure	теорема Фора
F 104	**Favard['s] measure** <of area> <IG>	Favardsches Flächenmaß *n*	mesure *f* [d'aire] de Favard	мера площади Фавара
F 105	**favourable case** <ST>	günstiger Fall *m*	cas *m* favorable, chance *f*	благоприятствующий случай
F 106	**favourable event** <ST>	günstiges Ereignis *n*	événement *m* favorable	благоприятствующее (благоприятное) событие
F 107	**FD-complex** <HA>	FD-Komplex *m*	FD-complexe *m*	FD-комплекс
F 108	**FD-homotopy** <HA>	FD-Homotopie *f*	FD-homotopie *f*	FD-гомотопия
	F-differentiable function (mapping) <FA>	*s.* F 581		
F 109	***F*-distribution,** Fisher['s] *F*-distribution, Fisher['s] distribution, variance ratio distribution <ST>	*F*-Verteilung *f*, Fishersche *F*-Verteilung (Verteilung *f*), Varianzquotientenverteilung *f*	distribution *f F* (de *F*, *F* de Fisher, de Fisher, du rapport des variances)	*F*-распределение, *F*-распределение Фишера, распределение Фишера (дисперсионного отношения)
F 110	**FD-module** <HA>	FD-Modul *m*	FD-module *m*	FD-модуль, свободный симплициальный модуль
	FD statistics <ST>	*s.* F 137		
	fe <FU>	*s.* M 175		
	feasibility <AL>	*s.* R 217		
F 111	**feasible base** <PG>	zulässige Basis *f*	base *f* réalisable	допустимая база
	feasible basic solution <PG>	*s.* 1. B 117; 2. S 970		
F 112	**feasible constraint,** feasible restriction <PG>	zulässige Nebenbedingung *f*	contrainte *f* réalisable	допустимое ограничение
F 113	**feasible perturbation** <PG>	zulässige Störung *f*	perturbation *f* admissible	допустимое возмущение
	feasible program[me] <PG>	*s.* F 115		
F 114	**feasible region** <PG>	zulässiger Bereich *m*	région *f* réalisable	допустимое множество, допустимая область, множество планов
	feasible restriction <PG>	*s.* F 112		
F 115	**feasible solution,** feasible program[me] <PG>	zulässige Lösung *f*, zulässiger Punkt (Vektor) *m*, ausführbare Lösung, Programm *n*, zulässiges (ausführbares) Programm	solution *f* (programme *m*) réalisable	допустимое решение, допустимая программа
F 116	**Fechner['s] correlation coefficient** <ST>	Fechnerscher Korrelationskoeffizient *m*, Korrelationskoeffizient von Fechner	coefficient *m* de corrélation de Fechner	коэффициент корреляции Фехнера
F 117	**Fedorov['s] solid,** convex parallelohedron <EG>	Fjodorowscher (Fedorovscher) Körper *m*, konvexes Paralleloeder *n*	corps *m* de Fedorov, parallélоèdre *m* convexe	тело Федорова, выпуклый параллелоэдр
F 118	**feeble solution,** generalized solution <of a linear partial differential equation> <DE>	schwache (verallgemeinerte) Lösung *f*	solution *f* faible (généralisée)	слабое (обобщенное) решение
F 119	**feeble stability** <DE>	schwache Stabilität *f*	stabilité *f* faible	слабая устойчивость
F 120	**feebly semi-separated space,** T_0-space, T_0 topological space <TO>	Kolmogorovscher Raum *m*, T_0-Raum *m*	espace *m* de Kolmogoroff, espace topologique quasi-séparé, T_0-espace *m*	пространство Колмогорова, колмогоровское пространство, T_0-пространство
	Fejér['s] average <SS>	*s.* F 126		
F 121	**Fejér['s] integral,** Fejér['s] operator <FA>	[singuläres] Fejérsches Integral *n*, Fejérscher Operator *m*, Integral (Operator) vom Fejérschen Typ	intégrale *f* de Fejér, opérateur *m* de Fejér	интеграл Фейера, фейеров интеграл, оператор Фейера, фейеров оператор
F 122	**Fejér['s] kernel** <FA>	Fejérscher Kern *m*	noyau *m* de Fejér	ядро Фейера, фейерово ядро
F 123	**Fejér-Lebesgue theorem** <SS>	Satz *m* von Fejér-Lebesgue, Fejér-Lebesguescher Satz	théorème *m* de Fejér-Lebesgue	теорема Фейера-Лебега
	Fejér['s] method [of summation] <LI, SS>	*s.* F 127		
	Fejér['s] operator <FA>	*s.* F 121		
F 124	**Fejér['s] polynomial** <AX, NU>	Fejérsches Polynom *n*, Treppenparabel *f*, Fejér-Polynom *n*	polynôme *m* de Fejér	многочлен (полином) Фейера
F 125	**Fejér-Riesz theorem** <FU>	Satz *m* von Fejér-Riesz (L. Fejér und F. Riesz), Fejér-Rieszscher Satz	théorème *m* de Fejér-Riesz (L. Fejér et F. Riesz)	теорема Фейера-Риса
F 126	**Fejér['s] sum,** Féjer['s] average <SS>	Fejérsche Summe *f*, Fejérsches Mittel *n*	somme *f* de Fejér, moyenne *f* de Fejér	сумма Фейера, фейерова сумма, среднее Фейера
F 127	**Fejér['s] summation,** Fejér['s] method [of summation] <for Fourier series> <LI, SS>	Fejérsche Summation *f*, Fejérsches Summationsverfahren *n*, *M*-Verfahren *n* für Fourier-Reihen	sommation (méthode) *f* de Fejér, méthode de sommation de Fejér	суммирование Фейера, метод суммирования Фейера, метод Фейера
F 128	**Fejér['s] theorem** <SS>	Satz *m* von Fejér, Fejérscher Satz	théorème *m* de Fejér	теорема Фейера
F 129	**Fejér-type kernel** <FA>	Kern *m* vom Fejérschen Typ	noyau *m* de type Fejér	ядро типа Фейера
F 130	**Feller-Arley process,** linear birth-and-death process <SP>	Feller-Arley-Prozeß *m*, linearer Geburts- und Todesprozeß *m*	processus *m* de Feller-Arley, processus de naissance et mort linéaire	процесс Феллера-Арлея, линейный процесс гибели и размножения
F 131	**Fermat['s] last theorem, Fermat['s] Last Theorem, Fermat['s] „last theorem"** <NT>	Fermatsche Vermutung *f*, großer Fermatscher Satz *m*, Fermat-Vermutung *f*, letzter Fermatscher Lehrsatz *m*	dernier (grand) théorème *m* de Fermat	великая (большая) теорема Ферма
	Fermat['s] lesser (little) theorem <AL>	*s.* F 134		
F 132	**Fermat['s] number** <NT>	Fermatsche (Gaußsche) Zahl *f*	nombre *m* de Fermat	число Ферма
	Fermat['s] prime <NT>	*s.* P 1298		
F 133	**Fermat['s] spiral,** parabolic spiral <GE>	Fermatsche Spirale *f*	spirale *f* de Fermat	спираль Ферма

No.	English	German	French	Russian
F 134	**Fermat['s] theorem,** Fermat['s] little (lesser) theorem, little Fermat theorem <AL>	Fermatscher Satz *m*, kleiner Fermatscher Satz	[petit] théorème *m* de Fermat; théorème de Fermat généralisé	малая теорема Ферма
F 135	**Fermat['s] theorem** <of the circle> <GE>	Fermatscher Satz *m* vom Kreis	théorème *m* de Fermat	теорема Ферма
F 136	**Fermi['s] co-ordinates** <DG>	Fermi-Koordinaten *fpl*	coordonnées *fpl* de Fermi	координаты Ферми
F 137	**Fermi[-Dirac] statistics,** FD statistics <ST>	Fermi[-Dirac]-Statistik *f*, Fermi-Diracsche Quantenstatistik *f*, FD-Statistik *f*	statistique *f* de Fermi [et Dirac], statistique Fermi-Dirac	статистика Ферми-Дирака, статистика Ферми
F 138	**Fermi-Thomas equation,** Thomas-Fermi equation, Thomas-Fermi differential equation <DE>	Thomassche Differentialgleichung *f*, Thomas-Fermische Differentialgleichung (Gleichung *f*), Thomas-Fermi-Differentialgleichung *f*, Thomas-Fermi-Gleichung *f*, Differentialgleichung von Thomas und Fermi, Fermi-Thomassche Gleichung, Gleichung von Fermi-Thomas	équation *f* de Fermi-Thomas, équation différentielle de Thomas-Fermi, équation de Thomas-Fermi	уравнение Ферми-Томаса, уравнение Томаса-Ферми, дифференциальное уравнение Томаса-Ферми
F 139	**Ferrari['s] solution for the general quartic** <AL>	Ferraris Lösung *f* der allgemeinen Gleichung vierten Grades	solution *f* algébrique de l'équation générale du quatrième degré par Ferrari	решение Феррари для общего уравнения четвертой степени
F 140	**Ferrers['] diagram,** Ferrers['] graph <GP>	Ferrers-Diagramm *n*	diagramme *m* de Ferrers	диаграмма Ферре, граф Ферре
	Ferrers['] graph <GP>	*s.* F 140		
F 141	**Feuerbach['s] hyperbola** <of a triangle> <EG>	Feuerbachsche Hyperbel *f*	hyperbole *f* de Feuerbach	гипербола Фейербаха
F 142	**Feuerbach['s] theorem,** nine-point circle theorem <of the triangle> <EG>	Feuerbachscher Satz *m*	théorème *m* de Feuerbach	теорема Фейербаха
	fibered <US>	*s.* fibred		
	fibering <US> <AT>	*s.* F 160		
	fibering relation <SE>	*s.* O 119		
F 143	**Fibonacci['s] number** <NT>	Fibonaccische Zahl *f*, Zahl von Fibonacci (Lamé)	nombre *m* de Fibonacci	число Фибоначчи
F 144	**Fibonacci['s] sequence,** series of Pisano, Pisano['s] series <FD, NT>	Fibonaccische Zahlenreihe (Reihe) *f*, Lamésche Reihe *f* der Ordnung 1, Fibonaccis Reihe *f*, Fibonacci-Folge *f*	suite *f* de Fibonacci, suite ordinaire de Lamé, suite de Lamé d'ordre 1	ряд Фибоначчи, последовательность Фибоначчи, числа Фибоначчи
F 145	**fibration,** Hurewicz['] fibre space, fibre map, Hurewicz['] fibre map <AT>	Faserraum *m* im Sinne von Hurewicz	fibre-espace *m* d'Hurewicz-Steenrod	расслоение, расслоенное пространство в смысле Гуревича, косое произведение в смысле Гуревича-Стинрода
F 146	**fibration** <TO>	Faserung *f*	fibration *f*	расслоение
	fibration <AT>	*s.* P 1649		
	fibration <CA>	*s.* F 147		
F 147	**fibration in the sense of Kan,** fibration <CA>	Faserabbildung *f* im Sinne von Kan	fibré *m* au sens de Kan	расслоение [в смысле Кана]
	fibration in the sense of Serre <AT>	*s.* W 62		
F 148	**fibre** <over *b*> <of a fibre space> <AT>	Faser *f* <über *b*>	fibre *f* <sur *b*>	слой <над точкой *b*>
F 149	**fibre** <of a mapping> <TO>	Faser *f*	tranche *f*	слой
	fibre <AT>	*s.* T 1153		
F 150	**fibre bundle,** twisted product <AT>	Faserbündel *n*	espace *m* fibré localement trivial, espace fibré	расслоение, пучок, расслоенное пространство, косое произведение, расслоенный пучок
	fibre bundle <AT>	*s.* L 1009		
F 151	**fibre bundle of Whitney** <AT>	Whitneysches Faserbündel *n*	fibré *m* de Whitney	расслоение Уитни
F 152	**fibred category** <CA>	gefaserte Kategorie *f*	catégorie *f* fibrée	расслоенная категория
F 153	**fibre degree,** degree with respect to the fibre <in a fibre space, filtration> <AT>	Fasergrad *m*, Grad *m* bezüglich der Faser	degré *m* fibre, degré-fibre *m*	степень по слою, степень по отношению к слою
F 154	**fibred in circumferences** <AT>	in Kreislinien gefasert	fibré en circonférences	расслоенный в окружностях
	fibred product <CA>	*s.* 1. P 2027; 2. P 2028		
F 155	**fibred sum,** [vertex of a] cocartesian square, amalgamated sum, pushout, amalgamized sum, union, cofibred sum <as an object> <CA>	Fasersumme *f*, Ecke *f* eines kokartesischen Quadrats, kokartesisches (cocartesisches) Quadrat *n*, verschmelzende (amalgamierte) Summe *f*	somme *f* fibrée (amalgamée), union *f*	расслоенная сумма, амальгама объектов A и B под объектом C, амальгама объектов A и B с объединенным объектом C, корасслоенная сумма
	fibred sum <CA>	*s.* P 2076		
F 156	**fibre homotopy** <TO>	Faserhomotopie *f*		послойная гомотопия
F 157	**fibre map** <AT>	Faserabbildung *f*	application *f* de fibres	послойное отображение, отображение расслоенных пространств
	fibre map <AT>	*s.* 1. F 145; 2. F 160		
F 158	**fibre of a correspondence R at x,** slice through x of R, x-section of R <SE>	Bild *n* eines Elements x bei einer Korrespondenz R, Schicht *f* R_x	coupe *f* de R suivant x	левое сечение элемента x в соответствии R, образ x при соответствии R, срез от R относительно x
	fibre preserving map <TO>	*s.* B 797		
F 159	**fibre preserving mapping** <AT>	fasertreue (faserungstreue) Abbildung *f*	application *f* conservant les fibres	преобразование, сохраняющее расслоенность

	English	German	French	Russian
	fibre product <AT>	*s.* W 243		
	fibre projection <AT>	*s.* P 1649		
F 160	**fibre space, fibring,** fibering <US>, fibre map, fibring, bundle <AT>	Faserraum *m*, gefaserter Raum *m*	espace *m* fibré; espace découpé	расслоение, расслоенное пространство
	fictitious example <GN>	*s.* C 2124		
F 161	**fictitious player** <TG>	fiktiver Spieler *m*	joueur *m* fictif	фиктивный игрок
F 162	**F-ideal** <of a partially ordered ring> <AL>	F-Ideal *n*	F-idéal *m*	F-идеал
F 163	**fiducial density** <ST>	Fiduzialdichte *f*	densité *f* fiducielle	фидуциальная плотность
F 164	**fiducial distribution** <ST>	Fiduzialverteilung *f*	distribution *f* fiducielle	фидуциальное распределение
F 165	**fiducial estimation** <ST>	fiduziale Schätzung *f*, Fiduzialschätzung *f*	estimation *f* fiducielle	фидуциальная оценка
F 166	**fiducial inference** <ST>	Fiduzialschluß *m*	inférence (induction) *f* fiducielle	фидуциальное заключение
F 167	**fiducial limit** <ST>	Fiduzialgrenze *f*	limite *f* fiducielle (fiduciaire)	фидуциальный предел
F 168	**fiducial probability** <ST>	Fiduzialwahrscheinlichkeit *f*, fiduzielle (fiduziale) Irrtumswahrscheinlichkeit *f*, inverse Wahrscheinlichkeit *f*, Irrtumswahrscheinlichkeit *f*	probabilité *f* fiducielle	фидуциальная вероятность
F 169	**fiducial region** <ST>	Fiduzialbereich *m*	région *f* fiducielle (fiduciaire)	фидуциальная область
F 170	**field,** commutative field, domain of rationality, // domain <AL>	Körper *m*, Rationalitätsbereich *m*, kommutativer Körper	corps *m*, corps commutatif (abélien, droit), champ *m*, domaine *m* de rationalité, // domaine orthoïde <König>, région *f* de rationalité	поле, коммутативное тело, область рациональности
F 171	**field** <DE, VA>	Feld *n* <Kurvenschar, bei der durch jeden Punkt genau eine Scharkurve geht>	champ *m*	поле
F 172	**field** <of a relation> <SE>	Feld *n*	champ *m*, support *m*; domaine *m* de définition <lorsqu'on représente la relation comme fonction propositionnelle>; domaine <d'une relation d'ordre>	поле
	δ-field <SE>	*s.* D 210		
	σ-field <ME, SE, TO>	*s.* S 810		
	σ-field of Borel sets <TO>	*s.* B 582		
F 173	**field algebraically closed in *K*** <AL>	relativ-algebraisch-abgeschlossener Teilkörper *m* in *K*, in *K* algebraisch abgeschlossener Körper *m*	corps *m* algébriquement fermé dans *K*	поле, алгебраически замкнутое в *K*
F 174	**field basis,** minimal basis, linearly independent basis <of a field> <AL>	Körperbais *f*, Basis *f*, // Minimalbasis *f*	base *f* du corps, base	база [поля], базис [поля]
	field between . . . <AL>	*s.* I 749		
F 175	**field characteristic,** characteristic <of a field> <AL>	Körpercharakteristik *f*, Charakteristik *f* <eines Körpers>	caractéristique *f* du corps, caractéristique	характеристика поля, характеристика
	field conjugate <AB>	*s.* C 1994		
F 176	**field degree,** degree <of a field> <AL>	Körpergrad *m*, Grad *m*	degré *m* du corps, degré	степень поля, степень
F 177	**field different** <of an algebraic number field> <AL>	Körperdifferente *f*, Verzweigungsideal *n*, Grundideal *n*, Differente *f*	différente *f* du corps, idéal *m* de ramification, idéal fondamental	дифферента поля
F 178	**field discriminant,** discriminant <of a field> <AL>	Körperdiskriminante *f*, Diskriminante *f* der Gattung, Diskriminante *f* <eines Körpers>	discriminant *m* <d'un corps>	дискриминант <поля>
	field extension <AL>	*s.* E 774		
F 179	**field extension soluble by radicals,** extension soluble by radicals <AL>	Erweiterung *f* durch Radikale	extension *f* radicielle	расширение, разрешимое в радикалах; радикальное расширение
F 180	**field generated over *k* by *x*,** field obtained by adjoining to *k* the element *x* <AL>	von *x* über *k* erzeugter Körper *m*	corps *m* engendré par *x* sur *k*	поле, порожденное элементом *x* над *k*
	field isomorphic over *k* <AL>	*s.* K 81		
	field obtained by adjoining to *k* the element *x* <AL>	*s.* F 180		
F 181	**field of algebraic functions,** algebraic function field <AL>	algebraischer Funktionenkörper *m*, Körper *m* algebraischer Funktionen	corps *m* de fonctions algébriques	поле алгебраических функций
F 182	**field of algebraic functions of *n* independent variables over *k*** <AL>	algebraischer Funktionenkörper *m* in *n* Variablen über *k*	corps *m* des fonctions algébriques à *n* variables sur le corps *k*, corps des fonctions algébriques à *n* indéterminées à coefficients dans *k*	поле алгебраических функций от *n* переменных над *k*
	field of Borel sets <ME, SE, TO>	*s.* S 810		
	field of Borel sets <TO>	*s.* B 582		
F 183/4	**field of characteristic *p*** <AL>	Körper *m* der Charakteristik *p*, Körper von der Charakteristik *p*	corps *m* de la caractéristique *p*	поле характеристики *p*

No.	English	German	French	Russian
F 185	**field of class two** <AL>	metabelscher Körper *m*	corps *m* métabélien	поле второго класса, метабелево поле
	field of complex numbers <AL>	*s.* C 1614		
F 186	**field of constants,** constant field <AL>	Konstantenkörper *m*	corps *m* des constantes	поле констант
F 187	**field of definition,** defining field <AG>	Definitionskörper *m*	corps *m* de définition	поле определения
F 188	**field of events,** algebra of events <ST>	Ereignisfeld *n*, Ereignisalgebra *f*	champ *m* (algèbre *f*) d'événements, espace *m* probabilisable	поле[случайных]событий, алгебра событий
F 189	**field of extremals** <VA>	Extremalenfeld *n*	champ *m* d'extrémales	поле экстремалей
F 190	**field of finite type** <AL>	endlich erzeugter Körper *m* <über dem Primkörper>	corps *m* de type fini, extension *f* de type fini du sous-corps premier	конечно порожденное поле, конечно порожденное расширение простого поля
F 191	**field of moments** <of a vector field> <VT>	Momentfeld *n*	champs *m* de moments	поле моментов
	field of Monge directions <DE>	*s.* M 823		
F 192	**field of *n*-frames** <AT>	Basisfeld *n*, *n*-Beinfeld *n*	champ *m* de *n*-repères	поле *n*-реперов
F 193	**field of *p*-adic numbers** <AL>	*p*-adischer Zahlkörper (Körper) *m*, Körper der *p*-adischen Zahlen	corps *m* *p*-adique, corps des nombres *p*-adiques	поле *p*-адических чисел, *p*-адическое поле (числовое поле)
	field of polynomial quotients <AL>	*s.* R 169		
	field of prime characteristic <AL>	*s.* F 194		
F 194	**field of prime number characteristic,** field of prime characteristic <AL>	Körper *m* von Primzahlcharakteristik	corps *m* de caractéristique première	поле характеристики, равной простому числу; поле простой характеристики
	field of quotients <AL>	*s.* Q 321		
F 195	**field of rational functions** <of an algebraic manifold> <AG>	algebraischer Funktionenkörper *m*, rationaler Funktionenkörper *m*	corps *m* des fonctions rationnelles, corps de fractions rationnelles	поле рациональных функций
F 196	**field of rational functions in *n* indeterminates over *K*** <AL>	rationaler Funktionenkörper *m* in *n* Unbestimmten über dem Körper *K*, rationaler Funktionenkörper von *n* Veränderlichen über *K*	corps *m* des fractions rationnelles à *n* variables sur le corps *K*, corps des fractions rationnelles à *n* indéterminées à coefficients dans *K*	поле рациональных функций от *n* переменных над *K*
F 197	**field of rationality** <of a divisor> <AL>	Rationalitätskörper *m*	corps *m* de rationalité	поле рациональности
F 197 a	**field of rationals,** number domain of all rational numbers <AL>	Körper *m* der rationalen Zahlen, rationaler Zahlkörper *m*	corps *m* des nombres rationnels, corps rationnel absolu	поле рациональных чисел
F 198	**field of real numbers,** number domain of all real numbers <AL>	Körper *m* der reellen Zahlen	corps *m* des nombres réels, corps des réels	поле вещественных чисел
F 199	**field of representatives,** representative field <AL>	Repräsentantenkörper *m*	corps *m* de représentants	поле представителей
	field of residue classes <AL>	*s.* R 893		
	field of scalars <AL>	*s.* G 441		
F 200	**field of sets,** ring of sets, Boolean ring of sets, field of subsets <closed with respect to union and symmetric difference> <SE>	Mengenkörper *m*, Mengenring *m*, Boolescher Ring *m*	corps *m* d'ensembles, corps de parties, corps	поле множеств, поле, тело множеств
	field of sets <SE>	*s.* S 638		
	σ-field of sets <ME, SE, TO>	*s.* S 810		
	σ-field of sets <SE>	*s.* S 823		
	field of subsets <SE>	*s.* 1. F 200; 2. S 638		
	field of tangents <DE>	*s.* D 563		
F 201	**field polynomial,** characteristic polynomial <of a field extension> <AL>	Hauptpolynom *n*, Körperpolynom *n*, charakteristisches Polynom *n*	polynôme *m* caractéristique	характеристический полином
F 202	**field polynomial of *x* relative to *k*, field polynomial of *x* over *k*** <AL>	charakteristisches Polynom *n* von *x* über *k*	polynôme *m* caractéristique de *x* sur *k*	характеристический многочлен *x* над *k*
	field satisfying Hasse's product formula <AL>	*s.* P 550		
F 203	**field separably generated over *k*** <AL>	über *k* separabel erzeugter Körper *m*	extension *f* de *k* admettant une base de transcendance séparante	сепарабельно порожденное поле над *k*
F 204/5	**field that can be ordered** <AL>	anordnungsfähiger Körper *m*	corps *m* ordonnable (admettant une structure d'ordre)	упорядочиваемое поле
F 206	**field that is not Galois;** non-normal field <AL>	nichtgaloisscher Körper *m*; Nichtnormalkörper *m*	corps *m* non galoisien; corps non normal	ненормальное поле
F 207	**field theory** <AL>	Körpertheorie *f*	théorie *f* des corps	теория полей
F 208	**field topology** <AL>	Körpertopologie *f*	topologie *f* du corps	топология поля
F 209	**field tower** <AL>	Körperturm *m*	tour *f* de corps	башня полей
	field vector <VT>	*s.* B 700		
	field with a valuation <AL>	*s.* F 211		
F 210	**field without affect** <AL>	affektloser Körper *m*	corps *m* sans affect	поле без аффекта
F 211	**field with valuation,** field with a valuation <AL>	bewerteter Körper *m*	corps *m* valué (normé, métrisé, métrique)	поле с оценкой (нормой), метризованное (нормированное) поле, нормированное тело
	fifteen-cornered polygon <EG>	*s.* Q 296		
	Fifteen Puzzle <CT>	*s.* B 620		

No.	English	German	French	Russian
	fifth-degree polynomial equation <AL>	*s.* Q 302		
F 212	**figurate number** <*r*-th> <of order *k*> <NT>	<*r*-te> figurierte Zahl *f* <der Ordnung *k*>	<*r*-e> nombre *m* figuré <d'ordre *k*>	<*r*-ое> фигурное число <порядка *k*>
F 213	**figurative** <VA>	Figurative *f*	figurative *f*	фигуратива
	figurative symbol <LO, SE>	*s.* V 55		
F 214	**figuratrix** <VA>	Figuratrix *f*	figuratrice *f*	фигуратриса
F 215	**figure**, cypher, cipher <of a number system> <NT>	Ziffer *f*, Grundziffer *f*	chiffre *m*	цифра
F 216	**figure**, numeral, number symbol <for natural numbers> <NT>	Zahlzeichen *n*, Zahlsymbol *n*, Ziffer *f*, Symbol *n*	symbole *m* numérique, signe *m* <d'un nombre>, nombre *m*, signe (caractère) *m* numéral, signe (caractère) numérique	числовой символ, цифра
F 217	**figure 8 [curve]**, eight curve <GE>	Achterkurve *f*, Acht *f*	figure *f* 8	восьмерка
F 218	**figure in perspective**, homothetic figure, radially related figure <GE>	ähnliche und ähnlich liegende (gelegene) Figur *f*, perspektivähnliche Figur, ähnliche und perspektive Figur, ähnliche und perspektiv ähnliche Figur, zentrisch ähnliche Figur, perspektiv liegende ähnliche Figur, homothetische Figur, ähnlich liegende (gelegene) Figur	figure *f* homothétique (semblable et semblablement située, semblablement située)	гомотетическая фигура, подобная [и подобно расположенная] фигура
F 219	**figure of equal area** <in the plane> <EG>	Figur *f* gleichen Flächeninhalts, flächengleiche Figur, inhaltsgleiche Figur	figure *f* équivalente	равновеликая фигура, фигура равной площади
	figure of equal volume <EG>	*s.* S 1252		
F 220	**figure of inclusion**, inference figure, syllogism <LO>	Schlußfigur *f*	figure *f* de dérivation	фигура умозаключения
F 221	**figure of intersection**, intersection figure <DS>	Durchdringungsfigur *f*	figure *f* d'intersection	фигура пересечения
F 222	**figures centrally symmetric to each other** <EG>	zentralsymmetrische Figuren *fpl*	figures *fpl* mutuellement centro-symétriques	взаимно центрально-симметричные фигуры
	figures in central perspective (projection) <DS, PJ>	*s.* P 515		
	figuring out <GN>	*s.* C 13		
	fill embankment <DS>	*s.* E 196		
F 223	**filter**, Bourbaki['s] filter <in a set> <SE>	Filter *m*, Bourbaki-Filter *m* <in (auf) einer Menge>	filtre *m*, filtre de Bourbaki <sur un ensemble>	фильтр, фильтр Бурбаки, центрированная система множеств <в множестве>
	filter <AL, SE, TO>	*s.* P 1786		
	filter <LA>	*s.* D 995		
F 224	**filter base**, base, raster <SE>	Filterbasis *f*, Raster *m*, Filter *m*	base *f* de filtre, base	базис фильтра, растр
F 225	**filtered category** <CA>	filtrierende Kategorie *f*	catégorie *f* filtrante	фильтрующаяся категория
F 226	**filtered colimit** <CA>	filtrierender Kolimes *m*	colimite *f* filtrante	фильтрующийся индуктивный предел
F 227	**filtered degree** <AL>	Filtergrad *m*	degré *m* filtrant	фильтрующая степень
F 228	**filtered group** <GR>	gefilterte Gruppe *f*, Gruppe mit Filtration	groupe *m* filtré	группа с фильтрацией
F 229	**filtered Lie algebra** <AL>	filtrierte (gefilterte) Liesche Algebra *f*	algèbre *f* de Lie filtrée	фильтрованная алгебра Ли
F 230	**filtered limit** <CA>	filtrierender Limes *m*	limite *f* filtrante	фильтрующийся проективный предел
F 231	**filtered ring** <AL>	filtrierter (gefilterter) Ring *m*	anneau *m* filtré	фильтрованное кольцо, кольцо с фильтрацией, профильтрованное кольцо; кольцо, на которое задана положительная фильтрация
	filtered set <SE>	*s.* 1. D 552; 2. Q 140		
F 232	**filter having a base of open sets** <TO>	offener Filter *m*	filtre *m* ayant une base d'ensembles ouverts	фильтр, обладающий базисом открытых множеств
	filtering <AL>	*s.* F 234		
F 233	**filter of sets** <SE>	Mengenfilter *m*	filtre *m* d'ensembles	фильтр множеств
	filtrant pre-ordered set <SE>	*s.* Q 140		
F 234	**filtration**, filtering <AL>	Filtration *f*	filtration *f*	фильтрация, задание фильтрации
	filtration <AL>	*s.* I 286		
	filtration convergent above <AL>	*s.* E 692		
	final decision <ST>	*s.* T 167		
F 235	**final element** <AT>	Endelement *n*	élément *m* final	концевой элемент
F 236	**final functor** <CA>	finaler Funktor *m*	foncteur *m* final	финальный функтор
F 237	**finally monotone (monotonic) sequence** <SS> ⌐<AL>	schließlich monotone Folge *f*	suite *f* finalement monotone	окончательно монотонная последовательность
F 238	**final rank** <of a *p*-group>	finaler Rang *m*	rang *m* final	финальный ранг
	final segment <SE>	*s.* R 789		
F 239	**final state** <PG>	Endzustand *m*	état *m* final	конечное состояние
F 240	**final topology** <FA, TO>	Finaltopologie *f*	topologie *f* finale	финальная топология
	finding of the root <AL, AR>	*s.* T 29		

F 241	**find the value of an indeterminate form / to** <DI>	einem unbestimmten Ausdruck einen Wert beilegen	lever l'indétermination	раскрывать неопределенность
F 242	**fine convergence-divergence theory for the Lagrange interpolation** <AX>	feine Interpolationstheorie *f*	théorie *f* de convergence-divergence fine de l'interpolation de Lagrange	тонкая теория сходимости-расходимости интерполяции Лагранжа
F 243	**fineness** <of a decomposition> <FA>	Feinheitsmaß *n*, Feinheit *f*	finesse *f*	мелкость
F 244	**finer covering** <TO>	feinere Überdeckung *f*	recouvrement *m* plus fin, recouvrement subordonné	более мелкое покрытие
F 245	**fine resolution** <of a sheaf> <AT>	feine Auflösung *f*	résolution *f* fine	тонкая резольвента
F 246	**finer partition** <of a set> <SE>	feinere Zerlegung *f*	partition *f* plus fine, sous-partition *f*	более мелкое разбиение
F 247	**finer topology,** larger topology, weaker topology, <*in some cases also:*> stronger topology <TO>	feinere (majorisierende, schwächere) Topologie *f*, <*manchmal auch:*> stärkere Topologie	topologie *f* plus fine (forte), topologie majorante	более тонкая (слабая) топология, мажорирующая топология, <*в некоторых случаях также:*> более сильная топология
F 248	**finer uniform structure** <TO>	feinere uniforme Struktur *f*	structure *f* uniforme plus fine	мажорирующая равномерная структура
F 249	**fine sheaf** <AT>	feine Garbe *f*	faisceau *m* fin	тонкий пучок
F 250	**finest topological structure** <TO>	schwächste topologische Zuordnung *f*, feinste topologische Struktur *f*	structure *f* topologique la plus fine	слабейшая топологическая структура, <*также:*> сильнейшая из топологических структур
	finest topology <TO>	*s.* L 98		
F 251	**fine topology** <PO>	feine Topologie *f*, „topologie fine" *f*	topologie *f* fine	тонкая топология
F 252	**finitary method** <Hilbert>, finitistic method <MM>	finitäre (finitistische, finite) Methode *f*	méthode *f* finitiste, méthode finie	финитный метод
F 253	**finitary operation** <UA>	finitäre (endlichstellige) Operation *f*, finitäre (endlichstellige) algebraische Verknüpfung *f*	opération *f* d'une arité finie	конечноместная операция, финитарная операция
F 254	**finitary proof** <MM>	finiter Beweis *m*	épreuve (démonstration) *f* finie	финитное доказательство
F 255	**finitary proof theory,** finitistic proof theory <MM>	finitäre Beweistheorie *f*	théorie *f* finitiste de la démonstration	финитная теория доказательства
F 256	**finite algebra** <UA>	endliches algebraisches System *n*, endliche universelle Algebra *f*	algèbre *f* finie	конечная [алгебраическая] система
	finite assemblage <SE>	*s.* F 316		
F 257	**finite automaton** <TA>	endlicher Automat *m*	automate *m* fini, machine *f* séquentielle	конечный автомат
F 258	**finite base** <of an almost periodic function>; finite basis <of a group> <AP, GR>	endliche Basis *f*	base *f* finie	конечный базис
	finite base <AL>	*s.* F 259		
F 259	**finite basis,** finite base <of an ideal> <AL>	endliche Basis *f*	système *m* générateur fini, base *f* finie	конечная база, конечный базис
	finite basis <AP, GR>	*s.* F 258		
	finite basis condition <AL>	*s.* H 320		
F 260	**finite cardinal [number],** inductive cardinal (number) <SE>	endliche Kardinalzahl *f*, endliche (induktive) Mächtigkeit *f*	cardinal *m* fini	конечное кардинальное число
F 261	**finite constructibility** <MM> ⌐<NT>	endliche Konstruierbarkeit *f*	constructibilité *f* finie	конечная конструктивность
	finite continued fraction	*s.* T 176		
F 262	**finite cyclic group** <GR>	endliche zyklische Gruppe *f*	groupe *m* cyclique (monogène fini)	конечная циклическая группа
F 263	**finite definability** <MM>	endliche Definierbarkeit *f*	définissabilité *f* finie	конечная определимость
F 264	**finite derivative,** proper derivative <DI>	endliche (eigentliche) Ableitung *f*	dérivée *f* finie, dérivée propre[ment dite]	конечная (собственная) производная
F 265	**finite development** <NT>	endliche Entwicklung *f*	développement *m* limité (fini)	конечное разложение
F 266	**finite-difference approximation** <AX, NU> ⌐<DE, NU>	Differenzenapproximation *f*, Differenzennäherung *f*	approximation *f* par différences finies	разностное приближение, разностная аппроксимация
	finite-difference method	*s.* L 145		
	finite-difference method <NU>	*s.* D 438		
	finite difference operator <FD, NU>	*s.* D 436		
F 267	**finite-dimensional extension field,** finite extension field, finite extension <AL>	endliche Körpererweiterung *f*, endlicher Erweiterungskörper *m*, endlich-algebraische Körpererweiterung (Erweiterung *f*), endlich-algebraischer Oberkörper *m*	extension *f* finie, extension de degré fini, extension algébrique finie, corps *m* algébrique, corps fini	конечное расширение поля
F 268	**finite dimensionality** <GE>	Endlichdimensionalität *f*	propriété *f* d'être de dimension finie	конечномерность
F 269	**finite-dimensional vector space,** finitely generated vector space <AL>	endlichdimensionaler Vektorraum *m*	espace *m* vectoriel de dimension finie	конечномерное векторное (линейное) пространство

F 270	**finite discontinuity** <DI>	Unstetigkeit *f* im Endlichen	discontinuité *f* dans le fini	разрыв в конечности
	finite discrete principal order <AL>	*s.* K 172		
F 271	**finite-element method,** method of finite elements <AN, NU>	Methode *f* der finiten Elemente, Finit[e]-Elemente-Methode *f*, Elementenmethode *f*	méthode *f* des éléments finis	метод финитных (конечных) элементов
F 272	**finite equation** <DE, NU>	finite Gleichung *f*, endliche Gleichung	équation *f* finie	конечное (недифференциальное) уравнение
	finite extension [field] <AL>	*s.* F 267		
F 273	**finite extension of the constant field** <of an algebraic function field> <AL>	endlich-algebraische Konstantenerweiterung *f*	extension *f* finie du corps des constantes	конечное расширение поля констант
	finite field <AL>	*s.* G 14		
	finite field over *k* <AL>	*s.* E 799		
F 274	**finite fraction** <AR, NT>	endlicher [systematischer] Bruch *m*	fraction *f* [systématique] limitée	конечная систематическая дробь
F 275	**finite function** <RF>	endliche Funktion *f*	fonction *f* [numérique] finie	конечная [числовая] функция
	μ-finite function <ME>	*s.* M 945		
F 276	**finite group,** group of finite order <GR>	endliche Gruppe *f*, Gruppe [von] endlicher Ordnung	groupe *m* fini (d'ordre fini)	конечная группа, группа конечного порядка
	finite group <SE>	*s.* F 316		
	finite increment <DI>	*s.* I 292		
F 277	**finite induction** <LO>	endliche Induktion *f*	induction *f* finie	конечная индукция
F 278	**finite integral domain** <AL>	endlicher Integritätsbereich *m*, affiner Ring *m*	anneau *m* affine	аффинное кольцо
F 279	**finitely additive measure** <ME>	endlich additives Maß *n*	mesure *f* finiment (simplement) additive	конечно-аддитивная мера
	finitely additive measure	*s.* C 2157		
F 280	**finitely axiomatizable (axiomatized) theory** <MM>	endlich (finit) axiomatisierbare Theorie *f*	théorie *f* finiment axiomatisable	конечно аксиоматизируемая теория
F 281	**finitely cocomplete category** <CA>	endlich[-] kovollständige Kategorie *f*, endlich rechtsvollständige Kategorie	catégorie *f* finiment cocomplète	конечно полная справа категория
F 282	**finitely compact metric space** <TO>	finit kompakter metrischer Raum *m*	espace *m* métrique finiment compact	конечнокомпактное метрическое пространство
F 283	**finitely complete category** <CA>	endlich linksvollständige Kategorie *f*, endlich[-] vollständige Kategorie	catégorie *f* finiment complète	конечно полная слева категория
F 284	**finitely connected domain,** domain of finite connectivity <TO>	endlich zusammenhängendes Gebiet *n*	domaine *m* finiment connexe, domaine de connection finie	конечносвязная область
F 285	**finitely generated abelian group,** abelian group of finite type <GR>	abelsche A_5-Gruppe *f*, abelsche Gruppe mit endlich vielen Erzeugenden, endlich erzeugbare abelsche Gruppe	groupe *m* abélien de type fini	абелева A_5-группа, абелева группа с конечным числом образующих [элементов], конечно-порожденная абелева группа
F 286	**finitely generated algebra** <AL>	endlich erzeugte Algebra *f*	algèbre *f* de type fini	конечно порожденная алгебра, алгебра конечного типа
F 287	**finitely generated extension field** <AL>	endlich-erzeugbarer Erweiterungskörper *m*, endlich-erzeugbare Körpererweiterung *f*, endlich erzeugte Körpererweiterung, endlich erzeugter Oberkörper *m*, algebraische Körpererweiterung <im Sinne von Kähler>	extension *f* de type fini [d'un corps]	конечно порожденное расширение [поля]
F 288	**finetely generated group** <GR>	endlich erzeugte Gruppe *f*, Gruppe mit endlich vielen Erzeugenden, endlich erzeugbare Gruppe	groupe *m* à engendrement fini, groupe de type fini, groupe à nombre fini de générateurs	конечнопорожденная группа, группа с конечным числом образующих [элементов]
F 289	**finitely generated ideal** <AL>	endlich erzeugtes Ideal *n*, Ideal endlichen Typs	idéal *m* de type fini	идеал конечного типа, конечнопорожденный идеал
F 290	**finitely generated module,** module of finite type <AL>	endlich erzeugter Modul *m*, Modul endlichen Typs	module *m* de type fini	конечнопорожденный модуль, модуль конечного типа
F 291	**finitely generated *R*-module,** *R*-module of finite type <AL>	endlicher *R*-Modul *m*, endlich-erzeugbarer *R*-Modul, endlich erzeugter *R*-Modul	*R*-module *m* de type fini	конечнопорожденный *R*-модуль, *R*-модуль конечного типа
	finitely generated vector space <AL>	*s.* F 269		
F 292	**finitely many elements,** a finite number of elements <SE>	endlich viele Elemente *npl*	éléments *mpl* d'un nombre fini	элементы конечного числа (количества)
F 293	**finitely nonzero function** <AN>	finite Funktion *f*		финитная функция <формальная линейная комбинация конечного числа элементов>
F 294	**finitely presented group** <GR>	endlich definierbare Gruppe *f*, endlich darstellbare Gruppe	groupe *m* de présentation finie, groupe finiment présentable	конечноопределенная (конечнопредставимая) группа, конечно копредставленная (определенная) группа

F 295	**finitely presented module** <AL>	endlich darstellbarer Modul *m*	module *m* de présentation finie	конечно представимый модуль
	finitely valued function <AN, GN>	*s.* F 320		
F 296	**finite measure** <ME>	endliches Maß *n*, finites Maß	mesure *f* finie	конечная мера
F 297	**finite model** <ST>	endliches Modell *n*	modèle *m* fini	конечная модель
	finite model <ST>	*s.* 1. M 730; 2. R 103		
F 298	**finite multiplier,** finite population correction <ST>	Endlichkeitsfaktor *m*	correction *f* pour sondage dans une population finie	поправочный множитель на конечность совокупности
F 299	**finiteness** <MM>	Finitheit *f*	propriété *f* d'être fini	финитность, конечность
F 300	**finiteness / in** <GN>	im Endlichen	dans le fini	в конечности, в конечном
	finiteness in the sense of double-well-ordered <SE>	*s.* T 82		
F 301	**finiteness of the system of invariants** <IV>	Endlichkeit *f* der Invarianten, Endlichkeit des vollen Invariantensystems (Komitantensystems)	finitude *f* du système des invariants	конечность системы инвариантов
F 302	**finiteness principle (theorem)** <LO>	Endlichkeitssatz *m*	théorème *m* de finitude	теорема конечности
F 303	**finite nilpotent group** <GR>	endliche nilpotente Gruppe *f*	groupe *m* nilpotent fini	конечная нильпотентная группа, специальная группа
	finite normal separable extension <AL>	*s.* G 12		
F 304	**finite normal separable extension of the prime subfield,** absolutely Galois field <AL>	absolut-Galoisscher (absolutgaloisscher) Körper *m*, Galoisscher Körper in bezug auf den Primkörper	corps *m* absolument de Galois, corps absolument galoisien	абсолютно сепарабельное нормальное поле
	finite norm operator <FA>	*s.* H 357		
	finite number of elements / a <SE>	*s.* F 292		
F 305	**finite order-type,** finite type <SE>	endlicher Ordnungstypus *m*	type *m* d'ordre fini	конечный порядковый тип
F 306	**finite ordinal [number],** ordinal number of the first class, number of the first class <SE>	endliche Ordnungszahl (Ordinalzahl) *f*	ordinal *m* fini	конечное порядковое число
F 307	**finite part** <of a modulus> <AB>	endlicher Bestandteil *m*	partie *f* finie	конечная часть
F 308	**finite part,** Hadamard['s] finite part <of a divergent integral> <DE, DI>	endlicher Anteil *m*, Hadamardscher endlicher Anteil, endlicher Bestandteil *m*	partie *f* finie	конечная часть
F 309	**finite partition** <SE>	endliche Zerlegung *f*	partition *f* finie	конечное разбиение
	finite *p*-group <GR>	*s.* P 1332		
F 310	**finite plane,** open plane <FT>	offene [komplexe] Zahlenebene *f*	plan *m* complexe ouvert	открытая комплексная плоскость
	finite plane <FT>	*s.* A 937		
	finite population correction <ST>	*s.* F 298		
	finite pregeometry <CT>	*s.* M 224		
F 311	**finite presentation** <of a group> <GR>	endliche Präsentation *f*	présentation *f* finie	конечное копредставление
F 312	**finite prime [spot],** nonarchimedean prime, non-Archimedean prime spot <NT>	endliche (nichtarchimedische) Primstelle *f*, Primdivisor *m*	diviseur *m* premier fini	конечный простой дивизор
F 313	**finite progression** <AR>	endliche Progression *f*	progression *f* finie (limitée)	прогрессия с конечным числом членов
F 314	**finite-rowed matrix** <MD>	endlichzeilige (endlichreihige) Matrix *f*	matrice *f* d'un nombre fini des lignes	конечно[-]строчная матрица
F 315	**finite series** <SS>	abbrechende (endliche) Reihe *f*	série *f* limitée (finie)	обрывающийся ряд, конечный ряд
	finite series <SS>	*s.* F 319		
F 316	**finite set,** inductive set, // finite group, finite assemblage <SE>	endliche Menge *f*, // endliche Mannigfaltigkeit *f* <Dedekind>	ensemble *m* fini, collection *f* finie	конечное множество
F 317	**finite set algebra** <SE>	endliche Mengenalgebra *f*	algèbre *f* finie (simple)	конечная алгебра множеств
	finite set in the sense of Tarski <SE>	*s.* T 83		
F 318	**finite-sheeted surface** <TO>	endlichblättrige Fläche *f*, endlich vielblättrige Fläche	surface *f* d'un nombre fini de feuillets	конечнолистная поверхность
F 319	**finite sum,** finite series <SS>	endliche Summe *f*	somme *f* finie, série *f* finie	конечная сумма
	finite trigonometric sum <AN>	*s.* T 946		
	finite type <SE>	*s.* F 305		
	finite type II algebra <FA> ⌐<FA>	*s.* W 8		
	finite type II *W-algebra**	*s.* W 8		
F 320	**finite-valued function,** finitely valued function <AN, GN>	endlichwertige Funktion *f*	fonction *f* à valeurs finies	конечнозначная функция
	finite variation <RF>	*s.* B 688/9		
F 321	**finitism** <FO>	Finitismus *m*; Hilbertscher Finitismus	finitisme *m*	финитизм; финитизм Гильберта
F 322	**finitist deduction** <MM>	finites Schließen *n*	déduction *f* finie	финитный вывод
	finitistic method <MM>	*s.* F 252		
	finitistic proof theory <MM>	*s.* F 255		

	English	German	French	Russian
F 323	**finitist point of view** <MM>	finiter Standpunkt *m*	point *m* de vue finitiste	финитная точка зрения
	Finslerian space <DG>	*s.* F 326		
	Finsler['s] manifold <DG>	*s.* F 326		
F 324	**Finsler['s] metric,** Finsler['s] quasimetric <DG>	Finslersche Metrik (Quasimetrik, Ersatzmetrik) *f*	métrique (quasimétrique) *f* de Finsler, métrique (quasimétrique) finslérienne	метрика (квазиметрика) Финслера
F 325	**Finsler['s] operation** <SE>	Finslersche Operation *f*	opération *f* de Finsler	операция Финслера
	Finsler['s] quasimetric <DG>	*s.* F 324		
F 326	**Finsler['s] space (variety),** Finslerian space, Finsler['s] manifold <DG>	Finslerscher Raum *m*, Finslersche Mannigfaltigkeit *f*, Finsler-Raum *m*	espace *m* de Finsler, espace finslérien, variété *f* finslérienne (de Finsler)	пространство (многообразие) Финслера, финслерово пространство
	fir <AL>	*s.* F 617		
	2-fir ring <AL>	*s.* G 102		
	first adjoint <FA, TO>	*s.* A 307		
F 327	**first and last term** <of a progression> <AR>	erstes und letztes Glied *n* <einer Progression>	extrêmes *mpl* <d'une progression>	первый и *n*-й члены <прогрессии>
F 328	**first axiom of countability,** first countability axiom <TO>	erstes Abzählbarkeitsaxiom *n*	premier axiome *m* de dénombrabilité [de Hausdorff]	первая аксиома счетности
	first Betti number <GP>	*s.* C 2891		
	first boundary condition <DE, PO>	*s.* D 613		
	first boundary [value] problem <DE, PO>	*s.* D 629		
	first canonical form <MD>	*s.* J 99		
	first characteristic function <AL>	*s.* C 551		
F 329	**first characteristic polynomial** <of a matrix> <MD>	erstes charakteristisches Polynom *n*	premier polynôme *m* caractéristique	первый характеристический многочлен
F 330	**first class,** first number-class <SE>	erste Zahlklasse (Zahlenklasse) *f*, erste ordinale (kardinale) Zahlklasse	première classe *f* <de nombres>	первый числовой класс
F 331	**first Clavius law,** Clavius['] law <LO>	Theorem *n* der falschen Annahme, Theorem der Selbstbestätigung, Schluß *m* ex contrario	loi *f* de rétorsion, [première] loi *f* de Clavius, consequentia *f* mirabilis	удивительное следование, consequentia mirabilis
F 332	**first comparison test,** comparison test of the first kind <for convergence> <SS>	Vergleichskriterium (Konvergenzkriterium, Kriterium) *n* erster (1.) Art, allgemeines Vergleichskriterium erster (1.) Art	règle *f* (critère *m*, théorème *m*) [de convergence] de première espèce, règle de comparaison directe, comparaison *f* directe	признак (критерий) сравнения первого рода, сравнительный признак (критерий) первого рода
F 333	**first component** <of a conjunction, disjunction, etc.> <LO>	Vorderglied *n*	première composante *f*	предыдущий член
	first component <LO>	*s.* A 695		
	first conjugate <FA, TO>	*s.* A 307		
F 334	**first co-ordinate,** first term <*a* is the first term, *b* the second term> <of an ordered pair> <SE>	erstes Element *n*, erstes Glied *n* <*a* ist erstes Glied, *b* zweites Glied>	première coordonnée *f*, abscisse *f*, première projection *f* <*a* avant *b*, *b* après *a*, *a* est le précédent de *b*, *b* est le suivant de *a*, *a* est antérieur à *b*, *b* est postérieur à *a*, *a* est inférieur à *b*, *b* est supérieur à *a*, *a* est plus petit que *b*, *b* est plus grand que *a*>	первая координата, первая проекция, абсцисса, первый элемент <*a* есть первый элемент, *b* второй элемент>
	first countability axiom <TO>	*s.* F 328		
F 335	**first countable metrizable space** <TO>	metrisierbarer Raum *m*, der dem ersten Abzählbarkeitsaxiom genügt	espace *m* métrisable de type dénombrable	метризуемое пространство, удовлетворяющее первой аксиоме счетности
F 336	**first countable [topological] space,** topological space satisfying the first axiom of countability <TO>	Raum *m*, der dem ersten Abzählbarkeitsaxiom genügt	espace *m* à caractère dénombrable	пространство с первой аксиомой счетности; пространство, удовлетворяющее первой аксиоме счетности; пространство со счетной локальной базой [в каждой точке]; пространство, в котором каждая точка обладает счетной фундаментальной системой окрестностей
	first Cousin problem <FT>	*s.* C 2594		
	first curvature <DG>	*s.* 1. C 2766; 2. M 302		
	first differential parameter of Lamé <DG>	*s.* L 55		
	first element <SE>	*s.* S 1219		
	first equation of Kolmogorov <SP>	*s.* K 117a		
F 337	**first fundamental form,** metric form <in Euclidean surface theory> <DG>	erste (I.) Grundform (Fundamentalform) *f*, erste (I.) Gaußsche Fundamentalform, metrische Grundform (Fundamentalform)	première forme *f* fondamentale, forme métrique	первая основвая [квадратичная] форма, первая дифференциальная форма Гаусса, метрическая форма
	first homotopy group <AT>	*s.* F 824		
F 338/9	**first integral** <DE>	erstes Integral *n*, Vorintegral *n*	intégrale *f* première	первый интеграл
	first isomorphism theorem <CA>	*s.* F 343		
	first isomorphism theorem <GR>	*s.* H 505		

No.	English	Deutsch	Français	Русский
F 340	**first law for powers** <AR>	Distributionsformeln *fpl* bei gleichem Exponenten <ein Potenzgesetz>	formules *fpl* de distribution pour des bases différentes	формулы $(ab)^n = a^n b^n$ и $(a:b)^n = a^n : b^n$
F 341	**first law of isomorphism,** parallelogram law, Noether['s] (second, diamond) isomorphism theorem <GR>	erster (1.) Isomorphiesatz *m*, Dedekind-Noetherscher Isomorphiesatz	théorème *m* d'isomorphie, principe *m* de réduction de Hasse	теорема Нетера об изоморфизме, теорема об изоморфизме
	first law of transposition <LO>	*s.* L 215		
F 342	**first Lemoine circle** <of a triangle> <EG>	erster Lemoinescher Kreis *m*	premier cercle *m* de Lemoine, cercle *m* triplicateur	первая окружность Лемуана
	first mean value theorem <DI>	*s.* M 327		
	first member <GN>	*s.* L 383		
	first member <SE>	*s.* S 1219		
F 343	**first Noether isomorphism theorem,** first isomorphism theorem <CA>	erster Isomorphiesatz *m*	premier théorème *m* d'isomorphie	первая теорема об изоморфизмах
	first normal <DG>	*s.* P 1449		
	first normal [unit] vector <DG>	*s.* P 1455		
	first number-class <SE>	*s.* F 330		
F 344	**first obstruction,** primary obstruction <AT>	erstes Hindernis *n*	première classe *f* obstruction	первое препятствие
	first octant <AY>	*s.* O 48		
	first-order calculus <LO>	*s.* 1. F 347; 2. F 349		
	first-order calculus with identity <LO>	*s.* F 348		
	first-order Cartesian tensor <VT>	*s.* V 92		
	first-order component <ST>	*s.* L 778		
	first-order first-class congruence of lines <DG, PJ>	*s.* N 166		
F 345	**first-order formula,** first-order sentence form, sentential formula in the functional calculus of the first order <LO>	einstufiger Ausdruck *m*, Ausdruck erster Stufe, Formel *f* des Prädikatenkalküls erster Stufe	formule *f* de premier niveau	формула первого порядка, формула исчисления предикатов первого порядка
	first-order functional calculus <LO>	*s.* 1. F 347; 2. F 349		
	first-order functional calculus with identity <LO>	*s.* F 348		
F 346	**first-order language** <MM>	Sprache *f* erster (der ersten) Stufe	langage *m* du premier ordre	язык первой (1-й) ступени, язык первого (1-го) порядка
F 347	**first-order logic,** elementary logic of predicates, elementary [predicate] logic, first-order [predicate] calculus, first-order functional calculus, lower predicate calculus, logic of first order, quantification theory <LO>	Prädikatenkalkül *m* erster (der ersten) Stufe, Prädikatenlogik *f* erster Stufe, Quantorenlogik *f* der ersten Stufe, engere Quantorenlogik, Prädikatenlogik *f* der ersten Stufe, engerer Prädikatenkalkül *m*	calcul *m* logique du premier échelon, calcul des prédicats du premier ordre, logique *f* fonctionnelle restreinte, logique élémentaire, logique du premier ordre	исчисление предикатов первого порядка, логика предикатов первого порядка, исчисление предикатов первой ступени, узкое исчисление предикатов, элементарная логика
F 348	**first-order logic with identity,** first-order functional calculus with identity, first-order [predicate] calculus with identity, elementary logic with identity (equality), system of logic with identity, functional calculus of first order with equality <LO>	Prädikatenkalkül *m* erster (der ersten) Stufe mit Identität, erweiterter Prädikatenkalkül der ersten Stufe, Prädikatenkalkül mit Identität, I-Kalkül *m*	calcul *m* logique du premier échelon, calcul des prédicats élargi, logique *f* de l'identité, calcul des prédicats du premier ordre avec constante d'égalité	расширенное исчисление предикатов
F 349	**first-order logic without identity,** functional calculus of the first order, first-order functional calculus, first-order [predicate] calculus, restricted functional (predicate) calculus, predicate logic, elementary logic without identity <LO>	Prädikatenkalkül *m* erster Stufe, engerer Prädikatenkalkül erster (der ersten) Stufe, engerer Prädikatenkalkül, Prädikatenkalkül der ersten Stufe ohne Identität, engerer Funktionenkalkül *m*, Prädikatenlogik *f*	calcul *m* des prédicats restreint, logique *f* du premier ordre sans égalité	исчисление предикатов первого порядка без равенства, узкое исчисление предикатов [без равенства]
	first-order pole <FT>	*s.* P 907		
	first-order predicate calculus <LO>	*s.* 1. F 347; 2. F 349		
	first-order predicate calculus with identity <LO>	*s.* F 348		
	first-order sentence form <LO>	*s.* F 345		
	first-order tensor <VT>	*s.* V 92		
F 350	**first-order theory** <LO>	Theorie *f* erster Stufe	théorie *f* du premier ordre	теория первого порядка, элементарная теория
	first plane [of projection] <DS>	*s.* H 566		

	English	German	French	Russian
	first principal line <DS>	*s.* H 172		
	first principal plane <DS>	*s.* H 173		
	first problem <DE, PO>	*s.* D 629		
	first projection <DS>	*s.* P 628		
F 351	**first quadrant,** quadrant I <AY>	Hauptquadrant *m*, erster Quadrant *m*, Quadrant I	premier quadrant *m*, quadrant I	первый квадрант, квадрант I
	first quartile <ST>	*s.* L 1158		
	first regular [matrix] representation <AL>	*s.* R 1249		
	first rule of transposition <LO>	*s.* R 1517		
	first shifting theorem <IT>	*s.* F 652		
	first system <SP>	*s.* K 117a		
F 352	**first term** <of a binary operation> <AL>	aktive Zahl *f*	nombre (terme) *m* actif, premier terme *m*	первый член
F 353	**first term,** initial term <US> <of a progression> <AR>	erstes Glied *n*, Anfangsglied *n*, Anfangszahl *f*	premier terme *m*, base *f*, nombre *m* primordial	первый член
F 354	**first term** <of a relation> <LO>	erstes Glied *n*	prédécesseur *m*	первый элемент
F 355	**first term** <of a continued fraction> <NT>	Anfangsglied *n*	premier terme *m*, terme *m* initial, membre *m* premier	первый элемент
F 356	**first term,** initial term <of an infinite product, sequence *or* series> <SS>	Anfangsglied *n*, erstes Glied *n*	premier terme *m*, terme *m* initial, membre *m* premier	первый член
	first term <AL, AR, SE>	*s.* A 1204		
	first term <SE>	*s.* F 334		
F 357	**first test for convergence** <of a sequence *or* series of positive numbers> <SS>	erstes (1.) Hauptkriterium *n*, erstes (1.) fundamentales Kriterium (Konvergenzkriterium) *n*	premier critère (test) *m* de convergence	первый признак сходимости
F 358	**first theorem of the mean** <for integrals> <DI>	erster Mittelwertsatz *m* [der Integralrechnung], Mittelwertsatz der Integralrechnung	première formule *f* de la moyenne, [premier] théorème *m* de la moyenne <du calcul intégral>	первая теорема о среднем, [первая] теорема о среднем интегрального исчисления
F 359	**first trace,** first trace point <of a line> <DS>	erster Spurpunkt *m*, erste Spur *f*	première trace *f*, premier point *m* trace	первый (горизонтальный) след <прямой>, след в горизонтальной плоскости <проекций>
F 360	**first trace [line],** horizontal trace [line] <of a plane> <DS>	erste Spurlinie (Spur) *f*, horizontale Spurlinie (Spur)	trace *f* horizontale, première trace	горизонтальный след <плоскости>, след в горизонтальной плоскости <проекций>
	first trace parallel <DS>	*s.* H 172		
	first trace point <DS>	*s.* F 359		
F 361	**Fischer-Riesz theorem,** Riesz-Fischer theorem <FA>	Fischer-Rieszscher Satz *m*, Riesz-Fischerscher Satz, Satz von Riesz-Fischer	théorème *m* de Riesz-Fischer	теорема Риса-Фишера
	Fisher-Behrens test <ST>	*s.* B 168		
	Fisher['s] distribution <ST>	*s.* F 109		
	Fisher['s] exact probability test <ST>	*s.* F 364		
	Fisher['s] *F*-distribution <ST>	*s.* F 109		
F 361a	**Fisher['s] information,** intrinsic accuracy <ST>	Fishersche Information *f*	information *f* de Fisher	информация по Фишеру, внутренняя точность
	Fisher['s] omnibus test <ST>	*s.* O 73		
	Fisher-Pitman test <ST>	*s.* P 492		
F 362	**Fisher['s] summation method** <ST>	Fishersches Summationsverfahren *n*	méthode *f* de sommation de Fisher	метод суммирования Фишера
	Fisher['s] test for independence <ST>	*s.* F 364		
	Fisher['s] test of linearity <ST>	*s.* T 213		
F 363	**Fisher['s] theorem** <ST>	Satz *m* von Fisher, Fisherscher Satz	théorème *m* de Fisher	теорема Фишера
	Fisher['s] transformation <ST>	*s.* Z 88		
F 364	**Fisher-Yates test,** Fisher['s] exact probability test, exact χ^2-test (chi-square test), Fisher['s] test for independence <ST>	Fisher-Yates-Test *m*, Fishers exakter Unabhängigkeitstest *m*, Fishers Wahrscheinlichkeitstest *m*, Fishers[cher] Test *m*, exakter Test von R. A. Fisher	test *m* de Fisher-Yates, test exact d'indépendance de Fisher, test exact de Fisher, test de probabilité de Fisher	критерий Фишера-Йейтса, точный критерий независимости Фишера, [точный вероятностный] критерий Фишера
	Fisher['s] z-distribution <ST>	*s.* Z 11		
	Fisher['s] *Z*-statistic <ST>	*s.* Z 86		
	Fisher['s] z-transformation <ST>	*s.* Z 88		
	fit <ER, ST>	*s.* F 368		
F 365	**fitted curve** <ER, NU>	ausgleichende Kurve *f*, Ausgleichskurve *f*	courbe *f* de lissage	выравнивающая кривая
F 366	**fitted function** <NU>	Ausgleichsfunktion *f*	fonction *f* de lissage	выравнивающая функция
F 367	**fitted line** <ER, NU>	ausgleichende Gerade *f*, Ausgleichsgerade *f*	droite *f* d'ajustement, droite de lissage	прямая выравнивания
F 368	**fitting,** fit <of observations> <ER, ST>	Ausgleichung *f*, Ausgleich *m*	ajustement *m*, lissage *m*	выравнивание

No.	English	German	French	Russian
F 369	**fitting** <of curves *or* functions> <NU, ST>	Fitten *n*, Anpassen *n*, Anpassung *f*	lissage *m* de points, ajustement *m*	вычерчивание (пригонка) по точкам, подгонка, выравнивание
F 370	**Fitting['s] decomposition** <of Lie algebras> <AL>	Fittingsche Zerlegung *f*	décomposition *f* de Fitting	разложение Фиттинга
F 371	**Fitting['s] group** <AL>	Fittingsche Gruppe *f*	groupe *m* de Fitting	группа Фиттинга
	Fitting['s] height <AL>	*s.* N 243		
F 372	**fitting parabola** <NU>	Ausgleichsparabel *f*, ausgleichende Parabel *f*	parabole *f* de lissage	парабола выравнивания
F 373	**Fitting['s] radical,** upper nilradical (radical) <of a ring> <AL>	Fittingsches (verallgemeinertes, oberes) Radikal *n*	radical *m* supérieur	радикал Фиттинга, верхний радикал
F 374	**Fitting['s] subgroup,** maximal normal nilpotent subgroup <of a group> <GR>	Fitting-Gruppe *f*, Fittinggruppe *f*, maximaler nilpotenter Normalteiler *m*	sous-groupe *m* nilpotent invariant maximal	максимальный нильпотентный нормальный делитель
	fitting with a handle of the first kind <AT>	*s.* I 53		
	fitting with a handle of the second kind <AT>	*s.* I 54		
F 375	**five-colour theorem** <GP>	Fünffarbensatz *m*	théorème *m* des cinq couleurs	теорема о пяти красках
F 376	**five-digit number, five-figure-number (decimal),** five-place decimal <NT>	fünfstellige Zahl *f*	nombre *m* [décimal] de cinq chiffres	пятиразрядное число
F 377	**five lemma** <CA, HA>	Fünferlemma *n*	lemme *m* des cinq	лемма о пяти морфизмах; лемма о пяти гомоморфизмах
	five-place decimal <NT>	*s.* F 376		
F 378	**five-place relation,** pentadic relation <LO>	fünfstellige Relation *f*	relation *f* pentadique	пятизначное отношение
F 379	**five-points problem** <PJ>	Fünfpunktaufgabe *f*, Problem *n* der fünf Punkte <Steiner>	problème *m* des cinq points	задача пяти точек
F 380	**five Sylvester planes** <of a cubic surface> <GE>	Sylvestersches (Sylvesters) Pentaeder *n*, Pentaeder [von Sylvester]	pentaèdre *m*	пентаэдр Сильвестра
F 381	**fixed block** <of a permutation group> <AL, GR>	Festblock *m*	sous-ensemble *m* invariant	инвариантное подмножество
	fixed effects model <ST>	*s.* M 730		
	fixed element <GE>	*s.* I 865		
	fixed element <PJ>	*s.* D 912		
	fixed error <ST>	*s.* B 269		
F 382	**fixed field** <in Galois theory> <AL>	Invariantenkörper *m*, Invarianzkörper *m*	corps *m* des invariants, corps fixe	поле инвариантов, неподвижное поле
	fixed line <PJ>	*s.* D 925		
	fixed model <ST>	*s.* M 730		
	fixed path <GE>	*s.* B 94		
	fixed plane <PJ>	*s.* D 933		
F 383	**fixed point,** invariant point, fixed-point <of a mapping> <TO>	Fixpunkt *m*, Koinzidenzpunkt *m*	point *m* fixe (invariant)	неподвижная (инвариантная) точка
	fixed point <AY, PJ>	*s.* D 935		
F 384	**fixed point calculation** <NU>	Festkommarechnung *f*	calcul *m* en virgule fixe	вычисление с фиксированной запятой
F 385	**fixed point formula** <AT>	Fixpunktformel *f*	formule *f* des points fixes	формула о неподвижной точке
F 386	**fixed point formula for correspondences,** Cayley-Brill formula, Chasles-Cayley-Brill [correspondence] formula, formula of Cayley-Brill <AG>	Koinzidenzformel *f*, Koinzidenzgleichung *f*; Cayley-Brillsches Korrespondenzprinzip *n*	formule (équation) *f* de coïncidence	формула Кэли-Брилля
	fixed point formula of Lefschetz <AT>	*s.* L 282		
	fixed-point-free homeomorphism <TO>	*s.* H 424		
F 387	**fixed point method** <DE>	Fixpunktmethode *f*	technique (méthode) *f* du point fixe	метод неподвижной точки
F 388	**fixed point property** <of a space> <TO>	Fixpunkteigenschaft *f*	propriété *f* du point fixe	свойство неподвижных точек
F 389	**fixed-point theorem, fixed point theorem** <TO>	Fixpunktsatz *m*, Fixpunktprinzip *n*	théorème *m* de points fixes, principe *m* de point fixe	принцип неподвижной точки, теорема о неподвижной точке
	fixed-point theorem of Borsuk <TO>	*s.* B 617		
	fixed-point theorem of Lefschetz <AT>	*s.* L 283		
F 390	**fixed sample** <ST>	feste Stichprobe *f*	échantillon *m* permanent	фиксированная выборка
F 391	**fixed simplex** <AT>	Fixsimplex *n*	simplexe *m* invariant	неподвижный симплекс
	fixed singularity <DE>	*s.* N 420		
	fixed vector <VT>	*s.* B 700		
F 392	***FK*-space,** Fréchet['s] coordinate space, Fréchet['s] sequence space <FA, TO>	*FK*-Raum *m*, Fréchetscher Koordinatenraum (Folgenraum) *m*	espace *m* [de type] *FK*, espace des coordonnées (suites) de Fréchet	координатное пространство Фреше, пространство последовательностей Фреше, пространство типа *FK*, *FK*-пространство
F 393	**flabbiness** <of a sheaf> <AT>	Welkheit *f*	flasquitude *f*	вялость
F 394	**flabby category** <CA>	welke Kategorie *f*	catégorie *f* flasque	вялая категория

No.	English	German	French	Russian
F 395	**flabby resolution** <of sheafs> <AL, TO>	welke Auflösung *f*	résolution *f* flasque, résolution *f* par des faisceaux flasques	вялая резольвента; резольвента пучка, состоящая из вялых пучков
F 396	**flabby sheaf,** welk sheaf <AT>	welke Garbe *f*	faisceau *m* flasque	вялый пучок
F 397	**flag** <GE>	Fahne *f*, Flagge *f*	drapeau *m*	флаг
F 398	**flag complex** <AL>	Titsscher Komplex *m*	complexe *m* de Tits	комплекс Титса
	flag manifold <DG>	*s.* M 64		
F 399	**flat** <in a vector space> <AL>	Lösungsmenge *f* eines inhomogenen linearen Gleichungssystems	ensemble *m* des solutions d'un système inhomogène d'équations linéaires	множество решений неоднородной системы линейных уравнений
	flat angle <EG>	*s.* S 1832		
	flat distribution <ST>	*s.* P 662		
F 400	**flat extension** <AL>	flache Erweiterung *f*	extension *f* plate	плоское расширение
F 401	**flat morphism** <AL>	flacher Morphismus *m*	morphisme *m* plat	плоский морфизм
F 402	**flatness** <of a module> <AL>	Flachheit *f*	platitude *f*	плоскость
	flatness <ST>	*s.* P 663		
F 403	**flat point,** planar point <of a surface> <DG>	Flachpunkt *m*	point *m* planaire	точка уплощения
F 404	**flat sheaf** <AT>	flache Garbe *f*	faisceau *m* plat	плоский пучок
F 405	**flat space** <AL>	flacher Raum *m*	espace *m* plat	плоское пространство
F 406	**flecflecnode** <of an algebraic curve> <AG>	Doppelinflexionsknoten *m*	nœud *m* d'inflexion double	двойная точка кривой, являющаяся для обеих ветвей точкой перегиба
F 407	**flecnode** <of a curve> <AG, DG>	Wendeknoten *m*, Fleknodalpunkt *m*, Inflexionsknoten *m*	point *m* flecnodal	флекнодальная точка
F 408	**flecnode curve** <of a surface> <DG>	Wendeknotenkurve *f*, Fleknodalkurve *f*	courbe *f* flecnodale	флекнодальная кривая; двойная точка кривой, являющаяся для одной из ветвей точкой перегиба
F 409	**flecnode surface** <of a surface> <DG>	Fleknodalfläche *f*	surface *f* flecnodale	флекнодальная поверхность
F 410	**flecnode tangent** <of a surface> <DG>	Fleknodaltangente *f*, Ruhtangente *f*	tangente *f* flecnodale	флекнодальная касательная, касательная в флекнодальной точке, «застойная» касательная
F 411	**Fletcher-Powell descent method for minimization** <PG>	Fletcher-Powellsches Verfahren *n*	méthode *f* de Fletcher et Powell	метод Флетчера-Поуэлла
	flex <DG, DI>	*s.* P 767		
F 412	**flexible ring** <AL>	flexibler Ring *m*	anneau *m* flexible	эластичное кольцо
	flex point <DG, DI>	*s.* P 767		
	flex tangent <DG>	*s.* I 503		
F 413	**floating point calculation** <NU>	Gleitkommarechnung *f*	calcul *m* en virgule flottante	вычисление с плавающей запятой
F 414	**floating-point notation (representation),** semilogarithmic representation <of a number> <NT, NU>	Darstellung *f* im Gleitkomma (beweglichen Komma), Darstellung mit gleitendem Komma, Gleitkommadarstellung *f*, halblogarithmische Zahlendarstellung *f* (Darstellung)	représentation *f* en (à) virgule flottante, notation *f* en (à) virgule flottante, représentation (notation) semilogarithmique	представление [чисел] в системе (виде) с плавающей запятой, полулогарифмическое представление
F 415	**flock [of Prüfer],** imperfect brigade, abstract coset <AL>	Schar *f*, Prüfersche Schar, unvollständige Brigade *f*, abstrakte Nebengruppe *f*	brigade *f* imparfaite	груда
	flooring <NU>	*s.* R 1420		
F 416	**Floquet['s] solution** <DE>	Floquetsche Lösung *f*	solution *f* de Floquet	решение Флоке
F 417	**Floquet['s] theorem** <DE>	Satz *m* von Floquet, Floquetscher Satz, Theorem *n* von Floquet, Floquetsches Theorem	théorème *m* de Floquet	теорема Флоке
F 418	**Floquet['s] theory** <DE>	Floquetsche Theorie *f*, Theorie von Floquet	théorie *f* de Floquet	теория Флоке
F 419	**flow** <GP>	Fluß *m*, Strom *m*	flot *m*	поток
F 420	**flow** <ME, SP>	Strömung *f*	courant *m*, écoulement *m*	поток
F 421	**flow line,** stream[-] line <ME, SP>	Stromlinie *f*	ligne *f* de courant	линия потока
F 422	**flow problem** <PG>	Flußproblem *n*	problème *m* du flot	задача о потоке
F 423	**flow ratio** <of a cycle> <GP>	Flußverhältnis *n*	rapport *m* de flux	потоковое отношение, отношение потоков
	FL-ring <AL>	*s.* F 717		
	fluctuation <RF>	*s.* O 508		
	fluctuation <ST>	*s.* S 1606		
F 424	**flux,** flux of the vector, vector flux, vectorial flux <through a surface> <VT>	Fluß *m* des Vektorfelds (Vektors), Vektorfluß *m*, Fluß	flux *m* du vecteur, flux vectoriel, flux	поток векторного поля, поток [вектора]
	fluxion <DI>	*s.* D 273		
F 425	**flux of the tensor,** tensor (tensorial) flux <through a surface> <VT>	Fluß *m* des Tensorfeldes (Tensors), Tensorfluß *m*	flux *m* du tenseur, flux tensoriel	поток тензорного поля, поток тензора
	flux of the vector <VT>	*s.* F 424		
	***F*-negligible module** <AL>	*s.* F 687		
F 426	**focal axis** <of a quadric> <AY>	Fokalachse *f*	axe *m* focal	фокальная ось
	focal chord <AY>	*s.* L 157		

F 427	**focal circle** <of a cubic> <AG>	Fokalkreis *m*	cercle *m* focal	фокальная окружность
F 428	**focal conic** <of a quadric> <AY>	Fokalkegelschnitt *m*, Brennlinie *f*	focale *f*, conique *f* focale	фокальное коническое сечение
F 429	**focal cubic** <AG>	fokale Kubik *f*	cubique *f* focale	фокальная кубическая кривая
F 430	**focal developable** <AY>	Fokaldeveloppable *f*	développable *f* focale	фокальная развертывающаяся поверхность
F 431	**focal distance,** focal length <of a conic> <AY>	Brennpunktsabstand *m*, Fokaldistanz *f*	distance *f* focale	фокусное расстояние
F 432	**focal ellipse** <AY>	Fokalellipse *f*	ellipse *f* focale	фокальный эллипс
	focal length <AY>	*s.* F 431		
F 433	**focal line** <AG>	Fokalkurve *f*, Fokale *f*, Brennpunktskurve *f*, Fokallinie *f*	focale *f*, courbe *f* focale	фокальная кривая, фокала
F 434	**focal line** <of a rectilinear congruence> <DG>	Brennlinie *f*, Leitlinie *f*, Leitgerade *f*, Direktrix *f*	ligne *f* focale	фокальная линия
F 435	**focal line,** focal straight line <GE>	Brenngerade *f*, Fokalgerade *f*, fokale Gerade *f*	droite *f* focale	фокусная прямая, фокальная прямая
F 436	**focal plane** <of a rectilinear congruence> <PJ>	Brennebene *f*, Fokalebene *f*	plan *m* focal, plan polaire	фокальная плоскость
F 437	**focal point,** focus <of a rectilinear congruence> <PJ>	Brennpunkt *m*, Fokalpunkt *m*	point *m* focal, foyer *m*	фокальная точка, фокус
	focal point <DE>	*s.* S 1531		
F 438	**focal property** <AY>	Brennpunktseigenschaft *f*, Fokaleigenschaft *f*	propriété *f* focale	фокальное свойство
F 439	**focal radius** <of a conic> <AY>	Brennstrahl *m*	rayon *m* focal	фокальный радиус-вектор
	focal straight line <GE>	*s.* F 435		
	focal strip <DE>	*s.* M 827		
F 440	**focal surface** <of a rectilinear congruence> <PJ>	Brennfläche *f*, Fokalfläche *f*	surface *f* focale	фокальная поверхность
	focal surface <DG>	*s.* G 543		
	focoids <AY, PJ>	*s.* C 2873		
F 441	**focus** <of a quadric *or* a plane algebraic curve> <AG>	Brennpunkt *m*, Fokalpunkt *m*	foyer *m*	фокус
F 442	**focus** <VA>	Brennpunkt *m*	foyer *m*	фокус
	focus <DE>	*s.* S 1531		
	focus <PJ>	*s.* F 437		
	focus-to-centre distance <AY>	*s.* L 790		
F 443	**Fokker-Planck equation** <DE>	Fokker-Planck-Gleichung *f*, Fokker-Plancksche Gleichung *f*, Einstein-Fokker-Plancksche (Fokker-Plancksche) Differentialgleichung *f*	équation *f* différentielle de Fokker-Planck, équation de Fokker-Planck	уравнение Эйнштейна-Фоккера (Фоккера-Планка, Эйнштейна-Фоккера-Планка), дифференциальное уравнение Фоккера-Планка
F 444	**folded normal distribution** <ST>	gefaltete Normalverteilung *f*	convolution *f* de la distribution normale	свертка нормального распределения
	folding <AN>	*s.* C 2409		
F 445	**foliated manifold** <TO>	geblätterte Mannigfaltigkeit *f*	variété *f* feuilletée	расслоенное многообразие
F 446	**foliated space** <TO>	geblätterter Raum *m*	espace *m* feuilleté	расслоенное пространство
F 447	**foliation** <TO>	Blätterung *f*	feuilletage *m*	расслоение
F 448	**folioid** <a plane curve> <GE>	Folioide *f*	folioïde *f*	фолиоида
F 449	**folium,** leaf <a plane curve> <GE>	Blatt *n*, Folium *n*, Blattkurve *f*	feuille *f*, folium *m*	лист
	folium of Descartes <AG>	*s.* C 164		
F 450	**follow / to** <LO>	folgen	se déduire	следовать
F 451	**follow / to,** to be greater <than>, to be over, to contain <$x \geqq y$> <SE>	enthalten, folgen <auf>, größer oder gleich sein	être plus grand que ou au plus égal <à>, être supérieur [ou égal] <à>, succéder <à>	
F 452	**follow a covering** α **/ to** <said of a covering> <SE, TO>	echt feiner sein als die Überdeckung α	être strictement plus fin que le recouvrement α	следовать за покрытием α
F 453	**foot** <of a perpendicular> <EG>	Lotfußpunkt *m*, Fußpunkt *m* <eines Lotes>	pied *m* <d'une perpendiculaire>	основание <перпендикуляра>
F 454	**forbidden path** <in transportation problems> <GP, PG>	verbotener Weg *m*	voie *f* interdite, chemin *m* interdit	запрещенный путь
F 455	**force** <of a theory> <MM>	Stärke *f*	force *f*	сила
F 456	**forcing condition** <SE>	„forcing"-Bedingung *f*	condition *f* de « forcing »	вынуждающее условие
F 457	**forcing method** <SE>	„forcing"-Methode *f*	méthode *f* de « forcing »	метод вынуждения
F 458	**Ford and Fulkerson algorithm,** general maximum flow algorithm <GP, PG>	Ford-Fulkersonscher Algorithmus *m*	algorithme *m* général pour le problème du flot maximum, algorithme de Ford et Fulkerson	алгоритм Форда-Фалкерсона
F 458 a	**forecasting,** prediction, prognosis <SP>	Vorhersage *f*, Prognostizierung *f*	prévision *f*, prédiction *f*	предсказание, прогноз[ирование]
	foreshortening <DS>	*s.* R 417		
F 459	**forest** <GP>	Wald *m*	forêt *f*	лес
F 460	**forgetful functor,** underlying functor <CA>	Vergißfunktor *m*, vergeßlicher (unterliegender, vergessender) Funktor *m*	foncteur *m* d'oubli, foncteur oubli	пренебрегающий (стирающий) функтор
	forking <GN>	*s.* B 725		

No.	English	German	French	Russian
F 461	**form,** homogeneous polynomial, quantic <of the n-th degree> <AL>	Form *f*, homogenes Polynom *n*, algebraische Form, Quantik *f* <Sylvester> <n-ten Grades>	forme *f*, polynôme *m* (forme) homogène, forme algébrique, quantique *f* <de degré n, du n-e degré, n-homogène>	форма, однородный многочлен, однородный полином, гомогенный многочлен <степени n>
	form <GN>	*s.* S 741		
	form <LO>	*s.* S 497		
	1-form <AN>	*s.* P 546		
	$a + ib$ form <AL, AN>	*s.* A 437		
	formal category <CA>	*s.* R 691		
F 462	**formal computation,** recursive computation <of the value of a function> <GN, MM>	rekursive Berechnung *f*	calcul *m* récursif	рекурсивное вычисление
F 463	**formal derivative** <of a polynomial> <AL>	formale Ableitung *f* <eines Polynoms>	polynôme *m* dérivé	формальная производная <многочлена>
	formalism <FO, LO, MM>	*s.* F 466		
F 464	**formalizability** <MM>	Formalisierbarkeit *f*	propriété *f* d'être formalisable, formalisabilité *f*	формализуемость
F 465	**formalized language,** calculus; formal language <MM>	formalisierte (künstliche) Sprache *f*; formale Sprache	langage *m* formalisé; langage formel	формализованный язык, искусственный язык; формальный язык
F 466	**formalized theory,** formalism <FO, LO, MM>	formalisierte Theorie *f*, Formalismus *m*, [interpretierter] Kalkül *m*, System *n*, Theorie	théorie *f* formalisée, formalisme *m*	формализованная теория, формализм, формальная система
	formal language <MM>	*s.* F 465		
F 467	**formal logic** <LO>	formale Logik *f*	logique *f* formelle (formalisée)	формальная логика
F 468	**formally consistent system of formulas** <MM>	syntaktisch (formal) widerspruchsfreie Menge *f* von Ausdrücken	système *m* de formules absolument consistant	формально непротиворечивая совокупность формул
F 469	**formally real field** <AL>	formal[-] reeller Körper *m*	corps *m* formellement réel	формально действительное (вещественное) поле, вещественное поле
F 470	**formal model** <PG>	formales Modell *n*	modèle *m* formel	формальная модель
F 471	**formal polynomial** <AL>	formales Polynom *n*	polynôme *m* formel (abstrait)	формальный полином
F 472	**formal power series,** formal series <AL>	formale Potenzreihe *f* (Reihe *f*)	série *f* [entière] formelle	формальный [степенной] ряд
	formal power series ring <AL>	*s.* R 1324		
	formal semantics <LO>	*s.* S 426		
	formal series <AL>	*s.* F 472		
F 473	**formal smoothness** <AL>	formale Glattheit *f*	lissité *f* formelle	формальная гладкость
F 474	**formal system,** logistic system <LO>	formales System *n*	système *m* formel, calcul *m*	формальная система
F 475	**formation,** Gaschütz['s] formation <of groups> <AL>	Formation *f* <von Gruppen> <Gaschütz>	formation *f* <de groupes>	формация <групп>
F 476	**formation of an equation,** setting up (of) an equation <GN>	Aufstellen *n* einer Gleichung	mise *f* en équation, établissement *m* (position *f*) d'une équation	составление (вывод) уравнения, описывание уравнением
F 477	**formation of the commutator-factor group,** abelianizing <of a group> <GR>	Abelschmachen *n*	abélisation *f*	взятие фактор-группы по коммутанту
F 478	**formation of the intersection of a countable family of sets** <SE>	abzählbare Durchschnittsbildung *f*	opération *f* d'intersection dénombrale	операция счетного пересечения
F 479	**formation of the Kronecker product** <of representations> <RE>	Bildung *f* des Kronecker-Produkts	formation *f* du produit kroneckérien	кронекерово умножение
F 480	**formation of the union of a countable collection of sets** <SE>	abzählbare Vereinigungsbildung *f*	opération *f* union dénombrable	операция счетного объединения
F 481	**formation of transvectants** <process> <IV>	Transvektion *f*, Überschiebung *f*, Zusammensetzung *f*	transvection *f*, composition *f*	трансвекция
F 482	**formation rule** <in a formal language> <LO>	Bildungsregel *f*	règle *f* de formation	правило образования
F 483	**form in n variables,** n-ary form <AL>	Form *f* in n Variablen, n-äre Form, Form von n Variablen	forme *f* de n variables, forme n-aire	n-арная форма
	form of interference <LO>	*s.* K 76		
F 484	**form of Maurer-Cartan,** Maurer-Cartan form <of a Lie group> <GR>	Maurer-Cartansche Form *f*	forme *f* de Maurer-Cartan	форма Маурера-Картана
	form of the fifth degree <AL>	*s.* Q 303		
	form of the fourth degree <AL>	*s.* Q 90		
	form of the sixth degree <AL>	*s.* S 729		
	form of the third degree <AL>	*s.* C 2743		
F 485	**form problem** <IV>	Formenproblem *n*	problème *m* des formes	проблема форм
F 486	**forms having no common variables** <AL>	variablenfremde Formen *fpl*	formes *fpl* sans variables communes	формы без общих переменных
	form the inner product / to <VT>	*s.* C 2257		

No.	English	German	French	Russian
F 487	**form the *n*-th multiple / to** <of> <AR>	ver-*n*-fachen	former le *n*-uple <de>	образовать *n*-кратное
F 488	**formula,** meaningful (well-formed, correct logical, correctly constructed) formula, expression <LO>	Formel *f*, zulässiger (sinnvoller, logischer) Ausdruck *m*, Ausdruck, logische Formel	formule *f*, expression *f* bien formée (faite), expression douée de sens	формула, допустимое (осмысленное) выражение, правильно образованная формула, поф
	formula <LO>	*s.* 1. M 307; 2. S 499		
	∀ formula <LO>	*s.* U 338		
	ζ-formula <NT>	*s.* Z 70		
	formula containing free individual variables <LO>	*s.* N 331		
F 489	**formulae for alephs** <SE>	Alephrelationen *fpl*, Alephformeln *fpl*	formules *fpl* pour des alephs	соотношения между алефами
	formulae of [Serret-] Frenet <DG>	*s.* F 643		
	formula for mechanical (numerical) cubature <DI, NU>	*s.* C 2721		
	formula free of quantifiers <LO>	*s.* Q 78		
	formula having a normal form <LO>	*s.* P 1225		
F 490	**formula having the same truth value** <LO>	wahrheitsgleicher Ausdruck *m*	formule *f* ayant la même valeur de vérité	формула, имеющая одинаковое значение истинности
	formula in prenex normal form <LO>	*s.* P 1225		
F 491	**formula in proof-theoretic normal form** <LO>	Ausdruck *m* in allgemeingültigkeitstheoretischer Skolemscher Normalform	∃∀-formule *f*	∃∀-формула
F 492	**formula in satisfaction-theoretic normal form** <LO>	Ausdruck *m* in erfüllbarkeitstheoretischer Normalform	∀∃-formule *f*	∀∃-формула, сколемовская формула; формула, имеющая нормальный вид Сколема
	formula in the prenex normal form <LO>	*s.* P 1225		
	formula involving free variables <LO>	*s.* N 331		
	formula in which no variable has a free occurrence <LO>	*s.* S 496		
F 493	**formula language,** language of formulas <GN>	Formelsprache *f*	langage *m* de formule	язык формул, формульный язык
	formula of a normal form <LO>	*s.* P 1225		
F 494	**formula of associativity** <for the intersection multiplicity> <AG>	Assoziativitätsformel *f*	formule *f* d'associativité	формула ассоциативности
	formula of Cayley-Brill <AG>	*s.* F 386		
F 495	**formula of computation,** computational (calculational) formula <NU>	Berechnungsformel *f*, Rechenformel *f*	formule *f* de calcul	расчетная формула
	formula of elementary logic <LO>	*s.* M 307		
F 496	**formula of Hirsch,** Hirsch['s] formula <AT>	Hirschsche Formel *f*	formule *f* de Hirsch	формула Хирша
F 497	**formula of Laguerre,** Laguerre['s] formula <for the angle of two lines> <AY, PJ>	Laguerresche Winkelformel (Formel) *f*, Satz *m* von Laguerre, Laguerrescher Satz	formule *f* de Laguerre	формула Лагерра
F 498	**formula of projection** <for the intersection multiplicity> <AG>	Projektionsformel *f*	formule *f* de projection	формула проекции
	formula of total probability <ST>	*s.* T 683		
F 499	**formulary,** collection of formulas, handbook of formulae <GN>	Formelsammlung *f*	recueil *m* de formules, formulaire *m*	сборник формул; собрание формул
	formulation of a problem <GN>	*s.* P 1049		
	formulation of the question <GN>	*s.* P 1049		
	forward derivative <DI>	*s.* R 1150		
	forward derivative function <RF>	*s.* R 1151		
	forward difference <FD>	*s.* D 313		
F 500	**forward difference operator** <FD, NU>	Operator *m* für aufsteigende Differenzen, Differenzenoperator *m*, ∇	opérateur *m* des différences ascendantes	оператор взятых назад [конечных] разностей
F 501	**forward difference quotient** <FD>	vorderer Differenzenquotient *m*	quotient *m* des différences en avant	разностное отношение «вперед»
	forward differentiability <DI>	*s.* R 1120		
	forward [differential] equation[s] [of Kolmogorov] <SP>	*s.* K 122		
	forward Dini['s] derivative <RF>	*s.* R 1154		

No.	English	German	French	Russian
	forward system <SP>	*s.* K 122		
F 502	**foundation,** justification, reasons <GN>	Begründung *f*	fondation *f*	обоснование
F 503	**foundations** <*e.g.:* of arithmetics, geometry, mathematics, set theory> <FO>	Grundlagen *fpl* <*z. B.:* der Arithmetik, Geometrie, Mathematik, Mengenlehre>	fondements *mpl* <*par exemple:* de l'arithmétique, de la géométrie, des mathématiques, de la théorie des ensembles>	основания <*например:* арифметики, геометрии, математики, теории множеств>
F 504	**foundations of higher mathematics** <FO>	Grundlagen *fpl* der höheren Mathematik	mathématiques *fpl* générales	основы высшей математики
F 505	**four-colour conjecture** <GP>	Vierfarbenvermutung *f*	conjecture *f* des quatre couleurs	гипотеза четырех красок
F 506	**four-colour problem, four colour problem,** problem of colouring maps in four colours, geographical problem of the four colours <GP>	Vierfarbenproblem *n*	problème *m* des quatre colours, problème de la carte	задача (проблема) четырех красок
F 507	**four-colour theorem** <GP>	Vierfarbensatz *m*	théorème *m* des quatre couleurs, théorème de Guthrie	теорема о четырех красках
F 508	**four-combination,** 4-combination, quaternary, quaternion <CT>	Kombination (Komplexion) *f* der (zur) vierten (4.) Klasse, Kombination zu je 4, Quaterne *f*, Quaternion *f*	quaterne *m*, tétrade *f*, groupe *m* de quatre, quaternion *f*	сочетание по 4, четверка
	four-component spinor <AL, GE>	*s.* S 1524		
F 509	**four-cusped curve** <GE>	vierspitzige (quadrikuspidale) Kurve *f*, Kurve mit vier Spitzen	courbe *f* quadricuspidale	кривая с четырьмя точками возврата
	four-cusped hypocycloid <GE>	*s.* A 1125		
	four-digit integer <NT>	*s.* F 511		
F 510	**four-dimensionality, four-dimensionalness** <GE>	Vierdimensionalität *f*	quadridimensionnalité *f*	четырехразмерность
	four-dimensional vector <DG, VT>	*s.* F 552		
F 511	**four-figure integer,** four-digit integer <NT>	vierstellige (vierziffrige) ganze Zahl *f*	entier *m* à quatre chiffres	четырехзначное целое число
F 512	**four-fold classification** <ST>	vierfache Klassifikation *f*	classification *f* à quatre entrées	классификация по четырем признакам
	four-fold symmetry <EG>	*s.* Q 92		
F 513	**four-fold table,** fourfold table, 2 · 2 table, 2 × 2 table, two-by-two contingency table <ST>	Vierfeldertafel *f*, 2 · 2-Tafel *f*, 2×2-Tafel *f*, Zwei-mal-zwei-Tafel, vierteilige Kontingenztafel *f*	tableau *m* (table *f*) à quatre cases, tableau 2 · 2 (2×2), tableau de contingence 2 · 2 (2×2), table 2 · 2 (2×2), table de contingence 2 · 2 (2×2)	четырехклеточная таблица (таблица корреляции), четырехпольная таблица, таблица 2 · 2 (2×2)
F 514	**four frame,** 4-frame, tetrahedral <DG>	Vierbein *n*, 4-Bein *n*	4-repère *m*, tétraèdre *m*	4-репер, тетраэдр
F 515	**Fourier['s] algebra** <AL>	Fouriersche Algebra *f*	algèbre *f* de Fourier	алгебра Фурье
F 516	**Fourier analysis,** harmonic analysis <AN, NU>	Fourier-Analyse *f*, harmonische Analyse *f*, Oberwellenanalyse *f*	analyse *f* harmonique (de Fourier)	гармонический анализ, анализ Фурье
F 517	**Fourier analyzer,** harmonic analyzer, periodometer <AN, IN>	harmonischer Analysator *m*, Fourier-Analysator *m*	analyseur *m* harmonique, analyseur de Fourier	гармонический анализатор, анализатор гармоник
F 518	**Fourier-Bessel formula** <AN, FU>	Formel *f* von Fourier-Bessel, Fourier-Besselsche Formel	formule *f* de Fourier-Bessel	формула Фурье-Бесселя
	Fourier-Bessel function <FU>	*s.* B 231		
F 519	**Fourier-Bessel series** <AN, NU, SS>	Fourier-Bessel-Reihe *f*, Fourier-Reihe *f* mit Zylinderfunktionen	série *f* de Fourier-Bessel	ряд Фурье-Бесселя
	Fourier-Bessel transform[ation] <IT>	*s.* H 84		
	Fourier-Bohr spectrum <AN>	*s.* S 1426		
F 520	**Fourier coefficient** <of an orthogonal expansion>; Euler coefficient <of a Fourier expansion> <AN, AP, AX, NU>	Fourier-Koeffizient *m*, Fourier-Konstante *f*, Entwicklungskoeffizient *m*, Koeffizient *m*, harmonischer Konstituent *m*, Euler-Fourier-Koeffizient *m*	coefficient *m* de Fourier	коэффициент Фурье
	Fourier component <AN, NU>	*s.* H 89		
F 521	**Fourier['s] cosine transform[ation]** <IT>	Fouriersche Kosinustransformation (cos-Transformation) *f*	transformation *f* cosinus de Fourier	косинус-преобразование Фурье
	Fourier['s] double series <SS>	*s.* D 916		
F 522	**Fourier-Ehrenpreis transform** <DE>	Fourier-Ehrenpreissche Transformierte *f*	transformée *f* de Fourier-Ehrenpreis	изображение по Фурье-Эренпрайсу
	Fourier-Euler['s] formulas <AN, NU, SS>	*s.* E 587		
F 523	**Fourier['s] expansion** <AN>	Fourier-Entwicklung *f*, Fourier-Zerlegung *f*	développement *m* en série de Fourier	разложение Фурье
F 524	**Fourier['s] exponent** <AP>	Fourier-Exponent *m*	exposant *m* de Fourier	показатель Фурье

No.	English	German	French	Russian
	Fourier function <FU>	*s.* B 231		
F 525	**Fourier['s] half-range series** <SS>	Fourier-Reihe *f* mit rein sinus- oder kosinusförmigen Bestandteilen	série *f* de Fourier à termes en sinus ou cosinus seulement	ряд Фурье только с синусоидальными или косинусоидальными членами
F 526	**Fourier['s] integral** <RF>	Fourier-Integral *n*, Fouriersches Integral *n*	intégrale *f* de Fourier	интеграл Фурье, тригонометрический интеграл
F 527	**Fourier['s] integral equation** <IE, IT>	Fouriersche Integralgleichung *f*	équation *f* intégrale de Fourier	интегральное уравнение Фурье
F 528	**Fourier['s] integral theorem,** integral theorem of Fourier <AN, NU>	Fouriersche Integraldarstellung (Integralformel, Formel) *f*	formule *f* de Fourier	интегральная формула Фурье, формула Фурье
	Fourier['s] integral transform <IT>	*s.* 1. F 541; 2. F 542		
	Fourier['s] integral transformation <IT>	*s.* F 542		
F 529	**Fourier['s] inversion formula (theorem)**	Fouriersche Umkehrformel *f*, Fourierscher Umkehrsatz *m*, Fourier-Umkehrsatz *m*	formule *f* d'inversion de Fourier, formule inverse de Fourier, formule de réciprocité de Fourier	теорема обращения Фурье
F 530	**Fourier['s] kernel** <IE>	Fourier-Kern *m*, Fourierscher Kern *m*	noyau *m* de Fourier	ядро Фурье
F 531	**Fourier['s] matrix** <AP>	Fouriersche Matrix *f*, Fourier-Matrix *f*	matrice *f* de Fourier	матрица Фурье
F 532	**Fourier['s] operator** <FA>	Fourier-Operator *m*	opérateur *m* de Fourier	оператор Фурье
F 533	**Fourier-Plancherel operator** <FA>	Fourier-Plancherel-Operator *m*, Fourier-Plancherel-Transformation *f*, Fourier-Plancherelsche Transformation *f*	transformation *f* (opérateur *m*) de Fourier-Plancherel	оператор (преобразование) Фурье-Планшереля
F 534	**Fourier['s] series,** trigonometric Fourier series <AN, SS>	Fourier-Reihe *f*, Fouriersche Reihe *f*, trigonometrische Fourier-Reihe	série *f* de Fourier, série de Fourier trigonométrique	ряд Фурье, тригонометрический ряд Фурье
F 535	**Fourier series** <of an almost periodic function *or* of a vector> <AP, FA>	Fourier-Reihe *f*, Fouriersche Reihe *f*	série *f* de Fourier	ряд Фурье
F 536	**Fourier['s] sine transform[ation]** <IT>	Fouriersche Sinustransformation (sin-Transformation) *f*	transformation *f* sinus de Fourier	синус-преобразование Фурье
F 537	**Fourier['s] space** <AN>	Fourier-Raum *m*	espace *m* de Fourier	пространство Фурье
F 538	**Fourier-Stieltjes['] series** <AN, NU, SS>	Fourier-Stieltjes-Reihe *f*	série *f* de Fourier-Stieltjes	ряд Фурье-Стилтьеса
F 539	**Fourier-Stieltjes transform[ation]** <IT>	Fourier-Stieltjes-Transformation *f*	transformation *f* de Fourier-Stieltjes	преобразование Фурье-Стилтьеса
F 540	**Fourier synthesis,** harmonic synthesis <AN, NU>	Fourier-Synthese *f*, harmonische Synthese *f*	synthèse *f* harmonique, synthèse de Fourier	гармонический синтез, синтез Фурье
F 541	**Fourier['s] transform,** Fourier['s] integral transform <IT>	Fourier-Transformierte *f*	transfouriée *f*, trans-Fourier *f* directe, transformée (image) *f* de Fourier	образ Фурье, фурье-образ, трансформанта (преобразование) Фурье, изображение [по] Фурье
F 542	**Fourier['s] transform[ation],** Fourier['s] integral transform[ation] <IT>	Fourier-Transformation *f*, Fouriersche Integraltransformation *f*	transformation *f* [intégrale] de Fourier	преобразование Фурье, фурье-преобразование, интегральное преобразование Фурье, трансформация Фурье
	four-index symbol <DG>	*s.* R 1040		
F 543	**four-leafed rose,** quadrifolium <GE>	Vierblatt *n*, Quadrifolium *n*, vierblättrige Rosenkurve *f*	quadrifolium *m*, rose *f* à quatre branches, rosace *f* à quatre branches (feuilles)	четырехлистник, четырехлепестковая роза
F 544	**four lemma** <CA, HA>	Viererlemma *n*	lemme *m* des quatre	лемма о четырех [гомо-] морфизмах
F 545	**four-place relation,** tetradic relation <LO>	vierstellige Relation *f*	relation *f* quaternaire	четырехместное отношение
F 546	**four-point problem**<TO>	Vierpunktproblem *n*	problème *m* des quatres points	проблема четырех точек
F 547	**four-point property** <of a semi-metric space> <TO>	Vierpunkteigenschaft *f*	propriété *f* des quatre points	свойство четырех точек
	fours-group <GR>	*s.* K 90		
F 548	**four squares theorem,** four-squares theorem, Lagrange['s] theorem [on four squares] <NT>	Vier-Quadrate-Satz *m*, Satz *m* von Lagrange, Lagrangescher Satz	théorème *m* de Lagrange	теорема Лагранжа
	four-termed equation <AL>	*s.* Q 61		
	fourth-degree polynomial equation <AL>	*s.* Q 88		
	fourth harmonic point <PJ>	*s.* H 93		
F 549	**fourth law for powers,** association law for powers <AR>	Assoziationsformel *f* für Potenzen	formule *f* d'association pour les puissances	закон показателей для степени степени
	fourth-order ten sor<VT>	*s.* T 154		
	fourth proportional [number] <AR>	*s.* G 253		
F 550	**four-valued logic** <LO>	vierwertige Logik *f*	logique *f* quadrivalente	четырехзначная логика
F 551	**four-valuedness,** quadruplicity <AN, LO>	Vierwertigkeit *f*	quadrivalence *f*	четырехзначность
F 552	**four-vector,** 4-vector, four-dimensional vector <DG, VT>	Vierervektor *m*, vierdimensionaler Vektor *m*	quadrivecteur *m*, 4-vecteur *m*, vecteur *m* quadridimensionnel (quadratique)	четыре-вектор, 4-вектор, четырехмерный вектор, четырехвектор

No.	English	German	French	Russian
F 553	**four-vertex theorem** <CS, GE>	Vierscheitelsatz *m*	théorème *m* des quatre sommets	теорема о четырех вершинах
F 554	***F*-permanent summation** <of Fourier series> <LI>	*F*-permanente Summation *f*	sommation *f* *F*-permanente	*F*-перманентный метод суммирования
F 554a	**fractal** <set of fractionary dimension> <TO>	Fractal *n*	fractal *m*	фракталь, множество дробной размерности
	fractile of order *p* <ST>	*s.* Q 81		
F 555	**fraction,** fraction expression <AL>	Bruch *m*	fraction *f* algébrique	дробь, алгебраическая дробь
F 556	**fraction,** fractional number <AR, NT>	Bruch *m*, gebrochene Zahl *f*, Bruchzahl *f*	fraction *f*, nombre *m* fractionnaire, rompu *m*	дробь, дробное число
F 557	**fractional arithmetic;** operations with fractions <AR>	Bruchrechnung *f*	calcul *m* des fractions; calcul fractionnaire	исчисление дробей
F 558	**fractional derivative** <DI>	Ableitung *f* gebrochener Ordnung	dérivée *f* d'ordre fractionnaire	производная дробного порядка
F 559	**fractional divisor** <AG, AL, FT>	gebrochener Divisor *m*	diviseur *m* fractionnaire	дробный дивизор
F 560	**fractional equation** <AL>	gebrochene algebraische Gleichung *f*	équation *f* fractionnaire	дробное алгебраическое уравнение
F 561	**fractional equation** <AR>	Bruchgleichung *f*	équation *f* fractionnaire	дробное уравнение
F 562	**fractional equivalence** <UA>	Faktoräquivalenzrelation *f*	équivalence *f* quotient	фактор-эквивалентность, дробная эквивалентность
F 563	**fractional exponent** <AL, AR>	gebrochener Exponent *m*, Bruchexponent *m*	exposant *m* fractionnaire	дробный показатель [степени]
F 564	**fractional function** <FT>	gebrochene Funktion *f*	fonction *f* fractionnaire	дробная функция
F 565	**fractional ideal of** $\mathfrak{o}$ <AL>	gebrochenes $\mathfrak{o}$-Ideal *n*	idéal *m* fractionnaire de $\mathfrak{o}$	дробный идеал в $\mathfrak{o}$
F 566	**fractional integral** <AN>	Integral *n* gebrochener Ordnung	intégrale *f* d'ordre fractionnaire	интеграл дробного порядка
	fractional line <GN>	*s.* F 571		
	fractional linear transformation <FT>	*s.* B 348		
	fractional number <AR, NT>	*s.* F 556		
F 567	**fractional part** <of a number> <NT>	gebrochener Teil *m*, ganzzahliger Rest *m* $\langle x\rangle = x - [x]$	partie *f* fractionnaire, mantisse *f*	дробная часть, $\{x\} = x - [x]$
F 568	**fractional rational function** <as a fraction of two prime polynomials> <AL, FT>	gebrochene rationale Funktion *f*, gebrochen[-]rationale Funktion	fonction *f* rationnelle fractionnaire	дробно-рациональная функция, дробно (дробная) рациональная функция
F 569	**fractional replication** <ST>	teilweise Wiederholung *f*	répétition *f* partielle (fractionnée)	частичное повторение
	fractionary dimension <TO>	*s.* H 137		
F 570	**fractionary ideal** <AB, AL>	gebrochenes Ideal *n*	idéal *m* fractionnaire	дробный идеал
F 571	**fraction bar,** fraction[al] line, horizontal line (rule); solidus, fraction stroke (/) <GN>	Bruchstrich *m*	barre *f* (trait *m*) de fraction, trait *m* de séparation, signe *f* de division, signe *f* fractionnaire	черта дроби, дробная черта, черта в дроби
	fraction expression <AL>	*s.* F 555		
	fraction field <AL>	*s.* Q 321		
F 572	**fraction in its lowest terms,** simplified fraction, reduced fraction <AL, NT>	gekürzter (reduzierter, irreduzibler, unkürzbarer, gehobener) Bruch *m*	fraction *f* irréductible (réduite à sa plus simple expression, simplifiée, réduite)	упрощенная (приведенная, сокращенная, несократимая) дробь
	fraction line <GN>	*s.* F 571		
	fraction of numbers <NT>	*s.* N 889		
F 573	**fraction of the Farey sequence,** term of the Farey sequence, Farey['s] fraction <NT>	Farey-Bruch *m*, Fareybruch *m*	fraction *f* de la suite de Farey	член последовательности Фарея
	fraction stroke <GN>	*s.* F 571		
F 574	**fraction that can be cancelled,** cancellable fraction <AL, AR>	kürzbarer Bruch *m*, reduktibler Bruch *m*	fraction *f* réductible (simplifiable)	сократимая дробь
	fraction with equal denominator <AL, NT>	*s.* S 868		
F 575	**F-radical** <of a ring> <AL>	F-Radikal *n*	F-radical *m*	F-радикал
F 576	**frame** <ST>	Rahmen *m*, Erhebungsgrundlage *f*, Auswahlgrundlage *f*	base *f*	основа обследования (выбора), представление в наглядной форме текущих выборочных данных
	4-frame <DG>	*s.* F 514		
	Fraser[']s diagram <FD, NU>	*s.* L 1176		
	***F*-ratio** <ST>	*s.* V 64		
F 577	**Frattini['s] factor [group]** <GR>	Faktorgruppe *f* nach der Frattini-Gruppe	groupe *m* quotient par le groupe principal	фактор-группа по Ф-подгруппе
	Frattini['s] subgroup <GR>	*s.* P 1424		
	freak value <ST>	*s.* O 553		
F 578	**Fréchet['s] axiom,** T_1-separation axiom <TO>	erstes (Fréchetsches) Trennungsaxiom *n*, T_1-Axiom *n*	axiome *m* de Fréchet, axiome T_1	аксиома [отделимости] Фреше, аксиома (T_1)
F 579	**Fréchet['s] base** <TO>	Fréchet-Raster *m*	base *f* du filtre de Fréchet	база фильтра Фреше
	Fréchet['s] co-ordinate space <FA, TO>	*s.* F 392		
F 580	**Fréchet['s] curve** <FA, GE, TO>	Fréchetsche Kurve *f*	courbe *f* de Fréchet	кривая Фреше

No.	English	German	French	Russian
F 581	**Fréchet differentiable function (mapping),** F-differentiable function (mapping) <FA>	Fréchet-differenzierbare Funktion (Abbildung) *f*, nach Fréchet differenzierbare Funktion (Abbildung)	fonction (application) *f* dérivable au sens de Fréchet	дифференцируемая по Фреше функция, дифференцируемое по Фреше отображение
F 582	**Fréchet['s] differential,** strong (total) differential <FA>	Fréchetsches Differential *n*, Differential nach Fréchet	différentielle *f* de Fréchet	дифференциал Фреше, сильный дифференциал
F 583	**Fréchet equivalent mapping** <FA, GE>	Fréchet-äquivalente Abbildung *f*	application *f* équivalente au sens de Fréchet	эквивалентное по Фреше отображение
F 584	**Fréchet['s] filter** <TO>	Fréchet-Filter *m*	filtre *m* de Fréchet	фильтр Фреше
	Fréchet-Riesz theorem <FA>	*s.* R 1061		
	Fréchet['s] sequence space <FA, TO>	*s.* F 392		
F 585	**Fréchet['s] space,** *F*-space, B_0-space <FA, TO>	Fréchet-Raum *m*, *F*-Raum *m*, B_0-Raum *m*, Fréchetscher Raum *m*	espace *m* de Fréchet, espac [de type] (*F*), *F*-espace *m*, espace [de type] (B_0)	епространство Фреше, *F*-пространство, B_0-пространство, пространство типа B_0
F 586	**Fréchet['s] surface** <FA, GE, TO>	Fréchetsche Fläche *f*	surface *f* de Fréchet	поверхность Фреше
F 587	**Fréchet['s] topological space,** semi-separated space, T_1-space, T_1 topological space <TO>	Fréchetscher Raum *m*, T_1-Raum *m*	espace *m* accessible, espace T_1	топологическое пространство в сильном смысле, достижимое пространство, T_1-пространство
F 588	**Fréchet['s] variation,** F-variation <of a function> <AN>	Fréchet-Variation *f*	variation *f* au sens de Fréchet	F-вариация, вариация в смысле Фреше
F 589	**Fredholm['s] alternative,** alternative of Fredholm <IE>	Fredholmsche Alternative *f*, [Fredholmscher] Alternativsatz *m*	alternative *f* de Fredholm, alternative de Riesz-Fredholm	альтернатива Фредгольма
F 590	**Fredholm['s] determinant** <IE>	Fredholmsche Determinante *f*, Fredholmscher Nenner *m*	déterminant *m* de Fredholm	знаменатель (определитель, детерминант) Фредгольма
F 591	**Fredholm['s] domain** <FA> Γ<IE>	Fredholm-Bereich *m*	domaine *m* de Fredholm	область Фредгольма
	Fredholm['s] equation	*s.* 1. F 594; 2. F 600		
	Fredholm['s] equation of the first kind <IE>	*s.* 1. F 593; 2. F 601		
	Fredholm['s] equation of the second kind <IE>	*s.* 1. F 594; 2. F 602		
F 592	**Fredholm['s] equation with symmetric kernel,** orthogonal integral equation <IE>	orthogonale Integralgleichung *f*, Fredholmsche Integralgleichung mit symmetrischem Kern	équation *f* de Fredholm avec noyau symétrique, équation intégrale orthogonale	уравнение Фредгольма с симметричным ядром, ортогональное интегральное уравнение
	Fredholm['s] integral equation <IE>	*s.* 1. F 594; 2. F 600		
F 593	**Fredholm['s] integral equation of the first kind,** Fredholm['s] equation of the first kind, linear integral equation [with fixed upper limit of integration] of the first kind <*e.g.*: with continuous kernel> <IE>	Fredholmsche Integralgleichung *f* erster Art, lineare Integralgleichung [mit fester oberer Integrationsgrenze] erster Art <*z. B.*: mit stetigem Kern>	équation *f* intégrale de Fredholm de première espèce, équation de Fredholm de première espèce, équation intégrale linéaire [à limite supérieure fixe d'intégration] de première espèce <*par exemple:* à noyau continu>	интегральное уравнение Фредгольма первого рода, уравнение Фредгольма первого рода, линейное интегральное уравнение [с постоянным верхним пределом] первого рода <*например:* с непрерывным ядром>
	Fredholm['s] integral equation of the first kind <IE>	*s.* F 601		
F 594	**Fredholm['s] integral equation of the second kind,** Fredholm['s] equation of the second kind, linear integral equation [with fixed upper limit of integration] of the second kind, Fredholm['s] [integral] equation <IE>	Fredholmsche Integralgleichung *f* zweiter Art, lineare Integralgleichung [mit fester oberer Integrationsgrenze] zweiter Art, Fredholmsche Integralgleichung	équation *f* intégrale de Fredholm de seconde (deuxième) espèce, équation de Fredholm de seconde (deuxième) espèce, équation intégrale linéaire [à limite supérieure fixe d'intégration] de seconde (deuxième) espèce, équation [intégrale] de Fredholm	интегральное уравнение Фредгольма второго рода, уравнение Фредгольма второго рода, линейное интегральное уравнение [с постоянным верхним пределом] второго рода, [интегральное] уравнение Фредфольма
	Fredholm['s] integral equation of the second kind <IE>	*s.* F 602		
F 595	**Fredholm['s] kernel (nucleus),** kernel, nucleus <IE> Γ<IE>	Fredholmscher Kern *m*	noyau *m* de Fredholm	ядро Фредгольма
F 596	**Fredholm['s] numerator**	Fredholmscher Zähler *m*	numérateur *m* de Fredholm	числитель Фредгольма
F 597	**Fredholm['s] operator** <FA>	Fredholm-Operator *m*, Fredholmscher Operator *m*	opérateur *m* (transformation *f*) de Fredholm	фредгольмов оператор, оператор Фредгольма, Ф-оператор, F-оператор
F 598	**Fredholm['s] point** <FA>	Fredholm-Punkt *m*	point *m* de Fredholm	точка Фредгольма
F 599	**Fredholm['s] radius** <FA, IE>	Fredholmscher Radius *m*, Fredholm-Radius *m*	rayon *m* de Fredholm	радиус Фредгольма
F 600	**Fredholm-type [integral] equation,** integral equation of [the] Fredholm type, Fredholm['s] [integral] equation, integral equation with fixed upper limit of integration <IE>	Integralgleichung *f* vom Fredholmschen Typ, Integralgleichung vom Fredholm-Typ, Fredholmsche Integralgleichung, Integralgleichung mit fester oberer Integrationsgrenze	équation *f* intégrale de (du) type Fredholm, équation [intégrale] de Fredholm, équation intégrale à limite supérieure fixe d'intégration	интегральное уравнение типа Фредгольма, интегральное уравнение Фредгольма, уравнение Фредгольма, интегральное уравнение с постоянным верхним пределом
F 601	**Fredholm-type [integral] equation of the first kind,** integral equa-	Integralgleichung *f* vom Fredholmschen Typ erster Art, Integralgleichung	équation *f* intégrale de (du) type Fredholm de première espèce, équation	интегральное уравнение типа Фредгольма первого рода, интегральное

and still: F 601	tion of [the] Fredholm type of the first kind, Fredholm['s] [integral] equation of the first kind, integral equation with fixed upper limit of integration of the first kind <IE>	vom Fredholm-Typ erster Art, Fredholmsche Integralgleichung erster Art, Integralgleichung [mit fester oberer Integrationsgrenze] erster Art	[intégrale] de Fredholm de première espèce, équation intégrale à limite supérieure fixe d'intégration de première espèce	уравнение Фредгольма первого рода, уравнение Фредгольма первого рода, интегральное уравнение с постоянным верхним пределом первого рода
F 602	**Fredholm-type [integral] equation of the second kind,** integral equation of [the] Fredholm type of the second kind, Fredholm['s] [integral] equation of the second kind, integral equation with fixed upper limit of integration of the second kind <IE>	Integralgleichung *f* vom Fredholmschen Typ zweiter Art, Integralgleichung vom Fredholm-Typ zweiter Art, Fredholmsche Integralgleichung zweiter Art, Integralgleichung [mit fester oberer Integrationsgrenze] zweiter Art	équation *f* intégrale de (du) type Fredholm de seconde (deuxième) espèce, équation [intégrale] de Fredholm de seconde (deuxième) espèce, équation intégrale à limite supérieure fixe d'intégration de seconde (deuxième) espèce	интегральное уравнение типа Фредгольма второго рода, [интегральное] уравнение Фредгольма второго рода, интегральное уравнение с постоянным верхним пределом второго рода
F 603	**Fredkin['s] game** <TG>	Fredkin-Spiel *n*	jeu *m* de Fredkin	игра Фредкина
F 604	**free approximation** <of a chain complex> <HA>	freie Approximation *f*	approximation *f* libre	свободная аппроксимация
F 605	**free automorphism** <AL>	freier Automorphismus *m*	automorphisme *m* libre	свободный автоморфизм
F 606	**free band,** free idempotent semigroup <AL>	freie idempotente Halbgruppe *f*	demi-groupe *m* d'idempotents libre	свободная связка, свободная подгруппа идемпотентов
	free basis <AL>	*s.* F 612		
	free commutative algebra <AL>	*s.* P 976		
F 607	**free decision variable,** free variable <PG, SP>	vorzeichenfreie Entscheidungsvariable (Steuervariable) *f*, freie Entscheidungsvariable (Steuervariable, Variable *f*)	variable *f* de décision libre, variable libre	свободная переменная решения, свободная [решающая] переменная
F 608	**free decomposition** <of groups> <GR>	freie Zerlegung *f*	décomposition *f* en produit libre	разложение в свободное произведение, свободное разложение
F 609	**free differential calculus** <AL>	freier Differentialkalkül *m*	calcul *m* différentiel libre	свободное дифференциальное исчисление
	freedom <AG>	*s.* D 499		
	freedom of contradiction <GN, LO>	*s.* C 2082		
F 610	**free extension** <of *L* over *k*> <AL>	freier Körper *m* <von *L* über *k*>	extension *f* libre <de *L* sur *k*>	свободное расширение <*L* над *k*>
F 611	**free factor** <AL, GR, UA>	freier Faktor *m*	facteur *m* libre	свободный множитель
F 612	**free generating set,** free basis <of a group *or* module> <AL>	freie Basis *f*, freies Erzeugendensystem *n*	base *f* libre, ensemble *m* libre de générateurs, système *m* de générateurs libre	множество свободных образующих, свободный базис, система свободных образующих
F 613	**free generating set** <UA>	System *n* freier Erzeugender	système *m* de générateurs libre	система свободных образующих
F 614	**free generator** <GR>	freie Erzeugende *f*	générateur *m* libre	свободная образующая
F 615	**free group,** word group <GR>	freie Gruppe *f*, Wortgruppe *f*	groupe *m* libre (de mots)	свободная группа, группа слов
F 616	**free groupoid** <CA>	freies Gruppoid *n*	groupoïde *m* libre, magma *m* libre	свободный группоид
F 617	**free ideal ring,** fir <AL>	Ring *m*, dessen Ideale frei vom Rang 1 sind	FI-anneau *m*	кольцо свободных идеалов, FI-кольцо
	free idempotent semigroup <AL>	*s.* F 606		
F 618	**free index,** identifying index, living index <GN, VT>	freier Index *m*	indice *m* libre (franc)	свободный индекс
	free join <CA>	*s.* C 2449		
F 619	**free liberty,** free mobility <GE>	freie Beweglichkeit *f*	libre mobilité *f*	свободная подвижность
F 620	**freely generated group** <GR>	frei erzeugte Gruppe *f*	groupe *m* librement engendré	свободно порожденная группа
F 621	**freely homotopic maps** <TO>	frei homotope (ineinander deformierbare) Abbildungen *fpl*	applications *fpl* librement homotopes	свободно гомотопные отображения
F 622	**freely indecomposable group** <GR>	frei unzerlegbare Gruppe *f*	groupe *m* indécomposable en produit libre	неразложимая [в свободное произведение] группа
F 623	**free maximum** <VA>	freies Maximum *n*	maximum *m* libre	безусловный максимум
F 624	**free minimum** <VA>	freies Minimum *n*	minimum *m* libre	безусловный минимум
	free mobility <GE>	*s.* F 619		
	free module over *R* <AL>	*s.* F 631		
F 625	**free monoid** <AL>	freies Monoid *n*	monoïde *m* libre	свободный моноид
F 626	**freeness** <of modules> <AL>	Freiheit *f*	liberté *f*	свобода
F 627	**free object,** left free object <CA>	freies Objekt *n*	objet *m* libre	свободный [слева] объект
F 628	**free polynomial ring** <AL>	freier Polynomring *m*	anneau *m* des polynômes libre	свободное кольцо многочленов
F 629	**free presentation** <of groups> <AL>	freie Präsentierung *f*	présentation *f* libre	свободное представление
F 630	**free product** <GR>	freies Produkt *n*	produit *m* libre	свободное произведение
F 631	**free *R*-module,** free module over *R* <AL>	freier *R*-Modul *m*, Vektorraum *m* über *R*	*R*-module *m* libre	свободный *R*-модуль (модуль над *R*)
F 632	**free semigroup** <AL>	freie Halbgruppe *f*	demi-groupe *m* libre, monoïde *m* libre	свободная полугруппа
F 633	**free set,** independent set <in a dependence relation> <AL>	unabhängige Menge *f*	ensemble *m* libre (indépendant)	свободное (независимое) множество

F 634	**free set of generators** <AL>	freies Erzeugendensystem *n*	ensemble *m* libre de générateurs	свободная система образующих
F 635	**free subscript** <GN, VT>	freier unterer Index *m*	indice *m* inférieur libre	свободный нижний индекс
F 636	**free substitution of terms** <LO>	freie Termeinsetzung *f*, freie Einsetzung *f* von Termen	substitution *f* libre de termes	свободная подстановка термов
F 637	**free variable,** real variable, unknown <LO>	freie Variable *f*	variable *f* libre	свободная переменная, значащая переменная
	free variable <PG, SP>	*s.* F 607		
F 638	**free vector** <VT>	freier Vektor *m*, // Pfeil *m* <Lotze>	vecteur *m* libre (non localisé)	свободный вектор
F 639	**Frege['s] syllogism,** self-distributive law of [material] implication <LO>	Theorem *n* des Distributionsschlusses, Dreierschluß *m*, Fregescher Dreierschluß (Kettenschluß *m*), implikative Fregesche Wahrform *f*, Wahrform (Form *f*) zum Dreierschluß, Prinzip *n* des Distributionsschlusses, Prinzip der verallgemeinerten Abtrennung	loi *f* de distributivité de l'implication par rapport à l'implication	самодистрибутивность (закон самодистрибутивности) импликации
F 640	**Frégier['s] line** <of a conic> <AY, EG>	Frégiersche Gerade *f*	droite *f* de Frégier	прямая Фрежье
F 641	**Frégier['s] point** <of a conic> <AY>	Frégierscher Punkt *m*	point *m* de Frégier	точка Фрежье
	Frégier['s] theorem <AY>	*s.* T 279		
F 642	***F*-regular element** <of a ring> <AL>	*F*-reguläres Element *n*	élément *m* *F*-régulier	*F*-регулярный элемент
F 643	**Frenet['s] (Frenet-Serret['s]) formulae,** Serret-Frenet['s] formulae, formulae of [Serret-] Frenet <of curve theory> <DG>	Frenetsche Formeln *fpl*, Frenet-Formeln *fpl*, Serretsche Formeln	formules *fpl* de Frenet, formules dues à Frenet et Serret	формулы Серре-Френе (Френе)
F 644	**frequency approach** <ST>	Häufigkeitsvorgehen *n*	approche *f* fréquentiste	частотный подход
F 645	**frequency chart,** frequency paper <IN, ST>	Häufigkeitsnetz *n*, Häufigkeitspapier *n*	diagramme (papier) *m* à échelle fonctionnelle de fréquence	частотная сетка, частотная бумага
F 646	**frequency curve** <ST>	Häufigkeitskurve *f*	courbe *f* des fréquences	кривая частот (частоты), частотная кривая
F 647	**frequency diagram** <ST>	Häufigkeitsdiagramm *n*	diagramme *m* des fréquences	диаграмма (график) частот, диаграмма (график) повторяемости
F 648	**frequency distribution** <ST>	Häufigkeitsverteilung *f*	distribution *f* des fréquences	частотное распределение, распределение частот
	frequency equation <DE>	*s.* A 1250		
F 649	**frequency function,** probability frequency function <ST>	Häufigkeitsfunktion *f*, Wahrscheinlichkeitshäufigkeitsfunktion *f*	fonction *f* de fréquence	функция частоты
F 650	**frequency method** <of solving the transportation problem> <PG>	Frequenzmethode *f*	méthode *f* des fréquences	метод частот
	frequency paper <IN, ST>	*s.* F 645		
F 651	**frequency polygon** <ST>	Häufigkeitspolygon *n*	polygone *m* de fréquence, polygone des fréquences, polygone de fréquences	полигон частот (повторяемости, распределения), многоугольник частот (повторяемости, распределения)
F 652	**frequency-shift theorem,** first shifting theorem, substitution property <of Laplace transform> <IT>	Dämpfungssatz *m*	règle *f* sur la multiplication de l'original par une exponentielle	теорема смещения
F 653	**frequency theory of probability** <ST>	Häufigkeitsinterpretation *f* der Wahrscheinlichkeit	interprétation *f* fréquentiste de la probabilité	частотная интерпретация теории вероятностей [по Мизесу]
F 654	**Fresnel[s] cosine integral** <FU>	Fresnelsches Kosinusintegral *n*	cosinus *m* intégral de Fresnel	косинус-интеграл Френеля
F 655	**Fresnel['s] integral** <FU>	Fresnelsches Integral *n*	intégrale *f* de Fresnel	интеграл Френеля
F 656	**Fresnel['s] sine integral** <FU>	Fresnelsches Sinusintegral *n*	sinus *m* intégral de Fresnel	синус-интеграл Френеля
F 657	**Fresnel['s] wave surface** <AG>	Fresnelsche Wellenfläche *f*	surface *f* des ondes de Fresnel	волновая поверхность Френеля
	Freudenthal['s] suspension <TO>	*s.* S 2387		
F 658	**Freudenthal['s] suspension theorem** <AT>	Freudenthalscher Einhängungssatz *m*	théorème *m* de suspension de Freudenthal	теорема Фрейденталя о надстройке
F 659	**Friedman (Friedman-Kendall) test** <ST>	Friedman[-Kendall]-Test *m*	test *m* de Friedman[-Kendall]	критерий Фридмана[-Кендалла]
F 660	**Friedrichs['s] inequality** <FT>	Friedrichssche Ungleichung *f*, Ungleichung von Friedrichs	inégalité *f* de Friedrichs	неравенство Фридрихса
F 661	**Friedrichs['s] method** <FA>	Friedrichssche Methode *f*, Methode von Friedrichs	méthode *f* de Friedrichs	метод Фридрихса
	friendly numbers <NT>	*s.* A 597		
	F. Riesz's representation theorem <FA>	*s.* R 1061		
F 662	**f-ring,** function ring <AL>	f-Ring *m*	f-anneau *m*	f-кольцо
	Frink['s] theorem <GP>	*s.* T 280		
F 663	**Frobenius['] algebra** <AL>	Frobenius-Algebra *f*	algèbre *f* frobeniusienne	фробениусова алгебра

F 664	**Frobenius['] automorphism,** Frobenius['] substitution <AB>	Frobenius-Automorphismus *m*, Frobenius-Substitution *f*	automorphisme *m* de Frobenius, Frobenius *m*, substitution *f* de Frobenius	подстановка (автоморфизм, элемент) Фробениуса
F 665	**Frobenius['] class** <AB>	Frobenius-Substitutionsklasse *f*	classe *f* de Frobenius	класс Фробениуса
F 666	**Frobenius['] duality** <AL>	Frobeniussche Dualität *f*	dualité *f* de Frobenius	двойственность Фробениуса
F 667	**Frobenius['] endomorphism,** Frobenius['] map <AB>	Frobenius-Endomorphismus *m*	endomorphisme *m* de Frobenius	эндоморфизм Фробениуса
F 668	**Frobenius['] extension** <AL>	Frobenius-Erweiterung *f*	extension *f* de Frobenius	фробениусово расширение
F 669	**Frobenius['] form,** rational canonical form <of a matrix> <MD>	erste Normalform *f*	matrice *f* de Frobenius	первая нормальная форма
F 670	**Frobenius['] group** <AL>	Frobenius-Gruppe *f*, Frobeniusgruppe *f*	groupe *m* de Frobenius	группа Фробениуса
F 671	**Frobenius['] homomorphism,** Frobenius['] map <AL>	Frobeniusscher Homomorphismus *m*	homomorphisme *m* frobeniusien	гомоморфизм (отображение) Фробениуса
	Frobenius['] inclusion theorem <DE>	*s.* I 248		
F 672	**Frobenius['] map** <AB>	Frobeniussche Abbildung *f*	application *f* de Frobenius	отображение Фробениуса
	Frobenius['] map <AB>	*s.* F 667		
	Frobenius['] map <AL>	*s.* F 671		
F 673	**Frobenius['] module** <AL>	Frobenius-Modul *m*	module *m* de Frobenius	модуль Фробениуса
F 674	**Frobenius['] reciprocity theorem** <RE>	Frobeniussches Reziprozitätsgesetz *n*	formule *f* de réciprocité de Frobenius, théorème *m* [de réciprocité] de Frobenius	закон взаимности (двойственности) Фробениуса, теорема двойственности Фробениуса
F 675	**Frobenius['] ring** <AL>	Frobenius-Ring *m*	anneau *m* frobeniusien	фробениусово кольцо
	Frobenius['] substitution <AB>	*s.* F 664		
F 676	**Frobenius['] symbol** <AB>	Frobenius-Symbol *n*, Frobeniussches Symbol *n*	symbole *m* de Frobenius	символ Фробениуса
	Frobenius['] theorem <AL, GR>	*s.* T 281		
	front adjunction <CA>	*s.* U 288		
	frontal axonometry <DS>	*s.* D 522		
F 677	**frontier,** boundary <of a set> <TO>	Begrenzung *f*, Rand *m*, Randpunktmenge *f*	frontière *f*	граница, граничное точечное множество, множество точек границы
	frontier <AT>	*s.* P 786		
F 678	**frontier point,** boundary point <of a set, is not contained in this set> <TO>	Begrenzungspunkt *m*, Grenzpunkt *m*, Randpunkt *m*	point *m* frontière, point-frontière *m*	граничная точка
F 679	**front line,** second principal line, second trace parallel, // vertical <in two-plane projection> <DS>	Frontlinie *f*, zweite Hauptlinie (Tafellinie, Streichlinie) *f*, Hauptlinie (Tafellinie, Streichlinie) zweiter Ordnung	frontale *f*, droite *f* frontale (de front), deuxième ligne *f* principale	фронталь, вторая главная (основная) линия, // вертикаль
F 680	**front plane,** second principal plane <in two-plane projection> <DS>	Frontebene *f*, zweite Hauptebene *f*, Hauptebene zweiter Ordnung	plan *m* frontal (de front), deuxième plan principal	фронтальная (вторая главная) плоскость
F 681	**frustum of cone,** frustum of right [circular] cone, truncated cone (right [circular] cone), conical frustum <EG>	Kegelstumpf *m*, gerader Kegelstumpf (Kreiskegelstumpf *m*)	cône *m* tronqué, tronc *m* de cône, cône [circulaire] droit tronqué, tronc du cône [circulaire] droit	усеченный конус, усеченный прямой [круговой] конус
F 682	**frustum of oblique cone** <EG>	schiefer Kegelstumpf *m*	cône *m* oblique tronqué	усеченный наклонный конус
F 683	**frustum of pyramid,** frustum of right pyramid, truncated pyramid <EG>	Pyramidenstumpf *m*, gerader (senkrechter) Pyramidenstumpf	pyramide *f* tronquée, tronc *m* de pyramide (pyramide droite), pyramide droite tronquée	усеченная пирамида (прямая пирамида)
	frustum of right [circular] cone <EG>	*s.* F 681		
	frustum of right pyramid <EG>	*s.* F 683		
F 684	**F_σ-set** <TO>	F_σ-Menge *f*, F_σ *n*	ensemble *m* F_σ, F_σ *m*	множество F_σ, множество типа F_σ, F_σ-множество
F 685	**F_{II}-space** <TO>	F_{II}-Raum *m* <metrischer Raum, in dem jede nichtleere abgeschlossene Teilmenge in sich von zweiter Kategorie ist>	F_{II}-espace *m*	F_{II}-пространство
	F-space <FA, TO>	*s.* F 585		
	F-statistic <ST>	*s.* V 64		
F 686	**F-test** <ST>	*F*-Test *m*	test *m F*	*F*-критерий
	F'-test <ST>	*s.* S 2192		
F 687	**F-torsion module,** *F*-negligible module <AL>	*F*-Torsionsmodul *m*	module *m F*-négligeable	модуль *F*-кручения
F 688	**Fubini['s] normal** <DG>	Normale *f* von Fubini, Fubinische Normale	normale *f* de Fubini	нормаль Фубини
F 689	**Fubini['s] theorem** <for distributions> <AN>	Theorem *n* von Fubini, Fubinisches Theorem	théorème *m* de Fubini	теорема Фубини
F 690	**Fubini['s] theorem** <for derivability or integrability of functional series> <ME, RF>	Satz *m* von Fubini, Fubinischer Satz	théorème *m* de Fubini (Fubini-Lebesgue, Lebesgue-Fubini)	теорема Фубини (Лебега-Фубини)
	Fuchs['s] equation <DE>	*s.* F 699		
	Fuchsian class <DE>	*s.* F 694		

	Fuchsian [differential] equation <DE>	*s.* F 699		
F 691	**Fuchsian function** <of the first *or* second kind> <FT>	Fuchssche Funktion *f*, Hauptkreisfunktion *f* <erster (1.) *oder* zweiter (2.) Art>	fonction *f* fuchsienne <de première *ou* deuxième espèce>	функция Фукса, фуксова функция <первого *или* второго рода>
F 692	**Fuchsian group** <FT>	Hauptkreisgruppe *f*, Fuchssche Gruppe *f*	groupe *m* fuchsien	фуксова группа, группа Фукса
F 693	**Fuchsian group of the first kind,** horocyclic group <FT>	Hauptkreisgruppe *f* erster (1.) Art, Fuchssche Gruppe *f* erster (1.) Art, Grenzkreisgruppe *f*, horozyklische Gruppe	groupe *m* fuchsien de première espèce, groupe horocyclique	фуксова группа первого рода, орициклическая группа
F 694	**Fuchsian type,** Fuchsian class <DE>	Fuchsscher Typ[us] *m*, Fuchssche Klasse *f*	type *m* Fuchs, classe *f* fuchsienne	тип Фукса, класс Фукса
F 695	**fuchsoid function** <FT>	fuchsoide Funktion *f*	fonction *f* fuchsoïde	фуксоидная функция
F 696	**Fuchsoid group,** horocyclic group of the second kind <FT>	fuchsoide Gruppe *f*, Grenzkreisgruppe *f* (horozyklische Gruppe) *f* zweiter (2.) Art	groupe *m* fuchsoïde, groupe horocyclique de deuxième espèce	фуксоидная группа, орициклическая группа второго рода
F 697	**Fuchs[']s radical** <of a ring> <AL>	Radikal *n* im Sinne von Fuchs, Fuchssches Radikal *n*	radical *m* de Fuchs	радикал [в смысле] Фукса
F 698	**Fuchs['s] (Fuchs') theorem** <DE>	Satz *m* von Fuchs, Fuchsscher Satz	théorème *m* de Fuchs	теорема Фукса
	Fuchs['s] theory <DE>	*s.* T 384		
F 699	**Fuchs-type [differential] equation,** Fuchs['s] equation, Fuchsian [differential] equation, differential equation of Fuchsian type, equation of the Fuchsian type, equation with regular singular points <DE>	Differentialgleichung *f* vom Fuchsschen Typ[us], Differentialgleichung der Fuchsschen Klasse	équation *f* différentielle du type Fuchs, équation du type Fuchs	уравнение фуксова типа, дифференциальное уравнение типа Фукса
F 700	**Fuhrmann['s] circle** <of a triangle> <EG>	Fuhrmannscher Kreis *m*	cercle *m* de Fuhrmann	окружность Фурмана
F 701	**fulfil / to,** to satisfy, to meet <a condition *or* requirement> <GN>	erfüllen, befriedigen <eine Bedingung *oder* Forderung>, genügen <einer Bedingung *oder* Forderung>	remplir <une condition *ou* demande>, satisfaire <[à] une condition *ou* demande>	удовлетворять <условию *или* требованию>, выполнять <условие *или* требование>
	fulfil / to <AL, AN>	*s.* S 60		
	fulfilment <LO>	*s.* S 55		
F 702	**full and faithful imbedding** <of a category> <CA>	volltreue Einbettung *f*	plongement *m* pleinement fidèle	вполное верное погружение
	full angle <EG>	*s.* P 440		
F 703	**full angle around a point** <on a surface> <GE>	voller Winkel *m* um einen Punkt	angle *m* plein autour d'un point	полный угол вокруг точки
	full conjunctive normal form <LO>	*s.* P 1402		
	full disjunctive normal form <LO>	*s.* P 1409		
F 704	**full dual space,** dual, linear dual, dual [vector] space <of a vector space> <AL, FA>	algebraischer Dual (Dualraum) *m*, dualer Raum *m*, algebraisch dualer (konjugierter) Raum *m*	espace *m* dual, dual *m* algébrique, espace vectoriel dual	сопряженное (дуальное, двойственное) пространство, алгебраическое сопряженное [пространство]
F 705	**full embedding** <of a functor> <CA>	volle Einbettung *f*	foncteur *m* pleinement fidèle qui est injectif sur les objets	вполне унивалентный функтор вложения
F 706	**full faithful functor,** fully faithful functor <CA>	völlig treuer Funktor *m*, volltreuer Funktor	foncteur *m* pleinement fidèle	вполне (полный) унивалентный функтор, вполне инъективный функтор
	full function-theoretical plane <FT>	*s.* E 762		
F 707	**full functor** <CA>	voller Funktor *m*	foncteur *m* plein	полный функтор
	full group of permutations <GR>	*s.* S 2441		
F 708	**full homomorphism** <of partial algebras> <UA>	überall definierter Homomorphismus *m*	homomorphisme *m* partout défini	всюду определенный гомоморфизм
	full hull <FA>	*s.* O 293		
F 709	**full image** <of a many-valued mapping> <SE>	volles Bild *n*	image *f* complète	полный образ
F 710	**full inhomogeneous Lorentz group** <GR>	volle inhomogene Lorentz-Gruppe *f*	groupe *m* de Lorentz inhomogène et orthochrone	полная неоднородная группа Лоренца
F 711	**full invariance** <of a subgroup> <GR>	Vollinvarianz *f*	invariance *f* complète	полная характеристичность
F 712	**full inverse image,** inverse-image set, counter image, inverse [image] <in a mapping> <SE, TO>	volles (vollständiges) Urbild *n*, Urbild, Originalmenge *f*, Urbildmenge *f*	image *f* réciproque (inverse), prototype *m* complet	полный прообраз
	full inverse image <SE, TO>	*s.* I 904		
F 713	**full isotropic plane,** null plane <DG>	vollisotrope (totalisotrope, ametrische) Ebene *f*	plan *m* totalement isotrope	вполне изотропная плоскость
F 714	**full isotropic surface,** null surface <DG>	vollisotrope (totalisotrope, ametrische) Fläche *f*	surface *f* totalement isotrope	вполне изотропная поверхность
F 715	**full isotropic variety,** null variety <DG>	vollisotrope (totalisotrope, ametrische) Mannigfaltigkeit *f*	variété *f* totalement isotrope	вполне изотропное многообразие

F 716	**full linear group,** complete linear group, general linear [homogeneous] group <of dimension *n*; over *K*> <GR>	volle (allgemeine, vollständige, generelle) lineare Gruppe *f*, allgemeine lineare homogene Gruppe <für *n* Variable; über dem Körper *K*>	groupe *m* linéaire général (et homogène général, complet), groupe linéaire <d'ordre *n*, à *n* variables, de degré *n*, de type *n*; défini sur *K*, sur le corps *K*>	полная (общая) линейная группа <от *n* переменных; над *K*>
F 717	**full linear ring,** FL-ring <AL>	FL-Ring *m*	FL-anneau *m*	FL-кольцо
	full lower triangular group <AL>	*s.* L 1170		
	full matrix algebra (ring) <AL>	*s.* T 677		
F 718	**full orthogonal group,** orthogonal group <GR>	volle (erweiterte) orthogonale Gruppe *f*	groupe *m* orthogonal complet, groupe orthogonal	полная ортогональная группа
	full plane <FT>	*s.* E 762		
F 719	**full reducibility** <of a representation> <RE>	vollständige Reduzibilität *f*	réductibilité *f* complète	полная приводимость
F 720	**full solid angle** <EG>	räumlicher Vollwinkel *m*	angle *m* solide total	полный телесный угол
	full sphere <DI, GE, TO>	*s.* B 38		
F 721	**full subcategory,** morphism-full subcategory, complete subcategory <CA>	volle Unterkategorie (Teilkategorie) *f*	sous-catégorie *f* pleine (complète)	полная подкатегория
F 722	**full subgraph** <CA, GP, UA>	voller Teilgraph *m*	sous-graphe *m* plein	полный подграф
	full symmetric group <GR>	*s.* S 2441		
	full transformation semigroup <AL>	*s.* S 2464		
F 723	**full unimodular group** <GR>	volle unimodulare Gruppe *f*	groupe *m* unimodulaire complet	полная унимодулярная группа
	full upper triangular group <AL>	*s.* U 441		
	fully characteristic subgroup <GR>	*s.* F 725		
	fully faithful functor <CA>	*s.* F 706		
F 724	**fully invariant congruence [relation]** <UA>	vollinvariante Kongruenzrelation *f*	congruence *f* complètement invariante	вполне инвариантная конгруэнция
F 725	**fully invariant subgroup,** fully characteristic subgroup <GR>	vollinvariante (vollcharakteristische) Untergruppe *f*	sous-groupe *m* complètement invariant	вполне характеристическая (инвариантная) подгруппа, отмеченная подгруппа
	fully normal space <TO>	*s.* P 78		
	fully ordered ring <AL>	*s.* L 819		
F 726	**fully reducible representation,** completely reducible representation, semi-simple representation <AL>	vollständig reduzible Darstellung *f*, vollreduzible (halbeinfache) Darstellung	représentation *f* semi-simple (complètement réductible)	вполне приводимое представление, полупростое (полностью приводимое) представление
F 727	**fully reducible star body** <GU>	vollreduzibler Sternkörper *m*	corps *m* étoilé complètement réductible	вполне приводимое звездное тело
F 728	**fully transitive group,** completely transitive group <AL>	volltransitive Gruppe *f*	groupe *m* complètement transitif	вполне транзитивная группа
	function <AN, FA>	*s.* M 96		
	function <LO>	*s.* S 497		
	function <SE>	*s.* S 1037		
F 729	**function / as a** <of> <GN>	in Abhängigkeit <von>, als Funktion <von>	en fonction <de>	в зависимости <от>
	(1—1)-function, 1—1 function <SE>	*s.* I 548		
	Γ-function <FU>	*s.* G 42		
	δ-function <FU>	*s.* D 211		
	ε-function <LO>	*s.* E 309		
	ζ-function <FU>	*s.* W 177		
	ζ-function <FU, NT>	*s.* R 1046		
	ϑ-function <FU>	*s.* 1. J 36; 2. T 409		
	Π-function <FU>	*s.* P 600		
	σ-function <FT>	*s.* W 165		
	φ-function <NT>	*s.* E 588		
F 730	**functional** <of the *n*-th degree on a linear space> <FA>	Funktional *n* <*n*-ten Grades, von *n*-tem Grade auf einem linearen Raum>	fonctionnelle *f* <de degré *n* sur un espace linéaire>	функционал <*n*-й степени в линейном пространстве>
F 731	**functional,** function of a function <VA>	Funktional *n*, Funktionenfunktion *f*, Funktionsfunktion *f*, Funktion *f* einer Funktion	fonctionnelle *f*, fonction *f* de fonction	функционал, функция от функции, сложная функция
	functional <AN, FA>	*s.* M 96		
F 732	**functional algebra** <FT>	Funktionalalgebra *f* <Pál Turán>	algèbre *f* fonctionnelle	функциональная алгебра
F 733	**functional analysis** <FA>	Funktionalanalysis *f*	analyse *f* fonctionnelle	функциональный анализ
F 734	**functional calculus** <FA, LO>; system of logic with functions, logical functional calculus, functional logical calculus <LO>	Funktionalkalkül *m*	calcul *m* fonctionnel	функциональное исчисление
	functional calculus <LO>	*s.* P 1183		
	functional calculus of first order with equality <LO>	*s.* F 348		
	functional calculus of higher order <LO>	*s.* H 304		

No.	English	German	French	Russian
	functional calculus of the first order <LO>	*s.* F 349		
	functional calculus of the second order <LO>	*s.* S 218		
	functional calculus of the third order <LO>	*s.* P 1184		
F 735	**functional calculus with identity,** system of logic with identity and functions <LO>	Funktionalkalkül *m* mit Identität	calcul *m* fonctionnel avec constante d'égalité	расширенное функциональное исчисление
	functional chart <NO>	*s.* F 756		
F 736	**functional concave in the Minkowski sense** <FA>	im Minkowskischen Sinne konkaves Funktional *n*	fonctionnelle *f* concave au sens de Minkowski	вогнутый в смысле Минковского функционал
F 737	**functional concentrated on a point** <FA>	auf einen Punkt konzentriertes Funktional *n*	fonctionnelle *f* à support ponctuel	функционал, сосредоточенный в точке
F 738	**functional congruence,** identical congruence <of polynomials> <NT>	algebraische (identische) Kongruenz *f*, Kongruenz	congruence *f* identique	тождественное сравнение
	functional constant <LO>	*s.* F 757		
F 739	**functional dependence** <AN>	funktionale Abhängigkeit *f*, Funktionalabhängigkeit *f*	dépendance *f* fonctionnelle	функциональная зависимость
	functional derivative <VA>	*s.* V 70		
	functional determinant <AN>	*s.* J 5		
	functional digraph <GP>	*s.* F 742		
F 740	**functional eigenvalue equation** <DE, FA>	Funktional-Eigenwertgleichung *f*	équation *f* aux valeurs propres fonctionnelle	функциональное уравнение на собственные значения
F 741	**functional equation for (of) the gamma function** <FU>	Funktionalgleichung *f* der (für die) Gammafunktion	équation *f* fonctionnelle de la fonction gamma	функциональное уравнение гамма-функции, основное соотношение для гамма-функции
F 742	**functional graph,** functional digraph <GP>	funktionaler Graph *m*	graphe *m* fonctionnel (univoque)	функциональный орграф
F 743	**functional invariant** <DE, DG, PJ>	Funktionalinvariante *f* <Clebsch>	invariant *m* fonctionnel	функциональный инвариант
	functionality <SE>	*s.* S 1040		
	functional logical calculus <LO>	*s.* F 734		
F 744	**function allowing a convolution** <FT>	faltbare Funktion *f*	fonction *f* convolable	свертывающаяся функция
	functionally closed set <TO>	*s.* Z 61		
	functionally closed space <TO>	*s.* H 284		
	functionally complete algebra <UA>	*s.* P 1255		
F 745	**functionally incomplete propositional calculus** <LO>	fragmentarischer Aussagenkalkül *m*, nicht funktional vollständiger Kalkül *m*	calcul *m* propositionnel fonctionnellement incomplet	функционально неполное исчисление высказываний
	functionally open set <TO>	*s.* C 2644		
	functionally strictly complete algebra <UA>	*s.* P 1255		
F 746	**functional matrix,** Jacobian matrix, jacobian matrix <AN>	Funktionalmatrix *f*, Jacobische Matrix *f*	matrice *f* fonctionnelle (jacobienne)	функциональная матрица
F 747/8	**functional method** <AG>	funktionale Methode *f* <Cayley>	méthode *f* fonctionnelle	функциональный метод
	function almost periodic on the left <AP>	*s.* L 292		
	function almost periodic on the right <AP>	*s.* R 1069		
	functional operator <FA>	*s.* F 753		
	functional relation <SE>	*s.* S 1042		
F 749	**functional relationship** <ST>	funktionale Beziehung *f*	relation (liaison) *f* fonctionnelle	функциональное соотношение
F 750	**functional representation** <of an abstract Hilbert space> <FA>	Funktionaldarstellung *f*	représentation *f* fonctionnelle	функциональное представление
	functional scale <NO>	*s.* F 756		
	functional series <SS>	*s.* F 775		
F 751	**functional space** <VA>	Funktionalraum *m*	espace *m* fonctionnel	функциональное пространство
F 752	**functional symbol,** operation sign, function symbol <LO>	Funktionssymbol *n*, Operationssymbol *n*, Funktionszeichen *n*	symbole *m* fonctionnel	функциональный символ, функциональная буква, знак функции
F 753	**functional transformation,** functional operator <FA>	Funktionaltransformation *f*, Funktionaloperator *m*, // Funktionaloperation *f*	transformation *f* fonctionnelle, opérateur *m* fonctionnel, // opération *f* fonctionnelle	функциональное преобразование, функциональный оператор, // функциональная операция
F 754	**function approximable in the mean** <AX>	im Mittel approximierbare Funktion *f*	fonction *f* approximable (approchable) en moyenne	аппроксимируемая (приближаемая) в среднем функция
F 755	**function bounded in measure** <ME>	dem Maß nach beschränkte Funktion *f*	fonction *f* bornée en mesure	функция, ограниченная по мере

No.	English	German	French	Russian
F 756	**function chart,** functional chart, function[al] scale, nomographic scale of a function <NO>	Funktionsskala *f*, Funktionsleiter *f*	échelle *f* fonctionnelle, échelle nomographique d'une fonction	функциональная шкала, шкала функции
F 757	**function constant,** functional constant, proper name of a function <LO>	Funktionskonstante *f*	constante *f* de fonctions	функциональная постоянная
	function continuous in the extended sense <AN>	*s.* C 2212		
F 758	**function continuous on the right,** right-[hand] continuous function <AN>	rechtsseitig (vorwärts) stetige Funktion *f*, rechtsstetige Funktion	fonction *f* continue vers le droit, fonction continue à droite	непрерывная справа функция
	function continuous with respect to μ <AN>	*s.* M 944		
	function differentiable in the sense of Stolz <DI>	*s.* T 644		
	function differentiable on the left <RF>	*s.* L 369		
	function differentiable on the right <RF>	*s.* R 1153		
F 759	**function[-] element,** element <of function> <FT>	Funktionselement *n*, Element *n*	élément *m* de fonction, élément fonctionnel, élément	элемент функции, элемент
F 760	**function field** <*e.g.:* of one indeterminate> <AL>	Funktionenkörper *m* <*z. B.:* in einer Unbestimmten>	corps *m* de fonctions, corps fonctionnel <*par exemple:* d'une variable>	поле функций, функциональное поле <*например:* одной переменной>
	function finite with respect to a measure μ <ME>	*s.* M 945		
	function having continuous derivatives of all orders <DI>	*s.* I 453		
	function integrable in the sense of Riemann <AN>	*s.* R 1014		
	function into . . . <SE>	*s.* M 103		
	function of a function <AN>	*s.* C 1678		
	function of a function <VA>	*s.* F 731		
F 761	**function of best approximation** <AX>	Funktion *f* kleinster Abweichung <von *f*>, Funktion bester Approximation <an *f*>	fonction *f* de la meilleure approximation	функция наилучшего приближения
F 762	**function of bounded variation,** function of limited variation <AN>	Funktion *f* von (mit) beschränkter (endlicher) Variation (Schwankung)	fonction *f* à variation bornée, fonction à oscillation [totale] limitée	функция с ограниченной (конечной) вариацией, функция с ограниченным (конечным) изменением, функция ограниченной вариации
	function of class α <TO>	*s.* B 593		
F 763	**function of equal increase (order)** <RF>	gleichstark (gleichermaßen) wachsende Funktion *f*, Funktion von (mit) gleichem Zuwachs, Funktion gleicher Ordnung	fonction *f* semblable	подобная функция, функция равного приращения (порядка), функция с равным приращением
	function of formal logic <LO>	*s.* T 1040		
F 764	**function of greater increase (order)** <than another function> <RF>	stärker wachsende Funktion *f*, Funktion von (mit) höherem (stärkerem) Zuwachs, Funktion größerer Ordnung	fonction *f* prépondérante <sur une autre>	превалирующая <над другой> функция, функция бóльшего приращения (порядка), функция высшего порядка, функция с бóльшим приращением
F 765	**function of lesser increase (order)** <than another function> <RF>	schwächer (geringer) wachsende Funktion *f*, Funktion von (mit) geringerem Zuwachs, Funktion kleinerer Ordnung	fonction *f* négligeable <devant une autre>	пренебрежимая <сравнительно с другой> функция, функция меньшего приращения (порядка), функция с меньшим приращением
	function of limited variation <AN>	*s.* F 762		
F 766	**function of negative jumps** <RF>	Funktion *f* der negativen Sprünge	fonction *f* des sauts négatifs	функция отрицательных скачков
F 767	**function of one variable,** singulary function <AL, AN>	Funktion *f* einer Variablen (Veränderlichen), einstellige Funktion	fonction *f* d'une variable	функция одной переменной, одноаргументная (одноместная, унарная) функция, функция с одним аргументом
	function of one variable obtained by holding constant all the other variables <AN>	*s.* S 230		
F 768	**function of positive jumps** <RF>	Funktion *f* der positiven Sprünge	fonction *f* des sauts positifs	функция положительных скачков
	function of representation <CA>	*s.* M 101		

	English	German	French	Russian
F 769	**function of several variables** <AL, AN>	Funktion *f* mehrerer Variabler (Veränderlicher), mehrstellige Funktion	fonction *f* de plusieurs variables	функция нескольких (многих) переменных, многоаргументная (многоместная) функция
F 770	**function of singularities,** singular part <of a real function> <RF>	singulärer Teil *m*, Funktion *f* der Singularitäten	fonction *f* des singularités, partie *f* singulière	функция особенностей, сингулярная составляющая (часть)
	function of support <CS>	*s.* S 2344		
	function of the elliptic cylinder <FU>	*s.* M 173		
F 771	**function of the first Baire class,** function of the 1st Baire class, Baire 1 function <RF, TO>	Funktion *f* erster Klasse	fonction *f* de première (I^e) classe [de Baire], fonction de classe 1	функция первого класса, функция первого класса по Бэру
	function of the parabolic cylinder <FU>	*s.* P 52		
	function of the position [of the point] <AN>	*s.* P 1053		
	function of two arguments <LO>	*s.* F 772		
F 772	**function of two variables,** binary function, function of two arguments <LO>	Funktion *f* zweier Variabler, Funktion zweier Veränderlicher	fonction *f* de deux variables	функция от двух аргументов, бинарная функция, двуместная функция
F 773	**function of unbounded variation** <AN>	Funktion *f* von unbeschränkter Schwankung	fonction *f* à variation illimitée	функция с неограниченной вариацией
	ζ-function of Weierstrass <FU>	*s.* W 177		
	σ-function of Weierstrass <FT>	*s.* W 165		
	function onto . . . <SE>	*s.* S 2378		
	(1—1)-function onto <SE>	*s.* B 330		
	function parameter <LO>	*s.* F 783		
	function periodic *n* times <AN>	*s.* N 716		
	function ring <AL>	*s.* F 662		
	function satisfying a global Lipschitz condition <AN, TO>	*s.* M 109		
	function satisfying a Hölder condition <AN>	*s.* H 387		
	function satisfying a Lipschitz condition <AN, TO>	*s.* 1. M 109; 2. M 110		
	function satisfying a Lipschitz condition <DE>	*s.* L 896		
	function satisfying a local Lipschitz condition <AN, TO>	*s.* L 983		
	function satisfying a punctual Lipschitz condition <AN, TO>	*s.* M 111		
	function scale <NO>	*s.* F 756		
F 774	**function sequence,** sequence of functions <SS>	Funktionenfolge *f*, Funktionsfolge *f*	suite *f* de fonctions, suite fonctionnelle	последовательность функций
F 775	**function series,** series of functions, functional series <SS>	Funktionenreihe *f*, Funktionsreihe *f*, Funktionalreihe *f*	série *f* de fonctions, série fonctionnelle, série à termes variables	функциональный ряд
F 776	**function[-] set,** insertion[-] set, set of all [possible] mappings of *N* into *M*, set of all insertions of *N* into *M* <SE>	Belegungsmenge *f*, Menge *f* aller Belegungen von *N* mit *M*, Menge der Abbildungen von *N* in *M*	ensemble *m* exponentiel de *N* avec *M*, exponentielle *f N* de *M*, ensemble des applications de *N* dans *M*	множество [всех] отображений [от] *N* в *M*
F 777	**functions inverse to each other** <AN>	zueinander inverse Funktionen *fpl*	fonctions *fpl* réciproquement inverses	взаимно обратные функции
F 778	**function space** <FA>	Funktionenraum *m*, Funktionsraum *m*, Funktionalraum *m*	espace *m* fonctionnel, espace de[s] fonctions	функциональное пространство, пространство функций
	function space <TO>	*s.* M 112		
	function symbol <LO>	*s.* F 752		
F 779	**function symbol of *n* arguments,** *n*-place function letter <LO, MM>	*n*-stelliges Funktionssymbol *n*; *n*-stelliges Operationssymbol *n*	symbole *m* fonctionnel à *n* places	*n*-местный функциональный символ
F 780	**function term** <LO>	Funktionsterm *m*, F-Term *m*	terme *m* de fonction	предметная функция
F 781	**function-theoretic** <FT>	funktionentheoretisch	en (de la, d'après la, au sens de la) théorie des fonctions de variables complexes	теоретико-функциональный
F 782	**function theory,** complex analysis, theory of functions <of one complex variable> <FT>	Funktionentheorie *f*, komplexe Funktionentheorie, Theorie *f* der Funktionen einer komplexen Variablen	théorie *f* des fonctions <d'une variable complexe>	теория функций комплексного переменного

No.	English	German	French	Russian
	function to . . . <SE>	*s.* M 103		
	function to be integrated <DI>	*s.* I 670		
F 783	**function variable,** operator variable, function parameter <LO>	Funktionsveränderliche *f*, Funktionsvariable *f*, F-Variable *f*	variable *f* fonctionnelle	функциональная переменная
F 784	**function with bounded support** <AN>	finite Funktion *f*, Funktion mit beschränktem Träger	fonction *f* à support borné	финитная функция
F 785	**function with integer arguments** <RF>	ganzzahlige Funktion *f*, ganze Zahlenfunktion *f*	fonction *f* à arguments entiers	целочисленная (целая числовая) функция
F 786	**functor** <CA, LO>	Funktor *m*	foncteur *m*	функтор <CA, LO>; предикатор, связка <LO>
F 787	**functor adjoint on the left** <CA>	linksseitig adjungierter Funktor *m*	foncteur *m* adjoint à gauche	сопряженный слева функтор
F 788	**functor category,** exponential category, category of functors; category of diagrams, diagram category <CA>	Funktorkategorie *f*; Diagrammkategorie *f*	catégorie *f* des foncteurs; catégorie de diagrammes	категория функторов; категория диаграмм
F 789	**functor Ext** <HA>	Ext-Funktor *m*	foncteur *m* Ext	функтор Ext
F 790	**functor Hom,** hom-functor, morphism (principal) functor <CA, HA>	Hom-Funktor *m*	foncteur *m* Hom	функтор Hom
F 791	**functorial colimit** <CA>	funktorieller Kolimes *m*	colimite *f* fonctorielle	функториальный прямой предел
	functorial isomorphism <CA>	*s.* N 26		
F 792	**functorial limit** <CA>	funktorieller Limes *m*	limite *f* fonctorielle	функториальный обратный предел
	functorial map <CA>	*s.* N 41		
F 793	**functorial property** <CA>	Funktoreigenschaft *f*	fonctorialité *f*, propriété *f* fonctorielle	функториальность
	functorial transformation <CA>	*s.* N 41		
F 794	**functor language** <CA>	funktorielle Sprache *f*	langage *m* fonctoriel	функторный язык
	functor morphism <CA>	*s.* N 41		
F 795	**functor of *n* arguments (variables),** *n*-variable functor <CA>	*n*-stelliger Funktor *m*, Funktor mit *n* Argumenten	foncteur *m* de *n* variables	функтор от *n* переменных, *n*-местный функтор
	functor of one argument <LO>	*s.* S 1132		
F 796	**functor of several variables** <CA>	Funktor *m* in mehreren Variablen, mehrstelliger Funktor, Funktor mit mehreren Argumenten, Multifunktor *m*	foncteur *m* de plusieurs variables, multifoncteur *m*	функтор от нескольких аргументов, многоместный функтор, мультифунктор, функтор от многих переменных
F 797	**functor of the second order,** predicate of predicates (second level), second-level predicate <LO>	Prädikatenprädikat *n*, Prädikat *n* der zweiten (2.) Stufe, Prädikat zweiter (2.) Stufe	prédicat *m* de prédicats, prédicat d'ordre deux (2)	предикат второго (2-го) порядка, предикат от предикатов, предикат предикатов
F 798	**functor of the third order** <LO>	Prädikat *n* dritter Stufe	prédicat *m* d'ordre 3	предикат третьего порядка
	functor of two arguments <LO>	*s.* B 360		
	functor of two variables <CA>	*s.* B 313		
F 799	**functor Tor** <HA>	Tor-Funktor *m*	foncteur *m* Tor	функтор Tor
F 800	**fundamental circuits,** basis associated with the spanning tree <GP>	Fundamentalsystem *n* <zu einem Gerüst gehöriges>	base *f* de cycles <associée à l'arbre maximal>	базис циклов <соответствующий остову>
F 801	**fundamental class** <of a field extension *or* manifold> <AB, AT>	Fundamentalklasse *f*	classe *f* fondamentale	фундаментальный класс
F 802	**fundamental cocycle** <AT>	Fundamentalkozyklus *m*	cocycle *m* fondamental	основной коцикл
F 803	**fundamental combinant** <of algebraic forms> <IV>	Fundamentalkombinante *f*	combinant *m* fondamental	основой (фундаментальный) комбинант
F 804	**fundamental concept,** basic concept <FO>	Grundbegriff *m*	notion *f* fondamentale (de base)	основное (фундаментальное) понятие
	fundamental cube <TO>	*s.* H 344		
F 805	**fundamental curve** <of a rational mapping> <AG>	Fundamentalkurve *f*	courbe *f* fondamentale	фундаментальная кривая
F 806	**fundamental curve** <of a net, pencil> <AY>	Fundamentalkurve *f*, Grundkurve *f*	courbe *f* fondamentale	главная кривая
F 807	**fundamental cycle** <AT>	Fundamentalzyklus *m*, Grundzyklus *m*	cycle *m* fondamental	основной цикл
F 808	**fundamental determinant** <DE, IV>	Fundamentaldeterminante *f* <DE, IV>, Grunddeterminante *f* <DE>	déterminant *m* fondamental	фундаментальный определитель <DE>; основной определитель <IV>
F 809	**fundamental discriminant** <AB>	Fundamentaldiskriminante *f*	discriminant *m* fondamental	фундаментальный дискриминант
F 810	**fundamental domain** <of an analytic function> <FT>	Fundamentalgebiet *n*, Fundamentalbereich *m*	domaine *m* fondamental	фундаментальная область, основная область
F 811	**fundamental domain,** region of discontinuity <*also:* in the stronger sense> <of a discontinuous group of automorphisms> <FT>	Fundamentalbereich *m*, Fundamentalraum *m*, Fundamentalgebiet *n*, Diskontinuitätsgebiet *n*, Diskontinuitätsbereich *m* <*auch:* im engeren Sinne>	domaine *m* fondamental (de discontinuité) <*aussi:* au sens étroit>	фундаментальная область, область разрывности <*также:* в узком смысле>

No.	English	German	French	Russian
F 812	**fundamental element** <of a curve> <DG>	Fundamentalgröße *f*	élément *m* fondamental	основной элемент
F 813	**fundamental equation** <of a field> <AL>	Fundamentalgleichung *f* <Kronecker>	équation *f* fondamentale	основное уравнение
	fundamental equation <DE>	*s.* C 542		
F 814	**fundamental equations** <DG>	Ableitungsgleichungen *fpl*, Grundgleichungen *fpl*, Fundamentalgleichungen *fpl*	équations *fpl* fondamentales	основные уравнения
F 815	**fundamental equations of Gauss,** equations of Gauss, Gauss['s] equations <DG>	Gaußsche Ableitungsgleichungen *fpl*, Ableitungsgleichungen (Ableitungsformeln, Fundamentalgleichungen) *fpl* von Gauß	équations *fpl* [fondamentales] de Gauss	[основные] уравнения Гаусса
F 816	**fundamental exact sequence** <of Galois cohomology groups>	fundamentale exakte Sequenz *f*	suite *f* exacte fondamentale	основная точная последовательность
F 817	**fundamental form** <AB>	Fundamentalform *f*	forme *f* fondamentale	фундаментальная форма
F 818	**fundamental form** <especially in surface theory> <DG>	Grundform *f*, Fundamentalform *f*; fundamentale Differentialform *f* <insbesondere der Hermiteschen Metrik>	forme *f* fondamentale	основная квадратичная форма, основная [дифференциальная] форма
F 819	**fundamental form,** Gauss['] fundamental form <in Euclidean surface theory> <DG>	Fundamentalform *f*, Grundform *f*, Gaußsche Fundamentalform (Grundform)	forme *f* fondamentale, forme fondamentale de Gauss	дифференциальная форма Гаусса <в евклидовой теории поверхностей>
F 820	**fundamental form,** groundform <IV>	Grundform *f*, Urform *f*	forme *f* fondamentale	основная форма
F 821	**fundamental formulae** <DG>	Grundformeln *fpl*, Fundamentalformeln *fpl*	formules *fpl* fondamentales	основные формулы
F 822	**fundamental function** <DE>	Fundamentalfunktion *f*	fonction *f* fondamentale	фундаментальная функция
	fundamental function <DE, IE>	*s.* E 57		
F 823	**fundamental group** <of a knot> <AT>	Knotengruppe *f*	groupe *m* du nœud	[фундаментальная] группа узла
F 824	**fundamental group,** Poincaré['s] group, first homotopy group, one-dimensional homotopy <based at x_0, with base point x_0> <AT>	Fundamentalgruppe *f*, erste Homotopiegruppe *f*, Poincaré-Gruppe *f* <zum Basispunkt x_0>	groupe *m* fondamental (de Poincaré, fondamental de Poincaré)	фундаментальная группа, группа Пуанкаре <в точке x_0>
F 825/6	**fundamental group** <having a base> <GR>	fundamentale Gruppe *f*	groupe *m* fondamental	фундаментальная группа
	fundamental group <AB>	*s.* I 24		
F 827	**fundamental groupoid,** category of path classes, track groupoid <TO>	Fundamentalgruppoid *n*	groupoïde *m* fondamental	фундаментальный группоид, категория классов путей
	fundamental homologies <AT>	*s.* F 844		
F 828	**fundamental homology class** <of a compact manifold> <AT>	fundamentale Homologieklasse *f*	classe *f* fondamentale	основной класс гомологий
F 829	**fundamental hypothesis of combinatorial topology,** "Hauptvermutung" of combinatorial topology, Hauptvermutung <AT>	Hauptvermutung *f* der kombinatorischen Topologie	conjecture *f* fondamentale de la topologie combinatoire, Hauptvermutung *f*	основная гипотеза комбинаторной топологии, «Hauptvermutung» комбинаторной топологии
F 830	**fundamental ideal** <of a group ring> <AL>	Fundamentalideal *n*	idéal *m* fondamental <d'une algèbre de groupe>; anneau *m* de Magnus <d'un groupe>	фундаментальный идеал
	fundamental ideal <AB>	*s.* D 441		
F 831	**fundamental identity** <IV>	Grundidentität *f*, Identität *f*	identité *f* fondamentale	основное тождество
F 832	**fundamental inequality of class field theory,** inequality of class field theory <first *or* second, numbering not unique> <AB>	fundamentale Ungleichung *f* der Klassenkörpertheorie <erste *oder* zweite>	inégalité *f* fondamentale de la théorie du corps de classes <première *ou* seconde>	основное неравенство теории полей классов <первое *или* второе>
F 833	**fundamental integral** <VA>	Grundintegral *n*, Extremalintegral *n*	intégrale *f* fondamentale	основной интеграл
F 834	**fundamental invariant** <of a system of linear differential equations> <DE>	Fundamentalinvariante *f*	invariant *m* fondamental	фундаментальный инвариант
F 835	**fundamental invariant** <IV>	Grundinvariante *f*, Invariantentyp *m*	invariant *m* fondamental	основной инвариант
	fundamental law of algebra <AL>	*s.* F 858		
	fundamental law of arithmetic <NT>	*s.* E 570		
	fundamental laws of logarithms <AR>	*s.* L 218		
F 836	**fundamental lemma** <VA>	Fundamentallemma *n*	lemme *m* fondamental	основная лемма
F 837	**fundamental line** <of a family of conics> <AY>	Grundgerade *f*, Grundtangente *f*, Basistangente *f*	tangente *f* fondamentale	основная линия

F 838	**fundamental matrix** <DE>	Grundmatrix *f*, Fundamentalmatrix *f*	matrice *f* fondamentale	фундаментальная матрица
	fundamental metric tensor <DG>	*s.* F 854		
	fundamental net <TO>	*s.* C 258		
	fundamental operation <AR>	*s.* A 949		
F 839	**fundamental parallelepipedon** <of a lattice> <NT>	Fundamentalparallelepiped *n*	parallélépipède *m* fondamental	основной параллелепипед
	fundamental period <AN, FU>	*s.* P 1368		
	fundamental period parallelogram <FT>	*s.* P 1369		
F 840	**fundamental point,** base point <of a birational transformation> <AG>	Fundamentalpunkt *m*, fundamentaler Punkt *m*	point *m* fondamental	фундаментальная точка
	fundamental point <PJ>	*s.* B 121		
F 841	**fundamental polygon** <of a discontinuous group> <FT>	Fundamentalpolygon *n*	polygone *m* fondamental	фундаментальный полигон
F 842	**fundamental probability set** <ST>	Menge (Gesamtheit) *f* der Elementarereignisse	ensemble *m* des événements élémentaires	множество элементарных событий
F 843	**fundamental semi-invariant,** basic semi-invariant <DG>	Grundhalbinvariante *f*	semi-invariant *m* fondamental (basique)	основной полуинвариант (семиинвариант)
	fundamental sequence <AN>	*s.* C 92		
	fundamental sequence <SS, TO>	*s.* C 268		
	fundamental series <FA>	*s.* C 269		
F 844	**fundamental set** <of homologies>, fundamental homologies <AT>	Fundamentalsystem *n* <von Homologien>	système *m* fondamental <d'homologies>	фундаментальная система <гомологий>
F 845	**fundamental set,** fundamental system <of integrals,> base, basis <for the solutions> <DE>	Hauptsystem *n*, Fundamentalsystem *n* <von Lösungen>, Integralbasis *f*	système *m* fondamental <d'intégrales>	фундаментальная система <решений, интегралов>
F 846	**fundamental set,** total set <of a linear topological space> <TO>	Grundmenge *f*, Grundsystem *n*, Fundamentalmenge *f*, abgeschlossenes (vollständiges) System *n*; totale Untermenge (Menge) *f* <speziell in separiertem lokalkonvexen Raum>	ensemble *m* fondamental (total)	основное (фундаментальное, тотальное) множество
F 847	**fundamental solution** <DE>	Grundlösung *f*, Fundamentallösung *f*	solution *f* principale (fondamentale)	основное (фундаментальное) решение
F 848	**fundamental substitution** <AL, DE>	Fundamentalsubstitution *f* <AL, DE>; Umlaufsubstitution <DE>	substitution *f* fondamentale	фундаментальная подстановка
F 849	**fundamental surface** <AG>	Fundamentalfläche *f*	surface *f* fondamentale	фундаментальная поверхность
F 850	**fundamental system** <of solutions of a linear recurrent equation> <AL>	Hauptsystem *n* <von Lösungen>	système *m* principal <de solutions>	фундаментальная система <решений>
F 851	**fundamental system** <of solutions *or* of chains of a complex> <AL, AT>	Fundamentalsystem *n* <von Lösungen *oder* Ketten>	système *m* fondamental <de solutions *ou* chaînes>	фундаментальная система <решений *или* цепей>
F 852	**fundamental system** <of periods of a *q*-periodical function> <FT>	Hauptsystem *n* <von Perioden einer *q*-periodischen Funktion>	système *m* principal <de périodes d'une fonction *q*-périodique>	главная система <периодов *q*-периодической функции>
F 853	**fundamental system** <of period *or* theta characteristics *or* of an Abelian integral of the second kind> <FU>	Fundamentalsystem *n*	système *m* fondamental	фундаментальная система
	fundamental system <DE>	*s.* F 845		
F 854	**fundamental tensor,** fundamental metric tensor, metric tensor <DG>	Maßtensor *m*, Grundtensor *m*, Fundamentaltensor *m*, metrischer Fundamentaltensor (Tensor *m*)	tenseur *m* fondamental, tenseur métrique	метрический тензор, фундаментальный тензор
F 855	**fundamental test,** main test <for convergence> <of a sequence *or* series> <SS>	Hauptkriterium *n*, fundamentales Kriterium *n*	critère (test) *m* fondamental <de convergence>	основной критерий
F 856	**fundamental tetrahedron** <of a lattice> <NT>	Fundamentaltetraeder *n*	tétraèdre *m* fondamental	фундаментальный тетраэдр
F 857	**fundamental theorem [for (of) abelian groups],** structure theorem for finitely generated modules <GR>	Basissatz *m* [für abelsche Gruppen], Hauptsatz *m* über [endlich erzeugte] abelsche Gruppen, Hauptsatz abelscher Gruppen, Basissatz für endlich erzeugte Moduln	théorème *m* de structure fondamental, théorème de Schering-Kronecker	основная теорема об абелевых группах с конечным числом образующих, структурная теорема для конечно порожденных модулей
F 858	**fundamental theorem of algebra,** fundamental law of algebra <AL>	Fundamentalsatz(Hauptsatz) *m* der Algebra, algebraisches Fundamentaltheorem *n*, Fundamentaltheorem der algebraischen Gleichungen, d'Alemberts Theorem *n*, algebraischer Hauptsatz der komplexen Zahlen	théorème *m* de d'Alembert-Gauss, théorème de d'Alembert, théorème fondamental de l'algèbre	основная теорема алгебры [комплексных чисел], теорема Д'Аламбера-Гаусса (Даламбера-Гаусса), теорема Гаусса о корнях многочлена

	fundamental theorem of arithmetic <NT>	*s.* E 570		
F 859	**fundamental theorem of calculus,** fundamental theorem of integral calculus <DI>	Fundamentalsatz *m* der Differential- und Integralrechnung	théorème *m* fondamental du calcul différentiel et intégral	теорема о взаимной обратности дифференцирования и интегрирования
	fundamental theorem of integral calculus <DI>	*s.* F 859		
	fundamental theorem of rational arithmetic <NT>	*s.* E 570		
F 860	**fundamental theorem of uniformization theory,** Koebe-Poincaré theorem <FT>	Hauptsatz *m* der Uniformisierungstheorie [von Koebe und Poincaré], Koebe-Poincarésches Grenzkreistheorem *n*	théorème *m* fondamental de la théorie d'uniformisation, théorème de Koebe-Poincaré	фундаментальная (основная) теорема теории униформизации
F 861	**fundamental transformation** <of surfaces> <AY>	Fundamentaltransformation *f*	transformation *f* fondamentale	основное преобразование
F 862	**fundamental unit** <AB>	Grundeinheit *f*	unité *f* fondamentale	основная единица
F 863	**fundamental variety** <AG>	fundamentale Untermannigfaltigkeit *f*	variété *f* fondamentale	фундаментальное многообразие
	"Fundierungsaxiom" <SE>	*s.* A 1291		
	funicular curve (line) <GE>	*s.* C 227		
	furcation <GN>	*s.* B 725		
F 864	**Furry-Yule process,** linear birth process <SP>	Furry-Yule-Prozeß *m*, linearer (einfacher) Geburtsprozeß (Geburtenprozeß) *m*, Yule-Furry-Prozeß *m*, Furry-Yulescher Prozeß *m*	processus *m* de Furry-Yule, processus de naissance linéaire	процесс Фарри-Юла, линейный процесс рождения
F 865	**fuzzy set** <SE>	mehrwertige Menge *f*, unbestimmtes Ereignis *n*, unbestimmte (unscharfe, „fuzzy") Menge	ensemble *m* flou, partie *f* floue	размытое (нечеткое) множество
	F-variation <FA>	*s.* F 588		

G

	g <GE>	*s.* G 357		
G 1	**Gagliardo['s] lemma** <FA>	Lemma *n* von Gagliardo, Gagliardosches Lemma	lemme *m* de Gagliardo	лемма Гальярдо
G 2	**Galerkin['s] equations** <NU, VA>	Galerkinsche Gleichungen *fpl*	équations *fpl* de Galerkin	уравнения Галеркина
G 3	**Galerkin['s] method** <NU>	Galerkinsche Methode *f*, Galerkinsches Verfahren *n*, Verfahren von Galerkin, Näherungsverfahren *n* von Ritz-Galerkin	méthode *f* de Galerkin	метод Галеркина (Бубнова-Галеркина, Галеркина-Петрова, моментов)
G 4	**Galileo['s] spiral** <GE>	Galileische Spirale *f*	spirale *f* de Galilée	спираль Галилея
G 5	**Galois['s] algebra** <AL>	galoissche Algebra *f*; uneigentlicher galoisscher Körper *m*	algèbre *f* galoisienne	алгебра Галуа
G 6	**Galois['s] closure** <of a Galois correspondence> <LA>	Galoissche Hülle *f*	fermeture *f* de Galois	замыкание Галуа
G 7	**Galois closure operation** <LA>	Galoissche Hüllenoperation *f*	fermeture *f* de Galois	операция замыкания Галуа
G 8	**Galois['s] cohomology** <AL>	Galois-Kohomologie *f*, Galoiskohomologie *f*	cohomologie *f* galoisienne	когомологии (когомология) Галуа
G 9	**Galois['s] connection (correspondence),** // **Galois['s] connexion** <LA>	Galois-Verbindung *f*, Galois-Korrespondenz *f*, Galoiskorrespondenz *f*	correspondance *f* de Galois	соответствие (связь) Галуа
G 10	**Galois covering** <AG>	galoissche Überlagerung *f*	revêtement *m* galoisien	накрытие Галуа
G 11	**Galois['s] equation,** separable normal equation <AL>	Galoissche Gleichung *f*, separable Normalgleichung *f*	équation *f* galoisienne (de Galois)	сепарабельное нормальное уравнение
G 12	**Galois['s] extension,** [finite] normal separable extension; Galois['s] extension field <AL>	galoissche Erweiterung (Körpererweiterung) *f*, [endliche] separable und normale Körpererweiterung, normale Erweiterung; Galoisscher Körper *m*	extension *f* galoisienne (normale et séparable); corps *m* de Galois	расширение Галуа, сепарабельное нормальное расширение, расширение поля Галуа
	Galois['s] extension field <AL>	*s.* G 12		
G 13	**Galois extension of *k*** <AL>	relativ-Galoisscher Körper *m* in bezug auf *k*	corps *m* de Galois relatif par rapport à *k*	расширение Галуа от *k*
G 14	**Galois['s] field,** finite field, strictly finite field <AL>	Galois-Feld *n*, Galoisfeld *n*, endlicher (Galoisscher) Körper *m*	corps (champ) *m* de Galois	поле Галуа, конечное поле
G 15	**Galois['s] group** <of an equation>, group of the equation <AL>	galoissche Gruppe *f*, Gruppe der Gleichung, // Gleichungsgruppe *f*	groupe *m* galoisien, groupe [de l'équation]	группа Галуа <уравнения>, группа уравнения
G 16	**Galois['s] group** <of *K* with respect to *k*> <GR>	Galoissche Gruppe *f*, Galois-Gruppe *f*, Galoisgruppe *f* <von *K* über *k*>	groupe *m* de Galois, groupe du corps de Galois (de *K* sur *k*)	группа Галуа <*K* над *k*>
G 17	**Galois group of a field extension** <AL>	Relativgruppe *f* <Galoissche Gruppe>	groupe *m* de Galois relatif	группа Галуа расширения поля

	English	German	French	Russian
G 18	**Galois['s] imaginary** <AL>	Galoissche (Galois') Imaginäre *f*	racine *f* « imaginaire de Galois », imaginaire *f* de Galois	«мнимый» корень Галуа
G 19	**Galois['s] lattice** <of a Galois correspondence> <LA>	Galoisscher Verband *m*	treillis *m* de Galois	решетка Галуа
G 20	**Galois['s] module** <AL>	Galois-Modul *m*, Galoismodul *m*	module *m* galoisien	модуль Галуа
G 21	**Galois['s] resolvent** <AL>	Galoissche Resolvente *f*	résolvante *f* de Galois	резольвента Галуа
G 22	**Galois['s] ring** <AL>	galoisscher Ring *m*	anneau *m* galoisien	кольцо Галуа
G 23	**Galois['s] theory** <AL>	Galoissche Theorie *f*	théorie *f* de Galois	теория Галуа
G 24	**Galton['s] apparatus (board), Galtonian board**; pinball board <IN, ST>	Galtonsches Brett *n*	appareil *m* (planche *f*) de Galton	доска (прибор, аппарат) Гальтона
G 25	**Galtonian curve, Galton ogive** <ST>	Galtonsche Ogive *f*, inverse Häufigkeitssummenkurve *f*	ogive *f* de Galton	огива Гальтона
G 26	**Galton[s'] rank order test** <ST>	Galtons[cher] Anordnungstest *m*	test *m* de rangs de Galton	порядковый критерий Гальтона
G 27	**Galton-Watson process** <SP>	Galton-Watson-Prozeß *m*, Verzweigungsprozeß *m* mit diskreter Zeit	processus *m* de Galton-Watson	процесс Гальтона-Уотсона (Гальтона-Ватсона)
	gamble <TG>	*s.* G 32		
G 28	**game** <TG>	Spiel *n*, Spielart *f*	jeu *m*	игра
G 29	**game against nature** <TG>	Spiel *n* gegen die Natur	jeu *m* contre la nature	игра с природой
	game in extensive form	*s.* P 1051		
G 30	**game in normalized form** <TG>	Spiel *n* in Normalform	jeu *m* en forme normale	игра в нормальной форме
G 31	**game in partition function form** <TG>	Spiel *n* in Zerlegungsform		игра в форме функции разбиения
G 32	**game of chance, game of hazard,** gamble <TG>	Glücksspiel *n*, Hasardspiel *n*	jeu *m* au hazard, jeu de probabilité, jeu de hasard	азартная игра
	game of complete information <TG>	*s.* G 40		
	game of perfect information <TG>	*s.* G 40		
G 33	**game of pursuit** <TG>	Verfolgungsspiel *n*	jeu *m* des poursuites	игра преследования
G 34	**game of survival** <TG>	Überlebensspiel *n*	jeu *m* de survie	игра на выживание
	game of timing <TG>	*s.* D 1042		
G 35	**game on the unit square** <TG>	Spiel *n* über dem Einheitsquadrat	jeu *m* sur le carré unité	игра на единичном квадрате
G 36	**game rule,** rule of the game <TG>	Spielregel *f*	règle *f* du jeu	правило игры
G 37	**game-theoretic** <TG>	spieltheoretisch	d'après la théorie des jeux, au sens de la théorie des jeux	теоретико-игровой
G 38	**game tree,** tree <of a game> <TG>	Spielbaum *m*, Baum *m* <eines Spiels>	arbre *m* d'un jeu	дерево игры
	game with complete information <TG>	*s.* G 40		
G 39	**game with infinitely many players** <TG>	Spiel *n* mit unendlich vielen Spielern	jeu *m* à une infinité de joueurs	игра с бесконечным множеством игроков
G 40	**game with perfect information,** game with complete information, game of perfect (complete) information <TG>	Spiel *n* mit vollständiger Information	jeu *m* avec information complète	игра с полной информацией
G 41	**gamma distribution,** Pearson type III <ST>	Gammaverteilung *f*, Γ-Verteilung *f*	distribution *f* gamma	гамма-распределение, Γ-распределение
	gamma-error <ST>	*s.* E 481		
G 42	**gamma[-] function,** Γ-function, factorial function, Eulerian (Euler['s]) integral of the second kind, Euler['s] second integral, generalized factorial function <FU>	Γ-Funktion *f*, Gammafunktion *f*, Gamma-Funktion *f*, Fakultätenfunktion *f*, Eulersches Integral *n* zweiter Art (Gattung), Euler-Integral *n* zweiter (2.) Art, vollständige Gammafunktion	fonction *f* Γ, fonction gamma, fonction gamma d'Euler, fonction eulérienne, seconde (deuxième) intégrale *f* eulérienne, intégrale (fonction) eulérienne de seconde espèce, fonction factorielle, factorielle *f*	Γ-функция, гамма-функция, гамма-функция Эйлера, эйлеров интеграл второго рода
G 43	**gamma[-] number,** γ-number, principal number of addition, principal ordinal of addition, principal ordinal for addition <SE>	additive Hauptzahl *f* <der Funktion $\alpha + \beta$>, γ-Zahl *f*, Gamma-Zahl *f*, Hauptzahl der Addition <Ordnungszahl>	nombre *m* principal additif, nombre-γ *m*, nombre gamma	гамма-число, γ-число
G 44	**gap** <of an ordering *or* in a power series> <SE, SS>	Lücke *f*	lacune *f*	пробел <SE>; лакуна, пропуск <SS>
G 45	**gap character,** character <of a gap> <in an ordered set> <SE>	Lückencharakter *m*, Charakter *m* <einer Lücke>	caractère *m* de lacune, caractère <d'une lacune>	характер пробела
G 46	**gap series,** lacunar[y] series, Taylor['s] series with gaps <FT, SS>	Potenzreihe *f* mit Lücken, Lückenreihe *f*, lakunäre Reihe *f*	série *f* lacunaire	лакунарный ряд, ряд с пропусками (лакунами)
G 47	**gap theorem,** Liouville['s] gap theorem <for elliptic functions> <FU>	Lückensatz *m*, Liouvillescher Lückensatz	théorème *m* des lacunes [de Liouville]	теорема о пропусках [Лиувилля]
G 48	**gap theorem** <for power series> <SS>	Lückensatz *m*, Lückentheorem *n*	théorème *m* des lacunes	теорема о лакунах (пробелах)
	gap theorem <SS>	*s.* H 10		
	gap theorem of Fabry <SS>	*s.* F 4		

	English	German	French	Russian
	gap theorem of Weierstrass <FT>	*s.* W 160		
G 49	**Gårding['s] inequality** <DE>	Gårdingsche Ungleichung *f*, Ungleichung von Gårding	inégalité *f* de Gårding	неравенство Гординга
G 50	**Gårding['s] space** <FA>	Gårdingscher Raum *m*	espace *m* de Gårding	пространство Гординга
	Gaschütz['s] formation <AL>	*s.* F 475		
G 51	**Gâteaux-analytic function,** analytic function in the sense of Gâteaux <FT>	Gâteaux-analytische Funktion *f*	fonction *f* analytique au sens de Gâteaux	аналитическая функция в смысле Гато
G 52	**Gâteaux[-] differentiable function (mapping),** weakly differentiable mapping <FA>	nach Gâteaux differenzierbare Funktion (Abbildung) *f*, Gâteaux-differenzierbare Funktion (Abbildung)	fonction (application) *f* dérivable au sens de Gâteaux	дифференцируемая по Гато функция; функция, дифференцируемая в смысле Гато; дифференцируемое по Гато отображение
G 53	**Gâteaux['s] differential,** weak differential <FA>	Gâteauxsches Differential *n*, Differential nach Gâteaux	différentielle *f* de Gâteaux	дифференциал Гато, слабый дифференциал, вариация Гато
G 54	**gauge,** distance function <CS, GE>	Distanzfunktion *f*, Strahldistanz *f*	jauge *f*, // distance *f* radiale	дистанционная функция
G 55	**gauge** <GE, IN>	Streckenabtrager *m*, Streckenübertrager *m*, Eichmaß *n*	étalon *m* de longueur, étalon	эталон длины
	gauge <FA>	*s.* M 630		
G 56	**gauge [function],** Minkowski['s] functional (gauge) <DG, GE>	Eichfunktion *f*	jauge *f*, fonction *f* étalon	калибровочная функция, функция-эталон
G 57	**gauge group** <DG>	Eichgruppe *f*	groupe *m* de jauge	группа калибровочных преобразований, калибровочная группа, группа преобразований масштаба
G 58	**gauge[-] invariance** <DG>	Eichinvarianz *f*	invariance *f* de jauge	калибровочная инвариантность, инвариантность относительно калибровочных преобразований, инвариантность относительно преобразований масштаба
G 59	**gauge surface** <DG>	Eichfläche *f*	surface *f* de jauge	нормирующая поверхность, калибровочная поверхность
G 60	**gauge transformation** <DG>	Eichtransformation *f*, Umeichung *f*	transformation *f* (changement *m*) de jauge	калибровочное преобразование, преобразование масштаба
G 61	**gauge variety** <GE>	Eichmannigfaltigkeit *f*	variété *f* de jauge, variété-étalon *f*	калибровочное многообразие, многообразие-эталон
	Gauss['s] analogies <EG>	*s.* G 71		
G 62	**Gauss['] approximation,** Gauss-type approximation <AX>	Gauß-Approximation *f*	approximation *f* de [type] Gauss	приближение (аппроксимация) гауссовского типа
G 63	**Gauss['] approximation problem,** Gauss['] problem <AX>	Gaußsche Approximationsaufgabe *f*, Gaußsches Approximationsproblem (Problem) *n*	problème *m* d'approximation de Gauss, problème de Gauss [d'approximation]	задача приближения (аппроксимации) гауссовского типа
	Gauss-Bonnet formula <DG>	*s.* G 64		
G 64	**Gauss-Bonnet theorem,** Gauss-Bonnet formula <DG>	Gauß-Bonnetsche Integralformel *f*, Bonnet[sche] Integralformel, Gauß-Bonnetsche Formel *f*, Integralformel (Formel) von Gauß-Bonnet, Integralformel (Formel) von Bonnet	formule *f* de Gauss et Bonnet	теорема Гаусса-Бонне
G 65	**Gauss-Christoffel formula** <for mechanical quadrature>, **Gauss-Christoffel quadrature formula** <AX, DI, NU>	Gauß-Christoffelsche [mechanische] Quadraturformel *f*, Gauß-Christoffelsche Formel *f*	formule *f* [de quadrature mécanique] de Gauss-Christoffel	формула [механических квадратур] Гаусса-Кристоффеля, квадратурная формула Гаусса-Кристоффеля
	Gauss-Codazzi equations [of the surface] <DG>	*s.* C 1003		
G 66	**Gauss['] condition** <of a simple ring> <AL>	Gaußsche Bedingung *f*	condition *f* de Gauss	условие Гаусса
G 67	**Gauss['] continued fraction expansion,** Gauss['] expansion <for the hypergeometric function> <FU>	Gaußscher Kettenbruch *m* <für die hypergeometrische Funktion>	fraction *f* continue de Gauss	цепная дробь Гаусса
	Gauss co-ordinates <DG>	*s.* C 2797		
	Gauss['s] curvature <DG>	*s.* T 621		
	Gauss['s] definition <FU>	*s.* G 70		
	Gauss distribution <ST>	*s.* N 558		
	Gauss['] divergence theorem <DI, VT>	*s.* G 427		
	Gauss-Doolittle method <AL, NU, ST>	*s.* D 891		
	Gauss['] elimination method <AL>	*s.* G 72		

No.	English	German	French	Russian
G 68	**Gauss['] equation,** Theorema egregium, Gauss['] formula <for total curvature> <DG>	Theorema *n* egregium [von Gauß], Gaußsche Gleichung *f*	équation (formule) *f* de Gauss <pour la courbure totale>	формула (уравнение) Гаусса <для полной кривизны>, теорема Гаусса, threorema egregium
G 69	**Gauss['] equations,** equations of Gauss <for the Riemann-Christoffel curvature tensor> <DG>	Gaußsche Gleichungen *fpl*	équations *fpl* de Gauss	уравнения Гаусса
	Gauss['] equations <DG>	*s.* F 815		
	Gauss['] error curve <ST>	*s.* E 471		
	Gauss error distribution curve <ST>	*s.* E 471		
	Gauss['] error function <ER, ST>	*s.* E 473		
	Gauss['] expansion <FU>	*s.* G 67		
G 70	**Gauss['s] formula,** Gauss['s] definition <of the Γ-function> <FU>	Gaußsche Definition (Darstellung, Formel) *f*	formule *f* de Gauss	гауссово представление (определение), формула Гаусса
	Gauss['] formula <AX, DI, NU>	*s.* G 83		
	Gauss['] formula <DG>	*s.* G 68		
	Gauss['] formula of interpolation <AX, FD, NU>	*s.* G 76		
G 71	**Gauss['s] formulas,** Gauss['s] analogies, Delambre['s] analogies <of spherical trigonometry> <EG>	Delambresche Formeln *fpl*, Gaußsche Formeln, Mollweidesche Formeln [der sphärischen Trigonometrie]	formules *fpl* de Delambre, analogies *fpl* de Delambre	формулы Деламбра
	Gauss['] fundamental form <DG>	*s.* F 819		
	Gauss['s] hypergeometric [differential] equation <DE>	*s.* H 690		
	Gauss['s] hypergeometric function <FU>	*s.* H 692		
	Gauss['s] hypergeometric series <SS>	*s.* H 694		
G 72	**Gaussian algorithm,** Gaussian elimination, elimination, Gauss['] [elimination] method, Gaussian triangularization <AL>	Gaußscher Algorithmus *m*, Gaußsches Eliminationsverfahren *n*	algorithme *m* de Gauss, méthode *f* d'élimination de Gauss, méthode de Gauss, méthode d'élimination	алгоритм Гаусса [исключения неизвестных], метод исключения Гаусса, метод Гаусса
G 73	**Gaussian brackets** <NT>	Gaußsche Klammern *fpl*	crochets *mpl* d'Euler, crochets de Gauss, parenthèses *fpl* d'Euler, parenthèses de Gauss, crochets d'Euler-Gauss	скобки Гаусса
	Gaussian complex integer (number) <NT>	*s.* G 75		
	Gaussian curvature <DG>	*s.* T 621		
	Gaussian curve [of error] <ST>	*s.* E 471		
	Gaussian differential equation <DE>	*s.* H 690		
	Gaussian distribution [law] <ST>	*s.* N 558		
G 74	**Gaussian elimination,** Gauss-Jordan elimination <AL>	Gaußsche Elimination *f*	élimination *f* de Gauss	исключение Гаусса
	Gaussian elimination <AL>	*s.* G 72		
	Gaussian error curve <ST>	*s.* E 471		
	Gaussian error function <ER, ST>	*s.* E 473		
	Gaussian hypergeometric series <SS>	*s.* H 694		
G 75	**gaussian integer, Gaussian integer,** Gaussian complex integer, complex integer, Gaussian complex number <NT>	ganze Gaußsche (komplexe) Zahl *f*, Gaußsche Zahl	entier *m* de Gauss, nombre *m* entier complexe	целое комплексное (гауссово) число, комплексное целое число, гауссово число
G 76	**Gaussian interpolation formula,** Newton-Gauss formula, Gauss['] interpolation formula, Gauss['] formula of interpolation, Newton-Gauss interpolation formula <AX, FD, NU>	Gaußsche Interpolationsformel *f*, Interpolationsformel von Gauß	formule *f* d'interpolation de Gauss	интерполяционная формула Гаусса
	Gaussian law <ST>	*s.* N 558		
	Gaussian law of error [distribution] <ER>	*s.* E 475		
	Gaussian lemniscate function <FT, FU>	*s.* L 559		
G 77	**Gaussian mean value theorem** <for potential functions>, theorem of the mean for harmonic functions, Gauss['] law of	Gaußscher Mittelwertsatz *m*, Mittelwertsatz der harmonischen Funktionen, Mittelwertsatz <der Potentialtheorie>; Gaußscher	théorème *m* de Gauss <pour les valeurs moyennes>	теорема о среднем арифметическом

	the arithmetic mean <PO>	Satz *m* vom arithmetischen Mittel <für holomorphe und harmonische Funktionen>		
G 78	**Gaussian multiplier** <AL>	Gaußscher Multiplikator *m*	multiplicateur *m* de Gauss	множитель Гаусса
G 79	**Gaussian number,** complex rational number <AL>	rationale komplexe Zahl *f*, Gaußsche Zahl *f*	nombre *m* de Gauss, nombre rationnel complexe	гауссово число, комплексное рациональное число
G 80	**Gaussian number field** <AB>	Körper *m* der Gaußschen Zahlen, Körper der rationalen komplexen Zahlen	corps *m* des nombres de Gauss, corps des nombres rationnels complexes	поле гауссовых чисел
G 81	**Gaussian number field** <NT>	Gaußscher Zahlkörper *m*	corps *m* des nombres de Gauss	числовое поле Гаусса, гауссово числовое поле
	Gaussian plane <FT>	*s.* A 937		
	Gaussian probability distribution <ST>	*s.* N 558		
G 82	**Gaussian process,** normal process <SP>	Gaußscher (normaler) Prozeß *m*	processus *m* de Gauss, processus gaussien (aléatoire gaussien, normal)	нормальный случайный процесс, гауссовский [случайный] процесс
	Gaussian psi-function (Ψ-function) <FU>	*s.* D 480		
G 83	**Gaussian quadrature formula,** Gauss['] [quadrature] formula; Gauss['] mechanical quadrature <AX, DI, NU>	Gaußsche Quadraturformel (Formel) *f*, Quadraturformel (Formel) von Gauß; Gaußsche mechanische Quadratur *f*	formule *f* de Gauss [pour l'intégration numérique]; méthode *f* de Gauss [pour l'intégration numérique]	квадратурная формула Гаусса, формула [механической] квадратуры Гаусса, формула Гаусса; гауссова квадратура, метод Гаусса [численного интегрирования]
	Gaussian representation <DG>	*s.* S 1464		
G 84	**Gaussian space** <AN>	Gaußscher Raum *m*, Gauß-Raum *m*	espace *m* gaussien	гауссово пространство
G 85	**Gaussian sum,** Gauss['] sum <NT>	Gaußsche Summe *f*; Lagrangesche Resolvente *f* <in der elementaren Zahlentheorie>	somme *f* de Gauss	сумма Гаусса, гауссова сумма
G 86	**Gaussian system** <of *k*-th order> <AX, DI, NU>	Gaußsches System *n* <der Ordnung *k*>	système *m* gaussien <d'ordre *k*>	гауссова система <*k*-го порядка>
	Gaussian theorem <DI, VT>	*s.* G 427		
	Gaussian transcendental function <ER, ST>	*s.* E 473		
	Gaussian triangularization <AL>	*s.* G 72		
G 87	**Gaussian type** <AX, DI, NU>	Gauß-Typus *m*	type *m* gaussien (de Gauss)	гауссов тип, тип Гаусса
G 88	**Gaussian type quadrature formula,** Gauss-type quadrature formula <AX, DI, NU>	Quadraturformel *f* vom Gauß-Typus	formule *f* [pour l'intégration numérique] de type Gauss, formule de quadrature du (de) type Gauss (gaussien)	квадратурная формула гауссова типа
	Gaussian variable <ST>	*s.* N 665		
G 89	**Gauss['s] inequality** <ST>	Gaußsche Ungleichung *f*	inégalité *f* de Gauss	неравенство Гаусса
G 90	**Gauss['] integral** <for the digamma function <FU>	Gaußsche Integraldarstellung *f*	intégrale *f* de Gauss	интеграл Гаусса
	Gauss['] interpolation formula <AX, FD, NU>	*s.* G 76		
	Gauss-Jordan elimination <AL>	*s.* G 74		
	Gauss['] law of the arithmetic mean <PO>	*s.* G 77		
	Gauss['s] law of reciprocity <NT>	*s.* Q 42		
G 91	**Gauss['] lemma** <AL>	Gaußscher Satz *m* [über Polynomteiler]	théorème *m* de Gauss	теорема Гаусса
G 92	**Gauss['] lemma** <for quadratic residues> <NT>	Gaußsches Lemma *n*	lemme *m* de Gauss	лемма Гаусса
	Gauss['] lemma <AL>	*s.* L 552		
G 93	**Gauss['s] logarithm,** addition logarithm <AL, AN>	Gaußscher (Leonellischer) Logarithmus *m*, Additionslogarithmus *m*	logarithme *m* de Gauss, logarithme d'addition	гауссов логарифм
G 94	**Gauss-Manin connection** <AG>	Gauß-Manin-Zusammenhang *m*	connexion *f* de Gauss-Manin	связность Гаусса-Манина
	Gauss-Markov estimator <ST>	*s.* B 244		
G 95	**Gauss-Markov theorem,** Markov['s] theorem <ST>	Gauß-Markov-Theorem *n*, Gauß-Markovsches Theorem *n*, Markovsches Theorem, Theorem von Markov	théorème *m* de Gauss-Markov, théorème de Markov	теорема Гаусса-Маркова, теорема Маркова
	Gauss['] mechanical quadrature <AX, DI, NU>	*s.* G 83		
G 96	**Gauss['] method** <of decomposing a quadratic form into squares> <NT>	Gaußsche Methode *f*	méthode *f* de Gauss <de décomposition en carrés>	метод Гаусса
	Gauss['] method <AL>	*s.* G 72		
	Gauss['s] multiplication theorem <FU>	*s.* M 1038		
	Gauss number plane <FT>	*s.* A 937		

No.	English	German	French	Russian
	Gauss paper <IN, ST>	*s.* N 640		
	Gauss plane <FT>	*s.* A 937		
G 97	**Gauss['] problem** <for Gaussian sums> <NT>	Gaußsches Problem *n* der Vorzeichenbestimmung <der Gaußschen Summen>	problème *m* de Gauss	проблема Гаусса
	Gauss['] problem <AX>	*s.* G 63		
	Gauss['s] psi-function (Ψ-function) <FU>	*s.* D 480		
	Gauss['] quadrature formula <AX, DI, NU>	*s.* G 83		
G 98	**Gauss-Seidel method,** single-step iteration [for solving linear equations], Seidel['s] method <AL, AX, NU>	Gauß-Seidelsches (Seidelsches) Iterationsverfahren *n*, Gauß-Seidelsches Verfahren *n*, Iterationsverfahren von Gauß-Seidel, Gauß-Seidel-Verfahren *n*	méthode *f* itérative de Gauss-Seidel, méthode de Gauss-Seidel	метод Сейделя (Гаусса-Сейделя)
	Gauss['s] sum <NT>	*s.* G 85		
G 99	**Gauss['s] test** <for convergence> <SS>	Gaußsches Kriterium (Konvergenzkriterium) *n*	critère *m* de Gauss, règle *f* de [convergence de] Gauss	признак (критерий) [сходимости] Гаусса
	Gauss['] theorem <DI, VT>	*s.* G 427		
G 100	**Gauss['] transformation** <for elliptic functions> <FU>	Gaußsche Transformation *f*	transformation *f* gaussienne	преобразование Гаусса
	Gauss-type approximation <AX>	*s.* G 62		
	Gauss-type quadrature formula <AX, DI, NU>	*s.* G 88		
G 101	**Gauss-Winckler inequality** <ST>	Gauß-Wincklersche Ungleichung *f*	inégalité *f* de Gauss-Winckler	неравенство Гаусса-Винклера
	g.c.d. <AL, NT>	*s.* G 404		
	G.C.D. <AL, NT>	*s.* G 404		
G 102	**GCD-domain,** HCF-ring, [commutative] weak Bézout domain, [commutative] 2-fir ring <AL>	pseudo-Bézoutscher Ring *m*, Ring mit g.g.T. <Ring, in dem jedes Paar von Elementen einen g.g.T. hat>	anneau *m* pseudo-bézoutien (à p.g.c.d.)	псевдобезу кольцо, [коммутативное] слабое кольцо Безу, [коммутативное] 2-FI-кольцо
	g.c.l.d. <AL>	*s.* G 405		
	g.c.r.d. <AL>	*s.* G 406		
	gd <FU>	*s.* G 539		
	Gd <FU>	*s.* G 539		
	ge <FU>	*s.* M 175		
G 103	**Geary['s] ratio** <ST>	Geary-Quotient *m*	rapport (quotient) *m* de Geary	отношение Гири
G 104	**Geary['s] test** <ST>	Geary-Test *m*	test *m* de Geary	критерий Гири
	gedanken experiment <ST>	*s.* T 440		
G 105	**Gegenbauer['s] function,** ultraspherical (metaspherical) function <FU>	Gegenbauersche (ultrasphärische, metasphärische) Funktion *f*	fonction *f* de Gegenbauer, fonction ultrasphérique (métasphérique)	функция Гегенбауэра, ультрасферическая (метасферическая) функция
G 106	**Gegenbauer['s] polynomial** <as a generalized Neumann polynomial> <FU>	Gegenbauersches Polynom *n* <$A_{n,\nu}(z)$⟩ *oder* ⟨$B_{n;\nu,\mu}(z)$>	polynôme *m* de Gegenbauer	многочлен (полином) Гегенбауэра
G 107	**Gegenbauer['s] polynomial,** ultraspherical polynomial <FU>	Gegenbauersches (ultrasphärisches) Polynom *n*, ultrasphärische Funktion *f*, *p*-dimensionale zonale Kugelfunktion *f* <$C_n^\lambda(z)$>	polynôme *m* de Gegenbauer, polynôme ultrasphérique	многочлен (полином) Гегенбауэра, ультрасферический многочлен (полином)
G 108	**Geidel factor** <ST>	Geidel-Faktor *m*	facteur *m* de Geidel	коэффициент Гейделя
G 109	**Gelfand-Dunford theorem** <ME>	Satz *m* von Gelfand-Dunford, Gelfand-Dunfordscher Satz	théorème *m* de Gelfand-Dunford	теорема Гельфанда-Данфорда
G 110	**Gelfand['s] homomorphism** <FA>	Gelfand-Homomorphismus *m*	homomorphisme *m* de Gelfand	гомоморфизм Гельфанда
G 111	**Gelfand['s] integral** <AN>	Integral *n* nach Gelfand	intégrale *f* de Gelfand	интеграл Гельфанда
G 112	**Gelfand-Neumark algebra** <FA>	Gelfand-Neumarksche Algebra *f*	algèbre *f* de Gelfand-Neumark	алгебра Гельфанда-Неймарка
G 113	**Gelfand-Neumark theorem,** theorem of Gelfand-Neumark <FA>	Satz *m* von Gelfand-Neumark, Gelfand-Neumarkscher Satz	théorème *m* de Gelfand-Neumark	теорема Гельфанда-Неймарка
G 114	**Gelfand['s] ring** <AL>	Gelfandscher Ring *m*	anneau *m* de Gelfand	кольцо Гельфанда
G 115	**Gelfand['s] topology** <FA, TO>	Gelfand-Topologie *f*	topologie *f* de Gelfand	топология Гельфанда
	Gelfond['s] theorem <NT>	*s.* T 282		
G 116	**geminant** <of a polynomial> <AL>	Geminante *f*, Zwillingsform *f*	géminant *m*	геминант
	Gemini <NT>	*s.* P 1325		
	general affirmative proposition <LO>	*s.* U 310		
G 117	**general algebra** <UA>	allgemeine (generelle) Algebra *f*	algèbre *f* générale	общая алгебра
G 118	**general algebraic equation,** general equation, general polynomial equation <of the *n*-th degree, of degree *n*> <AL>	allgemeine [algebraische] Gleichung *f* <*n*-ten Grades>	équation *f* générale, équation algébrique générale <du n^e degré, du n^e ordre>	общее алгебраическое уравнение, общее уравнение <*n*-ой степени>

No.	English	German	French	Russian
G 119	**general associative law** <AL, LO>	allgemeines Assoziativgesetz *n*	loi *f* d'associativité générale, loi d'association	обобщенный закон ассоциативности
	general axonometry <DS>	*s.* S 1160		
G 120	**general Burnside problem** <GR>	allgemeines Burnsidesches Problem *n*	problème *m* de Burnside général	общая проблема Бернсайда
G 121	**general case** <GN>	allgemeiner Fall *m*	cas *m* général	общий случай
	general continuum hypothesis <SE>	*s.* G 138		
	general convergence principle <SS>	*s.* C 234		
G 122	**general Dirichlet series,** generalized Dirichlet['s] series <SS>	allgemeine Dirichletsche Reihe *f*	série *f* de Dirichlet [générale], série de Lejeune Dirichlet	общий ряд Дирихле
G 123	**general distributive law** <AL>	allgemeines Distributivgesetz *n*, verallgemeinertes distributives Gesetz *n*	loi *f* distributive générale, loi de distributivité généralisée (complète), théorème *m* de distributivité générale, formule *f* générale de distributivité	обобщенный закон дистрибутивности
G 124	**general distributivity,** infinite distributivity <AL>	allgemeine (unendliche) Distributivität *f*	distributivité *f* générale	общая дистрибутивность
	general equation <AL>	*s.* G 118		
G 125	**general factor** <of an infinite product> <SS>	allgemeiner Faktor *m*	facteur *m* général	общий сомножитель
G 126	**general factor** <in factor analysis> <ST>	allgemeiner Faktor *m*, Generalfaktor *m*	facteur *m* général	основной фактор
	general form of a quadratic equation <AL>	*s.* G 174		
	general hyperplane <AG>	*s.* G 210		
	general indefinite Denjoy integral <RF>	*s.* D 528		
G 127	**general integral,** complete primitive <of an ordinary *or* exact differential equation of the first order> <DE>	allgemeines Integral *n*, Stammgleichung *f*; Stammfunktion *f* <linke Seite der Stammgleichung>	intégrale *f* générale	общий интеграл
G 128	**general integral,** general solution <of an ordinary *or* a partial differential equation *or* a system of such equations>; complementary function <of the auxiliary equation> <DE>	allgemeines Integral *n*, allgemeine Lösung *f*	intégrale *f* générale, solution *f* générale	общее решение; общий интеграл <обыкновенного дифференциального уравнения, если соотношение для общего решения дано в виде, не разрешенном относительно *y*>
	general isomorphism	*s.* H 500		
	generality quantifier <LO>	*s.* U 356		
G 129	**generalization** <LO> ┌<LO>	Generalisierung *f*, Allquantifizierung *f*	quantification *f* universelle, généralisation *f*	применение квантора [все]общности, обобщение
	generalization rule	*s.* R 1474		
G 130	**generalize / to** <LO>	generalisieren	universaliser	связывать квантором всеобщности, обобщать
G 131	**generalized almost periodic function** <AL, AP>	verallgemeinerte fastperiodische Funktion *f*	fonction *f* presque-périodique généralisée	обобщенная почти-периодическая функция
G 132	**generalized almost periodic function in the sense of A.S. Besicovich,** Besicovich['s] almost periodic function, B_p almost-periodic function <AP>	B^p-fastperiodische Funktion *f*, Besicovitch-fastperiodische Funktion *f*	fonction *f* presque-périodique [généralisée] de [A.] Besicovitch	[обобщенная] почти периодическая функция [в смысле] А. Безиковича
G 133	**generalized almost periodic function in the sense of V. V. Stepanov,** Stepanov['s] almost periodic function, S_p almost-periodic function <AP>	S^p-fastperiodische Funktion *f*, Stepanow-fastperiodische Funktion *f*	fonction *f* presque-périodique [généralisée] de [W.] Stepanoff	[обобщенная] почти периодическая функция в смысле В. В. Степанова
	generalized almost periodic function in the sense of Weyl <AL>	*s.* A 530		
	generalized almost periodic function in the sense of [H.] Weyl <AP>	*s.* A 531		
	generalized Artin symbol <AB>	*s.* C 629		
G 134	**generalized Boolean algebra** <AL>	verallgemeinerte Boolesche Algebra *f*	algèbre *f* de Boole généralisée	обобщенная булева алгебра
G 135	**generalized Boolean lattice** <LA>	verallgemeinerter Boolescher Verband *m*	algèbre *f* généralisée de Boole, corps *m* généralisé de Boole	обобщенная алгебра Буля
G 136	**generalized Burnside theorem** <AL>	verallgemeinerter Burnsidescher Satz *m*	théorème *m* de Burnside généralisé, théorème de densité	обобщенная теорема Бернсайда
	generalized Cauchy sequence <TO>	*s.* C 258		
G 137	**generalized continued fraction,** continued fraction <NT>	allgemeiner Kettenbruch *m*, Kettenbruch	fraction *f* continue généralisée	общая цепная дробь, цепная дробь

G 138	**generalized continuum hypothesis,** general continuum hypothesis, generalized hypothesis of the continuum <SE>	verallgemeinerte Kontinuumhypothese *f*	hypothèse *f* généralisée du continu, hypothèse du continu généralisée	обобщенная гипотеза континуума, обобщенная континуум-гипотеза
	generalized Dirichlet['s] series <SS>	*s.* G 122		
G 139	**generalized distance** <ST>	verallgemeinerter Abstand *m*	distance *f* généralisée	обобщенное расстояние
G 140	**generalized equalizer** <CA>	verallgemeinerter Differenzkern *m*	objet *m* des coïncidences <des morphismes>	обобщенный уравнитель
	generalized factorial <FD, FU>	*s.* F 38		
	generalized factorial function <FU>	*s.* G 42		
G 141	**generalized Fourier series** <of a function> <FA, SS>	verallgemeinerte Fourier-Reihe *f*	série *f* de Fourier généralisée	обобщенный ряд Фурье
	generalized function <AN>	*s.* D 753		
G 142	**generalized Green['s] function,** generalized induction function <DE>	verallgemeinerte Greensche Funktion *f*, Greensche Funktion im erweiterten Sinne	fonction *f* de Green généralisée	обобщенная функция Грина
	generalized hypothesis of the continuum <SE>	*s.* G 138		
	generalized induction function <DE>	*s.* G 142		
G 143	**generalized induction principle,** principle of noetherian induction <AL>	Prinzip *n* der noetherschen Induktion, Induktionsbedingung *f*	principe *m* de récurrence noethérienne	принцип нетеровой индукции, обобщенный принцип индукции, нетерова индукция
G 144	**generalized inverse,** general reciprocal, pseudoinverse, relative inverse element <AL>	relatives Inverses *n* <eines Elementes>	élément *m* relativement inverse	главный (относительно) обратный элемент
G 145	**generalized inverse,** relative inverse <of an operator> <FA>	relativer inverser Operator *m*, relative Inverse *f* <eines Operators>	opérateur *m* relativement inverse	обобщенно обратный оператор
	generalized inverse <AL>	*s.* 1. G 176; 2. R 723		
	generalized inverse limit <CA>	*s.* L 697		
G 146	**generalized Kronecker delta** <VT>	δ-Tensor *m*, Delta-Tensor *m*	tenseur-indicateur *m*, tenseur *m* indicateur [classique] de Kronecker	δ-тензор, дельта-тензор
	generalized Kronecker delta <DG, VT>	*s.* A 563		
	generalized Laguerre function <FU>	*s.* L 40		
	generalized Lamé equation <DE>	*s.* L 64		
G 147	**generalized limit** <of a divergent sequence> <LI>	verallgemeinerter Limes *m*, Limes im verallgemeinerten Sinne, *V*-Limes *m*	limité *f* généralisée	обобщенный предел
G 148	**generalized mean** <of a random variable> <ST>	verallgemeinerter Mittelwert *m*	moyenne *f* généralisée	обобщенное среднее
	generalized mean value theorem <DI>	*s.* 1. C 240; 2. T 102		
	generalized Parseval equation <FA>	*s.* P 178		
	generalized Parseval['s] equation <SS>	*s.* P 176		
	generalized partition of unity <FA>	*s.* S 1400		
G 149	**generalized point** <of an algebraic group> <AG>	verallgemeinerter Punkt *m*	point *m* généralisé	обобщенная точка
	generalized projective limit <CA>	*s.* L 697		
	generalized ratio test <SS>	*s.* D 4		
	generalized relation of completeness <FA>	*s.* P 178		
	generalized relation of completeness <SS>	*s.* P 176		
G 150	**generalized rule of detachment** <LO>	Dreierschlußregel *f*, Regel *f* des Distributionsschlusses, Regel der verallgemeinerten Abtrennung	règle *f* de détachement généralisé	обобщенное правило отделения
G 151	**generalized Schwarz['s] inequality** <in a linear space> <FA>	verallgemeinerte Schwarzsche Ungleichung *f*	inégalité *f* de Cauchy-Schwarz généralisée	обобщенное неравенство Буняковского (Шварца)
	generalized sequence <SE>	*s.* M 887		
G 152	**generalized simplex method** <PG>	verallgemeinerte Simplexmethode *f*	méthode *f* de simplexes généralisée	обобщенный симплекс-метод
	generalized solution <DE>	*s.* F 118		
	generalized spectral family <FA>	*s.* S 1400		

	generalized spectral function <FA>	*s.* S 1400		
G 153	**generalized sum** <of a divergent series> <LI>	verallgemeinerte Summe *f*, Summe im verallgemeinerten Sinne	somme *f* généralisée	обобщенная сумма
G 154	**generalized symmetric group,** complete monomial group, symmetry <of degree *n*> <GR>	volle monomiale Gruppe *f* <der Gruppe *H*>, Symmetrie *f* <der Gruppe *H*>, verallgemeinerte symmetrische Gruppe <bezüglich der Gruppe *H*> <vom Grad *n*>	groupe *m* symétrique généralisé <de degré *n*>	обобщенная симметрическая группа <степени *n*>
G 155	**generalized theorem of Stokes,** Stokes['s] integral formula <for multiple integrals in oriented manifolds> <AN, DI>	Stokessche (verallgemeinerte Stokessche) Integralformel *f*, Stokessche Formel *f*	formule *f* intégrale de Stokes, formule stokienne	обобщенная формула Стокса, формула Стокса
G 156	**generalized Todd genus,** T_y-genus <AG>	verallgemeinertes Toddsches Geschlecht *n*, T_y-Geschlecht *n*	genre *m* de Todd généralisé	обобщенный род Тодда, T_y-род
G 157	**generalized upper half plane of degree *n*,** upper half plane of degree *n* <FT>	obere Siegelsche Halbebene *f* vom Grade *n*	demi-plan *m* supérieur de Siegel de degré *n*	верхняя полуплоскость Зигеля рода *n*
G 158	**generalized Vandermonde determinant** <AL>	Potenzdeterminante *f*, Potentialdeterminante *f*, [verallgemeinerte] Vandermondesche Determinante *f*	déterminant *m* potentiel (de puissances)	обобщенный определитель Вандермонда
G 159	**generalized Waring problem** <NT>	verallgemeinertes Waringsches Problem *n*	problème *m* de Waring généralisé	обобщение проблемы Варинга
G 160	**general kernel** <IE>	allgemeiner Kern *m*	noyau *m* général, noyau de forme générale	ядро общего вида
G 161	**general Laplace transform[ation]** <IT>	allgemeine Laplace-Transformation *f*	transformation *f* de Laplace générale	общее преобразование Лапласа
G 162	**general linear equation** <AL>	allgemeine lineare Gleichung *f*	équation *f* linéaire générale	общее линейное уравнение
	general linear [homogeneous] group <GR>	*s.* F 716		
	general linear variety <AG>	*s.* G 212		
	generally recursive function <MM>	*s.* G 177		
	generally valid formula <LO>	*s.* U 349		
G 163	**general Mathieu equation** <DE>	allgemeine Mathieusche Differentialgleichung (Gleichung) *f*	équation *f* de Mathieu générale	общее уравнение Матье
	general maximum flow algorithm <GP, PG>	*s.* F 458		
G 164	**general mean** <ER, GN, ST>	allgemeines Mittel *n*	moyenne *f* générale	общее среднее
	general mean value theorem <DI>	*s.* T 102		
G 165	**general metric** <TO>	allgemeine Metrik *f*, Metrik	écart *m* <Fréchet>	общая метрика
G 166	**general multiplication of tensors** <VT>	allgemeine Multiplikation *f* von Tensoren	multiplication *f* des tenseurs, multiplication tensorielle	общее умножение тензоров
	general non-linear Riccati equation <DE>	*s.* R 977		
	general perspective affinity <DS>	*s.* S 1173		
	general plane section <AG>	*s.* G 214		
G 167	**general point,** generic point <over *k*> <AG>	allgemeiner Punkt *m* <über *k*>	point *m* générique (général) <sur *k*>	общая точка <над *k*>
G 168	**general point of *V* / for a** <Zariski>**,** for a sufficiently general point of *V* <Hodge-Pedoe> <AG>	fast überall auf *V*	presque partout sur *V*	почти всюду на *V*
G 169	**general polynomial** <of the *n*-th degree> <AL>	allgemeines Polynom *n* <*n*-ten Grades über *K*>	polynôme *m* général <du n^{me} degré>	общий многочлен <*n*-ой степени>
	general polynomial equation <AL>	*s.* G 118		
G 170	**general position** <GE>	allgemeine Lage *f*	position *f* générale	общее положение
G 171	**general principle of choice** <SE>	allgemeines Auswahlprinzip *n* <Zermelo>	principe *m* général du choix	общая теорема выбора
	General Principle of Convergence <SS, AN>	*s.* C 234		
G 172	**general product** <of groups> <GR>	allgemeines Produkt *n*, faktorisierte Gruppe *f* <in die Faktoren N_i>	produit *m* général	общее произведение
	general product <VT>	*s.* P 1596		
G 173	**general proposition,** universal proposition, general (universal) sentence, universally quantified formula, sentence of a universal character; A-proposition <traditional logic> <LO>	Allaussage *f*, Universalaussage *f*, Allsatz *m*, allgemeines Urteil *n*	proposition *f* universelle	общее суждение, универсальное высказывание, общее предложение, общезначимое высказывание

No.	English	German	French	Russian
	general purpose sample <ST>	*s.* M 155		
G 174	**general quadric,** general form of a quadratic equation, affected quadratic <AL>	allgemeine quadratische Gleichung *f*, allgemeine Gleichung zweiten (2.) Grades	équation *f* quadratique générale, équation générale du deuxième (2e) degré	общее квадратное уравнение, общее уравнение второй (2-ой) степени
G 175	**general quadrilateral** <GE>	allgemeines Viereck *n* <alle Seiten verschieden lang>	quadrangle *m* général	четырехугольник общего вида
G 176	**general reciprocal,** generalized inverse, pseudo[-]inverse <of a matrix> <AL>	verallgemeinerte (relative) Inverse *f*, Moore-Penrose-Inverse *f*, Pseudoinverse *f* <einer Matrix>	matrice *f* relativement inverse, matrice pseudo-inverse	главный обратный элемент <к матрице>, обобщенная обратная матрица, псевдообратная матрица
	general reciprocal <AL>	*s.* G 144		
G 177	**general[-]recursive [numerical] function,** generally recursive function <MM>	allgemeinrekursive (allgemein-rekursive, allgemein rekursive) Funktion *f*, allgemeinrekursive zahlentheoretische Funktion, quasirekursive (regelrecht auswertbare) Funktion	fonction *f* récursive générale, fonction généralement récursive, fonction récurrente générale	общерекурсивная (общая рекурсивная) функция
G 178	**general recursive predicate,** recursive predicate <MM>	allgemeinrekursives Prädikat *n*	attribut *m* récursif général, prédicat *m* général récursif	общерекурсивный предикат
G 179	**general recursive relation** <MM>	allgemeinrekursive Relation *f*	relation *f* récursive générale	общерекурсивное отношение
G 180	**general recursive sequence** <MM>	allgemeinrekursive Folge *f*	suite *f* récursive générale	общерекурсивная последовательность
G 181	**general recursivity** <LO>	allgemeine Rekursivität *f*	récursivité *f* générale	общая рекурсивность
	general regression <ST>	*s.* R 499		
G 182	**general renewal process,** modified renewal process <SP>	allgemeiner Erneuerungsprozeß *m*, modifizierter Erneuerungsprozeß	processus *m* général du renouvellement, processus du renouvellement modifié	общий процесс восстановления
	general Riccati equation <DE>	*s.* R 977		
	general sentence <LO>	*s.* G 173		
G 183	**general set theory,** pure (abstract) set theory <SE>	allgemeine (abstrakte) Mengenlehre *f*	théorie *f* générale des ensembles	общая теория множеств
	general similarity transformation <AY>	*s.* S 884		
G 184	**general solution** <of an equation> <AL>	allgemeine Lösung *f*	solution *f* générale (complète)	общее (полное) решение
	general solution <DE>	*s.* G 128		
	general Stokes theorem <DI>	*s.* C 158		
G 185	**general term** <of a series *or* sequence> <SS>	allgemeines Glied *n*	terme *m* général	общий член
	general topology <TO>	*s.* S 705		
	general uniformization theorem [of Koebe]	*s.* U 137		
G 186	**general validity,** universal validity, identity <LO>	Allgemeingültigkeit *f*	validité *f* générale, identité *f*	общезначимость, тождественная истинность, всегда-истинность, универсальная общезначимость, всеобщность
G 187	**general valuation,** Krull['s] valuation <AL>	allgemeine (Krullsche) Bewertung *f*	valuation *f* généralisée (de Krull)	нормирование Крулля, нормирование <произвольного ранга>
G 188	**general valuation of rank 1,** Krull['s] valuation of rank 1 <AL>	spezielle (einstufige) allgemeine Bewertung *f* <Wertgruppe hat Rang 1>	valuation *f* de rang 1, valuation ayant un groupe de valeurs archimédien	нормирование Крулля ранга 1
G 189	**general valuation of rank greater than 1,** Krull['s] valuation of rank greater than 1 <AL>	mehrstufige allgemeine Bewertung *f* <Wertgruppe hat Rang $\neq$ 1>	valuation *f* de rang supérieur à 1	нормирование Крулля ранга больше 1
	general zero <AG, AL>	*s.* G 217		
G 190	**generate / to** <*e.g.* a group> <AL>	erzeugen <*z. B.* eine Gruppe>	engendrer, générer <*par exemple*, un groupe>	порождать, образовать <*например*, группу>
	generate / to <AL>	*s.* S 1341		
G 191	**generated algebra** <by> <AL>	erzeugte Algebra *f*	algèbre *f* engendrée <par>	порожденная алгебра
G 192	**generated filter** <TO>	erzeugter Filter *m*	filtre *m* engendré	фильтр, порожденный некоторым множеством подмножеств
G 193	**generated group** <GR>	erzeugte Gruppe *f*	groupe *m* dérivé	порожденная группа
G 194	**generating class** <of a variety> <UA>	erzeugende Klasse *f*	classe *f* génératrice	порождающий класс
G 195	**generating cone** <of a partially ordered linear space> <AL>	erzeugender Kegel *m*	cône *m* générateur	образующий конус
G 196	**generating differential operator** <ST>	erzeugender Differentialoperator *m*	opérateur *m* différentiel générateur	производящий дифференциальный оператор
	generating element <GR>	*s.* G 207		
G 197	**generating function** <of a sequence of functions, especially of special polynomials> <AN>	erzeugende Funktion *f*, Erzeugende *f*	fonction *f* génératrice	генератриса, // женератриса
G 198	**generating function,** generator function <of a canonical transformation> <DE, VA>	Erzeugende *f*, erzeugende Funktion *f*, Substitutionsfunktion *f*	fonction *f* génératrice	производящая функция

No.	English	German	French	Russian
G 199	**generating function,** course-of-value function <FO>	erzeugende Funktion *f*, Wertverlaufsfunktion *f*	fonction *f* génératrice	производящая функция
G 200	**generating function** <of a random variable> <ST>	erzeugende Funktion *f*, Erzeugende *f*	fonction *f* génératrice	производящая функция
	generating function <NT>	*s.* E 274		
	generating function <ST>	*s.* P 1539		
G 201	**generating line,** curvilinear generator <GE>	erzeugende Kurve (Linie) *f*, Erzeugende *f*	ligne (courbe) *f* génératrice, génératrice *f* curviligne	образующая линия, криволинейная образующая
	generating line <EG>	*s.* G 205		
G 202	**generating relations,** defining relations, defining relator <of a semigroup *or* group> <AL, GR>	definierende Relationen *fpl*	relations *fpl* fondamentales, relations de définition, relations génératrices, relations définissantes	определяющие соотношения, определяющие отношения
G 203	**generating series** <SS>	erzeugende Reihe *f*	série *f* génératrice	производящий ряд
	generating set <AL, GR>	*s.* S 2519		
	generating set <CA>	*s.* F 84		
G 204	**generating subspace** <AL, TO>	erzeugender Unterraum *m*	sous-espace *m* générateur	порождающее подпространство
	generating system <AL, GR>	*s.* S 2519		
	generation <AY>	*s.* R 654		
G 205	**generator,** rectilinear generator, generating line, ruling element, generatrix <of a ruled surface, especially a cone *or* cylinder> <EG> ┌<CA>	Erzeugende *f*; Mantellinie *f*, Seitenlinie *f* <beim Kegel *oder* Zylinder>	génératrice *f*, génératrice rectiligne	образующая линия, образующая, прямолинейная образующая
G 206	**generator** <as an object>	Generator *m*	générateur *m*	образующий, образующая
G 207	**generator,** generating element <of a group> <GR>	Erzeugende *f*, erzeugendes Element *n*	générateur *m*, élément *m* générateur	порождающий элемент, порождающий, образующий элемент
	generator function <DE, VA>	*s.* G 198		
	generatrix <EG>	*s.* G 205		
G 208	**generically surjective map** <AG>	allgemein surjektive Abbildung *f*	application *f* génériquement surjective	общесюръективное отображение
G 209	**generic curve** <AG>	allgemeine Kurve *f*	courbe *f* générique (générale)	общая кривая
G 210	**generic hyperplane,** general hyperplane <AG>	allgemeine Hyperebene *f*	hyperplan *m* générique	общая гиперплоскость
G 211	**generic linear complex [of lines (rays)]** <AY, PJ>	allgemeiner linearer Komplex (Strahlenkomplex) *m*	complexe *m* linéaire générique	общий линейный комплекс [прямых (лучей)]
G 212	**generic linear variety,** general linear variety <AG>	allgemeine lineare Mannigfaltigkeit *f*	variété *f* linéaire générique	общее линейное многообразие
G 213	**generic pencil** <AG>	allgemeines Büschel *n*	faisceau *m* général	общий пучок
G 214	**generic plane section,** general plane section <AG>	allgemeiner Ebenenschnitt *m*	section *f* plane générique	общее плоское сечение
G 215	**generic point** <TO>	allgemeiner Punkt *m*	point *m* générique	общая точка
	generic point <AG>	*s.* G 167		
G 216	**generic specialization** <AG>	allgemeine Spezialisierung *f*	spécialisation *f* générique	общая специализация
G 217	**generic zero,** general zero <of a polynomial ideal> <AG, AL>	allgemeine Nullstelle *f*	zéro *m* générique	общий нуль
G 218	**genetic[al] method** <GN, LO>	genetische Methode *f*	méthode *f* génétique	генетический метод
G 219	**genus** <*pl*: genera> <of an algebra, an algebraic number field, a canonical product, closed system of exterior differential equations, coincidence, curve, curve point, discontinuous group, Fuchsian function, groups, pair of curves, Riemann matrix, ruled surface, *or* variety> <AB, AG, AL, AY, DE, FT, GR, TO>	Geschlecht *n*	genre *m*	род
G 220	**genus,** deficiency <of an algebraic surface> <AG>	Geschlecht *n*, Defekt *m*, // Rang *m*	genre *m*, déficience *f*	род, дефицient
G 221	**genus,** deficiency <Cayley> <of an algebraic curve> <AG>	Geschlecht *n*, Defekt *m*, Geschlechtszahl *f*, // Rang *m*, Defizient *m*, Deficient *m*, Klassenzahl *f*	genre *m*, déficience *f*, nombre *m* du genre, // nombre de classe, classe *f*	род, дефицient
G 222	**genus** <of an algebra> <AL>	Genus *n* <Hazlett>	genre *m*	род
G 223	**genus** <of an entire function> <FT>	Geschlecht *n* <Laguerre>, Höhe *f* <v. Schaper>	genre *m*, hauteur *f*	род
G 224	**genus** <of a graph> <GP>	Geschlecht *n*, Art *f*	genre *m*	тип, род
G 225	**genus** <of quadratic *or* bilinear forms> <NT>	Geschlecht *n*	genre *m*, genre de classes	род
G 226	**genus** <of a surface, especially a Riemann surface> <TO>	Geschlecht *n*, topologisches Geschlecht	genre *m*	род
	genus <AG, GE>	*s.* G 259		
G 227	**genus field** <NT>	Geschlechterklassenkörper *m*	corps *m* de genre	родовое поле
G 228	**genus group** <AB>	Geschlechtergruppe *f*	groupe *m* des genres	родовая группа, группа родов

	English	German	French	Russian
G 229	**genus theorem** <AG>	Geschlechtssatz *m*	théorème *m* du genre	теорема жанра
G 230	**geodesic,** geodesic line <DG>	Geodätische *f*, geodätische (geradeste) Linie *f*, Geodäte *f*	géodésique *f*, ligne *f* géodésique	геодезическая линия, геодезическая
	geodesically convex domain <VA>	*s.* E 865		
G 231	**geodesically parallel curve,** geodesic parallel curve <DG, VA>	geodätisch parallele Kurve *f*	courbe *f* géodésiquement parallèle	геодезически параллельная кривая
	geodesic circle <DG>	*s.* 1. G 238; 2. C 689		
G 232	**geodesic congruence,** congruence of geodesic lines <DG>	geodätische Kongruenz *f*, Kongruenz von geodätischen Linien	congruence *f* [de lignes] géodésique	геодезическая конгруэнция, конгруэнция геодезических линий
G 233	**geodesic co-ordinates,** geodesic parameters, central co-ordinates <in a Riemann space> <DG>	geodätische Koordinaten *fpl*, Zentralkoordinaten *fpl*	coordonnées *fpl* géodésiques (centrales)	геодезические (центральные) координаты
G 234	**geodesic curvature,** tangential curvature <DG>	geodätische Krümmung *f*, Abwickelkrümmung *f*, Tangentialkrümmung *f*	courbure *f* géodésique (tangentielle)	геодезическая кривизна
	geodesic curvature circle <DG>	*s.* C 689		
G 235	**geodesic deviation** <DG>	geodätische Abweichung *f*	déviation *f* géodésique	геодезическое отклонение
	geodesic displacement <DG>	*s.* I 479		
G 236	**geodesic distance** <DG, GE>	geodätische Entfernung *f* <im Riemannschen *oder* Finslerschen Raum>; geodätischer Abstand *m* <im metrischen Raum>	distance *f* géodésique	геодезическое расстояние
G 237	**geodesic distance,** eikonal <VA>	geodätischer Abstand *m*, Fundamentalfunktion *f*, Eikonal *n*	distance *f* géodésique, iconale *f*	основная функция
G 238	**geodesic distance[-] circle,** distance[-]circle, circle of geodesic distance, geodesic circle <of the first kind> <on a surface> <DG>	Entfernungskreis *m*, geodätischer Kreis *m* erster Art, geodätischer Entfernungskreis <nach Gauß>	cercle *m* de distance géodésique, cercle géodésique <de première espèce>, circonférence *f* géodésique	окружность [геодезического] расстояния, геодезическая окружность <первого рода>
G 239	**geodesic equidistance** <VA>	geodätische Äquidistanz *f*	équidistance *f* géodésique	геодезическая равноудаленность
G 240	**geodesic excess** <GE>	geodätischer Exzeß *m*	excès *m* géodésique	геодезический избыток (эксцесс)
G 241	**geodesic field** <VA>	geodätisches Feld (Röhrenfeld) *n*, Röhrenfeld	champ *m* géodésique	геодезическое поле
	geodesic line <DG>	*s.* G 230		
G 242	**geodesic manifold,** totally geodesic manifold <DG>	geodätische (total geodätische) Mannigfaltigkeit *f*	variété *f* géodésique (totalement géodésique)	геодезическое (вполне геодезическое) многообразие
G 243	**geodesic manifold in a point,** locally geodesic manifold <DG>	geodätische Mannigfaltigkeit *f* in einem Punkt, lokal geodätische Mannigfaltigkeit	variété *f* géodésique dans un point, variété localement géodésique	геодезическое многообразие в точке, локально геодезическое многообразие
G 244	**geodesic mapping,** Beltrami['s] mapping <DG>	geodätische (bahntreue, Beltramische) Abbildung *f*	application (représentation) *f* géodésique, application (représentation) de Beltrami	геодезическое отображение, отображение Бельтрами, проективное отображение; отображение, сохраняющее траектории
	geodesic parallel curve <DG, VA>	*s.* G 231		
G 245	**geodesic parameter** <of a surface> <DG>	geodätischer Flächenparameter *m*	paramètre *m* géodésique <d'une surface>	геодезический параметр <поверхности>
	geodesic plane <DG>	*s.* G 355		
G 246	**geodesic slope** <VA>	geodätisches Gefälle *n*	pente *f* géodésique	геодезический наклон
	geodesic space <DG>	*s.* G 536		
G 247	**geodesic torsion** <DG>	geodätische Torsion (Windung) *f*	torsion *f* géodésique	геодезическое кручение
	geographical problem of the four colours <GP>	*s.* F 506		
	geometric addition <VT>	*s.* V 93		
G 248	**geometrical construction [problem]** <EG>	geometrische Konstruktion (Konstruktionsaufgabe) *f*, geometrisches Konstruktionsproblem *n*	construction *f* géométrique	геометрическое построение, конструктивная задача
G 249	**geometrical element,** element <in a construction problem> <EG>	Element *n*	élément *m*, condition *f*	элемент
	geometrically obvious <GE>	*s.* I 856		
G 250	**geometrically parafactorial local ring** <AL>	geometrisch parafaktorieller lokaler Ring *m*	anneau *m* géométriquement parafactoriel	геометрически парафакториальное локальное кольцо
G 251	**geometrically unramified local ring** <AL>	geometrisch unverzweigter lokaler Ring *m*	anneau *m* local géométriquement unibranche	геометрически неразветвленное локальное кольцо
	geometrical problem <VA>	*s.* H 446		
G 252	**geometrical vector,** vector in the affine space <VT>	geometrischer Vektor *m*, Vektor im affinen Raum	vecteur *m* géométrique (dans l'espace affine)	геометрический вектор, вектор в аффинном пространстве
	geometric antecedent <AT>	*s.* G 267		
G 253	**geometric average,** geometric mean, mean proportional, fourth propor-	geometrisches Mittel *n*, mittlere (vierte) Proportionale *f*, proportionales	moyenne *f* géométrique, quatrième proportionnelle *f*, moyenne propor-	среднее геометрическое (пропорциональное), геометрическое сред-

No.	English	German	French	Russian
	tional [number] <AR>	Mittel *n*	tionnelle	нее, четвертая пропорциональности, неизвестный член пропорции
	geometric average <ST>	*s.* G 261		
	geometric body <EG>	*s.* S 1250		
	geometric boundary condition <DE>	*s.* E 489		
G 254	**geometric calculus,** Ausdehnungslehre <of H. Grassmann> <GE>	Wissenschaft *f* der extensiven Größe, Ausdehnungslehre *f* <Graßmann>	algèbre *f* extensive, théorie *f* des grandeurs extensives	учение о протяженных величинах, учение о протяженности
G 255	**geometric complex;** Euclidean complex <AT>	euklidischer (geometrischer) Komplex *m*	complexe *m* euclidien	евклидов (геометрический) комплекс
G 256	**geometric difference** <VT>	geometrische Differenz *f*, Vektordifferenz *f*	différence *f* géométrique	геометрическая (векторная) разность
G 257	**geometric difference equation** <of order *n*> <FD>	geometrische Differenzengleichung *f* <der Ordnung *n*>	équation *f* aux différences finies géométrique <d'ordre *n*>	геометрическое уравнение на конечных разностях <порядка *n*>
G 258	**geometric distribution** <ST>	geometrische Verteilung *f*	distribution *f* géométrique	геометрическое распределение
	geometric distribution <ST>	*s.* C 2209		
G 259	**geometric genus,** genus <of a surface *or* manifold> <AG, GE>	geometrisches Geschlecht *n* <AG, GE>; Flächengeschlecht *n* <AG>	genre *m* géométrique, genre	геометрический род (жанр)
G 260	**geometric lattice** <AL, GE>	geometrischer Verband *m*, Geometrie *f*	treillis *m* géométrique, géométrie *f*, treillis matroïde	геометрическая структура
	geometric locus <GE>	*s.* L 1018		
G 261	**geometric mean [value],** geometric average, logarithmic average, ordinary geometric mean [value] <ST>	geometrisches Mittel *n*, geometrischer Mittelwert *m*, logarithmisches Mittel, logarithmischer Mittelwert, gewöhnliches geometrisches Mittel, gewöhnlicher geometrischer Mittelwert	moyenne *f* géométrique, valeur *f* moyenne géométrique (logarithmique), moyenne géométrique ordinaire	среднее геометрическое, геометрическое среднее, геометрическая средняя [величина], логарифмическое среднее [значение], среднее логарифмическое, обычное (обыкновенное) геометрическое среднее
	geometric mean <AR>	*s.* G 253		
G 262	**geometric multiplication** <of versors> <VT>	geometrische Multiplikation *f*	multiplication *f* géométrique	геометрическое умножение
G 263	**geometric object of the same kind** <GE>	geometrisches Objekt *n* von gleicher Art, gleichartiges geometrisches Objekt	objet *m* géométrique de même sorte	геометрический объект одиночного рода
G 264	**geometric order** <in the set of polyhedral domains> <SE>	geometrische Halbordnung (Ordnungsrelation) *f*	ordre *m* géométrique	геометрическое отношение порядка
G 265	**geometric progression,** geometric sequence <AR>	geometrische Folge (Progression) *f*	progression *f* géométrique (par quotient), suite *f* géométrique	геометрическая прогрессия
G 266	**geometric proportion** <AR>	geometrische Proportion (Analogie) *f*	proportion *f* géométrique	геометрическая пропорция
G 267	**geometric realization,** geometric antecedent <of a complex> <AT>	geometrische Realisierung *f*	réalisation *f* géométrique	геометрическая реализация, геометрическое представление
	geometric relation <GE>	*s.* M 97		
	geometric sequence <AR>	*s.* G 265		
G 268	**geometric series** <AR>	geometrische Reihe *f*	série *f* géométrique	геометрический ряд
G 269	**geometric simplex,** linear simplex <of dimension *n*> <AT>	geradliniges Simplex *n*, euklidisches Simplex, geometrisches Simplex	simplexe *m* géométrique	геометрический симплекс <размерности *n*>
G 270	**geometric sum,** vectorial sum, vector sum, resultant <of vectors> <VT>	vektorielle Summe *f*, Vektorsumme *f*, geometrische Summe, Resultante *f*	somme *f* géométrique (vectorielle), résultante *f*	векторная (геометрическая) сумма
G 271	**geometrization** <GE>	Geometrisierung *f*	géométrisation *f*	геометризация
G 272	**geometrography** <EG>	Geometrographie *f*	géométrographie *f*	геометрография
G 273	**geometry of circles,** circular geometry <DG>	Kreisgeometrie *f*, Geometrie *f* der Kreise	géométrie *f* des cercles, géométrie circulaire	геометрия окружностей
	geometry of circles <DG>	*s.* L 658		
G 274	**geometry of compass** <EG>	Geometrie *f* des Zirkels [allein]	géométrie *f* du compas	геометрия циркуля
	geometry of lines <AY>	*s.* L 859		
G 275	**geometry of numbers** <GU, NT>	Geometrie *f* der Zahlen, Minkowskische Geometrie der Zahlen	géométrie *f* des nombres	геометрия чисел, геометрическая теория чисел
G 276	**geometry of ruler and compass** <EG>	Geometrie *f* von Lineal und Zirkel	géométrie *f* de la règle et du compas	геометрия линейки и циркуля
G 277	**geometry of spheres,** spherical geometry <DG>	Kugelgeometrie *f*, Geometrie *f* der Kugeln	géométrie *f* des sphères, géométrie sphérique	геометрия сфер, сферическая геометрия
	geometry of spheres <DG>	*s.* L 659		
G 278	**geometry of the circle** <AY, EG>	Kreisgeometrie *f*, Geometrie *f* des Kreises	géométrie *f* du cercle	геометрия окружности
G 279	**geometry of the complex domain,** complex geometry <GE>	komplexe Geometrie *f*	géométrie *f* complexe	комплексная геометрия
G 280	**geometry of the triangle** <EG>	Dreiecksgeometrie *f*, Geometrie *f* des Dreiecks	géométrie *f* du triangle	геометрия треугольника
G 281	**geometry of webs** <DG, TO>	Geometrie *f* der Waben (Gewebe), Wabengeometrie *f*, Textilgeometrie *f*	géométrie *f* des réseaux	геометрия сот
	***G*-equivalent fibre bundle** <AT>	*s.* E 431		
G 282	**Gergonne['s] point,** point of Gergonne <of a triangle> <EG>	Gergonnescher (Gergonnes) Punkt *m*	point *m* de Gergonne	точка Жергона (Жергонна)

G 283	**germ** <of a section of a sheaf, a function, *or* a divisor> <AL, AN, AT, FT, TO>	Keim *m*	germe *m*	росток
G 284	**germ** <of a filter> <TO>	Keim *m* <nach einem Filter>	germe *m* <suivant un filtre>	росток <относительно фильтра>
G 285	**germ** <of mappings> <TO>	Keim *m*	germe *m* <d'applications>	росток <отображений>, класс эквивалентных отображений
G 286	**Gerono['s] lemniscate** <GE>	Lemniskate *f* von Gerono, Geronos Lemniskate	lemniscate *f* de Gerono	лемниската Джероно
G 287	**Gershgorin['s] theorem** <on the position of the eigenvalues of a matrix> <MD, NU>	Gerschgorinscher Kreissatz *m*	théorème *m* de Gershgorin	теорема Гершгорина
G 288	**Gibbsian state** <SP>	Gibbsscher Zustand *m*	état *m* gibbsien	гиббсовское состояние
G 289	**Gibbs['] phenomenon** <for Fourier series> <SS>	Gibbssche Erscheinung *f*, Gibbssches Phänomen *n*	phénomène *f* de Gibbs	явление Гиббса
	Gibbs['] vector algebra <AL, GE>	*s.* V 95		
	Gibrat distribution <ST>	*s.* L 1042		
G 290	**girth,** length of the longest cycle <of a non-oriented graph> <GP>	Taillenweite *f*	calibre *m*, longueur *f* du plus long cycle	обход
G 291	**given quantity** <NU>	gegebene (vorgegebene) Größe *f*	grandeur *f* donnée [d'avance]	данная (заданная) величина
	given value of argument <AX, FD, NU>	*s.* I 779		
G 292	**glancing intersection** <of two curves> <NU>	schleifender Schnitt *m*	intersection *f* rasante	пересечение <двух кривых> под малым углом, касательное пересечение
	g.l.b., GLB <DI, SE>	*s.* G 411		
	GLB, g.l.b. <SE>	*s.* G 412		
G 293	**glissette** <GE>	Gleitkurve *f*	glissette *f*	кривая скольжения
G 294	**Glivenko['s] theorem** <ST>	Satz *m* von Gliwenko (Glivenko), Hauptsatz *m* der mathematischen Statistik, Gliwenko-Satz *m*, Glivenko-Satz *m*	théorème *m* de Glivenko	теорема Гливенко
G 295	**global Brauer group** <AG>	globale Brauersche Gruppe *f*	groupe *m* de Brauer global	глобальная группа Брауэра
G 296	**global class field theory** <AB>	globale Klassenkörpertheorie *f*	théorie *f* du corps de classe globale	глобальная теория полей классов
G 297	**global conductor** <of a character> <AB>	globaler Führer *m*	conducteur *m* global	[глобальный] кондуктор
G 298	**global continuity** <DI>	globale Stetigkeit *f*, Stetigkeit im Großen	continuité *f* globale	глобальная непрерывность
G 299	**global convergence** <NU, PG>	globale Konvergenz *f*	convergence *f* globale	глобальная сходимость
G 300	**global differential geometry,** differential geometry in the large <DG>	Differentialgeometrie *f* im Großen, globale Differentialgeometrie	géométrie *f* différentielle globale	глобальная дифференциальная геометрия, дифференциальная геометрия в целом, геометрия в целом
G 301	**global existence** <GN>	globale Existenz *f*, Existenz im Großen	existence *f* globale	существование в целом, глобальное существование
G 302	**globalization** <AL>	Globalisierung *f*	globalisation *f*	глобализация
G 303	**global limit theorem** <ST>	globaler Grenzwertsatz (Grenzverteilungssatz) *m*	théorème *m* limite global	глобальная предельная теорема
G 304	**global linearization** <PG>	globale Linearisierung *f*	linéarisation *f* globale	глобальная линеаризация
G 305	**global Lipschitz condition** <DE>	globale Lipschitz-Bedingung *f*	condition *f* de Lipschitz globale	глобальное условие Липшица
G 306	**global Lipschitz constant** <of a mapping> <TO>	Dehnungsschranke *f*, globale (einheitliche) Lipschitzsche Konstante *f*, Lipschitzsche Konstante	constante *f* de Lipschitz globale	граница растяжения, [глобальная] постоянная Липшица
G 307	**global mapping,** mapping in the large <SE>	Abbildung *f* im Großen, globale Abbildung	application *f* globale	отображение в целом
	global maximum <DI>	*s.* A 115		
	global minimum <DI>	*s.* A 117		
G 308	**global order** <of a distribution> <AN>	globale Ordnung *f*	ordre *m* global	глобальный порядок
G 309	**global reciprocity law** <AB>	globales Reziprozitätsgesetz *n*	loi *f* de réciprocité globale	глобальный закон взаимности
G 310	**global uniformization,** uniformization in the large <FT>	Uniformisierung *f* im Großen	uniformisation *f* globale	униформизация в большом (целом), глобальная униформизация
G 311	**globoidal curve** <GE>	globoidale Kurve *f*	courbe *f* globoïdale	глобоидальная кривая
G 312	**glued boundaries,** identified boundaries <TO>	verheftete Ränder *mpl*	bords *mpl* identifiés	склеенные (отождествленные) границы
	gluing <TO>	*s.* P 598		
	gluing of boundaries <TO>	*s.* P 297		
G 313	**gluing of manifolds** <TO>	Verheften *n* von Mannigfaltigkeiten	recollement *m* de variétés	склеивание многообразий
G 314	**gluing theorem** <GE>	Verheftungssatz *m* [von A. D. Aleksandrow]	théorème *m* de collage	теорема склеивания [А. Д. Александрова]
	Gnedenko['s] [local] limit theorem <ST>	*s.* G 316		
G 315	**Gnedenko test** <ST>	Gnedenko-Test *m*	test *m* de Gnedenko	критерий Гнеденко
G 316	**Gnedenko['s] theorem,** Gnedenko['s] local limit theorem, Gnedenko['s]	Satz (Grenzwertsatz, lokaler Grenzwertsatz) *m* von Gnedenko, Gnedenko-	théorème *m* de Gnedenko, théorème limite local de Gnedenko, théorème	теорема Гнеденко, локальная предельная теорема Гнеденко, пре-

No.	English	German	French	Russian
	limit theorem, local limit theorem of Gnedenko <ST>	scher Satz (Grenzwertsatz, lokaler Grenzwertsatz)	limite de Gnedenko	дельная теорема Гнеденко
G 317	**gnomon** <EG, NT>	Gnomon *n*	gnomon *m*	гномон
G 318	**gnomonic projection** <PJ>	gnomonische (orthodromische, gnomische) Projektion *f*	projection *f* gnomique	гномоническая проекция
G 319	**Godeaux['s] chain** <DG>	Godeaux-Kette *f*, Godeauxsche Kette *f*	chaine *f* de Godeaux	цепь Годо
G 320	**Godeaux-Rozet surface** <DG>	Fläche *f* von Godeaux-Rozet, Godeaux-Rozetsche Fläche	surface *f* de Godeaux-Rozet	поверхность Годо-Розе
G 321	**Godeaux['s] sequence** <DG>	Godeauxsche Folge *f*, Godeaux-Folge *f*	suite *f* de Godeaux	последовательность Годо
	Gödel['s] axiom of constructibility <SE>	*s.* A 1284		
	Gödel-Bernays axiom system of set theory <SE>	*s.* G 328		
G 322	**Gödel['s] completeness theorem,** K. Gödel['s] completeness theorem, completeness theorem of Gödel <MM>	Gödelscher Vollständigkeitssatz *m*, Gödelsches Vollständigkeitstheorem *n*	théorème *m* de Gödel [de complétude]	теорема Геделя о полноте, геделевская теорема о полноте, теорема полноты Геделя, геделева теорема полноты
G 323	**Gödel['s] β-function** <MM>	Gödelsche β-Funktion *f*	fonction *f* β de Gödel	β-функция Геделя
	Gödel['s] incompleteness theorem <MM>	*s.* G 327		
G 324	**Gödelization, gödelizing** <MM>	Gödelisierung *f*	gödelisation *f*, procédé *m* de Gödel	геделизирование
G 325	**Gödel['s] number,** code <MM>	Gödel-Zahl *f*, Gödelsche Zahl *f*, Gödel-Nummer *f*, Gödelzahl *f*	nombre *m* de Gödel, gödelien *m*	геделев номер
G 326	**Gödel[-] numbering** <MM>	Gödelsche Zuordnungsvorschrift *f*, Gödel-Numerierung *f*, Gödelsche Arithmetisierung *f*	arithmétisation *f* de Gödel	геделевская арифметизация
G 327	**Gödel['s] underivability theorem,** Gödel['s] incompleteness theorem <first *or* second> <MM>	Gödelscher Unvollständigkeitssatz (Satz) *m* <erster *oder* zweiter>	théorème *m* de Gödel [d'incomplétude] <premier *ou* second>	теорема Геделя о неполноте; первая теорема Геделя, теорема о неполноте [формальных систем], теорема о неполноте формализованной арифметики; вторая теорема Геделя [о неполноте], теорема Геделя о невозможности доказать непротиворечивость формальной системы средствами самой системы
G 328	**Gödel-von Neumann-Bernays set theory;** Gödel-Bernays axiom system of set theory <SE>	Gödel-von Neumann-Bernayssche Mengentheorie *f*	théorie *f* des ensembles de Gödel-Bernays	теория множеств Геделя-Бернайса, система Геделя-Бернайса, GB
	go into . . . without [a] remainder / to <NT>	*s.* B 162		
G 329	**Goldbach['s] conjecture (guess, hypothesis)** <NT>	Goldbachsche Vermutung *f*, Goldbachsches Problem *n*	hypothèse *f* (problème *m*) de Goldbach	гипотеза Гольдбаха, проблема Гольдбаха[-Эйлера]
G 330	**Goldbach['s] theorem** <NT>	Goldbachscher (Goldbachs) Satz *m*, Goldbachsches Gesetz *n*	proposition *f* (loi *f*, théorème *m*) de Goldbach	теорема Гольдбаха
	Goldbach-Waring problem <NT>	*s.* P 1563		
	golden rule <AR>	*s.* R 1512		
G 331	**golden section,** extreme and mean ratio, division in extreme and mean ratio <EG>	Goldener Schnitt *m*, stetige Teilung *f*, göttliche Proportion *f*, proportio *f* divina, sectio *f* divina	division *f* en moyenne et extrême raison, proportion *f* divine	золотое деление, золотое сечение, гармоническое деление, деление в крайнем и среднем отношении, непрерывное деление
G 332	**Goldie['s] dimension** <AL>	Goldiesche Dimension *f*	dimension *f* de Goldie	размерность Голди
G 333	**Goldie['s] ring** <AL>	Goldie-Ring *m*	anneau *m* de Goldie	кольцо Голди
G 334	**Goldie['s] theorem** <AL>	Satz *m* von Goldie, Goldiescher Satz	théorème *m* de Goldie	теорема Голди
G 335	**Gomory['s] condition** <PG>	Gomory-Bedingung *f*	condition *f* de Gomory	условие Гомори
G 336	**Gomory['s] cut** <PG>	Gomory-Schnitt *m*	section *f* de Gomory	сечение Гомори
	Gomory['s] method <PG>	*s.* C 2826		
G 337	**Gompertz['] formula (law)** <ST>	Gompertzsches Wachstumgesetz (Gesetz) *n*, Gompertz-Formel *f*, Gompertzsche Formel *f*	loi (formule) *f* de Gompertz	закон (формула) Гомперца
G 338	**Gompertz-Makeham['s] growth function** <ST>	Wachstumsfunktion *f* nach Gompertz-Makeham, Gompertz-Makehamsche Wachstumsfunktion, Gompertzsche Wachstumsfunktion (Funktion *f*)	fonction *f* de croissance de Gompertz-Makeham	функция Гомперца, функция роста Гомперца-Мейкхэма (по Гомперцу-Мейкхэму)
	gon <GE>	*s.* G 357		

No.	English	German	French	Russian
G 339	**goniometric equation** <EG>	goniometrische (reingoniometrische) Gleichung *f*	équation *f* goniométrique	гониометрическое уравнение
G 340	**good approximation,** close approximation <AX, NT>	gute Näherung *f*, gute (genaue) Annäherung *f*	bonne approximation *f*	хорошая аппроксимация, хорошее приближение
G 341	**goodness of fit** <ST>	Güte *f* der Anpassung	validité *f* de l'ajustement, qualité *f* d'ajustement	согласие
G 342	**good reduction** <AG>	gute Reduktion *f*	bonne réduction *f*	хорошая редукция
G 343	**Göpel['s] group** <for theta-functions> <FU>	Göpelsche Gruppe *f*	groupe *m* de Göpel	группа Гепеля
G 344	**Göpel['s] invariant** <for theta-functions> <FU>	Göpelsche Invariante *f*	invariant *m* de Göpel	инвариант Гепеля
	Göpel['s] tetrahedron <AG, FT, FU>	*s.* S 2552		
	Gordan['s] method <IV>	*s.* M 466		
G 345	**Gordan['s] series** <IV>	Gordansche Reihe *f*	série *f* de Gordan	ряд Гордана
	Gordan['s] theorem <AL>	*s.* T 283		
	gore <EG>	*s.* L 1188		
G 346	**Gorenstein['s] module** <AL>	Gorenstein-Modul *m*, Gorensteinmodul *m*	module *m* de Gorenstein	модуль Горенштейна
G 347	**Gorenstein['s] ring** <AL>	Gorenstein-Ring *m*, Gorensteinring *m*	anneau *m* de Gorenstein	кольцо Горенштейна, горенштейново кольцо
	gorge <DG>	*s.* S 1868		
G 348	**gorge circle** <of a one-sheet hyperboloid of revolution> <AY>	Kehlkreis *m*	cercle *m* de gorge	горловина, горловая окружность
G 349	**gorge ellipse** <of a one-sheet hyperboloid> <AY>	Kehlellipse *f*	ellipse *f* de gorge	горловина, горловой эллипс
	gorge line <DG>	*s.* S 1868		
G 350	**go through a maximum / to** <DI>	durch ein Maximum gehen	passer par un maximum	проходить через максимум
G 351	**go through a minimum / to** <DI>	durch ein Minimum gehen	passer par un minimum	проходить через минимум
G 352	**Goursat['s] formula** <FT>	Formel *f* von Goursat, Goursatsche Formel	formule *f* de Goursat	формула Гурса
G 353	**Goursat['s] problem** <DE>	Goursatsches Problem *n*	problème *m* de Goursat	задача Гурса
G 354	**Goursat['s] theorem** <FT>	Satz *m* von Goursat, Goursatscher Satz	théorème *m* de Goursat	теорема Гурса
G 355	**G-plane,** geodesic plane <DG>	G-Ebene *f*, geodätische Ebene *f*	G-plan *m*, plan *m* géodésique, plan (G)	G-плоскость, геодезическая плоскость
	gr <GE>	*s.* G 357		
	grad <GE>	*s.* G 357		
	grad <VT>	*s.* G 362		
	Grad <VT>	*s.* G 363		
G 356	**gradable object** <CA>	graduierbares Objekt *n*	objet *m* graduable	градуируемый объект
G 357	**grade,** grad, gon, ^{g}, gr <GE>	Gon *n*, Neugrad *n*, ^{g}	grade *m*, gon *m*, ^{g}, gr	град, гон, десятичный (метрический, новый) градус, ^{g}
	grade <AL>	*s.* D 262		
	grade <MD>	*s.* R 136		
	grade correlation <ST>	*s.* R 141		
G 358	**graded free category** <CA>	graduierte freie Kategorie *f*	catégorie *f* libre graduée	градуированная свободная категория
G 359	**graded group** <GR>	graduierte Gruppe *f*	groupe *m* gradué	градуированная группа; группа, снабженная градуировкой
G 360	**graded lattice** <LA>	Verband *m* mit Dimensionsfunktion	treillis *m* gradué	структура с функцией размерности
G 361	**gradient,** rate of change <of a function at a point> <DI, NU>	Steigung *f* <in einem Punkt>	gradient *m*, rapport *m* d'accroissement, taux *m* d'accroissement <dans un point>	скорость изменения, быстрота изменения, отношение приращений <в точке>
G 362	**gradient,** grad, **grad,** ∇ <of a scalar> <VT>	Gradient *m*, Gradientenvektor *m*, grad	gradient *m*, grad, **grad**	градиент, grad
	gradient <AN, DI, FD>	*s.* D 789		
	gradient at a surface of discontinuity <VT>	*s.* G 363		
	gradient method <AN, NU, PG>	*s.* M 485		
	gradient method <NU>	*s.* G 364		
G 363	**gradient of discontinuity,** gradient at a surface of discontinuity, surface gradient, areal gradient, Grad <VT>	Flächengradient *m*, Sprunggradient *m*, Grad	gradient *m* de discontinuité, gradient dans une surface de discontinuité, gradient de surface, gradient superficiel, Grad	градиент разрыва (на поверхности разрыва), поверхностный градиент, Grad
	gradient scale <DE>	*s.* G 366		
G 364	**gradient-step method,** gradient method <of a matrix eigenvalue problem> <NU>	Gradient-step-Verfahren *n*, Gradientenmethode *f*	méthode *f* du gradient	градиентный метод
G 365	**gradient tensor** <VT>	Gradiententensor *m*, Gradientaffinor *m*, Gradient *m*	tenseur *m* gradient	градиентный тензор, тензорный градиент
	graduated dividers <GE, IN>	*s.* P 1855		
G 366	**graduated fall line;** fall scale, slope scale, gradient scale <DS>	graduierte Fallinie *f*; Böschungsmaßstab *m*	ligne *f* de pente graduée; échelle *f* de pente	градуированная линия падения; масштаб падения (наклона, откоса)
G 367	**graduation** <*e.g.*: with values in a monoid> <AL>	Graduierung *f* <*z. B.*: mit Werten in einem Monoid>	graduation *f* <*par exemple:* suivant le monoïde>	градуировка (*например:* со значениями в моноиде, по моноиду>
G 368	**graduation bounded below,** bounded below graduation <AL>	nach unten beschränkte Graduierung *f*	graduation *f* bornée inférieurement	ограниченная снизу градуировка

No.	English	German	French	Russian
	graduation of the circle <NU>	s. C 2902		
	Graeco-Latin square <CT>	s. E 616		
G 369	**Gräffe['s] method, Graeffe['s] method, Gräffe['s] root-squaring method,** root-squaring method, Lobachevski method <AL, AX. NU>	Gräffesche Näherungsmethode f, Gräffesches Verfahren n, Verfahren von Gräffe, Verfahren der quadrierten Wurzeln, Gräffes Verfahren, // Graeffe-Verfahren n	méthode f de Gräffe (Graeffe), procédé m de Gräffe	метод Лобачевского (Греффе, Данделена)
G 370	**Gram-Charlier expansion (series)** <of type *A or B*> <ST>	Gram-Charlier-Reihe f, Gram-Charliersche Reihe f, Gram-Charlier-Entwicklung f, Gram-Charliersche Entwicklung f <vom Typ *A oder B*>	série f de Gram-Charlier, expansion f de Gram-Charlier <du type *A ou B*>	ряд Грама-Шарлье <типа *A или B*>
G 371	**Gram['s] determinant,** Gramian <AL, AN>	Gramsche Determinante f	déterminant m de Gram, gramien m	определитель (детерминант) Грама
G 372	**Gramian** <AL>	Gramsche Matrix f	matrice f de Gram	матрица Грама
	Gramian <AL, AN>	s. G 371		
G 373	**Grammel['s] method** <DE, NU>	Näherungsverfahren n von Grammel, Grammelsches Näherungsverfahren, Grammels[ches] Verfahren n	méthode f de Grammel	метод Граммеля
G 374	**Gram-Schmidt orthogonalization [procedure], Gram-Schmidt [orthogonalization] process,** Schmidt['s] [orthogonalization] process, Schmidt['s] orthogonalization <AL>	Orthogonalisierungsverfahren (Orthonormierungsverfahren) n von (nach) Gram-Schmidt (E. Schmidt, Erhard Schmidt, Hilbert-Schmidt), [Gram-]Schmidtsches Orthogonalisierungsverfahren (Orthonormierungsverfahren), Hilbert-Schmidtsches Orthogonalisierungsverfahren (Orthonormierungsverfahren), Schmidtscher Orthogonalisierungsprozeß m	procédé m (méthode f) d'orthogonalisation (d'orthonormalisation) de Schmidt (Gram-Schmidt, Hilbert-Schmidt), procédé d'orthogonalisation (d'orthonormalisation) dû à E. Schmidt, méthode d'orthogonalisation (d'orthonormalisation) due à E. Schmidt	метод (способ, процесс) ортогонализации (ортонормирования) Шмидта (Гильберта-Шмидта, Э. Шмидта, Грама-Шмидта), ортогонализация Грама-Шмидта
G 375	**Gram['s] theorem** <IV>	Gramscher Satz m	théorème m de Gram	теорема Грама
G 376	**grand average,** overall mean; average overall subsampling value <ST>	Gesamtmittel n	moyenne f générale (globale)	общее среднее; среднее по всем группам
G 377	**grand total** <ST>	Gesamtsumme f	somme f totale	общий итог, полная сумма
	grand total <AR>	s. T 615		
G 378	**graph** <of a correspondence> <AG>	Graph m	graphe m	граф
G 379	**graph** <of a partial operation> <AL>	Graph m	graphe m	график
G 380	**graph** <of a function *or* transformation> <AN, SE>	Graph m, Ensemble n représentatif	graphe m, courbe f représentative, ensemble m représentatif, graphe fonctionnel, graphique m	график, представляющее отношение (множество)
G 381	**graph** <of a lattice> <LA>	Graph m <eines Verbands>	graphe m latticiel	структурный граф
G 382	**graph** <of a binary relation> <SE>	Graph m	graphe m; représentation f matricielle, schéma m matriciel <graphe en forme matricielle>	граф
	graph <AN, NU>	s. D 408		
	graph <AT, GP>	s. T 517		
	graph <CA>	s. D 412		
	graph <GP>	s. A 147		
	graph <NO>	s. N 299		
	graph chart <IN, NU>	s. G 389		
	graph free of circuits <GP>	s. C 699		
G 383	**graphical calculation** <NU>	graphisches Rechnen n	calcul m graphique	графическое вычисление
G 384	**graphical integration** <DE, DI, NU>; graphical quadrature <DI, NU>	graphische Integration f <DE, DI, NU>; graphische Quadratur f <DI, NU>	intégration f graphique <DE, DI, NU>; quadrature f graphique <DI, NU>	графическое интегрирование <DE, DI, NU>
	graphically represented complex number <FT>	s. A 382		
	graphical quadrature <DI, NU>	s. G 384		
G 385	**graphical representation of [the] complex numbers** <AN>	geometrische Darstellung f komplexer Zahlen	représentation f géométrique des nombres complexes, représentation d'Argand-Cauchy	геометрическое изображение комплексных чисел
	graphic representation <AN, NU>	s. D 408		
G 386	**graphic solution** <NU>	graphische Lösung f; graphische Auflösung f	résolution f graphique	графическое решение
G 387	**graph obtained by retraction of a subgraph to a point** <GP>	Zusammenziehung f	graphe m obtenu par condensation (rétrécissement d'un sous-graphe)	
G 388	**graph of König,** König['s] graph <GP>	Königscher Graph m <schlichter paarer Graph>	graphe m de König	граф Кенига <обыкновенный двудольный граф>
	graph of multiplicity *n* <GP>	s. N 228		

No.	English	German	French	Russian
	graph of the logarithmic function <AN>	*s.* L 1035		
G 389	**graph paper,** graph chart <IN, NU>	Funktionspapier *n*, graphisches Papier *n*, Funktionsnetz *n*	papier (diagramme) *m* à échelle fonctionnelle	функциональная бумага (сетка)
G 390	**graph rank,** rank <of a graph> <GP>	Rang *m*	rang *m*	ранг
G 391	**graph with loops** <GP>	Graph *m* im weiteren Sinne <Schlingen zugelassen>	graphe *m* avec boucles	граф с петлями
G 392	**graph without chords** <GP>	sehnenloser Kreis *m*	graphe *m* sans cordes	граф без хорд
G 393	**graph without loops** <GP>	Graph *m* im engeren Sinne, Graph ohne Schlingen, schlingenloser Graph	graphe *m* sans boucles	граф без петлей
G 394	**graph without triangle** <GP>	dreikreisfreier Graph *m*, Graph ohne 3-Clique	graphe *m* sans triangle	граф без треугольника
	Grassmann['s] algebra <AL>	*s.* E 824		
G 395	**Grassmann['s] coordinates [of the first kind]** <PJ>	Graßmannsche Koordinaten *fpl* [erster (1.) Art], Π_p-Koordinaten *fpl*	coordonnées *fpl* grassmanniennes [de première espèce]	грассмановы координаты [первого рода]
G 396	**Grassmann['s] coordinates of the second kind** <PJ>	Graßmannsche Koordinaten *fpl* zweiter (2.) Art	coordonnées *fpl* grassmanniennes de seconde (deuxième) espèce	грассмановы координаты второго рода
	grassmannian <PJ>	*s.* G 397		
G 397	**Grassmann manifold,** Grassmann variety, grassmannian <PJ>	Graßmannsche Mannigfaltigkeit *f*	grassmannienne *f*, variété *f* de Grassmann, variété grassmannienne	грассманиан, грассмановское многообразие, многообразие Грассмана, грассманово многообразие
G 398	**Grassmann multiplication** <of segments *or* geometric elements> <PJ>	Graßmanns[che] Multiplikation *f*	multiplication *f* de Grassmann	умножение Грассмана
	Grassmann multiplication <AL>	*s.* E 840		
	Grassmann product <AL>	*s.* O 550		
G 399	**Grassmann['s] relations** <PJ>	Graßmann-Relationen *fpl*, quadratische *p*-Relationen *fpl* <zwischen Graßmannschen Koordinaten>	relations *fpl* de Grassmann	отношения Грассмана
	Grassmann variety <PJ>	*s.* G 397		
G 400	**great circle** <of the sphere> <EG>	Großkreis *m*, größter Kreis *m*, größter Kugelkreis *m*, Hauptkreis *m* <der Kugelfläche>	grand cercle *m*	большой круг, окружность большого круга
	great circle line <DG, VA>	*s.* O 440		
G 401	**greater** <than>, > <AN>	größer <als>, >	strictement supérieur <à>, plus grand [strictement] <que>, >	больше <чем>, >
G 402	**greater,** later <than>, > <NT, SE>	größer <als>, >	strictement supérieur <à>, plus grand <que>, plus grand strictement <que>, postérieur <à>, supérieur <à>, après	больше <чем>, более, >
G 403	**greater than or equal to,** $\geqq$, $\geq$ <AN, SE>	größer oder gleich, $\geqq$, $\gtrsim$	supérieur ou égal <à>, plus grand que ou moins <à>, plus grand ou égal <à> <AN, SE>; après ou égal <à> <SE>, $\geqq$, $\gtrsim$	больше или равно, не меньше <чем>, равный или больше <чем>, $\geqq$, $\geq$
	greater than relation <SE>	*s.* R 675		
G 404	**greatest common divisor,** highest common factor, G.C.D., g.c.d. <AL, NT>; greatest common measure <NT>	größter gemeinsamer (gemeinschaftlicher) Teiler *m*, größter Gemeinteiler *m*, g.g.T. <AL, NT>; größtes gemeinsames (gemeinschaftliches) Maß *n* <NT>	plus grand commun diviseur *m*, p.g.c.d.	наибольший общий делитель, общий наибольший делитель, о.н.д., н.о.д.
	greatest common divisor <AL>	*s.* H 310		
G 405	**greatest common left divisor,** g.c.l.d. <AL>	größter gemeinsamer Linksteiler *m*, GGLT	plus grand commun diviseur *m* à gauche	левый наибольший делитель
	greatest common measure <NT>	*s.* G 404		
G 406	**greatest common right divisor,** g.c.r.d. <AL>	größter gemeinsamer Rechtsteiler *m*, GGRT	plus grand commun diviseur *m* à droite	правый наибольший делитель
G 407/8	**greatest common submodule,** logical product, [set-theoretic] intersection <of modules> <AL>	Durchschnitt *m*	intersection *f*	пересечение
G 409	**greatest element,** largest number, last member, largest element, all element, unit, identity, universal element <of a partially ordered set> <SE>	größtes (letztes) Element *n*, Einselement *n*	élément *m* maximum, plus grand élément, élément universel, dernier élément, majorant *m* universel	наибольший (абсолютно максимальный, универсальный) элемент, максимум, максимальный элемент
G 410	**greatest ideal,** universally maximal ideal <AL>	größtes (universal maximales) Ideal *n*	idéal *m* maximum	наибольший (универсально максимальный) идеал
	greatest integer <NT>	*s.* I 645		

	greatest integer function <NT>	*s.* S 1552		
	greatest integer *x* <NT>	*s.* I 645		
	greatest left ideal <AL>	*s.* U 344		
G 411	**greatest lower bound,** infimum, inf, g.l.b., GLB <of a set *or* sequence of real numbers *or* of a real-valued function>, // lower boundary <DI, SE>	untere Grenze *f*, Infimum *n*, größte untere Schranke *f*, finis *m* inferior, inf, fin inf, fin, // untere Schranke	borne *f* inférieure stricte (précise), la plus grande borne inférieure, borne inférieure, la plus grande limite *f* inférieure, le plus grand minorant *m*, infimum *m*, minimum *m* absolu, minimum, limite minimum <Darboux>, inf	нижняя грань, точная нижняя грань, инфимум, inf <DI, SS>
G 412	**greatest lower bound,** meet, infimum, inf, GLB, g.l.b. <in a partially ordered set> <SE>	untere Grenze *f*, Infimum *n*, inf	borne *f* inférieure, le plus grand minorant *m*, borne inférieure stricte (précise), infimum *m*, inf	точная нижняя граница, наибольшая нижняя грань, пересечение, infimum
	greatest of the limits <DI, SS>	*s.* U 427		
	greatest square-free divisor <NT>	*s.* C 2456		
G 413	**Great Picard Theorem,** Picard['s] grand theorem, Picard['s] general theorem <FT>	großer (allgemeiner) Picardscher Satz *m*	grand théorème *m* de Picard, théorème général de Picard	большая теорема Пикара
	Grebe['s] point <EG>	*s.* L 564		
	Greco-Latin square <CT>	*s.* E 616		
	Greenberger['s] method <ST>	*s.* C 1918		
G 414	**Green-de Rham projector** <DG>	Green-de-Rham-Projektor *m*	projecteur *m* de Green-de Rham	проектор Грина-де Рама
G 415	**Green['s] first identity,** Green['s] formula of the first kind, first Green formula <DI, VT>	Greensche Formel *f* erster Art, erste Greensche Formel, Greensche Zwischenformel *f*	formule *f* de Green du premier genre, première formule de Green	первая (предварительная) формула Грина
	Green['s] formula of the first kind <DI, VT>	*s.* G 415		
	Green['s] formula of the second kind <DI, VT>	*s.* G 425		
G 416	**Green['s] function,** induction function, source function <DE, PO>	Greensche Funktion *f*, Einflußfunktion *f*, Quellenfunktion *f*, Riemannsche Funktion	fonction *f* de Green (source)	функция Грина (источника, влияния)
G 417	**Green['s] function in the most general sense,** induction function in the most general sense <DE>	allgemeinste Greensche Funktion *f*	fonction *f* de Green dans le sens le plus général	функция Грина в самом общем смысле
G 418	**Green['s] kernel** <DE>	Greenscher Kern *m*	noyau *m* de Green	ядро Грина
G 419	**Green['s] map** <AL>	Greensche Abbildung *f*	application *f* de Green	отображение Грина
G 420	**Green['s] matrix,** Green['s] tensor, dyadic Green['s] function <DE>	Greensche Matrix *f*, Greenscher Tensor *m*, tensorielle Greensche Funktion *f*	matrice *f* (tenseur *m*) de Green, fonction *f* de Green tensorielle	матрица (тензор) Грина, гринов тензор, тензорная функция Грина
G 421	**Green['s] normal** <DG>	Normale *f* von Green, Greensche Normale, Grat *m*	normale *f* de Green	нормаль Грина
G 422	**Green['s] operator** <DE>	Greenscher Operator *m*	opérateur *m* de Green	оператор Грина
G 423	**Green['s] polynomial** <AL>	Greensches Polynom *n*	polynôme *m* de Green	полином Грина
G 424	**Green['s] resolvent** <DE>	Greensche Resolvente *f*	résolvante *f* de Green	резольвента Грина
G 425	**Green['s] second identity,** Green['s] theorem, Green['s] formula of the second kind, second Green formula <DI, VT>	Greensche Formel *f*, Greensche Formel zweiter Art, zweite Greensche Formel	formule *f* de Green du deuxième genre, deuxième formule de Green	вторая формула Грина
G 426	**Green['s] space** <DE, PO>	Greenscher Raum *m*	espace *m* de Green	пространство Грина
	Green['s] tensor <DE>	*s.* G 420		
G 427	**Green['s] theorem,** Green['s] transformation, Ostrogradsky['s] theorem, divergence theorem, Gauss['] divergence theorem, integral theorem of Gauss, Gaussian theorem, Gauss['] theorem, integration by parts <DI, VT>	Gaußscher Satz *m* der Vektoranalysis (Integralrechnung), Gaußscher Satz, Gauß-Ostrogradskischer (Gaußscher) Integralsatz *m*, Integralsatz *m* von Gauß, Satz von Ostrogradski, Integralformel *f* von Gauß, Gaußsche (Ostrogradskische) Integralformel, Gaußsche (Gauß-Ostrogradskische, Ostrogradskische) Formel, Divergenzsatz *m*, Fundamentalsatz *m* der Vektoranalysis, Greensche Integralformel (Formel)	formule *f* (théorème *m*) d'Ostrogradsky, théorème de Gauss, identité *f* d'Ostrogradsky	формула Остроградского, теорема Остроградского [о дивергенции], формула Гаусса-Остроградского, теорема Гаусса
	Green['s] theorem <DI, VT>	*s.* G 425		
	Green['s] theorem for *n* = 2 <DI, VT>	*s.* R 1042		

No.	English	German	French	Russian
	Green['s] transformation <DI, VT>	*s.* G 427		
	Gregory['s] backward formula <AX, FD, NU>	*s.* N 201		
G 428	**Gregory['s] formula,** Gregory-Newton formula <for numerical quadrature> <FD, NU>	Gregorysche Integrationsformel (Integrationsregel, Formel) *f*	formule *f* de Gregory, formule d'intégration de Gregory, formule d'intégration mixte par différences latérale	формула Грегори, формула интегрирования Грегори
	Gregory['s] forward formula <AX, FD, NU>	*s.* N 202		
G 429	**Gregory['s] interpolation formulae, Gregory-Newton formula [for interpolation],** Newton['s] interpolation formulae <AX, FD, NU>	Gregory-Newtonsche Formeln *fpl*, Newtonsche Interpolationsformel[n] *f*[*pl*], Interpolationsformel[n] von Newton <mit absteigenden oder aufsteigenden Differenzen>	formules *fpl* d'interpolation de [Gregory-] Newton	формулы Грегори-Ньютона, интерполяционные формулы Грегори-Ньютона, интерполяционные формулы Ньютона, формулы Ньютона
	Gregory-Newton formula <FD, NU>	*s.* G 428		
G 430	**Gregory['s] series** <SS>	Arkustangensreihe *f*, arctan-Reihe *f*, Gregorysche Reihe *f*	série *f* de l'arctangente, développement *m* en série de l'arctangente, série de Gregory	ряд арктангенса, разложение арктангенса в степенной ряд
	Grelling-Nelson paradox of heterologicality <LO>	*s.* G 431		
G 431	**Grelling['s] paradox,** Grelling-Nelson paradox of heterologicality, paradox of heterologicality <LO>	heterologische Paradoxie *f*, Antinomie *f* von Grelling, Grellingsche Antinomie, Antinomie des Wortes „heterologisch", Antinomie des Bezeichnungsbegriffes	paradoxe *m* de Grelling (l'hétérologie)	парадокс Греллинга
	grid sampling <ST>	*s.* L 149		
G 432	**Griffith['s] theorem** <for a triangle> <EG>	Griffithscher Satz *m*	théorème *m* de Griffith	теорема Гриффита
G 433	**grill** <TO>	Sieb *n*	crible *m*	решето
	Grössencharakter <NT>	*s.* H 161		
G 434	**gross error,** blunder <ER>	grober Fehler *m*	faute *f* grossière, grosse faute	грубая ошибка (погрешность)
G 435	**Grothendieck['s] category** <CA>	Grothendieck-Kategorie *f*	anneau *m* de Grothendieck	категория Гротендика
G 436	**Grothendieck['s] group** <AL, CA>	Grothendieck-Gruppe *f*	groupe *m* de Grothendieck	группа Гротендика
G 437	**Grothendieck['s] homomorphism** <AL, CA>	Grothendieck-Homomorphismus *m*	homomorphisme *m* de Grothendieck	гомоморфизм Гротендика
G 438	**Grothendieck['s] ring** <AL>	Grothendieck-Ring *m*	anneau *m* de Grothendieck	кольцо Гротендика
G 439	**Grothendieck['s] topology** <CA>	Grothendieck-Topologie *f*	topologie *f* de Grothendieck	топология Гротендика
	Grötzsch['s] [distortion] theorem <FT>	*s.* T 284		
G 440	**ground field,** base field, basic field <AG, AL>	Grundkörper *m*	corps *m* de base	основное поле, базисное поле
G 441	**ground field,** scalar field, field of scalars <of a vector space> <AL>	Grundkörper *m*, Skalarenbereich *m*, Skalarkörper *m*	corps *m* des scalaires	основное поле, поле скаляров
G 442	**ground field characteristic,** characteristic <of the ground field> <AL>	Grundkörpercharakteristik *f*, Charakteristik *f*	caractéristique *f* du corps de base	характеристика основного поля
	groundform <IV>	*s.* F 820		
G 443	**ground line** <in two-plane method> <DS>	Rißachse *f*		ось проекций, линия пересечения плоскостей проекций
G 444	**group,** structure group, structural group <of a fibre bundle> <AT>	Strukturgruppe *f*	groupe *m* structural	структурная группа
G 445	**group** <*e.g.:* of order *n or* of rank 1> <GR>	Gruppe *f* <*z. B.:* *n*-ter Ordnung, der Ordnung *n oder* vom Rang 1>	groupe *m* <*par exemple:* de l'ordre *n ou* de rang un>	группа <*например:* порядка *n или* ранга 1>
G 446	**group,** class <ST>	Gruppe *f*, Klasse *f*	groupe *m*, classe *f*	группировка, группа, класс
G 447	**2-group** <GR>	2-Gruppe *f*	groupe *m* binaire	2-группа
G 448	**3-group** <GR>	3-Gruppe *f*	groupe *m* ternaire	3-группа
G 449	**Π-group** <GR>	Π-Gruppe *f*, p-Gruppe *f*	Π-groupe *m*	Π-группа
G 450	**Π'-group** <GR>	Π'-Gruppe *f*	Π'-groupe *m*	Π'-группа
	Ω-group <AL>	*s.* O 67		
G 451	**group acting freely** <AT>	fixpunktfreie Gruppe *f*	groupe *m* opérant librement	группа, действующая свободно; группа, действующая без неподвижных точек
G 452	**group algebra,** algebra of a group, group ring <AL>	Gruppenring *m*, Gruppenalgebra *f*	algèbre *f* de (d'un) groupe, anneau *m* de groupe, algèbre de Frobenius	групповая алгебра, групповое кольцо, алгебра группы
	group[-]automorphism <GR>	*s.* A 1229		
G 453	**group averaging** <AL>	Mittelung *f* über die Gruppe, Bildung *f* des Mittels über die Gruppe	prise *f* de moyenne sur le groupe	усреднение по группе
G 454	**group axioms** <GR>	Gruppenaxiome *npl*	axiomes *mpl* de groupes, postulats *mpl* de groupe	групповые аксиомы

No.	English	German	French	Russian
	group character <RE>	*s.* C 511		
	group character <AL, GR>	*s.* G 510		
G 455	**group comparison** <ST>	Gruppenvergleich *m*	comparaison *f* de groupes	сравнение группировок
	group composition <GR>	*s.* L 173		
G 456	**group determinant** <AL>	Gruppendeterminante *f*, Determinante *f* der Gruppe	déterminant *m* du groupe, Gruppendeterminant *m*	групповой детерминант
G 457	**grouped data** <ST>	gruppierte Daten *pl*	données *fpl* groupées	сгруппированные данные
	grouped group <GR>	*s.* I 142		
G 458	**grouped sample unit** <ST>	gruppenartige Stichprobeneinheit *f*	unité *f* de sondage en groupes, unité d'échantillonnage en groupes	элемент выборки по группам
G 459	**group element,** element <of order *n*, of infinite order> <of a group> <GR>	Gruppenelement *n*, Element *n*, // Operation *f* <[von] *n*-ter Ordnung, [von] unendlicher Ordnung>	élément *m* <d'ordre *n*, d'ordre infini>	элемент <порядка *n*, бесконечного порядка>
G 460	**group element of order 2** <or 1> <GR>	involutorisches Gruppenelement *n*	élément *m* du groupe involutif	элемент порядка 2 <или 1> в группе
	group extension <GR, NT>	*s.* E 785		
G 461	**group factor** <ST>	Gruppenfaktor *m*	facteur *m* de groupe	групповой фактор
G 462	**group factor model** <ST>	Gruppenfaktormodell *n*	modèle *m* des facteurs de groupe	модель групповых факторов
G 463	**group frequency** <ST>	Gruppenhäufigkeit *f*	fréquence *f* de groupe	групповая частота
G 464	**group generated by a given set of subgroups** <GR>	Erzeugnis *n*, Kompositum *n*, kleinstes gemeinsames Vielfaches *n*, Vereinigung *f*	sous-groupe *m* engendré par les éléments des sous-groupes donnés, groupe-réunion *m*	группа, порожденная множеством элементов данных подгрупп
G 465	**group generated by the translations** <AL, GR>	von Translationen erzeugte Gruppe *f*	translateur *m*	группа, порожденная сдвигами
	group[-] homomorphism <GR>	*s.* H 500		
G 466	**grouping** <ST>	Gruppierung *f*	groupement *m*	группировка
G 467	**grouping in cells (classes)** <ST>	Klasseneinteilung *f*	groupement *m* en classes	группировка (группирование) [в классах], разбиение на классы
	grouping symbol <FO>	*s.* P 2030		
G 468	**group integration** <AL>	Integration *f* über die Gruppe	intégration *f* sur le groupe	интегрирование по группе
G 469	**group-inverse,** inverse, inverse element <of a group element> <GR>	Gruppeninverses *n*, Inverses *n* <eines Elements in einer Gruppe>	inverse *m* <d'un élément du groupe>	обратный элемент <в группе>
	group[-] isomorphism <GR>	*s.* I 1131		
	group law <GR>	*s.* L 173		
G 470	**group LF (3,2) of order 168** <GR>	Kleinsche Gruppe *f*, Kleinsche Gruppe der Ordnung 168	groupe *m* de Klein d'ordre 168	группа Клейна порядка 168
G 471	**group mean** <ST>	Gruppenmittel *n*	moyenne *f* de (sur le) groupe	среднее внутри группы
	group metacyclic in the sense of Zassenhaus <GR>	*s.* Z 79		
G 472	**group moment** <ST>	Gruppenmoment *n*	moment *m* de groupes	групповой момент
	group multiplication <GR>	*s.* L 173		
G 473	**group object** <CA>	Gruppenobjekt *n*	objet *m* de groupe	групповой объект, группа категории
	group of automorphisms <AL>	*s.* 1. A 1230; 2. L 801		
G 474	**group of automorphisms over (relative to) F** <AL> Γ<AG>	relative Automorphismengruppe *f* über *F*	groupe *m* d'automorphismes sur *F*	группа автоморфизмов над *F*
G 475	**group of base points**	Basisgruppe *f*	groupe *m* de points fixes	базисное множество
	group of boundaries <AT, HA>	*s.* S 2109		
	group of chains <AT, HA>	*s.* C 473		
	group of classes of algebras <AL>	*s.* B 742		
G 476	**group of coefficients,** coefficient group <*n*-th> <AT, TO>	Koeffizientengruppe *f* <*n*-te>	groupe *m* des coefficients <n^{e}>	группа коэффициентов <*n*-я>
G 477	**group of components** <of a topological group> <GR>	Faktorgruppe *f* nach der Komponente des Einselements	groupe *m* quotient par la composante connexe de l'élément unité	фактор-группа по связной компоненте единицы
	group of cosets <GR>	*s.* F 27		
	group of curves <AY>	*s.* F 81		
G 478	**group of Eilenberg-MacLane,** Eilenberg-MacLane group <AT>	Eilenberg-MacLanesche Gruppe *f*	groupe *m* d'Eilenberg-MacLane	группа Эйленберга-Маклейна
G 479	**group of figures** <of a number> <AR, NT>	Ziffergruppe *f*	tranche *f*, série *f* de chiffres consécutifs	грань, группа цифр
	group of finite order <GR>	*s.* F 276		
G 480	**group of homomorphisms** <HA>	Hom-Gruppe *f*, Gruppe *f* der Homomorphismen	groupe *m* des homomorphismes	группа гомоморфизмов, группа Hom
G 481	**group of improper orthogonal transformations,** improper rotation group <AY>	Drehspiegelungsgruppe *f*, Drehspiegelgruppe *f*	groupe *m* des rotations et mirages, groupe des rotations	группа несобственных ортогональных преобразований, группа несобственных вращений
G 482	**group of invertible elements,** unit group, group of units <of a semigroup> <AL>	Gruppe *f* der umkehrbaren Elemente	groupe *m* des éléments inversibles	группа обратимых элементов

No.	English	German	French	Russian
G 483	**group of isometry** <AL>	Isometriegruppe *f*, Bewegungsgruppe *f*	groupe *m* d'isométrie, groupe isométrique	группа изометрий, изометрическая группа
G 484	**group of isotropy,** isotropy group, isotropy subgroup, stability subgroup, stabilizer, stable subgroup <of an element *x*> <AL, TO>	Isotropiegruppe *f*, Stabilisator *m* <eines Elements *x*>, Stabilitätsgruppe *f* <an der Stelle *x*>	groupe (sous-groupe) *m* d'isotropie, stabilisateur *m* <d'un élément *x*>	группа изотропии, стабилизатор, стационарная (стабильная) подгруппа <элемента *x*>
G 485	**group of left quotients** <of a semigroup> <AL>	Gruppe *f* linksseitiger Quotienten, Linksquotientengruppe *f*	groupe *m* des quotients à gauche	группа левых частных
G 486	**group of linear transformations** <AY>	Inversionsgruppe *f*, Gruppe *f* der linearen Transformationen	groupe *m* des transformations linéaires	группа линейных преобразований
	group of lower-triangular matrices with ones in the diagonal <GR>	*s.* U 292		
	group of matrices <GR>	*s.* M 192		
G 487	**group of motions (movement[s]),** movement group, group of proper motions (movements) <AY, GE>	Gruppe *f* der [eigentlichen] Bewegungen, Bewegungsgruppe *f* [erster Art], Kongruenzgruppe *f*	groupe *m* de mouvement, groupe des déplacements (déplacements directs)	группа движений (движений первого рода)
G 488	**group of *n*-boundaries** <AT, HA>	*n*-te (*n*-dimensionale) Rändergruppe *f*	groupe *m* des *n*-bords	*n*-я подгруппа границ
G 489	**group of *n*-cycles,** *n*-th subgroup of cycles <AT, HA>	*n*-dimensionale Zyklengruppe *f*, Gruppe *f* der *n*-Zyklen, *n*-Zyklengruppe *f*	groupe *m* des *n*-cycles	подгруппа *n*-циклов
G 490	**group of Néron-Severi,** Néron-Severi group<AL>	Néron-Severische Gruppe *f*	groupe *m* de Néron-Severi	группа Нерона-Севери <классов дивизоров>
G 491	**group of non-Euclidean motions** <GE>	nichteuklidische Bewegungsgruppe *f*	groupe *m* des déplacements non euclidiens	группа неевклидовых движений
G 492	**group of periods,** period group <of an Abelian function> <FT>	Periodengruppe *f*	groupe *m* de périodes	группа периодов
	group of permutations <GR>	*s.* P 487 a		
G 493	**group of permutations of the set *M*** <GR>	Permutationsgruppe *f* der Menge *M*	groupe *m* de permutations (transformations) de l'ensemble *M*	группа подстановок над множеством *M*
	group of permutations of *n* objects <GR>	*s.* S 2455		
G 494	**group of points,** point[-] group <on algebraic curves> <AG>	Punktgruppe *f*	groupe *m* de points, groupe ponctuel	точечная группа
	group of proper motions (movements) <AY, GE>	*s.* G 487		
G 495	**group of quotients,** quotient group <of a semigroup> <AL>	Quotientengruppe *f*	groupe *m* des fractions	группа дробей
G 496	**group of representatives** <in group extension> <GR>	Vertretergruppe *f*	groupe *m* de représentants	группа представителей
G 497	**group of residue classes modulo *m*** <of the integers> <AL>	Gruppe *f* der Restklassen mod *m*	groupe *m* [additif] des entiers modulo *m*	группа вычетов по модулю *m*
G 498	**group of residue classes relatively prime to *m*** <AL>	prime Restklassengruppe *f* modulo *m*	groupe *m* multiplicatif des classes modulo *m* qui sont premières avec *m*, groupe des classes résiduelles premières à *m*	группа простых классов вычетов по модулю *m*
	group of restricted homogeneous Lorentz transformations <AL>	*s.* P 1793		
G 499	**group of right quotients** <of a semigroup> <AL>	Rechtsquotientengruppe *f*	groupe *m* des quotients à droite	группа правых частных
G 500	**group of semilinear substitutions** <of a vector space> <AL>	allgemeine halblineare Gruppe *f*	groupe *m* des collinéations <d'un espace vectoriel>	полулинейная группа преобразований
G 501	**group of similarity transformations** <AL, GE>	Gruppe *f* der Ähnlichkeitstransformationen, äquiforme Gruppe <AL, GE>; Gruppe der äquiformen Transformationen <GE>	groupe *m* des transformations par similitude; groupe des similitudes	группа подобия (подобных преобразований); группа подобий
	group of symmetries <GE>	*s.* P 747		
	group of the equation <AL>	*s.* G 15		
G 502/3	**group of the graph** <GP>	Gruppe *f* des Graphen, Automorphismengruppe *f*	groupe *m* du graphe	группа графа, вершинная группа графа
	group of torsion <AT>	*s.* T 599		
	group of transformations <AL, AY>	*s.* T 769		
	group of translations <GE>	*s.* T 826		
G 504	**group of triangular matrices** <AL>	Dreiecksgruppe *f*, Gruppe *f* von Dreiecksmatrizen	groupe *m* de matrices triangulaires	группа треугольных матриц
	group of units <AL>	*s.* 1. G 482; 2. U 278		
	group of upper-triangular matrices with ones in the diagonal <AL>	*s.* U 444		

G 505	**groupoid** <AL>	Gruppoid *n*, binäre algebraische Struktur *f*, binäres System *n*, Operativ *n*	groupoïde *m*, groupoïde complet	группоид, мультипликативное множество, оператив
	groupoid <CA>	*s.* E 56		
G 506	**groupoid algebra** <AL>	Gruppoidalgebra *f*	algèbre *f* de groupoïde	алгебра группоида
G 507	**groupoid of paths** <of a diagram scheme> <CA>	Wegegruppoid *n*	groupoïde *m* de chemins	группоид путей
G 508	**groupoid with unit element** <AL>	Gruppoid *n* mit Einselement	groupoïde *m* unitaire (possédant un élément neutre), magma *m* unifère (unitaire)	группоид с 1
G 509	**group operation** <GR>	Gruppenoperation *f*, Gruppenverknüpfung *f*	opération *f* de groupe	групповая операция
	group product <GR>	*s.* P 1592		
G 510	**group property,** // group character <AL, GR>	Gruppeneigenschaft *f*	propriété *f* d'un groupe	групповое свойство, свойство (характер) группы
	group ring <AL>	*s.* G 452		
	group satisfying the maximal condition <GR>	*s.* N 284		
G 511	**group satisfying the maximum and minimum condition** <AL>	endliche Gruppe *f* [im Sinne der Kettensätze]	groupe *m* satisfaisant les conditions maximale et minimale	группа, которая удовлетворяет условию максимальности и минимальности
G 512	**group scheme** <AG>	Gruppenschema *n*	schéma *m* de groupes	групповая схема, схема групп
G 513	**group space** <of a topological group> <AL>	Gruppenraum *m*	espace *m* de groupe	групповое пространство
	group symmetry <GR>	*s.* I 927		
	group table <GR>	*s.* C 303		
G 514	**group[-]theoretical** <GR>	gruppentheoretisch	en (de, à, d'après la, au sens de la) théorie des groupes	теоретико-групповой, в теории групп
G 515	**group-theoretical function** <AL>	gruppentheoretische Funktion *f*	fonction *f* en théorie des groupes	теоретико-групповая функция
G 516	**group-theoretical transfer,** transfer, verlagerung <AB>	gruppentheoretische Verlagerung *f*, Verlagerung	transfert *m*	теоретико-групповое перенесение, перенесение
G 517	**group valued functor** <CA>	gruppenwertiger Funktor *m*	foncteur *m* dans une catégorie de groupes	функтор в категорию групп
G 518	**group variety,** connected algebraic group <AL, TO>	Gruppenmannigfaltigkeit *f*, Gruppenvarietät *f*, irreduzible algebraische Gruppe *f*	variété *f* de groupe, groupe *m* algébrique connexe	групповое многообразие, связная алгебраическая группа
	group which has a subnormal abelian series <GR>	*s.* S 1152		
	group with an abelian series <GR>	*s.* S 1238		
	group with an ascending normal series with cyclic factors <GR>	*s.* H 674		
G 519	**group with an increasing filtration** <AL>	aufsteigend filtrierte Gruppe *f*	groupe *m* à filtration croissante	группа с возрастающей фильтрацией
G 520	**group with a ring of operators,** operator[-]group, group with operators <GR>	Gruppe *f* mit Operatoren, Operatorgruppe *f*	groupe *m* à opérateurs, groupe avec opérateurs	группа с операторами, операторная группа
G 521	**group with decreasing filtration** <AL>	absteigend filtrierende Gruppe *f*	groupe *m* à filtration décroissante	группа с убывающей фильтрацией
G 522	**group with multiple operators** <GR>	Multioperatorgruppe *f*, Gruppe *f* mit Multioperatoren, Gruppe mit einem Multioperatorsystem	groupe *m* à multi-opérateurs	мультиоператорная группа, группа с мультиоператорами, группа с многоместными операторами
	group with operators <GR>	*s.* G 520		
G 523	**group without radical** <AL>	Gruppe *f* ohne Radikal	groupe *m* sans radical	группа, не имеющая радикала
G 524	**group without torsion,** torsion free group, torsion-free group, aperiodic group <GR>	torsionsfreie (lokal unendliche) Gruppe *f*	groupe *m* sans torsion, groupe apériodique	группа без кручения; группа, свободная от кручения; непериодическая (локально бесконечная) группа
	group with the normalizer condition <GR>	*s.* N 229		
G 525	**group with trivial centre** <AL>	Gruppe *f* ohne Zentrum	groupe *m* de centre réduit à *e*	группа без центра
	growing semi-martingale <ST>	*s.* S 2129		
G 526	**growth,** order <of a function> <FT>	Wachstumsordnung *f*, Ordnung *f*	ordre *m* de croissance, ordre	порядок роста
G 527	**growth** <FT, RF, ST>	Wachstum *n*	croissance *f*	рост
G 528	**growth curve** <ST>	Wachstumskurve *f*	courbe *f* de croissance	кривая роста
	growth curve <ST>	*s.* G 530		
G 529	**growth factor,** accumulation factor <AR>	Verzinsungsfaktor *m*, Aufzinsungsfaktor *m*	facteur *m* $(1 + r)$ ou r est le taux	множитель $(1 + r)$ в формуле $A = P(1 + r)^n$ сложных процентов
	growth formula <ST>	*s.* G 531		
G 530	**growth function,** growth curve <ST>	Wachstumsfunktion *f*, Wachstumskurve *f*	fonction *f* de croissance	функция роста
G 531	**growth law,** growth formula <ST>	Wachstumsgesetz *n*, Wachstumsformel *f*	loi (formule) *f* de croissance	формула (закон) роста
	growth order <SS>	*s.* O 346		

G 532	**growth process** <SP>	Wachstumsprozeß *m*	processus *m* de croissance	процесс роста
G 533	**growth rate** <ST>	Wachstumsrate *f*, Wachstumsgeschwindigkeit *f*	taux *m* de croissance	норма (скорость, темп) роста
	growth rate <FT, RF>	*s.* R 159		
G 534	**Grundy['s] function** <GP>	Grundy-Funktion *f*	fonction *f* de Grundy	функция Гранди
	Grün['s] lemma <GR>	*s.* L 553		
	Grün['s] theorem <GR>	*s.* T 285		
G 535	**Grünwald['s] cone [of dual numbers],** cone of dual numbers <PJ>	Grünwaldscher Kegel *m* der dualen Zahlen, Kegel der dualen Zahlen, Grünwaldscher Zahlenkegel *m*	cône *m* de Grünwald [des nombres duaux], cône des nombres duaux	конус Грюнвальда, конус дуальных чисел [Грюнвальда]
G 536	**G-space,** geodesic space <DG>	G-Raum *m*, geodätischer Raum *m*	G-espace *m*, espace *m* géodésique, espace G	G-пространство, геодезическое пространство
G 537	**G-surface,** two-dimensional G-space <DG>	G-Fläche *f*, zweidimensionaler G-Raum *m*	G-surface *f*, G-espace *m* bidimensionnel	G-поверхность, двумерное G-пространство
	G-test <ST>	*s.* S 2193		
G 538	**guard[ing] digit, guard position,** security digit <NU>	Schutzziffer *f*, Schutzstelle *f*	chiffre *m* de garde, position *f* de réserve	запасной знак, резервный разряд
	Gudermann['s] function <FU>	*s.* G 539		
G 539	**gudermannian, Gudermannian,** Gudermann['s] function, gd, Gd <FU>	Gudermann-Funktion *f*, Gudermannscher Winkel *m*, Hyperbelamplitude *f*, gd, Gd, 𝔄mp	goudermannien *m*, fonction *f* goudermannienne, amplitude *f* hyperbolique, angle *m* de Lambert, gd, Gd, amh.	гудерманиан, функция Гудермана, угол Гудермана, gd, Gd
G 540	**Gudermann['s] transformation** <AN>	Gudermannsche Transformation *f*	transformation *f* de Gudermann	преобразование Гудермана
	guess <GN>	*s.* S 706		
G 541	**Guichard-Bianchi surface** <DE>	Guichard-Bianchische Fläche *f*, Bianchi-Guichardsche Fläche	surface *f* de Guichard-Bianchi	поверхность Бианки-Гишара, поверхность Гишара-Бианки
G 542	**Guichard['s] congruence [of lines (rays)]** <DG>	Guichardsche Strahlenkongruenz (Linienkongruenz, Geradenkongruenz, Kongruenz) *f*, Guichardsches Strahlensystem *n*	congruence *f* [de droites] de Guichard	конгруэнция [прямых (лучей)] Гишара, конгруэнция
G 543	**Guichard['s] surface,** focal surface <of a Guichard congruence> <DG>	Guichardsche Fläche *f*, Brennfläche *f*	surface *f* de Guichard, surface focale	поверхность Гишара, фокальная поверхность
	Guldin['s] rule <DI, EG>	*s.* P 38		
	Gunter['s] scale <NO>	*s.* L 1048		
G 544	**Gutzmer['s] formula** <SS>	Gutzmersche Formel *f*	formule *f* de Gutzmer	формула Гуцмера
G 545	**g-valued automorphic function** <FT>	*g*-wertige automorphe Funktion *f*	fonction *f* automorphe *g*-valuée	*g*-значная автоморфная функция
G 546	**Gysin['s] homomorphism,** Thom-Gysin homomorphism <AT>	Gysin-Homomorphismus *m*	homomorphisme *m* de Gysin (Guisyn)	гомоморфизм Гизина
	Gysin['s] sequence <AT>	*s.* T 433		

H

H 1	**Haantjes curvature** <of a metric space> <GE>	Haantjessche Krümmung *f*	courbure *f* de Haantjes	кривизна Хантьеса
H 2	**Haar['s] condition** <RF>	Haarsche Bedingung *f*, Bedingung von Haar	condition *f* de Haar	условие Хаара
H 3	**Haar['s] lemma** <for double integrals> <AN>	Haarsches Lemma *n* für Doppelintegrale, Haarsches Variationslemma *n*, Variationslemma von Haar	lemme *m* de Haar	лемма Хаара
H 4	**Haar['s] measure** <on a topological group> <AL, TO>	Haarsches Maß *n*	mesure *f* de Haar	мера Хаара
H 5	**Haar['s] theorem** <NU, RF>	Theorem *n* von Haar, Haarsches Theorem	théorème *m* de Haar	теорема Хаара
H 6	**Hachette['s] cone** <GE>	Kegel *m* von Hachette, Hachettescher Kegel	cône *m* de Hachette	
H 7	**Hadamard['s] criterion** <FT>	Hadamardsches Kriterium *n*	critère *m* de Hadamard, critère d'Hadamard	критерий Адамара
H 8	**Hadamard['s] determinant theorem, Hadamard['s] determinantal inequality,** Hadamard['s] inequality <MD>	Hadamardscher Determinantensatz *m*, Hadamardsche Ungleichung *f*, Hadamardsche Abschätzung *f*	théorème *m* [du déterminant] de Hadamard, inégalité *f* (critère *m*) de Hadamard, théorème d'Hadamard, inégalité d'Hadamard	теорема Адамара об определителях, критерий Адамара для определителя, неравенство Адамара
	Hadamard['s] finite part <DE, DI>	*s.* F 308		
H 9	**Hadamard['s] gap condition** <SS>	Hadamardsche Lückenbedingung *f*	condition *f* [des lacunes] de Hadamard	условие Адамара [о лакунах], условие лакунарности Адамара
H 10	**Hadamard['s] gap theorem,** gap theorem <SS>	Hadamardscher Lückensatz *m*	théorème *m* des lacunes de Hadamard, théorème des lacunes	теорема о лакунах Адамара, теорема о пропусках [Адамара], теорема Адамара о лакунах (пропусках)
	Hadamard['s] inequality <MD>	*s.* H 8		

No.	English	German	French	Russian
H 11	**Hadamard['s] integration method** <DE>	Hadamardsche Integrationsmethode (Methode) *f*, Methode von Hadamard	méthode *f* d'intégration d'Hadamard	метод Адамара, метод интегрирования Адамара
H 12	**Hadamard['s] matrix** <a matrix with orthogonal rows having elements $\pm$ 1> <AL, CT>	Hadamardsche Matrix *f*	matrice *f* de Hadamard	матрица Адамара
H 13	**Hadamard['s] matrix, hadamard matrix,** matrix with dominating diagonal <MD>	Hadamardsche Matrix *f* Matrix mit überwiegender Hauptdiagonale, Matrix mit dominierender Diagonale	matrice *f* d'Hadamard, matrice à diagonale dominante	адамарова матрица, матрица Адамара, матрица с доминирующей диагональю
H 14	**Hadamard['s] method of descent** <DE>	Hadamardsche Absteigemethode *f*, Absteigemethode von Hadamard	méthode *f* de descente de Hadamard	метод спуска Адамара
H 15	**Hadamard['s] multiplication theorem** <SS>	Hadamardscher Multiplikationssatz *m*	théorème *m* de Hadamard, théorème de multiplication de Hadamard, théorème d'Hadamard	мультипликационная теорема Адамара, теорема Адамара умножения (об умножении) особенностей, теорема умножения Адамара
H 16	**Hadamard['s] product** <of power series> <SS>	Hadamardsches Produkt *n*	produit *m* de Hadamard, produit d'Hadamard	адамаровское произведение, адамаровская композиция, произведение Адамара
	Hadamard['s] product <MD>	*s.* K 163		
H 17	**Hadamard['s] theorems** <for power series> <SS>	Hadamardsche Sätze *mpl*	théorèmes *mpl* de Hadamard, théorèmes d'Hadamard	теоремы Адамара
H 18	**Hadamard['s] three-circles theorem,** three-circles theorem, three-circle theorem <FT>	Hadamardscher Dreikreisesatz *m*, Dreikreisesatz von Hadamard, Dreikreisesatz, Hadamard-Faber-Blumenthalscher Dreikreisesatz	lemme *m* des trois cercles, théorème *m* des trois cercles de Hadamard	теорема о трех кругах [Адамара], теорема Адамара о трех кругах
H 19	**Hadamard['s] three-spheres theorem** <FT>	Hadamardscher Dreikugelsatz *m*	théorème *m* des trois sphères [de Hadamard]	теорема о трех шарах Адамара
H 20	**Hagge['s] circle** <of a triangle> <EG>	Haggescher Kreis *m*	cercle *m* de Hagge	окружность Хагге
H 21	**Hagge['s] sphere** <of a polyhedron> <EG>	Haggesche Kugel *f*	sphère *f* de Hagge	сфера Хагге
H 22	**Hahn-Banach [extension] theorem** <FA>	Hahn-Banachscher Fortsetzungssatz *m*, Fortsetzungssatz (Fortsetzungsprinzip *n*, Satz *m*) von Hahn-Banach	théorème *m* de Hahn-Banach	теорема Хана-Банаха
H 23	**Hahn decomposition** <of a measurable set> <ME>	Hahnsche Zerlegung *f*	décomposition *f* de Hahn	разложение Хана
H 24	**Hahn['s] extension theorem** <for a measure> <ME>	Hahnscher Fortsetzungssatz *m*	théorème *m* de Hahn	теорема Хана
	half[-]algebra <UA>	*s.* P 180		
H 25	**half-angle** <EG>	halber Winkel *m*, Halbwinkel *m*	demi-angle *m*	половинный угол, половина угла, полуугол
H 26	**half[-]angle formulas (identities)** <of plane *or* spherical trigonometry> <EG>	Halbwinkelformeln *fpl*, Halbwinkelsatz *m*	formules *fpl* des demi-angles	формулы половинного угла, формулы функций (тангенса) половинного угла
	half-bounded [from] above <FA>	*s.* B 662		
	half-boundedness <FA>	*s.* S 334		
	half-bounded operator <FA>	*s.* S 335		
	half-bounded transformation <FA>	*s.* S 335		
	half-characteristic <DE>	*s.* S 339		
H 27	**half-closed interval,** half-open interval, partly open [and partly closed] interval, semi-closed interval, semi-open interval, half-interval, interval open at one end <AN, SE>	halboffenes Intervall *n*	intervalle *m* semi-fermé, intervalle semi-ouvert	полуинтервал, полуоткрытый интервал, полусегмент, полуоткрытый промежуток, полуотрезок
	half-closed interval on the left <AN, SE>	*s.* H 32		
	half-closed interval on the right <AN, SE>	*s.* H 31		
	half[-]cycle <AN, DE>	*s.* S 430		
H 28	**half[-]exact operation** <GR>	halbexakte Operation *f*	opération *f* semi-exacte	полуточная операция
	halfgroupoid <AL>	*s.* P 216		
	half-homomorphism <AL, GR>	*s.* S 389		
H 29	**half-integer, half-integral,** half-odd, half-odd integral, half numberly <NT, NU>	halbzahlig	demi-entier, semi-entier, demi-impair	полуцелый
	half-interval <AN, SE>	*s.* H 27		
	half-line <GE>	*s.* R 198		
H 30	**half-neighbourhood** <TO>	Halbumgebung *f*	demi-voisinage *m*	полуокрестность
	half numberly <NT, NU>	*s.* H 29		
	half odd <NT, NU>	*s.* H 29		

No.	English	German	French	Russian
	half-odd integral <NT, NU>	*s.* H 29		
	half-open interval <AN, SE>	*s.* H 27		
	half-open interval closed from the left <AN, SE>	*s.* H 32		
H 31	**half-open interval closed from the right, half-open interval open at the left,** half-closed interval on the right, half-open interval on the left <]*a*,*b*], (*a*,*b*], ⟨*a*,*b*⟩ > <AN, SE>	links[ ]halboffenes Intervall *n*	intervalle *m* semi-ouvert à gauche	полуинтервал слева, полуоткрытый интервал [, открытый] слева
H 32	**half-open interval open at the right,** half-open interval closed from the left, half-closed interval on the left, half-open interval on the right < [*a*,*b*[, [*a*,*b*), ⟨*a*,*b*⟩ > <AN, SE>	rechts[ ]halboffenes Intervall *n*	intervalle *m* semi-ouvert à droite	полуинтервал справа, полуоткрытый интервал [, открытый] справа
	half-open interval on the left <AN, SE>	*s.* H 31		
	half-open interval on the right <AN, SE>	*s.* H 32		
	half-period <AN, DE>	*s.* S 430		
	half-plane <AN>	*s.* I 450		
H 33	**half-plane of absolute convergence** <in Laplace transform> <IT>	Halbebene *f* absoluter Konvergenz	demi-plan *m* de convergence absolue	полуплоскость абсолютной сходимости
H 34	**half-plane of convergence** <of a Dirichlet series *or* in Laplace transform> <IT, SS>	Konvergenzhalbebene *f*	demi-plan *m* de convergence	полуплоскость сходимости
H 35	**half product** <GN>	halbes Produkt *n*	demi-produit *m*	полупроизведение
H 36	**halfquasigroup,** cancellation halfgroupoid <AL>	Halbgruppoid *n* mit Kürzungsregel	p-groupoïde *m* simplifiable	частичный группоид с сокращением
H 37	**half range,** semi range, half width <ST>	halbe Spannweite *f*, halbe Breite *f*	demi-étendue *f*, demi-largeur *f*	квазиразмах
H 38	**half-reduced transformation,** semi-reduced transformation <IV>	halbreduzierte Transformation *f*	transformation *f* semi réduit	полуприведенное преобразование
H 39	**half-replicate experiment** <ST>	Versuch *m* mit einer halben Wiederholung	expérience *f* avec demi-répétition	полуреплика
H 40	**half-sheet** <of a Riemann surface> <FT>	Halbblatt *n*	demi-surface *f* de Riemann	полулист
H 41	**half-side formulas** <of spherical trigonometry> <EG>	Halbseitenformeln *fpl*, Halbseitensatz *m*	formules *fpl* des demi-côtés	формулы тангенса половины стороны
H 42	**half-space,** infinite half-space, semi-infinite space <AN, GE>	Halbraum *m*, unendlicher Halbraum	demi-espace *m*, demi-espace infini	полупространство, бесконечное полупространство, полубесконечное пространство
	half-space of support <CS, GE>	*s.* S 2345		
H 43	**half sum, half-sum** <GN>	halbe Summe *f*, Halbsumme *f*	demi-somme *f*	полусумма
	half width <ST>	*s.* H 37		
H 44	**Hall['s] algebra** <AL>	Hallsche Algebra *f*	algèbre *f* de Hall	алгебра Холла
H 45	**Hall['s] base** <of a group *or* algebra> <AL>	Hall-Basis *f*, Hall-Base *f*	base *f* de Hall	холловская база
H 46	**Hall['s] enumeration principle** <AL>	Hallsches Abzählungsprinzip *n*	principe *m* énumératif de Hall	принцип перечисления Холла
	Hall['s] lemma <GR>	*s.* L 554		
H 47	**Hall['s] polynomial** <AL>	Hallsches Polynom *n*	polynôme *m* de Hall	многочлен Холла
H 48	**Hall['s] set** <AL>	Hallsche Menge *f*	ensemble *m* de Hall <dans un magma libre>	множество Холла
H 49	**Hall-subgroup,** Hall['s] subgroup <GR>	Hallsche Untergruppe *f*	sous-groupe *m* de Hall	подгруппа Холла
H 50	**Hall Π-subgroup** <GR>	Π-Hall-Gruppe *f*	Π-sous-groupe *m* de Hall	холловская Π-подгруппа
H 51	**Hall['s] theorem** <GR>	Satz *m* von Hall, Hallscher Satz	théorème *m* de Hall	теорема Холла
H 52	**Halphen['s] factorial function,** factorial function [of Halphen], factorial <FU>	Halphensche Faktoriell-Funktion *f*, Faktorial *n*	fonction *f* factorielle [de Halphen]	факториальная функция [Альфана], факториал Альфана
H 53	**Halphen['s] factorial function of the first kind;** cf; sf; ef <FU>	Halphensche Faktoriell-Funktion *f* der ersten Art, Faktorial *n* der ersten Art; cf; sf; ef	fonction *f* factorielle de première espèce; cf; sf; ef	факториальная функция [Альфана] первого рода; cf; sf; ef
H 54	**Halphen['s] factorial function of the second kind;** cg; sg; eg <FU>	Halphensche Faktoriell-Funktion *f* der zweiten Art, Faktorial *n* der zweiten Art; cg; sg; eg	fonction *f* factorielle de deuxième espèce; cg; sg; eg	факториальная функция [Альфана] второго рода; cg; sg; eg
H 55	**Halphen['s] point** <of a cubic in the plane *or* space *or* of a pencil of cubics> <AG>	Halphenscher Punkt *m*	point *m* de Halphen	точка Альфана; междусекущая точка <только пучка кривых третьего порядка>
	halving <EG, GN>	*s.* B 460		
H 56	**Hamburger['s] continued fraction** <NT>	Hamburgerscher Kettenbruch *m*	fraction *f* continue de Hamburger	цепная дробь Гамбургера
H 57	**Hamburger['s] problem of moments** <ST>	Hamburgersches Momentenproblem *n*, Momentenproblem von Hamburger	problème *m* des moments de Hamburger	проблема моментов Гамбургера

No.	English	German	French	Russian
H 58	**Hamel['s] base (basis), Hamel-basis,** algebraic basis, basis of Hamel, basis <of a linear space> <FA>	Hamelsche Basis *f*, Hamel-Basis *f*, algebraische (lineare) Basis, Basis	base *f* de Hamel, base hamelienne (algébrique), base	базис Хамеля, хамелевский (линейный, алгебраический) базис, базис Гамеля, базис [векторного пространства], хамелевская база
	Hamel['s] spiral <GE>	*s.* S 1530		
	Hamel['s] theorem <FA>	*s.* T 286		
H 59	**Hamilton['s] arc** <unoriented> <GP>	[offene] Hamiltonsche Linie *f*, [offene] Hamilton-Linie *f*	chaîne *f* hamiltonienne	гамильтонова цепь
	Hamilton-Cayley theorem <MD>	*s.* C 292		
H 60	**Hamilton['s] circuit,** Hamiltonian circuit, Hamilton['s] line <unoriented> <GP>	Hamiltonscher Kreis *m*, [geschlossene] Hamiltonsche Linie, Hamilton-Linie *f*, Hamilton-Kreis *m*	cycle *m* hamiltonien	гамильтонов цикл
H 61	**Hamilton-connected graph** <GP>	Hamilton-zusammenhängender Graph *m*	graphe *m* Hamilton-connecté	граф, в котором всегда имеется гамильтонова цепь с заданными концами
	Hamilton[s] equations <DE>	*s.* C 82		
H 62	**Hamilton['s] formula** <for a congruence of lines> <DG>	Hamiltonsche Gleichung (Formel) *f*, Formel von Hamilton	formule *f* de Hamilton	формула Гамильтона
H 63	**Hamilton['s] formulae** <VA>	Hamiltonsche Formeln *fpl*	formules *fpl* de Hamilton	формулы Гамильтона
H 64	**Hamilton['s] function,** Hamiltonian, characteristic function <DE, VA>	Hamiltonsche Funktion *f*, charakteristische Funktion [von Hamilton]	fonction *f* hamiltonienne, fonction d'Hamilton, fonction caractéristique	функция Гамильтона, характеристическая функция, гамильтониан
H 65	**Hamilton['s] hexagon** <EG>	Hamiltonsches Sechseck *n*	hexagone *m* de Hamilton	шестигранник Гамильтона
	Hamiltonian <DE, VA>	*s.* H 64		
	Hamiltonian <VT>	*s.* D 195		
H 66	**hamiltonian chain** <non-closed> <GP>	Hamiltonsche Kette (Linie) *f*	chaîne *f* hamiltonienne	гамильтонова цепь
H 67	**hamiltonian circuit** <oriented> <GP>	Hamiltonsche Linie *f*, Hamiltonscher Kreis *m*	circuit *m* hamiltonien	гамильтонов контур
	Hamiltonian circuit <GP>	*s.* H 60		
H 68	**hamiltonian cycle** <GP>	Hamiltonscher Zyklus *m*	cycle *m* hamiltonien	гамильтонов цикл
H 69	**Hamiltonian group** <GR>	Hamiltonsche Gruppe *f*, hamiltonsche Gruppe	groupe *m* hamiltonien, groupe d'Hamilton	группа Гамильтона, гамильтонова группа
H 70	**hamiltonian path,** complete path <GP>	Hamiltonscher Weg *m*, gerichtete Hamiltonsche Linie *f*, vollständige (Hamiltonsche) Bahn *f*	chemin *m* hamiltonien	гамильтонов путь
H 71	**Hamiltonian ring** <AL>	Hamiltonscher Ring *m*	anneau *m* hamiltonien	гамильтоново кольцо
	Hamiltonian system <DE>	*s.* C 82		
H 72	**Hamilton['s] Icosian Game,** Sir Wm. Hamilton's Icosian Game <GP>	Hamiltonsches Dodekaederspiel *n*, Hamiltonsches Spiel *n*	jeu *m* de Hamilton	игра Гамильтона
H 73	**Hamilton-Jacobi['s] equation, Hamilton-Jacobi['s] [partial] differential equation,** Hamilton['s] partial differential equation, partial differential equation of Hamilton-Jacobi <DE>	Hamilton-Jacobische [partielle] Differentialgleichung (Gleichung) *f*, Hamilton-Jacobi-Gleichung *f*, Hamiltonsche partielle Differentialgleichung, Eikonalgleichung *f*	équation *f* de Jacobi, équation aux dérivées partielles de Jacobi, équation différentielle d'Hamilton-Jacobi, équation d'Hamilton-Jacobi	уравнение Гамильтона-Якоби, дифференциальное уравнение Гамильтона-Якоби
	Hamilton['s] line <GP>	*s.* H 60		
	Hamilton['s] partial differential equation <DE>	*s.* H 73		
	Hamilton['s] partial differential operator <VT>	*s.* D 195		
	Hamilton['s] principal function <VA>	*s.* P 1421		
	Hamilton['s] quaternion <AL>	*s.* R 228		
H 74	**Hamilton['s] quaternion algebra** <AL>	Hamiltonsche (klassische) Quaternionenalgebra *f*	algèbre *f* des quaternions réels	алгебра вещественных кватернионов
H 75	**Hammerstein['s] equation** <IE>	Hammersteinsche Integralgleichung *f*	équation *f* de Hammerstein	[интегральное] уравнение Хаммерштейна
	handbook of formulae <GN>	*s.* F 499		
H 76	**hand computation** <NU>	Handrechnung *f*, Rechnen *n* mit der Hand	calcul *m* à la main	ручной счет
H 77	**handle,** handle of the first kind <TO>	Henkel *m*, Henkel erster Art, gelochte Ringfläche *f*	anse *f*	ручка, ручка первого рода
H 78	**handlebody** <TO>	Henkelkörper *m*	variété *f* d'anses	тело с ручками
	handle of the first kind <TO>	*s.* H 77		
	handle of the second kind <TO>	*s.* C 2687		
H 79	**hand-operated desk calculating machine, hand-operated desk calculator** <IN, NU>	Tisch[-Hand]rechenmaschine *f*	machine *f* [à calculer] de bureau, calculateur *m* de bureau, machine à main	настольная счетная (вычислительная) машина, арифмометр
	Hankel['s] Bessel function <FU>	*s.* H 81		

No.	English	German	French	Russian
	Hankel['s] Bessel function [of the third kind] <FU>	*s.* B 234		
H 80/1	**Hankel['s] determinant** <AN>	Hankelsche Determinante *f*, rekurrente Determinante	déterminant *m* de Hankel	определитель Ганкеля
	Hankel['s] function <FU>	*s.* B 234		
H 82	**Hankel['s] integral [equation]** <FU>	Hankelsche Integraldarstellung *f* [der Zylinderfunktionen]	intégrale *f* de Hankel	интеграл Ганкеля, интегральное представление Ганкеля
H 83	**Hankel['s] principle of permanence** <AL>	Hankelsches Permanenzprinzip *n*	principe *m* de permanence de Hankel	принцип перманентности Ганкеля
H 84	**Hankel['s] transform[ation],** Fourier-Bessel transform[ation] <IT>	Hankel-Transformation *f*	transformation *f* [intégrale] de Hankel, transformation de Fourier-Bessel	преобразование по Ганкелю, преобразование Ганкеля
	Hankel['s] type of Bessel function of the second kind <FU>	*s.* B 233		
H 85	**Hardy['s] class** <FT>	Hardysche Klasse *f*	classe *f* de Hardy	класс Харди
H 86	**Hardy['s] field** <TO>	Hardyscher Körper *m*, Hardy-Körper *m*	corps *m* de Hardy	поле Харди
H 87	**Hardy['s] inequality** <DE>	Hardysche Ungleichung *f*	inégalité *f* de Hardy	неравенство Харди
H 88	**Hardy-Littlewood['s] test** <for convergence of a Fourier series> <SS>	Hardy-Littlewoodsches Kriterium (Konvergenzkriterium) *n*	règle *f* (critère *m*, théorème *m*) de Hardy-Littlewood	признак (критерий) [сходимости] Харди-Литтльвуда
	Hardy['s] test <SS>	*s.* D 634		
	Hardy['s] theorem <DE, NT>	*s.* T 287		
H 89	**harmonic,** harmonic component, Fourier component, component <AN, NU>	Harmonische *f*, Fourier-Komponente *f*, harmonische Komponente *f*, harmonischer Term *m*	harmonique *m*, composante *f* harmonique, composante de Fourier	гармоника, гармоническая составляющая (компонента), фурье-компонента, составляющая (компонента) [ряда] Фурье
	harmonic analysis <AN, NU>	*s.* F 516		
	harmonic analyzer <AN, IN>	*s.* F 517		
	harmonic average <ER, ST>	*s.* H 102		
H 90	**harmonic balance** <DE>	harmonische Balance *f*	balance *f* harmonique	гармонический баланс
	harmonic balance method <DE>	*s.* M 467		
H 91	**harmonic complex,** Battaglini['s] complex <PJ>	Battaglinischer Komplex *m*, harmonischer Komplex	complexe *m* harmonique (de Battaglini)	гармонический комплекс, комплекс Баттальини
	harmonic component <AN, NU>	*s.* H 89		
H 92	**harmonic congruence of normals** <PJ>	harmonische Normalenkongruenz *f*, Dupinsches Strahlensystem *n*	congruence *f* harmonique de normales, congruence de Dupin	гармоническая конгруэнция нормалей
H 93	**harmonic conjugate** <of *z* with respect to *a* and *b*>, fourth harmonic point <PJ>	vierter harmonischer Punkt *m* <von *z* bezüglich *a* und *b*>	conjugué *m* harmonique <de *z* par rapport à *a* et *b*>, quatrième point *m* harmonique	точка гармонически сопряженная <к *z* относительно точек *a* и *b*>, четвертая гармоническая точка
H 94	**harmonic conjugate points** <of a triangle> <PJ>	harmonisch zugeordnete Punkte *mpl*, [harmonisch] assoziierte Punkte	points *mpl* conjugués harmoniques	гармонически сопряженные точки
H 95	**harmonic constant** <in the harmonic series> <SS>	harmonische Konstante *f*	constante *f* harmonique	гармоническая постоянная
H 96	**harmonic cross ratio** <PJ>	harmonisches Doppelverhältnis *n*	rapport *m* harmonique	гармоническое отношение
H 97	**harmonic differential equation,** harmonic equation <DE>	harmonische Differentialgleichung (Gleichung) *f*	équation *f* [différentielle] harmonique	гармоническое [дифференциальное] уравнение
H 98	**harmonic division** <AR>	harmonische Teilung *f*	division *f* harmonique	гармоническое деление, золотое сечение, деление в крайнем и среднем отношении
	harmonic equation <DE>	*s.* H 97		
H 99	**harmonic function,** potential function, potential <FT, PO>	harmonische Funktion *f*, Potentialfunktion *f*, Potential *n*	fonction *f* harmonique (potentielle), potentiel *m*	гармоническая (потенциальная) функция, потенциал
H 100	**harmonic group of points,** harmonic quadruplet <on a line> <PJ>	harmonisches Punktequadrupel (Punktquadrupel, Quadrupel) *n*, harmonische Punktgruppe *f*	groupe *m* de points harmonique, quaterne *m* harmonique	гармоническая четверка точек, [гармонический] точечный квадрупель
	harmonic homology <PJ>	*s.* H 104		
H 101	**harmonicity** <FT, GE>	Harmonizität *f*	harmonicité *f*	гармоничность
H 102	**harmonic mean [value],** harmonic average, inverse average <ER, ST>	harmonisches Mittel *n*, harmonischer Mittelwert *m*	moyenne *f* harmonique, valeur *f* moyenne harmonique	среднее гармоническое, гармоническое среднее
H 103	**harmonic measure** <FT>	harmonisches Maß *n*, Winkelmaß *n*, konformes (funktionentheoretisches) Maß	mesure *f* harmonique	гармоническая мера
H 104	**harmonic perspectivity,** harmonic homology <PJ>	harmonische Perspektivität *f*, projektive Spiegelung *f*	perspectivité (homologie) *f* harmonique	гармоническая гомология
H 105	**harmonic polar,** trilinear polar <of the triangle> <AY>	Harmonikale *f*, trilineare (harmonische) Polare *f*	polaire *f* harmonique (trilinéaire), droite *f* harmoniquement associée	гармоническая (трилинейная) поляра
H 106	**harmonic polar curve** <as a cubic> <AG>	harmonische Polarkurve *f*	courbe *f* polaire harmonique	гармоническая полярная кривая

No.	English	German	French	Russian
H 107	**harmonic polar line** <of the point of inflexion of a cubic> <AG>	harmonische Gerade *f*, harmonische Polare *f*	droite *f* harmonique, polaire *f* harmonique	гармоническая прямая, гармоническая поляра
H 108	**harmonic pole** <of a circle> <AG, DS>	harmonischer Pol *m*	pôle *m* harmonique	гармонический полюс
H 109	**harmonic pole,** trilinear pole <of a triangle> <AY>	harmonischer (trilinearer) Pol *m*	pôle *m* harmonique (trilinéaire)	гармонический (трилинейный) полюс
H 110	**harmonic position** <of four points> <PJ>	harmonische Lage *f*	position *f* harmonique	гармоническое расположение
H 111	**harmonic progression** <AR>	harmonische Progression (Reihe) *f*	progression *f* harmonique	гармоническая прогрессия
H 112	**harmonic proportion** <of three quantities> <AR>	harmonische (musikalische) Proportion *f*	proportion *f* harmonique (musicale)	гармоническая пропорция
H 113	**harmonic quadrilateral** <AY, EG>	harmonisches Sehnenviereck *n* (Kreisviereck *n*)	quadrilatère *m* harmonique	гармонический четырехугольник
	harmonic quadruplet <PJ>	*s.* H 100		
H 114	**harmonic series** <AN, FU>	harmonische Reihe *f*	série *f* harmonique	гармоничекий ряд
	harmonic synthesis <SS>	*s.* F 540		
	Harnack['s] first theorem on convergence <PO>	*s.* W 176		
H 115	**Harnack['s] inequality,** inequality of Harnack <PO>	Harnacksche Ungleichung (Doppelungleichung) *f*	inégalité *f* de Harnack	[двойное] неравенство Гарнака
H 116	**Harnack['s] principle [of convergence], Harnack['s] second convergence theorem, Harnack['s] theorem** <PO>	Harnacksches Konvergenzprinzip (Prinzip) *n*, Prinzip (Konvergenzprinzip) *n* von Harnack, zweiter Harnackscher Satz, Harnackscher Satz, Satz von Harnack	principe *m* de Harnack, théorème *m* de Harnack	принцип [сходимости] Гарнака (Харнака), теорема Гарнака, вторая теорема Гарнака
	Harriot-Descartes rule <AL>	*s.* D 304		
H 117/8	**Hartley['s] formula** <ST>	Hartleysche Formel *f*	formule *f* de Hartley	формула Хартли
H 119	**Hartley['s] range method** <ST>	Hartleysches Spannweitenverfahren *n*	méthode *f* [des étendues] de Hartley	метод Хартли, метод размахов Хартли
	Hartogs['] domain <FT>	*s.* S 340		
H 120	**Hartogs['] function** <FT>	Hartogssche Funktion *f*	fonction *f* de Hartogs	функция Хартогса
H 121	**Hartogs['] theorem,** theorem of Hartogs <FT, SE>	Satz *m* von Hartogs, Hartogsscher Satz	théorème *m* de Hartogs	теорема Хартогса
	Hasse-Arf theorem <AL>	*s.* T 288		
	Hasse['s] diagram <SE>	*s.* D 407		
H 122	**Hasse['s] function** <AB>	Hassesche Funktion *f*, Hasse-Funktion *f*	fonction *f* de Hasse	функция Хассе
H 123	**Hasse['s] local to global principle,** Hasse['s] principle, local-global principle <AL>	Hasse-Prinzip *n*	principe *m* de Hasse	принцип Хассе
H 124	**Hasse-Minkowski theorem** <NT>	Satz *m* von Hasse-Minkowski, Hasse-Minkowskischer Satz	théorème *m* de Hasse-Minkowski	теорема Минковского-Хассе
H 125	**Hasse['s] norm symbol** <AB>	Hassesches Normsymbol *n*	symbole *m* [de restes normiques] de Hasse	символ норменного вычета Хассе
H 126	**Hasse[s] norm theorem** <AL>	Hassescher Normensatz *m*	théorème *m* normique de Hasse	теорема Хассе о нормах
	Hasse['s] principle <AL>	*s.* H 123		
H 127	**Hasse['s] product formula** <AL>	Hassesche Produktformel *f*	formule *f* du produit de Hasse	формула произведения Хассе
H 128	**Hasse['s] reciprocity theorem,** product theorem for norm residue symbols <AB>	Hassesches Reziprozitätsgesetz *n*, Produktsatz *m* der Normsymbole	loi *f* de réciprocité de Hasse	закон взаимности Хассе
H 129	**Hasse['s] unit theorem** <AB>	Hassescher Einheitensatz *m*	théorème *m* de Hasse sur les unités	теорема Хассе о единицах
H 130	**Hasse-Witt invariant** <AL>	Hasse-Wittsche Invariante *f*	invariant *m* de Hasse-Witt	инвариант Хассе-Витта
H 131	**hat,** roof, ^ <as a mathematical symbol> <GN>	Dach *n*, Hut *m*, ^	accent *m* circonflexe, ^	крышка, ^
H 132	**hatchet planimeter** <GE, IN>	Beilplanimeter *n*, Schleppe *f*, Stangenplanimeter *n*, Hatchet-Planimeter *n*, Schneidenplanimeter *n*, Schneidenradplanimeter *n*	planimètre *m* à hachette, stangenplanimètre *m*, stangplanimètre *m*	планиметр с лезвийным диском, дисковый планиметр Фигута, планиметр-топорик, рычажный планиметр
H 133	**Hauck['s] theorem** <AY>	Hauckscher Satz *m*, Satz von Hauck	théorème *m* de Hauck	теорема Хаука
	"Hauptvermutung" [of combinatorial topology] <AT>	*s.* F 829		
H 134	**Hausdorff['s] axioms,** Hausdorff['s] postulates <TO>	Hausdorffsche Umgebungsaxiome *npl*	axiomes *mpl* de Hausdorff	аксиомы Хаусдорфа
	Hausdorff-closed space <TO>	*s.* A 85		
H 135	**Hausdorff['s] commutator** <of a Lie algebra> <AL>	Hausdorffscher Kommutator *m*	commutateur *m* de Hausdorff	коммутант Хаусдорфа
	Hausdorff['s] countability axioms <TO>	*s.* C 2555		
H 136	**Hausdorff['s] differentiation** <AL>	Hausdorffsche Differentiation *f*	différentiation *f* de Hausdorff	дифференцирование Хаусдорфа

No.	English	German	French	Russian
H 137	**Hausdorff['s] dimension,** fractionary dimension <TO>	Hausdorffsche Dimension *f*, Hausdorff-Dimension *f*, Besicovič-Dimension *f*, fraktionäre (nichtganzzahlige) Dimension	dimension *f* de Hausdorff, dimension fractionnaire	размерность Хаусдорфа, дробная размерность
H 138	**Hausdorff['s] distance** <of two sets> <TO>	Entfernung *f* <nach Hausdorff>	écart *m* mutuel	хаусдорфово расстояние
H 139	**Hausdorff['s] group** <AT>	Hausdorffsche Gruppe *f*	groupe *m* de Hausdorff	группа Хаусдорфа
	Hausdorff *k*-space <TO>	*s.* K 35		
	Hausdorff-Kuratowski maximal principle <GR>	*s.* H 141		
	Hausdorff['s] limitation method <LI>	*s.* H 380		
H 140	**Hausdorff['s] matrix,** $\mathfrak{H}$-matrix <SS>	Hausdorffsche Matrix *f*	matrice *f* de Hausdorff	матрица Хаусдорфа
H 141	**Hausdorff['s] maximal principle,** Kuratowski['s] maximal principle, Hausdorff-Kuratowski maximal principle, maximal chain principle, Kuratowski['s] lemma, maximal axiom <SE>	Hausdorff-Birkhoffscher Maximalkettensatz *m*, Satz *m* von Hausdorff (Hausdorff-Birkhoff, Birkhoff), Birkhoffscher Satz	théorème *m* de Hausdorff; axiome *m* de Hausdorff	теорема Хаусдорфа, принцип максимальности Хаусдорфа
H 142	**Hausdorff['s] mean** <LI>	Hausdorffsches Mittel *n*	moyenne *f* de Hausdorff	хаусдорфово среднее, среднее Хаусдорфа
H 143	**Hausdorff['s] measure** <ME>	Hausdorffsches Maß *n*	mesure *f* de Hausdorff	мера Хаусдорфа, хаусдорфова мера
	Hausdorff['s] method [of limitation] <LI>	*s.* H 380		
	Hausdorff['s] method [of summation] <LI>	*s.* H 381		
H 144	**Hausdorff['s] metric** <TO>	Hausdorffsche Metrik *f*	distance *f* de Hausdorff	метрика Хаусдорфа
H 145	**Hausdorff['s] operation,** δs-operation [of Mr. Hausdorff] <with basis *B*> <SE>	Hausdorffscher Operator *m*, δS-Funktion *f* <der Basis *B*>	fonction *f* de Hausdorff, opération *f* de Hausdorff, fonction δs <de base *B*>	операция Хаусдорфа <с базой *B*>
	Hausdorff['s] postulates <TO>	*s.* H 134		
H 146	**Hausdorff['s] problem of moments** <ST>	Hausdorffsches Momentenproblem *n*	problème *m* des moments de Hausdorff	проблема моментов Хаусдорфа
	Hausdorff['s] second denumerability axiom <TO>	*s.* S 202		
H 147	**Hausdorff['s] separation axiom,** T_2-separation axiom <TO>	Hausdorffsches (hausdorffsches, zweites) Trennungsaxiom *n*	axiome *m* de Hausdorff, axiome T_2	аксиома Хаусдорфа (отделимости Хаусдорфа), аксиома (T_2)
H 148	**Hausdorff['s] series** <of a Lie algebra> <AL>	Hausdorffsche Reihe *f*	série *f* de Hausdorff, formule *f* de Hausdorff	ряд Хаусдорфа
	Hausdorff['s] space <TO>	*s.* S 536		
	Hausdorff['s] summation method <LI>	*s.* H 381		
	Hausdorff['s] topological space <TO>	*s.* S 536		
H 149	**Hausdorff['s] topology** <TO>	Hausdorffsche (separierte) Topologie *f*	topologie *f* séparée (de Hausdorff)	отделимая (хаусдорфова) топология
H 150	**haversine, hav** <AN>	halber Sinusversus *m*	demi-sinus *m* versus	половина синуса-верзуса
H 151	**having the property that any two points are contained in a continuum** <TO>	kontinuaverknüpft	ayant la propriété que deux points quelquonques se laissent unir par un continuum	непрерывносвязный
	having the same sense <GE, TO>	*s.* S 876		
H 152	***H*-base** <of a polynomial ideal> <AL>	*H*-Basis *f*	*H*-base *f*	*H*-базис
	H.C.F. <AL>	*s.* H 310		
	HCF-ring <AL>	*s.* G 102		
H 153	**H-closedness** <of a space> <TO>	H-Abgeschlossenheit *f*	H-fermeture *f*, fermeture *f* absolue	H-замкнутость
	H-closed space <TO>	*s.* A 85		
H 154	**h-cobordism** <AL, AT>	h-Kobordismus *m*	h-cobordisme *m*, J-équivalence *f*	h-кобордизм
H 155	**H-cogroup** <AT>	H-Kogruppe *f*	H-cogroupe *m*	H-когруппа
	H-continuous function <AN>	*s.* H 387		
	head <GN>	*s.* T 3		
H 156	**head[s] or tail[s]** <ST>	Zahl (Schrift) *f* oder Wappen *n*, Bild *n* (Kopf *m*) oder Schrift (Adler *m*)	pile *f* ou face *f*, croix *f* ou pile	орел или решка, «герб» или «надпись»
	heart contour (line, shape) <AG>	*s.* C 129		
	Heaviside['s] calculus <DE>	*s.* O 167		
H 157	**Heaviside['s] expansion theorem** <DE>	Heavisidescher Entwicklungssatz *m*	théorème *m* d'expansion d'Heaviside (de Heaviside)	теорема разложения Хевисайда
H 158	**Heaviside['s] function,** unit function [of Heaviside], unit step [function], Heaviside['s] unit func-	Heavisidesche Funktion *f*, Sprungfunktion *f*, Heaviside-Funktion *f*, Heavisidesche Sprungfunktion	fonction *f* de Heaviside, fonction unité de Heaviside, fonction unité d'Heaviside, échelon *m*	единичный скачок, единичная функция [Хевисайда], функция Хевисайда, единичная

	tion <AN>	(Einheitsfunktion *f*, Stufenfunktion *f*), Einheitssprung *m*, Einheitssprungfunktion *f*	unité d'Heaviside, échelon d'unité, échelon d'Heaviside, fonction échelon-unité, fonction échelon-unité de Heaviside, fonction unitaire (unité)	ступенчатая функция, функция единичного скачка, функция с единичным скачком, единичная ступенька-функция Хевисайда
	Heaviside['s] operational calculus <DE>	*s.* O 167		
	Heaviside['s] unit function <AN>	*s.* H 158		
H 159	**Heawood['s] conjecture,** Heawood['s] map-colouring conjecture <GP>	Heawoodsche Vermutung *f*	hypothèse *f* d'Heawood	гипотеза Хивуда
H 160	**Heawood['s] formula** <GP>	Heawoodsche Formel *f*	formule *f* d'Heawood	формула Хивуда
	Heawood['s] map-colouring conjecture <GP>	*s.* H 159		
H 161	**Hecke['s] character,** Grössencharakter <NT>	Heckescher Größencharakter *m*, Größencharakter [nach Hecke]	« Grössencharakter » *m* [au sens] de Hecke, Grössencharacter *m*	характер Гекке
H 162	**Hecke['s] *L*-function** <NT>	Heckesche *L*-Funktion *f*	fonction *f L* de Hecke	*L*-функция Гекке
H 163	**Hecke['s] *L*-series** <NT>	Heckesche *L*-Reihe *f*	série *f L* de Hecke, série de Hecke	*L*-ряд Гекке, ряд Гекке
H 164	**Hecke *L*-series of Hecke characters** <AB>	Heckesche *L*-Reihe *f* mit Größencharakteren	série *f L* de Hecke « mit Grössencharaktere »	*L*-ряд Гекке характеров Гекке
H 165	**Hecke['s] operator** <of an elliptic modular form> <FT>	Hecke-Operator *m*	opérateur *m* de Hecke	оператор Гекке
H 166	**Hecke['s] zeta-function** <NT>	Heckesche Zetafunktion *f*	fonction *f* zêta de Hecke	дзета-функция Гекке
H 167	**Heegard diagram** <TO>	Heegard-Diagramm *n*	diagramme *m* de Heegard	диаграмма Хегора
H 168	**height,** rank <of an ideal> <AL>	Höhe *f*, Rang *m*	hauteur *f*, rang *m*	ранг, высота
H 169	**height,** cote <in topographic method> <DS>	Kote *f*, Höhe *f*, Kotenzahl *f*, Höhenzahl *f*	cote *f*, nombre *m* coté	числовая отметка, отметка <высоты>
H 170	**height;** size <of an algebraic number> <NT>	Höhe *f*	hauteur *f*	высота; размер
	height <AY>	*s.* A 815		
	height <LA, SE>	*s.* D 510		
H 171	**height circle,** contour circle <in one-plane projection> <DS>	Höhenkreis *m*	cercle *m* de niveau	окружность уровня
	height contour [line] <DS>	*s.* L 598		
H 172	**height line,** horizontal [line], first principal line, first trace parallel <in two-plane projection> <DS>	Höhenlinie *f*, erste Hauptlinie (Tafellinie, Streichlinie) *f*, Hauptlinie (Tafellinie, Streichlinie) erster Ordnung	horizontale *f*, première ligne *f* principale	горизонталь, первая главная (основная) линия
	height line <DS>	*s.* L 598		
H 173	**height plane,** first principal plane <in two-plane projection> <DS>	Höhenebene *f*, erste Hauptebene *f*, Hauptebene erster Ordnung	plan *m* horizontal, premier plan principal	горизонтальная (первая главная) плоскость
	height plane <DS>	*s.* L 600		
H 174	**Heine-Borel['s] theorem,** covering theorem of Borel <TO>	Heine-Borelscher Überdeckungssatz *m*, Satz *m* von Borel, Heine-Borelscher Satz, Satz (Überdeckungssatz) von Heine-Borel, Heine-Borelsches Theorem *n*, schwacher Überdeckungssatz von Heine-Borel	théorème *m* de Heine-Borel (Borel)	теорема (лемма) Гейне-Бореля [об открытом покрытии], теорема Бореля-Лебега; условие Бореля (Гейне-Бореля)
H 175	**Heine-Cantor theorem** <for trigonometric series> <SS>	Heine-Cantorscher Satz *m*	théorème *m* de Heine-Cantor	теорема Гейне-Кантора
H 176	**Heine['s] condition** <in a limit space> <TO>	Heinesches Stetigkeitskriterium *n*, Stetigkeitsbedingung *f* von Heine	condition *f* de Heine	условие Гейне
H 177	**Heine['s] factorial** <FU>	Heinesche Fakultät *f*	factorielle *f* de Heine	факториал Гейне
H 178	**Heine['s] polynomial** <FU>	Heinesches Polynom *n*	polynôme *m* de Heine	многочлен Гейне
H 179	**Heine['s] series** <SS>	Heinesche Reihe *f*	série *f* heinéenne (de Heine)	ряд Гейне
H 180	**Heine-Sommerfeld function** <FU>	Heine-Sommerfeld-Funktion *f*	fonction *f* de Heine-Sommerfeld	функция Гейне-Зоммерфельда
	Heine['s] theorem <AN, TO>	*s.* T 289		
H 181	**Heisenberg['s] algebra** <AL>	Heisenberg-Algebra *f*	algèbre *f* de Heisenberg	алгебра Гейзенберга
H 182	**Heisenberg['s] ring** <AL>	Heisenberg-Ring *m*, Heisenbergring *m*	anneau *m* de Heisenberg	гейзенбергово кольцо, кольцо Гейзенберга
	helical curve (line) <GE>	*s.* H 185		
	helical motion <GE>	*s.* S 181		
	helical surface <DG>	*s.* H 184		
H 183	**helicoid** <with a straight-line as the screwing line> <DG>	Helikoid *n*, Schraubenregelfläche *f*	hélicoïde *m* [gauche]	геликоид
	helicoidal displacement (motion) <GE>	*s.* S 181		

No.	English	German	French	Russian
H 184	**helicoidal surface, helicoid,** helical surface <with an arbitrary plane curve as the screwing line> <DG>	Schraubenfläche *f*, allgemeine Schraubenfläche, Helikoid *n*	surface *f* hélicoïdale, hélicoïde *m*	винтовая поверхность
H 185	**helix,** helical curve (line), cylindrical helix, screwline, screw (spiral) line, spiral <a space curve on a cylinder> <GE>	Schraubenlinie *f*, Schneckenlinie *f*, Böschungslinie *f*, Kurve *f* konstanter Neigung, Loxodrome *f* des Zylinders	hélice *f* [cylindrique], courbe *f* hélicoïde (héliçoide), ligne *f* (courbe) hélicoïdale, spirale *f* [cylindrique]	[цилиндрическая] винтовая линия, винтовая кривая, винтообразная линия, [пространственная] спираль, улиткообразная линия, улитка, винтовая дуга
	helix <GE>	*s.* C 718		
H 186	**Hellinger['s] integral** <FA>	Hellingersches Integral *n*	intégrale *f* de Hellinger	интеграл Хеллингера
H 187	**Hellinger-Toeplitz theorem,** theorem of Hellinger and Toeplitz <FA>	Hellinger-Toeplitzscher Satz *m*, Satz von Hellinger-Toeplitz (Hellinger und Toeplitz)	théorème *m* de Hellinger-Toeplitz	теорема Хеллингера-Теплица
H 188	**Helly['s] property** <of sets> <SE>	Helly-Eigenschaft *f*	propriété *f* de Helly	свойство Хелли
H 189	**Helly['s] selection theorem** <RF>	Hellyscher Satz *m*, Hellysches Auswahlprinzip *n*, Satz von Helly	principe *m* de choix	теорема Хелли
H 190	**Helly['s] space** <FA>	Hellyscher Raum *m*, Helly-Raum *m*	espace *m* de Helly	пространство Хелли
H 191	**Helly['s] theorem** <ST>	Satz *m* von Helly, Hellyscher Satz	théorème *m* de Helly	теорема Хелли
	Helmert['s] distribution <ST>	*s.* C 634		
	Helmert-Pearson distribution <ST>	*s.* C 634		
H 192	**hemicompact** <TO>	Halbkompaktum *n*	semi-compact *m*	полукомпакт
	hemicompact [topological] space <TO>	*s.* S 814		
	hemigroup <AL>	*s.* S 376		
	hen <DE, FU>	*s.* H 224		
	Hen <FU>	*s.* H 228		
H 193	**hendecagonal number** <a figurate number> <NT>	Elfeckszahl *f*, Endekagonalzahl *f*, elfeckige Zahl *f*	nombre *m* endécagonal (hendécagonal, hendécagone)	одиннадцатиугольное число
H 194	**Henkin['s] completeness theorem** <LO>	Henkinscher Vollständigkeitssatz *m*	théorème *m* de complétude de Henkin	теорема полноты Генкина
H 195	**Hensel['s] conditions** <AL>	Henselsche Bedingungen *fpl*	conditions *fpl* de Hensel	условия Гензеля
H 196	**henselization** <AL>	Henselisierung *f*	hensélisation *f*	гензелизация
H 197	**Hensel['s] lemma** <on polynomial congruences> <AL>	Henselsches Lemma *n*, Henselscher Hilfssatz (Satz) *m*	lemme *m* de Hensel	лемма Гензеля
H 198	**Hensel ring** <AL>	Henselscher Ring *m*	anneau *m* hensélien	гензелово кольцо
H 199	**Hensel['s] theorem on units** <AB>	Henselscher Einheitensatz *m*	théorème *m* des unités de Hensel	теорема Гензеля о единицах
H 200	**heptagonal number** <a figurate number> <NT>	Heptagonalzahl *f*, Siebeneckszahl *f*	nombre *m* heptagone (heptagonal)	семиугольное (гептагональное) число
H 201	**heptiamond** <GE>	Heptiamant *m*	heptiamant *m*	гептиамант
H 202	**heptomino** <GE>	Heptomino *n*	heptomino *m*	гептомино
H 203	**Herbrand['s] lemma** <AB, AL>	Herbrandsches Lemma *n*	lemme *m* d'Herbrand, lemme de Herbrand	лемма Эрбрана
H 204	**Herbrand['s] quotient,** quotient of Herbrand <AL>	Herbrandscher Index *m*		индекс Эрбрана, отношение Эрбрана
H 205	**Herbrand['s] theorem** <AL>	Satz *m* von Herbrand, Herbrandscher Satz	théorème *m* d'Herbrand	теорема Эрбрана
	Herbrand['s] theorem <LO>	*s.* T 290		
H 206	**Herbrand['s] unit theorem** <AB>	Herbrandscher Einheitensatz *m*	théorème *m* d'Herbrand sur les unités	теорема Эрбрана о единицах
H 207	**hereditarily enumerable set** <MM>	erblich aufzählbare Menge *f*	ensemble *m* héréditairement énumérable	наследственно-перечислимое множество
H 208	**hereditarily generating system** <of a group> <AL>	erbliches Erzeugendensystem *n*	système *m* générateur héréditaire	наследственная система образующих
H 209	**hereditarily indecomposable continuum** <TO>	erblich unzerlegbares Kontinuum *n*	continu *n* héréditairement indécomposable, continu de Knaster	наследственно неразложимый континуум, континуум Кнастера
H 210	**hereditarily normal space,** T_5-space, T_5 topological space <TO>	vollständig (erblich) normaler Raum *m*, T_5-Raum *m*	espace *m* héréditairement (complètement) normal, espace T_5	наследственно (вполне) нормальное пространство, вполне нормальное топологическое пространство, T_5-пространство
H 211	**hereditarily undecidable theory** <MM>	erblich unentscheidbare Theorie *f*	théorie *f* héréditairement indécidable	наследственно неразрешимая теория
H 212	**hereditarily unicoherent continuum** <TO>	erblich unikohärentes Kontinuum *n*	continu *m* héréditairement unicohérent	наследственно уникогерентный континуум
H 213	**hereditary class** <of closure spaces> <TO>	erbliche Klasse *f*	classe *f* héréditaire	наследственный класс
H 214	**hereditary property** <*e.g.:* of a topological space> <LO, SE, TO>	erbliche Eigenschaft *f* <LO, SE, TO>; kogrediente (ausschnittsinvariante) Eigenschaft <TO>	propriété *f* héréditaire	наследственное свойство
H 215	**hereditary radical,** torsion radical <CA>	erbliches Radikal *n*	idéal *m* héréditaire	наследственный радикал

No.	English	German	French	Russian
H 216	**hereditary set** <SE>	erbliche Menge *f*	ensemble *m* héréditaire	наследственное множество
H 217	**hereditary spectrum** <FA>	erbliches Spektrum *n*	spectre *m* héréditaire	наследственный спектр
H 218	**hereditary system of sets** <SE>	erbliches Mengensystem *n*	famille *f* héréditaire [d'ensembles]	наследственная система множеств, наследственное семейство
H 219	**heredity** <SE>	Erblichkeit *f*	hérédité *f*	наследственность
	Herglotz['s] theorem <GE>	*s.* T 291		
	Hermitean . . .	*s.* Hermitian		
H 220	**Hermite['s] [differential] equation** <DE>	Hermitesche Differentialgleichung *f*	équation [différentielle] d'Hermite	[дифференциальное] уравнение Эрмита
	Hermite['s] eigenvalue problem <DE>	*s.* H 229		
H 221	**Hermite-Fejér interpolation method** <AX>	Hermite-Fejérsches Interpolationsverfahren *n*	méthode *f* d'interpolation d'Hermite-Fejér	интерполяционный метод Эрмита-Фейера
H 222	**Hermite['s] formula,** Hermite['s] quadrature formula <AX, DI, NU>	Hermitesche Quadraturformel (Formel) *f*	formule *f* d'Hermite, formule d'intégration d'Hermite	формула [численного интегрирования] Эрмита
H 223	**Hermite['s] function,** A_i <DE, FU>	Hermitesche Funktion *f*, Hermite-Funktion *f*, A_i	fonction *f* d'Hermite, A_i	функция Эрмита, A_i
H 224	**Hermite['s] function of the second kind,** h_n, he_n <DE, FU>	Hermitesche Funktion *f* zweiter Art, h_n, he_n	fonction *f* d'Hermite de deuxième espèce, h_n, he_n	функция Эрмита второго рода, h_n, he_n
H 225	**Hermite['s] interpolation formula** <AX, FD, NU>	Hermitesche Interpolationsformel (Formel) *f*, Interpolationsformel (Formel) von Hermite	formule *f* d'interpolation d'Hermite	интерполяционная формула Эрмита
H 226	**Hermite['s] interpolation polynomial** <AX, FD, NU>	Hermitesches Interpolationspolynom *n*, Interpolationspolynom von Hermite	polynôme *m* d'interpolation d'Hermite	интерполяционный многочлен Эрмита
H 227	**Hermite['s] normal form,** normal form of Hermite <of a matrix> <MD>	Hermitesche Normalform *f*	forme *f* réduite d'Hermite	эрмитова нормальная форма
H 228	**Hermite['s] [orthogonal] polynomial,** orthogonal Hermite polynomial, Hermitian polynomial, H_n, He_n <FU>	Hermitesches (Tschebyscheff-Hermitesches) Polynom *n*, [Tschebyscheff-]Hermite-Polynom *n*, H_n, He_n	polynôme *m* d'Hermite, H_n, He_n	многочлен (полином) Чебышева-Эрмита, многочлен (полином) Эрмита, H_n
	Hermite-Ostrogradsky formula <DI>	*s.* O 536		
H 229	**Hermite['s] problem,** Hermite['s] eigenvalue problem <DE>	Hermitesche Eigenwertaufgabe *f*, Hermitesches Eigenwertproblem (Problem) *n*	problème *m* d'Hermite [aux valeurs propres]	задача Эрмита [на собственные значения]
	Hermite['s] quadrature formula <AX, DI, NU>	*s.* H 222		
H 230	**Hermite['s] reciprocity law** <for algebraic forms> <IV>	Hermitesches (Hermites) Reziprozitätsgesetz *n*	loi *f* de réciprocité d'Hermite	закон взаимности Эрмита
	Hermitian adjoint <MD>	*s.* H 235		
	Hermitian affinor <VT>	*s.* H 254		
	Hermitian affinor density <VT>	*s.* H 611		
H 231	**Hermitian bilinear functional,** Hermitian (symmetric bilinear, symmetric) functional <in a Hilbert space> <FA>	hermitesches bilineares Funktional *n*, hermitesches (symmetrisches bilineares, symmetrisches) Funktional	fonctionnelle *f* bilinéaire hermitienne, fonctionnelle hermitienne (bilinéaire symétrique, symétrique)	эрмитов билинейный фукционал, эрмитов (симметрический билинейный, симметрический) функционал
H 232	**Hermitian circle** <DG, PJ>	Hermitescher Kreis *m*	cercle *m* hermitien	окружность Эрмита
H 233	**hermitian congruence** <of matrices> <MD>	hermitesche Kongruenz (Äquivalenz) *f*	congruence *f* hermitique	эрмитова конгруэнтность
H 234	**Hermitian conjugate** <of an operator>, Hermitian conjugate operator <FA>	hermitesch Konjugierte *f*, hermitesch konjugierter Operator *m*	conjugué *m* hermitien	эрмитово[-]сопряженный оператор
H 235	**Hermitian conjugate [matrix], hermitian, conjugate matrix,** Hermitian adjoint (transpose), conjugate-transpose, [complex] conjugate transpose, conjugate transposed matrix, adjoint matrix, adjoint, associate matrix, $A^{\top}$, A^{H}, A^* <MD>	hermitesch (hermitisch) konjugierte Matrix *f*, adjungierte (begleitende, konjugiert transponierte, transponiert-konjugierte, transjugierte) Matrix, Adjungierte *f*	adjointe *f*, matrice *f* adjointe (associée, transposée [et] conjuguée), hermitique *f* conjuguée	эрмитово сопряженная матрица, эрмитово-сопряженная матрица, транспонированная и сопряженная матрица, сопряженная (присоединенная) матрица
	Hermitian conjugate operator <FA>	*s.* H 234		
H 236	**Hermitian continual reduction** <of quadratic forms> <NT>	Hermitesche Reduktion *f*	réduction *f* continuelle d'Hermite	эрмитово приведение
H 237	**Hermitian distance** <DG, PJ>	Hermitesche Entfernung *f*, Hermitescher Abstand *m*	distance *f* hermitienne	эрмитово расстояние
H 238	**hermitian endomorphism** <AL>	hermitescher Endomorphismus *m*	endomorphisme *m* hermitien	эрмитов эндоморфизм
H 239	**Hermitian extension** <of an operator> <FA>	hermitesche Fortsetzung (Erweiterung) *f*	extension *f* hermitienne (hermitique)	эрмитово расширение

H 240	**Hermitian form** <AL>	hermitesche Form *f*	forme *f* hermitienne (autoadjointe, d'Hermite, à indéterminées conjuguées); forme sesquilinéaire hermitienne	эрмитова форма
H 241	**Hermitian form bounded above** <FA>	oberhalbbeschränkte hermitesche Form *f*	forme *f* hermitienne semibornée supérieurement	полуограниченная сверху эрмитова форма
H 242	**Hermitian form bounded below** <FA>	unterhalbbeschränkte hermitesche Form *f*	forme *f* hermitienne semi[-]bornée inférieurement	полуограниченная снизу эрмитова форма
	Hermitian functional <FA>	*s.* H 231		
H 243	**Hermitian geometry** <DG, PJ>	Hermitesche Geometrie *f*	géométrie *f* hermitienne	эрмитова геометрия
H 244	**hermitian inner product module** <AL>	hermitescher Modul *m*	module *m* hermitien	эрмитов модуль
H 245	**hermitian inner product space,** hermitian space <over a ring> <AL>	hermitescher Raum *m*	espace *m* hermitien	эрмитово пространство
	hermitian inner product space <FA>	*s.* U 260		
H 246	**Hermitian kernel** <IE>	Hermitescher Kern *m*	noyau *m* hermitien (symétrique)	эрмитово ядро
H 247	**Hermitian manifold** <DG>	hermitesche Mannigfaltigkeit *f*	variété *f* hermitienne	эрмитово многообразие
H 248	**hermitian matrix,** Hermitian matrix, self-adjoint matrix <MD>	hermitesche (selbstadjungierte) Matrix *f*, Hermite-Matrix *f*	matrice *f* hermitienne (hermitique, autoadjointe)	эрмитова (эрмитовская, самосопряженная) матрица, матрица Эрмита
H 249	**Hermitian metric** <DG, PJ>	hermitesche Metrik *f*	métrique *f* hermitienne	эрмитова метрика
H 250	**Hermitian modular group** <AB>	Hermitesche Modulgruppe *f*	groupe *m* modulaire hermitien	эрмитова модулярная группа
H 251	**Hermitian operator,** symmetrical operator <FA>	hermitescher Operator *m*, Hermite-Operator *m*, symmetrischer Operator	opérateur *m* hermitien (hermitique, symétrique)	эрмитов (эрмитовский) оператор, оператор Эрмита, симметричный оператор
	Hermitian polynomial <FU>	*s.* H 228		
H 252	**Hermitian [scalar] product** <AL>	Hermitesches Skalarprodukt *n*	produit *m* [scalaire] hermitien	эрмитово-скалярное произведение
	Hermitian quantity <VT>	*s.* H 611		
H 253	**Hermitian space** <DG, PJ>	Hermitescher Raum *m*	espace *m* hermitien	эрмитово пространство
	hermitian space <AL>	*s.* H 245		
	hermitian space <FA>	*s.* U 260		
H 254	**hermitian [symmetric] tensor, Hermitian tensor,** Hermitian affinor <VT>	Hermitescher Tensor (Affinor) *m*	tenseur (affineur) *m* hermitien	эрмитов тензор (аффинор)
	Hermitian tensor density <VT>	*s.* H 611		
H 255	**Hermitian transformation** <AL>	hermitesche Transformation *f*	transformation *f* linéaire hermitienne, transformation d'Hermite	эрмитово линейное преобразование
	Hermitian vector space <FA>	*s.* U 260		
H 256	**hermiticity** <AL, AN>	Hermitezität *f*	hermiticité *f*, symétrie *f* hermitienne	эрмитовость, эрмитова симметричность
H 257	**Hero['s] (Heron['s]) formula** <EG>	heronische Dreiecksformel *f*, Heronische Inhaltsformel *f*, Heron-Dreiecksformel *f*	formule *f* de Héron [d'Alexandrie]	формула Герона
H 258	**Heron['s] parallelogram** <EG>	Heronisches Parallelogramm *n*	parallélogramme *m* rationnel (de Héron)	геронов параллелограмм
H 259	**Heron['s] quadrangle,** rational quadrangle <EG>	Heronisches (rationales) Viereck *n*	quadrangle *m* rationnel (de Héron)	геронов (рациональный) четырехугольник
H 260	**Heron['s] triangle,** rational triangle <EG>	Heronisches (rationales) Dreieck *n*	triangle *m* rationnel (de Héron)	геронов (рациональный) треугольник, треугольник Герона
	Hesse['s] configuration <AG, SG>	*s.* C 1872		
	Hesse['s] determinant <AL, DG, IV>	*s.* H 267		
	Hesse['s] determinant <DI>	*s.* H 269		
H 261	**Hesse['s] equation** <for elliptic functions> <FT>	Hessesche Gleichung *f*	équation *f* hessienne	уравнение Гессе
	Hesse['s] line <AY>	*s.* H 272		
H 262	**Hessenberg['s] method** <MD>	Hessenbergsches Verfahren *n*	méthode *f* de Hessenberg	метод Гессенберга
	Hessenberg['s] theorem <GE>	*s.* T 292		
H 263	**Hesse['s] normal form,** Hesse['s] standard form <of the equation of a line *or* plane>, normal equation of Hesse <of a line *or* plane> <AY>	Hessesche Normalform *f*, Normalform <der Geraden- *oder* Ebenengleichung>	forme *f* normale de Hesse <de l'équation d'une droite *ou* d'un plan>, équation normale (eulérienne) <d'une droite *ou* d'un plan>	нормальная форма Гессе <уравнения прямой *или* плоскости>, нормальная форма уравнения <прямой *или* плоскости>
H 264	**Hesse['s] principle [of transfer[ence]]** <DG>	Hesses[ches] Übertragungsprinzip *n*, Übertragungsprinzip von Hesse	principe *m* de transfert de [L. O.] Hesse	принцип перенесения (связности) Гессе
	Hesse['s] standard form <AY>	*s.* H 263		
H 265	**Hesse['s] theorem** <on perspective triangles> <PJ>	Hessescher Satz *m*	théorème *m* de Hesse	теорема Гессе
H 266	**Hessian** <of a plane curve> <AG>	Hessesche Kurve *f*	hessienne *f*, courbe *f* hessienne	гессиана, гессиан

H 267	**Hessian,** Hessian covariant, Hesse['s] determinant <of a form, curve, surface> <AL, DG, IV>	Hessesche Determinante (Kovariante, Invariante, Diskriminante) *f*, Hesse-Determinante *f*, Hessiana *f*	hessien *m*, déterminant (discriminant, invariant) *m* de Hesse, déterminant (covariant *m*) hessien, hessienne *f*	гессиан, определитель (детерминант) Гессе
H 268	**Hessian** <of a bundle of curves *or* a net of conics> <AY>	Hessesche Kurve *f*, Hessiane *f*, Tripelkurve *f*, Jacobische Kurve	courbe *f* de [L. O.] Hesse, hessienne *f*, courbe triple, Tripelkurve *f* du réseau, courbe de Jacobi, jacobienne *f*, jacobien *m*	гессиана, якобиана
H 269	**Hessian,** Hesse['s] determinant <of a function> <DI>	Hessesche Determinante *f*, Hesse-Determinante *f*	déterminant *m* hessien (de Hesse), hessien *m*	определитель Гессе, детерминант Гессе, гессиан
	Hessian covariant <AL, DG, IV>	*s.* H 267		
H 270	**Hessian group, Hessian-group** <AL>	Hessesche Gruppe *f*, Hessesche G_{216} *f*	groupe *m* hessien	группа Гессе
H 271	**Hessian hypersurface** <AG>	Hessesche Hyperfläche *f*, Kernhyperfläche *f*	hypersurface *f* hessienne	гиперповерхность Гессе
H 272	**Hessian line,** Hesse['s] line <AY>	Hessesche Gerade *f*	droite *f* de Hesse, droite hessienne	прямая Гессе
H 273	**Hessian matrix** <DI>	Hessesche Matrix *f*, Hesse-Matrix *f*	matrice *f* hessienne (de Hesse)	матрица Гессе
H 274	**Hessian point** <AY>	Hessescher Punkt *m*	point *m* de Hesse, point hessien	точка Гессе
H 275	**Hessian surface** <of a surface of *n*-th degree> <AG>	Hessesche Fläche *f*, Determinantenfläche *f*, Steinersche Kernfläche *f*	surface *f* hessienne, surface *f* du déterminant	поверхность Гессе
H 276	**Hessian triangle** <of a curve> <AG>	Hessesches Dreieck *n*	triangle *m* hessien	треугольник Гессе
	heterogeneity of variances <ST>	*s.* H 280		
	heterogeneous distribution <ST>	*s.* M 685		
H 277	**heterogeneous ring** <AL>	heterogener Ring *m*	anneau *m* hétérogène	гетерогенное кольцо
H 278	**heterograde statistics** <ST>	heterograde Statistik *f*, qualitative Statistik	statistique *f* hétérograde	статистика по качественному признаку
H 279	**heterologicality** <LO>	Heterologizität *f*; Eigenschaft *f*, heterologisch zu sein	hétérologie *f*	гетерологичность
H 280	**heteroscedasticity,** heterogeneity of variances <ST>	Heteroskedastizität *f*, Heterogenität *f* der Varianzen	hétéroscédasticité *f*, hétérogénéité *f* des variances	гетероскедастичность, неоднородность дисперсий
H 281	**heteroscedastic random variable** <ST>	heteroskedastisch verbundene Zufallsvariable *f*	variable *f* aléatoire hétéroscédastique	гетероскедастично связанная случайная величина
H 282	**Heuman['s] lambda (Λ-) function** <FU>	Lambdafunktion *f* von Heuman, Heumans Lambdafunktion (Λ-Funktion *f*)	fonction *f* lambda (Λ) de Heuman	
H 283	**Heun['s] [differential] equation** <DE>	Heunsche Differentialgleichung (Gleichung) *f*	équation *f* [différentielle] de Heun	[дифференциальное] уравнение Хойна
H 284	**Hewitt-Nachbin space, Hewitt['s] [Q-]space,** real[-]compact space, Q-space, saturated space, e-complete space, real[-]complete space, functionally closed space <TO>	Q-Raum *m*, Hewitt-Nachbin-Raum *m*, Hewittscher Q-Raum *m*, reellkompakter Raum *m*	espace *m* de Hewitt-Nachbin, espace replet	Q-пространство Хьюита, функционально замкнутое пространство, вещественно полное пространство
	hexadecimal notation <NT>	*s.* S 717		
	hexadecimal number system <NT>	*s.* S 718		
	hexagonal chart (graph) <NO>	*s.* H 287		
H 285	**hexagonal *m*-web** <GE, TO>	Sechseck-*m*-Gewebe *n*	*m*-réseau *m* hexagonal	шестиугольная *m*-сеть
H 286	**hexagonal net** <GE, TO>	Sechseckgewebe *n*	réseau *m* hexagonal	сеть шестиугольников, шестиугольная сеть
H 287	**hexagonal nomogram,** hexagonal chart (graph) <NO>	Hexagonaltafel *f*	abaque *m* hexagonal	гексагональная номограмма, гексагональная диаграмма
H 288	**hexagonal number** <a figurate number> <NT>	Hexagonalzahl *f*, Sechseckszahl *f*	nombre *m* hexagonal (hexagone)	шестиугольное (гексагональное) число
	hexagrammum mysticum [of Pascal] <PJ, SG>	*s.* P 287		
	hexahedral group <AL, GR>	*s.* O 41		
H 289	**hexahedral representation** <of a cubic surface> <AG>	Hexaederdarstellung *f* <Cremona>	représentation *f* hexaédrique	гексаэдрическое представление
H 290	**hexahedron** <EG>	Sechsflach *n*, Hexaeder *n*, Sechsflächner *m*	hexaèdre *m*	шестигранник, гексаэдр
	hexahedron <EG>	*s.* R 559		
H 291	**hexaspherical coordinates** <DG>	hexasphärische Koordinaten *fpl*; hexasphärisches Koordinatensystem *n*	coordonnées *fpl* hexasphériques; système *m* de coordonnées hexasphériques	гексасферические координаты; система гексасферических координат
H 292	**hexiamond** <GE>	Hexiamant *m*	hexiamant *m*	гексиамант
H 293	**hexomino** <GE>	Hexomino *n*	hexomino *m*	гексомино
H 294	**H-function of Jacobi,** eta-function of Jacobi, Jacobi['s] H-function (eta-function) < $H(2Kv) = \vartheta_1(v)$ *or* $H_1(2Kv) = \vartheta_2(v)$ > <FU>	Etafunktion (Eta-Funktion, H-Funktion) *f* von Jacobi, Jacobische Eta-Funktion (Etafunktion, H-Funktion) < $H(2Kv) = \vartheta_1(v)$ *oder* $H_1(2Kv) = \vartheta_2(v)$ >	fonction *f* êta de Jacobi < $H(2Kv) = \vartheta_1(v)$ *ou* $H_1(2Kv) = \vartheta_2(v)$ >	H-функция (эта-функция) Якоби < $H(2Kv) = \vartheta_1(v)$ *или* $H_1(2Kv) = \vartheta_2(v)$ >

H 295	***H*-group** <AT>	*H*-Gruppe *f*	*H*-groupe *m*	*H*-группа
H 296	***H*-homomorphism** <of an algebra> <AL>	*H*-Homomorphismus *m*	*H*-homomorphisme *m*	*H*-гомоморфизм
H 297	**hidden component,** latent component <ST>	versteckte Komponente *f*	composante *f* latente (cachée)	скрытая (ненаблюдаемая) компонента
H 298	**hidden replication** <ST>	verborgene Wiederholung *f*	répétition *f* cachée	скрытое повторение
	***H*-ideal** <AL>	*s.* H 437		
H 299	**hierarchical classification,** nested classification <ST>	hierarchische Klassifikation *f*	classification *f* hiérarchique	иерархическая (гнездовая) классификация
H 300	**hierarchy** <*e.g.:* of categories, logical types, sets> <CA, LO, SE>	Hierarchie *f* <*z. B.:* von Kategorien, logischer Typen, von Mengen>	hiérarchie *f* <*par exemple:* des catégories, types logiques, ensembles>	иерархия <*например:* категорий, логических типов, множеств>
	higher commutator <AL>	*s.* E 759		
H 301	**higher-decade subtraction** <AR>	Subtraktion *f* einer einstelligen Zahl von einer zweistelligen mit zweistelliger Differenz oder Subtraktion einer zweistelligen Zahl von einer zweistelligen mit einstelliger Differenz	soustraction *f* de nombres où le nombre à soustraire ou la différence est un nombre à un chiffre	вычитание чисел, при котором либо вычитаемое, либо разность является однозначным числом
	higher[-]degree term <AN>	*s.* T 179		
	higher derivative <DI>	*s.* D 276		
H 302	**higher dimensional space** <GE>	höherdimensionaler Raum *m*	espace *m* de dimension supérieure, espace d'ordre supérieur, espace supérieur	пространство более высокой размерности
H 303	**higher mathematics** <GN>	höhere Mathematik *f*	mathématiques *fpl* supérieures	высшая математика
	higher-order derivative <DI>	*s.* D 276		
	higher-order ellipse <GE>	*s.* E 191		
H 304	**higher-order logic, higher order logics,** higher predicate calculus, functional calculus of higher order <LO>	Prädikatenkalkül *m* (Prädikatenlogik *f*) höherer Stufe, erweiterte Quantorenlogik *f*	logique *f* fonctionnelle généralisée, logique supérieure (d'ordre supérieur)	исчисление (логика) предикатов высшего порядка, логика (исчисление предикатов) высших порядков
H 305	**higher order partial derivative,** partial derivative of higher order <DI>	höhere partielle Ableitung *f*, partielle Ableitung höherer Ordnung	dérivée *f* partielle d'ordre supérieur	частная производная высшего порядка
	higher-order ramification field <AB>	*s.* H 308		
H 306	**higher-order ramification group,** higher ramification group, ramification group of higher degree <AB>	Verzweigungsgruppe *f* höherer Art, höhere Verzweigungsgruppe	groupe *m* de ramification d'espèce supérieure	группа разветвления высшего порядка
	higher order term <AN>	*s.* T 179		
H 307	**higher plane curve,** plane algebraic curve of higher degree (order), algebraic plane curve of higher degree (order) <AG>	algebraische ebene Kurve *f* höherer <als zweiter> Ordnung, [ebene] algebraische Kurve höherer <als zweiter> Ordnung, ebene Kurve höherer <als zweiter> Ordnung, ebene Kurve höheren Grades, [ebene] algebraische Kurve höheren Grades	courbe *f* [algébrique] plane d'ordre (de degré) supérieur	плоская алгебраическая кривая высшего порядка, плоская кривая высшего порядка
	higher predicate calculus <LO>	*s.* H 304		
H 308	**higher ramification field,** higher-order ramification field, ramification field of higher order <AB>	Verzweigungskörper *m* höherer Art, höherer Verzweigungskörper	corps *m* de ramification d'espèce supérieure	поле ветвления высшего порядка
	higher ramification group <AB>	*s.* H 306		
H 309	**higher singularity** <of a curve *or* function> <AG, FT>	höhere Singularität *f*, Singularität höherer Ordnung	singularité *f* élevée (extraordinaire, d'ordre supérieur)	особенность высшего порядка
	highest coefficient <AL>	*s.* L 229		
H 310	**highest common factor,** greatest common divisor, H.C.F., sum <of ideals> <AL>	Idealsumme *f*, Summe *f*, größter gemeinsamer (gemeinschaftlicher) Teiler *m* <von Idealen>	plus grand commun diviseur *m*, somme *f* d'idéaux, borne *f* supérieure [d'une famille] d'idéaux	сумма идеалов
	highest common factor <AL, NT>	*s.* G 404		
	highest degree coefficient <AL>	*s.* L 229		
	highest degree term <AL>	*s.* L 232		
	highest dimension <AL>	*s.* D 503		
	highest figure <NT>	*s.* T 499		
	highest number <NT>	*s.* T 499		
H 311	**highest order,** most significant digit <of a number> <NU>	höchste gültige Ziffer *f*	digit *m* de poids supérieur	цифра самого старшего значащего разряда, старшая значащая цифра
H 312	**highest significant difference,** honest significant difference, hsd, HSD <ST>	Grenzdifferenz *f* des Tukey-Tests, HSD	la plus haute différence *f* significative, différence significative du test de Tukey, hsd	наибольшая значимая разность, значимая разность в критерии Тьюки

	highest term <AL>	*s.* L 232		
	highest weight <AL>	*s.* D 881		
H 313	**high indices theorems** <LI>	Lückenumkehrsätze *mpl*	théorèmes *mpl* de hautes indices	
H 314	**highly composite ideal** <NT>	hochzusammengesetztes Ideal *n*	idéal *m* hautement composé	высоко составной идеал
H 315	**highly composite number** <NT>	hochzusammengesetzte Zahl *f*	nombre *m* largement (hautement) composé	высоко составное число
H 316	**Higman['s] group** <GR>	Higmansche Gruppe *f*	groupe *m* d'Higman	группа Хигмена
H 317	**Hilbert algebra** <AL>	Hilbert-Algebra *f*	algèbre *f* hilbertienne	алгебра Гильберта, гильбертова алгебра
H 318	**Hilbert['s] automorphism** <NT>	Hilbertscher Automorphismus *m*	automorphisme *m* hilbertien	гильбертов автоморфизм
H 319	**Hilbert['s] axiomatic method** <MM>	axiomatische Methode *f* von Hilbert, Hilbertsche axiomatische Methode	méthode *f* axiomatique de Hilbert	аксиоматический метод Гильберта
H 320	**Hilbert base property,** finite basis condition, basis (base) condition <AL>	Hilbertsche Basiseigenschaft *f*	condition *f* de base finie	условие конечности базиса
H 321	**Hilbert['s] basis theorem,** Hilbert['s] theorem, basis theorem of Hilbert <AL>	Hilbertscher Basissatz *m*, Basissatz von Hilbert, Basissatz	théorème *m* de Hilbert (la base de Hilbert, la base finie, finitude de Hilbert)	теорема Гильберта о конечности базиса, теорема Гильберта о базисе
	Hilbert['s] boundary value problem <IE>	*s.* H 348		
	Hilbert['s] characteristic function <AG, AL>	*s.* C 550		
	Hilbert['s] class field <AB>	*s.* A 59		
H 322	**Hilbert['s] coefficient** <AL>	Hilbert-Koeffizient *m*, Hilbertkoeffizient *m*	coefficient *m* de Hilbert	коэффициент Гильберта
H 323	**Hilbert['s] construction** <EG>	Konstruktion *f* mit Lineal und Eichmaß, Hilbertsche Konstruktion	construction *f* de Hilbert	построение Гильберта
	Hilbert['s] co-ordinate space $[l^2]$ <FA>	*s.* S 1313		
	Hilbert['s] cube <TO>	*s.* H 344		
H 324	**Hilbert['s] dimension** <FA>	Hilbert-Dimension *f*, Hilbertsche Dimension *f*	dimension *f* hilbertienne	гильбертова размерность
	Hilbert['s] epsilon-symbol <LO>	*s.* H 360		
H 325	**Hilbert['s] existence theorem** <VA>	Hilbertscher Existenzsatz *m*	théorème *m* d'existence de Hilbert	теорема существования Гильберта
H 326	**Hilbert['s] formula** <IE>	Hilbertsche Formel *f*	formule *f* de Hilbert	формула Гильберта
	Hilbert['s] function <AG, AL>	*s.* C 550		
	Hilbert['s] ε-function <LO>	*s.* E 309		
	Hilbert['s] function space $[L^2]$ <FA>	*s.* S 1314		
H 327	**Hilbert['s] fundamental formula** <IE>	Hilbertsche Fundamentalformel *f*	formule *f* fondamentale de Hilbert	фундаментальная формула Гильберта
H 328	**Hilbert['s] homogeneous modular group** <AB>	[engere] homogene Hilbert-sche Modulgruppe *f*	groupe *m* modulaire homogène de Hilbert	однородная модулярная группа Гильберта
H 329	**Hilbertian field** <AL>	Hilbertscher Körper *m*	corps *m* hilbertien	гильбертово поле
H 330	**Hilbertian geometry** <DG>	Hilbertsche Geometrie *f*	géométrie *f* hilbertienne	гильбертова геометрия, геометрия Гильберта
	Hilbertian ring <AL>	*s.* J 38		
H 331	**Hilbert['s] independence theorem** <VA>	Hilbertscher (Beltrami-Hilbertscher) Unabhängigkeitssatz *m*, Unabhängigkeitssatz	théorème *m* d'indépendance de Hilbert	теорема независимости Гильберта
	Hilbert['s] independent integral <VA>	*s.* H 333		
H 332	**Hilbert['s] inequality** <for a double integral> <DI>	Hilbertsche Ungleichung *f*	inégalité *f* de Hilbert	неравенство Гильберта
	Hilbert['s] inequality <SS>	*s.* H 362		
H 333	**Hilbert['s] [invariant] integral,** Hilbert['s] independent integral <VA>	Hilbertsches Integral *n*, Hilbertsches invariantes (unabhängiges) Integral	intégrale *f* de Hilbert, intégrale invariante (indépendante) de Hilbert	инвариантный интеграл Гильберта, интеграл Гильберта
H 334	**Hilbert['s] irreducibility theorem** <AL>	Hilbertscher Irreduzibilitätssatz *m*	théorème *m* d'irréductibilité de Hilbert	теорема неприводимости Гильберта, теорема Гильберта о неприводимости
H 335	**Hilbert-Kamke problem** <NT>	Hilbert-Kamkesches Problem *n*	problème *m* de Hilbert-Kamke	проблема Гильберта-Камке
H 336	**Hilbert['s] lemma** <AB>	Hilbertscher Normensatz *m*	théorème *m* normique de Hilbert	теорема Гильберта о нормах (циклических расширениях)
H 337	**Hilbert['s] matrix** <FA>	Hilbert-Matrix *f*, H-Matrix *f*	matrice *f* de Hilbert	гильбертова матрица, матрица Гильберта
H 338	**Hilbert['s] modular form** <FT>	Hilbertsche Modulform *f*	forme *f* modulaire de Hilbert	модулярная форма Гильберта
H 339	**Hilbert['s] modular function** <FT>	Hilbertsche Modulfunktion *f*	fonction *f* de Hilbert	модулярная функция Гильберта
H 340	**Hilbert['s] modular group** <AB>	Hilbertsche Modulgruppe *f*	groupe *m* de Hilbert	модулярная группа Гильберта
H 341	**Hilbert['s] modular surface** <AG>	Hilbertsche Modulfläche *f*	surface *f* modulaire de Hilbert	модулярная поверхность Гильберта

No.	English	German	French	Russian
H 342	**Hilbert['s] norm residue symbol** <AB>	Hilbertsches Normenrestsymbol (Normsymbol) *n*	symbole *m* [de reste normique] de Hilbert	символ [норменного вычета] Гильберта
H 343	**Hilbert['s] Nullstellensatz,** Hilbert['s] theorem on zeros <AL>	Hilbertscher Nullstellensatz *m*, Nullstellensatz von Hilbert	Nullstellensatz *m* [de Hilbert], théorème *m* des zéros [de Hilbert]	теорема [Гильберта] о нулях (корнях)
H 344	**Hilbert['s] parallelotope,** Hilbert['s] cube, fundamental cube <of Hilbert space> <TO>	Hilbertscher Quader *m*, Hilbert-Quader *m*, Hilbertquader *m*, Fundamentalquader *m*	cube *m* fondamental de Hilbert, parallélépipède *m* de Hilbert	гильбертов кирпич, гильбертов куб, основной параллелепипед
H 345	**Hilbert *p*-class field** <AB>	*p*-Klassenkörper *m*	corps *m* de *p*-classes	гильбертово поле *p*-классов
H 346	**Hilbert *p*-class field tower** <AB>	*p*-Klassenkörperturm *m*	tour *m* de corps de *p*-classes	башня гильбертовых полей *p*-классов
H 347	**Hilbert-Poincaré boundary condition** <DE>	Hilbert-Poincarésche Randbedingung *f*, Poincarésche Randbedingung	condition *f* aux limites de Hilbert-Poincaré	краевое условие Гильберта-Пуанкаре
	Hilbert['s] postulate of completeness <GE>	*s.* A 1282		
H 348	**Hilbert['s] problem,** Hilbert['s] boundary value problem <IE>	Hilbert-Problem *n*, Hilbertsches Randwertproblem *n*, Hilbertsche Randwertaufgabe *f*	problème *m* de Hilbert, problème aux valeurs limites de Hilbert	краевая задача Гильберта, задача Гильберта
H 349	**Hilbert['s] problems** <FO>	Hilbertsche Probleme *npl*	problèmes *mpl* de Hilbert	проблемы Гильберта
H 350	**Hilbert['s] product formula** <AB>	Hilbertsche Produktformel *f*	formule *f* du produit de Hilbert	гильбертова формула произведения <для норменного вычета>
H 351	**Hilbert['s] program** <MM>	Hilbertsches Programm *n*	programme *m* de Hilbert	программа Гильберта
H 352	**Hilbert['s] proof theory** <MM>	Hilbertsche Beweistheorie *f*	théorie *f* hilbertienne de la démonstration	теория доказательств Гильберта
H 353	**Hilbert['s] ramification theory** <AB>	Hilbertsche Verzweigungstheorie *f*	théorie *f* de la ramification de Hilbert	теория разветвления Гильберта
	Hilbert['s] ring <AL>	*s.* J 38		
H 354	**Hilbert-Schmidt class,** Hilbert-Schmidt type <of operators> <FA>	Hilbert-Schmidtsche Klasse *f*, Hilbert-Schmidtscher Typ *m*	classe *f* (type *m*) de Hilbert-Schmidt	класс (тип) Гильберта-Шмидта
H 355	**Hilbert-Schmidt expansion theorem** <IE>	Hilbert-Schmidtscher Entwicklungssatz *m*, Entwicklungssatz von Hilbert und E. Schmidt	théorème *m* de Hilbert et E. Schmidt	теорема Гильберта-Шмидта
	Hilbert-Schmidt fundamental formula <IE>	*s.* S 133		
H 356	**Hilbert-Schmidt kernel,** Hilbert-Schmidt-type kernel, normalizable kernel, square-integrable kernel, quadratically integrable kernel <FA, IE>	Hilbert-Schmidtscher Kern *m*, Kern vom Hilbert-Schmidtschen Typ, normierbarer (quadratisch integrierbarer, quadratisch integrabler, quadratintegrabler) Kern	noyau *m* de Hilbert-Schmidt, noyau du (de) type de Hilbert-Schmidt, noyau de carré intégrable	ядро Гильберта-Шмидта, ядро типа Гильберта-Шмидта, нормируемое ядро, ядро с интегрируемым квадратом; ядро, интегрируемое с квадратом
H 357	**Hilbert-Schmidt operator,** Hilbert-Schmidt transformation, finite norm operator, operator (transformation) of Hilbert-Schmidt type (class) <FA>	Operator *m* (Transformation *f*) vom Hilbert-Schmidtschen Typ, Hilbert-Schmidt-Operator *m*, Hilbert-Schmidtsche Transformation	opérateur *m* (transformation *f*) de (du) type de Hilbert-Schmidt, opérateur (transformation) de Hilbert-Schmidt	оператор (преобразование) [типа] Гильберта-Шмидта
	Hilbert-Schmidt type <FA>	*s.* H 354		
	Hilbert-Schmidt-type kernel <FA, IE>	*s.* H 356		
	Hilbert['s] sequence space [l^2] <FA>	*s.* S 1313		
H 358	**Hilbert['s] space** <FA>	Hilbert-Raum *m*, Hilbertscher Raum *m*, Hilbertraum *m*	espace *m* de Hilbert, espace hilbertien, Hilbert *m*	гильбертово пространство
	Hilbert['s] space of functions <FA>	*s.* S 1314		
	Hilbert['s] space of sequences <FA>	*s.* S 1313		
	Hilbert['s] strong axiom of continuity <GE>	*s.* A 1282		
H 359	**Hilbert['s] subset** <AL>	Hilbertsche Untermenge *f*	sous-ensemble *m* hilbertien	гильбертово подмножество
H 360	**Hilbert['s] ε-symbol,** Hilbert['s] epsilon-symbol, ε-symbol <LO>	Hilberts ε-Symbol (Epsilon-Symbol) *n*	symbole *m* ε (epsilon) de Hilbert	ε-символ (эпсилон-символ) Гильберта
H 361	**Hilbert['s] system of axioms** <GE>	Hilbertsches Axiomensystem *n*	système *m* d'axiomes de Hilbert	система аксиом Гильберта
H 362	**Hilbert['s] theorem.** Hilbert['s] inequality <for a double series> <SS>	Hilbertscher Doppelreihensatz *m*, Hilbertsche Ungleichung *f*; ursprünglicher Hilbertscher Doppelreihensatz, Hilbertsche Ungleichung im engeren Sinne <für $p = p' = 2$>	théorème *m* (inégalité *f*) de Hilbert	теорема (неравенство) Гильберта, теорема Гильберта о двойных рядах
	Hilbert['s] theorem <AL>	*s.* H 321		
	Hilbert['s] theorem <DG>	*s.* T 293		
H 363	**Hilbert['s] theorem on [chains of] syzygies** <AL>	Hilberts[cher] Satz *m* vom Abbrechen der Syzygienkette	théorème *m* [des syzygies] de Hilbert	теорема Гильберта об обрыве цепей сизигий, теорема Гильберта о сизигиях
	Hilbert['s] theorem on zeros <AL>	*s.* H 343		

	English	German	French	Russian
H 364	**Hilbert['s] topology** <AG>	Hilbertsche Topologie *f*, Hilbert-Topologie *f*	topologie *f* de Hilbert	топология Гильберта
H 365	**Hilb['s] formula** <on Bessel functions> <FU>	Hilbsche Formel *f*	formule *f* de Hilb	формула Гильба
H 366	**Hill['s] determinant** <DE>	Hillsche Determinante *f*	déterminant *m* de Hill	определитель Хилла
H 367	**Hill['s] [differential] equation,** differential equation of Hill type <DE>	[G. W.] Hillsche Differentialgleichung *f*, Differentialgleichung vom Hillschen Typ[us]	équation *f* de Hill, équation différentielle de Hill	уравнение Хилла, дифференциальное уравнение Хилла
H 368	**Hill['s] function** <DE, FU>	Hillsche Funktion *f*	fonction *f* de Hill	функция Хилла
H 369	**Hill['s] system [of differential equations]** <DE>	Hillsches System (Differentialgleichungssystem) *n*	système *m* d'équations différentielles de Hill	система дифференциальных уравнений Хилла
	Hinčin['s] transfer principle <AX>	*s.* K 67		
	hinged tracing lever <GE, IN>	*s.* M 929		
H 370	**Hippocrates['s] lune,** lunula Hippokratis, lunula (crescent) of Hippocrates <EG>	Möndchen *n* (Mond *m*) des Hippokrates, lunula *f* Hippokratis	lunule *f* d'Hippocrate, lunula Hippokratis	гиппократова луночка
H 371	**hippopede,** horse fetter <AG>	Hippopede *f*, Hippopede des (von) Eudoxos, Pferdefessel *f*, Pferdeschlinge *f*	hippopède *f*	гиппопеда
	Hirsch['s] formula <AT>	*s.* F 496		
H 372	**Hirsch-Plotkin radical** <AL>	Hirsch-Plotkinsches Radikal *n*	radical *m* de Hirsch-Plotkin	радикал Хирша-Плоткина
H 373	**histogram,** area histogram <two-dimensional representation of frequency proportional to area> <ST>	Staffelbild *n* <Gesamtdarstellung>; Treppenpolygon *n*, Histogramm *n* <obere Begrenzung>	histogramme *m*	гистограмма
	histogram <GN>	*s.* B 60		
H 374	**history,** prehistory <PG>	Vorgeschichte *f*	histoire *f* [antérieure]	предыстория
H 375	**Hjelmslev plane** <GE>	Hjelmslev-Ebene *f*	plan *m* de Hjelmslev	плоскость Гельмслева
H 376	***H*-lim[it],** limit by Hölder['s] method <LI>	*H*-Limes *m*, Limes *m* nach dem *H*-Verfahren, *H*-lim	*H*-limite *f*, limite *f* par la méthode de Hölder, *H*-lim	[обобщенный] предел по методу Гельдера, [обобщенный] предел по Гельдеру, *H*-lim
H 377	**$\mathfrak{H}$-lim[it],** (H,p_n) limit, limit by Hausdorff's method, (H,p_n) lim <LI>	(H,p_n)-Limes, Limes *m* nach dem (H,p_n)-Verfahren, (H,p_n)-lim	(H,p_n)-limite *f*, limite *f* par la méthode de Hausdorff, (H,p_n)-lim	[обобщенный] предел по методу Хаусдорфа, [обобщенный] предел по Хаусдорфу, (H,p_n)-lim
H 378	**$\mathfrak{H}$-limitable sequence,** (H,p_n) limitable sequence, sequence limitable by Hausdorff's method <LI>	(H,p_n)-limitierbare (nach dem (H,p_n)-Verfahren limitierbare) Folge *f*	suite *f* limitable par la méthode de Hausdorff, suite $\mathfrak{H}$-limitable ((H,p_n)-limitable)	последовательность, лимитируемая методом Хаусдорфа; (H,p_n)-лимитируемая последовательность
H 379	***H*-limitable sequence,** sequence limitable by Hölder's method <LI>	*H*-limitierbare (nach dem *H*-Verfahren limitierbare) Folge *f*	suite *f* limitable par la méthode de Hölder, suite *H*-limitable	последовательность, лимитируемая методом Гельдера; *H*-лимитируемая последовательность
	***h*-line, h line** <GE>	*s.* H 633		
	$\mathfrak{H}$-matrix <SS>	*s.* H 140		
H 380	**$\mathfrak{H}$-method,** (H,p_n) method, Hausdorff['s] method [of limitation], Hausdorff['s] limitation method <for divergent sequences> <LI>	Hausdorffsches Limitierungsverfahren ((H,p_n)-Verfahren) *n*, (H,p_n)-Verfahren, Verfahren der Hausdorffschen Mittel, Hausdorff-Verfahren, Hausdorffsches Verfahren [(H,p_n)]	méthode *f* de Hausdorff, méthode (H,p_n) (des moyennes de Hausdorff, de limitation de Hausdorff)	метод [образования обобщенного предела] Хаусдорфа, метод средних Хаусдорфа
H 381	**$\mathfrak{H}$-method,** (H,p_n) method, Hausdorff['s] method [of summation], Hausdorff['s] summation method <for divergent series> <LI>	Hausdorffsches Summierungsverfahren ((H,p_n)-Verfahren) *n*, (H,p_n)-Verfahren, Verfahren *n* der Hausdorffschen Mittel, Hausdorff-Verfahren *n*, Hausdorffsches Verfahren [(H,p_n)]	méthode *f* de Hausdorff, méthode (H,p_n) (des moyennes de Hausdorff, de sommation de Hausdorff)	метод Хаусдорфа, метод суммирования [расходящихся рядов] Хаусдорфа, метод средних Хаусдорфа
	***H*-method** <LI>	*s.* 1. H 389; 2. H 393		
	h_n <DE, FU>	*s.* H 224		
	H_n <FU>	*s.* H 228		
H 382	**Hodge manifold** <DG, FT>	Hodge-Mannigfaltigkeit *f*	variété *f* de Hodge	многообразие Ходжа
H 383	**hodograph transformation** <DE>	Hodographentransformation *f*	transformation *f* de l'hodographe	преобразование годографа
H 384	**Hofmann['s] category** <CA>	Hofmannsche Kategorie *f*	catégorie *f* hofmannienne	хофманова категория
H 385	**Hölder['s] condition,** condition of Hölder <of order or index λ, $0 < \lambda \leqq 1$, with a constant *A*; more special: of order λ, $0 < \lambda < 1$ > <AN>	Hölder-Bedingung *f*, *H*-Bedingung *f*, Höldersche Bedingung *f* <mit dem Exponenten λ, $0 < \lambda \leqq 1$, und dem Koeffizienten *A*; spezieller: mit dem Exponenten λ, $0 < \lambda < 1$ >	condition *f* de Hölder (Lipschitz) <d'ordre ou d'exposant λ, $0 < \lambda \leqq 1$ et avec la constante *A*; plus spécial: d'ordre λ, $0 < \lambda < 1$ >	условие Гельдера <порядка λ, $0 < \lambda \leqq 1$ с постоянной или коэффициентом *A*; более специально: порядка λ, $0 < \lambda < 1$ >; условие Липшица <для числовых функций одного действительного переменного>
	Hölder['s] constant <AN>	*s.* C 2105		
H 386	**Hölder continuity,** property of satisfying a	Hölder-Stetigkeit *f*, H-Stetigkeit *f*,	propriété *f* de satisfaire à une condition de Hölder	свойство удовлетворять условию Гельдера,

and still: H 386	Hölder condition <AN>	Höldersche Stetigkeit *f*	(Lipschitz), propriété d'être höldérien, Hölder-continuité *f*	Н-непрерывность, непрерывность в смысле Гельдера, непрерывность по Гельдеру
H 387	**Hölder continuous function,** H-continuous function, function satisfying a Hölder condition <AN>	Hölder-stetige (H-stetige) Funktion *f*; Funktion, die eine Hölder-Bedingung (H-Bedingung) erfüllt	fonction *f* höldérienne (Hölder-continue), fonction satisfaisant à une condition de Hölder (Lipschitz)	гельдерова функция; функция, удовлетворяющая условию Гельдера; непрерывная в смысле Гельдера функция
	Hölder['s] index <AN>	*s.* O 261		
H 388	**Hölder['s] inequality** <AN>	Höldersche Ungleichung *f* <in der Reihen- *oder* Integralform>	inégalité *f* de Hölder	неравенство Гельдера <для сумм *или* интегралов>
H 389	**Hölder['s] limitation method,** Hölder['s] method [of limitation], *H*-method <for divergent sequences> <LI>	Höldersches Limitierungsverfahren *n*, *H*-Verfahren *n*	méthode *f* de limitation de Hölder, méthode de Hölder	метод [образования обобщенного предела] Гельдера
	Hölder['s] limitation method of *p*-th order <LI>	*s.* H 588		
H 390	**Hölder['s] mean** <of *p*-th order> <LI>	Höldersches Mittel *n* <*p*-ter Ordnung>	moyenne *f* de Hölder <d'ordre *p*>	среднее [арифметическое] Гельдера <*p*-го порядка>
	Hölder['s] method <LI>	*s.* H 393		
	Hölder['s] method [of limitation] <LI>	*s.* H 389		
	Hölder['s] method of *p*-th order <LI>	*s.* 1. H 587; 2. H 588		
	Hölder['s] method of summation <LI>	*s.* H 393		
H 391	**Hölder[s'] norm** <of matrices> <MD>	Höldersche Matrizennorm (Norm) *f*	norme *f* de Hölder	норма Гельдера
	Hölder['s] order <AN>	*s.* O 261		
H 392	**Hölder-Riesz inequality** <FA>	Hölder-Rieszsche Ungleichung *f*, Höldersche Ungleichung	inégalité *f* de Hölder-Riesz	неравенство Гельдера-Риса
	Hölder-Riesz space <FA>	*s.* S 1318		
H 393	**Hölder['s] summation method,** Hölder['s] method [of summation], *H*-method <for divergent series> <LI>	Höldersches Summierungsverfahren *n*, *H*-Verfahren *n*	méthode *f* de sommation de Hölder, méthode [des moyennes arithmétiques] de Hölder	метод Гельдера, метод суммирования [расходящихся рядов] Гельдера, метод средних арифметических Гельдера
	Hölder['s] summation method of *p*-th order <LI>	*s.* H 587		
H 394	**Hölder['s] theorem** <for ordered groups> <AL>	Hölderscher (Cartanscher) Satz *m*	théorème *m* de Hölder	теорема Гельдера
H 395	**Hölder['s] theorem** <for the gamma function> <FU>	Satz *m* von Hölder, Hölderscher Satz	théorème *m* de Hölder	теорема Гельдера
	Hölder['s] theorem <AL>	*s.* T 295		
H 396	**holoid** <AL>	Holoid *n*	holoïde *m*	голоид
H 397	**holomorph** <of a group> <GR>	Holomorph *n*, Holomorphie *f*	holomorphie *f*, holomorphe *m*, groupe *m* holomorphe	голоморф
H 398	**holomorph-convex manifold,** holomorphically convex manifold <FT>	holomorph-konvexe Mannigfaltigkeit *f*	variété *f* holomorphiquement convexe, variété holomorphe-convexe	голоморфно выпуклое многообразие, Н-выпуклое многообразие
	holomorphically complete complex space <FT>	*s.* S 1738		
	holomorphically complete manifold <FT>	*s.* S 1736		
	holomorphically convex manifold <FT>	*s.* H 398		
	holomorphically separable manifold <FT>	*s.* H 411		
H 399	**holomorphic complement** <of a real function> <RF>	holomorphe Ergänzung *f*	complément *m* holomorphe	голоморфное дополнение
H 400	**holomorphic completeness** <FT>	Holomorphievollständigkeit *f*	complétude *f* holomorphe	голоморфная полнота
H 401	**holomorphic convexity** <FT>	Holomorphiekonvexität *f*	convexité *f* holomorphe	голоморфная выпуклость
	holomorphic differential <FT>	*s.* A 11		
H 402	**holomorphic differential form,** holomorphic form <DG, FT>	holomorphe Differentialform (Form) *f*	forme *f* différentielle holomorphe, forme holomorphe	голоморфная дифференциальная форма, голоморфная форма
H 403	**holomorphic divisor,** non[-]negative divisor <AG, FT>	holomorpher (nichtnegativer) Divisor *m*	diviseur *m* holomorphe (non négatif)	голоморфный (неотрицательный) дивизор
	holomorphic form <DG, FT>	*s.* H 402		
H 404	**holomorphic function,** complex analytic function, analytic function <DG>	holomorphe (komplexanalytische, analytische) Funktion *f*	fonction *f* holomorphe (analytique complexe, analytique)	голоморфная (комплексно-аналитическая, аналитическая) функция

	English	German	French	Russian
H 405	**holomorphic function,** regular analytic function, regular function <FT>	holomorphe (regulär analytische, reguläre) Funktion *f*	fonction *f* holomorphe (synectique, analytique régulière, régulière)	голоморфная (регулярная аналитическая, регулярная, аналитическая, правильная) функция
H 406	**holomorphic manifold,** complex analytic manifold <DG>	holomorphe (komplexanalytische) Mannigfaltigkeit *f*	variété *f* à structure analytique[-]complexe, variété analytique[-]complexe, variété holomorphe	комплексно-аналитическое многообразие, голоморфное многообразие
H 407	**holomorphic mapping,** holomorphic transformation, complex analytic mapping (transformation), analytical mapping (transformation) <FT>	holomorphe (komplexanalytische, analytische) Abbildung *f*, holomorphe (komplexanalytische, analytische) Transformation *f*	application (transformation) *f* holomorphe (analytique complexe, analytique)	голоморфное (комплексно-аналитическое, аналитическое) отображение (преобразование)
H 408	**holomorphic mapping of a domain onto a domain** <FT, TO>	gebietstreue holomorphe Abbildung *f*	application *f* holomorphe d'un domaine sur un domaine	голоморфное отображение области на область
H 409	**holomorphic part** <of a Laurent expansion> <FT>	Nebenteil *m*	partie *f* régulière	голоморфная часть
	holomorphic rational mapping (transformation) <AG>	*s.* R 621		
H 410	**holomorphic separability** <FT>	Holomorphieseparierbarkeit *f*	séparabilité *f* holomorphe	голоморфная отделимость
	holomorphic transformation <FT>	*s.* H 407		
H 411	**holomorph-separable manifold,** holomorphically separable manifold <FT>	holomorph-separierbare Mannigfaltigkeit *f*	variété *f* holomorphiquement séparable, variété holomorphe-séparable	голоморфно отделимое многообразие, H-отделимое многообразие
H 412	**holomorphy** <of a function> <FT>	Holomorphie *f*	holomorphie *f*	голоморфность
H 413	**holonomic condition** <VA>	holonome Bedingung *f*	condition *f* holonome	голономное условие
H 414	**holonomic reference system** <DG>	holonomes Bezugssystem *n*	repère *m* holonome	голономный репер, голономная система отсчета
H 415	**holonomy** <DG>	Holonomie *f*	holonomie *f*	голономность, голономия
H 416	**holonomy group** <DG>	Holonomiegruppe *f*	groupe *m* d'holonomie	группа голономии, голономная группа
H 417	**Holtsmark-Larsen method** <ST>	Holtsmark-Larsensche Schachbrettmethode *f*	méthode *f* de Holtsmark-Larsen	[шахматный] метод Хольцмарка-Ларсена
H 418	**homaloidal net** <of algebraic curves> <AG>	homaloidisches (homaloidales) Netz *n*, Netz vom Grad $D = 1$	réseau *m* homaloïdal	гомалоидная сеть
H 419	**homaloidal surface** <AG>	homaloidische Fläche *f* <Sylvester, Cremona>	surface *f* homaloïdale (homaloïdique)	гомолоидная поверхность
H 420	**homeomorph** <TO>	homöomorphes Bild *n*	image *f* homéomorphe	гомеоморфный образ
H 421	**homeomorph[ic] graph,** topologically identical graph <GP>	homöomorpher Graph *m*	graphe *m* homéomorphe	гомеоморфный граф
	homeomorphic mapping <TO>	*s.* T 519		
	homeomorphic space <TO>	*s.* T 529		
H 422	**homeomorphic to a circle** <TO>	kreishomöomorph	homéomorphe à un disque	гомеоморфный кругу
H 423	**homeomorphism** <property> <TO>	Homöomorphie *f*	homéomorphie *f*	гомеоморфность
	homeomorphism <TO>	*s.* T 519		
H 424	**homeomorphism without fixed points,** fixed-point-free homeomorphism <TO>	fixpunktfreier (fixpunktloser) Homöomorphismus *m*	homéomorphisme *m* sans point fixe	гомеоморфизм, свободный от неподвижных точек; гомеоморфизм, не имеющий неподвижных точек
	hom-functor <CA, HA>	*s.* F 790		
H 425	**homogeneity formula** <for Weierstrass's *p*-funktion> <FU>	Homogenitätsformel *f*	formule *f* d'homogénéité	формула однородности
	homogeneity of variances <ST>	*s.* H 507		
H 426	**homogeneity relation** <of a function, also for the Bernoulli polynomials> <AN>	Homogenitätsrelation *f*	relation *f* d'homogénéité	соотношение однородности
	homogeneous boundary value problem <DE>	*s.* H 438		
	homogeneous canonical transformation <DE, VA>	*s.* M 177		
H 427	**homogeneous Cartesian co-ordinates,** homogeneous co-ordinates <AY>	homogene kartesische Koordinaten *fpl*, homogene Koordinaten	coordonnées *fpl* cartésiennes homogènes, coordonnées homogènes	однородные декартовы координаты, однородные координаты
	homogeneous chain <SP>	*s.* H 441		
H 428	**homogeneous** <*n*-> **cochain** <HA>	homogene Kokette *f* <vom Grade *n*>	cochaîne *f* homogène <de degré *n*>	однородная <*n*-> коцепь
H 429	**homogeneous component** <of a graduation> <AL>	homogene Komponente *f*, homogener Bestandteil *m*	composante *f* (composant *m*) homogène	однородная компонента (составляющая)
H 430	**homogeneous component** <of a socle> <AL>	Fuß *m*	pied *m*	основание

H 431	**homogeneous component** <of degree n> <of a polynomial> <AL>	homogene Komponente *f*, homogener Bestandteil (Teil) *m* <vom Grade n, n-ten Grades>	composante (partie) *f* <n-> homogène	однородная компонента (часть) <степени n>
H 432	**homogeneous component** <of degree n> <of a power series> <SS>	homogener Bestandteil *m* <n-ten Grades>	partie *f* homogène <de degré n>	однородная составляющая <n-й степени>
H 433	**homogeneous coordinates** <AY>	homogene Koordinaten *fpl*, Verhältniskoordinaten *fpl*	coordonnées *fpl* homogènes (projectives)	однородные координаты
	homogeneous coordinates <AY>	*s.* H 427		
H 434	**homogeneous coordinates of Segre** <AG>	Segresche homogene Koordinaten *fpl*	coordonnées *fpl* homogènes de Segre	однородные координаты Сегре
	homogeneous differential equation <DE>	*s.* 1. D 515; 2. H 439		
	homogeneous differential system <DE>	*s.* H 444		
	homogeneous dimension <AG>	*s.* P 1683		
H 435	**homogeneous element** <of a graded group> <GR>	homogenes Element *n*	élément *m* homogène; élément isobare	однородный элемент
	homogeneous equation <DE>	*s.* 1. D 515; 2. H 439		
H 436	**homogeneous function** <of degree n> <AN>	homogene Funktion *f* <vom Grade n, von der Dimension n, von der Ordnung n>	fonction *f* homogène <de degré n, de dimension n>	однородная функция <с измерением n, с показателем n, степени n>
	homogeneous graph of degree *n* <GP>	*s.* R 557		
H 437	**homogeneous ideal,** homogeneous polynomial ideal, H-ideal <AL>	homogenes Ideal *n*, H-Ideal *n*, homogenes Polynomideal *n*	idéal *m* homogène	однородный идеал, Н-идеал, гомогенный идеал
H 438	**homogeneous linear boundary value problem,** homogeneous boundary value problem <DE>	homogenes (vollhomogenes) lineares Randwertproblem *n*, homogenes Randwertproblem, homogene [lineare] Randwertaufgabe *f*	problème *m* aux limites [linéaire] homogène	однородная [линейная] краевая задача
H 439	**homogeneous linear differential equation,** homogeneous differential equation, homogeneous linear equation, homogeneous equation <of the n-th order> <DE>	homogene (verkürzte) lineare Differentialgleichung *f*, homogene Differentialgleichung <n-ter Ordnung>	équation *f* différentielle homogène (sans second membre), équation linéaire homogène, équation homogène (sans second membre) <d'ordre n, de n-e ordre>	однородное линейное дифференциальное уравнение, однородное дифференциальное (линейное) уравнение, однородное уравнение <порядка n, n-го порядка>
	homogeneous linear equation <DE>	*s.* H 439		
	homogeneous linear set (system) [of differential equations] with constant coefficients <DE>	*s.* D 1		
H 440	**homogeneously dimensional variety** <AT>	homogendimensionale Mannigfaltigkeit *f*	variété *f* purement dimensionnelle	размерно[-]однородное многообразие
	homogeneously *n*-dimensional complex <AT>	*s.* P 2058		
H 441	**homogeneous Markov chain,** homogeneous chain, stationary [Markov] chain <SP>	[zeitlich] homogene Markovsche Kette *f*, [zeitlich] homogene Kette, stationäre [Markovsche] Kette	chaîne *f* markovienne homogène, chaîne homogène, chaîne [markovienne] stationnaire	однородная цепь Маркова, однородная цепь, стационарная цепь [Маркова]
H 442	**homogeneous Markov process** <SP>	[zeitlich] homogener Markovscher Prozeß *m*	processus *m* de Markov homogène	однородный процесс Маркова
H 443	**homogeneous modular group** <FT>	homogene elliptische Modulgruppe *f*	groupe *m* modulaire homogène (arithmétique)	однородная эллиптическая модулярная группа
	homogeneous polynomial <AL>	*s.* F 461		
	homogeneous polynomial ideal <AL>	*s.* H 437		
	homogeneous problem <VA>	*s.* H 446		
	homogeneous *r*-cycle on *V* <AG>	*s.* R 207		
	homogeneous space <AL>	*s.* F 56		
	homogeneous system <AL>	*s.* H 445		
H 444	**homogeneous system [of differential equations],** homogeneous differential system <DE>	homogenes (verkürztes) [lineares] Differentialgleichungssystem *n*, homogenes lineares System *n* von gewöhnlichen Differentialgleichungen [in Normalform], verkürztes lineares System von gewöhnlichen Differentialgleichungen, homogenes (verkürztes) System	système *m* différentiel homogène, système d'équations différentielles linéaires homogènes, système d'équations linéaires homogènes, système homogène (sans second membre)	однородная система дифференциальных уравнений, однородная система

H 445	**homogeneous system of linear equations,** homogeneous system <of equations> <AL>	homogenes lineares Gleichungssystem *n*, homogenes Gleichungssystem (System *n*)	système *m* homogène d'équations linéaires, système homogène [d'équations]	однородная система линейных уравнений, однородная система [уравнений]
	homogeneous tangential co-ordinates of the line <AY>	*s.* L 856		
	homogeneous tangential co-ordinates of the plane <AY>	*s.* P 643		
H 446	**homogeneous variational problem,** homogeneous problem, geometrical problem <VA>	Variationsproblem *n* in Parametergestalt, homogenes Variationsproblem (Problem *n*), Kurvenproblem *n*, geometrisches Problem	problème *m* [variationnel] homogène, problème géométrique	однородная [вариационная] задача, геометрическая задача
H 447	**homogenized polynomial** <AG, AL>	homogen gemachtes Polynom *n*	polynôme *m* homogénisé	гомогенизованный многочлен
H 448	**homogenizing variable** <in a polynomial> <AG, AL>	homogenisierende Variable *f*	variable *f* d'homogénéité	переменная однородности
H 449	**homograde statistics** <ST>	homograde Statistik *f*	statistique *f* homograde	
H 450	**homographic chart,** homographic scale, projective chart (scale) <NO>	projektive Skala (Leiter) *f*	échelle *f* homographique (projective)	проективная (дробно-линейная) шкала
H 451	**homographic correspondence** <GE>	gebrochen[-]lineare Korrespondenz *f*	correspondance *f* homographique	гомографическое (дробно-линейное) соответствие
H 452	**homographic division,** related division, projective division <Baker> <PJ>	homographische Teilung *f* <Teilung mit gleichem Doppelverhältnis>	division *f* homographique	гомографическое деление
H 453	**homographic function,** linear fractional function <AL, AN, FT>	gebrochen[-]lineare Funktion *f*, lineare Funktion	fonction *f* homographique (linéaire)	дробно-линейная функция
	homographic invariant <AY>	*s.* I 871		
	homographic mapping <FT>	*s.* B 348		
	homographic scale <NO>	*s.* H 450		
	homography <AY, PJ>	*s.* C 1147		
	homography <FT>	*s.* B 348		
H 454	**homogroup** <AL>	Homogruppe *f*	homogroupe *m*, demi-groupe *m* avec éléments zéroïdes	гомогруппа
H 455	**homological algebra** <as a field of mathematics> <HA>	homologische Algebra *f*, Homologiealgebra *f*	algèbre *f* homologique	гомологическая алгебра, алгебра гомологий
	homological codimension <AL>	*s.* D 262		
H 456/7	**homological dimension,** projective (homology) dimension <AL, AT, CA>	homologische Dimension *f*	dimension *f* homologique	гомологическая размерность
H 458	**homological invariant** <AT>	Homologieinvariante *f*	invariant *m* homologique	гомологический инвариант
H 459	**homologically dependent chain** <AT>	homolog abhängige Kette *f*	chaîne *f* homologiquement liée	гомологически зависимая цепь
H 460	**homologically independent chain** <AT>	homolog unabhängige Kette *f*	chaîne *f* homologiquement indépendante	гомологически независимая цепь
	homologically locally connected space <AT>	*s.* S 1312		
H 461	**homological resolution** <HA>	homologische Auflösung *f*	résolution *f* homologique	гомологическая резольвента
	ε-homologous <AT>	*s.* E 310		
H 462	**homologous mappings** <of complexes> <AT>	homologe Abbildungen *fpl*, Abbildungen vom gleichen Homologietypus	applications *fpl* homologiques	гомологичные отображения
H 463	**homologous minor** <MD>	homologe Unterdeterminante *f*	sous-déterminant *m* homologue <de>	минор, принадлежащий тем же индексам строк и столбцов
H 464	**homologous points** <with respect to an algebraic correspondence> <AG>	homologe Punkte *mpl* <bezüglich einer algebraischen Korrespondenz>	points *mpl* homologues <pour une correspondance>	гомологичные точки <относительно алгебраического соответствия>
H 465	**homologous simplicial map** <AT>	homologe simpliziale Abbildung *f*, simpliziale Abbildung von demselben Homologietypus, simpliziale Abbildung vom selben Homologietypus	application *f* simpliciale homologique	гомологическое симплициальное отображение
H 466	**homologous to zero** <AT>	nullhomolog	homologique à zéro	гомологичный нулю
H 467	**homologous to zero with division allowed** <AT>	divisions-nullhomolog, schwach berandend (homolog Null)	faiblement homologique à zéro	слабо гомологичный нулю
H 468	**homologous with division allowed** <AT>	divisionshomolog, schwach homolog	faiblement homologique	слабо гомологичный
H 469	**homology,** Δ-homology, lower homology <AT>	Homologie *f*	homologie *f*	гомологии, Δ-гомологии, нижние гомологии
H 470	**homology** <of mappings> <as a property> <AT>	Homologie *f*	homologie *f*	гомологичность
H 471	**homology,** homology object <*n*-th> <CA>	Homologieobjekt *n* <*n*-tes>	objet *m* homologique <*n*-e>	объект гомологий <*n*-й>
	homology <PJ>	*s.* P 522		
	∇-homology <AT>	*s.* C 1085		

	Δ-homology <AT>	*s.* H 469		
H 472	**homology algebra** <AT>	Homologiealgebra *f*	algèbre *f* d'homologie	алгебра гомологий
	homology cell <AT>	*s.* C 316		
H 473	**homology class** <AT>	Homologieklasse *f*	classe *f* d'homologie	класс гомологий
H 474	**homology cross product** <HA>	homologisches Kreuzprodukt *n*		гомологическое прямое произведение
	homology dimension <AL, AT, CA>	*s.* H 456/7		
H 475	**homology-equivalence** <AT>	Homologieäquivalenz *f*	équivalence *f* d'homologie	гомологичная эквивалентность
H 476	**homology-equivalent complex** <AT>	homologie-äquivalenter Komplex *m*	complexe *m* homologiquement équivalent	гомологично эквивалентный комплекс
H 477	**homology functor** <AT, HA>	Homologiefunktor *m*	foncteur *m* homologique	гомологический функтор, функтор гомологии
H 478	**homology group** <*e.g.:* mod. *m*> <AT, HA>	Homologiegruppe *f* <*z. B.:* mod *m*>	groupe *m* d'homologie <*par exemple:* modulo *m*>	группа гомологии, группа гомологий <*например:* по модулю *m*> <AT, HA>; Δ-группа, [нижняя] группа Бетти <AT>
H 479	**homology group mod. 2** <AT>	Homologiegruppe *f* mod 2, Zusammenhangsgruppe *f*	groupe *m* d'homologie modulo 2	группа гомологий по модулю 2
H 480	**homology group with coefficients [in] *G*** <AT>	Homologiegruppe *f* mit Koeffizienten in *G*, Homologiegruppe bezüglich des Koeffizientenbereichs *G*	groupe *m* d'homologie à coefficients (valeurs) dans *G*	группа гомологий с коэффициентами в *G*, группа гомологий над *G*
H 481	**homology manifold** <AT>	Homologiemannigfaltigkeit *f*, H-Mannigfaltigkeit *f*	variété *f* homologique	гомологическое многообразие, h-многообразие, обобщенное многообразие
	homology Mayer-Vietoris sequence <AT>	*s.* M 283		
H 482	**homology module** <HA>	Homologiemodul *m*	module *m* d'homologie	модуль гомологий
	homology modulo the zero-divisors <AT>	*s.* H 492		
	homology object <CA>	*s.* H 471		
H 483	**homology operation** <AT>	Homologieoperation *f*	opération *f* d'homologie	гомологическая операция
H 484	**homology sequence** <AT, HA>	Homologiesequenz *f*	suite *f* d'homologie	последовательность гомологий, гомологическая последовательность
	homology sequence of the triple <HA>	*s.* E 654		
	homology sheaf <AT>	*s.* D 293		
H 485	**homology simplex** <AT>	Homologiesimplex *n*, H-Simplex *n*, einfacher Komplex *m* <Reidemeister>	simplexe *m* homologique	гомологический симплекс
H 486	**homology spectral sequence** <AT>	Spektralsequenz *f* der Homologie	suite *f* spectrale d'homologie	гомологическая спектральная последовательность, спектральная последовательность гомологий
H 487	**homology sphere** <AT>	Homologiesphäre *f*, H-Sphäre *f*, einfacher Komplex *m* <Reidemeister> <HS^n>	sphère *f* homologique	гомологическая сфера
	homology theory with coefficients Z <AT>	*s.* I 630		
H 488	**homology theory with compact carriers (supports)** <AT>	Homologietheorie *f* mit kompakten Trägern	théorie *f* homologique à supports compacts	теория гомологий с компактными носителями
H 489	**homology transgression** <AT>	homologische Transgression *f*	transgression *f* homologique	гомологическая трансгрессия
H 490	**homology type** <AT>	Homologietyp *m*, Homologietypus *m*	type *m* d'homologie	гомологический тип
H 491	**homology with coefficients *G*** <HA>	Homologie *f* bezüglich eines Koeffizientenbereichs *G*	homologie *f* à coefficients dans *G*	гомологии с коэффициентами в *G*
H 492	**homology with division allowed,** homology modulo the zero-divisors <AT>	Divisionshomologie *f*, Homologie *f* mit Division, schwache Homologie	homologie *f* faible	слабые гомологии
	homomorph <GR>	*s.* H 495		
H 493	**homomorphic group,** homomorphous group, // multiply isomorphic group <GR>	homomorphe (mehrstufig isomorphe, meriedrisch isomorphe, // meroedrisch isomorphe, isomorphe) Gruppe *f*	groupe *m* homomorphe (mériédriquement isomorphe, // isomorphe de rang multiple)	гомоморфная группа
H 494	**homomorphic image** <of a subgroup> <GR>	Teil *m* <einer Gruppe>, homomorphes Bild *n* <einer Untergruppe>	image *f* homomorphe	гомоморфный образ
H 495	**homomorphic image (map),** homomorph <of a group> <GR>	homomorphes Bild *n*, Bild bei einem Homomorphismus	image *f* homomorphe; homomorphe *m*, isomorphe *m* mériédrique	гомоморфный образ
	homomorphic mapping <AL>	*s.* 1. H 498; 2. R 1318		
	homomorphic mapping <GR>	*s.* H 500		
	homomorphic relation <CA>	*s.* C 2501		
H 496	**homomorphism** <of a Boolean algebra> <AL>	Homomorphismus *m*	homomorphisme *m* booléen, homomorphisme	гомоморфизм
H 497	**homomorphism** <of groups> <as a property> <AL>	Homomorphie *f*	homomorphisme *m*; // isomorphisme *m*	гомоморфизм

No.	English	German	French	Russian
H 498	**homomorphism,** homomorphic mapping <AL>	Homomorphismus *m*, homomorphe Abbildung *f*	homomorphisme *m*, homomorphie *f*, morphisme *m*, application *f* respectant (compatible avec) la loi de composition, représentation *f* partout définie	гомоморфизм, гомоморфное отображение
H 499	**homomorphism** <of graphs> <GP>	Homomorphismus *m*	homomorphisme *m*	гомоморфизм
H 500	**homomorphism,** homomorphism of groups, group[-] homomorphism, homomorphic mapping, representation, // general isomorphism, multiple isomorphism, meroedric isomorphism <GR>	Homomorphismus *m*, Gruppenhomomorphismus *m*, gruppentheoretischer Homomorphismus, homomorphe Abbildung *f*, // meroedrisch isomorphe Abbildung, mehrstufig isomorphe Abbildung, mehrstufiger Isomorphismus *m*, meroedrischer Isomorphismus, meriedrischer Isomorphismus, Isomorphismus	homomorphisme *m*, homomorphisme de groupes, homomorphie *f*, // isomorphisme *m* mériédrique, isomorphisme méroédrique	гомоморфизм, гомоморфизм группы, групповой гомоморфизм, гомоморфное отображение, многоступенчатый изоморфизм, мериедрический изоморфизм
H 501	**homomorphism** <of degree *d*> <of a graded group> <HA>	Homomorphismus *m* <vom Grade *d*>	homomorphisme *m* <de degré *d*>	гомоморфизм <степени *d*>
H 502	***-homomorphism** <FA>	*-Homomorphismus *m*	*-homomorphisme *m*	*-гомоморфизм
H 503	**1—1 homomorphism,** embedding, injection, monomorphism <of algebras> <UA>	eineindeutiger Homomorphismus *m*, Einbettung *f*, Injektion *f*, Monomorphismus *m*, monomorpher Homomorphismus *m*	morphisme *m* injectif, monomorphisme *m*	взаимно однозначный гомоморфизм, мономорфизм, моногомоморфизм
	homomorphism <AL>	*s.* 1. L 661; 2. L 662; 3. L 825; 4. M 776; 5. R 971/2; 6. R 1318		
	homomorphism <FA>	*s.* L 828		
	homomorphism <GP>	*s.* C 2036		
	homomorphism <LA>	*s.* L 124		
H 504	**homomorphism condition** <AL>	Homomorphiebedingung *f*	condition *f* d'homomorphisme	условие гомоморфизма
	homomorphism of groups <GR>	*s.* H 500		
	homomorphism of rings <AL>	*s.* R 1318		
H 505	**homomorphism theorem,** law of homomorphism, main homomorphism theorem, first isomorphism theorem, factor theorem <GR>	Homomorphiesatz *m*, spezieller Homomorphiesatz, erster (1.) Isomorphiesatz *m*, // Epimorphiesatz *m*	théorème *m* d'homomorphisme, théorème d'homomorphie	теорема о гомоморфизме (гомоморфизмах), теорема об эпиморфизмах
H 506	**homomorphism theorem** <for sets> <SE>	Homomorphiesatz *m* <für Mengen>	théorème *m* d'homomorphisme <pour des ensembles>	теорема о гомоморфизмах <множеств>
	homomorphism upon <AL>	*s.* O 127		
	homomorphous group <GR>	*s.* H 493		
H 507	**homoscedasticity,** homogeneity of variances <ST>	Homoskedastizität *f*, Homogenität *f* der Varianzen	homoscédasticité *f*, homogénéité *f* des variances	гомоскедастичность, однородность дисперсий
H 508	**homoscedastic random variable** <ST>	homoskedastisch verbundene Zufallsvariable *f*	variable *f* aléatoire homoscédastique	гомоскедастично связанная случайная величина
	homothetic <AL>	*s.* H 510		
H 509	**homothetic body** <GE>	homothetischer Körper *m*	corps *m* homothétique	гомотетичное тело
	homothetic centre <GE>	*s.* C 429		
	homothetic ellipse <ST>	*s.* E 157		
	homothetic ellipsoid <ST>	*s.* E 162		
	homothetic figure <GE>	*s.* F 218		
	homothetic ratio <GE>	*s.* R 192		
	homothetic transformation <DS>	*s.* H 511		
H 510	**homothety,** inner translation, multiplication, homothetic <corresponding to α, by α> <AL>	Homothetie *f*, Multiplikation *f* <mit α>	homothétie *f*, homothétie interne <de rapport α>	гомотетия, внутренний сдвиг <соответствующий элементу α>
H 511	**homothety,** homothetic transformation, perspective transformation of similitude <DS>	perspektive Ähnlichkeit *f*, Ähnlichkeit bei perspektiver Lage, Homothetie *f*, perspektive Ähnlichkeitstransformation *f*, zentrische Streckung *f*, homothetische Abbildung *f*	homothétie *f*, transformation *f* homothétique	гомотетия, центрально-подобное преобразование, преобразование гомотетии, гомотетическое преобразование
H 512	**homotopically equivalent space,** homotopy-equivalent space, space of the same homotopy type <TO>	homotopieäquivalenter Raum *m*, Raum von gleichem Homotopietyp, homotop äquivalenter Raum	espace *m* homotopiquement équivalent, espace homotopie-équivalent	гомотопно эквивалентное пространство
H 513	**homotopically trivial map,** mapping homotopic to a constant, inessential map[ping], null-homotopic map, null homotopic map[ping] <TO>	unwesentliche (nullhomotope, homotopisch triviale) Abbildung *f*, Abbildung homotop Null (0)	application *f* inessentielle (homotope à zéro (0), homotopiquement triviale)	несущественное отображение; отображение, гомотопное нулю; гомотопное нулю (постоянному) отображение, гомотопно тривиальное отображение

No.	English	German	French	Russian
H 514	**homotopic chain homomorphism** <HA>	homotope Kettentransformation *f*	homomorphisme *m* homotope	гомотопный гомоморфизм
	homotopic deformation <TO>	*s.* H 520		
H 515	**homotopic invariant** <TO>	Homotopieinvariante *f*	invariant *m* homotopique	гомотопический инвариант
H 516	**homotopic loop** <TO>	homotoper geschlossener Weg *m*	lacet *m* homotope (équivalent)	гомотопная петля
H 517	**homotopic map[ping]** <TO>	homotope Abbildung *f*	application *f* homotope	гомотопное отображение
H 518	**homotopic path** <TO>	homotoper Weg *m*	arc *m* paramétré homotope	гомотопный путь
H 519	**homotopism** <of a quasigroup> <AL>	Homotopismus *m*	homotopisme *m*	гомотопизм
H 520	**homotopy,** homotopic deformation <TO>	[stetige] Homotopie *f*, [homotope] Deformation *f*, stetige Abänderung *f*	homotopie *f*, déformation *f* continue (homotope)	гомотопия, гомотопная деформация
	ε-homotopy <TO>	*s.* E 311		
H 521	**homotopy[-]associative** <CA, TO>	homotopieassoziativ, h-assoziativ	homotopie-associatif	гомотопически ассоциативный
H 522	**homotopy associativity** <AL, CA, TO>	Homotopieassoziativität *f*, H-Assoziativität *f*	associativité *f* homotopique	гомотопическая ассоциативность
	homotopy category <CA, TO>	*s.* 1. H 524; 2. H 525		
H 523	**homotopy category of maps** <CA, TO>	Kategorie *f* der stetigen Abbildungen modulo Homotopie	catégorie *f* homotopique des applications continues	гомотопическая категория отображений
H 524	**homotopy category of pairs,** homotopy category <objects are topological pairs, morphisms are homotopy classes> <CA, TO>	Homotopiekategorie *f* der topologischen Paare, Kategorie *f* der topologischen Paare modulo Homotopie	catégorie *f* homotopique des couples topologiques	категория гомотопических типов пар
H 525	**homotopy category of topological spaces,** homotopy category, category of topological spaces modulo homotopy <CA, TO>	Kategorie *f* der topologischen Räume modulo Homotopie, Homotopiekategorie *f*	catégorie *f* homotopique d'espaces topologiques, catégorie homotopique	гомотопическая категория, категория гомотопических типов [топологических пространств], категория [всех] топологических пространств по модулю гомотопии, категория топологических пространств с классами гомотопных отображений в качестве морфизмов
H 526	**homotopy chain** <AT>	Homotopiekette *f*	chaîne *f* d'homotopie <de Reidemeister>	гомотопическая цепь
H 527	**homotopy class,** class of homotopic mappings <TO>	Homotopieklasse *f*, Abbildungsklasse *f*	classe *f* d'homotopie, classe d'applications	гомотопический класс, класс гомотопных между собою отображений, класс отображений
H 528	**homotopy classification** <TO>	Homotopieklassifikation *f*	classification *f* suivant l'homotopie	гомотопическая классификация
	homotopy class of paths <TO>	*s.* P 302		
H 529	**homotopy commutative diagram** <AT, HA>	homotopiekommutatives (h-kommutatives) Diagramm *n*	diagramme *m* homotopie-commutatif	гомотопически коммутативная диаграмма
	homotopy covering property <TO>	*s.* H 542		
H 530	**homotopy cylinder** <TO>	Homotopiezylinder *m*	cylindre *m* d'homotopie	цилиндр гомотопии
H 531	**homotopy equivalence** <TO>	Homotopieäquivalenz *f*, h-Äquivalenz *f*	homotopie-équivalence *f*, équivalence *f* d'homotopie, équivalence homotopique	гомотопическая (гомотопная) эквивалентность
	homotopy-equivalent space <TO>	*s.* H 512		
H 532	**homotopy excision theorem** <AT>	Exzisionstheorem *n* für die Homotopie	théorème *m* d'excision pour l'homotopie	теорема о гомотопическом вырезании
H 533	**homotopy extension** <TO>	Homotopieerweiterung *f*	extension *f* d'homotopie	продолжение гомотопии
H 534	**homotopy extension property** <with respect to *Y*> <TO>	Homotopieerweiterungseigenschaft *f*, Fortsetzungseigenschaft *f* der Homotopie	propriété *f* de l'extension d'homotopie	свойство продолжения гомотопии <относительно *Y*>; аксиома о распространении гомотопии
H 535	**homotopy functor** <AT>	Homotopiefunktor *m*	foncteur *m* d'homotopie	гомотопический функтор
H 536	**homotopy group,** homotopy group of Hurewicz <with base point x_0> <TO>	Homotopiegruppe *f* <mit dem Basispunkt x_0>	groupe *m* d'homotopie <relativement au point-base x_0>	группа гомотопий, гомотопическая группа <с отмеченной точкой x_0>
H 537	**homotopy group functor** <AT>	Homotopiegruppenfunktor *m*	foncteur *m* « groupe d'homotopie »	функтор гомотопических групп
	homotopy group of Hurewicz <TO>	*s.* H 536		
H 538	**homotopy inverse** <AT>	homotopieinvers, h-invers	homotopie-inverse	гомотопически обратный
H 539	**homotopy inverse** <of a map> <CA, TO>	Homotopieinverses *n*, homotop inverse Abbildung *f*	homotopie-inverse *m*	гомотопически обратное отображение
H 540	**homotopy length** <CA>	Homotopielänge *f*	longueur *f* homotopique	гомотопическая длина
H 541	**homotopy lifting** <TO>	Homotopiehochhebung *f*	relèvement *m* d'une homotopie	поднятие гомотопии
H 542	**homotopy lifting property,** homotopy	Hebungseigenschaft *f* der Homotopie, Homotopie-	propriété *f* du relèvement d'homotopie	свойство накрывающей гомотопии <относитель-

No.	English	German	French	Russian
	covering property <with respect to a space> <TO>	Hochhebungseigenschaft *f*, Deckhomotopieeigenschaft *f*, Homotopieliftungseigenschaft *f*		но пространства>
H 543	**homotopy operator** <HA>	Homotopieoperator *m*	opérateur *m* d'homotopie	оператор гомотопии
H 544	**homotopy pair** <AT>	Homotopiepaar *n*	couple *m* homotopique	пара гомотопий
H 545	**homotopy parameter** <TO>	Parameter *m* der Deformation, Homotopieparameter *m*	paramètre *m* d'homotopie	параметр гомотопии
H 546	**homotopy sequence** <AT>	Homotopiesequenz *f*	suite *f* d'homotopie	гомотопическая последовательность
H 547	**homotopy set** <AT>	Homotopiemenge *f*	ensemble *m* d'homotopie	гомотопическое множество
H 548	**homotopy sphere** <AT>	Homotopiesphäre *f*	sphère *f* homotopique (d'homotopie)	гомотопическая сфера
H 549	**homotopy theorem** <for mappings> <TO>	Homotopiesatz *m*	théorème *m* d'homotopie	теорема гомотопии
H 550	**homotopy theory** <TO>	Homotopietheorie *f*	théorie *f* d'homotopie	теория гомотопий (гомотопии), гомотопическая теория
H 551	**homotopy type** <TO>	Homotopietyp *m*, Homotopietypus *m*	type *m* d'homotopie	гомотопический тип
H 552	**homotopy with base point,** based homotopy <TO>	Homotopie *f* mit Grundpunkt, punktierte Homotopie	homotopie *f* avec point-base	гомотопия с отмеченной точкой
	honest significant difference <ST>	*s.* H 312		
H 553	**honest subgroup** <GR>	ehrliche Untergruppe *f*		честная подгруппа
	honeycomb pattern <FD, NU>	*s.* M 413		
H 554	**Hopf algebra** <over *R*> <AL>	Hopfsche Algebra *f* <über *R*>	algèbre *f* de Hopf, bigèbre *f* <sur *R*>	алгебра Хопфа, кольцевая группа, бигебра <над кольцом *R*>
H 555	**Hopf['s] bundle;** Hopf['s] fibring (fibration) <AT>	Hopfsches Bündel *n*	fibré *m* de Hopf	расслоение Хопфа
	Hopf['s] ergodic theorem <SP>	*s.* E 461		
H 556	**Hopf extension theorem** <AT>	Hopfscher Erweiterungssatz *m*	théorème *m* d'extension de Hopf	теорема Хопфа о продолжении
	Hopf['s] fibration (fibring) <AT>	*s.* H 555		
H 557	**hopfian group** <GR>	Hopfsche Gruppe *f*	groupe *m* de Hopf	хопфова группа
	Hopfian property <AL>	*s.* H 558		
H 558	**hopficity,** Hopfian property <AL>	Eigenschaft *f*, Hopfsche Gruppe zu sein	propriété *f* d'être un groupe de Hopf, propriété hopfienne	хопфовость
H 559	**Hopf['s] manifold** <AT>	Hopfsche Mannigfaltigkeit *f*, H-Mannigfaltigkeit *f*	variété *f* de Hopf	многообразие Хопфа
H 560	**Hopf['s] map** <of fibre bundles> <AT>	Hopfsche Abbildung *f*	application *f* de Hopf	отображение Хопфа
H 561	**Hopf['s] object** <CA>	H-Objekt *n*, Hopf-Objekt *n*	objet *m* de Hopf	объект Хопфа
	Hopf['s] problem <GR>	*s.* P 1564		
H 562	**Hopf['s] theorem** <AT>	Satz *m* von Hopf, Hopfscher Satz	théorème *m* de Hopf	теорема Хопфа
H 563	**Hopf['s] theorem** <on H spaces> <AT>	Hopfsches Theorem *n*, Theorem von Hopf	théorème *m* de Hopf	теорема Хопфа <об H-пространствах>
H 564	**Hopf['s] trace formula** <AT>	Hopfsche Spurformel *f*, Spurformel von H. Hopf, verallgemeinerte Euler-Poincarésche Formel *f*	formule *f* de Hopf	формула Хопфа
	horizon <DS>	*s.* L 869		
	horizontal <DS>	*s.* H 172		
H 565	**horizontal composition** <CA>	horizontale Komposition *f*	composition *f* horizontale	горизонтальная композиция
	horizontal line <DS>	*s.* H 172		
	horizontal line <GN>	*s.* F 571		
H 566	**horizontal plane [of projection],** horizontal projection plane, first plane [of projection] <in two-plane method> <DS>	Horizontalebene *f*, Grundrißebene *f*, erste Projektionsebene *f*, erste Tafel *f*, Grundrißtafel *f*	plan *m* horizontal [de projection], premier plan [de projection]	плоскость горизонтальной проекции
	horizontal projection <DS>	*s.* P 628		
	horizontal projection plane <DS>	*s.* H 566		
	horizontal row <MD>	*s.* R 1425		
	horizontal rule <GN>	*s.* F 571		
	horizontal trace [line] <DS>	*s.* F 360		
H 567	**horn** <AL, CA>	Horn *n*		колпачок
H 568	**Horn['s] class** <LO, UA>	Hornsche Klasse *f*	classe *f* de Horn	хорновский класс
H 569	**horned sphere,** Alexander['s] horned sphere <TO>	gehörnte Sphäre *f*	sphère *f* à cornes, sphère cornue	рогатая сфера
	horned syllogism <LO>	*s.* D 496		
H 570	**Horner['s] method** <for solving numerical equations of factorials> <AL, NU>	Hornersche (Horners) Methode *f*	méthode *f* de Horner	метод Горнера
H 571	**Horner['s] method, Horner['s] process, Horner['s] scheme** <AN, NU>	Hornersches Schema *n*, Horner-Schema *n*, Horners Schema	méthode *f* (schéma *m*) de Horner	способ (схема, правило) Горнера
H 572	**Horn['s] formula** <LO>	Hornscher Ausdruck *m*	formule *f* de Horn	хорновская формула

No.	English	German	French	Russian
H 573	**Horn['s] hypergeometric function** <FU>	Hornsche hypergeometrische Funktion *f*	fonction *f* hypergéométrique de Horn	гипергеометрическая функция Хорна
H 574	**Horn['s] sentence** <LO>	Hornsche Aussage *f*	énoncé *m* de Horn	хорновское предложение
H 575	**horocycle,** limit circle <FT>	Grenzkreis *m*, Horozykel *m*	horicycle *m*, horocycle *m*, cercle *m* limite	орицикл, предельный круг
H 576	**horocycle,** limit circle, oricycle <in hyperbolic geometry> <GE>	Grenzkreis *m*, Orizykel *m*, Horozykel *m*	horicycle *m*, horocycle *m*	орицикл, предельная окружность, предельная линия, предельная кривая
	horocyclic group <FT>	*s.* F 693		
H 577	**horocyclic group of the first kind** <FT>	Grenzkreisgruppe (horozyklische Gruppe) *f* erster (1.) Art	groupe *m* horocyclique de première espèce	орициклическая группа первого рода
	horocyclic group of the second kind <FT>	*s.* F 696		
H 578	**horopter curve** <PJ>	Horopterkurve *f*	horoptère *m*	гороптер
H 579	**horosphere,** limit sphere, orisphere <in hyperbolic geometry> <GE>	Grenzfläche *f*, Orisphäre *f*, Horosphäre *f*, Grenzkugel *f*	horisphère *f*	орисфера, предельная сфера, предельная поверхность
	horse fetter <AG>	*s.* H 371		
	Hospital['s] rule <DI>	*s.* D 208		
H 580	**Hostinsky['s] sphere** <DG>	Hostinskysche Kugel *f*	sphère *f* d'Hostinsky	сфера Хостинского
H 581	**Hotelling['s] [generalized Student] distribution, Hotelling['s] T^2 (*T*),** Hotelling['s] T^2 (*T*) distribution <ST>	Hotelling-Verteilung *f*, Hotellings T^2-Verteilung *f* (*T*-Verteilung *f*, T^2), T^2-Verteilung, Hotellings verallgemeinerte Studentsche Verteilung *f*	distribution *f* T^2 (*T*) d'Hotelling, distribution (répartition *f*) d'Hotelling, distribution de T^2	распределение Хотеллинга, T^2-распределение (*T*-распределение) Хотеллинга, T^2-распределение, *T*-распределение, обобщенное распределение Стьюдента
H 582	**Hotelling['s] T^2 (*T*),** T^2-statistic, *T*-statistic, T^2, *T* <ST>	[Hotellings[che]] T^2-Stichprobenfunktion *f* (*T*-Stichprobenfunktion *f*, T^2-Maßzahl *f*, *T*-Maßzahl) *f*, Hotellings T^2 (*T*) *n*, T^2, *T*	statistique *f* T^2 [d'Hotelling], statistique *T* [d'Hotelling], T^2 *m* [d'Hotelling], *T m* [d'Hotelling]	статистика T^2 [Хотеллинга], статистика *T* [Хотеллинга], T^2 [Хотеллинга], *T* [Хотеллинга]
	Hotelling['s] *T* (T^2) distribution <ST>	*s.* H 581		
H 583	**Hotelling['s] test; Hotelling['s] *T*-test,** *T*-test <ST>	Hotelling-Test *m*, Hotellingscher Test *m*; Hotellingscher *T*-Test *m*, *T*-Test	test *m* d'Hotelling; test *T* d'Hotelling, test *T*	критерий Хотеллинга; *T*-критерий [Хотеллинга], критерий *T* [Хотеллинга]
H 584	**Howard['s] algorithm** <ST>	Howard-Algorithmus *m*	algorithme *m* d'Howard	алгоритм Хоуарда
	h plane, *h*-plane <GE>	*s.* H 638		
H 585	**H_p-lim, (H,p) limit, H_p-limit,** limit by Hölder's method of p-th order <LI>	H_p-Limes *m*, (H,p)-Limes *m*, Limes *m* nach dem H_p-Verfahren, H_p-lim	H_p-limite *f*, limite *f* par la méthode de Hölder d'ordre *p*, H_p-lim	[обобщенный] предел по методу Гельдера *p*-го порядка, (H,p)-предел, H_p-предел, H_p-lim
H 586	**(H,p) limitable sequence, H_p-limitable sequence,** sequence limitable by Hölder's method of p-th order <LI>	H_p-limitierbare ((H,p)-limitierbare, nach dem H_p-Verfahren limitierbare) Folge *f*	suite *f* limitable par la méthode de Hölder d'ordre *p*, suite (H,p)-limitable	последовательность, лимитируемая методом Гельдера *p*-го порядка; (H,p)-лимитируемая последовательность
H 587	**(H,p) method, H_p-method,** Hölder['s] method of p-th order, Hölder['s] summation method of p-th order <for divergent series> <LI>	H_p-Verfahren *n*, (H,p)-Verfahren *n*, Höldersches Summierungsverfahren *n* der Ordnung *p*	méthode *f* de sommation de Hölder d'ordre *p*, méthode de Hölder d'ordre *p*, méthode H_p, méthode (H,p)	метод Гельдера *p*-го порядка, метод суммирования [расходящихся рядов] Гельдера *p*-го порядка, (H,p)-метод
H 588	**(H,p) method, H_p-method,** Hölder['s] method of p-th order, Hölder['s] limitation method of p-th order <for divergent sequences> <LI>	H_p-Verfahren *n*, (H,p)-Verfahren *n*, Höldersches Limitierungsverfahren *n* der Ordnung *p*	méthode *f* [de limitation] de Hölder d'ordre *p*	метод [образования обобщенного предела] Гельдера *p*-го порядка, (H,p)-метод
	(H,p_n) lim[it] <LI>	*s.* H 377		
	(H,p_n) limitable sequence <LI>	*s.* H 378		
	(H,p_n) method <LI>	*s.* 1. H 380; 2. H 381		
	(H,p_n)-sum <LI>	*s.* H 592		
	(H,p_n) summable series <LI>	*s.* H 594		
	h point, *h*-point <GE>	*s.* H 641		
	(H,p) sum, H_p-sum <LI>	*s.* S 2264		
H 589	**(H,p) summable series, H_p-summable series,** series summable by Hölder's method of p-th order <LI>	H_p-summierbare ((H,p)-summierbare, nach dem H_p-Verfahren summierbare) Reihe *f*	série *f* sommable par la méthode de Hölder d'ordre *p*, série H_p-sommable	ряд, суммируемый методом Гельдера *p*-го порядка; (H,p)-суммируемый ряд
	h-rotation <GE>	*s.* H 644		
	HSD, hsd <ST>	*s.* H 312		
	HSD (hsd) test [of Tukey] <ST>	*s.* T 1059		
H 590	**H-space** <AT>	Hopfscher Raum *m*, H-Raum *m*	espace *m* de Hopf, H-espace *m*	H-пространство
H 591	**H'-space** <TO>	H'-Raum *m*	espace *m* muni d'une H'-structure	H'-пространство
H 592	**$\mathfrak{H}$-sum,** (H,p_n)-sum, sum by Hausdorff's method <LI>	(H,p_n)-Summe *f*, Summe *f* nach dem (H,p_n)-Verfahren	somme *f* par la méthode de Hausdorff, (H,p_n)-somme *f*	[обобщенная] сумма по методу Хаусдорфа, [обобщенная] сумма по Хаусдорфу
	***H*-sum** <LI>	*s.* S 2263		

No.	English	German	French	Russian
H 593	***H*-summable series,** series summable by Hölder's method <LI>	*H*-summierbare (nach dem *H*-Verfahren summierbare) Reihe *f*	série *f* sommable par la méthode de Hölder, série *H*-sommable	суммируемый методом Гельдера ряд, *H*-суммируемый ряд
H 594	**ℌ-summable series,** (H,p_n) summable series, series summable by Hausdorff's method <LI>	(H,p_n)-summierbare (nach dem (H,p_n)-Verfahren summierbare) Reihe *f*	série *f* sommable par la méthode de Hausdorff, série *H*-sommable ((H,p_n)-sommable)	ряд, суммируемый методом Хаусдорфа; (H,p_n)-суммируемый ряд
	***H*-test** <ST>	*s.* K 178		
H 595	**Huard['s] method of centres,** centre method of Huard <PG>	Zentrenmethode *f* von Huard, Huardsche Zentrenmethode	méthode *f* des centres de Huard	метод центров
	hundred <NT>	*s.* U 289		
	hundred[']s place <NT>	*s.* P 620		
H 596	**Hungarian method,** König-Egerváry method <of solving the transportation problem <PG>	Ungarische (ungarische) Methode *f*, Differentialrentenmethode *f*	méthode *f* hongroise (de König-Egerváry)	венгерский метод
H 597	**Hungarian tree** <GP>	ungarischer Baum *m*	arbre *m* hongrois	венгерское дерево
	Hurewicz['] fibre map (space) <AT>	*s.* F 145		
H 598	**Hurewicz['s] homomorphism** <AT>	Hurewicz-Homomorphismus *m*, Hurewiczscher Homomorphismus *m*	homomorphisme *m* de Hurewicz	гомоморфизм Гуревича
H 599	**Hurewicz['s] isomorphism theorem,** isomorphism theorem of Hurewicz <AT>	Hurewiczscher Isomorphiesatz *m*, Satz *m* von Hurewicz	théorème *m* de Hurewicz	теорема Гуревича (Гуревича об изоморфизме)
H 600	**Hurewicz['s] theorem,** theorem of Hurewicz <AT> ⌐<TO>	Abbildungssatz *m* von Hurewicz, Hurewiczscher Abbildungssatz	théorème *m* de Hurewicz	теорема Гуревича
	Hurewicz['s] theorem	*s.* T 296		
	Hurewicz-Tumarkin theorem <TO>	*s.* T 297		
H 601	**Hurwitz['s] criterion** <on the roots of a polynomial> <AL>	Hurwitzsches Kriterium *n*	critère *m* de Hurwitz	критерий Рауса-Гурвица, критерий Гурвица
H 602	**Hurwitz['s] determinant** <AL>	Hurwitzsche Determinante *f*	déterminant *m* de Hurwitz	определитель Гурвица
H 603	**Hurwitz['s] equation** <AL>	Hurwitzsche Gleichung *f*	équation *f* de Hurwitz	уравнение Гурвица
H 604	**Hurwitzian continued fraction** <NT>	Hurwitzscher Kettenbruch *m*	fraction *f* continue de Hurwitz	цепная дробь Гурвица
H 605	**Hurwitz['s] integral** <on a Lie group> <AL>	Hurwitzsches Integral *n*	intégrale *f* de Hurwitz	интеграл Гурвица
H 606	**Hurwitz['s] polynomial** <AL>	Hurwitzsches Polynom *n*	polynôme *m* de Hurwitz	многочлен Гурвица
H 607	**Hurwitz['s] theorem,** theorem of Hurwitz <on a sequence of holomorphic functions> <FT>	Satz *m* von Hurwitz, Hurwitzscher Satz	théorème *m* de Hurwitz	теорема Гурвица
	Husimi['s] tree <GP>	*s.* C 2		
H 608	**Hutton['s] rule** <AL, NU>	Huttons Regel *f*	règle *f* de Hutton	правило Хаттона
H 609	**Huyghens['] [differential] equation** <DE>	Huygenssche Differentialgleichung (Gleichung) *f*	équation *f* [différentielle] d'Huygens	[дифференциальное] уравнение Гюйгенса
H 610	**Huyghens['] principle** <DE>	Huygenssches (Huygens') Prinzip *n*	principe *m* d'Huygens	принцип Гюйгенса
H 611	**hybrid quantity,** Hermitian quantity (tensor density, affinor density) <VT>	Hermitesche Größe (Tensordichte, Affinordichte) *f*, hybride Größe	grandeur *f* hybride (hermitienne), densité *f* tensorielle (affinorielle) hermitienne	эрмитова величина, эрмитова тензорная (аффинорная) плотность, гибридная величина
H 612	**hyperabelian function** <FT>	hyperabelsche Funktion *f*	fonction *f* hyperabélienne	гиперабелева функция
H 613	**hyperabelian group,** SI*-group <GR>	hyperabelsche Gruppe *f*	groupe *m* hyperabélien	
H 614	**hyperalgebraic manifold** <AG>	hyperalgebraische Mannigfaltigkeit *f*	variété *f* hyperalgébrique	гипералгебраическое многообразие
H 615	**hyperarchimedean f-ring** <AL>	hyperarchimedischer f-Ring *m*	anneau *m* réticulé hyperarchimédien	гиперабелева группа
H 616	**hyperarithmetical relation** <MM>	hyperarithmetische Relation *f*	relation *f* hyperarithmétique	гиперарифметическое отношение
H 617	**hyperatom** <LA>	Hyperatom *n*	hyperatome *m*	гиператом
H 618	**hyperbola of Apollonius,** Apollonius['s] hyperbola <GE>	Apollonische Hyperbel *f*	hyperbole *f* d'Apollonius	гипербола Аполлония, аполлониева гипербола
	hyperbolic automorphism <FT>	*s.* H 652		
	hyperbolic case <FT>	*s.* L 718		
H 619	**hyperbolic catenary** <GE>	hyperbolische Kettenlinie *f*	chaînette (caténaire) *f* hyperbolique	гиперболическая цепная линия
H 620	**hyperbolic cologarithm** <AN>	Ergänzung *f* des hyperbolischen Logarithmus, hyperbolischer Kologarithmus *m*	cologarithme *m* hyperbolique	гиперболический кологарифм
H 621	**hyperbolic corner** <of a normal polygon> <FT>	hyperbolische Ecke *f*	sommet *m* hyperbolique	гиперболическая вершина
H 622	**hyperbolic cosecant,** cosech, // csch <FU>	Hyperbelkosekans *m*, Cosecans *m* hyperbolicus, hyperbolischer Kosekans *m*, cosech, // Hyperbelcosecans *m*, hyperbolischer Cosecans, csch, ℭ𝔬𝔰𝔢𝔠	cosécante *f* hyperbolique, cosech, // csch	гиперболический косеканс, cosech, // csch

No.	English	German	French	Russian
H 623	**hyperbolic cosine,** cosh, // ch <FU>	Hyperbelkosinus *m*, Cosinus *m* hyperbolicus, hyperbolischer Kosinus *m*, cosh, // Hyperbelcosinus *m*, hyperbolischer Cosinus *m*, ch, Ch, ℭ𝔬𝔰	cosinus *m* hyperbolique, cosh, // ch	гиперболический косинус, ch, // cosh
H 624	**hyperbolic cosine integral,** Cih <FU>	hyperbolischer Integralkosinus (Integralcosinus) *m*, Cosinus *m* integralis hyperbolicus, Cih	cosinus *m* intégral hyperbolique, Cih	гиперболический интегральный косинус, Cih, cih
H 625	**hyperbolic cotangent,** coth, // ctgh, cth <FU>	Hyperbelkotangens *m*, Cotangens *m* hyperbolicus, hyperbolischer Kotangens *m*, coth, // Hyperbelcotangens *m*, hyperbolischer Cotangens *m*, cth, ctgh, Cth, ℭ𝔱𝔤	cotangente *f* hyperbolique, coth, // cth, ctgh	гиперболический котангенс, coth, // cth, ctgh
	hyperbolic differential equation <DE>	*s.* H 627		
H 626	**hyperbolic elliptic integral of the third kind** <FU>	hyperbolisches elliptisches Integral *n* dritter (3.) Gattung	intégrale *f* elliptique hyperbolique de troisième espèce	гиперболический эллиптический интеграл третьего рода
H 627	**hyperbolic equation,** hyperbolic differential equation, hyperbolic partial differential equation, [partial] differential equation of the hyperbolic type <DE>	hyperbolische (total-hyperbolische, normal-hyperbolische, normal hyperbolische) Differentialgleichung (Gleichung, partielle Differentialgleichung) *f*, Differentialgleichung vom hyperbolischen Typ[us]	équation *f* hyperbolique (de type hyperbolique, aux dérivées partielles hyperbolique)	гиперболическое уравнение, [дифференциальное] уравнение [в частных производных] гиперболического типа, гиперболическое дифференциальное уравнение [в частных производных]
H 628	**hyperbolic function** <FU>	Hyperbelfunktion *f*, hyperbolische Funktion *f*	fonction *f* hyperbolique	гиперболическая функция
H 629	**hyperbolic geometry,** Lobachevskian geometry <GE>	hyperbolische (Lobatschewskische, Bolyai-Lobatschewskische) Geometrie *f*, Geometrie von Lobatschewski-Bolyai, nichteuklidische Geometrie, // Lobatschefskysche Geometrie, imaginäre Geometrie	géométrie *f* hyperbolique (non euclidienne de Lobatchefski, de Lobatchefski, de Lobatchevski)	гиперболическая геометрия, геометрия Лобачевского
	hyperbolic homology <PJ>	*s.* N 483		
H 630	**hyperbolic inverse [point]** <AY>	hyperbolisch inverser Punkt *m*	point *m* réciproque hyperbolique, inverse *m* hyperbolique	гиперболически инверсная точка
H 631	**hyperbolic involution** <AY>	hyperbolische Involution *f*, entgegengesetzt projektive Involution	involution *f* hyperbolique	гиперболическая инволюция, гиперболическое инволюционное преобразование
H 632	**hyperbolicity** <DE>	Hyperbolizität *f*	hyperbolicité *f*	гиперболичность
H 633	**hyperbolic line,** *h*-line, h line, Lobachevski['s] line <GE>	hyperbolische Gerade *f*, h-Gerade *f*, Lobatschewskische Gerade	droite *f* hyperbolique (de Lobatchefski, de Lobatchevski, lobatchevskienne)	гиперболическая прямая, прямая Лобачевского, Л-прямая, прямая в гиперболической геометрии
	hyperbolic logarithm <AN>	*s.* N 31		
H 634	**hyperbolic metric determination** <PJ>	hyperbolische [projektive] Maßbestimmung *f*	détermination *f* métrique hyperbolique	гиперболическое [проективное] мероопределение
H 635	**hyperbolic motion** <GE>	hyperbolische Bewegung *f*, Bewegung im hyperbolischen Raum, Bewegung der hyperbolischen Geometrie	mouvement *m* hyperbolique	гиперболическое движение
H 636	**hyperbolic paraboloid** <AY>	hyperbolisches Paraboloid *n*, Sattelfläche *f*	paraboloïde *m* hyperbolique	гиперболический параболоид
	hyperbolic parallel postulate <GE>	*s.* L 912		
	hyperbolic partial differential equation <DE>	*s.* H 627		
	hyperbolic perspectivity <PJ>	*s.* N 483		
H 637	**hyperbolic plane** <AL>	hyperbolische Ebene *f*	plan *m* hyperbolique	гиперболическая плоскость
H 638	**hyperbolic plane,** *h*-plane, h plane, Lobachevski['s] plane <GE>	hyperbolische Ebene *f*, h-Ebene *f*, Lobatschewskische Ebene	plan *m* hyperbolique (de Lobatchefski, Lobatchevski, non euclidien hyperbolique, lobatchevskien)	гиперболическая плоскость, плоскость Лобачевского, Л-плоскость
H 639	**hyperbolic point** <of a plane curve> <DG>	hyperbolischer Punkt *m*	point *m* hyperbolique	гиперболическая точка
H 640	**hyperbolic point,** saddle point, col <of a surface> <DG>	hyperbolischer Punkt (Flächenpunkt) *m*, Sattelpunkt *m*, Paß *m*	point *m* hyperbolique, col *m*, point [de] col	гиперболическая точка <поверхности>, точка перевала, седловая точка, седло, седловина
H 641	**hyperbolic point,** *h*-point, h point, Lobachevski['s] point <in hyperbolic geometry> <GE>	hyperbolischer Punkt *m*, h-Punkt *m*, Lobatschewskischer Punkt	point *m* hyperbolique (de Lobatchefski, de Lobatchevski, lobatchevskien)	гиперболическая точка, точка Лобачевского, Л-точка
H 642	**hyperbolic programming** <PG>	hyperbolische Optimierung (Programmoptimierung, Programmierung) *f*	programmation (optimisation) *f* hyperbolique	гиперболическое программирование

No.	English	German	French	Russian
H 643	**hyperbolic Riemann surface** <FT>	hyperbolische Riemannsche Fläche *f*, Riemannsche Fläche vom hyperbolischen Typ	surface *f* riemannienne hyperbolique	гиперболическая риманова поверхность
H 644	**hyperbolic rotation,** h-rotation <in the hyperbolic plane> <GE>	hyperbolische Drehung *f*	rotation *f* hyperbolique	гиперболическое вращение, вращение в гиперболической плоскости
H 645	**hyperbolic secant,** sech, // sch <FU>	Hyperbelsekans *m*, Secans *m* hyperbolicus, hyperbolischer Sekans *m*, sech, // Hyperbelsecans *m*, hyperbolischer Secans, sch, Sek	sécante *f* hyperbolique, sech, // sch	гиперболический секанс, sech, // sch
H 646	**hyperbolic series** <AN>	Reihe *f* nach hyperbolischen Funktionen	série (ligne) *f* hyperbolique	ряд по гиперболическим функциям
H 647	**hyperbolic simplex method** <PG>	hyperbolisches Simplexverfahren *n*	méthode *f* simpliciale (du simplexe) hyperbolique	гиперболический симплексный метод
H 648	**hyperbolic sine,** sinh, // sh <FU>	Hyperbelsinus *m*, Sinus *m* hyperbolicus, hyperbolischer Sinus, sinh, // sh, Sh, Sin	sinus *m* hyperbolique, sinh, // sh	гиперболический синус, sh, // sinh
H 649	**hyperbolic sine integral,** Sih <FU>	hyperbolischer Integralsinus *m*, Sinus *m* integralis hyperbolicus, Sih	sinus *m* intégral hyperbolique, Sih	гиперболический интегральный синус, Sih, sih
H 650	**hyperbolic space,** Lobachevski['s] space <GE>	hyperbolischer (Lobatschewskischer) Raum *m*, h-Raum *m*	espace *m* lobatchefskien (lobatschewskien, hyperbolique, de Lobatchefski)	гиперболическое пространство, пространство Лобачевского, Л-пространство
H 651	**hyperbolic spiral,** reciprocal spiral <GE>	hyperbolische Spirale *f*	spirale *f* hyperbolique	гиперболическая спираль
H 652	**hyperbolic substitution,** hyperbolic automorphism <FT>	hyperbolische Abbildung (lineare Abbildung, lineare Transformation, Substitution, Kreisverwandtschaft, Möbius-Transformation) *f*	substitution *f* hyperbolique	гиперболическое дробно-линейное преобразование
H 653	**hyperbolic system [of [partial] differential equations]** <DE>	hyperbolisches (total[-] hyperbolisches, normal[-] hyperbolisches) System *n* [von partiellen Differentialgleichungen]	système *m* [d'équations aux dérivées partielles] hyperbolique	гиперболическая система [дифференциальных уравнений в частных производных]
H 654	**hyperbolic tangent,** tanh, // th, tgh <FU>	Hyperbeltangens *m*, Tangens *m* hyperbolicus, hyperbolischer Tangens, tanh, // th, tgh, Th, Tg	tangente *f* hyperbolique, tanh, // th, tgh	гиперболический тангенс, tanh, // th, tgh
	hyperbolic trigonometry <FU, GE>	*s.* T 386		
H 655	**hyperbolic type** <of a Riemann surface *or* a differential equation> <DE, FT>	hyperbolischer Typ[us] *m*	type *m* hyperbolique	гиперболический тип
H 656	**hyperbolism** <of a curve> <GE>	Hyperbolismus *m*	hyperbolisme *m*	гиперболизм
H 657	**hyperbolograph** <GE, IN>	Hyperbelzirkel *m*, Hyperbolograph *m*	hyperbolographe *m*	гиперболограф
H 658	**hyperboloidal position** <AY>	hyperboloidische Lage *f*	position *f* hyperboloïdale	гиперболоидальное [рас]положение
H 659	**hyperboloid of one sheet,** one-sheet hyperboloid <AY>	einschaliges (einmanteliges, einfaches) Hyperboloid *n*, // Miederfläche *f*	hyperboloïde *m* à une nappe	однополостный (однопольный) гиперболоид
H 660	**hyperboloid of revolution** <EG>	Drehhyperboloid *n*, Rotationshyperboloid *n*, Umdrehungshyperboloid *n*, // Konoid *n* <Archimedes>	hyperboloïde *m* de révolution	гиперболоид вращения
H 661	**hyperboloid of two sheets,** two-sheet hyperboloid, parted hyperboloid <AY>	zweischaliges (zweimanteliges, zweifaches) Hyperboloid *n*	hyperboloïde *m* à deux nappes	двуполостный (двупольный) гиперболоид
	hypercentral group <GR>	*s.* Z 1		
H 662	**hypercentre,** last term in the upper central series <of a group> <GR>	Hyperzentrum *n*	hypercentre *m*	гиперцентр
	ω-hypercentre <GR>	*s.* O 68		
H 663	**hyper-characteristic [normal] subgroup** <GR>	hypercharakteristischer Normalteiler *m*, hypercharakteristische Untergruppe *f*	sous-groupe *m* hypercaractéristique	гиперхарактеристическая подгруппа
H 664	**hypercircle,** circular hyperconic <as a hyperconic in the complex Euclidean plane> <DG>	Hyperkreis *m* <E. A. Weiss>	hypercercle *m*, hyperconique *f* circulaire	гиперокружность
H 665	**hypercircumference** <in the E_4> <DG>	Hyperkreis *m* <Fr. Teichert>	hypercirconférence *f* <O. Borůvka>	гиперокружность
H 666	**hypercohomology** <HA>	Hyperkohomologie *f*	hypercohomologie *f*	гиперкогомология
H 667	**hypercolumn** <of a matrix> <MD>	Hyperspalte *f*	hypercolonne *f*	обобщенный столбец
H 668	**hypercomplex function** <AL>	hyperkomplexe Funktion *f*	fonction *f* hypercomplexe	гиперкомплексная функция
H 669	**hypercomplex number** <AL>	hyperkomplexe Zahl *f*, komplexe Größe *f* höherer Ordnung, komplexe Größe	nombre *m* hypercomplexe (complexe d'ordre supérieur, complexe)	гиперкомплексное число

	hypercomplex number system <AL>	*s.* A 474		
	hypercomplex number system over the field of complex numbers <AL>	*s.* A 407		
	hypercomplex number system over the reals <AL>	*s.* S 324		
H 670	**hypercomplex number system without unity quantity** <AL>	hyperkomplexes Zahlensystem *n* ohne Einselement, System *n* ohne Haupteinheit, ausgeartetes System komplexer Größen	système *m* [de nombres complexes] dégénérescent	система гиперкомплексных чисел без единицы
	hypercomplex system <AL>	*s.* A 406		
H 671	**hyperconic** <DG>	Hyperkegelschnitt *m*	hyperconique *f*	гиперконическое сечение, гиперконика
	hypercurve <GE>	*s.* H 702		
H 672	**hypercycle** <AY>	Hyperzykel *m* <Study>	hypercycle *m*	гиперцикл
H 673	**hypercycle** <in hyperbolic geometry> <GE>	Überkreis *m*, Hyperzykel *m*; Abstandslinie *f*	hypercycle *m*	гиперцикл, эквидистанта
H 674	**hypercyclic group,** group with an ascending normal series with cyclic factors <GR>	hyperzyklische Gruppe *f*	groupe *m* hypercyclique	гиперциклическая группа
H 675	**hypercyclic ring** <AL>	hyperzyklischer Ring *m*	anneau *m* hypercyclique	гиперциклическое кольцо
H 676	**hypercyclide** <GE>	Hyperzyklide *f* <Study>	hypercyclide *f*	гиперциклида
H 677	**hypercycloid** <GE>	Hyperzykloide *f*	hypercycloïde *f*	гиперциклоида
H 678	**hyperdeterminant** <AL>	Hyperdeterminante *f*	hyperdéterminant *m*	гипердетерминант
H 679	**hyperdistributive function** <AN>	hyperdistributive Funktion *f*	fonction *f* hyperdistributive	гипердистрибутивная функция
H 680	**hyperelliptic field,** hyperelliptic function field <AL>	hyperelliptischer Körper (Funktionenkörper) *m*	corps *m* hyperelliptique	гиперэллиптическое поле <алгебраических функций>
H 681	**hyperelliptic function** <FT>	hyperelliptische Funktion *f*	fonction *f* hyperelliptique	гиперэллиптическая функция
	hyperelliptic function field <AL>	*s.* H 680		
H 682	**hyperelliptic integral** <*e.g.*: of the first kind> <FT>	hyperelliptisches Integral *n* <*z. B.*: erster Gattung>	intégrale *f* hyperelliptique <*par exemple:* de première espèce>	гиперэллиптический интеграл <*например:* первого рода>
H 683	**hyperelliptic theta-function** <FT, FU>	hyperelliptische Thetafunktion (ϑ-Funktion) *f*	fonction *f* thêta hyperelliptique	гиперэллиптическая тэта-функция
H 684	**hyperexponential group** <GR>	hyperexponentielle Gruppe *f*	groupe *m* hyperexponentiel	гиперэкспоненциальная группа
H 685	**hyperexponential law** <AL>	Hyperexponentialgesetz *n*	loi *f* hyperexponentielle	гиперэкспоненциальный закон
H 686	**hyperfinite C*-algebra** <FA>	hyperendliche *C**-Algebra *f*	*C**-algèbre *f* hyperfinie	гиперконечная *C**-алгебра
H 687	**hyperfuchsian function** <FT>	hyperfuchssche Funktion *f*	fonction *f* hyperfuchsienne	гиперфуксова функция
H 688	**hyperfuchsian group** <FT>	hyperfuchssche Gruppe *f*	groupe *m* hyperfuchsien	гиперфуксова группа
H 689	**hyperfunctor** <CA>	Hyperfunktor *m*	hyperfoncteur *m*	гиперфунктор
	hypergeodesic curve <DG>	*s.* P 32		
H 690	**hypergeometric differential equation,** hypergeometric equation, Gaussian differential equation, Gauss['s] hypergeometric [differential] equation <DE>	hypergeometrische Differentialgleichung (Gleichung) *f*, Gaußsche Differentialgleichung	équation *f* de Gauss, équation différentielle de Gauss, équation [différentielle] hypergéométrique	гипергеометрическое [дифференциальное] уравнение, [дифференциальное] уравнение Гаусса
H 691	**hypergeometric distribution,** hypergeometric probability distribution <ST>	hypergeometrische Verteilung *f*	distribution *f* hypergéométrique	гипергеометрическое распределение
	hypergeometric equation <DE>	*s.* H 690		
H 692	**hypergeometric function,** Gauss['s] hypergeometric function <FU>	hypergeometrische (Gaußsche hypergeometrische) Funktion *f*	fonction *f* hypergéométrique [de Gauss]	гипергеометрическая функция
H 693	**hypergeometric function of the second kind** <FU>	hypergeometrischeFunktion *f* zweiter Art	fonction *f* hypergéométrique de deuxième espèce	гипергеометрическая функция второго рода
	hypergeometric polynomial <FU>	*s.* J 28		
	hypergeometric probability distribution <ST>	*s.* H 691		
H 694	**hypergeometric series,** Gauss['s] hypergeometric series, Gaussian (classical) hypergeometric series <SS>	hypergeometrische (Gaußsche hypergeometrische, Gaußsche) Reihe *f*, // hypergeometrische Funktion *f*	série *f* hypergéométrique (hypergéométrique de Gauss)	гипергеометрический ряд, гипергеометрический ряд Гаусса, ряд Гаусса
H 695	**hyper graeco-latin square** <CT, ST>	hyper-griechisch-lateinisches Quadrat *n*	carré *m* hyper-gréco-latin	гипер-греко-латинский квадрат
	hypergraph <GP>	*s.* S 694		
	hypergraph with a faithful graph representation <GP>	*s.* C 1897		
	hypergroup <AL>	*s.* M 963		
H 696	**hyperharmonic series** <SS>	allgemeine harmonische Reihe *f*, hyperharmonische (harmonische) Reihe	série *f* hyperharmonique	гипергармонический ряд

H 697	**hyperhomology module** <HA>	Hyperhomologiemodul *m*	module *m* d'hyperhomologie	модуль гипергомологий
H 698	**hyperhyperboloid** <PJ>	Hyperhyperboloid *n*	hyperhyperboloïde *m*	гипергиперболоид
H 699	**hyperimmune set** <SE>	hyperimmune Menge *f*	ensemble *m* hyperimmune	гипериммунное множество
H 700	**hyper-Jacobian curve** <GE>	hyperjacobische Kurve *f* <Spottiswoode>	courbe *f* hyperjacobienne	гиперякобиева кривая
H 701	**hyper-Jacobian surface** <AG>	hyperjacobische Fläche *f*	surface *f* hyperjacobienne	гиперякобиева поверхность
H 702	**hyperline,** hypercurve, supercurve <Cayley> <GE>	Hyperkurve *f*, Überkurve *f*	hyperligne *f*, hypercourbe *f*	гиперлиния
H 703	**hypermatrix,** partition[ed] matrix, matrix of matrices <MD>	Hypermatrix *f*, Übermatrix *f*, Blockmatrix *f*, Matrix *f* von Matrizen, Kästchenmatrix *f*, in Kästchen eingeteilte Matrix, in Blöcke zerlegte Matrix	hypermatrice *f*, matrice *f* (tableau *m*) de matrices, matrice partitionnée (des matrices, décomposée en blocs)	гуперматрица, матрица матриц, блочная (клеточная, ящичная) матрица
	hypermaximal [Hermitian] operator <FA>	*s.* S 273		
	hypermaximal symmetrical operator <FA>	*s.* S 273		
H 704	**hypermetric topological group** <AL>	hypermetrische topologische Gruppe *f*	groupe *m* topologique hypermétrique	гиперметрическая топологическая группа
H 705	**hypernormal dispersion** <Lexis> <ST>	übernormale (hypernormale) Dispersion *f*	dispersion *f* hypernormale	гипернормальное рассеяние
H 706	**hyper-octahedral group** <AL>	Hyperoktaedergruppe *f*	groupe *m* hyperoctaédrique	гипероктаэдрическая группа подстановок
H 707	**hyperparallel half-lines** <in the hyperbolic plane> <GE>	überparallele Halbgeraden *fpl*	demi-droites *fpl* hyperparallèles	расходящиеся (гиперпараллельные) полупрямые
	hyperplane <LA>	*s.* C 965		
H 708	**hyperplane at infinity,** infinite hyperplane, ideal hyperplane, improper hyperplane <as an extension of the Euclidean space> <PJ>	unendlich[ ]ferne Hyperebene *f*, uneigentliche (ideale) Hyperebene, Fernhyperebene *f*, Fernraum *m*	hyperplan *m* à (de) l'infini, hyperplan idéal (impropre)	бесконечно удаленная гиперплоскость, несобственная гиперплоскость
H 709	**hyperplane co-ordinates,** tangential co-ordinates of the hyperplane <PJ>	Hyperebenenkoordinaten *fpl*, Koordinaten *fpl* der Hyperebene	coordonnées *fpl* [tangentielles] du hyperplan	гиперплоскостные координаты
H 710	**hyperplane of reference,** co-ordinate hyperplane <for hyperplane co-ordinates> <PJ>	Fundamentalhyperebene *f*, Koordinatenhyperebene *f*, Grundhyperebene *f*, Bezugshyperebene *f*	hyperplan *m* de référence (coordonnées), hyperplan fondamental	основная (координатная) гиперплоскость
H 711	**hyperplane of support,** supporting hyperplane, tac-hyperplane <CS, GE>	Stützhyperebene *f*	hyperplan *m* d'appui	опорная гиперплоскость
H 712	**hyperplane section** <of a manifold> <AG>	Hyperebenenschnitt *m*	section *f* hyperplane	гиперплоскостное сечение
H 713	**hyperprimary ideal** <AB>	hyperprimäres Ideal *n*	idéal *m* hyperprimaire	гиперпримарное число
H 714	**hyperprimary module** <AB>	Hyperprimärmodul *m*	module *m* hyperprimaire	гиперпримарный модуль
H 715	**hyperprimary number** <AB>	hyperprimäre Zahl *f*	nombre *m* hyperprimaire	гиперпримарное число
H 716	**hyperquadric,** quadric surface, quadric <in a higher-dimensional space> <GE>	Hyperquadrik *f*, Hyperfläche *f* zweiter (2.) Ordnung, Quadrik *f*, Hyperquadrifläche *f* <Segre>	hyperquadrique *f*, surface *f* hyperquadrique	гиперквадрика, гиперповерхность второго порядка
H 717	**hyperradial function** <FU>	hyperradiale Funktion *f*	fonction *f* hyperradiale	гиперрадиальная функция
H 718	**hyper-real ideal** <AL>	hyperreelles Ideal *n*	idéal *m* hyper[-]réel	гипервещественный идеал
H 719	**hyperrow** <of a matrix> <MD>	Hyperzeile *f*	hyperligne *f*	обобщенная строка
H 720	**hypersimple set** <MM>	hypereinfache Menge *f*	ensemble *m* hypersimple	гиперпростое множество
H 721	**hyperspace** <TO>	Hyperraum *m*	hyperespace *m*	гиперпространство
	hyperspace <TO>	*s.* Q 347		
H 722	**hyperspace curve** <GE>	Überraumkurve *f*	courbe *f* hyperspatiale	гиперпространственная кривая
H 723	**hypersphere,** hyperspherical surface <GE>	Hypersphäre *f*, Sphäre *f*, Hyperkugel *f*, Hyperkugelfläche *f*	hypersphère *f*, surface *f* hypersphérique	гиперсфера
H 724	**hypersphere** <in hyperbolic geometry> <GE>	Überkugel *f*, Hypersphäre *f*; Abstandsfläche *f*	hypersphère *f*	гиперсфера
H 725	**hypersphere** <including its interior points> <GE>	Hyperkugel *f*	hypersphère *f*	гипершар
	hyperspherical surface <GE>	*s.* H 723		
H 726	**hyperstonian space** <TO>	hyper-Stonescher Raum *m*, hyperstonescher Raum	espace *m* hyperstonien	гиперстоуново пространство
H 727	**hypersurface** <DG, GE>	Hyperfläche *f*, Überfläche *f*	hypersurface *f*	гиперповерхность
H 728	**hypersurface of the second class** <GE>	Hyperfläche *f* zweiter (2.) Klasse	hypersurface *f* de la deuxième classe	гиперповерхность второго класса
H 729	**hypersurface of the second degree** <F. Klein> <GE>	Hyperfläche *f* zweiten (2.) Grades	hypersurface *f* du deuxième degré	гиперповерхность второй степени
H 730	**hypoabelian group** <Dickson> <AL, GR>	hypoabelsche Gruppe *f* <linearer Substitutionen, Jordan>	groupe *m* hypoabélien	гипоабелева группа
	hypocentral group <GR>	*s.* Z 10		
H 731	**hypocompact space** <TO>	hypokompakter Raum *m*	espace *m* hypocompact	гипокомпактное пространство
H 732	**hypocontinuity** <FA>	Hypostetigkeit *f*	hypocontinuité *f*	гипонепрерывность

	English	German	French	Russian
H 733	**hypocontinuous bilinear mapping** <FA>	hypostetige bilineare Abbildung *f*	application *f* bilinéaire hypocontinue	гипонепрерывное билинейное отображение
H 734	**hypocycloid** <GE>	Hypozykloide *f*	hypocycloïde *f*	гипоциклоида
H 735	**hypoelliptic[al] operator** <DE>	hypoelliptischer Operator *m*	opérateur *m* hypoelliptique (différentiel hypo[-]elliptique)	гипоэллиптический оператор
H 736	**hypoellipticity** <DE>	Hypoelliptizität *f*	hypoellipticité *f*	гипоэллиптичность
H 737	**hypohamiltonian graph** <GP>	hypohamiltonscher Graph *m*	graphe *m* hypohamiltonien	гипогамильтонов граф
H 738	**hyponormal dispersion** <Lexis> <ST>	unternormale Dispersion *f*	dispersion *f* hyponormale	гипонормальное рассеяние, гипонормальная дисперсия
H 739	**hypotenuse** <of a rectangular triangle> <EG>	Hypotenuse *f*	hypoténuse *f*	гипотенуза
	hypothesis <LO>	*s.* 1. A 695; 2. P 1222		
	hypothesis <ST>	*s.* S 1694		
	hypothesis of the continuum <SE>	*s.* C 2247		
H 740	**hypothesize / to** <LO>	eine Hypothese aufstellen	poser une hypothèse	строить гипотезу
H 741	**hypothetical population,** hypothetical universe <ST>	hypothetische Grundgesamtheit *f*	population *f* (univers *m*) hypothétique	гипотетическая [генеральная] совокупность
	hypothetical proposition <LO> ⌐<LO>	*s.* C 1823		
	hypothetical syllogism	*s.* R 1467		
	hypothetical universe <ST>	*s.* H 741		
H 742	**hypothetico-deductive method** <LO>	hypothetisch-deduktive Methode *f*	méthode *f* hypothético-déductive	гипотетико-дедуктивный метод, метод гипотетической дедукции
H 743	**hypotrochoid** <GE>	Hypotrochoide *f*, // Hypotrochoidale *f*	hypotrochoïde *f*, hypocycloïde *f* raccourcie	гипотрохоида

I

	English	German	French	Russian
	I closed subset <SE>	*s.* R 789		
I 1	**iconic model** <PG>	bildhaftes Modell *n*, Bildmodell *n*, ikonisches Modell	modèle *m* imagé	портретная модель; модель, точно повторяющая объект
I 2	**icosahedral form** <AL>	Ikosaederform *f*	forme *f* icosaédrique	икосаэдрическая форма
I 3	**icosahedral group;** dodecahedral group <AL, GR>	Ikosaedergruppe *f*; Dodekaedergruppe *f*	groupe *m* de l'icosaèdre, groupe icosaédrique (icosaèdre, icosaédral); groupe du dodécaèdre, groupe dodécaédrique (dodécaédral)	группа икосаэдра, икосаэдрическая группа; группа додекаэдра, додекаэдрическая группа
I 4	**icosahedron** <EG>	Zwanzigflach *n*, Ikosaeder *n*, Zwanzigflächner *m*, 20-Flach *n*, 20-Flächner *m*	icosaèdre *m*	двадцатигранник, икосаэдр
	icosahedron <EG>	*s.* R 562		
I 5	**icosahedron equation** <AL>	Ikosaedergleichung *f*	équation *f* de l'icosaèdre, équation icosaédrique	уравнение икосаэдра
I 6	**ideal,** sum (additive) ideal <of a Boolean algebra> <AL>	Ideal *n*	idéal *m*, idéal booléen	идеал
I 7	**ideal** <of a Lie ring> <AL>	Ideal *n*, invarianter Teilring *m*	idéal *m*	идеал, лиев идеал
I 8	**ideal** <of a ring or semigroup> <*e.g.:* ideal $\mathfrak{a}'$ lies over the ideal $\mathfrak{a}$> <AL>	Ideal *n* <*z. B.:* Ideal $\mathfrak{a}'$ liegt über dem Ideal $\mathfrak{a}$>	idéal *m* <*par exemple:* idéal $\mathfrak{a}'$ est au-dessus de l'idéal $\mathfrak{a}$>	идеал <*например:* идеал $\mathfrak{a}'$ лежит над идеалом $\mathfrak{a}$>
I 9	**ideal** <of a lattice> <LA>	Ideal *n*, $\cup$-Ideal *n*, verbandstheoretisches Ideal	idéal *m*	идеал [решетки], теоретико-структурный идеал
I 10	**Φ-ideal,** Riesz['s] ideal <FA>	Φ-Ideal *n*, Riesz-Ideal *n*, Rieszideal *n*, Ideal *n* des Rieszschen Operators	Φ-idéal *m*, idéal *m* de Riesz	Φ-идеал, идеал Риса
	ideal <AL>	*s.* T 1116		
	ideal <SE>	*s.* U 425		
I 11	**ideal base (basis),** basis, set of generators <of an ideal> <AL>	Idealbasis *f*, Basis *f*	système *m* de générateurs, système générateur, base *f* <d'un idéal>	базис, образующие, база <идеала>
I 12	**ideal class group** <AB>	Idealklassengruppe *f*	groupe *m* des classes d'idéaux	группа классов идеалов
I 13	**ideal class in the usual sense** <AB>	Idealklasse *f* im gewöhnlichen Sinne	classe *f* d'idéaux au sens ordinaire	класс идеалов в обычном смысле
	ideal decomposable into primary ideals <AL>	*s.* D 51		
	ideal element <PJ>	*s.* E 123		
I 14	**ideal group** <AB>	Idealgruppe *f*	groupe *m* des idéaux [fractionnaires inversibles]	группа идеалов
	ideal hyperplane <PJ>	*s.* H 708		
I 15	**idealizer condition** <GR>	Idealisatorbedingung *f*		идеализаторное условие
I 16	**ideal length, ideal-length,** length <of an ideal> <AL>	Ideallänge *f*, Länge *f* <eines Ideals>	longueur *f* <d'un idéal>	кратность <идеала>
	ideal line <PJ>	*s.* L 852		
I 17	**ideal number** <AB>	ideale Zahl *f*, Idealzahl *f*, Ideal *n* <Kummer>	nombre *m* idéal, idéal *m*	идеальное число
	ideal of definition <AL, FA> ⌐<AL>	*s.* D 127		
	ideal of polynomials	*s.* P 988		
I 18	**ideal of the fundamental (principal) class** <AL>	Hauptklassenideal *n*, Ideal *n* der Hauptklasse	idéal *m* de la classe principale	идеал главного класса
	ideal plane <PJ>	*s.* P 640		

I 19	**ideal point** <of the hyperbolic plane> <GE>	Überpunkt *m*, idealer Punkt *m*	point *m* idéal	идеальная точка
	ideal point <PJ>	*s.* P 722		
I 20	**ideal theoretic** <AL>	idealtheoretisch	en théorie des idéaux	с точки зрения теории идеалов
	ideal which cannot be decomposed into a product <NT>	*s.* P 1315		
I 21	**ideal whose radical is a prime ideal** <AL>	Quasiprimärideal *n*	idéal *m* quasi[-]primaire	идеал, радикал которого является простым
I 22	**idele, idèle** <AB>	Idel *n*, Idèle *n*	idèle *m*	идель, идеальный элемент
I 23	**idele class group** <AB>	Idelklassengruppe *f*	groupe *m* des classes d'idèles	группа классов иделей (идеальных элементов Шевалле)
I 24	**idele group,** fundamental group <AB>	Idelgruppe *f*, Fundamentalgruppe *f* <der Idele>	groupe *m* des idèles	группа иделей
I 25	**idemfactor** <AL>	Idemfaktor *m*	idemfacteur *m*	неменяющий множитель
	idemfactor <VT>	*s.* U 298		
I 26	**idempotence** <for a closure operation> <TO>	Satz *m* der Abgeschlossenheit <für die Hüllenbildung>	idempotence <de l'opération de fermeture>	идемпотентность <операции замыкания>
I 27	**idempotence law** <LO>	Verschmelzungssatz *m*, Idempotenzgesetz *n*	loi *f* d'idempotence	закон идемпотентности
I 28	**idempotence law for disjunction, idempotence of disjunction** <LO>	Idempotenzgesetz *n* der Alternative, Verschmelzungssatz *m* für die Alternative	loi *f* d'idempotence de la disjonction	закон идемпотентности для дизъюнкции
I 29	**idempotency** <AL>	Idempotenz *f*	idempotence *f*	идемпотентность
I 30	**idempotent,** idempotent element (quantity) <AL>	Idempotent *n*, idempotentes Element *n*	élément *m* idempotent, idempotent *m*	идемпотент, идемпотентный элемент
I 31	**idempotent composition law** <AL>	idempotentes Verknüpfungsgesetz *n*	loi *f* idempotente	идемпотентное умножение
	idempotent element <AL>	*s.* I 30		
I 32	**idempotent groupoid** <AL>	idempotentes Gruppoid *n*	groupoïde *m* idempotent	группоид идемпотентов, идемпотентный группоид
I 33	**idempotent laws** <for a lattice> <LA>	Idempotenzgesetze *npl*	relations *fpl* d'idempotence	законы идемпотентности
I 34	**idempotent number** <of a hypercomplex number system> <AL>	idempotente Zahl *f*, Einheit *f* <Frobenius>	nombre *m* idempotent	идемпотентное число
	idempotent quantity <AL>	*s.* I 30		
I 35	**idempotent ring** <AL>	idempotenter Ring *m*	anneau *m* idempotent	кольцо с идемпотентным умножением
I 36	**idempotent semigroup,** band <AL>	Schief *n*, idempotente Halbgruppe *f*, Band *n*	demi-groupe *m* idempotent	полугруппа идемпотентов, связка, идемпотентная полугруппа
	idempotent subset <AL>	*s.* R 597		
I 37	**identical,** identically equal <to>, ≡ <AL, GN>	identisch, identisch gleich, ≡	identique, égal identiquement <à>, ≡	тождественный, тождественно равный, ≡
	identical <EG>	*s.* C 1935		
I 38	**identical automorphism,** identity automorphism <AL>	identischer Automorphismus *m*, Einheitsautomorphismus *m*	automorphisme *m* identique (unité)	тождественный автоморфизм, единичный автоморфизм
	identical congruence <NT>	*s.* F 738		
I 39	**identically congruent polynomial,** congruent polynomial <NT>	identisch (algebraisch) kongruentes Polynom *n*, kongruentes Polynom	polynôme *m* identiquement congruent	тождественно конгруэнтный многочлен
I 40	**identically distributed** <ST>	identisch verteilt	identiquement distribué	тождественно распределенный
	identically equal <AL, GN>	*s.* I 37		
	identically false formula <LO>	*s.* C 2277		
I 41	**identically false propositional function** <LO>	identisch falsche Aussagenfunktion *f*, immer falsche Aussage *f*, Kontradiktion *f*	fonction *f* propositionnelle identiquement fausse	тождественно ложная функция высказывания, всегда ложное высказывание
	identically true compound proposition <LO>	*s.* I 43		
	identically true formula <LO>	*s.* T 98		
I 42	**identically true or false formula** <LO>	aussagenlogische Identität *f* oder Kontradiktion *f*	formule *f* analytique	всегда-истинная или всегда ложная формула
	identically true sentence <LO>	*s.* U 349		
I 43	**identically true sentential combination,** identically true compound proposition <LO>	immer richtige Aussagenverbindung *f*, allgemeingültige Aussagenverbindung	proposition *f* composée identiquement vraie	всегда истинное сложное высказывание
	identically valid formula <LO>	*s.* U 349		
I 44	**identical morphism,** unit (identity) morphism, identity, unit <CA>	identischer Morphismus *m*, Identität *f*, Einsabbildung *f*	morphisme (homomorphisme) *m* identique, unité *f*	тождественный морфизм, тождественный (единичный) гомоморфизм, единичный морфизм, единичное отображение, единица
I 45	**identical operation,** identity <AL>	identische Operation *f*, Identität *f*, Identitätsoperation *f*	opération *f* identique	тождественный оператор
I 46	**identical relation** <in a group> <GR>	identische Relation *f*, Regel *f*, Identität *f*	identité *f*	тождественное [со]отношение, тождество

No.	English	German	French	Russian
I 47	**identical representation,** identity (unit, trivial) representation <RE>	identische (totalsymmetrische, triviale) Darstellung *f*, Einsdarstellung *f*	représentation *f* identique (unité)	тождественное (единичное, тривиальное) представление
I 48	**identical transformation,** unit (identity) transformation, identity <AN>	identische Transformation (Abbildung) *f*, Einheitstransformation *f*, Einheitsabbildung *f*	transformation (application) *f* identique, transformation(-)unité *f*, application (-)unité *f*	тождественное преобразование, единичное преобразование
I 49	**identifiability** <AL>	Identifizierbarkeit *f*	identifiabilité *f*, assimilabilité *f*	отождествляемость
I 50	**identification,** identifying <in passing to the quotient space> <TO>	Identifizierung *f*, Identifikation *f*	identification *f*	отождествление, идентификация
	identification <TO>	*s.* P 598		
I 51	**identification map[ping],** quotient mapping <TO>	Identifizierungsabbildung *f*	application *f* d'identification	отображение отождествления, идентифицирующее отображение
I 52	**identification of boundaries** <AT>	Randidentifikation *f*, Randidentifizierung *f*	identification *f* de frontières	отождествление границ
	identification of boundaries <TO>	*s.* P 297		
I 53	**identification of the first kind,** fitting with a handle of the first kind <AT>	Aufsetzen *n* eines Henkels erster Art	attachement *m* d'une anse	склеивание первого рода, приклеивание ручки первого рода
I 54	**identification of the second kind,** fitting with a handle of the second kind <AT>	Aufsetzen *n* einer Kreuzhaube		склеивание второго рода, приклеивание ручки второго рода
	identification space <TO>	*s.* Q 347		
	identification topology <TO> ┌<TO>	*s.* 1. Q 350; 2. Q 351		
	identified boundaries	*s.* G 312		
I 55	**identifier** <LO>	Identifikator *m*, Identifikationsoperator *m*	opérateur *m* d'identification	отождествитель
	identifying <TO>	*s.* I 50		
	identifying index <GN, VT>	*s.* F 618		
I 56	**identities of Kronecker** <for matrices> <MD>	Kroneckersche Identitäten *fpl*	identités *fpl* de Kronecker	тождества Кронекера
I 57	**identity** <between variables> <AL>	identische Gleichung *f*, Identität *f*, identische Gleichheit *f*	identité *f*, équation *f* identique	тождественное уравнение, тождественное равенство, тождество
I 58	**identity,** unit, identity (unit) element, unity quantity <of a field> <AL>	Einselement *n*, Eins *f*, Haupteinheit *f*	élément *m* unité, élément-unité *m*, unité *f* absolue (principale)	единичный элемент, единица, главная единица
I 59	**identity,** unit, identity (unit) element, unit-element, one <of a ring> <AL>	Einselement *n*, Einheitselement *n*	élément-unité *m*, élément *m* unité	единица кольца, единица, единичный элемент
I 60	**identity** <of primitive classes> <UA>	Identität *f*	identité *f*	закон, тождество, тождественное отношение
	identity <AL>	*s.* 1. I 45; 2. I 62; 3. N 183		
	identity <AL, SE, TO>	*s.* I 65		
	identity <AN>	*s.* I 48		
	identity <CA>	*s.* I 44		
	identity <EG>	*s.* C 1912		
	identity <GR>	*s.* I 63		
	identity <LO>	*s.* G 186		
	identity <SE>	*s.* 1. E 326; 2. G 409		
	identity automorphism <AL>	*s.* I 38		
I 61	**identity axiom** <LO>	Identitätsaxiom *n*, Satz *m* der Reflexivität <für die Identität>	axiome *m* d'identité	аксиома тождества, закон рефлексивности равенства
	identity dyad <VT>	*s.* U 273		
I 62	**identity element,** identity, unit element, unity, unity element, two-sided identity element <in a multiplicative composition> <AL>	Einselement *n*, Einheitselement *n*, Eins *f*, Einheit *f*, zweiseitiges Einselement	élément-unité *m*, élément *m* unité, unité *f*, élément identique (neutre), élément unité bilatère, élément-unité bilatère, élément neutre bilatère	единичный элемент, единица, двусторонняя единица, двусторонний нейтральный элемент
I 63	**identity element,** identity, unit element, unit-element, neutral element, neutral <GR>	Einselement *n*, Gruppeneins *f*, neutrales Gruppenelement (Element) *n*, Einheitselement *n*	élément *m* neutre, élément-unité *m*, unité *f* du groupe, élément identique (unitaire)	единичный элемент, единица [группы], нейтральный элемент
	identity element <AL>	*s.* 1. I 58; 2. I 59; 3. N 183		
	identity function <AL, SE, TO>	*s.* I 65		
I 64	**identity graph,** asymmetric[al] graph <GP>	asymmetrischer Graph *m* <Graph, der nur den identischen Automorphismus besitzt>	graphe *m* asymétrique (identique)	асимметрический (тождественный) граф
	identity law <LO>	*s.* L 189		
I 65	**identity map[ping],** identity [function] <AL, SE, TO>	identische Abbildung *f*, Identität *f*, Ruhabbildung *f*, identische Funktion *f*	application *f* identique, fonction *f* identité	тождественное отображение, тождественная функция
I 66	**identity matrix,** unit matrix, *I* <MD>	Einheitsmatrix *f*, *E*, 𝔈	matrice *f* unité, matrice-unité *f*, unité *f* matricielle, matrice unitaire, // système-unité *m*	единичная матрица
	identity morphism <CA>	*s.* I 44		
	identity of Euler <AL>	*s.* E 594		
I 67	**identity of Picone,** theorem of Picone <DE>	Identität (Formel) *f* von Picone, Piconesche Identität	identité *f* de Picone	формула Пиконе

No.	English	German	French	Russian
I 68	**identity operator,** unit operator <of an operator group> <AL>	identischer Operator *m*, Einsoperator *m*, Identitätsoperator *m*	opérateur *m* identique (identité, neutre, unité), transformation *f* identique, opérateur-unité *m*	тождественный оператор, единичный оператор
I 69	**identity permutation** <AL>	identische Permutation (Substitution) *f*	permutation (substitution) *f* identique, substitution-unité *f*	тождественная перестановка (подстановка), единичная подстановка
I 70	**identity problem,** word problem <AL>	Identitätsproblem *n*, Wortproblem *n*	problème *m* d'identité, problème des mots	проблема тождества <слов>, проблема слов
	identity relation <SE>	*s.* E 326		
	identity representation <RE>	*s.* 1. I 47; 2. T 1000		
	identity subgroup <GR>	*s.* U 304		
	identity tensor <VT>	*s.* U 298		
I 71	**identity theorem** <for holomorphic functions *or* power series> <FT, SS>	Identitätssatz *m*, Eindeutigkeitssatz *m*	théorème *m* sur l'identité	теорема о тождестве
	identity transformation <AN>	*s.* I 48		
	I-divergency <ST>	*s.* I 508		
	I-equivalent system <UA>	*s.* E 339		
I 72	**if and only if, iff,** // when and only when <GN>	wenn und nur wenn; dann und nur dann, wenn; genau dann, wenn	si et seulement si, ssi, lorsque . . . et réciproquement	когда и только когда, если и только если
I 73	**if . . . then . . .** <$p \to q$> <LO>	wenn . . ., so . . .	. . . entraîne . . ., . . . implique . . ., . . . a pour conséquence . . .	если. . ., то. . .
I 74	***i*-genus** <AG>	*i*-Geschlecht *n*	*i*-genre *m*	*i*-род
	***i, j* matrix element**	*s.* E 130		
	i-line <PJ, SG>	*s.* S 1726		
I 75	**ill-conditioned matrix** <AL, NU>	schlechtkonditionierte Matrix *f*	matrice *f* mal-conditionnée (mal conditionneé)	плохо обусловленная матрица
	ill posed problem <DE>	*s.* M 60		
I 76	**illusory correlation,** nonsense correlation <ST>	Scheinkorrelation *f*, illusorische Korrelation *f*, Nonsenskorrelation *f*	corrélation *f* illusoire	иллюзорная (ложная) корреляция
	Im <FT>	*s.* I 98		
I 77	**image,** image function, transform <of a functional transformation> <AN>	Bildfunktion *f*, Unterfunktion *f*, Resultatfunktion *f*, Transformierte *f*, Bild *n*	image *f*, fonction *f* image, transformée *f*	образ, изображение [функции], преобразованная функция (форма), результат преобразования, трансформанта, трансформа
I 78	**image** <of a mapping> <SE>	Bild *n*	image *f*, image directe	образ
	image <DS>	*s.* P 518		
	image <SE>	*s.* I 86		
I 79	**image by a univalent function** <SE>	umkehrbar eindeutiges Bild *n*, Bild bei einer umkehrbar eindeutigen Abbildung	image *f* biunivoque	образ при взаимно однозначном отображению
I 80	**image category** <CA>	Bildkategorie *f*	catégorie *f* image	образ категории
I 81	**image chain** <AT>	Bildkette *f*	chaîne *f* image	образ (отображение) цепи
	image curve <AN, NU>	*s.* D 408		
	image function <AN>	*s.* I 77		
I 82	**image group** <for a homomorphism> <AL>	Bildgruppe *f*	groupe *m* image	образ группы
I 83	**image line** <GE>	Bildgerade *f*	droite *f* image	прямая, являющаяся образом; прямая-образ
I 84	**image plane** <in central perspective> <DS>	Bildebene *f*	plan *m* de projection, plan-image *m*	картинная плоскость, плоскость проекций
I 85	**image point** <of a polynomial *or* in a mapping> <AN, TO>	Bildpunkt *m*	point *m* image <AN>; conséquent *m* <TO>	отображающая точка
I 86	**image set,** image, range <of a mapping> <SE>	Bildmenge *f*, Bild *n*	ensemble *m* des images, image *f*	множество образов, образ
I 87	**image set of a section** <of a sheaf *or* fibre bundle> <AL, TO>	Schnittfläche *f*	surface *f* de section	секущая поверхность
I 88	**image set of the zero section** <of a fibre bundle *or* sheaf> <AL, TO>	Nullschnittfläche *f*	surface *f* de section nulle	нулевая секущая поверхность
I 89	**image space** <of a functional transformation> <AN>	Bildraum *m*, Resultatraum *m*, Unterraum *m*, Bildbereich *m*, Resultatbereich *m*, Unterbereich *m*	espace *m* image, espace-image *m*	пространство образов (изображений), область образов (изображений)
I 90	**imaginary axis** <of complex co-ordinates>, axis of imaginaries <FT>	imaginäre Achse *f*	axe *m* imaginaire	мнимая ось
I 91	**imaginary circle** <AY>	nullteiliger (imaginärer) Kreis *m*	cercle *m* imaginaire	мнимая окружность
I 92	**imaginary ellipsoid** <AY>	imaginäres (nullteiliges) Ellipsoid *n*	ellipsoïde *m* imaginaire	мнимый эллипсоид
	imaginary experiment <ST>	*s.* T 440		
I 93	**imaginary line of the first kind** <PJ>	imaginäre Gerade *f* erster (1.) Art, niederimaginäre Gerade	droite *f* imaginaire de première espèce	мнимая прямая первого рода
I 94	**imaginary line of the second kind** <PJ>	imaginäre Gerade *f* zweiter (2.) Art, hochimaginäre Gerade	droite *f* imaginaire de deuxième espèce	мнимая прямая второго рода

No.	English	German	French	Russian
I 95	**imaginary logarithm** <AN>	imaginärer Logarithmus *m*	logarithme *m* imaginaire	имагинарный логарифм
I 96	**imaginary number** <$a + bi$, $b \neq 0$> <AL, FT, NT>	imaginäre Zahl *f*	nombre *m* imaginaire	мнимое число
I 97	**imaginary number,** pure (purely) imaginary number <$0 + bi$> <AL, FT, NT>	rein imaginäre Zahl *f*, reinimaginäre (imaginäre) Zahl	nombre *m* imaginaire pur, nombre [purement] imaginaire, imaginaire *m* [pur]	чисто мнимое число
	imaginary number <AL>	*s.* C 1632		
I 98	**imaginary part,** Im <FT>	Imaginärteil *m*, imaginärer Teil (Bestandteil *m*), Im, // $\mathfrak{Im}$, $\mathfrak{I}$	partie *f* imaginaire, Im	мнимая часть, Im
I 99	**imaginary point** <AY>	imaginärer Punkt *m*	point *m* imaginaire	мнимая (воображаемая) точка
I 100	**imaginary projection** <PJ>	Imaginärprojektion *f*	projection *f* imaginaire	мнимая проекция
I 101	**imaginary quadric,** null quadric <AY>	nullteilige Fläche *f* zweiten (2.) Grades, nullteilige Quadrik *f*, Nullfläche *f*, nullteilige Fläche zweiter (2.) Ordnung	quadrique *f* imaginaire	нулевая (мнимая) поверхность второй степени
	imaginary quaternion <AL>	*s.* P 2048		
I 102	**imaginary root** <AL>	imaginäre Wurzel *f*, // unmögliche (surdische) Wurzel	racine *f* imaginaire, // racine sourde	мнимый корень
I 103	**imaginary sphere** <AY>	imaginäre (nullteilige) Kugel *f*	sphère *f* imaginaire	мнимая сфера, пустой (мнимый) шар
I 104	**imaginary unit,** unit of imaginaries, i, // secondary unit <FT>	imaginäre Einheit *f*, i, // laterale Einheit	unité *f* imaginaire, i, // unité latérale, unité secondaire <Hamilton>	мнимая единица, i
I 105	**imbeddability,** embeddability <AL>	Einbettbarkeit *f*	plongeabilité *f*	погружаемость, вложимость
	imbedded manifold <AG>	*s.* I 118		
I 106	**imbedded primary component** <AL>	zu einem eingebetteten Primideal gehörige Primärkomponente *f*, eingebettete Primärkomponente	composante *f* primaire immergée	вложенная примарная компонента
I 107	**imbedded primary ideal** <of an ideal> <AL>	eingebettetes Primärideal (Oberideal) *n*	idéal *m* primaire immergé	погруженный примарный идеал
I 108	**imbedded prime ideal** <AL>	eingebettetes Primideal *n*	idéal *m* premier immergé	вложенный (неизолированный) простой идеал
I 109	**imbedding** <faithful functor which is injective on objects> <CA>	Einbettung *f* <treu und auf Objekten injektiv>	foncteur *m* fidèle qui est injectif sur les objets	функтор вложения
	imbedding <TO>	*s.* E 198		
	imbedding theorem <AL, FA, TO, VA>	*s.* E 202		
I 110	**imitated experiment,** constructed experiment <ST> ⌐<SE>	Modellversuch *m*	expérience *f* construite	модельный эксперимент
	immediate antecedent	*s.* I 115		
I 111	**immediate extension** <of a valued field> <AL>	unmittelbare Erweiterung *f*	extension *f* immédiate	непосредственное расширение
I 112	**immediate inference** <LO>	unmittelbares Schließen *n*	inférence *f* immédiate	непосредственное умозаключение
I 113	**immediately containing prime ideal** <AL>	unmittelbares Primoberideal *n*	suridéal *m* premier immédiat	непосредственный простой надидеал (надыдеал)
I 114	**immediate predecessor** <in a lattice> <LA>	unterer Nachbar *m*	voisin *m* inférieur	нижний сосед
I 115	**immediate predecessor,** immediate antecedent, direct predecessor <SE>	unmittelbarer Vorgänger *m*	prédécesseur *m* immédiat, prédécesseur, objet *m* immédiatement avant, précédent (antécédent) *m* immédiat	непосредственно предшествующий элемент, непосредственный предшественник
I 116	**immediate prime subideal** <AL>	unmittelbares Primunterideal *n*	sous-idéal *m* premier immédiat	непосредственный простой подидеал (подыдеал)
I 117	**immediate successor,** sequent, direct successor <SE>	unmittelbarer Nachfolger *m*	successeur *m* immédiat, successeur, suivant *m* immédiat, suivant <de>, successeur consécutif <à>	непосредственно последующий элемент
	immediate successor <LA, SE>	*s.* S 594		
I 118	**immersed manifold (variety),** imbedded manifold <AG>	eingebettete Mannigfaltigkeit *f*	variété *f* plongée	вложенное многообразие
I 119	**immersion** <of a variety into another one> <DG, TO>	Immersion *f*	immersion *f*	иммерсия, погружение
I 120	**immigration** <ST>	Immigration *f*, Einwanderung *f*	immigration *f*	иммиграция
I 121	**immune set** <LO, SE>	immune Menge *f*	ensemble *m* immune	иммунное множество
	imperfect brigade <AL>	*s.* F 415		
I 122	**imperfect field** <AL>	unvollkommener Körper *m*	corps *m* imparfait	несовершенное поле
I 123	**imperfectness** <AL>	Unvollkommenheit *f*	imperfection *f*	несовершенство
I 124	**imperfect number** <NT>	unvollkommene Zahl *f*	nombre *m* imparfait	несовершенное число
I 125	**implicate / to,** to imply <materially> <LO>	implizieren, subjungieren, bedingen	impliquer, entraîner	имплицировать, иметь следствием, заключать в себе, влечь

No.	English	Deutsch	Français	Русский
I 126	**implication,** → <LO>	Implikation *f*, logische Implikation, →	implication *f* [logique], conditionnel *m*, implication SI . . . ALORS, →	[логическая] импликация, отношение следования, следование, →
	implication <LO>	*s.* 1. C 1823; 2. M 161		
I 127	**implicational calculus of propositions,** implicational propositional calculus <LO>	*C*-Kalkül *m*, Implikationenkalkül *m*	calcul *m* implicationnel, système *m* implicationnel	импликативное пропозициональное исчисление
	implicational form <LO>	*s.* T 95		
	implicationally defined class <UA>	*s.* Q 232		
	implicational propositional calculus <LO>	*s.* I 127		
	implication in material meaning <LO>	*s.* M 161		
	implication in the material sense <LO>	*s.* M 161		
I 128	**implication rule,** rule of implication <LO>	Implikationsregel *f*	règle *f* d'implication	правило импликации
	implication sign (symbol) <LO>	*s.* S 852		
I 129	**implicative semi[-]lattice** <AL>	implikativer Halbverband *m*	demi-treillis *m* implicatif	импликативная полуструктура
I 130	**implicit definition** <LO>	implizite Definition *f*	définition *f* implicite (par postulat, axiomatique)	неявное определение; неявное задание
I 131	**implicit differential equation** <DE>	implizite (implizite gewöhnliche) Differentialgleichung *f*	équation *f* différentielle implicite	неразрешенное [обыкновенное] дифференциальное уравнение, [обыкновенное] дифференциальное уравнение в неразрешенном (неявном) виде
I 132	**implicit equation** <AL, AN>	implizite Gleichung *f*	équation *f* implicite	неявное уравнение
I 133	**implicit function** <DI>	implizite (implizit[e] dargestellte, unentwickelte) Funktion *f*	fonction *f* implicite	неявная функция
	implicit-function theorem <AN>	*s.* T 298		
I 134	**imply / to** <said of a relation> <SE>	implizieren	être plus fin <que>	быть более тонкое отношение <чем>
	imply / to <LO>	*s.* I 125		
I 135	**importation** <LO>	Importation *f*	importation *f*	внесение, импортация
	importation <LO>	*s.* L 190		
I 136	**impossibility proof** <GN>	Unmöglichkeitsbeweis *m*	démonstration *f* d'impossibilité	доказательство невозможности
I 137	**impossibility statement (theorem)** <GN>	Unmöglichkeitssatz *m*, Unmöglichkeitsbehauptung *f*	théorème *m* d'impossibilité, théorème de Arrow	теорема невозможности
I 138	**impossible event** <ST>	unmögliches Ereignis *n*	événement *m* impossible	невозможное событие
	impredicable definition <LO>	*s.* I 139		
I 139	**impredicative definition,** non-predicative (impredicable) definition <LO>	imprädikative (imprädikable, nichtprädikative) Definition *f*	définition *f* imprédicable (imprédicative, non prédicative)	непредикативное (импредикативное, импредикабельное) определение, непредикативная (импредикативная, импредикабельная) дефиниция
I 140	**impredicativity** <LO>	Imprädikativität *f*	imprédicabilité *f*	непредикативность
I 141	**imprimitive character,** improper character <modulo *m*> <NT>	uneigentlicher Charakter *m* <mod *m*>	caractère *m* impropre <relatif à un module *m*>	непримитивный (несобственный) характер <по модулю *m*>
I 142	**imprimitive group,** grouped group <Kirkman> <of permutations> <GR>	imprimitive (nichtprimitive) Gruppe *f*	groupe *m* non primitif, groupe imprimitif, permutation *f* composée du second genre <Ruffini>, équation *f* non primitive <Galois>, fonction *f* transitive <Cauchy>, groupe à lettres conjuguées <Betti>, groupe complexe <Betti>, groupe groupé <Kirkman>, système *m* secondaire <Jordan>, équation secondaire <Jordan>	импримитивная группа
I 143	**imprimitive linear group** <GR>	imprimitive lineare Gruppe *f*, imprimitive Substitutionsgruppe *f*	groupe *m* linéaire imprimitif	импримитивная линейная группа
I 144	**imprimitive matrix** <MD>	imprimitive Matrix *f*	matrice *f* imprimitive	импримитивная матрица
I 145	**imprimitive polynomial** <AL>	imprimitives Polynom *n* <vom Inhalt *d*>	polynôme *m* imprimitif	импримитивный полином
I 146	**imprimitive representation** <of a group> <RE>	imprimitive Darstellung *f*	représentation *f* imprimitive	импримитивное представление
	imprimitive subset <GR>	*s.* S 2520		
	imprimitive system <GR>	*s.* S 2520		
	imprimitive variety <GR>	*s.* S 2520 a		

I 147	**imprimitivity** <AL>	Imprimitivität *f*	imprimitivité *f*	импримитивность
I 148	**improper automorphic transformation, improper automorphism,** improper transformation into itself <of a form> <AL, NT>	uneigentliche automorphe Substitution; uneigentlicher Automorphismus *m* <einer quadratischen Form>	transformation (substitution) *f* automorphe impropre	несобственное автоморфное преобразование
	improper bisecant <GE>	*s.* I 149		
	improper character <NT>	*s.* I 141		
I 149	**improper chord,** improper bisecant <GE>	uneigentliche Sehne (Sekante, Bisekante) *f*	corde (bisécante) *f* impropre	несобственная хорда
I 150	**improper class** <is element of itself> <SE>	uneigentliche Klasse *f*	classe *f* impropre	несобственный класс
I 151	**improper component** <in intersection theory> <AG>	uneigentliche Komponente *f*	composante *f* excédentaire	несобственная компонента
I 152	**improper conic** <AY>	uneigentliche Kurve *f* zweiter Ordnung, uneigentlicher Kegelschnitt *m*	conique *f* (section *f* conique) impropre	несобственная кривая второго порядка, несобственное коническое сечение
I 153	**improper convex body** <CS, GE>	uneigentlicher konvexer Körper *m*	corps *m* convexe impropre	несобственное выпуклое тело
	improper derivative <DI>	*s.* I 442		
I 154	**improper differentiability** <DI>	uneigentliche Differenzierbarkeit *f*	dérivabilité *f* impropre	несобственная дифференцируемость
I 155	**improper divergence** <SS>	unbestimmte Divergenz *f*	divergence *f* impropre	несобственная расходимость
I 156	**improper divisor** <of an element of a ring> <AL>	uneigentlicher (trivialer) Teiler *m*	pseudo-diviseur *m*, diviseur *m* impropre	тривиальный (несобственный) делитель
I 157	**improper divisor** <NT>	unechter (trivialer) Teiler *m*	diviseur *m* impropre	тривиальный (несобственный) делитель
	improper element <PJ>	*s.* E 123		
I 158	**improper equivalence** <of forms> <NT>	uneigentliche Äquivalenz *f*	équivalence *f* impropre	несобственная эквивалентность
I 159	**improper Euclidean motion** <GE>	euklidische Umlegung *f*	antidéplacement *m* euclidien	несобственное евклидово движение
I 160	**improper expansion** <of a real number with nines from a certain place onward> <NT>	uneigentliche Entwicklung *f*	développement *m* impropre	несобственное значение
I 161	**improper face** <of a simplex> <AT>	uneigentliche Seite *f*	face *f* impropre	несобственная грань
I 162	**improper field** <VA>	uneigentliches Feld *n*	champ *m* impropre	несобственное поле
I 163	**improper filter** <AL, SE>	uneigentlicher Filter *m*	filtre *m* impropre	несобственный фильтр
I 164	**improper fraction** <AR>	unechter (uneigentlicher) Bruch *m*; unechtgebrochene Zahl *f*, // Bastardbruch *m*, fractio *f* spuria	fraction *f* impropre (irrégulière)	неправильная дробь
I 165	**improper function** <AN>	uneigentliche Funktion *f*	fonction *f* impropre	несобственная функция
	improper hyperplane <PJ>	*s.* H 708		
I 166	**improper ideal** <AL>	uneigentliches Ideal *n*	idéal *m* impropre	несобственный идеал
	improper ideal <AG, AL>	*s.* T 995		
I 167	**improper integral** <DI>	uneigentliches [Riemannsches] Integral *n*	intégrale *f* d'une fonction réglée par morceaux, intégrale impropre	несобственный (сингулярный) интеграл, интеграл кусочно линейчатой функции
I 168	**improper integral of the first kind,** infinite integral <DI>	uneigentliches Integral *n* mit unendlicher Integrationsgrenze	intégrale *f* impropre de première espèce	несобственный интеграл первого рода; несобственный интеграл, если интервал интегрирования не ограничен
I 169	**improper integral of the second kind** <DI>	uneigentliches Integral *n* über eine unbeschränkte Funktion	intégrale *f* impropre de deuxième espèce	несобственный интеграл второго рода; несобственный интеграл, если подынтегральная функция не ограничена
I 170	**improper limit** <DI>	uneigentlicher Grenzwert *m*	valeur *f* limite impropre	несобственный предел
I 171	**improper line** <as an extension of the affine space> <PJ>	uneigentliche Gerade *f*	droite *f* impropre	несобственная прямая
	improper line <PJ>	*s.* L 852		
I 172	**improperly divergent [infinite] continued fraction,** essentially divergent [infinite] continued fraction <NT>	uneigentlich divergenter unendlicher Kettenbruch *m*, oszillierender unendlicher Kettenbruch *m*, wesentlich divergenter Kettenbruch *m*	fraction *f* continue infinie discrépante	существенно расходящаяся цепная дробь
I 173	**improperly divergent infinite determinant** <MD>	uneigentlich divergente unendliche Determinante *f*	déterminant *m* infini improprement divergent	несобственно расходящийся бесконечный определитель
I 174	**improperly divergent sequence,** oscillating sequence <SS>	unbestimmt (uneigentlich) divergente Folge *f*, oszillierende Folge	suite *f* discrépante (improprement divergente, indéterminée, oscillante)	несобственно расходящаяся последовательность, осциллирующая последовательность
	improperly divergent series <SS>	*s.* O 504		
I 175	**improperly equivalent [quadratic] form** <NT>	uneigentlich äquivalente (äquivalente quadratische) Form *f*	forme *f* improprement équivalente	несобственно эквивалентная форма
	improperly posed problem <DE>	*s.* M 60		

No.	English	German	French	Russian
I 176	**improperly integrable function** <DI>	uneigentlich integrierbare Funktion *f*	fonction *f* improprement intégrable	несобственно интегрируемая функция
I 177	**improperly primitive [binary quadratic] form** <NT>	uneigentlich primitive [quadratische] Form *f*, quadratische Form zweiter Art, gerade quadratische Form	forme *f* [quadratique] improprement primitive	несобственно примитивная форма
I 178	**improper mapping,** improper transformation <AL, AN>	uneigentliche Abbildung (Transformation) *f*	transformation *f* impropre	несобственное отображение (преобразование)
I 179	**improper** <absolute or relative> **maximum** <of a functional> <VA>	uneigentliches Maximum *n*	maximum *m* impropre	несобственный максимум
	improper maximum <RF>	*s.* W 114		
I 180	**improper** <absolute or relative> **minimum** <of a functional> <VA>	uneigentliches Minimum *n*	minimum *m* impropre	несобственный минимум
	improper minimum <RF>	*s.* W 117		
I 181	**improper movement** <GE>	uneigentliche Bewegung *f* <erster, zweiter *oder* dritter Art>, Bewegung mit Umlegung, Umlegung *f*	antidéplacement *m*, isométrie *f* négative	несобственное движение
I 182	**improper number,** ∞ <AN, SE>	uneigentliche Zahl *f*, ∞	nombre *m* impropre, ∞	несобственное число, ∞
I 183	**improper orthogonal mapping,** improper orthogonal transformation, reversal, reflexotation, improper rotation, rotary reflection, orientation-reversing isometry <GE>	uneigentliche orthogonale Transformation (Abbildung) *f*, Drehung *f* und Spiegelung *f*, Drehspiegelung *f*, Umlegung *f*, Umwendung *f*, Operation *f* zweiter (2.) Art	transformation *f* orthogonale impropre, retournement *m*, rotation-réflexion *f*, antidéplacement *m*, anti-déplacement *m*, opération *f* de deuxième espèce, isométrie *f* négative	несобственное ортогональное отображение (преобразование), зеркальный поворот; поворот, сопровождаемый отражением; вращение с отражением, несобственное вращение, зеркальное отображение с поворотом (вращением), поворот второго рода, поворот с отражением
I 184	**improper orthogonal matrix** <MD>	uneigentlich orthogonale Matrix *f*	matrice *f* orthogonale gauche	несобственно ортогональная матрица
	improper orthogonal transformation <GE>	*s.* I 183		
	improper partial graph <GP>	*s.* I 198		
I 185	**improper plane** <as an extension of the affine space> <PJ>	uneigentliche Ebene *f*	plan *m* impropre	несобственная плоскость
	improper plane <PJ>	*s.* P 640		
I 186	**improper point** <as an extension of the affine space *or* infinite or ideal point of the hyperbolic plane <GE, PJ>	uneigentlicher Punkt *m*	point *m* impropre	несобственная точка
	improper point <PJ>	*s.* P 722		
I 187	**improper principal ordinal** <SE>	uneigentliche Hauptzahl *f*	nombre *m* principal impropre	несобственное главное число
	improper quadric <AG>	*s.* D 161		
I 188	**improper quotient object** <CA>	uneigentliches Faktorobjekt *n*	objet *m* quotient impropre	несобственный фактор-объект
I 189	**improper rational function,** rational function <the numerator polynomial of which having a degree higher than that of the denominator polynomial> <AL, FT>	unecht gebrochene rationale Funktion *f*, unecht gebrochen[-]rationale Funktion	fonction *f* rationnelle impropre	неправильная дробно-рациональная функция
I 190	**improper refinement** <of a normal series> <AL>	unechte Verfeinerung *f*	raffinement *m* impropre	несобственное уплотнение
I 191	**improper representation** <of a number by a quadratic form> <NT>	uneigentliche Darstellung *f* <einer Zahl durch eine quadratische Form>	représentation *f* impropre <d'un nombre par une forme quadratique>	несобственное представление <числа с помощью квадратичной формы>
I 192	**improper rotation** <DG>	uneigentliche Drehung *f* <erster, zweiter *oder* dritter Art>	rotation *f* impropre	несобственное вращение
	improper rotation <GE>	*s.* I 183		
	improper rotation group <AY>	*s.* G 481		
I 193	**improper set** <a set which is element of itself> <SE>	anormale (uneigentliche) Menge *f*	ensemble *m* impropre	несобственное (экстраординарное) множество
I 194	**improper singularity** <of an algebraic curve> <AG>	uneigentliche Singularität *f* <Cayley>	singularité *f* impropre	несобственная особенность
I 195	**improper Stieltjes integral** <AN>	uneigentliches Stieltjessches Integral *n*	intégrale *f* de Stieltjes impropre	несобственный интеграл Стилтьеса
I 196	**improper subalgebra** <AL>	uneigentliche Unteralgebra *f*	sous-algèbre *f* impropre	несобственная подалгебра
I 197	**improper subclass** <SE>	unechte Unterklasse *f*	sous-classe *f* pleine (impropre)	несобственный подкласс
I 198	**improper subgraph,** improper partial graph <GP>	unechter Teilgraph *m*	graphe *m* partiel impropre	несобственный частичный граф

No.	English	German	French	Russian
I 199	**improper subgroup** <GR>	unechte Untergruppe *f*	sous-groupe *m* impropre	несобственная подгруппа
I 200	**improper subobject** <CA>	uneigentliches Unterobjekt *n*	sous-objet *m* impropre	несобственный подобъект
I 201	**improper subset,** whole set considered as a subset of itself <SE>	unechte (uneigentliche) Teilmenge *f*, unechte Untermenge *f*	partie *f* pleine, sous-ensemble *m* impropre	наибольшее подмножество, полная часть, несобственное подмножество
I 202	**improper symbol,** syncategorematic symbol <LO>	uneigentliches Symbol *n*	symbole *m* impropre	несобственный символ
	improper transformation <AL, AN>	*s.* I 178		
	improper transformation into itself <AL, NT>	*s.* I 148		
I 203	**impulse response,** pulse response <AN>	Impulsübergang[sfunktion *f*] *m*, Impulsantwort[funktion] *f*, Stoßantwort[funktion] *f*	réponse *f* impulsionnelle (impulsive, percussionnelle)	импульсная переходная функция, импульсная (ударная) реакция
I 204	**impulsor,** ejector, torsor <GE>	Impulsor *m*, Ejektor *m*, Torsor *m* <Study>	impulseur *m*, éjecteur *m*, torseur *m*	импульсор, эжектор, торсор
I 205	**impure equation** <AL>	unreine Gleichung *f*, Gleichung mit mehreren Potenzen der Unbekannten, aequatio *f* affecta	équation *f* non binôme, équation polynôme	нечистое уравнение
I 206	**imputation** <TG>	Zuteilung *f*, Verteilung *f*	imputation *f*	предпосылка, дележ
I 207	**inaccessibility** <AN, SE, TO>	Unerreichbarkeit *f*	inaccessibilité *f*	недостижимость
	inaccessible aleph <SE>	*s.* I 209		
I 208	**inaccessible boundary point** <of the first *or* second kind> <in Dirichlet's problem> <DE, TO>	unerreichbarer Randpunkt *m* <erster *oder* zweiter Art>	point *m* inaccessible <de première (1re) *ou* deuxième (2e) espèce>	недостижимая граничная точка <первого *или* второго рода>
I 209	**inaccessible cardinal,** inaccessible aleph, cardinal number inaccessible from below <SE>	unerreichbare Kardinalzahl *f*, unerreichbarer Aleph *m*	cardinal (aleph) *m* inaccessible	недостижимое кардинальное число, недостижимый кардинал (алеф)
I 210	**inaccessible element,** element inaccessible from below <of a lattice> <LA>	unerreichbares Element *n*	élément *m* inaccessible	недостижимый элемент
I 211	**inaccessible number** <SE>	unerreichbare Zahl *f*	nombre *m* inaccessible	недостижимое число
I 212	**inaccessible ordinal** <regular initial number with a limit-index> <SE>	unerreichbare Ordnungszahl (Ordinalzahl) *f*	ordinal *m* inaccessible	недостижимое ординальное (порядковое) число
I 213	**inaccessible set** <SE>	unerreichbare Menge *f*	ensemble *m* inaccessible	недостижимое множество
I 214	**incalculability,** non-computability <FO>	Nichtberechenbarkeit *f*	propriété *f* d'être incalculable	невычислимость
I 215	**incalculable function,** non-computable function <FO>	nichtberechenbare (unberechenbare) Funktion *f*	fonction *f* incalculable	невычислимая функция; неисчислимая функция
I 216	**incentre,** centre of the inscribed circle <EG>	Mittelpunkt *m* des Inkreises (eingeschriebenen Kreises), Inkreismittelpunkt *m*	centre *m* du cercle inscrit	центр вписанной окружности
I 217	**incentre,** centre of the inscribed sphere <of a tetrahedron *or* another convex body> <EG>	Mittelpunkt *m* der Inkugel, Inkugelmittelpunkt *m*	centre *m* de la sphère inscrite	центр вписанной сферы
I 218	**incidence,** incidence relation[ship] <of a partial plane> <AL>	Inzidenzrelation *f*	relation *f* d'incidence	инцидентное отношение
I 219	**incidence** <with> <GE>	Inzidenz *f* <mit>, Enthaltensein *n* <in>, Inzidieren *n* <mit>	incidence *f* <à>	инцидентность <с>, принадлежность <к>
I 220	**incidence** <GP>	Inzidenz *f*	incidence *f*	инцидентность
	incidence coefficient <AT>	*s.* I 229		
I 221	**incidence condition** <GE>	Inzidenzbedingung *f*	condition *f* d'incidence	условие (требование) инцидентности
I 222	**incidence correspondence** <AG>	Inzidenzkorrespondenz *f*	correspondance *f* d'incidence	инцидентное соответствие
I 223	**incidence curve** <PJ>	Inzidenzkurve *f*	courbe *f* d'incidence	кривая инцидентности
I 224	**incidence formula** <AG>	Inzidenzformel *f* <Schubert>	formule *f* d'incidence	инцидентностная формула
I 225	**incidence geometry** <GE>	Inzidenzgeometrie *f*	géométrie *f* d'incidence	инцидентностная геометрия
I 226	**incidence map** <GP>	Inzidenzabbildung *f*	application *f* d'incidence	отображение инцидентности
I 227	**incidence matrix,** matrix of incidence <of a complex> <AT>	Inzidenzmatrix *f*, Berandungsmatrix *f*	matrice *f* d'incidence	матрица инцидентности
I 228	**incidence matrix,** vertex [incidence] matrix <of a graph> <GP>	Inzidenzmatrix *f*	matrice *f* d'incidence	матрица инциденций
I 229	**incidence number,** incidence-number, incidence coefficient <AT>	Berandungszahl *f*, Inzidenzzahl *f*, Inzidenzkoeffizient *m*	coefficient *m* d'incidence	коэффициент инцидентности
I 230	**incidence-preserving map** <GE>	inzidenzerhaltende Abbildung *f*	application *f* conservant l'incidence	отображение, сохраняющее инцидентность

No.	English	German	French	Russian
I 231	**incidence relation** <AT>	Berandungsrelation *f*, Berandungsbeziehung *f*	relation *f* d'incidence	отношение подчинения
I 232	**incidence relation** <GE>	Inzidenzbeziehung *f*, Beziehung *f* des Enthaltenseins, Beziehung der vereinigten Lage, Inzidenzrelation *f*	relation *f* d'incidence	отношение инцидентности, отношение принадлежности, соотношение инцидентности
	incidence relation[ship] <AL>	*s.* I 218		
	incidence structure <PJ>	*s.* P 249		
I 233	**incidence surface** <PJ>	Inzidenzfläche *f*	surface *f* d'incidence	поверхность инцидентности
	incidence system <PJ>	*s.* P 249		
I 234	**incidence table** <of a configuration> <TO>	Inzidenztafel *f* <einer Konfiguration>	table *f* d'incidence <d'une configuration>	таблица инциденций <конфигурации>
I 235	**incident** <GE, GP, SE>	inzident	incident	инцидентный
I 236	**incircle,** inscribed circle <of a triangle> <EG>	Inkreis *m*, einbeschriebener (eingeschriebener) Kreis *m*, Innenkreis *m*, Binnenkreis *m*	cercle *m* inscrit, circonférence *f* inscrite	вписанная окружность, вписанный круг
I 237	**inclination** <EG>	Neigung *f*	inclinaison *f*	наклон
	inclination <DS>	*s.* 1. A 664; 2. A 665		
I 238	**inclined line** <to a line *or* plane> <EG>	geneigte Gerade *f* <gegen eine Gerade *oder* Ebene>	droite *f* inclinée <vers une droite *ou* un plan>	наклонная [прямая] <к прямой *или* плоскости>
I 239	**include / to** <said of a relation> <SE>	enthalten	être moins fin <que>	быть более грубое отношение <чем>
I 239a	**include / to** <as a subset> $\supseteq$ <SE>	enthalten <als Untermenge>, $\supseteq$	contenir <comme partie>, $\supseteq$	содержать <как подмножество>, $\supseteq$
I 240	**included angle** <between two sides> <EG>	eingeschlossener Winkel *m* <von zwei Seiten>	angle *m* compris <entre deux côtés>	заключенный угол <между двумя сторонами>
	include properly / to <SE>	*s.* C 2154		
I 241	**including set,** superset, comprehending set <SE>	Obermenge *f*	sur-ensemble *m*	надмножество
I 242	**inclusion,** set-theoretic[al] inclusion, $\subseteq$ <of a subset> <SE>	Inklusion *f*, Enthaltensein *n*, $\subseteq$ <Gleichheit zugelassen>	inclusion *f*, inclusion large, inclusion au sens large, $\subseteq$	включение, $\subseteq$
	inclusion <LO>	*s.* L 1062		
	inclusion function <SE>	*s.* I 245		
I 243	**inclusion functor** <CA>	Inklusionsfunktor *m*, Inklusion *f* <einer Unterkategorie>	foncteur *m* d'inclusion	функтор включения
I 244	**inclusion homomorphism** <HA>	Inklusionshomomorphismus *m*	homomorphisme *m* d'inclusion	гомоморфизм включения
I 245	**inclusion map[ping],** inclusion (insertion) function <of a subset> <SE>	Inklusionsabbildung *f*, Einbettung *f*, kanonische Injektion *f*, Einbettungsabbildung *f*, Inklusion *f*, Einsetzungsabbildung *f*	injection *f*, application *f* canonique (d'inclusion), insertion *f*	отображение вложения, вложение, отображение включения
I 246	**inclusion relation,** subset (part-whole) relation, relation of inclusion (subset, set-inclusion) <SE>	Inklusionsbeziehung *f*, Beziehung *f* des Enthaltenseins, Enthaltenseinsbeziehung *f*, Enthaltenseinsrelation *f*, Inklusionsrelation *f*	relation *f* d'inclusion	отношение включения, соотношение включения
	inclusion relation <SE>	*s.* 1. O 336; 2. P 246		
I 247	**inclusion theorem** <DE, FA, IE>	Einschließungssatz *m*	théorème *m* d'inclusion	теорема двусторонней оценки, теорема включения
I 248	**inclusion theorem of Frobenius,** Frobenius['] inclusion theorem <DE>	Frobeniusscher Einschließungssatz *m*, Einschließungssatz *m* von Frobenius	théorème *m* d'inclusion de Frobenius	теорема включения Фробениуса
	inclusive disjunction <LO>	*s.* D 705		
I 249	**inclusive OR, inclusive "or"** <LO>	einschließendes ODER (Oder) *n*, inklusives ODER (Oder) *n*	OU *m* inclusif, « ou » *m* étant pris au sens inclusif, OU non exclusif	исключающее ИЛИ («или»), неразделительное ИЛИ («или»), ИЛИ («или») в неисключающем смысле, соединительно-разделительный союз «или», союз «или» в соединительно-разделительном значении, «или . . . или оба», и/или
	incoming edge <GP>	*s.* E 258		
I 250	**incommensurability** <GE, NT>	Inkommensurabilität *f*, // Asymmetrie *f*	incommensurabilité *f*, // asymétrie *f*	несоизмеримость
I 251	**incommensurable** <GE, NT>	inkommensurabel, ohne gemeinsames Maß, // asymmetrisch, unsymmetrisch	incommensurable, sourd, // asymétrique	несоизмеримый
	incommensurable line segments <GE>	*s.* I 253		
I 252	**incommensurable quantities** <GE, NT>	inkommensurable Größen *fpl*	grandeurs (quantités) *fpl* incommensurables, incommensurables *fpl*	несоизмеримые величины
I 253	**incommensurable segments,** incommensurable line segments <GE>	inkommensurable Strecken *fpl*	segments *mpl* incommensurables	несоизмеримые отрезки
	⌐<FA> **incommutable operators**	*s.* N 338		
I 254	**incompactness,** noncompactness <TO>	Nichtkompaktheit *f*	non-compacité *f*	некомпактность

I 255	**incomparability relation** <SE>	Unvergleichbarkeitsrelation *f*	relation *f* d'incomparabilité	отношение несравнимости
I 256	**incomparable methods of limitation** <LI>	unvergleichbare Limitierungsverfahren (*V*-Verfahren) *npl*	méthodes *fpl* de limitation non comparables	несравнимые методы перехода к обобщенному пределу
I 257	**incomparably greater element** <AL>	unvergleichbar größeres Element *n*	élément *m* incomparablement plus grand	несравнимо больший элемент
I 258	**incomparably smaller element** <AL>	unvergleichbar kleineres Element *n*	élément *m* incomparablement plus petit	несравнимо меньший элемент
I 259	**incompatibility,** inconsistency <GN>	Inkompatibilität *f*, Unvereinbarkeit *f*, Unverträglichkeit *f*	incompatibilité *f*	несовместимость, несовместность
	incompatibility <AL, LO>	*s.* S 763		
	incompatibility <LO>	*s.* I 279		
	incompatible axioms <FO>	*s.* I 284		
	incompatible elements <SE>	*s.* N 340		
	incompatible equations <AL, AN>	*s.* I 281		
	incompatible events <ST>	*s.* M 1101		
I 260/1	**incomplete Bessel function** <FU>	unvollständige Bessel-Funktion *f*	fonction *f* de Bessel incomplète	неполная бесселева функция, неполная функция Бесселя
I 262	**incomplete beta function** <FU>	unvollständige Beta-Funktion *f*	fonction *f* bêta incomplète	неполная бета-функция [Эйлера]
I 263	**incomplete Boolean algebra** <AL>	unvollständige Boolesche Algebra *f*	algèbre *f* de Boole non complète	неполная булева алгебра
	incomplete elliptic integral <FU>	*s.* E 178		
I 264	**incomplete equation** <of the *n*-th degree> <AL>	unvollständige Gleichung *f* <*n*-ten Grades>	équation *f* incomplète <de degré *n*>	неполное уравнение <степени *n*>
I 265	**incomplete factorial function** <FU>	unvollständige Fakultät *f*	factorielle *f* incomplète	неполный факториал
I 266	**incomplete gamma function** <FU>	unvollständige Gamma-Funktion *f*	fonction *f* gamma incomplète	неполная гамма-функция
I 267	**incomplete induction** <FO>	unvollständige Induktion *f*	induction *f* incomplète	неполная (несовершенная, проблематическая, обобщающая, расширяющая) индукция
I 268	**incomplete latin square,** partial latin square <CT, ST>	unvollständiges lateinisches Quadrat *n*	carré *m* latin incomplet	неполный латинский квадрат
I 269	**incomplete lattice** <LA>	unvollständiger Verband *m*	treillis (lattice) *m* incomplet	неполная решетка
	incompletely defined function <SE>	*s.* P 211		
I 270	**incompleteness theorem** <MM>	Unvollständigkeitssatz *m*	théorème *m* d'incomplétude	теорема о неполноте
I 271	**incomplete orthonormal system** <AN>	unvollständiges Orthonormalsystem *n*	système *m* orthonormal incomplet	неполная ортонормированная система
I 272	**incomplete polynomial** <AL>	unvollständiges Polynom *n*	polynôme *m* incomplet, fonction *f* rationnelle entière incomplète	неполный многочлен
I 273	**incomplete quadratic equation** <AL>	unvollständige quadratische Gleichung *f*	équation *f* quadratique incomplète	неполное квадратное уравнение
I 274	**incompressible measurable transformation** <ME>	inkompressible (nicht dissipative) meßbare Transformation *f*	transformation *f* mesurable incompressible	несжимаемое измеримое преобразование
I 275	**incongruence** <AL, NT>	Inkongruenz *f*	non-congruence *f*	несравнимость
I 276	**incongruence,** noncongruence <EG>	Inkongruenz *f*	non-congruence *f*, incongruence	неконгруэнтность
I 277	**incongruent** <AL>	inkongruent, nicht kongruent	incongru	несравнимый
I 278	**incongruent,** incongruous <EG>	inkongruent	incongru	неконгруэнтный, инконгруэнтный
	incongruous <EG>	*s.* I 278		
I 279	**inconsistency,** contradictoriness, self-contradictoriness, incompatibility <LO>	Widersprüchlichkeit *f*	inconsistance *f*, incohérence *f*	несовместимость, противоречивость
	inconsistency <GN>	*s.* I 259		
I 280	**inconsistent calculus** <LO>	widerspruchsvoller Kalkül *m*	calcul *m* contradictoire	противоречивое исчисление
	inconsistent equation <AL>	*s.* U 396		
I 281	**inconsistent equations,** incompatible equations, inconsistent system of equations <AL, AN>	unlösbare (unverträgliche) Gleichungen *fpl*, unlösbares Gleichungssystem *n*, System *n* unverträglicher Gleichungen	équations *fpl* incompatibles, système *m* incompatible, système d'équations incompatible (impossible, contradictoires)	несовместимые уравнения, несобственная система [уравнений], противоречивая система [уравнений], противоречивые уравнения
I 282	**inconsistent estimator** <ST>	inkonsistente Schätzung (Schätzfunktion) *f*	estimateur *m* non consistant, estimateur inconsistant	несостоятельная оценка
I 283	**inconsistent formal system** <LO>	widersprüchliches formales System *n*	système *m* formel inconsistant	противоречивая формальная система
I 284	**inconsistent system of axioms,** [self-]contradictory system of axioms, incompatible axioms <FO>	widerspruchsvolles (widersprüchliches) Axiomensystem *n*, sich widersprechende Axiome *npl*	système *m* axiomatique incompatible, système axiomatique contradictoire, axiomes *mpl* incohérents (inconsistants)	противоречивая (контрадикторная) система аксиом, несовместные (несовместимые, противоречащие) аксиомы

No.	English	German	French	Russian
	inconsistent system of equations <AL, AN>	*s.* I 281		
I 285	**incorrect proposition** <LO>	fehlerhafte Aussage *f*	énoncé *m* erroné	ошибочное высказывание
	increasing correspondence <SE>	*s.* O 354		
	increasing directed set <SE>	*s.* D 552		
I 286	**increasing filtration,** filtration <of a module> <AL>	aufsteigende Filtration *f*	filtration *f* croissante	возрастающая фильтрация
I 287	**increasing function,** isotonic (isotone, non-decreasing) function, monotonically (monotonic, monotone) increasing (non-decreasing) function <RF>	[monoton] wachsende (zunehmende, steigende, nicht abnehmende, nichtfallende) Funktion *f*, isotone Funktion	fonction *f* croissante (isotone), fonction monotone (monotonement) croissante (non décroissante), fonction croissante au sens large	возрастающая (небывающая, изотонная) функция, монотонно (монотонная) неубывающая (возрастающая) функция
	increasing function <SE>	*s.* I 1173		
I 288	**increasing homeomorphism** <TO>	wachsender Homöomorphismus *m*	homéomorphisme *m* croissant	возрастающий гомеоморфизм
I 289	**increasing progression,** monotonically increasing progression <AR>	wachsende (aufsteigende) Progression *f*	progression *f* ascendante (croissante)	возрастающая прогрессия
	increasing relation <SE>	*s.* O 357		
I 290	**increasing sequence** <of groups> <GR>	aufsteigende Folge *f*	suite *f* croissante	возрастающая последовательность
	increasing sequence <SS>	*s.* M 869		
I 291	**increasing transfinite sequence** <of type α>, **increasing α-sequence** <SE>	Fundamentalfolge *f* von Ordnungszahlen	suite *f* transfinie croissante <de type α>, α-suite (alpha-suite) *f* croissante	возрастающая трансфинитная последовательность <типа α>, возрастающая α-последовательность
I 292	**increment,** finite increment <of a function> <DI>	Zuwachs *m*, Inkrement *n*	accroissement *m*, incrément *m*	приращение
I 293	**increment graph** <GP>	Inkrementgraph *m*	graphe *m* d'incréments	граф приращений
	ind <FA>	*s.* I 337		
I 294	**indecomposability** <AL, SE, TO>	Unzerlegbarkeit *f*	indécomposabilité *f*	неразложимость
I 295	**indecomposable cardinal number** <SE>	unzerlegbare Mächtigkeit (Kardinalzahl) *f*	nombre *m* cardinal indécomposable	аддитивно неразложимое кардинальное число
	indecomposable matrix <MD>	*s.* N 352		
I 296	**indecomposable ordinal** <SE>	unzerlegbare (irreduzible) Ordnungszahl *f* <bezüglich einer Operation>, unzerlegbare Zahl *f*	ordinal *m* indécomposable	неразложимое порядковое число
I 297	**indefinability** <LO>	Undefinierbarkeit *f*	indéfinissabilité *f*	неопределяемость, неопределимость
I 298	**indefinite form** <AL>	indefinite Form *f*	forme *f* indéfinie	неопределенная форма
I 299	**indefinite game** <TG>	unbestimmtes Spiel *n*	jeu *m* indéfini	неопределенная игра
I 300	**indefinite integral** <as a function of its upper limit> <DI>	unbestimmtes Integral *n*	intégrale *f* indéfinie	неопределенный интеграл
	indefinite integral <DI>	*s.* P 1344		
I 301	**indefinitely increasing series,** infinitely increasing series <SS>	unbeschränkt (unbegrenzt, unendlich) wachsende Reihe *f*	série *f* infiniment (indéfiniment) croissante	неограниченно возрастающий ряд
I 302	**indefiniteness** <AL, AN>	Indefinitheit *f*	propriété *f* d'être indéfini	знаконеопределенность, неопределенность
	indefiniteness <GN>	*s.* I 322		
I 303	**indefinite operator** <FA>	indefiniter Operator *m*	opérateur *m* indéfini	неопределенный оператор
I 304	**indefinite total variation** <AN>	unbestimmte Totalvariation *f*	variation *f* totale indéfinie	неопределенная полная вариация
I 305	**in[-]degree,** demi-degree inward, in-valence <of a vertex> <GP>	Eingangsvalenz *f*, Eingangsgrad *m*, negativer Grad *m*	degré (demi-degré) *m* intérieur	отрицательная степень, полустепень захода
I 306	**independence** <of> <GN>	Unabhängigkeit *f* <von>	indépendance *f* <de>	независимость <от>
	independence <ST>	*s.* S 1793		
	independence number <GP>	*s.* S 1578		
	independence of the order of operation of two external laws of composition <AL>	*s.* A 1112		
I 307	**independence of valuations** <AL>	Annäherungsunabhängigkeit *f* von Bewertungen	indépendance *f* des valuations	независимость абсолютных значений
I 308	**independence proof** <FO> ⌐<AL>	Unabhängigkeitsbeweis *m*	démonstration *f* de l'indépendance	доказательство независимости
	independence theorem	*s.* W 34		
	independent absolute value <AL>	*s.* I 422		
	independent absolute values <AL>	*s.* I 319		
I 309	**independent axioms,** postulates independent as to consequences <FO>	unabhängige Axiome *npl*	axiomes *mpl* indépendants	независимые аксиомы
	independent edge family <GP>	*s.* D 887		
	independent event <ST>	*s.* S 1782		
I 310	**independent events** <ST>	unabhängige (in der Gesamtheit unabhängige, insgesamt unabhängige, en bloc unabhängige) Ereignisse *npl*	événements *mpl* indépendants	независимые события

No.	English	German	French	Russian
	independent points <GE>	*s.* L 813		
	independent random variable <ST>	*s.* I 321		
I 311	**independent representation** <of eigenvalues etc.> <AN>	independente (unabhängige) Darstellung *f*	représentation *f* indépendante	независящее представление
I 312	**independent sampling** <ST>	unabhängige Stichprobenauswahl (Stichprobennahme) *f*, unabhängiges Stichprobenerhebungsschema *n*	échantillonnage (sondage) *m* indépendant	независящий выбор
I 313	**independent set** <of a matroid> <GP>	independente (unabhängige) Menge *f*	ensemble *m* indépendant (libre)	независимое множество
I 314	**independent set,** unrelated set, internally stable set, stable set [from the inside] <of vertices> <GP>	unabhängige Knotenmenge (Menge) *f*, innerlich stabile Menge <von Knoten>	ensemble *m* indépendant (stable, intérieurement stable) <de sommets>	независимое множество, внутренне[е] устойчивое множество, несвязное множество, устойчивое [изнутри] множество <вершин>
I 315	**independent set** <of propositions *or* notions> <LO>	unabhängige Menge *f*	ensemble *m* indépendant	независимая (неизбыточная, минимальная) совокупность
I 316	**independent set** <of formulas> <MM>	unabhängige Menge *f*	ensemble *m* indépendant	независимое множество
	independent set <AL>	*s.* F 633		
	independent set of points <GE>	*s.* L 813		
I 317	**independent system of axioms** <FO>	unabhängiges Axiomensystem *n*, Basis *f*	système *m* d'axiomes indépendant	независимая система аксиом, система независимых аксиом
I 318	**independent tests,** orthogonal tests <ST>	unabhängige (orthogonale) Tests *mpl*	tests *mpl* indépendants (orthogonaux)	независимые (ортогональные) критерии
I 319	**independent valuations,** independent absolute values <AL>	annäherungsunabhängige Bewertungen *fpl*	valuations *fpl* indépendantes	независимые абсолютные значения
I 320	**independent variable,** argument <AN>	unabhängige Variable (Veränderliche) *f*, Argument *n*	variable *f* indépendante, variable [principale], argument *m*	независимая переменная, аргумент; значение аргумента
	independent variable <PG>	*s.* N 322		
I 321	**independent variate,** independent random variable <ST>	unabhängige Zufallsvariable *f*	variable *f* aléatoire indépendante	независимая случайная переменная
I 322	**indeterminacy,** indeterminedness, indefiniteness, indeterminateness, undeterminedness <GN>	Unbestimmtheit *f*	indétermination *f*, indéfinité *f*	неопределенность
I 323	**indeterminate** <AL>	Unbestimmte *f*	indéterminée *f*	неопределенная [величина], переменная
I 324	**indeterminate equation** <diophantine or not> <AL>	unbestimmte Gleichung *f*	équation *f* indéterminée	неопределенное уравнение
	indeterminate equation <NT>	*s.* D 532		
	indeterminate expression <DI>	*s.* I 325		
I 325	**indeterminate form,** indeterminate expression <DI>	unbestimmter Ausdruck *m*, unbestimmte Form *f*, unbestimmter (singulärer) Wert *m*	expression *f* [qui se présente sous une forme] indéterminée, forme *f* indéterminée (indéfinie, illusoire), valeur *f* indéterminée (singulière) <Cauchy>	неопределенное выражение, неопределенная форма, неопределенность
I 326	**indeterminate fraction** <DI>	unbestimmter Bruch *m*	fraction *f* indéterminée	неопределенная дробь
	indeterminateness <GN>	*s.* I 322		
I 327	**indeterminate product** <of generalized functions> <AN>	unbestimmtes Produkt *n*	produit *m* indéfini	неопределенное произведение
I 328	**indeterminate system of equations** <more unknowns than equations> <AL>	unbestimmtes Gleichungssystem *n*	système *m* indéterminé	неопределенная система уравнений
	indeterminedness <GN>	*s.* I 322		
I 329	**index** <of an algebraic correspondence> <AG>	Index *m*, Zahl *f*	indice *m*	индекс
I 330	**index** <cardinality of the generated sub-semigroup> <AL>	Index *m*, Ordnung *f*	exposant *m*	индекс, показатель
I 331	**index** <index *or* index + period, *pl.* indices, index pair> <AL>	Exponent *m*	exposant *m*	показатель <*pl.*: показатели, пара показателей>
I 332	**index,** order <of a root, radical> <AL>	Wurzelexponent *m*, Wurzelzeiger *m*, Wurzelindex *m*	ordre *m*, exposant *m*, indice *m* <d'une racine>	показатель корня
I 333	**index,** rank <of an equivalence relation> <AL, SE>	Index *m*, Anzahl *f* der Äquivalenzklassen	rang *m*	индекс [эквивалентности], ранг
I 334	**index** <of a fixed point> <AT>	Index *m* <eines Fixpunktes>, Fixpunktindex *m*	ordre *m* <d'un point invariant>	индекс <неподвижной точки>
I 335	**index** <of a vector field> <AT>	Index *m* <eines Vektorfelds>	indice *m* de giration <d'un champ de vecteurs, d'un vecteur autour d'une courbe fermée>	индекс <векторного поля>

No.	English	German	French	Russian
I 336	**index,** analytical index <of an elliptical differential operator *or* a complex of pseudodifferential operators> <DE>	Index *m*	indice *m*	индекс, аналитический индекс
I 337	**index,** ind <of an operator of finite deficiency and nullity> <FA>	Index *m*, ind	indice *m*, ind	индекс, ind
I 338	**index** <of a sine spiral> <GE>	Index *m*	indice *m*	показатель
I 339	**index** <as a mathematical sign> <GN>	Index *m*	indice *m*	индекс
I 340	**index** <of a subgroup> <GR>	Index *m*, Gruppenindex *m*	indice *m*, index *m*	индекс
I 341	**index,** number <of a line *or* column> <MD>	Index *m*, Nummer *f*	rang *m*, indice *m*	индекс
I 342	**index** <of a matrix> <MD>	Grad *m* der Minimalgleichung, Index *m*	degré *m* de l'équation minimale (minimum); classe *f* <d'une matrice dérogatoire> <Sylvester>	степень минимального уравнения
I 343	**index** <of a minor> <MD>	Index *m* <Summe der Zeilen- und Spaltenindizes>	indice *m*	индекс
I 344	**index** <of a number with respect to a primitive root> <NT>	Index *m*, Exponent *m*	indice *m*	индекс
I 345	**index;** number, place <of an element of a sequence> <SS>	Index *m*; Nummer *f*	indice *m*, rang *m*; place *f*	индекс; номер
I 346	**index** <of a point relative to a closed path, *or* to a curve> <TO>	Index *m*, Ordnung *f* <eines Punktes bezüglich eines geschlossenen Weges *oder* einer Kurve>	indice *m* <d'un point par rapport à un lacet *ou* à un circuit>	порядок, индекс <точки относительно замкнутого пути, кривой, контура *или* петли>
I 347	**index** <of the first *or* second kind> <of the Hermitian quantity> <VT>	Index *m* <erster (1.) *oder* zweiter (2.) Art>	indice *m* <de première *ou* deuxième espèce>	индекс <первого *или* второго рода>
	index <AL, AR>	*s.* E 730		
	index <FT, TO>	*s.* W 264		
	index <NT>	*s.* O 277		
	index <ST>	*s.* I 352		
I 348	**indexed** <GN>	indiziert; durchindiziert	indexé, indicié, affecté d'indices	индексированный, снабженный индексами
	indexed class <SE>	*s.* S 1042		
	indexed collection of elements <SE>	*s.* F 82		
	indexed point <CA>	*s.* B 103		
	indexed set of elements <SE> ⌐<SE>	*s.* F 82		
	indexed system of sets	*s.* F 86		
I 349	**index form** <VA>	Indexform *f*	forme *f* indicielle	индексная форма
I 350	**indexing,** labelling, labeling <GN>	Indizierung *f*, Bezeichnung *f* mit Indizes, Indexbezeichnung *f*	affectation *f* d'indices	индицирование, проиндицирование, снабжение индексами, помечение индексами, индексация
I 351	**indexing of a set *E* using as indices the elements of a set *F*** <SE>	Parameterdarstellung *f* einer Menge *E* mittels einer Menge *F*	représentation *f* paramétrique d'un ensemble *E* au moyen d'un ensemble *F*	представление множества *E* с помощью множества *F*
	indexing set <SE>	*s.* I 361		
	index law <AL, SE>	*s.* L 185		
	index line <NO>	*s.* I 1154		
I 352	**index number,** index <ST>	Indexzahl *f*, Index *m*	nombre *m* indice, indice *m*	индекс
	index of cograduation <ST>	*s.* S 1350		
	index of connection <AT>	*s.* B 252		
I 353	**index of correlation** <square of the correlation ratio> <ST>	Korrelationsindex *m*	indice *m* de corrélation	индекс корреляции
I 354	**index of imprimitivity** <of a matrix> <MD>	Imprimitivitätsindex *m*	indice *m* d'imprimitivité	индекс импримитивности
I 355	**index of inertia** <of a bilinear *or* quadratic form> <AL>	Trägheitsindex *m*, Index *m*	indice *m*, indice d'inertie, index *m*	индекс инерции, индекс
I 356	**index of multiplicity** <of a meromorphic function> <FT>	Verzweigtheitsindex *m*, Index *m* der algebraischen Verzweigtheit, Verzweigungsindex *m*	indice *m* de ramification	индекс ветвления
I 357	**index of nilpotency** <of an element, algebra, ideal> <AL>	Exponent *m*, Nilpotenzexponent *m*	indice *m* de nilpotence	индекс нильпотентности
I 358	**index of speciality** <of a linear series> <AG>	Spezialitätsindex *m*	indice *m* de spécialité	индекс специальности
	index pair <AL>	*s.* I 331		
I 359	**index-preserving projectivity** <of a group> <AL>	indexerhaltender Verbandsisomorphismus *m*	isomorphisme *m* de treillis conservant l'indice	сохраняющий индексы структурный изоморфизм
I 360	**index** <of a point> **relative to a cycle** <AT>	Ordnung *f* <eines Punktes> in bezug auf einen Zyklus, Ordnung (Ordnungszahl *f*) <eines Punktes> bezüglich eines Zyklus	indice *m* <d'un point> par rapport à un cycle	порядок <точки> относительно цикла
I 361	**index set,** indexing set, set of indices, domain of indexes, domain <SE>	Indexmenge *f*	ensemble *m* des indices, ensemble d'indices	множество индексов, индексирующее множество
I 362	**index set** <of an indexed collection> <SE>	Träger *m* <eines mengentheoretischen Komplexes>	ensemble *m* d'indices <d'une famille>	множество индексов <семейства>

	3-index symbol <DG>	*s.* C 667		
I 363	**index theorem** <FA>	Indextheorem *n*	théorème *m* de l'indice	теорема об индексе
I 364	**indicator,** Bernoulli['s] variable <of a random event> <ST>	Indikator *m*, Anzeiger *m*, Bernoullische Variable *f*	indicateur *m*, variable *f* de Bernoulli	индикатор, переменная Бернулли
	indicator <NT>	*s.* E 588		
I 365	**indicator function,** Phragmén-Lindelöf function <of an entire function> <FT>	Indikatrix *f*, Indikator *m*	indicatrice *f*, fonction *f* de Phragmén-Lindelöf	индикатриса, функция Фрагмена-Линделефа
I 366	**indicatrix** <of the Carathéodory metric> <FT>	Indikatrix *f* <der Carathéodoryschen Metrik>	indicatrice *f* <de la métrique de Carathéodory>	индикатриса <метрики Каратеодори>
	indicatrix <DG>	*s.* T 483		
	indicatrix of principal normals <DG>	*s.* S 1467		
I 367	**indicial equation** <of a homogeneous linear differential equation at a singular point, either a point of determinacy or a point of indeterminacy> <DE>	Indexgleichung *f*, charakteristische Gleichung *f*	équation *f* déterminante	определяющее уравнение
I 368	**indicial notation** <GN>	Indexschreibweise *f*	écriture (notation) *f* indicielle	индексная запись
I 369	**indifference class** <ST>	Indifferenzklasse *f*	classe *f* d'indifférence	класс безразличия
I 370	**indifference curve** <ST, TG>	Indifferenzkurve *f*	courbe *f* d'indifférence	кривая безразличия
I 371	**indifference region** <ST>	Indifferenzbereich *m*, indifferenter Bereich *m*	région *f* d'indifférence	область безразличия
I 372	**indifference section** <ST>	Indifferenzabschnitt *m*	section *f* d'indifférence	секция безразличия
I 373	**indifference surface** <ST>	Indifferenzfläche *f*	surface *f* d'indifférence	поверхность безразличия
I 374	**indifference zone** <ST>	Indifferenzzone *f*	zone *f* d'indifférence	зона безразличия
I 375	**indifferent continuity** <AN>	indifferente Stetigkeit *f*	continuité *f* indifférente	индифферентная непрерывность
	indirect analytic continuation <FT>	*s.* A 630		
I 376	**indirect bilinear transformation,** indirect Möbius transformation, quasi[-]linear transformation, anti-homography <FT>	lineare (allgemeine lineare, gebrochene lineare, gebrochen-lineare) Transformation (Abbildung, Substitution) *f* zweiter (2.) Art, quasilineare Transformation (Abbildung, Substitution), gegensinnige (indirekte, uneigentliche) Möbiussche Transformation (Kreisverwandtschaft *f*, Kreistransformation *f*), // Antihomographie *f*	transformation *f* homographique indirecte, homographie *f* indirecte, transformation quasilinéaire, correspondance *f* antihomographique	квазилинейное преобразование (отображение), непрямое дробно-линейное преобразование (отображение), непрямое преобразование Мебиуса, непрямое круговое преобразование, антигомография
I 377	**indirect boundary point** <FT>	mittelbare (indirekte) Randstelle *f*	point *m* frontière indirect	непрямая граничная точка
	indirect conformal mapping (transformation) <FT>	*s.* A 729		
	indirect demonstration ⌐<LO>	*s.* I 378		
	indirected graph <GP>	*s.* M 962		
	indirectly conformal mapping (transformation) <FT>	*s.* A 729		
	indirect Möbius transformation <FT>	*s.* I 376		
I 378	**indirect proof,** proof by reductio ad absurdum, reduction ad absurdum proof, indirect demonstration, reductio ad absurdum, reductio ad impossibile <LO>	indirekter Beweis *m*, Widerspruchsbeweis *m*, apagogisches Beweisverfahren *n*, apagogischer Beweis, reductio *f* ad absurdum, demonstratio *f* a contrario	démonstration *f* indirecte (par réduction à l'absurde), démonstration par l'absurde, raisonnement *m* par l'absurde, méthode *f* « ad absurdo », démonstration a contrario, démonstration apagogique, raisonnement apagogique, apagogie *f*, preuve *f* indirecte (par contradiction), reductio *f* ad absurdum	доказательство от противного, аналогическое косвенное доказательство, косвенное доказательство, непрямое доказательство, доказательство приведением к противоречию (нелепости, абсурду), рассуждение от противного, аналогическое доказательство
I 379	**indirect proof** <as the wider concept> <GN>	indirekter Beweis *m*	preuve *f* indirecte	косвенное доказательство
I 380	**indirect sampling** <ST>	indirekte Stichprobennahme *f*	échantillonnage (sondage) *m* indirect	косвенный выбор
I 381	**indiscrete [topological] space,** accrete space <TO>	indiskreter topologischer Raum *m*, trivialer Raum	espace *m* muni de la topologie indiscrète, espace trivial	пространство с тривиальной топологией, тривиальное (антидискретное) пространство
I 382	**indiscrete topology,** trivial (chaotic) topology <TO>	indiskrete (chaotische, triviale) Topologie *f*	topologie *f* triviale (grossière, chaotique, indiscrète)	тривиальная (нулевая, антидискретная, хаотическая) топология
	individual <LO>	*s.* 1. I 388; 2. O 2		
	individual <SE>	*s.* U 448		
	individual <ST>	*s.* S 31		
	individual constant <LO>	*s.* I 386		
I 383	**individual ergodic theorem,** Birkhoff['s] ergodic theorem <SP>	individueller Ergodensatz *m* [von G. D. Birkhoff], Ergodensatz von Birkhoff, Birkhoffscher Ergodensatz	théorème *m* ergodique individuel, théorème ergodique de Birkhoff	индивидуальная эргодическая теорема, эргодическая теорема Биркгофа (Бирхофа)

No.	English	German	French	Russian
384	**individually rational payoff configuration** <TG>	individuell rationale Konfiguration *f*	configuration *f* individuellement rationnelle	индивидуально рациональная конфигурация
	individual move <TG>	*s.* P 509		
385	**individual observation** <ST>	Einzelbeobachtung *f*	observation *f* individuelle	единичное (отдельное) наблюдение
386	**individual parameter,** individual constant, term <LO>	Individuenkonstante *f*, Objektkonstante *f*, Gegenstandskonstante *f*, konstanter Term *m*	constante *f* d'objet, objet *m* fixe	индивидная константа, предметная константа, предметная постоянная
387	**individual probability** <ST>	Einzelwahrscheinlichkeit *f*	probabilité *f* individuelle	индивидуальная (единичная) вероятность
388	**individual symbol,** individual <LO>	Individuensymbol *n*, nullstelliges Operationssymbol *n*	symbole *m* individuel, individu *m*	переменный символ для предметов
	individual [term] variable <LO>	*s.* O 11		
389	**individual variation** <ST>	Einzelvariation *f*	variation *f* individuelle	единичное отклонение (изменение)
390	**indivisibility** <AL>	Unteilbarkeit *f*	indivisibilité *f*	неделимость
391	**indivisible element** <AL>	unteilbares Element *n*	élément *m* indivisible	недилимый элемент
	indivisible group <GR>	*s.* D 581		
	induced bundle <AT>	*s.* I 394		
392	**induced cohomology homomorphism,** cohomology homomorphism <AT>	induzierter Homomorphismus *m* der Kohomologiegruppen	homomorphisme *m* induit des groupes de cohomologie	индуцированный гомоморфизм групп когомологий
393	**induced equivalence relation,** equivalence naturally induced <by a mapping>, [equivalence] kernel, kernel equivalence <of a map> <SE, UA>	induzierte Äquivalenzrelation *f* <durch eine Abbildung>, Kern *m* <einer Abbildung>	équivalence *f* d'application, équivalence associée à une application	отношение эквивалентности, естественно индуцированное отображением; ядро <отображения>, ядерная эквивалентность
394	**induced fibre bundle,** induced bundle <by a mapping> <AT>	induziertes Faserbündel *n*, Urbild *n* eines Faserbündels <vermöge einer Abbildung>	espace *m* fibré image réciproque, fibré *m* induit <par une application>	индуцированное косое произведение, индуцированное расслоенное пространство <отображением>
395	**induced partial composition** <on a subset> <AL>	induzierte partielle algebraische Verknüpfung *f*	composition *f* partielle induite	индуцированная частичная композиция
	induced subgraph <GP>	*s.* S 2105		
	induced topology <TO>	*s.* Q 350		
396	**induced uniformity** <on a subset>, relative uniformity <for a subset>, relativization of the uniformity <to a subset> <TO>	induzierte uniforme Struktur *f* <auf einer Untermenge>	structure *f* uniforme induite <sur une partie>	индуцированная равномерная структура <на подмножестве>
397	**induction** <as a counterpart to deduction> <LO>	Induktion *f*	induction *f*, raisonnement *m* par récurrence, raisonnement inductif	индукция
	induction <FO>	*s.* M 165		
	inductional assumption <LO>	*s.* I 398		
	induction axiom <FO, LO>	*s.* A 1281		
	induction condition <FO>	*s.* I 402		
	induction function <DE, PO>	*s.* G 416		
	induction function in the most general sense <DE>	*s.* G 417		
398	**induction hypothesis,** inductive hypothesis, inductional assumption <LO>	Induktionsannahme *f*, Induktionsvoraussetzung *f*	hypothèse *f* de récurrence	индукционная гипотеза, индуктивное предположение
	induction injection <CA>	*s.* I 544		
399	**induction on *n*** <FO, LO>	Induktion *f* nach *n*	récurrence *f* sur *n*	индукция по *n*
	induction principle <FO, LO>	*s.* P 1510		
	induction proof <FO>	*s.* P 1754/5		
400	**induction rule,** rule of induction <LO>	Induktionsregel *f*	règle *f* de l'induction complète	правило индукции
401	**induction scheme** <MM>	Induktionsschema *n*, Schema *n* der vollständigen Induktion	schéma *m* de l'induction	схема индукции
402	**induction step,** inductive step, induction condition <FO>	Induktionsschritt *m*, Induktionsschluß *m*, Schluß *m* von *n* auf $n+1$	établissement *m* de validité d'une proposition pour $n+1$, si la vérité de la n^{me} (précédente) est assurée	индукционный шаг, этап в доказательстве по индукции, индуктивный шаг
403	**induction variable** <LO>	Induktionsvariable *f*	variable *f* de récurrence	индукционная переменная; переменная, по которой производится индукция
	inductive cardinal <SE>	*s.* F 260		
404	**inductive closure system** <AL>	induktives Hüllensystem *n*	système *m* de fermeture inductif	индуктивная система замыканий
405	**inductive conclusion** <ST>	induktiver Schluß *m*, Induktionsschluß *m*, Repräsentationsschluß *m*, Schluß vom Teil aufs Ganze	conclusion *f* inductive	индуктивное заключение
406	**inductive cone,** direct cone <with range vertex *x* and base *d*> <of morphisms> <CA>	Kopinsel *m*, Copinsel *m*	cône *m* inductif	коконус, прямой конус, индуктивный конус (с конечной вершиной *x* и базой *d*>

No.	English	German	French	Russian
	inductive cone <CA>	*s.* L 726		
	inductive definition <FO>	*s.* D 140		
I 407	**inductive dimension** <TO>	induktive Dimension *f*	dimension *f* inductive	индуктивная размерность
	inductive family of mappings <CA, SE, TO>	*s.* C 1050		
	inductive hypothesis <LO>	*s.* I 398		
	inductive inference <LO>	*s.* R 238		
I 408	**inductive limit,** topological inductive limit <of spaces> <TO>	induktiver (direkter) Limes *m*, topologischer induktiver Limes <von Räumen>	espace *m* limite inductif	индуктивный предел <пространств>
	inductive limit <CA>	*s.* C 1130		
	inductive limit <TO>	*s.* D 576		
I 409	**inductive-limit topology** <TO>	Topologie *f* des induktiven Limes	topologie *f* limite inductive	топология прямого спектра
I 410	**inductively ordered set,** inductive set <SE>	induktive [halbgeordnete] Menge *f*; schrankeninduktive [halbgeordnete] Menge <jede Kette ist nach oben beschränkt>; grenzinduktive [halbgeordnete] Menge <jede Kette hat eine obere Grenze>	ensemble *m* ordonné inductif, ensemble inductif	индуктивное (индуктивно упорядоченное) множество
	inductive number <SE>	*s.* F 260		
	inductive proof <FO>	*s.* P 1754/5		
I 411	**inductive property** <of a set> <TO>	induktive (induzible) Eigenschaft *f*	propriété *f* inductive	индуктивное свойство
I 412	**inductive set** <as a partially ordered set *or* a finite set> <SE>	induktive Menge *f* <jede gerichtete Untermenge hat maximales Element, bzw. es gibt eine natürliche Zahl *n*, so daß die Menge genau *n* Elemente enthält>	ensemble *m* inductif	индуктивное множество
	inductive set <SE>	*s.* 1. F 316; 2. I 410		
	inductive step <FO, LO>	*s.* I 402		
	inductive system <AL, CA, SE>	*s.* D 610		
I 413	**inefficient estimator (estimating function)** <ST>	nichtwirksame Schätzung (Schätzfunktion) *f*	estimateur *m* inefficace, fonction *f* estimatrice inefficace	неэффективная оценка
I 414	**inequality** <property> <GN>	Ungleichheit *f*	non-égalité *f*	неравенство
I 415	**inequality,** inequation <formula> <GN>	Ungleichung *f*	inéquation *f*, inégalité *f*	неравенство
I 416	**inequality between the arithmetic and the geometric mean** <AN, ST>	Ungleichung *f* zwischen arithmetischem und geometrischem Mittel	théorème *m* de la moyenne	неравенство между арифметическим и геометрическим средними
I 417	**inequality constraint** <PG>	Ungleichungsnebenbedingung *f*, Nebenbedingung *f* in Ungleichungsform	contrainte *f* sous forme d'une inégalité	условие в виде неравенства
I 418	**inequality for a variance** <ST>	Varianzungleichung *f*, Streuungsungleichung *f*	inégalité *f* pour une variance	неравенство дисперсии
	inequality of class field theory <AB>	*s.* F 832		
	inequality of Harnack <PO>	*s.* H 115		
	inequality of König-Jourdain-Zermelo <SE>	*s.* K 136		
I 418a	**inequality of opposite sense** <GN>	gegensinnige Ungleichung *f*	inégalité *f* de sens contraire	неравенство противоположного смысла
I 419	**inequality of the same sense** <GN>	gleichsinnige Ungleichung *f*	inégalité *f* de même sens	неравенство одинакового смысла
I 420	**inequality sign,** symbol for the denial of equality, $\neq$ <GN>	Ungleichheitszeichen *n*, $\neq$	signe *f* d'inégalité, $\neq$	знак отрицания равенства, знак неравенства, $\neq$
	inequation <GN>	*s.* I 415		
I 421	**inequivalence** <of representations> <RE>	Inäquivalenz *f*	non-isomorphie *f*	неэквивалентность
I 422	**inequivalent valuation;** independent absolute value <AL>	nichtäquivalente (inäquivalente) Bewertung *f*	valuation *f* inéquivalente	неэквивалентное нормирование, независимое абсолютное значение
I 423	**inertia field** <AB>	Trägheitskörper *m*	corps *m* d'inertie	поле инерций (инерции)
I 424	**inertia form** <AL>	Trägheitsform *f*	forme *f* d'inertie	форма инерции
I 425	**inertia group** <AB>	Trägheitsgruppe *f*, nullte Verzweigungsgruppe *f*	groupe (sous-groupe) *m* d'inertie	группа инерций (инерции), подгруппа инерции
I 426	**inertial prime ideal** <AB>	träges Primideal *n*	idéal *m* premier inerte	инертный простой идеал
I 427	**inertial prime number** <AB>	träge Primzahl *f*	nombre *m* premier inerte	инертное простое число
I 428	**inertia ring,** semi-simple sub-algebra <Dickson> <AL>	Trägheitsring *m*	anneau *m* d'inertie	кольцо инерции
	inessential discontinuity <RF>	*s.* R 799		

No.	English	German	French	Russian
I 429	**inessential extension** <AL>	unwesentliche Erweiterung *f*	extension *f* inessentielle	несущественное расширение
I 430	**inessential game** <TG>	unwesentliches (außerwesentliches) Spiel *n*	jeu *m* non essentiel	несущественная игра
	inessentially divergent [infinite] continued fraction <NT>	*s.* P 1803		
	inessential map[ping] <TO>	*s.* H 513		
	inessential sequence <HA>	*s.* S 1537		
	inessential singularity <DE> ⌐<FT>	*s.* R 630		
	inessential singularity	*s.* R 631		
	inessential singular kernel <IE>	*s.* W 110		
	inessential singular point <FT>	*s.* R 631		
I 431	**inessential state** <SP>	unwesentlicher Zustand *m*	état *m* accessoire	несущественное состояние
	inf <DI, SE>	*s.* G 411		
	inf <SE>	*s.* G 412		
	inference <LO>	*s.* L 1062		
	inference <ST>	*s.* S 1695		
I 432	**inference according to the rule of detachment** <LO>	Grundschluß *m*	inférence *f* suivant la règle de séparation	заключение по правилу отрывания
	inference figure <LO>	*s.* F 220		
I 433	**inference figure schema** <LO>	Schlußfigurschema *n*	règle *f* (schéma *m*) de dérivation	схема умозаключения
I 434	**inference founded on the well-ordering principle** <FO, GN>	Wohlordnungsschluß *m*	inférence *f* fondée sur le bon ordre	заключение при помощи полного порядка
I 435	**inference pattern** <LO>	Schlußschema *n*	schéma *m* de déduction	схема заключения
	inference rule <LO>	*s.* R 1478		
	inferior approximate limit <RF>	*s.* L 1124		
	inferior limit <DI, SS>	*s.* L 1153		
	inferior limit <RF>	*s.* M 597		
	infimum <CA>	*s.* L 697		
	infimum <DI, SE>	*s.* G 411		
	infimum <LA>	*s.* M 362		
	infimum <SE>	*s.* G 412		
I 436	**infinitary operation,** infinite operation <AL>	infinitäre Operation *f*	opération *f* d'arité infinie	бесконечноместная операция
I 437	**infinitary property** <of a number sequence> <SS>	infinitäre Eigenschaft *f*	propriété *f* infinitaire	
I 438	**infinitary relation** <AL>	infinitäre Relation *f*	relation *f* d'arité infinie	бесконечноместное отношение
I 439	**infinite,** infinitely great <of order *n*> <AL, DI>	unendlich [groß] <von *n*-ter Ordnung>	infiniment grand, infini <d'ordre *n*, du n^e ordre>	бесконечно большой <*n*-го порядка>
	infinite assemblage <SE>	*s.* I 474		
I 440	**infinite cardinal,** transfinite cardinal [number], aleph, ℵ <SE>	unendliche (transfinite, überendliche) Kardinalzahl *f*, Aleph *n*, Alef *m*, ℵ	cardinal *m* infini (transfini), aleph *m*, ℵ	бесконечное (трансфинитное) кардинальное число, алеф, ℵ
	infinite continuous group <AL>	*s.* L 673		
I 441	**infinite decimal,** unending (non-terminating, never-ending) decimal <NT>	unendlicher (nichtabbrechender) Dezimalbruch *m*	fraction *f* décimale illimitée, décimale *f* illimitée	бесконечная десятичная дробь
I 442	**infinite derivative,** improper derivative <DI>	unendliche (uneigentliche) Ableitung *f*	dérivée *f* infinie (impropre)	бесконечная (несобственная) производная
I 443	**infinite descent** <AG, AL, LO, NT>	unendlicher Abstieg *m*, Descente *f* infinie	descente *f* infinie	бесконечный спуск
	infinite determinant <MD>	*s.* D 350		
I 444	**infinite-dimensional space,** ∞-dimensional space, space of infinite [number of] dimensions <AN, GE, TO>	unendlichdimensionaler (∞-dimensionaler) Raum *m*	espace *m* de dimension infinie	бесконечномерное пространство, пространство бесконечной размерности
I 445	**infinite distributivity** <LA>	vollständige Distributivität *f*	distributivité *f* complète	общая дистрибутивность
	infinite distributivity <AL>	*s.* G 124		
I 446	**infinite ∩-distributivity** <LA>	unendliche Durchschnittsdistributivität *f*	∩-distributivité *f* générale	общая ∩-дистрибутивность
I 447	**infinite ∪-distributivity** <LA>	unendliche Vereinigungsdistributivität *f*	∪-distributivité *f* générale	общая ∪-дистрибутивность
	infinite element <PJ>	*s.* E 123		
I 448	**infinite field extension** <AL>	unendliche Körpererweiterung *f*, Körpererweiterung von unendlichem Grad	extension *f* de type infini	бесконечное расширение (расширение поля)
I 449	**infinite function** <AN>	unendliche (infinite) Funktion *f*	fonction *f* infinie	бесконечная функция
I 450	**infinite half-plane,** semi-infinite plane, half-plane <AN>	unendliche Halbebene *f*, Halbebene	demi-plan *m* infini, demi-plan	бесконечная полуплоскость, полуплоскость
	infinite half-space <AN, GE>	*s.* H 42		
	infinite hyperplane <PJ>	*s.* H 708		

	English	German	French	Russian
I 451	**infinite induction** <MM>	unendliche Induktion *f*	récurrence *f* infinie	бесконечная индукция, правило Карнапа, ω-правило
	infinite integral <DI>	*s.* I 168		
I 452	**infinite interval** <AN>	unendliches Intervall *n*	intervalle *m* infini	бесконечный интервал
	infinite line <PJ>	*s.* L 852		
	infinitely adjacent point <DG>	*s.* I 460		
I 453	**infinitely continuously derivable (differentiable) function,** function having continuous derivatives of all orders <DI> ┌<PJ>	unendlich[ ]oft stetig differenzierbare Funktion *f*	fonction *f* indéfiniment continûment dérivable (différentiable)	бесконечно непрерывно дифференцируемая функция
	infinitely distant point	*s.* P 722		
	infinitely distributive lattice <LA>	*s.* C 1469		
I 454	**infinitively ∪-distributive lattice** <LA>	vollständig vereinigungsdistributiver Verband *m*	treillis *m* ∪-distributif général	вполне ∪-дистрибутивная структура
I 455	**infinitely ∩-distributive lattice** <LA>	vollständig durchschnittsdistributiver Verband *m*	treillis *m* ∩-distributif général	вполне ∩-дистрибутивная структура
I 456	**infinitely divisible distribution** <ST>	unbeschränkt (unbegrenzt) teilbare Verteilung *f*	distribution *f* indéfiniment divisible	безгранично делимое распределение
	infinitely divisible element <AL>	*s.* D 799		
I 457	**infinitely divisible measure** <ME, ST>	unendlich (unbegrenzt) teilbares Maß *n*	mesure *f* indéfiniment divisible	безгранично делимая мера
	infinitely divisible random variable <ST>	*s.* I 458		
I 458	**infinitely divisible variate,** infinitely divisible random variable <ST>	unbeschränkt (unbegrenzt) teilbare Zufallsgröße (Zufallsvariable) *f*	variable *f* aléatoire indéfiniment divisible	безгранично делимая случайная величина (переменная)
	infinitely great <AL, DI>	*s.* I 439		
	infinitely increasing series <SS>	*s.* I 301		
I 459	**infinitely many elements,** infinite number of elements, infinitude of elements <SE>	unendlich viele Elemente *npl*, unendliche Anzahl *f* von Elementen	infinité *f* d'éléments	бесконечное множество элементов
I 460	**infinitely near point,** [infinitely] adjacent point <DG>	unendlich benachbarter Punkt *m*	point *m* infiniment voisin, point consécutif <de premier ordre>	бесконечно близкая точка
I 461	**infinitely small,** infinitesimal <of order *n*> <AL, DI>	unendlich klein, infinitesimal, verschwindend klein <von *n*-ter Ordnung>	infiniment petit, infinitésimal, évanouissant <d'ordre *n*, du n^e ordre>	бесконечно малый, инфинитезимальный <*n*-го порядка>
	infinitely small magnitude <DI>	*s.* I 476		
I 462	**infinitely small of lower order,** infinitesimal of lower order <AN>	von niedrigerer Ordnung unendlich klein	infiniment petit d'ordre inférieur	бесконечно малый низшего порядка
I 463	**infinitely small of the same order,** infinitesimal of the same order <AN> ┌<DI>	von gleicher Ordnung unendlich klein	infiniment petit de même ordre	бесконечно малый одинакового порядка, эквивалентный
	infinitely small quantity	*s.* I 476		
I 464	**infinite matrix,** matrix of infinite order, doubly infinite array <MD>	unendliche Matrix *f*	matrice *f* infinie	бесконечная матрица
	infinite model <ST>	*s.* M 731		
	infinite number of elements <SE>	*s.* I 459		
I 465	**infinite of lower order,** of lower order [infinite] <AN>	von niedrigerer Ordnung unendlich	infini d'ordre inférieur	бесконечно большой низшего порядка
I 466	**infinite of the same order,** of the same order [infinite] <AN>	von gleicher Ordnung unendlich [groß]	infini de même ordre	бесконечно большой одинакового порядка, эквивалентный
	infinite operation <AL>	*s.* I 436		
	infinite ordinal [number] <SE>	*s.* T 746		
I 467	**infinite place,** prime at infinity, infinite prime [spot] <of an algebraic number field> <AB, AL>	unendliche Primstelle *f*, Primstelle *f*, unendliche Stelle *f*	place *f* à l'infini, place infinie	бесконечная точка
	infinite plane <PJ>	*s.* P 640		
I 468	**infinite point** <of the hyperbolic plane> <GE>	Randpunkt *m*, unendlich ferner Punkt *m*, Fernpunkt *m*	point *m* à (de) l'infini	бесконечно удаленная точка
	infinite point <PJ>	*s.* P 722		
	infinite prime [spot] <AB, AL>	*s.* I 467		
I 469	**infinite product,** continued product <SS>	unendliches Produkt *n*	produit *m* infini	бесконечное произведение
I 470	**infinite progression** <AR>	unendliche Progression *f*	progression *f* illimitée (infinie)	прогрессия с бесконечным числом членов
I 471	**infinite recurrent measurable transformation** <ME>	unendlich rekurrente meßbare Transformation *f*	transformation *f* mesurable infiniment récurrente	бесконечно возвратное измеримое преобразование
I 472	**infinite sequence,** [nonterminating] sequence <SE, SS>	unendliche Folge *f*	suite *f* illimitée (infinie)	бесконечная последовательность
I 473	**infinite sequence of arbitrary choices,** choice sequence <MM>	Wahlfolge *f*	suite *f* du choix	последовательность выбора

I 474	**infinite set,** infinite assemblage, non-inductive set <SE>	unendliche (transfinite, überendliche, nichtinduktive) Menge *f*, // unendliche Mannigfaltigkeit *f* <Dedekind>	ensemble *m* infini (transfini), collection *f* infinie	бесконечное множество
	infinite set in Dedekind['s] sense <SE>	*s.* D 90		
I 475	**infinite set without accumulation point** <TO>	divergente Punktmenge (Menge, Teilmenge) *f*	ensemble *m* infini dépourvu de points d'accumulation	бесконечное множество, не имеющее предельных точек
I 476	**infinitesimal,** infinitesimal quantity, infinitely small quantity (magnitude) <*e.g.:* of higher, the same, *or* lower order> <DI>	infinitesimale Größe *f*, Infinitesimalgröße *f*, unendlich kleine Größe <*z. B.:* höherer, gleicher *oder* niedrigerer Ordnung>	grandeur *f* infinitésimale (infiniment petite), infiniment petit *m*, quantité *f* infiniment petite, quantité infinitésimale <*par exemple:* d'ordre supérieur, du même ordre *ou* d'ordre inférieur>	бесконечно малая величина <*например:* высшего, одного [и того же] *или* низшего порядка>
	infinitesimal <AL, DI>	*s.* I 461		
	infinitesimal analysis (calculus) <DI>	*s.* D 449		
I 477	**infinitesimal contact transformation** <DE, VA>	infinitesimale Berührungstransformation *f*	transformation *f* de contact infinitésimale	бесконечно малое контактное преобразование
I 478	**infinitesimal deformation** <of a surface> <DG>	infinitesimale Verbiegung *f*	déformation *f* infinitésimale	инфинитезимальное (бесконечно малое) изгибание
I 479	**infinitesimal displacement,** geodesic displacement, Levi-Cività['s] parallel displacement, parallel displacement [in the sense] of Levi-Cività <DG>	infinitesimale (geodätische) Parallelverschiebung *f* [von Levi-Cività], Parallelverschiebung [im Sinne] von Levi-Cività, Levi-Civitàsche [infinitesimale] Parallelverschiebung	transport (déplacement) *m* parallèle infinitésimal ([au sens] de Levi-Cività), transport (déplacement) par parallélisme de Levi-Cività, transport (déplacement) par parallélisme infinitésimal (géodésique)	инфинитезимальное (геодезическое) [параллельное] перенесение
	infinitesimal generator <FA>	*s.* I 482		
I 480	**infinitesimal geometry,** local differential geometry, differential geometry in the small <DG>	Infinitesimalgeometrie *f*, Differentialgeometrie *f* im Kleinen, lokale Differentialgeometrie	géométrie *f* infinitésimale (différentielle locale)	инфинитезимальная (локальная дифференциальная) геометрия, [дифференциальная] геометрия в малом
	infinitesimal group <AL>	*s.* L 648		
I 481	**infinitesimally irreducible representation** <RE>	infinitesimal irreduzible Darstellung *f*	représentation *f* infinitésimalement irréductible	инфинитезимально неприводимое представление
	infinitesimal of lower order <AN>	*s.* I 462		
	infinitesimal of the same order <AN>	*s.* I 463		
I 482	**infinitesimal operator,** infinitesimal transformation, infinitesimal generator <of a semigroup of operators> <FA>	infinitesimaler Operator *m*, Infinitesimaloperator *m*, infinitesimale Transformation *f*	opérateur *m* infinitésimal, transformation *f* infinitésimale	инфинитезимальный (производящий, бесконечно малый) оператор, инфинитезимальное (бесконечно малое) преобразование
I 483	**infinitesimal operator** <SP>	infinitesimaler Operator *m*	opérateur *m* infinitésimal	инфинитезимальный оператор
	infinitesimal quantity <DI>	*s.* I 476		
I 484	**infinitesimal rigidity** <of surfaces> <DG>	infinitesimale Unverbiegbarkeit (Starrheit) *f*	rigidité *f* infinitésimale	инфинитезимальная жесткость
I 485	**infinitesimal ring** <of a Lie group> <AL>	infinitesimale Algebra *f*	algèbre *f* infinitésimale	инфинитезимальная алгебра
I 486	**infinitesimal rotation** <DG>	infinitesimale (elementare) Drehung *f*, infinitesimale (elementare) Rotation *f*, Elementardrehung *f*, Elementarrotation *f*	rotation *f* infiniment petite	бесконечно малое вращение, бесконечно малый поворот
I 487	**infinitesimal transformation** <AL, DE>	infinitesimale Transformation *f*	transformation *f* infinitésimale	инфинитезимальное преобразование
	infinitesimal transformation <FA>	*s.* I 482		
	infinitesimal variation <AN>	*s.* V 69		
	infinite spherical circle <AY, PJ>	*s.* A 63		
I 488	**infinite-stage system** <PG>	System *n* mit unendlich vielen Stufen	système *m* à une infinité d'étages	система с бесконечным количеством ступеней
I 489	**infinite system of differential equations** <DE>	unendliches System *n* von Differentialgleichungen, unendliches Differentialgleichungssystem *n*	système *m* infini d'équations différentielles	бесконечная система дифференциальных уравнений
I 490	**infinite system of linear equations** <AL, AN>	unendliches lineares Gleichungssystem *n*	système *m* d'équations linéaires à une infinité d'inconnues	бесконечная система линейных уравнений
I 491	**infinite-valued function** <DI, SE>	unendlich vieldeutige Funktion *f*	fonction *f* à une infinité de valeurs	бесконечнозначная функция
	infinitude <DI, GN>	*s.* I 494		
	infinitude of elements <SE>	*s.* I 459		

I 492	**infinitum / ad,** to infinity, continuing without end <AN>	ad infinitum	jusqu'à l'infini	до бесконечности, без конца
	infinity / to <AN>	*s.* I 492		
I 493	**infinity** <AN>	Unendlich *n*	infini *m*	бесконечность, область бесконечности
I 494	**infinity,** infinitude <DI, GN>	Unendlichkeit *f*	infinitude *f*	бесконечность
	infinity <FT>	*s.* P 723		
	infinity axiom <GE>	*s.* P 1120		
I 495	**infinity lemma** <FO, GP>	Unendlichkeitslemma *n*	lemme *m* de l'infini	лемма бесконечности
	infinity postulate <GE>	*s.* P 1120		
I 496	**infix** <LO>	Infix *n* <binärer Junktor zwischen zwei Aussagen>	infixe *m*	инфикс
I 497	**inflation** <AL, HA>	Inflation *f*	inflation *f*	раздувание <полугруппы>; гомоморфизм инфляции, инфляция, отображение инфляции
	inflation factor <NU, ST>	*s.* E 863		
	inflectional tangent <DG>	*s.* I 503		
	inflection point <DG>	*s.* P 768		
	inflection point <DG, DI>	*s.* P 767		
I 498	**inflexional asymptote** <of a plane curve> <DG>	Inflexionsasymptote *f*	asymptote *f* inflexionnelle, asymptote d'inflexion	касательная в бесконечно удаленной точке перегиба
I 499	**inflexional axis** <of a cubic> <AG>	Inflexionsachse *f*	axe *m* inflexionnel, axe d'inflexion	прямая, связывающая три точки перегиба
I 500	**inflexional curve,** curve of inflection points <DG, DI>	Wendepunktskurve *f*	courbe *f* des points d'inflexion	кривая перегибов
I 501	**inflexional curve** <of a surface> <DG>	Wendekurve *f*, Wendungskurve *f*, Inflexionskurve *f* <Bianchi>	courbe *f* d'inflexion	кривая перегибов
I 502	**inflexional line** <of an algebraic curve> <DG>	Wendelinie *f*, Wendepunktslinie *f*	ligne *f* des points d'inflexion	прямая перегибов
I 503	**inflexional tangent,** inflectional (stationary) tangent, flex tangent <of a curve> <DG>	Wendetangente *f*, stationäre Tangente *f*, Inflexionstangente *f*, Biegungstangente *f*	tangente *f* inflexionnelle (d'inflexion, au point d'inflexion, stationnaire)	касательная в точке перегиба, перегибная касательная
	inflexion point <DG>	*s.* P 768		
	inflexion point <DG, DI>	*s.* P 767		
I 504	**inflexion point of higher order** <of a space curve> <DG>	Wendeberührungspunkt *m*	point *m* d'inflexion d'ordre supérieur, point *m* de contact d'un plan [osculateur] stationnaire	точка перегиба высшего порядка
	inflexive relation <SE>	*s.* I 1056		
I 505	**informal interpretation** <LO>	inhaltliche Interpretation *f*		содержательная интерпретация
	information <ST>	*s.* I 506		
I 506	**information content,** amount (quantity, set, volume) of information, information volume, [statistical] information, decision content <ST>	Informationsgehalt *m*, Informationsbetrag *m*, Informationsmenge *f*, Informationsumfang *m*, Informationsvolumen *n*, Informationsinhalt *m*, [statistische] Information *f*, Anzahl *f* der Einzelinformationen (Einzelnachrichten), Nachrichtenmenge *f*, Nachrichtengehalt *m*	capacité *f* d'information, quantité *f* d'information, information *f* [statistique]	количество информации, информационное количество, объем информации, емкость информации, информационная емкость, [статистическая] информация, количество сведений на один элемент сообщения
I 507	**information domain** <TG>	Informationsbereich *m*	domaine *m* d'information	информационная область
I 508	**information for discrimination,** discriminant information, I-divergency <ST>	diskriminierende Information *f*, I-Divergenz *f*	information *f* discriminante, divergence *f* I	информация для дискриминации, количество информации для дискриминации
I 509	**information gain** <ST>	Informationsgewinn *m*	gain *m* d'information	прирост информации
I 510	**information set** <*e.g.:* of a player> <TG>	Informationsmenge *f* <*z. B.:* eines Spielers>	ensemble *m* d'information <*par exemple:* d'un joueur>	информационное множество <*например:* игрока>
I 511	**information source** <ST>	Informationsquelle *f*, Nachrichtenquelle *f*	source *f* d'information	источник информации (сообщений)
I 512	**information theory [of Shannon-Weaver],** mathematical theory of communication; coding theory, theory of coding <ST>	Informationstheorie *f* [von Shannon-Weaver], mathematische Theorie *f* der Nachrichtenübertragung; Kodierungstheorie *f*, Codierungstheorie *f*	théorie *f* de l'information [de Shannon et Weaver], théorie des communications mathématiques; théorie de codification (codage)	теория информации [Шеннона], математическая теория связи; теория кодирования
	information volume <ST>	*s.* I 506		
I 513	**infra-barrelled space** <FA>	infratonnelierter Raum *m*	espace *m* infratonnelé	инфрабочечное пространство
I 514	**infra-invariant subgroup** <GR>	infrainvariante Untergruppe *f*	sous-groupe *m* infra-invariant	инфраинвариантная подгруппа
I 515	**inhomogeneity correlation** <ST>	Inhomogenitätskorrelation *f*	corrélation *f* due à l'inhomogénéité	корреляция вследствие неоднородности
	inhomogeneous boundary value problem <DE> <AL>	*s.* N 396		
I 516	**inhomogeneous cochain**	inhomogene Kokette *f*	cochaine *f* non homogène	неоднородная коцепь
I 517	**inhomogeneous coordinates** <AY>	inhomogene Koordinaten *fpl*	coordonnées *fpl* inhomogènes	неоднородные координаты
	inhomogeneous differential equation <DE>	*s.* N 397		
I 518	**inhomogeneous integral equation,** inhomogeneous linear integral equation <IE>	inhomogene [lineare] Integralgleichung *f*	équation *f* intégrale [linéaire] inhomogène	неоднородное [линейное] интегральное уравнение

No.	English	German	French	Russian
	inhomogeneous linear boundary value problem <DE>	*s.* N 396		
	inhomogeneous linear differential equation <DE>	*s.* N 397		
	inhomogeneous linear integral equation <IE>	*s.* I 518		
I 519	**inhomogeneous linear recursion** <MM>	inhomogene lineare Rekursion *f*	récurrence *f* linéaire avec second membre	неоднородное линейное возвратное уравнение
	inhomogeneous linear system of [ordinary] differential equations <DE>	*s.* N 398		
I 520	**inhomogeneous Lorentz group,** Poincaré['s] group <GR>	inhomogene Lorentz-Gruppe *f*, Poincaré-Gruppe *f*	groupe *m* de Lorentz inhomogène, groupe de Poincaré	неоднородная группа Лоренца, группа Пуанкаре
	inhomogeneous problem <VA>	*s.* N 403		
	inhomogeneous system of [ordinary] differential equations <DE>	*s.* N 398		
	inhomogeneous variational problem <VA>	*s.* N 403		
	initial <SE>	*s.* I 536		
I 521	**initial approximation** <e.g. in an iterative procedure> <AX, NU>	Anfangsnäherung *f*, Lösungsansatz *m*; Startelement *n* <eindimensional>; Startvektor *m* <mehrdimensional>	approximation *f* initiale	начальное приближение
	initial column <GN, NU>	*s.* E 269		
	initial condition <FO, LO>	*s.* B 139		
I 522	**initial conditions,** initial values, Cauchy['s] conditions, Cauchy['s] initial conditions (values) <DE>	Anfangsbedingungen *fpl*, Anfangswerte *mpl*, Cauchysche Anfangsbedingungen (Anfangswerte), Cauchysche Bedingungen *fpl*	conditions (valeurs) *fpl* initiales, conditions de Cauchy, conditions (valeurs) initiales de Cauchy, données *fpl* de Cauchy	начальные условия, начальные значения, условия Коши, начальные условия (значения) Коши
	initial conditions <NU>	*s.* I 523		
	initial cone <CA>	*s.* C 1131		
I 523	**initial data,** initial information (values, conditions) <NU>	Anfangsdaten *pl*, Anfangsinformation *f*, Anfangswerte *mpl*, Anfangsbedingungen *fpl*	données (valeurs, conditions) *fpl* initiales, information *f* initiale	начальные (исходные) данные, начальная (исходная) информация, начальные условия (значения)
I 524	**initial diagram** <CA>	initiales Diagramm *n*	diagramme *m* initial	инициальная диаграмма
I 525	**initial distribution** <ST>	Anfangsverteilung *f*, Ausgangsverteilung *f*	distribution *f* initiale	начальное распределение
	initial end-point <GP>	*s.* I 543		
I 526	**initial error** <NU>	Anfangsfehler *m*	erreur *f* initiale	начальная (исходная) ошибка
I 527	**initial form** <AL>	Anfangsform *f*	forme *f* initiale	начальная форма
I 528	**initial functor** <CA>	initialer Funktor *m*	foncteur *m* initial	инициальный функтор
I 529	**initial index** <of a subgroup in a totally ordered group> <AL>	Anfangsindex *m*	indice *m* initial	начальный индекс
	initial information <NU>	*s.* I 523		
I 530	**initial manifold,** initial variety <DE>	Anfangsmannigfaltigkeit *f*	variété *f* initiale	начальное (исходное) многообразие
I 531	**initial moment** <ST>	Anfangsmoment *n*	moment *m* initial	начальный момент
	initial number <SE>	*s.* I 532		
	initial object <CA>	*s.* C 2316		
I 532	**initial ordinal [number],** initial number <of a given power> <SE>	Anfangszahl *f*, Cantorsche (ordinale) Anfangszahl <gegebener Mächtigkeit>	ordinal (nombre) *m* initial	начальное число, начальное ординальное число, начальное порядковое число
I 533	**initial point** <of an integral> <DE> ⌐<GE>	Anfangspunkt *m*	point *m* initial	начальная точка
I 534	**initial point** <of an arc>	Anfangspunkt *m*	origine *f*	начало
I 535	**initial point,** base, origin, point of application <of a vector> <VT>	Anfangspunkt *m*	origine *f*	начало, точка приложения
	initial point <TO>	*s.* O 425		
	initial row <GN, NU>	*s.* E 270		
I 536	**initial segment,** initial, left segment, subset closed below, M closed subset <of an ordered set> <SE>	Anfangsstück *n*, Anfang *m*, Abschnitt *m*	section (partie) *f* commençante, partie héréditaire, section initiale, segment (intervalle) *m* initial	начальный отрезок (сегмент), левый отрезок
	initial segment <SE>	*s.* S 242		
I 537	**initial set** <of objects> <CA>	initiale Menge *f*	ensemble *m* initial	инициальное множество
I 538	**initial solution** <PG>	Anfangslösung *f*, Ausgangslösung *f*	solution *f* initiale	начальное решение
I 539	**initial state** <PG>	Anfangszustand *m*	état *m* initial	исходное (начальное) состояние
I 540	**initial strip** <DE> ⌐TO>	Anfangsstreifen *m*, Ausgangsstreifen *m*	bande *f* initiale	начальная (исходная) полос[к]а
I 541	**initial structure** <AL,	initiale Struktur *f*	structure *f* initiale	инициальная структура
	initial term <AR>	*s.* F 353		
	initial term <SS>	*s.* F 356		
I 542	**initial topology** <TO>	Initialtopologie *f*, initiale Topologie *f*, Ausgangstopologie *f*	topologie *f* initiale	инициальная топология

	initial-value problem <DE>	*s.* C 261		
	initial values <DE>	*s.* I 522		
	initial values <NU>	*s.* I 523		
	initial variety <DE>	*s.* I 530		
I 543	**initial vertex,** initial end-point <of an arc> <GP>	Startpunkt *m*, Anfangspunkt *m*, linker Eckpunkt *m*, Anfangsknoten *m*, Anfangsknotenpunkt *m*	extrémité *f* initiale, sommet *m* initial	начало, начальная вершина
	injection <CA>	*s.* I 544		
	injection <SE>	*s.* I 548		
	injection <TO>	*s.* E 198		
	injection <UA>	*s.* H 503		
I 544	**injection morphism,** injection, induction (canonical) injection <in (of) a coproduct *or* colimit> <CA>	Injektion *f* <in ein Koprodukt *oder* einen Kolimes>	injection *f* <dans un coproduit *ou* dans une colimite>	вложение, каноническое вложение, каноническая инъекция <копроизведения *или* копредела>
	injective <CA>	*s.* I 549		
I 545	**injective dimension** <HA>	injektive Dimension *f*	dimension *f* injective	инъективная размерность
I 546	**injective envelope,** injective hull <AL>	injektive Hülle *f*	enveloppe *f* injective	инъективная оболочка
	injective function <SE>	*s.* I 548		
I 547	**injective graph** <GP>	injektiver Graph *m*	graphe *m* injectif	инъективный граф
	injective homomorphism <AL>	*s.* M 863		
	injective hull <AL>	*s.* I 546		
	injective hull <GR>	*s.* D 801		
I 548	**injective mapping,** injection, one-to-one mapping [into], 1—1 mapping [into], one-to-one mapping [into], one-to-one and into mapping, biunique mapping, univalent mapping, monomorphic mapping, one-to-one (one-one) transformation, one to one application, one-to-one representation, one-to-one correspondence (function), (1—1)-function, 1—1 function, univalent (injective) function <SE>	injektive Abbildung *f*, Injektion *f*, eineindeutige Abbildung (Abbildung in), umkehrbar[ ]eindeutige Abbildung, einwertige (monomorphe, schlichte) Abbildung, eineindeutige (umkehrbar eindeutige, injektive) Zuordnung *f*, eineindeutige Transformation *f*, eineindeutige (umkehrbar eindeutige, injektive) Funktion *f*	application *f* injective, injection *f*, application biunivoque [dans], représentation (transformation) *f* biunivoque, transformation (1,1), correspondance *f* biunivoque (injective), fonction *f* univalente (à valeurs distinctes, injective)	инъективное отображение, инъекция, взаимно однозначное отображение, одно-однозначное (однолистное, мономорфное) отображение, взаимно однозначное преобразование (соответствие), инъективное соответствие, инъективная функция, наложение, вложение
I 549	**injective object,** injective <CA>	injektives Objekt *n*	objet *m* injectif, injectif *m*	инъективный объект
	injective relation <SE>	*s.* O 119		
I 550	**injectivity** <AL, SE, TO>	Injektivität *f*	injectivité *f*	инъективность
I 551	**inner automorphism,** cogredient automorphism <of a group> <GR>	innerer Automorphismus *m*, kogredienter (cogredienter) Isomorphismus *m*	automorphisme *m* intérieur (cogrédient, interne)	внутренний автоморфизм
I 552	**inner capacity** <PO>	innere Kapazität *f*	capacité *f* intérieure	внутренняя емкость
	inner content <ME>	*s.* I 724		
I 553	**inner derivation** <AL>	innere Derivation *f*	dérivation *f* intérieure	внутренняя деривация, внутреннее дифференцирование
I 554	**inner direct sum** <of Hilbert spaces> <FA>	innere direkte Summe *f*	somme *f* directe intérieure	внутренняя прямая сумма
I 555	**inner integral** <within a multiple integral> <DI>	inneres Integral *n*	intégrale *f* intérieure	внутренний интеграл
	inner Jordan content <ME>	*s.* I 724		
I 556	**inner left translation,** left[-]multiplication <corresponding to *a*> <of a groupoid *or* ring> <AL>	linke Homothetie *f*, innere linksseitige Translation *f* <durch *a*>	homothétie *f* interne <correspondant à *a*>	внутренний левый сдвиг <соответствующий элементу *a*>
I 557	**inner multiplication,** multiplication and contraction, transvection, contraction, composition, inner tensor multiplication, überschiebung <of tensors> <operation> <VT>	Überschiebung *f* <von Indizes>, Multiplikation *f* und Faltung *f* <von Tensoren>	multiplication *f* contractée, transvection *f* <de tenseurs>	[тензорное] умножение со свертыванием, внутреннее умножение <тензоров>
	inner normal <DG>	*s.* I 735		
I 558	**inner point** <of a simplex> <AT>	innerer Punkt *m*, mittlerer Punkt	point *m* intérieur	внутренняя точка
I 559	**inner point** <of a convex set> <CS>	innerer Punkt *m*	point *m* interne	внутренняя точка
	inner point <EG, TO>	*s.* I 740		
I 560	**inner polar** <AG>	innere Polare *f*	polaire *f* interne	внутренняя поляра
I 561	**inner product** <of tensors>, tensor compounded from two given tensors, inner tensor product <result> <VT>	Überschiebung *f*, inneres Produkt *n* <von Tensoren>	produit *m* contracté, produit [tensoriel] intérieur <de tenseurs>	внутреннее произведение [тензоров]
	inner product <FA>	*s.* S 84		

No.	English	German	French	Russian
	inner product <SE>	*s.* I 802		
	inner product <VT>	*s.* S 86		
I 562	**inner product module** <AL>	Modul *m* mit innerem Produkt, Innenproduktmodul *m*	module *m* à produit intérieur	модуль со скалярным произведением
I 563	**inner product space** <a finitely generated projective inner product module> <AL, FA>	Innenproduktraum *m*, Raum *m* mit innerem Produkt	espace *m* à produit scalaire	пространство с внутренним произведением
	inner radius <FT>	*s.* I 741		
	inner ratio [of division] <AY, EG>	*s.* A 370		
I 564	**inner right translation,** right[-]multiplication <corresponding to *a*> <of a groupoid *or* ring> <AL>	rechte Homothetie *f*, innere rechtsseitige Translation *f* <durch *a*>	homothétie *f* interne <correspondant à *a*>	внутренний правый сдвиг <соответствующий элементу *a*>
	inner tensor multiplication <VT>	*s.* I 557		
	inner tensor product <VT>	*s.* I 561		
	inner translation <AL>	*s.* H 510		
	inner vertex <GP>	*s.* I 771		
I 565	**inparabola,** inscribed parabola <of a triangle> <EG>	Inparabel *f*, einbeschriebene Parabel *f*	parabole *f* inscrite	вписанная парабола
I 566	**input** <of a queueing system> <ST>	Kundenstrom *m*	entrée *f* <d'un système avec attente>	поток требований
	input <CA>	*s.* L 697		
I 567	**input alphabet** <TA>	Eingabealphabet *n*, Eingangsalphabet *n*	alphabet *m* d'entrée	входной алфавит
	input error <ER, NU>	*s.* E 474		
I 568	**input flow** <of a network> <GP> ⌐<ST>	Flußinput *m*	flux *m* entrant	входной поток
I 569	**input-output analysis**	Input-Output-Analyse *f*	analyse *f* entrée-sortie	анализ ввода-вывода
I 570	**input-output matrix** <ST>	Input-Output-Matrix *f*	matrice *f* entrée-sortie	матрица ввода-вывода
I 571	**input signal** <TA>	Eingabesignal *n*, Eingangssignal *n*	signal *m* d'entrée, signal incident	входной сигнал, сигнал на входе
I 572	**input state** <PG>	Eingangszustand *m*	état *m* d'entrée	входное состояние
I 573	**inquiry [all around],** poll <ST>	Umfrage *f*	enquête *f*, sondage *m*	опрос, анкета
I 574	**inradius,** radius of the inscribed sphere <of a tetrahedron *or* another convex body> <EG>	Radius *m* der Inkugel, Inkugelradius *m*	rayon *m* de la sphère inscrite	радиус вписанной сферы
I 575	**inradius,** radius of the inscribed circle <of a triangle> <EG>	Radius *m* des Inkreises, Inkreisradius *m*	rayon *m* du cercle inscrit	радиус вписанной окружности
I 576	**inscribed angle** <of a closed curve> <EG>	einbeschriebener Winkel *m*	angle *m* inscrit	вписанный угол
	inscribed angle <EG>	*s.* A 655		
	inscribed circle <EG>	*s.* I 236		
	inscribed parabola <EG>	*s.* I 565		
I 577	**inscribed polygon** <of an arc> <DG>	einbeschriebener Streckenzug *m*, Sehnenpolygon *n*	polygone *m* inscrit (de cordes)	вписанный многоугольник
I 578	**inscribed polygon** <of a circle> <EG> ⌐<EG>	Sehnenvieleck *n*	polygone *m* inscrit (inscriptible>	вписанный многоугольник; многоугольник, вписанный в окружность
	inscribed quadrangle	*s.* I 579		
	inscribed sphere <EG>	*s.* I 592		
I 579	**inscribed tetragon,** inscribed quadrangle <of a circle>, quadrilateral inscribed <in a circle> <EG>	Sehnenviereck *n*, Kreisviereck *n*	quadrangle *m* inscrit, quadrilatère *m* inscriptible	вписанный четырехугольник; четырехугольник, вписанный в окружность
I 580	**inscribed triangle** <EG>	einbeschriebenes Dreieck *n*	triangle *m* inscrit, inscrite *f*	вписанный треугольник
I 581	**inseparability** <AL>	Inseparabilität *f*	inséparabilité *f*	несепарабельность
I 582	**inseparability** <AN, SE, TO>	Untrennbarkeit *f*	non-séparabilité *f*	неотделимость
	inseparable degree <AL>	*s.* D 184		
I 583	**inseparable element** <AL>	inseparables Element *n*, inseparabel-algebraisches Element	élément *m* inséparable	несепарабельный элемент
I 584	**inseparable extension** <AL>	inseparable Körpererweiterung *f*, inseparabler Oberkörper *m*, Erweiterung (Körpererweiterung) *f* zweiter Art, inseparable Erweiterung *f*	extension *f* inséparable, extension non séparable, extension de seconde espèce	несепарабельное расширение <поля>
	inseparable factor of the degree <AL>	*s.* D 184		
I 585	**inseparable isogeny** <of algebraic groups> <AG>	inseparable Isogenie *f*	isogénie *f* inséparable, isogénie radicielle	несепарабельная изогения, радикальная изогения
I 586	**inseparable polynomial,** not separable polynomial <AL>	inseparables Polynom *n*, Polynom zweiter (2.) Art	polynôme *m* inséparable (non séparable)	несепарабельный многочлен
I 587	**insertion** <EG>	Einschiebung *f*	intercalation *f*	вставка
	insertion function <SE>	*s.* I 245		
I 588	**insertion of *m* further terms between two terms of an arithmetic sequence** <AR>	Einschalten *n* von *m* Gliedern in eine arithmetische Progression	insertion *f* de *m* moyens différentiels, insertion de *m* moyens arithmétique <entre deux nombres donnés>	введение *m* дальнейших членов в арифметическую прогрессию
I 589	**insertion of *N* into *M*,** mapping of *N* into *M*, distribution of *N* into *M* <SE>	Belegung *f* von *N* mit *M*, Abbildung *f* von *N* in *M*	représentation *f* de *N* avec *M*, application *f* de *N* dans *M*	отображение *N* в *M*

No.	English	German	French	Russian
I 590	**insertion ruler** <GE, IN>	Einschiebelineal *n*	règle *f* à glissière	вставка, накладная линейка
	insertion[-]set <SE>	*s.* F 776		
	inside <TO>	*s.* I 716		
	insoluble equation <AL>	*s.* U 396		
	inspection by attributes <ST>	*s.* A 167		
I 591	**inspection by variables,** variables inspection <ST>	Variablenprüfung *f*, messende Prüfung *f*	inspection *f* par les variables, contrôle *m* aux mesures, inspection quantitative	контроль (обследование, инспекция) по количественному признаку
I 592	**insphere,** inscribed sphere <of a tetrahedron *or* another convex body> <EG>	Inkugel *f*	sphère *f* inscrite	вписанная сфера
I 593	**instability** <of a solution> <DE>	Instabilität *f*, Labilität *f*	instabilité *f*	неустойчивость
	instantiation <LO>	*s.* P 271		
I 594	**insurance calculus** <GN>	Versicherungsrechnung *f*	calcul *m* d'assurance	страховое исчисление
I 595	**insurance statistics,** actuarial statistics <ST>	Versicherungsstatistik *f*	statistique *f* d'assurance	статистика страхования
I 596	**integer,** rational integer, integral number, whole [rational] number <of the same *or* of unequal parity> <NT>	ganze (ganzrationale, ganze rationale) Zahl *f* <von gleicher *oder* verschiedener Parität>	nombre *m* entier, entier *m*, entier rationnel (relatif), nombre *m* entier rationnel <de la même parité *ou* de parité inégale>	целое число, целое рациональное, целое <равной *или* разной четности>
I 597	**integer of many digits** <AR, NT>	vielstellige [ganze] Zahl *f*	nombre *m* à plusieurs chiffres	многоразрядное [целое] число
	integer optimization <PG>	*s.* I 600		
	integer part <NT>	*s.* I 645		
I 598	**integer point** <AG>	ganzer Punkt *m*	point *m* entier	целая точка
I 599	**integer polyhedron** <PG>	ganzzahliges Polyeder *n*, Polyeder mit ganzzahligen Eckpunkten	polyèdre *m* entier (en nombres entiers)	целочисленный многогранник, многогранник с целочисленными координатами вершин
I 600	**integer programming,** integer optimization <PG>	ganzzahlige Optimierung (Programmoptimierung, Programmierung) *f*	programmation (optimisation) *f* [discrète] en nombres entiers	целочисленное программирование, целочисленная оптимизация
I 601	**integer solution** <result> <AL>	ganzzahlige Lösung *f*, Lösung in ganzen Zahlen	solution *f* en entiers	решение в целых числах, целочисленное решение
I 602	**integer-valued entire function,** integer-valued integral function <FT>	ganzwertige ganze Funktion *f*	fonction *f* entière à valeurs intègres	целочисленная целая функция, целая функция с целыми значениями
I 603	**integer-valued function** <AL, AN>	ganzwertige Funktion *f*, Funktion mit ganzen Zahlen als Werten	fonction *f* à valeurs intègres	функция, принимающая целочисленные значения; функция с целыми значениями, целочисленная функция
	integer-valued integral function <FT>	*s.* I 602		
I 604	**integrability conditions,** conditions of integrability <AN, DG>	Integrierbarkeitsbedingungen *fpl*, Integrabilitätsbedingungen *fpl*, Integrabilitätsrelationen *fpl*	conditions *fpl* d'intégrabilité	условия интегрируемости
I 605	**integrability in the sense of Riemann** <AN>	Integrierbarkeit *f* im Riemannschen Sinne, Riemannsche Integrierbarkeit	intégrabilité *f* au sens de Riemann	интегрируемость в смысле Римана
	μ-integrable function <AN>	*s.* M 946		
I 606	**integrable group** <DE, DI>	integrierbare Gruppe *f*	groupe *m* intégrable	интегрируемая группа
	integrable in the sense of Denjoy-Khinchine <RF>	*s.* T 636		
	integrable Lie group <GR>	*s.* S 1280		
	integrable solid <DI>	*s.* C 2719		
I 607	**integrable system [of partial differential equations]** <DE>	integrables System *n* [von partiellen Differentialgleichungen]	système *m* intégrable [d'équations différentielles aux dérivées partielles]	интегрируемая система [дифференциальных уравнений в частных производных]
	integral <DE>	*s.* S 1263		
I 608	**integral algebraic quantity,** integral quantity <function *or* number> <AL>	ganze [algebraische] Größe *f*	quantité *f* algébrique entière	целая алгебраическая величина
I 609	**integral base (basis)** <AB>	Ganzheitsbasis *f*	base *f* entière (des entiers, rationnelle)	целочисленный базис
I 610	**integral calculus** <DI>	Integralrechnung *f*	calcul *m* intégral	интегральное исчисление
I 611	**integral chain,** chain over *I* <AT>	ganzzahlige Kette *f*, 𝔖-Kette *f*, ganzzahliger Komplex *m*	chaîne *f* à coefficients entiers	целочисленная цепь
I 612	**integral closure** <AL>	ganze Abschließung *f*, Integrität *f*, ganz[-]abgeschlossene Hülle *f*	clôture *f* intégrale	целое замыкание, цело-замыкание, вполне замкнутая оболочка
I 613	**integral closure of a ring in** *R* <AL>	ganzer Abschluß *m* eines Ringes in *R*	fermeture *f* intégrale d'un anneau dans *R*	целое замыкание кольца в *R*
I 614	**integral cohomology ring** <AT>	ganzzahliger Kohomologiering *m*	anneau *m* de cohomologie à coefficients entiers	кольцо когомологий с целочисленными коэффициентами
I 615	**integral conoid** <DE>	Integralkonoid *n*	conoïde *m* intégral	интегральный коноид
	integral convergence test <SS>	*s.* C 248		
	integral cosine <FU>	*s.* C 2531		
I 616	**integral covering surface** <FT>	Integralüberlagerungsfläche *f*	surface *f* de recouvrement intégrale	интегральная поверхность наложения

No.	English	German	French	Russian
I 617	**integral curvature** <DG>	Integralkrümmung *f*	courbure *f* intégrale	интегральная кривизна
I 618	**integral curve,** solution curve <DE>	Lösungskurve *f*, Integralkurve *f*	courbe (ligne) *f* intégrale	интегральная кривая
I 619	**integral dependence** <AL>	Ganzabhängigkeit *f*	dépendance *f* intégrale	целая зависимость
I 620	**integral domain,** ring without zero divisors, entire ring <AL>	nullteilerfreier Ring *m* <aus wenigstens 2 Elementen>, Ring ohne Nullteiler	anneau *m* sans diviseurs de zéro, anneau intègre	область целостности, кольцо без делителей нуля
	integral domain <AL>	*s.* D 869		
	integral domain of characteristic *p* <AL>	*s.* D 870		
	integral domain of characteristic zero <AL>	*s.* D 871		
I 621	**integral element** <DE>	Integralelement *n*	élément *m* intégral	интегральный элемент
I 622	**integral element over *R*,** *R*-integral element, element <of a ring> integrally dependent on *R* <AL>	ganz[-]abhängiges Element *n* von *R*, *R*-ganzes Element, ganzes Element über *R*	élément *m* entier sur *R*	целый элемент над *R*
I 623	**integral equation method,** method of integral equations <DE, PO>	Integralgleichungsmethode *f*	méthode *f* des équations intégrales	метод интегральных уравнений
	integral equation of Fredholm type <IE>	*s.* F 600		
	integral equation of Fredholm type of the first kind <IE>	*s.* F 601		
	integral equation of Fredholm type of the second kind <IE>	*s.* F 602		
	integral equation of the Fredholm type <IE>	*s.* F 600		
	integral equation of the Fredholm type of the first kind <IE>	*s.* F 601		
	integral equation of the Fredholm type of the second kind <IE>	*s.* F 602		
	integral equation of [the] Volterra type <IE>	*s.* V 206		
	integral equation with fixed upper limit of integration <IE>	*s.* F 600		
	integral equation with fixed upper limit of integration of the first kind <IE>	*s.* F 601		
	integral equation with fixed upper limit of integration of the second kind <IE>	*s.* F 602		
	integral equation with variable upper limit of integration <IE>	*s.* V 206		
I 624	**integral exponential,** exponential integral [function]; ei; Ei <FU>	Exponentialintegral *n*, Integralexponentielle *f*, Integralexponentialfunktion *f*; ei; Ei	intégrale *f* exponentielle, exponentielle *f* intégrale; ei; Ei	интегральная показательная функция, интегрально-показательная функция; ei; Ei
I 625	**integral filtration** <of a group> <GR>	ganze Filtration *f*	filtration *f* entière	целая фильтрация
	integral function <FT>	*s.* E 259		
I 626	**integral function of finite order** <FT>	ganze Funktion *f* von endlicher Ordnung, Hadamardsche Funktion	fonction *f* de Hadamard, fonction d'ordre fini	целая функция конечного порядка
I 627	**integral-geometric area (measure of area),** area <IG>	integralgeometrisches Maß (Flächenmaß) *n*	aire *f* <en géométrie intégrale>	площадь <в интегральной геометрии>
I 628	**integral homology functor** <AT>	ganzzahliger Homologiefunktor *m*	foncteur *m* d'homologie intégrale	функтор целочисленных гомологий
I 629	**integral homology group** <AT>	ganzzahlige Homologiegruppe *f*, Homologiegruppe mit Koeffizienten in **Z**	groupe *m* d'homologie à coefficients entiers	группа гомологий [с целочисленными коэффициентами]
I 630	**integral homology theory,** homology theory with coefficients **Z** <AT>	ganzzahlige Homologietheorie *f*	théorie *f* homologique à coefficients entiers	целочисленная теория гомологий, теория гомологий с коэффициентами в **Z**
I 631	**integral ideal of** $\mathfrak{o}$ <AL>	$\mathfrak{o}$-ganzes Ideal *n*	idéal *m* entier de $\mathfrak{o}$	целый идеал в $\mathfrak{o}$
I 632	**integral inequality** <IE>	Integralungleichung *f*	inéquation *f* intégrale	интегральное неравенство
	integral in the Riemann sense <DI>	*s.* R 1015		
I 633	**integral invariant** <DE, DG>	Integralinvariante *f*	invariant *m* intégral	интегральный инвариант
I 634	**integrality condition,** requirement of integrality <GN, PG>	Ganzzahligkeitsforderung *f*	demande (condition) *f* d'intégrité	требование (условие) целочисленности
I 635	**integrality theorem** <AT>	Ganzheitssatz *m*	théorème *m* d'intégrité	теорема целочисленности
	integral kernel <IE>	*s.* K 50		
	integrally closed domain <AL>	*s.* I 636		

No.	English	German	French	Russian
I 636	**integrally closed integral domain,** integrally closed domain <AL>	ganz[-]abgeschlossener (normaler) Integritätsbereich *m*	anneau *m* d'intégrité intégralement clos (fermé)	вполне замкнутая область целостности
I 637	**integrally closed ring** <AL>	ganz[-]abgeschlossener Ring *m*	anneau *m* intégralement clos (fermé)	целозамкнутое кольцо
I 638	**integral matrix** <AL>	ganzzahlige Matrix *f*	matrice *f* intégrale	интегральная (целочисленная) матрица
I 639	**integral matrix** <DE>	Integralmatrix *f*	matrice *f* intégrale	интегральная матрица
I 640	**integral monomial** <AL>	ganzes Monom *n*	monôme *m* entier	целый одночлен
	integral multiple <AR, NT>	*s.* M 987		
I 641	**integral neodomain** <AL>	nullteilerfreier Neoring *m*	néo-anneau *m* sans diviseurs de zéro	неокольцо без делителей нуля
I 642	**integralness,** integrity <AL, NT>	Ganzzahligkeit *f*, Ganzheit *f*	intégrité *f*, propriété *f* d'être entier	целостность, целочисленность
	integral number <NT>	*s.* I 596		
	integral of Cauchy type <AN>	*s.* C 246		
I 643	**integral operator** <FA>	Integraloperator *m*	opérateur *m* intégral	интегральный оператор
I 644	**integral over a closed surface,** closed surface integral <AN>	Hüllenintegral *n*	intégrale *f* sur une surface fermée	интеграл по замкнутой поверхности; [двойной] интеграл, взятый по замкнутой поверхности
I 645	**integral part,** integer part, entier, greatest integer <less than or equal to *x*>, ent *x*, E[*x*] <of a number *x*> <NT>	ganzer Teil *m*, größte ganze Zahl *f*, größtes Ganzes *n*, [*x*], E[*x*]	caractéristique *f* <de *x*>, le plus grand nombre *m* entier <inférieur ou égal à *x*>, entier *m* [le plus grand], partie *f* entière [par défaut], le plus grand entier, ent *x*, [*x*], E[*x*]	целая часть, антье <от *x* *или* [числа] *x*>, [*x*], E[*x*]
I 646	**integral point** <PG>	ganzzahliger Punkt *m*	point *m* entier	целочисленная точка
I 647	**integral polynomial** <AL>	ganzzahliges Polynom *n*	polynôme *m* à coefficients entiers	целочисленный многочлен, многочлен с целыми коэффициентами
I 648	**integral polynomial** <IE>	Integralpolynom *n*	polynôme *m* intégral	интегральный многочлен
I 649	**integral polynomial with highest coefficient ≡ 1** <NT>	primäre ganze ganzzahlige Funktion *f* <Polynom, dessen höchster Koeffizient ≡ 1 ist>	fonction *f* [rationnelle entière à coefficients entiers] primaire	целочисленный многочлен, старший коэффициент которого сравним with 1
I 650	**integral power series** <SS>	Integralpotenzreihe *f*	série *f* en puissances d'intégrales	интегро-степенной ряд
I 651	**integral prime ideal** <AB>	ganzes Primideal *n*	idéal *m* entier premier	целый простой идеал
	integral quantity <AL>	*s.* I 608		
I 652	**integral quaternion** <AL>	ganzzahlige Quaternion *f*	quaternion *m* entier	целочисленный кватернион
	integral rational function <AN>	*s.* E 262		
I 653	**integral relation** <DE>	Integralrelation *f*	relation *f* intégrale	интегральное отношение
I 654	**integral remainder** <in Taylor's formula> <DI>	Integraldarstellung *f* für das Restglied, Integralrestglied *n*	reste *m* intégral	остаточный член в интегральной форме
I 655	**integral representation,** representation by integral[s] <AN>	Integraldarstellung *f*	représentation *f* intégrale	интегральное представление
I 656	**integral representation** <of a function> <IE>	quellenmäßige Darstellung *f*	représentation *f* intégrale	интегральное представление
I 657	**integral representation module** <AL>	ganzzahliger Darstellungsmodul *m*	module *m* de représentation intégrale	целочисленный модуль представления
	integral ring <AL>	*s.* D 869		
I 658	**integral ring extension** <AL>	ganze Ringerweiterung *f*	extension *f* intégrale d'anneau	целое расширение кольца; целое кольцо
	integral secant <FU>	*s.* S 188		
I 659	**integral sign,** ∫ <DI>	Integralzeichen *n*, ∫	signe *m* d'intégration, ∫	знак интегрирования, ∫
	integral sine <FU>	*s.* S 1026		
I 660	**integral singular chain** <AT>	ganzzahlige singuläre Kette *f*	chaîne *f* singulière entière	целочисленная сингулярная цепь
I 661	**integral strip** <DE>	Integralstreifen *m*	bande *f* intégrale	интегральная полос[к]а
I 662	**integral subdomain** <AL>	Teilintegritätsbereich *m*, Unterintegritätsbereich *m*	sous-domaine *m* d'intégrité	подобласть целостности
	integral sum <DI>	*s.* R 1035		
I 663	**integral surface,** solution surface <of a partial differential equation> <DE>	Lösungsfläche *f*, Integralfläche *f*	surface *f* intégrale	интегральная поверхность
	integral surface <DE>	*s.* I 668		
I 664	**integral table** <AN>	Integraltafel *f*	table *f* des intégrales	таблица интегралов
	integral theorem of Cartan <DI>	*s.* C 158		
	integral theorem of Fourier <AN, NU>	*s.* F 528		
	integral theorem of Gauss <DI, VT>	*s.* G 427		
	integral theorem of Stokes <DI, VT>	*s.* S 1815		
	integral transcendental function <FT>	*s.* E 265		
I 665	**integral transform[ation]** <IT>	Integraltransformation *f*	transformation *f* intégrale	интегральное преобразование
I 666	**integral unimodular substitution** <AL>	ganzzahlige unimodulare Substitution *f*	substitution *f* unimodulaire intégrale	целочисленная унимодулярная подстановка
I 667	**integral valued polynomial** <NT>	ganzwertiges Polynom *n*	polynôme *m* à valeurs entières	целозначный многочлен

	English	German	French	Russian
I 668	**integral variety,** integral surface <of partial differential equations> <DE>	Integralmannigfaltigkeit *f*, Integralgebilde *n*, Integralfläche *f*, Integralverein *m*	variété *f* intégrale, surface *f* intégrale	интегральное многообразие, интегральная поверхность
I 669	**integral vector** <PG>	ganzzahliger Vektor *m*	vecteur *m* entier	целочисленный вектор, вектор с целочисленными компонентами
I 670	**integrand,** function (expression) to be integrated, // element of integration <DI>	Integrand *m*	fonction *f* intégrée, fonction à intégrer, expression (fonction, quantité) *f* [qui figure] sous le signe d'intégration, quantité à intégrer, coefficient *m* différentiel	подынтегральная (интегрируемая) функция, подынтегральное [подинтегральное] выражение, подынтегральная функция
I 671	**integraph** <AN, IN>	Integraph *m*	intégraphe *m*	интеграф
	integrated power function (spectrum) <SP>	*s.* S 1401		
I 672	**integrating factor,** Euler['s] multiplier <DE>	integrierender Faktor (Multiplikator) *m*, [Eulerscher] Multiplikator, Integrabilitätsfaktor *m*	facteur (multiplicateur) *m* intégrant, multiplicateur *m* d'Euler	интегрирующий множитель, множитель Эйлера
I 673	**integrating fraction** <DI>	integrierender Bruch *m*	fraction *f* intégrante	интегрирующая дробь
I 674	**integrating wheel,** wheel <AN, GE, IN>	Integrierrolle *f*	roulette *f* intégrante	интегрирующий ролик
I 675	**integration** <DI>	Integration *f*, Integrieren *n*	intégration *f*	интегрирование
	integration <DE>	*s.* 1. Q 49; 2. S 1262		
	integration as the inverse of differentiation <DI>	*s.* A 718		
I 676	**integration by differentiation,** solution by differentiation <DE>	Integration *f* durch Differentiation	intégration (solution) *f* par dérivation	интегрирование (решение) методом дифференцирования
I 677	**integration by parts,** integration per parts, partial integration <DI>	partielle (unvollständige, teilweise) Integration *f*, Integration nach Teilen, Teilintegration *f*, Produktintegration *f*	intégration *f* par parties	интегрирование по частям
	integration by parts <DI, VT>	*s.* G 427		
I 678	**integration by power series** <DE>	Integration *f* mittels (durch) Potenzreihen	intégration *f* par [développement en] séries entières	интегрирование при помощи степенных рядов
I 679	**integration by substitution,** method of substitution <DI>	Integration *f* durch Substitution (Einführung neuer Integrationsvariablen), Einführung *f* neuer Integrationsvariablen, Substitutionsmethode *f*	intégration *f* par substitution, méthode *f* de changement de variables	интегрирование подстановкой, метод замены переменных
	integration by terms <DI>	*s.* I 682		
I 680	**integration constant** <DI>	Integrationskonstante *f*	constante *f* d'intégration	постоянная интегрирования
	integration interval <DI>	*s.* L 751		
I 681	**integration operator** <AN>	Integrationsoperator *m*	opérateur *m* d'intégration	оператор интегрирования
	integration per parts <DI>	*s.* I 677		
I 682	**integration term by term,** integration by terms, term-by-term integration, termwise integration <DI>	gliedweise Integration *f*	intégration *f* terme à terme	почленное интегрирование, интегрирование по членам
I 683	**integration variable** <DI>	Integrationsvariable *f*, Integrationsveränderliche *f*	variable *f* d'intégration	переменная интегрирования
I 684	**integration** <of an integral> **with respect to a parameter** <DI>	Integration *f* unter dem Integralzeichen, Integration <eines Integrals> nach einem Parameter	intégration *f* <d'une intégrale> par rapport à un paramètre	интегрирование <интеграла> по параметру, интегрирование под знаком интеграла
I 685	**integration with respect to index** <DI>	Integration *f* nach dem Index	intégration *f* par rapport à l'indice	интегрирование по индексу
I 686	**integrator** <AN, IN>	Integrator *m*	intégrateur *m*	интегратор
I 687	**integrator** <in the Stieltjes integral> <AN>	Integratorfunktion *f*	intégrateur *m*	интегрирующая функция
I 688	**integrimeter** <AN, IN>	Integrimeter *n*	intégrimètre *m*	интегриметр
	integrity <AL, NT>	*s.* I 642		
I 689	**integro-differential equation** <DE>	Integrodifferentialgleichung *f*, Integro-Differentialgleichung *f*	équation *f* intégro-différentielle	интегро-дифференциальное уравнение
I 690	**integro-differential operator** <FA>	Integrodifferentialoperator *m*, Integro-Differentialoperator *m*	opérateur *m* intégro-différentiel	интегро-дифференциальный оператор
I 691	**intension,** denotation; connotation <classical logic>; sense <modern logic> <of a concept> <MM>	Intention *f*, Bedeutung *f*	intention *f*	интенция, содержание
I 692	**intensional logic** <LO>	intensionale Logik *f*	logique *f* intentionnelle	интенсиональная логика
I 693	**intensional property** <LO>	intensionale Eigenschaft *f*	propriété *f* intentionnelle	интенсиональное (содержательное) свойство

I 694	**intensity** <of a stochastic process, e.g. a Markov chain> <SP>	Intensität *f*	intensité *f*	интенсивность
I 695	**intensity function** <SP>	Intensitätsfunktion *f*	fonction *f* d'intensité	функция интенсивности
	inter <SE>	*s.* I 802		
I 696	**interblock information** <ST>	Zwischenblockinformation *f*	information *f* entre blocs	межблочная информация
I 697	**intercept** <of a curve *or* surface> <AY>	Achsenabschnitt *m*	intercepte *m*, point *m* de rencontre	отрезок, отсекаемый на координатной оси
I 698	**intercept chart,** compound nomogram [with points in a line], compound alignment chart (graph) <NO>	mehrteilige Fluchtlinientafel *f*, Verbundnomogramm *n*, Verbundtafel *f*	abaque *m* par alignement composé, abaque à points alignés composé	составная номограмма [из выравненных точек]
I 699	**intercept equation of a [straight] line, intercept form of the equation of a [straight] line** <AY>	Achsenabschnittsgleichung *f* [der Geraden], Achsenabschnittsform *f* der Geradengleichung, Abschnittsgleichung *f* der Geraden, Abschnittsform (Achsenschnittform) *f* der Geradengleichung	équation *f* d'une droite par segments	уравнение прямой в отрезках
	intercept on the axis of abscissas <AY>	*s.* X 1		
	intercept on the x-axis <AY>	*s.* X 1		
I 700	**intercept theorems** <EG>	Strahlensatz *m*, Hauptsatz *m* der Ähnlichkeitslehre	théorème *m* de Thalès (Thales)	теоремы о лучах (прямых) теоремы о свойствах параллельных прямых, пересекающих стороны угла
I 701	**interchange,** permutation <in the antecedent *or* succedent> <LO>	Vertauschung *f* <im Antezedent *oder* Sukzedent>	permutation *f* <dans l'antécédent *ou* conséquent>	перестановка <в антецеденте *или* сукцеденте>
	interchange graph <GP>	*s.* L 860		
I 702	**interchange of [two] lines, interchanging of lines,** interchanging of two lines <of a matrix> <MD>	Zeilenvertauschung *f*, Vertauschung *f* von [zwei] Zeilen	échange *m* de [deux] lignes	перестановка [двух] строк
	interchanging of the rows and columns <MD>	*s.* T 859		
	interchanging of two lines <MD>	*s.* I 702		
I 703	**interclass correlation,** between-class correlation, between-group correlation, correlation between classes (treatments), external correlation <ST>	Korrelation *f* zwischen den Klassen, Zwischenklassenkorrelation *f*, Zwischenkorrelation *f*, äußere Korrelation, Interklaßkorrelation *f*, Interklassenkorrelation *f*	corrélation *f* entre les classes, corrélation entre classes, corrélation interclasse (externe)	межгрупповая корреляция, корреляция между группами (классами), внешняя корреляция
I 704	**interclass variance,** between-group variance, between-class variance, variance between classes, external variance <ST>	Varianz *f* zwischen den Klassen, Zwischenklassenvarianz *f*, Zwischenvarianz *f*, äußere Varianz, Interklaßvarianz *f*, Interklassenvarianz *f*	variance *f* entre les classes, variance entre classes, variance interclasse (externe), variance	межгрупповая дисперсия, дисперсия между группами (классами), внешняя дисперсия
	intercorrelation <ST>	*s.* 1. C 2486; 2. C 2689		
	intercorrelation analysis <ST>	*s.* C 2690		
	intercorrelation coefficient <ST>	*s.* C 2691		
I 705	**interdecile range** <ST>	Dezilabstand *m*, interdezile Spannweite *f*	intervalle *m* interdécile, interdécile *m*	интердецильная широта, расстояние между децилями
I 706	**interdeducibility** <LO>	Deduktionsgleichheit *f*	interdéductibilité *f*	равенство по дедукции, дедуктивное равенство
I 707	**interdependent equations** <GN>	voneinander abhängige Gleichungen *fpl*	équations *fpl* interdépendantes	взаимно связанные уравнения
I 708	**interdiction of confusion** <LO>	Konfusionsverbot *n*	règle *f* d'interdiction des fausses homonymies	запрещение смешения
I 709	**interest,** simple interest <AR>	Zins *m*	intérêt *m*, intérêt simple	процент, простой процент
I 710	**interest** <in the interest formula> <AR>	Zinsertrag *m*	produit *m* de l'intérêt	взнос, приращенный взнос
	interest account <AR>	*s.* I 711		
I 711	**interest calculation (computation),** method of interest calculation, [simple] interest account <AR>	[einfache] Zinsrechnung *f*, Zinsenberechnung *f*, Interessenrechnung *f*	calcul *m* des intérêts [simples]	исчисление процентов (простых процентов)
I 712	**interest formula** <AR>	Zinsformel *f*	formule *f* des intérêts	формула [простых] процентов
	interference variety over *k* <AG>	*s.* K 185		
	intergroup deviance <ST>	*s.* I 713		
I 713	**intergroup sum of squares,** intergroup deviance, between-group sum of squares, between-group deviance <ST>	Summe *f* der Abweichungsquadrate zwischen den Gruppen, Quadratsumme *f* zwischen den Gruppen, Zwischengruppen-Quadratsumme *f*	somme *f* des carrés [des écarts] entre les groupes	межгрупповая сумма квадратов [отклонений от среднего значения]

No.	English	German	French	Russian
I 714	**interior** <of a Jordan curve> <GE>	Inneres *n*	intérieur *m*	внутренность, внутренняя часть
I 715	**interior** <of a domain> <TO>	Gebietsinneres *n*, Inneres *n* <eines Gebiets>	intérieure *m* <d'un domain>	внутренность области
I 716	**interior,** open kernel, inside <of a set> <TO>	Inneres *n*, offener Kern *m*, Kern	intérieur *m*	внутренность, открытое ядро, множество внутренних точек
I 717	**interior alternate angles,** alternate interior angles <US> <EG>	innere Wechselwinkel *mpl*	angles *mpl* alternes[-]internes	внутренние накрестлежащие углы
I 718	**interior angle** <of a circle> <EG>	Sehnenwinkel *m*	angle *m* intérieur au cercle	угол с вершиной внутри круга, вписанный угол
I 719	**interior angle** <EG>	Innenwinkel *m*	angle *m* intérieur	внутренний угол
I 720	**interior bisector (bisectrix)** <e.g. of the triangle> <EG>	Innenwinkelhalbierende *f*, innere Winkelhalbierende *f*	bissectrice *f* intérieure (d'un angle intérieur)	биссектриса (биссектор) внутреннего угла
I 721	**interior boundary [value] problem,** interior problem <DE, PO>	inneres Randwertproblem *n*, innere Randwertaufgabe *f*, Randwertproblem (Randwertaufgabe) für das Innengebiet, Innenproblem *n*	problème *m* intérieur, problème aux limites intérieur	внутренняя краевая задача, внутренняя задача
I 722	**interior centre of similarity (similitude)** <GE>	innerer Ähnlichkeitspunkt *m*	centre *m* de similitude intérieur	внутренний центр подобия
I 723	**interior closed cut** <on a surface> <AT>	Rückkehrschnitt *m*	rétrosection *f*	внутренний замкнутый разрез
I 724	**interior content,** inner content, interior (inner) Jordan content <ME>	innerer [Peano-Jordanscher] Inhalt *m*	aire *f* intérieure	внутренняя площадь, внутренняя жорданова мера
I 725	**interior cross-sectional measure** <CS, GE>	inneres Quermaß *n*	travers *m* intérieur, aire (étendue) *f* du travers intérieur	внутренняя поперечная мера
I 726	**interior derivative** <DG>	innere Ableitung *f*	dérivée *f* intérieure	внутренняя производная
I 727	**interior differential expression** <AN, DG>	innerer Differentialausdruck *m*	expression *f* différentielle intérieure	внутреннсс дифференциальное выражение
I 728	**interior Dirichlet problem** <DE>	inneres Dirichletsches Problem *n*	problème *m* de Dirichlet intérieur	внутренняя задача Дирихле
I 729	**interior domain** <TO>	Innengebiet *n*, Innenbereich *m*	région *f* intérieure, domaine *m* intérieur	внутренняя область
I 730	**interior edge** <GP>	innere Kante *f*	arête *f* intérieure	внутреннее ребро
	interior Jordan content <ME>	*s.* I 724		
I 731	**interior Lebesgue measure,** interior (lower) measure <ME>	inneres Lebesguesches Maß *n*, inneres L-Maß (Maß) *n*	mesure *f* intérieure lebesguienne, mesure [de Lebesgue] intérieure	нижняя мера, внутренняя мера <в смысле Лебега>
I 732	**interior map,** interior mapping, interior transformation <Stoilow> <TO>	innere Abbildung *f*	application *f* intérieure	внутреннее отображение
	interior map <TO>	*s.* O 142		
	interior mapping <TO>	*s.* 1. I 732; 2. O 142		
I 733	**interior measure,** lower measure <ME>	inneres Maß *n*	mesure *f* intérieure	внутренняя (нижняя) мера
	interior measure <ME>	*s.* I 731		
I 734	**interior multiplication** <AL>	innere Multiplikation *f*, // projektive Multiplikation	multiplication *f* intérieure <Grassmann>, // multiplication projective	внутреннее умножение
I 735	**interior normal,** inner (inward) normal <DG>	innere Normale *f*, Innennormale *f*	normale *f* intérieure	внутренняя нормаль
I 736	**interior operation** <TO>	Operation *f* der Bildung des inneren Kerns	opération *f* qui fait correspondre à chaque ensemble son intérieur	операция, при которой каждому множеству соответствует его внутренность
I 737	**interior operator** <TO>	Kernoperator *m*, Kontraktion *f* <dual zu Hüllenoperation>	opération *f* de l'intérieur	операция открытого ядра
I 738	**interior opposite angle** <EG>	innere entgegengesetzte (entgegengesetzt liegende) Winkel *mpl*	angles *mpl* co-internes, angles intérieurs du même côté de la sécante	внутренние односторонние углы
I 739	**interior Pfaff problem,** interior problem <DE>	inneres [Pfaffsches] Problem *n*	problème *m* [de Pfaff] intérieur	внутренняя задача [Пфаффа]
I 740	**interior point,** inner point <EG, TO>	innerer Punkt *m*	point *m* intérieur	внутренняя точка
	interior problem <DE>	*s.* I 739		
	interior problem <DE, PO>	*s.* I 721		
I 741	**interior radius,** inner radius <FT>	innerer [konformer] Radius *m*	rayon *m* intérieur	внутренний радиус
	interior transformation <TO>	*s.* 1. I 732; 2. O 142		
I 742	**interlace / to,** to intertwine, to be interlaced (intertwined) <TO>	sich verschlingen	s'entrelacer, entrelacer l'un l'autre	зацепляться
I 743	**interlaced cycle,** intertwined cycle <TO>	verschlungener Zyklus *m*	cycle *m* entrelacé	зацепленный цикл
I 744	**interlacing,** intertwining, link <TO>	Verschlingung *f*	entrelacement *m*	зацепление
	intermediacy <GE, SE>	*s.* R 678		
I 745	**intermediate base** <of an algebraic manifold> <AG>	Zwischenbasis *f*, intermediäre Basis *f*	base *f* intermédiaire	промежуточный базис
I 746	**intermediate calculation** <AR, GN>	Zwischenrechnung *f*	calcul *m* intermédiaire	промежуточное вычисление

I 747	**intermediate convergent,** intermediate fraction <of a continued fraction> <NT>	Nebennäherungsbruch *m* <zwischen zwei aufeinanderfolgenden Näherungsbrüchen eines Kettenbruchs>; eingeschalteter Bruch *m*, eingeschalteter (mittelbarer) Näherungsbruch *m*, intermediärer Bruch, Schaltbruch *m*, Zwischenbruch *m*	fraction *f* intermédiaire <entre deux réduites consécutives d'une fraction continue>, fraction secondaire, convergent *m* intermédiaire	промежуточная подходящая дробь, промежуточная (вставная) дробь
I 748	**intermediate differential** <FT> ⌐<DI>	intermediäres Differential *n*	différentielle *f* intermédiaire	промежуточный дифференциал
	intermediate differential	*s.* P 199		
I 749	**intermediate field,** field between . . .; subextension <AL>	Zwischenkörper *m* <zwischen>	corps *m* intermédiaire (commutatif intermédiaire), extension *f* intermédiaire <entre>; sous-extension *f*	промежуточное поле <между>
I 750	**intermediate field theorem** <of Galois' theory> <AL>	Zwischenkörpersatz *m* <Steinitz>	théorème *m* des corps intermédiaires	теорема о промежуточных полях
I 751	**intermediate form** <AL, FT>	Mittelform *f* <Klein>	forme *f* intermédiaire	промежуточная форма
	intermediate fraction <NT>	*s.* I 747		
I 752	**intermediate function,** Jacobian function, Jacobi['s] function <FT, FU>	Jacobische Funktion *f* <Frobenius>, intermediäre Funktion <Poincaré>	fonction *f* intermédiaire (de Jacobi)	промежуточная функция, функция Якоби
I 753	**intermediate group** <GR>	Zwischengruppe *f*	groupe *m* intermédiaire	промежуточная группа
I 754	**intermediate integral** <DE>	Zwischenintegral *n*, intermediäres Integral *n*, intermediäre Lösung *f*, Zwischenlösung *f*	intégrale *f* intermédiaire	промежуточный интеграл
I 755	**intermediate lattice** <GU>	Zwischengitter *n*	réseau *m* intermédiaire	промежуточная решетка
	intermediate product <AR>	*s.* P 251		
I 756	**intermediate result** <AR, GN>	Zwischenergebnis *n*	résultat *m* provisoire	промежуточный результат
I 757	**intermediate term** <of a series> <SS>	Zwischenglied *n*	terme *m* intermédiaire	промежуточный член
I 758	**intermediate value** <of a function> <RF>	Zwischenwert *m*	valeur *f* intermédiaire	промежуточное (среднее) значение
	intermediate value property <RF>	*s.* D 12		
	intermediate value theorem <RF>	*s.* L 1017		
I 759	**intermediate variable** <IV>	Zwischenvariable *f* <Clebsch>	variable *f* intermédiaire	промежуточная переменная
	intermediate vertex <GP>	*s.* I 771		
I 760	**internal composition [law],** binary internal composition <AL>	inneres Verknüpfungsgesetz *n*, innere Verknüpfung *f*	loi *f* de composition interne, composition *f* interne	внутренний закон композиции, закон внутренней композиции, внутренняя композиция
I 761	**internal correlation coefficient** <ST>	interner Korrelationskoeffizient *m*	coefficient *m* de corrélation interne	коэффициент внутренней корреляции
I 762	**internal direct product** <of groups> <GR>	[internes] direktes Produkt *n*	produit *m* direct	внутреннее прямое произведение
I 763	**internal direct sum** <AL>	interne direkte Summe *f*	somme *f* directe de sous-groupes	внутренняя прямая сумма
I 764	**internal division** <of a line segment> <EG>	innere Teilung *f* <einer Strecke>	division *f* interne	внутреннее деление, деление в среднем отношением <отрезка>
I 765	**internal least square** <ST> ⌐<GP>	internes kleinstes Quadrat *n*	moindre carré *m* interne	внутренний наименьший квадрат
	internally stable set	*s.* I 314		
I 766	**internally tangent** <GE>	[sich] von innen berührend, innenberührend	tangent intérieurement	имеющий внутреннее касание, касающийся внутренним образом
	internal ratio <AY, EG>	*s.* A 370		
I 767	**internal regression** <ST>	interne Regression *f*	régression *f* interne	внутренняя регрессия <Хартли>
I 768	**internal stability** <GP, TG>	innere (interne) Stabilität *f*	stabilité *f* interne	внутренняя устойчивость
I 769	**internal tangency** <GE>	innere Berührung *f*	tangence *f* intérieure, contact *m* intérieur	внутреннее касание
I 770	**internal transformation** <AT>	interne Transformation *f*	transformation *f* interne	внутреннее преобразование
	internal variance <ST>	*s.* W 273		
I 771	**internal vertex,** inner (intermediate) vertex <GP>	innerer Knotenpunkt *m*	sommet *m* intérieur	внутренняя вершина
I 772	**interpenetrating samples** <ST>	ineinandergreifende (überlagerte) Stichproben *fpl*	échantillons *mpl* superposés (enchevêtrés)	взаимно проникающие (пересекающиеся) выборки
I 773	**interpercentile range** <ST>	Perzentilabstand *m*, Zentilabstand *m*	intervalle *m* interpercentile, interpercentile *m*	интерпроцентильная широта, расстояние между процентилями
	interpolating function <AX, FD, NU>	*s.* I 775		
	interpolating polynomial <AX, FD, NU>	*s.* I 781		
	interpolating series <AX, FD, NU>	*s.* I 784		

I 773a	**interpolation** <AX, FD, NU>	Interpolation *f*, Einschalten *n* von Zwischenwerten	interpolation *f*	интерполяция; интерполирование
	interpolation <AX, FD, NU>	*s.* L 805		
I 774	**interpolation error** <AX, NU>	Interpolationsfehler *m*	erreur *f* d'interpolation	ошибка интерполяции
I 775	**interpolation function,** interpolating function <AX, FD, NU>	Interpolationsfunktion *f*	fonction *f* d'interpolation	интерполяционная (интерполирующая) функция
I 776	**interpolation indicatrix** <AX, FD, NU>	Interpolationsindikatrix *f*	indicatrice *f* d'interpolation	индикатриса интерполяции
I 777	**interpolation method** <AX, FD, NU>	Interpolationsverfahren *n*, Interpolationsmethode *f*	méthode *f* d'interpolation	интерполяционный метод, способ интерполяции
I 778	**interpolation method [of mechanical quadrature]** <DI, NU>	interpolatorisches mechanisches Quadraturverfahren *n*, interpolatorisches Verfahren *n* [der mechanischen Quadratur]	méthode *f* d'interpolation [de quadrature mécanique]	интерполяционный метод [механических квадратур]
I 779	**interpolation node,** given value of argument <in interpolation> <AX, FD, NU>	Stützstelle *f*, Interpolationsknoten *m*, Knoten *m*, Interpolationspunkt *m*, [interpolatorischer] Grundpunkt *m*, Stützpunkt *m*, Stützwert *m*	nœud *m* d'interpolation	узел [интерполяции], полюс интерполяции, узловая точка, заданная точка
I 780	**interpolation of *m* numbers between two terms of a geometric sequence** <AR>	Einschalten *n* von *m* Gliedern in eine geometrische Progression	insertion *f* de *m* moyens proportionnels (géométrique) <entre deux nombres donnés>	введение *m* дальнейших членов в геометрическую прогрессию
I 781	**interpolation polynomial,** interpolating polynomial <AX, FD, NU>	Interpolationspolynom *n*, Schaltpolynom *n*	polynôme *m* d'interpolation	интерполяционный (интерполирующий) многочлен
	interpolation polynomial of Lagrange <AX, NU>	*s.* L 23		
I 782	**interpolation problem,** problem of interpolation <AX, FD, NU>	Interpolationsaufgabe *f*, Interpolationsproblem *n*	problème *m* d'interpolation	интерполяционная задача
I 783	**interpolation quadrature formula** <DI, NU>	Quadraturformel (Formel) *f* vom Interpolationstyp, interpolatorische Quadraturformel	formule *f* de quadrature interpolatoire	квадратурная формула интерполяционного типа
I 784	**interpolation series,** interpolating series <AX, FD, NU>	Interpolationsreihe *f*	série *f* d'interpolation	интерполяционный ряд
I 785	**interpretability by models** <MM>	Modellinterpretierbarkeit *f*	interprétabilité *f* par des modèles	интерпретируемость при помощи моделей
I 786	**interpretable theory** <MM>	interpretierbare Theorie *f*	théorie *f* interprétable	интерпретируемая теория
I 787	**interpretation** <LO>	Interpretation *f*	interprétation *f*	интерпретация
I 788	**interpretation** <ST>	Interpretation *f*, Deutung *f*	interprétation *f*	интерпретация, истолкование, раскрытие смысла, смысл
	interpretation <LO>	*s.* P 780		
	interpretation <MM>	*s.* M 729		
I 789	**interpretation theorem** <LO, MM>	Interpretationssatz *m*	théorème *m* d'interprétation	теорема интерпретации
I 790	**interquartile mean** <ST>	Mittel *n* über den Quartilabstand, Quartilabstand[s]-mittel *n*	moyenne *f* interquartile	интерквартильное среднее, среднее по интерквартильной ширине
I 791	**interquartile range,** quartile range <ST>	Quartilabstand *m*, Hälftespielraum *m*, zwischenquartile Breite *f*, Bereich *m* des Quartils	écart (intervalle) *m* interquartile, interquartile *m*	интерквартильная широта, расстояние между квартилями
I 792	**intersect / to,** to be non-disjoint <said of sets> <SE>	sich treffen, sich schneiden, einen nichtleeren Durchschnitt haben, gemeinsame Elemente haben	se couper, être conjoints, se croiser, se rencontrer	пересекаться
	intersecting line <AG>	*s.* T 863		
I 793	**intersecting lines,** concurrent [straight] lines <EG>	sich schneidende Geraden *fpl*	droites *fpl* sécantes (concourantes)	пересекающиеся прямые; прямые, пересекающиеся в общей точке
I 794	**intersecting plane,** cutting plane, secant plane <EG>	schneidende Ebene *f*, Schnittebene *f*	plan *m* sécant	секущая плоскость
I 795	**intersecting planes** <EG>	sich schneidende Ebenen *fpl*	plans *mpl* sécants (qui se coupent)	пересекающиеся плоскости
I 796	**intersecting planes method** <DS>	Ebenenverfahren *n*	méthode *f* des plans sécants	метод секущих плоскостей
I 797	**intersection** <of linear systems> <AG>	Schnittsystem *n*	système *m* linéaire intersection	пересечение линейных систем
I 798	**intersection** <of two linear spaces> <AL, GE>	Schnittraum *m*	intersection *f* d'espaces, espace *m* intersection	пересечение пространств
I 799	**intersection,** meet <of morphisms> <CA>	Durchschnitt *m*	intersection *f*	левое пересечение
I 800	**intersection** <of cells *or* complexes, curves, solids, *or* surfaces> <GE>	Schnitt *m*; Durchdringung *f* <von Flächen oder Körpern>	intersection *f*	пересечение
I 801	**intersection** <of subgroups> <GR>	Durchschnitt *m*	intersection *f*, p. g. c. d. *m*	пересечение
I 802	**intersection,** product, meet, inner (logical) product, common part, set-theoretic[al] intersection, inter <of sets> <SE>	Durchschnitt *m*, logisches (inneres) Produkt *n*, Durchschnittsmenge *f*, Schnittmenge *f*	intersection *f*, partie *f* commune, produit *m*, produit logique, ensemble-produit *m*, inter	пересечение, общая часть, теоретико-множественное произведение

No.	English	German	French	Russian
	intersection <AL>	*s.* 1. G 407/8; 2. L 240		
	intersection <EG>	*s.* I 814		
	intersection <LA>	*s.* M 362		
	intersection angle <EG>	*s.* A 666		
I 803	**intersection coefficient,** intersection number, Kronecker['s] index <AT>	Schnittzahl *f*, Kroneckerscher Schnittindex *m*	coefficient *m* d'intersection	индекс пересечения
	intersection curve <AY, DS, EG>	*s.* C 2784		
I 804	**intersection cycle** <AG>	Schnittzyklus *m*	cycle *m* intersection	цикл-пересечение
	intersection figure <DS>	*s.* F 221		
I 805	**intersection formula** <AT>	Schnittformel *f*	formule *f* d'intersection	формула пересечения
I 806	**intersection graph** <GP>	Durchschnittsgraph *m*, Durchschnitt *m* von Graphen	graphe *m* d'intersections, intersection *f* de graphes	граф пересечений, пересечение графов
	intersection line <EG>	*s.* L 870		
I 807	**intersection multiplicity,** multiplicity of intersection <AG>	Schnittmultiplizität *f*, Schnittvielfachheit *f*	multiplicité *f* d'intersection	кратность пересечения
I 808	**intersection number** <of divisors> <AG>	Schnittzahl *f*	coefficient *m* d'intersection	индекс (кратность) пересечения
	intersection number <AT>	*s.* I 803		
I 809	**intersection of classes** <SE>	Durchschnittklasse *f*	classe *f* intersection	пересечение классов
I 810	**intersection of domains** <TO>	Produktgebiet *n*, Durchschnitt *m* von Gebieten	intersection *f* de domaines	произведение (пересечение) областей
I 811	**intersection of filters** <TO>	Durchschnittsfilter *m*, Durchschnitt *m* von Filtern	filtre *m* intersection	пересечение фильтров, фильтр-пересечение
I 812	**intersection of orders** <SE>	Durchschnitt *m* von Ordnungen	ordre *m* produit (intersection)	пересечение порядков
I 813	**intersection of topologies** <TO>	Durchschnittstopologie *f*	topologie *f* intersection	пересечение топологий
	intersection of two quadrics <AG>	*s.* E 187		
	intersection operation <SE>	*s.* M 371		
I 814	**intersection point,** point of intersection, intersection <EG>	Schnittpunkt *m*	point *m* d'intersection, point de concours	точка пересечения
I 815	**intersection point of the diagonals** <EG>	Diagonalenschnittpunkt *m*	point *m* d'intersection des diagonales	точка пересечения диагоналей
I 816	**intersection[-] product** <AG>	Schnittprodukt *n*	produit *m* d'intersection	пересечение-произведение
I 817	**intersection ring** <AT>	Schnittring *m*	anneau *m* d'intersection	кольцо пересечений
I 818	**intersection theorems** <AY>	Schnittpunktssätze *mpl*	théorèmes *mpl* d'intersection	теорема пересечения
I 819	**intersection theory, intersection-theory,** theory of intersections <AG>	Schnittheorie *f*	théorie *f* de l'intersection	теория пересечений
I 820	**intersect irreducibly / to** <between *a* and *b*> <TO>	irreduzibel schneiden <zwischen *a* und *b*>	couper irréductiblement <entre *a* et *b*>	неприводимо разрезать <между точками *a* и *b*>
I 821	**intersect transversally / to** <AG>	sich transversal schneiden	se couper transversalement	пересекаться трансверсально
	intertwine / to <TO>	*s.* I 742		
	intertwined cycle <TO>	*s.* I 743		
	intertwining <TO>	*s.* I 744		
I 822	**intertwining operator** <RE>	Intertwining-Operator *m*	opérateur *m* d'entrelacement	сплетающий оператор
I 823	**interval** <especially of the number line> <AN>	Intervall *n*	intervalle *m*	интервал
I 824	**interval,** step <FD, NU>	Schrittweite *f*, Spanne *f*, Maschenweite *f*, Tafelschritt *m*, Schritt *m*	intervalle *m*, pas *m*	шаг, интервал
I 825	**interval,** closed interval <of a lattice> <LA>	Intervall *n*, Quotientenverband *m*, Quotient *m*, abgeschlossenes Intervall *n*, Zwischenverband *m*	intervalle *m* fermé, intervalle, segment *m*	интервал (отрезок) структуры
I 826	**interval** <of an ordered set> <SE>	Stück *n*	section *f* <commençante, finissante *ou* moyenne>	интервал
	interval <AN>	*s.* O 140		
	interval <ST>	*s.* I 835		
I 827	**interval algebra** <NU, SE>	Intervallalgebra *f*, Intervall-Algebra *f*	algèbre *f* des intervalles	алгебра интервалов
I 828	**interval closed at the left,** unbounded interval closed at the left, $[a, +\infty)$ <AN>	linksabgeschlossenes [unbeschränktes] Intervall *n*	intervalle *m* non borné, fermé à gauche	неограниченный замкнутый слева интервал
I 829	**interval closed at the right,** unbounded interval closed at the right, $(-\infty, b]$ <AN>	rechtsabgeschlossenes [unbeschränktes] Intervall *n*	intervalle *m* non borné, fermé à droite	неограниченный замкнутый справа интервал
	interval estimate <ST>	*s.* C 1860		
I 830	**interval estimation** <ST>	Intervallschätzung *f*	estimation *f* par intervalle	интервальное оценивание, интервальная оценка
	interval estimation <ST>	*s.* C 1860		
I 831	**interval function** <AN>	Intervallfunktion *f*, Abschnittsfunktion *f*	fonction *f* d[e l]'intervalle	функция интервала, интервальная функция
I 832	**interval graph** <GP>	Intervallgraph *m*	graphe *m* d'intervalles	граф интервалов, граф отрезков
I 833	**interval of convergence** <AN>	Konvergenzintervall *n*	intervalle *m* de convergence	интервал сходимости

I 834	**interval of definition** <of a function> <AN>	Definitionsintervall *n*	intervalle *m* de variation	интервал определения
I 835	**interval of variation,** interval, spread <of a distribution> <ST>	Variationsintervall *n*	intervalle *m* de variation	интервал варьирования
	interval open at one end <AN, SE>	*s.* H 27		
I 836	**interval topology** <of a lattice> <TO>	Intervalltopologie *f*	topologie *f* segmentaire	интервальная топология
I 837	**interval, which is not an initial or finite segment** <of an ordered set> <SE>	Mittelstück *n*	section *f* moyenne, tronçon *m*	интервал, который не является граничным отрезком
I 838	**intra-block variance** <ST>	Innerblockvarianz *f*	dispersion (variance) *f* intra-bloc, dispersion (variance) à l'intérieur des blocs	внутриблочная дисперсия, дисперсия внутри блока
I 839	**intra-class correlation** <ST>	Innerklassenkorrelation *f*, Intraklaßkorrelation *f*, Paarkorrelation *f*	corrélation *f* intra-classe	корреляция внутри класса (группы), внутригрупповая (внутриклассовая) корреляция
I 840	**intra-class correlation coefficient** <ST>	Innerklassen-Korrelationskoeffizient *m*	coefficient *m* de corrélation intra-classe	коэффициент корреляции внутри группы (класса)
	intra-class variance <ST>	*s.* W 273		
	intra-group deviance <ST>	*s.* I 841		
I 841	**intra-group sum of squares,** intra-group deviance <ST>	Summe *f* der Abweichungsquadrate innerhalb der Gruppe, Quadratsumme *f* innerhalb der Gruppe, Innergruppen-Quadratsumme *f*	somme *f* des carrés [des écarts] intra-groupe, somme des carrés [des écarts] à l'intérieur du groupe	внутригрупповая сумма квадратов [отклонений от среднего значения]
	intra-group variation <ST>	*s.* B 143		
I 842	**intransitive group** <GR>	intransitive Gruppe *f*	groupe *m* intransitif	интранзитивная группа
	intransitiveness <GR>	*s.* I 844		
I 843	**intransitive relation** <SE>	intransitive (gegentransitive) Relation *f*	relation *f* intransitive	интранзитивное [со]отношение
I 844	**intransitivity** <of a group *or* relation> <GR, SE>; intransitiveness <of a group> <GR>	Intransitivität *f*	intransitivité *f*	интранзитивность
	intrinsic accuracy <ST>	*s.* F 361a		
	intrinsical equation <DG>	*s.* N 25		
	intrinsic co-ordinates <DG>	*s.* N 23		
	intrinsic equation <DG>	*s.* N 25		
I 845	**intrinsic geometry,** absolute geometry <e.g. of a surface> <DG>	innere (absolute) Geometrie *f*	géométrie *f* intrinsèque (absolue)	внутренняя (абсолютная) геометрия
I 846	**intrinsic invariant** <TO>	innere Invariante *f*	invariant *m* intrinsèque	внутренний инвариант
I 847	**intrinsic metric** <DG, GE>	innere Metrik *f*	métrique *f* intrinsèque	внутренняя метрика
I 848	**intrinsic orientation** <DG>	innere Orientierung *f*	orientation *f* intrinsèque	внутренняя ориентация
I 849	**intrinsic property,** absolute property <e.g. of a surface> <DG>	innere (absolute) Eigenschaft *f*	propriété *f* intrinsèque (absolue)	внутреннее (абсолютное) свойство
I 850	**introduction of the conjunction** <in the succedent *or* in the antecedent> <LO>	Konjunktionseinführung *f*, Und-Einführung *f* <im Sukzedens *oder* im Antezedens>	introduction *f* de la conjonction <dans le conséquent *ou* dans l'antécédent>	$\wedge$-введение, введение конъюнкции <в сукцеденте *или* в антецеденте>
I 851	**introduction of the disjunction** <in the succedent *or* in the antecedent> <LO>	Oder-Einführung *f* <im Sukzedens *oder* im Antezedens>	introduction *f* de la disjonction <dans le conséquent *ou* dans l'antécédent>	$\vee$-введение <в сукцеденте *или* в антецеденте>
	introduction of the existential quantifier in the antecedent <LO>	*s.* J 65		
	introduction of the existential quantifier in the succedent <LO>	*s.* J 66		
I 852	**introduction of the implication** <in the succedent *or* in the antecedent> <LO>	Folgt-Einführung *f* <im Sukzedens *oder* im Antezedens>	introduction *f* de l'implication <dans le conséquent *ou* dans l'antécédent>	введение импликации, $\supset$-введение, введение $\supset$ <в сукцеденте *или* в антецеденте>
I 853	**introduction of the negation** <in the succedent *or* in the antecedent> <LO>	Nicht-Einführung *f*, Negationseinführung *f* <im Sukzedens *oder* im Antezedens>	introduction *f* de la négation <dans le conséquent *ou* dans l'antécédent>	введение $\neg$ <в сукцеденте *или* в антецеденте>
	introduction of the universal quantifier in the antecedent <LO>	*s.* J 68		
	introduction of the universal quantifier in the succedent <LO>	*s.* J 69		
	intuitional logic <LO>	*s.* I 855		
I 854	**intuitionism** <MM>	Intuitionismus *m*	intuitionisme *m*, intuitionnisme *m*	интуиционизм
I 855	**intuitionist[ic] logic,** Brouwerian (intuitional) logic <LO>	intuitionistische (Brouwersche) Logik *f*	logique *f* intuition[n]iste	интуиционистская (брауэрова) логика
I 856	**intuitively geometric,** geometrically obvious <GE>	geometrisch anschaulich, anschaulich-geometrisch	géométriquement intuitif, d'une manière géométriquement intuitive	наглядно-геометрический
	in-valence <GP>	*s.* I 305		

No.	English	German	French	Russian
I 857	**invariance** <of an element *or* a property> <AL, GE, IV>	Invarianz *f*	invariance *f* <d'un élément *ou* d'une propriété>; fixité *f* <d'un élément>	инвариантность <элемента *или* свойства>; неподвижность, неизменность <элемента>
I 858	**invariance** <of a subgroup> <GR>	Normalteilereigenschaft *f* <einer Untergruppe>	invariance *f* <d'un sous-groupe>	инвариантность <подгруппы>
	invariance of domain <FT>	*s.* D 861		
	invariance of domain <TO>	*s.* I 859		
	invariance of domain theorem <TO>	*s.* B 781		
I 859	**invariance of interior points,** invariance of domain, Brouwer['s] invariance of domain <TO>	Gebietsinvarianz *f*	invariance *f* de domaine	инвариантность области (внутренних точек)
	invariance of the region <FT>	*s.* D 861		
	invariance of translation <AL, GE>	*s.* T 827		
	invariance property <IV>	*s.* I 876		
I 860/1	**invariance theorem** <AT, CA, GN>	Invarianzsatz *m*, Invarianzaussage *f*	théorème *m* d'invariance	теорема инвариантности
I 862	**invariance** <of a matrix> **with respect to transposition** <MD>	Umsturzinvarianz *f*	invariance *f* au rapport de transposition	инвариантность относительно транспонирования
	invariant <VT>	*s.* S 73		
I 863	**invariant [analytic] continuation** <FT>	[unmittelbare] invariante [analytische] Fortsetzung *f*	prolongement *m* [analytique] invariant	инвариантное [аналитическое] продолжение
I 864	**invariant derivative** <DG>	invariante Ableitung *f*	dérivée *f* invariante	инвариантная производная
I 865	**invariant element,** fixed (stable) element <of a mapping> <GE>	invariantes Element *n*, Fixelement *n*	élément *m* invariant (stable)	инвариантный (неподвижный, двойной) элемент
I 866	**invariant estimator** <ST>	invariante Schätzfunktion (Punktschätzung, Schätzung) *f*	estimateur *m* invariant	инвариантная оценка
I 867	**invariant factor** <of a module> <AL>	Invariantenteiler *m*, invarianter Faktor *m*	facteur *m* invariant	инвариантный множитель (фактор)
I 868	**invariant factor** <of a polynomial matrix> <AL>	Invariantenteiler *m*, invarianter Faktor *m*, invariantes Polynom *n*, *k*-ter (zusammengesetzter) Elementarteiler *m*	facteur *m* invariant	инвариантный множитель
	invariant factor <AL>	*s.* E 100		
I 869	**invariant Lie subgroup** <of a Lie group> <GR>	Liescher Normalteiler *m*, invariante Liesche Untergruppe *f*	sous-groupe *m* de Lie distingué	нормальный делитель Ли
I 870	**invariant metric** <on a group> <GR>	invariante Metrik *f* <auf einer Gruppe>	métrique *f* invariante, distance *f* invariante par translation, métrique flissante <sur un groupe>	инвариантная метрика <на группе>
I 871	**invariant of collineation,** homographic invariant <AY>	Invariante *f* der Kollineation, homographische Invariante	invariant *m* homographique	инвариант коллинеации
I 872	**invariant of contact,** osculant <of a conic *or* a system of surfaces> <DG>	Berührungsinvariante *f*, Oskulante *f*	invariant *m* de contact, osculant *m*	инвариант касания
I 873	**invariant of intersection** <AG>	Schnittinvariante *f*	invariant *m* d'intersection	инвариант пересечения
I 874	**invariant of Severi** <AG>	Severische Invariante *f*	invariant *m* de Severi	инвариант Севери
I 875	**invariant of structure** <of a matrix> <MD>	Strukturinvariante *f*	invariant *m* de structure	структурный инвариант
	invariant of structure <AL>	*s.* S 2010		
	invariant of Zeuthen-Segre <AG>	*s.* Z 76		
	invariant point <TO>	*s.* F 383		
I 876	**invariant property, invariance property** <IV>	invariante Eigenschaft *f*, Invarianteneigenschaft *f*, Invarianzeigenschaft *f*	propriété *f* invariante, propriété d'invariance, invariance *f*	инвариантное свойство, свойство инвариантности, свойство неизменения
I 877	**invariant representation** <of algebraic forms> <AL>	Invariantendarstellung *f*	représentation *f* invariante	инвариантное представление
I 878	**invariant ring,** duo-ring, two-sided ring <AL>	Duoring *m*	anneau *m* duo	дуо-кольцо
I 879	**invariant series** <AL, CA>	invariante Reihe *f*	suite *f* invariante	инвариантный ряд
I 880	**invariant set** <of a group> <GR>	invariante Menge *f*	ensemble *m* invariant	инвариантное множество
I 881	**invariant set,** strongly invariant set <relative to a measurable transformation> <ME, ST>	invariante (streng invariante) Menge *f* <bezüglich einer meßbaren Transformation>	partie *f* invariante (strictement invariante), ensemble *m* invariant (strictement invariant) <relatif à une transformation mesurable>	инвариантное множество, строго инвариантное множество <относительно измеримого преобразования>
I 882	**invariant subalgebra** <AL>	invariante Teilalgebra (Unteralgebra) *f*	sous-algèbre *f* invariante	инвариантная подалгебра, идеал алгебры
I 883	**invariant sub[-]group,** normal subgroup, distinguished subgroup,	Normalteiler *m*, invariante (ausgezeichnete, selbstkonjugierte) Unter-	sous-groupe *m* invariant (normal, distingué, conjugué de lui-même,	нормальный делитель, нормальная (инвариантная, самосопря-

No.	English	German	French	Russian
	self-conjugate sub[-] group, normal divisor <GR>	gruppe *f*, eigentlicher Teiler *m*, monotypische Untergruppe, // autojuger (selbstkonjugierter) Teiler <Netto>, ausgezeichneter (monotypischer) Teiler	invariable), diviseur *m* propre <Betti>, sous-groupe monotypique <Frobenius>, diviseur autoconjugué <Netto>, diviseur distingué (normal)	женная) подгруппа
I 884	**invariant subset** <with respect to a composition> <AL>	invariante Untermenge *f* <gegenüber einer Verknüpfung>	partie *f* stable <pour (par rapport à) une loi de composition>	инвариантное подмножество <относительно закона композиции>
I 885	**invariant subspace** <AL, FA>	invarianter Unterraum *m*	sous-espace *m* vectoriel stable (invariant), sous-espace *m* invariant	инвариантное подпространство <представления *или* относительно отображений>; допустимое подпространство <относительно множества *M* линейных отображений>; *M*-инвариантное (*M*-допустимое) подпространство
I 886	**invariant Sylow group** <GR>	Sylow-Normalteiler *m*	sous-groupe *m* invariant de Sylow	инвариантная силовская группа
I 887	**invariant test** <ST>	invarianter Test *m*	test *m* invariant	инвариантный критерий
I 888	**invariant theory,** theory of invariants <IV>	Invariantentheorie *f*	théorie *f* des invariants	теория инвариантов
I 889	**invariant with respect to mapping** <TO>	abbildungsinvariant	invariant par applications	инвариантный при отображениях
I 890	**inverse,** inverse element, reciprocal element <AL>	Inverses *n*, Inverse *f*, Reziprokes *n*, inverses Element *n*	élément *m* symétrique, symétrique *m* <en composition arbitraire>; inverse *m*, élément inverse <en composition arbitraire *ou* en notation multiplicative>; opposé *m* <en notation additive>	обратный элемент, обратный; симметричный элемент
I 891	**inverse** <of a point>, inverse point <with respect to a circle> <GE>	inverser Punkt *m* <in bezug auf einen Kreis>	point *m* réciproque, inverse *m*, conjugué *m* isogonal <d'un point>	образ точки, инверсная точка <при инверсии относительно окружности>
I 892	**inverse** <of an implication> <LO>	konträre Implikation *f*	implication *f* contraire	инверсная импликация
	inverse <AL>	*s.* 1. I 930; 2. R 723		
	inverse <AN>	*s.* I 912		
	inverse <GE>	*s.* I 901		
	inverse <GR>	*s.* G 469		
	inverse <LO>	*s.* I 945		
	inverse <MD>	*s.* R 251		
	inverse <NT>	*s.* I 929		
	inverse <SE>	*s.* I 941		
	inverse <SE, TO>	*s.* F 712		
	inverse affine transformation <AY>	*s.* N 86		
I 893	**inverse array** <MD>	komplementäre Matrix *f*	matrice *f* complémentaire	дополнительная матрица
I 894	**inverse automorphism** <AL>	inverser (reziproker) Automorphismus *m*	automorphisme *m* réciproque	обратный автоморфизм
	inverse average <ER, ST>	*s.* H 102		
I 895	**inverse basis,** reciprocal basis <AL>	reziproke (inverse) Basis *f*	base *f* réciproque	обратный базис
I 896	**inverse calculation,** back substitution <NU>	Rückrechnung *f*, inverse Rechnung *f*, Sicherung *f* durch Rückrechnung	calcul *m* inverse	обратный расчет (счет)
	inverse chain <SP>	*s.* I 928		
	inverse circular function <AN>	*s.* I 957		
	inverse cone <CA>	*s.* P 1673		
I 897	**inverse continued fraction** <NT>	inverser Kettenbruch *m*	fraction *f* continue inverse	обратная непрерывная (цепная) дробь
	inverse correlation <ST>	*s.* N 88		
I 898	**inverse cosecant,** arc cosecant, anticosecant, Arc cosec, arc cosec, arccsc, $\operatorname{cosec}^{-1}$ <principal value: arc cosec> <FU>	Arkuskosekans *m*, Arc cosec, arc cosec <Hauptwert: arc cosec>	arc *m* cosécante, cosécante *f* inverse, Arc cosec, arc cosec <détermination principale: arc cosec>, // arccsc	арккосеканс, аркускосеканс, Arc cosec, arc cosec <главное значение: arc cosec>
I 899	**inverse cosine,** arc cosine, anticosine, Arc cos, arc cos, $\cos^{-1}$ <principal value: arc cos> <FU>	Arkuskosinus *m*, Arc cos, arc cos <Hauptwert: arc cos>	arc *m* cosinus, cosinus *m* inverse, Arc cos, arc cos <détermination principale: arc cos>	арккосинус, аркускосинус, Arc cos, arc cos <главное значение: arc cos>
I 900	**inverse cotangent,** arc cotangent, anticotangent, Arc cot, arc cot, $\cot^{-1}$ <principal value: arc cot>, // Arc ctg, arc ctg <FU>	Arkuskotangens *m*, Arc cot, arc cot <Hauptwert: arc cot>, // Arc ctg, arc ctg	arc *m* cotangente, cotangente *f* inverse, Arc cot, arc cot <détermination principale: arc cot>, // Arc ctg, arc ctg	арккотангенс, аркускотангенс, Arc cot, arc cot <главное значение: arc cot>, // Arc ctg, arc ctg
I 901	**inverse curve,** inverse <of a curve> <GE>	inverse Kurve *f*	courbe *f* inverse	инверсная (обратная) кривая, образ кривой <при инверсии>
I 902	**inverse dependence** <GN>	umgekehrte Abhängigkeit *f*	dépendance *f* réciproque	обратная зависимость
I 903	**inverse distribution parameter** <DG>	Schränkung *f*, reziproker Drall *m*	paramètre *m* de distribution réciproque	«развод», обратный параметр распределения
	inverse element <AL>	*s.* I 890		
	inverse element <GR>	*s.* G 469		
I 904	**inverse fibre** <at a point>, full inverse image <of a point> <SE, TO>	vollständiges Urbild *n* <eines Punktes>	tranche *f* <d'une transformation>	комножество <отображения>

I 905	**inverse fibre of the correspondence** *R* **at** *y* <SE>	Urbild *n* des Elements *y* bei der Korrespondenz *R*, Schicht *f* R_y	coupe *f* de la correspondance réciproque du correspondance *R* suivant *y*	правое сечение элемента *y* при соответствии *R*, прообраз элемента *y* при соответствии *R*
I 906	**inverse figure** <GE>	inverse Figur *f*	figure *f* inverse	инверсная (обратная) фигура
I 907	**inverse form** <AL>	inverse (reziproke, reziproke quadratische) Form *f*	forme *f* inverse	обратная форма
I 908	**inverse fraction** <AL, AR>	inverser (reziproker) Bruch *m*, reziproker Wert *m* <eines Bruchs>	fraction *f* inverse	обратная дробь
I 909	**inverse function** <AN>	Umkehrfunktion *f*, inverse (reziproke) Funktion *f*	fonction *f* inverse (réciproque)	обратная функция
I 910	**inverse homomorphism** <AL>	inverser Homomorphismus *m*	homomorphisme *m* réciproque	обратный гомоморфизм
	inverse homothety <GE>	*s.* I 947		
	inverse hyperbolic cosine <FU>	*s.* A 922		
	inverse hyperbolic cotangent <FU>	*s.* A 923		
I 911	**inverse hyperbolic function,** area-hyperbolic function, antihyperbolic (arc-hyperbolic, ar) function <AN>	Areafunktion *f*, inverse hyperbolische Funktion *f*, inverse Hyperbelfunktion *f*, Umkehrfunktion *f* einer hyperbolischen Funktion, Ar-Funktion *f*	argument *m* d'une fonction hyperbolique, fonction *f* hyperbolique inverse (réciproque), aréafonction *f*	обратная гиперболическая фукция, ареафункциян
	inverse hyperbolic sine <FU>	*s.* A 924		
	inverse hyperbolic tangent <FU>	*s.* A 925		
I 912	**inverse[-] image,** pre[-]image, counter[-] image, inverse, antecedent, prototype, primitive, original <in a functional transformation> <AN>	Urbild *n*, Original *n*, inverses Bild *n*, Prototyp *m*	image *f* inverse (réciproque, anticipée), antécédent *m*, prototype *m*, original *m*	прообраз, оригинал, // первообраз
I 913	**inverse image** <of a sheaf> <AT>	garbentheoretisches inverses Bild *n*, inverses Bild	image *f* réciproque faisceautique, image réciproque	обратный образ <пучка>
	inverse image <SE, TO>	*s.* F 712		
	inverse-image set <SE, TO>	*s.* F 712		
I 914	**inverse inclusion** <SE>	umgekehrte Inklusion *f*	inclusion *f* inverse	обратное включение
I 915	**inverse interpolation** <AX, FD, NU>	inverse Interpolation *f*	interpolation *f* inverse	обратная интерполяция
	inverse-isomorphic <AL>	*s.* A 730		
I 916	**inverse isomorphism** <AL>	inverser Isomorphismus *m*, Inverses *n* <eines Isomorphismus>	isomorphisme *m* inverse	обратный изоморфизм
I 917	**inverse isoperimetric problem** <VA>	reziprokes isoperimetrisches Problem *n*	problème *m* isopérimétrique réciproque	обратная задача изопериметров
I 918	**inverse Laplace transform** <IT>	inverse Laplace-Transformation *f*	intégrale *f* de Mellin-Fourier, transformée inverse de Laplace	обратное преобразование Лапласа
I 919	**inverse law of double negation** <LO>	erstes Verneinungsgesetz *n*; Form *f* zur introductio inabsurdi	loi *f* de double négation inverse	обратный закон двойного отрицания
I 920	**inverse limit** <of groups> <GR>	inverse Grenzgruppe (Limesgruppe) *f*, inverser Limes *m*	groupe *m* limite inverse, limite *f* projective <d'une séquence de groupes>	обратная предельная группа
	inverse limit <AL, TO>	*s.* P 1697		
	inverse limit <CA>	*s.* 1. L 697; 2. L 736		
	inverse logarithm <AR>	*s.* A 741		
I 921	**inversely bounded set** <of a topological skew field> <AL>	invers beschränkte Menge *f*	ensemble *m* rétroborné	обратно ограниченное множество
	inversely conformal transformation <FT>	*s.* A 729		
I 922	**inversely congruent,** congruent and indirectly conformal <EG>	invers (ungleichsinnig) kongruent, kongruent mit Umlegung	indirectement coïncident (congru, égal)	зеркально-конгруэнтный, зеркально-равный, конгруэнтный с изменением направления обхода на противоположное
	inversely isomorphic <AL>	*s.* A 730		
	inversely ordered set <SE>	*s.* A 749		
I 923	**inversely proportional,** reciprocally proportional <to> <AR>	umgekehrt (indirekt) proportional <Dativ *oder* zu>	inversement (réciproquement) proportionnel <à>	обратно пропорциональный, обратно-пропорциональный, обратнопропорциональный
I 924/5	**inversely proportional division** <AR, NU>	umgekehrt proportionale Teilung *f*	partage *m* inversement proportionnel	обратно пропорциональное деление
	inversely well-ordered <SE>	*s.* A 790		
I 926	**inverse map[ping],** reciprocal map[ping] <SE>	inverse Abbildung *f*, Inverse *f*, Umkehrabbildung *f*, reziproke Abbildung	application *f* inverse (réciproque)	обратное отображение
I 927	**inverse mapping,** group symmetry <of a group> <GR>	Inversenabbildung *f*, Übergang *m* zum Inversen <jedes Element einer Gruppe wird auf Inverses abgebildet>	application *f* symétrique, symétrie *f* <d'un groupe>	отображение каждого элемента на обратный, симметрия <группы>

No.	English	German	French	Russian
	inverse mapping <AY>	*s.* I 972		
I 928	**inverse Markov chain,** inverse chain <SP>	inverse [Markovsche] Kette *f*	chaîne *f* [markovienne] inverse	обратная цепь [Маркова]
	inverse matrix <MD>	*s.* R 251		
I 929	**inverse number,** reciprocal [value], inverse [value] <of a number> <$z \to 1/z$> <NT>	inverse (reziproke, umgekehrte) Zahl *f*, Kehrwert *m*, Reziprokes *n*, reziproker Wert *m*	nombre *m* inverse (réciproque)	обратное число, обратная величина <числа> <*pl*: взаимнообратные числа>
I 930	**inverse operation,** inverse <of an operation> <AL>	inverse (umgekehrte) Operation *f*, Umkehroperation *f*, Umkehrung *f* <einer Operation>	opération *f* inverse, inverse *m* <d'une opération>	обратная операция
I 931	**inverse operator,** reciprocal operator <AL, FA>	Umkehroperator *m*, inverser (reziproker) Operator *m*	opérateur *m* inverse (réciproque)	обратный оператор
	inverse order / in <GN>	*s.* I 975		
	inverse order type <SE>	*s.* C 2374		
I 932	**inverse ordinal,** converse ordinal number <SE>	konverse Ordnungszahl *f*	nombre *m* ordinal converse	обратное порядковое число
I 933	**inverse permutation** <AL, CT>	inverse Permutation *f*	permutation *f* inverse (réciproque)	обратная перестановка
	inverse point <GE>	*s.* I 891		
	inverse probability <ST>	*s.* P 1107		
	inverse probability theorem <ST>	*s.* B 156		
I 934	**inverse problem** <GN>	Umkehrproblem *n*, inverses Problem *n*, umgekehrte Aufgabe *f*	problème *m* inverse	обратная задача, задача обращения
I 935	**inverse problem** <VA>	inverses Problem *n*	problème *m* inverse	обратная задача
I 936	**inverse proportionality** <AR, GN>	umgekehrte Proportionalität *f*	proportionnalité *f* inverse	обратная пропорциональность
I 937	**inverse proposition** <GN>	umgekehrte Aussage *f*	proposition *f* réciproque	обратное предложение
I 938	**inverse quasi-order** <SE>	konverse Quasiordnung *f*, konverse Vorordnung *f*	préordre *m* converse, quasi-ordre *m* converse	обратное отношение предпорядка, обратный квазипорядок
I 939	**inverse quaternion** <AL>	inverse (reziproke) Quaternion *f*	quaternion *m* inverse	обратный кватернион
I 940	**inverse ratio,** reciprocal ratio <of two numbers> <NT>	Verhältnis *n* der Reziproken	rapport *m* inverse	отношение обратных величин
	inverse ratio <AR>	*s.* R 258		
	inverse regression <ST>	*s.* N 107		
I 941	**inverse relation,** converse relation, converse, inverse, dual <of a relation> <SE>	konverse (inverse, inverse binäre, reziproke, duale, entgegengesetzte) Relation *f*, Umkehrrelation *f*	relation *f* converse (réciproque, inverse, opposée), réciproque *f*, symétrique *f* <d'une relation>	обратное отношение (соответствие), инверсное бинарное отношение
I 942	**inverse rule of inference** <LO>	inverse Schlußregel *f*	règle *f* de conclusion inverse	обратное правило вывода
I 943	**inverse rule of three** <AR>	umgekehrte Regeldetri *f* (Regel *f* de tri), regula *f* de tri conversa	règle *f* de trois inverse	обратное тройное правило
I 944	**inverse secant,** arc secant, antisecant, Arc sec, arc sec, $\sec^{-1}$ <principal value: arc sec> <FU>	Arkussekans *m*, Arc sec, arc sec <Hauptwert: arc sec>	arc *m* sécante, sécante *f* inverse, Arc sec, arc sec <détermination principale: arc sec>	арксеканс, аркуссеканс, Arc sec, arc sec <главное значение: arc sec>
I 945	**inverse sentence,** inverse <of given sentence> <LO>	konträre Aussage *f*	théorème *m* contraire <d'un autre>	инверсное высказывание, инверсное суждение
I 946	**inverse similarity (similitude)** <AL>	ähnlich unitäre Kollineation *f* mit Umlegung	similitude *f* inverse	обратное подобие
I 947	**inverse similitude,** negative similitude, inverse (negative) homothety <GE>	Ähnlichkeitstransformation (Homothetie) *f* mit negativem Ähnlichkeitsverhältnis	homothétie *f* inverse (négative)	обратная гомотетия, гомотетия с отрицательным коэффициентом
I 948	**inverse sine,** arc sine, antisine, Arc sin, arc sin, $\sin^{-1}$ <principal value: arc sin> <FU>	Arkussinus *m*, Arc sin, arc sin <Hauptwert: arc sin>	arc *m* sinus, sinus *m* inverse, Arc sin, arc sin <détermination principale: arc sin>	арксинус, аркуссинус, Arc sin, arc sin <главное значение: arc sin>
I 949	**inverse spectrum,** inverse system <AL>	projektive Familie *f*, projektives System *n*, inverses Spektrum *n*	système *m* projectif (inverse)	обратный спектр, проективная система
I 950	**inverse system** <CA>	projektives (inverses) System *n*	système *m* projectif	проективная система
I 951	**inverse system** <of sets over a directed set> <SE>	inverses System *n*	système *m* projectif	обратный спектр
I 952	**inverse system** <of topological spaces> <TO>	inverses (projektives) System *n*	système *m* projectif (inverse)	проективная система
	inverse system <AL>	*s.* I 949		
I 953	**inverse tangent,** arc tangent, antitangent, Arc tan, arc tan, $\tan^{-1}$ <principal value: arc tan>, // Arc tg, arc tg <FU>	Arkustangens *m*, Arc tan, arc tan <Hauptwert: arc tan>, // Arc tg, arc tg	arc *m* tangente, tangente *f* inverse, Arc tan, arc tan <détermination principale: arc tan>, // Arc tg, arc tg	арктангенс, аркустангенс, Arc tan, arc tan, <главное значение; arc tan>, // Arc tg, arc tg
I 954	**inverse theorem,** converse <of a theorem> <GN>	Umkehrung *f* <eines Satzes>, Umkehrsatz *m*, Umkehrtheorem *n*, Kehrsatz *m*	réciproque *f* <d'un théorème>, théorème *m* réciproque, proposition *f* inverse	обратная теорема, теорема обращения, обратное утверждение
I 955	**inverse transform** <of a curve> <GE>	Rücktransformierte *f* <einer Kurve bei Punkttransformation>	antécédente *f* <d'une courbe>	прообраз <кривой>
	inverse transform <AN>	*s.* O 426		

No.	English	German	French	Russian
I 956	**inverse transform[ation]** <AN>	inverse Transformation *f*, Umkehrtransformation *f*, Rücktransformation *f*, reziproke Transformation	transformation *f* inverse (réciproque)	обратное преобразование, обратная трансформация
I 957	**inverse trigonometric[al] function,** inverse circular function, arctrigonometric[al] function, antitrigonometric[al] function, cyclometric function <AN>	Arkusfunktion *f*, Arc-Funktion *f*, zyklometrische Funktion *f*, Kreisbogenfunktion *f*, inverse trigonometrische Funktion, Umkehrfunktion *f* einer trigonometrischen Funktion, inverse Kreisfunktion *f*	fonction *f* circulaire réciproque (inverse), fonction trigonométrique réciproque (inverse), fonction cyclométrique (goniométrique)	обратная тригонометрическая (круговая) функция, аркфункция, аркус[-]функция, аркус, циклометрическая (антитригонометрическая) функция
I 958	**inverse value** <AR, NU>	inverser Wert *m*, Kehrwert *m*, reziproker Wert	valeur *f* inverse	обратное значение
	inverse value <NT>	*s.* I 929		
I 959	**inverse variation** <GN>	umgekehrt proportionale Änderung *f*	variation *f* (changement *m*) inverse (réciproque)	изменение по закону обратной пропорциональности
I 960	**inverse vector iteration** <MD, NU>	inverse Vektoriteration *f*	itération *f* vectorielle inverse	обратная векторная итерация
I 961	**inversion** <in a permutation> <AL, CT>	Inversion *f*, Fehlstand *m*, Umstellung *f*, Derangement *m*, Abfolge *f*	inversion *f*, dérangement *m*, variation *f*	инверсия, беспорядок
I 962	**inversion** <of a substitution *or* an integral> <AL, DI>	Umkehrung *f* <einer Substitution *oder* eines Integrals>	inversion *f* <d'une substitution *ou* d'une intégrale>	обращение <подстановки *или* интеграла>
	inversion <GE>	*s.* 1. I 970; 2. I 971; 3. I 972		
	inversion <MD>	*s.* M 194		
I 963	**inversion formula,** conversion formula <GN>	Umkehrformel *f*	formule *f* d'inversion, formule de réciprocité	формула обращения
I 964	**inversion length** <of a curve> <AY>	Inversionslänge *f*	longueur *f* d'inversion	инверсионная длина
	inversion of the point <GE>	*s.* I 972		
I 965	**inversion principle** <LO>	Inversionsprinzip *n*	principe *m* d'inversion	инверсионный принцип
I 966	**inversion principles of number theory** <NT>	Umkehrungssätze *mpl* der Zahlentheorie	théorèmes *mpl* d'inversion de la théorie des nombres	теоремы обращения в теории чисел
I 967	**inversion problem** <for elliptic integrals> <FT>	Umkehrproblem *n*	problème *m* de l'inversion	задача обращения
I 968	**inversion test** <ST>	Inversionstest *m*	test *m* basé sur les inversions	критерий, основанный на инверсиях
I 969	**inversion theorem** <for Abelian functions> <FT>	Umkehrsatz *m* <für Abelsche Funktionen>	théorème *m* de l'inversion <pour les fonctions abéliennes>	теорема обращения <для абелевых функций>
I 970	**inversion with respect to a circle,** inversion <GE>	Inversion *f* am Kreis, Inversion	inversion *f* par rapport au cercle, inversion	инверсия относительно окружности, инверсия
	inversion with respect to a circle <GE>	*s.* I 972		
I 971	**inversion with respect to a sphere,** [spherical] inversion <GE>	Inversion *f* an der Kugel, Kugelinversion *f*, Inversion	inversion *f* par rapport à une sphère, inversion [dans l'espace]	инверсия относительно сферы, инверсия [в пространстве]
I 972	**inversion with respect to unit circle,** inversion with respect to a circle, inversion of the point, inversion, mathematical inversion, reciprocal mapping, inverse mapping <GE>	Abbildung *f* durch reziproke Radien (Radienvektoren), Transformation *f* durch reziproke Radien (Radienvektoren), Inversion (Spiegelung) *f* am Einheitskreis, Inversion	transformation (application) *f* par rayons vecteurs réciproques, inversion *f* par rapport au cercle unité, inversion, anastrophe *f* <Cauchy>	преобразование обратными радиус-векторами, инверсия относительно единичной окружности, точечная инверсия, инверсия
I 973	**inversive geometry** <Morley> <GE>	inversive Geometrie *f*	géométrie *f* inversive	инверсивная геометрия <геометрия треугольника внутри единичного круга>
	inversive plane <GE>	*s.* M 715		
I 974	**inversor** <GE, IN>	Inversor *m*	inverseur *m*	инверсор
	inversor of Peaucellier <GE, IN>	*s.* P 358		
I 975	**inverted order / in,** in inverse order, in [the] reverse order, reversed in order <GN>	in umgekehrter Reihenfolge (Anordnung)	en ordre inverse	в обратном порядке
	invertible arrow <CA>	*s.* I 1127		
I 976	**invertible element** <AL>	invertierbares (umkehrbares) Element *n*	élément *m* inversible (invertible); élément symétrisable	обратимый элемент; элемент, допускающий обратный; элемент, имеющий симметричный
I 977	**invertible element,** regular element <of a normed algebra> <FA>	invertierbares (reguläres) Element *n*	élément *m* inversible (régulier)	элемент, допускающий обратный; регулярный элемент
I 978	**invertible fractional ideal** <AL, NT>	umkehrbares gebrochenes Ideal *n*	idéal *m* fractionnaire inversible	обратимый дробный идеал
I 979	**invertible map[ping]** <SE>	umkehrbare Abbildung *f*	application *f* inversible	обратимое отображение
I 980	**invertible matrix** <over a ring> <AL>	invertierbare Matrix *f*	matrice *f* inversible	обратимая матрица
	invertible matrix <MD>	*s.* N 485		
I 981	**invertible measurable transformation,** measurable transformation having a measurable inverse <ME>	umkehrbare meßbare Transformation *f*	transformation *f* mesurable inversible (ayant un inverse mesurable)	обратимое измеримое преобразование; измеримое преобразование, обладающее измеримым обратным
I 982	**invertible measure preserving transformation** <ME>	umkehrbare maßtreue Transformation *f*	transformation *f* inversible conservant la mesure	обратимое преобразование, сохраняющее меру
I 983/4	**invertible module** <AL, TO>	umkehrbarer Modul *m*	module *m* inversible	обратимый модуль

No.	English	German	French	Russian
	invertible morphism <CA>	*s.* I 1127		
I 985	**invertible operator** <AL, FA>	invertierbarer Operator *m*	opérateur *m* inversible	обратимый оператор
I 986	**invertible sheaf** <AL, TO>	umkehrbare Garbe *f*	faisceau *m* inversible	обратимый пучок
I 987	**invertible substitution** <AL>	umkehrbare Substitution *f*	substitution *f* réversible (inversible)	обратимая подстановка
I 988	**invertible transformation** <AL, AN, GE>	umkehrbare Transformation *f*	transformation *f* inversible (réversible)	обратимое преобразование
	involute [of evolute] <DG>	*s.* E 648		
I 989	**involution** <*e.g.:* on algebraic curves *or* of higher degree *or* of conjugate diameters> <AG, AY>	Involution *f* <*z. B.:* auf algebraischen Kurven *oder* höheren Grades *oder* konjugierter Durchmesser>	involution *f* <*par exemple:* sur les courbes algébriques *ou* de degré supérieur *ou* de diamètres conjugués>	инволюция <*например:* на алгебраических кривых *или* высшей степени *или* сопряженных диаметров>
I 990	**involution** <in a field *or* of functions> <AL, DE>	Involution *f*	involution *f*	инволюция
I 991	**involution,** involutory map[ping], involutory transformation <AL, AY, SE, TO>	Involution *f*, involutorische Abbildung (Transformation) *f*, vertauschbare Abbildung	involution *f*, application (transformation) *f* involutive	инволюция, инволюционное преобразование (отображение), инволютивное преобразование (отображение)
	involution <AR>	*s.* R 54		
I 992	**involution condition,** condition of involution <DE>	Involutionsbedingung *f*	condition *f* d'involution	инволюционное условие
I 993	**involution curve** <PJ>	Involutionskurve *f*	courbe *f* involutive (d'involution)	инволюционная кривая
I 994	**involution in the pencil of lines** <Steiner> <GE>	Involution *f* im Strahlenbüschel, Strahlensystem *n* <Steiner>	involution *f* dans le faisceau de droites	инволюция в пучке прямых, система лучей
I 995	**involution net** <PJ>	Involutionsnetz *n*	réseau *m* d'involution, réseau involutif	инволюционная сеть
I 996	**involution of forms** <AL>	Formeninvolution *f* <Battaglini>	involution *f* de formes	инволюция форм
I 997	**involution of lines,** line involution <AY>	Geradeninvolution *f*, Strahleninvolution *f*	involution *f* de droites	инволюция прямых, инволюционное преобразование прямых
	involution of planes <AY>	*s.* P 648		
	involution of points <AY>	*s.* P 750		
I 998	**involution point** <PJ>	Involutionspunkt *m*	point *m* d'involution	инволюционная точка
I 999	**involutorial anti-automorphism** <AL>	involutorischer Antiautomorphismus *m*	antiautomorphisme *m* involutif	антиавтоморфизм порядка 2, инволютивный антиавтоморфизм
I 1000	**involutorial point ranges,** involutorial series <AY>	involutorische Punktreihen *fpl*	ponctuelles *fpl* involutives	инволюционные ряды точек
I 1001	**involutorial ring** <AL>	Ring *m* mit Involution	anneau *m* involutif (à involution)	инволютивное кольцо, кольцо с инволюцией
	involutorial series <AY>	*s.* I 1000		
I 1002	**involutory algebra** <AL>	Algebra *f* mit Involution	algèbre *f* involutive, algèbre à involution	алгебра с инволюцией, инволютивная алгебра
I 1003	**involutory correspondence** <AG, AY, PJ>	involutorische Entsprechung (Zuordnung) *f*	correspondance *f* involutive	инволютивное соответствие
I 1004	**involutory functions** <DE>	involutorische Funktionen *fpl*, in Involution liegende Funktionen	fonctions *fpl* involutives	инволютивные функции
I 1005	**involutory homology** <DS, PJ>	involutorische Perspektive *f*, perspektive Spiegelung *f*	homologie (perspective) *f* involutive	инволютивная (инволюционная) гомология (перспектива)
	involutory map[ping] <AL, AY, SE, TO>	*s.* I 991		
I 1006	**involutory matrix** <MD>	involutorische Matrix *f*	matrice *f* involutive (réciproque)	инволютивная (инволюционная) матрица
I 1007	**involutory Möbius transformation** <FT>	Möbius-Involution *f*, Möbiusinvolution *f*	transformation *f* de Möbius involutive	инволютивное преобразование Мебиуса
I 1008	**involutory movement** <GE>	involutorische Bewegung *f*, Umwendung *f*	mouvement *m* involutif	инволюционное (инволютивное) движение
I 1009	**involutory pair (points),** pair of involutory points <PJ>	involutorische Punkte *mpl*, involutorisches Punktepaar *n*	points *mpl* involutifs, couple *m* involutif, couple de points involutifs	инволютивные точки, пара инволютивных точек
I 1010	**involutory system** <of exterior differential equations> <DE>	Involutionssystem *n*	système *m* en involution	инволюционная система
	involutory system <DE>	*s.* C 1478		
	involutory transformation <AL, AY, SE, TO>	*s.* I 991		
	inward normal <DG>	*s.* I 735		
	iota operator <LO>	*s.* D 325		
I 1011	**I-regular group** <GR>	I-reguläre Gruppe *f*	groupe *m* I-régulier	I-регулярная группа
I 1012	**I-ring** <AL>	Zornscher Ring *m*, I-Ring *m*	anneau *m* de Zorn	кольцо Цорна, I-кольцо
	irrational <NT>	*s.* I 1019		
I 1013	**irrational algebraic expression,** surd <AL>	irrationaler [algebraischer] Ausdruck *m*, Irrationalität *f*	expression *f* [algébrique] irrationnelle, irrationnelle *f*	иррациональное [алгебраическое] выражение, иррациональность
I 1014	**irrational algebraic number of the second degree** <NT>	Irrationale *f* zweiten Grades	irrationnelle *f* du second degré	иррациональное алгебраическое число второй степени
I 1015	**irrational equation,** radical equation <AL, AN>	irrationale Gleichung *f*, Wurzelgleichung *f*	équation *f* irrationnelle	иррациональное уравнение; иррациональное алгебраическое уравнение

I 1016	**irrational fraction** <NT>	irrationaler (inkommensurabler) Bruch *m*	fraction *f* irrationnelle	иррациональная дробь
	irrational function <AN>	*s.* N 459		
I 1017	**irrationality** <as a property> <AN, NT>	Irrationalität *f*	irrationalité *f*	иррациональность
I 1018	**irrationality theorem of Stolz** <for a continued fraction> <NT>	Stolzscher Irrationalitätssatz *m*	théorème *m* d'irrationalité de Stolz	теорема иррациональности Штольца
I 1019	**irrational number,** irrational, // surd <NT>	irrationale Zahl *f*, Irrationalzahl *f*, Irrationalität *f*, Irrationale *f*, // surdische Größe *f* <Stifel>	nombre *m* irrationnel, irrationnelle *f*, // nombre *m* sourd, quantité *f* sourde	иррациональное число, иррациональность
I 1020	**irreducibility** <AL, GE, TO>	Irreduzibilität *f* <AL, GE, TO>; Unkürzbarkeit *f* <AL>	irréductibilité *f*	неприводимость <AL, GE, TO>; несократимость <AL>
I 1021	**irreducibility criterion** <AL>	Irreduzibilitätskriterium *n*	critère *m* d'irréductibilité	критерий (признак) неприводимости
I 1022	**irreducible affine algebraic variety over** *k* <AG>	irreduzible (unzerlegbare) affine algebraische *k*-Mannigfaltigkeit *f*, algebraische *k*-Mannigfaltigkeit, affine *k*-Varietät *f*	variété *f* algébrique affine irréductible sur *k*	неприводимое аффинное алгебраическое многообразие над *k*
I 1023	**irreducible algebraic correspondence,** irreducible correspondence <AG>	irreduzible [algebraische] Korrespondenz *f*	correspondance *f* irréductible	неприводимое алгебраическое соответствие
I 1024	**irreducible algebraic plane curve** <AG>	irreduzible (einfache) ebene algebraische Kurve *f*	courbe *f* plane algébrique irréductible (indécomposable, simple)	неприводимая плоская алгебраическая кривая
	irreducible algebraic set over *k* <AG>	*s.* I 1038		
I 1025	**irreducible algebraic variety,** variety, irreducible variety <AG>	irreduzible algebraische Mannigfaltigkeit *f*, Varietät *f*, irreduzible Mannigfaltigkeit (Vielfältigkeit *f*)	variété *f* algébrique irréductible, variété	неприводимое алгебраическое многообразие, многообразие
I 1026	**irreducible branch** <of an algebraic variety> <AG>	irreduzibler Mantel (Zweig) *m*	branche (nappe) *f* irréductible, nappe	неприводимая ветвь
I 1027	**irreducible case** <AL>	Casus *m* irreducibilis, irreduzibler Fall *m*	cas *m* irréductible	неприводимый случай
	irreducible chain <SP>	*s.* I 1040		
I 1028	**irreducible character** <RE>	irreduzibler Charakter *m*	caractère *m* irréductible	неприводимый (примитивный) характер
I 1029	**irreducible constituent** <of a representation> <AL>	irreduzibler Konstituent (Bestandteil) *m*	composante *f* (constituant *m*) irréductible	неприводимый конституант (конституэнт), неприводимая конституэнта
	irreducible correspondence <AG>	*s.* I 1023		
I 1030	**irreducible curve,** non decomposed curve <AY>	nicht zerfallende Kurve *f*	courbe *f* à une seule branche	нераспадающаяся кривая (линия)
I 1031	**irreducible element** <of a domain of integrity> <AL>	irreduzibles (unzerlegbares) Element *n*	élément *m* irréductible	неприводимый элемент
I 1032	**irreducible element,** extremal element, atom <of a ring> <AL>	unzerlegbares Element *n*	élément *m* extrémal (irréductible)	неприводимый (экстремальный, неразложимый) элемент, атом
I 1033	**irreducible element** <of a lattice> <LA>	irreduzibles Verbandselement (Element) *n* <eines Verbandes>	élément *m* indécomposable <d'un treillis>	неприводимый элемент <структуры>
	irreducible element <AL>	*s.* P 1292		
	∪-irreducible element <LA>	*s.* J 70		
I 1034	**irreducible equation** <AL>	irreduzible Gleichung *f*	équation *f* irréductible	неприводимое уравнение
I 1035	**irreducible factor** <of an entire function> <AL, AN>	irreduzibler Faktor *m*	facteur *m* irréductible	неприводимый фактор
	irreducible form <AB>	*s.* P 1302		
	irreducible function <AL>	*s.* P 1305		
I 1036	**irreducible generating set,** minimal system of generators, minimal generating set <GR>	irreduzibles (minimales) Erzeugendensystem *n*	système *m* de générateurs minimal, système générateur minimal (irréductible), partie *f* génératrice minimale, partie irréductible	неприводимая система образующих, минимальное (неприводимое) порождающее множество
I 1037	**irreducible in the real domain** <AL>	reell-irreduzibel	irréductible dans le domaine des nombres réels	вещественно неприводимый
	irreducible *K*-module <AL>	*s.* S 925		
I 1038	**irreducible *k*-set,** *k*-variety, irreducible algebraic set over *k*, *k*-irreducible algebraic set, irreducible variety over *k*, prime rational cycle over *k* <AG>	*k*-Varietät *f*, Varietät *f* über *k*, irreduzible [algebraische] *k*-Mannigfaltigkeit *f*, Mannigfaltigkeit (irreduzible Vielfältigkeit) *f* über *k*	*k*-variété *f*, variété *f* algébrique irréductible sur *k*	неприводимое [алгебраическое] *k*-многообразие, неприводимое [алгебраическое] многообразие над *k*, *k*-неприводимое алгебраическое множество
I 1039	**irreducible map** <GP>	irreduzible Karte *f*	carte *f* irréductible	неприводимая карта
I 1040	**irreducible Markov chain,** irreducible chain <SP>	irreduzible Markovsche Kette *f*, irreduzible Kette, unzerlegbare [Markovsche] Kette	chaîne *f* markovienne irréductible, chaîne irréductible	неприводимая (неразложимая) цепь Маркова, неприводимая (неразложимая) цепь
I 1041	**irreducible matrix** <MD>	irreduzible Matrix *f*	matrice *f* irréductible	неразложимая матрица
I 1042	**irreducible polynomial,** polynomial indecompos-	irreduzibles (unzerlegbares, nicht faktorisierbares)	polynôme *m* irréductible, fonction *f* [rationnelle	неприводимый (неразложимый на множители)

	able into factors, non-factorable polynomial <AL>	Polynom *n*	entière] indécomposable [en facteurs], fonction [rationnelle entière] absolument irréductible	многочлен
	irreducible projective *k*-set <AG>	*s.* P 1696		
I 1043	**irreducible proof** <MM>	irreduzibler (unverkürzbarer) Beweis *m*	démonstration *f* irréductible	несводимое доказательство
I 1044	**irreducible quadratic form** <AL>	elementare [quadratische] Form *f*, irreduzible [quadratische] Form	forme *f* [quadratique] élémentaire, forme [quadratique] irréductible	неприводимая квадратичная форма
I 1045	**irreducible representation,** simple representation <RE>	irreduzible Darstellung *f*	représentation *f* irréductible (simple)	неприводимое (простое) представление
I 1046	**irreducible *R*-module** <AL>	irreduzibler *R*-Modul *m* <im Sinne von Jacobson>	*R*-module *m* irréductible	неприводимый *R*-модуль
I 1047	**irreducible set** <with respect to a property> <SE>	irreduzible Menge *f* <bezüglich einer Eigenschaft>	ensemble *m* irréductible <par rapport à une propriété>	неприводимое множество <относительно свойства>
I 1048	**irreducible space,** irreducible topological space <TO>	irreduzibler (irreduzibler topologischer, unzerlegbarer) Raum *m*	espace *m* irréductible	неприводимое пространство
	irreducible topological space <TO>	*s.* I 1048		
	irreducible union <LA>	*s.* I 1054		
	irreducible variety <AG>	*s.* I 1025		
	irreducible variety over *k* <AG>	*s.* I 1038		
I 1049	**irreducibly connected space** <between *A* and *B*> <TO>	irreduzibel zusammenhängender Raum *m* <zwischen *A* und *B*>	espace *m* irréductiblement connexe <entre *A* et *B*>	неприводимо связное пространство <между множествами *A* и *B*>
I 1050	**irredundant covering** <of a group> <GR>	irreduzible Überdeckung *f*	revêtement *m* irréductible	неприводимое покрытие
I 1051	**irredundant intersection** <in a lattice> <LA>	unverkürzbarer Durchschnitt *m*	intersection *f* irréductible	несократимое пересечение
I 1052	**irredundant primary representation,** reduced primary representation <of an ideal> <AL>	normierte Zerlegung *f* [durch größte Primärideale], unverkürzbare (reduzierte) Darstellung *f* [durch größte Primärideale], normierte Primäridealzerlegung *f*, reduzierte (unverkürzbare) Primärzerlegung *f*	intersection *f* primaire normée, représentation *f* normée, décomposition *f* primaire réduite, décomposition réduite	несократимое примарное разложение, представление максимальными примарными идеалами, приведенное примарное представление, редуцированное примарное разложение
I 1053	**irredundant representation** <AG, AL>	unverkürzbare (kürzeste, gekürzte) Darstellung *f*	représentation *f* irréductible (réduite)	несократимое представление, несократимая запись
I 1054	**irredundant union,** irreducible union <in a lattice> <LA>	unverkürzbare Vereinigung *f*	réunion *f* irréductible	несократимое объединение
	irreflective relation <SE>	*s.* I 1056		
I 1055	**irreflexively partially ordered set, irreflexively quasi-ordered set** <SE>	irreflexiv halbgeordnete Menge *f*	ensemble *m* partiellement ordonné au sens strict	иррефлексивно полуупорядоченное множество
I 1056	**irreflexive relation,** antireflexive relation, irreflective relation, inflexive relation <SE>	irreflexive Relation (Beziehung) *f*, antireflexive Relation (Beziehung), inflexive Relation (Beziehung)	relation *f* antiréflexive (irréflexive, totalement irréflexive), inégalité *f*	иррефлексивное [бинарное] отношение, антирефлексивное отношение
I 1057	**irreflexivity,** anti-reflexiveness <of a relation> <SE>	Irreflexivität *f*, Antireflexivität *f*	irréflexivité *f*, antiréflexivité *f*	иррефлексивность, антирефлективность
I 1058	**irrefutability in the propositional calculus** <LO>	Unwiderlegbarkeit *f* im Aussagenkalkül	irréfutabilité *f* en calcul des propositions	неопровержимость в исчислении высказываний
I 1059	**irrefutable proposition** <LO>	unwiderlegbare Aussage *f*	proposition *f* irréfutable	неопровержимое высказывание
I 1060	**irregular birational transformation** <AG>	irreguläre birationale Transformation *f*	transformation *f* birationnelle irrégulière	иррегулярное бирациональное преобразование
I 1061	**irregular continued fraction** <NΓ>	unregelmäßiger Kettenbruch *m*	fraction *f* continue irrégulière	неправильная цепная дробь
I 1062	**irregular decomposition** <of a space> <TO>	irreguläre Zerlegung *f*	décomposition *f* irrégulière	иррегулярное разбиение
I 1063	**irregular determinant** <of a quadratic form> <NT>	irreguläre Determinante *f*	déterminant *m* irrégulier	иррегулярный определитель
I 1064	**irregular divisor class** <AL>	irreguläre Divisorenklasse *f*	classe *f* de diviseurs irrégulière	иррегулярный класс дивизоров
I 1065	**irregular eigenvalue problem** <DE>	irreguläre Eigenwertaufgabe *f*, irreguläres Eigenwertproblem *n*	problème *m* aux valeurs propres irrégulier	неправильная задача на собственные значения
I 1066	**irregularity** <of a surface> <AG>	Irregularität *f*	irrégularité *f*	иррегулярность
I 1067	**irregular point** <TO>	irregulärer Punkt *m*	point *m* irrégulier	иррегулярная точка
I 1068	**irregular prime,** irregular prime number <in Fermat['s] conjecture> <NT>	irreguläre Primzahl *f*	nombre *m* premier irrégulier	иррегулярное простое число
	irregular prime number <NT> Γ<DE>	*s.* I 1068		
	irregular singularity	*s.* I 1069		
I 1069	**irregular singular point,** irregular singularity, point of indetermination,	Stelle *f* der Unbestimmtheit, singuläre Stelle der Unbestimmtheit, Unbe-	point *m* singulier irrégulier, singularité *f* irrégulière, point d'indétermination,	существенная (существенно, иррегулярная) особая точка, особая

and still: I 1069	essential singular point, essential singularity <of a homogeneous linear differential equation> <DE>	stimmtheitsstelle *f*, wesentlich (wesentliche, stark) singuläre Stelle, irreguläre singuläre Stelle, irreguläre Singularität *f*	point singulier essentiel, singularité essentielle	точка неопределенности, точка определенности, иррегулярная особенность, сильно особая точка
	irresoluble equation <AL>	*s.* U 396		
I 1070	**irrotational field,** nonrotational field, noncircuital field, lamellar [vector] field, nonvortical field, vector field derivable from a scalar potential, potential field <VT>	potentiales (wirbelfreies, rotationsfreies, drehungsfreies, lamellares, laminares) Vektorfeld *n*, Potentialfeld *n*, Gradientenfeld *n*, wirbelfreies (rotationsfreies, drehungsfreies, lamellares, laminares) Feld *n*, wirbelfreies (reines) Quellenfeld *n*, Quellenfeld	vecteur *m* lamellaire, champ *m* de vecteurs lamellaire (irrotationnel), champ newtonien, vecteur newtonien, champ irrotationnel, champ à potentiel scalaire, champ non rotationnel, champ lamellaire, champ de potentiel, champ potentiel	безвихревое поле, скалярное потенциальное поле, поле без вихрей, невихревое поле, потенциальное поле, градиентное поле
I 1071	**isepiphanic problem** <CS>	isepiphanes Problem *n*	problème *m* des isépiphanes	
I 1072	**isobaric form** <AL>	isobare Form *f*	forme *f* isobare	изобарическая форма
I 1073	**isobaric polynomial** <AL>	isobares (isobarisches) Polynom *n*	fonction *f* isobare (rationnelle entière isobarique)	изобарический многочлен
	isobath <DS>	*s.* L 593		
I 1074	**isoclass,** class of [mutually] isomorphic [algebraic] systems <UA>	Klasse *f* isomorpher algebraischer Systeme, Klasse isomorpher universeller Algebren	classe *f* d'algèbres isomorphes	изокласс, класс изоморфных алгебраических систем
I 1075	**isocline** <DE>	Isokline *f*	isocline *f*	изоклина
I 1076	**isocyclic surface** <Demartres> <DG>	isozyklische Fläche *f*	surface *f* isocyclique	изоциклическая поверхность
I 1077	**isodynamic point,** Beltrami['s] point <EG>	isodynamischer (Beltramischer) Punkt *m*	point *m* isodynamique (de Beltrami)	изодинамический центр, изодинамическая точка, точка Бельтрами
I 1078	**isogeneous algebraic group** <AG, AL>	isogene algebraische Gruppe *f*	groupe *m* algébrique isogène	изогенная алгебраическая группа
I 1079	**isogeny** <AG, AL>	Isogenie *f*	isogénie *f*, isogénisme *m*	изогения
I 1080	**isogeny class** <of algebraic groups> <AG>	Isogenieklasse *f*	classe *f* d'isogénie	класс изогении
I 1081	**isogeny type** <of abelian varieties> <AG>	Isogenietyp *m*	type *m* d'isogénie	изогенный тип
I 1082	**isogon** <EG>	Isogon *n*	isogone *m*	изогон
I 1083/4	**isogonal affine transformation** <GE>	winkeltreue affine Transformation *f*	transformation *f* affine isogonale	изогональное аффинное преобразование
I 1085	**isogonal conformal mapping (transformation),** direct[ly] conformal mapping (transformation) <FT>	direkt[e] konforme Abbildung *f*, konforme Abbildung erster Art	application (représentation) *f* conforme directe (de première espèce)	конформное отображение первого рода
I 1086	**isogonal conjugate lines,** isogonal conjugates <of a triangle> <EG>	Winkelgegengeraden *fpl*	droites *fpl* conjuguées isogonales	продолжения сторон угла треугольника за вершину
I 1087	**isogonal conjugate point** <of a point with respect to a triangle> <EG>	isogonales Bild *n*, Winkelgegenpunkt *m*	inverse *m*, conjugué *m* isogonal, arguésienne *f*	
	isogonal conjugates <EG>	*s.* I 1086		
I 1088	**isogonal correspondence** <GE>	isogonale (gleichwinklige) Korrespondenz *f*	correspondance *f* isogonale	равноугольное (изогональное) соответствие
	isogonality <FT, GE>	*s.* P 1240		
	isogonal mapping <AY, GE>	*s.* A 669		
	isogonal mapping <FT>	*s.* C 1901		
I 1089	**isogonal surface** <GE>	isogonale Fläche *f*, Gleichwinkelfläche *f*, Isogonalfläche *f*	surface *f* isogonale	изогональная поверхность
I 1090	**isogonal trajectory** <DE, DG>	Isogonaltrajektorie *f*, isogonale Trajektorie *f*	trajectoire *f* isogonale	изогональная траектория
I 1091	**isogonal transformation** <EG>	isogonale Verwandtschaft *f*	transformation *f* arguésienne	дезаргово преобразование
	isogonal transformation <AY, GE>	*s.* A 669		
	isogonic mapping <AY, GE>	*s.* A 669		
I 1092	**isogonic points** <of a triangle> <EG>	isogonische (isogone) Punkte *mpl*	points *mpl* isogones	изогональные центры
	isogonic transformation <AY, GE>	*s.* A 669		
I 1093	**isogonological triangle** <EG>	isogonologes Dreieck *n*	triangle *m* isogonologique	изогонологический треугольник
I 1094	**isogram** <as a curve *or* domain> <FT>	Isogramme *f*	isogramme *m*	изограмма
I 1095	**isohedron** <EG>	Isoeder *n*	isoèdre *m*	изоэдр
	isohypse [line] <DS>	*s.* L 598		
I 1096	**isolated double point** <AG>	isolierter Doppelpunkt *m*	point *m* double isolé	изолированная двойная точка
I 1097	**isolated edge** <of a graph> <GP>	isolierte Kante *f*, elementarer Kreis *m*	arête *f* isolée	изолированное ребро
I 1098	**isolated element,** central element, element of the centre <of a group> <GR>	isoliertes (invariantes) Element *n*, Element des Zentrums, Zentrumselement *n*	élément *m* invariant, élément central (conjugué de lui-même, du centre, normal)	инвариантный элемент, центральный элемент
	isolated essential singularity (singular point) <FT>	*s.* E 527		

No.	English	German	French	Russian
	isolated extremum <DI>	*s.* S 1859		
	isolated ordinal <SE>	*s.* N 410		
1099	**isolated point** <also of a spectrum> <FA, TO>	isolierter Punkt *m*	point *m* isolé	изолированная точка
	isolated point <AG>	*s.* A 196		
1100	**isolated prime ideal** <of an ideal> <AL>	nichteingebettetes (isoliertes, minimales) Primideal *n*	idéal *m* premier minimal	изолированный простой идеал
	isolated set <TO>	*s.* D 672		
1101	**isolated singular point** <of an analytic *or* a quaternion function) <FT>	isolierter singulärer Punkt *m*, isolierte singuläre Stelle *f*, isolierte Singularität *f*	point *m* singulier isolé, singularité *f* isolée	изолированная особая точка
1102	**isolated subgroup,** convex subgroup <of an ordered group ><GR>	isolierte Untergruppe *f*	sous-groupe *m* isolé	изолированная (выпуклая) подгруппа
	isolated subgroup <GR>	*s.* P 2067		
	isolated subset <AL>	*s.* S 438		
1103	**isolated vertex** <GP>	isolierte Ecke *f*, isolierter Knotenpunkt (Knoten) *m*	sommet *m* isolé	изолированная вершина
	isolating of roots <AL, NU>	*s.* S 561		
	isomer <VT>	*s.* I 1104		
1104	**isomeric tensor,** isomer <of a tensor> <VT>	isomerer Tensor *m*	tenseur *m* isomérique, isomère *m*	изомерный тензор
	isometric axonometry <DS, PJ>	*s.* I 1113		
1105	**isometric chart,** isometric stereogram <ST>	isometrisches Stereogramm *n*	diagramme (stéréogramme) *m* isométrique	изометрическая стереограмма
1106	**isometric circle** <FT>	Isometriekreis *m*, isometrischer Kreis *m*	cercle *m* isométrique	изометрическая окружность
	isometric co-ordinate <DG>	*s.* I 1165		
1107	**isometric embedding** <of a metric space> <TO>	isometrische (kongruente) Einbettung *f*	plongement *m* isométrique	изометрическое вложение
1108	**isometric embedding,** length-preserving embedding <in a space having a metric defined by an element of length> <TO>	längentreue Einbettung *f*, isometrische Einbettung *f*	plongement *m* isométrique (conservant la longueur)	изометрическое (сохраняющее длину) вложение
1109	**isometric form,** equivalent form <AL>	isometrische Form *f*	forme *f* isométrique	изометрическая (эквивалентная) форма
	isometric lines <DG>	*s.* I 1168		
	isometric mapping <DG, TO>	*s.* I 1112		
	isometric metric space <TO>	*s.* I 1110		
	isometric net <DG>	*s.* I 1164		
	isometric parameter <DG>	*s.* I 1165		
	isometric projection <DS, PJ>	*s.* I 1113		
1110	**isometric space,** isometric metric space <TO>	isometrischer (isometrischer metrischer, kongruenter metrischer, kongruenter) Raum *m*	espace *m* isométrique (métrique isométrique)	изометрическое (конгруэнтное, изометрическое метрическое) пространство
	isometric stereogram <ST>	*s.* I 1105		
1111	**isometric surface,** applicable surface <DG>	isometrische (abwickelbare, abbildbare, verbiegbare, biegbare) Fläche *f*	surface *f* isométrique (applicable)	изометрическая (наложимая) поверхность
	isometric system [of curves] <DG>	*s.* I 1168		
	isometric transformation <DG, TO>	*s.* I 1112		
1112	**isometry,** isometric mapping (transformation), distance-preserving mapping <of metric spaces onto one another>; length-preserving mapping <if the metric is defined by an element of length only> <DG, TO>	isometrische Abbildung *f*, Isometrie *f*, abstandstreue Abbildung; isometrische Transformation *f* <auf sich>, Bewegung *f*, Verbiegung *f*, Biegung *f*; längentreue Abbildung, Abwicklung *f*, Abwickelung *f*	isométrie *f*, application (transformation) *f* isométrique	изометрия <на>, изометрическое отображение (изображение) <в>; изометрическое преобразование <на себе>, движение
1113	**isometry,** isometric projection, isometric axonometry <DS, PJ>	isometrische Projektion (Axonometrie, Parallelperspektive) *f*	perspective (projection) *f* isométrique	изометрия, изометрическая проекция
1114	**isometry** <of pseudometric spaces> <TO>	metrisch-treue Abbildung *f*	application *f* conservant la pseudo-distance	отображение, сохраняющее псевдорасстояние
	isometry <GE>	*s.* M 915		
1115	**isomorphic,** ≅ <AL, GR>	isomorph, ≅	isomorphe, ≅	изоморфный, ≅
1116	**isomorphic complex,** complex having the same combinatorial type, combinatorially equivalent complex <AT>	isomorpher (kombinatorisch äquivalenter) Komplex *m*, Komplex vom gleichen [kombinatorischen] Typus	complexe *m* isomorphe (combinatoirement équivalent, équivalent du point de vue combinatoire)	изоморфный (комбинаторно эквивалентный) комплекс; комплекс, имеющий один и тот же комбинаторный тип
	isomorphic correspondence <AL>	*s.* I 1126		
	isomorphic correspondence <GR>	*s.* I 1131		
	isomorphic extension field over k <AL>	*s.* K 81		
	isomorphic extension of k <AL>	*s.* K 81		

No.	English	German	French	Russian
I 1117	**isomorphic field** <AL>	isomorpher Körper *m*	corps isomorphe (de même type, identique abstraitement parlant)	изоморфное поле
	isomorphic field extension over *k* <AL>	*s.* K 81		
I 1118	**isomorphic graph** <GP>	isomorpher (gleicher) Graph *m*, Graph von derselben Struktur	graphe *m* isomorphe, assemblage *m* pareil <Jordan>	изоморфный граф
I 1119	**isomorphic group** <GR>	isomorphe (holoedrisch isomorphe, einstufig isomorphe, 1 — 1-isomorphe) Gruppe *f*, Gruppe vom gleichen Typus	groupe *m* isomorphe (en isomorphie), groupe isomorphe de rang un, groupe holoédriquement (hémiédriquement) isomorphe	изоморфная группа
I 1120	**isomorphic image (map)** <AL>	isomorphes Bild *n*	image *f* isomorphe	изоморфный образ
I 1121	**isomorphic mapping,** isomorphism <of a complex> <AT>	isomorphe Abbildung *f*, Isomorphie *f*	isomorphisme *m*	изоморфное отображение
	isomorphic mapping <AL>	*s.* I 1126		
	isomorphic mapping <GR>	*s.* I 1131		
	isomorphic object <CA>	*s.* E 445		
I 1122	**isomorphic partially ordered set,** similar partially ordered set <SE>	ähnliche (isomorphe) halbgeordnete Menge *f*, ähnliche geordnete Menge	ensemble *m* [partiellement] ordonné semblable	подобное частично упорядоченное множество
	isomorphic refinement <AL>	*s.* E 448		
I 1123	**isomorphic relation,** similar relation <SE>	isomorphe Relation *f*	relation *f* isomorphe (semblable)	изоморфное отношение
	isomorphic representation <RE>	*s.* E 449		
	isomorphic set <SE>	*s.* E 404		
I 1124	**isomorphic space,** equivalent space <DG>	isomorpher (äquivalenter) Raum *m*	espace *m* isomorphe (équivalent)	изоморфное (эквивалентное) пространство
I 1125	**isomorphic subobject** <CA>	äquivalenter Monomorphismus *m*, isomorphes Unterobjekt *n*	sous-objet *m* isomorphe	эквивалентный мономорфизм
I 1126	**isomorphism,** isomorphic mapping, isomorph mapping; isomorphic correspondence <AL>	Isomorphismus *m*, isomorphe Abbildung *f*, Isomorphie *f*	isomorphisme *m*, isomorphie *f*	изоморфизм, изоморфное отображение; изоморфное соответствие
I 1127	**isomorphism,** equivalence, invertible morphism (arrow), unit <as a morphism> <CA>	Isomorphismus *m*, Äquivalenz *f*, invertierbarer Pfeil *m*, umkehrbarer Morphismus *m*	isomorphisme *m*, morphisme *m* inversible	эквивалентность, изоморфизм, обратимый морфизм
I 1128	**isomorphism,** isomorphism functor <as a functor> <CA>	Isomorphismus *m*	isomorphisme *m*	изоморфизм
I 1129	**isomorphism** <of categories, of a graph, of lattices, *or* of uniform spaces> <CA, GP, LA, TO>	Isomorphismus *m*	isomorphisme *m*	изоморфизм
I 1130	***-isomorphism** <FA>	*-Isomorphismus *m*	*-isomorphisme *m*	*-изоморфизм
I 1131	**isomorphism,** isomorphism of groups, group[-]isomorphism, simple isomorphism, 1-isomorphism, isomorphic mapping; isomorphic correspondence <of groups> <GR>	Isomorphismus *m*, Gruppenisomorphismus *m*, gruppentheoretischer Isomorphismus, isomorphe Abbildung *f*, gruppenisomorphe Abbildung, einstufiger (holoedrischer) Isomorphismus, 1-Isomorphismus *m*	isomorphisme *m*, isomorphisme de groupes, isomorphisme holoédrique	изоморфизм, изоморфизм группы, групповой изоморфизм, изоморфное отображение, голоэдрический изоморфизм
I 1132	**isomorphism,** bijection <of algebras> <UA>	Isomorphismus *m*, Bijektion *f*	isomorphisme *m*	изоморфизм
	isomorphism <AT>	*s.* I 1121		
	isomorphism <SE>	*s.* O 356		
	1-isomorphism <GR>	*s.* I 1131		
I 1133	**isomorphism between sets** <SE>	Mengenisomorphismus *m*	isomorphisme *m* d'ensembles	теоретико-множественный изоморфизм
I 1134	**isomorphism class** <AL>	Isomorphieklasse *f*	classe *f* d'isomorphisme	класс изоморфизма
I 1135	**isomorphism class** <of fibre bundles> <AT>	Bündelklasse *f*	classe *f* de fibrés (fibrations) isomorphes	класс изоморфных расслоений
I 1136	**isomorphism condition** <LO>	Isomorphiebedingung *f*	condition *f* d'isomorphie	условие изоморфизма
	isomorphism functor <CA>	*s.* I 1128		
I 1137	**isomorphism invariant** <SP>	Isomorphieinvariante *f*	invariant *m* d'isomorphie	инвариант изоморфизма
	isomorphism of groups <GR>	*s.* I 1131		
I 1138	**isomorphism onto** <AL>	Isomorphismus *m* auf, Isomorphismus-auf *m*	isomorphie *f* (isomorphisme *m*) sur	изоморфизм на
	isomorphism over *k* <AL>	*s.* K 82		
	isomorphism over R_0 <AL>	*s.* R 724		
	isomorphism over the prime field <AL>	*s.* A 78		
I 1139	**isomorphism problem** <GR>	Isomorphieproblem *n*	problème *m* d'isomorphisme	проблема изоморфизма [слов]

No.	English	German	French	Russian
I 1140	**isomorphism theorem** <of class field theory> <AB>	Isomorphiesatz *m*	loi *f* d'isomorphisme	теорема изоморфизма
	isomorphism theorem of Hurewicz <AT>	*s.* H 599		
I 1141	**isomorphism theorems,** Dedekind-Noether isomorphism theorems, laws of isomorphism, isomorphy theorems <AL, CA>	Isomorphiesätze *mpl*	théorèmes *mpl* d'isomorphisme de Nœther	теоремы об изоморфизмах
I 1142	**isomorphism theorems of group theory** <GR>	Isomorphiesätze *mpl*, gruppentheoretische Isomorphiesätze	théorèmes *mpl* d'isomorphisme de la théorie des groupes	теоретико-групповые теоремы об изоморфизмах
I 1143	**isomorphism type** <UA>	Isomorphietyp *m*	type *m* d'isomorphie	тип изоморфизма
	isomorph mapping <AL>	*s.* I 1126		
I 1144	**isomorphy** <as a property> <AL, TO>	Isomorphie *f*	isomorphie *f*	изоморфность
I 1145	**isomorphy** <of groups> <as a property> <GR>	Isomorphie *f*	isomorphie *f*, isomorphisme *m*, isomorphisme holoédrique (réciproque), holomorphie *f* <Wigner>	изоморфизм
I 1146	**isomorphy** <of relations> <SE>	Isomorphie *f* <zwischen Relationen>	isomorphie *f*, identité *f* de structures <de relations>	изоморфизм <отношений>
	isomorphy theorems <AL, CA>	*s.* I 1141		
I 1147	**isoperimetric[al] deficiency** <CS, GE>	isoperimetrisches Defizit *n*	déficit *m* isopérimétrique	
I 1148	**isoperimetric[al] figure** <GE>	isoperimetrische Figur *f*	figure *f* isopérimétrique	изопериметрическая фигура
I 1149	**isoperimetric[al] inequality** <for convex bodies> <CS, GE>	isoperimetrische Ungleichung *f*	inégalité *f* isopérimétrique	изопериметрическое неравенство
I 1150	**isoperimetric[al] parameter** <VA>	isoperimetrischer Parameter *m*, isoperimetrische Konstante *f*	paramètre *m* isopérimétrique	изопериметрический параметр
I 1151	**isoperimetric[al] problem** <GE, VA>	isoperimetrisches Problem *n* <GE, VA>; Problem der Dido <VA>	problème *m* isopérimétrique (des isopérimètres)	задача изопериметров, изопериметрическая задача
I 1152	**isoperimetric[al] property** <GE>	isoperimetrische Eigenschaft *f*	propriété *f* isopérimétrique	изопериметрическое свойство
I 1153	**isoperimetry** <GE>	Isoperimetrie *f*	isopérimétrie *f*	изопериметрия
I 1154	**isopleth,** isoplethal, index line <NO>	Isoplethe *f*, beziffertes Element *n*	isoplèthe *f*, ligne *f* isoplèthe	изоплета
	isopleth <NO>	*s.* N 164		
	isoplethal <NO>	*s.* I 1154		
I 1155	**isopole** <of a triangle> <EG>	Isopol *m*	isopôle *m*	изополюс
I 1156	**isoptic curve** <of a curve *or* conic> <GE>	isoptische Kurve *f*, Kurve gleichen Gesichtswinkels	courbe *f* isoptique	изооптическая кривая
I 1157	**isosceles trapezoid** <EG>	gleichschenkliges Trapez *n*	trapèze *m* isocèle	равнобочная трапеция
I 1158	**isosceles triangle** <EG>	gleichschenkliges Dreieck *n*	triangle *m* isocèle	равнобедренный треугольник
I 1159	**isostrophic loop** <AL>	isostrophe Loop *f*	loop *m* isostrophique	изострофная лупа
I 1160	**isostrophic quasigroup** <AL>	isostrophe Quasigruppe *f*	quasigroupe *m* isostrophique	изострофная квазигруппа
I 1161	**isostrophy** <AL>	Isostrophie *f*	isostrophie *f*	изострофия
I 1162	**isothermal-asymptotic surface** <DG>	isotherm-asymptotische Fläche *f*	surface *f* isotherme-asymptote	изотермическая асимптотическая поверхность
I 1163	**isothermal[-] conjugate net** <DG>	isotherm-konjugiertes Netz *n*	réseau *m* isotherme conjugué	изотермическая сопряженная сеть (сетка)
	isothermal lines <DG>	*s.* I 1168		
I 1164	**isothermal net,** isometric net <on a surface> <DG>	isothermisches Netz (Kurvennetz) *n*, isometrisches Netz (Kurvennetz)	réseau *m* isotherme (isométrique)	изотермическая сетка (сеть)
I 1165	**isothermal parameter,** isometric parameter (co-ordinate), isothermic parameter <DG>	isothermer (isometrischer) Parameter *m*, isotherme Koordinate *f*	paramètre *m* isotherme (isométrique), variable (coordonnée) *f* isotherme	изотермический (изометрический) параметр, изотермическая координата
I 1166	**isothermal parameter curve** <DG>	isotherme Parameterlinie *f*	ligne *f* paramétrique isotherme	изотермическая параметрическая линия
I 1167	**isothermal surface** <DG>	Isothermfläche *f*	surface *f* isotherme	изотермическая поверхность
I 1168	**isothermal system [of curves],** isothermic system [of curves], isothermal lines, isometric system [of curves], isometric lines <on a surface> <DG>	Isothermensystem *n*, Isothermenschar *f*, isothermisches System *n* von Kurven	famille *f* isotherme, faisceau *m* (famille) de courbes isothermes, courbes *fpl* isothermes, système *m* isotherme [de courbes]	изотермическая система кривых, изометрическое семейство, изотермические кривые
	isothermic parameter <DG>	*s.* I 1165		
	isothermic system [of curves] <DG>	*s.* I 1168		
	isotone function <RF>	*s.* I 287		
	isotone many-one correspondence <SE>	*s.* I 1173		
	isotone mapping <SE>	*s.* I 1173		
	isotone sequence <SS>	*s.* M 869		
I 1169	**isotone transformation** <of a lattice> <LA>	Ordnungshomomorphismus *m*	application *f* isotone, morphisme *m* d'ordre, application croissante	изотонное отображение
I 1170	**isotone valuation** <LA>	monotone (isotone) Bewertung *f*	valuation *f* isotone	изотонное нормирование

	isotonic function <RF>	*s.* I 287		
I 1171	**isotonic injective mapping** <SE>	isotone injektive Abbildung *f*, isotone Injektion *f*	injection *f* croissante	изотонное инъективное отображение
I 1172	**isotonicity**, isotony <RF, SE>	Isotonie *f*	isotonie *f*	изотонность
I 1173	**isotonic mapping**, order[-]preserving mapping, monotone (isotone) mapping, isotone (order-preserving) many-one correspondence, order-preserving map, increasing (order-preserving) function, order (monotonic) homomorphism <of a partially ordered set> <SE>	isotone Abbildung *f*, monotone Abbildung, ordnungstreue Abbildung, Ordnungshomomorphismus *m*, ordnungserhaltende Abbildung	application *f* croissante, application isotone, application monotone, morphisme *m* d'ensembles ordonnés, morphisme d'ordre, homomorphisme *m*, fonction *f* isotone, application croissante au sens large	изотонное отображение, монотонное отображение, монотонный гомоморфизм, гомоморфизм упорядоченного множества, монотонное преобразование, возрастающее отображение, возрастающее в широком смысле отображение; отображение, сохраняющее порядок
	isotonic sequence <SS>	*s.* M 869		
I 1174	**isotonous operation** <in a pre-ordered set> <AL, SE>	isotone Operation *f*	opération *f* isotone	изотонная операция
I 1175	**isotony** <for a closure operation> <AL, AN, LO, TO>	Satz *m* der Monotonie, Monotoniesatz *m* <für die Hüllenbildung>	monotonie *f* <de l'opération de fermeture>	изотонность <операции замыкания>
	isotony <RF, SE>	*s.* I 1172		
	isotope [groupoid] <AL>	*s.* I 1179		
I 1176	**isotopic deformation**, isotopy <TO>	isotope Deformation *f*, Isotopie *f*	déformation *f* isotope, isotopie *f*	изотопическая деформация, изотопия
I 1177	**isotopic embedding** <TO>	isotope Einbettung *f*	plongement *m* isotope	изотопическое вложение
I 1178	**isotopic figure** <TO>	isotope Figur *f*	figure *f* isotope	изотопная фигура
I 1179	**isotopic groupoid**, isotope groupoid, isotope <of a groupoid> <AL>	isotopes Gruppoid *n*, Isotop *n* <eines Gruppoids>	groupoïde *m* isotope, isotope *m* <d'un groupoïde>	изотопный группоид, изотоп <группоида>
I 1180	**isotopic knot** <TO>	isotoper Knoten *m*	nœud *m* isotope	узел, принадлежащий к одному и тому же изотопическому типу
I 1181	**isotopic point sets**, isotopic sets <TO>	[zueinander] isotope Punktmengen *fpl*, isotope Mengen *fpl*	parties *fpl* isotopes	[взаимно] изотопные множества, [взаимно] изотопические множества
I 1182	**isotopic quasi-fields** <AL>	[zueinander] isotope Quasikörper *mpl*	quasi-corps *mpl* isotopes	[взаимно] изотопные квазиполя
	isotopic sets <TO>	*s.* I 1181		
I 1183	**isotopism** <AL>	Isotopismus *m*	isotopisme *m*	изотопизм
I 1184	**isotopy** <as a property> <AL, TO>	Isotopie *f*	isotopie *f*	изотопия
	isotopy <TO>	*s.* I 1176		
I 1185	**isotopy class** <TO>	Isotopieklasse *f*	classe *f* d'isotopie	изотопический класс
I 1186	**isotopy invariant** <TO>	Isotopieinvariante *f*	invariant *m* d'isotopie	изотопический инвариант
I 1187	**isotopy theorem** <TO>	Isotopiesatz *m*	théorème *m* d'isotopie	теорема об изотопии
I 1188	**isotopy type** <of a knot> <AT>	Isotopietyp *m*	type *m* d'isotopie	изотопический тип
I 1189	**isotropic circular transformation** <GE>	isotrope Kreistransformation (Kreisverwandtschaft) *f*	transformation *f* circulaire isotrope	изотропное круговое преобразование
I 1190	**isotropic Clifford translation of the first kind** <GE>	isotrope Cliffordsche Schiebung *f* erster Art, isotrope Cliffordsche Linksschiebung *f*	translation *f* de Clifford isotrope de première espèce	изотропный перенос Клиффорда первого рода
I 1191	**isotropic Clifford translation of the second kind** <GE>	isotrope Cliffordsche Schiebung *f* zweiter Art, isotrope Cliffordsche Rechtsschiebung *f*	translation *f* de Clifford isotrope de deuxième espèce	изотропный перенос Клиффорда второго рода
I 1192	**isotropic cone** <AY>	isotroper Kegel *m*, Minimalkegel *m*	cône *m* isotrope	изотропный конус
I 1193	**isotropic curvature** <DG>	isotrope Krümmung *f*	courbure *f* isotrope	изотропная кривизна
I 1194	**isotropic curve**, null curve, minimal curve <DG>	isotrope Kurve *f* [erster Art], Minimalkurve *f*, Minimallinie *f*, ametrische Kurve, Kurve der Länge Null	courbe *f* isotrope (minimale, isotropique), ligne *f* de longueur nulle	изотропная кривая, минимальная кривая, минимальная линия
I 1195	**isotropic half-line** <GE>	isotrope Halbgerade *f*	demi-droite *f* isotrope	изотропная полупрямая
I 1196	**isotropic line**, minimum line <AY, DG>	isotrope Gerade *f*, Minimalgerade *f*, Isotrope *f*, Gerade von der Länge Null, zirkulare Gerade	droite *f* isotrope (minimale), isotrope *f*	изотропная прямая
I 1197	**isotropic mean** <of a function $f(x)$ for a module r of x> <RF>	isotropes Mittel *n*	moyenne *f* isotropique <Cauchy>	изотропное среднее
I 1198	**isotropic minimal surface** <DG>	isotrope Minimalfläche *f*, Potentialfläche *f*	surface *f* minimale isotropique	изотропная минимальная поверхность
I 1199	**isotropic parabola** <GE>	parabolischer Kreis *m*, isotrope Parabel *f*	parabole *f* isotropique	изотропная парабола
I 1200	**isotropic parameter** <of a surface> <DG>	isotroper Flächenparameter (Parameter) *m*	paramètre *m* isotrope	изотропный параметр, изотропная координата
I 1201	**isotropic plane**, minimum plane <AY, DG, PJ>	[einfach] isotrope Ebene *f*, Minimalebene *f*	plan *m* isotrope (minimal)	изотропная плоскость
	isotropic points <AY, PJ>	*s.* C 2873		
I 1202	**isotropic process**, isotropic stochastic process <SP>	isotroper Prozeß (stochastischer Prozeß, statistischer Prozeß) *m*	processus *m* isotrope (stochastique isotrope)	изотропный процесс (случайный процесс)
I 1203	**isotropic projection** <GE>	isotrope Projektion *f*, Minimalprojektion *f*	projection *f* isotrope	изотропная проекция

No.	English	German	French	Russian
	isotropic stochastic process <SP>	*s.* I 1202		
I 1204	**isotropic surface** <DG>	isotrope Fläche *f*	surface *f* isotropique	изотропная поверхность
I 1205	**isotropic vector** <GE>	isotroper (ametrischer, lichtartiger) Vektor *m*	vecteur *m* isotrope	изотропный вектор
	isotropism <GE>	*s.* I 1206		
I 1206	**isotropy** <GE, ST>; isotropism <GE>	Isotropie *f*	isotropie *f*	изотропия <GE, ST>; изотропность <GE>
	isotropy [sub]group <AL, TO>	*s.* G 484		
	isotype <ST>	*s.* P 583		
I 1207	**isotypic ring** <AL>	isotyper Ring *m*	anneau *m* isotypique	изотипное кольцо
I 1208	**isovariant homotopy** <TO>	isovariante Homotopie *f*	homotopie *f* isovariante	изовариантная гомотопия
	isthmus <GP>	*s.* S 545		
	item <ST>	*s.* S 31		
	iterate <AN, SE, TO>	*s.* P 1595		
	iterated <AN, NU>	*s.* I 1211		
I 1209	**iterated connecting homomorphism (morphism)** <HA>	iterierter Verbindungshomomorphismus *m*	homomorphisme *m* de connexion itéré	итерированный связывающий гомоморфизм
I 1210	**iterated difference** <FD>	iterierte Differenz *f*	différence *f* itérée	итерированная разность
I 1211	**iterated function,** iterated <of a function> <AN, NU>	Iterierte *f*, iterierte (wiederholte) Funktion *f*	fonction *f* itérée (itérative)	итерированная функция, итерация [функции]
I 1212	**iterated functor** <CA>	iterierter Funktor *m*	itéré *m* <d'un foncteur>	итерированный функтор
I 1213	**iterated integral** <DI>	iteriertes Integral *n*	intégrale *f* itérée (répétée)	повторный интеграл
I 1214	**iterated kernel,** iteration kernel <*n*-th> <IE>	iterierter Kern *m* <*n*-ter>	noyau *m* itéré, itéré *m* <*n*-e>	итерированное (повторное) ядро <*n*-ое>
I 1215	**iterated limit** <AN>	iterierter Limes (Grenzwert) *m*; sukzessiver Grenzübergang *m*	limite *f* itérée; passage *m* successif à la limite	повторный предел; повторный предельный переход
I 1216	**iterated limit of rows** <SS>	iterierter Zeilenlimes *m*	limite *f* itérée de (par) lignes	повторный (итерированный) предел по строкам
I 1217	**iterated logarithm** <AN>	iterierter (wiederholter) Logarithmus *m*, $\log_k$	logarithme *m* itéré	повторный логарифм
I 1218	**iterated map** <FA>	iterierte Abbildung *f*, Iterierte *f*, Potenz *f*	application *f* itérée	повторное отображение
I 1219	**iterated series,** iterated sum, repeated series <SS>	iterierte (iterierte unendliche) Reihe *f*	série *f* itérée	повторный (итерированный) ряд
I 1220	**iterated Steenrod square** <AT>	iteriertes Steenrodsches Quadrat *n*	opération *f* de Steenrod itérée, carré *m* itéré	повторный квадрат Стинрода
I 1221	**iterated sum** <SS>	iterierte Summe *f*	somme *f* itérée	итерированная сумма
	iterated sum <SS>	*s.* I 1219		
I 1222	**iterating, iteration,** iteration process (procedure) <AN, NU>	Iterieren *n*, Iterationsprozeß *m*, Iteration *f*	procédé *m* d'itération, itération *f*	итерирование, процесс составления итераций, процесс итерации, повторение
I 1223	**iteration** <ST>	Iteration *f*	itération *f*	повторение, итерация
	iteration <AN, NU>	*s.* S 2231		
	iteration <ST>	*s.* R 1521		
	iteration kernel <IE>	*s.* I 1214		
	iteration method <AX, DE, IE, NU>	*s.* I 1229		
	iteration procedure <AN, NU>	*s.* I 1222		
	iteration process <AN, NU>	*s.* I 1222		
I 1224	**iteration step,** iterative step, step of iteration <AN, NU>	Iterationsschritt *m*	pas *m* d'itération	шаг итерации
	iteration theory <ST>	*s.* T 397		
I 1225	**iterative computation** <AX, NU>	iterative Berechnung *f*	calcul *m* itératif	итерационное вычисление, итерационный расчет
I 1226	**iterative cycle,** cycle <NU>	Iterationsschleife *f*	cycle *m* d'itération	итерационный цикл, цикл итерации
I 1227	**iterative equation** <DE>	Iterationsgleichung *f*	équation *f* itérative	итерационное уравнение
I 1228	**iterative invariant** <AN, NU>	Iterationsinvariante *f*	invariant *m* itératif	итерационный инвариант
I 1229	**iterative method,** iteration method, method of successive approximations <AX, DE, IE, NU>	iteratives Näherungsverfahren (Verfahren) *n*, Iterationsverfahren *n*, Iterationsmethode *f*, Verfahren des wiederholten Einsetzens, Methode *f* der Iteration[en] (sukzessiven Approximation[en], schrittweisen Näherung)	méthode *f* itérative (par itérations), procédé *m* (méthode) d'itération, méthode des approximations successives	итерационный метод, метод итераций, метод последовательных приближений
I 1230	**iterative method for eigenvalue problems,** Engesser-Vianello method <DE>	Iterationsverfahren *n*, Engesser-Vianello-Verfahren *n*	méthode *f* itérative [d'Engesser-Vianello] <pour les problèmes aux valeurs propres>	итерационный метод при задачах на собственные значения
	iterative step <AN, NU> NU>	*s.* I 1224		
	***i*-th column expansion** <MD>	*s.* E 706		
I 1231	**Ivory['s] theorem** <for conics> <AY>	Satz *m* von Ivory, Ivoryscher Satz	théorème *m* d'Ivory	теорема Ивори
I 1232	**Iwasawa decomposition** <of a group> <GR>	Iwasawasche (Iwasawa-Mostowsche) Zerlegung *f*	décomposition *f* d'Iwasawa-Mostow, décomposition d'Iwasawa	разложение Ивазавы

J

	English	German	French	Russian
	Jackson['s] approximation theorems <AN, AX>	*s.* J 3		
J 1	**Jackson['s] integral,** Jackson['s] singular integral <AN>	Jacksonsches singuläres Integral *n*	intégrale *f* [singulière] de Jackson	особый (сингулярный) интеграл Джексона
J 2	**Jackson['s] kernel** <IE>	Jacksonscher Kern *m*	noyau *m* de Jackson	ядро Джексона
	Jackson['s] singular integral <AN>	*s.* J 1		
J 3	**Jackson['s] theorems,** Jackson['s] approximation theorems, approximation theorems of Jackson <AN, AX>	Jacksonsche Approximationssätze (Sätze) *mpl,* Sätze (Approximationssätze) von [T.] Jackson	théorèmes *mpl* [d'approximation] de Jackson	теоремы о приближении Джексона, аппроксимационные теоремы Джексона
	Jacobi['s] algorithm <NT>	*s.* J 6		
J 4	**Jacobian** <of a web generated by 4 algebraic surfaces> <AG>	Jacobische Fläche *f,* Kernfläche *f*	surface *f* jacobienne (de Jacobi, nodale)	якобиева поверхность
J 5	**Jacobian,** Jacobian determinant, functional determinant <AN>	Funktionaldeterminante *f,* Jacobische Determinante (Funktionaldeterminante) *f,* alternierende Differentialfunktion *f* <Cauchy>	jacobien *m,* déterminant *m* fonctionnel (fonctionnel de Jacobi, de Jacobi)	якобиан, функциональный определитель [Якоби], определитель Якоби
	Jacobian <AG>	*s.* 1. J 9; 2. J 14		
J 6	**Jacobian algorithm,** Jacobi['s] algorithm, Jacobi['s] continued fraction algorithm, Jacobi-Perron algorithm <NT>	Jacobischer Algorithmus (Kettenbruchalgorithmus) *m,* Jacobis Kettenbruchalgorithmus, Jacobisches Verfahren *n,* Jacobi-Kettenalgorithmus *m,* Jacobi-Perronscher Algorithmus	algorithme *m* de Jacobi (Jacobi-Perron)	алгоритм Якоби-Перрона
	Jacobian amplitude <FT, FU>	*s.* A 605		
J 7	**Jacobian continued fraction** <NT>	Jacobi-Kettenbruch *m,* Jacobischer Kettenbruch *m*	fraction *f* continue de Jacobi	непрерывная дробь Якоби
J 8	**Jacobian covariant** <IV>	Jacobische Kovariante *f*	covariant *m* jacobien (de Jacobi)	ковариант Якоби
J 9	**Jacobian curve,** Jacobian <of a web of curves> <AG>	Jacobische Kurve *f,* Jacobiana *f,* Jacobischer Ort *m*	courbe *f* jacobienne, jacobienne *f*	якобиева кривая
	Jacobian determinant <AN>	*s.* J 5		
J 10	**Jacobian [elliptic] function,** Jacobi['s] elliptic function <of module *k*> <FU>	Jacobische elliptische Funktion *f,* Jacobische Funktion <mit dem Modul *k*>	fonction *f* elliptique de Jacobi, fonction de Jacobi <à module *k*>	эллиптическая функция Якоби, функция Якоби <с модулем *k*>
	Jacobian function <FT, FU>	*s.* I 752		
J 11	**Jacobi-Anger['s] formula** <for Bessel functions> <FU>	Jacobi-Angersche Formel *f*	formule *f* de Jacobi-Anger	формула Якоби-Ангера
	Jacobian interpolation node <AX, FD, NU>	*s.* J 12		
	Jacobian matrix <AN>	*s.* F 746		
J 12	**Jacobian node,** Jacobian interpolation node <AX, FD, NU>	Jacobi-Knoten *m,* Jacobischer Interpolationsknoten (Knoten) *m*	nœud *m* jacobien	якобиев узел, якобиева узловая точка
J 13	**Jacobian system,** Jacobi['s] system <of linear partial differential equations> <DE>	Jacobisches System *n*	système *m* jacobien	якобиева система
J 14	**Jacobian variety, jacobian variety,** Jacobi['s] variety, Jacobian <AG>	Jacobische Mannigfaltigkeit *f*	variété *f* jacobienne (de Jacobi), jacobienne *f*	якобиево многообразие
J 15	**Jacobian zeta function, Jacobian Z-function,** zeta function of Jacobi, Z-function of Jacobi, Jacobi['s] zeta function, Jacobi['s] Z-function, Z, zn <FU>	Zetafunktion (ζ-Funktion) *f* von Jacobi, Jacobische Zetafunktion (ζ-Funktion), zn	fonction *f* zêta (Z) de Jacobi, fonction de Jacobi de seconde espèce, Z, zn	дзета-функция (ζ-функция) Якоби, zn
J 16	**Jacobi['s] bracket** <of two functions> <DE>	Jacobische Klammer *f,* Jacobischer Klammerausdruck *m,* Mayersche Klammer	crochet *m* de Jacobi	скобка Якоби, скобка Майера
J 17	**Jacobi['s] canonical form** <of a matrix> <MD>	kanonische Normalform *f*	forme *f* canonique de Jacobi	каноническая нормальная форма
	Jacobi['s] complete integral <DE>	*s.* C 1444		
	Jacobi['s] continued fraction algorithm <NT>	*s.* J 6		
J 18	**Jacobi['s] criterion** <DI>	Jacobisches Kriterium *n,* Kriterium von Jacobi	critère *m* de Jacobi	критерий Якоби
	Jacobi['s] differential equation <DE>	*s.* J 19		

No.	English	German	French	Russian
	Jacobi['s] differential equation <VA>	*s.* J 20		
	Jacobi['s] elliptic function <FU>	*s.* J 10		
19	**Jacobi['s] equation,** Jacobi['s] differential equation <DE>	Jacobische Differentialgleichung (Gleichung) *f*	équation *f* (équation différentielle) de Jacobi	уравнение Якоби, дифференциальное уравнение Якоби
20	**Jacobi['s] equation,** Jacobi['s] differential equation <VA>	Jacobische (akzessorische) Differentialgleichung *f*, Variationsgleichung *f*	équation *f* differéntielle de Jacobi	дифференциальное уравнение Якоби, уравнение Якоби
	Jacobi['s] eta-function <FU>	*s.* H 294		
	Jacobi['s] function <FT, FU>	*s.* I 752		
	Jacobi['s] H-function <FU>	*s.* H 294		
21	**Jacobi['s] identity,** Jacobi['s] relation <AL>	Jacobische Identität *f*, Identität von Jacobi	identité *f* de Jacobi	тождество Якоби
22	**Jacobi['s] identity** <of three functions> <DE>	Jacobische Identität *f*, [A.] Mayersche Identität *f*	identité *f* de Jacobi	тождество Якоби (Майера)
23	**Jacobi['s] inversion problem** <FT>	Jacobisches Umkehrproblem *n*, Umkehrproblem von Jacobi	problème *m* de l'inversion de Jacobi	задача обращения Якоби
24	**Jacobi-Liouville formula** <DE>	Jacobi-Liouvillesche Formel *f*, Jacobische Formel	formule *f* de Jacobi-Liouville	формула Якоби-Лиувилля
	Jacobi['s] matrix <MD>	*s.* T 934		
25	**Jacobi['s] method** <for determination of characteristic values> <NU>	Jacobisches Verfahren *n*, Jacobi-Verfahren *n*	méthode *f* de Jacobi	метод Якоби
26	**Jacobi['s] method [of integration]** <DE>	Jacobische Integrationsmethode *f*, Integrationsmethode von Jacobi, Jacobische Methode *f*, Methode von Jacobi	méthode *f* [d'intégration] de Jacobi	метод [интегрирования] Якоби
27	**Jacobi['s] multiplier** <DE>	Jacobischer Multiplikator *m*	multiplicateur *m* de Jacobi	множитель Якоби
	Jacobi-Perron algorithm <NT>	*s.* J 6		
28	**Jacobi['s] polynomial,** hypergeometric polynomial <FU>	Jacobisches Polynom *n*, Jacobi-Polynom *n*, hypergeometrisches Polynom	polynôme *m* de Jacobi, polynôme hypergéométrique	многочлен Якоби, гипергеометрический многочлен
	Jacobi['s] relation <AL>	*s.* J 21		
29	**Jacobi['s] resolvent** <AL>	Jacobische Resolvente *f*	résolvante *f* de Jacobi, résolvante jacobienne	резольвента Якоби
30	**Jacobi['s] rotation** <MD, NU>	Jacobi-Rotation *f*, Jacobi-Drehung *f*	rotation *f* jacobienne	вращение Якоби
31	**Jacobi['s] sufficient condition,** sufficient condition of Jacobi <VA>	Jacobische S-Bedingung *f*, S-Bedingung von Jacobi, verschärfte (starke) Jacobische Bedingung *f*	condition *f* suffisante de Jacobi	достаточное (сильное) условие Якоби
32	**Jacobi['s] sum** <AB>	Faktorensystem *n* der Gaußschen Summe, Jacobische Summe *f*	somme *f* de Jacobi	сумма Якоби
	Jacobi-Sylvester Inertia Theorem <AL>	*s.* L 191		
33	**Jacobi['s] symbol** <NT>	Jacobisches Symbol *n*, Jacobi-Symbol *n*, Jacobis Symbol	symbole *m* de Jacobi (Legendre-Jacobi)	символ Якоби
	Jacobi['s] system <DE>	*s.* J 13		
34	**Jacobi['s] theorem** <in least squares method> <AX, NU>	Jacobisches Theorem *n*	théorème *m* de Jacobi	теорема Якоби
35	**Jacobi['s] theorem** <VA>	Jacobischer Fundamentalsatz *m*, Jacobischer Satz *m*, Satz von Jacobi	théorème *m* de Jacobi	теорема Якоби
36	**Jacobi['s] theta function,** elliptic theta-function, theta function, ϑ-function <of the first, second, third *or* fourth kind> <FU>	Jacobische Theta-Funktion *f*, elliptische Theta-Funktion, Theta-Funktion [von Jacobi], ϑ-Funktion *f* [von Jacobi] <erster, zweiter, dritter *oder* vierter Art>	fonction *f* thêta de Jacobi, fonction thêta [jacobienne], fonction ϑ [jacobienne] <du premier, deuxième, troisième *ou* quatrième genre>	тэта-функция Якоби, якобиева тэта-функция, тэта-функция, ϑ-функция <первого, второго, третьего *или* четвертого рода>
	Jacobi['s] variety <AG>	*s.* J 14		
	Jacobi['s] zeta (ζ-) function <FU>	*s.* J 15		
37	**Jacobson['s] radical** <of a ring> <AL>	Jacobson-Radikal *n*, Jacobsonsches Radikal *n*	radical *m* de Jacobson	радикал Джекобсона, джекобсоновский радикал
38	**Jacobson['s] ring,** Hilbert['s] ring, Hilbertian ring <AL>	Jacobsonscher Ring *m*	anneau *m* de Jacobson (Hilbert)	кольцо Джекобсона (Гильберта)
39	**Jacobson['s] schema** <AG>	Jacobsonsches Schema *n*	schéma *m* de Jacobson	схема Джекобсона
40	**Jacobson['s] space** <TO>	Jacobson-Raum *m*, Jacobsonscher Raum *m*	espace *m* de Jacobson	пространство Джекобсона
41	**Jacobson['s] topology** <AL>	Jacobsonsche Topologie *f*	topologie *f* de Jacobson	топология Джекобсона
	Jacobson-Witt algebra <AL>	*s.* W 282		

No.	English	German	French	Russian
J 42	**Janiszewski['s] space** <TO>	Janiszewskischer Raum *m*	espace *m* de Janiszewski	пространство Янишевского
J 43	**J-antisymmetric element** <AL>	J-antisymmetrisches Element *n*	élément *m* J-antisymétrique	J-антисимметрический элемент
J 44	**Janzen['s] area** <ME>	Janzensches Maß *n*	aire *f* de Janzen	площадь Янцена
J 45	**Japanese homomorphism** <AT>	japanischer Homomorphismus *m*	« Japanese homomorphism » *m*, homomorphisme *m* japonais	японский гомоморфизм
J 46	**Japanese ring** <AL>	japanischer Ring *m*	anneau *m* japonais	японское кольцо
J 47	**Jensen['s] function** <AP>	Jensensche Funktion *f*	fonction *f* de Jensen	функция Иенсена
J 48	**Jensen['s] inequality** <CS, FT>	Jensensche Ungleichung *f*	inégalité *f* de Jensen	неравенство Иенсена
J 49	**Jensen['s] theorem** <FT>	Jensenscher Satz *m*, Satz von Jensen-Nevanlinna, Jensen-Nevanlinnascher Satz	théorème *m* de Jensen	теорема Иенсена
J 50	**Jerabek['s] hyperbola** <in a triangle> <EG>	Jerabeksche (Jerabeks) Hyperbel *f*, Jerabeks Kurve *f*	hyperbole *f* de Jérabek (Jerabek), courbe *f* de Jérabek	гипербола Ерабека
J 51	**Jerrard['s] theorem** <on the equation of fifth order> <AL>	Jerrards (Jerrardscher) Satz *m*	théorème *m* de Jerrard	теорема Жеррара
J 52	**jet** <DG>	Jet *m*	jet *m*	струя
	Jeu de Taquin <CT>	*s.* B 620		
J 53	***J*-limit, *J*-lim** <LI>	*J*-Limes *m*, Limes *m* nach dem *J*-Verfahren, *J*-lim	*J*-limite *f*, *J*-lim	обобщенный предел по *J*-методу, *J*-предел, *J*-lim
J 54	***J*-limitable sequence** <LI>	*J*-limitierbare Folge *f*, nach dem *J*-Verfahren limitierbare Folge	suite *f* *J*-limitable	последовательность, лимитируемая *J*-методом
	J-matrix <MD>	*s.* T 934		
J 55	***J*-method,** *J*-method of summation, method [of summation] by means defined by integral functions <for series> <LI>	*J*-Verfahren *n*, Summierungsverfahren *n* mittels ganzer Funktionen	méthode *f* [de sommation] par moyennes définies par les fonctions entières	*J*-метод [суммирования]; метод суммирования средними, определенными целыми функциями
J 56	***J*-method of limitation,** method of limitation by means defined by integral functions <for sequences> <LI>	*J*-Verfahren *n*, Limitierungsverfahren *n* mittels ganzer Funktionen	méthode *f* de limitation par moyennes définies par les fonctions entières	*J*-метод [образования обобщенного предела], метод образования обобщенного предела средними, определенными целыми функциями
	***J*-method of summation** <LI>	*s.* J 55		
J 57	**Joachimsthal['s] surface** <DG>	Joachimsthalsche Fläche *f*	surface *f* de Joachimsthal	поверхность Иоахимсталя
J 58	**Joachimsthal['s] theorem** <AY, DG>	Joachimsthalscher Satz *m*	théorème *m* de Joachimsthal	теорема Иоахимсталя
J 59	**join,** sum, Boolean join <in lattices> <LA>	[verbandstheoretische] Vereinigung *f*	union *f*, borne *f* supérieure	объединение, точная верхняя грань
J 60	**join** <of equivalence relations> <UA>	Vereinigung *f*	réunion *f*	объединение
	join <SE>	*s.* 1. L 252; 2. U 201; 3. U 202		
J 61	**join-homomorphic image** <LA>	vereinigungshomomorphes Bild *n*	image *f* $\cup$-homomorphe	образ при гомоморфизме по объединению
J 62	**join-homomorphism, join homomorphism,** upper hemitropism <of the subgroup lattice> <GR>	Vereinigungshomomorphismus *m*, $\cup$-Homomorphismus *m* <des Untergruppenverbands>	$\cup$-homomorphisme *m* <du treillis des sous-groupes>	гомоморфизм по объединению <структуры подгрупп>
J 63	**join-homomorphism, join homomorphism** <LA>	Vereinigungshomomorphismus *m*, $\cup$-Homomorphismus *m*	$\cup$-homomorphisme *m*, $\vee$-homomorphisme *m*, $\cup$-morphisme *m*, $\vee$-morphisme *m*, homomorphisme *m* de jonction	гомоморфизм по объединению
J 64	**join-independence, join independence** <LA>	Vereinigungsunabhängigkeit *f*	$\cup$-indépendance *f*	$\cup$-независимость
	joining a superfluous universal quantifier <LO>	*s.* J 67		
J 65	**joining the existential quantifier to the antecedent,** introduction of the existential quantifier in the antecedent <LO>	vordere Partikularisierung *f*, Es-gibt-Einführung (Existenzeinführung) *f* im Antezedens	introduction *f* du quantificateur existentiel dans l'antécédent	$\exists$-введение в антецеденте, введение квантора существования в антецеденте
J 66	**joining the existential quantifier to the consequent,** introduction of the existential quantifier in the succedent <LO>	hintere Partikularisierung *f*, Es-gibt-Einführung *f* im Sukzedens, Existenzeinführung *f* im Sukzedens	introduction *f* du quantificateur existentiel dans le conséquent	$\exists$-введение в сукцеденте, введение квантора существования в сукцеденте
J 67	**joining the universal quantifier,** joining a superfluous universal quantifier <LO>	Alleinführung *f*	liaison *f* par quantificateur universel	$\forall$-введение, введение квантора общности
J 68	**joining the universal quantifier to the antecedent,** introduction of the universal quantifier in the antecedent <LO>	vordere Generalisierung *f*, Alleinführung *f* im Antezedens	introduction *f* du quantificateur universel dans l'antécédent	$\forall$-введение в антецеденте, введение квантора общности в антецеденте

No.	English	German	French	Russian
69	**joining the universal quantifier to the consequent,** introduction of the universal quantifier in the succedent <LO>	hintere Generalisierung *f*, Alleinführung *f* im Sukzedens	introduction *f* du quantificateur universel dans le conséquent	∀-введение в сукцеденте, введение квантора общности в сукцеденте
70	**join-irreducible element,** join irreducible element, ∪-irreducible element <of a lattice> <LA>	vereinigungsirreduzibles (∪-irreduzibles) Element *n*	élément *m* sup-irréductible (∪-irréductible, ∨-irréductible, irréductible par rapport à la jonction)	∪-неприводимый (неприводимый, ∪-неразложимый) элемент; элемент, неразложимый в объединение
71	**join-isomorphic mapping, join-isomorphism, join isomorphism** <AL, SE>	Vereinigungsisomorphismus *m*	∪-isomorphisme *m*, ∨-isomorphisme *m*	изоморфизм по объединению
	join of a complex with a point <AT>	*s.* C 1849		
	join of a point and a simplex <AT>	*s.* C 1850		
72	**join-preserving mapping** <of quasi-ordered sets> <SE>	Vereinigungshomomorphismus *m*	application *f* préservant l'union	отображение, сохраняющее объединение
73	**join-reducible element** <LA>	vereinigungsreduzibles (∪-reduzibles) Element *n*	élément *m* sup-réductible (∪-réductible)	∪-разложимый (∪-приводимый) элемент
	join-semilattice, join semilattice <AL>	*s.* U 436		
J 74	**join-stable,** closed under the union operation <SE>	abgeschlossen gegenüber Vereinigungsmengenbildung	fermé par les réunions	замкнутый относительно объединений
J 75	**joint consistency theorem** <FO>	Satz *m* über die gemeinsame Widerspruchsfreiheit	théorème *m* de la consistance conjointe	теорема о совместной непротиворечивости
	joint denial <LO>	*s.* S 2439		
	joint distribution <ST>	*s.* 1. B 480; 2. J 76; 3. M 1088		
J 76	**joint probability distribution,** joint distribution <ST>	gemeinsame Wahrscheinlichkeitsverteilung (Verteilung) *f*	distribution *f* de probabilités conjointe, distribution conjointe	совместное распределение [вероятностей]
J 77	**joint satisfiability** <LO>	gemeinsame Erfüllbarkeit *f*	satisfiabilité *f* commune	совместная выполнимость
J 78	**joint sufficient estimator** <ST>	gemeinsame erschöpfende Schätzfunktion *f*	estimateur *m* exhaustif conjoint	совместная достаточная оценка
J 79	**Jonquières['] domain** <PJ>	Jonquièressches Gebiet *n*	domain *m* de Jonquières	область Жонкьера
J 80	**Jonquières['] group,** de Jonquières['] group <AG>	Jonquièressche Gruppe *f*	groupe *m* de Jonquières	группа Жонкьера
J 81	**Jonquières['] transformation,** de Jonquières['] transformation <AG>	Jonquièressche Transformation *f*	transformation *f* de Jonquières	преобразование Жонкьера
J 82	**Jordan['s] algebra** <AL>	Jordan-Algebra *f*, Jordanalgebra *f*, Jordansche Algebra *f*	algèbre *f* de Jordan	жорданова алгебра, алгебра Жордана, // йорданова алгебра
	Jordan['s] arc <TO>	*s.* J 86		
J 83	**Jordan['s] automorphism,** semi-automorphism <of a ring> <AL>	Jordan-Automorphismus *m*, Semiautomorphismus *m*	automorphisme *m* de Jordan, semi-automorphisme *m*	жорданов автоморфизм, полуавтоморфизм
	Jordan['s] block <AL>	*s.* J 94		
J 84	**Jordan-Brouwer [separation] theorem,** Brouwer['s] generalization of the Jordan curve theorem <TO>	Jordan-Brouwerscher Satz *m*	théorème *m* de Jordan-Brouwer	теорема Жордана-Брауэра (Жордана-Броуэра), брауэровское обобщение теоремы Жордана о кривых
J 85	**Jordan canonical form theorem** <AL>	Satz *m* von der Existenz der Jordanschen Normalform	théorème *m* de la forme de Jordan	теорема о жордановой нормальной форме
	Jordan['s] content <ME>	*s.* C 2158		
J 86	**Jordan['s] curve,** simple arc, Jordan['s] arc, simple Jordan curve, simple continuous arc <TO>	Jordan-Kurve *f*, Jordansche Kurve *f*, Jordan-Bogen *m*, einfacher (Jordanscher) Kurvenbogen *m*, Bogen *m*, einfache offene Kurve	courbe *f* (arc *m*) de Jordan, arc de Jordan simple, ligne *f* de Jordan, courbe jordanienne, arc	кривая Жордана, жорданова кривая, кривая в смысле Жордана, простая дуга [кривой], жорданова дуга [кривой], простая незамкнутая кривая
	Jordan['s] curve <TO>	*s.* S 894		
	Jordan['s] curve theorem <TO>	*s.* J 103		
J 87	**Jordan-Dedekind chain condition** <AL, SE>	Jordan-Dedekindsche Kettenbedingung *f*	condition *f* de chaîne de Jordan-Dedekind, condition de Jordan-Dedekind	условие Жордана-Дедекинда
	┌<SS> **Jordan-Dirichlet test**	*s.* D 626		
J 88	**Jordan['s] division algebra** <AL>	Jordan-Körper *m*	algèbre *f* de Jordan à division	жорданово тело, // йорданово тело
J 89	**Jordan['s] domain,** Jordan['s] region <TO>	Jordanscher Bereich *m*, Jordan-Bereich *m*, Jordanbereich *m*	disque *m*, domaine *m* de Jordan	жорданова область
	Jordan['s] form <AL>	*s.* J 94		
J 90	**Jordan-Hölder[-Schreier] theorem,** theorem of Jordan-Hölder-Schreier-Zassenhaus <on composition series> <AL>	Satz *m* von Jordan-Hölder, Jordan-Hölderscher Satz	théorème *m* de Jordan-Hölder	теорема Жордана-Гельдера, теорема Жордана-Гельдера-Шрейера
J 91	**Jordan['s] homomorphism** <of a ring> <AL>	Jordan-Homomorphismus *m*	homomorphisme *m* de Jordan	жорданов гомоморфизм

No.	English	German	French	Russian
	Jordanian canonical form <MD>	*s.* J 99		
J 92	**Jordan['s] identity** <AL>	Jordansche Identität *f*	identité *f* de Jordan	жорданово тождество
J 93	**Jordan['s] lemma** <FT>	Lemma *n* von Jordan, Jordansches Lemma	lemme *m* de Jordan	лемма Жордана
J 94	**Jordan['s] matrix,** simple classical matrix, matrix in Jordan form, elementary Jordan matrix, Jordan['s] block, reduced matrix, Jordan['s] normal form, Jordan['s] form <AL>	Jordan-Matrix *f*, Jordansche Matrix *f*, Matrix *f* in Jordanscher Normalform	matrice (réduite) *f* de Jordan, matrice réduite [de Jordan]	клетка Жордана, жорданова матрица, жорданов ящик; матрица, имеющая жорданову форму
J 95	**Jordan matrix in lower triangular form** <of a matrix> <MD>	untere Jordan-Matrix (Tridiagonalmatrix) *f*	matrice *f* de Jordan en forme triangulaire inférieure	клетка Жордана в нижней треугольной форме
J 96	**Jordan['s] matrix in upper triangular form** <of a matrix> <MD>	obere Jordan-Matrix (Tridiagonalmatrix) *f*	matrice *f* de Jordan en forme triangulaire supérieure	клетка Жордана в верхней треугольной форме
J 97	**Jordan measurable** <ME>	Jordan-meßbar	mesurable au sens de Jordan	измеримый в смысле Жордана
	Jordan['s] measure <ME>	*s.* C 2158		
J 98	**Jordan['s] module** <AL>	Jordan-Modul *m*	module *m* de Jordan	модуль Жордана
J 99	**Jordan['s] normal form,** Jordanian canonical form, first canonical form, classical canonical form <MD>	Jordansche (dritte) Normalform *f*	forme *f* de Jordan, forme canonique (réduite) de Jordan, réduite *f* de Jordan	жорданова каноническая (нормальная) форма, нормальная (каноническая) жорданова форма, жорданова форма, нормальная форма Жордана, нормальная форма, жорданово представление
	Jordan['s] normal form <AL>	*s.* J 94		
J 100	**Jordan['s] product** <AL>	Jordan-Produkt *n*, Jordanprodukt *n*	produit *m* de Jordan	жорданово произведение
	Jordan['s] region <TO>	*s.* J 89		
J 101	**Jordan['s] representation** <AL>	Jordansche Darstellung *f*	représentation *f* de Jordan	жорданово (общее) представление <алгебры>
J 102	**Jordan['s] ring** <AL>	Jordan-Ring *m*, Jordanring *m*	anneau *m* de Jordan	жорданово кольцо, J-кольцо
J 103	**Jordan['s] [separation] theorem,** Jordan['s] curve theorem, theorem of Jordan <TO>	Jordanscher Kurvensatz *m*	théorème *m* de Jordan	теорема Жордана (Жордана о кривых, Жордана о замкнутых кривых)
J 104	**Jordan['s] variation** <of a function of one variable> <FT>	Jordan-Variation *f*	variation *f* de Jordan	вариация Жордана, жорданова вариация
J 105	**J-shaped distribution** <ST>	J-förmige Verteilung *f*	distribution *f* en J	J-образное распределение
J 106	***J*-sum** <LI>	*J*-Summe *f*, Summe *f* nach dem *J*-Verfahren	*J*-somme *f*	*J*-сумма
J 107	***J*-summable series** <LI>	*J*-summierbare Reihe *f*, nach dem *J*-Verfahren summierbare Reihe	série *f J*-sommable	*J*-суммируемый ряд
J 108	**J-symmetric element** <AL>	J-symmetrisches Element *n*	élément *m* J-symétrique	J-симметрический элемент
J 109	**judg[e]ment** <affirming or denying a proposition> <LO>	Urteil *n*	jugement *m*	суждение
	judg[e]ment <LO>	*s.* P 1865		
	judg[e]ment sampling <ST>	*s.* P 2075		
	Julia['s] direction <FT>	*s.* D 571		
J 110	**Julia['s] exceptional function,** exceptional function in the sense of Julia <FT>	Juliasche Ausnahmefunktion *f*	fonction *f* exceptionnelle [au sens] de Julia	исключительная функция [в смысле] Жюлия
	Julia['s] manifold <FA>	*s.* J 112		
J 111	**Julia['s] operator** <FA>	Juliascher Operator *m*	opérateur *m* de Julia	оператор Жюлия
J 112	**Julia['s] variety,** Julia['s] manifold <in a Hilbert space> <FA>	Juliasche Mannigfaltigkeit *f*	variété *f* de Julia	многообразие Жюлия
J 113	**jump** <in a linear system of subgroups of a loop, in metamathematics, *or* in Dedekind's cut> <AL, MM, SE>	Sprung *m*	saut *m*	скачок
J 114	**jump** <of a function> <AN, TO>	Sprung *m*, // Unstetigkeitssprung *m*	saut *m*	скачок
J 115	**jump discontinuity,** point of jump discontinuity, ordinary discontinuity <DI>	Sprungstelle *f*, Sprungpunkt *m*, Unstetigkeitsstelle *f* (Unstetigkeitspunkt *m*) mit Sprung	point *m* de saut [fini], point de discontinuité à saut [fini]	точка скачка (разрыва с конечным скачком)
J 116	**jump discontinuity** <property> <DI>	Unstetigkeit *f* durch Sprung	discontinuité *f* à (par) saut [fini]	разрыв со (с конечным) скачком
	jump function <AN>	*s.* S 1746		
J 117	**jump method** <AN, NU>	Sprungstellenverfahren *n*	méthode *f* des sauts	метод [А. Н.] Крылова
	junction <GP>	*s.* V 156		
	junction point <GP>	*s.* N 275		
J 118	**Jung['s] circle** <GE>	Jungscher Kreis *m*	cercle (disque) *m* de Jung	окружность Юнга
J 119	**Jung['s] theorem** <on convex bodies> <GE>	Jungscher Satz *m*	théorème *m* de Jung	теорема Юнга
J 120	**justifiable** <LO>	rechtfertigbar	justifiable	обосноваемый
	justification <GN>	*s.* F 502		

J 121	**justification theorem, justifying theorem** <FO>	Rechtfertigungssatz *m*	théorème *m* de légitimation	теорема узаконения
J 122	**just non-Cross variety,** almost-Cross variety <of groups> <UA>	Fast-Cross-Varietät *f*	variété *f* presque de Cross	почти-кроссово многообразие
J 123	**juxtaposition** <LO, NT>	Nebeneinandersetzen *n*, Nebeneinanderschreiben *n*, Nebensetzung *f*, Juxtaposition *f*	juxtaposition *f*	соединение, запись (помещение) рядом, сопоставление

K

K 1	***k*-abundant number** <NT>	*k*-abundante Zahl *f*	nombre *m* *k*-abondant	*k*-избыточное число
K 2	***k*-adic fraction** <NT>	*k*-adischer Bruch *m*	fraction *f* *k*-adique	*k*-ная [систематическая] дробь, *k*-ичная [систематическая] дробь
	Kaehlerian structure <DG>	*s.* K 4		
K 3	**Kähler['s] differential form** <DG>	Kählersche Differentialform *f*	forme *f* de Kähler	кэлерова дифференциальная форма
K 4	**Kählerian structure,** Kaehlerian structure <DG>	kählersche Struktur *f*	structure *f* kählérienne	кэлерова структура
K 5	**Kähler['s] manifold** <DG>	kählersche (Kählersche) Mannigfaltigkeit *f*	variété *f* kählérienne	кэлерово многообразие
K 6	**Kähler['s] metric** <DG>	kählersche (Kählersche) Metrik *f*	métrique *f* kählérienne	кэлерова метрика
	Kakeya-Eneström theorem <AL, FT>	*s.* E 239		
	***K*-algebra** <AL>	*s.* A 477		
K 7	**Kamke-Waring problem** <NT>	Kamke-Waringsches Problem *n*	problème *m* de Kamke-Waring	проблема Камке-Варинга
K 8	**kampyle of Eudoxus,** curve of Eudoxus <AG>	Kampyla *f* des Eudoxus, Kampyle *f* des Eudoxus	kampule *f* d'Eudoxe	кривая, имеющая уравнение $y^4 = a^2(x^2 + y^2)$
K 9	**Kan['s] complex** <CA>	Kan-Komplex *m*	complexe *m* de Kan	полное симплициальное множество
K 10	**Kan['s] condition** <CA>	Kan-Bedingung *f*	condition *f* de Kan	условие Кана
K 11	**Kan['s] construction** <CA>	Kan-Konstruktion *f*	construction *f* de Kan	конструкция Кана
K 12	**Kan['s] extension** <CA>	Kan-Erweiterung *f*	extension *f* de Kan	расширение Кана
K 13	***k*-anisotropic algebraic group** <AG>	*k*-anisotrope algebraische Gruppe *f*	groupe *m* algébrique *k*-anisotrope	*k*-анизотропная алгебраическая группа
K 14	**Kantor-Hervey point** <GE>	Kantor-Hervey-Punkt *m*	point *m* de Kantor-Hervey	точка Кантора-Хервея
K 15	**Kantor['s] line** <EG>	Kantor-Gerade *f*	droite *f* de [S.] Kantor	прямая Кантора
K 16	**Kantorovich['s] method of solution factor[s], Kantorovich['s] method of solving multipliers,** method of solution factors, method of solving multipliers <PG>	[Kantorowitschsche] Methode *f* der Auflösungsmultiplikatoren (lösenden Faktoren)	méthode *f* des multiplicateurs solvants [de Kantorovitch]	метод разрешающих множителей Канторовича
K 17	**Kantorovich['s] method of summands** <PG>	Kantorowitschsche Summandenmethode *f*	méthode *f* des termes additionnables de Kantorovitch	метод слагаемых Канторовича
	Kantorovich-space, Kantorovich['s] space <FA>	*s.* K 187		
K 18	**Kantor['s] point** <EG>	Kantor-Punkt *m*, Kantorpunkt *m*	point *m* de Kantor	точка Кантора
K 19	**Kaplansky['s] density theorem** <FA>	Kaplanskyscher Dichtigkeitssatz *m*	théorème *m* de densité de Kaplansky	теорема Капланского
	Kaplansky['s] theorem <AL>	*s.* T 301		
K 20	**kappa curve,** kappa <AG>	Kappakurve *f*, Quartik *f* von G. van Gutshoven, Gutschoven-Kurve *f*, Gutschovenkurve *f*, Gutschovensche Quartik *f*	courbe *f* de Gutschoven, courbe kappa, cappa *m*	каппа, кривая каппа <график $x^4 + x^2y^2 = a^2y^2$ >
K 21	**Kapteyn['s] integral,** Kapteyn['s] trigonometric integral <FU>	Kapteyns[ches] trigonometrisches Integral *n*	intégrale *f* de Kapteyn, intégrale trigonométrique de Kapteyn	интеграл Каптейна, тригонометрический интеграл Каптейна
K 22	**Kapteyn['s] series** <FU>	Kapteynsche Reihe *f*	série *f* de Kapteyn	ряд Каптейна
	Kapteyn['s] trigonometric integral <FU>	*s.* K 21		
K 23	***k*-arc connected graph** <GP>	*k*-fach bogenzusammenhängender (bezüglich der Bögen zusammenhängender) Graph *m*	graphe *m* *k*-arc-connexe	*k*-дугово-связный граф
K 24	**Karhunen representation** <ST>	Karhunen-Darstellung *f*	représentation *f* de Karhunen	представление Карунена
K 25	**Karnaugh map** <LO>	Karnaugh-Diagramm *n*, Karnaugh-Tafel *f*, K-Diagramm *n*, KD *n*	diagramme *m* de Karnaugh	карта Карнау
	karoubian category <CA>	*s.* P 1898		
	***k*-arrangement of *n* elements** <CT>	*s.* A 984		
K 26	**Kasner circle** <FT>	Kasner-Kreis *m*	cercle *m* de Kasner	окружность Казнера
K 27	**Kasner clock** <FT>	Kasner-Kreis *m* mit dem Mittelpunkt im Ursprung	cercle *m* de Kasner à son centre dans l'origine	окружность Казнера с центром в начале координат
	***k*-automorphism** <AL>	*s.* A 1233		

K 27a	**K-circle** <DG>	*K*-Kreis *m*	*K*-cercle *m*	*K*-окружность
K 28	**k-clique** <GP>	*k*-Clique *f*	*k*-clique *f*	*k*-клика
K 29	**k-combination,** sample of *k* elements without regard to order, subpopulation of *k* elements without regard to order, combination of the *k*-th class (order) <of the elements of a set> <CT>	Kombination *f* zur *k*-ten Klasse, Kombination *k*-ter Klasse (Ordnung), Kombination zu je *k*	combinaison *f k* à *k*, combinaison prise *k* à *k*, combinaison de la *k*-e classe	сочетание по *k*
K 30	**k-component** <of a *k*-set> <AG>	*k*-Komponente *f*	composante *f* sur *k*, *k*-composante *f*	неприводимая компонента над *k*
	k-connected graph <GP>	*s.* K 223		
K 31	**K-definiteness,** definiteness in Kamke's sense <DE>	K-Definitheit *f*, Kamke-Definitheit *f*	propriété *f* d'être défini au sens de Kamke	К-определенность, определенность в смысле Камке, определенность по Камке
K 32	**k-edge[-] connected graph** <GP>	*k*-fach kantenzusammenhängender (bezüglich der Kanten zusammenhängender) Graph *m*	graphe *m k*-arête-connexe, graphe *k* fois continu, assemblage *m* d'arêtes (de lignes) *k* fois continu, // graphe *k*-cohérent	*k*-реберно-связный граф
	kegly space <FA, TO>	*s.* B 67		
K 33	**Kelleyfication** <of a space> <process> <TO>	Kelleyschmachen *n*	kelleyification *f*, kelleyifier *m*	келлификация
K 34	**Kelleyfication** <of a space> <TO>	kelleysch gemachter Raum *m*	kelleyifié *m* <d'un espace>	келлификация <пространства>
K 35	**Kelley['s] space,** compactly generated Hausdorff space, compactly generated space, Hausdorff *k*-space <TO>	Kelley-Raum *m*, Kelleyscher (kompakt erzeugter Hausdorffscher) Raum	espace *m* de Kelley	каонное пространство, пространство Келли, компактно порожденное пространство, хаусдорфово *k*-пространство
K 36	**Kelley['s] topology** <TO>	Kelley-Topologie *f*	topologie *f* de Kelley	топология Келли
K 37	**Kelvin['s] function of the first kind,** bei function, bei <FU>	Kelvinsche Funktion *f* erster Art, Thomsonsche Funktion erster Art, bei-Funktion *f*, bei	fonction *f* de Kelvin de première espèce, fonction bei, bei	первая функция Томсона, функция Томсона нулевого порядка первого рода bei, функция bei, bei
K 38	**Kelvin['s] function of the second kind,** ber function, ber <FU>	Kelvinsche Funktion *f* zweiter Art, Thomsonsche Funktion zweiter Art, ber-Funktion *f*, ber	fonction *f* de Kelvin de seconde espèce, fonction ber, ber	вторая функция Томсона, функция Томсона нулевого порядка первого рода ber, функция ber, ber
K 39	**Kelvin['s] transformation,** Thomson['s] transformation <PO>	Kelvin-Transformation *f*, Thomson-Transformation *f*	transformation *f* de Kelvin (Thomson)	преобразование Кельвина, преобразование Томсона
	Kelvin['s] transformation <DI, VT>	*s.* S 1815		
K 40	**Kempe['s] curve** <GE>	Kempesche Kurve *f*	courbe *f* de Kempe	кривая Кемпе
K 41	**Kendall['s] coefficient of concordance,** coefficient of concordance, rank concordance coefficient <ST>	Kendallscher Konkordanzkoeffizient *m*, Konkordanzkoeffizient, Rangkonkordanzkoeffizient *m*	coefficient *m* de concordance de Kendall, coefficient de concordance, coefficient de concordance des rangs	коэффициент согласия Кендалла, коэффициент согласия, коэффициент рангового согласия
K 42	**Kendall['s] rank correlation coefficient** <ST>	Kendallscher Rangkorrelationskoeffizient *m*	coefficient *m* de corrélation [des rangs] de Kendall, coefficient de corrélation de rangs	коэффициент ранговой корреляции Кендалла
	Kepler['s] polyhedron <EG>	*s.* K 44		
K 43	**Kepler['s] rule,** prismoidal formula <for the volume of a solid> <EG, NU>	Simpsonsche Formel *f*	formule *f* de Simpson	формула Симпсона <для объемов тел>
	Kepler['s] rule <DI, NU>	*s.* S 1008		
K 44	**Kepler['s] solid,** Kepler['s] polyhedron <EG>	Keplerscher Körper *m*	solide *m* de Kepler, polyèdre *m* de Kepler	кеплерово тело, кеплеров многогранник, тело Кеплера
K 45	**ker-coker sequence;** snake lemma <CA, HA>	Ker-Koker-Sequenz *f*	diagramme *m* serpentin	змеевидная диаграмма
K 46	**Kern** <of three natural numbers> <NT>	Kern *m* <Dedekind>	noyau *m*	ядро
K 47	**kernel** <of a semigroup> <AL>	Kerngruppe *f*, Suschkewitschsche Kerngruppe, Suschkewitsch-Kern *m*, Kern *m* <einer Halbgruppe>	noyau *m* <d'un demi-groupe>	ядро <полугруппы>
K 48	**kernel** <e.g. of a homomorphism *or* linear map *or* an order homomorphism> <AL, CA, PO, SE>	Kern *m*	noyau *m*	ядро
K 49	**kernel** <of a graph> <GP>	Kern *m*, Nukleus *m*	noyau *m*	ядро
K 50	**kernel,** kernel function, integral kernel, nucleus <of an integral equation *or* an integral> <IE>	Kern *m*, Kernfunktion *f*, Integralkern *m*	noyau *m*, fonction-noyau *m*, noyau intégral, fonction *f* d'influence	ядро, керн-функция, функция влияния
	kernel <AL, FA>	*s.* N 797		
	kernel <CA>	*s.* E 327		
	kernel <FA>	*s.* S 1428		
	kernel <IE>	*s.* F 595		
	kernel <SE, UA>	*s.* I 393		
	kernel <TG>	*s.* P 318		
	kernel congruence <AL>	*s.* C 1929		
	kernel equivalence <SE, UA>	*s.* I 393		

K 51	**kernel function** <FT>	Kernfunktion *f*	fonction *f* noyau	керн-функция
	kernel function <FT>	*s.* B 195		
	kernel function <IE>	*s.* K 50		
K 52	**kernel matrix** <FA, IE>	Kernmatrix *f*	matrice *f* noyau	керн-матрица
K 53	**kernel of a derivation** <in a ring> <AL>	Konstantenring *m* einer Derivation	anneau *m* des constantes par rapport à une dérivation	кольцо констант относительно дифференцирования
K 54	**kernel of equal measure** <of a set> <ME>	maßgleicher Kern *m*, meßbarer Kern	intérieur *m* d'égale mesure	ядро равной меры
	kernel of finite rank <IE>	*s.* D 157		
K 55	**kernel preserving functor** <CA>	Funktor *m*, der Kerne respektiert	foncteur *m* préservant les noyaux	функтор, сохраняющий ядра
K 56	**kernel series** <of an infinite product> <SS>	Kernreihe *f*	série *f* de noyau	ряд ядер
K 57	**key** <of a nomogram> <NO>	Schlüssel *m*	clef *m*	ключ
K 58	**key equation** <NO>	Schlüsselgleichung *f*	équation *f* clef	ключевое уравнение
K 59	***k*-flat** <in R^n> <GE>	*k*-dimensionale affine lineare Mannigfaltigkeit *f* <im R^n>	variété *f* affine linéaire *k*-dimensionnelle <en R^n>	*k*-мерное аффинное линейное многообразие <в R^n>
K 60	***k*-fold isotropic manifold** <DG>	*k*-fach totalisotrope Mannigfaltigkeit *f* <Pinl>, *k*-fach isotrope Mannigfaltigkeit <Lense>, isotrope Mannigfaltigkeit von *k*-ter Art <Bompiani>	variété *f* *k* fois isotrope	*k*-кратно изотропное многообразие
K 61	***k*-fold root,** *k*-tuple root, *k*-tuple zero <of a polynomial> <AL>	*k*-fache Nullstelle *f*, *k*-fache Wurzel *f*	racine *f* multiple d'ordre *k*, racine de multiplicité *k*, zéro *m* d'ordre *k*	корень кратности *k*, *k*-кратный нуль, нуль *k*-го порядка
	***k*-fold transitive group** <GR>	*s.* 1. K 143; 2. K 196		
	***k*-fold transitive permutation group** <GR>	*s.* K 143		
	***k*-fold transitive transformation group** <GR>	*s.* K 196		
K 62	***k*-free number** <NT>	*k*-freie Zahl *f*	entier *m* libre de puissance *k*-ième	число, не делящееся на *k*-ю степень
K 63	**K-functor** <AL, CA, TO>	K-Funktor *m*	foncteur *m* K	K-функтор
K 64	**K-genus** <of a variety> <AT>	K-Geschlecht *n*	K-genre *m*	K-род
	K. Gödel['s] completeness theorem <MM>	*s.* G 322		
K 65	***k*-gonal algebraic curve** <AG>	*k*-gonale (*k*-seitige) algebraische Kurve *f*	courbe *f* algébrique *k*-gonale	*k*-гональная алгебраическая кривая
K 66	**Khinchine['s] law [of large numbers]** <ST>	Chintschinsches(Khintchinesches) Gesetz *n* [der großen Zahlen], Satz *m* von Chintschin (Khintchine), Chintschinscher (Khintchinescher) Satz	loi *f* [des grands nombres] de Khintchine	закон [больших чисел] Хинчина
K 67	**Khinchine['s] principle of transfer,** // Hinčin['s] transfer principle <AX>	Chintschinsches (Khintchinesches) Übertragungsprinzip *n*	principe *m* de transfert de Khintchine	принцип перенесения Хинчина
	Khinchine['s] process <SP>	*s.* S 1679		
K 68/9	**Kiefer-Wolfowitz process** <SP>	Kiefer-Wolfowitz-Prozeß *m*	processus *m* de Kiefer-Wolfowitz	процесс Кифера-Вольфовица
K 70	**Kiepert['s] triangles** <of a triangle> <EG>	Kiepertsche Dreiecke *npl*	triangles *mpl* de Kiepert	треугольники Киперта
K 71	**Killing['s] equation** <of a Lie group> <GR>	Killingsche Gleichung *f*, charakteristische Gleichung	équation *f* de Killing	уравнение Киллинга
K 72	**Killing['s] form,** Cartan-Killing form; Cartan inner product <of a Lie algebra> <AL>	Killing-Cartansche Bilinearform *f*, bilineare Fundamentalform *f*	forme *f* de Killing, forme bilinéaire de Killing	форма Киллинга, киллингова форма
K 73	**Killing['s] theorem,** theorem of Killing <for simple Lie groups> <GR>	Killingsches Theorem *n*, Theorem von Killing	théorème *m* de Killing	теорема Киллинга
K 74	**kind** <of an arithmetical operation> <AR>	Stufe *f* <einer Rechnungsart>	rang *m*, degré *m* <d'une opération arithmétique>	ступень <арифметического действия>
K 75	**$\mathfrak{K}$-indecomposable algebra** <AL>	$\mathfrak{K}$-unzerlegbare Algebra *f*	$\mathfrak{K}$-algèbre *f* indécomposable	$\mathfrak{K}$-неразложимая алгебра
K 76	**kind of syllogism,** form of inference <LO>	Schlußweise *f*	méthode *f* de déduction	метод вывода
K 77	**kinematic density** <IG>	Bewegungsdichte *f*, kinematische Dichte *f*	densité *f* cinématique	кинематическая плотность, плотность [группы] движений
K 78	**Kirkman['s] plane,** K-plane <SG>	Kirkman-Ebene *f*	plan *m* de Kirkman	плоскость Киркмана
K 79	**Kirkman['s] point** <SG>	Kirkmanscher Punkt *m*, Kirkman-Punkt *m*	point *m* de Kirkman	точка Киркмана
K 80	**Kirkman['s] [school girl] problem** <GP>	Kirkmansches Schulmädchenproblem (Problem) *n*, Schulmädchenproblem, Kirkmans Schulmädchenproblem, Kirkmansche Aufgabe *f*, Kirkmans Problem [der 15 Schulkinder], Problem der 15 Schulkinder	problème *m* de Kirkman (T. P. Kirkman), problème des 15 demoiselles	задача Киркмана о школьницах, задача о школьницах

No.	English	German	French	Russian
	k-irreducible algebraic set <AG>	*s.* I 1038		
K 81	**k-isomorphic field,** field isomorphic over *k*, isomorphic extension of *k*, isomorphic field extension over *k*, isomorphic extension field over *k* <AL>	äquivalente Körpererweiterung (Erweiterung) *f* über *k*, äquivalenter Erweiterungskörper *m* über *k*, isomorphe Körpererweiterung über *k*	extension *f* isomorphe sur *k*, extension *k*-isomorphe	эквивалентное расширение [поля] над *k*
K 82	**k-isomorphism,** isomorphism over *k*, conjugation <AL>	Isomorphismus *m* über *k*, *k*-Isomorphismus *m*	isomorphisme *m* sur *k*, *k*-isomorphisme *m*	*k*-изоморфизм
K 83	**k-isotropic algebraic group** <AG, GR>	*k*-isotrope algebraische Gruppe *f*	groupe *m* algébrique *k*-isotrope	*k*-изотропная алгебраическая группа
	kitchen drawer principle <CT>	*s.* B 705		
K 84	**kite,** deltoid <as a convex figure> <EG>	Deltoid *n*, Drachenfigur *f*, Drache *m*, Ochsenkopf *m*, caput *n* bubulum, Rhomboid *n*	deltoïde *m*	дельтоид, ромбоид
K 85	**Kleene['s] basis theorem** <FO>	Basissatz *m* von Kleene, Kleenescher Basissatz	théorème *m* de Kleene, théorème de la base de Kleene	теорема Клини о базисе
K 86	**Klein['s] bottle,** Klein['s] surface, non-orientable torus, sphere with two cross-caps <GE>	Kleinscher Schlauch *m*, Kleinsche Flasche *f*, einseitiger Schlauch, nichtorientierbare Ringfläche *f*	surface (vase, bouteille) *f* de Klein	бутылка (поверхность) Клейна
	Klein['s] configuration <SG>	*s.* C 1873		
K 87	**Klein['s] co-ordinates** <GE>	Kleinsche Koordinaten *fpl*	coordonnées *fpl* de Klein	координаты Клейна
	Kleinen / im <GN>	*s.* S 1213		
	Klein['s] Erlanger program[me] <GE>	*s.* E 465		
K 88	**Klein['s] form problem** <AL>	Kleinsches Formenproblem *n*	problème *m* des formes de Klein	задача о формах Клейна
	Klein['s] four[s]-group <GR>	*s.* K 90		
	Klein['s] σ-function <FT>	*s.* K 97		
K 89	**Klein['s] geometry** <GE>	Kleinsche Geometrie *f*	géométrie *f* de Klein	геометрия Клейна
K 90	**Klein['s] 4-group (group),** Klein['s] four-group, Klein['s] quadratic group, Klein['s] fours-group, Klein['s] Vierergruppe, fours-group, vierer group, Vierergruppe, quadratic group, axial group <GR>	Kleinsche Vierergruppe *f*, Vierergruppe	Vierergruppe (groupe) *m* de Klein, groupe du rectangle, groupe quadratique	четверная группа, группа Клейна, четверная группа Клейна
K 91	**Kleinian function** <FT>	Kleinsche Funktion *f*	fonction *f* kleinéenne	функция Клейна
K 92	**Kleinian group** <FT>	Kleinsche Gruppe *f*	groupe *m* kleinéen	группа Клейна
K 93	**Kleinmichel['s] criterion,** criterion of Kleinmichel <PG>	Kriterium *n* von Kleinmichel, Kleinmichelsches Kriterium	critère *m* de Kleinmichel	критерий Клейнмихеля
K 94	**Klein['s] model** <of lobachevskian geometry> <GE>	Kleins (Kleinsches) Modell *n* <der hyperbolischen Ebene *oder* Geometrie>	modèle *f* de Klein <de la géométrie hyperbolique>	модель Клейна <гиперболической геометрии>
K 95	**Klein['s] oscillation theorem** <DE>	Oszillationssatz *m* von Klein, Kleins[cher] Oszillationssatz	théorème *m* d'oscillation de Klein	теорема Клейна, теорема колебаний Клейна
K 96	**Klein['s] principle [of transfer[ence]]** <DG>	Kleins[ches] Übertragungsprinzip *n*, Übertragungsprinzip von [F.] Klein	principe *m* de corrélation (transfert) de [F.] Klein	принцип перенесения [Ф.] Клейна
	Klein['s] quadratic group <GR>	*s.* K 90		
K 97	**Klein['s] sigma[-] function,** Klein['s] σ function <FT>	Kleinsche σ-Funktion (Sigma-Funktion) *f*, σ-Funktion (Sigma-Funktion) von Klein	fonction *f* σ (sigma) de Klein	σ-функция (сигма-функция) Клейна
K 98	**Klein['s] space** <GE>	Kleinscher Raum *m*	espace *m* de Klein	пространство Клейна
	Klein['s] surface <GE>	*s.* K 86		
	Klein['s] Vierergruppe <GR>	*s.* K 90		
	k-line <AY>	*s.* P 291		
	K-lineal <FA>	*s.* V 113		
K 99	**k-linear algebra,** linear algebra <over *k*> <AL>	*k*-lineare Algebra *f*, lineare Algebra <über *k*>	algèbre *f* linéaire <sur *k*>	*k*-линейная алгебра, линейная алгебра <над *k*>
K 100	**Kloosterman[n] sum** <NT>	Kloostermansche Summe *f*, Kloosterman-Summe *f*	somme *f* de Kloosterman	сумма Клостермана
	knee <NU>	*s.* B 747		
K 101	**k-net** <as a partial plane> <AL>	*k*-Gewebe *n*, Gewebe *n*	*k*-tissu *m*	*k*-сеть
K 102	**knight's move** <CT>	Rösselsprung *m*	saut *m* (marche *f*, parcours *m*, course *f*) du cavalier <sur l'échiquier>	ход коня
K 103	**knight's move square** <ST>	Rösselquadrat *n*; Rösselsprunganlage *f*	carré *m* de la marche du cavalier	магический квадрат типа «ход конем»; блочный план типа «ход конем»
K 104	**Knopp['s] kernel theorem,** Knopp['s] theorem <LI, SS>	Knoppscher Kernsatz *m*	théorème *m* de Knopp	теорема Кноппа

No.	English	German	French	Russian
	Knopp-Schnee theorem <LI>	*s.* E 423		
	Knopp['s] theorem <LI, SS>	*s.* K 104		
	***k*-normal affine variety** <AG>	*s.* K 222		
	***k*-normal projective *k*-variety** <AG>	*s.* A 947		
K 105	***k*-normal variety** <AG>	*k*-normale Mannigfaltigkeit *f*	variété *f* *k*-normale	*k*-нормальное многообразие
K 106	**knot,** link of multiplicity one <AT>	Knoten *m*, topologischer Knoten	nœud *m*	узел
	knot <GP>	*s.* V 156		
K 107	**knot complement,** complement of a knot <TO>	Knotenaußenraum *m*	complément *m* d'un nœud	дополнительное пространство <узла>
K 108	**knot matrix** <AT>	Knotenmatrix *f* <Knotentheorie>	matrice *f* du nœud	матрица узла
	knot[-] singularity <AG>	*s.* N 272		
K 109	**knotted curve** <AT>	verknotete Kurve *f*	courbe *f* nouée	заузленная кривая
K 110	**knotted polygon** <TO>	verknotetes Polygon *n*	polygone *m* noué	заузленный полигон
K 111	**knot theory** <AT>	Knotentheorie *f*	théorie *f* des nœuds	теория узлов
	Kochansky['s] approximate construction <GE>	*s.* C 2130		
K 112	**Koch['s] method** <DE, NU>	Kochsches Verfahren *n*, Kochsche Methode *f*	méthode *f* de Koch	метод Коха
K 113	**Kodaira['s] dimension** <AG>	Kodaira-Dimension *f*	dimension *f* de Kodaira	размерность Кодаиры
K 114	**Koebe['s] constant** <FT>	Koebesche Konstante *f*	constante *f* de Koebe	постоянная Кебе
K 115	**Koebe['s] distortion theorem,** Koebe['s] theorem, theorem of Koebe <FT>	Verzerrungssatz *m* von Koebe [und Pick], Koebes Verzerrungssatz	théorème *m* de Koebe	теорема Кебе
	Koebe-Poincaré theorem <FT>	*s.* F 860		
	Koebe['s] theorem <FT>	*s.* K 115		
	Koenigsberg Bridge Problem <GP>	*s.* K 134		
K 116	**Koenigs['s] formula** <DG>	Formel *f* von Koenigs, Koenigssche Formel	formule *f* de Koenigs	формула Кенигса
	Kolmogorov-Alexander product <AT, HA>	*s.* C 2754		
	Kolmogorov['s] area <ME>	*s.* K 126		
K 117	**Kolmogorov['s] axiom system, Kolmogorov['s] axioms,** Kolmogorov['s] system of axioms <ST>	Kolmogorovsches Axiomensystem *n*, Kolmogorovsche (Kolmogoroffsche, Kolmogorowsche) Axiome *npl*, Axiome von Kolmogorov	système *m* des axiomes de Kolmogorov, axiomes *mpl* de Kolmogorov	система аксиом Колмогорова, аксиомы (аксиоматика) Колмогорова
K 117a	**Kolmogorov['s] backward [differential] equation,** backward [differential] equation[s], first equation of Kolmogorov, backward (first) system, Kolmogorov['s] retrospective equation <of the process> <SP>	Rückwärtsgleichung *f* [von Kolmogorov], Ausgangsgleichung *f* [von Kolmogorov], Kolmogorovsche Rückwärtsgleichung (Ausgangsgleichung), erste fundamentale Differentialgleichung *f*, retrospektive Gleichung *f*, erstes System *n* der Differentialgleichungen <des Prozesses>	équation *f* différentielle en arrière, équation différentielle du passé, première équation [aux dérivées partielles] de Kolmogoroff, équation rétrospective de Kolmogoroff, équation K_1, équation relative à l'instant initial [d'après A. Kolmogoroff], équation inverse [de Kolmogoroff], premières équations *fpl* de Kolmogoroff <du processus>	обратное (первое) уравнение [А. Н. Колмогорова], обратное дифференциальное уравнение [Колмогорова], обратные уравнения, обратная система уравнений <процесса>
K 118	**Kolmogorov['s] compatibility conditions** <ST>	Verträglichkeitsbedingungen *fpl* von Kolmogorov	conditions *fpl* de compatibilité de Kolmogorov	условия совместности Колмогорова
K 119	**Kolmogorov['s] criterion** <for normalization> <FA, TO>	Kolmogorovscher Normierungssatz *m*, Kolmogorovsches Normierbarkeitskriterium *n*, Normierungssatz von Kolmogorov	critère *m* de Kolmogoroff	критерий <нормируемости> Колмогорова
K 120	**Kolmogorov['s] distribution [function]** <ST>	Kolmogorov-Verteilung *f*, Kolmogorovsche Verteilung[sfunktion] *f*, Kolmogorov-Smirnovsche λ-Verteilung (Lambda-Verteilung) *f*	distribution *f* de Kolmogorov, fonction *f* de distribution de Kolmogorov	распределение (функция распределения) Колмогорова
K 121	**Kolmogorov['s] equations** <ST>	Kolmogorovsche Differentialgleichungen (Gleichungen) *fpl*	équations *fpl* [différentielles] de Kolmogorov	[дифференциальные] уравнения Колмогорова
	Kolmogorov['s] ergodic theorem <SP>	*s.* M 257		
	Kolmogorov Fokker-Planck [diffusion] equation <SP>	*s.* K 122		
K 122	**Kolmogorov['s] forward [differential] equation,** forward [differen-	Vorwärtsgleichung *f* [von Kolmogorov], Eingangsgleichung *f* [von Kolmo-	équation *f* différentielle en avant, équation différentielle de future, équation	прямое (второе) уравнение [А. Н. Колмогорова], прямое дифференциаль-

and still: K 122	tial] equation [of Kolmogorov], second equation of Kolmogorov, forward (second) system, forward [differential] equations [of Kolmogorov], system of forward equations, second equations of Kolmogorov, Kolmogorov Fokker-Planck [diffusion] equation <of the process> <SP>	gorov], Kolmogorovsche Vorwärtsgleichung (Eingangsgleichung), zweite fundamentale Differentialgleichung *f*, zweites System *n* der Differentialgleichungen <des Prozesses>	directe [de Kolmogoroff], seconde équation [aux dérivées partielles] de Kolmogoroff, équation prospective de Kolmogoroff, équation K_2, équation relative à l'instant final [d'après A. Kolmogoroff], secondes équations *fpl* de Kolmogoroff <du processus>	ное уравнение [Колмогорова], прямые уравнения, система прямых уравнений, прямая система уравнений, уравнение Колмогорова-Фоккера-Планка, уравнение типа Фоккера-Планка <процесса>
K 123	**Kolmogorov['s] inequality** <ST>	Kolmogorovsche Ungleichung (Wahrscheinlichkeitsabschätzung) *f*, Ungleichung von Kolmogorov	inégalité *f* de Kolmogoroff	неравенство Колмогорова
K 124	**Kolmogorov['s] integral** <AN>	Kolmogorovsches Integral *n*, Unterteilungsintegral *n*, Integral nach der Feinheit der Einteilung	intégrale *f* de Kolmogoroff	интеграл Колмогорова
K 125	**Kolmogorov['s] law of large numbers** <ST>	Kolmogorovsches Gesetz *n* [der großen Zahlen]	loi *f* des grands nombres de Kolmogorov	закон больших чисел Колмогорова
K 126	**Kolmogorov['s] measure** <of area>, Kolmogorov['s] area <ME>	axiomatisches Maß *n* von Kolmogorov, Maß von Kolmogorov, Kolmogorovsches Flächenmaß *n*	mesure (aire) *f* de Kolmogoroff	мера <площади> Колмогорова, площадь Колмогорова
	Kolmogorov['s] retrospective equation <ST>	*s.* K 117a		
K 127	**Kolmogorov-Seliverstov-Plessner theorem** <SS>	Satz *m* von Kolmogorov-Seliverstov-Plesner, Kolmogorov-Seliverstov-Plesnerscher Satz	théorème *m* de Kolmogoroff-Seliverstoff-Plessner	теорема Колмогорова-Селиверстова-Плеснера
K 128	**Kolmogorov-Sinai invariant,** entropy <of a dynamical system> <SP>	Kolmogorov-Sinai-Invariante *f*, Entropie *f*	invariant *m* de Kolmogorov-Sinai, entropie *f*	инвариант Колмогорова-Синая, энтропия
K 129	**Kolmogorov-Smirnov test** <ST>	Kolmogorov-Smirnov-Test *m*	test *m* de Kolmogorov-Smirnov	критерий Колмогорова-Смирнова
	Kolmogorov['s] system of axioms <ST>	*s.* K 117		
K 130	**Kolmogorov['s] test** <ST>	Kolmogorov-Test *m*	test *m* de Kolmogorov	критерий Колмогорова
K 131	**Kolmogorov['s] theorem** <on a polynomial of best approximation *or* on a precompact set> <AX, NU, TO>	Satz *m* von Kolmogorov, Kolmogorovscher Satz	théorème *m* de Kolmogoroff	теорема Колмогорова
	Kolmogorov['s] three-series theorem <ST>	*s.* T 464		
K 132	**Kolmogorov['s] zero-one law** <ST>	Kolmogorovsche Fassung *f* des Null-oder-Eins-Gesetzes, Null-Eins-Gesetz *n* von Kolmogorov	loi *f* de zéro ou un de Kolmogoroff	закон нуля или единицы Колмогорова
K 133	**Kondrashov['s] theorem** <DE>	Satz *m* von Kondraschow, Kondraschowscher Satz	théorème *m* de Kondrašov (Kondrachov)	теорема Кондрашова
	König-Egerváry method <PG>	*s.* H 596		
	König['s] graph <GP>	*s.* G 388		
	König['s] inequality <SE>	*s.* K 136		
K 134	**Königsberg Bridge Problem, Königsberg problem,** Koenigsberg Bridge Problem, problem of the Königsberg bridges, problem of the seven bridges of Königsberg <GP>	Brückenproblem *n*, Eulersches (Königsberger) Brückenproblem, Problem *n* der Königsberger Brücken, Problem der sieben Königsberger Brücken	problème *m* d'Euler	задача о мостах, задача Эйлера о мостах, задача о семи кенигсбергских мостах, задача о кенигсбергских мостах
K 135	**König['s] theorem** <GP>	Satz *m* von König, Königscher Satz	« Graphensatz » *m* de König	теорема Кенига
K 136	**König['s] theorem,** theorem of J. König, inequality of König-Jourdain-Zermelo, König['s] inequality <on cardinals> <SE>	Satz *m* von König, Königscher Satz	théorème *m* de J. König	теорема Кенига
K 137	**Korn['s] inequality** <DE>	Kornsche Ungleichung *f*	inégalité *f* [dite] de Korn	уравнение Корна
	Korovkin-type theorem <LA>	*s.* T 302		
K 138	**Koszul['s] complex** <HA>	Koszul-Komplex *m*	complexe *m* de Koszul	комплекс Козюля
K 139	**Kotelnikov['s] theorem** <ST>	Satz *m* von Kotelnikov, Kotelnikovscher Satz	théorème *m* de Kotelnikov	теорема Котельникова
K 140	**Köthe['s] ring** <AL>	Köthe-Ring *m*	anneau *m* de Köthe (Koethe)	кольцо Кете
K 141	**Köthe['s] space,** perfect space <FA, TO>	vollkommener Raum *m*, Köthe-Raum *m*	espace *m* de Köthe (Koethe), espace parfait (köthien, koethien)	совершенное пространство, пространство Кете
	***k*-perfect number** <NT>	*s.* M 982		

K 142	**k-plane** <GE>	*k*-dimensionale Ebene *f*	plan *m* *k*-dimensionnel	*k*-мерная плоскость
	K-plane <SG>	*s.* K 78		
K 143	**k-ply transitive [permutation] group,** *k*-fold transitive [permutation] group <GR>	*k*-fach transitive Permutationsgruppe (Gruppe) *f*, Permutationsgruppe vom Transitivitätsgrad *k*	groupe *m* [de permutations] *k* fois transitif, groupe [de permutations] *k*-uplement transitif	*k* раз транзитивная группа [подстановок], *k*-кратно транзитивная группа [подстановок]
	k-ply transitive [transformation] group <GR>	*s.* K 196		
K 144	**k-rank** <of an algebraic group> <GR>	*k*-Rang *m*	*k*-rang *m*	*k*-ранг
K 145	**k-rational point** <AG>	*k*-rationaler Punkt *m*	point *m* *k*-rationnel	*k*-рациональная точка
K 146	**Krawtschouk['s] polynomial** <FU, ST>	Krawtschuksches (Krawtschouksches) Polynom *n*	polynôme *m* de Krawtschouk	многочлен Кравчука
K 147	**Krein['s] method** <FA>	Kreinsche Methode *f*, Methode von Krein	méthode *f* de Krein	метод Крейна
K 148	**Krein-Milman theorem** <on extremal points> <CS, FA>	Krein-Milmanscher Satz *m*, Satz von Krein-Milman	théorème *m* de [M. G.] Krein- [D. P.] Milman	теорема Крейна-Мильмана
K 149	**Kristensen['s] method** <ST>	Methode *f* Kristensen, Kristensen-Methode *f*	méthode *f* de Kristensen	метод Кристенсена
	Krivine Löwenheim['s] theorem <LO>	*s.* L 1123		
	Kronecker['s] δ <AL, AN, GE>	*s.* K 152		
K 150	**Kronecker['s] criterion** <AL>	Kroneckersches Irreduzibilitätskriterium *n*	critère *m* de Kronecker	критерий неприводимости Кронекера
K 151	**Kronecker['s] curvature** <of a hypersurface> <DG>	Kroneckersches Krümmungsmaß *n*	courbure *f* de Kronecker (Gauss-Kronecker)	кривизна Кронекера
K 152	**Kronecker['s] delta [symbol],** Kronecker['s] δ, Kronecker['s] symbol <δ_i^k; δ_{ik}> <AL, AN, GE>	Kronecker-Symbol *n*, Kroneckersymbol *n*, Kroneckersches Symbol (Delta-Symbol, Delta, δ) *n*, Delta-Symbol, δ-Symbol	symbole *m* delta de Kronecker, indice *m* (symbole) de Kronecker, symbole diagonal	символ Кронекера, кронекеровский символ, кронекеровская дельта
K 153	**Kronecker['s] density theorem** <AB>	Kroneckerscher Dichtigkeitssatz *m*	loi *f* de densité de Kronecker	теорема плотности Кронекера
K 154	**Kronecker['s] existence theorem** <AT>	Kroneckerscher Existenzsatz *m*	théorème *m* d'existence de Kronecker	теорема существования Кронекера
K 155	**Kroneckerian reduction** <of a Hermitian matrix> <MD>	Kroneckersche Reduktion *f*	réduction *f* de Kronecker	кронекеровская редукция
K 156	**Kronecker['s] index** <of a 0-chain> <AT>	Kronecker-Index *m*, Kroneckerscher Index *m*, Index *m*	indice *m* de Kronecker	индекс Кронекера
	Kronecker['s] index <AT>	*s.* I 803		
K 157	**Kronecker integral** <AT>	Kroneckersches Integral *n*	intégrale *f* de Kronecker	интеграл Кронекера
K 158	**Kronecker['s] interpolation formula** <AX, NU>	Kroneckersche Interpolationsformel *f*, Interpolationsformel (Formel) *f* von Kronecker	formule *f* d'interpolation de Kronecker	интерполяционная формула Кронекера
K 159	**Kronecker['s] method** <for the factorization of polynomials> <AL>	Kroneckersche (lexikographische) Methode *f*	méthode *f* de Kronecker	метод Кронекера, лексикографический метод
K 160	**Kronecker['s] method [of elimination],** elimination method of Kronecker <AL>	Kroneckersche Eliminationsmethode (Methode) *f*	méthode *f* d'élimination de Kronecker	метод исключения Кронекера
K 161	**Kronecker power** <of a matrix> <MD>	Kroneckersche Potenz *f*	puissance *f* kroneckérienne (de Kronecker)	кронекеровская степень
K 162	**Kronecker product** <of algebraic theories> <CA>	Kronecker-Produkt *n*, Kroneckerprodukt *n*	produit *m* kroneckérien	кронекеровское произведение
K 163	**Kronecker['s] product,** direct product, tensor product, Hadamard['s] product, elementwise product <of matrices> <MD>	Kronecker-Produkt *n*, Kroneckerprodukt *n*, tensorielles Produkt *n*, Tensorprodukt *n*, Kroneckersche Produktmatrix	produit *m* tensoriel (kroneckérien, de Kronecker)	прямое (кронекеровское, поэлементное) произведение, произведение Адамара
K 164	**Kronecker['s] product,** direct product <of representations> <RE>	Kronecker-Produkt *n*, Kroneckerprodukt *n*, direktes Produkt *n*, Produkt, Komposition *f*, tensorielles (Kroneckersches) Produkt, Tensorprodukt *n*, Produktdarstellung *f*	produit *m* tensoriel (kroneckérien, direct, cartésien)	произведение Кронекера, тензорное произведение
	Kronecker['s] product <FA>	*s.* D 595		
K 165	**Kronecker['s] series** <FU>	Kroneckersche Reihe *f*	série *f* de Kronecker	ряд Кронекера
K 166	**Kronecker['s] symbol** <NT>	Kronecker-Symbol *n*	symbole *m* de Kronecker	символ Кронекера
	Kronecker['s] symbol <AL, AN, GE>	*s.* K 152		
	Kronecker['s] tensor <VT>	*s.* U 298		
K 167	**Kronecker['s] theorem** <in theory of cyclotomy> <AL>	Kroneckerscher Satz *m*	théorème *m* de Kronecker	теорема Кронекера

K 168	**Kronecker['s] theorem** <on the rank of matrices *or* for convergence> <MD, SS>	Satz *m* von Kronecker, Kroneckerscher Satz	théorème *m* de Kronecker	теорема Кронекера
K 169	**Kronecker['s] theorem** <for diophantine approximations> <NT>	Kroneckerscher Approximationssatz *m*, Kroneckerscher Satz *m* über diophantische Approximationen	théorème *m* de Kronecker	теорема Кронекера
	Kronecker-Weber theorem <AB>	*s.* T 304		
K 170	**Kronecker['s] youthful dream** <AB>	Kroneckerscher Jugendtraum *m*	« rêve *m* de jeunesse » de Kronecker	заветная мечта юности, «Jugendtraum» Кронекера
	Krull-Akizuki theorem <AL>	*s.* T 305		
K 171	**Krull['s] dimension** <AL>	Krullsche Dimension *f*, Krull-Dimension *f*	dimension *f* [au sens] de Krull, dimension [maximale]	размерность Крулля
K 172	**Krull['s] domain,** finite discrete principal order <AL>	endliche diskrete Hauptordnung *f*, Krullscher Ring *m*	anneau *m* de Krull, anneau normal noethérien	кольцо Крулля
K 173	**Krull['s] Hauptidealsatz,** Krull['s] Principal Ideal Theorem, principal ideal theorem <AL>	Krullscher Hauptidealsatz *m*	théorème *m* de l'idéal principal [de Krull]	теорема главных идеалов Крулля
K 174	**Krull['s] ordinal** <of a ring> <AL>	Krullsche Ordinalzahl *f*	ordinal *m* de Krull	порядковое число <кольца>
	Krull['s] Principal Ideal Theorem <AL>	*s.* K 173		
K 175	**Krull[-Remak]-Schmidt theorem,** Schmidt-Remak theorem <GR>	Satz *m* von Remak (Remak-Krull-Schmidt, Krull-Remak-Schmidt, Schmidt), Remak-Schmidtscher (Krull-Schmidtscher) Satz	théorème *m* de Remak (Krull-Remak-Schmidt)	теорема Шмидта (Ремака-Шмидта, Крулля-Ремака-Шмидта, Крулля-Шмидта)
K 176	**Krull['s] theorem** <AL>	Satz *m* von Krull, Krullscher Durchschnittssatz *m*	théorème *m* de Krull	теорема Крулля
K 177	**Krull['s] topology** <in Galois' theory> <AL>	Krullsche Topologie *f*	topologie *f* de Krull	топология Крулля
	Krull['s] valuation <AL>	*s.* G 187		
	Krull['s] valuation of rank 1 <AL>	*s.* G 188		
	Krull['s] valuation of rank greater than 1 <AL>	*s.* G 189		
K 178	**Kruskal-Wallis['] [*H*] test,** *H*-test <ST>	Kruskal-Wallis-Test *m*, Kruskal-Wallisscher *H*-Test *m*, *H*-Test [von Kruskal-Wallis]	test *m* de Kruskal-Wallis, test *H* de Kruskal-Wallis, test *H*	критерий Крускала-Валлиса, *H*-критерий [Крускала-Валлиса], критерий *H* [Крускала-Валлиса]
K 179	**Krylov[-Bogoliubov]-Weinstein theorem,** Weinstein['s] theorem <DE, FA>	Krylow-Bogoljubow-Weinsteinscher Einschließungssatz, Weinsteinscher Einschließungssatz *m*, Einschließungssatz von Bogoljubow-Krylow-Weinstein (Krylow-Bogoljubow-Weinstein)	théorème *m* de Weinstein, théorème de Krylov-[Bogolioubov-]Weinstein	теорема Вайнштейна, теорема Крылова-Боголюбова-Вайнштейна
K 180	***k* samples problem,** problem of *k* samples <ST>	*k*-Stichproben-Problem *n*	problème *m* des *k* échantillons	проблема *k* выборок
K 181	***k*-saturated graph** <GP>	*k*-gesättigter Graph *m*	graphe *m* *k*-saturé	*k*-насыщенный граф
K 182	***k*-section** <of a hypergraph> <GP>	*k*-Schnitt *m*	*k*-section *f*	*k*-сечение
K 183	**K-semidefinite,** semidefinite in Kamke's sense <DE>	K-semidefinit, semidefinit im Sinne von Kamke, Kamke-semidefinit	semi-défini au sens de Kamke	K-полуопределенный, полуопределенный в смысле Камке, полуопределенный по Камке
K 184	**K-semidefiniteness,** semidefiniteness in Kamke's sense <DE>	K-Semidefinitheit *f*, Kamke-Semidefinitheit *f*	propriété *f* d'être semi-défini au sens de Kamke	K-полуопределенность, полуопределенность в смысле Камке, полуопределенность по Камке
K 185	***k*-set,** algebraic set over *k*, algebraic *k*-set, bunch of varieties normally algebraic over *k* <Weil>, variety over *k* <Zariski>, algebraic variety over *k* <Hodge-Pedoe>, interference variety over *k* <Severi> <AG>	*k*-Menge *f*, algebraische Mannigfaltigkeit *f* über *k*, Vielfältigkeit *f* über *k* <van der Waerden>	*k*-ensemble *m*, ensemble *m* normalement algébrique sur *k*	*k*-множество, алгебраическое множество над *k*
K 186	***k*-simple variety,** variety relatively simple with reference to *k* <Weil>, simple variety <Zariski, Hodge-Pedoe> <AG>	*k*-einfache Mannigfaltigkeit *f*, einfache Mannigfaltigkeit über *k*	variété *f* *k*-simple	*k*-простое многообразие, простое многообразие над *k*

K 187	**K-space,** Kantorovich['s] space, Kantorovich-space <FA>	K-Raum *m*, Kantorowitsch-Raum *m*, Vektorverband *m*	K-espace *m*, espace *m* de Kantorovitch	K-пространство, пространство Канторовича, условно полная векторная структура
K 188	**k-space** <TO>	k-Raum *m*	k-espace *m*	k-пространство
K 189	***K*-sphere** <DG>	*K*-Kugel *f*	*K*-sphère *f*	*K*-сфера
K 190	***k*-statistic** <k_1, k_2, ...> <ST>	*k*-Stichprobenfunktion *f*, *k*-Maßzahl *f*, *k*-Statistik *f*	statistique *f k*, coefficient *m k*	*k*-статистика
K 191	**K3 surface** <AG>	K3-Fläche *f*	surface *f* K3	поверхность типа K3, K3-поверхность
K 192	**K-theory** <AL, AT, CA>	K-Theorie *f*	K-théorie *f*	K-теория
K 193	***k*-th moment,** moment of order *k* <ST>	*k*-tes Moment *n*, [gewöhnliches] Moment der Ordnung *k*	*k*-e moment *m*, moment d'ordre *k*	*k*-й момент, момент порядка *k*
K 194	***k*-th transvectant,** transvectant of index *k* <of an algebraic form> <IV>	*k*-te Überschiebung *f*, Elementarkovariante *f*	*k*-e transvection *f*	
	k-topology <TO>	*s.* T 566		
K 195	***k*-torus** <AL>	*k*-Torus *m*	*k*-tore *m*	*k*-тор, тор над *k*
K 196	***k*-transitive [transformation] group,** *k*-ply transitive [transformation] group, *k*-fold transitive [transformation] group <GR>	*k*-fach transitive Gruppe *f*, *k*-fach transitive Transformationsgruppe *f*	groupe *m k* fois transitif, groupe de transformations *k* fois transitif, groupe [de transformations] *k*-uplement transitif	*k* раз транзитивная группа [преобразований], *k*-кратно транзитивная группа [преобразований]
	***k*-tuple root** <AL>	*s.* K 61		
	***k*-tuple zero** <AL>	*s.* K 61		
K 197	**Kubota['s] formula** <CS>	Kubotasche Formel *f*	formule *f* de Kubota	формула Куботы
K 198	**Kuhn-Tucker conditions,** local Kuhn-Tucker conditions <PG>	Kuhn-Tucker-Bedingungen *fpl*, Kuhn-Tuckersche Bedingungen *fpl*, lokale Kuhn-Tucker-Bedingungen	conditions *fpl* de Kuhn-Tucker [locales]	условия Куна-Таккера
K 199	**Kuhn-Tucker optimization** <PG>	Kuhn-Tucker-Optimierung *f*	optimisation *f* de Kuhn et Tucker	оптимизация Куна-Таккера
K 200	**Kuhn-Tucker [saddle-point] theorem,** saddle-point theorem <PG>	Satz *m* (Theorem *n*) von Kuhn-Tucker, Kuhn-Tuckerscher Satz, Kuhn-Tuckersches Theorem, globale Kuhn-Tucker-Bedingung *f*, Sattelpunktkriterium *n*	théorème *m* de Kuhn et Tucker, théorème du point de selle, théorème de Kuhn-Tucker	теорема Куна-Таккера
K 201	**Kummer['s] character** <AB>	Kummerscher Charakter *m*	caractère *m* de Kummer	куммеров характер
K 202	**Kummer['s] cone** <of a quartic> <AG>	Kummerscher Kegel *m*	cône *m* de Kummer	конус Куммера
	Kummer['s] configuration <SG>	*s.* C 1874		
	Kummer['s] differential equation <DE>	*s.* C 1884		
K 203	**Kummer['s] equation** <AB>	Kummersche Gleichung *f*	équation *f* kummérienne	уравнение Куммера
	Kummer['s] equation <DE>	*s.* C 1884		
	Kummer extension <AL>	*s.* K 204		
K 204	**Kummer['s] field** <over *k*>, Kummer extension <of *k*> <AL>	Kummersche Erweiterung *f*, Kummersche Körpererweiterung *f* <von *k*>, Kummerscher Körper *m* <über *k*>; Kummerscher Zahlkörper *m*	corps *m* kummérien, corps de Kummer <sur *k*>, extension *f* de Kummer <de *k*>	расширение Куммера, куммерово расширение поля <от *k*>, куммерово поле; куммерово числовое поле <над *k*>
K 205	**Kummer['s] formula** <first *or* second> <for transformation of Kummer's function> <FU>	Kummersche Transformationsformel *f* <erste *oder* zweite>	formule *f* de Kummer <première *ou* deuxième>	формула Куммера <первая *или* вторая>
	Kummer['s] function <FU>	*s.* C 1885		
K 206	**Kummer['s] fundamental form,** Kummer['s] quadratic fundamental form <DG>	Kummersche Grundform (Fundamentalform) *f*, Kummersche quadratische Grundform (Fundamentalform)	forme *f* fondamentale de Kummer, forme quadratique fondamentale de Kummer	основная квадратичная форма Куммера, основная форма Куммера
K 207	**Kummer-Hilbert reciprocity law** <AB>	Kummer-Hilbertsches Reziprozitätsgesetz *n*	loi *f* de réciprocité de Kummer-Hilbert	закон взаимности Куммера-Гильберта
K 208	**Kummerian prime** <NT>	Kummersche Primzahl *f*	nombre *m* premier kummérien	куммерово простое число
	Kummer['s] quadratic fundamental form <DG>	*s.* K 206		
K 209	**Kummer['s] quartic surface,** Kummer surface <AG>	Kummersche Fläche *f*	surface *f* de Kummer	поверхность Куммера
	Kummer['s] series <FU>	*s.* C 1885 a		
	Kummer surface <AG>	*s.* K 209		
K 210	**Kummer['s] test** <for convergence> <SS>	Kummersches Kriterium (Konvergenzkriterium) *n*	critère *m* de Kummer	признак Куммера
	Kummer['s] theorem <AB>	*s.* T 307		
K 211	**Kummer['s] theory** <of field extension> <AL>	Kummersche Theorie *f*	théorie *f* de Kummer	теория Куммера

No.	English	German	French	Russian
K 212	**Künneth['s] formula** <AT, HA>	Künneth-Formel *f*, Künnethsche Formel *f*	formule *f* (théorème *m*) de Künneth, formule de Kunneth	формула Кюннета
K 213	**Künneth['s] relation** <AT> ⌐<AT>	Künneth-Relation *f*	relation *f* de Künneth	соотношение Кюннета
	Künneth['s] theorem	*s.* T 308		
K 214	**Kuratowski['s] closure axioms** <TO>	Kuratowskische Hüllenaxiome *npl*; Hülleneigenschaften *fpl*	axiomes *mpl* de fermeture de Kuratowski	аксиомы замыкания Куратовского
K 215	**Kuratowski['s] closure operator** <TO>	Kuratowskischer Hüllenoperator *m*	opération *f* de fermeture de Kuratowski	оператор замыкания Куратовского
K 216	**Kuratowski['s] graph** <GP>	Kuratowskischer Graph *m* <vom Typ 1 *oder* 2>	graphe *m* de Kuratowski	граф Понтрягина-Куратовского <первого *или* второго типа>
	Kuratowski['s] lemma (maximal principle) <SE>	*s.* H 141		
K 217	**Kuratowski['s] theorem** <GP>	Satz *m* von Kuratowski, Kuratowskischer Satz	théorème *m* de Kuratowski	теорема Куратовского
K 218	**Kurosh-Amitsur radical** <AL>	Radikal *n* im Sinne von Kurosch-Amitsur, Kurosch-Amitsur-Radikal *n*	radical *m* de Kuroš-Amitsur	радикал в смысле Куроша-Амицура
K 219	**Kurosh-Ore theorem** <AL>	Theorem *n* (Satz *m*) von Kurosch-Ore, Kurosch-Oresches Theorem	théorème *m* de Kurosch-Ore	теорема Куроша-Оре
K 220	**kurtosis** <ST>	Wölbung *f*, Koeffizient *m* der Wölbung	kurtosis *m*	выпуклость, коэффициент выпуклости
	kurtosis <ST>	*s.* E 674		
K 221	**Kushner['s] iterative method** <ST>	Iterationsverfahren *n* von Kushner, Kushnersches Iterationsverfahren	méthode *f* itérative de Kushner	итерационный метод Кашнера
	***k*-variety** <AG>	*s.* I 1038		
K 222	***k*-variety affinely normal over *k*,** *k*-normal affine variety <AG>	affin normale *k*-Mannigfaltigkeit *f*	*k*-variété *f* affinement normale	аффинно-нормальное *k*-многообразие
	k*-variety projectively normal over *k <AG>	*s.* A 947		
K 223	***k*-vertex connected graph,** *k*-connected graph <GP>	*k*-fach knotenzusammenhängender Graph *m*, *k*-fach [bezüglich der Knotenpunkte] zusammenhängender Graph, *k*-zusammenhängender Graph	graphe *m* *k*-connexe	*k*-связный граф

L

No.	English	German	French	Russian
	labeling <GN>	*s.* I 350		
L 1	**labelled graph,** signed graph <GP>	markierter Graph *m*	graphe *m* marqué	помеченный (перенумерованный) граф
	labelling <GN>	*s.* I 350		
L 2	**labile space** <TO>	labiler [metrischer] Raum *m*	espace *m* instable	неустойчивое пространство
L 3	**labyrinth** <GP>	Labyrinth *n*, Irrgarten *m*	labyrinthe *m*	лабиринт
L 4	**labyrinth problem** <GP>	Labyrinthproblem *n*, Labyrinthenproblem *n*, Problem *n* der Labyrinthe	problème *m* des labyrinthes	проблема лабиринта
L 5	**lack of fit** <ST>	unzureichende Anpassung *f*, Anpassungsmangel *m*	manque *m* d'ajustement	плохое согласование, отсутствие согласия
L 6	**lacunarity** <FT>	Lakunarität *f*	lacunarité *f*	лакунарность
L 7	**lacunarity** <SE, SS>	Lückenhaftigkeit *f*	propriété *f* d'être lacunaire	лакунарность
	lacunar series <FT, SS>	*s.* G 46		
L 8	**lacunary end** <of a Riemann surface> <FT>	lakunäres Ende *n*	« end » *m* lacunaire	лакунарный конец
L 9	**lacunary sequence** <SS>	lakunäre Folge *f*, Folge mit Lücken	suite *f* lacunaire	лакунарная последовательность
	lacunary series <FT, SS>	*s.* G 46		
L 10	**lacunary space** <FT>	lakunärer Raum *m*, // lacunärer Raum	espace *m* lacunaire	лакуна, пропущенная область
	lacunary value <FT>	*s.* E 671		
L 11	**ladder, scale** <NO>	Leiter *f*	échelle *f*	шкала
L 12	**ladder chart (diagram, graph)** <NO>	Leitertafel *f*, Leiterdiagramm *n*	abaque (nomogramme, diagramme) *m* à échelle	номограмма со шкалой
L 13	**lag** <ST>	Verzögerung *f*, Lag *n*	retard *m*, décalage *m*	запаздывание, отставание, отрицательный сдвиг фазы
L 14	**lag correlation** <ST>	Lagkorrelation *f*, Korrelation *f* mit Verzögerung	corrélation *f* avec retard, corrélation avec décalage	корреляция с запаздыванием аргумента, корреляция с запаздывающим (отклоняющимся) аргументом
L 15	**lag correlation coefficient** <ST>	Lagkorrelationskoeffizient *m*	coefficient *m* de corrélation avec retard (décalage)	коэффициент корреляции с запаздывающим аргументом
L 16	**lag covariance** <ST>	Lagkovarianz *f*, Kovarianz *f* mit Verzögerung	covariance *f* avec retard, covariance avec décalage	ковариация с запаздыванием аргумента, ковариация с запаздывающим (отклоняющимся) аргументом
	Lagrange-Abel polynomial <FU> ⌐<DE>	*s.* L 46		
	Lagrange['s] adjoint	*s.* A 290		
L 17	**Lagrange bracket** <DE>	Lagrangescher Klammerausdruck *m*, Lagrangesche Klammer *f*, Lagrange-Klammer *f*	crochet *m* de Lagrange	скобка Лагранжа

L 18	**Lagrange-Charpit method** <DE>	Lagrange-Charpitsche Methode *f*, Methode von Lagrange und Charpit	méthode *f* de Lagrange-Charpit	метод Лагранжа-Чарпита
L 19	**Lagrange['s] coefficient** <AX, NU>	Lagrange-Koeffizient *m*	coefficient *m* de Lagrange	коэффициент Лагранжа
	Lagrange['s] differential equation <DE>	*s.* D 450		
	Lagrange['s] factor <DI>	*s.* L 26		
	Lagrange['s] form [of the remainder] <DI>	*s.* L 30		
	Lagrange['s] formula <DI>	*s.* M 327		
	Lagrange['s] formula of interpolation <AX, DI, NU>	*s.* L 21		
L 20	**Lagrange['s] identity** <for square sums *or* differential equations> <AL, DE>	Lagrangesche (Lagranges) Identität *f*	formule *f* de Lagrange <pour les sommes carrés>; identité *f* de Lagrange <pour les expressions différentiels>	тождество Лагранжа
L 21	**Lagrange['s] interpolation formula,** Lagrange['s] formula of interpolation <AX, DI, NU>	Lagrangesche Interpolationsformel (Formel) *f*, Interpolationsformel (Formel) von Lagrange	formule *f* d'interpolation de Lagrange, formule de Lagrange	интерполяционная формула Лагранжа
L 22	**Lagrange['s] interpolation polynomial,** Lagrangian interpolation polynomial <AX, FD, NU>	Interpolationspolynom *n* von Lagrange, Lagrangesches Interpolationspolynom	polynôme *m* d'interpolation de Lagrange	интерполяционный многочлен Лагранжа
L 23	**Lagrange['s] interpolation polynomial,** Lagrange['s] parabola, interpolation polynomial of Lagrange, standard polynomial <AX, NU>	Lagrangesche interpolatorische Grundfunktion *f* <zum Grundpunkt x_k>, Grundpolynom *n* <zum Interpolationsknoten x_k>, Lagrangesche Parabel *f*	polynôme *m* d'interpolation de Lagrange, parabole *f* de Lagrange	интерполяционный коэффициент Лагранжа, интерполяционный многочлен Лагранжа
	Lagrange['s] mean value formula <DI>	*s.* M 327		
L 24	**Lagrange['s] method [of integration]** <DE>	Lagrangesche Integrationsmethode *f*, Integrationsmethode von Lagrange, Lagrangesche Methode *f*	méthode *f* [d'intégration] de Lagrange	метод [интегрирования] Лагранжа
	Lagrange['s] method of multipliers <DI, PG, VA>	*s.* L 25		
L 25	**Lagrange['s] method of undetermined multipliers,** method of undetermined multipliers, Lagrange['s] method of multipliers, method of Lagrangian multipliers, method of multipliers, Lagrangian procedure <DI, PG, VA>	Lagrangesche Multiplikatormethode (Methode) *f*, Multiplikatormethode, Methode der Lagrangeschen Multiplikatoren, Multiplikatorenregel (Methode) *f* von Lagrange, Multiplikatorenregel, Euler-Lagrangesche Multiplikatorenregel, Lagrangesches Multiplikatorenverfahren *n*, klassische Lagrange-Methode (Lagrangesche Methode) *f*	méthode *f* de Lagrange, méthode des multiplicateurs de Lagrange, méthode des multiplicateurs	метод множителей Лагранжа, метод множителей
L 26	**Lagrange['s] multiplier,** Lagrange['s] undetermined multiplier, undetermined multiplier, Lagrange['s] factor, Lagrangian factor (multiplier) <DI>	Lagrangescher Multiplikator *m*, Lagrange-Faktor *m*	multiplicateur *m* de Lagrange	множитель Лагранжа, лагранжев множитель
L 27	**Lagrange['s] number** <NT>	Lagrangesche Zahl *f*	nombre *m* de Lagrange	число Лагранжа
	Lagrange['s] parabola <AX, NU>	*s.* L 23		
L 28	**Lagrange['s] polynomial** <FU>	Lagrangesches Polynom *n*	polynôme *m* de Lagrange	многочлен (полином) Лагранжа
L 29	**Lagrange['s] problem,** problem of Lagrange <in the calculus of variations> <VA>	Lagrangesches Variationsproblem *n*, Problem *n* von Lagrange	problème *m* de Lagrange	задача Лагранжа
L 30	**Lagrange['s] remainder,** Lagrange['s] form [of the remainder] <in Taylor's formula> <DI>	Lagrangesches Restglied *n*, Lagrangesche Form *f* des Restgliedes <der Taylor-Reihe>, Restglied von Lagrange, Restglied in der Lagrangeschen Form, Restglied der Taylorschen Formel in der Form von Lagrange	reste *m* (terme *m* résiduel) de Lagrange	остаточный член Лагранжа, остаток Лагранжа, остаточный член [формулы Тейлора] в форме Лагранжа
L 31	**Lagrange['s] resolvent** <AL>	Lagrangesche Resolvente *f*, Lagrangesche Wurzelzahl *f*, Lagranges Resolvente	résolvante *f* de Lagrange, nombre *m* radical, résolvante de Lagrange-Hilbert	резольвента Лагранжа
L 32	**Lagrange['s] reversion theorem** <FT>	Lagrangesches Reversionstheorem *n*, Reversionstheorem von Lagrange	théorème *m* de réversion de Lagrange	теорема обращения Лагранжа

L 33	**Lagrange['s] series,** Bürmann[-Lagrange] series <FT>	Bürmann-Lagrangesche Reihe *f*, Lagrangesche Reihe	série *f* de Lagrange, série de Bürmann-Lagrange	ряд Лагранжа, ряд Бюрмана-Лагранжа
L 34	**Lagrange['s] spectrum** <AX>	Lagrange-Spektrum *n*	spectre *m* de Lagrange	спектр Лагранжа
L 35	**Lagrange['s] theorem** <GR>	Satz *m* von Lagrange, Lagrangescher Satz	théorème *m* de Lagrange	теорема Лагранжа
	Lagrange['s] theorem <DI>	*s.* M 327		
	Lagrange['s] theorem [on four squares] <NT>	*s.* F 548		
L 36	**Lagrange['s] theorem [on quadratic irrationalities]** <NT>	Lagrangescher Satz *m* über periodische Kettenbrüche	théorème *m* de Lagrange sur des irrationalités quadratiques	теорема Лагранжа <о квадратических иррациональностях>
	Lagrange['s] undetermined multiplier <DI>	*s.* L 26		
L 37	**Lagrangian,** Lagrangian expression, Lagrangian function <VA>	Lagrange-Funktion *f*, Lagrangesche Funktion *f*, Grundfunktion *f*	lagrangien *m*, fonction *f* lagrangienne, fonction de Lagrange	лагранжиан, функция Лагранжа, лагранжева функция
	Lagrangian derivative <VA>	*s.* V 70		
	Lagrangian expression <VA>	*s.* L 37		
	Lagrangian factor <DI>	*s.* L 26		
	Lagrangian function <VA>	*s.* L 37		
	Lagrangian interpolation polynomial <AX, FD, NU>	*s.* L 22		
	Lagrangian multiplier <DI>	*s.* L 26		
	Lagrangian procedure <DI, PG, VA>	*s.* L 25		
L 38	**lag regression** <ST>	Lagregression *f*, Regression *f* mit Verzögerung	régression *f* avec retard (décalage)	регрессия с запаздыванием аргумента, регрессия с запаздывающим (отклоняющимся) аргументом
	lag theorem <IT>	*s.* T 479		
L 39	**Laguerre['s] differential equation,** Laguerre['s] equation <DE>	Laguerresche Differentialgleichung (Gleichung) *f*	équation *f* différentielle de Laguerre, équation de Laguerre	дифференциальное уравнение Лагерра, уравнение Лагерра
	Laguerre['s] equation <DE>	*s.* L 39		
	Laguerre['s] formula <AY, PJ>	*s.* F 497		
L 40	**Laguerre['s] function,** generalized Laguerre function <FU>	[verallgemeinerte] Laguerresche Funktion *f*, [verallgemeinerte] Laguerre-Funktion *f*	fonction *f* de Laguerre (Laguerre généralisée)	функция Лагерра, лагерровская функция, обобщенная функция Лагерра
L 41	**Laguerre['s] function of the second kind** <FU>	Laguerresche Funktion *f* der zweiten Art	fonction *f* de Laguerre de deuxième espèce	функция Лагерра второго рода
	Laguerre['s] geometry <DG>	*s.* L 43		
L 42	**Laguerre['s] geometry in the plane, Laguerre['s] geometry of circles,** Laguerre['s] geometry of the space of *K*-circles <DG>	Laguerresche Geometrie *f* der Kreisebene (Kreise), Laguerresche Geometrie für die Kreisebene, Geometrie von Laguerre für die Kreisebene, ebene Laguerresche Geometrie	géométrie *f* de Laguerre de cercles, géométrie de Laguerre dans le plan	геометрия Лагерра окружностей, геометрия окружностей Лагерра, геометрия Лагерра в плоскости
L 43	**Laguerre['s] geometry of spheres,** Laguerre['s] geometry of the space of *K*-spheres, Laguerre['s] geometry <DG>	Laguerresche Geometrie *f* des Kugelraums, Laguerresche Geometrie der Kugeln, Laguerresche Geometrie für den Kugelraum, Geometrie von Laguerre für den Kugelraum, Laguerresche Geometrie, Geometrie von Laguerre, Laguerre-Geometrie *f*	géométrie *f* de Laguerre de sphères (l'espace des sphères *K*), géométrie de Laguerre	геометрия Лагерра сфер, геометрия сфер Лагерра, геометрия Лагерра
	Laguerre['s] geometry of the space of *K*-circles <DG>	*s.* L 42		
	Laguerre['s] geometry of the space of *K*-spheres <DG>	*s.* L 43		
L 44	**Laguerre['s] group** <in the space of *K*-spheres> <DG>	Gruppe *f* von Laguerre, Laguerresche Transformationsgruppe *f*	groupe *m* de Laguerre	группа Лагерра
L 45	**Laguerre['s] orthogonal function** <DE, FU>	Laguerresche Orthogonalfunktion *f*	fonction *f* orthogonale de Laguerre	ортогональная функция Лагерра
L 46	**Laguerre['s] polynomial,** Lagrange-Abel polynomial <FU>	Laguerresches (Tschebyscheff-Laguerresches) Polynom *n*, [Tschebyscheff-] Laguerre-Polynom *n*, Kummersches (Lagrange-Abelsches) Polynom, verallgemeinertes Laguerresches Polynom	polynôme *m* de Laguerre (Lagrange-Abel)	многочлен Чебышева-Лагерра (Лагерра, Лагранжа-Абеля)
L 47	**Laguerre['s] polynomial in the narrow sense** <FU>	Laguerresches Polynom *n* im engeren Sinne	polynôme *m* de Laguerre au sens étroit	многочлен Чебышева-Лагерра в узком смысле

No.	English	German	French	Russian
L 48	**lambda-conversion,** λ-conversion <LO>	λ-Konversion *f*, Lambda-Konversion *f*	λ-conversion *f*, lambda-conversion *f*	λ-конверсия, лямбда-конверсия
L 49	**lambda-definable function,** λ-definable function <FO>	lambda-definierbare (λ-definierbare) Funktion *f*	fonction *f* lambda-définissable (λ-définissable)	ламбда-определимая (λ-определимая) функция
	lambda-matrix <AL>	*s.* P 999		
	lamdba[-]operator <LO>	*s.* A 152		
L 50	**lambda-ring,** Λ-ring <AL>	Λ-Ring *m*, Lambda-Ring *m*	Λ-anneau *m*, lambda-anneau *m*	Λ-кольцо, ламбда-кольцо
L 51	**lambda variation,** λ-variation, τ (λ) <RF>	λ-Variation *f*, Lambda-Variation *f*, τ (λ)	variation *f* λ, variation lambda, τ (λ)	λ-вариация, ламбда-вариация, τ (λ)
L 52	**Lambert['s] series** <FU, NT>	Lambertsche Reihe *f*, Lambert-Reihe *f*	série *f* de Lambert	ряд Ламберта
L 53	**Lambert['s] theorems** <on the parabola> <GE>	Lambertsche Parabelsätze *mpl*	théorèmes *mpl* de Lambert	теоремы Ламберта
L 54	**Lamé['s] curve** <DG>	Lamésche Kurve *f*	courbe *f* de Lamé	кривая Ламе
	Lamé['s] differential equation <DE>	*s.* L 56		
L 55	**Lamé['s] differential parameter of the first order,** first differential parameter of Lamé <DG>	erster (1.) Differentialparameter *m* von Lamé, Laméscher Differentialparameter erster (1.) Ordnung	paramètre *m* différentiel de Lamé du premier ordre	дифференциальный параметр Ламе первого рода
	Lamé['s] differential parameter of the second order <DE, DG, DI, PO>	*s.* L 91		
L 56	**Lamé['s] equation,** Lamé['s] differential equation <DE>	Lamésche Differentialgleichung (Gleichung) *f*	équation *f* de Lamé, équation différentielle de Lamé	уравнение Ламе, дифференциальное уравнение Ламе
	Lamé['s] equation <DE>	*s.* L 64		
L 57	**Lamé['s] family of surfaces** <DG>	Lamésche Flächenschar *f*	famille *f* de surfaces de Lamé	семейство поверхностей Ламе
L 58	**Lamé['s] function,** ellipsoidal function <FU>	Lamésche Funktion *f*	fonction *f* de Lamé, fonction ellipsoïdale	функция Ламе, эллипсоидальная функция
L 59	**Lamé['s] function of the first kind** <FU>	Lamésche Funktion *f* erster (1.) Gattung <1., 2., 3. *oder* 4. Art>	fonction *f* de Lamé de première (1re) espèce	функция Ламе первого (1-го) рода
L 60	**Lamé['s] function of the second kind,** associate Lamé function <FU>	Lamésche Funktion *f* zweiter (2.) Gattung, zugeordnete Lamésche Funktion	fonction *f* de Lamé de deuxième (seconde, 2de) espèce, fonction de Lamé associée	функция Ламе второго (2-го) рода
	lamellar [vector] field <VT>	*s.* I 1070		
L 61	**Lamé['s] number** <DI>	Lamésche Zahl *f*	nombre *m* de Lamé	число Ламе
L 62	**Lamé['s] polynomial** <FU>	Lamésches Polynom *n*	polynôme *m* de Lamé	многочлен Ламе
	Lamé['s] series of *n*-th order <NT>	*s.* N 748		
L 63	**Lamé['s] theorem** <FD>	Satz *m* von Lamé, Laméscher Satz	théorème *m* de Lamé	теорема Ламе
L 64	**Lamé['s] wave equation,** generalized Lamé equation, Lamé['s] equation <DE>	Lamésche Wellengleichung (Differentialgleichung) *f*, verallgemeinerte Lamésche Differentialgleichung	équation *f* des ondes de Lamé, équation de Lamé généralisée, équation de Lamé	волновое (обобщенное) уравнение Ламе, уравнение Ламе
L 65	**Lamé['s] wave function,** ellipsoidal wave function <FU>	Lamésche Wellenfunktion *f*	fonction *f* d'onde de Lamé, fonction d'onde ellipsoïdale	эллипсоидальная волновая функция, волновая функция Ламе
L 66	**Lancret['s] equation** <DG>	Lancretsche Gleichung *f*	équation *f* de Lancret	уравнение Ланкре
	Landau order symbols <AN>	*s.* O 393		
L 67	**Landau['s] polynomial** <FU>	Landausches Polynom *n*	polynôme *m* de Landau	многочлен Ландау
L 68	**Landau['s] radius** <FT>	Landauscher Radius *m*	rayon *m* de Landau	радиус Ландау
L 69	**Landau['s] theorem** <FT>	Landauscher Satz *m*, Satz von Landau	théorème *m* de Landau	теорема Ландау
L 70	**Landen['s] transformation** <FT, FU>	Landensche Transformation *f*	transformation *f* de Landen	преобразование Ландена
	language of formulas <GN>	*s.* F 493		
L 71	**Laplace-Beltrami operator** <of a form> <AN>	Laplace-Beltrami-Operator *m*	opérateur *m* de Laplace-Beltrami	оператор Лапласа-Бельтрами
L 72	**Laplace['s] cascade method,** cascade method <DE>	Kaskadenmethode *f* [von Laplace], Laplacesche Kaskadenmethode	méthode *f* de cascade [de Laplace]	каскадный метод [Лапласа], метод Лапласа
L 73	**Laplace['s] cycle,** periodic Laplace sequence <DG>	Laplacescher Zyklus *m*, Laplace-Zyklus *m*, periodische Laplacesche Folge *f*	cycle *m* de Laplace, suite *f* de Laplace périodique	цикл Лапласа, периодическая последовательность Лапласа
	Laplace['s] differential equation <PO>	*s.* L 75		
	Laplace['s] differential operator <DE, DG, DI, PO>	*s.* L 91		
L 74	**Laplace['s] distribution** <ST>	Laplace-Verteilung *f*, Laplacesche Verteilung *f*	distribution *f* de Laplace, distribution laplacienne	распределение Лапласа
L 75	**Laplace['s] equation,** Laplace['s] differential equation, potential equation <PO>	Laplacesche Differentialgleichung (Gleichung) *f*, [Laplacesche] Potentialgleichung *f*	équation *f* de Laplace, équation différentielle de Laplace, laplacienne *f*, formule *f* de Laplace	уравнение Лапласа, дифференциальное уравнение Лапласа, уравнение потенциального поля
L 76	**Laplace['s] expansion** <of a determinant> <MD>	Laplacescher Entwicklungssatz (Determinantensatz, Zerlegungssatz) *m*, Laplacesche Formel *f*, Laplacescher Satz *m* [für Determinanten]	développement *m* (règle *f*) de Laplace	теорема Лапласа <об определителях>, теорема разложения Лапласа

No.	English	German	French	Russian
L 77	**Laplace['s] expansion** <of a determinant> <process> <MD>	Entwicklung *f* nach dem Laplaceschen Entwicklungssatz, Unterdeterminantenentwicklung *f*	développement *m* suivant la règle de Laplace, développement de Laplace	разложение Лапласа (по минорам)
L 78	**Laplace['s] formula,** Laplace['s] quadrature formula <DI, NU>	Laplacesche Quadraturformel (Formel) *f*	formule *f* de Laplace, formule d'intégration de Laplace	формула Лапласа (численного интегрирования Лапласа)
L 79	**Laplace['s] integral** <of Legendre polynomials> <FU>	Laplacesche Integraldarstellung *f*; Laplace-Integral *n*, erzeugendes Integral *n*, erzeugende Funktion *f*	intégrale *f* de Laplace, intégrale génératrice	интеграл Лапласа
L 80	**Laplace['s] integral** <in Laplace transform> <IT>	Laplacesches Integral *n*, Laplace-Integral *n*	intégrale *f* de Laplace	интеграл Лапласа
L 81	**Laplace['s] invariant** <DE>	Laplacesche Invariante *f*	invariant *m* de Laplace	инвариант Лапласа
L 82	**Laplace['s] kernel** <DE>	Laplacescher Kern *m*	noyau *m* de Laplace	ядро Лапласа
	Laplace['s] limit theorem <ST>	*s.* M 806		
L 83	**Laplace['s] linear equation** <as an ordinary differential equation> <DE>	Laplacesche gewöhnliche Differentialgleichung *f*	équation *f* linéaire de Laplace	линейное [дифференциальное] уравнение Лапласа
	Laplace['s] operator <DE, DG, DI, PO>	*s.* L 91		
L 84	**Laplace['s] polynomial** <FU>	Laplacesches Polynom *n*	polynôme *m* de Laplace	многочлен (полином) Лапласа
	Laplace['s] quadrature formula <DI, NU>	*s.* L 78		
	Laplace['s] sequence <DG>	*s.* S 581		
L 85	**Laplace['s] series** <FU, SS>	Laplacesche Reihe *f*	série *f* de Laplace	ряд Лапласа
L 86	**Laplace['s] spherical function (harmonic)** <FU>	Laplacesche (allgemeine) Kugelfunktion *f*	fonction *f* [harmonique] sphérique de Laplace, fonction [harmonique] sphérique générale, harmonique *f* sphérique générale (de Laplace)	шаровая (сферическая) функция Лапласа
L 87	**Laplace-Stieltjes transform[ation]** <IT>	Laplace-Stieltjes-Transformation *f*	transformation *f* [intégrale] de Laplace-Stieltjes	преобразование Лапласа-Стилтьеса
L 88	**Laplace['s] transform** <IT>	Laplace-Transformierte *f*, L-Transformierte *f*, Unterfunktion *f*, Bildfunktion *f*, Resultatfunktion *f*	transformée *f* [de Laplace], fonction *f* image, image *f*, image de Laplace	изображение [по Лапласу], изображение Лапласа, преобразованная по Лапласу функция
L 89	**Laplace['s] transform[ation]** <IT>	Laplace-Transformation *f*, Laplacesche Transformation *f*, Transformation (Integraltransformation *f*) nach Laplace	transformation *f* de Laplace, transformation intégrale de Laplace	преобразование Лапласа, интегральное преобразование Лапласа
L 90	**Laplace['s] transformation** <on a surface in a projective space> <DG>	Laplace-Transformation *f*	transformation *f* de Laplace	преобразование Лапласа
L 91	**Laplacian,** laplacian, Laplace['s] operator, Laplace['s] differential operator, delta operator, delta, Laplacian derivative, Δ, ∇^2; [Lamé['s]] differential parameter of the second order, second differential parameter [of Lamé] <in differential geometry only> <DE, DG, DI, PO>	Laplace-Operator *m*, Laplaceoperator *m*, Laplacescher Operator *m*, Delta-Operator *m*, Delta *n*, Δ, ∇^2 <allgemein>; Laplacescher Differentialausdruck (Ausdruck) *m* <DG, PO>; zweiter (2.) Differentialparameter *m* [von Lamé], [Laméscher] Differentialparameter zweiter (2.) Ordnung <DG>	laplacien *m*, opérateur *m* laplacien (delta), Δ, ∇^2; paramètre *m* différentiel [de Lamé] du second ordre <en géométrie différentielle>	лапласиан, оператор Лапласа, дельта-оператор, Δ-оператор, Δ, ∇^2; дифференциальный параметр [Ламе] второго рода <в дифференциальной геометрии>
L 92	**Laplacian** <of a vector field> <grad div — rot rot> <VT>	Laplace-Operator *m*, Laplacescher Operator *m* <eines Vektorfeldes>	laplacien *m* vectoriel	векторный лапласиан
	Laplacian derivative <DE, DG, DI, PO>	*s.* L 91		
L 92 a	**large / in the,** globally <adv.> <GN>	im Großen, global, // im großen	globalement	в целом, глобально, в большом
	large category <CA>	*s.* B 318		
	large inductive dimension <TO>	*s.* S 1957		
	larger topology <TO>	*s.* F 247		
L 93	**large sample** <ST>	große Stichprobe *f*	grand échantillon *m*	большая выборка
L 94	**large sample analysis** <ST>	Verfahren *n* für große Stichproben, Analyse *f* großer Stichproben	méthode (analyse) *f* des grands échantillons	анализ больших выборок
L 95	**large-sample test** <ST>	Test *m* für große Stichproben	test *m* pour les grands échantillons	критерий для больших выборок
L 96	**large sieve method** <NT>	Methode *f* des großen Siebes	méthode *f* du grand crible	метод «большого решета»
	largest covering manifold <TO>	*s.* U 326		
	largest element <SE>	*s.* G 409		
L 97	**largest Hausdorff quotient** <of a topological space> <TO>	größter Hausdorffscher Quotientenraum *m*	espace-quotient *m* séparé maximum	максимальное хаусдорфово факторпространство
	largest normal divisor	*s.* M 240		
	largest number <SE>	*s.* G 409		
L 98	**largest topology,** finest topology <TO>	feinste Topologie *f*	topologie *f* la plus fine	сильнейшая топология, самая тонкая топология
	largest value <DI>	*s.* A 115		

L 99	**laskerian ring** <AL>	laskerscher Ring *m*	anneau *m* laskérien	ласкерово кольцо
L 100	**Lasker-Noether decomposition theorem** <AL>	Satz *m* von Lasker-Noether, Lasker-Noetherscher Satz, Zerlegungssatz *m* der Idealtheorie, Zerlegungssatz, Laskersches Theorem *n*	théorème *m* de Lasker-Noether (décomposition)	теорема Ласкера-Нетера (разложения)
L 101	**Lasker['s] theorem** <AL>	Laskerscher Satz *m*	théorème *m* de Lasker	теорема Ласкера
L 102	**last digit** <of a number> <NT, NU>	letzte Ziffer (Stelle) *f*, Endziffer *f*	chiffre *m* des unités, dernier chiffre	одноциферное окончание, последняя цифра
	last member <SE>	*s.* G 409		
L 103	**last multiplier** <DE>	letzter Multiplikator *m*	dernier multiplicateur *m* [de Jacobi]	последний умножитель
L 104	**last multiplier theorem** <DE>	Satz *m* vom letzten Multiplikator	théorème *m* du dernier multiplicateur	теорема последнего умножителя
L 105	**last term** <of a series> <SS>	Endglied *n*, letztes Glied *n*	dernier terme *m*, terme final	концевой член
	last term in the upper central series <GR>	*s.* H 662		
	latent component <ST>	*s.* H 297		
	latent domain <SE>	*s.* D 856		
	latent equation <AL, MD>	*s.* C 540		
L 106	**latent range,** range carrier <of a correspondence> <SE>	Zielbereich *m*, Nachbereich *m*	ensemble *m* d'arrivée, ensemble final	множество прибытия
	latent range <SE, TO>	*s.* R 123		
	latent root <MD>	*s.* E 61		
	latent vector <MD>	*s.* E 65		
	later <NT, SE>	*s.* G 402		
L 107	**lateral area** <of a polyhedron> <area of the lateral surface> <EG>	Mantelfläche *f*, Mantel *m*, Seitenfläche *f*	aire *f* latérale	площадь боковой поверхности
L 108	**lateral convergence** <of a double sequence> <SS>	laterale Konvergenz *f*	convergence *f* latérale	боковая сходимость
L 109	**lateral edge** <of a pyramid> <EG>	Seitenkante *f*	arête *f* latérale	боковое ребро
	lateral edge <EG>	*s.* E 11		
	lateral face <EG>	*s.* F 7		
	lateral side <EG>	*s.* L 526		
L 110	**lateral surface,** curved surface <of a cone *or* cylinder> <EG>	Mantel *m*, Mantelfläche *f*, Seitenfläche *f*	surface latérale (courbe)	боковая поверхность
L 111	**lateral surface** <of a polyhedron> <sum of the lateral faces> <EG>	Seitenfläche *f*	surface *f* latérale	боковая поверхность
L 112	**latin cube** <ST>	lateinischer Würfel *m*	cube *m* latin	латинский куб
L 113	**latin rectangle,** semi latin square <CT, ST>	lateinisches Rechteck *n*	rectangle *m* latin	латинский прямоугольник
L 114	**latin (Latin) square,** magic latin square <CT, ST>	[magisches] lateinisches Quadrat, LQ	carré *m* [magique] latin, permutation *f* carrée	латинский квадрат, латинский магический квадрат
	latin square in standard form <CT, ST>	*s.* S 1634		
L 115	**Latin square of *m*-th order, Latin square of order** *m*, $m \times m$ latin square <CT>	lateinisches Quadrat *n* der Seitenlänge *m*, *m*-reihiges lateinisches Quadrat	carré *m* latin de côté *m*	латинский квадрат порядка *m*
L 116	**lattice** <AL, AX, NU>	Gitter *n*	réseau *m*	решетка <AL>; сетка <AX, NU>
L 117	**lattice,** structure <LA>	Verband *m*, // Dualgruppe *f*	treillis *m*, structure *f*, lattice *m*, ensemble *m* réticulé (ordonné réticulé), ordre *m* latticiel, réseau *m* ordonné, réticulé *m*, lattis *m*, // groupe *m* double, système *m* de choses <Glivenko>, logique *f* ramifiée <Moisil>	структура, решетка, решеточно упорядоченное множество, латтис, связка, упорядоченная сеть
	lattice <ST>	*s.* L 120		
	σ-lattice <LA>	*s.* S 827		
L 118	**lattice constant** <ST>	Gitterkonstante *f*	pas *m* <de la distribution arithmétique>	шаг <решетчатого распределения>
L 119	**lattice covering** <GE, NT>	gitterförmige Überdeckung *f*	recouvrement *m* réticulaire	решетчатое покрытие
L 120	**lattice design,** lattice <ST>	Gitteranlage *f*, Gitter *n*	plan *m* en lattice (treillis), treillis *m*, lattice *m*, lattis *m*	решетчатый план, решетка
L 121	**lattice distribution** <ST>	gitterförmige Verteilung *f*, Gitterverteilung *f*	distribution *f* réticulaire (en réseau)	решетчатое распределение
L 122	**lattice function** <AX, DE, IE, NU>	Gitterfunktion *f*	fonction *f* de réseau, fonction donnée aux points d'un réseau	сеточная функция; функция, заданная на сетке
L 123	**lattice-homomorphic group,** l-homomorphic group <GR>	verbandshomomorphe Gruppe *f*	groupe *m* homomorphe structuralement, groupe structure-homomorphe	структурно гомоморфная группа, l-гомоморфная группа
L 124	**lattice[-] homomorphism,** homomorphism <of a lattice> <LA>	Verbandshomomorphismus *m*, Homomorphismus *m* <eines Verbands>	homomorphisme *m* <d'un treillis>, morphisme *m* de treillis, morphisme <d'un treillis>	структурный гомоморфизм, гомоморфизм решеток, гомоморфизм <структуры>
	lattice homomorphism <GR>	*s.* L 629		
L 125	**lattice identity** <LA>	Verbandsidentität *f*	identité *f* latticielle	структурное тождество

No.	English	German	French	Russian
	lattice-isomorphism, lattice isomorphism <GR, LA>	*s.* P 1735		
L 126	**lattice octahedron** <GU, NT>	Gitteroktaeder *n*	octaèdre *m* latticiel	решетчатый октаэдр
L 127	**lattice of congruence relations,** congruence lattice <LA>	Kongruenzrelationenverband *m*, Kongruenzenverband *m*	treillis *m* des congruences	структура конгруэнций
L 128	**lattice of cubes** <GE>	Würfelgitter *n*	réseau *m* de cubes	решетка кубов
L 129	**lattice of normal divisors** <LA>	Normalteilerverband *m*	treillis *m* des sous-groupes invariants	структура нормальных делителей
L 130	**lattice of partitions** <of a set> <SE>	Zerlegungsverband *m*	treillis *m* des partitions	структура разбиений
L 131	**lattice of periods** <of a doubly periodic function> <FT>	Periodengitter *n*, Periodennetz *n*	réseau *m* de parallélogrammes [de périodes], réseau de périodes	решетка периодов
L 132	**lattice of relations** <LA>	Relationenverband *m*	treillis *m* d'ensembles des parties	структура отношений
L 133	**lattice of sets** <AL, SE>	Mengenverband *m*	treillis *m* de parties, treillis d'ensembles	структура множеств
L 134	**lattice of subgroups** <GR>	Untergruppenverband *m*	lattice (treillis) *m* de sous-groupes, lattice du groupe	структура подгрупп
L 135	**lattice operation** <LA>	Verbandsoperation *f*	opération *f* latticielle	структурная операция
L 136	**lattice-ordered algebra** <AL>	verbandsgeordnete Algebra *f*	algèbre *f* réticulée	структурно упорядоченная алгебра, структурная алгебра
L 137	**lattice-ordered group,** l-group <LA>	Verbandsgruppe *f*, l-Gruppe *f*	groupe *m* réticulé	структурно (решеточно) упорядоченная группа, l-группа
L 138	**lattice-ordered groupoid** <AL>	Gruppoid-Verband *m*	groupoïde *m* ordonné en treillis	структурно упорядоченный группоид
	lattice[-]ordered Lie group <GR>	*s.* L 666		
L 139	**lattice-ordered module** <AL>	verbandsgeordneter Modul *m*	module (vectoriel) *m* en treillis, module (vectoriel) réticulé	структурно упорядоченный модуль
L 140	**lattice-ordered ring,** l-ring <AL>	verbandsgeordneter Ring *m*	anneau *m* ordonné réticulé, anneau réticulé	структурно (решеточно) упорядоченное кольцо, l-кольцо
	lattice[-]ordered semigroup <AL>	*s.* A 1110		
L 141	**lattice ordering** <AL, SE>	verbandsmäßige Ordnung *f*, Verbandsordnung *f*	ordre *m* latticiel	структурный (решеточный) порядок
L 142	**lattice ordering structure** <AL, UA>	Verbandsordnungsstruktur *f*	structure *f* d'ordre latticiel	решеточно-упорядоченная структура
L 143	**lattice packing** <GE, GU>	gitterförmige Anordnung (Lagerung) *f*	empilement *m* réticulaire	решетчатая упаковка
	lattice point <NT>	*s.* P 771		
L 144	**lattice point at the boundary** <NU>	Randgitterpunkt *m*	sommet *m* sur la frontière	граничная точка сетки
L 145	**lattice-point method** <DE, IE, NU>; finite-difference method <DE, NU>	Gitterpunktmethode *f* <DE, IE, NU>; Differenzenverfahren *n*, Differenzenmethode *f* <DE, NU>	méthode *f* des réseaux <DE, IE, NU>; méthode *f* des différences finies, méthode de différences finies <DE, NU>	метод сеток <DE, IE, NU>; конечно разностный метод, метод конечных разностей, разностный метод <DE, NU>
L 146	**lattice polynomial** <LA>	Verbandspolynom *n*	« polynôme *m* latticiel »	решеточный многочлен
L 147	**lattice-preserving mapping** <of a partially ordered set> <SE>	Verbandshomomorphismus *m*	application *f* préservant la structure de treillis	структурный гомоморфизм
L 148	**lattice-quasi-ordered class** <SE>	verbandsmäßig quasigeordnete Klasse *f*	classe *f* quasi-ordonné en treillis	решеточно-квазиупорядоченный класс
L 149	**lattice sampling,** grid sampling <ST>	Gitterstichprobenverfahren *n*	échantillonnage *m* treillis (lattice)	решетчатый выбор
	lattice satisfying the descending and ascending chain condition <LA>	*s.* D 665		
L 150	**lattice-stable** <quasi-ordered class> <SE>	abgeschlossen gegenüber Durchschnitts- und Vereinigungsbildung	stable pour les intersections et les réunions	замкнутый относительно пересечений и объединений
L 151	**lattice structure** <LA>	Verbandsstruktur *f*	structure *f* de treillis (lattice)	решетчатая структура
L 152	**lattice theoretic,** lattice-theoretic <LA>	verbandstheoretisch	d'après la théorie des structures, au sens de la théorie des structures	теоретико-структурный
L 153	**lattice theory,** theory of lattices <LA>	Verbandstheorie *f*, Theorie *f* der Verbände	théorie *f* des treillis (structures)	теория структур (решеток)
L 154	**lattice transformation** <AL>	Gittertransformation *f*	transformation *f* du réseau	решеточное преобразование
	lattice variety <UA>	*s.* E 337		
L 155	**lattice with a positive valuation** <LA>	positiv bewerteter Verband *m*	treillis *m* à valuation positive	положительно нормированная структура
L 156	**lattice with a valuation** <AL>	bewerteter Verband *m*	treillis *m* valué	нормированная структура
L 157	**latus rectum,** focal chord, *p* <of a conic> <AY>	Parameter *m*, latus *n* rectum	paramètre *m*, latus rectum *m*, corde *f* focale	фокальный параметр, умноженный на два
L 158	**Laurent['s] expansion;** Laurent['s] series <FT>	Laurentsche Entwicklung *f*, Laurent-Entwicklung *f*; Laurentsche Reihe *f*, Laurent-Reihe *f*	développement *m* de Laurent; série *f* de Laurent	разложение [в ряд] Лорана, лораново разложение; ряд Лорана
L 159	**Laurent['s] integral** <of the Legendre functions> <FU>	Laurentsche Integraldarstellung *f*	intégrale *f* de Laurent	интеграл Лорана

	Laurent['s] series <FT>	*s.* L 158		
L 160	**Laurent['s] theorem** <FT>	Laurentscher Satz *m*, Satz von Laurent, Laurents Satz	théorème *m* de Laurent	теорема Лорана
L 161	**L-automorphism,** structural automorphism, auto[-]projectivity <of a group> <GR>	Verbandsautomorphismus *m*	automorphisme *m* structural	структурный автоморфизм
L 162	**law "ex falso quodlibet",** Don Scotus['] law, law of Don Scotus <LO>	Prinzip *n* des „ex falso quodlibet sequitur", aktiver Widerspruchseffekt *m*, Ex falso quodlibet *n*; Wahrform *f* zum Schluß „ex falso quodlibet", Form *f* zum Schluß aus Widerlegtem, Dun-Scot-Regel *f*, „Ex contradictione quodlibet" *n*, Regula *f* falsi, Unableitbarkeitsprinzip *n*	principe *m* de l'inconsistance, ex falso sequitur quodlibet *m*, loi *f* de Duns Scot (Scotus)	из ложного следует все, что угодно; ex falso quodlibet; из противоречия следует все, что угодно
L 163	**law for joining the universal quantifier to the consequent of an implication** <LO>	Prinzip *n* der zulässigen hinteren Generalisierung, Gesetz *n* der Einführung des Allquantors in das Hinterglied	loi *f* d'introduction du quantificateur universel dans le conséquent	закон ∀-введения в сукцеденте
	law of absorption <LA>	*s.* A 138		
L 164	**law of adding implications by sides** <LO>	Regel *f* der Addition der Implikationen, Satz *m* von der beiderseitigen Addition von Implikationen	loi *f* de combinaison terme à terme de deux implications	
L 165	**law of addition,** principle of addition <LO>	Verdünnungsgesetz *n* für ∨, Theorem *n* der alternativen Verdünnung; Form *f* zur ∨-Verdünnung	principe *m* de simplification pour ∨	закон расширения
L 166	**law of addition of antecedents,** law of combining antecedents into a disjunction <LO>	Theorem *n* der vorderen Kopplung, Additionsgesetz *n* der Vorderglieder, Prinzip *n* der vorderen Kopplung; Form *f* zur Vordergliedisjugation	loi *f* de disjonction des prémisses, principe *m* de composition [pour les antécédents]	закон сложения антецедентов
	law of affirmation of the consequent <LO>	*s.* L 206		
	law of alteration of universal quantifiers <LO>	*s.* L 172		
L 167	**law of a new element,** principle of summation <LO>	Form *f* zur Oder-Nachsetzung; Regel *f* des neuen Summanden	loi *f* de compatibilité de la disjonction pour l'implication	
L 168	**law of a new factor** <LO>	Form *f* zur ∧-Nachsetzung; Form zur ∧-Vorsetzung	loi *f* de compatibilité de la conjonction pour l'implication	закон нового сомножителя
L 169	**law of categorical syllogism** <LO>	Prinzip *n* des kategorischen Syllogismus	principe *m* du syllogisme catégorique	простой категорический силлогизм
	law of combination <AL>	*s.* M 1028		
	law of combining antecedents into a disjunction <LO>	*s.* L 166		
L 170	**law of combining the consequents into a conjunction,** law of multiplication of consequents <LO>	Theorem (Prinzip) *n* der hinteren Kopplung, Multiplikationsgesetz *n* für die Hinterglieder; Form *f* zur Hintergliedkonjugation	principe *m* de composition <pour les conséquents>	закон умножения сукцедентов
L 171	**law of commutation** <LO>	Theorem *n* (Prinzip *n*, Satz *m*) der Prämissenvertauschung, Gesetz *n* der Vertauschung der Voraussetzungen, Wahrform *f* des Tausches der Vorderglieder, Wahrform (Form *f*) zum Tausch der Vorderglieder, Fregesches Axiom *n* 3	loi *f* de commutation (symétrie des prémisses)	закон дистрибутивности [импликации], закон перестановки антецедентов, перестановка посылок, закон перестановки посылок
	law of commutation <AL, LO>	*s.* C 1262		
	law of commutation <SS>	*s.* C 1252		
	law of commutativity <AL, LO>	*s.* C 1262		
L 172	**law of commutativity of universal quantifiers,** law of alteration of universal quantifiers <LO>	Gesetz *n* der Vertauschung der Allquantifikatoren	loi *f* de permutation des doubles quantifications universelles	закон перестановки кванторов всеобщности
L 173	**law of composition** <in a group>, group composition, group multi-	Gruppengesetz *n*, Kompositionsgesetz *n* in einer Gruppe, Gruppen-	loi *f* de groupe, loi de composition dans un groupe	групповой закон, композиция группы

No.	English	German	French	Russian
and still: L 173	plication, group law <GR>	operationen *fpl*, Gruppenmultiplikation *f*, Multiplikation *f*		
	law of composition <AL>	*s.* M 1028		
	law of compound constructive dilemma <LO>	*s.* C 1607		
L 174	**law of compound transposition** <LO>	erweitertes Kontrapositionsgesetz *n*	loi *f* de transposition composée	теорема сложной контрапозиции
L 175	**law of contradiction,** principle of contradiction, law of non-contradiction <LO>	Prinzip *n* (Satz *m*) vom ausgeschlossenen Widerspruch, Satz vom Widerspruch, Theorem *n* des ausgeschlossenen Widerspruchs, lex *f* contradictionis, principium *n* contradictionis	principe *m* de contradiction [exclue], loi *f* de contradiction (non-contradiction), principe de non-contradiction	закон противоречия, [формально-] логический закон противоречия, принцип противоречия (запрещения противоречия), закон отрицания противоречия, закон непротиворечия
	law of contraposition <LO>	*s.* C 1450		
L 176	**law of cosines,** cosine law, cosine rule <of plane *or* spherical trigonometry> <EG>	Kosinussatz *m*	théorème *m* des cosinus, théorème du cosinus	теорема косинусов
L 177	**law of decomposition** <AB>	Zerlegungsgesetz *n*	loi *f* de décomposition	закон разложения
L 178	**law of deduction,** deduction law (theorem) <LO>	Deduktionstheorem *n*	théorème *m* de [la] déduction	теорема [о] дедукции
	law of detachment <FO, LO>	*s.* L 213		
L 179	**law of distributivity of the existential and universal quantifier with respect to an equivalence** <LO>	Theorem *n* der gliedweisen Quantifizierung einer Äquivalenz	loi *f* de quantification de l'équivalence générale	закон дистрибутивности кванторов относительно эквиваленции
L 180	**law of distributivity of the existential quantifier with respect to a disjunction** <LO>	Gesetz *n* der Verteilung des Existenzquantifikators auf eine Alternative	loi *f* de quantification existentielle d'une disjonction	закон дистрибутивности квантора существования относительно дизъюнкции
L 181	**law of distributivity with respect to implication** <LO>	Distributivgesetz *n* bezüglich Implikation, Gesetz *n* der Verteilung auf eine Implikation	semi-distributivité *f* par rapport à l'implication, loi *f* de quantification de l'implication générale	полудистрибутивность относительно импликации
	law of Don Scotus <LO>	*s.* L 162		
L 182	**law of double negation,** complete law of double negation <equivalence> <LO>	Gesetz *n* der doppelten Negation, Satz *m* über die doppelte Verneinung; Form *f* zur reductio inabsurdi und Form zur introductio inabsurdi	loi *f* de double négation, loi de la double négation, principe *m* de [la] double négation, involution *f*	эквивалентность двойного отрицания утверждению, закон отрицания отрицания, полный закон двойного отрицания, // закон двойного отрицания
L 183	**law of double negation** <LO>	zweites Verneinungsgesetz *n*, Form *f* zur reductio inabsurdi	loi *f* de double négation	закон снятия двойного отрицания, закон двойного отрицания
	law of errors <ER>	*s.* E 475		
L 184	**law of excluded middle,** law (principle) of the excluded middle, law (principle) of the excluded third, tertium exclusum (non datur) <LO>	Satz *m* (Prinzip *n*) vom ausgeschlossenen Dritten, Prinzip des ausgeschlossenen Dritten, Tertium *n* non datur, principium *n* exclusi tertii	principe *m* (loi *f*) du tiers exclu, principe logique du tiers exclu, principium *m* tertii exclusi	закон (принцип) исключенного третьего, формально-логический закон исключенного третьего, третьего не дано, tertium non datur
L 185	**law of exponentiation (exponents),** exponential law, index law <AL, SE>	Potenzgesetz *n*, Potenzregel *f*	loi *f* de l'élévation aux puissances, règle *f* du calcul des puissances	закон показателей, свойство степеней, правило действия с показателями
L 186	**law of exportation,** exportation <LO>	Theorem *n* des Übergangs zur Prämissenzerlegung, Exportationsgesetz *n*	loi *f* d'expédition, exportation *f*	закон экспортации, экспортация
L 187	**law of formation** <LO>	Bildungsgesetz *n*	loi *f* de formation	закон образования
	law of homomorphism <GR>	*s.* H 505		
	law of identity <LO>	*s.* L 189		
L 188	**law of identity for equivalence** <LO>	Reflexivgesetz *n*, Gesetz *n* der Reflexivität <der Äquivalenz>, Identitätsgesetz *n*	loi *f* de réflexivité <de l'équivalence>, loi d'identité	закон тождества, закон идентичности
L 189	**law of identity for implication,** law of identity, identity law, repetition, reflexive law of [material] implication <LO>	Satz *m* von der Identität, [aussagenlogisches] Gesetz *n* der Identität, lex *f* identitatis, Gesetz der Reflexivität der Implikation, Satz der Selbstimplikation	principe *m* d'identité, loi *f* de réflexivité de l'implication	закон тождества (рефлексивности материальной импликации), принцип тождества
L 190	**law of importation,** importation <LO>	Theorem *n* des Übergangs zur Prämissenverbindung, Importationsgesetz *n*	loi *f* d'importation, loi de réunion des prémisses	закон импортации, импортация
L 191	**law of inertia,** Sylvester['s] law of inertia, Sylvester['s] law, Jacobi-Sylvester Inertia Theorem <for Hermitian	Sylvestersches (Sylvesters) Trägheitsgesetz *n*, Trägheitsgesetz, Trägheitsgesetz von Sylvester; Trägheitsgesetz der	loi *f* d'inertie, loi d'inertie de Sylvester (J. J. Sylvester); loi d'inertie des formes quadratiques	закон инерции, теорема Сильвестра; закон инерции квадратичных форм

No.	English	German	French	Russian
	forms>; **law of inertia for quadratic forms** <AL>	quadratischen Formen, Satz *m* von Sylvester, Sylvesterscher Satz		
L 192	**law of iterated logarithm,** law of the iterated logarithm <ST>	Gesetz *n* vom (des) iterierten Logarithmus	loi *f* du logarithme itéré, loi des logarithmes itérés	закон повторного логарифма
	law of joining a superfluous quantifier <LO>	*s.* R 1474		
	law of joining a superfluous universal quantifier <LO>	*s.* R 1452		
L 193	**law of large numbers** <ST>	Gesetz *n* der großen Zahlen	loi *f* des grands nombres	закон больших чисел
	law of left-side cancellation <AL>	*s.* L 309		
L 194	**law of logic** <general truth of logic> <LO>	logisches Gesetz *n*	loi *f* logique, tautologie *f*, formule *f* analytique	логический закон, закон мышления (логики)
	law of monotony <AL, SE>	*s.* M 877		
	law of multiplication <AL>	*s.* M 1028		
	law of multiplication of consequents <LO>	*s.* L 170		
L 195	**law of multiplying implications by sides** <LO>	Regel *f* der Multiplikation der Implikationen, Satz *m* von der beiderseitigen Multiplikation von Implikationen	loi *f* de combinaison terme à terme de deux implications	
L 196	**law of negating a conjunction** <LO>	Verneinungsgesetz *n* (Gesetz *n* der Negation) der Konjunktion	loi *f* de négation de la conjonction	закон отрицания конъюнкции
L 197	**law of negating a disjunction** <LO>	Verneinungsgesetz *n* der Disjunktion, Gesetz *n* der Negation der Alternative; Regel *f* der Negation der Alternative	loi *f* de négation de la disjonction	закон отрицания дизъюнкции
L 198	**law of negating an equivalence** <LO>	Verneinungsgesetz *n* (Gesetz *n* der Negation) der Äquivalenz	loi *f* de négation de l'équivalence	закон отрицания эквивалентности
L 199	**law of negating an implication** <LO>	Verneinungsgesetz *n* (Gesetz *n* der Negation) der Implikation	loi *f* de négation de l'implication	закон отрицания импликативного суждения, закон отрицания импликации
L 200	**law of negating the existential quantifier,** <LO>	Gesetz *n* der Negation des Existenzquantifikators; Gesetz der Ersetzung des Allquantifikators durch den Existenzquantifikator und die Negation	principe *m* de la négation des existentielles, négation *f* de l'existence	закон отрицания квантора существования
L 201	**law of negating the universal quantifier** <LO>	Gesetz *n* der Negation des Allquantifikators, Gesetz der Ersetzung des Existenzquantifikators durch den Allquantifikator und die Negation	principe *m* de la négation des universelles, négation *f* de la totalité	закон отрицания квантора всеобщности
	law of non-contradiction <LO>	*s.* L 175		
L 202	**law of nullity,** Sylvester['s] law of nullity <for the product of two matrices> <MD>	Sylvestersche Ungleichung *f* <für das Produkt zweier Matrizen>	théorème *m* des nullités [de Sylvester]	неравенство Сильвестра
L 203	**law of omitting superfluous existential quantifiers** <LO>	Gesetz *n* der Existenzbeseitigung	loi *f* d'exclusion du quantificateur existentiel	закон ∃-удаления
	law of operation <AR>	*s.* R 1498		
	law of probability <SE>	*s.* T 926		
	law of quadratic reciprocity <NT>	*s.* Q 42		
	law of rare events <ST>	*s.* P 833		
	law of recurrence of order k <FD, NT>	*s.* R 309		
	law of reductio ad absurdum <LO>	*s.* R 442		
	law of right-side cancellation <AL>	*s.* R 1089		
	law of signs <AL, AR>	*s.* R 1505		
L 204	**law of similarity transformation,** similarity principle <of Laplace transform> <IT>	Ähnlichkeitssatz *m*	théorème *m* de similarité, règle *f* de similitude	теорема подобия
L 205	**law of simple constructive dilemma** <LO>	Gesetz *n* des einfachen konstruktiven Dilemmas	loi *f* des prémisses disjointes	закон простой конструктивной дилеммы
L 206	**law of simplification,** law of affirmation of the consequent <LO>	Satz *m* der Prämissenbelastung, Theorem *n* der Prämissenvorschaltung, Schluß *m* „verum ex quodlibet", Wahrform *f* zum Schluß „verum ex quodlibet", Wahrform (Form *f*) zur Vorschaltung eines Vordergliedes, Verum *n* sequitur ad quodlibet; Regula *f* veri	loi *f* d'adjonction d'une implication à une proposition, loi de simplification, Verum *m* sequitur ad quodlibet	закон утверждения консеквента импликации, добавление антецедента, [закон] verum ex quodlibet

L 207	**law of simplification [for ∧]** <LO>	Verdünnungsgesetz *n* für ∧, Theorem *n* der konjunktiven Verdünnung; Form *f* zur ∧-Verdünnung	principe *m* de simplification pour ∧	закон удаления конъюнкции
L 208	**law of sines,** sine law (rule) <of plane *or* spherical trigonometry> <EG>	Sinussatz *m*	théorème *m* du (des) sinus	теорема синусов
	law of small numbers <ST>	*s.* P 833		
L 209	**law of specification (substitution),** law of transition from the general to the particular, law of transition from a general to a particular case, universal specification, rule for omitting the universal quantifier <LO>	Allbeseitigung *f*	loi *f* de vérification relationnelle <pour le quantificateur universel>	правило специализации, аксиома простого категорического силлогизма, аксиома для «все», правило ∀-исключения
L 210	**law of tangents,** tangent law <of plane trigonometry> <EG>	Tangenssatz *m* <der ebenen Trigonometrie>	théorème *m* des tangentes	формула Региомонтана (тангенсов), теорема тангенсов
L 211	**law of tautology** <LO>	Kürzungsgesetz *n*	loi *f* de tautologie	закон идемпотентности
	law of the conditional syllogism <FO, LO>	*s.* L 213		
L 212	**law of the excluded fourth** <LO>	Satz *m* vom ausgeschlossenen Vierten	principe *m* du quart exclu	принцип исключенного четвертого, четвертого не дано
	law of the excluded middle (third) <LO>	*s.* L 184		
L 213	**law of the hypothetical syllogism,** theorem on the transitivity of implication, law of the conditional syllogism, law of detachment <FO, LO>	Satz *m* vom gewöhnlichen Kettenschluß, Theorem *n* des Kettenschlusses, Gesetz *n* des hypothetischen Syllogismus, Form *f* zum Grundschluß, Abtrennungseffekt *m*; Wahrform *f* des Kettenschlusses, Form zum Kettenschluß, Form zur Hintergliednachsetzung, Wahrform des modus barbara (ponens); Wahrform zum modus ponendo ponens	syllogisme *m* conditionnel (conditionnel ex toto), transitivité *f* du →, transitivité du conditionnel, loi *f* de transitivité de l'implication, principe *m* (loi) du syllogisme hypothétique, Implicatif *m* modus ponens, principe d'inférence, principe de séparation	правило (теорема) силлогизма, закон гипотетического силлогизма, закон силлогизма
	law of the iterated logarithm <ST>	*s.* L 192		
	law of the mean <DI>	*s.* M 327		
	law of the propagation of errors <ER>	*s.* P 1764		
	law of transition from a general to a particular case <LO>	*s.* L 209		
	law of transition from the general to the particular <LO>	*s.* L 209		
L 214	**law of transitivity of identity** <LO>	Transitivität *f* der Gleichheit	raisonnement *m* d'égalité	закон транзитивности равенства
L 215	**law of transposition,** first law of transposition <LO>	erstes Kontrapositionsgesetz *n*, Gesetz *n* der Kontraposition, Gesetz der Wendung; Form *f* zur schwachen Kontraposition	[première] loi *f* de contraposition	[простой] закон контрапозиции
	law of trichotomy <SE>	*s.* T 926		
L 216	**law of unique prime factorization,** theorem of unique prime factorization <AL>	Satz *m* von der eindeutigen Primfaktorzerlegung, ZPE-Satz *m*, Satz von der [im wesentlichen] eindeutigen Primelementzerlegung	théorème *m* de la factorisation unique	теорема о единственности разложения на простые сомножители
L 217	**laws for changing the order of quantifiers,** laws of commutativity of quantifiers <LO>	Gesetze *npl* der Quantorenvertauschung (Vertauschung der Quantoren)	lois *fpl* de permutation des doubles quantifications de même nom	законы перестановки кванторов
L 218	**laws for logarithms,** fundamental laws of logarithms <AR>	Logarithmengesetze *npl*	lois *fpl* pour les logarithmes	свойства логарифмов
L 219	**laws of combining** <LO>	Theoreme *npl* der Kopplung	principes *mpl* de composition	законы сложения и умножения
	laws of commutativity of quantifiers <LO>	*s.* L 217		
L 220	**laws of distributing quantifiers, laws of distributivity** <of quantifiers> <LO>	Distribuierungsprinzipien *npl* <für „alle" und „es gibt">, Distributionstheoreme *npl* <der Quantoren>, Gesetze *npl* der Quantorenverteilung	lois *fpl* de distributivité <pour les quantificateurs>	законы распределения <кванторов>
L 221	**laws of double negation** <LO>	Gesetze *npl* der doppelten Negation	lois *fpl* de double négation	законы двойного отрицания
L 222	**laws of importation and exportation,** export-import law <LO>	Importations- und Exportationsgesetz *n*, Gesetz *n* der Prämissenverbindung, Exportations- und Importationsgesetz *n*, Satz *m* der	loi *f* d'importation et d'exportation	закон объединения посылок

		Prämissenverbindung, Prinzip *n* des Übergangs von der Prämissenzerlegung zur Prämissenverbindung und umgekehrt		
L 223	**laws of integral exponents** <AL>	Potenzgesetze *npl* für ganzzahlige Exponenten	règles *fpl* du calcul des puissances entières	правила действия с целыми показателями
	laws of isomorphism <AL, CA>	*s.* I 1141		
L 224	**laws of negating** <LO>	Verneinungsgesetze *npl*	lois *fpl* de négation, principes *mpl* de la négation	образование противоположности для некоторой формулы, законы отрицания
	laws of negating the quantifiers <LO>	*s.* D 220		
L 225	**laws of transposition** <LO>	Kontrapositionssätze *mpl*, Kontrapositionsgesetze *npl*, Gesetze *npl* der Kontrapositionen	lois *fpl* de contraposition	теоремы контрапозиции
	layer <FT>	*s.* S 759		
L 226	**layer-extremal group** <GR>	geschichtete extremale Gruppe *f*		слойно экстремальная группа
	layerity <MM, SE>	*s.* N 113		
	layout scheme <ST>	*s.* S 119		
	lb <AR, NU>	*s.* B 369 a		
L 227	**ℒ-class,** equivalence class mod ℒ <in a semigroup> <AL>	ℒ-Äquivalenzklasse *f*	ℒ-classe *f*	ℒ-класс, класс эквивалентности по модулю ℒ
	l.c.l.m. <AL>	*s.* L 239		
	L.C.M. <AL>	*s.* L 240		
	l.c.m., L.C.M. <AL, AR, NT>	*s.* L 241		
	l.c.r.m. <AL>	*s.* L 242		
L 228	**L-distribution,** Lévy['s] distribution <ST>	L-Verteilung *f*, Lévy-Verteilung *f*, Lévysche Verteilung *f*	distribution *f* L (de L, de Lévy)	L-распределение, распределение Леви
	lead <AY>	*s.* P 610		
L 229	**leading coefficient,** highest degree coefficient, highest coefficient <of a polynomial> <AL>	höchster Koeffizient *m*, Anfangskoeffizient *m*, Leitkoeffizient *m*, zum Leitglied gehöriger Koeffizient	coefficient *m* dominant (principal, de la plus haute puissance, directeur)	старший коэффициент, коэффициент при старшем члене
	leading diagonal <MD>	*s.* M 34		
	leading element <MD>	*s.* D 381		
L 230	**leading ideal,** associated graded ideal <of an ideal> <AL>	Leitideal *n*	idéal *m* gradué associé, « Leitideal » *m*	ведущий идеал
L 231	**leading submodule,** associated submodule <AL>	zugeordneter graduierter Untermodul *m*, Leitmodul *m*	sous-module *m* gradué associé	ассоциированный градуированный подмодуль
L 232	**leading term,** highest degree term, highest term <of a polynomial> <AL>	höchstes Glied *n*, Leitglied *n*, Glied mit dem höchsten Exponenten, Anfangsglied *n*	terme *m* directeur (ayant la plus grande puissance)	старший член
	leading term <IV>	*s.* S 1294		
L 233	**leading zero** <zero before the first non-zero digit> <NU>	führende Null *f*	zéro *m* guidant	ведущий нуль
L 234	**leaf** <AT, GP>	Blatt *n*	feuille *f*	слой <AT>; кусок, лист <GP>
L 235	**leaf** <of a rose> <GE>	Blatt *n*	branche *f*	лепесток
	leaf <GE>	*s.* F 449		
L 236	**learning automaton** <TA>	lernender Automat *m*	automate *m* apprenant	обучающийся автомат
L 237	**least absolute remainder** <modulo *n*>, minimal residue <NT>	absolut[-] kleinster Rest *m*	reste *m* minimum	абсолютно наименьший вычет
L 238	**least common denominator,** [lowest] common denominator, L.C.D. <AL, NT>	Hauptnenner *m*, Generalnenner *m*, // kleinster gemeinsamer Nenner *m*	plus petit commun dénominateur *m*, dénominateur commun	наименьший общий знаменатель, общий [наименьший] знаменатель
L 239	**least common left multiple,** l.c.l.m. <AL>	kleinstes gemeinsames Linksvielfaches *n*, KGLV	plus petit commun multiple *m* à gauche	левое наименьшее кратное
L 240	**least common multiple,** [set-theoretic] intersection, L.C.M. <of ideals> <AL>	Durchschnitt *m*, kleinstes gemeinschaftliches Vielfaches *n*, k. g. V.	plus petit commun multiple *m*, intersection *f*	пересечение
L 241	**least common multiple,** lowest (smallest) common multiple, l.c.m., L. C. M. <AL, AR, NT>	kleinstes gemeinsames (gemeinschaftliches) Vielfaches, k. g. V., KGV, // Dividuus *m*	plus petit (bas) commun multiple *m*, p. p. c. m., P. P. C. M., P. B. C. M.	наименьшее общее кратное, общее наименьшее кратное
L 242	**least common right multiple,** l.c.r.m. <AL>	kleinstes gemeinsames Rechtsvielfaches *n*, KGRV	plus petit commun multiple *m* à droite	правое наименьшее кратное
L 242 a	**least common supermodule,** logical sum, sum <of modules> <AL>	Summe *f* <zweier Moduln>	somme *f* de deux modules	сумма <двух модулей>
	least deviation <AX>	*s.* B 240 a		
	least element <LA>	*s.* Z 31		
	least element <SE>	*s.* S 1219		
L 243	**least integer which is greater or equal to a given number** <NT>	kleinste ganze Zahl größer oder gleich einer gegebenen Zahl	partie *f* entière par excès, quantité *f* voisine <de *x*> par excès, [*x*]*	наименьшее целое число, которое не меньше данного числа

No.	English	German	French	Russian
L 244	**least linear system containing the given linear systems** <AG>	kleinstes Linearsystem *n*, das die gegebenen Linearsysteme enthält	système *m* linéaire conjoignant	наименьшая линейная система, содержащая данные линейные системы
	least mean square error <ER, ST>	*s.* R 1379		
	least non-negative residue <NT>	*s.* P 1467		
L 245	**least number *k* with $a_k \neq 0$** <SS>	kleinste Zahl *f k* mit $a_k \neq 0$	valuation *f* de la suite $a_0, a_1, \ldots, a_n, \ldots$	наименьший номер *k*, для которого $a_k \neq 0$
L 246	**least-number operator** <FO>	Operator *m* der kleinsten Zahl	opérateur *m* du nombre minimum	оператор наименьшего числа
L 247	**least number principle,** principle of the smallest number, minimum principle <AN, FO>	Satz *m* vom kleinsten Element <gibt es eine natürliche Zahl mit der Eigenschaft *E*, so gibt es eine kleinste natürliche Zahl mit der Eigenschaft *E*>	principe *m* de l'élément minimum	принцип наименьшего числа
	least of the limits <DI, SS>	*s.* L 1153		
	least residue <NT>	*s.* P 1467		
	least right ideal	*s.* U 346		
	least significant difference <ST> ⌐<NU>	*s.* C 2674		
L 248	**least significant digit**	letzte gültige Ziffer *f*	dernier chiffre *m* significatif	самый младший разряд
	least square fitting procedure <ER, NU>	*s.* L 250		
L 249	**least squares approximation,** approximation by least squares [method] <AX>	Approximation *f* mit (nach) der Methode der kleinsten Quadrate	approximation *f* par moindres carrés	аппроксимация (приближение) по методу наименьших квадратов, аппроксимация (приближение) в смысле наименьших квадратов
L 250	**least squares method,** method (principle) of least squares, least square fitting procedure <ER, NU>	Methode *f* der kleinsten Quadrate (Fehlerquadrate, Quadratsummen), Fehlerquadratmethode *f*, MKQ	méthode *f* des moindres carrés	метод наименьших квадратов, способ квадратичной погрешности
L 251	**least squares [method] estimator** <ST>	MKQ-Schätzung *f*, Schätzung *f* nach der Methode der kleinsten Quadrate, Gaußsche Schätzfunktion (Schätzung) *f*	estimateur *m* par [la] méthode des moindres carrés, estimateur par les moindres carrés, estimateur gaussien (de Gauss)	оценка методом наименьших квадратов, оценка по методу наименьших квадратов, гауссовская оценка
L 252	**least upper bound,** lowest upper bound, supremum, sup, l.u.b., LUB <of a set *or* sequence of real numbers *or* a real-valued function, *or* in a partially ordered set> <DI, SE>; join <in a partially ordered set> <SE>; // upper boundary <DI, SE>	obere Grenze *f*, kleinste obere Schranke *f*, Supremum *n*, sup, finis *m* superior, fin sup, $\overline{\text{fin}}$, // obere Schranke <Pasch>	borne *f* supérieure stricte (précise), la plus petite borne supérieure, borne supérieure, moindre limite *f* supérieure, moindre (le plus petit) majorant *m*, suprémum *m*, maximum *m* [absolu], sup; union *f* <en un ensemble ordonné>	верхняя грань, точная (наименьшая) верхняя грань, супремум, sup; объединение <в полуупорядоченном множестве>
L 253	**least upper bound of the distances** <$d(x, y)$ for $x \in A$ and $y \in B$ of two sets> <TO>	obere Entfernung *f* <zweier Mengen *A* und *B*>	suprémum *m* des distances $d(x, y)$ pour $x \in A$ et $y \in B$ <de deux ensembles>	верхняя грань расстояний <$d(x, y)$, когда *x* пробегает *A*, а *y* пробегает *B*>
	least value <DI>	*s.* A 117		
	leave no remainder / to <NT>	*s.* B 162		
L 254	**Lebesgue['s] algebra** <AL>	Lebesguesche Boolesche Algebra *f*	algèbre *f* de Lebesgue	лебеговская булева алгебра
L 255	**Lebesgue['s] area** <of a surface> <DG>	Lebesguescher Inhalt (Flächeninhalt) *m*	aire *f* [au sens] de Lebesgue	площадь по Лебегу, площадь в смысле Лебега
L 256	**Lebesgue['s] constant** <SS>	Lebesguesche Konstante *f*	constante *f* de Lebesgue	константа Лебега
L 257	**Lebesgue covering,** countable open covering <TO>	abzählbare offene Überdeckung *f*	recouvrement *m* ouvert dénombrable	счетное открытое покрытие
	Lebesgue['s] covering lemma <TO>	*s.* L 263		
L 258	**Lebesgue['s] curve** <VA>	Lebesguesche Kurve *f*	courbe *f* de Lebesgue	кривая Лебега
L 259	**Lebesgue['s] decomposition** <of a real function> <RF>	Lebesguesche Zerlegung *f*	décomposition *f* de Lebesgue	разложение Лебега
	Lebesgue['s] dimension <TO>	*s.* C 2625		
L 260	**Lebesgue['s] function** <AN, LI>	Lebesguesche Funktion *f*	fonction *f* de Lebesgue	функция Лебега
L 261	**Lebesgue integrable,** (L)-integrable, L-integrable <AN>	Lebesgue-integrierbar, L-integrierbar, (L)-integrierbar	intégrable au sens de Lebesgue	интегрируемый в смысле Лебега, интегрируемый по Лебегу
I 262	**Lebesgue['s] integral,** L-integral <AN>	Lebesguesches Integral *n*, L-Integral *n*, Lebesgue-Integral *n*, Integral im Lebesgueschen Sinne	intégrale *f* de Lebesgue, intégrale au sens de Lebesgue	интеграл Лебега, L-интеграл, интеграл в смысле Лебега
L 263	**Lebesgue['s] lemma,** Lebesgue['s] covering lemma <for a metric space> <TO>	Lebesguesches Lemma *n*	lemme *m* de Lebesgue	лемма Лебега
	Lebesgue measurable function <ME>	*s.* L 910		
L 264	**Lebesgue['s] measure,** (L) measure, L measure <ME>	Lebesguesches Maß *n*, L-Maß *n*, Youngsches Maß, Borel-Lebesguesches Maß	mesure *f* de Lebesgue, mesure (L), mesure lebesguienne	мера Лебега, лебегова мера, мера в смысле Лебега

L 265	**Lebesgue['s] measure algebra** <AL, ME>	Lebesguesche Maßalgebra *f*	algèbre *f* de Lebesgue à mesure	алгебра Лебега с мерой
L 266	**Lebesgue['s] method of summation** <LI>	Summationsverfahren *n* von Lebesgue, Lebesguesches Summationsverfahren	méthode *f* (procédé *m*) de sommation de Lebesgue	метод суммирования Лебега
L 267	**Lebesgue number** <of a covering> <TO>	Lebesguesche Zahl *f*	nombre *m* de Lebesgue	лебегово число
	Lebesgue['s] outer measure <ME>	*s.* O 547		
L 268	**Lebesgue['s] point** <with respect to a function> <AN>	Lebesguescher Punkt *m*, L-Punkt *m* <bezüglich einer Funktion>	point *m* de Lebesgue <par rapport à une fonction>	точка Лебега <относительно функции>
L 269	**Lebesgue['s] problem** <CS>	Lebesguesches Deckelproblem (Problem, Tafelproblem) *n*	problème *m* de couvercle de Lebesgue	проблема Лебега
L 270	**Lebesgue['s] set** <ME, TO>	Lebesguesche Menge *f*	ensemble *m* de Lebesgue	множество Лебега
L 271	**Lebesgue['s] "small" theorem** <FA>	„kleiner" Satz *m* von Lebesgue	« petit » théorème *m* de Lebesgue	«малая» теорема Лебега
L 272	**Lebesgue['s] space,** space L^p (L_p) <FA>	Lebesguescher Raum *m*, Lebesgue-Raum *m*, Raum $L^p(\mu)$	espace *m* de Lebesgue, espace L^p	пространство Лебега, пространство L_p
L 273	**Lebesgue-Stieltjes integral,** Radon-Stieltjes integral, Radon['s] integral <AN>	Lebesgue-Stieltjessches Integral *n*, Radon-Stieltjessches Integral *n*, Radonsches Integral *n*	intégrale *f* de Stieltjes-Lebesgue (Lebesgue-Stieltjes), intégrale de Radon-Stieltjes, intégrale de Radon	интеграл Лебега-Стилтьеса, интеграл Радона-Стилтьеса, интеграл Радона
L 274	**Lebesgue-Stieltjes measure** <ME>	Lebesgue-Stieltjessches Maß *n*	mesure *f* de Lebesgue-Stieltjes	мера Лебега-Стилтьеса
L 275	**Lebesgue['s] sum,** L-sum <DI>	Lebesguesche Summe *f*, L-Summe *f*	somme *f* [au sens] de Lebesgue, somme (L)	сумма Лебега (по Лебегу, в смысле Лебега)
L 276	**Lebesgue['s] surface** <VA>	Lebesguesche Fläche *f*	surface *f* de Lebesgue	поверхность Лебега
L 277	**Lebesgue['s] test** <for convergence of a Fourier series> <SS>	Lebesguesches Kriterium *n*	critère *m* (règle *f*) de Lebesgue	признак Лебега
L 278	**Lebesgue['s] theorem** <on the derivative of a monotone function> <FA>	Satz *m* von Lebesgue, Lebesguescher Satz	théorème *m* de Lebesgue	теорема Лебега
L 279	**"Leerstelle",** vacant (argument) place, blank <of a functional symbol> <AL, AN, SE, TO>	Leerstelle *f*	place *f* vide	незаполненное (пустое) место, пробел
L 280	**Lefschetz['s] condition** <AT>	Lefschetz-Bedingung *f*	condition *f* de Lefschetz	условие Лефшеца
L 281	**Lefschetz['s] duality theorem** <AT>	Lefschetzscher Dualitätssatz *m*	théorème *m* de dualité de Lefschetz	теорема двойственности Лефшеца
L 282	**Lefschetz['s] fixed-point formula, Lefschetz['s] fixed point formula,** fixed point formula of Lefschetz, Lefschetz-Hopf formula <AT>	allgemeiner Fixpunktsatz *m*, Lefschetzsche Fixpunktformel *f*, [Lefschetz-Hopfsche] Spurformel *f*	formule *f* de Lefschetz (Lefschetz des points fixes), formule des traces de Lefschetz	теорема Лефшеца о неподвижной точке, формула Лефшеца-Хопфа
L 283	**Lefschetz['s] fixed-point theorem,** fixed-point theorem of Lefschetz <AT>	Lefschetzscher Fixpunktsatz *m*	théorème *m* de points fixes de Lefschetz	теорема Лефшеца о неподвижных точках
L 284	**Lefschetz['s] group** <of *X* modulo *F*> <AT>	Lefschetzsche Gruppe *f* <von *X* modulo *F*>	groupe *m* de Lefschetz <de *X* modulo *F*>	группа Лефшеца <пространства *X* по модулю *F*>
	Lefschetz-Hopf formula <AT>	*s.* L 282		
L 285	**Lefschetz['s] number** <of a continuous mapping> <AT>	Lefschetzsche Zahl *f*, Spureninvariante *f*	nombre *m* de Lefschetz	число Лефшеца
L 286	**Lefschetz['s] principle** <AG>	Lefschetzsches Prinzip *n*	principe *m* de Lefschetz	принцип Лефшеца
L 287	**Lefschetz['s] product** <AT>	Lefschetzsches Produkt *n*	produit *m* de Lefschetz	лефшецевское произведение
L 288	**left action** <AL>	linke Wirkung *f*	action *f* gauche	левое действие
L 289	**left action** <of a monoid> <CA>	Linksoperation *f*	action *f* à gauche	левое действие
L 290	**left adherent point** <TO>	linksseitiger Berührungspunkt *m*	point *m* adhérent à gauche	левая точка прикосновения
	left-adjoint, left adjoint <CA>	*s.* A 295		
L 291	**left adjoint homomorphism** <AL>	linksadjungierter Homomorphismus *m*	adjoint *m* à gauche <d'un homomorphisme>	сопряженный слева гомоморфизм
L 292	**left almost periodic function,** function almost periodic on the left <on a topological group> <AP>	links-fastperiodische Funktion *f*	fonction *f* presque périodique à gauche	почти периодическая слева функция
L 293	**left alternative division ring** <AL>	Linksalternativkörper *m*	corps *m* alternatif à gauche	левоальтернативное поле
L 294	**left alternative law** <AL>	Linksalternativgesetz *n*	loi *f* alternative à gauche	левый альтернативный закон
L 295	**left alternative ring** <AL>	Linksalternativring *m*	anneau *m* alternatif à gauche	левоальтернативное кольцо
L 296	**left amenable** <AL>	linksamenabel	aménable (moyennable) à gauche	левоаменабельный, левоусреднимый
L 297	**left[-]analytic function** <FT>	linksanalytische Funktion *f*	fonction *f* analytique à gauche	аналитическая слева функция, левоаналитическая функция

L 298	**left-analytic hypercomplex function** <AN>	linksanalytische hyperkomplexe Funktion *f*	fonction *f* hypercomplexe analytique à gauche	аналитическая слева гиперкомплексная функция, левоаналитическая функция, леворегулярная функция гиперкомплексного переменного
L 299	**left and right distributive** <AL, LO>	beiderseits distributiv	distributif des deux côtés	дистрибутивный слева и справа
L 300	**left[-]annihilating** <AL>	links-annullierend	annihilant à gauche	левоуничтожающий
L 301	**left annihilator, left-annihilator, left annihilator ideal** <AL>	linker Annulator (Annullator) *m*, Linksannulator *m*, Linksannullator *m*	annulateur *m* à gauche	левый аннулятор
L 302	**left artinian ring,** ring with left DCC <AL>	linksartinscher Ring *m*	anneau *m* artinien à gauche	артиново слева кольцо, левоартиново кольцо
L 303	**left-artinian semigroup** <AL>	linksartinsche Halbgruppe *f*	demi-groupe *m* artinien à gauche	артинова слева полугруппа, левоартинова полугруппа
L 304	**left associate** <of a matrix> <AL, MD>	linksassoziierte Matrix *f*, Linksassoziierte *fpl*	matrice *f* associée à gauche	левоассоциированная матрица
L 305	**left associated element** <in a ring> <AL>	linksassoziiertes Element *n*	élément *m* associé à gauche	ассоциированный слева элемент, левоассоциированный элемент
	left-associatedness	*s.* P 1843		
	left associator <AL>	*s.* L 444		
L 306	**left balanced functor** <CA>	linksausgeglichener Funktor *m*	foncteur *m* balancé à gauche	сбалансированный слева функтор
L 307	**left bimodule** <AL>	Bilinksmodul *m*, Doppellinksmodul *m*	bimodule *m* à gauche	левый бимодуль
	left bound <SE>	*s.* L 1129		
	left-bounded ordered set <SE>	*s.* O 319		
	left-bounded set <SE>	*s.* S 639		
	left bracket <GN>	*s.* L 382		
	left cancellability <AL>	*s.* R 573		
	left cancellable element <AL>	*s.* E 137		
L 308	**left-cancellation halfgroupoid** <AL>	Halbgruppoid *n* mit Linkskürzungsregel	p-groupoïde *m* simplifiable à gauche	частичный группоид с левым сокращением
L 309	**left[-]cancellation law,** law of left-side cancellation <AL>	Linkskürzungsregel *f*, linksseitige Kürzungsregel *f*	règle *f* de simplification à gauche	закон левостороннего сокращения
L 310	**left cancellative groupoid** <AL>	Gruppoid *n* mit Linkskürzungsregel	groupoïde *m* vérifiant la règle de simplification à gauche	группоид с левым сокращением (законом сокращения)
L 311	**left cancellative semigroup** <AL>	Halbgruppe *f* mit Linkskürzungsregel, linksreguläre Halbgruppe *f*	semi-groupe *m* à gauche	полугруппа с левым сокращением, полугруппа с левым законом сокращения
L 312	**left chain ring** <AL>	Ring *m*, dessen Linksideale linear geordnet sind	anneau *m* dont l'ensemble des idéaux à gauche est linéairement ordonné	кольцо, для которого множество левых идеалов линейно упорядочено
L 313	**left closed object, left-closed object** <for Σ> <CA>	linksabgeschlossenes Objekt *n* <bezüglich Σ>	objet *m* fermé à gauche <relativement à Σ>	замкнутый слева объект <относительно Σ>
	left cofinality <SE>	*s.* C 1119		
	left-cofinal set <SE>	*s.* C 1121		
L 314	**left coherent ring** <AL>	links-kohärenter Ring *m*	anneau *m* cohérent à gauche	когерентное слева кольцо
L 315	**left comaximal elements** <AL>	linkskomaximale Elemente *npl*	éléments *mpl* comaximaux à gauche	комаксимальные слева элементы
L 316	**left commensurable elements** <in a ring> <AL>	linkskommensurable Elemente *npl*	éléments *mpl* possédant un multiple à gauche commun	элементы, которые обладают общим левым кратным
L 317	**left commutator** <of two elements of a group> <GR>	linker Kommutator *m*	commutateur *m* à gauche	левый коммутатор
L 318	**left compatibility,** left regularity (homogeneity) <of a relation> <UA>	linksseitige Kompatibilität *f*, linksseitige Verträglichkeit *f*	compatibilité *f* à gauche, régularité *f* à gauche	левая совместность (стабильность, регулярность)
L 319	**left compatible relation,** left regular (homogeneous) relation <AL>	linkskompatible Relation *f*	relation *f* régulière (compatible, permise) à gauche	стабильное (регулярное, однородное) слева отношение
	left complete category, left-complete category <CA>	*s.* C 1416		
L 320	**left completion,** left-handed completion <of a topological group> <GR, TO>	linksseitige Vervollständigung *f*	complété *m* à gauche	левостороннее пополнение
L 321	**left composition algebra** <AL>	Linkskompositionsalgebra *f*	algèbre *f* de composition à gauche	левокомпозиционная алгебра
L 322	**left congruence** <on a groupoid> <UA>	linksseitige Kongruenzrelation *f*	équivalence *f* régulière à gauche, équivalence *f* compatible à gauche, congruence *f* à gauche	левая конгруэнция, стабильная слева эквивалентность
L 323	**left congruent element** <of a group> <GR>	linkskongruentes Element *n*, linkskongruentes Gruppenelement *n*	élément *m* équivalent à gauche	левый конгруэнтный элемент
	left-continuous <AN>	*s.* C 2231		
L 324	**left continuous functor,** continuous functor, limit preserving functor <CA>	linksstetiger Funktor *m*, stetiger Funktor *m*; Funktor *m*, der Limiten respektiert	foncteur *m* continu, foncteur *m* préservant les limites [projectives]	функтор, перестановочный с обратными пределами; функтор, сохраняющий обратные пределы

L 325	**left coprime elements** <AL>	linksteilerfremde Elemente *npl*	éléments *mpl* sans diviseurs à gauche communs, éléments étrangers à gauche	копростые слева элементы, взаимно простые слева элементы, левовзаимнопростые элементы
L 326	**left coset** <of a group> <GR>	linke Restklasse *f*, linke Nebenklasse *f*, linksseitige Restklasse *f*, linke Nebengruppe *f*, linksseitige Nebenklasse *f*, Linksnebenklasse *f*	classe *f* à gauche, complexe *m* associé à gauche, classe *f* latérale à gauche	левый смежный класс, левосторонний смежный класс
L 327	**left coset decomposition (expansion),** decomposition into left cosets <modulo, with respect to> <of a group *or* quasigroup> <AL, GR>	linksseitige (linke) Restklassenzerlegung *f*, linksseitige Zerlegung *f*, Linkszerlegung *f*, Zerlegung in linke Restklassen <nach, modulo>	décomposition *f* en complexes à gauche, décomposition <d'un groupe> en ses complexes à gauche, décomposition en classes à gauche <suivant>	левостороннее (левое) разложение <по>
L 328	**left coset relative to *H*** <GR>	linksseitige Nebenklasse (Restklasse) *f* modulo *H*, Linksnebenklasse *f* modulo *H*	classe *f* à gauche modulo (suivant) *H*, complexe *m* associé à gauche à *H*	левый класс смежности по *H*, левосторонний смежный класс по *H*
	left coset space <AL, TO>	*s.* S 1322		
	left decomposition <AL>	*s.* L 492		
L 329	**left-degenerate semi-linear mapping** <AL>	linksausgeartete halblineare Abbildung *f*	application *f* sesquilinéaire dégénérée à gauche	вырожденное слева полуторалинейное отображение
L 330	**left denominator** <AL>	Linksnenner *m*	dénominateur *m* à gauche	левый знаменатель
L 331	**left derivation** <AL>	linke Derivation *f*	dérivation *f* gauche	левое дифференцирование
L 332	**left derivative** <of a matrix> <DI, MD>	linke Ableitung *f*	dérivée *f* à gauche	левая производная
	left derivative <DI>	*s.* L 367		
	left derivative function <RF>	*s.* L 368		
L 333	**left derived functor** <*n*-th> <CA>	linksabgeleiteter Funktor *m* <*n*-ter>	foncteur *m* dérivé gauche <*n*-e>	левая производная <функтора> <*n*-я>, левый производный функтор <*n*-й>
L 334	**left differentiability,** left-hand differentiability, differentiability on the left, back[ward] differentiability <DI>	linksseitige Differenzierbarkeit *f*, hintere Differenzierbarkeit	dérivabilité *f* à gauche	дифференцируемость слева, левосторонняя (левая) дифференцируемость
L 335	**left differential** <of a Lie group> <GR>	linkes Differential *n*	différentielle *f* gauche	левый дифференциал
	left Dini derivative <RF>	*s.* L 370		
L 336	**left[-]directed partial order,** directed downward partial order <SE>	konvers gerichtete Halbordnung *f*, nach unten gerichtete (filtrierende) Halbordnung	ordre *m* filtrant à gauche, ordre filtrant inférieurement	направленный вниз частичный порядок
L 337	**left-directed preordered set,** left-directed quasi-ordered set <SE>	nach unten quasigerichtete Menge *f*	ensemble *m* préordonné filtrant à gauche	квазиупорядоченное множество, направленное вниз
L 338	**left-directed quasi-order,** left direction, directed downward quasi-order <SE>	nach unten gerichtete (filtrierende) Quasiordnung *f*, konvers gerichtete Quasiordnung	préordre *m* filtrant à gauche, préordre filtrant inférieurement	направленный вниз квазипорядок
	left-directed quasi-ordered set <SE>	*s.* L 337		
	left-directed set <SE>	*s.* D 543		
	left direction <SE>	*s.* L 338		
L 339	**left direct product** <of matrices> <MD>	linkes direktes Produkt *n*	produit *m* direct à gauche	левое прямое произведение
L 340	**left distributive** <over, with respect to> <AL, LO, SE>	linksdistributiv, linksseitig distributiv <bezüglich>	distributif à gauche <par rapport à>	дистрибутивный слева <относительно>
L 341	**left distributive composition law** <AL>	linksdistributives Verknüpfungsgesetz *n*	loi *f* [de composition] distributive à gauche	дистрибутивный слева закон композиции
L 342	**left distributive law,** left-side distributive law <AL>	Linksdistributivgesetz *n*, linksseitiges Distributivgesetz *n*	condition *f* de distributivité à gauche, loi *f* de distributivité à gauche; loi *f* distribuée à gauche <loi externe>	закон левой дистрибутивности, левый закон дистрибутивности, левый дистрибутивный закон, левосторонний распределительный закон
L 343	**left distributivity** <AL>	linksseitige Distributivität *f*, Linksdistributivität *f*	distributivité *f* à gauche	дистрибутивность слева
L 344	**left[-]division** <AL, SE>	linksseitige Division *f*; linke Division <in einer Quasigruppe>	division *f* à gauche	левое деление
L 345	**left division algorithm** <AL>	linksseitiger Divisionsalgorithmus *m*, Linksdivisionsalgorithmus *m*	division *f* généralisée à gauche, algorithme *m* de la division à gauche	левый алгоритм деления
L 346	**left divisor,** left-hand divisor <AL, SE>	Linksteiler *m*, linker Teiler *m*	diviseur *m* à gauche	левый делитель
	left divisor of zero <AL>	*s.* L 522		
	left domain <SE>	*s.* D 854		
L 347	**left dual couple** <FA>	Linksdualsystem *n*	couple *m* d'espace associés à gauche	левая дуальная пара
L 348	**left eigenvector** <AL>	Linkseigenvektor *m*	vecteur *m* propre à gauche	левый собственный вектор
	left end point <AN>	*s.* L 376		
L 349	**left Engel element** <of a group> <GR>	links-engelsches Element *n*	élément *m* engelien à gauche	лево-энгелев элемент

No.	English	German	French	Russian
	left equalizer <CA>	*s.* E 327		
L 350	**left-equivalent matrix** <AL>	linksäquivalente Matrix *f*	matrice *f* équivalente à gauche	лево-эквивалентная матрица
L 351	**left essential extension** <of a ring> <AL>	linke wesentliche Erweiterung *f*	extension *f* essentielle à gauche	левое существенное расширение
L 352	**left exact functor** <CA>	linksexakter Funktor *m*	foncteur *m* exact à gauche	точный слева функтор
L 353	**left exactness** <of a functor> <CA>	Linksexaktheit *f*	exactitude *f* à gauche	лево-точность
L 354	**left exponent** <AL>	Linksexponent *m*	exposant *m* à gauche	левый показатель
L 355	**left external composition law** <AL>	linksseitige äußere Verknüpfung *f*	loi *f* de composition externe à gauche, loi *f* externe à gauche	левая внешняя композиция
	left extremity <AN>	*s.* L 376		
L 356	**left factor** <of an unknown> <AL>	Linksfaktor *m*	facteur *m* gauche	левый множитель
L 357	**left faithful functor** <on the object *A*> <CA>	linkstreuer Funktor *m* <auf dem Objekt *A*>	foncteur *m* fidèle à gauche <sur l'objet *A*>	унивалентный слева <на объекте *A*> функтор
L 358	**left faithful ring** <AL>	linkstreuer Ring *m*	anneau *m* fidèle à gauche	точное слева кольцо
L 359	**left formal power series** <AL>	linke formale Potenzreihe *f*	série *f* formelle gauche	левый формальный степенной ряд
	left free object <CA>	*s.* F 627		
L 360	**left global homological (projective) dimension** <of a ring> <AL>	linke globale homologische (projektive) Dimension *f*	dimension *f* homologique globale à gauche	левая глобальная гомологическая размерность
L 361	**left Goldie dimension** <AL>	linke Goldie-Dimension *f*	dimension *f* de Goldie à gauche	левая размерность Голди
L 362	**left Goldie ring** <AL>	Links-Goldie-Ring *m*	anneau *m* de Goldie à gauche	левое кольцо Голди
L 363	**left Haar measure,** left-invariant Haar measure <AL>	linkes Haar-Maß *n*	mesure *f* de Haar à gauche	левая мера Хаара, левоинвариантная мера Хаара
L 364	**left Haar module** <AL>	linker Haar-Modul *n*	module *m* de Haar à gauche	левый модуль Хаара
L 365	**left half-tangent,** left-side (left-hand) half-tangent <DG>	linke (linksseitige, hintere) Halbtangente *f*	demi-tangente *f* à gauche	левая полукасательная
L 366	**left-hand cancellation,** left-side cancellation <AL>	linksseitige Kürzung *f*, linksseitiges Kürzen *n*	simplification *f* à gauche	левостороннее сокращение
	left-hand continuous <AN>	*s.* C 2231		
L 367	**left-hand derivative,** derivative on the left, left derivative, left-handed derivative, back (backward) derivative <of a function> <DI>	linksseitige Ableitung (Derivierte) *f*, hintere (linke) Ableitung (Derivierte), Linksableitung *f*, Linksderivierte *f*, linksseitiger (hinterer) Differentialquotient *m*	dérivée *f* à gauche, semi-dérivée *f* à gauche	производная слева, левосторочняя производная, [односторонняя] левая производная
L 368	**left-hand derivative function,** left derivative function, derivative function on the left, back[ward] derivative function <RF>	linksseitige Derivierten-funktion *f*, hintere Deriviertenfunktion	fonction *f* dérivée à gauche	производная функция слева, левосторонняя производная функция, левая производная функция
	left-hand differentiability <DI>	*s.* L 334		
L 369	**left-hand differentiable function,** function differentiable on the left <RF>	linksseitig (nach links) differenzierbare Funktion *f*	fonction *f* dérivable à gauche	дифференцируемая слева функция
L 370	**left-hand Dini derivative,** left (back, backward) Dini derivative, Dini['s] derivative on the left, D_1 <RF>	linksseitige Derivierte *f* (Ableitungszahl *f*), hintere Derivierte *f*, D_h, D_l	nombre *m* dérivé à gauche	левое производное число
	left-hand divisor <AL, SE>	*s.* L 346		
	left-handed completion <GR, TO>	*s.* L 320		
L 371	**left-handed co-ordinate system,** left-handed system, left system <of co-ordinates, of co-ordinate axes> <AY>	linkshändiges Koordinatensystem *n*, Linkssystem *n*, linkshändiges System *n*; Linkskreuz *n*	système *m* sinistrogyre, système *m* gauche [des axes de coordonnées], système *m* de rotation à gauche, système *m* rétrograde [de coordonnées], système *m* de coordonnées à gauche, système *m* à gauche	левовращающаяся система, левовращающаяся система координат, левая система [координат], левая координатная система, левовинтовая система
L 372	**left-handed curve,** sinistrorse curve, sinistrorsum curve <GE>	linkswendige (linksgewundene, linksgängige) Kurve *f*	courbe *f* sinistrorsum	кривая левого вращения, завитая влево кривая
	left-handed derivative <DI>	*s.* L 367		
	left-handed helix <GE>	*s.* S 1133		
L 373	**left-handed rotation,** negative rotation, counterclockwise rotation <EG>	Linksdrehung *f*, negative Drehung *f*	rotation *f* gauche, rotation *f* négative	левое (отрицательное) вращение, вращение влево (против часовой стрелки)
	left-handed ruled surface <GE>	*s.* S 1134		
	left-handed screw <GE>	*s.* L 486		
	left-handed system <AY>	*s.* L 371		

No.	English	German	French	Russian
L 374	**left-handed trihedral** <of vectors> <VT>	linkshändiges Dreibein *n* (Tripel *n* von Vektoren), negativ orientiertes Dreibein *n*	trièdre *m* [de sens] indirect, trièdre rétrograde (négativement orienté)	левая упорядоченная тройка векторов
L 375	**left-handed upper limit,** left upper limit, upper left-handed limit, upper limit on the left <DI>	oberer linksseitiger Limes (Hauptlimes) *m*	limite *f* supérieure à gauche	левосторонний верхний предел, верхний предел слева
L 376	**left-hand end-point,** left end point, left extremity <of an interval> <AN>	linker Endpunkt *m*	extrémité *f* à gauche	левый конец
	left-hand half-tangent <DG>	*s.* L 365		
	left-hand helix <GE>	*s.* S 1133		
L 377	**left-hand inclusion,** ⊂ <SE>	linksseitige Inklusion *f*, ⊂	inclusion *f* à gauche, ⊂	левостороннее включение, ⊂
	left-hand limit <DI>	*s.* L 740		
L 378	**left-hand lower approximate limit** <AN>	linksseitiger unterer approximativer Limes (Hauptlimes) *m*	limite *f* approximative inférieure à gauche	левосторонний (левый) нижний аппроксимативный предел
L 379	**left-hand lower continuous** <AN>	linksseitig unterhalb[ ] stetig, linksseitig nach unten stetig, linksseitig abwärts stetig	continu inférieurement à gauche	слева непрерывный снизу
L 380	**left-hand lower Dini['s] derivative,** lower Dini['s] derivative on the left <of a function> <RF>	untere linksseitige (hintere) Derivierte *f*, linksseitige (linke) untere Derivierte (Ableitungszahl *f*)	nombre *m* dérivé inférieur à gauche, nombre dérivé à gauche par défaut	нижнее левое производное число, нижнее производное число слева
L 381	**left-hand lower limit,** left lower limit, lower left-hand limit, lower limit on the left <DI>	unterer linksseitiger Limes (Hauptlimes) *m*	limite *f* inférieure à gauche	нижний левосторонний (левый) предел, нижний предел слева
L 382	**left-hand parenthesis,** left parenthesis; left bracket, (<GN>	linke Klammer *f*, Klammer auf, (	parenthèse *f* ouvrante, (	левая скобка, (
	left-hand ruled surface <GE>	*s.* S 1134		
	left-hand screw <GE>	*s.* L 486		
L 383	**left-hand side,** left hand side, LHS, left side, left member, first member <of an equation *or* inequality> <GN>	linke Seite *f*, erste Seite	membre *m* gauche, premier membre, partie *f* gauche, membre à gauche, côté *m* gauche	левая сторона, левая часть
L 384	**left-hand symmetrizable kernel** <FA>	linksseitig symmetrisierbarer Kern *m*	noyau *m* symétrisable à gauche	симметризируемое слева ядро
L 385	**left-hand system** <of linear equations> <in a non-commutative ring> <AL>	linksseitiges lineares Gleichungssystem *n*	système *m* d'équations linéaires à gauche	левосторонняя система линейных уравнений
L 386	**left-hand upper approximate limit** <AN>	linksseitiger oberer approximativer Limes (Hauptlimes) *m*	limite *f* approximative supérieure à gauche	левосторонний (левый) верхний аппроксимативный предел
L 387	**left-hand upper continuous** <AN>	linksseitig oberhalb[ ]stetig, linksseitig nach oben stetig, linksseitig aufwärts stetig	continu supérieurement à gauche	слева непрерывный сверху
L 388	**left-hand upper Dini['s] derivative,** upper Dini['s] derivative on the left <of a function> <RF>	obere linksseitige Derivierte *f*, obere hintere Derivierte, linksseitige (linke) obere Derivierte (Ableitungszahl) *f*	nombre *m* dérivé supérieur à gauche, nombre dérivé à gauche par excès, dérivée *f* supérieure à gauche de Dini	верхнее левое производное число, верхняя левая производная Дини
	left-hand zero-element <AL>	*s.* L 523		
L 389	**left hereditary ring** <AL>	linkserblicher Ring *m*	anneau *m* héréditaire à gauche	наследственное слева кольцо
L 390	**left heredity** <of a ring> <AL>	Linkserblichkeit *f*	hérédité *f* à gauche	наследственность слева
L 391	**left Hermite ring** <AL>	linkshermitescher Ring *m*	anneau *m* hermitien à gauche	левоэрмитово кольцо
	left homogeneity <UA>	*s.* L 318		
	left homogeneous relation <AL>	*s.* L 319		
	left homothetic (homothety) <AL, GR>	*s.* L 512		
L 392	**left homotopy inverse,** left inverse in the homotopy category <CA, TO>	Links-Homotopieinverses *n*, Linksinverses *n* in der Kategorie der topologischen Räume modulo Homotopie	homotopie-inverse *m* à gauche	левый гомотопический обратный [элемент], гомотопически левообратное отображение, левый обратный элемент в категории гомотопических типов
L 393	**left ideal** <AL, CA>	Linksideal *n*, linksseitiges Ideal *n*	idéal *m* à gauche	левый идеал
L 394	**left ideal of** ο <AL>	ο-Linksideal *n*	idéal *m* à gauche de ο	левый идеал в ο
	left identity <AL>	*s.* L 516		
	left identity <AL, GR>	*s.* L 395		
L 395	**left identity element,** left unity, left unit-element, left unit, left identity; left neutral element <AL, GR>	Linkseinselement *n*, linksseitiges Einselement *n*, Linkseinheit *f*, Linkseins *f*; linksneutrales Element; linkes Hauptelement *n* erster Art <in einem Gruppoid>	élément *m* unité à gauche, élément-unité *m* à gauche, unité *f* gauche; élément *m* neutre à gauche	левый единичный элемент, левая единица, левосторонний единичный элемент; левый нейтральный элемент

No.	English	German	French	Russian
L 396	**left injective dimension** <AL>	linke injektive Dimension *f*	dimension *f* injective à gauche	левая инъективная размерность
L 397	**left injective ring** <AL>	linksinjektiver Ring *m*	anneau *m* injectif à gauche	левоинъективное кольцо
L 398	**left inner product** <of *p*-forms> <AL>	linkes inneres Produkt *n*	produit *m* intérieur gauche	левое внутреннее произведение
L 399	**left-invariance, left invariance** <of a measure> <AL>	Linksinvarianz *f*	invariance *f* à gauche	левоинвариантность
	left-invariant Haar measure <AL>	*s.* L 363		
L 400	**left-invariant infinitesimal transformation** <AL>	linksinvariante infinitesimale Transformation *f*	transformation *f* infinitésimale invariante à gauche	левоинвариантное (инвариантное слева) инфинитезимальное преобразование
L 401	**left-invariant mean** <AL>	linksinvariantes Mittel *n*	moyenne *f* invariante à gauche	левоинвариантное среднее
L 402	**left-invariant measure** <on a group> <GR>	linksinvariantes Maß *n*	mesure *f* invariante par translation à gauche	левоинвариантная мера
L 403	**left[-]invariant metric** <of a group> <GR>	linksinvariante Metrik *f*	distance *f* invariante à gauche	левоинвариантная метрика
L 404	**left inverse** <AL>	linksinvers	symétrique à gauche <loi arbitraire>; inverse à gauche <en particulier, loi multiplicative>	симметричный слева <в общем>; левый обратный <в частности, для умножения>
L 405	**left inverse** <of a linear mapping> <AL>	Linksreziproke *f*, Linksinverse *f* <einer linearen Abbildung>	inverse *f* à gauche <d'une application linéaire>	левое обратное отображение
	left inverse <AL>	*s.* L 406		
	left inverse <AL, MD>	*s.* L 407		
	left inverse <FA>	*s.* L 408		
L 406	**left inverse element,** left inverse <of an element> <AL>	Linksinverses *n*, linksseitiges Inverses *n*, linksinverses Element *n*	élément *m* inverse à gauche, inverse *f* de gauche, inverse *f* à gauche; élément *m* symétrique à gauche	левый обратный элемент, обратный слева [элемент], левосторонний обратный элемент
	left inverse in the homotopy category <CA, TO>	*s.* L 392		
L 407	**left inverse matrix,** left inverse <of a[n infinite] matrix> <AL, MD>	Linksinverse *f*, linke (vordere) Reziproke *f*, linksinverse Matrix *f*	inverse *f* à gauche <d'une matrice [infinie]>	левая обратная матрица
L 408	**left inverse operator,** left inverse <of a linear operator> <FA>	linksinverser Operator *m*	opérateur *m* inverse à gauche	левый обратный оператор
L 409	**left inverse with respect to e** <AL>	Linksinverses *n* bezüglich *e*	inverse *f* à gauche par rapport à *e*	левый обратный элемент относительно *e*
L 410	**left-invertible element** <AL>	linksinvertierbares Element *n*	élément *m* inversible à gauche; élément *m* symétrisable à gauche	обратимый слева элемент
L 411	**left-invertible mapping** <AL>	linksinvertierbare Abbildung *f*	application *f* inversible à gauche	обратимое слева отображение
L 412	**left-isolated point,** point isolated from the left <in ordered spaces> <TO>	von links isolierter Punkt *m*	point *m* isolé à gauche	изолированная слева точка
L 413	**left isotropic line** <PJ>	Linksisotrope *f*	droite *f* isotrope à gauche	левая изотропная прямая
L 414	**left iteration** <of a transfinite function> <SE>	Linksiteration *f*	itération *f* à gauche	левая итерация
L 415	**left Jacobson radical** <of an ideal> <AL>	linkes Jacobson-Radikal *n*	radical *m* de Jacobson à gauche	левый радикал Джекобсона
L 416	**left Kan extension** <of *T* along the insertion *K*> <CA>	linksseitige Kan-Erweiterung *f* <von *T* längs der Einsetzung *K*>	extension *f* de Kan à gauche	левостороннее расширение Кана
L 417	**left kernel** <with respect to a bilinear form> <AL>	links-konjugierter Modul *m* <bezüglich einer Bilinearform>	noyau *m* de l'application linéaire associée à gauche <à une forme bilinéaire>	ядро слева <билинейной формы>
L 418	**left kernel** <of a bilinear mapping> <GR>	linksseitiger Kern *m*	noyau *m* à gauche	ядро слева
L 419	**left *K*-module** <AL>	*K*-Linksmodul *m*, Linksvektorraum *m* über *K*	*K*-module *m* à gauche, espace *m* vectoriel à gauche sur *K*	левый *K*-модуль
L 420	**left Krull dimension** <of a ring> <AL>	linke Krullsche Dimension *f*	dimension *f* de Krull à gauche	левая размерность Крулля
L 421	**left length** <of a module or ring> <AL>	linke Länge *f*	longueur *f* à gauche	левая длина
	left liberty [map] <CA>	*s.* L 644		
	left limit <CA>	*s.* L 697		
	left limit <DI>	*s.* L 740		
L 422	**left linearly dependent over *K*, left linearly *K*-dependent** <AL>	linksseitig linear abhängig über *K*	linéairement dépendant sur *K* à gauche	линейно зависимый слева над *K*, линейно *K*-зависимый слева
L 423	**left linearly *K*-independent** <AL>	linksseitig linear unabhängig über *K*	linéairement indépendant sur *K* à gauche	линейно *K*-независимый слева
L 424	**left linear topology** <on a ring> <AL>	linkslineare Topologie *f*	topologie *f* linéaire à gauche	линейная слева топология
L 425	**left localization** <of a ring> <AL>	linksseitige Lokalisierung *f*	localisation *f* à gauche	левая локализация
	left lower limit <DI>	*s.* L 381		
L 426	**left mean** <of a function on a topological group> <AL>	linker Mittelwert *m*	moyenne *f* à gauche	левое среднее
	left member <GN>	*s.* L 383		
	left modular ideal <AL>	*s.* R 581		
L 427	**left module** <AL>	Linksmodul *m*	module *m* à gauche	левый модуль
	left module over R <AL>	*s.* L 484		

No.	English	German	French	Russian
L 428	**left[-] monotonicity** <AL, SE>	linksseitige Monotonie *f*	monotonie *f* à gauche	монотонность слева
L 429	**left-monotonic law** <AL, SE>	linksseitiges Monotoniegesetz *n*	loi *f* de monotonie à gauche	закон монотонности слева
L 430	**left-monotonic operation** <AL, SE>	linksmonotone Operation *f*	opération *f* monotone à gauche	монотонная слева операция
L 431	**left multimodule** <AL>	Multilinksmodul *m*	multimodule *m* à gauche	левый мультимодуль
L 432	**left multiple** <AL, SE>	Linksvielfaches *n*, linksseitiges Vielfaches *n*	multiple *m* à gauche	левое кратное
L 433	**left[-]multiplication,** pre[-]multiplication, pre[-]multiplying, multiplication on the left <AL>	Multiplikation *f* von links, Linksmultiplikation *f*, linksseitige Multiplikation, Prämultiplikation *f*	multiplication *f* à gauche, prémultiplication *f*, pré-multiplication *f*	умножение слева, умножение начиная слева
	left multiplication <AL>	*s.* I 556		
	left multiplication <AL, GR>	*s.* L 512		
L 434	**left multiplication group** <of a quasigroup> <AL>	Gruppe *f* der Linksmultiplikationen	groupe *m* des multiplications à gauche	группа левых умножений
L 435	**left multiplication ring** <of a ring> <AL>	Ring *m* der Linksmultiplikationen	anneau *m* des multiplications à gauche	кольцо левых умножений
L 436	**left multiplicative domain,** left operator domain <AL>	Linksoperatorenbereich *m*, Linksmultiplikatorenbereich *m*, Linksoperatorenmenge *f*	ensemble *m* des opérateurs à gauche, domaine *m* d'opérateurs à gauche	область левых операторов
L 437	**left neat ring** <AL>	linksseitiger Nettoring *m*, Linksnettoring *m*	anneau *m* net à gauche	
L 438	**left *n*-Engel element,** bounded left Engel element <of a group> <GR>	beschränkt links-Engelsches Element *n*, *n*-links-Engelsches Element	élément *m* engelien à gauche borné	ограниченный левоэнгелев элемент, *n*-левоэнгелев элемент
	left neutral element <AL, GR>	*s.* L 395		
L 439	**left Noetherian (noetherian) ring** <AL>	linksnoetherscher Ring *m*	anneau *m* noethérien à gauche	нетерово слева кольцо, лево нетерово кольцо
L 440	**left noetherian semigroup** <AL>	linksnoethersche Halbgruppe *f*	demi-groupe *m* noethérien à gauche	нетерова слева полугруппа
L 441	**left-nondegenerate bilinear form** <AL>	linksnichtausgeartete Bilinearform *f*	forme *f* bilinéaire non dégénérée à gauche	невырожденная слева [билинейная] форма
L 442	**left nonsingular form** <AL>	linksnichtsinguläre Form *f*	forme *f* [bilinéaire] non singulière à gauche	неособая слева форма
L 443	**left non-zerodivisor,** left regular element <of a ring> <AL>	Linksnichtnullteiler *m*, Nichtlinksnullteiler *m*, linksreguläres Element *n*	élément *m* non diviseur de zéro à gauche, élément *m* simplifiable à gauche	левый неделитель нуля, сократимый слева элемент, левый регулярный элемент
L 444	**left nucleus,** left associator <of a loop> <AL>	linker Nukleus *m*		левое ядро
L 445	**left operator** <AL>	Linksoperator *m*, vorderer Operator *m*	opérateur (multiplicateur) *m* à gauche	левый оператор
	left operator domain <AL>	*s.* L 436		
L 446	**left order** <of a ring> <AL>	linke Ordnung *f*	ordre *m* à gauche	левый порядок
L 447	**left-ordered group** <GR>	linkshalbgeordnete Gruppe *f*	groupe *m* ordonné à gauche	левая частично упорядоченная группа, левоупорядоченная группа
L 448	**left-ordered set** <AL>	linkshalbgeordnete Menge *f*	ensemble *m* ordonné à gauche	левоупорядоченное множество
L 449	**left Ore condition** <for a non-commutative ring> <AL>	linke Ore-Bedingung *f*	condition *f* d'Ore à gauche	левое условие Оре
L 450	**left Ore domain (ring)** <AL>	linker Ore-Ring *m*	anneau *m* d'Ore à gauche	левое кольцо Оре
L 451	**left Ore set** <AL>	linke Ore-Menge *f*	ensemble *m* d'Ore à gauche	левое множество Оре
	left parenthesis <GN>	*s.* L 382		
L 452	**left periodic group** <GR>	linksperiodische Gruppe *f*	groupe *m* périodique à gauche	периодическая слева группа
	left PID <AL>	*s.* P 1440		
	left pir <AL>	*s.* P 671		
L 453	**left primary element** <of an ordered semi-group> <AL>	linksprimäres Element *n*	élément *m* primaire (premier) à gauche	примарный слева элемент
L 454	**left primitive algebra** <AL>	linksprimitive Algebra *f*	algèbre *f* primitive [à gauche]	примитивная [слева] алгебра
L 455	**left primitive ideal** <AL>	linksprimitives Ideal *n*	idéal *m* primitif à gauche	примитивный слева идеал
L 456	**left primitive ring** <AL>	linksprimitiver Ring *m*	anneau *m* primitif à gauche, anneau *m* primitif	примитивное [слева] кольцо
L 457	**left principal fibration** <AT>	linksseitiges Prinzipalfaserbündel *n*	fibration *f* principale à gauche, faisceau *m* principal à gauche	левое главное расслоение
	left principal ideal ring <AL>	*s.* P 671		
L 458	**left projective space** <AL>	linksprojektiver Raum *m*	espace *m* projectif à gauche	проективное слева пространство
L 459	**left pseudo-compact ring** <AL>	links-pseudokompakter Ring *m*	anneau *m* pseudo-compact à gauche	псевдокомпактное слева кольцо
L 460	**left quasi-field** <AL>	Linksquasikörper *m*, linksdistributive kartesische Gruppe *f*	quasi-corps *m* à gauche	левое квазиполе
L 461	**left quasigroup** <AL>	Linksquasigruppe *f*	quasi-groupe *m* à gauche	левая квазигруппа
L 462	**left quasi inverse** <of an element of a ring> <AL>	linkes Quasiinverses *n*	adverse *m* à gauche	левый квазиобратный [элемент] <для>
L 463	**left quasi-invertible element, left[-]quasi-regular element** <of a ring> <AL>	linksquasireguläres Element *n*	élément *m* quasi régulier à gauche	лево-квазирегулярный элемент

No.	English	German	French	Russian
L 464	**left quasi-regularity** <AL>	Linksquasiregularität *f*	quasi-régularité *f* à gauche	левая квазирегулярность
L 465	**left quasi-simple ring,** ring quasi-simple from the left <AL>	links-quasieinfacher Ring *m*	anneau *m* quasi-simple à gauche	квазипростое слева кольцо
L 466	**left quotient** <AL>	Linksquotient *m*	quotient *m* à gauche	левое частное
L 467	**left quotient** <of a division algorithm> <AL>	linksseitiger Quotient *m*	quotient *m* à gauche	левое неполное частное
L 468	**left quotient field** <AL>	Linksquotientenschiefkörper *m*	corps *m* des quotients à gauche	левое тело частных
L 469	**left quotient ring** <AL>	linker Quotientenring *m*	anneau *m* des fractions à gauche	левое кольцо частных
L 470	**left quotient ring** <with respect to a left Ore set>, ring of left quotients <AL>	Linksquotientenring *m*	anneau *m* de fractions à gauche <de *A* pour *S*>	левое кольцо частных
L 471	**left radical** <AL>	linkes Radikal *n*	radical *m* à gauche	левый радикал
L 472	**left regular element** <of a ring *or* a semigroup> <AL>	linksreguläres Element *n*	élément *m* régulier à gauche	регулярный слева элемент
	left regular element <AL>	*s.* 1. E 137; 2. L 443		
L 473	**left regularity** <of a semigroup> <AL>	Linksregularität *f*	régularité *f* à gauche	левая регулярность
	left regularity <AL>	*s.* R 573		
	left regularity <UA>	*s.* L 318		
	left regular matrix representation <AL>	*s.* L 474		
	left regular relation <AL>	*s.* L 319		
L 474	**left regular representation,** left regular matrix representation <of an algebra> <AL>	linke (zweite) reguläre Matrizendarstellung (Darstellung) *f*	représentation *f* matricielle régulière à gauche	левое регулярное матричное представление
	left regular representation <AL>	*s.* R 512		
L 475	**left regular ring** <AL>	linksregulärer Ring *m*	anneau *m* régulier à gauche	регулярное слева кольцо
L 476	**left regular semigroup** <AL>	linksreguläre Halbgruppe *f*	demi-groupe *m* inversif à gauche, semi-groupe *m* régulier à gauche	регулярная слева полугруппа
L 477	**left remainder** <of a division algorithm> <AL>	linksseitiger Rest *m*	reste *m* à gauche	левый остаток
L 478	**left representation** <of a category> <CA>	linke Darstellung *f*	représentation *f* à gauche	левое представление
L 479	**left representative** <AL>	Linksrepräsentant *m*	représentant *m* à gauche	левый представитель
L 480	**left representative system** <AL>	Linksrepräsentantensystem *n*, Linksvertretersystem *n*	système *m* de représentants à gauche	левая система представителей
L 481	**left resolution** <of an object> <CA>	linke Auflösung *f*	résolution *f* à gauche	левая резольвента
L 482	**left reversible semigroup** <AL>	linksreversible Halbgruppe *f*	semi-groupe *m* réversible à gauche	реверсивная слева полугруппа, полугруппа с общими слева кратными
L 483	**left Riemann integral** <of a matrix ><AN>	linkes Riemannsches Integral *n*	intégrale *f* de Riemann à gauche	левый интеграл Римана
L 484	**left R-module,** left module over *R* <AL>	*R*-Linksmodul *m*, Linksmodul *m* über *R*, Linksmodul mit *R* als Operatorenbereich	module *m* à gauche sur *R*, *R*-module *m* à gauche	левый *R*-модуль (модуль над *R*)
	left root <CA>	*s.* 1. E 327; 2. L 697		
L 485	**left satellite** <of a functor> <CA>	linker Satellit *m*	satellite *m* gauche	левый сателлит
L 486	**left screw,** left-hand[ed] screw, left-twisted screw, sinistrorse screw <GE>	Linksschraube *f*	vis *f* à gauche, vis sinistrorsum, vis à torsion gauche (sinistre)	левый винт
L 487	**left secondary element** <AL>	linkssekundäres Element *n*	élément *m* secondaire à gauche	вторичный слева элемент
L 488	**left secondary radical** <AL>	linkes sekundäres Radikal *n*	radical *m* secondaire à gauche	левый вторичный радикал
	left segment <SE>	*s.* I 536		
L 489	**left self-injective ring** <AL>	linksseitig selbstinjektiver Ring *m*	anneau *m* self-injectif à gauche	самоинъективное слева кольцо
L 490	**left semi-hereditary ring** <AL>	links-halberblicher Ring *m*	anneau *m* semi-héréditaire à gauche	полунаследственное слева кольцо
	left semi-isomorphism <CA>	*s.* C 2464		
L 491	**left semilinear mapping** <AL>	linkshalblineare Abbildung *f*	application *f* sesquilinéaire à gauche	полуторалинейное слева отображение
	left side <GN>	*s.* L 383		
	left-side cancellation <AL>	*s.* L 366		
L 492	**left-sided decomposition,** left decomposition <AL>	linksseitige Zerlegung *f*, Linkszerlegung *f*	décomposition *f* à gauche	левостороннее разложение, левое разложение
	left-side distributive law <AL>	*s.* L 342		
L 493	**left-sided Peirce decomposition** <of a ring> <AL>	linksseitige Peircesche Zerlegung *f*	décomposition *f* de Peirce à gauche	левостороннее пирсовское разложение
	left-side half-tangent <DG>	*s.* L 365		
L 494	**left simple groupoid** <AL>	linkseinfaches Gruppoid *n*	groupoïde *m* simple à gauche	простой слева группоид
L 495	**left simple semigroup** <AL>	linkseinfache Halbgruppe *f*	demi-groupe *m* simple à gauche	простая слева полугруппа

L 496	**left singular ideal** <AL>	singuläres Linksideal *n*	idéal *m* singulier à gauche	сингулярный левый идеал
L 497	**left singular semigroup** <AL>	linkssinguläre Halbgruppe *f*	demi-groupe *m* dont tous les éléments sont permis à gauche	вырождающаяся слева полугруппа, левосингулярная полугруппа, полугруппа левых нулей
L 498	**left socle** <of a ring> <AL>	Linkssockel *m*, linksseitiges Antiradikal *n*	socle *m* gauche	левый цоколь
L 499	**left-solvable** <AL>	linksseitig lösbar	résoluble à gauche	леворазрешимый
L 500	**left structure** <of a ring> <AL>	Linksstruktur *f*	structure *f* à gauche	левая структура
L 501	**left symbolic power** <in a non-commutative ring> <AL>	linke symbolische Potenz *f*	puissance *f* symbolique à gauche	левая символическая степень
	left system <AY>	*s.* L 371		
L 502	**left tangent** <DG>	linke (linksseitige, hintere) Tangente *f*	tangente *f* à gauche	левая касательная
L 503	**left tensor product** <AL>	linksseitiges Tensorprodukt *n*	produit *m* tensoriel gauche	левое тензорное произведение
L 504	**left tertiary radical** <AL>	linkes tertiäres Radikal *n*	radical *m* tertiaire à gauche	левый терциарный радикал
L 505	**left topological divisor of zero** <in a Banach algebra> <FA>	Linksnullteiler *m* im verallgemeinerten Sinn	diviseur *m* de zéro topologique à gauche	левый топологический делитель нуля
L 506	**left topological module** <AL>	topologischer Linksmodul *m*	module *m* topologique à gauche	левый топологический модуль
L 507	**left topological vector space** <AL>	topologischer Linksvektorraum *m*	espace *m* vectoriel topologique à gauche	левое топологическое векторное пространство
L 508	**left topology** <on an ordered set> <TO>	Linkstopologie *f*	topologie *f* gauche	левая топология
L 509	**left translate** <of a function on a group> <AL>	durch Linkstranslation aus einer Funktion hervorgehende Funktion *f*	fonction *f* translatée à gauche	левый сдвиг <функции>
L 510	**left translation** <of a function on a group> <AL>	linksseitige Translation *f*	translation *f* à gauche	левый сдвиг
L 511	**left translation** <of a groupoid *or* ring> <AL>	Linkstranslation *f*	homothétie *f* externe à gauche	сдвиг слева, левый сдвиг
L 512	**left translation,** left multiplication (homothety, homothetic) <by *a*> <AL, GR>	linke Translation *f*, Linkstranslation *f*, linke Homothetie (Multiplikation) *f*, linksseitige Multiplikation (Translation) <durch *a*>	homothétie *f* à gauche, translation *f* à gauche <correspondant à *a*, par rapport à *a*, d'amplitude *a*>	левая гомотетия, сдвиг слева, левый сдвиг, левый перенос <соответствующий элементу *a*>
	left-twisted helix <GE>	*s.* S 1133		
	left-twisted screw <GE>	*s.* L 486		
L 513	**left uniformity** <of a topological group> <AL, TO>	links-uniforme Struktur *f*, Linksuniformität *f*, linksseitige uniforme Struktur	structure *f* uniforme gauche	левая равномерная структура
L 514	**left-unique relation** <converse relation is unique> <LO>	voreindeutige Beziehung *f*, linkseindeutige Relation *f*	relation *f* univoque à gauche	левооднозначное отношение
L 515	**left unit** <of a semigroup> <AL>	Linkseinheit *f*	élément *m* inversible à gauche	обратимый слева элемент
L 516	**left unit,** left identity <modulo α> <AL>	Linkseinselement *n*, Linkseinheit *f*, relatives Einselement *n* <modulo α>	unité *f* à gauche, élément *m* unité à gauche <modulo α>	левая единица <по модулю α>
L 517	**left unit,** range unit <of an element, for an element> <AL>	Linkseins *n* <eines Elements>	unité *f* gauche <d'un élément>	левая единица <элемента>
	left unit <AL, GR>	*s.* L 395		
L 518	**left-unitary kernel,** unitary kernel on the left <IE>	linksunitärer Kern *m*	noyau *m* unitaire à gauche	унитарное слева ядро
	left unit-element <AL, GR>	*s.* L 395		
L 519	**left unit subsemigroup** <of a semigroup> <AL>	Unterhalbgruppe *f* der Linkseinheiten	sous-demigroupe *m* des éléments inversibles à gauche	подполугруппа [всех] обратимых слева элементов
	left unity <AL, GR>	*s.* L 395		
L 520	**left universal solution** <CA>	linke universelle Lösung *f*	solution *f* universelle à gauche	левое универсальное решение
	left upper limit <DI>	*s.* L 375		
L 521	**left vector space** <AL>	Linksvektorraum *m*	espace *m* vectoriel à gauche	левое векторное пространство
L 522	**left zero divisor,** left divisor of zero <AL>	linker Nullteiler *m*, Linksnullteiler *m*	diviseur *m* de zéro à gauche, diviseur *m* gauche de zéro, diviseur *m* de zéro de première espèce	левый делитель нуля
L 523	**left zero element,** left-hand zero-element <of a groupoid> <AL>	linkes Nullelement *n*, Linksnullelement *n*, linkes Hauptelement *n* zweiter Art, linksseitiges absorbierendes Element *n*	élément *m* permis à gauche	левый нуль, левый нулевой элемент
L 524	**left zeroid [element]** <of a semi-group> <AL>	linksseitiges Zeroidelement *n*, Linkszeroid *n*	élément *m* zéroïde à gauche	левый зероид
L 525	**left zero morphism** <CA>	Links-Nullmorphismus *m*	morphisme *m* nul à gauche	левый нулевой морфизм
L 526	**leg,** side, lateral side, non-parallel sides <of a trapezium *or* trapezoid> <EG>	Schenkel *m*	côté *m* <*pl.:* côtés non parallèles>	боковая сторона
L 527	**leg** <of a compass> <GE, IN>	Schenkel *m*	branche *f*	ножка
	leg <EG>	*s.* 1. O 540; 2. S 784		
	Legendre['s] associated function [of the first kind] <FU>	*s.* A 1075		

	Legendre['s] associated function of the second kind <FU>	*s.* A 1076		
L 528	**Legendre['s] condition** <VA>	Legendresche Bedingung *f* (Bedingung im engeren Sinne)	condition *f* de Legendre	неравенство (условие) Лежандра
	Legendre contact transformation <DE>	*s.* L 541		
	Legendre['s] differential equation <DE>	*s.* 1. L 529; 2. L 533		
	Legendre['s] duplication formula <FU>	*s.* D 1065		
	Legendre['s] elliptic integral <FU>	*s.* E 178		
L 529	**Legendre['s] equation,** Legendre['s] differential equation <DE>	Legendresche Differentialgleichung (Gleichung) *f*	équation *f* [différentielle] de Legendre	[дифференциальное] уравнение Лежандра
	Legendre['s] equation <DE>	*s.* L 533		
	Legendre['s] form <FT>	*s.* L 535		
	Legendre['s] form of the elliptic integral <FU>	*s.* E 178		
L 530	**Legendre['s] function** <having arbitrary indices ν, μ> <FU>	[allgemeine] Legendresche Funktion (Kugelfunktion) *f*, Kugelfunktion mit beliebigen Indizes	fonction *f* de Legendre	[сферическая] функция Лежандра, сферическая функция [по имени Лежандра]
	Legendre['s] function <NT>	*s.* S 1552		
L 531	**Legendre['s] function of the first kind,** spherical harmonic of the first kind <ν arbitrary, $\mu = 0$ omitted> <FU>	Legendresche Funktion (Kugelfunktion) *f* erster Art, Kugelfunktion erster (1.) Art	fonction *f* de Legendre de première espèce, fonction sphérique [primitive] de première espèce	[сферическая] функция Лежандра первого рода, сферическая функция [по имени Лежандра] первого рода
L 532	**Legendre['s] function of the second kind,** spherical harmonic of the second kind, surface zonal harmonic of the second kind <ν arbitrary, $\mu = 0$ omitted> <FU>	Legendresche Funktion (Kugelfunktion) *f* zweiter Art, Kugelfunktion zweiter (2.) Art	fonction *f* de Legendre de deuxième (seconde) espèce, fonction sphérique [primitive] de deuxième (seconde) espèce	[сферическая] функция Лежандра второго рода, сферическая функция [по имени Лежандра] второго рода
L 533	**Legendre['s] general differential equation, Legendre['s] general equation,** Legendre['s] differential equation, Legendre['s] equation, differential equation of the spherical harmonics, associated Legendre equation <DE>	allgemeine Legendresche Differentialgleichung *f*, Legendresche Differentialgleichung (Gleichung *f*), [allgemeine] Differentialgleichung der Kugelfunktionen	équation *f* différentielle des fonctions de Legendre associée, équation différentielle [générale] des fonctions harmoniques sphériques, équation [différentielle] générale de Legendre, équation [différentielle] de Legendre	общее [дифференциальное] уравнение Лежандра, [дифференциальное] уравнение Лежандра, дифференциальное уравнение сферических функций
	Legendre['s] integral <FU> ⌐<NT>	*s.* E 178		
	Legendre-Jacobi symbol	*s.* L 539		
L 534	**Legendre['s] modulus** <of an elliptic integral> <FU>	Legendrescher Modul *m*	module *m*, k^2	параметр, k^2
L 535	**Legendre['s] normal form,** Legendre['s] standard form, Legendre['s] form <of an elliptic differential> <FT>	Legendresche Normalform *f*, Normalform Legendres	forme *f* normale de Legendre	нормальная (стандартная) форма Лежандра
	Legendre['s] normal form of the elliptic integral <FU>	*s.* E 178		
L 536	**Legendre['s] polynomial,** Legendrian; zonal spherical harmonic, zonal harmonic [function] <in spherical coordinates> <FU>	Legendresches Polynom *n*, Legendrescher Koeffizient *m*, Legendre-Polynom *n*; zonale Kugelfunktion (Harmonische) *f*	polynôme *m* de Legendre, fonction *f* sphérique primitive (fondamentale); fonction (harmonique *f*) zonale, fonction harmonique zonale	многочлен Лежандра, сферический многочлен [по имени Лежандра], полином Лежандра; зональная гармоническая (сферическая функция), многочлен (полином) Лежандра первого рода
L 537	**Legendre['s] relation** <for elliptic integrals> <FT>	Legendresche Relation *f*	relation *f* de Legendre	соотношение Лежандра
	Legendre['s] standard form <FT>	*s.* L 535		
	Legendre['s] standard [form of the elliptic] integral <FU>	*s.* E 178		
L 538	**Legendre['s] sufficient condition** <VA>	Legendresche S-Bedingung *f*, verschärfte (starke) Legendresche Bedingung, Legendresche Bedingung *f* in der verschärften Form	condition *f* suffisante de Legendre	достаточное условие Лежандра, сильное условие Лежандра
L 539	**Legendre['s] symbol,** Legendre-Jacobi symbol <NT>	Legendresches Symbol *n*, Legendre-Symbol *n*, Legendresymbol *n*, Legendres Symbol	symbole *m* de Legendre	символ Лежандра, квадратичный символ
L 540	**Legendre['s] theorem,** theorem of Legendre <on spherical triangles> <EG>	Legendrescher Satz *m*	théorème *m* de Legendre	теорема Лежандра

No.	English	German	French	Russian
L 541	**Legendre['s] transform[ation],** Legendre contact transformation <DE>	Legendresche Transformation (Berührungstransformation) *f*, Berührungstransformation von Legendre, Legendre-Transformation *f*	transformation *f* de Legendre	преобразование Лежандра, лежандрово преобразование
	Legendrian <FU>	*s.* L 536		
L 542	**legit** <ST>	Legit *m*	légit *m*	легит
L 543	**legit transformation** <ST>	Legittransformation *f*, Legit *m*	transformation *f* légit	легит-преобразование
L 544	**"Le Her" game** <TG>	„Le Her"-Spiel *n*, „Le Her" *n*	jeu *m* « Le Her », « Le Her » *m*	игра «проходящий туз»
L 545	**Lehmus['] theorem,** theorem of Lehmus <on the triangle> <EG>	Satz *m* von Lehmus, Lehmusscher Satz	théorème *m* de Lehmus	теорема Лемуса
	Leibnitz . . .	*s.a.* Leibniz . . .		
	Leibniz['s] alternating series test <SS>	*s.* A 559		
	Leibniz['s] formula <DI>	*s.* L 548		
L 546	**Leibniz['] law** <LO>	Leibnizsches (identitätstheoretisches) Ersetzbarkeitstheorem *n*	loi *f* de Leibniz	закон Лейбница
	Leibniz['s] rule <DI>	*s.* L 548		
	Leibniz['s] rule <SS>	*s.* A 559		
L 547	**Leibniz['s] series,** alternating harmonic series <SS>	Leibnizsche (alternierende harmonische) Reihe *f*, harmonische Reihe mit alternierenden Vorzeichen	série *f* harmonique alternée, série de Leibniz	знакопеременный гармонический ряд, ряд Лейбница
	Leibniz['s] test (theorem) <SS>	*s.* A 559		
L 548	**Leibniz['s] theorem,** Leibniz['s] formula (rule) <for the *n*-th derivative of a product>, // Leibnitz['s] formula (rule, theorem) <DI>	Leibnizsche Formel (Produktenregel) *f*	formule *f* de Leibniz (d'Alembert), // formule de Leibnitz	формула Лейбница
L 549	**Leibniz['s] triangle** <FD>	harmonisches (Leibnizsches) Dreieck *n*	triangle *m* de Leibniz, triangle harmonique	треугольник Лейбница
L 550	**lemma** <GN>	Lemma *n*, Hilfssatz *m*	lemme *m*	лемма, вспомогательная теорема, вспомогательное предложение
	9 lemma <CA, HA>	*s.* N 260		
L 551	**lemma of Artin-Rees,** Artin-Rees lemma <AL>	Artin-Reessches Lemma *n*	lemme *m* d'Artin-Rees	лемма Артина-Риса
L 552	**lemma of Gauss,** Gauss['s] lemma <AL>	Gaußscher Satz *m* über Polynome, Gaußscher Satz [über primitive Polynome]	lemme *m* de Gauss pour les anneaux factoriels	лемма Гаусса
L 553	**lemma of Grün,** Grün['s] lemma <GR>	Lemma *n* von Grün, Grünsches Lemma	lemme *m* de Grün	лемма Грюна
L 554	**lemma of Hall,** Hall['s] lemma <GR>	Lemma *n* von Hall, Hallsches Lemma	lemme *m* de Hall	лемма Холла
L 555	**lemma of Harish-Chandra** <AL>	Lemma *n* von Harish-Chandra, Harish-Chandrasches Lemma	lemme *m* de Harish-Chandra	лемма Хариш-Чандры
	lemma of Loewner <FT>	*s.* L 1021		
L 556	**lemma of Study** <AL>	Studysches Lemma *n*	lemme *m* de Study	лемма Штуди
L 557	**lemma of the connecting morphism** <CA>	Verbindungslemma *n*	lemme *m* sur l'homomorphisme de connexion	лемма о связывающем морфизме
L 558	**lemniscate,** lemniscate of *n*-th order <GE>	Lemniskate *f*, allgemeine Lemniskate	lemniscate, *f* lemniscate d'ordre *n*	лемниската, лемниската *n*-го порядка
L 559	**lemniscate function,** Gaussian lemniscate function <cos lemn, cl *or* sin lemn, sl> <FT, FU>	Lemniskatenfunktion *f*, lemniskatische Funktion *f*	fonction *f* lemniscatienne	лемнискатическая функция
L 560	**lemniscate of Bernoulli,** Bernoulli['s] lemniscate <AG>	Bernoullische (hyperbolische) Lemniskate *f*	lemniscate *f* [de Bernoulli]	лемниската [Я.] Бернулли, лемниската
	lemniscate of Booth <AG>	*s.* B 564		
	lemniscate of *n*-th order <GE>	*s.* L 558		
L 561	**Lemoine['s] circle** <of a triangle> <EG>	Lemoines[cher] Kreis *m*	cercle *m* de Lemoine	окружность Лемуана
L 562	**Lemoine['s] hexagon** <EG>	Lemoinesches Sechseck *n*	hexagone *m* de Lemoine	шестиугольник Лемуана
L 563	**Lemoine['s] line,** Lemoine['s] straight line <of a triangle> <EG>	Lemoines[che] Gerade *f*	droite *f* de Lemoine	прямая Лемуана
L 564	**Lemoine['s] point,** Grebe['s] point <EG>	Lemoinescher (Grebescher) Punkt *m*, Symmedianpunkt *m*, Lemoines Punkt	point *m* de Lemoine, centre *m* des symédianes, point de Grebe	точка Лемуана
	Lemoine['s] straight line <EG>	*s.* L 563		
L 565	**Lemoine['s] triangle** <EG>	Lemoinesches Dreieck *n*, Mitteldreieck *n*	triangle *m* de Lemoine, triangle moyen	треугольник Лемуана
L 566	**length** <of a cycle>, degree, order <of a cyclic permutation> <AL>	Länge *f* <eines Zyklus>, Zyklenlänge *f*, Ordnung *f* <einer zyklischen Permutation>	longueur *f*, degré *m*, ordre *m* <d'un cycle>	длина <цикла>, порядок <циклической подстановки>
L 567	**length** <of a chain> <SE>	Länge *f*, Dimension *f*, verbandstheoretische Dimension	longueur *f*, rang *m*	длина

	length <AL>	*s.* 1. I 16; 2. W 290		
	length <LA>	*s.* D 509		
	length <SE>	*s.* D 511		
	length <VT>	*s.* M 24		
L 568/9	**length of a composition series** <of a group> <GR>	Kompositionslänge *f*, Länge *f* der Kompositionsreihe, Länge *f*, Jordansche Invariante *f*	longueur *f* de la suite de Jordan-Hölder	композиционная длина, длина композиционного ряда
L 570	**length of arc,** length of curve, arc length <DG>	Bogenlänge *f*, Länge *f* des Bogens, Länge der Kurve	longueur *f* de l'arc, longueur de la courbe	длина дуги, длина кривой
	length of class interval <ST>	*s.* C 794		
	length of curve <DG>	*s.* L 570		
L 571	**length of iteration,** length of run <ST>	Länge *f* der Iteration	longueur *f* de la suite, longueur de l'itération	длина итерации
L 572	**length of queue** <ST>	Warteschlangenlänge *f*, Länge *f* der Warteschlange	longueur *f* de la file d'attente	длина очереди
	length of radius vector <AY>	*s.* P 887		
	length of run <ST>	*s.* L 571		
L 573	**length of tangent,** tangent <GE>	Tangentenlänge *f*, Länge *f* der Tangente	longueur *f* de la tangente	длина касательной
	length of the chord <EG>	*s.* C 655		
L 574	**length of the gap** <SS>	Länge *f* der Lücke	longueur *f* de la lacune	длина лакуны
	length of the longest cycle <GP>	*s.* G 290		
L 575	**length of the period** <of a recurring decimal> <AR>	Periodenlänge *f*	grandeur *f* de la période	длина периода
	length-preserving embedding <TO>	*s.* I 1108		
	length-preserving mapping <DG, TO>	*s.* I 1112		
L 576	**lens** <as a convex body> <CS, GE>	Linse *f*	lentille *f*	линза
L 577	**lens space,** // **lense-space** <TO>	Linsenraum *m*	espace *m* lenticulaire, « lens space » *m*, « Linsenraum » *m*	линзовое пространство
L 578	**Leontief['s] matrix** <PG>	Leontief-Matrix *f*	matrice *f* de Leontief	матрица Леонтьева
L 579	**leptokurtic distribution,** peaked distribution <ST>	hochgipflige (leptokurtische) Verteilung *f*	distribution *f* leptokurtique	островершинное распределение, распределение с эксцессом больше нормального
L 580	**leptokurtosis,** positive kurtosis (excess), peakedness <ST>	Hochgipfligkeit *f*, positiver Exzeß *m*	excès *m* positif	островершинность, положительный эксцесс
L 581	**$\mathcal{L}$-equivalence** <in a semigroup> <AL>	$\mathcal{L}$-Äquivalenz *f*	$\mathcal{L}$-équivalence *f*	$\mathcal{L}$-эквивалентность
L 582	**$\mathcal{L}$-equivalent elements** <of a semigroup> <AL>	$\mathcal{L}$-äquivalente Elemente *npl*	éléments *mpl* $\mathcal{L}$-équivalents	$\mathcal{L}$-эквивалентные элементы
	Leray-Hirsch theorem <AT>	*s.* T 309		
L 583	**Leray['s] method** <FA, TO>	Leraysche Methode *f*	méthode (contribution) *f* de Leray	метод Лерэ
L 584	**Lerch['s] theorem** <in Laplace transform> <IT>	Satz *m* von Lerch, Lerchscher Satz	théorème *m* de Lerch	теорема Лерха
	Lerch['s] theorem <NT>	*s.* T 310		
L 585	**less** <than>, smaller <than>, $<$ <AN, SE>; earlier <than>, preceding, $<$ <SE>	kleiner <als>, $<$	plus petit <que>, plus petit strictement, inférieur, strictement inférieur <à>, $<$ <AN, SE>; antérieur, avant, $<$ <SE>	меньше <чем>, $<$
	less pollent set <SE>	*s.* S 651		
L 586	**less than or equal** <to>, $\leqq$, $\leq$ <AN, SE>	kleiner oder gleich, $\leqq$, $\leq$	inférieur ou égal <à>, plus petit que ou au plus égal <à>, inférieur <à>, $\leqq$, $\leq$ <AN, SE>; avant ou égal <à>, $\leqq$, $\leq$ <SE>	меньше или равно, не больше, $\leqq$, $\leq$
L 587	**less-than-or-equal-to relation** <SE>	„kleiner-gleich"- Relation *f*	relation *f* « inférieur ou égal à », comparaison *f*	отношение меньше или равный
L 588	**less-than-or-equal-to relation** *or* **greater-than-or-equal-to relation** <SE>	„kleiner-gleich"-Relation *f* oder „größer-gleich"-Relation *f*	relation *f* d'égalité-inégalité	отношение нестрогого неравенства
L 589	**less-than-or-equal-to sign,** $\leqq$, $\leq$ <GN>	„kleiner-gleich"-Zeichen *n*, $\leqq$, $\leq$	signe *m* de comparaison, signe d'ordre, $\leqq$, $\leq$	знак «меньше или равный», $\leqq$, $\leq$
	less than relation <SE>	*s.* R 676		
L 590	**less-than sign,** $<$ <GN>	„kleiner"-Zeichen *n*, $<$	signe *m* d'ordre, signe d'ordre strict, $<$	знак «меньше чем», $<$
L 590a	**let ... be** <GN>	es sei ..., // sei ...	soit ...	пусть ...
L 591	**let invariant / to** <an element> <AL, GE, IV>	invariant lassen, fest lassen <ein Element>	laisser invariant, conserver <un élément>	оставлять на месте <элемент>
L 592	**level** <of a module system> <AL>	Stufe *f* <Kronecker>, Rang *m*	rang *m*, degré *m*	ступень
L 593	**level,** order <of a set in ramified theory of types> <FO, SE>	Ordnung *f* <einer Menge im verzweigten Stufenkalkül>	ordre *m* <d'un ensemble>	порядок <множества>
L 594	**level** <of a factor>, factor level <ST>	Stufe *f*, Faktorenstufe *f*	niveau *m*, niveau du facteur	уровень, уровень фактора
L 595	**level** <in Morse's theory> <TO, VA>	Höhe *f*	niveau *m*	уровень

No.	English	German	French	Russian
	level <ST>	*s.* S 842		
L 596	**level cross** <SP>	Niveauschnitt *m*	point *m* d'intersection de niveau	точка пересечения уровня
L 597	**level curve,** level line <of a surface *or* of a function *or* of a scalar field> <DG, RF, ST>	Niveaulinie *f*	ligne (courbe) *f* de niveau	линия уровня
L 598	**level line,** contour line, height line; isohypse [line], height contour [line] <with positive co-ordinate>; isobath, depth contour [line] <with negative co-ordinate> <in one-plane method> <DS>	Höhenlinie *f*, Schichtenlinie *f*; Isohypse *f*; Isobathe *f*	ligne (courbe) *f* de niveau; courbe isohypse, isohypse *f*; courbe isobathe, isobathe *f*	линия уровня, уровенная линия, горизонталь; изогипса; изобата
	level line <DG, RF, ST>	*s.* L 597		
	level of error <ST>	*s.* 1. L 599; 2. S 842		
L 599	**level of error of the first kind,** type I error rate, error rate, error probability, level of error <ST>	Irrtumswahrscheinlichkeit *f*, Wahrscheinlichkeit *f* des Fehlers erster Art, Wahrscheinlichkeit für den Fehler erster Art, Fehlerwahrscheinlichkeit *f*, Fehlerrate *f*	probabilité *f* d'erreur [de première espèce], probabilité de l'erreur de première espèce	вероятность ошибки [первого рода]
	level of significance <ST>	*s.* S 842		
L 600	**level plane,** contour plane, height plane <in one-plane projection> <DS>	Höhenebene *f*, Schichtenebene *f*	plan *m* de niveau	плоскость уровня
L 601	**level surface,** contour surface <of a real-valued function *or* a scalar field> <DG, RF, ST>	Niveaufläche *f*	surface *f* de niveau	поверхность уровня
	Levi-Cività connection <DG>	*s.* R 1004		
	Levi-Cività['s] parallel displacement <DG>	*s.* I 479		
L 602	**Levi-Cività parallelism,** parallelism of Levi-Cività <DG>	Parallelismus *m* von Levi-Cività, Levi-Civitàscher Parallelismus	parallélisme *m* de Levi-Cività	параллелизм Леви-Чивита
	Levi-Civita symbol <DG, VT>	*s.* A 563		
	Levi-Civita['s] tensor <DG, VT>	*s.* A 563		
L 603	**Levi['s] decomposition** <of a Lie algebra *or* group> <AL>	Levische Zerlegung *f*	décomposition *f* de Levi	разложение Леви
	Levi['s] function <DE>	*s.* P 150		
L 604	**Levi['s] problem** <on a Stein space> <FT>	Levisches Problem *n*	problème *m* de Levi	проблема Леви
	Levi['s] space <FA>	*s.* B 193		
L 605	**Levitan['s] almost-periodic function,** almost-periodic function in the sense of Levitan, N-almost-periodic function <AP>	L-fastperiodische (N-fastperiodische, Levitan-fastperiodische) Funktion *f*	fonction *f* presque-périodique de Levitan	почти-периодическая функция в смысле Левитана, N-почти-периодическая функция
L 606	**Levitan['s] polynomial** <FU>	Levitansches Polynom *n*	polynôme *m* de Levitan	многочлен (полином) Левитана
L 607	**Levi['s] theorem** <on ordered groups> <GR>	Satz *m* von Levi, Levischer Satz	théorème *m* de Levi	теорема Леви
	Levi['s] theorem <AL>	*s.* T 311		
	Levi['s] theorem <FA>	*s.* B 495		
L 608	**Levitzki['s] inequality** <AL>	Levitzkische Ungleichung *f*	inégalité *f* de Levitzki	неравенство Левицкого
L 609	**Levitzki['s] radical** <of a ring> <AL>	Levitzkisches Radikal *n*	radical *m* de Levitzki	локально нильпотентный радикал Левицкого
L 610	**Lévy-Cramér['s] theorem** <ST>	Lévy-Cramérscher Satz *m*, Satz von Lévy-Cramér	théorème *m* de Lévy-Cramér	теорема Леви-Крамера
	Lévy['s] distribution <ST>	*s.* L 228		
L 611	**Lévy-Khinchine['s] representation** <ST>	Lévy-Chintschin-Darstellung *f*, Lévy-Khintchine-Darstellung *f*	représentation *f* de Lévy-Khintchine	представление Леви-Хинчина
L 612	**Lévy['s] theorem** <ST>	Lévyscher Satz *m*, Satz von Lévy	théorème *m* de Lévy	теорема Леви
L 613	**Lexell['s] circle** <of spherical triangles> <EG>	Lexellscher Kreis *m*	cercle *m* de Lexell	окружность Лекселла
L 614	**Lexell['s] theorem** <on spherical triangles> <EG>	Lexellscher Satz *m*	théorème *m* de Lexell	теорема Лекселла
	lexicographical order <SE>	*s.* L 619		
L 615	**lexicographic direct product** <of groups> <GR>	lexikographisches direktes Produkt *n*	produit *m* direct lexicographique	лексикографическое прямое произведение
L 616	**lexicographic direct sum** <of groups> <GR>	lexikographische direkte Summe *f*	somme *f* directe lexicographique	лексикографическая прямая сумма
L 617	**lexicographic function** <SE>	lexikographische Funktion *f* <J. Schmidt>	fonction *f* lexicographique	лексикографическая функция

No.	English	German	French	Russian
L 618	**lexicographic method** <of Dantzig, Orden, and Wolfe> <PG>	lexikographische Methode *f* von Dantzig, Orden und Wolfe; Dantzig-Orden-Wolfesche Methode	méthode *f* lexicographique	лексикографический метод
L 619	**lexicographic order[ing],** dictionary order, order by first difference[s], lexicographical order, ordering according to the principle of first differences, alphabetical order <SE>	lexikographische Ordnung *f*, Ordnung nach ersten Differenzstellen, lexikographische Anordnung *f*, alphabetische Ordnung (Anordnung)	ordre *m* lexicographique, ordre d'après le principe des premières différences, ordre dit du dictionnaire, ordre alphabétique	лексикографическое упорядочение, упорядочение в словарном порядке, алфавитный порядок; лексикографическая упорядоченность
L 620	**lexicographic [partial] ordering,** partial ordering according to the principle of first differences, partial order by first differences <SE>	lexikographische Halbordnung *f*, Halbordnung nach ersten Differenzstellen	ordre *m* lexicographique, ordre [partiel] d'après le principe des premières différences	лексикографическое полуупорядочение, частичное упорядочение в словарном порядке
L 621	**Lexis['] distribution** <ST>	Lexissche Verteilung *f*	distribution *f* de Lexis	распределение Лексиса
L 622	**Lexis['] ratio** <ST>	Lexissche Zahl *f*	rapport *m* de Lexis	отношение Лексиса
L 623	**Lexis['s] theory [of dispersion]** <ST>	Lexissche Dispersionstheorie *f*	théorie *f* de dispersion de Lexis, théorie de Lexis	теория Лексиса, теория дисперсии Лексиса
L 624	**Lexis variation** <ST>	Lexis-Variation *f*	variation *f* (schéma *m*) de Lexis	дисперсия Лексиса
L 625	***l*-fold [Markov] chain** <SP>	*l*-fache Markovsche Kette *f*, *l*-fache Kette	chaîne *f* markovienne *l*-uple, chaîne *l*-uple	*l*-кратная цепь Ма́ркова, *l*-кратная цепь
L 626	***L*-function** <NT>	*L*-Funktion *f*	fonction *f* *L*	*L*-функция
L 627	***L*-function,** logarithmico-exponential function <RF>	*L*-Funktion *f*	fonction *f* (H)	функция (H)
	lg <AN>	*s.* L 1039		
	lg <AR>	*s.* L 1028		
	lg <AR, NU>	*s.* B 754		
	l-group <LA>	*s.* L 137		
	l-homomorphic group <GR>	*s.* L 123		
L 628	**l-homomorphism** <of l-rings> <AL>	Homomorphismus *m* <verbandsgeordneter Ringe>	homomorphisme *m* <d'anneaux réticulés>	гомоморфизм <l-колец>
L 629	**L-homomorphism,** lattice homomorphism <of a group> <GR>	Verbandshomomorphismus *m*, Strukturhomomorphismus *m*	homomorphisme *m* structural	структурный гомоморфизм
	l'Hôpital['s] rule <DI>	*s.* D 208		
	L'Hospital['s] rule <DI>	*s.* D 208		
	LHS <GN>	*s.* L 383		
L 630	**l'Huilier['s] formula** <for a triangle *or* in spherical trigonometry> <EG>	l'Huiliersche Gleichung *f*	formule *f* de l'Huilier	формула Люилье
L 631	**l'Huilier['s] problem** <EG>	l'Huiliersche Aufgabe *f*	problème *m* de l'Huilier	задача Люилье
L 632	**l'Huilier['s] theorem** <EG>	Vieleckssatz *m* von l'Huilier, l'Huiliers[cher] Satz *m*	théorème *m* de l'Huilier	теорема Люилье
	li; Li <FU>'	*s.* L 1041		
L 633	**Liapunov['s] condition** <PO, ST>	Ljapunovsche Bedingung *f*	condition *f* de Liapounoff	условие Ляпунова
	Liapunov['s] direct method <DE>	*s.* L 639		
L 634	**Liapunov['s] first method** <DE>	Ljapunovs[che] erste Methode *f*, erste Methode von Ljapunov	première méthode *f* de Liapounoff	первый метод Ляпунова
	Liapunov['s] formula <SS>	*s.* P 175		
L 635	**Liapunov['s] fraction** <ST>	Ljapunovscher Bruch *m*	fraction *f* de Liapounoff	дробь Ляпунова
L 636	**Liapunov['s] function** <DE>	Ljapunovsche Funktion *f*	fonction *f* de Liapounoff	функция Ляпунова
L 637	**Liapunov['s] inequality** <ST>	Ljapunovsche Ungleichung *f*	inégalité *f* de Liapounoff	неравенство Ляпунова
L 638	**Liapunov['s] number,** characteristic number <DE>	Ljapunovsche (charakteristische) Zahl *f*	nombre *m* de Liapounoff, nombre caractéristique	число Ляпунова, характеристическое число
L 639	**Liapunov['s] second method,** Liapunov['s] direct method <DE>	Ljapunovs[che] zweite (direkte) Methode *f*, zweite (direkte) Methode von Ljapunov	deuxième méthode *f* de Liapounoff, méthode directe de Liapounoff	второй (прямой) метод Ляпунова
L 640	**Liapunov['s] surface** <DE>	Ljapunovsche (Ljapunowsche, Liapounoffsche) Fläche *f*	surface *f* de Liapounoff	поверхность Ляпунова
L 641	**Liapunov['s] theorem** <of stability>, stability theorem of Liapunov <DE>	Ljapunovscher Stabilitätssatz *m*, Stabilitätssatz von Ljapunov	théorème *m* de Liapounoff (stabilité de Liapounoff)	теорема Ляпунова (устойчивости Ляпунова)
L 642	**Liapunov['s] theorem** <ST>	Satz *m* von Ljapunov, Ljapunovscher Satz	théorème *m* de Liapounoff	теорема Ляпунова
	liar paradox <LO>	*s.* E 296		
L 643	**liberty** <of fields> <AL>	Freiheit *f*	liberté *f*	свобода
L 644	**liberty morphism,** left liberty, left liberty map, universal arrow to, universal arrow <CA>	universeller Pfeil *m* nach	flèche *f* universelle	освобождающий морфизм, освобождающий слева морфизм

No.	English	German	French	Russian
L 645	**liberty theorem** <GR>	Freiheitssatz *m* <Magnus, Dehn-Magnus>	théorème *m* de liberté	теорема о свободе
L 646	**l-ideal** <of an l-ring> <AL>	verbandsgeordnetes Ideal *n*, l-Ideal *n*	idéal *m* réticulé	l-идеал
L 647	**l-ideal,** normal subspace <of an l-group> <AL>	l-Ideal *n*	idéal *m* réticulé, famille *f* presque complète	l-идеал
L 648	**Lie['s] algebra,** // infinitesimal group <AL>	Liesche Algebra *f*, Lie-Algebra *f*, infinitesimale Gruppe *f*	algèbre *f* de Lie, // groupe *m* infinitésimal	алгебра Ли, лиева алгебра, // инфинитезимальная группа [Ли]
L 649	**Lie algebra** <of a Lie group> <AL>	Liesche Algebra *f*, Liescher Ring *m* <einer Lieschen Gruppe>	algèbre *f* de Lie <d'un groupe de Lie>	алгебра Ли <группы Ли>
L 650	**Lie 𝔄-module** <AL>	𝔄-Lie-Modul *m*, Lie-Modul *m* über *A*	𝔄-module *m* de Lie	𝔄-модуль Ли
L 651	**Liebmann['s] approximation method, Liebmann['s] method [of approximation]** <AX, NU, PO>	Liebmannsches Mittelungsverfahren *n*, Liebmann-Verfahren *n*, Liebmannsches Näherungsverfahren *n*, Liebmannsche Methode *f*	méthode *f* de Liebmann, méthode Liebmann	метод Либмана
L 652	**Lie['s] bracket** <of two vector fields> <DG>	Liesches Klammerprodukt *n*	crochet *m* de Lie	скобка Ли
	Lie['s] bracket <AL>	*s.* 1. B 710; 2. L 672		
L 653	**Lie['s] characteristic function,** characteristic function <in infinitesimal contact transformation> <DE, VA>	Liesche charakteristische Funktion *f*, charakteristische Funktion [von Lie]	fonction *f* caractéristique de Lie, fonction caractéristique	характеристическая функция [Ли]
L 654	**Lie continuous group** <GR>	Liesche kontinuierliche Gruppe *f*, liesche Gruppe	groupe *m* continu de Lie	непрерывная группа Ли
L 655	**Lie['s] derivative** <with respect to a vector field> <DG>	Liesche Ableitung *f*, Variationstransformation *f* <bezüglich eines Vektorfelds>	dérivée *f* de Lie <par rapport à un champ vectoriel>	производная Ли, лиева производная <относительно векторного поля>
L 656	**Lie['s] differential** <DG>	Liesches Differential *n*	différentielle *f* de Lie	дифференциал Ли
L 657	**Lie['s] division ring** <AL>	Liescher Schiefkörper *m*	anneau *m* de Lie à division	кольцо Ли с делением
	Lie['s] geometry <DG>	*s.* L 659		
L 658	**Lie['s] geometry in the plane, Lie['s] geometry of circles,** geometry of circles <DG>	Liesche Geometrie *f* der Kreisebene (Kreise), Liesche Geometrie für die Kreisebene, Geometrie von Lie für die Kreisebene, Kreisgeometrie *f*, ebene Liesche Geometrie	géométrie *f* de Lie de cercles, géométrie des cercles, géométrie de Lie dans le plan	геометрия Ли окружностей, геометрия окружностей Ли, геометрия окружностей, геометрия Ли в плоскости
L 659	**Lie['s] geometry of spheres,** geometry of spheres, Lie['s] geometry <DG>	Liesche Geometrie *f* des Kugelraums, Liesche Geometrie der Kugeln, Liesche Geometrie für den Kugelraum, Geometrie von Lie für den Kugelraum, Kugelgeometrie *f*, Liesche Geometrie, Geometrie von Lie	géométrie *f* de Lie de sphères, géométrie des sphères, géométrie de Lie	геометрия Ли сфер, геометрия сфер Ли, геометрия сфер (Ли)
L 660	**Lie['s] group** <*e.g.:* of type (*N*)> <GR>	Liesche Gruppe *f*, Lie-Gruppe *f* <*z. B.:* vom Typ (*N*)>	groupe *m* de Lie <*par exemple:* de type (*N*)>	группа Ли <*например:* принадлежащая типу (*N*)>
L 661	**Lie homomorphism,** homomorphism <of Lie groups> <AL>	Homomorphismus *m* Liescher Gruppen	morphisme (homomorphisme) *m* de groupes de Lie	гомоморфизм групп Ли
L 662	**Lie homomorphism,** homomorphism <of Lie algebras> <AL>	Homomorphismus *m* Liescher Algebren	morphisme (homomorphisme) *m* d'algèbres de Lie	гомоморфизм алгебр Ли
L 663	**Lie['s] hyperalgebra** <AL>	Liesche Hyperalgebra *f*	hyperalgèbre *f* de Lie	гиперaлгебра Ли
L 664	**Lie['s] identities** <for the structure constants of a continuous group> <GR>	Liesche Identitäten *fpl*	identités *fpl* de Lie	тождества Ли
L 665	**Lie['s] invariant** <GR>	Liesche Invariante *f*	invariant *m* de Lie	инвариант Ли
L 666	**Lie l-group,** lattice[-] ordered Lie group <GR>	verbandsgeordnete Liesche Gruppe *f*	groupe *m* de Lie réticulé	структурно упорядоченная группа Ли
L 667	**Lie['s] method [of integration]** <DE>	Liesche Integrationsmethode *f*, Integrationsmethode von Lie, Liesche Methode *f*	méthode *f* [d'intégration] de Lie	метод [интегрирования] Ли
L 668	**Lie['s] minimal surface** <DG>	Liesche Minimalfläche *f*	surface *f* minimale de Lie	минимальная поверхность Ли
L 669	**Lie['s] module** <AL>	Lie-Modul *m*	module *m* de Lie	модуль Ли
	Lie['s] multiplication <AL>	*s.* B 710		
L 670	**Liénard['s][differential] equation** <DE>	Liénardsche Differentialgleichung (Gleichung) *f*	équation *f* [différentielle] de Liénard	[дифференциальное] уравнение Лиенара
L 671	**Lie['s] polynomial** <AL>	Lie-Polynom *n*	polynôme *m* de Lie	многочлен Ли
L 672	**Lie['s] product,** commutator, Lie['s] bracket <in a Lie algebra> <AL>	Kommutator *m*	crochet *m*, crochet (produit *m*) de Lie	основная операция, коммутант, коммутатор, скобочное произведение
L 673	**Lie['s] pseudogroup,** infinite continuous group <AL>	Liesche Pseudogruppe *f*, Pseudo-Lie-Gruppe *f* unendliche kontinuierliche Gruppe *f*	pseudo-groupe *m* de Lie, groupe *m* infini et continu	псевдогруппа Ли, бесконечная непрерывная группа

L 674	**Lie['s] quadric,** Lie surface of second order <DG>	Liesche Quadrik *f*, Lie-Quadrik *f*, Liesche Fläche *f* zweiter (II.) Ordnung, Lie-Fläche zweiten (II.) Grades, Lie-F_2 *f*	quadrique *f* de Lie, surface *f* de deuxième ordre de Lie	квадрика Ли, поверхность второго порядка Ли
L 675	**Lie['s] quasisubgroup** <AL>	Liesche Quasiuntergruppe *f*	quasi-sous-groupe *m* de Lie	квазиподгруппа Ли
	Lie-Riemann-Helmholtz[-Hilbert] problem of the foundations of geometry <GE>	*s.* R 1001		
L 676	**Lie['s] ring** <AL>	Liescher Ring *m*, Lie-Ring *m*	anneau *m* de Lie	кольцо Ли, лиево кольцо
L 677	**Lie['s] series** <AL, SS>	Lie-Reihe *f*	série *f* de Lie	ряд Ли, лиев ряд
L 678/9	**Lie['s] subring** <of a Lie ring> <AL>	Liescher Teilring *m*	sous-anneau *m* de Lie	подкольцо Ли
	Lie['s] surface of second order <DG>	*s.* L 674		
L 680	**Lie['s] theory** <DE>	Liesche Theorie *f*	théorie *f* de Lie	теория Ли
L 681	**Lie['s] transformation group** <AL>	Liesche Transformationsgruppe *f*, Gruppe *f* von Lie	groupe *m* de transformations de Lie	лиева группа преобразований
L 682	**life,** life[]time <ST>	Lebensdauer *f*	vie *f*, durée *f* de vie	наработка на отказ
	life [game] <TG>	*s.* C 2415		
	life table <ST>	*s.* M 907		
	life[]time <ST>	*s.* L 682		
	lift <TO>	*s.* L 684		
L 683	**lifting** <AL, TO>	Anhebung *f*, Liftung *f*, Anheben *n*, Liften *n*	relèvement *m*, lifting *m*, remonte *f*	подъем, поднятие
L 684	**lifting,** lift <of a mapping> <TO>	geliftete Abbildung *f*, Liftung *f* <einer Abbildung>	application *f* relévée	поднятие <отображения>
L 685	**lifting map** <TO>	Liftungsabbildung *f*	application *f* de relèvement	отображение поднятия
L 686	**lifting of a point** <AG>	Liften *n* eines Punkts	relèvement *m* d'un point	поднятие точки
L 687	**lifting theorem** <TO>	Liftungssatz *m*, Hochhebungssatz *m*	théorème *m* du relèvement	теорема о поднятии
L 688	**Light['s] associativity test** <for a groupoid> <AL>	Assoziativitätstest *m* von Light, Lightscher Assoziativitätstest	test (critère) *m* d'associativité de Light	критерий ассоциативности по Лайту
L 689	**likelihood** <ST>	Likelihood *f*, Plausibilität *f*, Stichprobenwahrscheinlichkeit *f*	vraisemblance *f*	правдоподобие
L 690	**likelihood function** <ST>	Likelihoodfunktion *f*	fonction *f* de vraisemblance	функция правдоподобия
L 691	**likelihood ratio** <ST>	Likelihoodquotient *m*, Likelihoodverhältnis *n*	rapport *m* des vraisemblances	отношение правдоподобия
L 692	**likelihood ratio test,** probability ratio test, maximum likelihood ratio test <ST>	Likelihoodquotiententest *m*, Likelihoodverhältnistest *m*, Maximum-Likelihood-Quotiententest *m*, Wahrscheinlichkeitsverhältnistest *m*, Maximum-Likelihood-Verhältnistest *m*, // Likelihood-Ratiotest *m*	test *m* du rapport des vraisemblances, test du maximum du rapport des vraisemblances, test du maximum de vraisemblance, test du rapport des probabilités	критерий отношения правдоподобия (наибольшего правдоподобия), критерий правдоподобия (отношения вероятностей)
	likely possible event <ST>	*s.* E 331		
L 693	**like operation** <UA>	gleichnamige Operation *f*	opération *f* semblable	одноименная операция
L 694	**like power** <AR>	gleiche (ähnliche) Potenz *f*, gleich[ ]hohe Potenz	puissance *f* semblable	одинаковая степень
L 695	**like term,** similar term <AL, AR, GN>	ähnliches (gleichnamiges, entsprechendes) Glied *n*	terme (monôme) *m* semblable	подобный член
L 696	**Lill['s] construction (method)** <AL, NU>	Lillsche Konstruktion (Methode) *f*, Lillsches Verfahren *n*	méthode (construction) *f* de Lill	метод (построение) Лилля
	lim <DI, SS, TO>	*s.* L 698		
	l.i.m. <ST>	*s.* L 732		
	$\underline{\lim}$ <DI, SS>	*s.* L 1153		
	$\overline{\lim}$ <DI, SS>	*s.* U 427		
	limaçon <GE>	*s.* P 290		
	lim ap <RF>	*s.* A 831		
	limes in medio <ST>	*s.* L 732		
	limes number <SE>	*s.* L 743		
	lim inf <DI, SS>	*s.* L 1153		
	lim inf ap <RF>	*s.* L 1124		
L 697	**limit,** left limit, [generalized] projective limit, [generalized] inverse limit, left root, infimum, input <CA>	Limes *m*, inverser (projektiver) Limes, Infimum *n*, Linkswurzel *f*	limite *f* projective, limite	проективный (обратный) предел
L 698	**limit,** limit of indeterminacy, limiting value, lim <of a number sequence> <DI, SS, TO>	Häufungsgrenze *f*, Grenzwert *m*, Hauptlimes *m*, Limes *m*, Unbestimmtheitsgrenze *f*, lim	limite *f*, limite d'indétermination, valeur *f* limite, lim	предел последовательности (неопределенности), граница неопределенности, предел, предельное значение, lim
L 699	**limit,** extremum, maximum and minimum <of a set of real numbers *or* a function at a point> <RF, SE>	Hauptlimes *m*, Häufungsgrenze *f*, Unbestimmtheitsgrenze *f* <einer Menge reeller Zahlen *oder* einer Funktion in bezug auf einen Filter>	limite *f*, limites *fpl* supérieure et inférieure	предел, верхний и нижний пределы <функции по фильтру>
L 700	**limit** <of a sequence of sets> <SE, TO>	topologischer (abgeschlossener) Limes *m*	limite *f* topologique, limite	топологический предел, предел

No.	English	German	French	Russian
L 701	**limit** <of a double sequence> <SS, TO>	Limes *m*, Doppellimes *m*, Hauptlimes *m*	limite *f* <d'une suite infinie à double entrée>	двойной предел
L 702	**limit** <of a filter> <TO>	Limes *m*	limite *f*	предел
L 703	**limit** <of a map with respect to a filter> <TO>	Grenzwert *m*, Limes *m* <bezüglich eines Filters>	limite *f* <suivant un filtre>	предельное (граничное) значение <по фильтру>
	limit <SE>	*s.* L 730		
L 704	**φ-limit** <AL>	φ-Grenzwert *m*	limite *f* par rapport à la valuation φ	φ-предел
L 705	**limitability** <SS>	Limitierbarkeit *f*	limitabilité *f*	лимитируемость
L 706	**limitation** <of sequences> <LI>	Limitierung *f*	limitation *f*	образование обобщенного предела, переход к обобщенному пределу
L 707	**limitation method,** method of limitation <LI>	Limitierungsverfahren *n*, *V*-Verfahren *n*	méthode *f* de limitation, procédé *m* de limite	метод образования обобщенного предела [расходящейся последовательности], метод перехода к обобщенному пределу
L 708	**limitation theorem** <of class field theory> <AB>	Abgrenzungssatz *m*	loi *f* de limitation	лимитационная теорема, теорема ограничения
L 709	**limitative transformation** <TO>	Schränkungstransformation *f*	transformation *f* limitative	ограничивающее отображение
L 710	**limit body** <of a convex body> <CS, GE>	Limeskörper *m*	corps *m* limite	предельное тело
	limit by Abel's method <LI>	*s.* A 491		
	limit by arithmetic means <LI>	*s.* C 831		
	limit by Borel's method <LI>	*s.* B 589		
	limit by Borel's method of order *r* <LI>	*s.* B 761		
L 711	**limit by Cesàro's method,** *C*-limit, *C*-lim <LI>	*C*-Limes *m*, Limes *m* nach dem *C*-Verfahren, *C*-lim	limite *f* par la méthode de Cesàro, *C*-limite *f*, *C*-lim	[обобщенный] предел по [методу] Чезаро
L 712	**limit by Cesàro's method of *k*-th order,** (C,k) limit, C_k-limit, C_k-lim <LI>	C_k-Limes *m*, (C,k)-Limes *m*, Cesàro-Limes *m*, Limes *m* nach dem C_k-Verfahren, C_k-lim	limite *f* par la méthode de Cesàro d'ordre *k*, C_k-limite *f*, C_k-lim, (C,k) lim	[обобщенный] предел по [методу] Чезаро *k*-го порядка, (C,k)-lim, C_k-lim
L 713	**limit by columns,** column limit <of a double sequence> <SS>	Spaltenlimes *m*, Kolonnenlimes *m*	limite *f* par colonnes, limite de colonne	предел по столбцам (столбцу)
	limit by Euler's method <LI>	*s.* E 155		
	limit by Euler's method of *p*-th order <LI>	*s.* E 302		
	limit by Hausdorff's method <LI>	*s.* H 377		
	limit by Hölder['s] method <LI>	*s.* H 376		
	limit by Hölder's method of *p*-th order <LI>	*s.* H 585 *s.* H 585		
	limit by Nörlund's method <LI>	*s.* N 717		
	limit by Riesz's method <LI>	*s.* R 1348		
L 714	**limit by row,** row limit <of a double sequence> <SS>	Zeilenlimes *m*	limite *f* par lignes, limite de ligne	предел по строке
	limit case <GN>	*s.* B 573		
L 715	**limit characteristic** <DE>	Grenzcharakteristik *f*	caractéristique *f* limite	предельная характеристика
L 716	**limit circle** <DE>	Grenzkreis *m*	« Grenzkreis » *m*, cercle *m* limite	предельный круг
	limit circle <FT>	*s.* H 575		
	limit circle <GE>	*s.* H 576		
L 717	**limit circle case** <DE>	Grenzkreisfall *m*	cas *m* « Grenzkreis »	случай предельного круга
L 718	**limit-circle case,** hyperbolic case; limit-circle uniformization <FT>	Grenzkreisfall *m*, hyperbolischer Fall *m*; Grenzkreisuniformisierung *f*	cas *m* du cercle limite, cas hyperbolique	случай предельного круга, гиперболический случай
	limit circle type <DE>	*s.* D 451		
	limit-circle uniformization <FT>	*s.* L 718		
L 719	**limit-cycle, limit cycle** <DE>	Grenzzykel *m*	cycle *m* limite, cycle-limite *m*	предельный цикл
	limited abstraction principle <LO, SE>	*s.* A 1293		
	limited sequence <SS>	*s.* B 683		
	limited variation <AN>	*s.* B 687		
L 720	**limit element** <of an ordered set *or* a convergent sequence> <SE, AN>	Limeselement *n* <SE>; Grenzelement *n* <AN>	élément *m* limite	предельный элемент
L 721	**limit element,** limit point, limiting point <of a sequence> <TO>	Häufungspunkt *m*, Berührungspunkt *m*, Häufungsstelle *f*, Häufungswert *m*	valeur *f* d'adhérence, élément *m* d'accumulation, point *m* limite	предельная точка, предельное значение
	limit form of Cauchy's root test <SS>	*s.* C 259		

No.	English	German	French	Russian
	limit from above <DI>	*s.* L 741		
	limit from below <DI>	*s.* L 740		
	limit from the left <DI>	*s.* L 740		
	limit from the right <DI>	*s.* L 741		
L 722	**limit function** <of a sequence *or* series of functions> <AN>	Grenzfunktion *f*	fonction *f* limite, fonction-limite *f*, limite *f*	предельная функция
L 723	**limit function** <RF>	Limesfunktion *f*, Schrankenfunktion *f*	fonction *f* limite	граничная функция
L 724	**limit[-]index** <SE>	Limeszahl *f* als Index, Limesindex *m*	indice *m* nombre limite	предельный ординал как индекс
L 725	**limit inferior,** restricted limit <of a sequence of point sets> <SE>	mengenalgebraischer (algebraischer) unterer Limes *m*, unterer algebraischer Limes, unterer Limes, Limes (limes) *m* inferior	ensemble *m* limite restreint, ensemble-limite *m* restreint, limite *f* restreinte (inférieure), la plus petite limite, limes *m* inférior	нижний предел в смысле общей теории множеств, нижний предел
	limit inferior <DI, SS>	*s.* L 1153		
	limiting case <GN>	*s.* B 573		
L 726	**limiting cone,** universal (terminal, inductive) cone, co-cone <from *F*>, cone from a functor <CA>	Limeskegel *m*, universeller Kegel *m* <von *F* aus>	cône *m* terminal	предельный (терминальный) конус
L 727	**limiting distribution** <ST>	Grenzverteilung *f*, Grenzverteilungsgesetz *n*	distribution *f* limite, loi *f* [de distribution] limite	предельное распределение, предельный закон распределения
L 728	**limiting distribution function** <ST>	Grenzverteilungsfunktion *f*	fonction *f* de distribution limite	функция предельного распределения
	limiting error <ER, NU>	*s.* L 738		
	limiting number <TO>	*s.* A 188		
	limiting ordinal <SE>	*s.* L 743		
	limiting point <FA>	*s.* L 745		
	limiting point <TO>	*s.* 1. A 188; 2. L 721		
L 729	**limiting position** <GE>	Grenzlage *f*	position *f* limite	предельное положение
	limiting process <DI, GN>	*s.* P 295		
L 730	**limiting set,** limit <of a sequence of sets> <SE>	Mengenlimes *m*, Grenzmenge *f*, Limes *m*, algebraischer Limes, mengenalgebraischer Limes	ensemble *m* limite, limite *f* unique, limite <au sens de la théorie générale des ensembles>	предельное множество, предел в теоретико-множественном смысле, предел <в смысле общей теории множеств>
L 731	**limiting set** <TO>	Limesmenge *f*	ensemble *m* limite	предельное множество
	limiting value <DI, SS, TO>	*s.* L 698		
	limiting value <TO>	*s.* A 188		
L 732	**limit in the mean,** limes in medio, l.i.m. <ST>	Grenzwert (Limes) *m* im Mittel, limes *m* in medio, l.i.m.	limite *f* en moyenne, l.i.m.	предел в среднем, l.i.m.
L 733	**limit in the sense of pointwise convergence,** simple limit <of functions> <AN>	gewöhnlicher Limes *m*, Limes im Sinne der punktweisen Konvergenz	limite *f* simple	предел в смысле обычной сходимости
	limit in the sense of uniform convergence <AN>	*s.* U 146		
L 734	**limit line** <DE>	Grenzlinie *f*	ligne *f* limite, ligne-limite *f*	предельная линия
L 735	**limit model** <MM, SE>	Limesmodell *n*	modèle *m* limite	предельная модель
	limit[-]number <SE>	*s.* L 743		
	limit number <TO>	*s.* A 188		
L 736	**limit object,** inverse limit, projective limit <of a functor> <CA>	Limesobjekt *n*, inverser (projektiver) Limes *m*	objet *m* limite	проективный предел, обратный предел
L 737	**limit of a sequence of groups** <GR>	Grenzgruppe *f*, Limesgruppe *f*	limite *f* d'une séquence de groupes	предельная группа
L 738	**limit of error,** maximum error, limiting error <ER, NU>	Fehlergrenze *f*, Grenzfehler *m*, Maximalfehler *m*, Höchstfehler *m*	limite *f* d'erreur, erreur *f* limite, erreur maximale	максимальная (наибольшая) погрешность
	limit of indeterminacy <DI, SS, TO>	*s.* L 698		
L 739	**limit of integration** <DI>	Integrationsgrenze *f*	limite *f* d'intégration, limite de l'intégrale	предел интегрирования
	limit on one side <AN>	*s.* O 110		
L 740	**limit on the left,** limit from the left, limit to the left, limit from below, left-hand limit, left limit <of a function> <DI>	linksseitiger Limes *m*, linksseitiger Grenzwert *m*, hinterer Limes *m*, hinterer Grenzwert *m*	limite *f* à gauche, valeur *f* limite à gauche	предел <функции> слева, левосторонний предел <функции>, левый предел <функции>
L 741	**limit on the right,** limit from (to) the right, limit from above, right[-hand] limit <of a function> <DI>	rechtsseitiger Limes (Grenzwert) *m*, vorderer Limes (Grenzwert)	limite *f* (valeur *f* limite) à droite	предел <функции> справа, правосторонний (правый) предел <функции>
L 742	**limit order type,** limit type <SE>	Limestyp *m*	type *m* limite	предельный [порядковый] тип
L 743	**limit ordinal,** limit[-] number, limes number, ordinal (number) of the second kind, ordinal of the second class, limiting ordinal <SE>	Limeszahl *f*, Grenzzahl *f*, ordinale Limeszahl, Zahl *f* zweiter Art, Ordnungszahl *f* zweiter Art	nombre (ordinal) *m* limite, nombre ordinal limite, nombre de seconde espèce	предельное число (порядковое число), предельный ординал, предельное трансфинитное число

L 744	**limit point** <DE>	Grenzpunkt *m*	« Grenzpunkt » *m*	предельная точка
L 745	**limit point,** limiting point <of the spectrum of an operator> <FA>	Häufungspunkt *m*, Häufungsstelle *f*	point *m* limite, point-limite *m*	предельная точка <спектра оператора>
L 746	**limit point** <of an analytic function> <FT>	Grenzstelle *f*, Randpunkt *m* des Existenzbereichs	point *m* limite, point-limite *m*	предельная точка, граничная точка
L 747	**limit point** <of a sequence> <TO>	Limespunkt *m*, Grenzpunkt *m*	point *m* limite, point-limite *m*	предельная точка
	limit point, limit-point <TO>	*s.* A 188		
	limit point <TO>	*s.* L 721		
L 748	**limit-point case** <DE>	Grenzpunktfall *m*	cas *m* « Grenzpunkt »	случай предельной точки
L 749	**limit-point case,** parabolic case; limit-point uniformization <FT>	Grenzpunktfall *m*, parabolischer Fall *m*; Grenzpunktuniformisierung *f*	cas *m* du point limite, cas parabolique	случай предельной точки, параболический случай
	limit point type <DE>	*s.* D 452		
	limit-point uniformization <FT>	*s.* L 749		
	limit preserving functor <CA>	*s.* L 324		
L 750	**limit relation** <AN>	Limesbeziehung *f*, Limesrelation *f*	relation *f* limite	предельное соотношение
L 751	**limits of integration,** integration interval <DI>	Integrationsgrenzen *fpl*, Integrationsintervall *n*	limites *fpl* d'intégration, intervalle *m* d'intégration	пределы интегрирования, интервал интегрирования
	limit space <TO>	*s.* L 1179		
L 752	**limit spectrum,** cluster spectrum <FA>	Häufungsspektrum *n*, Verdichtungsspektrum *n*	spectre *m* limite	предельный спектр, спектр сгущения
	limit sphere <GE>	*s.* H 579		
L 753	**limit superior,** complete limit <of a sequence of point sets> <SE>	mengenalgebraischer oberer Limes *m*, oberer algebraischer Limes, algebraischer oberer Limes, oberer Limes, Limes superior, limes superior	ensemble *m* limite complet, ensemble-limite *m* complet, limite *f* complète (supérieure), la plus grande limite, limes *m* superior	верхний предел в смысле общей теории множеств, верхний (полный) предел
	limit superior <DI, SS>	*s.* U 427		
L 754	**limit surface** <of a congruence of lines> <DG>	Grenzfläche *f*	surface *f* limite	предельная поверхность, геометрическое место граничных точек
L 755	**limit theorem** <ST>	Grenzwertsatz *m*, Grenzverteilungssatz *m*	théorème *m* limite	предельная теорема
	limit theorem of Laplace <ST>	*s.* M 806		
	limit theorem of Poisson <ST>	*s.* P 833		
	limit theorems <AN>	*s.* T 370		
	limit to the left <DI>	*s.* L 740		
	limit to the right <DI>	*s.* L 741		
	limit type <SE>	*s.* L 742		
	limit value <TO>	*s.* A 188		
L 756	**limit variation** <of a sequence of functions> <FT>	Grenzschwankung *f*	variation *f* limite	предельное колебание (изменение)
	lim sup <DI, SS>	*s.* U 427		
	lim sup ar <AN>	*s.* U 406		
L 757	**Lindeberg['s] condition,** Lindeberg-Feller condition <ST>	Lindebergsche (Lindeberg-Fellersche) Bedingung *f*	condition *f* de Lindeberg (Lindeberg-Feller)	условие Линдеберга (Линдеберга-Феллера)
	Lindeberg-Feller condition <ST>	*s.* L 757		
L 758	**Lindeberg-Feller['s] theorem** <ST>	Satz *m* von Lindeberg-Feller, Lindeberg-Fellerscher Satz	théorème *m* de Lindeberg-Feller	теорема Линдеберга-Феллера
L 759	**Lindeberg-Lévy['s] theorem** <ST>	Satz *m* von Lindeberg-Lévy, Lindeberg-Lévyscher Satz	théorème *m* de Lindeberg-Lévy	теорема Линдеберга-Леви
L 760	**Lindelöf['s] construction** <VA>	Lindelöfsche Konstruktion *f*	construction *f* de Lindelöf	построение Линделефа
L 761	**Lindelöf['s] μ-function (mu-function)** <NT>	Lindelöfsche μ-Funktion (My-Funktion) *f*	μ-fonction (mu-fonction) *f* de Lindelöf	μ-функция (мю-функция) Линделефа
L 762	**Lindelöf['s] hypothesis** <NT>	Lindelöfsche Vermutung *f*	hypothèse *f* de Lindelöf	гипотеза Линделефа
L 763	**Lindelöfian map** <FT>	Lindelöfsche Abbildung *f*	application *f* lindelöfienne	преобразование Линделефа
L 764	**Lindelöf['s] principle** <FT>	Lindelöfsches Prinzip *n*, Lindelöf-Prinzip *n*, Prinzip von Lindelöf	principe *m* de Lindelöf	принцип Линделефа
L 765	**Lindelöf property** <TO>	Lindelöfsche Überdeckungseigenschaft *f*	propriété *f* de Lindelöf	свойство Линделефа
L 766	**Lindelöf['s] space** <TO>	Lindelöf-Raum *m*, Lindelöfraum *m*	espace *m* de Lindelöf	пространство Линделефа, линделевское [топологическое] пространство
L 767	**Lindelöf['s] theorem** <for convergence> <FT>	Konvergenzsatz *m* von Lindelöf, Lindelöfscher Konvergenzsatz	théorème *m* de Lindelöf	теорема Линделефа
	Lindelöf['s] theorem <DE>	*s.* T 312		
	Lindelöf['s] theorem <TO>	*s.* T 313		
	Lindelöf['s] theorem <VA>	*s.* T 314		
L 768	**Lindemann['s] theorem** <NT>	Lindemannscher Satz *m*	théorème *m* de Lindemann-Weierstrass	теорема Линдемана
L 769	**Lindenbaum['s] algebra** <MM>	Lindenbaumsche Algebra *f*	algèbre *f* de Lindenbaum	алгебра Линденбаума

No.	English	German	French	Russian
L 770	**Lindenbaum['s] theorem,** theorem of Lindenbaum, completion theorem of Lindenbaum <LO>	Lindenbaumscher Vervollständigungssatz (Satz, Ergänzungssatz) *m*	théorème *m* Lindenbaum	теорема (лемма) Линденбаума
	Lindenbaum['s] theorem <LO>	*s.* T 315		
L 771	**Lindstedt['s] method** <DE>	Methode *f* von Lindstedt, Lindstedtsche Methode, Verfahren *n* von Lindstedt	méthode *f* de Lindstedt	метод Линдстедта
L 772	**line,** ray <DG>	Gerade *f*, Strahl *m*	droite *f*, rayon *m*	прямая, луч
	line <EG>	*s.* S 1836		
	line <GP>	*s.* E 12		
	line <MD>	*s.* R 1425		
	lineal element <DE, DG, VA>	*s.* L 858		
	linear algebra <AL>	*s.* K 99		
L 773	**linear associative algebra,** algebra <AL>	lineare assoziative Algebra *f*	algèbre *f* associative linéaire	линейная ассоциативная алгебра
	linear associative algebra <AL>	*s.* A 406		
	linear associative algebra of finite order <AL>	*s.* A 474		
	linear basis <AL>	*s.* V 97		
	linear birth-and-death process <SP>	*s.* F 130		
	linear birth process <SP>	*s.* F 864		
	linear chart <NO, NU>	*s.* U 178		
L 774	**linear closure** <AL>	lineare Hülle *f*	enveloppe *f* linéaire	линейная оболочка, линейное замыкание
	linear closure of *M* <AL, FA>	*s.* S 2187		
L 775	**linear combination** <AL, PG>	Linearkombination *f*	combinaison *f* linéaire	линейная комбинация
L 776	**linear complex,** linear complex of lines (rays) <DG, PJ>	linearer Strahlenkomplex (Geradenkomplex, Komplex) *m*, Strahlengewinde *n*, Strahlgewinde *n*, Gewinde *n*	complexe *m* linéaire, complexe de droites linéaire, complexe linéaire de droites, complexe du premier ordre	линейный комплекс [прямых (лучей)]
	linear complex <AT, GP>	*s.* T 517		
	linear complex of lines (rays) <DG, PJ>	*s.* L 776		
L 777	**linear complex of spheres** <DG>	Kugelgebüsch *n*, linearer Kugelkomplex *m* im engeren Sinne	buisson *f* de sphères, complexe *m* [linéaire] de sphères	линейный комплекс сфер
L 778	**linear component,** first-order component, component of the first degree (order) <of regression> <ST>	lineare Komponente *f*, Komponente ersten Grades, Komponente erster Ordnung	composante *f* linéaire (de premier ordre)	линейная компонента, компонента первого порядка
L 779	**linear congruence of curves** <PJ>	lineare Kurvenkongruenz *f*	congruence *f* de courbes linéaire	линейная конгруэнция кривых
	linear connectivity <TO>	*s.* C 2059		
	linear contrast <ST>	*s.* C 2293		
L 780	**linear convergence** <PG, SS>	lineare Konvergenz *f*	convergence *f* linéaire	линейная сходимость
L 781	**linear Coxeter group** <AL>	lineare Coxeter-Gruppe (Coxetergruppe) *f*	groupe *m* de Coxeter linéaire	линейная группа Коксетера, ЛГК
	linear deformation ratio <GE>	*s.* R 191		
	linear dependence <GN>	*s.* L 837		
L 782	**linear difference equation** <of the *n*-th order> <FD>	lineare Differenzengleichung *f* <*n*-ter Ordnung, der Ordnung *n*>	équation *f* linéaire aux différences finies <de *n*-e ordre>	линейное разностное уравнение, линейное уравнение в конечных разностях <*n*-го порядка>
L 783	**linear differential** <AL, AN>	lineares (einfaches) Differential *n*	différentielle *f* linéaire	линейный дифференциал
L 784	**linear differential equation,** ordinary linear differential equation <of the *n*-th order> <DE>	lineare (lineare gewöhnliche) Differentialgleichung *f* <*n*-ter Ordnung>	équation *f* [différentielle] linéaire <de *n*-e ordre>	линейное (линейное обыкновенное) дифференциальное уравнение <*n*-го порядка>
L 785	**linear differential equation with constant coefficients** <DE>	lineare Differentialgleichung *f* mit konstanten Koeffizienten	équation *f* différentielle linéaire à coefficients constants	линейное дифференциальное уравнение с постоянными коэффициентами
	linear differential expression (form) <AN>	*s.* P 546		
L 786	**linear dimension** <of a linear space> <FA>	lineare Dimension *f*	dimension *f* linéaire	линейная размерность
L 787	**linear discriminant score,** discriminant score <ST>	linearer Trennwert *m*, Trennwert	valeur *f* discriminatoire [linéaire]	значение [линейной] дискриминантной функции
L 788	**linear disjointness** <AL>	lineare Disjunktheit *f*	propriété *f* d'être linéairement disjoint	линейная разделенность
L 789	**linear displacement,** pseudo-parallelism <GE>	Pseudoparallelismus *m*	pseudo-parallélisme *m*	псевдопараллелизм
	linear dual <AL, FA>	*s.* F 704		
L 790	**linear eccentricity,** focus-to-centre distance <of a conic> <AY>	lineare Exzentrizität *f*	excentricité *f* linéaire	линейный эксцентрицитет
	linear element <DG, DI>	*s.* D 465		
L 791	**linear equation,** simple equation, equation of the first degree <AL>	lineare Gleichung *f*, Gleichung ersten Grades	équation *f* linéaire (du premier degré), // équation simple	линейное уравнение, уравнение первой степени

L 792	**linear equivalence** <of divisors> <AG>	lineare (rationale) Äquivalenz *f*, Äquivalenz *f*	équivalence *f* linéaire (rationnelle)	линейная (рациональная) эквивалентность
L 792a	**linear extrapolation** <AX>	lineare Extrapolation *f*	extrapolation *f* linéaire	линейная экстраполяция; линейное экстраполирование
	linear factor <GP>	*s.* P 418		
L 793	**linear form** <on a *K*-module> <AL>	Linearform *f* <eines *K*-Moduls, auf einem *K*-Modul>	forme *f* linéaire, covecteur *m* <sur un *K*-module>	линейная форма <*K*-модуля>
	linear form module <AL>	*s.* D 1015		
	linear fractional function <AL, AN, FT>	*s.* H 453		
L 794	**linear fractional group** <AL>	Gruppe *f* der gebrochenlinearen Transformationen	groupe *m* des transformations homographiques	дробно-линейная группа
L 795	**linear fractional group,** pSL_n (*K*) <of dimension *n*; over *K*> <GR>	spezielle (unimodulare) projektive Gruppe *f*, projektive unimodulare Gruppe <für *n* Variable; über dem Körper *K*>	groupe *m* unimodulaire projectif <de degré *n*, à *n* variables, de type *n*; défini sur *K*, sur le corps *K*>	проективная унимодулярная группа <от *n* переменных; над *K*>
	linear fractional transformation <FT>	*s.* B 348		
L 796	**linear function** <homogeneous> <GN>	lineare Funktion *f*, Funktion ersten Grades	fonction *f* linéaire	линейная функция, функция первой степени
	linear function <GN>	*s.* A 355		
L 797	**linear functional** <FA> ⌈<AG>	lineares Funktional *n*, Linearform *f*	fonctionnelle *f* linéaire, forme *f* linéaire continue	линейный функционал
L 798	**linear genus** <of a surface>	Kurvengeschlecht *n*	genre *m* linéaire	род кривых
L 799	**linear genus** <of an ⌈<AL> algebraic function field>	lineares Geschlecht *n*, Irregularität *f*	genre *m* linéaire	линейный род
	linear graph <AT, GP>	*s.* T 517		
L 800	**linear group** <in an *n*-dimensional vector space of *n* variables> <AL>	lineare (lineare homogene) Gruppe <für *n* Variable, von *n* Variablen>	groupe *m* linéaire <d'ordre *n*, à *n* variables>	линейная группа <от *n* переменных>
L 801	**linear group,** group of automorphisms <of a module> <AL>	lineare Gruppe *f*, Automorphismengruppe *f*	groupe *m* des automorphismes, groupe linéaire	линейная группа, группа автоморфизмов
	linear homogeneous transformation <AY, PJ>	*s.* C 1147		
L 802	**linear independence of points,** affine independence of points <GE>	affine Unabhängigkeit *f* von Punkten	indépendance *f* affine de points	линейная (аффинная) независимость точек
L 803	**linear integral equation;** <especially:> linear integral equation with fixed upper limit of integration <IE>	lineare Integralgleichung *f*; <insbesondere:> lineare Integralgleichung mit fester oberer Integrationsgrenze	équation *f* intégrale linéaire; <en particulier:> équation intégrale linéaire à limite supérieure fixe d'intégration	линейное интегральное уравнение; <в частности:> линейное интегральное уравнение с постоянным верхним пределом
	linear integral equation of the first kind <IE>	*s.* F 593		
	linear integral equation of the second kind <IE>	*s.* F 594		
L 804	**linear integral equation of the third kind,** linear integral equation with fixed upper limit of integration of the third kind <IE>	lineare Integralgleichung *f* dritter Art, lineare Integralgleichung mit fester oberer Integrationsgrenze dritter Art	équation *f* intégrale linéaire de troisième espèce, équation intégrale linéaire à limite supérieure fixe d'intégration de troisième espèce	линейное интегральное уравнение третьего рода, линейное интегральное уравнение с постоянным верхним пределом третьего рода
	linear integral equation with fixed upper limit of integration <IE>	*s.* L 803		
	linear integral equation with fixed upper limit of integration of the first kind <IE>	*s.* F 593		
	linear integral equation with fixed upper limit of integration of the second kind <IE>	*s.* F 594		
	linear integral equation with fixed upper limit of integration of the third kind <IE>	*s.* L 804		
	linear integral equation with variable upper limit of integration <IE>	*s.* V 206		
805	**linear interpolation,** interpolation <AX, FD, NU>	lineare Interpolation *f*, Interpolation	interpolation *f* linéaire, interpolation	линейная интерполяция, интерполяция; линейное интерполирование
806	**linear isomorphism,** vector space isomorphism <AL>	Vektorraumisomorphismus *m*	isomorphisme *m* d'espaces vectoriels	изоморфизм векторных пространств
807	**linearity** <GN>	Linearität *f*	linéarité *f*	линейность, свойство линейности
808	**linearization** <DE, PG>	Linearisierung *f*	linéarisation *f*	линеаризация
809	**linearized system** <of differential equations> <DE>	linearisiertes System *n*, System der ersten Näherung	système *m* linéarisé, système de la première approximation	линеаризированная система, система первого приближения
810	**linearly compact module** <AL>	linear[ ]kompakter Modul *m*	module *m* linéairement compact	линейно компактный модуль
811	**linearly dependent points,** affinely dependent points, affinely dependent set <of points> <GE>	affin abhängige Punkte *mpl*	points *mpl* affinement dépendants	аффинно зависимые точки, аффинно зависимое подмножество <точек>, линейно зависимые точки

No.	English	German	French	Russian
L 812	**linearly dependent set (system)** <of elements> <AL>	linear abhängiges System *n*, linear abhängige Familie (Menge) *f* <von Elementen>	système *m* <d'éléments> lié (linéairement dépendant), famille *f* liée	линейно зависимая система, множество линейно зависимых элементов
	linearly independent basis <AL>	*s.* F 174		
L 813	**linearly independent points,** [affinely] independent points, affinely independent subset <of points>, [linearly] independent set of points <GE>	affin unabhängige Punkte *mpl*, unabhängige Punkte	famille *f* de points affinement libre, système *m* affinement libre, points *mpl* affinement indépendants	линейно (аффинно) независимые точки, независимое подмножество <точек>
	linearly independent set <AL>	*s.* L 814		
	linearly independent set of points <GE>	*s.* L 813		
L 814	**linearly independent system,** linearly independent set <of elements> <AL>	linear unabhängiges System *n*, freie (linear unabhängige) Menge *f*; linear unabhängige Teilmenge *f*, freie Untermenge *f*	système *m* linéairement indépendant, système (partie *f*, famille *f*) libre	линейно независимая система, свободная часть, множество линейно независимых элементов
L 815	**linearly ordered class** <SE>	streng (strikt, linear) geordnete Klasse *f*, geordnete Klasse	classe *f* ordonnée, classe totalement ordonnée	линейно упорядоченный класс
L 816	**linearly ordered domain of integrity** <AL>	geordneter (angeordneter) Integritätsbereich *m*	domaine *m* d'intégrité totalement ordonné	упорядоченная область целостности
	linearly ordered group <GR>	*s.* S 1001		
L 817	**linearly ordered groupoid** <AL>	angeordnetes Gruppoid *n*	groupoïde *m* linéairement ordonné	вполне упорядоченный группоид
L 818	**linearly ordered monoid** <AL>	angeordnetes Monoid *n*	monoïde *m* totalement ordonné	вполне упорядоченный моноид
L 819	**linearly ordered ring,** fully ordered ring <AL>	angeordneter (linear geordneter, geordneter, vollständig geordneter, einfach geordneter) Ring *m*	anneau *m* totalement ordonné, anneau ordonné	вполне (совершенно) упорядоченное кольцо
L 820	**linearly ordered semigroup** <AL>	angeordnete Halbgruppe *f*	demi-groupe *m* totalement ordonné	линейно упорядоченная полугруппа
L 821	**linearly ordered semiring,** ordered semi-ring <AL>	geordneter Halbring *m*	demi-anneau *m* totalement ordonné	[линейно] упорядоченное полукольцо
L 822	**linearly ordered set,** chain, ordered set, simply ordered set, totally ordered set, completely ordered set, serially ordered set <SE>	Kette *f*, Ordnung *f*, total (vollständig, linear) geordnete Menge *f*, linearer Verband (Verein) *m*, geordnete (einfach[]-geordnete, angeordnete, k-geordnete) Menge *f*, ordnungstheoretische Kette, vollgeordnete (geordnete, voll geordnete, streng geordnete, konnex geordnete) Menge, lineare (volle, vollständige) Ordnung, Vollordnung *f*, totale (strenge, einfache, konnexe) Ordnung, k-Ordnung *f*	ensemble *m* totalement ordonné, chaîne *f*, ensemble ordonné linéairement, ensemble muni d'une relation d'ordre complet, ensemble ordonné	линейно упорядоченное множество, цепь, совершенно упорядоченное множество, упорядоченное множество, связно (просто) упорядоченное множество, линейная структура
L 823	**linearly topological module** <AL>	lineartopologischer Modul *m*	module *m* linéairement topologisé	линейно топологизированный модуль
L 824	**linear manifold,** linear variety <FA, GE>	lineare Mannigfaltigkeit *f*	ensemble *m* (variété *f*) linéaire	линейное многообразие (множество)
	linear manifold <AL>	*s.* V 128		
	linear manifold <AL, TO>	*s.* L 843		
L 825	**linear map,** linear mapping, homomorphism <of>, linear transformation <of, on>, linear operator <on> <a vector space> <AL>	lineare Abbildung (Transformation) *f*, Homomorphismus *m*, Lineartransformation *f* <von Vektorräumen>	application *f* linéaire, homomorphisme *m* <d'espaces vectoriels>	линейное отображение (преобразование), гомоморфизм <векторных пространств>
	linear map <FA>	*s.* L 828		
	linear mapping <AL>	*s.* L 825		
	linear mapping <FA>	*s.* L 828		
	linear mapping <FT>	*s.* B 348		
	linear mapping <GN>	*s.* A 355		
L 826	**linear measure** <ME>	lineares Maß *n*, eindimensionales Flächenmaß *n*	mesure *f* linéaire	линейная мера
L 827	**linear method [of limitation]** <LI>	lineares Limitierungsverfahren (Verfahren) *n*	méthode *f* (procédé *m*) linéaire [de limitation]	линейный метод [образования обобщенного предела]
L 828	**linear operator,** linear map[ping], linear transformation, operator, homomorphism <FA>	linearer Operator *m*, lineare Abbildung *f*, lineare Transformation *f*, Operator, Homomorphismus *m*	opérateur *m* linéaire, application *f* linéaire, transformation *f* linéaire, opération *f* linéaire, opérateur, homomorphisme *m*	линейный оператор, линейное отображение, линейное преобразование, оператор, гомоморфизм
	linear operator <AL>	*s.* 1. L 825; 2. M 775		
	linear operator into itself <AL, FA>	*s.* E 228		
	linear optimization <PG>	*s.* L 833		
L 829	**linear order (orderedness)** <as a property> <SE>	lineare Ordnung *f*	ordre *m* linéaire	линейная упорядоченность

L 830	**linear ordering,** total ordering, complete ordering, simple ordering, ordering, order[-]relation <reflexive *or* irreflexive> <SE>	Ordnung *f*, einfache Ordnung, k-Ordnung *f*, Anordnung *f*, lineare (totale, vollständige, konnexe, kettenmäßige) Ordnung, Totalordnung *f*, Vollordnung *f*, Anordnungsrelation *f*, Anordnungsbeziehung *f*	ordre *m* linéaire (total, complet), relation *f* d'ordre complet (total), échelle *f*	линейное упорядочение, отношение линейной упорядоченности, линейный (совершенный) порядок
	linear partial differential equation <DE>	*s.* P 219		
L 831	**linear pencil,** pencil, bunch <linear system of ∞^1 algebraic varieties> <AG, AY>	Büschel *n*	faisceau *m*	пучок
L 832	**linear planimeter** <GE, IN>	Linearplanimeter *n*	planimètre *m* linéaire	линейный (прямолинейный) планиметр
L 833	**linear programming,** linear optimization, LP <PG>	lineare Optimierung (Programmoptimierung, Programmierung) *f*, Linearoptimierung *f*, Linearprogrammierung *f*, Linearprogrammieren *n*	programmation (optimisation) *f* linéaire	линейное программирование, линейная оптимизация
	linear projective mapping <AY, PJ>	*s.* C 1147		
	linear projectivity <AY, PJ>	*s.* C 1147		
	linear rank <AL>	*s.* D 172		
L 834	**linear recurrence relation** <of order *m*> <GN>	lineare Rekursionsgleichung *f* <*m*-ter Ordnung>	formule *f* linéaire de récurrence <du *m*-e ordre>	линейная рекуррентная формула <*m*-го порядка>
	linear recurrent series <NT>	*s.* R 304		
	linear recurring sequence <NT>	*s.* R 304		
L 835	**linear reflexive transitive relation** <SE>	lineare reflexive transitive Relation *f*	relation *f* de préférence, quasi-ordre *m*	линейное рефлексивное транзитивное отношение
L 836	**linear regression** <ST>	lineare (geradlinige) Regression *f*	régression *f* linéaire	линейная регрессия
L 837	**linear relationship,** straight line relationship, linear dependence <GN>	lineare Beziehung (Abhängigkeit) *f*	relation (dépendance) *f* linéaire	линейная зависимость (закономерность)
	linear scale <NO, NU>	*s.* U 178		
L 838	**linear series** <of divisors> <AG>	lineare Divisorenschar (Schar) *f*	série *f* linéaire	линейное семейство дивизоров
	linear series <AG>	*s.* L 840		
L 839	**linear series of dimension two** <AG>	Netz *n*, Divisorenschar *f* vom Rang 3	réseau *m* de diviseurs, série *f* linéaire de dimension 2	линейное семейство дивизоров размерности 2
L 840	**linear series of point groups,** linear series <on an algebraic surface> <AG>	lineare Punktschar *f*, Punktgruppenschar *f*, Äquivalenzschar *f*, Schar *f* von Punktgruppen	système *m* de groupes ponctuels	линейная система точечных групп
	linear set of differential equations <DE>	*s.* L 848		
	linear simplex <AT>	*s.* G 269		
	linear space <AL>	*s.* V 125		
L 841	**linear span** <AY>	affine Hülle *f*, aufgespannter linearer Unterraum *m*	enveloppe *f* affine	аффинная оболочка
	linear strict ordering <SE>	*s.* S 1914		
L 842	**linear string of symbols** <FO, LO>	Zeichenfolge *f*, Zeichenreihe *f*	assemblage *m* [de signes], suite (série, succession) *f* de signes	упорядоченная структура, знакосочетание, цепочка знаков
L 843	**linear subspace,** subspace, linear manifold <of a [topological] linear space; not necessarily closed> <AL, TO>	Teilraum *m*, Unterraum *m*, lineare Mannigfaltigkeit *f*	sous-espace *m* vectoriel	векторное (линейное) подпространство, линейное многообразие
L 844	**linear subsystem** <of a linear system> <AG>	lineares Teilsystem *n*, enthaltenes Linearsystem *n*	système *m* linéaire subordonné	линейная подсистема
	linear symplectic group <GR>	*s.* S 2479		
L 845	**linear system** <AG>	lineare Schar *f*, lineares System *n*, Linearschar *f*, Linearsystem *n*, Schar *f*	système *m* (série *f*) linéaire	линейная система, линейное семейство
	linear system <DE>	*s.* L 848		
L 846	**linear system generated by two linear systems** <AG>	Verbindungssystem *n* zweier Linearsysteme	système *m* linéaire engendré par deux systèmes linéaires	линейная система, порожденная двумя линейными системами
L 847	**linear system of curves** <AG>	lineares Kurvensystem *n*, Linearsystem *n* von Kurven	système *m* linéaire de courbes	линейная система кривых
L 848	**linear system of differential equations,** linear set of differential equations, linear system <DE>	lineares Differentialgleichungssystem *n*, lineares System *n* [von Differentialgleichungen]	système *m* linéaire [d'équations différentielles]	линейная система [дифференциальных уравнений]
	linear system of dimension 2 <AG>	*s.* W 132		
	linear system of dimension *n* <AG>	*s.* N 709		
	linear system of functions <AN>	*s.* S 2527		

L 849	**linear system of ∞^3 linear complexes** <in the projective space P_3> <PJ>	Komplexgebüsch *n*	système *m* linéaire de ∞^3 complexes linéaires	линейная система ∞^3 линейных комплексов
L 850	**linear system of ∞^4 linear complexes** <in the projective space P_3> <PJ>	Komplexwald *m*	système *m* linéaire de ∞^4 complexes linéaires	линейная система ∞^4 линейных комплексов
L 851	**linear system virtually free of base points** <AG>	lineares System *n* virtuell ohne Basispunkte	système *m* linéaire virtuellement sans points-base	линейная система, виртуальная без базисных точек
	linear transformation <AL>	*s.* L 825		
	linear transformation <FA>	*s.* L 828		
	linear transformation <FT>	*s.* B 348		
	linear transformation into itself <AL, FA>	*s.* E 228		
	linear variety <FA, GE>	*s.* L 824		
	linear vector space <AL>	*s.* V 125		
L 852	**line at infinity,** infinite (ideal, improper) line <as an extension of the Euclidean space> <PJ>	unendlich[]ferne Gerade *f*, uneigentliche (ideale) Gerade, Ferngerade *f*	droite *f* à (de) l'infini, droite idéale (impropre)	бесконечно удаленная прямая, несобственная прямая
L 853	**line bundle** <AT>	Geradenbündel *n*	fibration *f* rectiligne	линейное расслоение, одномерное векторное расслоение, расслоение на прямые
	line-chromatic number <GP>	*s.* C 669		
	line congruence <AY, DG>	*s.* C 1923		
L 854	**line conic, line-conic,** conic envelope, curve of the second class <AY>	Hüllkegelschnitt *m*, Tangentenkegelschnitt *m*, Linienkegelschnitt *m*, Kurve *f* zweiter Klasse	enveloppe *f* de deuxième classe	пучок прямых второго класса, кривая второго класса
L 855	**line containing the line segment** <EG>	Trägergerade *f* <einer Strecke>	support *m* d'un segment	прямая, на которой лежит отрезок
L 856	**line co-ordinates,** tangential co-ordinates [of the line], homogeneous tangential co-ordinates of the line <dual to point co-ordinates> <AY>	Linienkoordinaten *fpl*, Koordinaten *fpl* der Geraden, homogene Linienkoordinaten (Koordinaten der Geraden, Geradenkoordinaten) *fpl*	coordonnées *fpl* tangentielles [de la droite], coordonnées tangentielles homogènes [de la droite], coordonnées homogènes de la droite, coordonnées de la droite, coordonnées linéaires	тангенциальные координаты прямой, координаты прямой, однородные тангенциальные координаты прямой, линейные (линейчатые) координаты
	line co-ordinates <AY>	*s.* P 676		
L 857	**line-critical graph,** edge-critical graph <GP>	kantenkritischer Graph *m*	graphe *m* arête-critique	реберно-критический граф
L 858	**line element,** lineal element <DE, DG, VA>	Linienelement *n*	élément *m* linéaire	линейный элемент; вектор поля направления <DE>
	line element <DG, DI>	*s.* D 465		
L 859	**line geometry,** geometry of lines, Plücker['s] geometry <AY>	Liniengeometrie *f*, Plückersche Liniengeometrie	géométrie *f* réglée (des droites, linéaire, de Plücker)	линейчатая (линейная) геометрия
L 860	**line graph,** interchange graph, derived graph <of a graph> <GP>	Liniengraph *m*, „interchange"-Graph *m*, dualer Graph *m*	graphe *m* dual	смежностный граф, граф смежности, сопряженный граф
	line graph <GP>	*s.* R 856		
	line index <MD>	*s.* R 1429		
	line integral <DI, FT>	*s.* C 2800		
	line integral along a closed contour (curve, line, path) <AN>	*s.* C 734a		
	line integral along a contour <AN>	*s.* C 734a		
	line involution <AY>	*s.* I 997		
L 861	**line locally above a graph** <RF>	lokal oberhalb eines Graphen gelegene Gerade *f*, Gerade lokal oberhalb eines Graphen	droite *f* localement au-dessus d'un graphe	прямая[, лежащая] локально выше графика
L 862	**line locally below a graph** <RF>	lokal unterhalb eines Graphen gelegene Gerade *f*, Gerade lokal unterhalb eines Graphen	droite *f* localement au-dessous d'un graphe	прямая[, лежащая] локально ниже графика
L 863	**line locally on a graph** <RF>	lokal auf einem Graphen gelegene Gerade *f*, Gerade lokal auf einem Graphen	droite *f* localement sur un graphe	прямая[, лежащая] локально на графике
L 864	**line of affine curvature** <DG>	Affinkrümmungslinie *f*	ligne *f* de courbure affine	линия аффинной кривизны
	line of application <VT>	*s.* P 1050		
L 865	**line of centres** <of the conics of a family> <AY>	Mittelpunktsgerade *f*, Mittengerade *f*	droite *f* des centres	прямая центров
L 866	**line of centres,** centre line <DS, EG>	Zentrale *f*	ligne *f* des centres	линия центров
L 867	**line of centres of gravity,** centre of gravity line <EG>	Schwerpunktslinie *f*	ligne *f* des centres de gravité	линия центров тяжести
	line of constant slope <GE>	*s.* S 1207		
L 868	**line of curvature** <DG>	Krümmungslinie *f*	ligne *f* de courbure	линия кривизны, линия главных кривизн
	line of discontinuity <DE>	*s.* D 643		
L 869	**line of horizon,** horizon <in central perspective> <DS>	Horizont *m*	ligne *f* d'horizon, horizon *m*	линия горизонта

No.	English	German	French	Russian
	line of integration <AN>	*s.* P 309		
L 870	**line of intersection,** intersection line <of two planes> <EG>	Schnittgerade *f*	droite *f* d'intersection	прямая пересечения
	line of latitude <GE>	*s.* P 89		
	line of longitude <GE>	*s.* M 395		
	line of numbers <AN, SE>	*s.* N 872		
L 871	**line of projection** <GE>	Projektionslinie *f*	ligne *f* de rappel	проектирующая линия
	line of regression <ST>	*s.* R 498		
L 872	**line of slope,** curve of slope, slope curve <VA>	Gefällkurve *f*	courbe *f* de pente	кривая наклона (спуска)
	line of steepest slope <DS>	*s.* F 75		
	line of striction <DG>	*s.* 1. S 1867; 2. S 1868		
	line of support <CS, GE>	*s.* S 2346		
L 873	**line of vector,** vector line <DG, VT>	Vektorlinie *f*, Feldlinie *f* des Vektorfelds	ligne *f* vectorielle (de vecteurs)	векторная линия, линия вектора (векторного поля)
L 874	**line sampling** <ST>	Linienstichprobenverfahren *n*, Linientaxation *f*	échantillonnage (sondage) *m* en ligne	метод линейной выборки, линейная выборка, выборка по линиям
L 875	**line segment,** cut off <by a [straight] line> from the *y*-axis <AY>	Achsenabschnitt (Abschnitt) *m* auf der *y*-Achse, Absolutglied *n* der Geradengleichung	ordonnée *f* <de la droite> à l'origine	начальная ордината прямой <коэффициент *b* в уравнении прямой $y = ax + b$>
L 876	**line segment,** straight[-] line segment, segment <of a line> <EG>	Strecke *f*	segment *m* linéaire (de droite), segment	отрезок прямой, отрезок
	line system <AY, DG>	*s.* C 1923		
L 877	**line with heights,** coted line <in topographic projection> <DS>	kotierte Linie *f*	ligne *f* cotée	линия с численными отметками
	linguistic paradox <FO, LO>	*s.* S 312		
L 878	**link,** linkage <of polygons> <TO>	verkettetes System *n* von Polygonen, Verkettung *f*		зацепление
	link <GP>	*s.* E 12		
	link <TO>	*s.* I 744		
L 879	**linked product** <of groups> <GR>	Kettenprodukt *n*		цепное произведение
L 880	**link group** <AT>	Verkettungsgruppe *f*	groupe *m* d'enchainements	группа переплетений
	linking coefficient (number) <AT>	*s.* L 1106		
L 881	**link integral** <AT>	Verschlingungsintegral *n*	intégrale *f* d'entrelacement	интеграл зацепления
L 882	**link of chain** <TO>	Kettenglied *n*	chaînette *f*	звено (ребро) цепи
	link of multiplicity one <AT>	*s.* K 106		
L 883	**link relative** <ST>	Gliedziffer *f*	chaîne *f* de rapports	
	Linnik['s] theorem <NT>	*s.* T 316		
	(L)-integrable, L-integrable <AN>	*s.* L 261		
	L-integral <AN>	*s.* L 262		
L 884	**Liouville['s] formula** <for the Wronskian> <DE>	Liouvillesche Formel *f* <für die Wronskische Determinante>, Formel von Ostrogradski-Liouville	formule *f* de Liouville <pour la déterminante de Wronski>	формула Остроградского-Лиувилля <для вронскиана>
L 885	**Liouville['s] formula** <for curvatures> <DG>	Liouvillesche Formel *f*	formule *f* de Liouville	формула Лиувилля
	Liouville['s] gap theorem <FU>	*s.* G 47		
	Liouville-Neumann series <IE>	*s.* N 181		
L 886	**Liouville['s] normal form** <of a second-order equation with eigenvalue parameter> <DE>	Liouvilles[che] Normalform *f*	forme *f* normale de Liouville	нормальный вид Лиувилля
L 887	**Liouville['s] number** <NT>	Liouvillesche [transzendente] Zahl *f*	nombre *m* transcendant de [J.] Liouville, nombre de Liouville	число Лиувилля
	Liouville['s] residue theorem <FU>	*s.* R 902		
L 888	**Liouville['s] surface,** surface of Liouville <DG>	Liouvillesche Fläche *f*	surface *f* de Liouville	поверхность Лиувилля
L 889	**Liouville['s] theorem,** Cauchy-Liouville theorem <for entire functions> <FT>	Liouvillescher Satz *m*, Satz von Liouville	théorème *m* de Liouville	теорема Лиувилля, лиувиллева теорема, теорема Коши-Лиувилля
L 890	**Liouville['s] theorem** <on algebraic numbers> <NT>	Liouvillescher Satz *m* <über algebraische Zahlen>	théorème *m* de Liouville	теорема Лиувилля <о приближениях иррациональных чисел рациональными>
	Liouville['s] theorem <NT>	*s.* T 317		
	Liouville['s] theorem of residues <FU>	*s.* R 902		
L 891	**Liouville['s] theorems** <for elliptic functions> <FT, FU>	Liouvillesche Sätze *mpl*	théorèmes *mpl* de Liouville	теоремы Лиувилля

No.	English	German	French	Russian
L 892	**Lipschitz['s] condition,** condition of Lipschitz <of order α, $\alpha > 0$, with the Lipschitz constant M; especially: of order 1> <DE, FA>	Lipschitz-Bedingung *f*, Lipschitzsche Bedingung *f* <mit dem Exponenten α, $\alpha > 0$, und der Konstanten (dem Koeffizienten) M; *spezieller:* mit dem Exponenten 1>	condition *f* de Lipschitz <d'ordre α, $\alpha > 0$, avec la constante de Lipschitz M; spécialement d'ordre 1>	условие Липшица <порядка α, $\alpha > 0$, с постоянной M; особенно: порядка 1>
L 893	**Lipschitz['s] condition in a point,** punctual Lipschitz condition <AN>	punktale Lipschitz-Bedingung (Lipschitzsche Bedingung) *f*, Lipschitz-Bedingung (Lipschitzsche Bedingung) in einem Punkt	condition *f* de Lipschitz dans un point, condition de Lipschitz ponctuelle	условие Липшица в точке, точечное условие Липшица
	Lipschitz['s] constant <DE>	*s.* C 2106		
L 894	**Lipschitz continuity,** property of satisfying a Lipschitz condition <DE>	Lipschitz-Stetigkeit *f*, Lipschitzsche Stetigkeit *f*	propriété *f* de satisfaire à une condition de Lipschitz, propriété d'être lipschitzien	липшицево свойство, свойство удовлетворять условию Липшица, непрерывность в смысле Липшица
L 895	**Lipschitz continuous boundary** <DE>	Lipschitz-stetiger Rand *m*	frontière *f* lipschitzienne	липшицева граница; граница, удовлетворяющая условию Липшица
L 896	**Lipschitz continuous function,** function satisfying a Lipschitz condition <DE>	Lipschitz-stetige Funktion *f*; Funktion, die eine Lipschitz-Bedingung erfüllt	fonction *f* lipschitzienne (satisfaisant à une condition de Lipschitz)	липшицевая функция; функция, удовлетворяющая условию Липшица; непрерывная в смысле Липшица функция
L 897	**Lipschitz continuous mapping,** Lipschitz['s] mapping <TO>	Lipschitz-stetige (lipschitz-stetige) Abbildung *f*	application *f* lipschitzienne, représentation *f* de Lipschitz	липшицево отображение; отображение, удовлетворяющее условию Липшица
	Lipschitz continuous mapping <AN, TO>	*s.* M 109		
L 898	**Lipschitz-Dini test** <for convergence of a Fourier series> <SS>	Lipschitz-Dinisches Kriterium *n*	critère *m* (règle *f*, théorème *m*) de Lipschitz-Dini	признак Липшица-Дини
	Lipschitz['s] index <DE>	*s.* O 264		
	Lipschitz['s] mapping <TO>	*s.* L 897		
	Lipschitz['s] order <DE>	*s.* O 264		
L 899	**Lipschitz space** <of distributions> <AT>	Lipschitzscher Raum *m*	espace *m* de Lipschitz	пространство Липшица
L 900	**Lipschitz['s] test** <for convergence of a Fourier series> <SS>	Lipschitzsches Kriterium *n*	critère *m* (règle *f*, théorème *m*) de Lipschitz	признак Липшица
L 901	**l-isomorphic groups** <GR>	verbandsisomorphe Gruppen *fpl*	groupes *mpl* structuralement isomorphes	структурно изоморфные между собой группы
	L-isomorphism <GR, LA>	*s.* P 1735		
L 902	**Listing['s] knot** <TO>	Listingscher Knoten *m*	nœud *m* de Listing	узел Листинга
L 903	**Listing['s] theorem** <TO>	Listings Satz *m*	théorème *m* de Listing	теорема Листинга
L 904	**literal expression** <AL, GN>	Buchstabenausdruck *m*, allgemeiner Ausdruck *m*	expression *f* littérale	буквенное выражение
L 905	**literal number** <AL, GN>	Buchstabengröße *f*, algebraische Größe *f*, allgemeine Zahl *f*	quantité *f* algébrique, grandeur *f* algébrique	алгебраическая величина
	little Fermat theorem <AL>	*s.* F 134		
L 906	**Little Picard Theorem / the,** Picard['s] small theorem <FT>	kleiner Picardscher Satz *m*	petit théorème *m* de Picard	малая теорема Пикара
L 907	**lituus** <*pl.*: litui> <GE>	Lituus *m*, Krummstab *m*	lituus *m*	жезл, спираль «жезл» <график $\rho^2 = a/\Theta$>
L 908	**Liusternik-Ditkin method** <AN, NU>	Methode *f* von Ljusternik und Ditkin, Ljusternik-Ditkinsche Methode	méthode *f* de Liousternik-Ditkin	метод Люстерника-Диткина
	living index <GN, VT>	*s.* F 618		
L 909	**L-measurability,** measurability in Lebesgue's sense, measurability in the sense of Lebesgue <ME>	L-Meßbarkeit *f*, Lebesgue-Meßbarkeit *f*, Meßbarkeit *f* im Lebesgueschen Sinne	L-mesurabilité *f*, mesurabilité *f* au sens de Lebesgue, mesurabilité lebesguienne	измеримость по Лебегу, измеримость в смысле Лебега
L 910	**L-measurable function,** Lebesgue measurable function, measurable function <ME>	L-meßbare Funktion *f*, Lebesgue-meßbare Funktion, im Lebesgueschen Sinne meßbare Funktion, bezüglich des Lebesgueschen Maßes meßbare Funktion, meßbare Funktion	fonction *f* L-mesurable, fonction mesurable au sens de Lebesgue, fonction mesurable de Lebesgue, fonction mesurable	измеримая по Лебегу функция, измеримая в смысле Лебега функция, измеримая функция
	(L) measure, L measure <ME>	*s.* L 264		
	ln <AN>	*s.* N 31		
	loaded integral equation <IE>	*s.* M 690		
L 911	**loading,** factor loading, saturation <ST>	Ladung *f*, Faktorladung *f*, Saturation *f*	facteur (coefficient) *m* de pondération	факторный коэффициент
	Lobachevskian geometry <GE>	*s.* H 629		
L 912	**lobachevskian parallel postulate,** hyperbolic parallel postulate <GE>	hyperbolisches Parallelenaxiom *n*	axiome *m* des parallèles de la géométrie hyperbolique	аксиома параллельности Лобачевского

	Lobachevski['s] function <GE>	*s.* P 92		
	Lobachevski['s] line <GE>	*s.* H 633		
	Lobachevski method <AL, AX, NU>	*s.* G 369		
	Lobachevski['s] plane <GE>	*s.* H 638		
	Lobachevski['s] point <GE>	*s.* H 641		
	Lobachevski['s] space <GE>	*s.* H 650		
L 913	**local algebra** <AL>	lokale Algebra *f*	algèbre *f* locale (primaire)	локальная алгебра
L 914	**local arc[-]wise connectedness** <TO>	lokaler bogenweiser Zusammenhang *m*	connexité *f* locale par arcs	локальная связность с помощью дуг
L 915	**local Artin homomorphism** <in class field theory> <AB>	lokaler Artin-Homomorphismus *m*	homomorphisme *m* d'Artin local	локальный гомоморфизм Артина, гомоморфизм норменного вычета
	local base [at a point] <TO>	*s.* B 92		
	local base of neighbourhoods of a point <TO>	*s.* B 92		
	local basis [at a point] <TO>	*s.* B 92		
L 916	**local Betti group** <AT>	lokale Bettische Gruppe *f*	groupe *m* de Betti local	локальная группа Бетти, локальная Δ-группа
L 917	**local Borel set** <TO>	lokal Borelsche Menge *f*	ensemble *m* localement borélien	локально борелевское множество
L 918	**local class field theory** <AB>	lokale Klassenkörpertheorie *f*	théorie *f* locale des corps de classes, théorie du corps de classes local	локальная теория полей классов
L 919	**local compactness** <TO>	lokale Kompaktheit *f*, Lokalkompaktheit *f*	compacité *f* locale	локальная компактность
L 920	**local continuity** <of a mapping> <TO>	lokale Stetigkeit *f*	continuité *f* locale	локальная непрерывность
L 921	**local continuous transformation group** <AL>	lokale kontinuierliche Transformationsgruppe *f*, kontinuierliche Familie *f* von Transformationen, // Transformationsgruppe	groupe *m* continu local de transformations	локальная непрерывная группа преобразований
L 922	**local convergence** <PG, TO>	lokale Konvergenz *f*	convergence *f* locale	локальная сходимость
L 923	**local convexity** <GE>	Konvexität *f* im Kleinen, lokale Konvexität	convexité *f* locale	локальная выпуклость
	local co-ordinate system <AG, DG>	*s.* C 595		
L 924	**local degree** <of a mapping> <AT>	lokaler Abbildungsgrad *m*, lokaler Grad *m* <der Abbildung>	degré *m* local <d'une application>	локальная степень <отображения>
	local degree <GP>	*s.* D 176		
L 925	**local dendrite** <TO>	Baum *m* im Kleinen	dendrite *f* locale	локальный дендрит
	local differential geometry <DG>	*s.* I 480		
L 926	**local direct product** <of topological groups> <GR>	lokales direktes Produkt *n*	produit *m* direct local	локальное прямое произведение
L 927	**local disconnection** <TO>	Eigenschaft *f*, lokal unzusammenhängend zu sein	disconnexion *f* locale	локальная несвязность
L 928	**local domain** <AL>	lokaler Integritätsbereich *m*, nullteilerfreier Stellenring *m*	anneau *m* local noethérien d'intégrité	локальное кольцо без дивизоров нуля
L 929	**local duality theorem** <AG>	lokaler Dualitätssatz *m*	théorème *m* de dualité locale	локальная теорема двойственности
L 930	**local extremum,** relative extremum, extremum in the small <DI>	lokales Extremum *n*, Extremum im Kleinen, relatives Extremum, relativer Extremwert *m*	extrémum *m* local (relatif)	локальный (относительный) экстремум, экстремум в малом
	local function <AN>	*s.* P 1053		
	local-global principle <AL>	*s.* H 123		
L 931	**local group** <AL>	Gruppenkeim *m*, lokale Gruppe *f*	germe *m* de groupe, groupe *m* local	локальная группа
L 932	**local group** <of *x*> <AT>	Homologiegruppe *f* <in einem Punkt *x*>	groupe *m* d'homologie locale <de *x*>	локальная группа гомологий <в точке *x*>
L 933	**local isomorphism** <GR>	lokaler Isomorphismus *m*, Isomorphismus im Kleinen, lokal isomorphe Abbildung *f*	isomorphisme *m* local	локальный изоморфизм
L 934	**localization** <of a module *or* ring> <AL>	Lokalisierung *f*	localisé *m* <résultat>; localisation *f* <procédé>	локализация
L 935	**localization** <TO>	Lokalisierung *f*, Lokalisation *f*	localisation *f*	локализация
L 936	**localization principle** <for Fourier series> <SS>	Lokalisationsprinzip *n*	principe *m* de localisation	принцип локализации
	localization principle <LO>	*s.* C 1300		
	localized vector <VT>	*s.* B 701		
L 937	**localizing functor** <AL, CA>	Funktor *m* Lokalisierung	foncteur *m* localisation	функтор локализации
L 938	**localizing subcategory** <CA>	lokalisierende Unterkategorie *f*	sous-catégorie *f* localisante	локализующая подкатегория
	local Kuhn-Tucker conditions <PG>	*s.* K 198		

L 939	**local Lie group,** analytical local Lie group <GR>	lokale Liesche Gruppe *f*, Liescher Gruppenkeim *m*, analytische lokale Liesche Gruppe	germe *m* de groupe de Lie, groupe *m* local de Lie, germe de groupe analytique, groupuscule *m* de Lie	локальная группа Ли, росток группы Ли, аналитическая группа Ли, групускула Ли
L 940	**local Lie quasisubgroup** <AL>	lokale Liesche Quasiuntergruppe *f*	quasi-sous-groupuscule *m* de Lie	квязиподгрупускула Ли
L 941	**local Lie subgroup** <AL>	lokale Liesche Untergruppe *f*	sous-groupuscule *m* de Lie, sous-groupe *m* local de Lie	локальная подгруппа Ли, подгрупускула Ли
L 942	**local limit theorem** <ST>	lokaler Grenzwertsatz (Grenzverteilungssatz) *m*	théorème *m* limite local	локальная предельная теорема
	local limit theorem of Gnedenko <ST>	*s.* G 316		
	local limit theorem of [de] Moivre-Laplace <ST>	*s.* M 807		
L 943	**local Lipschitz condition** <AN>	lokale Lipschitz-Bedingung *f*	condition *f* de Lipschitz locale	локальное условие Липшица
	locally <GN>	*s.* S 1213		
L 944	**locally analytic[al] function** <FT>	lokalanalytische Funktion *f*	fonction *f* localement analytique	локальное аналитическая функция
L 945	**locally and colocally small category** <CA>	lokal kleine und lokale kokleine (cokleine) Kategorie *f*	catégorie *f* localement et colocalement petite	локально малая категория
L 946	**locally arc[-]wise connected space** <TO>	lokal bogenverknüpfter (bogenzusammenhängender) Raum *m*	espace *m* localement connexe par arcs	локально дугообразно связное пространство, локально жорданосвязное пространство
L 947	**locally bounded function** <TO>	lokalbeschränkte Funktion *f*	fonction *f* localement bornée	локально ограниченная функция
L 948	**locally cartesian group** <GR>	lokal-euklidische (lokaleuklidische topologische) Gruppe *f*, Parametergruppe *f*	groupe *m* localement euclidien	локально евклидова группа
L 949	**locally closed set** <TO>	lokalabgeschlossene (lokal abgeschlossene) Menge *f*	ensemble *m* localement fermé, partie *f* localement fermée	локально замкнутое множество
	locally collapsible space <TO>	*s.* L 958		
	locally compact Hausdorff space <TO>	*s.* L 951		
L 950	**locally compact mapping** <TO>	lokal[ ]kompakte Abbildung *f*	application *f* localement compacte	локально[-]компактное отображение
L 951	**locally compact space,** locally compact Hausdorff space <TO>	lokal[]kompakter Raum *m*, im Kleinen kompakter Hausdorffscher Raum	espace *m* localement compact	локально[-]компактное пространство, локально бикомпактное пространство
L 952	**locally compact space being the union of a countable number of compact subsets** <TO>	im Unendlichen abzählbarer lokal[ ]kompakter Raum *m*	espace *m* localement compact dénombrable à l'infini	счетное в бесконечности локально[-]компактное пространство
L 953	**locally connected continuum,** Peanian continuum <TO>	lokal zusammenhängendes Kontinuum *n*, Peanosches Kontinuum	continu *m* localement connexe, continu péanien	локально[-]связный метрический континуум, континуум Пеано
	locally connected dendroid <TO>	*s.* D 225		
L 954	**locally connected set,** connected im kleinen point set, regular point set <at [a point] *P*> <TO>	lokal (im Kleinen) zusammenhängende Punktmenge *f* <in [einem Punkte] *P*>	ensemble *m* localement connexe <en *P*>	локально[-]связное множество <в [точке] *P*>, связное в точке *P* множество
L 955	**locally connected [topological] space in dimension *r*** <TO>	lokal zusammenhängender [topologischer] Raum *m* in der Dimension *r*, in der Dimension *r* lokal zusammenhängender [topologischer] Raum	espace *m* localement connexe en dimension *r* <au point *P*>	локально[-]связное в размерности *r* пространство
L 956	**locally constant function** <from a topological space> <TO>	lokal[ ]konstante Abbildung *f*	application (fonction) *f* localement constante	локально постоянная функция
L 957	**locally constant sheaf,** locally simple sheaf, locally trivial sheaf <AL, TO>	lokal[ ]konstante Garbe *f*	faisceau *m* localement constant (simple)	локально простой пучок
L 958	**locally contractible space,** locally collapsible space <TO>	lokal (im Kleinen) zusammenziehbarer Raum *m*	espace *m* localement contractile; espace localement contractile dans soi	локально стягиваемое пространство
L 959	**locally convex algebra** <FA>	lokalkonvexe (im Kleinen konvexe) Algebra *f*	algèbre *f* localement convexe	локально выпуклая алгебра
L 960	**locally convex space,** convex linear space <FA, TO>	lokalkonvexer Vektorraum (Raum) *m*	espace *m* [vectoriel topologique] localement convexe, espace linéaire à semi-normes	[локально] выпуклое пространство
L 961	**locally convex topology** <FA, TO>	lokalkonvexe (im Kleinen konvexe) Topologie *f*	topologie *f* localement convexe	локально выпуклая топология
L 962	**locally Euclidean connection,** locally Euclidean transfer, locally flat connection (transfer) <DG>	lokal-euklidische (lokal ebene, lokalebene, lokal-ebene, holonome) Übertragung *f*, lokal-euklidischer (lokal ebener, lokal[-]ebener, holonomer) Zusammenhang *m*	connexion *f* localement euclidienne, transfert *m* localement euclidien	локально евклидова (плоская) связность, локально евклидово (плоское) перенесение
L 963	**locally Euclidean manifold,** locally flat manifold <DG>	lokal-euklidische (lokal ebene, lokal[-]ebene, holonome) Mannigfaltigkeit *f*	variété *f* localement euclidienne	локально евклидово (плоское) многообразие

	English	German	French	Russian
L 964	**locally Euclidean [topological] space** <TO>	lokaleuklidischer Raum *m*	espace *m* [topologique] localement euclidien	локально евклидово пространство
	locally Euclidean transfer <DG>	*s.* L 962		
L 965	**locally faithful representation** <of a topological group> <RE>	lokal treue Darstellung *f*	représentation *f* localement fidèle	локально точное представление
L 966	**locally finite category,** category locally of finite type <CA>	lokal[-]endliche Kategorie *f*	catégorie *f* localement finie (de type fini)	локально-конечная категория
L 967	**locally finite complex** <AT>	lokal[-]endlicher (lokaleuklidischer, euklidischer) Komplex *m*	complexe *m* localement fini	локально конечный комплекс
L 968	**locally finite family of [sub]sets** <TO>	lokal[-]endliches System *n* von Teilmengen, lokal[-]endliches Mengensystem *n*, lokal[-]endliche Menge *f*	famille *f* localement finie [de parties], ensemble *m* localement fini [de parties]	локально-конечная система множеств, локально-конечное семейство [подмножеств], локально-конечное множество
L 969	**locally finite graph** <GP>	Graph *m* von endlichem Grade, lokal[-]endlicher (lokalfiniter) Graph	graphe *m* localement fini	локально конечный граф
L 970	**locally finitely generated module** <AL>	lokal endlich erzeugter Modul *m*	module *m* localement de type fini	локально конечно-порождаемый модуль
L 971	**locally finite radical** <AL>	lokal[-]endliches Radikal *n*	noyau *m* localement fini	локально-конечный радикал
L 972	**locally finite sum** <of sheafs> <AL, TO>	lokal[-]endliche direkte Summe *f*	somme *f* directe localement finie	прямая сумма локально-конечной совокупности пучков
L 973	**locally finite sum** <of functions> <TO>	lokal[-]endliche Summe *f*	somme *f* localement finie	локально-конечная сумма
	locally flat connection <DG> ⌐<DG>	*s.* L 962		
	locally flat manifold	*s.* L 963		
	locally flat transfer <DG>	*s.* L 962		
L 974	**locally free module** <AL>	lokal[ ]freier Modul *m*	module *m* localement libre	локально свободный модуль
L 975	**locally free sheaf** <AL, TO>	lokal[ ]freie Garbe *f*	faisceau *m* localement libre	локально свободный пучок
L 976	**locally generated sheaf** <AL, TO>	lokal erzeugte Garbe *f*	faisceau *m* localement engendré	локально порождаемый пучок
	locally geodesic manifold <DG>	*s.* G 243		
L 977	**locally holonomic connection (transfer)** <DG>	lokal holonome Übertragung *f*, lokal holonomer Zusammenhang *m*	connexion *f* (transfert *m*) localement holonome	локально голономная связность, локально голономное перенесение
L 978	**locally homeomorphic** <TO>	lokal homöomorph	localement homéomorphe	локально-гомеоморфный
L 979	**locally homomorphic continuous group** <GR>	im Kleinen homomorphe kontinuierliche Gruppe *f*, lokal (infinitesimal) homomorphe kontinuierliche Gruppe, meriedrisch isomorphe kontinuierliche Gruppe im Kleinen, // meroedrisch isomorphe kontinuierliche Gruppe im Kleinen	groupe *m* continu localement homomorphe, // groupe continu localement mériédriquement isomorphe	локально гомоморфная непрерывная группа
L 980	**locally homomorphic function** <FA>	lokalhomomorphe Funktion *f*	fonction *f* localement homomorphe	локально гомоморфная функция
L 981	**locally isomorphic group** <GR>	lokal isomorphe Gruppe *f*, holoedrisch isomorphe Gruppe im Kleinen, im Kleinen isomorphe Gruppe	groupe *m* localement isomorphe	локально изоморфная группа
L 982	**locally *k*-normal [*k*-] variety,** variety relatively normal with respect to *k* <Weil>, locally normal *k*-variety <Zariski> <AG>	lokal normale *k*-Mannigfaltigkeit *f*	variété *f* localement *k*-normale	локально *k*-нормальное многообразие
L 983	**locally Lipschitz continuous function (mapping, transformation),** mapping (transformation, function) satisfying a local Lipschitz condition <AN, TO>	lokal dehnungsbeschränkte Abbildung (Transformation, Funktion) *f*; Abbildung (Transformation, Funktion), die einer lokalen Lipschitz-Bedingung genügt	application (transformation, fonction) *f* localement lipschitzienne	отображение (преобразование), удовлетворяющее локальному условию Липшица; функция, удовлетворяющая локальному условию Липшица
L 984	**locally nilpotent group** <GR>	lokal-nilpotente (lokal nilpotente) Gruppe *f*, lokal spezielle Gruppe	groupe *m* localement nilpotent	локально-нильпотентная группа, локально нильпотентная группа
L 985	**locally nilpotent group of automorphisms** <GR>	lokal-nilpotente (lokal nilpotente) Gruppe *f* von Automorphismen, äußerlich lokal-nilpotente (lokal nilpotente) Gruppe von Automorphismen	groupe *m* d'automorphismes localement nilpotent	локально-нильпотентная (локально нильпотентная) группа автоморфизмов, внешне локально-нильпотентная (локально нильпотентная) группа автоморфизмов
L 986	**locally nilpotent radical** <of a group> <GR>	Plotkinsches (lokal-nilpotentes, lokal nilpotentes) Radikal *n*	radical *m* localement nilpotent	радикал Плоткина, локально-нильпотентный (локально нильпотентный) радикал
L 987	**locally nilpotent ring** <AL>	lokal-nilpotenter (lokal nilpotenter) Ring *m*, semi-nilpotenter Ring	anneau *m* localement nilpotent	локально нильпотентное кольцо

L 988	**locally noetherian (Noetherian) group** <GR>	lokal Noethersche Gruppe *f*, lokalnoethersche Gruppe	groupe *m* localement noethérien	локально нетерова группа
L 989	**locally noetherian (Noetherian) prescheme** <AG>	lokal Noethersches Präschema *n*, lokal-noethersches Präschema	préschéma *m* localement noethérien	локально нетерова пресхема
	locally normal *k*-variety <AG>	*s.* L 982		
	locally normal variety <AG>	*s.* N 666		
L 990	**locally ordered group** <GR>	lokal halbgeordnete Gruppe *f*	groupe *m* localement ordonné	локально частично упорядоченная группа
L 991	**locally path[-]connected space** <TO>	lokal wegzusammenhängender Raum *m*, lokal wegeweise zusammenhängender Raum	espace *m* localement connexe par chemins	локально линейно связное пространство, локально связное по путям пространство
L 992	**locally periodic radical** <GR>	lokal periodisches Radikal *n*	radical *m* localement périodique	локально периодический радикал
L 993	**locally regular confidence region** <ST>	lokal-regulärer Konfidenzbereich *m*	région *f* de confiance localement régulière	локально-регулярная доверительная область
L 994	**locally separable space** <TO>	lokal separabler Raum *m*	espace *m* localement séparable	локально сепарабельное пространство
	locally simple sheaf <AL, TO>	*s.* L 957		
L 995	**locally small category,** well-powered category, well powered category <CA>	lokal kleine Kategorie *f*	catégorie *f* localement petite, catégorie « well powered »	локально малая слева категория, локально малая категория
L 996	**locally soluble (solvable) group** <GR>	lokal auflösbare Gruppe *f*	groupe *m* localement résoluble	локально разрешимая группа
L 997	**locally subnormal element** <of a group> <GR>	lokal subnormales Element *n*	élément *m* localement sous-normal	локально достижимый элемент
L 998	**locally supersoluble group** <GR>	lokal überauflösbare Gruppe *f*	groupe *m* localement hyper-résoluble	локально сверхразрешимая группа
L 999	**locally trivial embedding** <TO>	lokal[ ]triviale Einbettung *f*	plongement *m* localement trivial	локально тривиальное погружение
	locally trivial fibration <AT>	*s.* L 1009		
	locally trivial sheaf <AL, TO>	*s.* L 957		
L 1000	**locally unbiased test** <ST>	lokal unverzerrter (unverfälschter) Test *m*, wirksamer Test	test *m* localement sans biais, test localement non biaisé, test efficace	локально несмещенный критерий, эффективный критерий
L 1001	**locally uniformizing function** <FT>	Ortsuniformisierende *f*	fonction *f* localement uniformisante	локально униформизирующая функция
L 1002	**locally uniformizing parameter, locally uniformizing variable** <FT>	lokale uniformisierende Variable *f*, lokal[er] uniformisierender Parameter *m*, // Ortsuniformisierende *f*	paramètre *m* localement uniformisant, variable *f* localement uniformisante	локально униформизирующий параметр, локально униформизирующая переменная
L 1003	**locally uniformly convergent sequence** <SS, TO>	lokal gleichmäßig konvergente Folge *f*	suite *f* localement uniformément convergente	локально равномерно сходящаяся последовательность
L 1004	**locally zero function** <TO>	lokal verschwindende Funktion *f*	fonction *f* localement zéro	локально нулевая функция
L 1005	**local maximum,** relative maximum, maximum in the small, maximum turning value <of a function> <DI>	lokales Maximum, Maximum im Kleinen, relatives Maximum, relativer Maximalwert *m*	maximum *m* local (relatif), maximé *m* relatif	локальный (относительный) максимум, максимум в малом
L 1006	**local minimum,** relative minimum, minimum in the small, minimum turning value <of a function> <DI>	lokales Minimum *n*, Minimum im Kleinen, relatives Minimum, relativer Minimalwert *m*	minimum *m* local (relatif), minimé *m* relatif	локальный (относительный) минимум, минимум в малом
L 1007	**local parameter,** uniformizing parameter, uniformizing element <AL>	lokaler (uniformisierender) Parameter *m*	paramètre *m* local, uniformisante *f*	локальный (униформизирующий) параметр, униформизирующий элемент, униформизирующая
L 1008	**local point of view** <GN>	lokale Betrachtungsweise *f*	point *m* de vue local	локальная точка зрения
L 1009	**local product,** locally trivial fibration, fibre bundle <AT>	lokal[]triviales Bündel *n*	espace *m* fibré localement trivial, espace fibré classique	локально тривиальное расслоенное пространство, классическое расслоенное пространство, локально тривиальное расслоение
L 1010	**local product** <of topological groups> <GR>	lokales Produkt *n*	produit *m* local	локальное произведение
L 1011	**local ring** <AL>	Stellenring *m*, lokaler Ring *m*	anneau *m* local	локальное кольцо
L 1012	**local ringed space** <AG>	lokal geringter Raum *m*	espace *m* annelé en anneaux locaux, espace localement annelé	локально окольцованное пространство
L 1013	**local separation point** <of a continuum> <TO>	lokaler Zerlegungspunkt *m*	point *m* de séparation locale	точка локального разделения
	local sub[-]base at a point *x* <TO>	*s.* S 2062		
L 1014	**local to global principle** <AB, AL>	„lokal-global"-Prinzip *n*	principe *m* de « passage du local au global »	локально-глобальный принцип
L 1015	**local uniformization (uniformizing)** <FT>	lokale Uniformisierung *f*	uniformisation *f* locale	локальная униформизация
	local value <NT>	*s.* P 624		

No.	English	German	French	Russian
L 1016	**local weight** <in a topological space> <TO>	Gewicht *n* in einem Punkt	poids *m* local	локальный вес
	location of the roots <AL, NU>	*s.* S 561		
	location parameter <ST>	*s.* P 1058		
L 1017	**location principle (theorem),** intermediate value theorem, theorem of intermediate values; Bolzano['s] theorem, theorem of Bolzano-Cauchy <RF>	Zwischenwertsatz *m*; Bolzanoscher Satz *m*, Satz von Bolzano <für $z = 0$>	théorème *m* de la valeur intermédiaire, théorème sur les valeurs intermédiaires; théorème de Bolzano (Bolzano-Cauchy)	промежуточная теорема
L 1018	**locus,** geometric locus <GE>	geometrischer Ort *m*, // aufgelöster Ort	lieu *m* géométrique, // lieu résolu	геометрическое место [точек]
L 1019	**Loewner['s] coefficient theorem,** coefficient theorem of Loewner <SS>	Koeffizientensatz *m* von Löwner, Löwnerscher Koeffizientensatz	théorème *m* des coefficients de Loewner	теорема коэффицентов Левнера
L 1020	**Loewner['s] ellipsoid** <of a convex body> <CS, GE>	Löwnersches Ellipsoid *n*	ellipsoïde *m* de Loewner	эллипсоид Левнера
L 1021	**Loewner['s] lemma,** lemma of Loewner <FT>	Lemma *n* von Löwner, Löwnersches Lemma	lemme *m* de Loewner	лемма Левнера
L 1022	**Loewy['s] inequality** <for the characteristic of a matrix <MD>	Loewysche Ungleichung *f*	inégalité *f* de Loewy	неравенство Лови
L 1023	**Loewy['s] invariant** <of a module> <AL>	Loewy-Invariante *f*, Loewysche Invariante *f*	invariant *m* de Loewy	инвариант Лови
L 1024	**Loewy['s] module** <AL>	Loewy-Modul *m*	module *m* de Loewy	модуль Лови
L 1025	**Loewy['s] ring** <AL>	Loewy-Ring *m*	anneau *m* de Loewy	кольцо Лови
L 1026	**Loewy['s] series** <GR>	Loewysche Kompositionsreihe *f*, Loewy-Reihe *f*	série *f* de Loewy	ряд Лови
L 1027	**Loewy['s] submodule** <AL>	Loewy-Untermodul *m*	sous-module *m* de Loewy	подмодуль Лови
	log <AN>	*s.* 1. L 1039; 2. N 31		
	log <AR>	*s.* L 1028		
	log, $\log_{10}$ <AR, NU>	*s.* B 754		
	loge <AN>	*s.* N 31		
	$\log_2$ <AR, NU>	*s.* B 369 a		
L 1028	**logarithm,** log <of a number> <*e.g.*: to base *a*, $\log_a$>, // lg <AR>	Logarithmus *m*, log <*z. B.*: zur Basis *a*, $\log_a$>, // lg	logarithme *m*, log <*par exemple:* de base *a*, $\log_a$>, // lg	логарифм, log <*например:* при основании *a*, $\log_a$>, // lg
	logarithm <AN>	*s.* L 1039		
L 1029	**logarithmetics** <*e.g.*: of a quasigroup> <AL>	Logarithmetik *f* <*z. B.*: einer Quasigruppe>	logarithmétique *f* <*par exemple:* d'un quasigroupe>	логарифметика <*например:* квазигруппы>
	logarithmic <AN>	*s.* L 1035		
L 1030	**logarithmically bounded function** <AN>	logarithmisch beschränkte Funktion *f*	fonction *f* logarithmiquement bornée	логарифмически ограниченная функция
	logarithmic average <ST>	*s.* G 261		
L 1031	**logarithmic branch[-] point** <of a Riemann surface> <FT>	logarithmischer Verzweigungspunkt (Windungspunkt) *m*	point *m* de ramification logarithmique	логарифмическая точка ветвления (разветвления), логарифмическая точка
	logarithmic branch[-] point <FT>	*s.* L 1051		
L 1032	**logarithmic calculation,** computing with logarithms, calculation with logarithms <AR>	logarithmisches Rechnen *n*, logarithmische Rechnung *f*	calcul *m* logarithmique	логарифмическое вычисление
	logarithmic chart <IN, NU>	*s.* L 1043		
L 1033	**logarithmic convergence** <SS>	logarithmische Konvergenz *f*	convergence *f* logarithmique	логарифмическая сходимость
L 1034	**logarithmic convexity** <GE>	logarithmische Konvexität *f*	convexité *f* logarithmique	логарифмическая выпуклость
L 1035	**logarithmic curve,** logarithmic, graph of the logarithmic function <AN>	logarithmische Kurve *f*, Logarithmuskurve *f*, Graph *m* der Logarithmusfunktion	logarithmique *f*, courbe *f* logarithmique, graphe *m* de la fonction logarithmique	логарифмика, график логарифмической функции
L 1036	**logarithmic derivative** <DI>	logarithmische Ableitung *f*	dérivée *f* logarithmique	логарифмическая производная
L 1037	**logarithmic ellipse** <as a spatial curve of fourth order> <AG>	logarithmische Ellipse *f*	ellipse *f* logarithmique	логарифмический эллипс
L 1038	**logarithmic equation** <AN, AR>	logarithmische Gleichung *f*	équation *f* logarithmique	логарифмическое уравнение; уравнение, содержащее логарифм неизвестного
L 1039	**logarithmic function,** logarithm, log, // lg <AN>	Logarithmusfunktion *f*, logarithmische Funktion *f*, Logarithmus *m*, log, // lg	fonction *f* logarithmique, logarithme *m*, log, // lg	логарифмическая функция, логарифм, log, // lg
L 1040	**logarithmic hyperbola** <as a spatial curve of fourth order> <AG>	logarithmische Hyperbel *f*	hyperbole *f* logarithmique	логарифмическая гипербола
L 1041	**logarithmic integral, logarithmic[-]integral function;** li; Li <FU>	Integrallogarithmus *m*, Logarithmus *m* integralis, Logarithmusintegralfunktion *f*; li; Li	logarithme *m* intégral; li; Li	интегральный логарифм; li; Li
L 1042	**logarithmic normal distribution,** logarithmico-normal distribution, log-normal distribution, lognormal distribution,	logarithmisch normale Verteilung *f*, logarithmische Normalverteilung *f*, Lognormalverteilung *f*, Normalver-	distribution (répartition) *f* logarithmonormale, répartition (distribution) normale logarithmique, loi *f* normale logarith-	логарифмически нормальное распределение, логарифмически-нормальное распределение, логарифмическое нор-

No.	English	German	French	Russian
and still: L 1042	Gibrat distribution <ST>	teilung zweiter (2.) Art, logarithmisch-normales Verteilungsgesetz *n*, Gibrat-Verteilung *f*	mique, loi logarithmique de répartition normale, loi gausso-logarithmique, distribution logarithmico-normale, distribution de Gibrat, loi de Gibrat (Galton)	мальное распределение, логарифмически нормальный закон распределения, распределение Жибра
	logarithmico-exponential function <RF>	*s.* L 627		
	logarithmico-normal distribution <ST>	*s.* L 1042		
L 1043	**logarithmic paper,** logarithmic chart <IN, NU>	Logarithmenpapier *n*, logarithmisches Papier (Netz) *n*	papier *m* à échelle logarithmique, diagramme *m* logarithmique	логарифмическая бумага (сетка), диаграмма с логарифмическим масштабом
L 1044	**logarithmic parabola** <as a spatial curve of the fourth order> <AG>	logarithmische Parabel *f*	parabole *f* logarithmique	логарифмическая парабола
L 1045	**logarithmic part** <of an integral> <AN>	logarithmischer Anteil *m*	partie *f* logarithmique	логарифмическая часть
L 1046	**logarithmic period** <of an integral> <FT>	logarithmische Periode *f*	période *f* logarithmique	логарифмический период
	logarithmic potential method <PG>	*s.* M 472		
L 1047	**logarithmic residue** <FT>	logarithmisches Residuum *n*	résidu *m* logarithmique	логарифмический вычет
L 1048	**logarithmic scale,** Gunter['s] scale <NO>	logarithmische Skala *f*, Gunter-Skala *f*	échelle *f* logarithmique (des logarithmes)	логарифмическая шкала, шкала Гунтера
L 1049	**logarithmic series** <SS>	logarithmische Reihe *f*	série *f* logarithmique	логарифмический ряд
L 1050	**logarithmic singularity** <of a *p*-form> <DG>	logarithmische Singularität *f*	singularité *f* logarithmique	логарифмическая особенность
L 1051	**logarithmic singularity (singular point),** logarithmic branch[-] point <of a function>	logarithmische Singularität *f*, logarithmisch-singulärer Punkt *m*, logarithmisch singulärer Punkt, logarithmische singuläre Stelle *f*	point *m* singulier logarithmique, singularité *f* logarithmique	логарифмическая особенность (критическая точка, особая точка), логарифмическая точка разветвления
	logarithmic slide rule <IN, NU>	*s.* S 1199		
L 1052	**logarithmic space** <AB>	Logarithmenraum *m*	espace *m* logarithmique	логарифмическое пространство
L 1053	**logarithmic spiral,** equiangular spiral, logistic spiral <GE>	logarithmische (gleichwinklige) Spirale *f*	spirale *f* logarithmique (équiangle)	логарифмическая спираль
	logarithmic system <AR>	*s.* S 2528		
	logarithmic table <AR, IN, NU>	*s.* L 1057		
L 1054	**logarithmic test** [for convergence] <of 0-th, first, . . ., *n*-th order> <of integrals> <DI>	logarithmisches Kriterium (Konvergenzkriterium) *n* <nullter, erster, . . ., *n*-ter Ordnung>	critère *m* logarithmique [de convergence] <d'ordre 0, 1, . . ., *n*>	логарифмический признак (критерий) [сходимости] <нулевого, первого, . . ., *n*-го порядка>
L 1055	**logarithmic test** [for convergence] <of the first *or* second kind> <SS>	logarithmisches Kriterium (Konvergenzkriterium) *n* <erster *oder* zweiter Art>	critère *m* logarithmique [de convergence], règle *f* (théorème *m*) logarithmique [de convergence], critère [de convergence] <de première *ou* seconde (deuxième) espèce>	логарифмический признак (критерий) [сходимости] <первого *или* второго рода>
	logarithmic unit <ST>	*s.* L 1084		
L 1056	**logarithmoid** <GE>	Logarithmoide *f*	logarithmoïde *f*	логарифмоида
L 1057	**logarithm table,** logarithmic table, table of logarithms <AR, IN, NU>	Logarithmentafel *f*	table *f* des (de) logarithmes, table logarithmique	логарифмическая таблица, таблица логарифмов
	logarithm to base 10 <AR, NU>	*s.* B 754		
	logarithm to base e	*s.* N 31		
	logarithm to the base 10 <AR, NU>	*s.* B 754		
L 1058	**log-convex function,** multiplicatively convex function <RF>	logarithmisch konvexe Funktion *f*	fonction *f* logarithmiquement convexe	логарифмически выпуклая функция
	logical addition <LO>	*s.* D 706		
	logical algebra <LO>	*s.* A 475		
	logical conjunction <LO>	*s.* C 2017		
	logical connective <LO>	*s.* L 1061		
L 1059	**logical consequence,** consequence <LO>	Konsequenz *f*, logische Konsequenz	conséquence *f*	следствие
L 1060	**logical consistency,** consistency <LO>	Folgerichtigkeit *f*	logique *f*	последовательность, консеквентность
L 1061	**logical constant,** constant, logical connective, // syncategorematic word <LO>	logische Konstante *f*; Konstante der Mengenlehre	constante *f* logique, constante	константа, логическая постоянная (константа), логический символ
	logical constant <LO>	*s.* S 498		
L 1062	**logical deduction,** deduction, inference, inclusion <LO>	logisches Schließen *n*, Schließen, logischer Schluß *m*, Schluß	déduction *f* logique, inférence	логическое заключение, умозаключение
L 1063	**logical diagram,** logic diagram <LO, SE>	logisches Diagramm *n*	diagramme *m* logique	логическая диаграмма
	logical equivalence <LO>	*s.* E 411		

No.	English	German	French	Russian
	logical function <LO>	*s.* L 1067		
	logical functional calculus <LO>	*s.* F 734		
	logical identity <LO>	*s.* U 349		
	logically complete axiom system <FO>	*s.* C 1410		
	logically equivalent <LO>	*s.* E 427		
L 1064	**logically false proposition** <LO>	logisch falsche Aussage *f* <entsteht aus Kontradiktion durch Belegung>	proposition *f* logiquement fausse	логически ложное высказывание
L 1065	**logically true proposition** <LO>	logisch wahre Aussage *f* <entsteht durch Belegung aus Tautologie>	proposition *f* logiquement vraie	логически истинное высказывание
	logically true sentence <LO> ⌐<LO>	*s.* U 349		
	logically valid formula	*s.* U 349		
L 1066	**logical matrix,** matrix <AL, LO>	logische Matrix *f*	matrice *f* logique	логическая матрица
	logical multiplication <LO>	*s.* C 2018		
L 1067	**logical operation,** logic[al] function <LO>	logische Operation (Verknüpfungsoperation) *f*	opération (fonction) *f* logique	логическая операция, логическое действие, логическая функция
L 1068	**logical paradox,** mathematical paradox, paradox of set theory, set-theoretic[al] antinomy, mathematical antinomy <LO>	logische Paradoxie (Antinomie) *f*, logisches Paradoxon *n*	paradoxe *m* logique (mathématique)	логический парадокс
	logical product <AL>	*s.* G 407		
	logical product <LO>	*s.* C 2017		
	logical product <SE>	*s.* I 802		
L 1069	**logical schema** <LO>	logisches Schema *n*	schéma *m* logique	логическая схема
	logical sum <AL>	*s.* L 242 a		
	logical sum <LO>	*s.* D 705		
	logical sum <SE>	*s.* U 202		
	logical symbol <LO>	*s.* S 498		
L 1070	**logical variable** <LO>	logische Variable *f*	variable *f* logique	логическая переменная
L 1071	**logic calculus** <LO>	Logikkalkül *m*, logischer Kalkül *m*	calcul *m* logique	логическое (формальное) исчисление
	logic diagram <LO, SE>	*s.* L 1063		
	logic function <LO>	*s.* L 1067		
L 1072	**logicism** <FO>	Logizismus *m*	logicisme *m*	логицизм
L 1073	**logicistic point of view** <MM>	logizistischer Standpunkt *m*	point *m* de vue logiciste	логицистическая точка зрения
	logic of first order <LO>	*s.* F 347		
	logic of propositions <LO>	*s.* P 1868		
	logic of quantifiers <LO>	*s.* P 1183		
L 1074	**logic of relations** <LO>	Relationslogik *f*	logique *f* des relations	логика отношений
	logic of second order <LO>	*s.* S 218		
L 1075	**logico-mathematical model** <PG>	mathematisch-logisches Modell *n*	modèle *m* mathématico-logique	логико-математическая (математико-логическая) модель
	logic product <LO>	*s.* C 2017		
	logic sum <LO>	*s.* D 705		
L 1076	**logic without identity,** predicate calculus without identity <LO>	Prädikatenkalkül *m* ohne Identität	logique *f* sans égalité	исчисление предикатов без равенства
L 1077	**logistic** <as a curve> <GE>	Logistica *f*	logistique *f*	логистика
L 1078	**logistic curve,** logistic trend, Pearl-Reed curve <ST>	logistische Kurve *f*, logistischer Trend *m*	courbe (tendance) *f* logistique, courbe autocatalytique	логистическая кривая, логистический тренд
L 1079	**logistic distribution** <ST>	logistische Verteilung *f*	distribution *f* logistique	логистическое распределение
L 1080	**logistic function,** Verhulst['s] growth function, Robertson['s] growth function, autocatalytic function <ST>	logistische Funktion *f*, Wachstumsfunktion *f* nach Verhulst (Robertson), Verhulstsche (Robertsonsche) Wachstumsfunktion, autokatalytische Funktion	fonction *f* logistique, fonction de croissance de Verhulst (Robertson), fonction autocatalytique	логистическая функция, функция роста Робертсона (Верхульста, по Верхульсту), автокаталитическая функция
L 1081	**logistic method** <MM>	logistische Methode *f*	méthode *f* logistique	метод формализации
L 1082	**logistic process** <SP>	logistischer Prozeß (Wachstumsprozeß) *m*	processus *m* logistique	логистический процесс
	logistics <LO>	*s.* M 166		
	logistic spiral <GE>	*s.* L 1053		
	logistic system <LO>	*s.* F 474		
L 1083	**logistic system consistent in the sense of Post,** system consistent in Post's sense <LO>	widerspruchsfreies System *n* im Sinne von Post	système *m* consistant au sens de Post	непротиворечивая система в смысле Поста
	logistic trend <ST>	*s.* L 1078		
L 1084	**logit,** logarithmic unit <ST>	Logit *m*	logit *m*	логит
L 1085	**log-log paper,** double logarithmic paper <IN, NU>	doppelt[ ]logarithmisches Papier *n*, Potenzpapier *n*, log-log-Papier *n*, Exponentialpapier *n*	papier *m* à double échelle logarithmique, papier bilogarithmique (logarithmique, log-log)	логарифмическая бумага <с двойной логарифмической шкалой>, двойная логарифмическая бумага, log-log-бумага
L 1086	**log-log transformation** <ST>	log-log-Transformation *f*, Log-Log-Transformation *f*	transformation *f* bilogarithmique	преобразование повторным логарифмированием, двойное логарифмическое преобразование
	log[-]normal distribution <ST>	*s.* L 1042		

No.	English	German	French	Russian
	logocyclic <AG>	*s.* S 2007		
L 1087	**log transformation** <ST>	log-Transformation *f*, Log-Transformation *f*	transformation *f* logarithmique	логарифмическое преобразование
L 1088	**Lommel['s] function** <FU>	Lommelsche Funktion *f*	fonction *f* de Lommel	функция Ломмеля
L 1089	**Lommel-Malmstén formulae** <DE>	Lommel-Malmsténsche Formeln *fpl*, Formeln von Lommel und Malmstén	formules *fpl* de Lommel-Malmstén	формулы Ломмеля-Мальмстена
L 1090	**Lommel['s] polynomial** <FU>	Lommelsches Polynom *n*	polynôme *m* de Lommel	многочлен (полином) Ломмеля
L 1091	**long Čech homology sequence** <AT>	lange Čechsche Homologiesequenz *f*	suite *f* longue d'homologie de Čech	длинная последовательность гомологий Чеха
L 1092	**Longchamps['s] circle,** circle of Longchamps <of the triangle> <EG>	Longchampsscher Kreis *m*	cercle *m* de Longchamps	окружность Лоншама
L 1093	**Longchamps['s] sphere,** sphere of Longchamps <of a polyhedron> <EG>	Longchampssche Kugel *f*	sphère *f* de Longchamps	сфера Лоншама
L 1094	**Longchamps['s] theorems** <EG>	Longchampssche Sätze *mpl*	théorèmes *mpl* de Longchamps	теоремы Лоншама
	Longchamps['s] trisectrix <GE>	*s.* T 983		
L 1095	**long division,** longhand (unabridged) division <of numbers *or* polynomials>, // division transformation <AL, AR>	lange (unabgekürzte) Division *f*	division *f* non abrégée	деление с выписыванием всех промежуточных шагов, деление на бумаге, несокращенное (полное) деление
L 1096	**longevity,** long life[time] <ST>	Langlebigkeit *f*, Betriebsbrauchbarkeitsdauer *f*	longévité *f*, longue vie *f*	долговечность
L 1097	**long exact sequence** <CA, HA>	lange exakte Folge *f*	suite *f* exacte longue	длинная точная последовательность
	longhand division <AL, AR>	*s.* L 1095		
L 1098	**long homotopy sequence** <AT>	lange Homotopiesequenz *f*	suite *f* longue d'homotopie	длинная гомотопическая последовательность
L 1099	**longitudinal multiplication** <CA>	longitudinale Multiplikation *f*	multiplication *f* longitudinale	продольное умножение
	long life[time] <ST>	*s.* L 1096		
	long radius <EG>	*s.* C 738		
L 1100	**long root** <in a Lie group> <GR>	lange Wurzel *f*	racine *f* « longue »	длинный корень
L 1101	**Looman-Menchoff theorem** <FT>	Satz *m* von Looman-Menchoff, Looman-Menchoffscher Satz	théorème *m* de Looman-Menchoff	
L 1102	**loop** <AL>	Loop *f*, Quasigruppe *f* mit neutralem Element	loop *m*, quasi-groupe *m* avec élément unité	лупа
L 1103	**loop,** self loop <GP>	Schlinge *f*, singuläre Kante *f*, Einkreis *m*, Schleife *f*	boucle *f*, impasse *f*, autoliaison *f*	петля
L 1104	**loop** <of a curve> <TO>	Schlinge *f*	lacet *m*	петля
	loop <AN>	*s.* C 2252		
	loop <GP>	*s.* E 98		
	loop <TO>	*s.* C 892		
L 1105	**loop algebra** <AL>	Loopalgebra *f*	algèbre *f* de loop	алгебра лупы
L 1106	**looping coefficient,** linking number (coefficient) <AT>	Verschlingungszahl *f*	nombre *m* d'entrelacements	коэффициент зацепления
L 1107	**loop integral** <DI>	Schleifenintegral *n*	intégrale *f* prise le long d'une boucle	интеграл по петле
L 1108	**loop space,** space of loops <based at γ_0> <TO>	Schleifenraum *m* <mit Basispunkt γ_0>	espace *m* des lacets <à point base γ_0>	пространство петель <с отмеченной точкой γ_0>
	loop with operators <AL>	*s.* O 194		
L 1109	**Lopatinsky['s] conditions** <DE>	Lopatinskijsche Bedingungen *fpl*, Lopatinskij-Bedingungen	conditions *fpl* de Lopatinskij	условия Лопатинского
L 1110	**Lorentz['s] group** <GR>	Lorentz-Gruppe *f*, Lorentzgruppe *f*	groupe *m* de Lorentz	группа Лоренца, лоренцова группа
L 1111	**Lorentz['s] transformation** <AL>	Lorentz-Transformation *f*	transformation *f* de Lorentz	преобразование Лоренца, лоренцово преобразование
L 1112	**loss function** <ST>	Verlustfunktion *f*	fonction *f* de perte	функция потерь
L 1113	**loss of accuracy (precision)** <ER>	Genauigkeitsverlust *m*	perte *f* de précision	потеря точности, погрешность промежуточных вычислений
	loss of generality / without <GN>	*s.* W 274		
L 1114	**loss probability** <ST>	Verlustwahrscheinlichkeit *f*	probabilité *f* de perte	вероятность потери
L 1115	**loss system** <ST>	Verlustsystem *n*	système *m* de perte	система с потерями
L 1116	**lot;** batch <ST>	Posten *m*, Los *n*; Charge *f*	lot *m*, lot technique	партия, группа
L 1117	**lot fraction defective** <ST>	Ausschußanteil *m* eines Postens	proportion *f* de pièces défectueuses dans un lot	доля дефектных изделий в партии
L 1118	**lot quality protection** <ST>	Qualitätsschutz *m* für Einzelposten	protection *f* de la qualité d'un lot	гарантия качества партии
L 1119	**lottery sampling** <ST>	Auslosungsstichprobenverfahren *n*	échantillonnage *m* par tirage (loterie)	лотерейная выборка
L 1120	**lot tolerance fraction (percent) defective** <ST>	Schlechtgrenze *f*, Ablehngrenze *f*, Ablehnungsgrenze *f*, Ausschußtoleranz *f* von Posten, Schlechtlage *f*	proportion *f* tolérée de pièces défectueuses dans un lot, proportion maximum de déchets tolérable dans un lot	верхний контрольный предел
L 1121/2	**Löwdin['s] orthogonalization procedure,** weighted (symmetrical) orthogonalization process <MD, NU>	Löwdinsches (gewichtetes, symmetrisches) Orthogonalisierungsverfahren *n*	procédé *m* (méthode *f*) d'orthogonalisation symétrique (de Löwdin), procédé d'orthogonalisation pondéré	метод (процесс) ортогонализации Левдина, взвешенный (симметричный) метод ортогонализации

	Löwenheim-Skolem paradox	*s.* S 1191		
L 1123	**Löwenheim-Skolem [-Tarski] theorem, Löwenheim['s] theorem,** Skolem-Löwenheim theorem, theorem of Löwenheim-Skolem[-Gödel], Krivine Löwenheim['s] theorem <LO>	Löwenheim-Skolemsches Theorem *n*, Theorem von Löwenheim und Skolem, Reduktionssatz *m* von Löwenheim und Skolem	théorème *m* de Löwenheim-Skolem, théorème de Löwenheim	теорема Лёвенгейма-Сколема, теорема Сколема-Лёвенгейма, теорема Левенгейма, теорема Лёвенгейма-Скулема
L 1124	**lower approximate limit,** inferior approximate limit, lim inf ap <of a function> <RF>	unterer approximativer Limes (Hauptlimes, extremer Limes) *m*, untere approximative Unbestimmtheitsgrenze (Häufungsgrenze) *f*, lim inf ap	limite *f* approximative inférieure, limite inférieure approximative, lim inf ap	нижний аппроксимативный предел, lim inf ap
L 1125	**lower arithmetics** <AR>	niedere Arithmetik *f*	arithmétique *f* inférieure	низшая арифметика
L 1126	**lower asymptotic density** <AB>	asymptotische Dichte *f*, Dichte im Großen	densité *f* asymptotique inférieure	нижняя асимптотическая плотность
	lower base <EG>	*s.* B 85		
L 1127	**lower bound** <of a set *or* sequence of real numbers *or* a real-valued function> <DI, SS>	untere (linke) Schranke *f*	borne (limite) *f* inférieure, minorant *m*	нижняя грань (граница)
L 1128	**lower bound** <of a symmetric operator> <FA>	untere Grenze (Schranke) *f*	borne *f* inférieure	нижняя грань
L 1129	**lower bound,** minorant, left bound <of a partially ordered set> <SE>	untere Schranke *f*, Minorante *f*, linke Schranke	borne *f* inférieure, minorant *m*, élément *m* minorant, minorante *f*	нижняя граница, миноранта, нижняя грань
	lower boundary <DI, SE>	*s.* G 411		
	lower cell limit <ST>	*s.* L 1133		
L 1130	**lower central chain** <GR>	untere Zentralkette *f*	chaîne *f* centrale descendante	нижняя центральная цепь
L 1131	**lower central series** <of a group> <GR>	absteigende (unterste) Zentralfolge *f*, absteigende Zentrenfolge (Zentralreihe, Zentrenreihe) *f*	série *f* centrale inférieure (descendante)	нижняя центральная цепь, нисходящий (нижний) центральный ряд
L 1132	**lower class** <in a Dedekind cut> <AN, SE>	Unterklasse *f*, erste (untere) Klasse *f*	classe *f* inférieure	нижний (левый, первый) класс
L 1133	**lower class limit,** lower cell limit <ST>	untere Klassengrenze *f*	limite *f* inférieure de classe	нижний предел класса, нижняя граница класса
	lower complete square <CA>	*s.* P 2077		
	lower continuous function <RF>	*s.* L 1163		
L 1134	**lower control limit** <ST>	untere Kontrollgrenze *f*	limite *f* inférieure de contrôle	нижняя контрольная граница
L 1135	**lower Darboux integral,** lower Riemann integral, lower integral <AN>	unteres Darbouxsches (Riemannsches) Integral *n*, unteres Integral, [Riemannsches] Unterintegral *n*	intégrale *f* par défaut, intégrale inférieure de Darboux (Riemann), intégrale inférieure	нижний интеграл Дарбу (Римана), нижний интеграл
L 1136	**lower Darboux sum,** lower sum <AN, DI>	Darbouxsche Untersumme *f*, Untersumme	somme *f* inférieure de Darboux, somme inférieure	нижняя сумма Дарбу, нижняя [интегральная] сумма
L 1137	**lower degree** <AL>	niederer Grad *m*	degré *m* inférieur	низшая степень
L 1138	**lower density** <of a power series> <SS>	untere Dichte *f*	densité *f* inférieure	нижняя плотность
L 1139	**lower deviation,** downward deviation <AX>	Abweichung *f* nach unten	écart *m* en (vers le) bas	отклонение вниз, отклонение в сторону уменьшения
L 1140	**lower Dini['s] derivative** <RF>	untere Derivierte (Hauptderivierte, Ableitungszahl) *f*	nombre *m* dérivé inférieur	нижнее производное число
	lower Dini['s] derivative on the left <RF>	*s.* L 380		
	lower Dini['s] derivative on the right <RF>	*s.* R 1163		
L 1141	**lower Dini['s] partial derivative** <of a real-valued function> <RF>	untere partielle Derivierte *f*	dérivée *f* partielle inférieure de Dini	нижнее частное производное число, нижняя частная производная Дини
L 1142	**lower Dirichlet density** <AB>	untere Dirichlet-Dichte *f*	densité *f* de Dirichlet inférieure	нижняя плотность Дирихле
L 1143	**lower double limit** <of a double sequence> <SS>	unterer Doppellimes *m*	double limite *f* inférieure	нижний двойной предел
L 1144	**lower envelope** <of a family of functions> <AN>	untere Enveloppe (Grenze, Hüllfunktion) *f*	enveloppe *f* inférieure	нижняя огибающая
	lower estimate <AN, AX, ER>	*s.* M 649		
	lower hemitropism <GR>	*s.* M 367		
	lower homology <AT>	*s.* H 469		
L 1145	**lower implicative semilattice** <AL>	implikativer ⌒-Halbverband *m*	inf-demi-treillis *m* implicatif	нижняя импликативная полуструктура
L 1146	**lower index,** subscript <GN>	unterer (tiefgestellter) Index *m*	indice *m* inférieur (en bas)	нижний (подстрочный) индекс

No.	English	German	French	Russian
L 1147	**lowering** <of indices> <VT>	Herunterziehen *n*	faire *m* descendre, faire passer de haut en bas	опускание
L 1148	**lowering map** <TO>	dimensionserniedrigende Abbildung *f*	application *f* abaissante la dimension	понижающее размерность отображение
	lowering of order <MD>	*s.* R 430		
L 1149	**lowering of the degree** <of an equation> <AL>	Erniedrigung *f* des Grades, Reduktion *f* des Grades, Graderniedrigung *f*	abaissement *m* [du degré], réduction *f* du degré	понижение степени
L 1150	**lowering of the order** <of a differential equation>, depression of the order of an equation <DE>	Erniedrigung *f* der Ordnung, Reduktion *f* der Ordnung	abaissement *m* de l'ordre, réduction *f* de l'ordre	понижение порядка, уменьшение порядка
L 1151	**lower integral,** ∫ <AN>	unteres Integral *n*, Unterintegral *n*, ∫	intégrale *f* inférieure, ∫	нижний интеграл, ∫
	lower integral <AN>	*s.* L 1135		
L 1152	**lower Lebesgue sum** <AN>	Lebesguesche Untersumme *f*, untere Lebesguesche Summe *f*	somme *f* inférieure de Lebesgue	нижняя сумма Лебега
	lower left-hand limit <DI>	*s.* L 381		
L 1153	**lower limit,** inferior limit, limit inferior, minimum limit, least of the limits, lim inf, lim <of a number sequence> <DI, SS>	unterer Limes (Hauptlimes) *m*, Limes (limes) *m* inferior, untere Häufungsgrenze (Unbestimmtheitsgrenze) *f*, lim inf, lim, // untere Grenze *f* <Pasch>	limite *f* inférieure (inférieure d'indétermination), la plus petite *f* des limites, la plus petite limite, limite minimum, lim inf, lim	нижний (наименьший) предел, нижняя граница неопределенности, lim inf, lim
L 1154	**lower limit,** lower topological limit, lt <of a sequence of sets> <TO>	unterer topologischer (abgeschlossener) Limes *n*, lt, *F*-lim	limite *f* inférieure topologique, limite topologique inférieure, limite inférieure	нижний топологический предел, нижний предел
	lower limit <RF>	*s.* M 597		
	lower limit on one side <DI>	*s.* L 1156		
	lower limit on the left <DI> ┌<DI>	*s.* L 381		
	lower limit on the right	*s.* R 1164		
L 1155	**lower logarithmic density** <AB>	untere logarithmische Dichte *f*	densité *f* logarithmique inférieure	нижняя логарифмическая плотность
	lower measure <ME>	*s.* 1. I 731; 2. I 733		
	lower nilradical <AL>	*s.* L 1159		
L 1156	**lower one-sided limit,** one-sided lower limit, lower limit on one side <DI>	unterer einseitiger Limes (Hauptlimes, Grenzwert) *m*	limite *f* inférieure à un seul côté, limite inférieure unilatérale	нижний односторонний предел
	lower order / [infinite] of <AN>	*s.* I 465		
	lower predicate calculus <LO>	*s.* F 347		
L 1157	**lower pure value,** lower value <of a game> <TG>	unterer reiner Wert *m*, unterer Wert	valeur *f* inférieure pure, valeur inférieure	нижнее чистое значение, нижнее значение
L 1158	**lower quartile,** first quartile <ST>	unteres (erstes, 1., 25%iges) Quartil *n*	quartile *m* inférieur, premier quartile	первый (нижний) квартиль
L 1159	**lower radical,** lower nilradical <of a ring> <AL>	unteres Radikal *n*	radical *m* inférieur	нижний радикал
	lower Riemann integral <AN> ┌<DI>	*s.* L 1135		
	lower right-hand limit	*s.* R 1164		
L 1160	**lower semi[-]continuity** <AN, TO>	Halbstetigkeit *f* nach unten, untere Halbstetigkeit	semi-continuité *f* inférieure[ment]	полунепрерывность снизу
L 1161	**lower semi-continuous decomposition** <of a space> <TO>	nach unten halbstetige Zerlegung *f*, unterhalbstetige Zerlegung <zu offener Äquivalenzrelation gehörig>	décomposition *f* semi-continue inférieurement	полунепрерывное снизу разбиение
L 1162	**lower semi[-]continuous equivalence** <TO>	unterhalbstetige (nach unten halbstetige) Äquivalenzrelation *f*	relation *f* d'équivalence semi-continue inférieurement	полунепрерывное снизу отношение эквивалентности
L 1163	**lower semi-continuous function,** lower semicontinuous function, lower continuous function <RF>	nach unten halbstetige Funktion *f*, unterhalbstetige (unterhalb stetige, abwärts halbstetige, abwärts stetige, nach unten stetige) Funktion *f*	fonction *f* semi-continue (continue) inférieurement	полунепрерывная (непрерывная) снизу функция
L 1164	**lower semi[-]lattice,** semi[-]lattice, meet-semilattice <AL>	⌒-Halbverband *m*, Durchschnittshalbverband *m*	demi-treillis *m* relatif à l'intersection, ∧-demi-treillis *m*, ensemble *m* semi-réticulé inférieurement, demi-treillis *m* inférieur, inf-demi-treillis *m*, inf demi-treillis	полуструктура, полурешетка, семилаттис, полусвязка, нижняя полурешетка, нижняя полуструктура
L 1165	**lower semi-modular lattice** <LA>	nach unten semimodularer Verband *m*, ⌒-semimodularer Verband	treillis *m* semi-modulaire inférieurement	полумодулярная снизу структура
L 1166	**lower subsemilattice** <AL>	Teil-⌒-Halbverband *m*	sous-inf-demi-treillis *m*	нижняя подполуструктура
L 1167	**lower sum** <AN>	Untersumme *f*	somme *f* inférieure	нижняя сумма
	lower sum <AN, DI>	*s.* L 1136		
L 1168	**lower surface,** base surface, base <of frustum>	Grundfläche *f*, Basis *f*; Grundkreis *m* <Kegelstumpf>	surface *f* à bas	нижнее основание

No.	English	German	French	Russian
L 1169	**lower the degree / to** <of an equation> <AL>	den Grad <einer Gleichung> erniedrigen	abaisser <une équation>	понижать степень <уравнения>
	lower topological limit <TO>	*s.* L 1154		
L 1170	**lower triangular group,** full lower triangular group, triangular group <AL>	Gruppe *f* der unteren Dreiecksmatrizen (Halbmatrizen)	groupe *m* trigonal large inférieur, groupe des matrices triangulaires inférieures	группа нижних треугольных матриц
L 1171	**lower triangular matrix,** subdiagonal matrix <MD>	untere Halbmatrix (Dreiecksmatrix) *f*	matrice *f* triangulaire (trigonale) inférieure, triangulaire *f* inférieure	нижняя треугольная матрица
	lower triangular matrix with ones in the diagonal <MD>	*s.* U 284		
	lower unitriangular group <GR>	*s.* U 292		
	lower unitriangular matrix <MD>	*s.* U 284		
	lower value <TG>	*s.* L 1157		
	lower variation <AN>	*s.* N 115		
	lowest common denominator <AL, NT>	*s.* L 238		
	lowest common multiple <AL, AR, NT>	*s.* L 241		
L 1172	**lowest term** <of a polynomial> <AL>	niedrigstes Glied *n*, Glied niedrigster Ordnung	terme *m* ayant la plus petite puissance	младший член
	lowest upper bound <DI, SE>	*s.* L 252		
	lowest value <DI>	*s.* A 117		
L 1173	**loxodrome [curve],** loxodromic curve (line, spiral), rhumb (Rhumb) line, rhumb, spherical helix <on a sphere *or* spheroid, especially on earth's surface> <EG>	Loxodrome *f* im engeren Sinne, Loxodrome, Kursgleiche *f*, Schieflaufende *f*, Rhumblinie *f*, loxodromische Linie *f*	loxodromie *f*, ligne *f* loxodromique	локсодрома, локсодромия, локсодромная спираль (кривая)
	loxodromic automorphism <FT>	*s.* L 1175		
	loxodromic curve (line) <EG>	*s.* L 1173		
	loxodromic mapping <FT>	*s.* L 1175		
L 1174	**loxodromic matrix** <FT>	loxodromische Matrix *f*	matrice *f* loxodromique	локсодромическая матрица
	loxodromic spiral <EG>	*s.* L 1173		
L 1175	**loxodromic transformation,** loxodromic automorphism (mapping) <FT>	loxodromische Abbildung (Transformation, lineare Transformation, Kreisverwandtschaft, Substitution) *f*	transformation (substitution, application) *f* loxodromique	локсодромическое преобразование (отображение)
L 1176	**lozenge diagram,** Fraser['\]s diagram <FD, NU>	Rautendiagramm *n*, Fraser-Diagramm *n*, Lozengediagramm *n*, Diagramm *n* von Fraser, Frasersches Diagramm	diagramme *m* des losanges	диаграмма ромбов
	LP <PG>	*s.* L 833		
L 1177	***L*-reduced direct product,** reduced product <of algebras> <UA>	reduziertes direktes Produkt *n* <mod *L*>, *L*-reduziertes [direktes] Produkt	produit *m* direct réduit <mod. *L*>	приведенное произведение <по модулю *L*>
	l-ring <AL>	*s.* L 140		
	LSD <ST>	*s.* C 2674		
	l-semigroup <AL>	*s.* A 1110		
L 1178	***L*-series** <NT>	*L*-Reihe *f*, Abelsche *L*-Funktion *f*	série *f L*, série *L* de Dirichlet	*L*-ряд
L 1179	**L-space,** limit space <TO>	*L*-Raum *m*, Limesraum *m*	espace *m* $\mathfrak{L}^*$, espace $\mathfrak{L}_t$	$\mathfrak{L}^*$-пространство
L 1180	**l-subring** <AL>	verbandsgeordneter Unterring *m*	sous-anneau *m* réticulé	структурно упорядоченное подкольцо
	L-sum <DI>	*s.* L 275		
	L-summable series <DI>	*s.* S 2278		
	$\overline{\textbf{lt}}$ <TO>	*s.* U 428		
	$\underline{\textbf{lt}}$ <TO>	*s.* L 1154		
	l.u.b., LUB <DI, SE>	*s.* L 252		
L 1181	**Lubbock['s] formula** <AN, AX, NU>	Lubbocksche Formel *f*	formule *f* de Lubbock	формула Луббока
	Lucas cubic <AG>	*s.* C 2740		
L 1182	**Lucas['] number** <NT>	Lucassche Zahl *f*	nombre *m* de Lucas	число Люка́
	Lucas['] series <NT>	*s.* S 616		
L 1183	**Lucas['] theorem** <FT>	Lucasscher Satz *m*	théorème *m* de Lucas	теорема Люка́
L 1184	**Luchterhand['s] theorem** <EG>	Luchterhandscher Satz *m*	théorème *m* de Luchterhand	теорема Люхтерханда
	Ludolphian number <AN, GE>	*s.* N 804		
	Ludolph['s] number <AN, GE>	*s.* N 804		
L 1185	**Lukacs['s] theorem** <ST>	Satz *m* von Lukacs, Lukacsscher Satz	théorème *m* de Lukacs	теорема Лукача
L 1186	**Łukasiewicz['s] algebra** <LO>	Łukasiewiczsche Algebra *f*	algèbre *f* de Łukasiewicz, algèbre łukasiewiczienne	алгебра Лукасевича
L 1187	**Łukasiewicz['s] notation,** Polish notation, Polish parenthesis-free notation <LO>	klammerfreie Schreibweise *f* nach Łukasiewicz, Łukasiewiczsche klammerfreie Schreibweise	notation *f* polonaise (de Łukasiewicz)	бесскобочная символика в логической системе Я. Лукасевича

No.	English	German	French	Russian
L 1188	**lune,** biangle, spherical lune (digon), gore <EG>	Zweieck *n*, Mond *m*, Möndchen *n*, sphärisches Zweieck, Kugelzweieck *n*	fuseau *m*, lunule *f*, biangle *m*, fuseau sphérique	двуугольник, луночка, лунка, сферический двуугольник, [сферическая] долька
L 1189	**Lüneburg plane** <GE>	Lüneburg-Ebene *f*	plan *m* de Lüneburg	плоскость Люнебурга
	lunula Hippokratis (of Hippocrates) <EG>	*s.* H 370		
L 1190	**Lüroth['s] theorem** <AL>	Satz *m* von Lüroth, Lürothscher Satz *m*	théorème *m* de Lüroth	теорема Люрота
L 1191	**Lusin['s] condition** <ME, RF>	Lusinsche Bedingung *f* (N)	condition *f* de Lusin	условие Лузина
L 1192	**Lusin-Denjoy theorem** <SS>	Lusin-Denjoyscher Satz *m*, Satz von Lusin-Denjoy	théorème *m* de Lusin-Denjoy	теорема Лузина-Данжуа
L 1193	**Lusin-Privalov theorem** <FT>	Satz *m* von Lusin und Priwalow, Satz von Luzin und Privalov, Lusin-Priwalowscher Satz	théorème *m* de Lusin et Privalov (Privaloff)	теорема Лузина-Привалова
L 1194	**Lusin['s] sieve** <SE>	Lusinsches Sieb *n*	crible *m* de Lusin	решето Лузина
L 1195	**Lusin['s] space** <TO>	Lusinscher Raum *m*	espace *m* de Lusin, espace lusinien	пространство Лузина
L 1196	**Lusin['s] theorem,** theorem of Lusin <ME>	Lusinscher Satz *m*, Satz von Lusin	théorème *m* de Lusin	теорема Лузина
	Lyusternik-Schnirelman[n] category <TO>	*s.* C 205		

M

No.	English	German	French	Russian
M 1	**Macaulay['s] ring, Macaulay-Cohen ring,** Cohen-Macaulay ring, semi-regular ring, U-ring <AL>	Macaulay-Ring *m*, Cohen-Macaulay-Ring *m*	anneau *m* de Cohen-Macaulay	кольцо Коэна-Маколея
M 2	**Mac-Cay['s] cubic** <AG>	Mac-Caysche Kubik *f*	cubique *f* de Mac-Cay	кривая Мак-Кэя
M 3	**MacCullagh['s] theorem** <for the ellipse> <EG>	MacCullaghscher Satz *m*	théorème *m* de MacCullagh	теорема Маккаллега
M 4	**Macdonald['s] (MacDonald['s]) function,** Mcdonald['s] function, modified Hankel function, modified [cylindrical] Bessel function of the second kind, Basset['s] function <of order ν> <FU>	modifizierte Hankel-Funktion *f*, Macdonald-Funktion *f*, Mcdonald-Funktion *f*, Macdonaldsche Funktion *f*, Bassetsche Funktion *f*, Basset-Funktion *f*, modifizierte Bessel-Funktion *f* zweiter Art [mit nichtganzzahligem rein imaginärem Argument] <der Ordnung ν>	fonction *f* de Macdonald, fonction de Basset, fonction de Bessel modifiée de seconde espèce <d'indice ν>	функция Макдональда, функция Бассета, модифицированная функция Бесселя второго рода, модифицированная цилиндрическая (бесселева) функция второго (2-го) рода <порядка ν>
M 5	**machine computation (computing)** <NU>	Maschinenrechnen *n*	calcul *m* à la machine	машинный расчет, машинное вычисление
M 6	**Mackey-Arens theorem** <TO>	Theorem *n* (Satz *m*) von Mackey-Arens, Mackey-Arens-Theorem *n*	théorème *m* de Mackey-Arens [bornologique]	теорема Макки-Аренса
M 7	**Mackey-closed set,** set closed in the Mackey topology, (M)-closed set <TO>	Mackey-abgeschlossene Menge *f*	ensemble *m* Mackey-fermé, ensemble M-fermé, ensemble bornologiquement fermé	множество, замкнутое в топологии Макки; (М)-замкнутое множество
M 8	**Mackey['s] theorem** <FA>	Satz *m* von Mackey, Mackeyscher Satz	théorème *m* de Mackey	теорема Макки
M 9	**Mackey['s] toplogy** <FA, TO>	Mackey-Topologie *f*, Mackeysche Topologie *f*	topologie *f* de Mackey	топология Макки
M 10	**MacLane['s] category** <CA>	MacLanesche Kategorie *f*	catégorie *f* de MacLane	маклейнова категория
	Maclaurin-Cauchy test <SS>	*s.* 1. C 248; 2. C 259		
M 11	**Maclaurin['s] expansion;** Maclaurin['s] series, Stirling['s] formula <DI>	Maclaurinsche Entwicklung *f*, Maclaurin-Entwicklung *f*, Entwicklung in eine Maclaurinsche Reihe; Maclaurinsche Reihe *f*, // MacLaurinsche Reihe	développement *m* [en série] de Maclaurin; série *f* de Maclaurin, // série de Mac-Laurin	разложение [в ряд] Маклорена; ряд Маклорена
M 12	**Maclaurin['s] formula,** tangent formula, midpoint formula, tangent-trapezoid[al] formula, Maclaurin['s] rule, tangent rule (method), tangent-trapezoid[al] rule (method) <DI, NU>	Tangententrapezregel *f*, Tangentenregel *f*, Tangententrapezformel *f*, Tangentenformel *f*, Maclaurinsche Formel (Regel) *f*, Maclaurinsche Quadraturformel *f*, Tangententrapezmethode *f*, Tangentenmethode *f*	formule *f* de Maclaurin, formule des tangentes, formule du point central, règle (méthode) *f* des tangentes	формула касательных (Маклорена), правило касательных (Маклорена), метод касательных (Маклорена)
M 13	**Maclaurin['s] formulae** <DI, NU>	Maclaurinsche Quadraturformeln *fpl*	formules *fpl* de Maclaurin	формулы Маклорена
	Maclaurin['s] rule <DI, NU>	*s.* M 12		
	Maclaurin['s] series <DI>	*s.* M 11		
	Maclaurin['s] tetrad <AG>	*s.* T 228		

M 14	**Maclaurin['s] theorem** <on Maclaurin's expansion> <DI>	Satz *m* von Maclaurin, Maclaurinscher Satz	théorème *m* de Maclaurin	теорема Маклорена
	Maclaurin['s] trisectrix <GE>	*s.* T 984		
	MacNeille['s] completion <SE>	*s.* D 83		
M 15	**MacRobert['s] *E*-function,** *E*-function of MacRobert <FU>	*E*-Funktion *f* von MacRobert, MacRobertsche *E*-Funktion	*E*-fonction *f* de MacRobert	*E*-функция МакРоберта
M 16	**m-adic ring** <AL>	m-adischer Ring *m*	anneau *m* m-adique	m-адическое кольцо
M 17	**magic circle** <CT>	magischer Kreis *m*	cercle *m* magique	магический круг
M 18	**magic cube** <CT>	magischer Würfel *m*, Zauberwürfel *m*	cube *m* magique	магический куб
M 19	**magic figure** <CT>	magische Figur *f*	figure *f* magique	магическая фигура
	magic latin square <CT, ST>	*s.* L 114		
M 20	**magic square** <of order *n*> <CT>	magisches (vollmagisches) Quadrat *n*, Zauberquadrat *n*, Quadrat <von der Seite *n*, der Ordnung *n*>	carré *m* magique <de *n*, du *n*-e ordre, de côté *n*>	магический (волшебный) квадрат <порядка *n*>
M 21	**magic square with compartments** <CT>	[magisches] Quadrat *n* mit Abteilen	carré *m* magique à compartiments	
M 22	**magic square with cross** <CT>	[magisches] Quadrat *n* mit Kreuz	carré *m* magique à croix	
M 23	**magic star** <CT>	magischer Stern *m*	étoile *f* magique	магическая звезда
	magic sum <CT>	*s.* R 1440		
M 24	**magnitude,** length, value, absolute value, modulus <of a vector>; Euclidean norm, norm <of a vector in R^n> <VT>	Betrag *m*, Länge *f*, absoluter Betrag, Modul *m*; euklidische Norm *f*, Norm	module *m*, magnitude *f*, mesure *f*, grandeur *f*, intensité *f*, valeur *f* absolue, tenseur *m*; norme *f* euclidienne, norme	модуль, длина, величина, абсолютная величина; евклидова норма, норма
	magnitude <AN>	*s.* A 131		
	magnitude <NU>	*s.* O 349		
M 25	**magnitude of the discontinuity** <of a distribution function> <ST>	Sprunghöhe *f*, Höhe *f* des Sprungs	magnitude *f* de la discontinuité	величина скачка
M 26	**Magnus['s] algebra** <AL>	Magnus-Algebra *f*, Magnussche Algebra *f*	algèbre *f* de Magnus	алгебра Магнуса
M 27	**Magnus['s] group** <GR>	Magnussche Gruppe *f*	groupe *m* de Magnus	группа Магнуса
	Magnus['s] theorem <GR>	*s.* T 318		
M 28	**Mahalanobis['] [generalized] distance** <ST>	Mahalanobisscher Abstand *m*, verallgemeinerter Abstand von Mahalanobis, verallgemeinerter Abstand [nach Mahalanobis], Mahalanobis' D^2 *n*, D^2-Maßzahl *f* von Mahalanobis	distance *f* de Mahalanobis, distance généralisée de Mahalanobis	расстояние Махаланобиса, обобщенное расстояние Махаланобиса
M 29	**Mahler['s] classification** <NT>	Mahlersche Klassifikation *f*, Mahlersche Klasseneinteilung *f*	classification *f* de Mahler	классификация Малера, малеровская классификация чисел
M 30	**Mahler['s] conjecture** <NT>	Mahlersche Vermutung *f*	hypothèse *f* de Mahler	гипотеза Малера
M 31	**Mahler['s] inequalities** <GU>	Mahlersche Ungleichungen *fpl*	inégalités *fpl* de Mahler	неравенства Малера
M 32	**Mahler['s] selection theorem,** selection theorem of Mahler <GU>	Mahlerscher Auswahlsatz *m*	théorème *m* de sélection de Mahler	теорема выбора Малера
	Mainardi-Codazzi equations (relations) <DG>	*s.* C 1003		
	Mainardi['s] equations <DG>	*s.* C 1003		
M 33	**main branch,** track, branch <of a tree> <GP>	Ast *m* <von *P* entspringender>, Zweig *m*	branche *f*	ветвь
M 34	**main diagonal,** leading (principal, major) diagonal, diagonal <of a matrix> <MD>	Hauptdiagonale *f*; Hauptschräge *f*	diagonale *f* principale, grande diagonale, diagonale	главная диагональ, первая диагональ
	main diagonal sum <MD>	*s.* T 712		
	main homomorphism theorem <GR>	*s.* H 505		
M 35	**main involution** <of a Clifford algebra> <AL>	Hauptinvolution *f*	automorphisme *m* principal; involution *f* principale <d'une algèbre graduée>	главная инволюция
	main test <SS>	*s.* F 855		
	main value <AN>	*s.* C 260		
M 36	**majorant,** majorant function <AN>	Majorantenfunktion *f*, Majorante *f* <einer Funktion>	majorante *f*, fonction *f* majorante	мажорантная функция, мажоранта, мажорирующая функция
	majorant <SE>	*s.* U 411		
	majorant <SS>	*s.* M 37		
	majorant criterion <FT, SS>	*s.* C 1327		
	majorant function <AN>	*s.* M 36		
M 37	**majorant series,** majorant <SS>	Majorante *f*, Majorantenreihe *f*, Oberreihe *f*	série *f* majorante, majorante *f*, série dominante	превосходящий (мажорантный, мажорирующий, доминирующий) ряд

M 38	**major axis** <of an ellipse> <AY>	große Achse *f*, Hauptachse *f*; Länge *f* der Hauptachse (großen Achse)	grand axe *m*, axe principal	большая ось, главная ось
	major diagonal <MD>	*s.* M 34		
M 39	**majority decision element** <LO, TA>	Schwellenwertelement *n*	élément *m* à seuil	пороговый элемент
M 40	**majority decision function**, threshold function <LO, TA>	Schwellenfunktion *f*, Schwellenwertfunktion *f*	fonction *f* de seuil, fonction majorité	пороговая функция
M 41	**majority function** <AL>	Majoritätsfunktion *f*	fonction *f* de majorité, fonction de quorum	функция большинства, мажоритарная функция
M 42	**majority game** <TG>	Majoritätsspiel *n*	jeu *m* majoritaire	мажоритарная игра
M 43	**majority logic** <TA>	Mehrheitslogik *f*	logique *f* majoritaire	мажоритарная логика
	majorizable series <SS>	*s.* M 48		
M 44	**majorizable set** <of almost periodic functions> <AP>	majorisierbare Menge *f*	ensemble *m* majoré	мажорируемое множество
	majorization <AN, AX, ER>	*s.* M 49		
M 45	**majorize / to**, to dominate <a series> <SS>	majorisieren <eine Reihe>	majorer <une série>	мажорировать <ряд>
M 46	**majorized chain** <SE>	nach oben beschränkte Kette *f*	chaine *f* majorée	мажорированная цепь
	majorized ordered set <SE>	*s.* B 664		
M 47	**majorized sequence**, sequence with summable majorant <FA>	Folge *f* mit summierbarer Majorante	suite *f* majorée	последовательность с суммируемой мажорантой
	majorized sequence <SS>	*s.* B 665		
M 48	**majorized series**, dominated series, majorizable series <SS>	majorisierte Reihe *f*, majorisierbare Reihe	série *f* majorée	мажорируемый ряд
M 49	**majorizing**, majorization, upper estimate <AN, AX, ER>	Majorisierung *f*, Abschätzung *f* nach oben	majoration *f*	мажорирование, оценка сверху
M 50	**majorizing set** <AP>	majorisierende Menge *f*	ensemble *m* majorant	мажорирующее множество
M 51	**major premise** <in a categorial syllogism, the premise that contains the major term> <LO>	praemissa *f* major	majeure *f*	бóльшая (главная) посылка
	major rearrangement theorem <SS>	*s.* C 275		
M 52	**major star**, barycentric star dual to a vertex <AT>	baryzentrischer Stern *m* eines Eckpunkts	étoile *f* barycentrique duale au sommet	главная (барицентрическая) звезда, сопряженная вершине
M 53	**major term** <in a categorical syllogism, the term that is the predicate of the conclusion> <LO>	terminus *m* major	majeur *m*, grand terme *m*	бóльший термин
M 54	**major theorem of Desargues** <GE>	großer Desarguesscher Satz *m*	théorème *m* général de Desargues	великая теорема Дезарга
	make well-ordered / to <SE>	*s.* W 209		
M 55	**Malcev['s] algebra**, Mal'tsev['s] algebra <AL>	Malcev-Algebra *f*, Malzew-Algebra *f*, M-L-Algebra *f*	algèbre *f* de Malcev	алгебра Мальцева
M 56	**Malcev['s] condition** <GR>	Malcev-Bedingung *f*, Malzew-Bedingung *f*, Bedingung *f* von Malzew	condition *f* de Malcev	условие Мальцева, постулат Мальцева
M 57	**Malcev['s] module** <AL>	Malcev-Modul *m*, Malzew-Modul *m*	module *m* de Malcev	модуль Мальцева
M 58	**Malfatti['s] problem** <EG>	Malfattische Aufgabe (Berührungsaufgabe) *f*	problème *m* de Malfatti	проблема Малфати
M 59	**Malmquist['s] theorem** <DE>	Satz *m* von Malmquist, Malmquistscher Satz	théorème *m* de Malmquist	теорема Мальмквиста
M 60	**mal-posed problem**, non-well posed problem, ill (improperly) posed problem <for a partial differential equation> <DE>	unsachgemäßes (inkorrekt gestelltes) Problem *n*	problème *m* mal (incorrectement) posé	некорректно (неправильно) поставленная задача, некорректная (неточная) задача
	Mal'tsev['s] algebra <AL>	*s.* M 55		
M 61	**manifold**, variety <*e.g.*: of class *r*> <AG, DG, TO>	Mannigfaltigkeit *f* <*z. B.*: der Klasse *r*>	variété *f* <*par exemple*: de classe *r*>, // multiplicité *f*	многообразие <*например*: класса *r*>
	manifold <AT>	*s.* P 955		
	manifold <SE>	*s.* S 637		
	2-manifold <GE>	*s.* S 2355		
M 62	**manifold classification**, multiple classification <ST>	mehrfache Klassifikation *f*, Mehrfachklassifikation *f*	classification *f* multiple (à plusieurs entrées)	множественная классификация
M 63	**manifold embeddable without singularities** <GE>	singularitätenfrei einbettbare Mannigfaltigkeit *f*	variété *f* plongeable sans singularités	неособо вложимое многообразие; многообразие, вложимое без особенностей
	manifold free from singularities <AG>	*s.* V 83		
M 64	**manifold of flags**, flag manifold <in C_q> <DG>	Fahnenmannigfaltigkeit *f*, Flaggenmannigfaltigkeit *f*, Mannigfaltigkeit *f* der <in C_q situierten> Fahnen	variété *f* de drapeaux <en C_q>; variété des Borels	многообразие флагов, пространство флагов <в C_q>
M 65	**manifold of ∞^1 sliding vectors** <GE, VT>	Stabfläche *f*	variété *f* de ∞^1 vecteurs glissants	многообразие ∞^1 скользящих векторов
M 66	**manifold of ∞^2 sliding vectors** <GE, VT>	Stabkongruenz *f*	variété *f* de ∞^2 vecteurs glissants	многообразие ∞^2 скользящих векторов

M 67	**manifold of ∞^3 sliding vectors** <GE, VT>	Stabkomplex *m*	variété *f* de ∞^3 vecteurs glissants	многообразие ∞^3 скользящих векторов
M 68	**manifold of ∞^4 sliding vectors** <GE, VT>	Stabwald *m*	variété *f* de ∞^4 vecteurs glissants	многообразие ∞^4 скользящих векторов
M 69	**manifold of support** <CS, GE>	Stützmannigfaltigkeit *f*	variété *f* d'appui	опорное многообразие
M 70	**manifold without boundary** <TO>	unberandete Mannigfaltigkeit *f*	variété *f* sans bord	многобразие без края
M 71	**Mannheim['s] curve** <of the first *or* second kind *or* of a plane curve> <DG>	Mannheimsche Kurve *f* <erster (1.) *oder* zweiter (2.) Art *oder* einer ebenen Kurve>	courbe *f* de Mannheim <de première *ou* seconde espèce *ou* d'une courbe plane>	кривая Мангейма (Манхейма) <первого *или* второго рода *или* плоской кривой>
M 72	**Mannheim['s] formula** <for the distribution parameter> <DG>	Mannheimsche Formel *f*, Formel von Mannheim <für den Drall>	formule *f* de Mannheim <pour le paramètre de distribution>	формула Мангейма (Манхейма) <для параметра распределения>
M 73	**Mannheim['s] theorem** <DG>	Mannheimscher Satz *m*, Satz von [A.] Mannheim	théorème *m* de Mannheim	теорема Мангейма (Манхейма)
M 74	**Mann['s] *k*-test** <ST>	Manns *k*-Test *m*, Mannscher *k*-Test	test *m k* de Mann	*k*-критерий Манна
M 75	**Mann['s] theorem** <AB>	Mannscher Satz *m*	théorème *m* de Mann	теорема Манна
	Mann-Whitney statistic <ST>	*s.* U 461		
	Mann-Whitney test <ST>	*s.* W 257		
	MANOVA <ST>	*s.* M 1087		
M 76	**mantissa** <of a logarithm> <AR>	Mantisse *f*	mantisse *f*, partie *f* décimale	мантисса
M 77	**manydimensional problem of Diophantine approximation** <NT>	mehrdimensionales Problem *n* der diophantischen Approximation	problème *m* multidimensionnel d'approximation diophantienne	многомерная задача диофантова приближения
	many-dimensional space <GE>	*s.* M 957		
	manyness <SE>	*s.* C 123		
	many-one correspondence <SE>	*s.* S 1042		
M 78	**many-one reducible set** <FO>	mehr-ein-reduzible Menge *f*		много-односводимое множество
	many-one relation <SE>	*s.* S 1042		
	many-place[d] predicate <LO>	*s.* M 891		
	many-place predicate calculus <LO>	*s.* C 28		
M 79	**many-sheeted surface** <FT, TO>	mehrblättrige (vielblättrige) Fläche *f*	surface *f* à plusieurs feuilles	многолистная поверхность
	many-sorted elementary logic <LO>	*s.* S 714		
M 80	**many-to-many mapping** <SE>	mehrmehrdeutige (vielvieldeutige) Abbildung *f*	application *f* multiforme dans les deux sens	много-многозначное (взаимно-многозначное) отображение
	many-to-one relation <SE>	*s.* S 1042		
M 81	**many-valued composition law** <SE>	mehrdeutiges Verknüpfungsgesetz *n*	loi *f* [de composition] multiforme	многозначный закон композиции
M 82	**many-valued disjunction** <LO>	mehrwertige Alternative *f*	disjonction *f* multi-valuée	многозначная дизъюнкция
M 83	**many-valued function,** multiple-valued function, multiple valued function <contrary to single-valued function> <AN>	mehrdeutige (nichteindeutige) Funktion *f*	fonction *f* multivoque (multivaluée, à déterminations multiples)	многозначная (неоднозначная) функция
	many-valued function <FT>	*s.* M 1083		
	many-valued function <SE>	*s.* M 85		
M 84	**many-valued logic[s],** multi-valued logic, multivalued logic <LO>	mehrwertige Logik *f*	logique *f* à plusieurs valeurs, logique plurivalente (polyvalente), calcul *m* plurivalent (multivalent, polyvalent)	многозначная логика
M 85	**many-valued mapping,** multi-valued mapping, many-valued function, multi[-]application, multifunction <SE>	mehrdeutige Abbildung (Funktion) *f*, Abbildung, vieldeutige Abbildung (Funktion)	multiapplication *f*, application *f* multivoque, application-multivoque *f*, correspondance *f* multivoque, représentation *f* non univoque, fonction *f* multivoque (multivalente)	многозначное отображение, многозначная функция
M 86	**many-valuedness,** multiple[-]valuedness <AN>	Mehrdeutigkeit *f*	multivocité *f*	многозначность
M 87	**many-valuedness** <LO>	Mehrwertigkeit *f*	multivalence *f*, plurivalence *f*	многозначность
M 88	**many-valuedness,** multivaluedness, multiple valuedness, multiple-valuedness <SE>	Mehrdeutigkeit *f*, Vieldeutigkeit *f*; Mehrwertigkeit *f*	multiformité *f*, multidromie *f*, multivocité *f*, multivalence *f*	многозначность
	many-valued operation <UA>	*s.* M 979		
M 89	**many-valued partial mapping** <of ... in ...> <SE>	mehrdeutige Abbildung *f* <aus ... in ...>	représentation *f* <de ... dans ...>	многозначное частичное отображение <... в ...>
M 90	**many-valued partial mapping of *E*, the image of which has greater cardinality than *E*** <SE>	mehrdeutige Abbildung *f* aus *E*, deren Bildmenge größere Mächtigkeit als *E* hat	*E*-explosion *f*	многозначное частичное отображение *E*, при котором мощность образа больше мощности *E*

No.	English	German	French	Russian
M 91	**many-valued partial mapping of *E*, the image of which has lower cardinality than *E*** <SE>	mehrdeutige Abbildung *f* aus *E*, deren Bildmenge kleinere Mächtigkeit als *E* hat	*E*-contraction *f*	многозначное частичное отображение *E*, при котором мощность образа меньше мощности *E*
M 92	**many-valued partial mapping of *E*, the image of which has lower cardinality than the range** <SE>	mehrdeutige Abbildung *f* aus *E*, bei der das Bild geringere Mächtigkeit als der Nachbereich hat	*E*-plongement *m*	многозначное частичное отображение *E*, при котором мощность образа меньше мощности противоположной области
M 93	**many-valued partial mapping of *E*, the image of which has the same cardinality as *E*** <SE>	mehrdeutige Abbildung *f* aus *E*, deren Bildmenge dieselbe Mächtigkeit hat wie *E*	*E*-injection *f*	многозначное частичное отображение *E*, при котором образ имеет одинаковую мощность как *E*
M 94	**many-valued partial mapping of *E*, the image of which has the same cardinality as the range** <SE>	mehrdeutige Abbildung *f* aus *E*, bei der die Mächtigkeit der Bildmenge gleich der Mächtigkeit des Nachbereichs ist	*E*-surjection *f*	многозначное частичное отображение *E*, при котором образ и противоположная область имеют одинаковую мощность
	map <AN, FA>	*s.* M 96		
	map <CA>	*s.* M 899		
	map <NO>	*s.* N 299		
	map <TO>	*s.* C 2227		
	ε-map <TO>	*s.* E 312		
M 95	**map-colouring problem** <GP>	Färbungsproblem *n* von Karten	problème *m* de coloration des cartes	задача о раскрашивании карт
	map induced by *k* <CA>	*s.* C 1723		
	map onto . . . <SE>	*s.* S 2378		
M 96	**mapping,** map, application, representation, correspondence; transformation; function; operator, abstract function <domain and codomain: a function or Hilbert space>; functional <codomain: a set of real or complex numbers> <AN, FA>	Abbildung *f*, Zuordnung *f*; Transformation *f*; Funktion *f*; Operator *m*, abstrakte Funktion; Funktional *n*	application *f*, représentation *f*; transformation *f*; fonction *f*; opérateur *m*, fonction abstraite, opératon *f*; fonctionnelle *f*	отображение, соответствие; преобразование; функция; оператор, абстрактная функция; функционал
M 97	**mapping,** transformation, [geometric] relation <GE>	Abbildung *f*, Transformation *f*, [geometrische] Verwandtschaft (Beziehung) *f*, geometrische Abhängigkeit *f*	application *f*, transformation *f*, relation *f* [géométrique], affinité *f*	отображение, преобразование, соответствие, [геометрическое] родство (соотношение)
	mapping <FA, TO>	*s.* C 2227		
	mapping <SE>	*s.* S 1037		
	mapping / into <SE>	*s.* M 103		
	1—1 mapping <SE>	*s.* I 548		
	ε-mapping <TO>	*s.* E 312		
	mapping by parallel normals <GE>	*s.* T 764		
M 98	**mapping cone** <AT>	Abbildungskegel *m*	cône *m* d'application	конус отображения
M 99	**mapping cylinder** <AT>	Abbildungszylinder *m*	cylindre *m* d'application, « mapping cylinder » *m*	цилиндр отображения
M 100	**mapping function,** transforming function <AN>	Abbildungsfunktion *f*	fonction *f* de transformation (représentation)	отображающая функция
M 101	**mapping function,** arrow function, function of representation <functor applied to morphisms> <CA>	Abbildungsfunktion *f*, Pfeilabbildung *f*	foncteur *m* appliqué aux morphismes	функтор, применяемый к морфизмам
	mapping homotopic to a constant <TO>	*s.* H 513		
M 102	**mapping in itself,** transformation <AN, SE, TO>	Abbildung *f* in sich, Selbstabbildung *f*, Transformation *f*	application *f* en soi, autofonction *f*, transformation *f*	отображение <множества> в себя, преобразование
	mapping in the large <SE>	*s.* G 307		
M 103	**mapping into . . .,** function to . . ., function into . . ., into mapping <SE>	Abbildung *f* in . . .	application *f* dans . . .	отображение в . . .
	1—1 mapping into <SE>	*s.* I 548		
M 104	**mapping norm,** norm of a linear mapping <FA>	Abbildungsnorm *f*, Norm *f* einer linearen Abbildung	norme *f* d'une application [linéaire]	норма [линейного] отображения
	mapping of bundles <TO>	*s.* B 797		
	mapping of *N* into *M* <SE>	*s.* I 589		
M 105	**mapping of sets** <SE>	Mengenabbildung *f*	application (transformation) *f* d'ensembles	отображение множеств
M 106	**mapping of the boundary** <FT>	Randabbildung *f*	application *f* de la frontière	отображение границы
M 107	**mapping on a slit-region** <FT>	Schlitzabbildung *f*	représentation *f* conforme sur un domaine muni de fentes	отображение на область с разрезами (надрезами)
	mapping onto . . . <SE>	*s.* S 2378		
	(1 — 1)-mapping onto <SE>	*s.* B 330		
M 108	**mapping onto a point** <SE>	Abbildung *f* auf einen Punkt	application *f* sur un point	нуль-отображение
	mapping radius <FT>	*s.* C 1904		
	mapping relation <SE>	*s.* S 1042		

M 109	**mapping satisfying a [global] Lipschitz condition,** transformation (function) satisfying a [global] Lipschitz condition, Lipschitz continuous mapping <AN, TO>	dehnungsbeschränkte Abbildung (Transformation, Funktion) *f*; Abbildung (Transformation, Funktion), die einer [globalen] Lipschitz-Bedingung genügt	application (transformation, fonction) *f* [globalement] lipschitzienne	отображение (преобразование), удовлетворяющее [глобальному] условию Липшица; функция, удовлетворяющая [глобальному] условию Липшица; отображение (преобразование), ограниченное при растяжении
M 110	**mapping satisfying a Lipschitz condition,** transformation (function) satisfying a Lipschitz condition <AN, TO>	Abbildung (Transformation, Funktion) *f*, die einerLipschitz-Bedingung <mit der Lipschitz-Konstanten k> genügt	application (transformation, fonction) *f* lipschitzienne <de rapport *k*>	отображение (преобразование), удовлетворяющее условию Липшица; функция, удовлетворяющая условию Липшица
	mapping satisfying a local Lipschitz condition <AN, TO>	*s.* L 983		
M 111	**mapping satisfying a punctual Lipschitz condition,** transformation (function) satisfying a punctual Lipschitz condition <AN, TO>	punktal dehnungsbeschränkte Abbildung (Transformation, Funktion) *f*; Abbildung (Transformation, Funktion), die einer punktalen Lipschitz-Bedingung genügt	application (transformation, fonction) *f* ponctuellement lipschitzienne	отображение (преобразование), удовлетворяющее точечному условию Липшица; функция, удовлетворяющая точечному условию Липшица
M 112	**mapping space,** function space <TO>	Abbildungsraum *m*, Raum *m* der stetigen Abbildungen <von X in Y>	espace *m* des applications	пространство отображений
M 113	**mapping transformation** <of fibre bundles> <AT>	Abbildungstransformation *f*	transformation *f* d'application	преобразование отображения
	mapping upon . . . <SE>	*s.* S 2378		
M 114	**Marcinkiewicz['s] space** <FA, NT>	Marcinkiewicz-Raum *m*	espace *m* de Marcinkiewicz	пространство Марцинкевича
M 115	**marginal density** <ST>	Randdichte *f*, Dichte *f* der Randverteilung	densité *f* marginale	краевая плотность
M 116	**marginal distribution** <ST>	Randverteilung *f*, Marginalverteilung *f*	distribution *f* marginale	маргинальное распределение, безусловное распределение <компоненты многомерной случайной величины>, граничное распределение
M 117	**marginal distribution density function,** density function of the marginal distribution <ST>	Randverteilungsdichte *f*	densité *f* de distribution marginale	плотность маргинального распределения
M 118	**marginal distribution function,** reduced distribution function <ST>	Randverteilungsfunktion *f*	fonction *f* de distribution (répartition) marginale	функция маргинального распределения; функция, определяющая маргинальное распределение; краевая функция распределения
M 119	**marginal subgroup** <GR>	marginale Untergruppe *f*	sous-groupe *m* marginal	маргинальная подгруппа
M 120	**marginal sum** <of a matrix> <MD>	Spalten- oder Zeilensumme *f*	somme *f* de colonne ou de ligne	сумма по столбцу или по строке
M 121	**marked ruler** <GE, IN>	normiertes Lineal *n*; Lineal mit Eichmaß	règle *f* graduée	нормированная линейка
M 122	**market [model]** <TG>	Marktmodell *n*	modèle *m* du marché	модель рынка
M 123	**marking off angles** <GE>	Winkelabtragung *f*, Abtragung *f* von Winkeln	transfert *m* d'angles	откладывание (отложение) углов
M 124	**marking off segments** <EG>	Streckenabtragung *f*, Abtragung *f* von Strecken	transfert *m* de segments	откладывание отрезков, отложение отрезков
	Markoff . . .	*s.* Markov . . .		
M 125	**Markov['s] chain** <of quadratic forms> <NT>	Markovsche Kette *f*	chaîne *f* markovienne	маркова цепочка
M 126	**Markov['s] chain** <SP>	Markovsche (Markowsche, Markoffsche) Kette *f*, Kette	chaîne *f* markovienne (de Markov), chaîne de Markoff	цепь Маркова
M 127	**Markov-computable function** <MM>	Markov-berechenbare Funktion *f*	fonction *f* calculable au sens de Markov	вычислимая по Маркову функция
M 128	**Markov['s] condition** <ST>	Markovsche Bedingung *f*	condition *f* de Markov	условие Маркова
M 129	**Markov['s] decision process,** Markovian decision process <PG, SP>	Markovscher Entscheidungsprozeß *m*	processus *m* des décisions markovien	процесс решения Маркова, марковский процесс решения
	Markov['s] distribution <ST>	*s.* P 920		
M 130	**Markov['s] equation** <ST>	Markovsche Gleichung *f*	équation *f* de Markov	уравнение Маркова
M 131	**Markov['s] formulas** <of numerical integration> <DI, NU>	Markovsche Formeln *fpl*, Formeln [der numerischen Integration] von Markov	formules *fpl* de Markov	формулы Маркова
M 132	**Markovian controllable process** <SP>	Markovscher steuerbarer Prozeß *m*	processus *m* markovien contrôlable	марковский управляемый процесс
M 133	**Markovian controlled process** <SP>	Markovscher gesteuerter Prozeß *m*	processus *m* markovien contrôlé	марковский управленный процесс
	Markovian decision process <PG, SP>	*s.* M 129		
	Markovian process <SP>	*s.* M 143		

M 134	**Markovian property,** Markov['s] property <SP>	Markovsche Eigenschaft *f*	propriété *f* markovienne	марковское свойство
	Markovian spectrum <AX, NU>	*s.* M 145		
	Markovian stochastic process <SP>	*s.* M 143		
M 135	**Markovian strategy** <SP>	Markovsche Strategie *f*	stratégie *f* markovienne	марковская стратегия
M 136	**Markov['s] inequality** <for polynomials> <AN>	Markovsche Ungleichung *f*; Ungleichung von A. A. Markov <für die 1. Ableitung>; Ungleichung von V. A. Markov <für die höheren Ableitungen>	inégalité *f* de Markov	неравенство Маркова
M 137	**Markov['s] inequality** <ST>	Markovsche Ungleichung *f* <in der Wahrscheinlichkeitsrechnung>	inégalité *f* de Markov	неравенство Маркова
M 138	**Markov-Kakutani theorem** <on fixed points of affine maps> <TO>	Fixpunktsatz *m* von Markov-Kakutani, Markov-Kakutanischer Fixpunktsatz	théorème *m* de Markov-Kakutani	теорема Маркова-Какутани
M 139	**Markov['s] matrix** <ST>	Markovsche Matrix *f*	matrice *f* markovienne	марковская матрица
M 140	**Markov['s] minimal form** <GU>	Markovsche Minimalform *f*	forme *f* minimale de Markov	минимальная форма Маркова
	Markov['s] normal algorithm <FO>	*s.* N 536		
M 141	**Markov['s] number** <NT>	Markovsche Zahl *f*	nombre *m* de Markov	число Маркова
M 142	**Markov['s] period** <of a continued fraction> <NT>	Markovsche Periode *f*	période *f* de Markov	период Маркова
M 143	**Markov['s] process,** Markovian [stochastic] process <of *m*-th order> <SP>	Markovscher Prozeß (stochastischer Prozeß *m*, Markowscher (Markoffscher) Prozeß <*m*-ter Ordnung>	processus *m* de Markov, processus markovien (marcovien, de Markoff) <d'ordre *m*>	марковский процесс, марковский стохастический процесс <*m*-го порядка>
M 144	**Markov['s] process with homogeneous increments** <SP>	Markovscher Prozeß *m* mit homogenen Zuwächsen	processus *m* markovien avec incréments homogènes	процесс Маркова с однородными приращениями
	Markov['s] property <SP>	*s.* M 134		
M 145	**Markov['s] spectrum,** Markovian spectrum <AX, NU>	Markov-Spektrum *n*	spectre *m* de Markov	спектр Маркова
M 146	**Markov-Stieltjes inequality** <FU>	Markov-Stieltjessche Ungleichung *f*	inégalité *f* de Markov-Stieltjes	неравенство Маркова-Стилтьеса
M 147	**Markov['s] theorem** <ST>	Satz *m* von [A. A.] Markov, Markovscher Satz	théorème *m* de Markov	теорема Маркова
	Markov['s] theorem <ST>	*s. a.* G 95		
	Markov['s] time <SP>	*s.* S 1826		
M 148	**Markov['s] transform[ation]** <SS>	Markovsche Reihentransformation *f*	transformation *f* de Markov	преобразование Маркова
M 149	**marriage problem,** dancing problem <CT>	Heiratsproblem *n*	problème *m* de mariage	задача о выборе
M 150	**Martin['s] boundary** <PO>	Martinscher Rand *m*	frontière *f* de [R. S.] Martin	граница Мартина
M 151	**martingale** <SP>	Martingal *n*	martingale *f*	мартингал
M 152	**Martos['s] algorithm,** algorithm of Martos<PG>	Algorithmus *m* von Martos, Martos-Algorithmus *m*	algorithme *m* de Martos	алгоритм Мартоша
M 153	**Martus['s] formula** <EG>	Martussche Formel *f*	formule *f* de Martus	формула Мартуса
	Mascheroni['s] constant <FU>	*s.* E 579		
M 154	**Maschke['s] theorem** <DG, GR>	Satz *m* von [H.] Maschke, Maschkescher Satz	théorème *m* de Maschke	теорема Машке
M 155	**master sample,** general purpose sample <ST>	Primärstichprobe *f*	échantillon *m* principal	выборка для будущих подвыборок
M 156	**matched pairs** <ST>	gepaarte Werte *mpl*	valeurs *fpl* appariées	сходные пары
M 157	**matching,** packing <GP>	Verkettung *f*, Paarung *f*, Matching *n* <Kantenmenge so, daß keine zwei Kanten daraus benachbart sind>	couplage *m*	паросочетание
M 158	**"matching pennies"** <TG>	Zahl- oder Wappenspiel *n*	jeu *m* de pile ou face	игра в «орлянку», игра в орла и решку
M 159	**matching theorems** <for bipartite graphs> <GP>	Matchingtheoreme *npl*, „matching"-Theoreme *npl*	théorèmes *mpl* de couplage	теоремы паросочетания
M 160	**material equivalence,** truth-functional biconditional, equivalence, biconditional <LO>	materiale Äquivalenz *f*, Bisubjunktion *f*, Bijunktion *f*, Äquivalenz	équivalence *f* matérielle, biconditionnel *m*	материальная эквивалентция
M 161	**material implication,** implication in the material sense, implication in material meaning, implication, truth-functional conditional, conditional, seq, $\Rightarrow$, $\rightarrow$ <LO>	materiale (alternäre) Implikation *f*, Implikation, Subjunktion, seq, $\Rightarrow$, $\rightarrow$	implication *f* matérielle (formelle), seq, $\Rightarrow$, $\rightarrow$	материальная импликация, seq, $\Rightarrow$, $\rightarrow$
	material non-equivalence <LO>	*s.* E 687		
	material non-implication <LO>	*s.* N 406		

	English	German	French	Russian
M 162	**material operator** <LO>	materialer Operator *m* <Lewis>	opérateur *m* matériel	материальный оператор
M 163	**material relation** <between propositions> <LO>	materiale Relation *f* <Lewis>	relation *f* matérielle	материальное отношение
M 164	**mathematical analysis,** analysis <AN>	Analysis *f*	analyse *f* [mathématique]	математический анализ
	mathematical antinomy <LO>	*s.* L 1068		
	mathematical expectation <ST>	*s.* E 719		
M 165	**mathematical induction,** induction, complete induction, method of induction, method of complete induction <FO>	vollständige Induktion *f*, Methode *f* der vollständigen Induktion	induction *f* complète, récurrence, méthode *f* de l'induction complète, méthode d'induction complète	математическая индукция, полная [математическая] индукция, совершенная (бесконечная) индукция, метод математической (полной, совершенной) индукции
	mathematical inversion <GE>	*s.* I 972		
M 166	**mathematical logic,** modern (symbolic, symbolical) logic, // logistics <LO>	mathematische (theoretische, symbolische) Logik *f*, Logistik *f*	logique *f* mathématique (symbolique), // logistique *f*	математическая (символическая, теоретическая) логика, // логистика
M 167	**mathematical model** <PG>	mathematisches Modell *n*, mathematisch-analytisches Modell	modèle *m* mathématique	математическая модель
M 168	**mathematical object** <GN>	mathematisches Objekt *n*	être (objet) *m* mathématique	математический объект
	mathematical paradox <LO>	*s.* L 1068		
M 169	**mathematical procedure,** method of calculation <GN, NU>	Rechengang *m*, Rechnungsgang *m*	procédé *m* mathématique, méthode *f* de calcul	ход расчета, ход решения
M 170	**mathematical programming,** programming, optimization <PG>	Optimierung *f*, Programmoptimierung *f*, mathematische Optimierung (Programmoptimierung), // [mathematische] Programmierung *f*, [mathematisches] Programmieren *n*	programmation *f* [mathématique], programmation optimum, optimisation *f*	математическое программирование, программирование, оптимальное программирование, оптимизация
M 171	**mathematical rigor,** rigor <GN>	mathematische Strenge *f*, Strenge	rigueur *f* mathématique, rigueur	математическая строгость, строгость
	mathematical ruler <GE, IN>	*s.* R 1518		
	mathematical theory of communication <ST>	*s.* I 512		
	Mathieu['s] canonical transformation <DE, VA>	*s.* M 177		
M 172	**Mathieu['s] [differential] equation** <DE>	Mathieusche (Webersche) Differentialgleichung *f*, Differentialgleichung [der Funktionen] des elliptischen Zylinders	équation *f* [différentielle] de Mathieu, équation [différentielle] des fonctions du cylindre elliptique	уравнение Матье, дифференциальное уравнение Матье
M 173	**Mathieu['s] function,** function of the elliptic cylinder, elliptic cylinder function <FU>	Mathieusche Funktion *f*, Funktion des elliptischen Zylinders, elliptische Zylinderfunktion *f*	fonction *f* de Mathieu, fonction du cylindre elliptique	функция Матье, функция эллиптического цилиндра
	Mathieu function <FU>	*s.* P 455		
M 174	**Mathieu['s] function of imaginary argument** <FU>	Mathieusche Funktion *f* mit rein imaginärem Argument	fonction *f* de Mathieu d'argument imaginaire	функция Матье чисто мнимого аргумента
	Mathieu function of the first kind <FU>	*s.* P 455		
M 175	**Mathieu['s] function of the second kind;** fe; ge <FU>	Mathieusche Funktion *f* zweiter Art, Mathieusche Funktion [ganzer Ordnung] der zweiten Art; fe; ge	fonction *f* de Mathieu de la deuxième espèce; fe; ge	функция Матье второго рода; fe; ge
M 176	**Mathieu['s] group** <GR>	Mathieusche Gruppe *f*, fünffach transitive Gruppe von Mathieu	groupe *m* de Mathieu	группа Матье
M 177	**Mathieu['s] transformation,** Mathieu['s] canonical transformation, homogeneous canonical transformation, canonical transformation of Mathieu <DE, VA>	homogene kanonische Transformation *f*, homogene Berührungstransformation *f*, Mathieusche kanonische Transformation, Mathieusche Transformation	transformation *f* canonique homogène, transformation canonique de Mathieu	однородное каноническое преобразование, каноническое преобразование Матье, преобразование Матье
	matric algebra <AL>	*s.* M 182		
M 178	**matricial antirepresentation** <RE>	reziproke Matrizendarstellung *f*	anti-représentation *f* matricielle	матричное антипредставление
M 179	**matricial rank** <of a ring> <AL>	Matrizenrang *m*	rang *m* matriciel	матричный ранг
	matricial representation <AL>	*s.* M 208		
	matricial representation <GR>	*s.* M 210		
	matric notation <GN>	*s.* M 198		
M 180	**matrix,** array <AL>	Matrix *f*, // System *n*	matrice *f*, tableau *m*, // système *m*	матрица
M 181	**matrix,** quantifier-free portion <of a prenex	Kern *m* <einer pränexen Normalform>	partie *f* sans quantificateurs <d'une formule prénexe>	матрица <для формулы в пренексной форме>,

No.	English	German	French	Russian
and still:	formula> <LO>			бескванторная часть <предваренной формулы>
M 181	**matrix** <AL, LO>	*s.* L 1066		
	matrix <MD>	*s.* S 1558		
	λ-matrix <AL>	*s.* P 999		
	matrix / 1-by-*n* <MD>	*s.* N 65		
M 182	**matrix algebra,** matric algebra <of finite *or* infinite order> <AL>	Matrizenalgebra *f*, Matrixalgebra *f* <endlicher *oder* unendlicher Ordnung>	algèbre *f* matricielle, algèbre de matrices <d'ordre fini *ou* infini>	матричная алгебра, алгебра матриц <конечного *или* бесконечного порядка>
M 183	**matrix algebra** <as a theory> <MD>	Matrizenalgebra *f*	algèbre *f* des matrices, algèbre matricielle	алгебра матриц
M 184	**matrix analysis** <as a theory> <MD>	Matrizenanalysis *f*	analyse *f* matricielle	матричный анализ
M 185	**matrix calculation (calculus),** matrix theory <MD>	Matrizenrechnung *f*, Matrizenkalkül *m*, Matrizentheorie *f*	calcul *m* matriciel (de matrices), calcul des matrices, analyse *f* matricielle, théorie *f* des matrices	матричное исчисление, исчисление матриц, теория матриц
M 186	**matrix congruent in the hermitian sense,** conjunctive matrix <MD>	hermitesch kongruente Matrix *f*, hermitesch-kongruente Matrix, hermitesch äquivalente Matrix, konjunktive Matrix	matrice *f* hermitiquement congruente	эрмитово-конгруэнтная матрица
M 187	**matrix decomposed into diagonal blocks,** blocked diagonal matrix, quasi-diagonal matrix <MD>	zerfallende (quasidiagonale) Matrix *f*, verallgemeinerte Diagonalmatrix *f*, Stufenmatrix *f*, [vollständig] zerfallende quadratische Matrix	matrice *f* quasi-diagonale (quasi diagonale, diagonale par blocs, diagonale de matrices)	квазидиагональная (клеточно-диагональная, распавшаяся, обобщенная диагональная) матрица
M 188	**matrix equation** <AL>	Matrizengleichung *f*	équation *f* matricielle	матричное уравнение (равенство)
M 189	**matrix form** <AL>	Matrixgestalt *f*, Matrixform *f*, Matrizenform *f*	forme *f* d'une matrice, forme matricielle	матричная форма
M 190	**matrix function** <AL, AN>	Matrixfunktion *f*	fonction *f* matricielle	матричная функция
M 191	**matrix game,** $m \times n$ game <TG>	Matrixspiel *n*, $m \times n$-Spiel *n*	jeu *m* matriciel, jeu $m \times n$	матричная игра, $m \times n$-игра
M 192	**matrix group,** group of matrices <GR>	Matrizengruppe *f*	groupe *m* de matrices, groupe matriciel	группа матриц, матричная группа
M 193	**matrix having in each line and in each row at most one non-vanishing element** <MD> ┌<AL>	solitäre Matrix *f*	matrice *f* contenant dans chaque ligne et colonne au plus un élément non nul	матрица, имеющая в каждом столбце и в каждой строке не более одного отличного от нуля элемента
	matrix in Jordan form	*s.* J 94		
M 194	**matrix inversion,** inversion <of a matrix> <MD>	Matrixinversion *f*, Matrizenumkehrung *f*, Inversion *f*, Umkehrung *f* <einer Matrix>, Bestimmung *f* der Kehrmatrix	inversion *f* <d'une matrice>	обращение матрицы
M 195	**matrix method** <LI>	Matrixverfahren *n*	méthode *f* matricielle	матричный метод
M 196	**matrix norm,** norm <of a matrix> <AL, MD, NU>	Matrixnorm *f*, Norm *f* <einer Matrix>	norme *f* <d'une matrice>	матричная норма, норма <матрицы>
M 197	**matrix norm** <FA>	Matrixnorm *f*	norme *f* matricielle	матричная норма
M 198	**matrix notation,** matric notation <GN>	Matrizenschreibweise *f*, Matrixschreibweise *f*	écriture *f* matricielle; langage *m* matriciel	матричная запись, матричное обозначение, запись в матричной форме
M 199	**matrix of coefficients,** matrix of the coefficients <GN>	Koeffizientenmatrix *f*	matrice *f* des coefficients	матрица коэффициентов
	matrix of degree *n* <MD>	*s.* N 723		
	matrix of eigenvectors <AL>	*s.* M 722		
	matrix of incidence <AT>	*s.* I 227		
	matrix of infinite order <MD>	*s.* I 464		
	matrix of matrices <MD>	*s.* H 703		
	matrix of moments <ST>	*s.* M 812		
	matrix of order $m \times n$ <MD>	*s.* M 285		
	matrix of $p \times p$ minors <MD>	*s.* P 2017		
M 200	**matrix of relations** <of a module> <AL>	Relationenmatrix *f*	matrice *f* des relations	матрица соотношений
	matrix of size *m* by *n* <MD>	*s.* M 285		
	matrix of solutions <FD>	*s.* S 1270		
	matrix of the coefficients <AL>	*s.* S 2511		
	matrix of the coefficients <GN>	*s.* M 199		
M 201/2	**matrix of the same dimension[s] (size)** <MD> ┌<AL>	Matrix *f* gleichen Typs (Formats), gleichartige Matrix	matrice *f* du même type (sorte)	матрица одинакового размера, однородная матрица
	matrix of the system	*s.* S 2511		
M 203	**matrix of the transformation,** transformation matrix, change of basis matrix, transition matrix <of a base transformation> <AL>	Transformationsmatrix *f*, Koeffizientenmatrix *f* <der Transformation>, Übergangsmatrix *f* <von einer Basis zu einer anderen>	matrice *f* de passage (transition) <d'une base à l'autre>	матрица преобразования (перехода) <при базисном преобразовании>

No.	English	German	French	Russian
M 204	**matrix operator** <FA>	Matrixoperator *m*	opérateur *m* matriciel, opération-matrice *f*	матричный оператор
M 205	**matrix polynomial** <AL>	Matrizenpolynom *n*	polynôme *m* matriciel	матричный полином (многочлен)
M 206	**matrix power series** <SS>	Matrizenpotenzreihe *f*	série *f* de puissances de matrices	матрично-степенной ряд, степенной ряд матриц
M 207	**matrix product** <MD>	Matrizenprodukt *n*; Produktmatrix *f*	produit *m* de matrices, produit matriciel; matrice *f* produit	произведение матриц, матричное произведение; матрица-произведение
	matrix reducible to a triangular matrix <MD>	*s.* T 907		
M 208	**matrix representation,** matricial representation, representation by matrices <of degree *n*> <of an algebra> <AL>	Matrizendarstellung *f*, Darstellung *f* durch Matrizen, Darstellung <*n*-ten Grades>	représentation *f* matricielle <de degré *n*>	матричное представление <степени *n*>
M 209	**matrix representation** <of an operator> <FA>	Matrixdarstellung *f*	représentation *f* matricielle	матричное представление
M 210	**matrix representation,** matricial representation <of degree *n*> <of a group> <GR>	Matrizendarstellung *f*, lineare Darstellung *f*, Darstellung <*n*-ten Grades>	représentation *f* matricielle <de degré *n*>	матричное представление <степени *n*>
	matrix ring <AL>	*s.* R 1327		
M 211	**matrix semigroup** <AL>	Matrizenhalbgruppe *f*	demi-groupe *m* de matrices	полугруппа матричного типа
M 212	**matrix series,** series of matrices <SS>	Matrizenreihe *f*, Reihe *f* von Matrizen	série *f* matricielle	матричный ряд
M 213/4	**matrix solution** <AL, AN>	Matrixlösung *f*	solution *f* matricielle	матричное решение
M 215	**matrix symmetric with respect to the secondary diagonal** <MD>	nebensymmetrische Matrix *f*, symmetrische Matrix in bezug auf die Nebendiagonale	matrice *f* symétrique par rapport à la seconde diagonale	матрица, симметричная относительно побочной диагонали
	matrix theory <MD>	*s.* M 185		
M 216	**matrix transformation** <FA>	Matrixtransformation *f*	transformation *f* matricielle	матричное преобразование
M 217	**matrix tree theorem** <GP>	Matrix-Gerüst-Satz *m*, Satz *m* von Kirchhoff-Trent, Kirchhoff-Trentscher Satz	théorème *m* de Kirchhoff-Trent	матричная теорема о деревьях, теорема Кирхгофа-Трента
M 218	**matrix unit, matrix-unit** <in a matrix ring> <AL>	Matrizeneinheit *f*, Matrixeinheit *f*, Matriceseinheit *f*	unité *f* matricielle	матричная единица
M 219	**matrix-valued** <AL>	matrixwertig	à valeurs matrices	матричнозначный
	matrix with dominating diagonal <MD>	*s.* H 13		
M 220/1	**matrix with elements in R** <AL> ⌐<MD>	Matrix *f* über *R*, Matrix mit Elementen in *R*	matrice *f* sur *R*, matrice à éléments dans *R*	матрица над *R*, матрица с элементами в *R*
M 222	**matrix with no entries**	leere Matrix *f*	matrice *f* vide	пустая матрица
M 223	**matrizant** <DE>	Matrizant *m*	matrizant *m*	матрицант
M 224	**matroid;** finite pregeometry <CT>	Matroid *n*	matroïde *m*, stigmier *m*; prégéométrie *f* finie	матроид
	matroid [lattice] <LA>	*s.* E 677		
	Maurer-Cartan equations <GR>	*s.* E 350/1		
	Maurer-Cartan form <GR>	*s.* F 484		
	maverick <ST>	*s.* N 469		
	max <DI, GN>	*s.* M 250		
M 225	**maximal** <VA>	Maximale *f*	maximale *f*	максималь
M 226	**maximal abelian extension,** maximum Abelian extension <of a field> <AL>	maximale abelsche Erweiterung *f*	clôture *f* abélienne, extension *f* abélienne maximale	максимальное абелево расширение
	maximal axiom <SE>	*s.* H 141		
M 227	**maximal chain,** connected chain <of a partially ordered set> <SE>	maximale (zusammenhängende, unverfeinerbare) Kette *f*, Hauptkette *f*, Hauptreihe *f*	chaîne *f* maximale, suite *f* normale	максимальная цепь, главный ряд
	maximal chain <LA, SE>	*s.* C 2026		
	maximal chain principle <SE>	*s.* H 141		
M 228	**maximal complete field** <AL>	maximal perfekter Körper *m*	corps *m* maximal et complet	максимальное полное поле
M 229	**maximal connected subgraph,** connected component, component <of a graph> <GP>	Komponente *f*, zusammenhängender Bestandteil *m*	sous-graphe *m* simplement connexe, composante *f* connexe, composante	компонента, связная компонента
	maximal degree <GP>	*s.* D 175		
M 230	**maximal deviation** <AX, NU>	maximale Abweichung *f*	écart *m* maximal	максимальное отклонение
M 231	**maximal element,** maximal member <SE>	maximales Element *n*	élément *m* maximal	максимальный элемент
M 232	**maximal equivalent order,** maximal order <of a ring> <AL>	Maximalordnung *f*	ordre *m* maximal, « Maximalordnung » *f*	максимальный порядок
M 233	**maximal Hermitian operator,** maximal symmetric operator, maximal operator <FA>	maximaler hermitescher (symmetrischer) Operator *m*, maximaler Operator, maximale hermitesche Transformation *f*	opérateur *m* maximal symétrique (hermitien), opérateur maximal, transformation *f* maximale symétrique	максимальный симметрический оператор, максимальный эрмитов оператор, максимальный оператор
M 234	**maximal ideal,** divisorless ideal <of a ring *or* lattice> <AL, LA>	maximales (teilerloses) Ideal *n*	idéal *m* maximal (sans diviseurs)	максимальный идеал

	English	German	French	Russian
M 235	**maximal ideal space** <AN, TO>	Raum *m* der maximalen Ideale	espace *m* des idéaux maximaux	пространство максимальных идеалов
M 236	**maximal index** <of a curve *or* surface> <DG>	Maximalindex *m*, Maximalklassenindex *m*	indice *m* maximal	максимальный индекс
	maximal invariant series <GR>	*s.* P 1472		
M 237	**maximality,** maximal property <GN>	Maximalität *f*, Maximaleigenschaft *f*	maximalité *f*, propriété *f* maximale	максимальность, свойство максимальности; свойство максимума
M 238	**maximal Lie submodule** <AL>	Modulnukleus *m* <maximaler Liescher Teilmodul>	sous-module *m* de Lie maximal	максимальный лиев подмодуль
M 239	**maximal matrix ring** <FA>	maximaler Matrizenring *m*	anneau *m* matriciel maximal	максимальное кольцо матриц
	maximal member <SE>	*s.* M 231		
M 240	**maximal normal divisor,** largest normal divisor <GR>	maximaler (größter) Normalteiler *m*, invariante Maximaluntergruppe *f*	sous-groupe *m* invariant (distingué) maximal, plus grand diviseur *m* normal, sous-groupe invariant maximé (maximum)	максимальный нормальный делитель, наибольший нормальный делитель
	maximal normal nilpotent subgroup <GR>	*s.* F 374		
	maximal operator <FA>	*s.* M 233		
	maximal order <AL>	*s.* M 232		
	maximal path-connected subspace <TO>	*s.* P 304		
	maximal periodic subgroup <GR>	*s.* T 608		
	maximal property <GN>	*s.* M 237		
M 241	**maximal R-order** <of a field> <AL>	*R*-Hauptordnung *f*, maximale *R*-Ordnung *f*	*R*-ordre *m* maximal	максимальный *R*-порядок
M 242	**maximal separable extension,** separable closure, separable algebraic closure, separable hull <of a field> <AL>	maximale separable Körpererweiterung *f*, separable (separabel-abgeschlossene, absolute separable) Hülle *f*, separabler Abschluß *m*	clôture (fermeture) *f* séparable	сепарабельное алгебраическое замыкание, сепарабельное замыкание, сепарабельная оболочка
M 243	**maximal strip** <of an almost periodic function> <AP>	Maximalstreifen *m*	bande *f* maximale	максимальная полос[к]а
	maximal symmetric operator <FA>	*s.* M 233		
M 244	**maximal tree [subgraph],** skeleton, scaffolding, spanning tree, tree <of a graph> <GP>	maximaler Baum *m*, Gerüst *n*, aufspannender Baum *m* <eines Graphen>; spannende Arboreszenz *f* <eines gerichteten Graphen>	arbre *m* maximal	покрывающее дерево, остов, остовное дерево, каркас, максимальное дерево
M 245	**maximal type** <of a meromorphic function> <FT>	Maximaltypus *m*, Maximaltyp *m*	type *m* maximal	максимальный тип
	maximal unramified abelian extension <AB>	*s.* A 59		
	maximal valency <GP>	*s.* D 175		
	maximal value <DI, GN>	*s.* M 250		
M 246	**maximant** <VA>	Maximante *f*	maximante *f*	максиманта
M 247	**maximin** <PG, TG>	Maximin *n*, Maxmin *n*	maximin *m*	максимин
M 248	**maximization; maximizing** <PG>	Maximierung *f*, // Maximalisierung *f*, Maximisierung *f*	maximisation *f*	максимизация; максимизирование, обеспечение максимума
M 249	**maximizing sequence** <VA>	Maximalfolge *f*	suite *f* maximisante	максимизирующая последовательность
M 250	**maximum,** max, maximum value, maximal value <DI, GN>	Maximum *n*, max, Maximalwert *m*	maximum *m*, max, valeur *f* maximale (maximum)	максимум, max, максимальное значение
M 251	**maximum,** upper (superior) limit <of a function at a point> <RF>	oberer Hauptlimes (Limes, extremer Limes) *m*, obere Unbestimmtheitsgrenze (Häufungsgrenze) *f* <einer Funktion bezüglich eines Filters, längs eines Filters>	limite *f* supérieure <d'une fonction suivant un filtre>	верхний предел <числовой функции по фильтру>
M 252	**maximum** <of a sequence> <SS>	Maximum *n*, reales Maximum	maximé *m*, maximum *m* réel	максимум
	maximum <DI>	*s.* A 115		
	maximum Abelian extension <AL<>	*s.* M 226		
	maximum and minimum <RF, SE>	*s.* L 699		
M 253	**maximum at the boundary** <of a function> <AN>	Randmaximum *n*, Maximum *n* auf dem Rand	maximum *m* au bord	граничный максимум
	maximum chain <SP>	*s.* M 262		
M 254	**maximum condition** <for a partially ordered set> <AL>	Maximalbedingung *f*	condition *f* maximale	условие максимальности
	maximum condition for invariant subgroups <GR>	*s.* A 1032		
M 255	**maximum correlation** <ST>	Maximalkorrelation *f*	corrélation *f* maximale (maximum)	максимальная корреляция

	English	German	French	Russian
M 256	**maximum density** <of a power series><SS>	Maximaldichte *f*	densité *f* maximum	максимальная плотность
M 257	**maximum ergodic theorem,** Kolmogorov['s] ergodic theorem <SP>	maximaler Ergodensatz *m*, Ergodensatz von Kolmogorov, Kolmogorovscher Ergodensatz	théorème *m* ergodique maximal (maximum), théorème ergodique de Kolmogoroff	эргодическая теорема Колмогорова, максимальная эргодическая теорема
	maximum error <ER, NU>	*s.* L 738		
	maximum figure <NT>	*s.* T 499		
	maximum flow theorem <GP, PG>	*s.* T 278		
	maximum integral <DE>	*s.* M 273		
	maximum in the large <DI>	*s.* A 115		
	maximum in the narrow sense <DI>	*s.* S 1902		
	maximum in the small <DI>	*s.* L 1005		
M 258	**maximum likelihood equations** <ST>	Maximum-Likelihood-Gleichungen *f pl*	équations *fpl* du maximum de vraisemblance	уравнения максимального правдоподобия
M 259	**maximum likelihood estimate** <ST>	wahrscheinlichster Schätzwert (Wert) *m*, wahrscheinlichste Schätzung *f*, plausibelster Schätzwert (Wert), plausibelste Schätzung, Maximum-Likelihood-Schätzung *f*	estimation *f* la plus vraisemblable	оценка максимального правдоподобия
M 260	**maximum likelihood estimating function, maximum likelihood estimator** <ST>	Maximum-Likelihood-Schätzung *f*, Maximum-Likelihood-Schätzfunktion *f*, plausibelste Schätzung (Schätzfunktion) *f*	estimateur *m* du maximum de vraisemblance, estimateur par la méthode du maximum de vraisemblance, fonction *f* estimatrice du maximum de vraisemblance	оценка максимального правдоподобия
M 261	**maximum likelihood method (principle),** method of maximum likelihood, principle of maximum likelihood <ST>	Maximum-Likelihood-Methode *f*, Maximal-Stichprobenwahrscheinlichkeits-Methode *f*, Maximale-Stichprobenwahrscheinlichkeits-Methode *f*, Methode *f* der maximalen Stichprobenwahrscheinlichkeit, Maximum-Likelihood-Prinzip *n*, Methode der größten Dichte	méthode *f* du maximum de vraisemblance, principe *m* du maximum de vraisemblance	метод максимального правдоподобия, метод наибольшего правдоподобия, принцип максимального правдоподобия, принцип наибольшего правдоподобия
	maximum likelihood ratio test <ST>	*s.* L 692		
	maximum limit <DI, SS>	*s.* U 427		
M 262	**maximum Markov chain,** maximum chain <SP>	unverfeinerbare [Markovsche] Kette *f*	chaîne *f* [markovienne] maximale	максимальная цепь [Маркова]
M 263	**maximum matching** <GP>	maximale Verkettung *f*	couplage *m* maximum (maximal)	наибольшее паросочетание
M 264	**maximum metric** <FA>	Maximummetrik *f*	métrique *f* maximum	метрика максимума
	maximum-minimum principle <PG, TG>	*s.* M 589		
M 265	**maximum modulus** <of a holomorphic function> <FT>	Maximalbetrag *m*	module *m* maximum	максимум модуля
M 266	**maximum modulus** <ST>	maximaler Betrag *m*	module *m* maximum	максимальный модуль
M 267	**maximum modulus principle (theorem)** <for holomorphic functions>; maximum principle, principle of the maximum <for harmonic functions> <FT>	Maximumprinzip *n*, Satz *m* (Prinzip *n*) vom Maximum, Prinzip des Maximums; Prinzip des absoluten Betrages <für holomorphe Funktionen>	principe *m* du module maximum <pour les fonctions holomorphes>; principe (théorème *m*) du maximum <pour les fonctions harmoniques *ou* holomorphes>	принцип модуля, принцип максимума модуля <для голоморфных функций>; принцип (теорема) максимума <для гармонических *или* голоморфных функций>; принцип экстремума <для гармонических функций>
	maximum number <NT>	*s.* T 499		
M 268	**maximum or minimum condition** <for a partially ordered set> <SE>	Extremalbedingung *f*	condition *f* maximale ou minimale	условие максимальности или минимальности
M 269	**maximum point,** point of maximum, position of maximum <DI>	Maximalstelle *f*, Maximumstelle *f*	point *m* maximal (de maximum), point où la fonction admet un maximum	максимальная точка, точка максимума; точка, в которой функция принимает максимум
M 270	**maximum principle,** principle of maximum <for potentials> <PO>	Maximumprinzip *n* <für Potentiale>, erstes Maximumprinzip, Maximumprinzip von O. Frostman	principe *m* du maximum <pour les potentiels>	принцип максимума <для потенциалов>
	maximum principle <FT>	*s.* M 267		
M 271	**maximum problem** <DI>	Maximumaufgabe *f*, Maximumproblem *n*	problème *m* de maximum	задача на максимум, максимальная задача, проблема максимума
M 272	**maximum property** <ST>	Maximumseigenschaft *f*	propriété *f* du maximum	свойство максимума

M 273	**maximum solution,** maximum integral <DE>	Maximalintegral *n*, Oberfunktion *f*	intégrale *f* maximale, solution *f* maximale	верхнее (максимальное) решение, верхний (максимальный) интеграл, верхняя функция
M 274	**maximum strategy** <TG>	maximale Strategie *f*	stratégie *f* maximale	максимальная стратегия
M 275	**maximum term** <of a power series> <SS>	Maximalglied *n*	terme *m* maximal	максимальный член
	maximum turning value <DI>	*s.* L 1005		
	maximum value <DI>	*s.* A 115		
	maximum value <DI, GN>	*s.* M 250		
M 276	**maximum with a condition (constraint),** constraint maximum, relative maximum <DI, PG, VA>	Maximum *n* unter (mit) einer Nebenbedingung, gebundenes (relatives) Maximum	maximum *m* sous une condition (contrainte), maximum contraint (relatif)	максимум с условием (ограничением), условный (относительный) максимум
M 277	**Max Noether['s] theorem** <AG>	Satz *m* von [Max] Noether, Noetherscher Satz	théorème *m* de Noether	теорема Нетера
	Maxwell-Boltzmann distribution [law] <ST>	*s.* M 279		
	Maxwell-Boltzmann law <ST>	*s.* M 279		
M 278	**Maxwell-Boltzmann statistics,** Boltzmann statistics, classical [Boltzmann] statistics <ST>	Maxwell-Boltzmann-Statistik *f*, Boltzmann-Statistik *f*, klassische Statistik *f* [Boltzmanns]	statistique *f* de Maxwell-Boltzmann (Boltzmann), statistique classique [de Boltzmann]	статистика Максвелла-Больцмана, статистика Больцмана, классическая статистика Больцмана
M 279	**Maxwellian distribution, Maxwell['s] distribution, Maxwell['s] distribution function (law), Maxwell['s] distribution of velocities, Maxwell['s] equilibrium distribution law, Maxwellian equilibrium (velocity) distribution,** Maxwell['s] velocity distribution [law], Maxwell-Boltzmann distribution [law], Maxwell-Boltzmann law	Maxwell-Verteilung *f*, Maxwellsche Verteilung (Geschwindigkeitsverteilung, Gleichgewichtsverteilung) *f*, Maxwell-Boltzmann-Verteilung *f*, Maxwell-Boltzmannsche Verteilung, Maxwell [-Boltzmann]sche Verteilungsfunktion *f*, Maxwell[-Boltzmann]sches Verteilungsgesetz *n*, Maxwellsches Geschwindigkeitsverteilungsgesetz *n*	distribution *f* de Maxwell[-Boltzmann], distribution maxwellienne, distribution des vitesses de Maxwell[-Boltzmann], répartition *f* de Maxwell[-Boltzmann], répartition maxwellienne, loi *f* de Maxwell (distribution maxwellienne), fonction *f* de distribution maxwellienne (de Maxwell)	распределение Максвелла, максвелловское распределение [скоростей], максвеллово распределение, функция распределение Максвелла
	Maxwell-Todd relations <AG>	*s.* R 686		
	Maxwell['s] velocity distribution [law] <ST>	*s.* M 279		
	Mayer['s] complex <AT, HA>	*s.* C 466		
M 280	**Mayer['s] field** <VA>	Mayersches Feld *n*	champ *m* de Mayer	поле Майера
M 281	**Mayer['s] method** <of integration> <DE>	Mayersche Integrationsmethode *f*, Integrationsmethode von Mayer, Mayersche Methode *f*	méthode *f* [d'intégration] de Mayer	метод [интегрирования] Майера
M 282	**Mayer-Vietoris cohomology sequence,** cohomology Mayer-Vietoris sequence <AT>	Mayer-Vietorissche Kohomologiesequenz *f*	suite *f* cohomologique de Mayer-Vietoris	когомологическая точная последовательность Майера-Виеториса
M 283	**Mayer-Vietoris homology sequence,** homology Mayer-Vietoris sequence <AT>	Mayer-Vietorissche Homologiesequenz *f*	suite *f* homologique de Mayer-Vietoris	гомологическая точная последовательность Майера-Виеториса
M 284	**Mayer-Vietoris sequence** <AT>	Mayer-Vietoris-Sequenz *f*	suite *f* de Mayer-Vietoris	последовательность Майера-Виеториса
	Mazur-Gelfand theorem <AL, FA>	*s.* T 319		
M 285	***m*-by-*n* (*m* by *n*) matrix,** matrix of size *m* by *n*, matrix of order $m \times n$ <MD>	(*m*,*n*)-Matrix *f*, $m \times n$-Matrix *f*, Matrix *f* vom Typ (*m*,*n*), Matrix vom Format (*m*,*n*), (*m*,*n*)-reihige Matrix, Matrix mit *m* Zeilen und *n* Spalten	matrice *f* à *n* colonnes et *m* lignes, matrice à *m* lignes et *n* colonnes, matrice $m \times n$, matrice de type (*m*,*n*)	матрица размера $m \times n$, матрица с *m* строками и *n* столбцами
M 286	𝔪 **categorical theory,** theory categorical in power 𝔪 <MM>	𝔪-kategorische Theorie *f*	théorie *f* 𝔪-catégorique	𝔪-категоричная теория; теория, категоричная в мощности 𝔪
	Mcdonald['s] function <FU>	*s.* M 4		
	(M)-closed set <TO>	*s.* M 7		
M 287	𝔪**-closed subset** <of a topological space> <TO>	𝔪-abgeschlossene Untermenge *f*	partie *f* 𝔪-fermée	𝔪-замкнутое подмножество
	M closed subset <SE>	*s.* I 536		
M 288	**McNemar test** <ST>	McNemar-Test *m*	test *m* de McNemar	критерий Мак-Немара
M 289	𝔪**-compact space** <TO>	𝔪-kompakter Raum *m*	espace *m* 𝔪-compact	𝔪-компактное пространство
M 290	𝔪**-complete Boolean algebra,** Boolean 𝔪-algebra <AL>	𝔪-vollständige Boolesche Algebra *f*	algèbre *f* de Boole 𝔪-complète	𝔪-полная булева алгебра
M 291	𝔪**-complete field of sets,** 𝔪-field of sets <AL>	𝔪-vollständige Mengenalgebra *f*	corps *m* d'ensembles 𝔪-complet	𝔪-полная алгебра множеств

M 292	**m-complete filter,** m-filter <SE>	m-vollständiger Filter *m*	filtre *m* m-complet	m-полный фильтр
	M-convex subset <CS, TO>	*s.* M 494		
	MD <ST>	*s.* M 305		
M 293	**meager set,** thin set, set of [the] first category, set of first category according to Baire, set of the first species, exhaustible set <TO>	magere Menge *f*, Menge (Punktmenge *f*) [von] erster Kategorie	ensemble *m* de première (I[e]) catégorie, ensemble gerbé (maigre)	тощее множество, множество первой (I-ой) категории, множество первой категории по Кантору
M 294	**meager subset,** subset of [the] first category <of a topological space> <TO>	magere Teilmenge *f*, Teilmenge [von] erster Kategorie	partie *f* de première (I[e]) catégorie, partie gerbée (maigre)	тощее подмножество, подмножество первой (I-ой) категории
M 295	**Mealy['s] machine, Mealy['s] automaton** <TA>	Mealy-Automat *m*, Mealyscher Automat *m*	automate *m* de Mealy, réseau *m* de Mealy	автомат Мили
M 296	**mean** <of a function with respect to *n* arguments *or* to a point set> <AN>	Mittelwert *m*	moyenne *f*	среднее
M 297	**mean,** mean term <of a proportion> <AR>	inneres Glied *n*, Innenglied *n*, Mittelglied *n*, mittleres Glied *n*	terme *m* moyen, moyen *m*	средний член
M 298	**mean,** mean value, average, average value <ST>	Mittel *n*, Mittelwert *m*	moyenne *f*, valeur *f* moyenne	среднее, среднее значение, средняя величина
	mean <ST>	*s.* E 719		
M 299	**mean continuity** <of a kernel> <IE>	mittlere Stetigkeit *f*	continuité *f* moyenne	средняя непрерывность
	mean convergence <FA, RF>	*s.* C 2341		
	mean convergence <ST>	*s.* C 2342		
	mean convergence of *p*-th order <FA, RF>	*s.* S 1934		
M 300	**mean cross-sectional measure, Quermass-integral** <*m*-th> <of a convex body> <CS, GE>	Minkowskisches Quermaßintegral *n*, Quermaßintegral [Minkowskis] <*m*-tes>		поперечная мера <*m*-я>
M 301	**mean curvature** <of a piece of a hypersurface> <DG>	durchschnittliche Krümmung *f*	courbure *f* moyenne	средняя кривизна
M 302	**mean curvature,** mean normal curvature, circular (first) curvature <of a surface> <DG>	mittlere Krümmung (Flächenkrümmung) *f*	courbure *f* moyenne <d'une surface>	средняя кривизна <поверхности>
M 303	**mean density** <NT>	mittlere Dichtigkeit (Dichte) *f*	densité *f* moyenne, pourcentage *m*	средняя плотность
M 304	**mean derivative** <FT>	mittlere Ableitung (Derivierte) *f*	dérivée *f* moyenne	средняя производная
	mean deviation <ST>	*s.* A 1254		
M 305	**mean difference,** MD <ST>	mittlere Differenz *f*, MD	différence *f* moyenne	средняя разность, среднее разрождение
	mean error <ER, ST>	*s.* 1. A 1255; 2. R 1379		
M 306	**mean geodesic curvature** <Darboux> <DG>	mittlere geodätische Krümmung *f*	courbure *f* géodésique moyenne	средняя геодезическая кривизна
M 307	**meaningful formula,** correctly constructed formula, well-formed formula, formula <of predicate calculus>; expression of elementary logic, formula of elementary logic <LO>	prädikatenlogischer Ausdruck *m*, Ausdruck des Prädikatenkalküls, P-Ausdruck *m*	expression *f* bien faite (formée), formule *f* <du calcul des prédicats>	формула исчисления предикатов
	meaningful formula <LO>	*s.* 1. F 488; 2. S 499		
M 308	**meaningful proposition,** significant proposition <LO>	sinnvolle Aussage *f*	proposition *f* pleine (douée) de sens	осмысленное высказывание
	meaningful significant figure <NU>	*s.* S 846		
M 309	**meaningless proposition,** proposition without sense <LO>	sinnlose Aussage *f*	proposition *f* dénuée de sens (contenu)	бессмысленное высказывание; высказывание, не имеющее смысла
M 310	**mean life [time]** <ST>	mittlere Lebensdauer *f*	vie *f* moyenne, durée *f* de vie moyenne	наработка [до первого отказа], среднее время работы
	meanline <EG>	*s.* M 355		
	mean normal curvature <DG>	*s.* M 302		
	mean of sample <ST>	*s.* S 20		
M 311	**mean ordinate** <of a curve> <DI, NU>	mittlere Ordinate (Kurvenordinate) *f*	ordonnée *f* moyenne <d'une courbe>	средняя ордината <кривой>
M 312	**mean oscillation** <of a function> <AN>	mittlere Schwankung *f*	oscillation *f* moyenne	среднее колебание
M 313	**mean over the column,** column mean (average) <ST>	Spaltenmittel *n*, Spaltendurchschnitt *m*	moyenne *f* sur (de) la colonne	среднее по столбцу, постолбцевое среднее
M 314	**mean over the period** <AN, NU>	Mittel *n* (Mittelwert *m*) über die Periode, Periodenmittel *n*	moyenne *f* sur la période	среднее по периоду
M 315	**mean over the row,** row mean <ST>	Zeilenmittel *n*, Zeilendurchschnitt *m*	moyenne *f* sur (de) la ligne	среднее по строке, построчное среднее
M 316	**mean product [deviation]** <ST>	mittleres Abweichungsprodukt *n*	produit *m* moyen des écarts	среднее произведение отклонений
	mean proportional <AR>	*s.* G 253		
M 317	**mean range** <ST>	mittlere Spannweite *f*	étendue *f* moyenne	средний размах

	mean Riemannian curvature <DG>	*s.* R 983		
M 318	**mean square,** mean square deviation, MS <ST>	mittleres Abweichungsquadrat *n*, MQ	carré *m* moyen des écarts	среднее квадратичное [отклонение], среднеквадратичное [отклонение], средний квадрат отклонений
M 319	**mean square contingency** <ST>	mittlere quadratische Kontingenz *f*	carré *m* moyen de contingence	средняя квадратичная сопряженность [признаков], среднеквадратичная сопряженность [признаков]
	mean square deviation <ST>	*s.* 1. M 318; 2. S 1606; 3. V 62		
	mean square error <ER, ST>	*s.* R 1379		
M 320	**mean square of error** <AX>	mittleres Fehlerquadrat *n*	carré *m* moyen d'erreur, moyenne *f* du carré de l'erreur	средний квадрат ошибки, среднее квадрата ошибки
M 321	**mean term** <of a progression> <AR>	mittleres Glied *n*	terme *m* médian	средний член
	mean term <AR>	*s.* M 297		
M 322	**mean type** <of a meromorphic function> <FT>	Mitteltypus *m*, Mitteltyp *m*, Normaltypus *m*, Normaltyp *m*	type *m* moyen	средний тип
M 323	**mean value** <of a real-valued function with respect to an interval> <AP, RF>	Integralmittelwert *m*, Mittelwert *m*	valeur *f* moyenne, moyenne *f*	среднее значение, среднее
	mean value <ST>	*s.* 1. E 719; 2. M 298		
M 324	**mean value function** <NT>	Mittelwertfunktion *f*	fonction *f* valeur moyenne	функция, дающая среднее значение; функция среднего значения
M 325	**mean value method** <of integration> <AX, DE, NU>	Mittelwertmethode *f*	méthode *f* des [valeurs] moyennes	метод средних, метод средних значений
M 326	**mean value property** <DE>	Mittelwerteigenschaft *f*	propriété *f* de la valeur moyenne	свойство среднего значения
M 327	**mean value theorem,** first mean value theorem, law of the mean, Lagrange['s] [mean value] formula, Lagrange['s] theorem <of the differential calculus> <DI>	erster (gewöhnlicher) Mittelwertsatz *m* [der Differentialrechnung], Mittelwertsatz der Differentialrechnung, Lagrangesche Formel *f*, Formel von Lagrange	théorème *m* de Lagrange, théorème des accroissements finis, formule *f* des accroissements finis	теорема Лагранжа (о конечных приращениях), теорема о конечном приращении, теорема (формула) конечных приращений, формула Лагранжа, теорема о среднем дифференциального исчисления
M 328	**mean vector** <ST>	Mittelwertvektor *m*	vecteur *m* de moyenne	вектор среднего
	measurability in Borel['s] sense <ME>	*s.* B 512		
	measurability in Lebesgue's sense <ME>	*s.* L 909		
	measurability in the sense of Borel <ME>	*s.* B 512		
	measurability in the sense of Lebesgue <ME>	*s.* L 909		
	measurable (B) <ME>	*s.* B 592		
M 329	**measurable function;** measurable transformation; measurable mapping <FA, ME, SP>	meßbare Funktion *f*; meßbare Transformation *f*; meßbare Abbildung *f*	fonction *f* mesurable; transformation *f* mesurable; application *f* mesurable	измеримая функция; измеримое преобразование; измеримое отображение
	measurable function <ME>	*s.* L 910		
	μ-measurable function <ME, RF>	*s.* M 1092		
	measurable function in the sense of Borel <ME>	*s.* B 513		
	[μ-]measurable hull <ME>	*s.* M 1093		
M 330	**[μ-]measurable kernel** <of a set> <ME>	μ-meßbarer Kern *m*, μ-Kern *m*, meßbarer Kern	intérieur *m* μ-mesurable (mesurable)	μ-измеримое (измеримое) ядро, μ-измеримая (измеримая) внутренность
M 331	**measurable mapping** <of measurable sets on measurable sets> <ME>	meßbare (reguläre) Abbildung *f*	application *f* mesurable	измеримое отображение
	measurable mapping <FA, ME, SP>	*s.* M 329		
	measurable transformation <FA, ME, SP>	*s.* M 329		
	measurable transformation having a measurable inverse <ME>	*s.* I 981		
M 332	**measure,** measure function <ME>	Maß *n*, Maßfunktion *f*, positives Maß	mesure *f*	мера, функция меры
M 333	**measure admitting a convolution** <ME>	faltbares Maß *n*	mesure *f* convolable	свертывающаяся мера
M 334	**measure algebra** <AL, ME>	Maßalgebra *f*; Maßring *m*, Maßverband *m*	algèbre *f* à mesure	алгебра с мерой; булева σ-структура с мерой, обладающая единицей
	measure equation <NU>	*s.* N 909		
	measure function <ME>	*s.* M 332		
M 335	**measure of angle** <GE>	Winkelmaß *n*	mesure *f* de l'angle	угловая мера
M 336/7	**measure of angle in degrees** <GE>	Gradmaß *n* des Winkels	mesure *f* d'angle en degrés	градусная мера угла
	measure of angle in radians <GE>	*s.* R 12		

	measure of area <ME>	*s.* S 1560		
M 338	**measure of concentration,** concentration measure <ST>	Konzentrationsmaß *n*, Disparitätsmaß *n* <Gumbel>	mesure *f* de concentration	мера кучности
M 339	**measure of curvature**	Krümmungsmaß *n*	mesure *f* de courbure	мера кривизны
M 340	**measure of dispersion** <ST>	Streuungsmaß *n*	mesure *f* de dispersion	мера рассеивания
M 341	**measure of skewness,** skewness <according to Charlier, Pearson, Bowley, von Mises, *or* Lindeberg ><ST>	Schiefheitsmaß *n*, Schiefe *f* <nach Charlier, Pearson, Bowley, von Mises *oder* Lindeberg>	mesure *f* de dissymétrie, dissymétrie *f* <selon Charlier, Pearson, Bowley, von Mises *ou* Lindeberg>	мера асимметрии, асимметрия <по Шарлье, Пирсона, Боули, фон Мизеса *или* Линдеберга>
M 342	**measure of transcendence** <of a transcendental number> <NT>	Transzendenzmaß *n*	mesure *f* de transcendance	мера трансцендентности
M 343	**measure preserving [measurable] transformation** <ME>	maßtreue (m-treue, m-invariante) [meßbare] Transformation *f*	transformation *f* [mesurable] conservant la mesure	[измеримое] преобразование, сохраняющее меру; [измеримое] преобразование с сохранением меры
M 344	**measure space** <ME>	Maßraum *m*	espace *m* mesuré (mesurable)	пространство с мерой, измеримое пространство
M 345	**measure theory** <ME>	Maßtheorie *f*	théorie *f* des mesures, théorie de la mesure	теория меры
M 346	**measure zero,** zero measure <ME>	Maß *n* Null (0), Nullmaß *n*	mesure *f* nulle (zéro)	нулевая мера, мера нуль
M 347	**measuring error,** error of measurement <ST>	Meßfehler *m*	erreur *f* de mesure	погрешность (ошибка) измерения
M 348	**measuring rule,** comparing rule, rule <GE, IN>	Maßstab *m*, Maßstablineal *n*	règle *f* à échelle, règle divisée	масштабная линейка, масштаб
	mechanical cubature <AX, DI, NU>	*s.* N 879		
M 349	**mechanically calculable function** <MM>	mechanisch berechenbare Funktion *f*	fonction *f* calculable par machine	машинно-вычислимая функция
	mechanical quadrature formula <AX, DI, NU>	*s.* Q 51		
M 350	**mechanical quadrature method** <AX, DI, NU>	mechanisches Quadraturverfahren *n*	méthode *f* de quadrature mécanique	метод механической квадратуры
	medial algebra <AL>	*s.* A 7		
M 351	**medial correlation coefficient** <ST>	Medialkorrelationskoeffizient *m*	coefficient *m* de corrélation du test de Quenouille	срединный коэффициент корреляции
	medial graph <GP>	*s.* D 994		
M 352	**medial groupoid,** abelian groupoid <AL>	bisymmetrisches Gruppoid *n*	groupoïde *m* bisymétrique	медиальный группоид
	mediality <AL>	*s.* E 266		
	medial quasi[-]group <AL>	*s.* A 25		
M 353	**medial test** <ST>	Medialtest *m*, Quadrantentest *m*	test *m* de Quenouille	срединный критерий
M 354	**median** <of a tetrahedron> <EG>	Mediane *f*	médiane *f*	медиана
M 355	**median,** midline, meanline <of a trapezoid> <EG>	Mittellinie *f*, Mediane *f*	base *f* moyenne, ligne *f* centrale	средняя линия
M 356	**median** <of a triangle> <EG>	Seitenhalbierende *f*, Mitteltransversale *f*, Mediane *f*, Schwerelinie *f*	médiane *f*	медиана
M 357	**median,** median value <ST>	Median *m* (*n*), Medianwert *m*, Zentralwert *m*, Mediane *f*, 50%iges Quantil (Quartil) *n*	médiane *f*, valeur *f* médiane, médiale *f*, médiante *f*, moyenne *f* de position, valeur équiprobable	медиана, величина (значение) медианы, медианное (центральное, среднее) значение
	median envelope <DG>	*s.* M 528		
	median plane <DG>	*s.* M 531		
	median point <DG>	*s.* M 533		
	median point <EG>	*s.* C 418		
	median surface <DG>	*s.* M 537		
M 358	**mediant** <of Farey fractions> <NT>	Mediante *f*, komponierter Bruch *m*	médiante *f*	медианта
M 359	**median test** <ST>	Mediantest *m*	test *m* de la médiane	критерий, основанный на медиане
	median value <ST>	*s.* M 357		
M 360	**mediate inference** <LO>	mittelbares Schließen *n*	déduction *f* médiate	опосредствованное умозаключение
M 361	**medium number** <between minimum and maximum> <NU>	mittlere Zahl *f*	nombre *m* moyen	среднее число
M 362	**meet,** intersection, crosscut, Boolean meet, product, cap, infimum, $\frown$ <read: cap> <LA>	Durchschnitt *m*, verbandstheoretischer Durchschnitt	section *f*, borne *f* inférieure, intersection *f*, infimum *m*, p.g.c.d. *m* <d'éléments d'un treillis>; produit *m* booléien, produit booléen <d'éléments d'une algèbres de Boole>	пересечение, точная нижняя грань <элементов структур>; булево произведение <элементов булевых алгебр>
	meet <CA>	*s.* I 799		
	meet <SE>	*s.* 1. G 412; 2. I 802		
	meet / to <GN>	*s.* F 701		
M 363	**meet-automorphism** <AL>	Durchschnittsautomorphismus *m*	$\wedge$-automorphisme *m*	автоморфизм по пересечению
M 364	**meet-endomorphism** <AL>	Durchschnittsendomorphismus *m*	$\frown$-endomorphisme *m*, $\wedge$-endomorphisme *m*	гомоморфизм по пересечению
M 365	**meet-epimorphism** <AL>	Durchschnittsepimorphismus *m*	$\wedge$-épimorphisme *m*	эпиморфизм по пересечению
M 366	**meet-homomorphic image** <LA>	durchschnittshomomorphes Bild *n*	image *f* $\frown$-homomorphe	образ при гомоморфизме по пересечению
M 367	**meet-homomorphism,** meet homomorphism, lower hemitropism <of the subgroup lattice> <GR>	Durchschnittshomomorphismus *m*, $\frown$-Homomorphismus *m* <des Untergruppenverbands>	$\frown$-homomorphisme *m* <du treillis des sous-groupes>	гомоморфизм по пересечению <структуры подгрупп>

	English	German	French	Russian
M 368	**meet-homomorphism,** meet homomorphism <LA>	Durchschnittshomomorphismus *m*, ⌒-Homomorphismus *m*	⌒-homomorphisme *m*, ∧-morphisme *m*, homomorphisme *m* d'intersection	гомоморфизм по пересечению
M 369	**meet-irreducible element,** meet irreducible element <LA>	durchschnittsirreduzibles (⌒-irreduzibles) Element *n*	élément *m* inf-irréductible, élément ∧-irréductible (⌒-irréductible, irréductible par rapport à l'intersection)	⌒-неразложимый элемент, ⌒-неприводимый элемент; элемент, неразложимый в пересечение; элемент, неприводимый по пересечению
M 370	**meet-isomorphic mapping, meet-isomorphism** <AL>	Durchschnittsisomorphismus *m*, ⌒-Isomorphismus *m*	∧-isomorphisme *m*	⌒-изоморфизм
M 371	**meet operation,** intersection operation <SE>	Durchschnittsbildung *f*, Operation *f* der Durchschnittsbildung	opération *f* d'intersection, formation *f* de l'intersection	операция пересечения, произведение
M 372	**meet-preserving mapping** <of partially ordered sets> <SE>	Durchschnittshomomorphismus *m*	application *f* préservant l'intersection	отображение, сохраняющее пересечение
M 373	**meet-reducible element,** reducible element <LA>	durchschnittsreduzibles Element *n*, ⌒-reduzibles Element	élément *m* inf-réductible (∧-réductible)	⌒-разложимый элемент, ⌒-приводимый элемент
	meet-semilattice <AL>	*s.* L 1164		
M 374	**meet-stable,** closed under intersection <quasi-ordered class> <SE>	abgeschlossen gegenüber Durchschnittsbildung	stable pour les intersections	замкнутый относительно пересечений
M 375	**Mehler['s] integral** <of spherical functions> <FU>	Mehlersche Integraldarstellung *f* <der Kugelfunktionen>	intégrale *f* de Mehler	интеграл Мелера
M 376	**mehrstellen method** <DE, NU>	Mehrstellenverfahren *n*, Mehrstellenmethode *f*	« mehrstellenmethode » *f*	многоточечный метод [конечных разностей]
M 377	**Meissel['s] formula** <for prime numbers> <NT>	Meißelsche Primzahlformel *f*	formule *f* de Meissel	формула Мейселя
M 378	**Mellin['s] kernel** <DE>	Mellinscher Kern *m*	noyau *m* de Mellin	ядро Меллина
M 379	**Mellin['s] transform[ation]** <IT>	Mellin-Transformation *f*, Mellins[che] Transformation *f*, Mellinsche Integraltransformation *f*	transformation *f* de Mellin	преобразование Меллина, интегральное преобразование Меллина
M 380	**member,** side <of an equation *or* inequality> <GN>	Seite *f*	membre *m*, partie *f*, côté *m*	часть, сторона
M 381	**member,** summand, component, element <of the disjunction *or* of the logical sum> <LO>	Alternativglied *n*, Disjunktionsglied *n*, disjunktives Glied *n*, Glied, logischer Summand *m*, Summand	terme *m*, facteur *m*	слагаемое, дизъюнктивный член, член дизъюнкции
M 382	**member,** factor, component <of a conjunction> <LO>	Glied *n* der Konjunktion, Faktor *m*, Konjunktionsglied *n*, konjunktives Glied *n*	facteur *m* [de conjonction]	конъюнктивный член, член конъюнкции, множитель
	member <AL>	*s.* T 162		
	member <SE>	*s.* E 87		
M 383	**member of the uniformity,** entourage <of a uniform structure> <TO>	Nachbarschaft *f*, ,,entourage" *f*	entourage *m*	окружение
M 384	**membership** <of an element> <SE>	Enthaltensein *n*	appartenance *f*	принадлежность
M 385	**membership relation** <SE>	Elementbeziehung *f*	relation *f* d'appartenance, appartenance *f*	отношение принадлежности, ∈-отношение
	membership relation symbol <SE>	*s.* S 856		
	membership sign <SE>	*s.* S 856		
M 386	**membrane** <GE>	Membran *f*, zweidimensionaler Punktkomplex *m*	membrane *f*	мембрана
M 387	**Menelaos['s] theorem** <AY, EG>	Satz *m* des (von) Menelaos (Menelaus), Menelaosscher (Menelausscher) Satz, Regel *f* der sechs Größen (Stücke), Menelaus' Transversalensatz *m*, regula *f* sex quantitatum	théorème *m* de Ménélaüs (Ménélaos, Ménélas, la transversale), théorème des transversales, règle *f* des six quantités	теорема Менелая
M 388	**Menelaus['s] [straight] line** <AY>	Menelaus-Gerade *f*, Menelaos-Gerade *f*	droite *f* de Ménélaus	прямая Менелая
M 389	**Menger['s] algebra** <UA>	Menger-Algebra *f*	algèbre *f* de Menger	алгебра Менгера
M 390	**Menger['s] curvature** <in a metric space> <GE>	Mengersche Krümmung *f*	courbure *f* de Menger	кривизна Менгера
	Menger['s] graph theorem <GP>	*s.* V 165		
	Menger-Nöbeling theorem <TO>	*s.* T 320		
	Menger['s] theorem <GP>	*s.* V 165		
	Menger-Urysohn dimension <TO>	*s.* W 69		
	mensuration <GE>	*s.* M 501		
M 391	**mental arithmetic** <AR>	Kopfrechnen *n*, mündliches Rechnen *n*	calcul *m* mental (oral), compte *f* (calcul) de tête	устный счет, вычисление в уме
	mental experiment <ST>	*s.* T 440		
	mercantile arithmetic <AR>	*s.* B 818		
M 392	**Mercator['s] function** <DS>	Merkator-Funktion *f*, Merkatorfunktion *f*	fonction *f* de Mercator	функция Меркатора
M 393	**Mercer['s] theorem** <IE>	Mercerscher Satz *m*, Satz von Mercer	théorème *m* de Mercer	теорема Мерсера

M 394	**Mercer['s] theorem** <LI>	Mercer-Satz *m*	théorème *m* de Mercer	теорема Мерсера
M 395	**meridian,** meridian curve (line), line (meridian) of longitude <of a surface *or* body of revolution> <GE>	Meridianlinie *f*, Meridiankurve *f*, Meridian *m*	courbe (ligne) *f* méridienne, méridienne *f*	меридиан, меридианная кривая, меридианная линия
	meridian <AY, EG>	*s.* M 398		
	meridian curve <GE>	*s.* M 395		
M 396	**meridian ellipse** <AY>	Meridianellipse *f*	ellipse *f* méridienne	меридианный эллипс
	meridian line <GE>	*s.* M 395		
	meridian of longitude <GE>	*s.* M 395		
M 397	**meridian plane,** plane of the meridian, meridional plane <GE>	Meridianebene *f*	plan *m* méridien, méridien *m*	плоскость меридиана, меридианная (меридиональная) плоскость
M 398	**meridian section,** meridian <of a surface *or* body of revolution> <GE>	Meridianschnitt *m*, Meridianbereich *m*	section *f* méridienne, méridienne *f*	меридианное сечение, меридиональное сечение
M 399	**meridian surface** <of a complex surface> <GE>	Meridianfläche *f*	surface *f* méridienne	меридианная поверхность
	meridional plane <GE>	*s.* M 397		
	meroedric isomorphism <AL>	*s.* R 1318		
	meroedric isomorphism <GR>	*s.* H 500		
M 400	**meromorphic differential** <of *n*-th order> <FT>	meromorphes Differential *n*, Differential <*n*-ten Grades>	différentielle *f* méromorphe <d'ordre *n*>	мероморфный дифференциал <*n*-го порядка>
M 401	**meromorphic function** <FT>	meromorphe Funktion *f*	fonction *f* méromorphe	мероморфная функция
M 402	**meromorphic function element** <FT>	gebrochenes analytisches Funktionselement *n*, meromorphes Funktionselement	élément *m* de fonction méromorphe	мероморфный элемент функции
M 403	**meromorphic function for $\|z\| < 1$** <FT>	bruchartige Funktion *f*, meromorphe Funktion für $\|z\| < 1$	fonction *f* méromorphe pour $\|z\| < 1$	мероморфная функция для $\|z\| < 1$
M 404	**meromorphic mapping,** meromorphism <GR>	Meromorphismus *m*, meromorphe Abbildung *f*	méromorphisme *m*, application *f* méromorphe	мероморфизм, мероморфное отображение
	meromorphic part <FT>	*s.* P 1460		
	meromorphism <GR>	*s.* M 404		
M 405	**meromorphy** <of a fractional rational function> <FT>	Meromorphie *f*, Charakter *m* <einer gebrochenen rationalen Funktion> <Weierstraß>	méromorphie *f*, caractère *m* <d'une fonction rationnelle fractionnaire>	мероморфность
M 406	**Mersenne['s] number** <NT>	Mersennesche Zahl *f*	nombre *m* de Mersenne	число Мерсенна
M 407	**Mersenne['s] prime** <NT>	Mersennesche Primzahl *f*	nombre *m* premier de Mersenne	простое число Мерсенна
M 408	**Mertens['s] formula** <NT>	Mertenssche Formel *f*	formule *f* de Mertens	формула Мертенса
	Mertens['s] function <NT>	*s.* M 710		
M 409	**Mertens['s] hypothesis** <NT>	Mertenssche Hypothese *f*	hypothèse *f* de Mertens	гипотеза Мертенса
M 410	**Mertens['s] theorem** <on the Cauchy product of two series> <SS>	Satz *m* von Mertens, Mertensscher Satz	théorème *m* de Cauchy-Mertens	теорема Мертенса
	Mertens['s] theorems <AB>	*s.* T 371		
M 411	**mesh** <of a complex, triangulation> <AT>	Feinheitsgrad *m*	finesse *f*	мелкость
M 412	**mesh** <of a covering> <TO>	Feinheit *f*	finesse *f*	мелкость
M 413	**mesh of regular hexagons,** honeycomb pattern <FD, NU>	Sechseck[s]netz *n*, Honigwabengitter *n*, Honigwabenmuster *n*, Netz *n* aus regulären Sechsecken	réseau *m* d'hexagons réguliers	шестиугольная сетка
M 414	**mesh of triangles,** triangular pattern (net) <FD, NU>	Dreiecksnetz *n*	réseau *m* triangulaire (de triangles)	треугольная сетка
M 415	**mesh point** <NU>	Gitterpunkt *m*	nœud *m*	узел, точка <сетки>
M 416	**mesokurtic distribution** <ST>	mesokurtische Verteilung *f*	distribution *f* mésokurtique	распределение, имеющее нормальный эксцесс
M 417	**mesolabe** <AR, IN>	Mesolabium *n* <des Eratosthenes>	mesolabe *m*	мезолябия [Эратосфена]
M 418	**meta-axiom of choice** <LO, SE>	Metaauswahlaxiom *n*	métaaxiome *m* de choix	мета-аксиома выбора
M 419	**metabelian group** <GR>	metabelsche (zweistufig metabelsche, zweistufig auflösbare) Gruppe *f*, nilpotente Gruppe von der Klasse 2, von der Klasse 2 nilpotente Gruppe	groupe *m* métabélien (de spécialité 2)	метабелева (двусторонне разрешимая) группа, нильпотентная группа класса 2, двухступенно разрешимая группа
M 420	**metabelian group** <of class *n*> <GR>	metabelsche Gruppe *f*	groupe *m* métabélien	метабелева группа
M 421	**metabelian product** <AL>	metabelsches Produkt *n*	produit *m* métabélien	метабелево произведение
M 422	**metacanonical matrix** <DE>	metakanonische Matrix *f*	matrice *f* métacanonique	метаканоническая матрица
M 423	**metacategory** <CA>	Metakategorie *f*	métacatégorie *f*	метакатегория
M 424	**metacompact topological space** <TO>	metakompakter topologischer Raum *m*	espace *m* métacompact	метакомпактное пространство
M 425	**metacyclic equation,** solvable equation <in Galois' theory> <AL>	auflösbare Gleichung *f*, metazyklische Gleichung	équation *f* métacyclique (résoluble)	метациклическое уравнение, разрешимое уравнение

M 426	**metacyclic group** <GR>	metazyklische Gruppe *f*	groupe *m* métacyclique	метациклическая группа
M 427	**metageometry** <any geometry more general than the Euclidean geometry, of which the Euclidean one is a special case> <GE>	Metageometrie *f*	métagéométrie *f*	метагеометрия
M 428	**metagraph** <CA>	Metagraph *m*	métagraphe *m*	метаграф
M 429	**metahamiltonian group** <GR>	metahamiltonsche Gruppe *f*	groupe *m* méta-hamiltonien	метагамильтонова группа
M 430	**metaharmonic function** <AN>	metaharmonische Funktion *f*	fonction *f* métaharmonique	метагармоническая функция
M 431	**metaharmonic triangle** <EG>	metaharmonisches Dreieck *n*	triangle *m* métaharmonique	метагармонический треугольник
M 432	**metalanguage,** second-order language; U-language <combinatory language> <FO>	Metasprache *f*, Sprache *f* der zweiten Stufe	métalangue *f*, métalangage *m*	метаязык, язык второй ступени
M 433	**metalogical symbol** <LO>	metalogisches Symbol *n*	symbole *m* métalogique	металогический символ
M 434	**metalogic of predicates** <LO>	Metaprädikatenlogik *f*	métalogique *f* des prédicats	металогика предикатов
M 435	**metameter** <ST>	Metameter *m*	métamètre *m*	метаметр, преобразованная мера <когда преобразование не зависит от параметра>
M 436	**metanilpotent group** <GR>	metanilpotente Gruppe *f*	groupe *m* méta-nilpotent	метанильпотентная группа
M 437	**meta-proposition** <LO>	Metaaussage *f*	métaproposition *f*	метавысказывание, высказывание о высказываниях
M 438	**metarule** <FO>	Metaregel *f*, Superregel *f*	métarègle *f*	метаправило
	metaspherical function <FU>	*s.* G 105		
M 439	**metatheorem** <FO>	Metasatz *m*	métathéorème *m*	метатеорема
M 440	**metavariable** <LO>	Metavariable *f*	métavariable *f*	метапеременная
M 441	**meta word problem** <GR>	Meta-Wortproblem *n*	métaproblème *m* des mots	метапроблема тождества
	Metelka['s] configuration <SG>	*s.* C 1875		
	method by means defined by integral functions <LI>	*s.* J 55		
M 442	**method of aligned points** <NO>	Methode *f* der fluchtrechten Punkte	méthode *f* des points alignés	метод выравненных точек
M 443	**method of arithmetic means,** C_1-method, $(C,1)$ method, *M*-method <for divergent sequences *or* series> <LI>	Verfahren *n* der arithmetischen Mittel, *M*-Verfahren *n*, $(C,1)$-Verfahren *n*, C_1-Verfahren *n*	méthode *f* des moyennes arithmétiques, méthode $(C,1)$, méthode C_1	метод средних арифметических
	method of artificial variable <PG>	*s.* A 1005		
M 444	**method of ascending indices** <GP, PG>	Methode *f* der aufsteigenden Indizes	méthode *f* des indices ascendants	метод восходящих индексов
M 445	**method of ascent** <NT, PG>	Aufstiegsmethode *f*, Methode *f* des Aufsteigens	méthode *f* de l'ascente	метод подъема
M 446	**method of balayage,** sweeping-out method, sweep out method, method of sweeping out <DE>	Balayage-Methode *f*, Balayage-Verfahren *n*	méthode *f* de balayage	метод выметания [Пуанкаре]
M 447	**method of Banachiewicz,** Banachiewicz['s] method <AL, NU>	Verfahren *n* von Banachiewicz, Banachiewiczsches Verfahren	méthode *f* de Banachiewicz	метод Банахевича
	method of calculation <GN, NU>	*s.* M 169		
M 448	**method of Cesàro-Abel type** <LI>	Verfahren *n* vom Cesàro-Abel-Typ	procédé *m* du type de Cesàro-Abel	метод типа Чезаро-Абеля
M 449	**method of characteristic curves** <AX, DE, NU>	Charakteristikenverfahren *n*, Massausche Gitterkonstruktion *f*, Gitterkonstruktion nach Massau	méthode *f* des caractéristiques	метод характеристик
	method of Cholesky <AL, NU>	*s.* C 646		
M 450	**method of [coefficient] comparison, method of comparison of coefficients,** method of undetermined coefficients, method of equating coefficients, comparison of coefficients [method], coefficient comparison <GN>	Methode *f* (Verfahren *n*) der unbestimmten Koeffizienten, Methode des Koeffizientenvergleichs, Koeffizientenvergleich *m*, Koeffizientenvergleichung *f*	méthode *f* des coefficients indéterminés, méthode par identification [des coefficients], méthode de comparaison des coefficients, identification *f* [des coefficients], comparaison *f* des coefficients	метод неопределенных коэффициентов, метод сравнения [коэффициентов], метод приравнивания [коэффициентов], метод выравнивания, приравнение коэффициентов [при одинаковых степенях], уравнивание (сравнивание, сравнение) коэффициентов
	method of complete induction <FO>	*s.* M 165		
M 451	**method of computation,** calculating method <of numerical values> <NU>	Berechnungsmethode *f*, Rechenmethode *f*, Rechenverfahren *n*	méthode *f* de calcul	расчетный (вычислительный) метод, метод расчета (вычисления), способ вычисления
M 452	**method of conjugate gradients** <NU>	konjugierte Gradientenmethode *f*	méthode *f* du gradient conjugué	метод сопряженных градиентов
M 453	**method of conjugate nets** <FA>	Methode *f* der konjugierten Netze	méthode *f* des réseaux conjugués	метод сопряженных сетей

No.	English	German	French	Russian
M 454	**method of construction** <Russell> <MM>	Konstruktionsmethode *f*	méthode *f* de construction	метод конструкции
M 455	**method of descending indices** <GP, PG>	Methode *f* der fallenden Indizes	méthode *f* des indices descendants	метод нисходящих индексов
M 456	**method of descent** <NT>	Abstiegsmethode *f* <Satz von Mordell-Weil>	méthode *f* de la descente	метод спуска
M 457	**method of descent** <of Fermat> <NT>	Fermats Methode *f* des Herabsteigens, Methode des Zurückführens	méthode *f* de descente de Fermat	метод спуска Ферма
	method of diagonals <SE>	*s.* D 393a		
M 458	**method of Dirichlet's discontinuity factor** <AN, NT>	Methode *f* des diskontinuierlichen Faktors	méthode *f* du facteur de discontinuité	метод разрывного множителя
	method of Doolittle <AL, NU, ST>	*s.* D 891		
M 459	**method of elimination,** elimination method <AL>	Eliminationsmethode *f*, Eliminationsverfahren *n*	méthode *f* (procédé *m*) d'élimination; algorithme *m* d'élimination	метод исключения, способ исключения <неизвестных>
M 460	**method of equating** <in elimination> <AL>	Gleichsetzungsmethode *f*, Gleichsetzungsverfahren *n*, Methode *f* der Gleichsetzung, Komparationsmethode *f*	méthode *f* par identification (comparaison)	метод приравнивания
	method of equating coefficients <GN>	*s.* M 450		
M 461	**method of estimation** <ST>	Schätzverfahren *n*, Schätzung *f*	méthode *f* d'estimation	метод оценки
M 462	**method of exhaustion[s],** method of geometric exhaustion <GE>	[Archimedische] Exhaustionsmethode *f*, Exhaustion *f*, Methode *f* der Ausschöpfung, Ausschöpfungsmethode *f*	méthode *f* d'exhaustion, procédure *f* d'exhaustion d'Eudoxe	метод исчерпывания
M 463	**method of false position,** rule of false position, regula falsi, Regula falsi, binary chopping, double position <AN, NU>	Regula *f* falsi, Eingabeln *n* der Nullstelle, Sekantenverfahren *n*, Regel *f* vom falschen Ansatz, Regula duorum falsorum, Verfahren *n* der linearen Interpolation	règle *f* de fausse position, algorithme *m* des parties proportionnelles	метод хорд (ложного положения), правило (способ) ложного положения, метод секущих (линейного интерполирования)
	method of finite elements <AN, NU>	*s.* F 271		
M 464	**method of fractional steps,** method of splitting <DE, NU>	Verfahren *n* (Methode *f*) der eingeschalteten Halbschritte, Zwischenschrittverfahren *n*	méthode *f* à pas fractionnaires	метод дробных шагов
	method of geometric exhaustion <GE>	*s.* M 462		
M 465	**method of good lattice points,** method of optimal coefficients <DI, NU>	Methode *f* der optimalen Koeffizienten <von N. M. Korobow>	méthode *f* des « bons treillis »	метод оптимальных коэффициентов <Н. М. Коробова>
M 466	**method of Gordan,** Gordan['s] method <IV>	Gordansche Methode *f*	méthode *f* de Gordan	метод Гордана
M 467	**method of harmonic balance,** harmonic balance method <DE>	Methode *f* der harmonischen Balance, Krylow-Bogoljubow-Methode *f*	méthode *f* [de la] balance harmonique	метод (принцип) гармонического баланса, метод Крылова-Боголюбова
M 468	**method of indeterminates** <*e.g.:* for proving the theorem of primitive elements> <AL>	Methode *f* der Unbestimmten	méthode *f* des indéterminées	метод неопределенных
	method of induction <FO>	*s.* M 165		
M 469	**method of infinite descent** <LO>	Methode *f* des unendlichen Abstiegs	méthode *f* de la descente infinie	метод бесконечного спуска
	method of integral equations <DE, PO>	*s.* I 623		
	method of interest calculation <AR>	*s.* I 711		
M 470	**method of interpretations,** model method <FO, LO>	Modellmethode *f*	méthode *f* des interprétations	метод интерпретаций, метод моделей
	method of inverse probability <ST, TG>	*s.* B 150		
	method of Lagrangian multipliers <DI, PG, VA>	*s.* L 25		
	method of least squares <ER, NU>	*s.* L 250		
	method of limitation <LI>	*s.* L 707		
	method of limitation by means defined by integral functions <LI>	*s.* J 56		
M 471	**method of link relatives** <ST>	Gliedziffernmethode *f*	méthode *f* de la chaîne de rapports	
M 472	**method of logarithmic potential,** logarithmic potential method <PG>	Methode *f* des logarithmischen Potentials <von Frisch>, Frischsche Methode des logarithmischen Potentials	méthode *f* du potentiel logarithmique	метод логарифмического потенциала
	method of maximum likelihood <ST>	*s.* M 261		
	method of moments <ST>	*s.* M 814		

	method of multipliers <DI, PG, VA>	*s.* L 25		
	method of optimal coefficients <DI, NU>	*s.* M 465		
M 473	**method of orbits** <for Lie algebras> <AL>	Orbitmethode *f*	méthode *f* des orbites	метод орбит
M 474	**method of partial fractions** <AN>	Partialbruchmethode *f*	méthode *f* des fractions simples	метод элементарных дробей
	method of partitioning the variables <DE, PG>	*s.* S 562		
M 475	**method of path coefficients,** path coefficient method, path analysis <ST>	Pfadkoeffizientenmethode *f*, Pfadanalyse *f* <von Wright>	méthode (analyse) *f* des coefficients de direction	метод путевых коэффициентов, анализ пути
	method of penalty functions <PG>	*s.* P 372		
	method of phase diagram <DE>	*s.* P 559		
	method of postulation <MM>	*s.* A 1272		
	method of potentials <PG>	*s.* S 1749		
M 476	**method of power series** <DE>	Potenzreihenmethode *f*	méthode *f* de série entière	метод степенного ряда
M 477	**method of principal axes (axis)** <ST>	Hauptachsenmethode *f*	méthode *f* des axes principaux	метод главных осей
M 478	**method of principal components** <ST>	Hauptkomponentenmethode *f*	méthode *f* des composantes principales	метод основных компонент
M 479	**method of Puiseux,** Puiseux['] method <FT>	Puiseuxsche Methode *f*	méthode *f* de Puiseux	метод Пюизе
M 480	**method of representatives** <AL>	Repräsentantenmethode *f*, Repräsentationsmethode *f*	méthode *f* des représentants	метод представителей
M 481	**method of Riesz['s] arithmetic means** <LI>	Verfahren *n* der Rieszschen arithmetischen Mittel	méthode *f* des moyennes arithmétiques de [M.] Riesz	метод средних арифметических [М.] Риса
M 482	**method of Riesz['s] logarithmic means** <LI>	Verfahren *n* der Rieszschen logarithmischen Mittel	méthode *f* des moyennes logarithmiques de [M.] Riesz	метод средних логарифметических [М.] Риса
M 483	**method of Riesz['s] typical means** <of the first *or* second kind> <LI>	Verfahren *n* der Rieszschen typischen Mittel <erster (1.) *oder* zweiter (2.) Art>	méthode *f* des moyennes typiques de [M.] Riesz <de première *ou* deuxième (seconde) espèce>	метод средних типичных [М.] Риса <первого *или* второго рода>
	method of Runge and Kutta <DE, NU>	*s.* R 1524		
	method of saddle points <DI	*s.* M 486		
	method of solution factors <PG>	*s.* K 16		
	method of solving multipliers <PG>	*s.* K 16		
	method of splitting <DE, NU>	*s.* M 464		
	method of statistical testing <NU, ST>	*s.* M 878		
M 484	**method of steepest ascent[s],** steepest-ascent method, steepest ascent method <AN, NU, PG>	Methode *f* (Verfahren *n*) des steilsten Anstiegs	méthode *f* de la plus grande ascension	метод скорейшего (наискорейшего, быстрейшего, крутого) восхождения, метод восхождения
M 485	**method of steepest descent[s],** steepest-descent method, steepest descent method, gradient method <AN, NU, PG>	Methode *f* des steilsten Abstiegs (Abfalls), Methode des größten Gefälles, Prinzip (Verfahren) *n* des steilsten Abstiegs, Prinzip (Verfahren) des steilsten Abfalls, Gradientenmethode *f*, Gradientenverfahren *n*, Abstiegsverfahren *n*, Abstiegsmethode *f*	méthode *f* de la plus profonde descente, méthode de la plus grande pente	метод скорейшего (наискорейшего, быстрейшего) спуска, метод спуска
M 486	**method of steepest descent[s],** steepest-descent method, steepest descent method, saddle-point method, method of saddle points, saddle point approximation <DI>	Sattelpunktmethode *f*, Paßmethode *f*, Methode *f* der Sattelpunkte	méthode *f* du col	метод перевала (наибольшего ската, седловых точек, седловой точки, наискорейшего спуска, наибыстрейшего спуска)
M 487	**method of straight lines** <DS>	Geradenverfahren *n*	méthode *f* des droites	метод прямых
	method of subdomains <DE>	*s.* S 2099		
	method of substitution <DI>	*s.* I 679		
M 488	**method of successive approximations,** contracting mapping principle <AN, DE, TO>; Picard['s] method (iteration) <DE>	Methode *f* (Verfahren *n*) der sukzessiven Approximation[en], Prinzip *n* der kontrahierenden Abbildung, Methode der kontraktiven Abbildung <AN, DE, TO>; Iterationsmethode *f* (Iterationsverfahren *n*) von Picard-Lindelöf, Picardsche Iteration *f*, Picardsches Verfahren <DE>	méthode *f* des approximations successives, méthode de l'application contractante <AN, DE, TO>; méthode de Picard, intégration *f* par itération <DE>	метод последовательных приближений, метод (принцип) сжатых отображений <AN, DE, TO>; метод [итерации] Пикара, метод последовательных приближений Пикара-Линделефа <DE>

	method of successive approximations <NU>	*s.* I 1129		
	method of summation <LI>	*s.* S 2287		
	method of summation by means defined by integral functions <LI>	*s.* J 55		
	method of sweeping out <DE>	*s.* M 446		
M 489	**method of the cutting plane** <by Kelley> <PG>	Schnittebenenmethode *f* von Kelley, Kelleysche Schnittebenenmethode	méthode *f* des plans sécants	способ секущих плоскостей
	method of transfinite induction <GN, MM>	*s.* T 744		
	method of undetermined coefficients <GN>	*s.* M 450		
	method of undetermined multipliers <DI, PG, VA>	*s.* L 25		
	method of variation of the constants (parameters) <DE>	*s.* V 80		
	method of zero-one verification <LO>	*s.* Z 49		
	method with variable metric <AX, NU>	*s.* N 207		
M 490	**metric,** metrics <TO>	Metrik *f*, metrische Struktur *f*	stucture *f* métrique	метрика, метрическая структура
M 491	**metric,** metric function, distance-function, distance [function] <on a set> <as a functional> <TO>	Metrik *f*, eigentliche Metrik <auf einer Menge>	métrique *f* <sur un ensemble>	метрика <на множестве>
M 492	**metrically connected manifold (variety)** <DG>	metrisch zusammenhängende Mannigfaltigkeit *f*	variété *f* métriquement connexe	метрически связное многообразие
M 493	**metrically convergent sequence** <TO>	metrisch konvergente Folge (Mengenfolge) *f*	suite *f* métriquement convergente	метрически сходящаяся последовательность
M 494	**metrically convex subset,** convex subset, M-convex subset <of a metric space> <CS, TO>	metrisch konvexe Teilmenge *f*, konvexe Teilmenge <Menger>	partie *f* métriquement convexe, partie convexe	метрически выпуклое подмножество, М-выпуклое (выпуклое по Менгеру, выпуклое в смысле Менгера) подмножество
M 495	**metrically dense** <TO>	metrisch dicht	métriquement dense	метрически плотный
	metrically transitive flow (transformation) <ME>	*s.* E 463		
	metric axioms <TO>	*s.* D 731		
M 496	**metric Baire space** <TO>	metrischer Bairescher Raum *m*, G_{II}-Raum *m* <Hausdorff>	espace *m* métrique de Baire	метрическое пространство Бэра
M 497	**metric base,** base <of a semi-metric space> <TO>	metrische Basis *f*, Basis	base *f* métrique, base	метрический базис, базис
M 498	**metric connection,** metric transfer <DG>	metrische (maßtreue) Übertragung *f*, metrischer (maßtreuer) Zusammenhang *m*	connexion *f* métrique, transfert *m* métrique	метрическая связность, метрическое перенесение
M 499	**metric convergence** <of sequences of sets> <FA, TO>	metrische Konvergenz *f*	convergence *f* métrique	метрическая сходимость
M 500	**metric convexity** <TO>	metrische Konvexität *f*	convexité *f* métrique	метрическая выпуклость
M 501	**metric determination,** mensuration <GE>	Maßbestimmung *f*, metrische Bestimmung *f*	détermination *f* métrique	мероопределение
M 502	**metric differential geometry** <DG>	metrische (maßtreue) Differentialgeometrie *f*	géométrie *f* différentielle métrique	метрическая дифференциальная геометрия
M 503	**metric form,** metric fundamental form <of a surface> <DG>	metrische Fundamentalform (Grundform) *f*, Maßform *f*	forme *f* métrique, forme fondamentale métrique	метрическая (квадратичная основная) форма, метрика
	metric form <DG>	*s.* F 337		
M 504	**metric function** <GE>	Maßfunktion *f*, metrische Funktion *f*	fonction *f* métrique	метрическая функция
	metric function <TO>	*s.* M 491		
	metric fundamental form <DG>	*s.* M 503		
M 505	**metric limit** <of a sequence of sets> <TO>	metrischer Limes *m*, lm	limite *f* métrique	метрический предел
M 506	**metric line** <of a metric space> <TO>	metrische (gerade) Linie *f*, Gerade *f*	droite *f* métrique	метрическая прямая
	metrics <TO>	*s.* M 490		
M 507	**metric segment,** segment <in a metric space> <DG>	metrische Strecke *f*, Strecke	segment *m* métrique, segment	метрический отрезок, отрезок
M 508	**metric space** <TO>	metrischer Raum *m*	espace *m* métrique (distancié, doté d'une métrique)	метрическое пространство
	metric tensor <DG>	*s.* F 854		
M 509	**metric theory of continued fractions** <NT>	metrische Kettenbruchlehre (Kettenbruchtheorie) *f*	théorie *f* métrique des fractions continues	метрическая теория цепных дробей
	metric topology <TO>	*s.* S 2003		
	metric topology <TO>	*s.* T 564		

	metric transfer <DG>	*s.* M 498		
M 510	**metric which defines a given topology** <TO>	mit einer Topologie verträgliche Metrik	distance *f* compatible avec une topologie	расстояние, согласующееся с топологией
M 511	**metrizability** <TO>	Metrisierbarkeit *f*	métrisabilité *f*	метризуемость
M 512	**metrizable group** <GR>	metrisierbare Gruppe *f*	groupe *m* métrisable	метризуемая группа
M 513	**metrizable topology** <TO>	metrisierbare Topologie *f*	topologie *f* métrisable	метризуемая топология
M 514	**metrizable uniform space** <TO>	[uniform] metrisierbarer uniformer Raum *m*	espace *m* uniforme métrisable	метризуемое равномерное пространство
M 515	**metrization** <TO>	Metrisierung *f*, Metrisation *f*	métrisation *f*	метризация, введение метрики
M 516	**metrization theorem of Urysohn,** Urysohn['s] theorem <TO>	Urysohnscher Metrisationssatz *m*, Metrisationssatz von Urysohn	théorème *m* de métrisation d'Urysohn	метризационная теорема Урысона
M 517	**Meusnier['s] sphere** <GE>	Meusniersche Kugel *f*	sphère *f* de Meusnier	сфера Менье
M 518	**Meusnier['s] theorem,** theorem of Meusnier <DG>	Satz *m* von Meusnier, Meusnierscher Satz	théorème *m* de Meusnier	теорема Менье
	Meyer['s] theorem <NT>	*s.* T 321		
	m-field of sets <AL>	*s.* M 291		
	m-filter <SE>	*s.* M 292		
M 519	***M*-flat module** <AL>	*M*-flacher Modul *m*	module *m* *M*-plat	*M*-плоский модуль, модуль плоский относительно модуля *M*
M 520	***m*-form** <AL>	*m*-Form *f*	*m*-forme *f*	*m*-форма
M 521	**m-generators** <of an m-subalgebra> <AL>	m-Erzeugende *fpl*	m-générateurs *mpl*	m-образующие
	M-group <GR>	*s.* M 753		
M 522	**mid-coefficient** <in a formula> <GN>	mittlerer Koeffizient *m*	coefficient *m* moyen	средний коэффициент
M 523	**middle associator (nucleus)** <of a groupoid> <AL>	mittlerer Nukleus *m*		среднее ядро
M 524	**middle plane,** midplane <of a tetrahedron> <EG>	Mittelebene *f*	plan *m* médian	срединная плоскость
M 525	**middle term** <LO>	terminus *m* medius	moyen terme *m*	средний термин
M 526	**middle term** <of a syllogism> <LO>	Mittelbegriff *m*, Mittelglied *n*	moyen terme *m*	средний член
	middle third set <TO>	*s.* C 91		
M 527	***M*-ideal** <AL>	*M*-Ideal *n*	*M*-idéal *m*	*M*-идеал
M 528	**midenvelope,** median envelope <of a congruence of lines *or* of a surface> <DG>	Mittenhüllfläche *f*, Mittenenveloppe *f*, Mittenevolute *f*, Mittelhüllfläche *f*, Mittelenveloppe *f*, Mittelevolute *f*, mittlere Enveloppe *f*	enveloppe *f* médiane (moyenne)	срединная огибающая
	midline <EG>	*s.* M 355		
M 529	**mid[-]perpendicular** <of a line segment> <EG>	Mittelsenkrechte *f*	médiatrice *f*	медиатриса <отрезка *AB* или точек *A* и *B*>, серединный перпендикуляр <к отрезку *AB*>, симметраль <отрезка *AB*, точек *A* и *B*>
M 530	**midperpendicular [plane]** <of a segment> <as a plane> <EG>	Mittelsenkrechte *f* <Ebene>	plan *m* médiateur d'un segment, médiateur *m*	перпендикулярная плоскость, восстановленная в середине отрезка
	mid[-]perpendicular <EG>	*s.* R 1087		
M 531	**midplane,** median plane <of a line of a congruence of lines *or* of a surface> <DG>	Mittenebene *f*, Mittelebene *f*	plan *m* médian	срединная плоскость
	midplane <EG>	*s.* M 524		
M 532	**midpoint** <of an interval> <AN>	Intervallmitte *f*, Mitte *f* <eines Intervalls>	milieu *m* <d'un intervalle>	середина <интервала>
M 533	**midpoint,** median point <of a line in a congruence of lines> <DG>	Mittenpunkt *m*, Mittelpunkt *m*	point *m* médian	средняя точка
	midpoint <AT>	*s.* C 394		
	midpoint <EG>	*s.* B 459		
	midpoint formula <DI, NU>	*s.* M 12		
M 534	**mid[-]range** <ST>	Spannweitenmitte *f*, Mitte *f* des Variationsintervalls	centre *m* d'étendue	полусумма крайних значений, середина области измерения
M 535	**mid-rank method** <ST>	Mittelrangmethode *f*	méthode *f* des rangs moyens	метод связанных (объединенных) рангов
M 536	**mid-square method** <ST>	Quadratmittenmethode *f*	méthode *f* des centres du carré	метод середин квадрата
M 537	**midsurface,** median surface <of a congruence of lines *or* of a surface> <DG>	Mittenfläche *f*, Mittelfläche *f*	surface *f* médiane (moyenne)	срединная поверхность
	military perspective <DS>	*s.* B 444		
M 538	**millimetre squared paper** <IN, NU>	Millimeterpapier *n*	papier *m* millimétré (millimétrique, quadrillé en millimètres)	миллиметровая бумага, миллиметровка
M 539	**Milloux['s] theorem** <FT>	Satz *m* von Milloux, Millouxscher Satz	théorème *m* de Milloux	теорема Милью
M 540	**Milne['s] [integral] equation** <IE>	Milnesche Integralgleichung *f*	équation *f* [intégrale] de Milne	[интегральное] уравнение Милне

	English	German	French	Russian
M 541	**Milne-Thomson polynomial** <FU>	Milne-Thomson-Polynom *n*	polynôme *m* de Milne-Thomson	многочлен Милне-Томсона
M 542	**Milnor['s] ball** <AG>	Milnor-Kugel *f*	boule *f* de Milnor	шар Милнора
M 543	**Milnor['s] fibration** <AT>	Milnorsche Faserung *f*	fibration *f* de Milnor	расслоение Милнора
M 544	**Milnor['s] number** <AG>	Milnor-Zahl *f*	nombre *m* de Milnor	число Милнора
	min <DI, GN>	*s.* M 596		
	min <GE>	*s.* 1. C 340; 2. M 659		
M 545	**Minding['s] problem** <of isometric surfaces> <GE>	Mindingsches Problem *n* <isometrischer Flächen>	problème *m* de Minding <des surfaces isométriques>	задача Миндинга <изометрических поверхностей>
	Minding['s] rule <AL>	*s.* R 1487		
M 546	**minimal** <VA> ⌐<TA>	Minimale *f*	minimale *f*	минималь
M 547	**minimal automaton**	minimaler Automat *m*	automate *m* minimal	минимальный автомат
M 548	**minimal base** <of an algebraic variety *or* group> <AG, GR>	Minimalbasis *f*	base *f* minima	минимальный базис
M 549	**minimal base** <IV>	Minimalbasis *f*	base *f* minimale	минимальный базис
	minimal base <AB>	*s.* M 550		
M 550	**minimal basis,** minimal base <of order h> <AB>	Minimalbasis *f* <h-ter Ordnung>	base *f* minimale <d'ordre h>	минимальный базис <порядка h>
	minimal basis <AL>	*s.* F 174		
M 551	**minimal Cauchy filter** <TO>	minimaler Cauchy-Filter *m*	filtre *m* de Cauchy minimal	минимальный фильтр Коши
	minimal congruence relation <UA>	*s.* P 1400		
M 552	**minimal containing prime ideal** <of an ideal> <AL>	minimales Primoberideal *n*, höchstes Primoberideal	suridéal *m* premier minimal	минимальный простой идеал
M 553	**minimal containing pure subgroup** <GR>	Servanzhülle *f*	sous-groupe *m* pur minimal contenant	сервантная оболочка
M 554	**minimal co-ordinates** <AY>	Minimalkoordinaten *fpl*	coordonnées *fpl* minimales	минимальные координаты
	minimal curve <DG>	*s.* I 1194		
M 555	**minimal degree,** class <of a permutation group> <GR>	Minimalgrad *m*, Klasse *f* <Netto>	classe *f*	минимальная степень
	minimal degree <GP>	*s.* M 580		
M 556	**minimal dimension** <of a prime ideal> <AL>	Minimaldimension *f*	dimension *f* minimale	минимальная размерность
M 557	**minimal equation** <in field theory> <AL>	Minimalgleichung *f* <für ein Körperelement α über K>, zu α über K gehörige irreduzible Gleichung *f*	équation *f* minimale	минимальное уравнение
	minimal fixed block <GR>	*s.* D 874		
M 558	**minimal form** <AL, NT>	[quadratische] Minimalform *f*	forme *f* minimale	минимальная форма
	minimal generating set <GR> , ⌐<DG>	*s.* I 1036		
	minimal geodesic curve	*s.* N 773		
M 559	**minimal graph** <GP>	Minimalgraph *m*	graphe *m* minimal	минимальный граф
M 560	**minimal identity** <for algebras> <AL>	Minimalidentität *f*	identité *f* minimale	минимальное тождество
M 561	**minimality,** minimal property <GN>	Minimalität *f*, Minimaleigenschaft *f*	minimalité *f*, propriété *f* minimale	минимальность, свойство минимальности; свойство минимума
	minimal left ideal <AL>	*s.* S 927		
M 562	**minimally connected graph** <GP>	minimal zusammenhängender Graph *m*	graphe *m* connexe-minimal	реберно-критический граф относительно сильной связности
M 563	**minimal manifold,** minimal variety <DG>	Minimalmannigfaltigkeit *f*	variété *f* minimale	минимальное многообразие
M 564	**minimal model** <AG>	minimales Modell *n*, Minimalmodell *n*	modèle *m* minimum (minimal)	минимальная модель
M 565	**minimal normal subgroup** <of a group> <GR>	minimaler (kleinster) Normalteiler *m*, Fuß *m*	sous-groupe *m* distingué minimal, petit diviseur *m* normal, sous-groupe *m* invariant minimal	минимальный нормальный делитель
M 566	**minimal polynomial** <of an element α over a field k> <AL>	Minimalpolynom *n* <von α über k>, zu α über k gehöriges irreduzibles Polynom *n*	polynôme *m* minimal <de α sur k>	минимальный полином <элемента α над k>
M 567	**minimal polynomial,** minimum function, reduced characteristic function <of a matrix> <MD>	Minimalpolynom *n*	polynôme *m* minimal (minimum)	минимальный многочлен, минимальный аннулирующий многочлен
M 568	**minimal prime ideal** <AL>	minimales Primideal *n*	idéal *m* premier minimal	минимальный простой идеал
M 569	**minimal principle** <SE>	Minimalprinzip *n*	principe *m* de minimalité	принцип минимальности
	minimal property <GN>	*s.* M 561		
M 570	**minimal propositional calculus** <LO>	Minimalkalkül *m*	logique *f* minimale, logique minimale de Johansson	минимальная логика, минимальное исчисление высказываний
M 571	**minimal quasiprimitive class, minimal quasivariety,** atomic quasivariety <UA>	minimale Quasimannigfaltigkeit (Quasivarietät) *f*	quasi-variété *f* minimale	минимальное квазимногообразие, атомарное квазимногообразие
M 572	**minimal representation as a join of $\cup$-irreducible elements** <of a lattice> <LA>	minimale vereinigungsirreduzible Zerlegung *f*	représentation *f* $\vee$-irréductible minimale, représentation $\vee$-irréductible sans élément superflu	минимальное $\cup$-представление с $\cup$-неразложимыми элементами

M 573	**minimal representation as a meet of irreducible elements** <LA>	minimale durchschnitts-irreduzible Zerlegung *f*	représentation *f* ∧-irréductible minimale	минимальное ⌒-представление с ⌒-неразложимыми элементами
	minimal residue <NT>	*s.* L 237		
	minimal right ideal <AL>	*s.* S 947		
	minimal solution <AX>	*s.* E 131a		
	minimal spanning set <AL>	*s.* V 97		
M 574	**minimal subcover** <TO>	in einer Überdeckung enthaltene minimale Überdeckung *f*, minimale Teilüberdeckung *f*	sous-recouvrement *m* minimal	минимальное подпокрытие
M 575	**minimal sufficient estimator,** minimum sufficient estimator <ST>	minimale hinreichende Punktschätzung (Schätzung, Schätzfunktion) *f*, notwendige und hinreichende Punktschätzung (Schätzung, Schätzfunktion)	estimateur *m* exhaustif minimal, fonction *f* estimatrice exhaustive minimale	минимальная достаточная оценка
M 576/7	**minimal surface** <DG>	Minimalfläche *f*	surface *f* minimale	минимальная поверхность
M 578	**minimal system of generators** <of a closure operation> <TO>	minimales Erzeugendensystem *n*	système *m* générateur minimal (irréductible, sans éléments superflus)	минимальное порождающее множество
	minimal system of generators <GR>	*s.* I 1036		
M 579	**minimal type** <of a meromorphic function> <FT>	Minimaltypus *m*, Minimaltyp *m*	type *m* minimal	минимальный тип
M 580	**minimal valency,** minimal degree <of a graph> <GP>	Minimalvalenz *f*	degré *m* minimum	минимальная степень
M 581	**minimal variety,** atomic variety, equationally complete class <UA>	minimale Mannigfaltigkeit (Varietät) *f*, minimale primitive Klasse *f*	classe *f* primitive minimale	минимальное многообразие, атомарное многообразие, эквационально полный класс
	minimal variety <DG>	*s.* M 563		
M 582	**minimant** <VA>	Minimante *f*	minimante *f*	миниманта
M 583	**minimax** <PG, TG>	Minimax *n*, Minmax *n*	minimax *m*	минимакс
M 584	**minimax decision function** <ST>	Minimax-Entscheidungsfunktion *f*	fonction *f* de décision minimax	минимаксная решающая функция
M 585	**minimax equality,** min-max equality <TG>	Minmaxgleichung *f*	égalité *f* du minimax	равенство минимакса
M 586	**minimax group** <GR>	Minimaxgruppe *f*	groupe *m* minimax	минимаксная группа
M 587	**minimax inequality** <TG>	Minimaxungleichung *f*, Minimax-Ungleichung *f*	inégalité *f* du minimax	неравенство минимакса
M 588	**minimax principle** <DE>	Minimaxprinzip *n*, Mini-Max-Prinzip *n*, Courantsches (Courants) Mini-Max-Prinzip, [Courantsches] Minimum-Maximum-Prinzip *n*, [Courantsches] Maximum-Minimum-Prinzip *n*, Courants Maximum-Minimum-Prinzip, Minimum-Maximum-Prinzip (Maximum-Minimum-Prinzip) von Courant, Minimaxtheorem *n*, Courant-Fischer-Theorem *n*	principe *m* minimax	принцип минимакса
M 589	**minimax principle,** maximum-minimum principle <PG, TG>	Minimaxprinzip *n*, Mini-Max-Prinzip *n*, Minimum-Maximum-Prinzip *n*, Maximin-Prinzip *n*	principe *m* minimax, principe du (de) minimax	принцип минимакса
M 590	**minimax solution** <PG>	minimaxe Lösung *f*, Minimaxlösung *f*	solution *f* minimax	минимаксное решение
M 591	**minimax strategy** <TG>	Minimaxstrategie *f*, Minimax-Strategie *f*, Maximinstrategie *f*, Maximin-Strategie *f*, Vorsichtstrategie *f*	stratégie *f* minimax	минимаксная стратегия, стратегия минимакса
	minimax technique <AX, NU>	*s.* C 600		
M 592	**minimax theorem,** min-max theorem <PG, TG>	Minimaxtheorem *n* [der Spieltheorie], Min-Max-Theorem *n* [J. von Neumanns], Hauptsatz *m* für Matrixspiele, Minimaxsatz *m*, Minmax-Satz *m*	théorème *m* du (de) minimax, théorème minimax	теорема [Неймана] о минимаксе, теорема минимакса, основная теорема [теории матричных] игр [Дж. фон Неймана]
M 593	**minimization; minimizing** <PG>	Minimierung *f*, // Minimalisierung *f*, Minimisierung *f*	minimisation *f*	минимизация; минимизирование, обеспечение минимума
M 594	**minimizing method** <AX, DE>	„minimizing method" *f*, Minimierungsmethode *f*	méthode *f* de minimisation	метод минимизации
M 595	**minimizing sequence** <VA>	Minimalfolge *f*	suite *f* minimisante	минимизирующая последовательность

No.	English	German	French	Russian
M 596	**minimum,** min, minimum value <DI, GN>	Minimum *n*, min, Minimalwert *m*	minimum *m*, min, valeur *f* minimale (minimum)	минимум, min, минимальное значение
M 597	**minimum,** lower (inferior) limit <of a function at a point> <RF>	unterer Limes (Hauptlimes, extremer Limes) *m*, untere Unbestimmtheitsgrenze (Häufungsgrenze) *f* <einer Funktion in bezug auf einen Filter, nach einem Filter, längs eines Filters>	limite *f* inférieure <d'une fonction suivant un filtre>	нижний предел <числовой функции по фильтру>
M 598	**minimum** <of a sequence> <SS>	Minimum *n*, reales Minimum	minimé *m*, minimum *m* réel	минимум
	minimum <DI>	*s.* A 117		
M 599	**minimum at the boundary** <of a function> <AN>	Randminimum *n*, Minimum *n* auf dem Rand	minimum *m* au bord	граничный минимум
	minimum chi-squared method <ST>	*s.* M 609		
M 600	**minimum condition** <for a partially ordered set> <AL, SE>	Minimalbedingung *f*	condition *f* minimale	условие минимальности
M 601	**minimum covering** <GP>	minimale Überdeckung *f*	recouvrement *m* minimal	минимальное реберное разделение
M 602	**minimum covering problem** <GP>	Problem *n* der minimalen Überdeckung	problème *m* de recouvrement minimal	задача минимального реберного разделения
M 603	**minimum density** <of a power series> <SS>	Minimaldichte *f*	densité *f* minimum	минимальная плотность
M 604	**minimum distance method** <ST>	Verfahren *n* (Methode *f*) des minimalen Abstandes	méthode *f* de la distance minimum	метод минимального расстояния
	minimum equation <AL, MD>	*s.* R 342		
M 605	**minimum function** <of the general quantity> <of an algebra> <AL>	Rangpolynom *n*, Grundpolynom *n*, Minimalpolynom *n* <eines allgemeinen Elements>	polynôme *m* principal	ранговый полином
M 606	**minimum function** <of an element of an algebra> <AL>	Minimalpolynom *n*	polynôme *m* minimal	минимальный многочлен
	minimum function <MD>	*s.* M 567		
M 607	**minimum ideal** <of a matrix> <AL>	Minimumideal *n*	idéal *m* minimum	минимальный идеал
	minimum integral <DE>	*s.* M 617/8		
	minimum in the large <DI>	*s.* A 117		
	minimum in the narrow sense <DI>	*s.* S 1904		
	minimum in the small <DI>	*s.* L 1006		
	minimum limit <DI, SS>	*s.* L 1153		
	minimum line <AY, DG>	*s.* I 1196		
M 608	**minimum matrix procedure** <PG>	Minimalkostenregel *f*, Regel *f* der minimalen Kosten	règle *f* des coûts minimaux	правило минимальных издержек
M 609	**minimum χ^2-method,** minimum chi-squared method <ST>	Minimum-χ^2-Methode *f*, Minimum-Chi-Quadrat-Methode *f*, χ^2-Minimum-Methode *f*, Chi-Quadrat-Minimum-Methode *f*	méthode *f* de χ^2 minimum, méthode de chi carré minimum	метод минимума χ^2, метод минимума хи-квадрата
M 610	**minimum modulus** <of an operator> <FA>	Minimalmodul *m*	module *m* minimum	минимум модуля
M 611	**minimum modulus** <of a holomorphic function> <FT>	Minimalbetrag *m*	module *m* minimum	минимум модуля
M 612	**minimum-modulus principle** <FT>	Satz *m* vom Minimum	principe *m* du module minimum	принцип минимума модуля
	minimum plane <AY, DG, PJ>	*s.* I 1201		
M 613	**minimum point,** point (position) of minimum <DI>	Minimalstelle *f*, Minimumstelle *f*	point *m* minimal (de minimum), point où la fonction admet un minimum	минимальная точка, точка минимума; точка, в которой функция принимает минимум
M 614	**minimum principle,** principle of minimum <for eigenvalue problems> <DE>	Minimalprinzip *n*	principe *m* du minimum	принцип минимума
	minimum principle <AN, FO>	*s.* L 247		
M 615	**minimum problem** <DI>	Minimumaufgabe *f*, Minimumproblem *n*	problème *m* de minimum	задача на минимум, минимальная задача, проблема минимума
M 616	**minimum property** <ST>	Minimumseigenschaft *f*	propriété *f* du minimum	свойство минимума
M 617/8	**minimum solution,** minimum integral <DE>	Minimalintegral *n*, Unterfunktion *f*	intégrale (solution) *f* minimale	нижнее решение, нижний (минимальный) интеграл
	minimum solution <AX>	*s.* E 131a		
	minimum solution <ST>	*s.* B 154		
M 619	**minimum strategy** <TG>	minimale Strategie *f*	stratégie *f* minimale	минимальная стратегия
	minimum sufficient estimator <ST>	*s.* M 575		

	minimum turning value <DI>	*s.* L 1006		
	minimum value <DI>	*s.* A 117		
	minimum value <DI, GN>	*s.* M 596		
	minimum variance unbiased estimator <ST>	*s.* M 909		
M 620	**minimum vector** <GU>	Minimalvektor *m*	vecteur *m* minimum	минимизирующий вектор
M 621	**minimum with a condition (constraint),** constraint minimum, relative minimum <DI, PG, VA>	Minimum *n* unter (mit) einer Nebenbedingung, gebundenes (relatives) Minimum	minimum *m* sous une condition (contrainte), minimum contraint (relatif)	минимум с условием (ограничением), условный (относительный) минимум
M 622	**minischeme** <AG>	Minischema *n*	minischéma *m*	минисхема
M 623	**Minkowskian addition** <of point sets> <CS, GE>	Minkowskische Addition *f*	addition *f* minkowskienne	сложение Минковского
	Minkowskian geometry <CS, GE>	*s.* M 631		
M 624	**Minkowskian linear combination** <of point sets> <CS, GE>	Minkowskische Linearkombination *f*	combinaison *f* linéaire minkowskienne	линейная комбинация Минковского
M 625	**Minkowskian space,** Minkowski space <CS, DG>	Minkowskischer Raum *m*	espace *m* de Minkowski	пространство Минковского
M 626	**Minkowski['s] approximation theorem** <for convex bodies> <CS, GE>	Minkowskischer Approximationssatz *m*	théorème *m* d'approximation de Minkowski	аппроксимационная теорема Минковского
M 627	**Minkowski['s] conjecture** <for linear forms> <CS, GE>	Minkowskische Vermutung *f*	hypothèse *f* de Minkowski	гипотеза Минковского
M 628	**Minkowski['s] convex body theorem,** Minkowski['s] theorem <GU>	Minkowskischer Gitterpunktsatz *m*, Gitterpunktsatz von Minkowski, Minkowskischer Fundamentalsatz (Hauptsatz, Satz) *m*, Fundamentalsatz der Geometrie der Zahlen	théorème *m* fondamental de Minkowski	фундаментальная теорема Минковского в геометрии чисел
	Minkowski['s] convexity <CS, GE>	*s.* C 2394		
M 629	**Minkowski['s] determinant inequality (theorem),** determinant inequality of Minkowski <MD>	Minkowskische Ungleichung *f* <für Determinanten>	inégalité *f* de Minkowski <pour des déterminants>	неравенство Минковского <для определителей>
M 630	**Minkowski['s] functional,** Minkowski gauge, gauge <on a linear space> <FA>	Minkowski-Funktional *n*, Minkowskisches Funktional *n*, Distanzfunktion *f*	fonctionnelle *f* de Minkowski	функционал Минковского, опорная функция, функция Минковского
	Minkowski['s] functional <DG, GE>	*s.* G 56		
	Minkowski gauge <DG, GE>	*s.* G 56		
	Minkowski gauge <FA>	*s.* M 630		
M 631	**Minkowski['s] geometry,** Minkowskian geometry <CS, GE>	Minkowskische Geometrie *f*	géométrie *f* de Minkowski, géométrie minkowskienne	геометрия Минковского
	Minkowski-Hajós theorem <GU>	*s.* T 322		
M 632	**Minkowski['s] inequalities;** theorem of Minkowski <CS, GE>	Minkowskische Ungleichungen *fpl*; Minkowskische Ungleichheit *f*	inégalités *fpl* de Minkowski	неравенства Минковского
M 633	**Minkowski['s] inequality** <for series *or* integrals> <DI, SS>	Minkowskische Ungleichung *f*	inégalité *f* de Minkowski	неравенство Минковского
M 634	**Minkowski['s] lemma** <NT>	Minkowskisches Lemma *n*	lemme *m* de Minkowski	лемма Минковского
	Minkowski['s] linear forms theorem <GU>	*s.* M 638		
M 635	**Minkowski['s] mixed volume** <of a convex solid> <CS, GE>	Mischvolumen *n*, gemischtes Volumen *n*, gemischter Inhalt *m*	étendue *f* (volume *m*) mixte	смешанный объем
	Minkowski space <CS, DG>	*s.* M 625		
	Minkowski space <FA>	*s.* S 1318		
M 636	**Minkowski['s] sum** <of point sets> <CS, GE>	Minkowskische Summe *f*	somme *f* des corps convexes	сумма выпуклых тел
M 637	**Minkowski['s] theorem** <on convex surfaces> <CS, DG>	Satz *m* von Minkowski, Minkowskischer Satz	théorème *m* de Minkowski	теорема Минковского
	Minkowski['s] theorem <GU>	*s.* M 628		
M 638	**Minkowski['s] theorem about linear forms,** Minkowski['s] linear forms theorem <GU>	Minkowskischer Linearformensatz *m*	théorème *m* de Minkowski sur les formes linéaires	теорема Минковского о линейных формах
M 639	**Minkowski['s] theorem on units, Minkowski['s] unit theorem** <AB>	Minkowskischer Einheitensatz *m*	théorème *m* de Minkowski sur les unités	теорема Минковского об алгебраических единицах
	min-max equality <TG>	*s.* M 585		
	min-max technique <AX, NU, TG>	*s.* C 600		
	min-max theorem <PG,	*s.* M 592		

M 640	**minor** <of a matroid> <CT>	Minor *m*	mineur *m*	минор
M 641	**minor,** minor determinant, subdeterminant <*p*-rowed, *p*-th order> <MD>	Unterdeterminante *f*, Minor *m*, Subdeterminante *f*, Partialdeterminante *f*, partielle Determinante, // partiale Determinante *f* <*p*-reihig, *p*-ter Ordnung>	sous-déterminant *m*, mineur *m*, déterminant *m* partiel (extrait), déterminant dérivé <Cauchy> <d'ordre *p*>	минор, субдетерминант <порядка *p*>
M 642	**minorant,** minorant series <SS>	Minorante *f*, Minorantenreihe *f*, Unterreihe *f*	minorant *m*, série *f* minorante	миноранта, минорирующий ряд
	minorant <DI>	*s.* M 643		
	minorant <SE>	*s.* L 1129		
M 643	**minorant function,** minorant <DI>	Minorantenfunktion *f*, Minorante *f*	fonction *f* minorante, minorante *f*	минорантная функция, миноранта, минорирующая функция
	minorant series <SS>	*s.* M 642		
M 644	**minor arc** <in Farey dissection> <NT>	kleiner Bogen *m*, ,,minor arc" *m*	arc *m* mineur	меньшая дуга
	minor array <MD>	*s.* S 2130		
M 645	**minor axis,** shorter axis <of an ellipse> <AY>	kleine Achse *f*, Nebenachse *f*, konjugierte Achse, Querachse *f*; Länge *f* der Nebenachse (kleinen Achse)	petit axe *m*, axe secondaire, axe non focal, axe conjugué, second axe	малая ось
	minor determinant <MD>	*s.* M 641		
M 646	**minor in principal position,** chief minor <*p*-th> <MD>	Hauptabschnittsdeterminante *f*, Hauptunterdeterminante *f* in der linken oberen Ecke <*p*-te>	mineur *m* principal correspondant aux indices 1, . . ., *p*	главный минор, соответствующий индексам 1, . . ., *p*
	minorization <AN, AX, ER>	*s.* M 649		
M 647	**minorized chain** <SE>	nach unten beschränkte Kette *f*	chaîne *f* minorée	минорированная цепь
	minorized ordered set <SE>	*s.* O 319		
	minorized sequence <SS>	*s.* B 666		
M 648	**minorized series** <SS>	minorisierte (minorisierbare) Reihe *f*	série *f* minorée	минорируемый ряд
M 649	**minorizing,** minorization, lower estimate <AN, AX, ER>	Minorisierung *f*, Abschätzung *f* nach unten	minoration *f*	минорирование, оценка снизу
M 650	**minorizing set** <SE>	minorisierende Menge *f*	ensemble *m* minorant	минорирующее множество
	minor of a_{ik} <MD>	*s.* S 2083		
M 651	**minor of the Fredholm determinant** <*p*-th> <IE>	Minor *m* der Fredholmschen Determinante, Fredholmscher Minor <*p*-ter>	mineur *m* du déterminant de Fredholm <*p*-e>	минор определителя Фредгольма <*p*-й>
M 652	**minor premise** <in a categorical syllogism, the premise that contains the minor term> <LO>	praemissa *f* minor	mineure *f*	меньшая (младшая) посылка
M 653	**minor term** <in a categorical syllogism, the term that is the subject of the conclusion> <LO>	terminus *m* minor	mineur *m*, petit terme *m*	меньший термин
M 654	**minor theorem of Desargues** <GE>	kleiner Desarguesscher Satz *m*	petit théorème *m* de Desargues, théorème de Desargues	малая теорема Дезарга
M 655	**minterm** <AL, SE, LO>	Boolesches Elementarpolynom *n*, Konstituent *m*	produit *m* fondamental, minterme *m*	элементарный многочлен, конституента
M 656	**minuend** <AR, SE>	Minuend *m*, Minuendus *m*	minuende *m*	уменьшаемое
M 657	**minus infinity,** $-\infty$ <AN>	minus Unendlich *n*, $-\infty$	infini *m* négatif, moins l'infini, $-\infty$	минус бесконечность, $-\infty$
M 658	**minus mark (sign),** minus symbol, negative sign, — <AR>	Minuszeichen *n*, negatives Vorzeichen (Zeichen) *n*, —	signe *m* moins (négatif), —	знак минус, минус, отрицательный знак, —
	minus sign (symbol) <AR>	*s.* S 2216		
	minus symbol <AR>	*s.* M 658		
M 659	**minute, minute of angle (arc),** angular (sexagesimal) minute, ′, min <GE>	Minute *f*, Winkelminute *f*, Bogenminute *f*, Altminute *f*, ′	minute *f*, minute de l'angle, minute d'arc, minute angulaire (sexagésimale), ′	минута, минута угла (дуги), угловая минута, ′
M 660	**Miquel['s] circle** <GE>	Miquelscher Kreis *m*	cercle *m* de Miquel	окружность Микеля
M 661	**Miquel-Clifford configuration** <SG>	Miquel-Cliffordsche Konfiguration *f*	configuration *f* de Miquel-Clifford	конфигурация Микеля-Клиффорда
M 662	**Mirimanov['s] theorem** <NT>	Satz *m* von Mirimanow, Mirimanowscher Satz	théorème *m* de Mirimanov	теорема Мириманова
M 663	**mirror image,** reflected image, reflection <GE>	Spiegelbild *n*	image *f* symétrique	зеркальное отображение
	miscalculation <ER, NU>	*s.* C 1756		
	missing experimental unit <ST>	*s.* M 665		
	missing observation (plot) <ST>	*s.* M 665		
M 664	**missing plot technique** <ST>	Ergänzungsverfahren *n* fehlender Versuchseinheiten	technique *f* des unités expérimentales manquantes	метод дополнения выпавших единиц опыта
M 665	**missing value,** missing observation, missing plot, missing experimental unit <ST>	fehlender Wert *m*, fehlende Angabe (Beobachtung, Versuchseinheit) *f*, fehlendes Teilstück *n*, fehlende Parzelle *f*	valeur (donnée, observation) *f* manquante, unité *f* expérimentale manquante, parcelle *f* manquante	недостающее значение, недостающее наблюдение, недостающая экспериментальная единица, недостающая делянка
M 666	**mistake** <ER>	Irrtum *m*	faute *f*, bévue *f*	ошибка, промах

M 667	**mitre angle** <GE>	Winkel *m* von 45°, 45°-Winkel *m*	onglet *m*	угол 45°
M 668	**Mittag-Leffler['s] expansion; Mittag-Leffler['s] formula** <FT>	Mittag-Lefflersche Entwicklung *f*	développement *m* de M. Mittag-Leffler, développement (M)	разложение Миттаг-Леффлера
M 669	**Mittag-Leffler['s] function** <E_α> <FT>	Mittag-Lefflersche Funktion (E_α-Funktion) *f*	fonction *f* <E_α> de Mittag-Leffler	функция <E_α> Миттаг-Леффлера
M 670	**Mittag-Leffler['s] generalized theorem,** Mittag-Leffler['s] theorem <for general meromorphic functions> <FT>	verallgemeinerter Mittag-Lefflerscher Satz *m*, Mittag-Lefflerscher Satz	théorème *m* de Mittag-Leffler [généralisé]	[обобщенная] теорема Миттаг-Леффлера
M 671	**Mittag-Leffler['s] matrix** <FA>	Mittag-Lefflersche Matrix *f*	matrice *f* de Mittag-Leffler	матрица Миттаг-Леффлера
M 672	**Mittag-Leffler['s] method [of summation],** Mittag-Leffler summation method <LI>	Mittag-Lefflersches Summationsverfahren *n*, Borelsches Summationsverfahren für Potenzreihen	méthode *f* (procédé *m*) [de sommation] de Mittag-Leffler	метод [суммирования] Миттаг-Леффлера
M 673	**Mittag-Leffler['s] [R-]module** <AL>	Mittag-Lefflerscher Modul *m*	module *m* de Mittag-Leffler	модуль Миттаг-Леффлера
M 674	**Mittag-Leffler['s] star** <FT>	Holomorphiestern *m*, Hauptstern *m*, Mittag-Lefflerscher Stern *m*	étoile *f* d'holomorphie	звезда Миттаг-Леффлера, звезда гомоморфизма
M 675	**Mittag-Leffler sum,** B_α-sum <LI>	Mittag-Lefflersche Summe *f*, B_α-Summe *f*	somme *f* de Mittag-Leffler, B_α-somme *f*	[обобщенная] сумма по Миттаг-Леффлеру
	Mittag-Leffler summation method <LI>	*s.* M 672		
M 676	**Mittag-Leffler['s] theorem** <for expansion of a fractional meromorphic function> <FT>	Mittag-Lefflerscher Partialbruchsatz *m*, Mittag-Lefflerscher Satz *m*, Satz von Mittag-Leffler, Weierstraßscher Satz <zur Partialbruchzerlegung gebrochener Funktionen>	théorème *m* de Mittag-Leffler	теорема Миттаг-Леффлера
M 677	**Mittag-Leffler['s] theorem** <for existence of a certain meromorphic function> <FT>	Mittag-Lefflerscher Anschmiegungssatz *m*	théorème *m* de Mittag-Leffler	теорема Миттаг-Леффлера
	Mittag-Leffler['s] theorem <FT>	*s.* M 670		
M 678	**Mittag-Leffler['s] transform** <SS>	Mittag-Lefflersche Transformierte *f*	transformée *f* de Mittag-Leffler	трансформанта (изображение) Миттаг-Леффлера
M 679	**mixed area** <of a plane convex figure> <CS, GE>	gemischter Flächeninhalt (Inhalt) *m*	aire *f* mixte	смешанная площадь
M 680	**mixed-base notation,** mixed base (radix) notation <in number representation> <NT>	Gemischtbasisschreibweise *f*, Gemischtbasiszifferndarstellung *f*	système *m* de notation à base mixte	смешанная система счисления, представление чисел в системе со смешанным основанием, представление чисел в позиционной системе счисления с различными основаниями
	mixed boundary problem <DE, PO>	*s.* T 421		
	mixed boundary value problem <DE>	*s.* M 695		
	mixed boundary value problem <DE, PO>	*s.* T 421		
M 681	**mixed concomitant** <IV>	gemischte Konkomitante *f*, Zwischenform *f*, Divariante *f* <Salmon>	concomitant *m* mixte, forme *f* intermédiaire, divariant *m*, forme adjointe, concomitante *f* mixte	смешанный конкомитант
	mixed constraint <PG>	*s.* M 697		
M 682	**mixed covariant** <IV>	gemischte Kovariante *f*, Divariante *f*	covariant *m* mixte, divariant *m*	смешанный ковариант
M 683	**mixed cross-sectional measure** <CS, GE>	gemischtes Quermaß *n*	aire *f* mixte des travers, travers *m* extérieur mixte	смешанная поперечная мера
	mixed derivative <DI>	*s.* M 692		
	mixed differential equation <DE>	*s.* E 336		
M 684	**mixed differential parameter,** ∇ (U,V) <DG, VT>	gemischter Beltramischer Differentialparameter (Differentiator) *m*, gemischter Differentialparameter (Differentiator) von Beltrami, ∇ (U,V)	paramètre *m* différentiel mixte [de Beltrami], ∇ (U,V)	смешанный дифференциальный параметр [Бельтрами], ∇ (U,V)
M 685	**mixed distribution,** heterogeneous distribution <ST>	gemischte (heterogene) Verteilung *f*	distribution *f* complexe (hétérogène)	смешанное распределение, неоднородное распределение
	mixed distribution <ST>	*s.* C 1729		
	mixed extrapolation and interpolation method <DE, NU>	*s.* P 1202		
	mixed fraction <AR>	*s.* M 691		
M 686	**mixed game** <TG>	gemischtes Spiel *n*	jeu *m* mixte	смешанная игра
M 687	**mixed graph** <GP>	gemischter Graph *m*	graphe *m* mixte	смешанный граф
M 688	**mixed group** <AL>	Mischgruppe *f*, Loewysches Gruppoid *n*, Transmutationssystem *n*	groupoïde *m* de Loewy	смешанная группа
M 689	**mixed ideal** <AL>	gemischtes Ideal *n*	idéal *m* non équidimensionnel	смешанный идеал
M 690	**mixed integral equation,** loaded integral equation <IE>	gemischte (belastete) Integralgleichung *f*	équation *f* intégrale mixte	смешанное (нагруженное) интегральное уравнение

M 691	**mixed number,** mixed quantity (fraction) <AR>	gemischte Zahl *f*, gemischter Bruch *m*, // Bastardbruch *m*	nombre *m* composé (fractionnaire, mixte), fraction *f* mixte, expression *f* *f* mixte, expression *f* fractionnaire	смешанное число, смешанная дробь
M 692	**mixed partial derivative,** mixed derivative <DI>	gemischte Ableitung *f*	dérivée *f* mixte (croisée)	смешанная частная производная, смешанная производная
	mixed partial differential equation <DE>	*s.* E 336		
M 693	**mixed periodic decimal** <AR>	gemischtperiodischer Dezimalbruch *m*	fraction *f* décimale périodique mixte	смешанная бесконечная (периодическая) десятичная дробь
M 694	**mixed periodic fraction** <AR>	gemischtperiodischer (unrein periodischer) Bruch *m*	fraction *f* périodique mixte	смешанная периодическая дробь
M 695	**mixed problem,** mixed boundary value problem <for a hyperbolic *or* parabolic differential equation> <DE>	Anfangs-Randwertproblem *n*, Anfangswert-Randwert-Problem *n*, gemischtes Problem (Randwertproblem) *n*, Anfangs-Randwertaufgabe *f*, gemischte Randwertaufgabe *f*	problème *m* mixte (mêlé), problème de Fourier, problème aux limites mixte (mêlé)	смешанная краевая задача
	mixed problem <DE, PO>	*s.* T 421		
	mixed product <VT>	*s.* P 101		
M 695a	**mixed quadratic [equation]** <AL>	gemischtquadratische Gleichung *f*	équation *f* quadratique complète (mêlée)	полое квадратное уравнение
	mixed quantity <AR>	*s.* M 691		
	mixed radix notation <NT>	*s.* M 680		
M 696	**mixed sampling** <ST>	gemischtes Stichprobenverfahren *n*	sondage (échantillonnage) *m* mixte	смешанный выбор
M 697	**mixed side condition,** mixed constraint <PG>	gemischte Nebenbedingung (Zusatzbedingung) *f*	condition *f* subsidiaire mixte, contrainte *f* mixte	смешанное дополнительное условие
M 698	**mixed spectrum** <of a linear operator> <FA>	gemischtes Spektrum *n*	spectre *m* mixte	смешанный спектр
M 699	**mixed strategy,** randomized strategy <PG, TG>	gemischte (randomisierte) Strategie *f*	stratégie *f* mixte (combinée, randomisée, pondérée)	смешанная (комбинированная, рандомизированная) стратегия
M 700	**mixed tensor,** cocontravariant tensor <of order *or* valence (p,q) *or* $p+q$> <VT>	gemischter Tensor *m* <der Stufe (p,q) *oder* $p+q$>	tenseur *m* mixte <d'ordre *ou* valence (p,q) *ou* $p+q$>	смешанный тензор <ранга *или* валентности (p,q) *или* $p+q$>
M 701	**mixed term** <of a quadratic form having the shape $a_{ij}x_ix_j$> <AL>	gemischtes Glied *n*	terme *m* rectangle, rectangle *m*, terme « rectangle »	член вида $a_{ij}x_ix_j$ в квадратичной форме
	mixed type <DE>	*s.* E 336		
M 702	**mixed variation** <VA>	gemischte Variation *f*	variation *f* mixte	смешанная вариация
M 703	**mixed vertex** <GP>	gemischter Knotenpunkt *m*	sommet *m* mixte	смешанная вершина
M 704	**mixing** <in flows> <ST>	Mischung *f*	mélange *f*	перемешивание
M 705	**mixing,** symmetrization <over *s* indices> <of a tensor> <VT>	Mischung *f*, Mischen *n*, Symmetrisierung *f* <über *s* Indizes>	symétrisation *f* <sur *s* indices>	циклирование <по *s* индексам>
	mixing measurable transformation <ME>	*s.* S 1978		
M 706	**mixing problem** <PG>	Mischungsaufgabe *f*, Mischungsproblem *n*	problème *m* de mélange	задача на смеси, задача на правило смешения
M 707	**mixing theorem** <for measurable transformations> <ST>	Mischungssatz *m*	théorème *m* de mélange	теорема о перемешивании
	mixing transformation <ME>	*s.* S 1978		
	m-lattice <LA>	*s.* M 1045		
	***M*-method** <LI>	*s.* M 443		
	$m \times m$ latin square <CT>	*s.* L 115		
M 708	**(m,n) correspondence,** m-to-n correspondence <of sets> <SE>	(m,n)-deutige Relation (Korrespondenz) *f*	correspondance *f* m-n-voque	(m,n)-значное соответствие
	$m \times n$ game <TG>	*s.* M 191		
	Möbius['s] band <TO>	*s.* M 717		
M 709	**Möbius['s] equation** <for a linear complex> <AY>	Gleichung *f* von Möbius, Möbiussche Gleichung	équation *f* de Möbius	уравнение Мебиуса
M 710	**Möbius['s] function,** Mertens['s] function <NT>	Möbiussche Funktion *f*, Mertenssche Funktion	fonction *f* de Möbius, fonction μ de Möbius	функция Мебиуса
M 711	**Möbius['s] geometry,** Möbius['s] geometry of spheres (the space of *K*-spheres), conformal geometry in the space <GE>	Möbiussche Geometrie *f* des Kugelraums, Möbiussche Geometrie der Kugeln, Möbiussche Geometrie [für den Kugelraum], Geometrie von Möbius, Möbius-Geometrie *f*	géométrie *f* de Moebius, géométrie de Moebius de sphères	геометрия Мебиуса, геометрия Мебиуса сфер, геометрия сфер Мебиуса
M 712	**Möbius['s] geometry in the plane, Möbius['s] geometry of circles,** Möbius['s] geometry of the space of *K*-circles, conformal geometry in the plane <GE>	Möbiussche Geometrie *f* der Kreisebene (Kreise), Möbiussche Geometrie für die Kreisebene, Geometrie von Möbius für die Kreisebene, ebene Möbiussche Geometrie, Möbiussche Geometrie [in der Ebene], Geometrie der reziproken Radien, Inversionsgeometrie *f*	géométrie *f* de Moebius de cercles (l'espace des cercles *K*), géométrie de Moebius dans le plan, géométrie anallagmatique	геометрия Мебиуса окружностей, геометрия окружностей Мебиуса, геометрия Мебиуса в плоскости, геометрия Мебиуса, круговая геометрия, инверсионная геометрия, геометрия обратных радиусов

	Möbius['s] geometry of spheres <DG>	*s.* M 711		
	Möbius['s] geometry of the space of *K*-circles <DG>	*s.* M 712		
	Möbius['s] geometry of the space of *K*-spheres <GE>	*s.* M 711		
M 713	**Möbius['s] group** <in the space of *K*-spheres> <DG>	Gruppe *f* von Möbius, Möbiussche Gruppe (Transformationsgruppe) *f*	groupe *m* de Moebius	группа Мебиуса
M 714	**Möbius['s] inversion formula (principle)** <NT>	Möbiussche Umkehrformel (Umkehrung) *f*	formule *f* (théorème *m*) d'inversion de Möbius	формула обращения [Чебышева-]Мебиуса
M 715	**Möbius['s] plane, Möbius-plane,** inversive plane <GE>	Möbius-Ebene *f*, Möbius-ebene *f*, (M)-Ebene *f*	plan *m* de Möbius	плоскость Мебиуса
M 716	**Möbius['s] spherical triangle,** Möbius['s] triangle <EG>	Möbiussches sphärisches Dreieck *n*	triangle *m* [sphérique] de Möbius	[сферический] треугольник [в смысле] Мебиуса
	Möbius['s] spherical triangular co-ordinates <EG>	*s.* S 1496		
M 717	**Möbius['s] strip,** Möbius['s] band, Moebius['s] band <TO>	Möbiussches Band *n*, Möbius-Band *n*, Möbius-band *n*, // Möbiussche Fläche *f*	ruban *m* de Möbius, bande *f* de Möbius, ceinture *f* de Möbius, // surface *f* de Möbius	лист Мебиуса, поверхность Мебиуса
M 718	**Möbius['s] symbol** <for continued fractions> <NT>	Möbius' Symbol *n*	symbole *m* de Möbius	символ Мебиуса
	Möbius['s] transformation <FT>	*s.* B 348		
	Möbius['s] triangle <EG>	*s.* M 716		
	mod. <AL, NT>	*s.* M 786		
	modal calculus <LO>	*s.* M 725		
M 719	**modal class** <ST>	Modalklasse *f*	classe *f* modale	модальный класс
	modal column <MD>	*s.* E 65		
M 720	**modality,** mode <LO>	Modalität *f*	modalité *f*	модальность
M 721	**modality logics, modal logic** <LO>	modale Logik *f*, Modalitätenlogik *f*	logique *f* modale (des modalités)	модальная логика
	modality of truth <LO>	*s.* T 1046		
M 722	**modal matrix,** polar matrix, matrix of eigenvectors <of a matrix> <AL>	Matrix *f* der Eigenvektoren, Eigenvektorenmatrix *f*	matrice *f* des vecteurs propres	матрица собственных векторов
M 723	**modal proposition** <LO>	modale Aussage *f*	proposition *f* modale	модальное высказывание
M 724	**modal propositional calculus** <LO>	modaler Aussagenkalkül *m*	calcul *m* de propositions modal	модальное исчисление высказываний
M 725	**modal system,** modal calculus <LO>	Modalitätenkalkül *m*	calcul *m* modal	модальное исчисление
M 726	**modal truth functor** <LO>	modaler Funktor *m*	opérateur *m* modal	модальный оператор
M 727	**modal value, mode,** most probable value <ST>	Modalwert *m*, Mode *m*, Modus *m*, Dichtemittel *n*, Dichtewert *m*, wahrscheinlichster (häufigster, plausibelster, dichtester) Wert *m*, Gipfelwert *m*, Scheitelwert *m*, Scheitel *m*	mode *m*, valeur *f* normale, normale *f*, valeur dominante, dominante *f*, valeur la plus probable, valeur modale, milieu *m*, centre *m* de la classe la plus nombreuse, moyenne *f* de fréquence	наиболее вероятное значение, наивероятное (наивероятнейшее) значение, мода
	mode <LO>	*s.* M 720		
M 728	**model** <of a category> <CA>	Modell *n*	modèle *m*, objet *m* modèle	модель
M 729	**model,** interpretation <MM>	Modell *n*	modèle *m*	модель, реализация, интерпретация <системы аксиом>
	model <UA>	*s.* R 673		
M 730	**model I,** fixed effects model, fixed model, finite model <of variance analysis> <ST>	Modell *n* I, Modell mit festen Effekten, Modell „fix", endliches Modell	modèle *m* I, modèle à effets fixes, modèle fixe, modèle fini	модель I, модель с постоянными факторами, конечная модель
M 731	**model II,** random effects model, random model, infinite model <of variance analysis> <ST>	Modell *n* II (mit zufälligen Effekten, „zufällig"), unendliches Modell	modèle *m* II (à effets aléatoires, aléatoire, infini)	модель II (со случайными факторами), бесконечная модель
M 732	**model-complete theory** <MM>	modellvollständige Theorie *f*		модельно-полная теория
	model method <FO, LO>	*s.* M 470		
M 733	**model of moving means,** moving means model <ST>	Modell *n* der gleitenden Mittel[werte]	modèle *m* de moyennes mobiles	модель скользящих средних
M 734	**model-theoretic** <AL, LO>	modelltheoretisch	en théorie des modèles	теоретико-модельный
M 735	**model theory** <AL, LO>	Modelltheorie *f*	théorie *f* des modèles	теория моделей
	modern logic <LO>	*s.* M 166		
M 736	**modified [cylindrical] Bessel function [of the first kind]** <FU>	modifizierte Bessel-Funktion *f* [erster Art], modifizierte Besselsche Funktion *f* [erster Art], modifizierte Zylinderfunktion *f* erster Art	fonction *f* de Bessel [cylindrique] modifiée, fonction de Bessel de première espèce modifiée	модифицированная бесселева функция [первого рода], модифицированная функция Бесселя [первого рода], модифицированная цилиндрическая функция [первого рода], цилиндрическая функция мнимого аргумента
	modified [cylindrical] Bessel function of the second kind <FU>	*s.* M 4		

	English	German	French	Russian
M 737	**modified difference** <FD, NU>	modifizierte Differenz *f*	différence *f* modifiée	модифицированная разность
	modified Dirichlet problem <IE>	*s.* M 1097		
	modified Hankel function <FU>	*s.* M 4		
M 738	**modified Mathieu equation** <DE>	modifizierte Mathieusche (Webersche) Differentialgleichung *f*, modifizierte Differentialgleichung der Funktionen des elliptischen Zylinders	équation *f* de Mathieu modifiée	модифицированное уравнение Матье
M 739	**modified Mathieu function** <FU>	modifizierte Mathieusche Funktion *f*, modifizierte Funktion des elliptischen Zylinders, modifizierte elliptische Zylinderfunktion *f*	fonction *f* de Mathieu modifiée	модифицированная функция Матье
	modified mean	*s.* C 2475		
	modified renewal process <SP>	*s.* G 182		
M 740	**modified Schnirelmann density** <AB>	modifizierte Schnirelmann-Dichte *f*	densité *f* modifiée	модифицированная плотность [Шнирельмана]
M 741	**mod. *p* Steenrod algebra,** Steenrod['s] algebra mod. *p* <AT>	Steenrodsche Algebra *f* mod *p*	algèbre *f* de Steenrod relative à l'entier premier *p*, algèbre *f* de Steenrod mod. *p*	алгебра Стинрода по модулю *p*
	modular axiom <LA>	*s.* M 755		
M 742	**modular category** <CA>	modulare Kategorie *f*	catégorie *f* modulaire	модулярная категория
M 743	**modular character** <RE>	modularer Charakter *m*	caractère *m* modulaire	числовой характер
M 744	**modular correspondence** <AG>	Modularkorrespondenz *f*	correspondance *f* modulaire	модулярное соответствие
M 745	**modular equation** <for elliptic functions> <FU>	Modulargleichung *f*, Jacobische Modulargleichung *f*	équation *f* modulaire	модулярное уравнение
M 746	**modular figure** <FT>	Modulfigur *f*	figure *f* modulaire	модулярная фигура
M 747	**modular form** <AG, AL>	Modulform *f* <AG>; Modularform <AL>	forme *f* modulaire	модулярная форма
M 748	**modular form** <of degree *m*> <FT>	Modulform *f* <*m*-ten Grades>	forme *f* modulaire <de degré *m*>	модулярная форма <*m*-ой степени>
M 749	**modular function** <AL>	Modulfunktion *f*	fonction *f* modulaire (module)	функция модуля
M 750	**modular function** <of degree *n*> <FT>	Modulfunktion *f* <*n*-ten Grades>	fonction *f* modulaire <de degré *n*>	модулярная функция <*n*-ой степени>
	modular function <FT>	*s.* E 184		
M 751	**modular group** <of degree *n*> <AL>	Modulgruppe *f* <*n*-ten Grades>	groupe *m* modulaire <de degré *n*>	модулярная группа <*n*-ой степени>
M 752	**modular group** <AB, AL, FT>	Modulgruppe *f*	groupe *m* modulaire <AL, FT>; groupe *m* arithmétique <AB, AL>	модулярная группа
M 753	**modular group,** M-group <GR>	modulare Gruppe *f*	groupe *m* modulaire	модулярная группа
M 754	**modular Hilbert algebra** <AL, FA>	modulare Hilbert-Algebra *f*	algèbre *f* hilbertienne modulaire	модулярная алгебра Гильберта
	modular ideal <AL>	*s.* R 563		
M 755	**modular identity,** Dedekind['s] law, modular law modular axiom, Dedekind['s] axiom <LA>	modulare Identität *f*, modulares Gesetz *n*, Modulgesetz *n*, Modularitätsgesetz *n*; Modularitätsaxiom *n*	identité *f* modulaire, égalité *f* modulaire, loi *f* modulaire; axiome *m* de modularité	закон модулярности, модулярный закон
M 756	**modular inequality** <LA>	modulare Ungleichung *f*	inégalité *f* modulaire	модулярное неравенство
M 757	**modular interval** <LA>	modulares Intervall *n*	intervalle *m* modulaire	модулярный интервал
M 758	**modular invariant** <AL>	Modularinvariante *f*	invariant *m* modulaire	модулярный инвариант
M 759	**modular lattice,** Dedekind['s] lattice (structure), B-lattice <LA>	modularer Verband *m*, Dedekindscher Verband, // Dualgruppe *f* vom Modultypus	treillis *m* modulaire (de Dedekind, mesurable), structure *f* (lattice *m*) modulaire	дедекиндова структура, модулярная структура, модулярная решетка
	modular law <LA>	*s.* M 755		
	modular left ideal <AL>	*s.* R 581		
M 760	**modular matrix** <of degree *m*> <AL>	Modulmatrix *f* <*m*-ten Grades>	matrice *f* modulaire <de degré *m*>	модулярная матрица <*m*-ой степени>
M 761	**modular matrix** <FT>	Modulmatrix *f*	matrice *f* unimodulaire	модулярная матрица
M 762	**modular pair** <LA>	modulares Paar *n*	couple *m* modulaire	модулярная пара
M 763	**modular property** <LA>	Modularitätseigenschaft *f*	propriété *f* de modularité	модулярное свойство
M 764	**modular representation** <RE>	modulare Darstellung *f*	représentation *f* modulaire	модулярное представление
	modular right ideal <AL>	*s.* R 622		
M 765	**modular space** <FA>	Betragsraum *m*	espace *m* muni d'une métrique invariante par translation	пространство с метрикой инвариантной относительно переносов
M 766	**modular substitution** <FT>	Modulsubstitution *f*	substitution *f* modulaire	модулярная подстановка
M 767	**modular surface** <a universal covering surface> <FT>	Modulfläche *f*	surface *f* modulaire	модулярная поверхность
	modular surface <FT>	*s.* R 784		
M 768	**modular system** <AB>	Modulsystem *n*, Divisorensystem *n* <Kronecker>	système *m* modulaire (de diviseurs, de modules)	модулярная система
M 769	**modular triangle** <of a modular group> <FT>	Moduldreieck *n*, Elementardreieck *n*	triangle *m* modulaire	модулярный треугольник

No.	English	German	French	Russian
	modular variety <AG, FT>	*s.* V 85		
M 770	**module** <as an algebraic structure> <AL>	Modul *m*	module *m*	модуль
M 771	**module** <of an Euclidean algorithm> <NT>	Modulus *m* <Gauss>	module *m*	модуль
	module <AN>	*s.* A 131		
	module <FU>	*s.* M 794		
M 772	**π-module** <AL>	π-Modul *m*	π-module *m*	π-модуль
M 773	**module base** <IV>	Modulbasis *f*	base *f* de module	базис модуля
M 774	**module basis,** base <of a module> <AL>	Modulbasis *f*, Basis *f*, Erzeugendensystem *n*	base *f*	базис, база
	module direct sum <AL>	*s.* V 127		
M 775	**module endomorphism,** linear operator <AL>	Modulendomorphismus *m*	opérateur *m* linéaire, endomorphisme *m* <d'un module>	эндоморфизм модулей
M 776	**module homomorphism,** homomorphism <of modules> <AL>	Modulhomomorphismus *m*, Homomorphismus *m*, lineare Abbildung *f*	homomorphisme *m*, morphisme *m*, application *f* linéaire	гомоморфизм модулей, гомоморфизм
M 777	**module of boundaries** <HA>	Rändermodul *m*	module *m* des bords	модуль границ
M 778	**module of extensions,** Ext-module <HA>	Ext-Modul *m*, Modul *m* der Erweiterungen	module *m* des extensions	модуль расширений
	module of finite type <AL>	*s.* F 290		
M 779	**module of homomorphisms** <AL>	Homomorphiemodul *m*, Hom-Modul *m*	module *m* des homomorphismes	модуль гомоморфизмов
	module of linear forms <AL>	*s.* D 1015		
	module of periods <FT>	*s.* P 462		
M 780	**module of quotients** <in torsion theory> <AL>	Quotientenmodul *m*	module *m* de fractions	модуль частных
M 781	**module of syzygies,** syzygy module <AL>	Syzygienmodul *m*	module *m* de syzygies	модуль сизигий
	module over a polynomial ring <AL>	*s.* P 1001		
	module over R <AL>	*s.* R 1351		
M 782	**module structure** <AL>	Modulstruktur *f*	structure *f* de module	структура модуля
M 783	**module theory,** theory of modules <AL>	Modultheorie *f*	théorie *f* des modules	теория модулей
	module with differentiation <AL>	*s.* D 464		
	module with operators <AL>	*s.* O 195		
	module without torsion <AL>	*s.* T 596		
M 784	**moduli problem,** problem of moduli <AL, FT>	Moduliproblem *n*, Problem *n* der Moduli	problème *m* des modules	проблема модулей
M 785	**moduli space** <AG>	Moduliraum *m*	espace *m* des modules	пространство модулей
M 786	**modulo, mod.** <AL, NT>	modulo, mod	modulo, mod.	по модулю, mod.
M 787	**modulo-*n* check** <AR, NU>	Querrestkontrolle *f*, Quersummenrestkontrolle *f*	cléf *m* par *n*, essai *m* modulo *n*, preuve *f* par *n*, contrôle *m* de preuve par *n*	проверка по модулю *n*
M 788	**modulus,** algebraic divisor <AB>	Modul *m*, algebraischer Divisor *m* <Kronecker>	module *m*, diviseur *m* algébrique	модуль
M 789	**modulus** <*pl.*: moduli> <AB>	Kongruenzmodul *m*, Stellenmodul *m*, Modul *m*; Idealmodul *m*	module *m* de congruence	модуль сравнения
M 790	**modulus,** cross-ration of four tangents from a point <of a cubic curve> <AG>	Modul *m*, charakteristisches Doppelverhältnis *n*	module *m*	модуль, двойное отношение четырех касательных из произвольной точки K_3
M 791	**modulus** <of an almost-periodic function> <AP>	Modul *m*	module *m*	модуль
M 792	**modulus** <of a logarithmic system> <AR>	Modul *m* <eines Logarithmus>	module *m* <d'un système de logarithmes>	модуль <при переходе от одной системы логарифмов к другой>
M 793	**modulus** <of a domain> <FT>	Modul *m* <eines Gebietes>	module *m* <d'un domaine>	модуль <области>
M 794	**modulus,** module <of an elliptic function *or* integral> <FU>	Modul *m*, // Modulus *m*	module *m*	модуль, параметр *k*
M 795	**modulus,** parameter, κ <of a theta function> <FU>	Modul *m*, Parameter *m*	module *m*, paramètre *m*	модуль, параметр
M 796	**modulus** <of a congruence> <NT>	Modul *m*, Modul ganzer Zahlen	module *m* <d'une congruence>	модуль сравнения
	modulus <AN>	*s.* A 131		
	modulus <FA>	*s.* A 132		
	modulus <VT>	*s.* M 24		
	modulus / in <AL, AN>	*s.* T 25		
M 797	**modulus of continuity** <of a function> <AN>	Stetigkeitsmodul *m*, Schwankungsmodul *m*	module *m* de continuité	модуль непрерывности
M 798	**modulus of convexity** <FA>	Konvexitätsmodul *m*	module *m* de convexité	модуль выпуклости
M 799	**modulus of periodicity** <of an Abelian *or* elliptic integral> <FT>	Periodizitätsmodul *m*, Modul *m*, Modul (Index *m*) der Periodizität, Periode *f*	module (indice) *m* de périodicité, module	модуль периодичности
M 800	**modulus of precision** <ST>	Präzisionsmaß *n*, Genauigkeitszahl *f*, Genauigkeitsmodul *m*, Maß *n* der Präzision	mesure *f* (module *m*, paramètre *m*) de précision	мера (модуль) точности

	English	German	French	Russian
	modus ponendo ponens <LO>	*s.* R 1467		
M 801	**modus ponendo tollens** <LO>	modus *m* ponendo tollens	modus *m* ponendo tollens, conjonctif *m* modus ponendo tollens	modus ponendo tollens
	modus ponens [rule] <LO>	*s.* R 1467		
	modus tollendo ponens <LO>	*s.* R 1494		
M 802	**modus tollens,** rule modus tollendo tollens <LO>	modus *m* tollens, Modus *m* tollens, Regel *f* des modus tollens, Regel des modus tollendo tollens, Verwerfungsregel *f*, Widerlegungsregel *f*	modus *m* tollens	деструктивный силлогизм, вторая форма гипотетического силлогизма, отрицательный способ гипотетического силлогизма, отрицание по следствию, отрицательный модус условного силлогизма, отрицательная форма условного силлогизма, правило «опровержение», modus tollens
	Moebius['s] band <TO>	*s.* M 717		
M 803	**Mohr-Mascheroni construction,** construction by (with) compass alone <EG>	Mohr-Mascheronische Konstruktion *f*, Konstruktion mit dem Zirkel allein	construction *f* de Mohr-Mascheroni, construction au moyen d'un compas	построение Мора-Маскерони, построение с помощью [только] одного циркуля
M 804	**Moishezon['s] space** <AG>	Mojšezonscher Raum *m* <Artin>	espace *m* de Moisezon	пространство Мойшезона
M 805	**Moivre['s] formula,** de Moivre['s] formula <for cos ($n\varphi$) *or* sin ($n\varphi$)> <AN>	Moivresche Formel *f*	formule *f* de Moivre	формула Муавра
M 806	**Moivre-Laplace['s] limit theorem,** de Moivre-Laplace['s] limit theorem, [de] Moivre-Laplace['s] theorem, Laplace['s] limit theorem, limit theorem of Laplace <ST>	Grenzwertsatz *m* von de Moivre-Laplace, [klassischer] zentraler Grenzwertsatz von de Moivre-Laplace, de Moivre-Laplacescher Grenzwertsatz, Moivre-Laplacescher Grenzwertsatz, Laplacescher Grenzwertsatz, [de] Moivre-Laplacescher Satz *m*, Satz von [de] Moivre-Laplace, globaler Grenzwertsatz von [de] Moivre-Laplace, Integralgrenzwertsatz *m* von Moivre-Laplace	théorème *m* limite de [de] Moivre-Laplace, théorème limite central de [de] Moivre-Laplace, théorème limite de Laplace, théorème de [de] Moivre-Laplace	теорема Муавра-Лапласа, предельная теорема Муавра-Лапласа, классическая предельная теорема Муавра-Лапласа, интегральная [предельная] теорема Муавра-Лапласа, предельная теорема Лапласа, теорема Лапласа
M 807	**Moivre-Laplace['s] local limit theorem,** de Moivre-Laplace['s] local limit theorem, local limit theorem of [de] Moivre-Laplace <ST>	lokaler Grenzwertsatz *m* von [de] Moivre-Laplace	théorème *m* limite local de [de] Moivre-Laplace	локальная предельная теорема Муавра-Лапласа
	Moivre-Laplace['s] theorem <ST>	*s.* M 806		
M 808	**Moivre['s] theorem,** de Moivre['s] theorem, DeMoivre['s] theorem, Demoivre['s] theorem <AN>	Moivrescher Lehrsatz (Satz) *m*, Satz von Moivre, Moivresche Formel *f*, Moivre-Formel *f*	formule *f* de Moivre	формула Муавра
M 809	**Moldenhauer factor** <ST>	Moldenhauer-Faktor *m*	facteur *m* de Moldenhauer	коэффициент Мольденгауэра
	molding surface <DG>	*s.* M 924		
	molecular formula <LO>	*s.* A 1190		
	molecular proposition <LO>	*s.* C 1745		
M 810	**Mollweide['s] analogies (formulae)** <of plane trigonometry> <EG>	Mollweidesche Formeln *fpl* [der ebenen Trigonometrie]	formules (analogies) *fpl* de Mollweide	формулы Мольвейде
M 811	**moment generating function** <ST>	momenterzeugende Funktion *f*, Momenterzeugende *f*, Momentenerzeugende *f*	caractéristique *f* de Laplace, fonction *f* génératrice des moments	производящая функция моментов
M 812	**moment matrix,** matrix of moments <ST>	Momentenmatrix *f*	matrice *f* des moments	матрица моментов
	moment of order *k* <ST>	*s.* K 193		
	moment problem <AN, ST>	*s.* P 1567		
M 813	**moment ratio** <ST>	Momentenquotient *m*	rapport *m* de moments	отношение моментов
M 814	**moments method,** method of moments <ST>	Momentenmethode *f*	méthode *f* des (de) moments	метод моментов
M 815	**monad,** triple, triad, dual standard construction, monoid <CA>	Monade *f*, duale Standardkonstruktion *f*, Tripel *n*, Monoid *n*, Triade *f*	triplet *m*	триплет, тройка
M 816	**monadic algebra** <UA>	monadische Algebra *f* <Halmos>	algèbre *f* monadique	монадическая алгебра
M 817	**monadic functor,** tripleable functor <CA>	monadischer Funktor *m*	foncteur *m* monadique	монадический функтор

No.	English	German	French	Russian
	monadic predicate <LO>	*s.* O 94		
	monadic predicate calculus <LO>	*s.* O 95		
	monadic predicate calculus of first order <LO>	*s.* C 19		
M 818	**Monge-Ampère equation,** equation of the Monge-Ampère type <DE>	Monge-Ampèresche Differentialgleichung *f*, Monge-Ampèresche Gleichung *f*	équation *f* [dite] de Monge-Ampère, équation différentielle de Monge-Ampère	уравнение (дифференциальное уравнение) Монжа-Ампера
M 819	**Monge['s] axis** <DE>	Mongesche Achse *f*	axe *m* de Monge	ось Монжа
M 820	**Monge['s] cone,** cone of the first order <DE>	Mongescher Kegel *m*, Richtungskegel *m*, Kegel (Richtungskegel) erster (1.) Ordnung, Elementarkegel *m*, T-Kegel *m*	cône *m* de Monge (premier ordre)	конус Монжа (первого порядка)
M 821	**Monge['s] curve** <of a partial differential equation of the first order> <DE>	Mongesche Kurve *f*, Fokalkurve *f*, Integralkurve *f*	courbe *f* de Monge	кривая Монжа
	Monge['s] differential equation <DG>	*s.* M 824		
M 822	**Monge['s] direction** <DE>	Mongesche Richtung *f*	direction *f* de Monge	направление Монжа
M 823	**Monge direction field,** field of Monge directions <DE>	Mongesches Richtungsfeld *n*	champ *m* des directions de Monge	поле направлений Монжа
M 824	**Monge['s] equation,** Monge['s] differential equation <DG>	Mongesche Differentialgleichung *f*, Mongesche Gleichung *f*	équation *f* (équation différentielle) de Monge	уравнение (дифференциальное уравнение) Монжа
M 825	**Monge['s] point** <of a tetrahedron> <EG>	Mongescher Punkt *m*	point *m* de Monge	точка Монжа
M 826	**Monge['s] problem** <DE>	Mongesches (Monges) Problem *n*	problème *m* de Monge	задача Монжа
M 827	**Monge['s] strip,** focal strip <DE>	Mongescher Streifen *m*, Fokalstreifen *m*	bande *f* de Monge, bande focale	фокальная полос[к]а, полос[к]а Монжа
M 828	**Monge['s] surface** <GE>	Mongesche Fläche *f*	surface *f* de Monge	поверхность Монжа
M 829	**Monge['s] theorem** <GE>	Mongescher Satz *m*	théorème *m* de Monge	теорема Монжа
M 830	**moniamond** <GE>	Moniamant *m*	moniamant *m*	мониамант
M 831	**monic,** monomorphic <CA>	monomorph, hinten kürzbar, injektiv, monic	monomorphe	мономорфный, инъективный, моно
	monic [arrow] <CA>	*s.* M 864		
	monic morphism <CA>	*s.* M 864		
M 832	**monic polynomial,** normed polynomial <AL>	Polynom *n* mit höchstem Koeffizienten Eins, normiertes Polynom	polynôme *m* unitaire (normalisé)	многочлен со старшим коэффициентом 1, унитарный (приведенный, нормированный) многочлен, нормированный полином, многочлен с единичным старшим коэффициентом; многочлен, старший коэффициент которого равен [+] 1; отмеченный многочлен
M 833	**monocyclic complex** <AT>	monozyklischer Komplex *m*	complexe *m* monocyclique	моноциклический комплекс
M 834	**monocyclic system** <AL>	monozyklisches (einkreisiges) System *n*	système *m* monocyclique	моноциклическая система
M 835	**monodromy** <DE, FT, TO>	Monodromie *f*	monodromie *f*	монодромия
M 836	**monodromy group** <DE, GR, TO>	Monodromiegruppe *f* <DE, GR, TO>; Gruppe *f* <DE>	groupe *m* de monodromie	группа монодромии
M 837	**monodromy theorem,** principle of monodromy <FT>	Monodromiesatz *m*, Monodromieprinzip *n*, Eindeutigkeitssatz *n*	théorème *m* de monodromie	теорема однозначности (монодромии, о монодромии)
M 838	**monodromy transformation** <AG>	Monodromietransformation *f*	transformation *f* de monodromie	преобразование монодромии
M 839	**monofunctor** <CA>	Monofunktor *m*	monofoncteur *m*	монофунктор
M 840	**monogenic admissible subgroup** <GR>	zulässige zyklische Untergruppe *f*, monogene Untergruppe	sous-groupe *m* monogène permis	допустимая циклическая подгруппа
M 841	**monogenic [analytic] function,** complete [analytic] function <FT>	vollständige (vollständige analytische, monogene, monogene analytische) Funktion *f*	fonction *f* monogène (monogène analytique), fonction [analytique] complète	полная функция, полная аналитическая функция [по Вейерштрассу], полная аналитическая функция в смысле Вейерштрасса, моногенная (моногенная аналитическая, дифференцируемая) функция
	σ-monogenic function <FT>	*s.* S 829		
M 842	**monogenic loop** <AL>	monogene Loop *f*	loop *m* monogène	моногенная лупа
	monogenic module <AL>	*s.* C 2862		
M 843	**monogenic representation module,** cyclic representation module <AL>	monogener (zyklischer) Darstellungsmodul *m*	module *m* de la représentation monogène	моногенный (циклический) модуль представления
M 844	**monogenic subgroup** <of an operator group> <GR>	monogene Untergruppe *f*	sous-groupe *m* monogène	моногенная подгруппа

No.	English	German	French	Russian
M 845	**monoid,** semigroup with identity element, semigroup with unit-element <AL>	Halbgruppe *f* mit Einselement, Halbgruppe mit neutralem Element, Monoid *n*, Monoide *f*	monoïde *m* unitaire, demi-groupe *m* possédant un élément[-]unité, demi-groupe inversible, monoïde à élément[-]unité, monoïde	полугруппа с выделенной единицей, полугруппа с главной единицей, полугруппа с нейтральным элементом, моноид
M 846	**monoid** <CA>	H-Menge *f*, Monoid *n*	monoïde *m*	моноид
M 847	**monoid** <as a curve> <PJ>	monoidale Kurve *f*, Monoid *n*	courbe *f* monoïdale	моноид
M 848	**monoid** <as a hypersurface> <PJ>	Monoid *n*, Monoidfläche *f*	monoïde *m*	моноид
	monoid <AL>	*s.* S 376		
	monoid <CA>	*s.* M 815		
	monoidal category <CA>	*s.* C 222		
M 849	**monoidal representation** <of an algebraic space curve> <AG>	monoidale Darstellung *f* <Cayley>	représentation *f* monoïdale	моноидальное представление
M 850	**monoidal transformation,** dilatation <AG>	monoidale Transformation *f*	transformation *f* monoïdale	моноидальное преобразование
	monoidal transformation with non-singular centre <AG>	*s.* B 510		
M 851	**monoid homomorphism** <AL>	Monoidhomomorphismus *m*	homomorphisme *m* de monoïdes	моноидный гомоморфизм
M 852	**monoid of graduation** <AL>	Graduierungsmonoid *n*	monoïde *m* de graduation	моноид степеней
M 853	**monomial;** monomial (one-termed, one-term) expression <AL>	Monom *n*; eingliedriger Ausdruck *m*	monôme *m*; expression *f* monôme, expression à un terme	одночлен, моном; одночленное выражение
M 854	**monomial alternant** <IV>	monomiale Alternante (alternierende Funktion) *f*	alternant *m* monomial	моночленный (мономиальный) альтернант
M 855	**monomial equation** <AL>	monomiale Gleichung *f*	équation *f* monomiale	мономиальное уравнение
	monomial expression <AL>	*s.* M 853		
M 856	**monomial factor** <of an expression> <AL, GN>	Monom *n* als Faktor	facteur *m* monomial	одночленный фактор
M 857	**monomial form** <of a covariant> <AL>	monomiale Form *f*	forme *f* monomiale	мономиальная форма
M 858	**monomial group** <GR>	monomiale Gruppe *f*	groupe *m* monomial	мономиальная группа
M 859	**monomial representation** <RE>	monomiale Darstellung *f*, Monomialdarstellung *f*	représentation *f* monomiale	мономиальное представление
M 860	**monomial symmetric function** <AL>	monomiale symmetrische Funktion *f*, Potenzproduktsumme *f*	fonction *f* symétrique monomiale	мономиальная симметрическая функция
M 861	**monomino** <GE>	Monomino *n*	monomino *m*	мономино
	monomorphic <CA>	*s.* M 831		
	monomorphic <MM>	*s.* C 198		
M 862	**monomorphic axiom system** <FO>	monomorphes Axiomensystem *n*	système *m* d'axiomes monomorphe	мономорфная система аксиом
	monomorphic mapping <SE>	*s.* I 548		
M 863	**monomorphism,** injective homomorphism <AL>	Monomorphismus *m*, Isomorphismus *m* in, Isomorphismus-in *m*, injektiver Homomorphismus *m*, Einlagerung *f*	monomorphisme *m*, homomorphisme *m* biunivoque	мономорфизм, вложение
M 864	**monomorphism,** monic morphism, monic arrow, monic <CA>	Monomorphismus *m*, monomorpher Pfeil *m*, Monomorphie *f*	monomorphisme *m*	мономорфизм, инъективный морфизм;612 гомоморфизм
	monomorphism <UA>	*s.* H 503		
	monomorphy <MM>	*s.* C 204		
	monotone class <SE>	*s.* M 874		
	monotone decreasing function <RF>	*s.* D 80		
	monotone decreasing sequence <SS>	*s.* M 868		
	monotone function <RF>	*s.* M 870		
	monotone increasing function <RF>	*s.* I 287		
	monotone increasing sequence <SS>	*s.* M 869		
	monotoneity <AN, SE>	*s.* M 871		
	monotone mapping <SE>	*s.* I 1173		
M 865	**monotone mapping into itself** <of a partially ordered set> <SE>	Endomorphismus *m*, monotone Abbildung *f* in sich	application *f* monotone dans lui-même	монотонное отображение в себя
	monotone non-decreasing function <RF>	*s.* I 287		
	monotone non-increasing function <RF>	*s.* D 80		
	monotone non-increasing sequence <SS>	*s.* M 868		
M 866	**monotone quasi-order** <SE>	lineare Quasiordnung *f*	préordre *m* complet, ordre *m* faible (simple), préordre total	линейный квазипорядок
	monotone set (system of sets) <SE>	*s.* M 874		
	monotonically decreasing function <RF>	*s.* D 80		

No.	English	German	French	Russian
M 867	**monotonically decreasing geometric sequence,** decreasing geometric sequence <AR>	fallende geometrische Progression *f*	progression *f* [géométrique] décroissante	убывающая геометрическая прогрессия
M 868	**monotonically decreasing sequence,** monotonically non-increasing sequence, monotonic (monotone) decreasing (non-increasing) sequence, decreasing (non-increasing, antitonic, antitone) sequence <SS>	monoton fallende (abnehmende, nicht wachsende) Folge *f*, abnehmende (fallende [monotone], nicht wachsende, niemals wachsende, niemals zunehmende, nicht zunehmende, antitone) Folge [im weiteren Sinne]	suite *f* monotonement décroissante, suite décroissante [au sens large], suite non croissante, suite antitone	монотонно убывающая последовательность, убывающая (невозрастающая, антитонная) последовательность, убывающая монотонная последовательность
	monotonically increasing function <RF>	*s.* I 287		
	monotonically increasing progression <AR>	*s.* I 289		
M 869	**monotonically increasing sequence,** monotonic (monotone) increasing sequence, increasing (isotonic, isotone) sequence <SS>	monoton wachsende (zunehmende, nicht[] fallende) Folge *f*, wachsende (zunehmende, nicht[ ]fallende, niemals fallende, niemals abnehmende, nicht abnehmende, isotone, aufsteigende) Folge	suite *f* croissante (isotone, non décroissante), suite croissante au sens large, suite monotone[ment] croissante	монотонно возрастающая последовательность, возрастающая (неубывающая, изотонная) последовательность
	monotonically non-decreasing function <RF>	*s.* I 287		
	monotonically non-increasing function <RF>	*s.* D 80		
	monotonically non-increasing sequence <SS>	*s.* M 868		
	monotonic decreasing function <RF>	*s.* D 80		
	monotonic decreasing sequence <SS>	*s.* M 868		
M 870	**monotonic function,** monotone function <RF>	monotone Funktion *f* [im weiteren Sinne], eindeutige Funktion	fonction *f* monotone [au sens large]	монотонная функция
	monotonic homomorphism <SE>	*s.* I 1173		
	monotonic increasing function <RF>	*s.* I 287		
	monotonic increasing sequence <SS>	*s.* M 869		
M 871	**monotonicity,** monotoneity, monotony <AN, SE>	Monotonie *f*	monotonie *f*	монотонность
M 872	**monotonicity theorem** <SS>	Monotoniesatz *m*, spezielles Konvergenzprinzip *n*, Monotonieprinzip *n* für beschränkte Folgen, Monotonieprinzip	théorème *m* de monotonie	теорема монотонности
	monotonic law <AL, SE>	*s.* M 877		
M 873	**monotonic law of multiplication** <AL>	Monotoniegesetz *n* der Multiplikation	loi *f* de monotonie de la multiplication	закон (свойство) монотонности умножения
	monotonic non-decreasing function <RF>	*s.* I 287		
	monotonic non-increasing function <RF>	*s.* D 80		
	monotonic non-increasing sequence <SS>	*s.* M 868		
M 874	**monotonic system of sets,** monotone system of sets, monotone class (set), nest, tower, chain <of sets> <SE>	Mengenkette *f*, linearer Mengenverein *m*, Kette *f* <von Mengen>	famille *f* d'ensembles monotone	монотонное семейство множеств
M 875	**monotonic transformation** <TO>	monotone Transformation (Abbildung) *f*	transformation *f* monotone	монотонное преобразование (отображение)
	monotony <AN, SE>	*s.* M 871		
M 876	**monotony interval** <of a function> <AN>	Monotonieintervall *n*	intervalle *m* de monotonie	интервал монотонности
M 877	**monotony law,** law of monotony, monotonic law <AL, SE>	Monotoniegesetz *n*	loi *f* de monotonie	закон монотонности (однородности), свойство монотонности
	Monte Carlo computation <NU, ST>	*s.* C 1758		
M 878	**Monte Carlo method,** Monte-Carlo method (technique), method of statistical testing <NU, ST>	Monte-Carlo-Methode *f*, Monte-Carlo-Verfahren *n*, Monte-Carlo-Technik *f*, Methode *f* der statistischen Versuche	méthode *f* [de] Monte-Carlo, méthode [de] Monte Carlo, technique *f* de Monte-Carlo, technique de Monte Carlo	метод Монте-Карло, метод статистических испытаний

	English	German	French	Russian
M 879	**Monte-Carlo simulation** <NU, ST>	Monte-Carlo-Simulation *f*	simulation *f* [de] Monte-Carlo	моделирование методом Монте Карло
	Monte-Carlo technique <NU, ST>	*s.* M 878		
M 880	**Montel['s] principle** <FT>	Montelsches Prinzip *n*	principe *m* de Montel	принцип Монтеля
M 881	**Montel space,** (M)-space <FA>	Montel-Raum *m*, M-Raum *m*	espace *m* de Montel, espace (M), espace de type (M)	монтелево пространство, пространство Монтеля, монтелевское пространство, (M)-пространство
	Montel['s] theorem <FT>	*s.* T 323		
M 882	**Montgomery['s] $\mathcal{M}$-operation** <TO>	Montgomerysche $\mathcal{M}$-Operation *f*	opération *f* $\mathcal{M}$ de Montgomery	$\mathcal{M}$-операция Монтгомери
M 883	**mood** <LO>	Modus *m*	modus *m*, mode *m*	модус
M 884	**Moore['s] automaton,** Moore['s] machine	Moore-Automat *m*, Moorescher Automat *m*	réseau *m* de Moore, automate *m* de Moore	автомат Мура
	Moore closure <AL, LO, TO>	*s.* C 940		
	Moore['s] machine <TA>	*s.* M 884		
M 885	**Moore-Postnikov sequence** <of fibrations> <AT>	Moore-Postnikov-Sequenz*f*	suite *f* de Moore-Postnikov	система Постникова, последовательность Мура-Постникова
M 886	**Moore-Smith convergence,** convergence in the Moore-Smith sense <FA, TO>	Moore-Smith-Konvergenz *f*, Konvergenz im Moore-Smithschen Sinne	convergence *f* de (à la) Moore-Smith, convergence au sens de Moore-Smith	сходимость Мура-Смита, сходимость в смысле Мура-Смита, обобщенная сходимость
M 887	**Moore-Smith family (sequence),** net, generalized sequence, directed system <SE>	Moore-Smith-Folge *f*, gerichtetes System *n*, gerichtete Familie *f*, Netz *n*	famille *f* de Moore-Smith, système *m* filtrant, famille filtrante, suite *f* généralisée	направленная система, обобщенная последовательность, сеть, последовательность Мура-Смита, фильтрующаяся система, фильтрующееся семейство
M 888	**Mordell['s] conjecture** <AG>	Mordells Vermutung *f*	conjecture *f* de Mordell	гипотеза Морделла
M 889	**Mordell-Weil theorem** <AG>	Satz *m* von Mordell-Weil, Mordell-Weilscher Satz	théorème *m* de Mordell-Weil	теорема Морделла-Вейля
M 890	**more complex algebraic structure** <AL>	reichere [algebraische] Struktur *f*	structure *f* plus riche	более богатая структура
M 891	**more-place predicate,** relation, many-place[d] (multiplace) predicate, predicate with many argument places <LO>	mehrstelliges Prädikat (Attribut) *n*, Relation *f*, Beziehung *f*, mehrstelliges Prädikativ *n*	prédicat *m* à plus d'une place, prédicat polyadique (relatif, de relation, à plusieurs places, à plusieurs arguments, à plusieurs variables), relation *f*, prédicat (fonction *f* propositionnelle) portant sur plusieurs objets	многоместный предикат, отношение
M 892	**Morera['s] theorem** <FT>	Satz *m* von Morera, Morerascher Satz	théorème *m* de Morera	теорема Морера
M 893	**Morita['s] duality** <AL>	Morita-Dualität *f*	dualité *f* de Morita	двойственность Морита
M 894	**Morita-equivalent rings** <AL>	Morita-äquivalente Ringe *mpl*	anneaux *mpl* Morita-équivalents	морита-эквивалентные кольца
M 895	**Morita property** <of a ring> <AL>	Morita-Eigenschaft *f*	propriété *f* de Morita	морита-свойство
M 896	**Morley-Petersen theorem** <in the Euclidean space> <GE>	Morley-Petersenscher Satz *m*	théorème *m* de Morley-Petersen	теорема Морли-Петерсена
M 897	**Morley['s] theorem** <on a triangle> <GE>	Morleyscher Satz *m*	théorème *m* de Morley	теорема Морли
M 898	**Morley['s] triangle** <of a triangle> <GE>	Morleysches Dreieck *n*	triangle *m* de Morley	треугольник Морли
M 899	**morphism,** map, arrow <CA>	Morphismus *m*, Pfeil *m*	morphisme *m*, homomorphisme *m*, flèche *f*	морфизм, гомоморфизм, стрела
M 900	**2-morphism** <of a 2-category> <CA>	2-Morphismus *m*	2-morphisme *m*	морфизм второго ранга
	morphism-full subcategory <CA>	*s.* F 721		
	morphism functor <CA, HA>	*s.* F 790		
	morphism of bundles <TO>	*s.* B 797		
M 901	**morphism of finite type** <AG>	Morphismus *m* von endlichem Typ	morphisme *m* de présentation (type) fini	морфизм конечного типа
	morphism of functors <CA>	*s.* N 41		
M 902	**morphism of Segre** <AG>	Segrescher Morphismus *m*	morphisme *m* de Segre	морфизм Сегре
	morphism which is both a monomorphism and an epimorphism <CA>	*s.* B 353		
	Morse['s] function <TO, VA>	*s.* N 231		
M 903	**Morse['s] inequalities** <TO, VA>	Morsesche Ungleichungen *fpl*	inégalités *fpl* de Morse	неравенства Морсе
	Morse['s] normal form <VA>	*s.* C 68		
M 904	**Morse['s] theory** <TO, VA>	Morsesche Theorie *f*	théorie *f* de Morse	теория Морса
M 905	**mortality intensity** <ST>	Sterblichkeitsintensität *f*	taux *m* instantané de mortalité	интенсивность смертности

M 906	**mortality rate,** death rate <ST>	Sterblichkeitsrate *f*, Sterbezahl *f*	taux *m* de mortalité	коэффициент гибели, доля (норма) смертности
M 907	**mortality table,** life table <ST>	Sterbetafel *f*	table *f* (tableau *m*) de mortalité	таблица смертности
M 908	**Moses['s] test** <of extreme reactions> <ST>	Moses-Test *m* <zur Prüfung extremer Effekte>	test *m* de Moses <des effets extrêmes>	критерий Мозеса <для экстремальных реакций>
M 909	**most efficient estimating function, most efficient estimator,** minimum variance unbiased estimator <ST>	wirksamste Schätzfunktion (Schätzung, Punktschätzung) *f*, höchsteffiziente Schätzfunktion (Schätzung), Minimum-Varianz-Schätzfunktion *f*, Minimum-Varianz-Schätzung *f*, erwartungstreue (unverzerrte, unverfälschte, biasfreie) Schätzfunktion (Punktschätzung, Schätzung) mit kleinster Varianz, erwartungstreue (unverzerrte, unverfälschte, biasfreie) wirksamste Schätzfunktion (Schätzung)	estimateur *m* le plus efficace, fonction *f* estimatrice la plus efficace, estimateur (fonction estimatrice) [sans biais] à variance minimum (minimale)	наиболее эффективная оценка, оценка с наименьшей дисперсией, несмещенная оценка с минимальной дисперсией
M 910	**most favourable value** <ER>	günstigster (plausibelster) Wert *m*	valeur *f* la plus favorable	наиболее благоприятное (достоверное) значение
M 911	**most *n*-dimensionally connected space / at** <TO>	höchstens *n*-dimensional zusammenhängender Raum *m*	espace *m* à connexité au plus *n*-dimensionnelle	не более чем *n*-мерно связное пространство
M 912	**most powerful test** <ST>	trennschärfster Test *m*	test *m* le plus puissant	наиболее мощный критерий
	most probable value <ST>	*s.* M 727		
	most selective confidence interval <ST>	*s.* S 771		
	most significant digit <NU>	*s.* H 311		
M 913	**most stringent critical range** <ST>	strengster kritischer Bereich *m*	région *f* critique la plus rigoureuse	наиболее строгая критическая область
M 914	**most stringent test** <ST>	strengster Test *m*	test *m* le plus rigoureux	наиболее строгий критерий
M 915	**motion,** movement, displacement, isometry <GE>	Bewegung *f*	mouvement *m*, déplacement *m*, isométrie *f*	движение
	motion <GE>	*s.* P 1813		
	motion along a helix <GE>	*s.* S 181		
M 916	**motive** <of a manifold> <AG>	Motiv *n*	motif *m*	мотив
M 917	**motor** <GE>	Motor *m* <Study>	moteur *m*	мотор
M 918	**motor symbolism** <GE>	Motorrechnung *f*	symbolisme (calcul) *m* des moteurs	моторное исчисление, исчисление моторов
M 919	**Moufang identities** <AL>	Moufang-Identitäten *fpl*	identités *fpl* de Moufang	тождества Муфанга
M 920	**Moufang-Lie ring** <AL>	Moufang-Lie-Ring *m*	anneau *m* de Moufang-Lie	кольцо Муфанга-Ли
M 921	**Moufang['s] loop** <AL>	Moufang-Loop *f*	loop *m* de Moufang	лупа Муфанг[а]
M 922	**Moufang['s] plane** <PJ>	Moufang-Ebene *f*	plan *m* de Moufang	муфангова плоскость
M 923	**Moufang['s] theorem** <AL>	Satz *m* von Moufang, Moufangscher Satz	théorème *m* de Moufang	теорема Муфанга
M 924	**moulding surface,** molding surface <US> <DG>	Gesimsfläche *f*	surface *f* moulure	резная (карнизная) поверхность
M 925	**Moutard['s] quadric** <AY>	Moutardsche Quadrik *f*	quadrique *f* de Moutard	квадрика (поверхность второго рода) Мутара
M 926	**Mouton['s] method** <of interpolation> <FD, NU>	Moutonsche Interpolationsmethode *f*, Interpolationsmethode (Methode) *f* von Mouton	méthode *f* <d'interpolation> de Mouton	интерполяционный метод Мутона, метод <интерполяции> Мутона
M 927	**movable singularity** <DE>	bewegliche (verschiebbare) Singularität *f*	singularité *f* mobile (variable)	подвижная особенность
M 928	**move** <TG>	Zug *m*	coup *m*, trait *m*, marche *f*	ход
	movement <GE>	*s.* 1. M 915; 2. P 1813		
	movement group <AY, GE>	*s.* G 487		
M 929	**moving arm,** hinged tracing lever <of a planimeter> <GE, IN>	Fahrarm *m*, Fahrstange *f*	bras *m* traceur	обводной рычаг
M 930	**moving average,** sliding average, consecutive (overlapping, running) mean <ST>	gleitendes Mittel *n*, gleitender Durchschnitt *m*	moyenne *f* mobile (glissante)	скользящее среднее
	moving average <ST>	*s.* M 931		
M 931	**moving average method;** moving average <ST>	Gleitmittelverfahren *n*, Methode *f* des gleitenden Durchschnitts, Verfahren *n* der gleitenden Durchschnittsbildung; gleitende Durchschnittsbildung *f*	méthode *f* des moyennes mobiles, méthode de la moyenne mobile; procédé *m* des moyennes mobiles	метод скользящих средних; вычисление скользящих средних
M 932	**moving curve** <GE>	Polkurve *f*, rollende (abrollende) Kurve *f*	courbe *f* mobile (roulante)	производящая (катящаяся) кривая

No.	English	German	French	Russian
	moving means model <ST>	*s.* M 733		
M 933	**moving *n*-hedral, moving *n*-hedron,** "repère mobile" [of Darboux] <of a curve> <DG>	begleitendes *n*-Bein *n*, [Darbouxsches] „repère *n* mobile"	*n*-èdre *m* mobile (principal, attaché à la courbe, de Serret-Fresnel), repère *m* mobile [de Darboux], repère naturel	подвижный (основной, сопровождающий, переменный) *n*-гранник
	moving part <IN>	*s.* C 2760		
	moving point <GE, IN>	*s.* T 718		
M 934	**moving trihedral (trihedron)** <of a curve> <DG>	begleitendes Dreibein *n*, Hauptdreikant *n*, begleitendes Dreikant (Tripel) *n*	trièdre *m* mobile (principal), trièdre attaché à la courbe, trièdre de Serret-Fresnel, repère *m* mobile, repère naturel	подвижный (основной, сопровождающий, переменный) трехгранник (триэдр, триедр), естественный трехгранник, сопровождающий трехгранник Дарбу
M 935	***m*-partite number** <AB>	„*m*-partite number" *f*	« *m*-partite number » *m*	*m*-дольное число
M 936	***M*-regular element** <AL>	*M*-reguläres Element *n*	élément *m* *M*-régulier	*M*-регулярный элемент
	***M*--regular sequence** <AL>	*s.* M 939		
M 937	**m-regular subalgebra** <of a Boolean algebra> <AL>	m-reguläre Unteralgebra *f*	sous-algèbre *f* m-régulière	m-регулярная подалгебра
	m.s. <AL>	*s.* M 1051		
	MS <ST>	*s.* M 318		
M 938	***m*-sequence** <of a ring> <AL>	*m*-Folge *f*	*m*-suite *f*	*m*-последовательность
M 939	***M*-sequence,** *M*-regular sequence <AL>	*M*-Sequenz *f*, *M*-Folge *f*, reguläre *M*-Folge	suite *f* *M*-régulière	*M*-регулярная последовательность
	m-sequence <AL>	*s.* M 1050		
	(M)-space <FA>	*s.* M 881		
	***M*-subgroup** <GR>	*s.* A 337		
M 940	**m-system** <McCoy> <AL>	m-System *n*	m-système *m*	m-система
	M-test <FT, SS>	*s.* W 168		
	***m*-to-*n* correspondence** <SE>	*s.* M 708		
M 941	**much greater (larger)** <than>, $\gg$ <GN, NU>	groß gegen, groß gegenüber, $\gg$	très supérieur <à>, très grand <devant>, $\gg$	значительно больше <чем>, сильно (значительно) превышающий, великий по сравнению <с>, $\gg$
M 942	**much less (smaller)** <than>, $\ll$ <GN, NU>	klein gegen[über], wesentlich kleiner <als>, $\ll$	très inférieur <à>, négligeable <devant>, petit devant, $\ll$	значительно меньше <чем>, [очень] малый по сравнению <с>, $\ll$
M 943	**mu-continuity,** μ-continuity, continuity with respect to <a measure> μ <of a set function> <AN>	μ-Stetigkeit *f*, My-Stetigkeit *f*, μ-Totalstetigkeit *f*, My-Totalstetigkeit *f*, μ-Regularität *f*, My-Regularität *f*	continuité *f* par rapport à <la mesure> μ	μ-непрерывность, мю-непрерывность, непрерывность относительно <меры> μ
M 944	**mu-continuous function,** μ-continuous function, function continuous with respect to <a measure> μ <AN>	stetige (my-stetige) Funktion *f*, reguläre (absolut[ ]stetige, totalstetige) Funktion bezüglich <eines Maßes> μ	fonction *f* continue par rapport à <une mesure> μ, fonction μ-continue (mu-continue)	непрерывная функция относительно <меры> μ, μ-непрерывная (мю-непрерывная) функция
M 945	**mu-finite function,** μ-finite function, function finite with respect to a measure μ <ME>	μ-endliche (my-endliche) Funktion *f*, endliche Funktion in bezug auf ein Maß μ	fonction *f* μ-finie (mu-finie), fonction finie pour (par rapport à) la mesure μ	μ-конечная (мю-конечная) функция, конечная функция относительно меры μ
M 946	**mu-integrable function,** μ-integrable function <AN>	μ-integrierbare (my-integrierbare) Funktion *f*	fonction *f* μ-intégrable (mu-intégrable, intégrable pour [la mesure] μ)	μ-интегрируемая (мю-интегрируемая) функция
M 947	**Muir['s] symbol** <of a continued fraction> <NT>	Muirsches Symbol *n*	symbole *m* de Muir	символ Мюира
M 948	**multi-additive mapping** <AL>	multiadditive Abbildung *f*	application *f* multi-additive (*Z*-multi-linéaire)	многократно-аддитивное отображение
M 949	**multi-algebra** <UA>	Multialgebra *f*	multi-algèbre *f*	мультиалгебра
	multi[-]application <SE>	*s.* M 85		
M 950	**multicollinearity** <ST>	Multikollinearität *f*	multicollinéarité *f*	мультиколлинеарность
M 951	**multi-covector** <AL, DG, VT>	Multikovektor *m*, *p*-Kovektor *m*	multicovecteur *m*	поликовектор
M 952	**multicyclic** <AL>	mehrfach zyklisch	multicyclique	многоциклический
	multi-decision problem <ST>	*s.* M 994		
M 953	**multidegree** <AL>	Multigrad *m*	multidegré *m*	многостепень
M 954	**multidifferential field** <AL>	Multidifferentialkörper *m*	corps *m* multidifférentiel	многократно дифференциальное поле, мультидифференциальное поле
M 955	**multidigit number,** multiplace number <NT>	mehrstellige [ganze] Zahl *f*	nombre *m* de plusieurs chiffres	многозначное [целое] число, многоразрядное [целое] число
M 956	**multidimensional determinant,** determinant of higher dimension <MD>	Determinante *f* höheren Ranges, mehrdimensionale Determinante	déterminant *m* à plusieurs dimensions	многомерный определитель (детерминант)
	multidimensional distribution <ST>	*s.* M 1088		
	multidimensional distribution function <ST>	*s.* M 1089		

No.	English	German	French	Russian
	multidimensional random variate <ST>	*s.* R 115		
M 957	**multidimensional space,** many-dimensional space <GE>	mehrdimensionaler Raum *m*	espace *m* multidimensionnel	многомерное пространство
	multidimensional statistics <ST>	*s.* M 1090		
	multidimensional variate <ST>	*s.* R 115		
M 958	**multi-factor model** <ST>	Mehrfaktormodell *n*	modèle *m* multifactoriel	многофакторная модель
	multiform <DG>	*s.* P 553		
	multifunction <SE>	*s.* M 85		
M 959	**multigrade congruence** <NT>	mehrgradige (multigrade) Kongruenz *f*	congruence *f* multigrade	многостепенное сравнение
M 960	**multigrade equation** <NT>	multigrade (mehrgradige) Gleichung *f* <vom Grade *n*, der Ordnung *m* und dem Range *r*>	multigrade *f*, équation *f* multigrade	многостепенное уравнение
M 961	**multigraduation** <AL>	Multigraduierung *f*	multigraduation *f*	многоградуировка
M 962	**multigraph,** indirected graph <GP>	Multigraph *m*, ungerichteter Graph *m*	multigraphe *m*	мультиграф
M 963	**multigroup,** hypergroup <AL>	Multigruppe *f*, Hypergruppe *f*	hypergroupe *m*	мультигруппа, гипергруппа
M 964	**multihomogeneous equation** <AL>	mehrfach homogene Gleichung *f*	équation *f* multi[-]homogène	многократно однородное уравнение
M 965	**multihomogeneous polynomial** <AL>	mehrfach homogenes Polynom *n*	polynôme *m* multi[-]homogène	многократный многочлен
M 966	**multihomology** <AT>	Multihomologie *f*	multi-homologie *f*	мультигомология
M 967	**multilateral,** polylateral <GE>	Vielseit *n*	multilatère *m*, polylatère *m*	многосторонник
M 968	**multi[-]lattice** <AL>	Multiverband *m*	multistructure *f*	мультиструктура
M 969	**multilinear algebra** <AL>	multilineare Algebra *f*	algèbre *f* multilinéaire	полилинейная (мультилинейная) алгебра
M 970	**multilinear form** <AL, VT>	Multilinearform *f*, multilineare Form *f*, mehrfach lineare Form	forme *f* multilinéaire	полилинейная форма
M 971	┌<AL> **multilinear function**	multilineare Funktion *f*	fonction *f* multilinéaire	полилинейная функция
M 972	**multi-modal distribution [function]** <ST>	mehrgipflige (multimodale) Verteilung[sfunktion] *f*	distribution *f* plurimodale, fonction *f* de distribution plurimodale	многовершинное (мультимодальное) распределение, многовершинная (мультимодальная) функция распределения
M 973	**multimodule** <AL>	Multimodul *m*	multimodule *m*	мультимодуль
M 974	**multinomial,** polynomial in several variables <AN>	Polynom *n* in mehreren Variablen	polynôme *m* à plusieurs variables	многочлен от некоторых переменных
M 975	**multinomial coefficient** <AL, AN>	Polynomialkoeffizient *m*, Multinomialkoeffizient *m*	coefficient (nombre) *m* multinomial, coefficient polynomial	полиномиальный коэффициент
	┌<ST> **multinomial distribution**	*s.* P 981		
M 976	**multinomial expansion,** polynomial expansion <AL, DI>	Polynomialentwicklung *f*, polynomische Entwicklung *f*	développement *m* multinomial (polynomial)	полиномиальное разложение
M 977	**multinomial series** <SS>	Polynomialreihe *f*, Polynomreihe *f*	série *f* polynomiale	полиномиальный ряд
M 978	**multinomial theorem** <AL>	polynomischer Lehrsatz (Satz) *m*, Polynomialsatz *m*	théorème *m* multinomial (polynomial), formule *f* du multinôme	полиномиальная теорема
M 979	**multi-operation,** many-valued operation <UA>	Multioperation *f*, mehrwertige Operation *f*	multi-opération *f*	мультиоперация, многозначная операция
M 980	**multipartite graph** <GP>	mehrfach teilbarer Graph *m*	graphe *m* multiparti (séquentiel)	многодольный граф
M 981	┌<AB> **multipartite number**	„multipartite number" *f*	« multipartite number » *m*	расчлененное число
M 982	**multi[-]perfect number,** multiply perfect number, pluperfect number; *k*-perfect number <NT>	mehrfach perfekte (vollkommene) Zahl *f*, multiperfekte Zahl; *k*-perfekte Zahl	nombre *m* multiparfait; nombre *k*-parfait	кратно[-]совершенное число, многократно совершенное число; *k*-совершенное число
	multi-periodic function <AN>	*s.* M 1073		
M 983	**multi-person game** <TG>	Mehrpersonenspiel *n*	jeu *m* à plusieurs personnes	игра нескольких лиц (игроков)
M 984	**multi-phase sampling** <ST>	Mehrphasen-Stichprobenverfahren *n*, mehrphasiges Stichprobenverfahren	sondage *m* à plusieurs phases, échantillonnage *m* à plusieurs phases	многофазный выбор, метод многофазной выборки
	multiplace number <NT>	*s.* M 955		
	multiplace predicate <LO>	*s.* M 891		
M 985	**multiplane method (projection)** <DS>	Mehrtafelverfahren *n*, Mehrtafelprojektion *f*	projection *f* (méthode *f* des projections) sur plusieurs <deux ou trois> plans	комплексный чертеж, способ проекции на две или три плоскости
M 986	**multiple** <of an element> <AL, AR>	Vielfaches *n*, Multiplum *n*	multiple *m*	кратное
M 987	**multiple,** integral (whole) multiple <of an integer> <AR, NT>	Vielfaches *n*, ganzes Vielfaches, Dividuus *m*	multiple *m*	кратное
M 988	**multiple arc** <of an oriented graph> <GP>	mehrfacher Bogen *m*	arc *m* multiple	кратная дуга
	multiple classification <ST>	*s.* M 62		
M 989	**multiple coefficient of determination** <ST>	mehrfaches (multiples) Bestimmtheitsmaß *n*	coefficient *m* de détermination multiple	квадрат множественного коэффициента корреляции, множественный коэффициента смешанной корреляции

No.	English	German	French	Russian
M 990	**multiple comparison of means** <ST>	multipler Mittelwertvergleich *m*	comparaison *f* multiple des moyennes	множественное сравнение средних [значений]
M 991	**multiple contact** <DG, GE>	mehrpunktige Berührung *f*	contact *m* multiple	кратное касание
M 992	**multiple correlation** <ST>	multiple (mehrfache) Korrelation *f*	corrélation *f* multiple	множественная корреляция
M 993	**multiple correlation coefficient,** coefficient of multiple correlation <ST>	mehrfacher (multipler) Korrelationskoeffizient *m*	coefficient *m* de corrélation multiple	множественный коэффициент корреляции, коэффициент множественной корреляции
M 994	**multiple decision problem,** multi-decision problem <ST>	multiples Entscheidungsproblem *n*	problème *m* de décisions multiples	проблема с многими решениями, задача на статистическое решение при наличии нескольких альтернативных гипотез
M 995	**multiple edge,** parallel elements <GP>	mehrfache Kante *f*, Mehrfachkante *f*, Mehrfachstrecke *f*, parallele Kanten *fpl*	arête *f* multiple	кратное ребро, параллельные ребра
M 996	**multiple exponential sum** <NT>	mehrfache Exponentialsumme *f*	somme *f* exponentielle multiple	кратная экспоненциальная сумма
M 997	**multiple Fourier series** <SS>	mehrfache Fourier-Reihe *f*	série *f* de Fourier multiple	кратный ряд Фурье
M 998	**multiple *F*-test** <ST>	multipler *F*-Test *m*	test *m F* multiple	множественный *F*-критерий
M 999	**multiple Gauss[ian] sum** <NT>	mehrfacheGaußscheSummes *f* <Weber>	omme *f* multiple de Gauss, somme de Gauss multiple	кратная сумма Гаусса
M 1000	**multiple hypergraph** <GP>	Mehrfach-Hypergraph *m*	hypergraphe *m* multiple	мультигиперграф
M 1001	**multiple integral** <DI>	mehrfaches Integral *n*, Mehrfachintegral *n*	intégrale *f* multiple	кратный интеграл
	multiple isomorphism <GR>	*s.* H 500		
M 1002	**multiple Markov process** <SP>	multipler Markovscher Prozeß *m*	processus *m* markovien multiple	множественный марковский процесс
M 1003	**multiple negation** <LO>	mehrfache Verneinung *f*	négation *f* multiple	кратное отрицание
M 1004	**multiple operator** <AL>	Multioperator *m*	multi-opérateur *m*	мультиоператор, многоместный оператор
M 1005	**multiple order** <of a set> <SE>	mehrfache Ordnung *f*	ordre *m* multiple	кратный упорядок
M 1006	**multiple point** <of a curve *or* manifold> <DG>	mehrfacher Punkt *m*, Vielfachpunkt *m*, Mehrfachpunkt *m*	point *m* multiple	кратная точка
	multiple point <AG>	*s.* S 1105		
M 1007	**multiple primitivity** <of a permutation group> <GR>	mehrfache Primitivität *f*	primitivité *f* plusieurs fois	многократная примитивность
M 1008	**multiple range test** <ST>	multipler Spannweitetest *m*	test *m* d'étendue multiple	множественный критерий размаха
M 1009	**multiple recursion** <FO>	mehrfache Rekursion *f*	récursion *f* multiple	многократная рекурсия
M 1010	**multiple regression** <ST>	mehrfache (multiple) Regression *f*	régression *f* multiple	множественная регрессия
M 1011	**multiple regression coefficient** <ST>	multipler Regressionskoeffizient *m*	coefficient *m* de régression multiple	коэффициент множественной регрессии
M 1012	**multiple root,** repeated root, multiple zero <AL, AN>	mehrfache Wurzel *f*, mehrfache Nullstelle *f*	racine *f* (zéro *m*) multiple	кратный корень (нуль)
M 1013	**multiple roots** <AL>	mehrfache Wurzeln *fpl*	racines *fpl* confondues	кратные корни
M 1014	**multiple sequence** <SS>	mehrfach unendliche Folge *f*, Mehrfachfolge *f*, mehrfache Folge	suite *f* multiple	кратная последовательность
M 1015	**multiple series** <SS>	mehrfach unendliche Reihe *f*, Mehrfachreihe *f*, mehrfache Reihe, // Reihe mit mehrfachem Eingang, vielfache Reihe	série *f* multiple (à multiple entrée)	кратный ряд
M 1016	**multiple stratification** <ST>	mehrfache Schichtung *f*	stratification *f* multiple	множественное расслоение
M 1017	**multiple tangent** <DG>	mehrfache (vielfache) Tangente *f*	tangente *f* multiple	кратная касательная
	multiple tangent <AG>	*s.* S 1125		
	multiple tangential plane <AG>	*s.* S 1126		
M 1018	**multiple test** <ST>	multipler Test *m*, Test zum multiplen Vergleich	test *m* multiple	множественный критерий
M 1019	**multiple *t*-test** <ST>	multipler *t*-Test *m*	test *m t* multiple	множественный *t*-критерий
	multiple-valued function <FT>	*s.* M 1083		
	multiple-valued function, multiple valued function <AN>	*s.* M 83		
	multiple valuedness, multiple-valuedness <AN>	*s.* M 86		
	multiple valuedness, multiple-valuedness <SE>	*s.* M 88		
M 1020	**multiple Weyl sum** <NT>	mehrfache Weylsche Summe *f*	somme *f* de Weyl multiple	кратная экспоненциальная сумма Вейля
M 1021	**multiplex method** <PG>	Multiplexmethode *f*	méthode *f* multiplex	мультиплексный метод, мультиплекс-метод, многократный метод
	multiple zero <AL, AN>	*s.* M 1012		
M 1022	**multipliable family** <AN, TO>	multiplizierbare Familie *f*	famille *f* multipliable	перемножаемое семейство

M 1023	**multipliable sequence** <in a normed algebra> <FA>	multiplizierbare Folge *f*	suite *f* multipliable	перемножаемая последовательность
M 1024	**multiplicand** <of a product> <AR, SE>	Multiplikand *m*, Multiplikandus *m*, erster Faktor *m*	multiplicande *m*, // efficient *m* <Girard>	множимое
M 1025	**multiplication** <by> <AL, AR>	Multiplikation *f* <mit>	multiplication *f* <par>	умножение <на>
	multiplication <AL>	*s.* H 510		
	multiplication <AL, CT>	*s.* C 1695		
M 1026	**multiplication algebra** <*e.g.:* of an algebra> <AL>	Algebra *f* der Multiplikationen <*z. B.:* einer Algebra>	algèbre *f* des multiplications <*par exemple:* d'une algèbre>	алгебра умножений <*например:* алгебры>
	multiplication and contraction <VT>	*s.* I 557		
M 1027	**multiplication and division by means of detached coefficients** <of polynomials> <AL>	abgekürzte Multiplikation und Division <nur die Koeffizienten werden hingeschrieben>	multiplication *f* et division *f* abrégées	сокращенное умножение и деление
	multiplication by numbers <MD>	*s.* S 80		
	multiplication constant <AL>	*s.* C 2108		
M 1028	**multiplication law,** law of multiplication (combination), combination law, rule of combination, law of composition <AL>	Verknüpfungsgesetz *n*, Verknüpfungsvorschrift *f*, Zusammensetzungsvorschrift *f*	loi *f* de composition	закон композиции (умножения)
M 1029	**multiplication method** <of elimination> <AL>	Multiplikationsmethode *f*	méthode *f* des multiplicateurs <Bézout>	способ умножения, метод умножения
	multiplication of cardinal numbers <SE>	*s.* C 121 a		
M 1030	**multiplication of consequents** <LO>	hintere Kopplung *f*	composition *f* des conséquents	умножение сукцедентов
	multiplication of ordinal numbers <SE>	*s.* O 375		
	multiplication of partitioned matrices <MD>	*s.* D 583		
	multiplication on the left <AL>	*s.* L 433		
	multiplication on the right <AL>	*s.* R 1211		
M 1031	**multiplication operator** <FA>	Multiplikationsoperator *m*	opérateur *m* de multiplication	оператор умножения
M 1032	**multiplication ring** <of a ring> <AL>	Ring *m* der Multiplikationen	anneau *m* des multiplications	кольцо умножений
	multiplication rule <MD>	*s.* R 1488		
M 1033	**multiplication table** <AR>	Multiplikationstafel *f*, Multiplikationstabelle *f*, Einmaleins *n*, Produktentafel *f*, Produkttafel *f*, Pythagoräische Tabelle (Tafel) *f*	table *f* de multiplication (multiplication des entiers), table pythagorique (pythagorienne, de Pythagore)	таблица умножения
	multiplication table <AL>	*s.* C 295		
M 1034	**multiplication table for a basis** <of an algebra> <AL>	Multiplikationstafel *f* bezüglich einer Basis <einer Algebra>	table *f* de multiplication par rapport à une base <d'une algèbre>	таблица умножения базы <алгебры>
M 1035	**multiplication table from eleven to twenty** <AR>	großes Einmaleins *n*	table *f* de multiplication de 11 à 20	таблица умножения от одиннадцати до двадцати
M 1036	**multiplication table up to ten** <AR>	kleines Einmaleins *n*	table *f* de Pythagore (multiplication)	малая (маленькая) таблица умножения, таблица умножения до десяти
M 1037	**multiplication theorem** <also for Dirichlet and Fourier series> <AP, FD, FU, SS>	Multiplikationssatz *m* <AP, FU, SS>; Multiplikationstheorem *n* <FD, FU>	théorème *m* de multiplication	теорема умножения
M 1038	**multiplication theorem,** Gauss['s] multiplication theorem <for the gamma function> <FU>	Gaußsches Multiplikationstheorem *n*	formule *f* de multiplication de Legendre-Gauss	теорема (формула) умножения [Лежандра-] Гаусса
M 1039	**multiplication theorem** <of probability theory> <ST>	Multiplikationssatz *m* <der Wahrscheinlichkeiten>	théorème *m* de multiplication <des probabilités>	теорема умножения <вероятностей>
M 1040	**multiplicative axiom** <SE>	multiplikatives Axiom *n*	axiome *m* multiplicatif	мультипликативная аксиома, аксиома мультипликативности
	multiplicative axiom <SE>	*s.* A 1280		
M 1041	**multiplicative base** <of order *h*> <NT>	multiplikative Basis *f* <*h*-ter Ordnung>	base *f* multiplicative <d'ordre *h*>	мультипликативный базис <порядка *h*>
M 1042	**multiplicative character** <e.g. of a ring> <AL, NT>	Multiplikativcharakter *m* <AL>; multiplikativer Charakter *m* <AL, NT>	caractère *m* multiplicatif	мультипликативный характер
M 1043	**multiplicative composition law** <AL>	multiplikatives Kompositionsgesetz *n*, multiplikative Verknüpfung *f*	loi *f* multiplicative, loi de multiplication	мультипликативный закон композиции
	multiplicative Cousin problem <FT>	*s.* C 2595		
M 1044	**multiplicative group** <of a field *or* skew field> <AL>	Multiplikationsgruppe *f*, Multiplikativgruppe *f*, Einheitengruppe *f*	groupe *m* multiplicatif	мультипликативная группа
M 1045	**multiplicative lattice,** m-lattice <LA>	multiplikativer Verband *m*	treillis *m* multiplicatif, groupoïde *m* réticulé	мультипликативная структура (решетка), структура (решетка) с умножением
	multiplicatively closed set <AL>	*s.* M 1051		

No.	English	German	French	Russian
M 1046	**multiplicatively commutative ordinal numbers,** ordinal numbers commutative with respect to multiplication <SE>	multiplikativ vertauschbare Ordnungszahlen *fpl*	nombres *mpl* ordinaux commutables pour la multiplication	мультипликативно перестановочные порядковые числа
	multiplicatively convex function <RF>	*s.* L 1058		
M 1047	**multiplicatively invariant lattice** <GU>	multiplikativ-invariantes Gitter *n*	réseau *m* multiplicativement invariant	мультипликативно инвариантная решетка
M 1048	**multiplicative prime number theory** <NT>	multiplikative Primzahltheorie *f*	théorie *f* multiplicative des nombres premiers	мультипликативная теория простых чисел
	multiplicative principle <SE>	*s.* A 1280		
M 1049	**multiplicative product,** product <of a distribution and a function> <AN>	multiplikatives Produkt *n*, Produkt <von Distribution und Funktion>	produit *m* multiplicatif, produit <d'une distribution avec une fonction>	мультипликативное произведение, произведение <обобщенной функции с функцией>
M 1050	**multiplicative sequence,** m-sequence <of polynomials> <AL>	multiplikative Folge *f*, m-Folge *f*	suite *f* multiplicative, m-suite *f*	мультипликативная последовательность, m-последовательность
M 1051	**multiplicative system,** multiplicatively closed set, m.s. <of a ring> <AL>	multiplikativ abgeschlossenes System *n*, multiplikativ abgeschlossener Bereich *m*	partie *f* multiplicative, système *m* multiplicativement fermé, ensemble *m* multiplicativement stable	мультипликативно замкнутая система, мультипликативно замкнутое подмножество, мультипликативное подмножество, мультипликативная система
	multiplicative system <AL>	*s.* P 216		
	multiplicative variety <AG>	*s.* D 828		
M 1052	**multiplicativity** <of a function> <AL, NT>	Multiplikativität *f*	multiplicativité *f*	мультипликативность
	multiplicator <FU>	*s.* M 1066		
	multiplicator <GR>	*s.* S 153		
M 1053	**multiplicator equation** <for elliptic functions> <FU>	Multiplikatorgleichung *f*	équation *f* du multiplicateur	уравнение множителя
M 1054	**multiplicity** <of points, etc. in an algebraic variety> <AG>	Multiplizität *f*, Vielfachheit *f*	multiplicité *f*	кратность
M 1055	**multiplicity,** order <of a [multiple] point of a curve> <AG, DG>	Vielfachheit *f*, Ordnung *f*	ordre *m*, multiplicité *f*	кратность, порядок
M 1056	**multiplicity** <of an ideal *or* a [semi-]local ring *or* a ray of solution> <AL>	Multiplizität *f*	multiplicité *f*	кратность
M 1057	**multiplicity** <of an elementary divisor *or* eigenvalue> <AL, DE, FA>	Vielfachheit *f*	multiplicité *f*	кратность
M 1058	**multiplicity,** order <of a root, zero> <AL, FT>	Vielfachheit *f*, Multiplizität *f*, Ordnung *f*	ordre *m* de multiplicité, multiplicité *f*, ordre	кратность, множественность, порядок кратности
M 1059	**multiplicity** <as a root of the characteristic equation>, algebraic multiplicity <of an eigenvalue> <AL, MD>	algebraische Vielfachheit *f*, Vielfachheit, Ordnung *f*, Rang *m*	multiplicité *f* algébrique	кратность, ранг
M 1060	**multiplicity** <of an intersection point> <AY>	Schnittpunktsmultiplizität *f*, Multiplizität *f* <eines Schnittpunkts>	multiplicité *f* <d'un point d'intersection>	кратность <точки пересечения>
M 1061	**multiplicity** <of an edge> <GP>	Multiplizität *f* <einer Kante in bezug auf eine Kantenfolge>	multiplicité *f* <d'un arête>; ordre *m* de multiplicité <d'une ligne dans un multigraphe>	кратность <ребра>
	multiplicity <AT>	*s.* N 831		
	multiplicity of intersection <AG>	*s.* I 807		
	multiplicity type <UA>	*s.* T 1141		
M 1062	**multiplier** <of an invariant> <AL>	Multiplikator *m*	multiplicateur *m*	умножитель
M 1063	**multiplier** <of a semi-linear substitution> <AL>	Multiplikator *m*	multiplicateur *m*	коэффициент подобия
M 1064	**multiplier** <of an almost periodic function *or* a difference equation> <AP, FD>	Multiplikator *m*	multiplicateur *m*	множитель
M 1065	**multiplier** <AR>	Multiplikator *m*	multiplicateur *m*, // coefficient *m* <Girard, Viète>	множитель
M 1066	**multiplier,** multiplicator <of elliptic functions> <FU>	Multiplikator *m*	multiplicateur *m*	множитель
	multiplier <AL>	*s.* F 12		
	multiplier <GR>	*s.* S 153		
M 1067	**multiply connected domain (region)** <TO>	mehrfach[ ]zusammenhängendes Gebiet *n*, mehrfach[ ]zusammenhängender Bereich *m*	domaine *m* multiplement connexe, domaine à connexion multiple, domaine multiconnexe	многосвязная область, неодносвязная область
M 1068	**multiply connected sequence** <of functors> <CA>	mehrfach verbundene Sequenz *f*	suite *f* multiplement connexe	многократно связанная последовательность
M 1069	**multiply connected space,** not simply connected space <TO>	mehrfach[ ]zusammenhängender Raum *m*, nicht einfach[ ]zusammenhängender Raum	espace *m* multiplement connexe	многосвязное пространство

	multiply criss[-]cross / to <AL>	*s.* C 2706		
	multiply crosswise / to <AL>	*s.* C 2706		
M 1070	**multiplying out** <AL>	Ausmultiplizieren *n*, Ausmultiplikation *f*	multiplication *f*	перемножение
	multiply isomorphic group <GR>	*s.* H 493		
M 1071	**multiply monotone sequence** <SS>	mehrfach monotone Folge *f*	suite *f* plusieurs fois monotone	кратно-монотонная последовательность
M 1072	**multiply ordered class** <SE>	mehrfach geordnete Klasse *f*	classe *f* multi-ordonnée	кратно-упорядоченный класс
	multiply perfect number <NT>	*s.* M 982		
M 1073	**multiply periodic[al] function,** multi-periodic function <AN>	mehrfach periodische Funktion *f*	fonction *f* plusieurs fois périodique, fonction multiplement périodique, fonction multipériodique	кратно-периодическая функция, многократно-периодическая функция
M 1074	**multiply primitive** <AL>	mehrfach primitiv	plusieurs fois primitif	кратно-примитивный
M 1075	**multiply projective space** <PJ>	mehrfach projektiver Raum *m*	espace *m* plusieurs fois projectif, espace multi-projectif	кратно-проективное пространство
M 1076	**multiply rooted graph** <GP>	Graph *m* mit mehreren Wurzeln	graphe *m* à plusieurs racines	многокорневой граф
M 1077	**multiply transitive group** <GR>	mehrfach[ ]transitive Gruppe *f*	groupe *m* plusieurs fois transitif	кратно-транзитивная группа
M 1078	**multi-rooted equation,** equation with multiple roots <AL>	Gleichung *f* mit mehrfachen Wurzeln (Nullstellen)	équation *f* à zéros (racines) multiples	многокорневое уравнение, уравнение с многократными нулями
M 1079	**multistage competition** <PG>	Mehrstufenkonkurrenz *f*	compétition *f* à plusieurs étages	многоступенчатая конкуренция
M 1080	**multi-stage game** <TG>	Mehrschrittspiel *n*	jeu *m* à plusieurs pas	многошаговая игра
	multistage optimization <PG>	*s.* M 1081		
M 1081	**multistage programming,** multistage optimization <PG>	Mehrstufenoptimierung *f*	programmation (optimisation) *f* en plusieurs étages	многоступенчатое программирование, многоступенчатая оптимизация
M 1082	**multi-stage sampling** <ST>	mehrstufiges Stichprobenverfahren *n*, Mehrstufen-Stichprobenverfahren *n*	sondage *m* à plusieurs degrés, échantillonnage *m* à plusieurs degrés	многоступенчатый выбор, метод многоступенчатой выборки
M 1083	**multivalent function,** multiple-valued function, many-valued function, ramified (branched) function <contrary to univalent function> <FT>	mehrwertige (polydrome, multivalente, mehrblättrige, verzweigte, mehrdeutige, nichteindeutige, polytrope) Funktion *f*; *p*-wertige (*p*-valente) Funktion	fonction *f* multiforme (polytrope, polydrome, multivalente, non[-]uniforme); fonction *p*-valente	многолистная (многозначная, неоднозначная, разветвленная) функция; *p*-листная (*p*-значная) функция
M 1084	**multi[-]valued decision** <ST>	mehrwertige Entscheidung *f*	décision *f* plurivalente (à plusieurs valeurs, polyvalente)	многозначное решение
	multi[-]valued logic <LO>	*s.* M 84		
	multi-valued mapping <SE>	*s.* M 85		
M 1085	**multi[-]valued negation** <LO>	mehrwertige Negation *f*	négation *f* multi-valuée	многозначное отрицание
M 1086	**multivaluedness** <of a representation> <RE>	Mehrdeutigkeit *f*	multivalence *f*	многозначность
	multi-valuedness <SE>	*s.* M 88		
M 1087	**multivariate analysis of variance,** analysis of dispersion, dispersion analysis, MANOVA <ST>	multivariable Varianzanalyse *f*, mehrdimensionale Varianzanalyse, Dispersionsanalyse *f*, MANOVA	analyse *f* de variance à plusieurs variables	многомерный дисперсионный анализ
M 1088	**multivariate distribution,** multidimensional (joint) distribution <ST>	multivariable (mehrdimensionale, multivariate) Verteilung *f*	distribution *f* à plusieurs variables (dimensions), distribution multidimensionnelle	многомерное распределение
M 1089	**multivariate distribution function,** multidimensional distribution function <ST>	multivariable (mehrdimensionale, multivariate) Verteilungsfunktion *f*	fonction *f* de distribution à plusieurs variables (dimensions), fonction de distribution multidimensionnelle	многомерная функция распределения
M 1090	**multivariate statistics,** multidimensional statistics <ST>	multivariate (multivariable, mehrdimensionale) Statistik *f*	statistique *f* multivariate, statistique à plusieurs variables (dimensions)	многомерная статистика
M 1091	**multivector of rank *p*,** alternating tensor of rank *p*, *p*-vector, alternate *p*-linear function <AL, GE, VT>	Multivektor *m* *p*-ter Stufe, Multivektor der Stufe *p*, *p*-Vektor *m*, vollständig alternierender Tensor *m* *p*-ter Stufe, zusammengesetzte Größe *f* *p*-ter Stufe, Komplexgröße *f* *p*-ter Stufe	multivecteur *m* de rang *p*, *p*-vecteur *m*	поливектор (мультивектор) валентности *p*, *p*-вектор
M 1092	**mu-measurable function,** μ-measurable function <ME, RF>	μ-meßbare (my-meßbare) Funktion *f*, meßbare Funktion bezüglich <eines Maßes> μ	fonction *f* μ-mesurable (mu-mesurable)	μ-измеримая (мю-измеримая) функция
M 1093	**mu-measurable hull,** μ-measurable hull, measurable hull <ME>	μ-meßbare (my-meßbare) Hülle *f*, μ-Hülle *f*, My-Hülle *f*, meßbare Hülle	enveloppe *f* μ-mesurable (mu-mesurable), enveloppe mesurable	μ-измеримая (мю-измеримая) оболочка, измеримая оболочка
M 1094	**Müntz['s] theorem** <FD>	Satz *m* von Müntz, Müntzscher Satz	théorème *m* de Müntz	теорема Мюнца

M 1095	**mu-singular function,** μ-singular function <ME>	μ-singuläre (my-singuläre) Funktion *f*, singuläre Funktion bezüglich μ	fonction *f* μ-singulière (mu-singulière)	μ-сингулярная (мю-сингулярная) функция
M 1096	**Muskhelishvili['s] problem,** modified Dirichlet problem <IE>	Muschelischwilisches Problem *n*, modifiziertes Dirichletsches Problem	problème *m* de Muskhelishvili, problème modifié de Dirichlet	задача Мусхелишвили, модифицированная задача Дирихле
M 1097	**mu-summable function,** μ-summable function <AN>	μ-summierbare (my-summierbare) Funktion *f*	fonction *f* μ-sommable (mu-sommable)	μ-суммируемая (мю-суммируемая) функция
M 1098	**mutual commutant** <GR>	gegenseitige Kommutatorgruppe *f*	commutant *m* mutuel	взаимный (противоположный) коммутант
M 1099	**mutual information,** synentropy <ST>	Synentropie *f*, gegenseitige (wechselseitige, übertragene) Information *f*	information *f* mutuelle, information réciproque, synentropie *f*	взаимная информация, синэнтропия
M 1100	**mutually coprime elements** <AL>	paarweise teilerfremde Elemente *npl*	éléments *mpl* étrangers l'un à l'autre	взаимно простые элементы
M 1101	**mutually disjoint events,** mutually exclusive events, incompatible events, antithetic events <ST>	unvereinbare Ereignisse *npl*, [einander] ausschließende Ereignisse, sich ausschließende Ereignisse, unverträgliche (disjunkte, fremde) Ereignisse	événements *mpl* incompatibles (disjoints, s'excluant mutuellement)	взаимно исключающие события, несовместимые (несовместные) события, [взаимно] непересекающиеся события
M 1102	**mutually disjoint subsets,** mutually exclusive subsets, pairwise disjoint subsets <SE>	paarweise disjunkte (durchschnittsfremde, elementfremde, fremde) Untermengen *fpl*	sous-ensembles *mpl* mutuellement disjoints, sous-ensembles disjoints deux à deux	попарно непересекающиеся (дизъюнктные) подмножества, взаимно непересекающиеся подмножества
	mutually exclusive events <ST>	*s.* M 1101		
	mutually exclusive subsets <SE>	*s.* M 1102		
M 1103	**mutually independent events,** two-by-two [mutually] independent events, pairwise independent events <ST>	paarweise unabhängige Ereignisse *npl*	événements *mpl* indépendant[s] deux à deux, événements indépendant l'un à l'autre	попарно независимые события, независимые друг от друга события
M 1104	**mutually inscribed tetrahedra** <associated with a twisted cubic> <AG>	Möbiussche Tetraeder *npl*	tétraèdres *mpl* de Möbius	тетраэдры Мебиуса
M 1105	**mutually inscribed tetrahedra** <AY, SG>	Möbiussches Vierflachpaar *n*, Möbiussche Tetraeder (Vierflache) *npl*	tétraèdres *mpl* de Möbius	тетраэдры Мебиуса
M 1106	**mutually perpendicular / to be** <EG>	senkrecht [aufeinander-] stehen	être perpendiculaire (orthogonal)	быть ортогональным
	mutually prime elements <AL>	*s.* R 751		
	mutually prime ideals <AL>	*s.* C 1174		
	mutually relatively prime numbers <NT>	*s.* N 840		

N

N 1	***n*-abelian group** <GR>	*n*-abelsche Gruppe *f*	groupe *m n*-abélien	*n*-абелева группа
	nabla [operator] <VT>	*s.* D 195		
	nabla vector <VT>	*s.* D 195		
	***n*-adic group** <GR>	*s.* P 917		
	***n*-adic predicate** <LO>	*s.* P 1189		
	***n*-adic relation** <CA, SE>	*s.* N 17		
N 2	**Nagata-Smirnov metrization theorem** <TO>	Satz *m* von Nagata und Smirnov, Satz von J. Nagata und J. M. Smirnov, [Nagata-] Smirnovscher Metrisierungssatz *m*	théorème *m* de Nagata-Smirnov	теорема Нагата-Смирнова, метризационная теорема Нагата-Смирнова
N 3	**Nagayev['s] inequality** <ST>	Ungleichung *f* von Nagaev (Nagajew), Nagaevsche Ungleichung	inégalité *f* de Nagayev	неравенство Нагаева
N 4	**Nagel['s] point** <of a triangle> <EG>	Nagelscher Punkt *m*	point *m* de Nagel	точка Нагеля
	Nagumo['s] uniqueness theorem <DE>	*s.* U 226		
	NAH-plane <GE>	*s.* N 68		
N 5	**naive set theory** <SE>	naive Mengentheorie *f*	théorie *f* naïve (élémentaire) des ensembles	наивная теория множеств
N 6	**Nakayama['s] lemma** <AL>	Lemma *n* von Nakayama, Nakayamas Lemma	lemme *m* de Nakayama	лемма Накаямы
	N-almost-periodic function <AP>	*s.* L 605		
	Naperian logarithm <AN>	*s.* N 31		
N 7	**Napier['s] analogies,** Neper['s] analogies <EG>	Napiersche Analogien *fpl*, Nepers[che] Analogien	analogies *fpl* de Napier (Néper), analogies népériennes	неперовы аналогии
	Napierian (Napier['s]) logarithm <AN>	*s.* N 31		
N 8	**Napier['s] rods** <IN, NU>	Nepersche Stäbchen *npl* (Rechenstäbchen *npl*, Stäbe *mpl*), Napiersche Rechenstäbchen, Rechenstäbchen, Rechen-	réglettes *fpl* (bâtons *mpl*) de Néper, baguettes *fpl* népériennes, bâtons népériens	палочки Непера, неперовы счетные палочки, счетные палочки

No.	English	German	French	Russian
and still: N 8		stäbchen von Neper, Rechenstäbe *mpl* von John Neper, virgulae *fpl* numeratrices		
N 9	**Napier['s] rules,** Neper['s] rules <of circular parts> <EG>	Napiersche (Nepersche) Regel *f*	règle *f* de Néper	правило Непера, неперовс правило
N 10	**Napoleon['s] theorem** <for the triangle> <EG>	Napoleons Satz *m*	théorème *m* de Napoléon	теорема Наполеона
	nappe <GE>	*s.* S 760		
N 11	***n*-arc theorem** <TO>	*n*-Beinsatz *m* <Menger>	« *n*-Beinsatz » *m*, théorème *m* de Menger	теорема Менгера
N 12	**narrow sense / in the,** in the strict sense, in the restricted sense <GN>	im engeren Sinne, i.e.S.	au (en, dans le) sens étroit, au (en, dans le) sens strict, au (en, dans le) sens restreint	в узком смысле
N 13	***n*-ary attribute** <LO>	*n*-stelliges Attribut *n*	attribut *m* *n*-adique	*n*-местный признак
N 14	***n*-ary domain** <PJ>	Gebiet *n* *n*-ter Stufe	domain *m* *n*-aire	*n*-арная область
	***n*-ary form** <AL>	*s.* F 483		
N 15	***n*-ary operation,** *n*-place operation, operation of rank *n*, operation of *n* arguments <UA>	*n*-stellige (*n*-äre, *n*-stellige algebraische) Operation *f*, *n*-stellige (*n*-äre) algebraische Verknüpfung *f*	opération *f* interne *n*-aire, opération interne à *n* places (arguments)	*n*-арная (*n*-местная) операция, операция с *n* аргументами, *n*-членная (*n*-арная) алгебраическая операция
	***n*-ary predicate** <LO>	*s.* P 1189		
N 16	***n*-ary predicate variable** <LO>	*n*-stellige Prädikatenvariable *f*	variable *f* de prédicat à *n* places	переменный предикат от *n* переменных
N 17	***n*-ary relation,** *n*-adic relation, relation of rank *n*, *n*-place relation <CA, SE>	*n*-stellige (*n*-äre) Relation *f*	relation *f* *n*-aire (d'ordre *n*, de degré *n*)	*n*-арное (*n*-местное) отношение, отношение с *n* аргументами
N 18	**Nasik['s] cube** <CT>	Würfel *m* von Nasik, Nasikscher Würfel	cube *m* de Nasik	куб Назика
N 19	**Nasik['s] square** <a special magic square> <CT>	Quadrat *n* von Nasik	carré *m* de Nasik	квадрат Назика
N 20	**Natani['s] [differential] equation** <DE>	Natanische Differentialgleichung (Gleichung) *f*	équation *f* [différentielle] de Natani	[дифференциальное] уравнение Натани
N 21	**natural boundary** <of an analytic function> <FT>	natürliche Grenze *f*	coupure *f*, frontière *f* naturelle	естественная граница
N 22	**natural boundary condition** <VA>	natürliche Randbedingung *f*	condition *f* aux limites naturelle	естественное краевое условие
N 23	**natural co-ordinates,** intrinsic co-ordinates <of a space curve> <DG>	natürliche Koordinaten *fpl*	coordonnées *fpl* intrinsèques (naturelles)	естественные координаты
N 24	**natural deduction** <LO>	natürliches Schließen *n* <Gentzen>	déduction *f* naturelle	натуральный вывод, натуральная дедукция
	natural deduction system <LO>	*s.* S 2531		
	natural φ-density <AB>	*s.* A 1159		
N 25	**natural equation,** intrinsic (intrinsical) equation <of a curve> <DG>	natürliche Gleichung *f*	équation *f* intrinsèque	натуральное (естественное, внутреннее) уравнение
N 26	**natural equivalence,** natural isomorphism, functorial isomorphism <CA>	natürliche Äquivalenz *f*, natürlicher (funktorieller) Isomorphismus *m*, Isomorphismus	équivalence *f* naturelle, isomorphisme *m* de foncteurs, isomorphisme fonctoriel	естественная эквивалентность, функторный (естественный) изоморфизм, изоморфизм <функторов>
N 27	**natural exponent** <AL, NT>	natürlicher Exponent *m*	exposant *m* entier positif	целый положительный показатель
	natural frame <DG>	*s.* N 40		
N 28	**natural geometry** <by Cesaro> <DG>	natürliche Geometrie *f*	géométrie *f* naturelle [basée sur les équations intrinsèques]	натуральная (естественная) геометрия
	natural homomorphism <AL>	*s.* C 70		
	natural image <AL, SE>	*s.* C 73		
N 29	**natural injection** <AL, CA>	natürliche Injektion *f*	injection *f* naturelle	естественное вложение
	natural isomorphism <CA>	*s.* N 26		
N 30	**natural language** <LO>	natürliche Sprache *f*	langage *m* naturel	натуральный язык
N 31	**natural logarithm,** logarithm to base e, Napierian (Naperian, Napier['s], hyperbolic) logarithm, ln, $\log_e$, // log <AN>	natürlicher (Neperscher, Napierscher, hyperbolischer) Logarithmus *m*, Logarithmus zur Basis e, ln, $^e\log$, $\log_e$, // log	logarithme *m* naturel (népérien, hyperbolique, de base e), ln, $\log_e$, // log	натуральный (гиперболический, неперов) логарифм, ln, $\log_e$, // log
	naturally ordered factor-group (factor group) <GR>	*s.* C 76		
N 32	**natural mapping,** canonical mapping, projection, quotient map, projection map <of a set onto a decomposition of the set> <SE>	kanonische (natürliche) Abbildung *f*, Mengenhomomorphismus *m*, Projektion *f*, Projektionsabbildung *f* <einer Menge auf die Quotientenmenge>	application *f* canonique <d'un ensemble sur l'ensemble quotient>	каноническое (естественное) отображение, проекция <множества на фактор-множество>
	natural mapping <AL>	*s.* C 77		
N 33	**natural number,** positive integer <NT>	natürliche Zahl *f*, natürliche ganze Zahl	entier *m* naturel, nombre *m* entier naturel, nombre arithmétique	натуральное число, натуральное
N 34	**natural operation** <SE>	natürliche Operation *f*	opération *f* naturelle	натуральная операция

No.	English	German	French	Russian
N 35	**natural [partial] ordering** <AL, SE>	natürliche Halbordnung *f*; Halbordnung durch Inklusion	ordre *m* [partiel] naturel; ordre par inclusion	естественный частичный порядок, естественное упорядочение; упорядочение по включению
N 36	**natural product** <of ordinal numbers> <SE>	natürliches Produkt *n*	produit *m* naturel	натуральное произведение
N 37	**natural scale** <NT>	natürliche Zahlenreihe *f*	suite *f* naturelle, suite naturelle de[s] nombres, suite immédiate des nombres naturels	натуральный ряд, натуральный ряд чисел
N 38	**natural sine** <contrary to sine logarithm> <AN>	natürlicher Wert *m* des Sinus, natürlicher Sinus *m*	sinus *m* naturel	натуральный синус
N 39	**natural sum** <of ordinal numbers> <SE>	natürliche Summe *f*	somme *f* naturelle	натуральная сумма
N 40	**natural system** <of coordinates>, natural frame <DG>	natürliches Koordinatensystem (System) *n*	système *m* de coordonnées naturelles, système naturel <de coordonnées>; repère *m* naturel	естественная система <координат>
	natural topology <TO>	*s.* T 564		
N 41	**natural transformation,** morphism of functors, functor morphism, functorial map, functorial transformation <of functors> <CA>	natürliche Transformation *f*, funktorieller Morphismus *m*	morphisme *m* fonctoriel, triplet *m* définissant une transformation naturelle, transformation *f* naturelle, homomorphisme *m* [fonctoriel], application *f* naturelle	естественное (функторное) преобразование, функторный морфизм, морфизм функторов, [функторный] гомоморфизм <функтора в функтор>
	***n*-ball** <GE>	*s.* C 900		
N 42	***n*-boundary** <AT, HA>	*n*-dimensionaler Rand *m*	bord *m* de dimension *n*	граница размерности *n*, *n*-граница
	***n* by *n* array** <MD>	*s.* N 723		
	***n*-by-*n* matrix, *n* by *n* matrix** <MD>	*s.* N 723		
	***n* by *n* square matrix** <MD>	*s.* N 723		
N 43	***n*-category** <CA>	*n*-Kategorie *f*	*n*-catégorie *f*	*n*-категория
N 44	***n*-cell,** *n*-dimensional cell, topological *n*-cell <AT>	*n*-dimensionales Element *n*, krumme *n*-dimensionale Zelle *f*, *n*-dimensionale krumme Zelle, *n*-dimensionales topologisches Element, *n*-dimensionale [topologische] Zelle	*n*-cellule *f* [topologique], *n*-élément *m*	*n*-мерная кривая клетка; пространство, гомеоморфное замкнутому шару B_n
N 45	***n*-centre** <of a group> <GR>	*n*-Zentrum *n*	*n*-centre *m*	*n*-центр
N 46	***n*-chain** <AT>	*n*-Kette *f*, *n*-dimensionale Kette *f*	*n*-chaîne *f*, chaîne *f* de dimension *n*	цепь размерности *n*, *n*-цепь, *n*-мерная цепь
N 47	***n*-chromatic graph** <GP>	*n*-chromatischer (*n*-chromer) Graph *m*	graphe *m* *n*-chromatique	*n*-хроматический граф
N 48	***n*-coboundary,** *n*-dimensional coboundary <AT, HA>	*n*-dimensionaler Korand *m*, *n*-Korand *m*	cobord *m* de degré *n*	кограница степени *n*
N 49	***n*-cocycle** <AT, HA>	*n*-dimensionaler Kozyklus *m*	cocycle *m* de degré *n*	коцикл степени *n*
N 50	***n*-colourable graph** <GP>	*n*-färbbarer Graph *m*	graphe *m* *n*-colorable	*n*-раскрашиваемый граф
N 51	***n*-colouring** <GP>	*n*-Färbung *f*	*n*-coloration *f*	*n*-цветная раскраска
N 52	***n*-commutable elements** <of a group> <GR>	*n*-vertauschbare Elemente *npl*	éléments *mpl* *n*-commutables	*n*-перестановочные элементы
N 53	***n*-commutator** <AL>	*n*-Kommutator *m*	*n*-commutateur *m*	*n*-коммутатор
N 54	***n*-complex** <AT>	*n*-dimensionaler Komplex *m*	complexe *m* *n*-dimensionne	l*n*-мерный комплекс
N 55	***n*-connected space** <TO>	*n*-zusammenhängender Raum *m*, [bis zur Dimension] *n* zusammenhängender Raum *m*	espace *m* à connexité *n*-dimensionnelle	*n*-связное (*n*-мерно связное) пространство
N 56	***n*-cube,** *n*-dimensional cube <GE, TO>	*n*-dimensionaler Würfel (Kubus) *m*	cube *m* à *n* dimensions, cube de dimension *n*, *n*-cube *m*	*n*-мерный куб
N 57	***n*-cube scheme** <CA>	*n*-faches Produkt *n* eines Diagrammschemas mit sich		*n*-кратное произведение диаграммной схемы с собой
N 58	***n*-cycle,** cycle of length *n* <of a permutation> <AL>	Zyklus *m* der Länge *n*, *n*-elementiger (*n*-gliedriger) Zyklus	cycle *m* de longueur *n*, cycle *n*-aire, cycle de degré *n*	цикл длины *n*
N 59	***n*-cycle,** *n*-dimensional cycle <AT>	*n*-dimensionaler Zyklus *m*, *n*-Zyklus *m*	*n*-cycle *m*, cycle *m* de dimension *n*	цикл размерности *n*, *n*-цикл
	***n*-digit number** <NT>	*s.* N 714		
	***n*-dimensional cell** <AT>	*s.* N 44		
	***n*-dimensional closed interval** <GE, RF>	*s.* C 887		
	***n*-dimensional coboundary** <AT, HA>	*s.* N 48		
N 59a	***n*-dimensional column vector,** 1- by -*n* matrix <MD>	*n*-reihige Spaltenmatrix *f*	matrice *f* colonne à *n* lignes	столбец размерности (высоты) *n*
	***n*-dimensional continuum** <AN, GE>	*s.* C 167		
	***n*-dimensional cube** <GE, TO>	*s.* N 56		
	***n*-dimensional cycle** <AT>	*s.* N 59		
	***n*-dimensional elementary chain** <AT>	*s.* E 113		
	***n*-dimensional homotopy group** <TO>	*s.* N 737		

	English	German	French	Russian
N 60	***n*-dimensional interval,** *n*-interval <GE, RF>	*n*-dimensionales [achsenparalleles] Intervall *n*, achsenparalleles Intervall	pavé *m* [à *n* dimensions]	кирпич, *n*-мерный кирпич (интервал)
	***n*-dimensional manifold** <GE, TO>	*s.* N 264		
N 61	***n*-dimensional open interval** <GE, RF>	*n*-dimensionales [achsenparalleles] offenes Intervall *n*, offenes achsenparalleles Intervall	pavé *m* [à *n* dimensions], pavé ouvert [à *n* dimensions]	полиинтервал [в *n*-мерном пространстве], открытый параллелепипед [*n*-мерного пространства], открытый кирпич
N 62	***n*-dimensional parallelepiped[on]** <GE>	*n*-dimensionales Parallelepiped[on] *n*	parallélépipède *m* à *n* dimensions, parallélépipède de dimension *n*, parallélépipède *n*-dimensionnel	параллелепипед в *n*-мерном пространстве, *n*-мерный параллелепипед
	***n*-dimensional projective space** <PJ>	*s.* P 1713		
N 63	***n*-dimensional pseudomanifold without boundary,** absolute *n*-circuit <AT>	*n*-dimensionale geschlossene Pseudomannigfaltigkeit *f*	*n*-circuit *m* absolu	псевдомногообразие размерности *n* без края, абсолютный *n*-мерный цикл
	***n*-dimensional real vector bundle** <AT>	*s.* N 715		
N 64	***n*-dimensional rectangular parallelepiped** <GE>	*n*-dimensionaler Quader *m*	pavé *m* à *n* dimensions	*n*-мерный кирпич
N 65	***n*-dimensional row vector,** 1-by-*n* matrix <MD>	*n*-reihige Zeilenmatrix *f*, *n*-reihiger Zeilenvektor *m*	matrice *f* ligne à *n* colonnes	строка размерности (длины) *n*
	***n*-dimensional simplex** <TO>	*s.* N 726		
N 66	***n*-dimensional skeleton,** *n*-section <of a complex> <AT>	*n*-dimensionales Gerüst (Skelett) *n*	squelette *m* à *n* dimensions, squelette de dimension *n*	*n*-мерный остов
	***n*-dimensional solid sphere** <GE>	*s.* C 900		
	***n*-dimensional space** <GE, TO>	*s.* N 728		
N 67	***n*-dimensional standard skeleton complex,** standard simplicial *n*-complex <AT>	*n*-dimensionaler Standardeckpunktbereich *m*	schéma *m* simplicial type de dimension *n*	стандартная симплициальная схема размерности *n*
	***n*-disk** <TO>	*s.* C 886		
	***N*(0,1) distribution** <ST>	*s.* S 1623		
N 68	**near affine Hjelmslev plane,** NAH-plane <GE>	fastaffine Hjelmslev-Ebene *f*	plan *m* de Hjelmslev presque affine	почти аффинная плоскость Гельмслева
N 69	**near-field** <AL>	Fastkörper *m*	presque-corps *m*	почти-поле
N 70	**nearly poised [Saalschütz] series** <SS>	Saalschützsche Reihe *f* zweiter Art	série *f* de Saalschütz de la deuxième espèce	почти уравновешенный ряд [Заальшютца], ряд Заальшютца второго рода
N 71	**near-ring** <AL>	Fastring *m*	presque-anneau *m*	почти-кольцо
N 72	**neat complex** <AL>	Nettokomplex *m*	complexe *m* net	
N 73	**neat subgroup** <GR>	schwache Servanzuntergruppe *f*		слабо сервантная подгруппа
N 74	**necessary and sufficient condition,** characteristic condition <GN>	notwendige und hinreichende Bedingung *f*, charakteristische Bedingung	condition *f* nécessaire et suffisante, condition caractéristique	необходимое и достаточное условие, характеристическое условие, критерий, необходимый и достаточный признак
	necessary truth <LO>	*s.* A 642		
N 75	**necessity** <GN>	Notwendigkeit *f*	nécessité *f*	необходимость
	NED <ST>	*s.* N 565		
N 76	***n*-edged solid angle,** *n*-faced solid angle <EG>	*n*-Kant *n*, *n*-kantige körperliche Ecke *f*	angle *m* *n*-èdre	*n*-гранный угол
N 77	**needle point,** point <of a compass> <GE, IN>	Spitze *f*	pointe *f*	острие
	needle problem <ST>	*s.* B 792		
	negate <SE>	*s.* C 1358		
N 78	**negation** <as an operation> <LO>	Negation *f*, logische Negation	négation *f*	отрицание, логическое отрицание, операция не
N 79	**negation,** complement <of a proposition> <LO>	Negat *n*, Negation *f*, kontradiktorisches Gegenteil *n*, negierte Aussage *f*	propositon *f* négative, négation *f*	отрицание, дополнение <высказывания>
N 80	**negation** <of a relation> <SE>	Negation *f* <einer Relation>	relation *f* contradictoire	отрицание <отношения>
	negation <SE>	*s.* C 1387		
	negation bar <LO>	*s.* N 85		
N 81	**negation consistency,** consistency <LO>	klassische Widerspruchsfreiheit *f*, Widerspruchsfreiheit	non-contradiction *f*, cohérence *f*	внутренняя непротиворечивость, непротиворечивость
	negation consistent system <LO>	*s.* S 2509		
N 82	**negation functor** <LO>	Negationsfunktor *m*	foncteur *m* de négation	функтор отрицания
N 83	**negation law for the equivalence** <LO>	Prinzip (Theorem) *n* der gliedweisen Verneinung	loi *f* de négation de l'équivalence	закон четности эквивалентности
N 84	**negationless intuitionistic mathematics** <MM>	intuitionistische Mathematik *f* ohne Negation	mathématique *f* intuitioniste sans négation	интуиционистская математика без отрицания
N 85	**negation sign (symbol),** symbol of negation; negation bar; ¬-symbol, ¬ <*read:* negation of . . ., not . . ., non . . . <LO>	Zeichen *n* der Negation, Negationszeichen *n*, Nicht-Zeichen *n*, Negator *m*; Negationsstrich *m*, ¬ <*lies:* nicht, non>	symbole *m* (signe *f*) de négation, ¬ <*se lit:* négation de . . ., non . . .>	знак отрицания, негатор, отрицатель, ¬ <*читается:* не . . .; . . . сложно; не верно, что . . .; отрицание . . .>

No.	English	Deutsch	Français	Русский
N 86	**negative affine mapping,** inverse affine transformation <AY>	affine Abbildung *f* mit negativer Determinante	affinité *f* à déterminante négative	отрицательное аффинное отображение
	negative binomial [series] distribution <ST>	*s.* P 285		
N 87	**negative complex,** chain complex <HA>	negativer Komplex *m*, Kettenkomplex *m*	complexe *m* négatif	отрицательный (цепной) комплекс
N 88	**negative correlation,** inverse (antithetic) correlation <ST>	negative Korrelation *f*	corrélation *f* inverse (négative)	отрицательная корреляция
N 89	**negative definite eigenvalue problem** <DE>	negativ definite Eigenwertaufgabe *f*, negativ definites Eigenwertproblem *n*	problème *m* aux valeurs singulières (caractéristiques, critiques, propres) défini négatif	отрицательно определенная задача на собственные значения
N 90	**negative definite Hermitian form,** negatively definite Hermitian form <AL>	negativ definite hermitesche Form *f*	forme *f* hermitienne négative non dégénérée	отрицательная невырожденная эрмитова форма
N 91	**negative definite inner product space** <AL>	Raum *m* mit negativ definitem innerem Produkt	espace *m* à produit scalaire défini négatif	пространство с отрицательно определенным внутренним произведением
N 92	**negative definiteness** <AL, AN>	negative Definitheit *f*	propriété *f* d'être défini négatif, négativité *f* stricte	отрицательная определенность
N 93	**negative definite quadratic form,** negatively definite quadratic form <AL>	negativ definite quadratische Form *f*	forme *f* quadratique strictement (définie) négative	отрицательно определенная квадратичная форма
	negative direction <GE, GN>	*s.* C 835		
N 94	**negative divergence** <of a tensor *or* vector> <VT>	negative Divergenz *f*, Konvergenz *f*	divergence *f* négative	отрицательная дивергенция
	negative entropy <ST>	*s.* E 267		
	negative excess <ST>	*s.* P 663		
	negative factorial function <FU>	*s.* R 246		
N 95	**negative formula** <LO>	negierte Formel *f*	négation *f* d'une formule	негативная формула
N 96	**negative function,** strictly negative function << 0> <AL, AN>	negative (strikt negative, echt negative, streng negative) Funktion *f*	fonction *f* négative (strictement négative)	отрицательная (строго отрицательная, существенно отрицательная, негативная) функция
N 97	**negative gradient** <of a scalar> <VT>	negativer Gradient *m*, Konvergenz *f*	gradient *m* négatif	отрицательный градиент
	negative homothety <GE>	*s.* I 947		
	negative kernel <IE>	*s.* N 98		
	negative kurtosis <ST>	*s.* P 663		
	negatively definite Hermitian form <AL>	*s.* N 90		
N 98	**negatively definite kernel,** negative kernel <IE>	negativ definiter Kern *m*	noyau *m* défini négatif	отрицательно определенное ядро
	negatively definite quadratic form <AL>	*s.* N 93		
N 99	**negatively oriented base** <of a vector space> <AL>	negativ orientierte Basis *f*, Linkssystem *n*	base *f* négative (rétrograde, négativement orientée)	левый упорядоченный базис
N 100	**negatively related** <simplex and a face> <AT>	mit Inzidenzzahl —1	à coefficient d'incidence —1	с коэффициентом инцидентности — 1
N 101	**negatively related base** <AL, GE, TO>	entgegengesetzt orientierte Basis *f*	base *f* de sens rétrograde, base d'orientation opposée	базис противоположной ориентации, разноименный базис, противоположно ориентированный базис
	negatively semidefinite Hermitian form <AL>	*s.* N 110		
N 102	**negatively semi[-]definite operator,** negative semi[-]definite operator <FA>	negativ semidefiniter Operator *m*	opérateur *m* semi-défini négatif	отрицательно полуопределенный оператор
	negatively semi[-]definite quadratic form <AL>	*s.* N 111		
N 103	**negatively stable solution** <DE>	negativ stabile Lösung *f*	solution *f* négativement stable	отрицательно устойчивое решение
	negative matrix <AL, MD>	*s.* N 448		
N 104	**negative part** <of an element in an l-group *or* space *or* of a Hermitian operator> <AL, FA>	negativer Teil *m*, Negativteil *m*	partie *f* négative	отрицательная часть, компонента отрицательности
N 105	**negative particular proposition** <LO>	negatives (verneinendes) partikuläres Urteil *n*, partikulär verneinendes Urteil	proposition *f* particulière négative	частноотрицательное (частное отрицательное) суждение
	negative pedal <GE>	*s.* A 752		
N 106	**negative proposition** <LO>	negative Aussage *f*, verneinendes Urteil *n*	énoncé *m* négatif	отрицательное суждение
N 107	**negative regression,** inverse regression <ST>	negative Regression *f*	régression *f* inverse (négative)	отрицательная регрессия
	negative rotation <EG>	*s.* L 373		
N 108	**negative semi[-]definite eigenvalue problem** <DE>	negativ semidefinite Eigenwertaufgabe *f*, negativ semidefinites Eigenwertproblem *n*	problème *m* aux valeurs singulières (caractéristiques, critiques, propres) semi-défini négatif	отрицательно полуопределенная задача на собственные значения
N 109	**negative semi[-]definite form** <AL>	negativ semidefinite Form *f*	forme *f* négative (semi-définie négative)	отрицательная (неположительная, неположительно определенная) форма

	English	German	French	Russian
N 110	**negative semidefinite Hermitian form,** negatively semidefinite Hermitian form <AL>	negativ semidefinite hermitesche Form *f*	forme *f* hermitienne négative, forme hermitienne négative semi-définie	отрицательная эрмитова форма
	negative semi-definite matrix <AL, MD>	*s.* N 448		
	negative semi[-]definite operator <FA>	*s.* N 102		
N 111	**negative semi[-]definite quadratic form,** negatively semi[-]definite quadratic form <AL>	negativ semidefinite quadratische Form *f*	forme *f* quadratique négative (semi-définie négative)	отрицательная квадратичная форма, отрицательно полуопределенная квадратичная форма, неположительная (неположительно полуопределенная) квадратичная форма
	negative sense <GE, GN>	*s.* C 835		
	negative sign <AR>	*s.* M 658		
	negative similitude <GE>	*s.* I 947		
N 112	**negative skewness** <ST>	negative Schiefe *f*	dissymétrie (asymétrie) *f* négative	отрицательная асимметрия
N 113	**negative transitivity,** layerity <of a relation> <MM, SE>	negative Transitivität *f*	transitivité *f* négative	
N 114	**negative value of error** <ER>	Korrektur *f*, negativer Wert *m* des Fehlers	valeur *f* négative de l'erreur	отрицательная величина погрешности
N 115	**negative variation,** lower variation <of a [set] function> <AN>	negative (untere) Variation *f*	variation *f* négative (inférieure)	отрицательная (нижняя) вариация
	negentropy <ST>	*s.* E 267		
N 116	**neglect / to** <AX, NU>	vernachlässigen	négliger	пренебрегать, отбрасывать
N 117	**negligible** <with respect to> <AX, NU>	vernachlässigbar [klein] <gegen, gegenüber>	négligeable <devant>	пренебрежимый, пренебрегаемый, пренебрежимо малый, незначительно <по сравнению с>
N 118	**negligible function** <AX, NU>	vernachlässigbare Funktion *f*	fonction *f* négligeable	пренебрежимая функция
N 119	**negligible quantity** <AX, NU>	vernachlässigbare (zu vernachlässigende) Größe *f*	quantité *f* négligeable	пренебрежимая (незначительная) величина
N 120	**negligible *R*-module** <AL>	vernachlässigbarer *R*-Modul *m*	*R*-module *m* négligeable	пренебрегаемый *R*-модуль
N 121	**neighbour,** consecutive member <of an ordered set> <SE>	Nachbar *m*, benachbartes (konsekutives) Element *n*	élément *m* adjacent <à>, voisin *m*	сосед, последовательный элемент
N 122	**neighbourhood** <TO>	Umgebung *f*	voisinage *m*	окрестность
N 123	**neighbourhood** <TO>	Nachbarschaft *f*	entourage *m*; proximité *f* <dans l'espace de proximité>	соседство, окрестность, близость
N 124	**neighbourhood,** neighbourhood in the sense of Bourbaki <open or not> <TO>	Umgebung *f*, Nachbarschaft *f*	voisinage *m*	окрестность
	neighbourhood <TO>	*s.* O 144		
	ε-neighbourhood <TO>	*s.* E 313		
N 125	**neighbourhood axioms** <TO>	Umgebungsaxiome *npl*	axiomes *mpl* pour les voisinages	аксиомы окрестностей
N 126	**neighbourhood base (basis), neighbourhood-basis,** basis for the neighbourhoods <TO>	Umgebungsbasis *f*	base *f* d'ouverts <de la topologie>, base de voisinages	базис окрестностей
N 127	**neighbourhood filter** <TO>	Umgebungsfilter *m*	filtre *m* des voisinages	фильтр окрестностей
N 128	**neighbourhood filter** <in a uniform space> <TO>	Nachbarschaftsfilter *m*	filtre *m* d'entourages	фильтр окружений
N 129	**neighbourhood function** <TG>	Umgebungsfunktion *f*	fonction *f* de voisinage	окрестностная функция
	neighbourhood in the sense of Bourbaki <TO>	*s.* N 124		
N 130	**neighbourhood of *P* / in the,** around P <TO>	in der Umgebung von *P*	dans un voisinage (entourage) de *P*	в окрестности точки *P*
N 131	**neighbourhood of the [von] Neumann type** <TG>	Umgebung *f* des Von-Neumann-Typs, Umgebung vom von Neumannschen Typ	voisinage *m* du type de [von] Neumann	окрестность типа Неймана
N 132	**neighbourhood of zero** <AL, FA>	Umgebung *f* der Null <AL>; Nullumgebung *f* <FA>	voisinage *m* de zéro	окрестность нуля
N 133	**neighbourhood on the left** <of a real number> <TO>	linksseitige Umgebung *f*	voisinage *m* à gauche	левосторонняя окрестность
N 134	**neighbourhood on the right** <of a real number> <TO>	rechtsseitige Umgebung *f*	voisinage *m* à droite	правосторонняя окрестность
N 135	**neighbourhood retract** <TO>	Umgebungsretrakt *m*	rétracte *m* de voisinage	окрестностный ретракт
N 136	**neighbourhood space** <TO>	Umgebungsraum *m*	espace *m* à voisinage	окрестностное пространство; пространство, топология которого задана при помощи окрестностей
N 137	**neighbourhood system,** system of neighbourhoods <of a topological space> <TO>	Umgebungssystem *n*	système *m* de voisinages	система окрестностей; отображение, относящее каждой точке пространства некоторую фундаментальную систему ее окрестностей

No.	English	German	French	Russian
N 138	**neighbourhood topology** <TO>	Umgebungstopologie *f*, U-Topologie *f*	topologie *f* définie par un système de voisinages	топология, заданная при помощи окрестностей
N 139	**neighbouring form,** neighbouring quadratic form <AL>	benachbarte Form *f*, forma *f* contigua	forme *f* contiguë	соседняя форма
N 140	**neighbouring fundamental region** <FT, TO>	Nachbarbereich *m*, Nachbar *m* <eines Fundamentalbereichs>, spatium *n* confinium <Möbius>	région *f* voisine	соседняя фундаментальная область
N 141	**neighbouring prime numbers,** consecutive prime numbers <NT>	benachbarte (aufeinanderfolgende) Primzahlen *fpl*	nombres *mpl* premiers consécutifs	последовательные простые числа
	neighbouring quadratic form <AL>	*s.* N 139		
N 142	**neighbouring vertex** <AT>	benachbarte Ecke *f*	sommet *m* voisin (incident)	соседняя вершина
	Neil['s] parabola <AG>	*s.* S 353		
N 143	***n*-element set,** *n*-set <SE>	*n*-elementige Menge *f*	ensemble *m* à *n* éléments, ensemble *n*-aire, *n*-uple *m*, ensemble de *n* éléments non ordonnés	множество из *n* элементов
N 144	**neofield,** division neoring <AL>	Neokörper *m*	néocorps *m*	неотело, неополе
N 145	**neoring** <AL>	Neoring *m*	néo-anneau *m*	неокольцо
	Neper['s] analogies <EG>	*s.* N 7		
	Neper['s] rules <EG>	*s.* N 9		
N 146	**nephroid** <GE>	Nephroide *f*, Nierenkurve *f*	néphroïde *f*	нефроида
	neq <LO>	*s.* S 2439		
N 147	***n*-equivalence** <AT>	*n*-Äquivalenz *f*	*n*-équivalence *f*	*n*-эквивалентность
N 148	**Néron['s] form** <AG>	Néronsche Form *f*	forme *f* de Néron	форма Нерона
N 149	**Néron['s] model** <AG>	Néronsches Modell *n*	modèle *m* de Néron	модель Нерона
	Néron-Severi group <AL>	*s.* G 490		
N 150	**nerve** <of a covering *or* a set system> <TO>	Nerv *m*	nerf *m*	нерв
	nest <SE>	*s.* M 874		
	nest <TO>	*s.* N 157		
	nested classification <ST>	*s.* H 299		
N 151	**nested fields** <AL>	ineinandergeschachtelte Körper *mpl*	corps *mpl* emboîtés	вложенные поля
N 152	**nested Hilbert space** <FA>	Gelfandsches Raumtripel *n*	espace *m* hilbertien équipé	оснащенное гильбертово пространство
N 153	**nested interval property** <AN>	Stetigkeitssatz *m* der reellen Zahlen, Stetigkeitsprinzip *n*	théorème *m* de complétion, principe *m* des segments emboîtés, principe *m* de Cantor	принцип непрерывности
N 154	**nested intervals,** nest of intervals <AN>	ineinandergeschachtelte Intervalle *npl*	intervalles *mpl* emboîtés	вложенные промежутки, совокупность вложенных интервалов
N 155	**nested recursion** <MM>	eingeschachtelte (eingeschachtelte mehrfache, verschränkte) Rekursion *f*		рекурсия со вставками
	nested sample <ST>	*s.* C 949		
N 156	**nested sampling** <ST>	hierarchische Stichprobennahme *f*	échantillonnage *m* hiérarchique, sondage *m* hiérarchique	гнездовой выбор, метод гнездового выбора
N 157	**nesting,** nest <TO>	Schachtelung *f*	emboîtement *m*	шихтовка
N 158	**nest of intervals** <whose lengths form a null sequence>; collection of nested intervals <without fulfilling the condition mentioned> <AN>	Intervallschachtelung *f*, Schachtelung *f*	fractionnement *m*; emboîtement *m*	стягивающаяся система отрезков; последовательность (совокупность) вложенных интервалов, шихтовка
	nest of intervals <AN>	*s.* N 154		
N 159	**net,** two-parameter linear system <of algebraic curves> <AG>	Netz *n*, Linearsystem *n* der Stufe 2	réseau *m* [ponctuel], système *m* linéaire [ponctuel] de deuxième espèce	линейная система размерности 2
N 160	**net** <linear system of ∞^2 algebraic varieties> <AG>	Bündel *n*, Netz *n*	réseau *m*	связка
N 161	**net** <of conics> <AY>	Kegelschnittnetz *n*, [lineares] Kegelschnittsystem *n* zweiter (2.) Stufe	réseau *m* ponctuel, réseau <de coniques>	связка кривых второго (2-го) порядка
N 162	**net** <of curves *or* surfaces> <DG>	Netz *n* <von Kurven *oder* Flächen>	réseau *m* <de courbes *ou* surfaces>	сеть <кривых *или* поверхностей>
N 163	**net** <TO>	Überdeckung *f* eines Intervalls durch Intervalle	recouvrement *m* d'un intervalle par des intervalles	покрытие интервала интервалами
	net <DG, PJ>	*s.* N 166		
	net <SE>	*s.* M 887		
	3-net <AL, PJ>	*s.* T 456 a		
	ε-net <TO>	*s.* E 314		
N 164	**net chart (graph),** bunch graph (chart, map), nomogram with radial lines, isopleth <NO>	Netztafel *f*, Kurventafel *f*, Isoplethentafel *f*, Isoplethenkarte *f*	abaque *m* à radiantes, nomogramme *m* (abaque) à réseau, abaque	сетчатая номограмма, абак
N 165	**net of curves** <DG>	Kurvennetz *n*	réseau *m* de courbes	криволинейная сеть, сеть <кривых>
	net of curves <AY>	*s.* B 801		
N 166	**net of lines,** net of rays, net, first-order first-class congruence of lines <DG, PJ>	Strahlennetz *n*, Netz *n*	réseau *m* de droites, réseau, congruence *f* de droites de premier ordre et de première classe	сеть прямых (лучей), сеть конгруэнция прямых первого порядка и первого класса
	net of normals <DG>	*s.* N 628		
N 167	**net of quadrics** <AG>	Flächenbündel *n* zweiter (2.) Ordnung	réseau *m* de quadriques	связка поверхностей второго порядка

	English	German	French	Russian
	net of rays <DG, PJ>	*s.* N 166		
N 168	**net of surfaces** <GE>	Flächennetz *n*, // Flächenbündel *n*, Flächenfamilie *f*	réseau *m* de surfaces	связка поверхностей
N 169	**network** <GP>	Netzwerk *n*, Austauschnetz *n*, Netz *n*	réseau *m*, réseau de transfert	сеть
N 170	**network** <PG>	Netzplan *m*, Netzwerk *n*, Netzwerkdiagramm *n*	réseau *m*	сетевой график, сетевая модель
N 171	**network analysis** <GP, PG>	Netzwerktechnik *f*, Netzwerkplanung *f*, Netzwerkanalyse *f*	analyse *f* des réseaux	сетевое планирование и управление, СПУ
N 172	**Neuberg['s] cubic curve** <GE>	Neubergsche Kubik *f*	cubique *f* de Neuberg	кубическая кривая Нейберга
N 173	**Neuberg's theorem** <for a tetrahedron> <EG>	Neubergscher Satz *m*	théorème *m* de Neuberg	теорема Нейберга
	Neumann['s] algebra / [von] <FA>	*s.* W 4		
N 174	**Neumann algebra of purely infinite class / [von]** <FA>	[von] Neumannsche Algebra *f* von rein unendlicher Klasse	algèbre *f* de [von] Neumann de classe purement infinie	алгебра [фон] Неймана чисто бесконечного класса
N 175	**Neumann-Bernays [-Gödel] set theory / [von]** <SE>	[von] Neumann-Bernaysscher Aufbau *m* der Mengenlehre, [von] Neumann-Bernayssche Begründung *f* der Mengenlehre	théorie *f* des ensembles de Neumann-Bernays	аксиоматическая система теории множеств [фон] Неймана
	Neumann['s] Bessel function [of the second kind] <FU>	*s.* B 233		
N 176	**Neumann['s] boundary condition,** second boundary condition <for a partial differential equation>; boundary condition of the second kind <also for an ordinary differential equation of the second order> <DE, PO>	Neumannsche (zweite, 2.) Randbedingung *f*; Randbedingung zweiter (2.) Art	condition *f* aux limites de (du type) Neumann, deuxième condition aux limites; condition aux limites de deuxième (seconde) espèce	второе краевое условие, краевое условие Неймана, условие Неймана; краевое условие второго рода
	Neumann['s] boundary [value] problem <DE, PO>	*s.* N 180		
	Neumann['s] ergodic theorem <SP>	*s.* S 1693		
	Neumann['s] factor <FU> ⌐<FU>	*s.* N 178		
	Neumann['s] function	*s.* B 233		
N 177	**Neumann['s] function** <PO>	Neumannsche Funktion *f*	fonction *f* de Neumann	функция Неймана
N 178	**Neumann['s] number / [von],** Neumann['s] factor, ε_n <FU>	Neumannsche Zahl *f*	nombre *m* de Neumann	число Неймана
N 179	**Neumann['s] polynomial** <DE, FU>	Neumannsches Polynom *n*	polynôme *m* de Neumann	многочлен (полином) Неймана
N 180	**Neumann['s] problem,** Neumann['s] boundary [value] problem, second boundary [value] problem, second problem <for a partial differential equation>; boundary value problem of the second kind <also for an ordinary differential equation of the second order> <DE, PO>	Neumannsches Problem (Randwertproblem) *n*, Neumann-Problem *n*, Neumannsche Randwertaufgabe *f*, zweites Randwertproblem, zweite Randwertaufgabe; Randwertproblem (Randwertaufgabe) zweiter Art	problème *m* de Neumann, deuxième problème aux limites, deuxième problème; problème aux limites de deuxième espèce	вторая краевая задача, краевая задача второго рода <для обыкновенных дифференциальных уравнений второго порядка или дифференциальных уравнений в частных производных>; задача Неймана, краевая задача Неймана <в теории потенциала>
N 181	**Neumann['s] series,** Liouville-Neumann series <IE>	Neumannsche Reihe *f*	série *f* de Neumann	ряд Неймана
	Neumann['s] sphere <FT>	*s.* R 1030		
N 182	**Neumark['s] theorem** <FA>	Satz *m* von Neumark, Neumarkscher Satz	théorème *m* de Neumark	теорема Неймарка
	neutral <AL>	*s.* N 183		
	neutral <GR>	*s.* I 63		
N 183	**neutral element,** identity element, identity, neutral, unit element, two-sided identity element <with respect to a composition> <AL>	neutrales Element *n*, [zweiseitiges] Einselement *n*	élément *m* neutre, neutre *m*, élément neutre bilatère	нейтральный (двусторонний нейтральный) элемент, [двусторонняя] единица
N 184	**neutral element** <of a lattice> <LA>	neutrales Element *n*	élément *m* neutre (distribuant)	нейтральный элемент
	neutral element <GR>	*s.* I 63		
N 185	**neutral ideal,** distributive ideal <in a lattice> <LA>	neutrales Ideal *n*	idéal *m* neutre	нейтральный идеал
N 186	**neutral line,** vanishing line <DS>	Verschwindungslinie *f*, Verschwindungsgerade *f*	ligne (droite) *f* neutre	нейтральная линия
N 187	**neutral plane,** vanishing plane <plane through vertex of projection parallel to the projection plane> <DS>	Verschwindungsebene *f*	plan *m* neutre	нейтральная плоскость
N 188	**neutral point,** vanishing point <in central perspective> <DS>	Verschwindungspunkt *m*	point *m* neutre	нейтральная точка

N 189	**neutral quadratic form** <AL>	neutrale quadratische Form *f*	forme *f* quadratique neutre	нейтральная квадратичная форма
N 190	**neutrice** <AL>	Neutrix *f*	neutrice *f*	нейтрализатор, нейтриса
N 191	**Nevanlinna['s] class** <FT>	Nevanlinnasche Klasse *f*	classe *f* de Nevanlinna	неванлинновский класс
N 192	**Nevanlinna['s] function** <FD>	Nevanlinnasche Funktion *f*	fonction *f* de Nevanlinna	функция Неванлинны
	never-ending decimal <NT>	*s.* I 441		
N 193	**Newman['s] algebra** <AL>	Newmansche Algebra *f*	algèbre *f* de Newman	алгебра Ньюмена
N 194	**Newman-Keuls test,** Student-Newman-Keuls test <ST>	Newman-Keuls-Test *m*, Student-Newman-Keuls-Test *m*	test *m* de Newman-Keuls, test de Student-Newman-Keuls	критерий Ньюмена-Койлса, критерий Стьюдента-Ньюмена-Койлса
	Newton['s] approximation formula <AX, NU>	*s.* N 206		
N 195	**Newton-Cotes formulae,** Cotes['] quadrature formulae, Cotes['s] formulae, Cotes['] rule <DI, NU>	Cotessche (Newton-Cotessche) Formeln *fpl*, Formeln von Newton-Cotes	formules *fpl* de Cotes (Newton-Cotes)	формулы Котеса, квадратурные формулы Ньютона-Котеса
N 196	**Newton['] diagram,** Newton['s] polygon <AL, FT>	Newtonsches Polygon (Diagramm) *n*, Puiseux-Diagramm *n*, Puiseuxsches Diagramm, Diagramm von Puiseux (Newton)	polygone *m* de Newton, ligne *f* polygonale de Newton	многоугольник Ньютона
N 197	**Newton['s] factor** <AX, DI, NU>	Newtonscher Faktor *m*	facteur (coefficient) *m* de Newton	коэффициент Ньютона
N 198	**Newton['s] formula,** Newton['s] quadrature formula <for numerical quadrature> <AX, DI, NU>	Newtonsche Quadraturformel (Formel) *f*	formule *f* de Newton, formula d'intégration de Newton	формула [численного интегрирования] Ньютона
	Newton-Gauss [interpolation] formula <AX, FD, NU>	*s.* G 76		
N 199	**Newtonian kernel** <PO>	Newtonscher Kern *m*	noyau *m* newtonien	ньютоново ядро
N 200	**Newton['s] identities,** Newton['s] relations <for elementary symmetric functions> <AL>	Newtonsche Formeln (Gleichungen) *fpl*	formules *fpl* de Newton	тождества Ньютона
	Newton['s] indefinite integral <DI>	*s.* P 1344		
	Newton['s] interpolation formulae <AX, FD, NU>	*s.* G 429		
N 201	**Newton['s] interpolation formula with backward differences,** Gregory['s] backward formula <AX, FD, NU>	Newtonsche Interpolationsformel *f* mit aufsteigenden Differenzen, zweite Gregory-Newtonsche Formel *f*, Newtonsche Interpolationsformel für rückwärtsgreifende Differenzen	formule *f* d'interpolation de Newton par différences ascendantes	интерполяционная формула [Грегори-]Ньютона для интерполирования назад, формула Ньютона для интерполирования назад
N 202	**Newton['s] interpolation formula with forward differences,** Gregory['s] forward formula <AX, FD, NU>	Newtonsche Interpolationsformel *f* mit absteigenden Differenzen, erste Gregory-Newtonsche Formel *f*, Newtonsche Interpolationsformel für vorwärtsgreifende Differenzen	formule *f* d'interpolation de Newton par différences descendantes	интерполяционная формула [Грегори-]Ньютона для интерполирования вперед, формула Ньютона для интерполирования вперед, интерполяционная формула Ньютона
N 203	**Newton['s] interpolation polynom** <AX, FD, NU>	Interpolationspolynom *n* von Newton, Newtonsches Interpolationspolynom <mit dividierten Differenzen>	polynôme *m* d'interpolation de Newton	интерполяционный многочлен Ньютона
N 204	**Newton['s] interpolation series** <AX, NU>	Newtonsche Interpolationsreihe (Reihe) *f*	série *f* d'interpolation de Newton	интерполяционный ряд Ньютона
N 205	**Newton['s] interpolation sum** <AX, NU>	Newtonsche Interpolationssumme *f*	somme *f* d'interpolation de Newton	интерполяционная сумма Ньютона
N 206	**Newton['s] method,** Newton-Raphson algorithm, Newton-Raphson formula, Newton-Raphson method, second-order Newton-Raphson process, quadratically convergent Newton-Raphson process; Newton['s] approximation formula, Newton-Raphson formula <AX, NU>	Newtonsches Verfahren *n*, Newton-Verfahren *n*, Newtonsches Näherungsverfahren (Iterationsverfahren) *n*, Newton-Raphsonsche Methode *f*, Newtonsche (Newtons) Näherungsmethode *f*, Verfahren von Newton, Tangentenmethode *f*	méthode de Newton, méthode d'approximation de Newton, méthode de résolution approchée de Newton-Raphson, méthode de Newton-Raphson	метод Ньютона (касательных, Ньютона-Рафсона)
N 207	**Newton['s] method with variable metric,** method with variable metric <AX, NU>	Quasi-Newton-Verfahren *n*, [Newtonsches] Verfahren *n* mit variabler Metrik	méthode *f* [de Newton] à métrique variable	метод Ньютона с переменной метрикой
	Newton['s] polygon <AL, FT>	*s.* N 196		
N 208/9	**Newton['s] potential** <PO>	Newtonsches Potential *n*	potentiel *m* de Newton	потенциал Ньютона, ньютонов потенциал

No.	English	German	French	Russian
N 210	**Newton['s] potential kernel,** potential kernel <PO>	Newtonscher Potentialkern *m*, Potentialkern	noyau *m* potentiel [de Newton]	потенциальное ядро [Ньютона]
N 211	**Newton-Puiseux expansion,** Puiseux['] series expansion <FT>	Puiseux-Entwicklung *f*, Puiseuxentwicklung *f*	développement *m* de Puiseux	разложение Пюизе
	Newton['s] quadrature formula <AX, DI, NU>	*s.* N 198		
	Newton-Raphson algorithm (formula, method) <AX, NU>	*s.* N 206		
	Newton['s] relations <AL>	*s.* N 200		
N 212	**Newton['s] rule of the parallelogram,** Puiseux['] rule <FT>	Puiseuxsche (Puiseux') Regel *f*, Newtons Regel vom Parallelogramm	règle *f* du parallélogramme de Newton, règle de Puiseux	правило Пюизе (параллелограмма Ньютона)
	Newton-Stirling interpolation formula <AN, NU>	*s.* S 1778		
	Newton['s] three-eighths rule <DI, NU>	*s.* T 450		
	next state function <TA>	*s.* T 795		
N 213	**Neyman['s] allocation** <ST>	Neymansche Stichprobenaufteilung *f*	allocation (répartition) *f* de Neyman	распределение объектов в выборке по Нейману
N 214	**Neyman['s] distribution of type A,** type A distribution <ST>	Neyman-Verteilung *f* vom Typ A, Typ-A-Verteilung *f*	distribution *f* de Neyman de type A, distribution de type A	распределение Неймана типа A, распределение типа A
N 215	**Neyman['s] distribution of type B,** type B distribution <ST>	Neyman-Verteilung *f* vom Typ B, Typ-B-Verteilung *f*	distribution *f* de Neyman de type B, distribution de type B	распределение Неймана типа B, распределение типа B
N 216	**Neyman['s] distribution of type C,** type C distribution <ST>	Neyman-Verteilung *f* vom Typ C, Typ-C-Verteilung *f*	distribution *f* de Neyman de type C, distribution de type C	распределение Неймана типа C, распределение типа C
N 217	***n*-face** <of a simplex *or* polyhedron> <AT, CS>	*n*-dimensionale Seite *f* <eines Simplex *oder* Polyeders>; *n*-dimensionale Kante *f* <eines Polyeders>	face *f* de dimension *n*, face *n*-dimensionnelle	*n*-мерная грань
	***n*-faced solid angle** <EG>	*s.* N 76		
N 218	***n*-field** <UA>	*n*-Körper *m*	*n*-corps *m*	*n*-поле
N 219	***n*-fold classification,** *n*-way classification <ST>	*n*-fache Klassifikation *f*, *n*-fach-Klassifikation *f*, *n*-Weg-Klassifikation *f*	classification *f* à *n* entrées	классификация по *n* признакам
N 220	***n*-fold extension** <AL, CA>	*n*-fache Erweiterung *f*	extension *f* *n*-uple	*n*-кратное расширение
N 221	***n*-fold series** <SS>	*n*-fache Reihe *f*	suite *f* *n*-uple	*n*-кратная последовательность
N 222	***n*-fold symmetric product** <AL>	symmetrisches *n*-faches Produkt *n*	produit *m* symétrique *n*-uple	*n*-кратное симметрическое произведение
N 223	***n*-frame** <GE>	*n*-Bein *n*	*n*-repère *m*	*n*-репер
N 224	**N-function** <in an Orlicz space> <AN>	N-Funktion *f*	N-fonction *f*	N-функция
N 225	***n*-gon** <EG>	*n*-Eck *n*	polygone *m* de *n* côtés	*n*-угольник
N 226	***n*-gonal number,** polygonal number with *n* sides <*r*-th> <NT>	*n*-eckzahl *f*, *n*-gonalzahl *f* <*r*-te>	nombre *m* *n*-gonal <*r*-e>	*n*-угольное число <*r*-е>
N 227	***n*-graded module** <AL>	*n*-fach graduierter Modul *m*	module *m* *n*-gradué	*n*-кратно градуированный модуль
N 228	***n*-graph,** graph of multiplicity *n* <GP>	*n*-Graph *m*	*n*-graphe *m*, graphe de degré *n*	*n*-граф
N 229	**N-group,** group with the normalizer condition <GR>	N-Gruppe *f*	N-groupe *m*	N-группа
	***n*-group** <GR>	*s.* P 917		
	***n*-hedron** <EG>	*s.* P 966		
N 230	***n*-homogeneous variety** <with respect to a transformation group> <AL, TO>	*n*-homogene Mannigfaltigkeit *f*	variété *f* *n* fois homogène	*n*-кратно однородное многообразие
	***n*-homogeneous W*-algebra** <FA>	*s.* W 6		
N 231	**nice function,** Morse['s] function <TO, VA>	Morsesche Funktion *f*	fonction *f* excellente, fonction de Morse	функция Морсе
	nice imbedding <TO>	*s.* T 35		
	nicely imbedded <TO>	*s.* T 36		
N 232	**"nichtgabelbar" axiom system** <MM>	nichtgabelbares Axiomensystem *n*		неразветвляемая система аксиом
	***n*-ic non-residue** <NT>	*s.* N 744		
	Nicomedean conchoid <GE>	*s.* C 1784		
	Nicomedes['] conchoid <GE>	*s.* C 1784		
N 233	***n*-ic residue of *m*,** power residue of *m* of the *n*-th order <NT>	*n*-ter Potenzrest *m* modulo *m*	résidu *m* (puissance *f*) *n*-e modulo *m*, résidu de puissance *n*-e suivant *m*	вычет степени *n* по модулю *m*
	Nielsen-Hankel function <FU>	*s.* B 233		
N 234	**Nielsen['s] operation (transformation)** <GR>	Nielsensche Transformation *f*	opération *f* de Nielsen	преобразование Нильсена
	Nikodým['s] distance <ME>	*s.* D 736		
N 235	**Nikodým['s] domain** <DE>	Nikodýmscher Bereich *m*	ouvert (domaine) *m* de Nikodým	область Никодима

N 236	**Nikodým['s] metric** <ME>	Nikodýmsche Metrik *f*	métrique *f* de Nikodým	метрика Никодима
N 237	**nil algebra** <AL>	Nilalgebra *f*	nilalgèbre *f*	нильалгебра
N 238	**nil-automorphism** <GR>	Nilautomorphismus *m*	nil-automorphisme *m*	нильавтоморфизм
N 239	**nil-group** <GR>	Nilgruppe *f*	nil-groupe *m*	нильгруппа
N 240	**nil ideal** <AL>	Nilideal *n*	nil[-]idéal *m*	нильидеал
N 241	**nil left ideal** <AL>	linksseitiges Nilideal *n*	nil-idéal *m* à gauche	левый нильидеал
N 242	**nil polynomial, nil-polynomial** <AL>	Nilpolynom *n*	nil-polynôme *m*	нильмногочлен
N 243	**nilpotence class (length),** class, Fitting['s] height <of a nilpotent group> <AL>	Klasse *f* der Nilpotenz <einer Gruppe>	spécialité *f* <d'un groupe>	класс <нильпотентной группы>
N 244	**nilpotency** <AL, GR>	Nilpotenz *f*	propriété *f* d'être nilpotent, nilpotence *f*	нильпотентность
N 245	**nilpotent algebra** <of index of nilpotency *n*, of step *n*> <AL>	nilpotente Algebra *f* <vom Grad *n*, vom Exponenten *n*>	algèbre *f* nilpotente <d'indice de nilpotence *n*>	нильпотентная алгебра <с индексом нильпотентности *n*>
N 246	**nilpotent element** <AL>	nilpotentes Element *n*	nilpotent *m*, élément *m* nilpotent	нильпотентный элемент
N 247	**nilpotent group** <GR>	nilpotente (spezielle) Gruppe *f*; speziell-nilpotente Gruppe <Kurosch>	groupe *m* nilpotent (spécial)	нильпотентная группа; специальная группа
N 248	**nilpotent group of class *k*** <AL>	nilpotente Gruppe *f* von der Klasse *k*	groupe *m* spécial de spécialité *k*	нильпотентная группа класса *k*
N 249	**nilpotent ideal** <AL>	nilpotentes Ideal *n*	idéal *m* nilpotent	нильпотентный идеал
N 250	**nilpotent Lie algebra** <AL>	nilpotente Liesche Algebra *f*, nilpotenter Liescher Ring *m*, infinitesimale Gruppe *f* vom Range Null	algèbre *f* de Lie nilpotente	нильпотентная алгебра Ли
N 251	**nilpotent matrix** <AL>	nilpotente Matrix *f*	matrice *f* nilpotente	нильпотентная матрица
N 252	**nilpotent number** <AL>	nilpotente Zahl *f*, Wurzel *f* der Null	racine *f* de zéro, nombre *m* nilpotent, pseudo-nul *m*, nombre pseudo-nul	нильпотентное число
N 253	**nilpotent part** <of an endomorphism> <AL>	nilpotente Komponente *f*	composante *f* nilpotente	нильпотентная компонента
N 254	**nilpotent product** <of groups> <GR>	nilpotentes Produkt *n*	produit *m* nilpotent	нильпотентное произведение
N 255	**nilpotent radical** <AL>	nilpotentes Radikal *n*	radical *m* nilpotent	нильпотентный радикал
N 256	**nil-radical, nil radical,** null-radical <AL>	Nilradikal *n*, Radikalideal *n* <Jacobson>	nil[-]radical *m*, idéal *m* radical, radical *m* nilpotent	нильрадикал
N 257	**nil right ideal** <AL>	rechtsseitiges Nilideal *n*	nil-idéal *m* à droite	правый нильидеал
N 258	**nil ring, nil[-]ring** <AL>	Nilring *m*	nil-anneau *m*	нилькольцо
N 259	**nil-semigroup** <AL>	Nilhalbgruppe *f*	nildemi-groupe *m*	нильполугруппа
N 260	**nine lemma,** 9 lemma, three-by-three lemma <CA, HA>	Neunerlemma *n*, 3×3-Lemma *n*	lemme *m* 3×3	девятилемма, 3×3-лемма
N 261	**nine-point circle** <EG>	Feuerbachscher Kreis *m*, Neunpunktekreis *m*	cercle *m* des neuf points, cercle d'Euler, cercle de Feuerbach	девятиточечная окружность, окружность Эйлера (Фейербаха, девяти точек)
	nine-point circle theorem <EG>	*s.* F 142		
N 262	**nine-point conic** <EG>	Neunpunktekegelschnitt *m*	conique *f* des neuf points	коническое сечение девяти точек
	nine test <AR>	*s.* C 193		
	***n*-interval** <GE, RF>	*s.* N 60		
N 263	**nivellateur** <MD>	Nivellator *m*	nivellateur *m*	матрица системы линейных матричных уравнений
	NLP <PG>	*s.* N 412		
N 264	***n*-manifold,** *n*-dimensional manifold <GE, TO>	*n*-dimensionale Mannigfaltigkeit *f*	variété *f* à *n* dimensions	*n*-мерное многообразие
N 265	**(*n*,*n*) correspondence** <of sets> <SE>	(*n*,*n*)-deutige Relation (Korrespondenz) *f*	correspondance *f* *n*-*n*-voque (bi-*n*-voque)	(*n*,*n*)-значное соответствие
N 266	***n*-nilpotent group** <GR>	*n*-nilpotente Gruppe *f*	groupe *m* *n*-nilpotent	*n*-нильпотентная группа
N 267	**no-classes theory** <Russell> <LO>	klassenfreie Theorie *f*	théorie *f* sans classes	теория без классов
N 268	**nodal curve** <singularity of an algebraic surface> <AG>	Knotenkurve *f*, Wendekurve *f*	courbe *f* nodale	узловая кривая
N 269	**nodal curve** <of a bundle of quadrics> <GE>	Kernkurve *f*, Quadrupelkurve *f* <eines Flächenbündels zweiter Ordnung>	courbe *f* nodale (jacobienne) <d'un réseau de quadriques>	штейнерова кривая <связки поверхностей второго порядка>
N 270	**nodal set** <TO>	abgeschlossene Menge *f*, die Berührungspunkte der Komplementärmenge enthält	ensemble *m* fermé contenant des points d'adhérence de son ensemble complémentaire	замкнутое множество, содержащее точки прикосновения своего дополнения
	nodal singularity <DE>	*s.* N 273		
N 271	**nodal surface** <inverse of a surface of fourth order> <GE>	Knotenfläche *f*	surface *f* nodale	узловая поверхность
N 272	**node,** crunode, knot[-] singularity <of a curve> <AG>	gewöhnlicher Doppelpunkt *m*, Knotenpunkt *m*, eigentlicher Doppelpunkt	point *m* double à tangentes distincts, point double ordinaire, nœud *m*, nœud en croix, point crunodal (crucial)	обыкновенная двойная точка, двойная точка, точка самопересечения, узловая точка
N 273	**node,** nodal singularity <DE>	Knotenpunkt *m*, Knoten *m*	point *m* nodal, nœud *m*	узел
N 274	**node** <of a family of curves> <GE>	Knotenpunkt *m*	point *m* nodal	узел, узловая точка

No.	English	German	French	Russian
N 275	**node,** junction point, cross point <of a graph> <GP>	Kreuzungspunkt *m*, Verzweigungspunkt *m*, Verzweigung *f*, eigentlicher Knotenpunkt *m*, Mehrfachknotenpunkt *m*, Knotenpunkt vom Grad > 2	nœud *m*, carrefour *m*, sommet *m* de degré > 2, point *m* de croisement, sommet de branchement	точка разветвления
	node <GP>	*s.* V 156		
N 276	**node-locus** <AG>	Ort *m* der Doppelpunkte, Knotenort *m*	lieu *m* des points doubles	место двойных точек
N 277	**nodoid** <a surface of revolution of constant mean curvature> <GE>	Nodoid *n*	nodoïde *f*	нодоида
N 278	**Noether['s] condition** <for polynomial ideals> <AL>	Noethersche Bedingung *f*	condition *f* de Noether	условие Нетера
N 279	**Noether['s] fundamental theorem** <AL>	Noetherscher Fundamentalsatz *m*, Fundamentalsatz von Noether, Noetherscher Satz *m*, Noethers Fundamentalsatz; Fundamentalsatz der algebraischen Funktionen	théorème *m* fondamental de Noether, théorème de Noether; théorème fondamental sur les fonctions algébriques	фундаментальная теорема Нетера
N 280	**noetherian algebra** <AL>	noethersche Algebra *f*	algèbre *f* noethérienne	нетерова алгебра
N 281	**noetherian category** <CA>	noethersche Kategorie *f*	catégorie *f* noethérienne	нетерова категория
N 282	**noetherian conductor,** conductor <of a Noetherian domain of integrity> <AL>	Führer *m*	conducteur *m*	нетеров кондуктор, кондуктор
N 283	**noetherian domain** <AL>	noetherscher Integritätsbereich *m*	anneau *m* intègre noethérien	нетерова область [целостности]
N 284	**noetherian group,** group satisfying the maximal condition <GR>	Noethersche Gruppe *f*, Gruppe mit Maximalbedingung	groupe *m* noethérien	нетерова группа, группа с условием максимальности
N 285	**noetherian induction** <AG, AL>	noethersche Induktion *f*	récurrence *f* noethérienne	нетерова индукция
N 286	**Noetherian module** <AL>	noetherscher Modul *m*	module *m* noethérien	нетеров модуль, // нэтеров модуль
N 287	**noetherianness** <AL>	Noetherschsein *n*	propriété *f* d'être noethérien	нетеровость
N 288	**noetherian object** <CA>	noethersches Objekt *n*	objet *m* noethérien	нетеров объект
N 289	**Noetherian partially ordered set,** partially ordered set satisfying the ascending chain condition <SE>	der aufsteigenden Kettenbedingung genügende halbgeordnete Menge *f*; halbgeordnete Menge, die der aufsteigenden Kettenbedingung genügt	ensemble *m* ordonné noethérien, ensemble ordonné satisfaisant à la condition de chaîne ascendante	частично упорядоченное множество, удовлетворяющее условию обрыва возрастающих цепей
N 290	**noetherian prescheme** <AG>	noethersches Präschema *n*	préschéma *m* noethérien	нетерова пресхема
N 291	**Noetherian (noetherian) ring** <AL>	noetherscher Ring *m*, Ring mit Teilerkettensatz, *O*-Ring *m*	anneau *m* noethérien	нетерово кольцо
N 292	**noetherian scheme** <AG>	noethersches Schema *n*	schéma *m* noethérien	нетерова схема
N 293	**noetherian semigroup** <AL>	noethersche Halbgruppe *f*	demi-groupe *m* noethérien	нетерова полугруппа
N 294	**Noetherian [topological] space** <TO>	noetherscher [topologischer] Raum *m*	espace *m* noethérien	нетерово [топологическое] пространство
	Noether['s] isomorphism theorem <GR>	*s.* F 341		
N 295	**Noether['s] normalization lemma** <AL>	Noethersches Normalisierungslemma *n*	lemme *m* de normalisation de [E.] Noether	лемма Нетера о нормализации
N 296	**Noether['s] relation** <AG>	Noethersche Relation *f*	relation *f* de Noether	формула Нетера
N 297	**nominal definition** <FO>	Nominaldefinition *f*	définition *f* nominale	номинальное (формальное) определение
N 298	**nominal value** <AR>	Nennwert *m*	valeur *f* nominale	номинальная величина, номинальное значение
N 299	**nomogram,** nomograph, graph, nomographic chart (map), chart, map, abac <NO>	Nomogramm *n*, Rechentafel *f*, graphische Rechentafel, Abakus *m*	abaque *m*, nomogramme *m*, diagramme *m* nomographique	номограмма, график, номографическая диаграмма, вычислительная таблица
	nomogram with moving transparents <NO>	*s.* S 1200		
	nomogram with points in a line <NO>	*s.* A 490		
	nomogram with radial lines <NO>	*s.* N 164		
N 300	**nomogram with three parallel lines** <NO>	Dreileitertafel *f*	abaque *m* à trois droites parallèles	номограмма с тремя параллельными прямолинейными шкалами
	nomograph <NO>	*s.* N 299		
N 301	**nomographability,** nomographic representability <NO>	Nomographierbarkeit *f*	nomographisabilité *f*, représentabilité *f* en nomogramme	номографируемость
	nomographic chart (map) <NO>	*s.* N 299		
	nomographic representability <NO>	*s.* N 301		
	nomographic representation <NO>	*s.* N 302		
	nomographic scale of a function <NO>	*s.* F 756		
N 302	**nomographing,** nomographic representation <NO>	Nomographierung *f*	nomographisation *f*	номографирование

	nomograph with moving transparents <NO>	s. S 1200		
N 303	**nomography of net charts** <NO>	Flächennomographie f, Nomographie der Netztafeln	nomographie f des abaques à radiantes	номография сетчатых номограмм
N 304	**non-abelian extension [field]** <AB>	nichtabelsche Erweiterung (Körpererweiterung) f	extension f non abélienne	неабелево расширение [поля]
	non[-]abelian group <GR>	s. N 334		
N 305	**non-absolutely convergent series** <SS>	nichtabsolut konvergente Reihe f	série f non absolument convergente	неабсолютно сходящийся ряд
	non-absolute model <FO>	s. N 493		
N 306	**non-additivity** <AL, AN>	Nichtadditivität f	non-additivité f	неаддитивность
N 307	**non-adjacent edges** <of a graph> <GP>	knotenfremde Kanten fpl	arêtes fpl non adjacentes	несмежные ребра
N 308	**nonagonal number** <a figurate number> <NT>	Neuneckzahl f, Enneagonalzahl f	nombre m ennéagonal (ennéagone)	девятиугольное число
N 309	**non-aliquot part** <of a number> <NT>	nicht aufgehender Teil m, kleinere nicht aufgehende Zahl f	aliquante f, quantité f aliquante, partie f aliquante (non aliquote)	неделитель, меньше данного числа
	non-archimedean absolute value <AL>	s. N 314		
	non-Archimedean case <AL>	s. N 313		
N 310	**non-Archimedean domain;** non-archimedean magnitudes <AL, GE>	nichtarchimedisches Größensystem n, nichtarchimedische Größen fpl	système m de grandeurs non archimédien; grandeurs fpl non archimédiennes	неархимедова система величин; неархимедовы величины
N 311	**non-Archimedean field** <AL>	nichtarchimedisch geordneter Körper m	corps m non archimédien	неархимедово поле
N 312	**non-archimedean geometry** <GE>	nichtarchimedische Geometrie f	géométrie f non archimédienne	неархимедова геометрия
	non-archimedean magnitudes <AL, GE>	s. N 310		
	non-archimedean prime <NT>	s. F 312		
	non-Archimedean prime spot <NT>	s. F 312		
N 313	**non-Archimedean property;** non-Archimedean case <AL>	Nicht-Archimedizität f, Nichtarchimedischsein n	propriété f d'être non archimédien	неархимедовость
N 314	**non-archimedean valuation,** ultrametric valuation; valuation, non-archimedean absolute value <AL>	nichtarchimedische Bewertung f	valuation f non archimédienne; valeur f absolue non archimédienne	неархимедово (ультраметрическое) нормирование; неархимедово (ультраметрическое) абсолютное значение
N 315	**non-Aristotelian logics** <LO>	nichtchrysippinische (nichtaristotelische) Logik f	logique f non chrysippienne	нехризиппова логика
N 316	**nonary** <AL, NT>	nonär	nonaire	девятиричный
N 317	**non-associate** <AL>	nichtassoziiertes Element n	élément m non associé	неассоциированный элемент
N 318	**non-associative ring** <AL>	nichtassoziativer Ring m	anneau m non associatif	неассоциативное кольцо, NA-кольцо
N 319	**non-asymmetric relation** <SE>	nicht asymmetrische Relation f	relation f non asymétrique	неасимметричное отношение
	non-atomic Boolean algebra <AL>	s. A 1195		
	non-atomic measure <ME>	s. A 1196		
N 320	**nonbasic block** <PG>	Nichtbasisblock m	bloc m des variables indépendantes	блок небазисных переменных
N 321	**non-basic cell** <PG>	Nichtbasiszelle f	cellule f non basique	небазисная ячейка
N 322	**nonbasic variable,** independent variable <PG>	Nichtbasisvariable f	variable f indépendante	внебазисная (небазисная, независимая) переменная
N 323	**non-bounding** <AT>	nichtberandend	non bordant	неограничивающий, неокаймляющий
	non-cancellable element <AL>	s. N 465		
N 324	**non-categorical axiom system** <MM>	nichtkategorisches Axiomensystem n <d. h. ohne Vollständigkeitsaxiom>	système m d'axiomes non catégorique	некатегоричная система аксиом
N 325	**non-categoricity** <MM>	Nichtkategorizität f	non-catégoricité f	некатегоричность
N 326	**non-central** <χ^2-, F- or t-> **distribution** <ST>	nichtzentrale <χ^2-, F- oder t-> Verteilung f	distribution f <de χ^2, F ou t> non centrale	нецентральное <χ^2-, F- или t-> распределение
	non-central element <AL>	s. A 194		
N 327	**non-centrality parameter** <ST>	Nichtzentralitätsparameter m	paramètre m de non-centralité, paramètre d'excentricité	параметр нецентральности
N 328	**non-characteristic strip** <DE>	allgemeiner (nichtcharakteristischer) Streifen m	bande f non caractéristique	нехарактеристическая полос[к]а
	non-circuital field <VT>	s. I 1070		
N 329	**non-closed continuous group** <GR>	offene kontinuierliche Gruppe f	groupe m continu non fermé	незамкнутая непрерывная группа
N 330	**non-closed field** <AL>	nicht algebraisch abgeschlossener Körper m	corps m non algébriquement clos	незамкнутое поле
N 331	**nonclosed formula,** formula involving free variables, open sentence, open formula, formula containing free individual variables <LO>	nichtabgeschlossener (offener) Ausdruck m, nichtgeschlossene Aussageform f, offener Satz m, Satzformel f, Formel f mit freien Variablen, Formel	formule f qui contient des variables libres	незамкнутая формула; формула, содержащая свободные переменные; открытая формула

No.	English	German	French	Russian
N 332	**non-closed group** <GR, TO>	nichtgeschlossene Gruppe *f*	groupe *m* non fermé	незамкнутая группа
	non-closed surface <TO>	*s.* O 158		
N 333	**non-closure** <LO>	Unabgeschlossenheit *f*, Nichtabgeschlossenheit *f*	non-clôture *f*	незамкнутость
	non-commutability <AL, AN>	*s.* N 337		
	non-commutative division ring <AL>	*s.* D 813		
N 334	**non-commutative group,** non[-]abelian group <GR>	nichtkommutative (nichtabelsche) Gruppe *f*	groupe *m* non commutatif (abélien)	некоммутативная (неабелева) группа
N 335	**non-commutative ring** <AL>	nichtkommutativer Ring *m*, Schiefring *m*	anneau *m* non commutatif	некоммутативное кольцо
N 336	**non-commutative valuation** <AL>	nichtkommutative allgemeine Bewertung *f*	valuation *f* de Krull non commutative	некоммутативное нормирование Крулля
N 337	**non-commutativity,** non-commutability <AL, AN>	Nichtkommutativität *f*, Nichtvertauschbarkeit *f*	non-commutativité *f*, non-commutabilité *f*	некоммутативность, неперестановочность
N 338	**non-commuting operators,** incommutable (non-interchangeable) operators <FA>	nicht kommutierende (vertauschbare) Operatoren *mpl*	opérateurs *mpl* non commutants (commutables, interchangeables), opérateurs impermutables	некоммутирующие (неперестановочные) операторы
N 339	**non-compact group** <GR>	nichtkompakte Gruppe *f*	groupe *m* non compact	некомпактная группа, не компактная группа, открытая группа
	non-compactness <TO>	*s.* I 254		
N 340	**non-comparable elements,** incompatible elements <of a partial order> <SE>	unvergleichbare Elemente *npl*	éléments *mpl* non comparables	несравнимые элементы
	non-computability <FO>	*s.* I 214		
	non-computable function <FO>	*s.* I 215		
N 341	**nonconcordantly oriented simplex** <AT>	ungleichsinnig orientiertes Simplex *n*	simplexe *m* d'orientation différente	неравно ориентированный симплекс
N 342	**nonconcurrent lines** <EG>	nicht durch einen Punkt gehende Geraden *fpl*, sich nicht schneidende Geraden	droites *fpl* non concourantes, droites sans point commun	непересекающиеся прямые
	non-congruence <EG>	*s.* I 276		
	non-conjunction <AL, LO>	*s.* S 763		
N 343	**non-connected relation** <SE>	nichtkonnexe Relation *f*	relation *f* non connective	несвязное отношение
N 344	**non-constant polynomial** <AL>	echtes (nichtkonstantes) Polynom *n*	véritable polynôme *m*	непостоянный многочлен
N 345	**non-constructive proof of existence** <FO>	nichtkonstruktiver Existenzbeweis *m*	demonstration *f* d'existence non constructive	неконструктивное доказательство существования
N 346	**non-constructivity** <FO>	Nichtkonstruktivität *f*	propriété *f* d'être non constructif	неконструктивность
N 347	**non-continuable cocycle** <AT>	nichtfortsetzbarer Kozyklus *m*	cocycle *m* non prolongeable	непродолжаемый ∇-цикл
	non-contradictory theory <FO>	*s.* C 2100		
	non-correlation <ST>	*s.* A 54		
N 348	**non-creativity** <LO>	Nichtkreativität *f*	non-créativité *f*	некреативность
N 349	**non-critical point** <in Morse's theory> <VA>	gewöhnlicher (nichtkritischer) Punkt *m*	point *m* non critique	некритическая точка
N 350	**non-critical value** <of a function in Morse's theory> <VA>	gewöhnlicher (nichtkritischer) Wert *m*	valeur *f* non critique	некритическое значение
N 351	**non-cyclicity** <GR>	Nichtzyklizität *f*	propriété *f* d'être non cyclique	нецикличность
N 352	**non-decomposable matrix,** indecomposable matrix <MD>	unzerlegbare Matrix *f*	matrice *f* non décomposable	неразложимая матрица
	non decomposed curve <AY>	*s.* I 1030		
	non-decreasing function <RF>	*s.* I 287		
N 353	**non-deducibility** <LO>	Nichtableitbarkeit *f*	non-déductibilité *f*	невыводимость
N 354	**non-deducibility proof** <LO>	Nichtableitbarkeitsbeweis *m*	démonstration *f* de non-déductibilité	доказательство невыводимости
N 355	**nondegeneracy, non-degeneracy** <AL, TO, VA>	Nichtentartung *f*, Nichtausartung *f*, Nichtausgeartetheit *f*	non-dégénérescence *f*	невырождение, отсутствие вырождения, невырожденность
	non-degenerate affinity <AY>	*s.* R 509		
	non-degenerate bilinear form <AL, FA>	*s.* N 479		
N 356	**non-degenerate collineation,** collineatory transformation, non-singular collineation <AY, PJ>	nicht ausgeartete Kollineation *f*, Kollineation mit regulärer Matrix	application *f* projective non dégénérée	невырожденное проективное отображение, проективное соответствие
N 357	**non-degenerate conic [section],** regular conic [section], conic [section] <AY>	nichtentarteter (regulärer, nicht zerfallender) Kegelschnitt *m*, nichtentartete Kurve *f* zweiter Ordnung	section *f* conique non dégénérée (régulière, décomposée), conique *f* non dégénérée (régulière, décomposée), section conique, conique	невырожденное (правильное, регулярное) коническое сечение, невырожденная кривая второго порядка
N 358	**non-degenerate correlation,** non-singular correlation <PJ>	nichtausgeartete Korrelation *f*	corrélation *f* non dégénérée	невырожденная корреляция

N 359	**non[-]degenerate critical point** <Morse> <TO, VA>	nichtausgearteter kritischer Punkt *m*	point *m* critique non dégénéré, point non dégénéré, point de Morse	невырожденная критическая точка
N 360	**non-degenerate distribution** <ST>	eigentliche (wirkliche) Verteilung *f*, nichtentartete (nicht ausgeartete) Verteilung	distribution *f* non dégénérée	невырожденное (собственное) распределение
N 361	**non-degenerate set** <SE>	Menge *f* mit mindestens zwei Elementen	ensemble *m* contenant plus qu'un élément	множество, содержащее более одного элемента
N 362	**non-degenerate simplex** <AT>	nichtausgeartetes Simplex *n*	simplexe *m* simple (non singulier)	невырожденный (простой) симплекс
N 363	**non-degenerate type [of distribution]** <ST>	eigentlicher Verteilungstyp (Typ) *m*	type *m* [de distribution] non dégénéré	невырожденный тип [распределения]
	non-dense continuum containing more than one point <TO>	*s.* C 1801		
N 364	**non[-]dense set** <SE>	nichtdichte (apantachische) Menge *f*	ensemble *m* non[-]dense, ensemble apantachique	неплотное множество
	nondense set <TO>	*s.* N 704		
	nondense subset <TO>	*s.* N 705		
N 365	**non-denumerability,** uncountability, non-enumerability <SE>	Überabzählbarkeit *f*, Nichtabzählbarkeit *f*	propriété *f* d'être non dénombrable, innombrabilité *f*	несчетность
N 366	**non-denumerable set,** non-enumerable set, uncountable set <SE>	nichtabzählbare (nicht abzählbare) Menge *f*, überabzählbare [unendliche] Menge, unabzählbare Menge, // nicht abzählbare Mannigfaltigkeit *f*, unzählbare Mannigfaltigkeit	ensemble *m* innombrable (non dénombrable, indénombrable)	несчетное (бесчисленное, несчетное бесконечное, более чем счетное) множество
N 367	**non-denumerably many elements** <SE>	überabzählbar viele Elemente *npl*	une infinité *f* indénombrable d'éléments	несчетное количество элементов
N 368	**nonderogatory matrix** <AL>	nichtderogatorische Matrix *f*	matrice *f* non dérogatoire (privilégiée)	простая матрица
N 369	**non Desarguesian geometry** <AL, GE>	nichtdesarguessche Geometrie *f*	géométrie *f* nonarguésienne, géométrie dans laquelle le théorème de Desargues n'est pas valable	недезаргова геометрия; геометрия, в которой не имеет места предложение Дезарга
	nondeterminating sequence <SE, SS>	*s.* I 472		
	non-determination <ST>	*s.* C 1030		
N 370	**non-deterministic automaton** <TA>	nichtdeterministischer Automat *m*	automate *m* non déterminé	недетерминированный автомат
N 371	**non-developable ruled surface,** warped (twisted, skew ruled, skew) surface <GE>	windschiefe Fläche (Regelfläche) *f*, nicht abwickelbare Regelfläche	surface *f* gauche, surface réglée non développable	косая [линейчатая] поверхность, линейчатая неразвертывающаяся поверхность
N 372	**non-diagonal element,** off-diagonal element <MD>	Nichtdiagonalelement *n*	élément *m* non diagonal	недиагональный элемент
N 373	**non-diagonal term** <of a quadratic form> <AL>	Nichtdiagonalglied *n*	terme *m* non diagonal, terme rectangle	член вида $a_{ij} x_i x_j$, $i \neq j$
	non-directed graph <GP>	*s.* N 437		
N 374	**non-discrete space** <TO>	nichtdiskreter Raum *m*	espace *m* non discret	недискретное пространство
N 375	**non-disjointness;** overlapping <of sets> <SE>	Nichtdisjunktheit *f*	propriété *f* de n'être pas disjoint	частичное совпадение, пересечение
N 376	**non-disjoint sets;** overlapping sets <SE>	nichtdisjunkte Mengen *fpl*, Mengen mit nichtleerem Durchschnitt	ensembles *mpl* conjoints	пересекающиеся множества
	non-disjunction <LO>	*s.* S 2439		
N 377	**non-dualizability** <AL, AN, GE>	Nichtdualisierbarkeit *f*	propriété *f* de n'être pas dualisable	недуализируемость
N 378	**non-effective proof of existence** <FO>	nichteffektiver Existenzbeweis *m*	démonstration *f* de l'existence non effective	неэффективное доказательство существования
	non-empty set <SE>	*s.* N 517		
N 379	**non-enumerability** <FO>	Nichtaufzählbarkeit *f*	innumérabilité *f*	неперечислимость
	non-enumerability <SE>	*s.* N 365		
N 380	**non-enumerable set** <FO>	nichtaufzählbare Menge *f*	ensemble *m* innumérable (non énumerable)	неперечислимое множество
	non-enumerable set <SE>	*s.* N 366		
	non-equicharacteristic case <AL>	*s.* C 183		
N 381	**non-equivalence** <of sets> <SE>	Nichtäquivalenz *f*	non-équipotence *f*	неравномощность, неэквивалентность
	non-equivalence <LO>	*s.* E 687		
N 382	**non-euclidean geometry, non-Euclidean geometry,** non-euclidian geometry, non-Euclidian geometry <GE>	nichteuklidische Geometrie *f*; astralische Geometrie <Schweikart>	géométrie *f* non euclidienne	неевклидова геометрия
N 383	**non-Euclidean motion** <GE>	nichteuklidische Bewegung *f*, Bewegung im nichteuklidischen Raum, Bewegung der nichteuklidischen Geometrie	déplacement *m* non euclidien	неевклидово движение
N 384	**non-euclidean space** <GE>	nichteuklidischer Raum *m*	espace *m* non euclidien	неевклидово пространство
N 385	**non-Euclidean translation** <GE>	nichteuklidische Schiebung *f*	translation *f* non euclidienne	неевклидов перенос

No.	English	German	French	Russian
N 386	**non-Euclidean (non-euclidean) trigonometry** <GE>	nichteuklidische Trigonometrie *f*	trigonométrie *f* non euclidienne	неевклидова тригонометрия
	non-euclidian (non-Euclidian) geometry <GE>	*s.* N 382		
N 387	**non-exact square root** <AR, NT>	nicht aufgehende Quadratwurzel *f*	racine *f* carrée non exacte	неточный квадратичный корень
N 388	**non-existence,** nonexistence <GN>	Nichtexistenz *f*	non-existence *f*	несуществование
	nonfactorable polynomial <AL>	*s.* I 1042		
N 389	**non-finite set** <in constructive mathematics> <SE>	nichtendliche Menge *f*	ensemble *m* non fini	неконечное множество
N 390	**non-formalized theory** <FO, LO>	nicht formalisierte Theorie *f*	théorie *f* non formalisée	неформализированная теория
N 391	**non generally valid formula** <LO>	nicht allgemeingültiger Ausdruck *m*	formule *f* réalisable (synthétique, invalide)	не универсально верная формула
N 392	**non-generator** <of an algebra> <UA>	Nichterzeugende *f*	élément *m* non générateur	необразующий [элемент]
N 393	**non-harmonic Fourier series** <SS>	nichtharmonische Fourier-Reihe *f*	série *f* de Fourier non harmonique	негармонический ряд Фурье
N 394	**non-Hausdorff space,** non-separated space <TO>	nicht-Hausdorffscher Raum *m*, nichtseparierter Raum	espace *m* non séparé	неотделимое пространство
N 395	**non[-]holonomic constraint** <VA>	nichtholonome Bedingung *f*	contrainte *f* non holonome	неголономная связь, неголономное условие
	non-holonomic co-ordinates <GE>	*s.* Q 134		
	non-homogeneous boundary value problem <DE> ⌐<SP>	*s.* N 396		
	non-homogeneous chain	*s.* N 400		
	non-homogeneous differential equation <DE>	*s.* N 397		
N 396	**non-homogeneous linear boundary value problem,** inhomogeneous linear boundary value problem, non-homogeneous (inhomogeneous) boundary value problem <DE>	inhomogene (unhomogene) [lineare] Randwertaufgabe *f*, inhomogenes (unhomogenes) [lineares] Randwertproblem (Problem) *n*	problème aux limites [linéaire] inhomogène (non homogène), problème [linéaire] inhomogène (non homogène)	неоднородная [линейная] краевая задача, неоднородная [линейная] задача
N 397	**non-homogeneous linear differential equation,** inhomogeneous linear differential equation, nonhomogenous (inhomogeneous) differential equation <DE>	inhomogene (vollständige, nichthomogene, unhomogene) lineare Differentialgleichung *f*, inhomogene (nichthomogene, unhomogene) Differentialgleichung (Gleichung *f*)	équation *f* différentielle [linéaire] non homogène, équation différentielle [linéaire] inhomogène (avec (à) second membre), équation non homogène	неоднородное [линейное] дифференциальное уравнение
N 398	**non-homogeneous linear system of [ordinary] differential equations,** non-homogeneous (inhomogeneous) system of [ordinary] differential equations, inhomogeneous linear system of [ordinary] differential equations <DE>	nichthomogenes (inhomogenes) [lineares] System *n* von [gewöhnlichen] Differentialgleichungen	système *m* [linéaire] inhomogène (non homogène) d'équations différentielles [ordinaires]	неоднородная [линейная] система [обыкновенных] дифференциальных уравнений
N 399	**non-homogeneous line co-ordinates,** nonhomogeneous tangential co-ordinates of the line <AY>	nichthomogene Linienkoordinaten *fpl*	coordonnées *fpl* tangentielles non homogènes de la droite	неоднородные тангенциальные координаты прямой
N 400	**non-homogeneous Markov chain,** nonhomogeneous chain <SP>	inhomogene Markovsche Kette *f*, inhomogene Kette	chaîne *f* markovienne non homogène, chaîne non homogène	неоднородная цепь Маркова, неоднородная цепь
N 401	**non-homogeneous plane co-ordinates,** nonhomogeneous tangential co-ordinates of the plane <AY>	nichthomogene Ebenenkoordinaten *fpl*	coordonnées *fpl* tangentielles non homogènes du plan	неоднородные тангенциальные координаты плоскости
N 402	**non-homogeneous Plücker co-ordinates** <AY>	inhomogene (normierte) Plückersche Linienkoordinaten *fpl*	coordonnées *fpl* plückériennes inhomogènes	неоднородные плюккеровы координаты
	non-homogeneous problem <VA>	*s.* N 403		
	non-homogeneous system of [ordinary] differential equations <DE>	*s.* N 398		
	non-homogeneous tangential co-ordinates of the line <AY>	*s.* N 399		
	non-homogeneous tangential co-ordinates of the plane <AY>	*s.* N 401		
N 403	**non-homogeneous variational problem,** inhomogeneous variational problem, nonhomogeneous (inhomogeneous) problem <VA>	inhomogenes Variationsproblem (Problem) *n*, Funktionenproblem *n*	problème *m* [variationnel] inhomogène	неоднородная [вариационная] задача

N 404	**non-Hopfian group** <GR>	nicht hopfsche Gruppe *f*	groupe *m* non de Hopf	нехопфова группа
N 405	**non-iconic model** <PG>	nicht bildhaftes Modell *n*	modèle *m* non imagé	непортретная модель
N 406	**non-implication,** material non-implication <. . . but not . . .> <LO>	Nichtimplikation *f*	non-conditionnelle *f*	антиимпликация, non-implicatio <. . . , но не . . .>
N 407	**non-inclusion,** ⊄ <SE>	Nichtenthaltensein *n*, ⊄	non-inclusion *f*, ⊄	невключение, ⊄
	non-increasing function <RF>	*s.* D 80		
	non-increasing sequence <SS>	*s.* M 868		
	non-inductive set <SE>	*s.* I 474		
	non-interchangeable operators <FA>	*s.* N 338		
	non-intersecting sets <SE>	*s.* D 703		
	non-invariant subgroup <GR>	*s.* N 430		
	non-invertible matrix <MD>	*s.* S 1094		
N 408	**nonion** <AL>	Nonion *f*	nonion *m*	нонион
N 409	**non-irreflexivity** <of a relation> <SE>	Nichtirreflexivität *f*	non-irréflexivité *f*	неиррефлексивность
	non-isotropic line <PJ>	*s.* A 682		
	non-isotropic plane <PJ>	*s.* A 683		
N 410	**non-limiting ordinal,** ordinal of [the] first kind, ordinal number of [the] first kind, number of [the] first kind, successor ordinal, isolated ordinal <SE>	Nichtlimeszahl *f*, Zahl *f* erster Art, Ordnungszahl *f* erster Art, isolierte Zahl (Ordnungszahl)	nombre *m* [ordinal] de la première espèce, nombre de première espèce	непредельное число, непредельное порядковое число, число первого рода
N 411	**non[-]linearity** <AL, AN, SE>	Nichtlinearität *f*	non-linéarité *f*; non-complétude *f* <d'une relation d'ordre>	нелинейность
N 412	**nonlinear optimization (programming),** NLP <PG>	nichtlineare Optimierung (Programmoptimierung, Programmierung) *f*, nichtlineares Programmieren *n*	programmation (optimisation) *f* non linéaire	нелинейное программирование, нелинейная оптимизация
N 413	**nonlinear trend,** curvilinear trend <ST>	nichtlinearer Trend *m*	tendance *f* curviligne	нелинейный тренд
N 414	**non-logical axiom** <LO>	außerlogisches Axiom *n*	axiome *m* non logique	нелогическая аксиома
N 415	**non-logical constant,** extralogical constant <LO, SE>	außerlogische Konstante *f*	constante *f* non logique	нелогическая константа
N 416	**non-meager set,** set of [the] second category, set of the second species <TO>	Menge *f* [von] zweiter (2.) Kategorie, nicht magere Menge, Punktmenge *f* [von] zweiter Kategorie	ensemble *m* de seconde (deuxième, IIe) catégorie, ensemble non maigre, ensemble inépuisable	множество второй (II-ой) категории [по Кантору], не тощее множество
N 417	**non-measurable [point] set** <ME>	nichtmeßbare Punktmenge (Menge) *f*	ensemble *m* non mesurable, ensemble immensurable	неизмеримое [точечное] множество
N 418	**non-membership relation,** ∉ relation <SE>	Nichtelementbeziehung *f*	non-appartenance *f*	∉-отношение, отношение непринадлежности
	non-modular group <GR>	*s.* S 919		
N 419	**non-modular representation** <AL>	nichtmodulare Darstellung *f*	représentation *f* non modulaire	немодулярное представление
N 420	**non-movable singularity,** fixed singularity <DE>	feste Singularität *f*	singularité *f* fixe (non mobile)	неподвижная особенность
N 421	**non[-]negative combination** <PG>	Nichtnegativkombination *f*	combinaison *f* non négative	неотрицательная комбинация
N 422	**non[-]negative divisor,** effective divisor <AG>	effektiver (nichtnegativer, ganzer) Divisor *m*; Polygon *n* <arithmetische Theorie der algebraischen Funktionen>	diviseur *m* positif (entier)	целый (эффективный) дивизор
	non[-]negative divisor <AG, FT>	*s.* H 403		
N 423	**non[-]negative number** <NT>	nichtnegative Zahl *f*	nombre *m* non négatif, nombre positif (arithmétique)	неотрицательное число
	non[-]negative root, <AL, FO>	*s.* A 967		
N 424/5	**non[-]negative semi[-]definite matrix,** positive [semi[-]definite] matrix <MD>	positiv semidefinite Matrix *f*	matrice *f* semi-positive	положительно полуопределенная матрица
N 426	**non[-]negativity requirement** <PG>	Nichtnegativitätsforderung *f*, Forderung *f* der Nichtnegativität	demande (réquisition) *f* de non-négativité	требование неотрицательности
N 427	**non-nil ideal, nonnil ideal** <AL>	Nicht-Nilideal *n*	non-nil-idéal *m*	ниль-идеал
N 428	**non-noetherian ring** <AL>	nichtnoetherscher Ring *m*	anneau *m* non noethérien	ненетерово кольцо
	non-normal distribution <ST>	*s.* A 46		
	non-normal extension <AL>	*s.* E 810		
	non-normal field <AL>	*s.* F 206		
N 429	**non-normal population,** non-normal universe <ST>	nicht normalverteilte Grundgesamtheit *f*	population *f* non normale, univers *m* non normal	[генеральная] совокупность с отличным от нормального распределением

N 430	**non-normal subgroup,** non-invariant subgroup <GR>	Nichtnormalteiler *m*	sous-groupe *m* non invariant	неинвариантная подгруппа; подгруппа, не являющаяся нормальным делителем
	non-normal universe <ST>	*s.* N 429		
N 431	**non-numerical calculation** <GN>	nichtnumerische Rechnung *f*	calcul *m* non numérique	нечисленный расчет
N 432	**non-numeric algorithm** <FO>	nichtnumerischer Algorithmus *m*	algorithme *m* non numérique	нечисловой алгоритм
N 433	**nonobjective approach** <to theory of categories> <CA>	objektfreier Zugang *m*	traitement *m* sans objets	безобъектный подход
	non-ordered pair <SE>	*s.* U 371		
N 434	**non-orientability** <GE, TO>	Nichtorientierbarkeit *f*	non-orientabilité *f*	неориентируемость
N 435	**non-orientable contour** <TO>	nichtorientierbarer Rand *m*	contour *m* non orientable	неориентируемый контур
N 436	**non-orientable surface** <GE, TO>	nichtorientierbare Fläche *f*	surface *f* non orientable	неориентируемая поверхность
	non-orientable torus <GE>	*s.* K 86		
N 437	**non[-]oriented graph,** ordinary graph, non-directed graph, undirected graph, symmetric graph <GP>	ungerichteter (nichtorientierter) Graph *m*, Graph	graphe *m* non dirigé (orienté)	ненаправленный (неориентированный) граф, граф
N 438	**non-orthogonal factor,** oblique factor <ST>	nichtorthogonaler (schiefwinkliger) Faktor *m*	facteur *m* non orthogonal, facteur oblique	неортогональный фактор
N 439	**non-overlapping** <TO>	nicht überlappend	sans points intérieurs communs	неперекрывающийся, не имеющий общих внутренних точек
N 440	**non-overlapping intervals** <AN>	nichtüberlappende Intervalle *npl*	intervalles *mpl* n'empiétant pas l'un sur l'autre, intervalles qui n'empiètent pas l'un sur l'autre	неналегающие интервалы; интервалы, не имеющие общих внутренних точек
	non-overlapping sets <SE>	*s.* D 703		
	non-parallel sides <EG>	*s.* L 526		
N 441	**non-parametric confidence region** <ST>	nichtparametrischer (verteilungsfreier, parameterfreier) Konfidenzbereich (Vertrauensbereich) *m*	région *f* de confiance non paramétrique	непараметрическая доверительная область
N 442	**non-parametric estimation** <ST>	parameterfreie (verteilungsfreie, nichtparametrische) Schätzung *f*	estimation *f* non paramétrique	непараметрический метод оценки, непараметрическая оценка
N 443	**non-parametric test,** distribution[-] free test, parameter-free test <ST>	parameterfreier (verteilungsfreier, nichtparametrischer) Test *m*	test *m* non paramétrique	непараметрический критерий
N 444	**non-Pascalian geometry** <GE>	nichtpascalsche Geometrie *f*	géométrie *f* non pascalienne	непаскалева геометрия
N 445	**non-perfect set** <TO>	imperfekte Menge *f*	ensemble *m* imparfait	несовершенное множество
N 446	**non-periodic decimal [fraction]** <NT>	nichtperiodischer [unendlicher] Dezimalbruch *m*	fraction *f* décimale illimitée non périodique	непериодическая десятичная (бесконечная десятичная) дробь
N 447	**non-planar graph** <GP>	nichtplanarer Graph *m* <Graph vom Geschlecht > 0>	graphe *m* gauche	неплоский граф
	non-plane curve <DG>	*s.* S 1306		
N 448	**non-positive semidefinite matrix,** negative [semi-definite] matrix <AL, MD>	negativ semidefinite Matrix *f*	matrice *f* semi-négative	отрицательно полуопределенная матрица
N 449	**non-positivity** <AL, NT>	Nichtpositivität *f*	propriété *f* d'être non positif	неположительность
N 450	**non-potent semigroup** <AL>	Halbgruppe *f* ohne idempotente Elemente	demi-groupe *m* sans éléments idempotents	полугруппа без идемпотентных элементов
	non-predicative definition <LO>	*s.* I 139		
N 451	**non-prime divisor** <AL>	zusammengesetzter <d. h. nicht primer> Divisor *m*	diviseur *m* composé	непростой дивизор
N 452	**non-prime ideal** <AB, AL>	zusammengesetztes (nichtprimes) Ideal *n*	idéal *m* composé (non premier)	непростой идеал; невзаимно-простой идеал
N 453	**non-primitive root of unity** <NT>	nicht primitive Einheitswurzel *f*	racine *f* de l'unité imprimitive	непервообразный корень из единицы
N 454	**non-principal character** <NT>	Nichthauptcharakter *m*	caractère *m* non principal	неглавный характер
N 455	**nonprincipal filter** <AL, SE>	Nichthauptfilter *m*	filtre *m* non principal	неглавный фильтр
	non-proximal <TO>	*s.* D 742		
N 456	**non-ramified extension,** unramified [field] extension <AL>	unverzweigte Erweiterung (Körpererweiterung) *f*, unverzweigter Körper *m*	extension *f* non ramifiée, corps *m* non ramifié	неразветвленное расширение <поля>
N 457	**non-randomized test** <ST>	nichtrandomisierter Test *m*	test *m* non randomisé	нерандомизированный критерий
N 458	**non-random sample** <ST>	nichtzufällige Stichprobe *f*, Stichprobe mit bewußter Auswahl	échantillon *m* non aléatoire	неслучайная выборка
N 459	**non-rational function,** irrational function <AN>	irrationale (nichtrationale) Funktion *f*	fonction *f* irrationnelle	иррациональная функция
N 460	**non-real number** <AL, NT>	nichtreelle Zahl *f*	nombre *m* non réel	невещественное (недействительное) число
N 461	**non-recurrent circulant matrix** <AL>	Zirkulante *f* ohne Wiederholungen	circulante *f* non récurrente	циркулянтная матрица без повторения
N 462	**non-recurring digit** <of a periodic decimal> <AR, NT>	Ziffer *f* der Vorperiode, Vorperiodenziffer *f*	chiffre *m* irrégulier (précédant la période)	цифра предпериода

N 463	**non-recurring digits** <of a decimal fraction> <AR, NT>	Vorperiode *f*	chiffres *mpl* devant la période	предпериод
	non-reflexive set <SE>	*s.* D 88		
N 464	**non[-]reflexivity** <of a relation> <SE>	Nichtreflexivität *f*	non-réflexivité *f*	нерефлексивность
N 465	**non-regular element,** non-cancellable element <in a composition> <AL>	nichtreguläres (nichtkürzbares, singuläres) Element *n*	élément *m* non régulier, élément singulier	нерегулярный (несократимый) элемент
N 466	**non-regular function element** <FT>	irreguläres Funktionselement *n*	élément *m* de fonction non régulier	нерегулярный элемент функции
N 467	**non-removable discontinuity** <DI>	nicht[ ]hebbare Unstetigkeit *f*	discontinuité *f* essentielle	неустранимый разрыв
N 468	**non-removable discontinuity,** point of non-removable discontinuity <DI>	nicht[ ]hebbare Unstetigkeitsstelle *f*	discontinuité *f* essentielle, point *m* de discontinuité essentielle	неустранимый разрыв, точка неустранимого разрыва
N 469	**non-representative sampling,** maverick <ST>	nichtrepräsentative Stichprobennahme *f*	échantillonnage (sondage) *m* non représentatif	непредставительный выбор; выбор, не представительный для совокупности
N 470	**non[-]residue** <NT>	Nichtrest *m*	non-résidu *m*	невычет
N 471	**non-Riemannian geometry** <DG>	nicht-Riemannsche Geometrie *f*, nichtriemannsche (Nichtriemannsche) Geometrie	géométrie *f* non riemannienne	нериманова геометрия
	non-rotational field <VT>	*s.* I 1070		
N 472	**non-satisfiability** <LO>	Unerfüllbarkeit *f*	non-satisfiabilité *f*	невыполнимость
	non satisfiable formula <LO>	*s.* C 2277		
N 473	**non-scalar matrix** <AL>	nichtskalare Matrix *f*	matrice *f* non scalaire	нескалярная матрица
N 474	**non-secant [half-line]** <in hyperbolic geometry> <GE>	Nichtschneidende *f*, nichtschneidende Halbgerade *f*	demi-droite *f* non sécante, non-sécante *f*	несекущая полупрямая, несекущая
	nonsense correlation <ST>	*s.* I 76		
N 475	**non-separable graph,** nonseparable graph, biconnected graph <GP>	artikulationsfreier (zweizusammenhängender, 2-zusammenhängender, nichtartikulierter) Graph *m*, Graph ohne Artikulationspunkt, Stern *m*	graphe *m* inarticulé (biconnexe, 2-connexe)	граф без сочленений (точек сочленения), звезда
	non-separated space <TO>	*s.* N 394		
N 476/7	**non[-]simple path** <in an oriented graph> <GP>	nichtelementare Bahn *f*	chemin *m* composé	непростой путь
	non[-]singular affine transformation <AY>	*s.* R 509		
N 478	**non[-]singular algebraic variety** <AG>	nichtsinguläre algebraische Mannigfaltigkeit *f*	variété *f* algébrique non singulière, variété algébrique lisse	неособенное алгебраическое многообразие
N 479	**non[-]singular bilinear form,** non-degenerate bilinear form <AL, FA>	nichtausgeartete (nichtentartete, nicht-entartete) Bilinearform *f*	forme *f* bilinéaire non dégénérée	невырожденная (неособая) билинейная форма
	non-singular collineation <AY, PJ>	*s.* N 356		
N 480	**non[-]singular complex [of lines (rays)],** non[-]singular linear complex [of lines (rays)] <PJ>	Gewinde *n*, nichtsingulärer [linearer] Strahlenkomplex (Geradenkomplex, Komplex) *m*	complexe *m* [de droites] non singulier, complexe [de droites] linéaire non singulier	неособый (несингулярный) комплекс [прямых (лучей)], неособый (несингулярный) линейный комплекс [прямых (лучей)]
	non-singular correlation <PJ>	*s.* N 358		
N 481	**non-singular curve** <AG>	singularitätenfreie Kurve *f*	courbe *f* non singulière	кривая без особенностей, регулярная кривая
N 482	**non-singular divisor** <AG>	singularitätenfreier Divisor *m*	diviseur *m* non singulier	неособый дивизор
N 483	**non[-]singular homology,** non[-]singular perspectivity, hyperbolic homology (perspectivity) <PJ>	nichtsinguläre Perspektivität (Homologie) *f*, hyperbolische Perspektivität (Homologie)	homologie *f* non singulière, homologie hyperbolique	неособенная (гиперболическая) гомология
	non[-]singular linear complex <PJ>	*s.* N 480		
	non[-]singular linear complex of lines (rays) <PJ>	*s.* N 480		
N 484	**non[-]singular linear transformation** <AL, GE>	nichtsinguläre (nichtausgeartete) lineare Transformation *f*	transformation *f* [linéaire] ordinaire	невырожденное линейное преобразование
N 485	**non-singular matrix,** regular matrix, invertible matrix <MD>	nichtsinguläre (reguläre, invertierbare, nichtausgeartete) Matrix *f*	matrice *f* non singulière, matrice régulière (inversible)	неособенная (невырожденная, обратимая, регулярная) матрица
N 486	**non-singular model** <AG>	singularitätenfreies Modell *n*	modèle *m* sans singularités	неособая модель
	non[-]singular perspectivity <PJ>	*s.* N 483		
	non-singular system <AL>	*s.* C 2650		
N 487	**non-solvability** <of an equation> <AL>	Unauflösbarkeit *f*	irrésolubilité *f*	неразрешимость
N 488	**non-solvable group** <GR>	unauflösbare (nichtauflösbare) Gruppe *f*	groupe *m* non résoluble	неразрешимая группа

No.	English	German	French	Russian
N 489	**non-special group** <GR>	nichtspezielle Gruppe *f*	groupe *m* non spécial	неспециальная группа
N 490	**non-special [linear] system** <AG>	nicht-spezielle [lineare] Schar *f*	système *m* linéaire non spécial	неспециальная линейная система
N 491	**non-stable homotopy group** <AT>	instabile Homotopiegruppe *f*	groupe *m* d'homotopie instable (non stable)	группа нестабильной гомотопии
N 492	**non-stable integrality theorem** <AT>	instabiler Ganzheitssatz *m*	théorème *m* d'intégrité non stable	нестабильная теорема целочисленности
N 493	**non-standard model,** non-absolute model <FO>	Nichtstandardmodell *n*	modèle *m* non standard	нестандартная модель
	non-straightness <GN>	*s.* O 556		
N 494	**non-stratetic game** <TG>	nichtstrategisches Spiel *n*	jeu *m* non stratégique	нестратегическая игра
N 495	**non-symbolic factorization** <IV>	unsymbolische Zerlegung *f*	factorisation *f* non symbolique	несимволическая факторизация
N 496	**nonsymmetric relation** <SE>	unsymmetrische Relation *f*	relation *f* non symétrique	несимметричное отношение
N 497	**nonsymmetry** <of a relation> <SE>	Nichtsymmetrie *f*, Unsymmetrie *f*	non-symétrie *f*, antisymétrie *f*	несимметрия
N 498	**non-synectic two-dimensional chain** <PJ>	nichtsynektische zweidimensionale Kette *f*	chaîne *f* bidimensionnelle non synectique	несинэктическая двумерная цепь
N 499	**non-tangency condition** <VA>	„non-tangency"-Bedingung *f*, non-tangency-Bedingung *f*	condition *f* de non-tangence	условие некасания
N 500	**non-terminating continued fraction** <NT>	unendlicher (nichtabbrechender) Kettenbruch *m*	fraction *f* continue infinie (illimitée, d'ordre infini)	бесконечная непрерывная дробь
	non-terminating decimal <NT>	*s.* I 441		
N 501	**nontransitivity** <of a relation> <SE>	Nichttransitivität *f*	non-transitivité *f*	нетранзитивность
	non-trivial absolute value <AL>	*s.* N 507		
N 502	**non-trivial congruence [relation]** <on an algebra> <UA>	nichttriviale Kongruenz[-relation] *f*	congruence *f* non triviale	нетривиальная конгруэнция
	non-trivial cycle <AT>	*s.* C 2841		
N 503	**non-trivial derivation** <AL>	nichttriviale Derivation *f*	dérivation *f* non nulle	нетривиальное дифференцирование
N 504	**non-trivial element;** nonzero element <of a group> <GR>	Nichteinselement *n*, vom Einselement verschiedenes Element *n*	élément *m* non neutre	нееденичный элемент
N 505	**non-triviality** <AL>	Nichttrivialität *f*	non-trivialité *f*	нетривиальность
N 506	**non-trivial solution,** non-vanishing solution <AL>	nichttriviale (eigentliche) Lösung *f*	solution *f* non nulle (triviale, banale)	ненулевое (нетривиальное, отличное от нуля) решение
	non-trivial subcategory <CA>	*s.* P 1830		
N 507	**non-trivial valuation;** non-trivial absolute value <AL>	nichttriviale (nicht identische) Bewertung *f*	valuation *f* propre; valeur *f* absolue propre	нетривиальное нормирование; собственное абсолютное значение
N 508	**nonuniform continuity** <AN, TO>	nichtgleichmäßige (ungleichmäßige) Stetigkeit *f*	continuité *f* non uniforme	неравномерная сходимость
N 509	**nonuniform convergence,** non-uniform convergence <SS, TO>	ungleichmäßige (nichtgleichmäßige) Konvergenz *f*	convergence *f* non uniforme	неравномерная сходимость
N 510	**non-uniqueness**<AL, AN>	Nichteindeutigkeit *f*	non-unicité *f* <d'une solution>; propriété *f* d'être non univoque, ambiguïté *f* <d'une application>	неединственность <решения>; неоднозначность <отображения>
N 511	**non-unit** <of a ring> <AL>	Nichteinheit *f*	élément *m* non inversible	неделитель единицы
N 512	**non-unital left module** <AL>	Linkspseudomodul *m*, nichtunitärer Linksmodul *m*	pseudomodule *m* à gauche	левый псевдомодуль
N 513	**non-unital module** <AL>	Pseudomodul *m*, nichtunitärer Modul *m*	pseudomodule *m*	псевдомодуль
N 514	**non-unital right module** <AL>	Rechtspseudomodul *m*, nichtunitärer Rechtsmodul *m*	pseudomodule *m* à droite	правый псевдомодуль
	non-vacuous set <SE>	*s.* N 517		
	non-valence correspondence <AG>	*s.* S 1057		
N 515	**non-vanishing** <GN>	Nichtverschwinden *n*	non-nullité *f*	необращение в нуль, неравенство нулю; необращаемость
	non-vanishing <GN>	*s. a.* N 519		
	non-vanishing solution <AL>	*s.* N 506		
	non-vanishing vector <AL, VT>	*s.* N 521		
N 516	**nonvoid proper subset** <SE>	nichtleere echte Untermenge *f*, eigentliche Untermenge	partie *f* régulière	правильная часть, истинное подмножество
N 517	**nonvoid set,** non-empty (non-vacuous) set <SE>	nichtleere Menge *f*	ensemble *m* non vide	непустое множество
	non-vortical field <VT>	*s.* I 1070		
N 518	**non well-chained set** <TO>	unzusammenhängende Menge *f* im Cantorschen Sinne	ensemble *m* mal enchaîné, ensemble discontinu	множество, не обладающее свойством, что каждые две точки при любом $\varepsilon > 0$ соединимы ε-цепью, состоящей из точек множества
	non-well posed problem <DE>	*s.* M 60		
N 519	**non-zero,** non-vanishing, different from zero <GN>	ungleich Null, von Null verschieden, nicht verschwindend, verschieden von Null	différent de zéro	ненулевой, отличный от нуля, неравный нулю, не обращающийся в нуль, неисчезающий

No.	English	German	French	Russian
	non-zero divisor <AL>	*s.* R 540		
	non-zero divisor <GR>	*s.* P 1849		
	nonzero element <GR>	*s.* N 504		
N 520	**non-zero-sum game** <TG>	Nicht-Nullsummenspiel *n*	jeu *m* à somme différente de zéro	игра с ненулевой суммой
N 521	**non-zero vector,** non-vanishing vector <AL, VT>	vom Nullvektor verschiedener Vektor *m*, von Null verschiedener Vektor *m*, Vektor ungleich Null	vecteur *m* différent de zéro, vecteur non zéro	ненулевой вектор
N 522	**Nörlund['s] limitation method,** Nörlund['s] method [of limitation], (N,p_n) method <for divergent sequences> <LI>	Nörlundsches Limitierungsverfahren *n*, (N,p_n)-Verfahren *n*	méthode *f* (procédé *m*) de limitation de Nörlund, méthode (procédé) de Nörlund	метод Вороного, метод образования обобщенного предела Вороного
N 523	**Nörlund['s] mean** <of order *m*> <LI>	Nörlundsches Mittel *n* <*m*-ter Ordnung>	moyenne *m* de Nörlund <d'ordre *m*>	среднее Вороного (по Вороному)
N 524	**Nörlund['s] method,** Nörlund['s] summation method, Nörlund['s] method of summation, (N,p_n) method <for divergent series> <LI>	Nörlundsches Summierungsverfahren *n*, (N,p_n)-Verfahren *n*	méthode *f* (procédé *m*) de Nörlund, méthode (procédé) de sommation de Nörlund	метод Вороного, метод суммирования [расходящихся рядов] Вороного
	Nörlund['s] method [of limitation] <LI>	*s.* N 522		
	Nörlund['s] method of summation <LI>	*s.* N 524		
	Nörlund['s] summation method <LI>	*s.* N 524		
N 525	**norm / to** <a space *or* an algebra> <FA>	normieren <einen Raum *oder* eine Algebra>	normer <un espace *ou* une algèbre>	нормировать <пространство *или* алгебру>
N 526	**norm** <of a quaternion> <AL>	Norm *f*, Quadrat *n* des Tensors	norme *f*, norme algébrique	квадрат нормы, алгебраическая норма
N 527	**norm** <of an algebra, algebraic element, ideal *or* divisor> <AL, NT>	Norm *f*	norme *f*	норма
N 528	**norm** <of an element, a function, *or* a functional> <FA>	Norm *f*	norme *f*	норма
N 529	**norm** <of a group> <GR>	Kern *m*, Norm *f*	norme *f*	норма
N 530	**norm** <of a vector> <VT>	Norm *f*, Quadrat *n* der Länge, Längenquadrat *n*	norme *f*	квадрат модуля
	norm <AL, MD, NU>	*s.* M 196		
	norm <FA>	*s.* O 197		
	norm <MD>	*s.* E 565		
	norm <VT>	*s.* M 24		
N 531	**normability** <FA>	Normierbarkeit *f*	normabilité *f*	нормируемость
N 532	**normable [linear] space** <FA, TO>	normierbarer Raum *m*, normierbarer linearer Raum	espace *m* linéaire normable	нормируемое линейное пространство
N 533	**normal,** normal line <to a curve> <first, second, . . ., *s*-th> <DG>	Normale *f*, Kurvennormale *f* <erste, zweite, . . ., *s*-te>	normale *f* <première, seconde, . . ., *s*-e>	нормаль <первая, вторая, . . ., *s*-я>
	normal <DG>	*s.* N 663		
N 534	**normal addition theorem** <ST>	Additionssatz *m* der Normalverteilung	théorème *m* d'addition de la distribution normale	теорема сложения нормально распределенных случайных величин
	normal algebra <AL>	*s.* C 342		
N 535	**normal algorithm** <FO>	Normalalgorithmus *m*	algorithme *m* normal	нормальный алгоритм, метод конструктивного подбора
N 536	**normal algorithm,** Markov['s] normal algorithm <FO>	Markovscher Algorithmus *m*, Algorithmus im Sinne von Markov	algorithme *m* markovien, algorithme de Markov	алгоритм Маркова, нормальный алгоритм, нормальный алгоритм Маркова
N 537	**normal automorphism** <of a group> <GR>	normaler Automorphismus *m*, Zentrumsautomorphismus *m*	automorphisme *m* normal (central)	нормальный (центральный) автоморфизм
	normal axonometry <DS>	*s.* O 443		
N 538/9	**normal base** <of a space> <TO>	Normalbasis *f*, normale Basis *f*	base *f* normale	нормальная база
N 540	**normal basis** <of a Galois extension> <AB, AL>	Normalbasis *f*	base *f* normale	нормальный базис
N 541	**normal basis theorem** <AB, AL>	Satz *m* von der Normalbasis, Normalbasissatz *m*	théorème *m* de la base normale	теорема о нормальном базисе
N 542	**normal bundle** <as a fibre bundle> <AT>	Normalbündel *n*, Normalenbündel *n*	fibré *m* normal	нормальное расслоение
	normal chain <GR>	*s.* N 647		
N 543	**normal characteristic** <of a theta function> <FT, FU>	Normalcharakteristik *f*	caractéristique *f* normale	нормальная характеристика
N 544	**normal class** <SE>	normale Klasse *f*	classe *f* normale	нормальный (собственный) класс
	normal closed non-orientable surface of genus *p* <AT>	*s.* S 1439		
	normal closed orientable surface of genus *p* <AT>	*s.* S 1440		
N 545	**normal cone** <CS, GE>	Normalenkegel *m*	cône *m* normal	конус нормалей
N 546	**normal congruence,** congruence of normals <DG>	Normalenkongruenz *f*	congruence *f* de normales	конгруэнция нормалей, нормальная конгруэнция

	normal convergence <FA>	*s.* A 64		
	normal convergence <SS>	*s.* D 883		
N 547	**normal co-ordinates** <DG>	Normalkoordinaten *fpl*	coordonnées *fpl* normales	нормальные координаты
N 548	**normal correlation** <ST>	Normalkorrelation *f*	corrélation *f* normale	нормальная корреляция
N 549	**normal curvature** <of a surface> <DG>	Normalkrümmung *f*	courbure *f* normale	нормальная кривизна
N 550	**normal curvature vector** <DG>	erzwungener Krümmungsvektor *m*, Normalkrümmungsvektor *m*	vecteur *m* de courbure normal	нормальный вектор кривизны
N 551	**normal curve** <AG, FT>	normale Kurve *f* <AG>; Normalkurve *f*, Normkurve *f* <AG, FT>	courbe *f* normale	нормальная кривая
	normal curve <ST>	*s.* E 471		
N 552	**normal derivative** <of a function> <DI>	Normalableitung *f*, Ableitung *f* in Normalenrichtung	dérivée *f* suivant la normale, dérivée normale	производная по нормали, нормальная производная
N 553	**normal determinant** <MD>	Kochsche Normaldeterminante *f*, normale Determinante *f*, Normaldeterminante	déterminant *m* normal de H. von Koch, déterminant normal	нормальный детерминант
N 554	**normal deviate (deviation)** <ST>	normale Abweichung *f*	écart *m* normal	нормальное отклонение
N 555	**normal difference** <of a normal series of modules> <GR>	Faktor *m*	facteur *m*, quotient *m*	фактор
N 556	**normal discrete group** <GR>	normal-diskontinuierliche Transformationsgruppe *f*	groupe *m* discret normal	нормальная дискретная группа
N 557	**normal dispersion** <Lexis> <ST>	normale Dispersion *f*	dispersion *f* normale	нормальное рассеяние, нормальная дисперсия
N 558	**normal distribution,** Gaussian (Gauss) distribution, Gaussian probability distribution, Gaussian [law], normal (Gaussian) distribution law <ST>	Normalverteilung *f*, Gaußsche Normalverteilung (Verteilung *f*), Gauß-Verteilung *f*, Gaußsche Wahrscheinlichkeitsverteilung *f*, Normalverteilungsgesetz *n*, Gauß-Laplacesche Verteilung	loi *f* normale (de Gauss, de Laplace-Gauss, générale de Laplace), deuxième loi de Laplace, loi de répartition gaussienne, répartition (distribution) *f* gaussienne, distribution (répartition) de Gauss (Laplace-Gauss), distribution (répartition) normale	нормальное (гауссово, гауссовское) распределение, распределение Гаусса, гауссиан, нормальный закон распределения Гаусса, закон нормального распределения, закон Гаусса-Лапласа, закон Гаусса, распределение Гаусса-Лапласа, второй закон Лапласа, распределение Лапласа-Гаусса
	normal distribution curve <ST>	*s.* E 471		
N 559	**normal distribution function,** cumulative normal distribution <ST>	normale Verteilungsfunktion *f*, kumulative Normalverteilung *f*	fonction *f* de distribution normale, distribution *f* normale cumulée	нормальная функция распределения, нормальное распределение
	normal distribution law <ST>	*s.* N 558		
	normal divisor <GR>	*s.* I 883		
N 560	**normal eigenvalue problem,** normal self-adjoint eigenvalue problem <DE>	normale (normale selbstadjungierte, selbstadjungierte normale) Eigenwertaufgabe *f*	problème *m* normal aux valeurs propres	нормальная задача на собственные значения
	normal elliptic integral in Legendre's notation <FU>	*s.* E 178		
N 561	**normal endomorphism** <with respect to a Hermitian form> <AL>	normaler Endomorphismus *m* <bezüglich einer hermiteschen Form>	endomorphisme *m* normal <relativement à une forme hermitienne>	нормальный эндоморфизм <относительно эрмитовой формы>
N 562	**normal endomorphism** <of a group> <GR>	normaler Endomorphismus *m*, // normaler Automorphismus *m*	endomorphisme *m* distingué	нормальный эндоморфизм
N 563	**normal equation** <over *k*> <AL>	Normalgleichung *f*, normale Gleichung <über *k*>	équation *f* normale <sur *k*>	нормальное уравнение <над *k*>
	normal equation <AY>	*s.* C 62		
	normal equation <GE>	*s.* S 1608		
	normal equation of Hesse <AY>	*s.* H 263		
N 564	**normal equations,** simultaneous regression equations, standard equations <of least squares method> <ER, ST>	Normalgleichungen *fpl* <der Methode der kleinsten Quadrate>	équations *fpl* normales (types), équations-types *fpl*, équations de régression simultanées <de la méthode des moindres carrés>	нормальные уравнения <метода наименьших квадратов>
N 565	**normal equivalent deviate (deviation),** NED <ST>	Normalfraktil *n*	écart *m* réduit normal	нормальный квантиль
	normal error curve <ST>	*s.* E 471		
N 566	**normal error model,** error model <ST>	normales Fehlermodell *n*, Fehlermodell	modèle *m* des erreurs [accidentelles]	модель нормальных ошибок, модель ошибок
	normal expansion <SE>	*s.* N 581		
N 567	**normal exponential valuation** <AL>	normierte Exponentenbewertung *f*	valuation *f* exponentielle normalisée	нормализированная аддитивная нормировка
N 568	**normal extension** <of *k*, over *k*>, normal field <over *k*> <not necessarily separable> <AL>	normale Erweiterung *f*, Normalkörper *m* <über *k*>	extension *f* normale (quasi-galoisienne), corps *m* normal <sur *k*, de *k*>	нормальное расширение [поля] <над *k*>
N 569	**normal family** <of functions> <AN>	normale Familie (Funktionenfamilie) *f*, Normalschar *f*, Normalfamilie *f*	famille *f* normale	нормальное семейство

N 570	**normal family** <of spaces in dimension theory> <TO>	Normalbereich *m* <Hurewicz>	famille *f* héréditaire et F_σ-additive	нормальное семейство
	normal field <AL>	*s.* N 568		
N 571	**normal form** <of a quadratic form> <AL>	Normalform *f*	forme *f* normale	нормальный вид
N 572	**normal form** <of a second-order equation> <DE>	Normalform *f*, reduzierte Form *f*	forme *f* normale	нормальный вид
N 573	**normal form** <first *or* second> <of a difference equation> <FD>	Normalform *f* <erste *oder* zweite>	forme *f* normale <première *ou* deuxième>	нормальный вид <первый *или* второй>
N 574	**normal form** <of a linear transformation> <FT>	Normalform *f*	forme *f* normale	нормальный вид
N 575	**normal form,** standard form <of elliptic differentials and integrals> <FT>	Normalform *f*	forme *f* normale	нормальная (стандартная, каноническая) форма
N 576	**normal form** <IV>	Normalform *f* <Deruyts>	forme *f* normale	нормальная форма
N 577	**normal form** <LO>	Normalform *f*	forme *f* normale	нормальная форма
N 578	**normal form,** canonical form <of a matrix> <MD>	Normalform *f*	forme *f* canonique	нормальная форма, канонический вид, каноническая форма
N 579	**normal form** <of a recursive function> <MM>	Kleenesche Normalform *f*	forme *f* normale de Kleene	нормальная форма Клини
N 580	**normal form** <of a polar equation> <PJ>	Normalform *f*	forme *f* normale	нормальный вид
N 581	**normal form,** normal expansion <of an ordinal number> <SE>	Cantorsche Normaldarstellung *f*, Cantorsche Normalform *f*	forme *f* normale, développement *m* normal	нормальная форма
N 582	**normal form** <of a *k* person game> <TG>	Normalform *f* <eines *k*-Personen-Spiels>	forme *f* normale (normalisée, simultanée) <d'un jeu à *k* personnes>	нормальная форма <игры *k* лиц>
N 583	**normal form** <of a surface> <TO>	Normalform *f*	forme *f* normale	нормальный вид, стандартная форма
	normal form <LO>	*s.* P 1226		
	normal form of Hermite <MD>	*s.* H 227		
N 584	**normal form of Weierstrass,** Weierstrass['s] normal form <of an elliptic differential> <FT>	Weierstraßsche Normalform *f*, Normalform *f* Weierstraß'	forme *f* normale de Weierstrass, forme *f* réduite de Weierstrass	нормальная форма Вейерштрасса
N 585	**normal form theorem** <for a recursive function> <MM>	Normalformsatz *m*	théorème *m* de la forme normale	теорема о нормальной форме
N 586	**normal form transformation** <AL, AN, LO>	Transformation *f* auf die Normalform, Normalformtransformation *f*	transformation *f* à la forme normale	преобразование к нормальному виду
N 587	**normal form without identity** <LO>	identitätsfreie Normalform *f*	forme *f* normale sans identité	нормальная форма без тождества
	normal frequency curve <ST>	*s.* E 471		
N 588	**normal function,** normal mapping <of ordinals> <SE>	Normalfunktion *f*	fonction *f* normale	нормальная функция
N 589	**normal function of Poincaré** <AG>	Poincarésche Normalfunktion *f*	fonction *f* normale de Poincaré	нормальная функция Пуанкаре
N 590	**normal Hall subgroup** <AL>	Hallscher Normalteiler *m*	sous-groupe *m* invariant de Hall	нормальный делитель Холла
N 591	**normal homomorphism** <AT>	Normalhomomorphismus *m*	homomorphisme *m* normal	нормальный гомоморфизм
N 592	**normal integral,** Thomé['s] normal integral <DE>	Normalintegral *n*, Thomésches Normalintegral	intégrale *f* normale [de Thomé]	нормальный интеграл [Томе]
N 593	**normal integral** <of the first, second *or* third kind> <of Abelian functions> <FT>	Normalintegral *n* <erster, zweiter *oder* dritter Gattung>	intégrale *f* normale <de première, deuxième *ou* troisième espèce>	нормальный интеграл <первого, второго *или* третьего рода>
	normal irrational number <NT>	*s.* N 629		
N 594	**normality** <AL, CA, FT, ST>	Normalität *f*	normalité *f*	нормальность
N 595	**normality axiom,** T_4-separation axiom <TO>	viertes (Tietzesches) Trennungsaxiom *n*, T_4-Axiom *n*	premier axiome *m* de Tietze, axiome de normalité, axiome T_4 (IV de séparation)	аксиома Титце, первая аксиома Титце, аксиома нормальности, аксиома T_4, аксиома (T_4), аксиома (O_V)
N 596	**normality domain,** domain of normality <FT>	Normalitätsgebiet *n*	domaine *m* de normalité	область нормальности
N 597	**normalizable fixed point** <AT>	normalisierbarer Fixpunkt *m*	point *m* fixe normalisable	нормализуемая неподвижная точка
	normalizable function <AN>	*s.* S 1557		
	normalizable kernel <FA, IE>	*s.* H 356		
N 598	**normalization** <of a variety> <AG>	Normalisierung *f*	normalisée *f*; normalisation *f*	нормализация
N 599	**normalization** <AL, AN>	Normierung *f*	normalisation *f*	нормирование
N 600	**normalization** <of a frequency function> <ST>	Transformation *f* in eine Normalverteilung	normalisation *f* <d'une fonction de fréquences>	преобразование плотности распределения в нормальную
	normalization factor <GN>	*s.* N 618		
N 601	**normalization lemma** <AL>	Normalisierungslemma *n*	lemme *m* de normalisation	лемма о нормализации

No.	English	German	French	Russian
N 602	**normalize / to** <vectors *or* functions> <AN, VT>	normieren <Vektoren *oder* Funktionen>	normaliser, normer <des vecteurs *ou* des fonctions>	нормировать <векторы *или* функции>
N 603	**normalized additive character** <AL>	normierter Additivcharakter *m*	caractère *m* additif normé	нормированный аддитивный характер
N 604	**normalized basis** <AN>	normierte Basis *f*	base *f* normée	нормированный базис
N 605	**normalized [boundary] condition** <DE>	genormte Randbedingung *f*	condition *f* [aux limites] normée	нормированное [краевое] условие
N 606	**normalized discrete valuation** <AL>	normierte diskrete Bewertung *f*	valuation *f* discrète normée	нормализованное [дискретное] нормирование
N 607	**normalized eigenvector,** normalized pole <of a matrix> <MD>	normierter Eigenvektor *m*	vecteur *m* propre normé	нормированный собственный вектор
N 608	**normalized function** <AN>	normierte Funktion *f*	fonction *f* normée	нормированная (приведенная) функция
N 609	**normalized function** <FA>	normalisierte Funktion *f*	fonction *f* normalisée	нормализованная функция
N 610	**normalized measure** <AL>	normiertes Maß *n*	mesure *f* normalisée	нормализованная мера
	normalized measure <ME, ST>	*s.* P 1541		
N 611	**normalized metric** <ME>	normierte Metrik *f*	métrique *f* normée	нормированная метрика
	normalized orthogonal basis <AL>	*s.* O 489		
	normalized orthogonal system <AL, AN, FA>	*s.* O 495		
	normalized pole <MD>	*s.* N 607		
N 612	**normalized quaternion,** quaternion of norm 1, unit quaternion, versor <AL>	Versor *m*, normierte (genormte) Quaternion *f*, Einheitsquaternion *f*	verseur *m*, quaternion *m* normé, quaternion de norme 1	нормированный кватернион, кватернион с нормой 1, верзор
N 613	**normalized sequence** <in a Banach space> <FA>	normierte Folge *f*	suite *f* normale (normée)	нормированная последовательность
N 614	**normalized solution** <AL>	normierte Lösung *f*	solution *f* normalisée	нормированное решение
N 615	**normalized standard complex** <HA>	normierter Standardkomplex *m*	complexe *m* standard normé	нормализованный стандартный комплекс
N 616	**normalized vector,** unit vector <of a normed space> <TO>	normierter Vektor *m*, Einheitsvektor *m*	vecteur *m* normé (unité), vecteur-unité *m*	нормированный (единичный) вектор
	normalized vector <VT>	*s.* U 302		
N 617	**normalizer** <GR>	Normalisator *m*	normalisateur *m*, normalisant *m*, sous-groupe *m* normalisant	нормализатор
N 618	**normalizing factor,** normalization factor <GN> ⌐<ER>	Normierungsfaktor *m*	facteur *m* de normalisation, facteur normalisant	нормировочный коэффициент, нормировочный (нормирующий) множитель
	normal law of errors	*s.* E 475		
	normal line <DG>	*s.* N 533		
N 619	**normally convergent integral** <RF>	normal konvergentes Integral *n*	intégrale *f* normalement convergente	нормально сходящийся интеграл
N 620	**normally convergent series** <SS>	normal (maximal) konvergente Reihe *f*	série *f* normalement convergente	нормально (правильно) сходящийся ряд
N 621	**normally exhaustible** <AN>	normal ausschöpfbar	normalement exhaustible	нормально исчерпываемый
N 622	**normally ordered group** <GR>	normal geordnete Gruppe *f*	groupe *m* normalement ordonné	нормально упорядоченная группа
	normally ordered set <SE>	*s.* W 210		
N 623	**normally solvable operator** <FA>	normal auflösbarer Operator *m*	opérateur *m* normalement résoluble	нормально разрешимый оператор
N 624	**normal mapping** <of a group> <GR>	normale Abbildung *f*	application *f* distinguée	нормальное отображение
	normal mapping <FA>	*s.* N 634		
	normal mapping <SE>	*s.* N 588		
N 625	**normal matrix** <MD>	normale Matrix *f*	matrice *f* normale	нормальная матрица
N 626	**normal matrix** <in interpolation> <NU>	normale Abszissenfolge *f*, Normalmatrix *f*	matrice *f* normale	нормальная матрица
N 627	**normal morphism** <as a product of normal epimorphism and normal monomorphism> <CA>	normaler Morphismus *m*	morphisme *m* normal	нормальный мономорфизм
N 628	**normal net,** net of normals <DG>	Normalennetz *n*	réseau *m* de normales	сеть нормалей
N 629	**normal number,** normal irrational number <NT>	normale Zahl (Irrationalzahl) *f*	nombre *m* normal (irrationnel normal)	нормальное число
	normal of Sullivan <DG>	*s.* S 2251		
	normal of the surface <DG>	*s.* N 663		
N 630	**normaloid matrix** <FA>	normaloide Matrix *f*	matrice *f* normaloïde	нормалоидная матрица
N 631	**normaloid operator** <FA>	normaloider Operator *m*	opérateur *m* (transformation *f*) normaloïde	нормалоидный оператор
N 632	**normal operator** <of an operator group> <AL>	normaler Operator *m*	opérateur *m* distingué	нормальный оператор
N 633	**normal operator** <DE, FD>	Normaloperator *m*	opérateur *m* normal	нормальный оператор
N 634	**normal operator,** normal transformation, normal mapping <FA>	normaler Operator *m*, normale Transformation (Abbildung) *f*	opérateur *m* normal, transformation (application, opération) *f* normale	нормальный оператор, нормальное преобразование (отображение)
N 635	**normal order,** right order <in a permutation> <CT>	natürliche (richtige) Reihenfolge *f*, richtige Anordnung *f*, normale Anordnung (Reihenfolge)	ordre *m* normal	нормальное (естественное) расположение, нормальный (естественный) порядок, естественный порядок следования
	normal orthogonal basis <AL>	*s.* O 489		

No.	English	German	French	Russian
N 636	**normal plane** <DG>	Normalebene *f*	plan *m* normal	нормальная плоскость
N 637	**normal polygon** <FT>	Normalpolygon *n*	polygone *m* normal	нормальный многоугольник
N 638	**normal polynomial** <over *k*> <AL>	Normalpolynom *n*, normales Polynom *n* <über *k*>	fonction *f* normale, polynôme *m* normal <sur *k*>	нормальный полином <над *k*>
N 639	**normal population,** normal universe <ST>	normale Grundgesamtheit *f*	population *f* normale, univers *m* normal	нормальная [генеральная] совокупность
	normal probability curve <ST>	*s.* E 471		
N 640	**normal probability paper,** Gauss paper <IN, ST>	Gauß-Papier *n*, Gaußsches Papier *n*, Wahrscheinlichkeitspapier *n*	papier *m* à échelle gaussienne	нормальная вероятностная бумага
	normal process <SP>	*s.* G 82		
N 641	**normal prolongation** <of a transformation> <FA>	normale Fortsetzung (Erweiterung) *f*	prolongement *m* normal	нормальное продолжение
	normal random variable <ST>	*s.* N 665		
N 642	**normal representation** <of a principal order> <AL>	Normaldarstellung *f*	représentation *f* normale	нормальное представление
N 643	**normal resolution** <CA>	normale Auflösung *f*	résolution *f* normale	нормальная резольвента
N 644	**normal section** <of a surface> <DG>	Normalschnitt *m*	section *f* normale	нормальное сечение
	normal self-adjoint eigenvalue problem <DE>	*s.* N 560		
	normal separable extension <AL>	*s.* G 12		
N 645	**normal sequence** <of functions> <FT>	normale Funktionenfolge *f*	suite *f* normale <de fonctions>	нормальная последовательность <функций>
N 646	**normal series,** Thomé['s] normal series <DE>	Normalreihe *f*, Thomésche Normalreihe	série *f* normale [de Thomé]	нормальный ряд [Томе]
N 647	**normal series,** normal chain, normal tower [of subgroups] <of a group> <GR>	Normalreihe *f*, Normalkette *f* <Zassenhaus>, // Kompositionsreihe *f*	suite *f* de composition [ordinaire], série *f* normale, chaîne *f* normale (de sous-groupes normale), suite normale, chaîne de composition ascendante	нормальный ряд, нормальная цепь, нормальная башня [подгрупп]
N 648	**normal series** <of a lattice> <LA>	Normalreihe *f*	série *f* normale	нормальный ряд
	normal series with abelian factors <GR>	*s.* A 30		
N 649	**normal series with repetitions** <GR>	Normalreihe *f* mit Wiederholungen	suite *f* de composition avec répétitions	нормальный ряд с повторениями
N 650	**normal set** <SE>	gewöhnliche (normale) Menge *f* <enthält sich nicht selbst als Element>	ensemble *m* normal	нормальное (собственное, ординарное) множество
N 651	**normal simple surface with *r* contours** <AT>	Kugel *f* mit *r* Löchern, Kugel mit *r* Konturen	sphère *f* à *r* contours	нормальная простая поверхность с *r* контурами
N 652	**normal simplicial mapping** <AT>	normale simpliziale Abbildung *f*	application *f* simpliciale normale	нормальное [симплициальное] отображение, нормальный сдвиг
N 653	**normal solubility (solvability)** <of an operator equation> <FA>	normale Auflösbarkeit *f*	résolubilité *f* normale	нормальная разрешимость
N 654	**normal space,** T_4-space, T_4 topological space <not necessarily T_1> <TO>	normaler Raum *m*, T_4-Raum *m*; im weiteren Sinne normaler Raum <nicht notwendig T_1>	espace *m* normal, espace T_4	нормальное пространство, T_4-пространство
N 655	**normal space which is closed in any containing normal space** <TO>	n-abgeschlossener Raum *m*	espace *m* normal tel que chaque image homéomorphe dans un espace normal est fermée	нормальное пространство *E* такое, что для любого его гомеоморфизма *f* в нормальное пространство *f*(*E*) замкнуто
N 656	**normal Stiefel-Whitney class** <*n*-th> <of a manifold> <AT>	normale Stiefelsche Klasse *f* <*n*-te>	classe *f* normale de Stiefel-Whitney <*n*-e>	нормальный класс Штифеля-Уитни <*n*-й>
	normal subgroup <GR>	*s.* I 883		
	normal subspace <AL>	*s.* L 647		
N 657	**normal surface** <AG>	Normalfläche *f*, Normfläche *f*	surface *f* normale	нормальная поверхность
N 658	**normal surface** <of a curve on a surface> <DG>	Normalenfläche *f*	surface *f* des normales	поверхность нормалей
N 659	**normal system** <of subgroups> <GR>	Normalsystem *n*, normales [vollständiges geordnetes] System *n*	système *m* normal	нормальная система
N 660	**normal system of interpolation nodes** <NU>	normales Punktsystem (Grundpunktsystem, Knotensystem) *n*, normal verteilte Punkte *mpl*	système *m* normal de nœuds <d'interpolation>	нормальная система узлов
N 661	**normal tensor** <VT>	Normaltensor *m*, Normalaffinor *m*	tenseur *m* normal	нормальный тензор
N 662	**normal topology** <TO>	normale Topologie *f*	topologie *f* normale	нормальная топология
N 663	**normal to the surface,** surface normal, normal of the surface, normal <DG>	Flächennormale *f*, Normale *f* der Fläche, Normale	normale *f* à la surface	нормаль к поверхности
	normal tower [of subgroups] <GR>	*s.* N 647		
	normal transformation <FA>	*s.* N 634		
	normal transformation <LI>	*s.* R 643		

	normal unit vector <DG>	*s.* N 669		
	normal universe <ST>	*s.* N 639		
N 664	**normal valuation** <AL>	normierte Bewertung *f*	valuation *f* normale	нормализованное нормирование
N 665	**normal variate,** normal random variable, Gaussian variable <ST>	normale (normalverteilte, Gaußsche) Zufallsvariable, normale (normalverteilte) Variable *f*	variable *f* aléatoire normale, variable normale (gaussienne, laplacienne)	нормальная случайная величина (переменная), гауссова переменная
N 666	**normal variety** <Weil>, locally normal variety, absolutely normal variety, absolutely locally normal variety <Zariski> <AG>	normale (normale algebraische) Mannigfaltigkeit *f*, normale Varietät *f*	variété *f* normale (absolument normale), *k*-variété *f* normale	нормальное многообразие
N 667	**normal variety** <UA>	normale Mannigfaltigkeit (Varietät) *f*	variété *f* normale	нормальное многообразие
N 668	**normal vector** <of a curve> <DG>	Normalvektor *m*, Normalenvektor *m*	vecteur *m* normal (de la normale)	вектор нормали
N 669	**normal vector,** unit normal vector, unit normal, normal unit vector <of a surface> <DG>	Normalvektor *m*, Normaleneinheitsvektor *m*, Normalenvektor *m*	vecteur *m* normal (unitaire normal, unitaire de la normale), normale-unité *f*	вектор нормали, единичный вектор нормали, орт нормали, нормальный единичный вектор, единичный нормальный вектор
N 670	**norm axioms** <FA>	Axiome *npl* für eine Norm, Normaxiome *npl*	axiomes *mpl* d'une norme	аксиомы нормы
N 671	**normed algebra** <AL>	normierte (bewertete) Algebra *f*	algèbre *f* normée	нормированная алгебра, алгебра с нормой
N 672	**normed algebra,** normed ring <FA>	normierte Algebra *f*	algèbre *f* normée, anneau *m* normé	нормированное кольцо, нормированная алгебра
	normed algebra with an involution <FA>	*s.* S 272		
N 673	**normed linear space,** normed vector space, normed space <FA, TO>	normierter linearer Raum *m*, normierter Vektorraum *m* (Raum), linearer normierter Raum	espace *m* linéaire normé, espace [vectoriel] normé, espace muni d'une norme	нормированное линейное пространство, нормированное [векторное] пространство; пространство, снабженное нормой; пространство, в котором введена норма
	normed polynomial <AL>	*s.* M 832		
N 674	**normed random variable,** normed variate <ST>	normierte Zufallsgröße (Zufallsvariable) *f*	variable *f* [aléatoire] normée	нормированная случайная величина
	normed random variable <ST>	*s. a.* S 1626		
	normed ring <FA>	*s.* N 672		
	normed space <FA, TO>	*s.* N 673		
	normed variable <ST>	*s.* S 1626		
	normed variate <ST>	*s.* 1. N 674; 2. S 1626		
	normed vector space <FA, TO>	*s.* N 673		
N 675/6	**norm factor group** <AB>	Normfaktorgruppe *f*, Normenfaktorgruppe *f*	groupe *m* quotient par le groupe des normes	норменная факторгруппа
N 677	**norm form** <on *A* over *Γ*> <AL, NT>	Normform *f* <auf einer Algebra>	forme *f* norme (normique) <d'ordre *i*>, // forme décomposable	норменная форма, // разложимая форма
N 678	**norm group** <in class field theory> <AB>	Normengruppe *f*	groupe *m* des normes	группа норм, норменная подгруппа
N 679	**norm homomorphism** <of a Clifford group> <GR>	Normenhomomorphismus *m*	homomorphisme *m* normique	норменный гомоморфизм
N 680	**norm isomorphism** <FA>	Normisomorphismus *m*, normisomorphe Abbildung *f*	isomorphisme *m* conservant la norme	изоморфизм, сохраняющий норму
N 681	**normit** <ST>	Normit *n*	normit *m*	нормит
N 682	**norm mapping** <AL, NT>	Normabbildung *f*, Normoperation *f*	application *f* norme, opération *f* de norme	норменное отображение
N 683	**norm metric** <on an inner product space> <FA, TO>	Normmetrik *f*	métrique *f* définie par la norme	метрика, определенная нормой
N 684	**norm nonresidue** <AB>	Normennichtrest *m*	non-résidu *m* de norme	норменный невычет
	norm of a linear mapping <FA>	*s.* M 104		
N 685	**norm-preserving mapping** <AN>	normerhaltende Abbildung *f*	application *f* conservant la norme	сохраняющее норму отображение
N 686	**norm-preserving prolongation** <FA>	normerhaltende Fortsetzung *f*	prolongement *m* conservant la norme	сохраняющее норму продолжение
N 687	**norm residue** <AL>	Normenrest *m*	reste *m* normique, résidu *m* de norme	норменный вычет, нормвычет
N 688	**norm residue relatively prime to *m*** <AB>	primer Normenrest modulo *m*	reste *m* normique premier à *m*	простой норменный вычет по модулю *m*
N 689	**norm residue symbol,** norm symbol <AB>	Normenrestsymbol *n*, Normsymbol *n*	symbole *m* de reste normique, symbole de restes normiques	символ норменного вычета
	norm symbol <AB>	*s.* N 689		
N 690	**norm theorem** <AB>	Normensatz *m*	théorème *m* sur la norme, théorème normique	теорема о нормах
N 691	**norm topology,** uniform [operator] topology <FA>	Normtopologie *f*, gleichmäßige Topologie *f*, uniforme Operatortopologie *f*	topologie *f* définie par la norme	равномерная операторная топология, нормированная топология
	norm topology <TO>	*s.* S 2003		
	north-west corner <PG>	*s.* U 426		
N 692	**northwest-corner (North-West corner) rule** <in transport optimization> <GP, PG>	Nordwesteckenregel *f*		правило северно-западного угла

No.	English	Deutsch	Français	Русский
N 693	**Norwich['s] spiral** <GE>	Sturmsche Spirale *f*, Spirale von Norwich, Norwichs Spirale	spirale *f* de Norwich	спираль Штурма (Норвича)
	not an *n*-th power remainder <NT>	*s.* N 744		
	not a subset / to be <SE>	*s.* N 698a		
N 694	**notation** <GN>	Bezeichnung *f*	notation *f*	обозначение
N 695	**notation,** scoring <ST>	Bonitur *f*	notation *f*	бонитировка
N 696	**notation** <of a number> **in form of a nonterminating decimal** <NT>	Darstellung *f* <einer Zahl> als unendlicher Dezimalbruch	figuration *f* infinie	представление <числа> в виде бесконечной десятичной дроби
N 697	**notation** <of a number> **in form of a periodic decimal** <NT>	Darstellung *f* <einer Zahl> als periodischer Dezimalbruch	figuration *f* infinie périodique	представление <числа> в виде периодической десятичной дроби
N 698	**notation of Pringsheim** <of continued fractions> <NT>	Pringsheimsche Bezeichnung *f*	notation *f* de Pringsheim	обозначение Прингсгейма
	notation without brackets <LO>	*s.* P 163		
	not equal <GN>	*s.* U 94		
	. . . not equivalent to . . . <LO>	*s.* O 254		
	NOT-IF-THEN <LO>	*s.* E 686		
N 698a	**not included** <in a set> / **to be,** to be not a subset <of a set>, $\subsetneq$, $\not\subset$ <SE>	nicht enthalten sein <in einer Menge>, nicht Untermenge sein <von einer Menge>, $\subsetneq$, $\not\subset$	n'être pas inclus (contenu) <dans un ensemble>, n'être pas une partie <d'un ensemble>, $\subsetneq$, $\not\subset$	не содержаться, $\subsetneq$, $\not\subset$
N 699	**notion of between** <GE> ┌<GN>	„zwischen"-Begriff *m*, Zwischenbegriff *m*	notion *f* « entre »	понятие «между»
	notion of the infinite	*s.* C 1778		
	. . . not materially equivalent to . . . <LO>	*s.* O 254		
	not separable polynomial <AL>	*s.* I 586		
	not simply connected space <TO>	*s.* M 1069		
N 700	**novenic surface** <AG>	Fläche *f* neunter Ordnung	surface *f* de degré neuf (9)	поверхность девятой степени
N 701	**nowhere commutative semigroup** <AL>	antikommutative Halbgruppe *f*	demi-groupe *m* anti-commutatif	антикоммутативная полугруппа
N 702	**nowhere convergent sequence** <SS, TO>	nirgends konvergente Folge *f*	suite *f* nulle part convergente	всюду расходящаяся последовательность
N 703	**nowhere convergent series** <SS, TO>	nirgends konvergente Reihe *f*	série *f* nulle part convergente	всюду расходящийся ряд
N 704	**nowhere dense set, nowhere-dense set,** nondense set <TO>	nirgends[]dichte Menge *f*, nirgends[]dichte Punktmenge *f*, rare Menge	ensemble *m* rare, ensemble partout non dense, ensemble nulle part dense, ensemble non dense, ensemble dense nulle part	нигде не плотное множество, нигде не плотное точечное множество, разреженное множество
N 705	**nowhere dense subset, nowhere-dense subset,** nondense subset <TO>	nirgends[]dichte Untermenge (Teilmenge) *f*	partie *f* rare, sous-ensemble *m* nulle part dense, ensemble *m* rare	нигде не плотное подмножество
N 706	**nowhere differentiable function** <FA>	nirgends differenzierbare Funktion *f*	fonction *f* sans dérivée, fonction nulle part dérivable	нигде не дифференцируемая функция; функция, не имеющая производной ни в одной точке
N 707	***n*-parameter family** <GE>	*n*-parametrige Schar *f*	famille *f* à *n* paramètres	*n*-параметрическое семейство
N 708	***n*-parameter Lie group** <GR>	*n*-parametrige (*n*-gliedrige) Liesche Gruppe *f*	groupe *m* de Lie à *n* paramètres	*n*-параметрическая группа Ли
N 709	***n*-parameter linear system,** [linear] system of dimension *n* <AG>	lineares System *n* *n*-ter Stufe, *n*-fach unendliches lineares System, ∞^n-System *n*, lineares System von der Dimension *n*, lineares System von der Mannigfaltigkeitsstufe *n*	système *m* linéaire ponctuel de rang *n*, système linéaire de *n*-e espèce	линейная система размерности *n*
N 710	***n*-parametric complex continuous group** <GR>	kontinuierliche Gruppe *f* von *n* komplexen Parametern, [*n*-parametrige] komplexe kontinuierliche Gruppe	groupe *m* continu complexe de *n* paramètres	непрерывная группа от *n* комплексных параметров
N 711	***n*-parametric continuous group** <GR>	kontinuierliche Gruppe *f* von *n* Parametern, *n*-parametrige (*n*-gliedrige) Gruppe	groupe *m* continu de *n* paramètres	непрерывная группа от *n* параметров
N 712	***n*-partite graph** <GP>	*n*-fach teilbarer Graph *m*	graphe *m* *n*-parti	*n*-дольный граф
N 713	***n*-person game** <TG>	*n*-Personen-Spiel *n*	jeu *m* à *n* personnes	игра *n* лиц
	***n*-place function letter** <LO, MM>	*s.* F 779		
N 714	***n*-place number,** *n*-digit number <NT>	*n*-stellige (*n*-ziffrige) Zahl *f*	nombre *m* [naturel] de *n* chiffres	*n*-значное (*n*-разрядное) число
	***n*-place operation** <UA>	*s.* N 15		
	***n*-place predicate** <LO>	*s.* P 1189		
	***n*-place relation** <CA, SE>	*s.* N 17		
N 715	***n*-plane bundle,** *n*-dimensional real vector bundle, *n*-dimensional real vector bundle <AT>	*n*-dimensionales reelles Vektorraumbündel *n*	espace *m* fibré à fibre vectorielle réelle *n*-dimensionnelle	действительное *n*-мерное векторное расслоение
	***n*-ple** <AL, SE>	*s.* N 750		
N 716	***n*-ply periodic function,** *n* times periodic function, function periodic *n* times <AN>	*n*-fach periodische Funktion *f*	fonction *f* *n* fois périodique	*n*-кратно периодическая функция, *n*-периодическая функция

No.	English	German	French	Russian
N 717	**(N,p_n) lim[it],** limit by Nörlund's method <LI>	(N,p_n)-Limes *m*, Limes *m* nach dem (N,p_n)-Verfahren, (N,p_n)-lim	(N,p_n)-limite *f*, limite *f* par la méthode de Nörlund, (N,p_n)-lim	[обобщенный] предел по методу Вороного, [обобщенный] предел по Вороному
N 718	**(N,p_n) limitable sequence,** sequence limitable by Nörlund's method <LI>	(N,p_n)-limitierbare (nach dem (N,p_n)-Verfahren limitierbare) Folge *f*	suite *f* limitable par la méthode de Nörlund, suite (N,p_n)-limitable	последовательность, лимитируемая методом Вороного
	(N,p_n) method <LI>	*s.* 1. N 522; 2. N 524		
N 719	**(N,p_n) sum,** sum by Nörlund's method <LI>	(N,p_n)-Summe *f*, Summe *f* nach dem (N,p_n)-Verfahren	(N,p_n)-somme *f*, somme *f* par la méthode de Nörlund	[обобщенная] сумма по методу Вороного, [обобщенная] сумма по Вороному
N 720	**(N,p_n)-summable series,** series summable by Nörlund's method <LI>	(N,p_n)-summierbare (nach dem (N,p_n)-Verfahren summierbare) Reihe *f*	série *f* sommable par la méthode de Nörlund, série (N,p_n)-sommable	суммируемый методом Вороного ряд
N 721	***n*-point contact** <GE>	*n*-punktige Berührung *f*	contact *m* à *n* points	*n*-кратное касание
N 722	***N*-product** <GR>	*N*-Produkt *n*	*N*-produit *m*	*N*-произведение
N 723	***n*-rowed [square] matrix,** *n* by *n* square matrix, *n* by *n* matrix, *n*-by-*n* matrix, *n* by *n* array, square matrix of order *n*, matrix of degree *n*, *n*-th order matrix <MD>	*n*-reihige quadratische Matrix *f*, quadratische Matrix der Ordnung *n*, *n*-gliedrige quadratische Matrix	matrice *f* carrée de degré *n*, matrice carrée d'ordre *n*	квадратная матрица порядка *n*, квадратная матрица *n*-го порядка
	***n*-section** <AT>	*s.* N 66		
	***n*-set** <SE>	*s.* N 143		
	N-set <TO>	*s.* C 2644		
N 724	***n*-sheeted surface** <TO>	*n*-blättrige Fläche *f*	surface *f* à *n* feuilles	*n*-листная поверхность
N 725	***n*-sided pyramid** <EG>	*n*-seitige Pyramide *f*	pyramide *f* à *n* arêtes	*n*-угольная пирамида
N 726	***n*-simplex,** *n*-dimensional simplex <TO>	*n*-Simplex *n*, *n*-dimensionales Simplex *n*	*n*-simplexe *m*, simplexe *m* de dimension *n*	*n*-мерный симплекс
N 727	***n*-soluble group** <AL>	*n*-auflösbare Gruppe *f*	groupe *m* *n*-résoluble	*n*-разрешимая группа
N 728	***n*-space,** *n*-dimensional space <GE, TO>	*n*-dimensionaler Raum *m*	espace *m* à *n* dimensions, espace d'ordre *n*	*n*-мерное пространство, пространство *n* измерений
N 729	***n*-sphere,** S^n <GE, TO>	*n*-dimensionale Sphäre *f*, *n*-Sphäre *f*; *n*-dimensionaler sphärischer Raum *m*	*n*-sphère *f*	*n*-мерная сфера
	***n*-sphere** <TO>	*s.* T 537		
N 730	***n*-sphere bundle** <AT>	Bündel *n* von *n*-Sphären	espace *m* fibré, fibré en *n*-sphères	расслоение на *n*-мерные сферы
N 731	***n*-termed module of linear forms** <AL>	*n*-gliedriger Linearformenmodul *m*	module *m* de formes linéaires à *n* paramètres	*n*-членный модуль линейных форм
	***n*-termed sequence** <AL, SE>	*s.* N 750		
N 732	***n*-th cohomology group** <AT, HA>	*n*-te (*n*-dimensionale) Kohomologiegruppe *f*	groupe *m* de cohomologie pour la dimension *n*	*n*-мерная ∇-группа, *n*-мерная верхняя группа Бетти, группа ∇^n <AT>; *n*-я группа когомологий, группа когомологий размерности *n* <AT, HA>
N 733	***n*-th column** <of a matrix> <MD>	*n*-te Spalte (Kolonne) *f*, Spalte vom Index *n*	colonne *f* de rang *n*, *n*-e colonne, colonne d'indice *n*	*n*-й столбец
N 734	***n*-th cyclotomic polynomial,** cyclotomic polynomial of order *n* <AL>	*n*-tes Kreisteilungspolynom *n*	polynôme *m* cyclotomique d'indice *n*	*n*-й круговой многочлен, многочлен деления круга на *n* равных частей
N 735	***n*-th denominator,** denominator of the *n*-th convergent <of a continued fraction> <NT>	*n*-ter Näherungsnenner *m*	dénominateur *m* de la *n*-e réduite	знаменатель подходящей дроби порядка *n*
N 736	***n*-th homology group** <AT, HA>	*n*-te (*n*-dimensionale) Homologiegruppe *f*	groupe *m* d'homologie pour la dimension *n*	*n*-я группа гомологий, группа гомологий размерности *n* <AT, HA>; *n*-я $\triangle$-группа, *n*-мерная группа Бетти <AT>
N 737	***n*-th homotopy group,** *n*-dimensional homotopy group <TO>	*n*-te (*n*-dimensionale) Homotopiegruppe *f*	*n*-e groupe *m* d'homotopie	*n*-я гомотопическая группа
	***n*-th mean value theorem** <DI>	*s.* T 102		
N 738	***n*-th member,** *n*-th term <of a sequence> <SS>	*n*-tes Glied *n*	terme *m* de rang *n*, *n*-e terme, ennième terme	*n*-й член
N 739	***n*-th member of the upper central series** <GR>	*n*-tes Glied *n* der aufsteigenden Zentralfolge	*n*-e ensemble (groupe) *m* central, *n*-e centre *m*, centre d'ordre *n*	*n*-й член возрастающего центрального ряда
N 740	***n*-th Miquel polygon** <GE>	*n*-tes Miquel-Vieleck (Fußpunktvieleck) *n*	*n*-e polygone *m* de Miquel	*n*-й многоугольник Микеля
N 741	***n*-th numerator,** numerator of the *n*-th convergent <of a continued fraction> <NT>	*n*-ter Näherungszähler *m*	numérateur *m* de la *n*-e réduite	числитель подходящей дроби порядка *n*
	***n*-th order matrix** <MD>	*s.* N 723		
N 742	***n*-th partial quotient** <of a continued fraction> <NT>	*n*-ter Teilbruch *m*, *n*-tes Glied *n*	*n*-e fraction *f* partielle (composante), $(n+1)$-e terme *m*	*n*-е звено, звено *n*-го порядка
N 743	***n*-th partial sum** <of a series> <SS>	*n*-te Partialsumme (Teilsumme) *f*	somme *f* à l'ordre *n*	частичная сумма *n*-го порядка, *n*-я частичная сумма
	$(n-2)$-th polar <AG>	*s.* P 845		

No.	English	German	French	Russian
N 744	**n-th power non-residue,** not an n-th power remainder, n-ic non-residue <NT>	n-ter Potenznichtrest *m*	n-e non-résidu *m*, non-reste *f* de puissance n	невычет степени n
N 745	**n-th power operation** <AT>	Operation *f* der Erhebung in die n-te Potenz	opération *f* puissance n-e	возведение в n-ю степень
N 746	**n-th power residue symbol,** power residue symbol of the n-th order <NT>	n-tes Potenzrestsymbol *n*	symbole *m* de n-e puissance, symbole de puissance n-e	символ вычета степени n
	n-th projection <AL, SE>	s. P 1657		
N 747	**n-th root** <AL>	n-te Wurzel *f*, Wurzel n-ten Grades	n-e racine *f*, racine d'indice n, racine du degré n, racine n (n-e)	корень (радикал) n-ой степени
N 748	**n-th series of Lamé,** Lamé['s] series of n-th order, series of Lamé of n-th order <NT>	Laméscbe Reihe *f* n-ter Ordnung, Laméscbe Zahlenreihe *f* n-ter Ordnung	suite (série) *f* de Lamé d'ordre n	последовательность Ламе порядка n
	n-th subgroup of cycles <AT, HA>	s. G 489		
	n-th term <SS>	s. N 738		
N 749	**n times continuously differentiable function** <DI>	n-mal stetig differenzierbare Funktion *f*	fonction *f* n fois continûment différentiable (dérivable), fonction dérivable de classe C^n	n раз непрерывно дифференцируемая функция
	n times periodic function <AN>	s. N 716		
N 750	**n-tuple,** n-tuplet, ordered n-tuple[t], ordered sequence of n terms, ordered sample of n elements, n-termed sequence, n-ple <AL, SE>	n-Tupel *n*, geordnetes n-Tupel *n*, geordneter Komplex *m* von n Elementen, Cortege *n* vom Rang n	n-uplet *m*, n-tuple *m*, cortège *m*, suite *f* de n objets, séquence *f* de n éléments, séquence de degré n	n-набор, n-ка, упорядоченная n-ка, упорядоченный комплекс из n элементов, кортеж, набор из n элементов; набор из n чисел
N 751	**n-tuple complex** <AL>	n-facher Komplex *m*	complexe *m* n-uple	n-кратный комплекс
	n-tuplet <AL, SE>	s. N 750		
N 752	**n-tuply connected domain** <TO>	n-fach zusammenhängendes Gebiet *n*	domaine *m* n-connexe	n-связная область
N 753	**n-tuply ordered set** <Cantor> <SE>	n-fach geordnete Menge *f*	ensemble *m* n fois ordonné	n-кратно упорядоченное множество
N 754	**n-tuply well-ordered set** <Lindenbaum> <SE>	n-fach wohlgeordnete Menge *f*	ensemble *m* n fois bien ordonné	n-кратно вполне упорядоченное множество
N 755	**nuclear operator** <FA>	nuklearer Operator *m*	opérateur *m* nucléaire	ядерный оператор
N 756	**nuclear space** <FA>	nuklearer Raum *m*	espace *m* nucléaire	ядерное пространство
N 757	**nucleolus** <TG>	Nukleolus *m*		n-ядро
N 758	**nucleus** <of a set> <TO>	insichdichter Kern *m*	noyau *m*	плотное в себе ядро
	nucleus <IE>	s. 1. F 595; 2. K 50		
N 759	**nuisance parameter,** deranging parameter <ST>	lästiger (störender) Parameter *m*	paramètre *m* dérangeant	мешающий параметр
	null <AL, AN>	s. Z 18		
N 760	**nullary function** <UA>	nullstellige Funktion *f*	fonction *f* nullaire (à aucune place)	нульместная функция
N 761	**nullary operation,** 0-ary operation <UA>	nullstellige (nulläre) Operation *f*	opération *f* interne nullaire	нульарная (0-арная) операция, 0-арный (постоянный) оператор
N 762	**nullary partial operation** <UA>	nullstellige partielle [algebraische] Verknüpfung *f*, nullstellige partielle Operation *f*	opération *f* partielle interne nullaire	нульарная частичная операция
N 763/4	**nullary polynomial** <UA>	nulläres Polynom *n*	polynôme *m* nullaire	нульарный многочлен
	null circle <AY>	s. P 727		
N 765	**null-class,** empty class, void class <LO, SE>	leere Klasse *f*, Nullklasse *f*	classe *f* vide	пустой (нулевой) класс
	null curve <DG>	s. I 1194		
N 766	**null divisor,** divisor of zeros <of an algebraic function field> <AL, FT>	Nullstellendivisor *m*, Zählerdivisor *m*	diviseur *m* des zéros	дивизор нулей
	null element <AL>	s. 1. Z 14; 2. Z 17		
	null element <LA>	s. Z 31		
N 767	**null ellipse,** point ellipse <AY>	Punktellipse *f*	ellipse *f* réduite à un point	эллипс, выродившийся в точку; нулевой эллипс
N 768	**null expansion** <FD, NU>	Nullentwicklung *f*, Nulldarstellung *f* <Newtonsche Interpolationsreihe>	développement *m* nul	нулевое разложение
N 769	**null-form** <in a local ring> <AL>	Nullform *f*	forme *f* nulle	нулевая форма
N 770	**Null (null) form, null-form** <indefinite form capable to represent the zero element> <AL>	Nullform *f*, quadratische Nullform	forme *f* annulable; forme nulle	нулевая форма
N 771	**null-form** <binary or ternary quadratic form all the invariants of which are equal to zero> <IV>	Nullform *f*	forme *f* nulle	нулевая форма
N 772	**null formula** <LO>	leere Formel *f*	formule *f* vide	пустая формула
	null function <AN>	s. Z 32		
N 773	**null geodesic,** minimal geodesic curve <DG>	Nullgeodätische *f*	géodésique *f* isotrope	изотропная геодезическая
	null homotopic (null homotopic) map <TO>	s. H 513		

No.	English	German	French	Russian
	null-homotopic mapping <TO>	*s.* H 513		
N 774	**null[-]homotopic path** <TO>	nullhomotoper Weg *m*, Weg homotop Null (0)	lacet *m* homotope à un point	гомотопный нулю путь, гомотопно тривиальный путь
N 775	**null homotopy** <TO>	Nullhomotopie *f*	homotopie *f* à zéro	гомотопия в постоянное отображение
N 776	**null hypersphere** <AY>	entartete Hyperkugel *f*, Nullsphäre *f*	hypersphère *f* de rayon nul	нулевая гиперсфера
N 777	**null hypothesis** <ST>	Nullhypothese *f*, Testhypothese *f*	hypothèse *f* nulle	нулевая (основная) гипотеза
	null ideal <AL>	*s.* Z 35		
	nullify / to <GN>	*s.* E 334		
N 778	**nullity** <of a linear mapping of a vector space> <AL>	Defekt *m*	défaut *m*	дефект
N 779	**nullity** <dimension of the null space of a linear operator> <FA>	Nulldefekt *m*, Nullzahl *f*	nullité *f*	дефект
N 780	**nullity** <of a matrix> <MD>	Rangdefekt *m*, Rangabfall *m*, Nullität *f*, Defekt *m*, Exzeß *m*	nullité *f*, défaut *m*, ordre *m* de la dégénérescence	дефект
N 781	**nullity** <of a critical point *or* a critical extremal> <VA>	Rangdefekt *m*	nullité *f*	степень вырождения
	nullity <GP>	*s.* C 2891		
N 782	**null line** <of a vector system> <GE>	Nullgerade *f*, Nullstrahl *m*	droite *f* nulle	нулевая прямая
N 783	**null matrix,** zero matrix <MD>	Nullmatrix *f*	matrice *f* nulle (zéro), // matrice zéroïdale	нулевая матрица, нуль-матрица
N 784	**null object,** terminal object <CA>	terminales Objekt *n*, Endobjekt *n*, Punktobjekt *n*, Ende *n*, Punkt *m*	∅-produit *m*, objet *m* final	терминальный (финальный) объект, правый нуль, конечный объект
	null object <CA>	*s.* Z 44		
N 785	**null plane** <AY, PJ>	Nullebene *f*	plan *m* nul	нулевая плоскость, нуль-плоскость
	null plane <DG>	*s.* F 713		
N 786	**null point** <for a null system> <AY, PJ>	Nullpunkt *m*	point *m* nul	нулевая точка, нуль-точка
	null polarity <PJ>	*s.* N 801		
N 787	**null polynomial,** zero polynomial <AL>	Nullpolynom *n*	polynôme *m* nul	нуль-многочлен
	null quadric <AY>	*s.* I 101		
	null-radical <AL>	*s.* N 256		
N 788	**null ray** <of a null system> <PJ>	Nullstrahl *m*, Direktrix *f*, Leitstrahl *m*	rayon *m* directeur	нулевой луч
N 789	**null-recurrent state** <SP>	nullrekurrenter Zustand *m*, Nullzustand *m*, N-Zustand *m*, RN-Zustand *m*	état *m* nul récurrent	нулевое возвратное состояние
	null relation <SE>	*s.* E 215		
N 790	**null representation** <AL>	Nulldarstellung *f*	représentation *f* nulle	нулевое представление
N 791	**null representation module** <AL>	Nulldarstellungsmodul *m*	module *m* de représentation nulle	модуль нулевого представления
N 792	**nullring, null ring** <AL>	Nullring *m*	anneau *m* réduit à 0 (zéro)	нулевое кольцо
	null semigroup <AL>	*s.* Z 59		
N 793	**null sequence,** sequence tending to zero <SS>	Nullfolge *f*; Folge *f*, die unendlich klein wird	suite *f* convergeant vers zéro (0), suite tendant vers [le] zéro, suite nulle, // suite élémentaire <Heine>, variante *f* infiniment petite <Méray>	нулевая (стремящаяся к нулю) последовательность, нуль-последовательность, 0-последовательность
	null set <ME>	*s.* S 666		
	null-set, null set <SE>	*s.* V 204		
N 794	**null sheaf,** zero sheaf <AL, AT>	Nullgarbe *f*, konstante Garbe *f* des Nullmoduls	faisceau *m* nul	нулевой пучок
N 795	**null solution** <FA, IE>	Nullösung *f*	solution *f* nulle	нулевое решение
N 796	**null space** <with respect to a symmetric form> <AL>	Nullraum *m* <bezüglich einer symmetrischen Form>	espace *m* zéro <par rapport à une forme symétrique>	нуль-пространство <относительно симметрической формы>
N 797	**null[-] space,** kernel <of a linear transformation> <AL, FA>	Nullraum *m*	espace *m* zéro, noyau *m*	нуль-пространство, нуль-простанство, ядро
	null sphere <AY>	*s.* P 792		
N 798/9	**Nullstellenkörper,** zero field <AL>	Nullstellenkörper *m*	corps *m* de zéros	поле нулей
N 800	**Nullstellensatz,** theorem on zeros <AL>	Nullstellensatz *m*	Nullstellensatz *m*, théorème *m* des zéros	теорема о нулях вой шар
	null subspace <AL>	*s.* S 296		
	null surface <DG>	*s.* F 714		
N 801	**null system,** null polarity <PJ>	Nullsystem *n*, Nullkorrelation *f*	système *m* nul	нулевая система
N 802	**null transformation** <AN>	Nulltransformation *f*	transformation *f* nulle	нулевое преобразование (отображение)
	null variation <RF>	*s.* Z 67		
	null variety <DG>	*s.* F 715		
	null variety <UA>	*s.* Z 68		
N 803	**null vector,** zero vector <VT>	Nullvektor *m*	vecteur *m* nul (zéro)	нулевой вектор, нуль-вектор, нульвектор
	null vector <AL>	*s.* Z 30		
N 804	**number π;** Ludolphian number, Ludolph['s] number <AN, GE>	Zahl *f* π; Ludolfsche Zahl, Ludolfine *f*, Ludolphische Zahl	nombre *m* π; nombre d'Archimède, Ludolfin *m*, nombre de Ludolf	число π; лудолфово число
	number <MD>	*s.* I 341		
	number <SS>	*s.* I 345		
	δ-number <SE>	*s.* D 212		

	γ-number <SE>	*s.* G 43		
	ε-number <SE>	*s.* E 315		
	number axis <AN, SE>	*s.* N 872		
	number-class, number class <SE>	*s.* C 124		
N 805	**number code** <NU>	Zahlencode *m*	code *m* numérique	цифровой код
	number congruent 0 mod 4 <NT>	*s.* N 852		
N 806	**number consisting of the last k digits** <NT>	aus den letzten k Stellen gebildete Zahl *f*	nombre *m* formé par les k derniers chiffres à droite	последняя k-циферная грань, k-циферное окончание <числа>
N 807	**number consisting of the last two digits** <NT>	aus den letzten beiden Stellen gebildete Zahl *f*	nombre *m* formé par les deux derniers chiffres à droite	двуциферное окончание <числа>
	number couple <AL>	*s.* N 834		
N 808	**number defined by the Dedekind cut** <AN>	Schnittzahl *f*, Dedekindsche Schnittzahl	nombre *m* section	рубеж <сечения Дедекинда>
N 809	**number domain** <NT>	Zahlenbereich *m*, Zahlengebiet *n*	domaine *m* de nombres	числовая область
	number domain <NT>	*s. a.* N 811		
	number domain of all rational numbers <AL>	*s.* F 197 *a*		
	number domain of all real numbers <AL>	*s.* F 198		
	number e <AN>	*s.* E 1		
N 810	**numbered set** <SE>	numerierte (durchnumerierte) Menge *f*	ensemble *m* numéroté	занумерованное множество
	number example <GN>	*s.* N 888		
N 811	**number field,** number domain <NT>	Zahlkörper *m*, Zahlenkörper *m*, arithmetischer Körper *m*	corps *m* de nombres, corps numérique (arithmétique)	числовое поле
	number field <NT>	*s. a.* A 451		
	number field with Archimedean ordering <AL>	*s.* A 901		
	number group <NT>	*s.* B 507		
	number indecomposable with respect to addition <SE>	*s.* P 1285		
	numbering <GN>	*s.* C 2229		
	numbering <SE>	*s.* N 861		
N 812	**number interval** <DI>	Zahlenintervall *n*	intervalle *m* de nombres	числовой сегмент (интервал)
	number language <FO>	*s.* N 860		
	number line <AN, SE>	*s.* N 872		
N 813	**number[-]manifold** <AL>	Zahlenmannigfaltigkeit *f* <im Sinne von Lie>	variété *f* de nombres	многообразие чисел
N 814	**number module** <NT>	Zahlenmodul *m*	module *m* de nombres	числовой модуль
N 815	**number notation,** number representation <NT, NU>	Zahlendarstellung *f*, Zahldarstellung *f*	représentation *f* des nombres, notation *f* des nombres	представление числа, представление чисел
N 816	**number of boundaries** <TO>	Ränderzahl *f*	nombre *m* de bords	число границ
N 817	**number of classes,** class number <ST>	Klassenzahl *f*, Anzahl *f* der Klassen	nombre *m* des classes	число классов, количество классов
N 818	**number of columns** <of a matrix> <MD>	Spaltenzahl *f*	longueur *f* nombre *m* de colonnes	число столбцов
N 819	**number of compositions** <NT>	Kompositionsanzahl *f*, Zergliederungsanzahl *f*	nombre *m* de compositions	количество композиций
	number of digits <NT>	*s.* N 827		
N 820	**number of divisors** <of a number> <NT>	Teileranzahl *f*	nombre *m* de diviseurs	число делителей
N 821	**number of elements** <of a regular multiplet> <SE>	Elementezahl *f* <eines Tupels>	degré *m* <d'une séquence>	число элементов <кортежа>
	number of elements <AL>	*s.* O 257		
N 822	**number of external stability,** domination (dominance, edge independence) number <GP>	äußere Stabilitätszahl *f*	nombre *m* d'absorption, nombre de stabilité externe	число внешней устойчивости, реберное число независимости
N 823	**number of figures** <AR, NU>	Ziffernzahl *f*, Zahlenlänge *f*	nombre *m* de chiffres	длина числа, количество цифр
	number of first kind <SE>	*s.* N 410		
N 824	**number of ideal classes in the restricted sense** <AB>	Idealklassenzahl *f* im engeren Sinne	nombre *m* de classes d'idéaux au sens restreint	число классов идеалов в узком смысле
N 825	**number of inversions** <in a permutation> <AL, CT>	Anzahl *f* der Inversionen, Inversionsanzahl *f*, Inversionszahl *f*	nombre *m* d'inversions (des inversions)	число инверсий, число беспорядков
	number of permutations <CT>	*s.* N 828		
N 826	**number of Picard** <AL>	Picardsche Zahl *f*	nombre *m* de Picard	число Пикара
N 827	**number of places,** number of digits <of a number> <NT>	Stellenzahl *f*	nombre *m* des chiffres, index *m*	число разрядов, количество разрядов, число знаков
N 828	**number of reorderings,** number of permutations <CT>	Anzahl *f* der Anordnungen (Permutationen)	nombre *m* des permutations	число подстановок
N 829	**number of repetitions (replications)** <ST>	Wiederholungszahl *f*	nombre *m* de répétitions	число повторений
N 830	**number of rows** <of a matrix> <MD>	Zeilenzahl *f*	hauteur *f*, nombre *m* de lignes	число строк

N 831	**number of sheets,** multiplicity <of a covering projection> <AT>	Blätterzahl *f*, Blätteranzahl *f*, Vielfachheit *f* der Überlagerung	nombre *m* de feuilles	число листов, кратность
	number of signed fixed points <AT>	*s.* A 452		
	number of the first class <SE>	*s.* F 306		
	number of the first kind <SE>	*s.* N 410		
N 832	**number of the form $2^{n+1}(2m+1)$** <NT>	ungerad-gerade Zahl *f*, Zahl der Form $2^{n+1}(2m+1)$	nombre *m* impairement pair	целое число вида $2^{n+1}(2m+1)$
	number of the form $4n+2$ <NT>	*s.* N 853		
	number of the second class <SE>	*s.* O 377		
	number of the second kind <SE>	*s.* L 743		
	number of turns <FT, TO>	*s.* W 264		
N 833	**number of variations [in sign], number of variations of sign** <AL>	Anzahl *f* der Zeichenwechsel	nombre *m* des variations (changements de signe)	число перемен [знаков]
	number operator <DE>	*s.* N 899		
N 834	**number pair,** number couple, pair of numbers <AL>	Zahlenpaar *n*	paire *f* (couple *m*) de nombres, nombre *m* binaire <Pasch>	пара чисел
	number plane <AN, GE>	*s.* E 566		
	number plane <FT>	*s.* A 937		
N 835	**number polygon** <NT>	Zahlenpolygon *n*, Zahlenvieleck *n*	polygone *m* arithmétique	арифметический многоугольник
N 836	**number ray** <NT>	Zahlenstrahl *m*, Zahlstrahl *m*	rayon *m* de nombres	положительная полуось
	number representation <NT, NU>	*s.* N 815		
	number representation system <NT>	*s.* N 842		
	number ring <NT>	*s.* R 1328		
N 837	**number scale,** scale <GN>	Zahlenfolge *f*, // Zahlenreihe *f*	suite *f* numérique (de nombres), série *f* numérique	ряд чисел, последовательность чисел
	number scale <AN, SE>	*s.* N 872		
	number scale <NT>	*s.* C 1538		
N 838	**number scheme** <GN>	Zahlenschema *n*	schéma *m* de nombres	числовая схема
	number series <SS>	*s.* N 903		
	number set <NT>	*s.* S 670		
	numbers prime to each other <NT>	*s.* C 2447		
N 839	**number square** <NT>	Zahlenquadrat *n*, Zahlenviereck *n*	carré *m* arithmétique	арифметический квадрат
N 840	**numbers relatively prime in pairs,** coprime (mutually relatively prime) numbers <NT>	paarweise relativ prime Zahlen *fpl*, paarweise teilerfremde Zahlen	nombres *mpl* sans diviseur commun deux à deux, nombres premiers deux à deux	попарно [взаимно] простые числа
	number symbol <NT>	*s.* F 216		
N 841	**number symbolism** <GN>	Zahlensymbolik *f*	symbolisme *m* de nombres	числовая символика
N 842	**number system,** system of numbers, numeration, [system], number representation system, numeral system <in the base *n*> <NT>	Zahlensystem *n*, Numerationssystem *n*, Zahlsystem *n* <zur Basis *n*>	système *m* de nombres (numérotation, numération), système numérique <à (de) base *n*>	числовая система, система представления чисел, система счисления (нумерации) <по основанию *n*>
N 843	**number tetraeder** <AL>	Zahlentetraeder *n*	tétraèdre *m* arithmétique	арифметический тетраэдр
N 844	**number the logarithm of which has to be taken** <AR>	Logarithmand *m* <zu logarithmierende Zahl>	nombre *m* dont le logarithme est cherché	логарифмируемое число
N 845	**number-theoretic[al]** <NT>	zahlentheoretisch	d'après la théorie des nombres, au sens de la théorie des nombres	теоретико-числовой
N 846	**number-theoretical case** <AL>	zahlentheoretischer Fall *m*	cas *m* arithmétique	теоретико-числовой случай
	number-theoretical proof <NT>	*s.* A 964		
N 847	**number-theoretic formula,** arithmetical formula <LO, NT>	zahlentheoretische (arithmetische) Formel *f*	formule *f* arithmétique	теоретико-числовая формула, арифметическая формула
N 848	**number theorist** <NT>	Zahlentheoretiker *m*	arithméticien *m*	арифметик
N 849	**number theory,** theory of numbers, arithmetic <NT>	Zahlentheorie *f*, Arithmetik *f*, Zahlenlehre *f*, // Arithmologie *f* <Wolff>	théorie *f* des nombres, arithmétique *f*, // arithmologie *f*	теория чисел, арифметика
N 850	**number transformation** <NT>	Zahlentransformation *f*	transformation *f* de nombres	преобразование чисел
	number triangle <AR, CT>	*s.* P 293		
N 851	**number tuple,** ordered sequence of numbers <GN>	Zahlentupel *n*	multiplet *m* (séquence *f*) de nombres	числовой набор
N 852	**number twice an even number,** number congruent 0 mod 4 <NT>	gerad-gerade Zahl *f*, gerade-gerade Zahl, gleich-gleiche Zahl, numerus *m* pariter par, Zahl kongruent 0 mod 4, durch 4 teilbare Zahl	nombre *m* pairement pair, nombre également égal, nombre divisible par 4, nombre de la forme 4*n*	число, делимое на 4

No.	English	German	French	Russian
N 853	**number twice an odd number,** number of the form $4n + 2$ <NT>	Zahl *f* kongruent 2 mod 4, gerad-ungerade Zahl, ungerad-gerade Zahl, Zahl der Form $4n + 2$	nombre *m* pairement impair, nombre de la forme $4n + 2$	число вида $4n + 2$
N 854	**number unit** <AR>	Zahleneinheit *f*, numerische Einheit *f*	unité *f* numérique	числовая единица
N 855	**number variable** <LO>	Zahlenvariable *f*	variable *f* numérique	числовая переменная
N 856	**number which is not product of the same primes** <NT>	nicht aus denselben Primzahlen zusammengesetzte Zahl *f*	nombre *m* hétérogène	число, которое не обладает теми же простыми делителями
N 857	**number which is product of the same primes** <NT>	aus denselben Primzahlen zusammengesetzte Zahl *f*	nombre *m* homogène	число, которое обладает теми же простыми делителями
N 858	**number written in reverse order,** reversion <of a number> <*a b c* . . . → . . . *c b a*> <NT>	umgekehrte Zahl *f*, in umgekehrter Reihenfolge der Ziffern geschriebene Zahl	nombre *m* écrit en ordre inverse	обращенное число
N 859	**numerable bundle** <AT>	numerierbares Faserbündel *n*	fibré *m* numérable	нумерируемое расслоение
	numeral <NT>	*s.* F 216		
N 860	**numeral language,** number language <FO>	Ziffernschreibweise *f*, Ziffernsprache *f*	langage *m* arithmétique	язык чисел
	numeral system <NT>	*s.* N 842		
N 861	**numeration,** numbering <SE>	Numerierung *f*	numérotage *m*, numérotation *f*	нумерация
	numeration [system] <NT>	*s.* N 842		
N 862	**numerator** <of a fraction> <AR>	Zähler *m*	numérateur *m*, // note *f* supérieure <Girard>	числитель
N 863	**numerator and denominator** <of a fraction> <AR>	Zähler und Nenner *m* <eines Bruchs>	termes *mpl* <d'une fraction>	члены <дроби>
N 864	**numerator determinant** <AL>	Zählerdeterminante *f*	déterminant *m* numérateur	определитель-числитель
N 865	**numerator divisor** <AL>	Zählerdivisor *m*	numérateur *m* <d'un diviseur>	дивизор-числитель
N 866	**numerator function** <AL>	Zählerfunktion *f*	fonction *f* numérateur	функция-числитель
N 867	**numerator of a convergent** <of a continued fraction> <NT>	Näherungszähler *m*	numérateur *m* d'une réduite	числитель подходящей дроби
	numerator of the *n*-th convergent <NT>	*s.* N 741		
N 868	**numerator parameter** <of the generalized hypergeometric series> <FU>	Zählerparameter *m*	paramètre *m* du numérateur	параметр числителя
N 869	**numerical algebra** <NU, UA>	numerische Algebra *f*	algèbre *f* numérique	числовая алгебра <UA>; численная алгебра <NU>
N 870	**numerical analysis,** numerical calculus <NU>	numerische Analysis *f*	calcul *m* (analyse *f*) numérique	приближенный (численный) анализ
N 871	**numerical attribute,** numerical predicate <LO>	Zahlenprädikat *n*, Zahlenattribut *n*	attribut *m* numérique	числовой предикат
N 872	**numerical axis,** line of numbers, numeric[al] line, uniform (number) scale, number axis (line), real axis (line), continuum, continuum of [real] numbers, arithmetical continuum <AN, SE>	Zahlengerade *f*, arithmetisches Kontinuum *n*, Zahlenkontinuum *n*	droite *f* numérique, continu *m* linéaire, continu de la ligne droite, axe *m* numérique, droite des nombres, continu, droite réelle (euclidienne)	действительная прямая, числовая ось (прямая), числовой континуум
N 873	**numerical calculation** <NU>	numerische Berechnung *f*	calcul *m* numérique	численный расчет, численное вычисление
	numerical calculus <NU>	*s.* N 870		
	numerical check <AR, NU>	*s.* C 618		
N 874	**numerical coefficient** <GN>	Zahlenkoeffizient *m*	coefficient *m* numérique	численный коэффициент
N 875	**numerical coefficient,** numerical factor <GN>	Zahlenfaktor *m*, Zahlfaktor *m*	coefficient (facteur) *m* numérique	числовой коэффициент (множитель), численный множитель
N 876	**numerical computation** <NU>	numerisches Rechnen *n*, Zahlenrechnen *n*	calcul *m* numérique	численный счет
N 877	**numerical constant** <GN>	Zahlenkonstante *f*	constante *f* numérique	численная постоянная
N 878	**numerical continued fraction** <NT>	numerischer Kettenbruch *m*, Zahlenkettenbruch *m*	fraction *f* continue numérique	числовая цепная дробь
N 879	**numerical cubature,** approximate cubature, mechanical cubature <AX, DI, NU>	numerische (genäherte, mechanische) Kubatur *f*	cubature *f* numérique (approximative, mécanique)	численное интегрирование двойных интегралов, численная (приближенная, механическая) кубатура
N 880	**numerical data,** numerics <GN>	Zahlenangaben *fpl*, numerische Werte *mpl*, Zahlenwerte *mpl*	données *fpl* numériques	числовые (численные, цифровые) данные
N 881	**numerical density** <NT>	Zahlendichte *f*	densité *f* numérique	числовая плотность
N 882/3	**numerical determinant** <MD>	Determinante *f* mit Zahlen als Elementen, Zahlendeterminante *f*, numerische Determinante *f*	déterminant *m* numérique	численный определитель
N 884	**numerical differentiation** <DI, NU>	numerische Differentiation *f*	dérivation (différentiation) *f* numérique	числовой определитель, численное дифференцирование
	numerical eccentricity <AY>	*s.* E 8		

No.	English	German	French	Russian
N 885	**numerical equality** <GN>	Zahlengleichheit *f*	égalité *f* numérique	числовое равенство
N 886	**numerical equation** <the coefficients of which being definite numbers> <GN>	Zahlengleichung *f*, numerische Gleichung *f*, Gleichung mit Zahlenkoeffizienten	équation *f* numérique	числовое уравнение
N 887	**numerical error** <ER, NU>	numerischer Fehler *m*, Rechenfehler *m*	erreur *f* numérique	числовая погрешность
N 888	**numerical example,** number example <GN>	Zahlenbeispiel *n*	exemple *m* numérique	численный (числовой) пример
	numerical factor <GN>	*s.* N 875		
N 889	**numerical fraction,** fraction of numbers <NT>	Zahlenbruch *m*, numerischer Bruch *m*	fraction *f* numérique	числовая дробь
N 890	**numerical function** <AN, NU>	Zahlenfunktion *f*, numerische Funktion *f*	fonction *f* numérique (réelle)	числовая (вещественная) функция
N 891	**numerical inequality** <GN>	Zahlenungleichung *f*, numerische Ungleichung *f*, Ungleichung zwischen Zahlen	inégalité *f* numérique	числовое неравенство
N 892	**numerical integral** <NT>	summatorische Funktion *f*, Summenfunktion *f*	fonction *f* sommatoire, intégrale *f* numérique (arithmétique)	сумматорная функция
N 893	**numerical integration;** numerical quadrature <especially of simple integrals> <AX, DI, NU>	numerische Integration *f*; numerische Quadratur *f*, Näherungsquadratur *f*	intégration *f* numérique; quadrature *f* numérique (approchée)	численное (приближенное) интегрирование; численная квадратура
N 894	**numerical interpolation** <AX, NU>	numerische Interpolation *f*	interpolation *f* numérique	численное интерполирование
N 895	**numerical invariant** <of a matrix> <MD>	numerische Invariante *f*	invariant *m* numérique	числовая постоянная
	numerical line <AN, SE>	*s.* N 872		
N 896	**numerical mathematics** <NU>	numerische Mathematik *f*	mathématiques *fpl* numériques	численная математика
N 897	**numerical method** <NU>	numerisches Verfahren *n*, numerische Methode *f*	méthode *f* numérique	численный метод
N 898	**numerical minimization** <PG>	numerische Minimierung *f*	minimisation *f* numérique	численная минимизация
N 899	**numerical operator,** number operator <in the Heaviside calculus> <DE>	Zahlenoperator *m*	opérateur *m* numérique	числовой оператор
N 900	**numerical parameter** <GN>	Zahlenparameter *m*, numerischer Parameter *m*	paramètre *m* numérique	численный параметр
	numerical predicate <LO>	*s.* N 871		
N 901	**numerical problem** <AR, GN>	Zahlenaufgabe *f*, numerische Aufgabe *f*	problème *m* numérique	численная задача
	numerical quadrature <AX, DI, NU>	*s.* N 893		
N 902	**numerical quantity** <AL>	Zahlengröße *f* <Weierstraß>	quantité *f* numérique	численная величина
N 903	**numerical series,** number series <SS>	Zahlenreihe *f*	série *f* numérique	числовой ряд
N 904	**numerical solution** <NU>	numerische Lösung *f*	solution *f* numérique	численное решение
N 905	**numerical stability** <NU>	numerische Stabilität *f*	stabilité *f* numérique	численная устойчивость
N 906	**numerical table** <NU>	Zahlentafel *f*, Zahlentabelle *f*	tableau *m* (table *f*) de nombres, table numérique	числовая таблица
N 907	**numerical term** <LO>	Zahlterm *m*	terme *m* numérique	числовой терм
N 908	**numerical value** <NU>	Zahlenwert *m*, numerischer Wert *m*	valeur *f* numérique	численное (числовое) значение
	numerical value <AN>	*s.* A 131		
N 909	**numerical value equation,** measure equation, equation between numerical values <NU>	Zahlenwertgleichung *f*	équation *f* aux valeurs numériques	уравнение численных значений
	numeric line <AN, SE>	*s.* N 872		
	numerics <GN>	*s.* N 880		
N 910	**numeri idonei** <NT>	numeri *mpl* idonei <Euler>, taugliche Zahlen *fpl*	numeri *mpl* idonei	удобные числа
	***n*-universal bundle** <AT>	*s.* U 315		
N 911	***n*-universal element** <AT>	*n*-universelles Element *n*	élément *m* *n*-universel	*n*-универсальный элемент
	***n*-universal principal bundle** <AT>	*s.* U 315		
	***n*-variable functor** <CA>	*s.* F 795		
	***n*-way classification** <ST>	*s.* N 219		

O

No.	English	German	French	Russian
O 1	**obelisk** <EG>	Obelisk *m*, Spitzsäule *f*	obélisque *m*, tronc *m* polyédrique, tas *m* de sable	обелиск
O 2	**object,** individual <LO>	Gegenstand *m*, Objekt *n*, Individuum *n*	individu *m*, objet *m* individuel	предмет, индивидуум, индивидуальный предмет
O 3	**object-full subcategory** <CA>	Unterkategorie *f*, die alle Objekte der gegebenen Kategorie enthält	sous-catégorie *f* contenant tous les objets de la catégorie donnée	подкатегория, содержащая все объекты данной категории
O 4	**object function** <corresponding a functor to> <CA>	Objektabbildung *f*, Objektfunktion *f*	fonction *f* d'objet, application *f* des objets	отображение объектов
	object function <AN>	*s.* O 426		
O 5	**objection** <TG>	Drohung *f*	menace *f*	угроза
O 6	**objective function,** preference (cost, performance) function <PG>	Zielfunktion *f*	fonction *f* économique	целевая функция, функция цели, критерий эффективности

No.	English	German	French	Russian
O 7	**object language** <contrary to metalanguage> <LO>	Objektsprache *f*, Sprache *f* der ersten Stufe	langue-objet *f*	язык-объект, предметный язык
O 8	**object of connection** <DG>	Objekt (Objektfeld) *n* des Zusammenhangs	objet *m* de connexion	объект связности
	object representing a functor <CA>	*s.* R 857		
	object space <FA>	*s.* O 427		
O 9	**object theorem** <contrary to metatheorem> <MM>	Objektsatz *m*	théorème-objet *m*	предметная теорема, объектная теорема
O 10	**object theory** <MM>	Objekttheorie *f*	théorie-objet *f*	предметная теория
O 11	**object variable,** individual variable, individual term variable, term variable <LO>	Gegenstandsvariable *f*, Dingvariable *f*, Individuenvariable *f*, Variable *f* für Individuen, Objektvariable *f*, Namenvariable *f*, Dingveränderliche *f*	variable *f* d'objet, variable d'individu, variable individuelle, objet *m* variable	предметная переменная, переменный предмет, индивидная переменная, предметное переменное, индивидуальная переменная
O 12	**object with differentiation** <CA>	Objekt *n* mit Differentiation	objet *m* différentiel	дифференциальный объект
O 13	**oblate ellipsoid [of revolution], oblate spheroid** <EG>	abgeplattetes (zusammengedrücktes) Drehellipsoid (Rotationsellipsoid, Ellipsoid) *n*	ellipsoïde *m* [de révolution] aplati	сплюснутый (сплющенный, сжатый) эллипсоид [вращения]
O 14	**oblique astroid** <GE>	schiefe Astroide *f*	astroïde *f* oblique	косая астроида
O 15	**oblique circular cone,** oblique cone <EG>	schiefer Kreiskegel (Kegel) *m*	cône *m* circulaire oblique, cône oblique	наклонный круглый (круговой) конус, косой круглый (круговой) конус, наклонный (косой) конус
O 16	**oblique circular cylinder** <EG>	schiefer Kreiszylinder *m*	cylindre *m* circulaire oblique (incliné)	наклонный (косой) круговой цилиндр
	oblique cone <EG>	*s.* O 15		
O 17	**oblique co-ordinates** <AY>	schiefwinklige Koordinaten *fpl*	coordonnées *fpl* obliques	косоугольные координаты
O 18	**oblique co-ordinate system** <AY>	schiefwinkliges Koordinatensystem *n*	système *m* de coordonnées en axes obliques	косоугольная система координат
	oblique factor <ST>	*s.* N 438		
	obliquely truncated cone <EG>	*s.* T 1024		
	obliquely truncated cylinder <EG>	*s.* T 1025		
O 19	**oblique parallelepipedon** <EG>	schiefes Parallelepiped *n*	parallélépipède *m* oblique	наклонный параллелепипед
O 20	**oblique prism** <EG>	schiefes Prisma *n*	prisme *m* oblique	косая (наклонная) призма
	oblique projection <DS>	*s.* 1. S 1179; 2. S 1180		
O 21	**oblique pyramid** <EG>	schiefe Pyramide *f*	pyramide *f* oblique	наклонная (косая) пирамида
O 22	**oblique strophoid,** strophoid <GE>	schräge Strophoide *f*, Knotenfokale *f*, Fokale *f* mit Knoten, Fokale Quételets, Strophoide	strophoïde *f* oblique, focale *f* à nœud, focale de Quételet, strophoïde	косая строфоида, фокала Кветеле, строфоида
O 23	**oblique three-leafed rose** <GE>	schiefes Dreiblatt (Kleeblatt) *n*	rose *f* à trois branches oblique	косая трехлепестковая роза
O 24	**oblique triangle** <EG>	schiefwinkliges Dreieck *n*	triangle *m* obliquangle	косоугольный треугольник
O 25	**observable component** <ST>	beobachtbare Komponente *f*	composante *f* observable	[непосредственно] наблюдаемая компонента
O 26	**observational error** <ER>	Beobachtungsfehler *m*	erreur *f* d'observation	ошибка наблюдения, погрешность при наблюдении
O 27	**observation function** <of confidence region> <ST>	Kennfunktion *f*	fonction *f* des observations	вероятность покрытия
	obstacle problem <DE>	*s.* U 186		
O 28	**obstruction** <AL>	Obstruktion *f*, Hindernis *n*	obstruction *f*	препятствие
O 29	**obstruction cocycle** <AT>	Hinderniskozyklus *m*	cocycle *m* d'obstruction	препятствующий ∇-цикл
O 30	**obstruction theory** <AT>	Hindernistheorie *f*	théorie *f* des obstructions	теория препятствий
O 31	**obstruction to extending a cross-section** <of a fibre bundle> <AT>	Hindernis *n* gegen das Fortsetzen eines Schnitts	obstacle *m* par rapport à l'extension d'une section	препятствие к расширению сечения
O 32	**obstruction to lifting** *f* <AT>	Hindernis *n* gegen das Liften von *f*	obstacle *m*	препятствие к поднятию отображения *f*
O 33	**obtuse angle** <EG>	stumpfer Winkel *m*	angle *m* obtus	тупой угол
O 34	**obtuse triangle** <EG>	stumpfwinkliges Dreieck *n*	triangle *m* obtusangle	тупоугольный треугольник
O 35	**occupancy probability,** occupation probability <ST>	Besetzungswahrscheinlichkeit *f*	probabilité *f* d'occupation	вероятность размещения (заполнения)
O 36	**occupancy problem** <PG>	Belegungsproblem *n*	problème *m* d'occupation	задача о размещении
	occupation probability <ST>	*s.* O 35		
	OC curve (function) <ST>	*s.* O 165		
O 37	**(o)-complete Boolean algebra** <AL>	(o)-vollständige Boolesche Algebra *f*	algèbre *f* de Boole (o)-complète	(o)-полная алгебра
	(o)-convergence <FA>	*s.* O 292		
O 38	**octadic surface** <surface of fourth degree having 8 nodes> <AG>	oktadische Fläche *f*	surface *f* octade	
O 39	**octagonal number** <as a figurate number> <NT>	Oktagonalzahl *f*, Achteckszahl *f*	nombre *m* octogonal (octogone)	восьмиугольное число
O 40	**octahedral form** <AL>	Oktaederform *f*, Oktaederfunktion *f*	forme *f* octaédrique, forme de l'octaèdre, fonction *f* octaédrique	октаэдрическая форма

O 41	**octahedral group;** hexahedral group <AL, GR>	Oktaedergruppe *f*; Hexaedergruppe *f*, Würfelgruppe *f*	groupe *m* de l'octaèdre, groupe octaédrique (octaèdre), groupe octaédral; groupe du cube, groupe de l'hexaèdre, groupe hexaédrique (hexaédral)	группа октаэдра, октаэдрическая группа; группа гексаэдра, гексаэдрическая группа
O 42	**octahedron** <EG>	Achtflach *n*, Oktaeder *n*, Achtflächner *m*	octaèdre *m*	октаэдр, восьмигранник, четырехугольная бипирамида
	octahedron <EG>	*s.* R 601		
O 43	**octahedron equation** <AL>	Oktaedergleichung *f*	équation *f* de l'octaèdre, équation octaédrique	уравнение октаэдра
O 44	**octal arithmetic** <NT>	oktale Arithmetik *f*	arithmétique *f* octale	восьмеричная арифметика
O 45	**octal digit** <NT>	Oktalziffer *f*	chiffre *m* octal	восьмеричный разряд, цифра восьмеричной системы счисления
O 46	**octal notation,** octonary notation <NT>	Oktalschreibweise *f*, oktale Schreibweise (Zahlendarstellung) *f*	notation *f* octale	представление чисел в восьмеричной системе, восьмеричное представление
O 47	**octal [number] system** <NT>	Oktalsystem *n*	système *m* de numération octal	восьмеричная система [счисления]
O 48	**octant I,** first octant <AY>	Hauptoktant *m*, erster Oktant *m*, Oktant I	premier octant *m*, octant I	первый октант, октант I
O 49	**octavic** <AL>	Form *f* achter Ordnung	forme *f* de degré huit (8)	октавика, форма степени восемь (8)
O 50	**octiamond** <EG>	Oktiamant *m*	octiamant *m*	октиамант
O 51	**octomino** <EG>	Oktomino *n*	octomino *m*	октомино
	octonary notation <NT>	*s.* O 46		
	odd arrangement <CT>	*s.* O 61		
O 52	**odd circuit** <of a curve> <AG>	unpaarer Zug *m*	trait *m* impair	нечетный поток
O 53	**odd-dimensional space,** odd-measured space <GE, TO>	Raum *m* mit (von) ungerader Dimension, ungeradzahligdimensionaler Raum	espace *m* à un nombre de dimensions impair	нечетномерное пространство
O 54	**odd function** <DI>	ungerade Funktion *f*	fonction *f* impaire (antisymétrique)	нечетная функция
O 55	**odd half-integer** <NT>	halbzahlige Zahl *f*	nombre *m* demi-entier	полуцелое число
	odd-measured space <GE, TO>	*s.* O 53		
O 56	**odd-multiple zero** <AL, AN>	Nullstelle *f* [von] ungerader Vielfachheit	zéro *m* de multiplicité impaire	нечетнократный нуль
O 57	**oddness** <AR>	Ungeradheit *f*	imparité *f*	нечетность
O 58	**odd number,** uneven number <AR, NT>	ungerade Zahl *f*	nombre *m* impair	нечетное число
	odd-numbered value <AR>	*s.* O 62		
O 59	**odd part** <of a continued fraction> <NT>	Näherungsbruch *m* ungeradzahliger Ordnung	réduite *f* d'ordre impaire	подходящая дробь нечетного порядка
O 60	**odd permutation** <operation> <AL>	ungerade Permutation (Substitution) *f*, Substitution von ungeradem Grade	permutation (substitution) *f* impaire, permutation de deuxième classe, // substitution négative	нечетная подстановка
O 61	**odd permutation,** odd arrangement <CT>	ungerade Permutation (Anordnung, Komplexion) *f*, Komplexion zweiter (der zweiten) Klasse	arrangement *m* de deuxième classe, complexion *f* impaire	нечетная перестановка
O 62	**odd value,** uneven (odd-numbered) value <AR>	ungerader (ungeradzahliger) Wert *m*	valeur *f* impaire	нечетное значение, нечетная величина
	off-diagonal element <MD>	*s.* N 372		
O 62a	**O*-group** <GR>	O*-Gruppe *f*	O*-groupe *m*	доупорядочиваемая группа, у*-группа, O*-группа
O 63	**(o)-limit** <in a partially ordered linear space> <AN, TO>	ordnungstheoretischer Limes *m*, (*o*)-Limes *m*	(*o*)-limite *f*	(*o*)-предел
	Olmstead-Tukey corner test <ST> ┌<SE>	*s.* C 2469		
O 64	**omega,** ω <as an ordinal>	Omega *n*, ω	oméga *m*, ω	омега, ω
O 65	**omega-completeness, omega-completion,** ω-completeness, ω-completion <MM>	ω-Vollständigkeit *f*, Omega-Vollständigkeit *f*	propriété *f* d'être ω-complet (oméga-complet), ω-complétude *f*, oméga-complétude *f*	ω-полнота, омега-полнота
O 66	**omega-consistency,** ω-consistency <LO, MM>	ω-Widerspruchsfreiheit *f*, Omega-Widerspruchsfreiheit *f*	ω-consistance *f*, oméga-consistance *f*	ω-непротиворечивость, омега-непротиворечивость
O 67	**omega-group,** Ω-group <AL>	Ω-Gruppe *f*, Omega-Gruppe *f*, Gruppe *f* mit einem System von Multioperatoren Ω	Ω-groupe *m*, oméga-groupe *m*	Ω-группа, омега-группа, группа с системой мультиоператоров Ω
O 68	**omega-hypercentre,** ω-hypercentre <of a group> <GR>	ω-Hyperzentrum *n*, Omega-Hyperzentrum *n*	ω-hypercentre *m*, oméga-hypercentre *m*	ω-гиперцентр, омега-гиперцентр
O 69	**omega-incomplete theory,** ω-incomplete theory <MM>	ω-unvollständige (omega-unvollständige) Theorie *f*	théorie *f* ω-incomplète (oméga-incomplète)	ω-неполная (омега-неполная) теория
	omega-squared test <ST>	*s.* C 2649		
O 70	**omega-structure,** Ω-structure <UA>	Ω-Struktur *f*, Omega-Struktur *f*	Ω-structure *f*, oméga-structure *f*	структура с отношениями над областью предикатов Ω, Ω-структура, омега-структура
	omitting parentheses <AL, LO>	*s.* S 993		

	English	German	French	Russian
O 71	**omitting the existential quantifier** <LO>	Existenzbeseitigung *f*	élimination *f* du quantificateur existentiel	∃-удаление, удаление квантора существования
	omnibus estimate <ST>	*s.* O 566		
O 72	**omnibus test,** overall test <ST>	Omnibustest *m*	test *m* omnibus	критерий объединения, омнибус-критерий
O 73	**χ^2 omnibus test,** χ^2 overall test, chi-squared omnibus (overall) test, Fisher['s] omnibus test <ST>	χ^2-Omnibustest *m*, Chi-Quadrat-Omnibustest *m*, Fisherscher Omnibustest *m*	test *m* χ^2 omnibus, test chi carré omnibus, test omnibus de Fisher	χ^2-критерий объединения, критерий хи-квадрат объединения, критерий объединения Фишера
O 74	**once primed quantity** <e.g.: a'> <GN>	eingestrichene (einfach gestrichene) Größe *f*	quantité *f* une fois primée	величина с одним штрихом
	one <AL>	*s.* I 59		
O 75	**one and only one** x <LO>	genau ein x <mit>	un et un seul x	единственный x <такой, что>
	one-column array (matrix) <MD>	*s.* C 1164		
O 76	**one-cycle,** 1-cycle, cycle of length one <of a permutation> <AL, CT>	Einerzyklus *m*	cycle *m* unaire	цикл длины 1
	one-digit number <NT>	*s.* O 93		
	one-dimensional Betti number <TO>	*s.* C 2059		
O 77	**one-dimensional boundary value problem** <DE>	eindimensionales Randwertproblem *n*, eindimensionale Randwertaufgabe *f*, Randwertproblem (Randwertaufgabe) bei einer gewöhnlichen Differentialgleichung *n*-ter Ordnung	problème *m* aux limites unidimensionnel	одномерная краевая задача
O 78/9	**one-dimensional character** <RE>	eindimensionaler (linearer) Charakter *m*	caractère *m* d'une représentation de degré 1	одномерный характер
	one-dimensional complex <AT, GP>	*s.* T 517		
	one-dimensional compression <GE>	*s.* S 897		
O 80	**one-dimensional differential equation,** one-dimensional equation <DE>	gleichgradige Differentialgleichung *f*, homogene Differentialgleichung im erweiterten Sinne <*n*-ter Ordnung>, eindimensionale Differentialgleichung <Jacobsthal>, gleichgradige algebraische Differentialgleichung	équation *f* différentielle unidimensionnelle, équation unidimensionnelle	равноразмерное дифференциальное уравнение
	one-dimensional distribution <ST>	*s.* U 309		
	one-dimensional elongation <GE>	*s.* S 906		
	one-dimensional equation <DE>	*s.* O 80		
	one-dimensional homotopy <AT>	*s.* F 824		
	one-dimensional integral <DI>	*s.* S 923		
	one-dimensional quadric <AG, AY>	*s.* C 1944		
	one-dimensional simplex <AT>	*s.* S 240		
O 81	**one-dimensional space,** 1-space, one-space <AN, GE>	eindimensionaler Raum *m*	espace *m* unidimensionnel (à une dimension)	одномерное пространство
	one-dimensional strain <GE>	*s.* S 906		
O 82	**one-dimensional subspace** <of a vector space> <AL>	eindimensionaler Untervektorraum *m*, eindimensionaler Unterraum *m*	sous-espace *m* vectoriel monogène, sous-espace [vectoriel] à une dimension, droite *f* homogène	одномерное подпространство
	one-dimensional torus group <GR>	*s.* T 578		
O 83	**one-dimensional vector space** <AL>	eindimensionaler Vektorraum *m*	espace *m* vectoriel monogène	одномерное векторное пространство
O 84	**one-element class** <SE>	einelementige Klasse *f*	classe *f* singulaire	одноэлементный (одночленный) класс
O 85	**one-element group,** trivial group, unity group, zero group <GR>	Einsgruppe *f*, Einheitsgruppe *f*, Nullgruppe *f*	groupe *m* réduit à l'élément neutre, groupe trivial (unitaire)	одноэлементная (тривиальная, единичная) группа, нульгруппа
O 86	**one-element set,** singleton, unit set, unit-set, set consisting of a single element <SE>	einelementige Menge *f*, Einermenge *f*	ensemble *m* à un élément, ensemble réduit à un seul élément, singleton *m*, ensemble unitaire, ensemble monaire	одноэлементное множество, одиночка, единичное множество
	one-figure number <NT>	*s.* O 93		
O 87	**one-headed group** <GR>	Gruppe *f* mit einem einzigen maximalen Normalteiler	groupe *m* à sous-groupe distingué maximal unique	группа с единственным максимальным нормальным делителем
O 88	**one-leafed covering** <TO>	einblättrige Überlagerung *f*	revêtement *m* à un feuillet	однолистное наложение
O 89	**one-manyness** <of a relation> <SE>	Einmehrdeutigkeit *f*	co-univocité *f*	одномногозначность
	one-many relation <SE>	*s.* O 119		
	one-one relation <SE>	*s.* O 124		
	one-one transformation <SE>	*s.* I 548		

No.	English	German	French	Russian
O 90	**one-parameter family of curves,** single-parameter family of curves <AN, GE>	einparametrige Kurvenschar *f*	famille *f* de courbes à un [seul] paramètre, famille de courbes uniparamétrique	однопараметрическое семейство кривых
O 91	**one-parameter group** <GR>	einparametrige Gruppe *f*, Gruppe eines Parameters	groupe *m* à un paramètre, groupe à un seul paramètre, groupe uniparamétrique	однопараметрическая группа
O 92	**one-person game,** single-person game <TG>	Einpersonenspiel *n*, Einzelspiel *n*, Solospiel *n*	jeu *m* à une personne	игра с одним участником
O 93	**one-place number,** one-digit (one-figure, single-digit) number, digit <NT>	einstellige Zahl *f*	nombre *m* d'un seul chiffre, nombre à un chiffre	одноместное число, одноразрядное число
	one-place operation <AL>	*s.* U 36		
O 94	**one-place predicate,** monadic predicate, single-valued predicate, univalent predicate, unary predicate, predicate of one argument <LO>	einstelliges Prädikat (Attribut) *n*, Eigenschaft *f*, einstelliges Prädikativ *n*	prédicat *m* monadique (absolu, de propriétés), prédicat d'une variable, prédicat à un argument, prédicat singulier, expression *f* atomique de prédicat, propriété *f*, prédicat	свойство, одноместное отношение, одноместный предикат, монадичный предикат, унарный (одинарный, 1-арный, сингулярный) предикат, предикат от одной переменной
O 95	**one-place predicate calculus,** monadic predicate calculus, singulary functional calculus <LO>	einstelliger Prädikatenkalkül *m*, Logik *f* der Eigenschaften, einstellige Prädikatenlogik *f*	logique *f* des propriétés, logique des prédicats absolus (d'une seule variable)	исчисление (логика) одноместных предикатов, логика предикатов с одной переменной
O 96	**one-place predicate parameter,** unary predicate parameter <LO>	einstellige Prädikatenvariable *f*	variable *f* de prédicats à un argument	переменный предикат от одной переменной
	one-place relation <AL, LO>	*s.* U 37		
O 97	**one-plane method (projection)** <DS>	Eintafelverfahren *n*	projection *f* sur un [seul] plan, méthode *f* de projection sur un [seul] plan	метод проектирования на одну плоскость, проектирование на одну плоскость
O 98	**one-plane projection** <DS>	Eintafelprojektion *f*	projection *f* sur un [seul] plan	проекция на одну плоскость; проектирование на одну плоскость
O 99	**one-point compactification,** Alexandroff['s] one point compactification, Alexandroff['s] compactification <TO>	Alexandroffsche (Aleksandrovsche) Kompaktifizierung *f*, Alexandroffsche Kompaktifikation *f*, Ein-Punkt-Kompaktifizierung *f*, Ein-Punkt-Kompaktifikation *f*	compactifié *m* d'Alexandroff, compactification *f* par un seul point, compactification d'Alexandroff, compactifié d'Aleksandrov	одноточечное компактное расширение, компактификация Александрова, одноточечная компактификация, бикомпактное расширение Александрова
	one-point set <SE>	*s.* D 162		
O 100	**one-point space** <TO>	Einpunktraum *m*	espace *m* réduit à un point	одноточечное пространство
	one-point union <TO>	*s.* W 149		
O 101	**one-sample method** <ST>	Einstichprobenverfahren *n*	méthode *f* à un seul échantillon	метод одной выборки
	ones digit <NT>	*s.* U 295		
	one-sheet hyperboloid <AY>	*s.* H 659		
O 102	**one-sided condition,** one-sided Ore condition <AL>	einseitige Ore-Bedingung *f*, einseitige Bedingung *f*	condition *f* de Ore unilatère	одностороннее условие Оре
O 103	**one-sided continuity,** continuity on one side <AN>	einseitige Stetigkeit *f*	continuité *f* vers (à) un seul côté, continuité unilatérale	односторонняя непрерывность
O 104	**one-sided derivative,** derivative on one side, unilateral derivative <AN>	einseitige Ableitung *f*, einseitiger Differentialquotient *m*	semi-dérivée *f*, dérivée *f* à un seul côté, dérivée unilatérale	односторонняя производная
O 105	**one-sided differentiability,** differentiability on one side, unilateral differentiability <AN>	einseitige Differenzierbarkeit *f*	dérivabilité *f* à un seul côté, dérivabilité unilatérale	односторонняя дифференцируемость
O 106	**one-sided Dini derivative,** Dini['s] derivative from one side <AN>	einseitige extreme (Dinische) Derivierte *f*, einseitige Derivierte	nombre *m* dérivé de Dini à un seul côté	одностороннее производное число [по Дини]
O 107	**one-sided ideal** <AL>	einseitiges Ideal *n*	idéal *m* unilatéral	односторонний идеал
O 108	**one-sided inequality** <NU>	einseitige Ungleichung *f*	inégalité *f* au sens unique	простое неравенство
O 109	**one-sided Jordan curve** <TO>	einufrige Jordan-Kurve *f*	courbe *f* de Jordan à un seul côté	одноберяжная жорданова кривая
	one-sided Laplace transform[ation] <IT>	*s.* U 188		
O 110	**one-sided limit,** limit on one side, unilateral limit <AN>	einseitiger Grenzwert *m*, einseitiger Limes *m*	limite *f* à un seul côté, limite unilatérale	односторонний предел [функции]
O 111	**one-sided lower approximate limit** <AN>	einseitiger unterer approximativer Limes (Hauptlimes) *m*	limite *f* approximative inférieure à un seul côté	односторонний нижний аппроксимативный (асимптотический) предел
O 112	**one-sided lower continuous** <AN>	einseitig unterhalb[]stetig, einseitig nach unten stetig, einseitig abwärts stetig	continu inférieurement à un seul côté	односторонний непрерывный снизу
	one-sided lower limit <DI>	*s.* L 1156		
O 113	**one-sided order** <of a ring> <AL>	einseitige Ordnung *f*	ordre *m* unilatère	односторонний порядок

No.	English	German	French	Russian
	one-sided Ore condition <AL>	*s.* O 102		
O 114	**one-sided surface,** surface of one side, one-side surface, unilateral surface <DG, GE>	einseitige Fläche *f*	surface *f* unilatérale (unilatère)	односторонняя поверхность
O 115	**one-sided test,** single-tail test <ST>	einseitiger Test *m*	test *m* unilatéral, test à une queue	односторонний критерий
O 116	**one-sided upper approximate limit** <AN>	einseitiger oberer approximativer Limes (Hauptlimes) *m*	limite *f* approximative supérieure à un seul côté	односторонний верхний аппроксимативный (асимптотический) предел
O 117	**one-sided upper continuous** <AN>	einseitig oberhalb[ ]stetig, einseitig nach oben stetig, einseitig aufwärts stetig	continu supérieurement à un seul côté	односторонний непрерывный сверху
	one-side surface <DG, GE>	*s.* O 114		
	one-space <AN, GE>	*s.* O 81		
	one-sphere <TO>	*s.* S 894		
	one-term[ed] expression <AL>	*s.* M 853		
O 118	**one test** <in substitution method> <PG>	Einsprobe *f*	preuve *f* par un	проверка с помощью числа 1
O 119	**one-to-many correspondence,** one-many correspondence, one-to-many (one-many) relation, fibering relation, injective relation <SE>	ein[-]mehrdeutige Relation *f*, ein[-]mehrdeutige Beziehung *f*, injektive Relation *f*, linkseindeutige Relation *f*	relation *f* co-univoque, relation *f* injective	одно[-]многозначное соответствие, инъективное отношение
O 120	**one-to-many mapping,** one-to-many transformation <AN>	einmehrdeutige Abbildung (Transformation) *f*	application (transformation) *f* multiforme (non univoque)	одномногозначное отображение (преобразование)
	one-to-many relation <SE>	*s.* O 119		
	one-to-many transformation <AN>	*s.* O 120		
	one-to-one and into mapping <SE>	*s.* I 548		
	one-to-one and onto mapping <SE>	*s.* B 330		
	one-to-one application <SE>	*s.* I 548		
	one-to-one bicontinuous transformation <TO>	*s.* T 519		
O 121	**one-to-one correspondence,** (1 — 1) correspondence, reciprocal correspondence <between two sets> <SE>	eineindeutige Korrespondenz (Zuordnung) *f*, umkehrbar eindeutige Beziehung *f*, Paarung *f*	correspondance *f* biunivoque (parfaite, uniunivoque, univoque et réciproque, bijective)	взаимно однозначное соответствие, биективное соответствие, (1 — 1)-соответствие, одно-однозначное (взаимно обратное) соответствие
	one-to-one correspondence <SE>	*s.* 1. B 330; 2. I 548; 3. O 124		
	one-to-one function <SE>	*s.* I 548		
	one-to-one mapping <GE>	*s.* O 125		
	one-to-one mapping [into] <SE>	*s.* I 548		
O 122	**one-to-one mapping of a set onto itself,** bijective mapping of a set onto itself, permutation of a set <SE>	eineindeutige Abbildung *f* einer Menge auf sich, Permutation (Substitution) *f* einer Menge	application *f* biunivoque d'un ensemble sur lui-même, permutation *f* d'un ensemble	взаимно однозначное соответствие множества с собой, подстановка множества (в множестве)
	one-to-one mapping onto <SE>	*s.* B 330		
O 123	**one-to-one partial mapping of *A* into *B*** <SE>	eineindeutige Abbildung *f* aus *A* in *B*	application *f* partielle biunivoque de *A* dans *B*	точное частичное мультиотображение из *A* в *B*
O 124	**one-to-one relation,** one-one relation, perfect relation, one-to-one correspondence <SE>	eineindeutige (vollkommene, umkehrbar eindeutige) Relation *f*, verschiedenwertige Funktion *f*	relation *f* biunivoque	взаимно однозначное отношение
O 125	**one-to-one representation,** one-to-one mapping <of a surface onto a surface> <GE>	eineindeutige Abbildung *f*	représentation *f* biunivoque	однолистное отображение
	one-to-one representation <SE>	*s.* I 548		
O 126	**one-to-one sequence,** sequence of distinct points <TO>	Folge *f* verschiedener Punkte	suite *f* de points distincts	последовательность попарно различных точек
	one-to-one transformation <SE>	*s.* I 548		
	one-unit <NT> ⌐FT>	*s.* U 233		
	one-valued function <AN,	*s.* S 1036		
	one-valued function <SE>	*s.* S 1037		
	one-way classification <ST>	*s.* S 893		
	onto function <SE>	*s.* S 2378		
O 127	**onto homomorphism,** surjection, epimorphism, homomorphism upon, surjective homomorphism, epic morphism <AL>	Homomorphismus *m* auf, Homomorphismus-auf *m*, Surjektion *f*, Epimorphismus *m*, surjektiver Homomorphismus, epimorpher Homomorphismus, Epihomomorphismus *m*	épimorphisme *m*, morphisme *m* surjectif, homomorphisme *m* sur, surjection *f*	эпиморфизм, сюръективный гомоморфизм, эпигомоморфизм, эпи, эпигомо

No.	English	German	French	Russian
	onto mapping <SE>	*s.* S 2378		
	open and closed set <TO>	*s.* C 838		
	open-and-closed subset <TO>	*s.* C 838		
	open arc progression <GP>	*s.* O 132		
O 128	**open ball,** open [solid] sphere, spherical region <GE>	offene Kugel *f*	boule *f* ouverte, boule euclidienne ouverte	открытый [евклидов] шар, внутренность сферы, открытая сфера
O 129	**open ball,** open sphere, open solid sphere, spheroid <in a metric space> <TO>	offene Kugel *f*	boule *f* ouverte (inachevée), boule de deuxième espèce, sphère *f* généralisée ouverte	открытая сфера, открытый шар
	open base <TO>	*s.* 1. B 134; 2. B 138		
	open connected set <TO>	*s.* D 855		
O 130	**open cover[ing]** <TO>	offene Überdeckung *f*, Überdeckung	recouvrement *m* ouvert	открытое покрытие
O 131	**open curve** <TO>	offene (nichtgeschlossene) Kurve *f*	courbe *f* ouverte	незамкнутая (разомкнутая) кривая
O 132	**open directed-edge sequence,** open arc progression <of an oriented graph> <GP>	offene gerichtete Kantenprogression *f*	chemin *m* non fermé	незамкнутый ориентированный маршрут
O 133	**open disk** <AN, TO>	offene Kreisscheibe *f*, offener Kreis *m*, Kreisscheibe *f* ohne Rand	disque *m* ouvert, cercle *m* non circonférencié	открытый круг
	open domain <TO>	*s.* R 602		
O 134	**open edge train** <of an undirected graph> <GP>	offene Kantenfolge (Kantenprogression) *f*, offener Kantenzug *m*	chaîne *f* ouverte	незамкнутый маршрут
O 135	**open-ended cell (class)** <ST>	offene Klasse *f*	classe *f* ouverte	открытый класс
O 136	**open equivalence relation** <TO>	offene Äquivalenzrelation *f*	relation *f* d'équivalence ouverte, équivalence *f* ouverte	открытое отношение эквивалентности
O 137	**open eulerian graph** <GP>	offener Eulerscher Graph *m*	graphe *m* eulérien ouvert	незамкнутый эйлеров граф
	open formula <LO>	*s.* N 331		
	open function <TO>	*s.* O 142		
O 138	**open half space, open half-space** <GE>	offener Halbraum *m*	demi-espace *m* ouvert	открытое полупространство
O 139	**open injective mapping** <FA>	offene Injektion *f*	application *f* injective ouverte	открытое инъективное отображение
O 140	**open interval,** interval <(a,b), $]a,b[$> <AN>	offenes Intervall *n*	intervalle *m* ouvert	[открытый] промежуток, [открытый] интервал
	open interval <SE>	*s.* O 353		
	open kernel <TO>	*s.* I 716		
O 141	**open manifold,** relative manifold <TO>	berandete Mannigfaltigkeit *f*	variété *f* à bord	многообразие с краем
O 142	**open map[ping],** open function, interior map[ping], interior transformation <TO>	offene Abbildung *f*, innere Abbildung	application *f* ouverte, fonction (transformation) *f* intérieure, morphisme *m* ouvert	открытое отображение, внутреннее отображение
O 143	**open mapping theorem,** theorem of the open mapping of Banach <for complete metric linear spaces> <FA, TO>	Prinzip *n* der offenen Abbildung, Satz *m* über offene Abbildungen, Satz von Banach-Schauder, Banach-Schauderscher Satz	théorème *m* sur les applications ouvertes	теорема об открытом отображении
	open *n*-ball <TO>	*s.* O 154		
O 144	**open neighbourhood,** neighbourhood <TO>	offene Umgebung *f*, Umgebung, absolute Umgebung	voisinage *m* ouvert, voisinage	открытая окрестность, окрестность
O 145	**openness** <TO>	Offenheit *f*	propriété *f* d'être ouvert	открытость
O 146	**open ordered set,** unbounded linearly ordered set <SE>	offene geordnete Menge *f*, offene (unbegrenzte geordnete) Menge	ensemble *m* ordonné sans élément maximum et sans élément minimum	неограниченное линейно упорядоченное множество, упорядоченное множество без наибольшего и наименьшего элементов
O 147	**open parallelepipedon** <*n*-dimensional> <GE>	offenes Parallelepiped[on] *n*	parallélépipède *m* ouvert	открытый параллелепипед, полиинтервал
	open plane <FT>	*s.* F 310		
	open point set <TO>	*s.* O 153		
	open polygon <GE>	*s.* B 775		
O 148	**open rectangular parallelepiped** <TO>	offener Quader *m*	pavé *m* ouvert	открытый кирпич
O 149	**open relation** <LO>	offene Relation *f*	relation *f* ouverte	открытое отношение
O 150	**open segment** <GE>	offene Strecke *f*	segment *m* ouvert	открытый отрезок
O 151	**open semi-circle** <TO>	offener Halbkreis *m*	demi-cercle *m* ouvert	открытая полуокружность
	open sentence <LO>	*s.* N 331		
O 152	**open sequential scheme** <ST>	offenes Sequentialschema *n*	schéma *m* séquentiel (progressif) ouvert	открытая последовательная схема
O 153	**open set [of points],** open point set, domain <TO>	offene Menge (Punktmenge) *f*, // Bereich *m*	ouvert *m*, partie *f* ouverte, ensemble *m* ouvert	открытое множество, открытое точечное множество
O 154	**open solid *n*-sphere,** spherical region in R^n, spherical neighbourhood in R^n, open *n*-ball <TO>	*n*-dimensionale offene Kugel *f*, offene Kugel im R^n, sphärische Umgebung *f* im R^n, offene *n*-dimensionale Kugel	boule *f* ouverte à *n* dimensions, boule euclidienne ouverte *n*-dimensionnelle	*n*-мерный открытый шар (евклидов шар), внутренность *n*-мерной гиперсферы (сферы)
	open solid sphere <GE>	*s.* O 128		
	open solid sphere <TO>	*s.* O 129		
	open sphere <GE>	*s.* O 128		

No.	English	German	French	Russian
	open sphere <TO>	*s.* O 129		
O 155	**open star** <AT>	offener Stern *m*, Büschel *n*	étoile *f* ouverte	открытая звезда
O 156	**open statement form** <LO>	offene Aussageform *f*	forme *f* propositionnelle qui contient des variables libres	открытая форма высказывания
O 157	**open sub-base,** sub-base of open sets <of a topological space> <TO>	offene Subbasis *f*	sous-base *f* ouverte	открытая предбаза
O 158	**open surface,** non-closed surface <TO>	offene (nichtgeschlossene) Fläche *f*	surface *f* non fermé, surface ouverte	открытая поверхность, некомпактная поверхность без края
O 159	**open-type quadrature formula** <AX, DI, NU>	Quadraturformel (Formel) *f* vom offenen Typ	formule *f* [pour l'intégration numérique] de type ouvert	квадратурная формула открытого типа
O 160	**operand** <AR, NU>	Operand *m*, Rechengröße *f*	opérande *f*	операнд, вычисляемая величина, объект действия; величина, над которой производят операции
O 161	**operand** <LO, MM>	Operand *m*	opérande *f*	операнд; величина, над которой производят операции
	operate continuously / to <GR, TO>	*s.* A 197		
O 162	**operate effectively / to,** to operate regularly <said of a group> <AL>	effektiv operieren	opérer effectivement (fidèlement)	эффективно действовать, регулярно действовать
O 163	**operate holomorphically / to** <on a set> <said of a group> <DG>	holomorph operieren <auf einer Menge>	opérer holomorphiquement <sur un ensemble>	действовать голоморфно <на множестве>
	operate on a set / to <GR>	*s.* A 202		
O 164	**operate properly / to** <said of a group> <AL, TO>	eigentlich operieren	opérer proprement	действовать совершенно
	operate regularly / to <AL>	*s.* O 162		
O 165	**operating characteristic,** OC function; OC curve <ST>	Operationscharakteristik *f*, OC-Funktion *f*, O-C-Funktion *f*, Annahmekennlinie *f*, Testcharakteristik *f*; OC-Kurve *f*	courbe *f* caractéristique, courbe OC, courbe d'efficacité	оперативная характеристика
	operating with letters <AR>	*s.* A 425		
O 166	**o-operation** <AL>	Kreisoperation *f*		присоединенное умножение
	operation <NU>	*s.* C 1760		
	operation <UA>	*s.* A 455		
	operation / 0-ary <UA>	*s.* N 761		
	operation δs [of Mr. Hausdorff] <SE>	*s.* H 145		
O 167	**operational calculus,** operator calculus, Heaviside['s] calculus, Heaviside['s] operational calculus <DE>	Operatorenrechnung *f*, Heavisidesche Operatorenrechnung, Operatorenkalkül *m*, Heavisidescher Operatorenkalkül (Operationskalkül) *m*, Heaviside-Kalkül *m*	calcul *m* symbolique (opératoire, opérationnel, opératoriel), analyse *f* symbolique	операционное исчисление, операторное исчисление, символическое исчисление, метод Хэвисайда, операторное исчисление Хэвисайда, хэвисайдово исчисление
O 168	**operational definition** <MM>	operative Definition *f*	définition *f* opératoire	операционное определение
O 169	**operational inference figure** <LO>	Verknüpfungs-Schlußfigur *f*	règle *f* opératoire (de dérivation proprement dite)	
O 170	**operationally related** <AL>	operationell verknüpft	lié par opération	операционно связанный
	operational notation <DE>	*s.* S 2418		
	operational symbol <AL>	*s.* O 180		
O 171	**operation completely defined** <on ...> total operation <AL, SE>	überall definierte Operation *f*, auf ganz ... definierte Operation, vollständige Operation	opération *f* définie partout <sur ...>, opération complète	всюду <на ...> определенная операция, полностью определенная операция <на ...>
	operation of arithmetic <AR>	*s.* R 1498		
O 172	**operation of different kind** <AR>	ungleichstufige Operation *f*	opération *f* de rang distinct	действие разной ступени
O 173	**operation of higher kind** <AR>	Operation (Rechenoperation) *f* höherer Stufe	opération *f* de rang supérieur	действие высшей ступени
	operation of *n* arguments <UA>	*s.* N 15		
	operation of rank 1 <AL>	*s.* U 36		
	operation of rank *n* <UA>	*s.* N 15		
O 174	**operation of rewriting** <GN>	Umformungsoperation *f*	opération *f* de transformation	операция преобразования
O 175	**operation of set difference** <SE>	Mengensubtraktion *f*	formation *f* de la différence entre deux ensembles	образование разности множеств
O 176	**operation of several arguments** <AL>	mehrstellige Operation *f*	opération *f* à plusieurs arguments	операция с несколькими аргументами
O 177	**operation of symmetric difference** <SE>	Operation *f* der Bildung der symmetrischen Differenz	opération *f* différence symétrique	операция разностного сложения, операция симметрической разности
O 178	**operation of the same kind** <AL, AR>	gleichstufige Operation *f*	opération *f* de même rang	действие (операция) одинаковой ступени
	operation of two arguments <AL>	*s.* B 372		

O 179	**operation on a set** <AL>	Operation *f* auf (über) einer Menge	opération *f* [définie] sur un ensemble, opération dans un ensemble, loi *f* de composition interne dans un ensemble	операция на множестве
	operation sign <LO>	*s.* F 752		
	operations with fractions <AR>	*s.* F 557		
O 180	**operation symbol,** operational symbol, operative sign, operator <AL>	Operationssymbol *n*, Operationszeichen *n*	signe (symbole) *m* d'opération, symbole (signe) opératoire, connecteur *m*	знак операции (действия)
	operation with sets <SE>	*s.* S 699		
O 181	**operative mathematics** <FO>	operative Mathematik *f*	opérativisme *m*, mathématiques *fpl* opératoires	оперативная математика
	operative sign <AL>	*s.* O 180		
	operator <AL>	*s.* O 180		
	operator <AN, FA>	*s.* M 96		
	operator <FA>	*s.* L 828		
	operator <LO>	*s.* 1. Q 77; 2. S 1132		
	ι operator <LO>	*s.* D 325		
	λ-operator, operator λ <LO>	*s.* A 152		
O 182	**operator[-]algebra,** algebra with operators <UA>	Operatoralgebra *f*	algèbre *f* à opérateurs	алгебра с операторами
O 183	**operator automorphism** <AL>	Operatorautomorphismus *m*	automorphisme *m* d'opérateurs; automorphisme d'un groupe à opérateurs	операторный автоморфизм
O 184	**operator bounded below,** bounded below operator, operator semi-bounded below, operator half-bounded below, operator semi-bounded (half-bounded) from below <FA>	nach (von) unten halbbeschränkter Operator *m*, unterhalbbeschränkter Operator	opérateur *m* semi-borné (semiborné) inférieurement	полуограниченный снизу оператор
	operator calculus <DE>	*s.* O 167		
O 185	**operator defined on a dense subset** <FA>	dichtdefinierter Operator *m*	opérateur *m* défini sur une partie dense	оператор, определенный на плотном множестве
	operator domain <AL>	*s.* O 204		
O 186	**operator equation** <FA>	Operatorgleichung *f*, Operatorengleichung *f*	équation *f* opératorielle	операторное уравнение
O 187	**operator function,** operator-valued function <DE>	Operatorfunktion *f*	fonction *f* opérateur	операторная функция
	operator[-]group <GR>	*s.* G 520		
	operator half-bounded [from] below <FA>	*s.* O 184		
O 188	**operator-homomorphic** <AL>	operator-homomorph	homomorphe à opérateurs	операторно-гомоморфный
O 189	**operator homomorphism** <of an algebra with operators> <AL>	Operatorhomomorphismus *m*, operatorhomomorphe Abbildung *f*, Homomorphismus *m*, homomorphe Abbildung, Deformation *f*	homomorphisme *m* d'opérateurs, homomorphisme d'une structure à opérateurs	операторный гомоморфизм, оператор-гомоморфизм
O 190	**operator homomorphism** <of a group> <GR>	Operatorgruppenhomomorphismus *m*, operatorhomomorphe Abbildung *f*	homomorphisme *m* d'un groupe à opérateurs, homomorphisme d'opérateurs	операторный гомоморфизм
O 191	**operator-isomorphic** <AL>	operatorisomorph	isomorphe à opérateurs	операторно-изоморфный, операторно изоморфный
O 192	**operator isomorphism** <AL, GR>	Operatorisomorphismus *m*, Operatorisomorphie *f*	isomorphisme *m* opérateur; isomorphisme d'une structure à opérateurs	операторный изоморфизм, оператор-изоморфизм
O 193	**operator isomorphy** <property> <AL>	Operatorisomorphie *f*	isomorphie *f* opérateur	операторный изоморфизм
	operator lambda <LO>	*s.* A 152		
O 194	**operator loop, operator-loop,** loop with operators <AL>	Operatorloop *f*	loop *m* à opérateurs	лупа с операторами
	operator method <DE>	*s.* S 2416		
O 195	**operator module, operator-module,** module with operators <AL>	Operatormodul *m*	module *m* à opérateurs	модуль с операторами, операторный модуль
O 196	**operator necessity** <in modal logic> <LO>	Funktor *m* der Notwendigkeit	opérateur *m* de nécessité, connecteur *m* nécessité	операция необходимости, необходимость
O 197	**operator norm,** norm, bound <of an operator> <FA>	Operatornorm *f*, Norm *f* <eines Operators>	norme *f* <d'un opérateur>	норма <оператора>
O 198	**operator object** <CA>	Operatorobjekt *n*	objet *m* à opérateurs	операторный объект
O 199	**operator of finite rank** <FA>	endlichdimensionaler Operator *m*, Operator von endlichem Rang, Operator endlichen Ranges	opérateur *m* de rang fini	оператор конечного ранга, конечномерный оператор
	operator of Hilbert-Schmidt class (type) <FA>	*s.* H 357		
O 200	**operator of left translation** <of a group> <AL>	Linkstranslationsoperator *m*	opérateur *m* de translation à gauche	оператор левого сдвига

O 201	**operator of right translation** <of a group> <AL>	Rechtstranslationsoperator *m*	opérateur *m* de translation à droite	оператор правого сдвига
O 202	**operator possibility** <in modal logic> <LO>	Funktor *m* der Möglichkeit	opérateur *m* « possible », connecteur *m* possibilité, opérateur modal de la possibilité	модальный оператор «возможно», операция возможности
O 203	**operator ray** <FA>	Operatorstrahl *m*	rayon *m* d'opérateur	луч оператора
	operator semi-bounded [from] below <FA>	*s.* O 184		
O 204	**operator set,** operator domain, domain of operators (multipliers) <of an algebraic structure> <AL>	Operatorenbereich *m*, Operatorenmenge *f*, Multiplikatorenbereich *m*	ensemble *m* des opérateurs, domaine *f* d'opérateurs	область операторов
	operator-valued function <DE>	*s.* O 187		
	operator variable <LO>	*s.* F 783		
O 205	**operator with continuous spectrum** <FA>	Operator *m* mit kontinuierlichem Spektrum	opérateur *m* doué de spectre continu, opérateur à spectre continu	оператор с непрерывным спектром
O 206	**ophiuride** <GE>	Ophiuride *f*, Schlangenschwanzkurve *f*, Schlangenschwanzlinie *f*	ophiuride *f*	
O 207	**opposite,** opposite in direction, oppositely directed, of opposite direction, antiparallel <GE>	entgegengesetzt gerichtet, entgegengerichtet, antiparallel	opposé, de sens opposé, antiparallèle	противоположно направленный, противоположный, антипараллельный
O 208	**opposite algebra,** algebra inversely isomorphic <to>, reciprocal algebra <AL>	entgegengesetzte Algebra *f*	algèbre *f* opposée	инверсная алгебра
O 209	**opposite and equal;** of the same magnitude, but oppositely directed; equal of magnitude, but opposite of sign <GN>	entgegengesetzt gleich	opposé, égal et opposé	равный по величине, но противоположный по знаку
O 210	**opposite angles** <EG>	entgegengesetzte (entgegengesetzt liegende) Winkel *mpl*	angles *mpl* opposés	односторонние углы
	opposite category <CA>	*s.* D 979		
	opposite composition <AL>	*s.* C 2280		
O 211	**opposite composition law** <AL>	entgegengesetztes Verknüpfungsgesetz *n*	loi *f* de composition opposée	противоположный закон композиции
O 212	**opposite Dini['s] derivative** <RF>	entgegengesetzte Derivierte (Ableitungszahl) *f*	nombre *m* dérivé opposé	противоположное производное число <по Дини>
	opposite direction / of <GE>	*s.* O 207		
O 213	**opposite face** <of a simplex> <AT>	gegenüberliegende Seite *f*	face *f* opposée	противоположная грань
O 214	**opposite form** <NT>	entgegengesetzte <quadratische> Form *f*, forma *f* opposita	forme *f* opposée	противоположная форма
O 215	**opposite graduation** <AL>	entgegengesetzte Graduierung *f*	graduation *f* opposée	противоположное градуирование
O 216	**opposite group** <GR>	Gegengruppe *f*	groupe *m* opposé	инверсная группа
	opposite in direction <GE>	*s.* O 207		
O 217	**opposite Lie group** <AL>	entgegengesetzte Liesche Gruppe *f*	groupe *m* de Lie opposé	инверсная лиева группа
	oppositely directed <GE>	*s.* O 207		
O 218	**opposite number** <$z \to -z$> <NT>	entgegengesetzte Zahl *f*, Gegenzahl *f*, umgekehrte (inverse) Zahl	opposé *m*, symétrique *m*, nombre symétrique (égal et de signe contraire)	противоположное число
O 219	**opposite quantity** <AL>	entgegengesetzte Größe *f*	quantité *f* de signe contraire	противоположная величина
O 220	**opposite ring** <AL>	Gegenring *m*, entgegengesetzter Ring *m*	anneau *m* opposé	противоположное (антиизоморфное) кольцо
O 221	**opposite semigroup** <AL>	Gegenhalbgruppe *f*	demi-groupe *m* opposé	противоположная полугруппа
O 222	**opposite side** <of a complete quadrangle> <GE>	Gegenseite *f*, gegenüberliegende Seite *f*	côté *m* opposé	противоположная сторона
O 223	**opposite side** <in Pascal's hexagrammum mysticum> <EG>	Gegenseite *f*	côté *m* opposé	противоположная сторона
O 224	**opposite side,** opposite small side <of a rectangular triangle> <EG>	Gegenkathete *f*	côté *m* opposé	противолежащий катет
O 225	**opposite side** <of a triangle> <EG>	<dem Winkel> gegenüberliegende Seite *f*	côté *m* opposé	противолежащая сторона
O 226	**opposite sign** <AL>	entgegengesetztes Vorzeichen (Zeichen) *n*	signe *m* contraire (opposé)	противоположный знак
O 227	**opposite simplex** <AT>	Gegensimplex *n*, gegenüberliegendes Simplex *n*	simplexe *m* opposé	противоположный симплекс
O 228	**opposite skew field** <AL>	entgegengesetzter Schiefkörper *m*	corps *m* opposé	противоположное тело
	opposite small side <EG>	*s.* O 224		
O 229	**opposite topological group** <AL>	topologische Gegengruppe *f*, entgegengesetzte topologische Gruppe *f*	groupe *m* topologique opposé	противоположная топологическая группа

O 230	**opposite vector,** vector equal in length and opposite in direction <VT>	entgegengesetzter Vektor *m*, verkehrt gleicher Vektor	vecteur *m* opposé	противоположный вектор
O 231	**opposite vertex** <of a complete quadrilateral> <GE>	Gegenecke *f*, gegenüberliegende Ecke *f*	sommet *m* opposé, antisommet *m*	противолежащая вершина
O 232	**opposite vertex** <in Pascal's hexagrammum mysticum> <GE>	Gegenpunkt *m* <Steiner>	point *m* opposé	противоположная точка
O 233	**opposition** <LO>	Entgegensetzung *f*, Opposition *f*	opposition *f* [logique]	противоположение
O 234	**OP-ring,** outer product ring <AL>	OP-Ring *m*, Außenproduktring *m*	OP-anneau *m*	OP-кольцо
O 235	**optimality** <TG>	Optimalität *f*	optimalité *f*	оптимальность
O 236	**optimality criterion,** criterion of optimality <PG>	Optimalitätskriterium *n*, Optimierungskriterium *n*, Optimalkriterium *n*	critère *m* d'optimalité	критерий оптимальности
	optimality principle <PG>	*s.* B 175		
	optimality principle <PG, ST, TG>	*s.* P 1511		
O 237	**optimal policy** <in decision theory> <PG>	optimale Politik *f*, Optimalpolitik *f*	stratégie *f* optimale	оптимальная стратегия
O 238	**optimal stopping** <SP>	optimales Stoppen *n*	arrêt *m* optimal	оптимальная остановка
	ε-optimal strategy <SP, TG>	*s.* Q 212		
O 239	**optimization;** optimizing <PG>	Optimierung *f*, // Optimisierung *f*, Optimalisierung *f*	optimisation *f*, optimalisation *f*	оптимизация, доведение до оптимума
	optimization <PG>	*s. a.* M 170		
	0—1 optimization <PG>	*s.* Z 50		
O 240	**optimization problem** <PG>	Optimierungsproblem *n*	problème *m* d'optimisation	задача оптимизации
	optimizing <PG>	*s.* O 239		
O 241	**optimum,** optimum value <PG>	Optimum *n*, Optimalwert *m*	optimum *m*, valeur *f* optimale (optimum)	оптимум, оптимальная величина, оптимальное значение
	optimum point <PG>	*s.* O 243		
	optimum program[me] <PG>	*s.* O 243		
O 242	**optimum property** <ST>	optimale Eigenschaft *f*, Optimumeigenschaft *f*	propriété *f* optimale (optimum)	оптимальное свойство
O 243	**optimum solution,** optimum program[me]; optimum vector <multidimensional>; optimum point <one-dimensional> <PG>	Optimallösung *f*, optimale Lösung *f*, optimales Programm *n*; Optimalvektor *m*, optimaler Vektor *m*; Optimalpunkt *m*, optimaler Punkt *m*	solution *f* optimale, programme *m* optimum; vecteur *m* optimum; point *m* optimal (optimum)	оптимальный план, оптимальное решение, оптимальная программа; оптимальный вектор; оптимальная точка
O 244	**optimum strategy** <TG>	optimale Strategie *f*	stratégie *f* optimale	оптимальная стратегия
	optimum value <PG>	*s.* O 241		
	optimum vector <PG>	*s.* O 243		
O 245	**option,** choice <MM>	Wahlfreiheit *f*	liberté *f* du choix	свобода выбора
O 246	**optional sampling (selection)** <ST>	Auswahl *f* aufs Geratewohl, willkürliche Auswahl	choix *f* (sélection *f*, sondage *m*) arbitraire	произвольный выбор
O 247	**orbiform [curve],** curve of constant breadth <CS, GE>	Orbiforme *f*, Gleichdick *n*, gleichdicke Kurve *f*, ebener Körper *m* konstanter Breite, Körper konstanter Breite in der Ebene, Kurve konstanter Breite	courbe *f* orbiforme, courbe de largeur constante, orbiforme *m*	кривая постоянной ширины
O 248	**orbit,** transitivity set <GR>	Orbit *m* <durch *x* unter der Operation von *G*>, Transitivitätsklasse *f* <von *x* unter *G*>	orbite *f*, trajectoire *f*, classe *f* de transitivité	орбита, класс транзитивности
	orbit <DE>	*s.* T 722		
	orbit <GR>	*s.* D 874		
O 249	**orbitally stable integral curve** <DE>	orbital stabile Integralkurve *f*	courbe *f* intégrale orbitalement stable	орбитно устойчивая интегральная кривая
O 250	**orbital map** < <of a Lie group> <GR>	Orbitabbildung *f*	application *f* orbitale	орбитальное отображение
O 251	**orbital stability** <DE>	orbitale Stabilität *f*	stabilité *f* orbitale	орбитальная устойчивость
O 252	**orbital topology** <TO>	orbitale Topologie *f*	topologie *f* orbitale	орбитальная топология
O 253	**orbit space** <of the action of a group> <TO>	Bahnenraum *m*	espace *m* des trajectoires	пространство орбит <действия группы>, пространство траекторий
	orbit space <TO>	*s.* Q 348		
O 254	**. . . or . . . but not both,** . . . <is> not [materially] equivalent to . . . <LO>	entweder . . . oder . . .	ou bien . . . ou bien . . .	неверно, что . . . и . . .
O 255	**order** <of a field> <AB>	Ordnung *f* <Dedekind>, Spezies *f*, Species *f*, Art *f* <Kronecker>, Ring *m* algebraischer Größen <Hilbert>, Integritätsbereich *m* <Kronecker>, Zahlring *m* <Hilbert>	ordre *m*, espèce *f*, anneau *m* d'intégrité, domaine *m* d'intégrité, domaine holoïde, anneau	порядок
O 256	**order,** dimension <of an algebra> <AL>	Rang *m*, Grad *m* <Scheffers>	rang *m*, ordre *m*	размерность
O 257	**order** <of a conjugacy class>, number of elements <in a conjugacy class> <AL>	Ordnung *f*, Elementezahl *f* <einer Klasse konjugierter Elemente>	nombre *m* d'éléments <d'une classe de conjugaison>	порядок <класса [сопряженных элементов]>

No.	English	German	French	Russian
O 258	**order** <of an element with respect to a prime element at a place> <AL>	Ordnung *f* <eines Elements bezüglich eines Primelements>	valuation *f*, ordre *m*, hauteur *f* <d'un élément par rapport à un élément premier>	порядок, высота <элемента относительно простого элемента>
O 259	**order** <of the factor groups of a composition series> <AL>	Faktor *m* der Zusammensetzung	facteur *m* de composition, facteur de composition de Jordan <d'un groupe>	порядок фактор-групп композиционного ряда
O 260	**order** <of a permutation> <AL, CT>	Ordnung *f*, Ordnungszahl *f*, Grad *m*	ordre *m*, degré *m*	порядок
O 261	**order** <in the condition of Hölder>, Hölder['s] order, Hölder['s] index <AN>	Exponent *m* <in der Hölder-Bedingung>, Hölder-Exponent *m*, Hölderscher Exponent *m*	exposant (ordre) *m* [dans la condition] de Hölder	порядок условия (в условии) Гельдера
O 262	**order** <of an *o*-place> <AT>	Index *m*, Vielfachheit *f*	ordre *m*	индекс
O 263	**order** <of a Latin square> <CT>	Seitenlänge *f*, Reihenzahl *f*	côté *m*	порядок
O 264	**order** <in the condition of Lipschitz>, Lipschitz['s] order, Lipschitz['s] index <DE>	Exponent *m* <in der Lipschitz-Bedingung>, Lipschitz-Exponent *m*, Lipschitzscher Exponent	exposant (ordre) *m* [dans la condition] de Lipschitz	порядок условия (в условии) Липшица
O 265	**order** <of a congruence *or* complex> <DG>	Ordnung *f*, Grad *m*	ordre *m*, degré *m*	порядок
O 266	**order** <of a derivative> <DI>	Ordnung *f*, Grad *m*, Ableitungsordnung *f*	ordre *m*, degré *m*, indice *m* de dérivation	порядок
O 267	**order** <of a branch point> <FT>	Verzweigungsordnung *f*, Ordnung *f* <eines Verzweigungspunktes>	ordre *m* <d'un point de ramification>	индекс (порядок) ветвления (точки разветвления)
O 268	**order** <of an entire function> <FT>	Ordnung *f* <v. Schaper>	ordre *m* apparent, ordre	порядок
O 269	**order,** degree <of an elliptic function> <FU>	Ordnung *f*, Grad *m*	ordre *m*	порядок
O 270	**order** <of a point with respect to a curve> <GE>	Ordnung *f*, Punktordnung *f* <eines Punktes bezüglich einer Kurve>	ordre *m* <d'un point par rapport à une courbe>	порядок <точки относительно кривой>
O 271	**order,** period <of a group> <GR>	Ordnung *f*	ordre *m*, // diviseur *m* indicatif <Cauchy>	порядок, период
O 272	**order,** period <of an element of a group> <GR>	Ordnung *f* <eines Gruppenelements>	ordre *m* <d'un élément d'un groupe>	порядок <элемента группы>
O 273	**order** <of an expression> <LO>	Ausdrucksstufe *f*, Stufe *f* <eines Ausdrucks>	niveau *m*	порядок
O 274	**order** <of a matrix *or* determinant> <MD>	Ordnung *f*, Grad *m*, Reihenzahl *f*	ordre *m*, degré *m*	порядок
O 275	**order** <of a p-adic number> <NT>	Ordnungszahl *f*	ordre *m*	порядок
O 276	**order,** place, position rank <in a number representation> <NT>	Stelle *f*, Ziffernstelle *f*, Position *f*	poids *m*, rang *m*, position *f*	разряд, место, позиция
O 277	**order,** index <of a number mod. *m*> <NT>	Ordnung *f*, Index *m*	ordre *m*	порядок
O 278	**order** <of a system of sets *or* of a covering> <SE, TO>	Ordnung *f*	ordre *m*	кратность
	order <AB>	*s.* A 1169		
	order <AG>	*s.* 1. D 169; 2. D 170		
	order <AG, DG>	*s.* M 1055		
	order <AL>	*s.* 1. A 686; 2. D 173; 3. I 332; 4. L 566; 5. O 334		
	order <AL, FT>	*s.* M 1058		
	order <AL, VT>	*s.* R 133		
	order <CT>	*s.* A 983		
	order <FO, SE>	*s.* L 593		
	order <FT>	*s.* G 526		
	order <GN>	*s.* A 992		
	order <GN, SE>	*s.* O 350		
	order <MD>	*s.* S 1149		
	order <NU>	*s.* O 349		
	order <SE>	*s.* C 123		
	order <SS>	*s.* U 73		
	order <UA>	*s.* C 120		
O 279	**orderability** <AL>	Ordnungsfähigkeit *f*	ordonnabilité *f*	упорядочиваемость
O 280	**orderable set** <SE>	ordnungsfähige Menge *f*	ensemble *m* ordonnable	упорядочиваемое множество
	order according to the principle of last differences <SE>	*s.* A 735		
O 281	**order** <of an algebraic function> **at a point** <AL>	Ordnung *f* in einem Punkt	ordre *m* en un point	порядок в точке
O 282/3	**order** <of a meromorphic function> **at a point** <FT>	Ordnungszahl (Ordnung) *f* <einer meromorphen Funktion> an einer Stelle	ordre *m* <d'une fonction méromorphe> en un point	порядок <мероморфной функции> в точке
O 284	**order automorphism, order-automorphism** <of a partially ordered group> <GR>	Ordnungsautomorphismus *m*	automorphisme *m* croissant (d'un groupe ordonné)	порядковый автоморфизм, у-автоморфизм
O 285	**order automorphism, order-automorphism** <of a linearly ordered set> <SE>	Ordnungsautomorphismus *m*	automorphisme *m* d'un ensemble ordonné	автоморфизм упорядоченного множества
O 286	**order axioms,** ordering axioms <SE>	Ordnungsaxiome *npl*	axiomes *mpl* d'ordre	аксиомы порядка
O 287	**order boundedness** <SE>	Ordnungsbeschränktheit *f*	propriété *f* d'être borné (majoré et minoré)	ограниченность по упорядочению

O 288	**order-bounded set,** bounded set <SE>	beschränkte halbgeordnete Menge *f*, ordnungsbeschränkte Menge	ensemble *m* borné (ordonné majoré et minoré)	ограниченное частично упорядоченное множество
	order by first difference[s] <SE>	*s.* L 619		
	order by last differences <SE>	*s.* A 735		
O 289	**order compatible topology** <AN, TO>	mit der Ordnung verträgliche Topologie *f*	topologie *f* compatible avec l'ordre	совместимая с порядком топология
	order-complete quasi-ordered class <SE>	*s.* C 1551		
O 290	**order-complete set,** Dedekind complete set, conditionally complete set <SE>	vollständige halbgeordnete Menge *f*, bedingt vollständige Menge	ensemble *m* conditionnellement complet	условно полное множество
O 291	**order-continuous topology** <AN, TO>	ordnungsstetige Topologie *f*, stetige Topologie bezüglich der Ordnung	topologie *f* continue par rapport à l'ordre	топология, непрерывная по упорядочению
O 292	**order convergence,** (*o*)-convergence <in a partially ordered linear space> <FA>	Ordnungskonvergenz *f*, halbgeordnete Konvergenz *f*, ordinäre Konvergenz, (*o*)-Konvergenz *f*	(*o*)-convergence *f*	(*o*)-сходимость
O 293	**order-convex hull,** full hull <FA>	ordnungskonvexe Hülle *f*		(*o*)-выпуклая оболочка
	order dual <AN, TO>	*s.* A 1095		
O 294	**ordered Abelian group** <GR>	geordnete (angeordnete) abelsche Gruppe *f*	groupe *m* abélien totalement ordonné	линейно упорядоченная абелева группа
	ordered according to magnitude <SE>	*s.* O 296		
O 295	**ordered affine plane** <GE>	angeordnete affine Ebene *f*	plan *m* affine ordonné	упорядоченная аффинная плоскость
	ordered Archimedean field <AL>	*s.* A 900		
	ordered Archimedean number field <AL>	*s.* A 901		
	ordered arrangement <CT>	*s.* A 983		
	ordered arrangement <GN>	*s.* A 992		
O 296	**ordered by magnitude,** ordered according to magnitude <SE>	der Größe nach geordnet	ordonné d'après la grandeur	упорядоченный по величине
O 297	**ordered chain complex** <AT>	geordneter Kettenkomplex *m*	complexe *m* de chaînes ordonnées	упорядоченный цепной комплекс
	ordered class <CA, SE>	*s.* P 226		
O 298	**ordered class of subobjects** <of an object> <CA>	Potenzklasse *f*	classe *f* ordonnée des sous-objets	упорядоченный класс подобъектов
	ordered couple <SE>	*s.* O 307		
O 299	**ordered direct product** <GR>	geordnetes direktes Produkt *n*	produit *m* direct ordonné	упорядоченное прямое произведение
O 300	**ordered direct sum** <GR>	geordnete direkte Summe *f*	somme *f* directe ordonnée	прямая упорядоченная сумма
O 301	**ordered factor group** <GR>	geordnete (halbgeordnete) Faktorgruppe *f*	groupe *m* ordonné quotient	упорядоченная фактор-группа
O 302	**ordered field** <AL>	angeordneter (linear geordneter, vollständig geordneter, einfach geordneter) Körper *m*	corps *m* ordonné (totalement ordonné)	упорядоченное (вполне упорядоченное) поле
O 303	**ordered field** <AL>	geordneter Körper *m*, partiell (teilweise) geordneter Körper	corps *m* ordonné	упорядоченное поле
O 304	**ordered field extension** <AL>	angeordnete Körpererweiterung *f*, angeordneter Oberkörper *m*	extension *f* ordonnée	упорядоченное расширение поля
	ordered field having an Archimedean order <AL>	*s.* A 900		
O 305	**ordered group,** partially ordered group, po-group <GR>	halbgeordnete (geordnete) Gruppe *f*, teilweise (partiell) geordnete Gruppe	groupe *m* ordonné (semi-ordonné)	упорядоченная (частично упорядоченная) группа
	ordered group <GR>	*s.* S 1001		
	ordered loop <AL>	*s.* S 1002		
O 306	**ordered module** <AL>	geordneter Modul *m*, halbgeordneter Modul	module *m* ordonné	частично упорядоченный модуль
	ordered *n*-tuple[t] <AL, SE>	*s.* N 750		
O 307	**ordered pair,** ordered couple, couple <SE>	geordnetes Paar *n*	couple *m*, paire *f* ordonnée, couple ordonné, doublet *m*, séquence *f* de degré 2	упорядоченная пара
O 308	**ordered partition** <NT>	geordnete Partition *f*	partition *f* ordonnée	упорядоченное разбиение
O 309	**ordered polynomial** <AL>	geordnetes Polynom *n*	polynôme *m* ordonné [par rapport aux puissances d'une lettre]	расположенный многочлен
O 310	**ordered product** <of groups> <GR>	geordnetes Produkt *n*	produit *m* ordonné	упорядоченное произведение
O 311	**ordered product,** product <of types> <SE>	Produkt *n* <von Ordnungstypen>	produit *m* <de types ordinaux>	произведение <порядковых типов>
O 312	**ordered projective plane** <PJ>	angeordnete projektive Ebene *f*	plan *m* projectif ordonné	упорядоченная проективная плоскость
	ordered pythagorean field <AL>	*s.* P 2085		

No.	English	German	French	Russian
O 313	**ordered quadruplet** <SE>	geordnetes Quadrupel *n*, geordneter Vierer *m*	quadriplet *m*, séquence *f* de quatre éléments	упорядоченная четверка
O 314	**ordered quasi-field** <AL>	angeordneter Quasikörper *m*	quasi-corps *m* totalement ordonné	вполне упорядоченное квазиполе
O 315	**ordered ring,** partially ordered ring <AL>	geordneter Ring *m*, partiell (teilweise) geordneter Ring	anneau *m* ordonné (partiellement ordonné)	упорядоченное кольцо, частично упорядоченное кольцо
O 316	**ordered sample,** ordered series <ST>	geordnete Stichprobe *f*, Positionsstichprobe *f*, Variationsreihe *f*, Ordnungsstatistik *f*	échantillon *m* ordonné, série *f* ordonnée	ранжированный ряд распределения, ранжированный вариационный ряд, упорядоченная выборка, вариационный ряд, ряд распределения
	ordered sample <SE>	*s.* T 1061		
	ordered sample function <ST>	*s.* O 362		
	ordered sample of *n* elements <AL, SE>	*s.* N 750		
O 317	**ordered semi-group,** partially ordered semi-group <AL>	teilweise geordnete Halbgruppe *f*, geordnete Halbgruppe	demi-groupe *m* ordonné; monoïde *m* ordonné	упорядоченная полугруппа
	ordered semi-ring <AL>	*s.* L 821		
	ordered sequence <SE>	*s.* T 1061		
	ordered sequence of *n* terms <AL, SE>	*s.* N 750		
	ordered sequence of numbers <GN>	*s.* N 851		
	ordered series <ST>	*s.* O 316		
O 318	**ordered set,** strictly (separatively, antireflexively) ordered set <SE>	irreflexiv (antireflexiv) geordnete Menge *f*, [lineare] strikt geordnete Menge	ensemble *m* strictement ordonné	вполне упорядоченное множество, строго упорядоченное множество
	ordered set <SE>	*s. a.* 1. L 822; 2. P 231		
O 319	**ordered set bounded [from] below,** minorized (left-bounded) ordered set, ordered set bounded on the left <SE>	nach unten beschränkte (ordnungsbeschränkte) halbgeordnete Menge *f*, nach links beschränkte halbgeordnete Menge	ensemble *m* ordonné minoré (borné inférieurement, borné en bas)	ограниченное снизу полуупорядоченное множество
	ordered set bounded on the left <SE>	*s.* O 319		
	ordered set bounded on the right <SE>	*s.* B 664		
O 320	**ordered set no two segments of which are similar** <SE>	geordnete Menge *f*, von der keine zwei Segmente ähnlich sind	ensemble *m* rangé	упорядоченное множество, никакие два отрезка которого не подобны
O 321	**ordered set with gaps** <SE>	geordnete Menge *f* mit Lücken	échelle *f* (ordre *m*) lacunaire	упорядоченное множество с пробелами
O 322	**ordered set without gaps** <SE>	lückenlos geordnete Menge *f*, geordnete Menge ohne Lücken	échelle *f* fermée (non lacunaire), ensemble *m* sans trous	множество без дыр (пробелов)
O 323	**ordered simplex** <AT>	geordnetes Simplex *n*	simplexe *m* ordonné	упорядоченный симплекс, упорядоченный остов
O 324	**ordered singular boundary** <AT>	geordneter singulärer Rand *m*	bord *m* singulier ordonné	упорядоченная сингулярная граница
O 325	**ordered singular cycle** <AL>	geordneter singulärer Zyklus *m*	cycle *m* singulier ordonné	упорядоченный сингулярный цикл
O 326	**ordered skew field** <AL>	geordneter (angeordneter) Schiefkörper *m*	corps *m* gauche [totalement] ordonné	упорядоченное тело
O 327	**ordered subclass** <CA, SE>	halbgeordnete Unterklasse *f*	sous-classe *f* ordonnée	полуупорядоченный подкласс
O 328	**ordered triplet** <SE>	geordnetes Tripel *n*, geordneter Drilling (Dreier) *m* <drei der Reihe nach geordnete Elemente>	triplet *m*, séquence *f* de trois éléments, séquence de degré 3	упорядоченная тройка
	ordered vector space ⌐<AL, FA>	*s.* P 234		
O 329	**order epimorphism** <of a partially ordered group> <GR>	Ordnungsepimorphismus *m*	épimorphisme *m* croissant (d'un groupe ordonné)	порядковый эпиморфизм, у-эпиморфизм
O 330	**order function** <on a module> <AL>	Ordnungsfunktion *f* <auf einem Modul>	fonction *f* d'ordre <sur un module>	функция порядка <на модуле>
O 331	**order-homomorphic group** <GR>	ordnungshomomorphe Gruppe *f*	groupe *m* ordonné homomorphe	порядково-гомоморфная группа
O 332	**order-homomorphic image** <of a partially ordered group> <GR>	ordnungshomomorphes Abbild *n*	image *f* par un homomorphisme croissant	образ при порядковом гомоморфизме
O 333	**order homomorphism** <of a partially ordered group or semigroup> <AL, GR>	Ordnungshomomorphismus *m*	homomorphisme *m* croissant	порядковый гомоморфизм, у-гомоморфизм, о-гомоморфизм
	order homomorphism <SE>	*s.* I 1173		
O 334	**order ideal,** order, annihilator <of an element of an *R*-module> <AL>	Ordnungsideal *n*, Annullator *m*	annulateur *m*	порядковый идеал, порядок, аннулятор
	order ideal <AL>	*s.* A 686		
O 334a	**order** <of a space> **in a point** <TO>	Ordnung *f* in einem Punkt	ordre *m* en un point	порядок в точке
O 335	**ordering** <[of] a set> <SE>	Ordnen *n*	ordination *f*	упорядочивание
	ordering <CT>	*s.* A 983		
	ordering <GN>	*s.* A 985		
	ordering <GN, SE>	*s.* O 350		
	ordering <SE>	*s.* 1. L 830; 2. P 246		
	ordering according to the principle of first differences <SE>	*s.* L 619		

	English	German	French	Russian
	ordering[-] addition <in lattices> <SE>	*s.* A 230		
	ordering axioms <SE>	*s.* O 286		
	ordering in the weak sense <SE>	*s.* O 336		
	ordering relation <SE>	*s.* O 359		
	ordering relation in the strict sense <SE>	*s.* S 1909		
O 336	**ordering relation in the weak sense,** ordering in the weak sense, partial order, partial ordering [relation], proper quasi-order, inclusion relation <SE>	reflexive Halbordnung *f*, Halbordnung zweiter (2.) Art, Halbordnungsrelation *f*, Halbordnung *f*	ordre *m* [réflexif], ordre [au sens] large, relation *f* d'ordre [au sens] large, relation d'ordre, pré-ordre *m* antisymétrique, relation d'ordre partiel (non stricte), ordre partiel, ordre partiel large (non strict), comparaison *f*	рефлексивное частичное упорядочение, частичное упорядочение
	ordering theorem <AT>	*s.* C 786		
O 337	**order interval, order-interval** <of a partially ordered set> <SE>	abgeschlossenes Intervall *n*	intervalle *m* fermé, segment *m*	интервал, отрезок
	order-isomorphic correspondence <SE>	*s.* O 356		
O 338	**order-isomorphic field** <AL>	ähnlich-isomorpher Körper *m*	corps *m* isomorphe par similitude, corps isomorphe et semblable	подобно изоморфное поле
O 339	**order-isomorphic group** <GR>	ordnungsisomorphe [geordnete] Gruppe *f*	groupe *m* ordonné isomorphe	порядково-изоморфная группа, у-изоморфная группа
	order-isomorphic mapping <SE>	*s.* O 356		
O 340	**order-isomorphism** <of ordered modules *or* rings> <AL>	anordnungstreue (ähnlich-isomorphe) Abbildung *f*	isomorphisme *m* maintenant l'ordre	преобразование, сохраняющее расположение
O 341	**order isomorphism** <of partially ordered groups> <GR>	Ordnungsisomorphismus *m*	isomorphisme *m* croissant (de groupes ordonnés)	порядковый изоморфизм, у-изоморфизм
	order isomorphism <SE>	*s.* O 356		
O 342	**order line** <DS>	Ordner *m*, Ordnungslinie *f*	ligne *f* d'ordre	порядковая линия
	order linearly / to <SE>	*s.* O 361		
O 343	**order of an infinitesimal** <AN, SS>	Ordnung *f* der unendlich kleinen Größen, Ordnung des Verschwindens <einer Folge *oder* Funktion>	ordre *m* de petitesse, ordre des infiniment petits, ordre de l'infiniment petit, ordre infinitésimal	порядок малости, порядок бесконечно малой
O 344	**order of connectivity,** connectivity <of a domain> <TO>	Zusammenhangszahl *f*, Zusammenhang *m* <*z. B.:* *k*-facher>, Grad *m* der Konnexität	connectivité *f*	связность, порядок связности
O 345	**order of contact** <DG>	Ordnung *f* der Berührung	ordre *m* du (de) contact	порядок касания
O 346	**order of growth,** growth order <of a sequence> <SS>	Ordnung *f* des Anwachsens	ordre *m* de croissance	порядок роста
O 347	**order of infinities (infinity)** <AN, SS>	Ordnung *f* des Unendlichwerdens	ordre *m* d'infinitude, degré *m* de grandeur	порядок роста
O 348	**order of inseparability** <AL>	Inseparabilitätsordnung *f*	ordre *m* d'inséparabilité	несепарабельный порядок
O 349	**order of magnitude,** magnitude, order <of a number> <NU>	Größenordnung *f*	ordre *m* de grandeur, ordre	порядок величины, порядок
O 350	**order of sequence (succession),** sequence, order, ordering, ordinal succession <GN, SE>	Reihenfolge *f*	ordre *m*	порядок, чередование, последовательность
O 351	**order of the group of a graph,** symmetry number <of a graph> <GP>	Symmetriegrad *m*, Ordnung *f* der Gruppe eines Graphen	ordre *m* de symétrie	порядок группы графа, симметрическое число
O 352	**order of units** <NT>	Stellenindex *m*, Stellenzeiger *m* <Leibniz>	indice *m* de position	индекс
O 353	**order-open interval,** open interval <in an ordered set> <SE>	offenes Intervall *n*	intervalle *m* ouvert	открытый интервал
O 354	**order-preserving correspondence,** increasing correspondence <SE>	ordnungstreue Korrespondenz *f*	correspondance *f* isotone	сохраняющее порядок соответствие; соответствие, сохраняющее отношение порядка
	order-preserving function <SE>	*s.* I 1173		
O 355	**order-preserving isomorphism** <AL>	ordnungstreuer Isomorphismus *m*	isomorphisme *m* conservant l'ordre	сохраняющий порядок изоморфизм
O 356	**order-preserving isomorphism,** [order] isomorphism, similar mapping, similarity, similar one-to-one correspondence, similarity mapping (transformation), order-isomorphic correspondence (mapping), strictly order-preserving mapping <of partially ordered sets> <SE>	Ordnungsisomorphismus *m*, Ähnlichkeitsabbildung *f*, Isomorphismus *m*, isomorphe Abbildung *f*, Ähnlichkeit *f*, ordnungsisomorphe (ähnliche) Abbildung	isomorphisme *m* d'ordre, isomorphisme, bijection *f* monotone croissante, similitude *f*, transformation *f* compatible avec l'ordre, isomorphisme d'ensembles ordonnés	отображение (соответствие) подобия, подобное отображение, порядковый изоморфизм, [монотонный] изоморфизм, сохраняющая порядок функция, сохраняющее порядок отображение; отображение, сохраняющее строгие включения
	order-preserving many-one correspondence <SE>	*s.* I 1173		
	order[-] preserving map[ping] <SE>	*s.* I 1173		

O 357/8	**order[-] preserving relation,** increasing relation <SE>	ordnungstreue Relation *f*	relation *f* isotone	отношение, сохраняющее порядок
O 359	**order-relation, order relation,** relation of order, ordering relation <SE>	Ordnungsrelation *f*, Ordnung *f*, Ordnungsbeziehung *f*	relation *f* d'ordre	отношение порядка, соотношение порядка
	order relation, order-relation <SE>	*s. a.* 1. L 830; 2. P 246		
O 360	**order-simple group** <GR>	ordnungseinfache halbgeordnete Gruppe *f*	groupe *m* ordonné qui non contient pas des sous-groupes invariants convexes non triviaux	у-простая группа
O 361	**order simply / to,** to order linearly <said of a relation> <SE>	linear ordnen	ordonner linéairement	линейно упорядочивать
O 362	**order statistic,** ordered sample function <ST>	Positionsstichprobenfunktion *f*, Positionsfunktion *f*, Ranggröße *f*, Anordnungsstichprobenfunktion *f*, Stichprobenfunktion *f* der Anordnung, Ordnungsmaßzahl *f*, Anordnungsmaßzahl *f*, Anordnungswert *m*, Ordnungswert *m*, Ordnungsstatistik *f*	statistique *f* d'ordre, fonction *f* des observations de l'échantillon ordonné	порядковая статистика
O 363	**order statistics** <as a field of statistics> <ST>	Ordnungsstatistik *f*	statistique *f* d'ordre	порядковая статистика
O 364	**order structure** <SE>	Ordnungsstruktur *f*	structure *f* d'ordre	структура порядка
	order test <ST>	*s.* R 152		
O 365	**order topology,** (*o*)-topology <AN, TO>	Ordnungstopologie *f*	topologie *f* d'ordre	топология упорядочения, (*o*)-топология, топология упорядоченности, топология порядка
	order type <SE>	*s.* O 381		
O 366	**order type of a densely ordered set** <SE>	dichter Ordnungstypus *m*	type *m* [d'ordre] dense	плотный порядковый тип
O 367	**order type of an open ordered set** <SE>	unbegrenzter Ordnungstyp *m*	type *m* d'ordre d'un ensemble totalement ordonné sans élément maximum et sans élément minimum	порядковый тип неограниченного линейно упорядоченного множества
O 368	**order** <of connectives> **with respect to their strength** <LO>	Ordnung *f* <der Operatoren> nach ihrer Bindungsstärke	hiérarchie *f* <des opérateurs>	порядок <связок> относительно их сил
O 369	**ordinal,** ordinal number <SE>	Ordnungszahl *f*, Ordinalzahl *f*, Wohlordnungstypus *m*	ordinal *m*, nombre *m* ordinal (d'ordre), numéro *m*, type *m* du bon ordre	порядковое число, ординал, ординальное число
O 370	**ordinal addition,** addition of ordinal numbers <SE>	Addition *f* von Ordinalzahlen	addition *f* ordinale, addition des nombres ordinaux	ординальное сложение, сложение порядковых чисел
O 371	**ordinal arithmetic,** arithmetic of ordinals <SE>	Arithmetik *f* der Ordinalzahlen, Ordinalzahlarithmetik *f*	arithmétique *f* ordinale (des nombres ordinaux)	арифметика порядковых чисел
O 372	**ordinal character** <of a quadratic form in *n* variables> <NT>	Ordnungszahl *f*, determinierende Zahl *f*	invariant *m*	инвариант
O 373	**ordinal exponentiation** <SE>	Potenzierung *f* einer Ordnungszahl mit einer Ordnungszahl als Exponent	exponentiation *f* ordinale	потенцирование порядковых чисел
O 374	**ordinal function** <SE>	ordinale Funktion *f*	fonction *f* ordinale	порядковая функция
	ordinally similar set <SE>	*s.* S 878		
O 375	**ordinal multiplication,** multiplication of ordinal numbers <SE>	Multiplikation *f* von Ordinalzahlen	multiplication *f* ordinale, multiplication des nombres ordinaux	ординальное умножение, умножение порядковых чисел
	ordinal number <SE>	*s.* O 369		
O 376	**ordinal number class** <SE>	ordinale Zahlklasse *f*	classe *f* ordinale de nombres	ординальный класс чисел
	ordinal number of first kind <SE>	*s.* N 410		
	ordinal number of the first class <SE>	*s.* F 306		
	ordinal number of the first kind <SE>	*s.* N 410		
O 377	**ordinal number of the second class,** number of the second class <SE>	Ordnungszahl *f* der zweiten Zahlklasse	nombre *m* de la seconde classe	трансфинитное число второго класса
	ordinal numbers commutative with respect to addition <SE>	*s.* A 258		
	ordinal numbers commutative with respect to multiplication <SE>	*s.* M 1046		
	ordinal of [the] first kind <SE>	*s.* N 410		
	ordinal of the second class (kind) <SE>	*s.* L 743		
O 378	**ordinal product** <of partially ordered sets> <SE>	ordinales Produkt *n*	produit *m* ordinal (d'ordres)	ординальное произведение
O 379	**ordinal product** <of algebras> <UA>	Ordinalprodukt *n*	produit *m* ordinal	ординальное произведение
O 380	**ordinal series** <SE>	Folge *f* der Ordinalzahlen	suite *f* des nombres ordinaux	последовательность порядковых чисел
	ordinal succession <GN, SE>	*s.* O 350		

No.	English	German	French	Russian
O 381	**ordinal type,** order type, type <SE>	Ordnungstypus *m*, Ordnungstyp *m*	type *m* d'ordre, type ordinal	порядковый тип
O 382	**ordinary algebraic branch[-]point (ramification point, singularity),** regular algebraic singularity (branch[-]point, ramification point), ordinary (regular) singularity (branch[-]point, ramification point) <of a many-valued analytic function> <FT>	regulärer (gewöhnlicher) Verzweigungspunkt *m*, Verzweigungspunkt von regulärem Typ, Verzweigungspunkt vom regulären Typ, singuläre Stelle (Singularität) *f* vom regulären Typ	point *m* critique régulier (ordinaire), singularité *f* régulière (ordinaire), point de ramification ordinaire	точка разветвления (ветвления) регулярного типа, обыкновенная критическая точка
	ordinary arithmetic mean <AL, ER, ST>	*s.* A 961		
	ordinary branch[-]point <FT>	*s.* O 382		
O 383	**ordinary congruence,** additive congruence <AL>	gewöhnliche Kongruenz *f* <additiv>	congruence *f* ordinaire (additive)	обыкновенное (аддитивное) сравнение
O 384	**ordinary continued fraction** <NT>	gewöhnlicher Kettenbruch *m*	fraction *f* continue ordinaire, fraction continue algébrique	обыкновенная (простейшая) цепная дробь
	ordinary convergence <FA, TO>	*s.* S 1935		
	ordinary convergence <ST>	*s.* C 2332		
	ordinary cuspidal point <GE>	*s.* C 2814		
O 385	**ordinary differential equation,** differential equation <DE>	gewöhnliche Differentialgleichung *f*, Differentialgleichung	équation *f* différentielle ordinaire, équation différentielle	обыкновенное дифференциальное уравнение, дифференциальное уравнение
	ordinary Dirichlet series <SS>	*s.* D 631		
	ordinary discontinuity <DI>	*s.* J 115		
O 386	**ordinary field** <of algebraic functions of one variable> <AL>	ordinärer Körper *m*	corps *m* ordinaire	ординарное поле
	ordinary fraction <AR>	*s.* C 1234		
	ordinary geometric mean [value] <ST>	*s.* G 261		
	ordinary graph <GP>	*s.* 1. N 437; 2. S 918		
O 387	**ordinary indirect proof** <LO>	gewöhnlicher indirekter Beweis *m*	démonstration *f* indirecte ordinaire	обыкновенное косвенное доказательство
O 388	**ordinary inflection point** <DG>	gewöhnlicher Wendepunkt *m* <3punktige Berührung>	point *m* d'inflexion ordinaire	обыкновенная точка перегиба
O 389	**ordinary integral element** <DE>	gewöhnliches Integralelement *n*	élément *m* intégral ordinaire	обыкновенный интегральный элемент
	ordinary linear differential equation <DE>	*s.* L 784		
O 390	**ordinary multiple point,** ordinary singularity <of an algebraic curve> <AG>	gewöhnlicher mehrfacher Punkt *m*, gewöhnliche Singularität *f*	point *m* multiple ordinaire, singularité *f* ordinaire	обыкновенная многократная точка
	ordinary point <AG>	*s.* S 936		
	ordinary point <DE>	*s.* R 613		
	ordinary ramification point <FT>	*s.* O 382		
O 391	**ordinary singularity** <of an algebraic surface> <AG>	gewöhnliche Singularität *f*	singularité *f* ordinaire	обыкновенная особенная точка
	ordinary singularity <AG>	*s.* O 390		
	ordinary singularity <FT>	*s.* O 382		
	ordinate difference <AY>	*s.* R 1340		
O 392	**ordoid** <AL>	Ordoid *n*	ordoïde *m*	ордоид
O 393	**ordo-symbols,** Landau order symbols <*O and o*> <AN>	Landau-Symbole *npl*, Landausche Symbole *npl* <*O bzw. o*>	symboles *mpl* de Landau <*O et o*>; symbole *m* O de Bachmann-Landau	символы Ландау <*O и o*>
O 394	**Ore['s] condition** <AL>	Ore-Bedingung *f*	condition *f* de Ore	условие Оре
O 395	**Ore['s] congruences** <AB>	Oresche Kongruenzen *fpl*	congruences *fpl* de Ore	сравнения Оре
	Ore['s] domain <AL>	*s.* O 396		
O 396	**Ore['s] ring,** Ore['s] domain <AL>	Ore-Ring *m*	anneau *m* de Ore	кольцо Оре, кольцо Орэ
O 397	**Ore['s] theorem** <LA>	Theorem *n* von Ore, Oresches Theorem	théorème *m* de Ore	теорема Оре
	oricycle <GE>	*s.* H 576		
O 398	**orientability** <GE, TO>	Orientierbarkeit *f*	orientabilité *f*	ориентируемость
O 399	**orientable contour** <TO>	orientierbarer Rand *m*	contour *m* orientable	ориентируемый контур
	orientable manifold of connectivity $2p+1$ <AT>	*s.* S 1440		
	orientable manifold of genus p <AT>	*s.* S 1440		
O 400	**orientable surface** <TO>	orientierbare Fläche *f*	surface *f* orientable	ориентируемая поверхность
O 401	**orientation** <of an arc> <GP>	Sinn *m*, Richtung *f*	orientation *f*	ориентация
O 402	**orientation by propagation** <of a complex> <AT>	sukzessive Orientierung *f*	orientation *f* successive	последовательное ориентирование
O 403	**orientation class** <of a bundle> <AT>	Orientierungsklasse *f*	classe *f* d'orientation	класс ориентации

	orientation class <GE, TO>	*s.* S 492		
	orientation in the same direction <GE, GN>	*s.* D 587		
O 404	**orientation preserving automorphism** <AL, GE>	orientierungstreuer Automorphismus *m*	automorphisme *m* conservant l'orientation	автоморфизм, сохраняющий ориентацию
	orientation-preserving isometry <TO>	*s.* E 560		
O 405	**orientation preserving isomorphism** <of complexes> <AT>	orientierungserhaltende Isomorphie *f*	isomorphisme *m* conservant l'orientation	изоморфизм, сохраняющий ориентацию
O 406	**orientation-preserving parameter transformation** <DG, TO>	orientierungstreue Parametertransformation *f*	transformation *f* des paramètres conservant l'orientation	преобразование параметров, сохраняющее ориентацию
O 407	**orientation-reversing** <GE, TO>	orientierungsumkehrend, gegensinnig	renversant l'orientation	обращающий ориентацию
	orientation-reversing isometry <GE>	*s.* I 183		
	oriented arc length function <AN, GE>	*s.* A 904		
O 408	**oriented chain complex** <AT>	orientierter Kettenkomplex *m*	complexe *m* de chaines orientées	ориентированный цепной комплекс, комплекс ориентированных цепей
O 409	**oriented circle,** cycle <AY>	orientierter (gerichteter) Kreis *m*, Zykel *m*	cercle *m* orienté, cycle *m*	направленная окружность, цикл, ориентированный цикл (круг)
	oriented circuit <GP>	*s.* D 540		
O 410	**oriented contour** <TO>	orientierter Rand *m*	contour *m* orienté, bord *m* orienté	ориентированный контур, ориентированная граница
O 411	**oriented direction,** direction, sense <in a space> <GE>	orientierte Richtung *f*, Richtung	direction *f* orientée, direction	ориентированное направление, направление
	oriented element <GP>	*s.* A 883		
O 412	**oriented graph** <GP>	orientierter Graph *m*	graphe *m* orienté	ориентированный граф
O 413	**oriented homology group** <*n*-th> <AT>	orientierte Homologiegruppe *f* <*n*-te>	groupe *m* d'homologie orientée <pour la dimension *n*>	группа ориентированных гомологий <*n*-мерная, *n*-я>
O 414	**oriented intersection** <of cells, chains> <AT>	orientierter Schnitt *m*	intersection *f* orientée	ориентированное пересечение
O 415	**oriented intersection** <of oriented linear spaces> <GE>	orientierter Durchschnitt *m*	intersection *f* orientée	ориентированное пересечение
O 416	**oriented line,** oriented straightline, directed line (straightline) <GE>	orientierte (gerichtete) Gerade *f*; // Strahl *m*	droite *f* orientée (dirigée)	ориентированная (направленная) прямая
O 417	**oriented plane** <GE>	orientierte (gerichtete) Ebene *f*	plan *m* orienté	ориентированная плоскость
O 418	**oriented polygon** <GE>	gerichtetes (orientiertes) Vieleck *n*	polygone *m* orienté	ориентированный полигон
O 419	**oriented space** <GE>	orientierter (gerichteter) Raum *m*	espace *m* orienté	ориентированное пространство
O 420	**oriented sphere bundle** <AT>	orientiertes Sphärenbündel *n*	fibré *m* orienté (en sphères)	ориентированное расслоение на сферы
	oriented straightline <GE>	*s.* O 416		
O 421	**origin** <of co-ordinates>, co-ordinate origin <AY>	Koordinatenursprung *m*, Koordinatennullpunkt *m*, Koordinatenanfangspunkt *m*, Ursprung *m*, Nullpunkt *m*, Anfangspunkt *m* <des Koordinatensystems>	origine *f* <des coordonnées>	начало, начальная точка <координат>
O 422	**origin** <of an arrow> <CA>	Anfang *m*, Anfangspunkt *m*, linker Eckpunkt *m*	source *f*, extrémité *f* initiale	начало
O 423	**origin** <of an element of contact> <DE, DG>	Träger *m* <eines Elements>; Trägerpunkt *m* <eines Linienelements>	support *m*	точка-носитель
O 424/5	**origin,** initial point <of a path> <TO>	Anfangspunkt *m*	origine *f*	начало
	origin <AL>	*s.* Z 30		
	origin <AY>	*s.* P 902		
	origin <GP>	*s.* I 543		
	origin <VT>	*s.* I 535		
O 426	**original,** original function, superior function, object function, determining function; inverse transform <in a functional transformation> <AN>	Originalfunktion *f*, Oberfunktion *f*, Objektfunktion *f*, Stammfunktion *f*, determinierende Funktion *f*; Rücktransformierte *f*	fonction *f* originale, original *m*, fonction supérieure; transformée *f* inverse, image *f* réciproque	оригинал [преобразования], функция-оригинал, первообразная функция; обратная трансформанта, обратное изображение (преобразование)
	original <AN, SE>	*s.* I 912		
	original function <AN>	*s.* O 426		
	original order <CT>	*s.* S 1630		
O 427	**original space,** superior space, object space <in a functional transformation> <FA>	Originalraum *m*, Objektraum *m*, Oberraum *m*, Originalbereich *m*, Objektbereich *m*, Oberbereich *m*	espace *m* original (supérieur)	пространство-оригинал, оригинальное пространство
O 428	**origin of the edge** <of a complex> <AT>	Anfangspunkt *m* der Kante	origine *f* de l'arête	начало ребра

No.	English	German	French	Russian
	orisphere <GE>	*s.* H 579		
O 429	**Orlicz['s] class** <FA>	Orlicz-Klasse *f*	classe *f* d'Orlicz (de Orlicz)	класс Орлича
O 430	**Orlicz['s] space** <FA>	Orlicz-Raum *m*	espace *m* d'Orlicz (de Orlicz)	пространство Орлича
O 431	**OR-operator** <LO>	ODER-Operator *m*, logisches ODER *n*	opérateur *m* OU	ИЛИ-оператор
O 432	**orthocentre** <of a triangle *or* tetrahedron> <EG>	Höhenpunkt *m*, Höhenschnittpunkt *m*, Orthozentrum *n*	orthocentre *m*	ортоцентр
O 433	**orthocentric quadrangle** <EG>	orthozentrisches Viereck *n*	quadrangle *m* orthocentrique	ортоцентрический четырехугольник
O 434	**orthocentric tetrahedron,** orthotetrahedron <EG>	Vierflach *n* mit Höhenpunkt, orthozentrisches Vierflach, Orthotetraeder *n*	tétraèdre *m* orthocentrique, orthotétraèdre *m*	ортоцентрический четырехгранник (тетраэдр), ортотетраэдр
O 435	**orthocentroidal sphere** <of a tetrahedron> <EG>	orthozentroidale Kugel *f*	sphère *f* orthocentroïdale	ортоцентроидальная сфера
O 436	**orthochronous Lorentz transformation** <AL>	orthochrone Lorentz-Transformation *f*	transformation *f* [de Lorentz] orthochrone	ортохронное преобразование Лоренца
O 437	**orthocomplement,** orthogonal (disjoint) complement, annihilator <AL>	disjunktes Komplement *n*	orthocomplément *m*	дизъюнктное дополнение
	orthocomplement <AL, FA>	*s.* O 447		
	orthocomplement <LA>	*s.* P 843		
O 438	**orthocomplementation** <LA>	Orthokomplement-bildung *f*	orthocomplémentation *f*	переход к ортодополнению
O 439	**orthocomplemented lattice** <LA>	orthokomplementärer Verband *m*	treillis *m* orthocomplémenté	структура с ортодополнениями
O 440	**orthodrome,** great circle line <as a geodesic on a sphere> <DG, VA>	Orthodrome *f*, Großkreisbogen *m*	orthodromie *f*	ортодромия, дуга большого круга
O 441	**orthogonal,** perpendicular <EG>	orthogonal, senkrecht; senkrecht (rechtwinklig) aufeinanderstehend; sich rechtwinklig schneidend	orthogonal, perpendiculaire	ортогональный, перпендикулярный
O 442	**orthogonal affinity** <GE>	senkrecht-affine Abbildung *f*	affinité *f* orthogonale	ортогонально-аффинное отображение
	orthogonal and normalized system <AL, AN, FA>	*s.* O 495		
O 443	**orthogonal axonometry,** normal axonometry <DS>	senkrechte (orthogonale) Axonometrie *f*	axonométrie *f* orthogonale (normale)	ортогональная аксонометрия
O 444	**orthogonal base (basis)** <with respect to a hermitian form> <AL>	orthogonale Basis *f*, Orthogonalbasis *f* <für eine hermitesche Form>	base *f* orthogonale <pour une forme hermitienne>	ортогональный базис <относительно эрмитовой формы>
	orthogonal Cartesian co-ordinates <AY>	*s.* C 161		
O 445	**orthogonal circle** <of a pencil of circles> <AY>	Orthogonalkreis *m*, Mongescher Kreis *m*	cercle *m* orthogonal	ортогональный круг
	orthogonal circles <GE>	*s.* C 694		
O 446	**orthogonal closedness** <FA>	orthogonale Abgeschlossenheit *f*	propriété *f* d'être orthogonalement fermé	ортогональная замкнутость
O 447	**orthogonal complement,** orthocomplement <in a Hilbert space>; annihilator <in a normed linear space> <AL, FA>	orthogonales Komplement *n*; Orthogonalraum *m*	complément *m* orthogonal, orthocomplément *m*, supplémentaire *m* orthogonal, orthogonal *m*	ортогональный комплемент, ортодополнение
	orthogonal complement <AL>	*s.* O 437		
	orthogonal complement <LA>	*s.* P 843		
	orthogonal co-ordinates <AY>	*s.* R 279		
O 448	**orthogonal co-ordinate system,** orthogonal system [of co-ordinates] <AY>	rechtwinkliges Koordinatensystem *n*, orthogonales Koordinatensystem *n*, Orthogonalsystem *n*	système *m* de coordonnées orthogonales, système de coordonnées rectangulaires	прямоугольная система [координат], система прямоугольных координат, ортогональная система [координат]
O 449	**orthogonal data** <ST>	orthogonale Daten *npl*	données *fpl* orthogonales	ортогональные данные
O 450	**orthogonal decomposition** <AL, FA>	orthogonale Zerlegung *f*, Orthogonalzerlegung *f*	décomposition *f* orthogonale <d'un élément>; partition *f* orthogonale <d'un espace hilbertien>	ортогональное разложение
O 451	**orthogonal equivalence,** orthogonal similarity <of matrices> <MD>	orthogonale Ähnlichkeit *f*	similitude *f* par une transformation orthogonale	ортогональное подобие
O 452	**orthogonal expansion,** expansion in an orthogonal series <of a function> <process> <AN>	Entwicklung *f* in eine Orthogonalreihe, Orthogonalentwicklung *f*	développement *m* orthogonal (en série orthogonale)	ортогональное разложение, разложение в ортогональный ряд
	orthogonal expansion <AN>	*s.* O 477		
	orthogonal family <AN>	*s.* O 484		
O 453	**orthogonal group** <of *n* variables> <GR>	orthogonale Gruppe *f*, erweiterte orthogonale Gruppe <von *n* Variablen>	groupe *m* orthogonal, groupe élargi des rotations <à *n* variables>	ортогональная группа <от *n* переменных>
	orthogonal group <GR>	*s.* F 718		
O 454	**orthogonal groups** <to each other> <GR>	orthogonale Gruppen *fpl*, orthogonales Gruppenpaar (Paar) *n*	groupes *mpl* orthogonaux	ортогональные группы

No.	English	German	French	Russian
O 455	**orthogonal group with respect to the form Q** <AL>	orthogonale Gruppe *f* in bezug auf die Form Q	groupe *m* orthogonal associé à Q	ортогональная группа формы Q
	orthogonal Hermite polynomial <FU>	*s.* H 228		
	orthogonal integral equation <IE>	*s.* F 592		
O 456	**orthogonal invariance** <IE>	Orthogonalinvarianz *f*	invariance *f* orthogonale	инвариантность относительно ортогональных преобразований
O 457	**orthogonal invariant** <of a form> <AL, AY>	orthogonale Invariante *f*, Orthogonalinvariante *f*	invariant *m* orthogonal	ортогональный инвариант
O 458	**orthogonal involution** <AY>	Rechtwinkelinvolution *f*, rechtwinklige (orthogonale) Involution *f*; zirkulares Strahlensystem *n* <im Strahlenbüschel> <Steiner>	involution *f* orthogonale (rectangulaire)	ортогональная инволюция, ортогональное инволюционное преобразование
O 459	**orthogonality,** perpendicularity <AL, GE>	Orthogonalität *f*	orthogonalité *f*, perpendicularité *f*	ортогональность, перпендикулярность
O 460	**orthogonality of columns** <MD>	Spaltenorthogonalität *f*	orthogonalité *f* des colonnes	ортогональность по столбцам
O 461	**orthogonality of lines (rows)** <AL>	Zeilenorthogonalität *f*	orthogonalité *f* des lignes	ортогональность по строкам
O 462	**orthogonality relation** <DE, FA, RE>	Orthogonalitätsrelation *f*, Orthogonalitätsbeziehung *f*	relation *f* d'orthogonalité	соотношение ортогональности, отношение ортогональности
	orthogonalization and normalization <AN, GE>	*s.* O 492		
O 463	**orthogonalization procedure (process)** <AL, FA, GE>	Orthogonalisierungsverfahren *n*, Orthogonalisierungsprozeß *m*	procédé *m* d'orthogonalisation, méthode *f* d'orthogonalisation	метод ортогонализации, процесс ортогонализации
	orthogonal latin square <CT, ST>	*s.* O 480		
O 464	**orthogonal linear manifolds** <GE>	senkrechte lineare Mannigfaltigkeiten *fpl*	variétés *fpl* linéaires perpendiculaires	ортогональные линейные многообразия
	orthogonal linear transformation <AL, AY>	*s.* O 486		
O 465	**orthogonally closed set** <FA>	orthogonalabgeschlossene Menge *f*	ensemble *m* orthogonalement fermé	ортогонально замкнутое множество
O 466	**orthogonally irreducible representation** <RE>	orthogonal irreduzible Darstellung *f*	représentation *f* orthogonalement irréductible	ортогонально неприводимое представление
	orthogonal manifold <GE>	*s.* T 658		
	orthogonal mapping <AL, AY>	*s.* O 486		
O 467	**orthogonal matrix,** orthonormal matrix <MD>	orthogonale (orthonormierte) Matrix *f*	matrice *f* orthogonale (orthonormale)	ортогональная матрица, ортонормированная матрица
	orthogonal normalized system <AL, AN, FA>	*s.* O 495		
	orthogonal operator <FA>	*s.* U 253		
O 468	**orthogonal pair** <of elements in involution> <AY>	Rechtwinkelpaar *n*	couple *m* orthogonal	ортогональная пара
O 469	**orthogonal polynomial expansion,** expansion in orthogonal polynomials <AN>	Entwicklung (Reihenentwicklung) *f* nach orthogonalen Polynomen, Orthogonalpolynomentwicklung *f*	développement *m* suivant les polynômes orthogonaux	разложение в ряд по ортогональным многочленам
O 470	**orthogonal polynomials** <AN>	Orthogonalpolynome *npl*, Orthogonalsystem *n* von Polynomen, orthogonale Polynome *npl*, orthogonales Polynomsystem *n*	polynômes *mpl* orthogonaux	ортогональные многочлены
	orthogonal process <SP>	*s.* O 481		
O 471	**orthogonal projection** <of a convex body> <CS, GE>	Normalriß *m*	travers *m* extérieur, travers	ортогональная проекция
O 472	**orthogonal projection** <DS>	orthogonale Parallelprojektion *f*, Orthogonalprojektion *f*, orthogonale (senkrechte) Projektion *f*	projection *f* orthogonale	ортогональная (прямоугольная) проекция; ортогональное проектирование
	orthogonal projection <FA>	*s.* P 1737		
	orthogonal projector <FA>	*s.* P 1737		
O 473	**orthogonal random measure,** random measure <ME, ST>	orthogonales zufälliges Maß *n*, zufälliges Maß	mesure *f* aléatoire orthogonale, mesure aléatoire	ортогональная случайная мера, случайная мера
O 474	**orthogonal reciprocant** <IV>	Orthogonalreziprokante *f*	réciprocant *m* orthogonal	ортогональный реципрокант
O 475	**orthogonal semi-similarity [transformation]** <AL>	halbähnlich orthogonale Transformation *f*	semi-similitude *f* orthogonale	ортогональное преобразование полуподобия
O 476	**orthogonal sequence** <FA>	Orthogonalfolge *f*	suite *f* orthogonale	ортогональная последовательность
O 477	**orthogonal series,** orthogonal expansion <of a function> <AN>	Orthogonalreihe *f*, Orthogonalentwicklung *f*, Fourier-Reihe *f*	série *f* orthogonale, développement *m* orthogonal	ортогональный ряд, ортогональное разложение

No.	English	German	French	Russian
	orthogonal set <AN>	*s.* O 484		
	orthogonal similarity <MD>	*s.* O 451		
	orthogonal similar matrix <MD>	*s.* C 1940		
O 478	**orthogonal space** <FA>	Orthogonalraum *m*	espace *m* orthogonal	ортогональное пространство
O 479	**orthogonal sphere** <AY>	Orthogonalkugel *f*, orthogonale Kugel *f*	sphère *f* orthogonale	ортогональная сфера
O 480	**orthogonal square,** orthogonal latin square <CT, ST>	orthogonales [lateinisches] Quadrat *n*	carré *m* orthogonal, carré latin orthogonal	ортогональный [латинский] квадрат
O 481	**orthogonal stochastic process,** orthogonal process, process with orthogonal increments <SP>	orthogonaler stochastischer Prozeß *m*, orthogonaler Prozeß, Prozeß mit orthogonalen Zuwächsen	processus *m* aléatoire (stochastique) orthogonal, processus orthogonal, processus avec incréments orthogonaux	ортогональный [случайный] процесс, [случайный] процесс с ортогональными приращениями
O 482	**orthogonal submodule** <AL>	totalsenkrechter (orthogonaler) Untermodul *m*	sous-module *m* [totalement] orthogonal	ортогональный подмодуль
O 483	**orthogonal substitution,** orthogonal transformation <AL, AY>	orthogonale Substitution (Transformation) *f* <von einem rechtwinkligen Koordinatensystem in ein anderes>	substitution *f* orthogonale	ортогональная подстановка
O 484	**orthogonal system,** orthogonal family (set) <of functions> <AN>	Orthogonalsystem *n* <von Funktionen>	système *m* orthogonal <de fonctions>	ортогональная система <функций>
	orthogonal system [of co-ordinates] <AY>	*s.* O 448		
	orthogonal tests <ST>	*s.* I 318		
O 485	**orthogonal trajectory** <DE, DG>	orthogonale Trajektorie *f*, Orthogonaltrajektorie *f*	trajectoire *f* orthogonale, trajectoire normale	ортогональная траектория
O 486	**orthogonal transformation,** orthogonal linear transformation, orthogonal mapping <AL, AY>	orthogonale Transformation (Abbildung) *f*, lineare Transformation mit orthogonaler Matrix	transformation *f* linéaire orthogonale, automorphisme *m* orthogonal, transformation (application *f*) orthogonale	ортогональное [линейное] преобразование, ортогональный автоморфизм, ортогональное отображение
	orthogonal transformation <AL, AY>	*s. a.* O 483		
O 487	**orthological triangle** <EG>	orthologes Dreieck *n*	triangle *m* orthologique	ортологический треугольник
	orthomorphic projection <DS>	*s.* C 1903		
O 488	**orthomorphism** <GR>	Orthomorphismus *m*	orthomorphisme *m*	ортоморфизм
	orthonormal base <AL>	*s.* O 489		
	orthonormal base <AN, FA>	*s.* C 1543		
O 489	**orthonormal basis,** normal (normalized) orthogonal basis, orthonormal base <AL>	orthonormale Basis *f*, Orthonormalbasis *f*, orthonormierte Basis	base *f* orthonormale (orthonormée)	ортонормированный базис
	orthonormal co-ordinates <AY>	*s.* C 161		
O 490	**orthonormality** <AL, AN, GE>	Orthonormalität *f*, Orthonormiertheit *f*	orthonormalité *f*	ортонормированность
O 491	**orthonormality relation** <e.g. in a Hilbert space> <FA>	Orthonormalitätsrelation *f*	relation *f* d'orthonormalité	отношение ортонормированности
O 492	**orthonormalization,** orthogonalization and normalization <AN, GE>	Orthonormierung *f*, Orthogonalisierung *f* und Normierung *f*	orthonormalisation *f*, orthogonalisation *f* et normalisation *f*	ортонормирование, ортонормировка, ортогонализация и нормировка, ортонормализация
O 493	**orthonormalization process** <AL, AN>	Orthonormierungsverfahren *n*	procédé (méthode *f*) d'orthonormalisation	метод (способ) ортонормирования
	orthonormal matrix <MD>	*s.* O 467		
O 494	**orthonormal sequence,** countably infinite orthonormal system <FA>	Orthonormalfolge *f*, orthonormierte Folge *f*, abzählbar unendliches Orthonormalsystem *n*	suite *f* orthonormale, suite orthonormée, système *m* orthonormal dénombrablement infini	ортонормированная последовательность, счетно-бесконечная ортонормированная система
O 495	**orthonormal system,** orthogonal [and] normalized system, normalized orthogonal system <AL>	Orthonormalsystem *n*, orthonormiertes System *n*, normiertes Orthogonalsystem *n*, orthogonales [und] normiertes System, normiertes orthogonales System	système *m* orthonormal (orthonormé), système orthogonal [et] normé, système normé orthogonal, famille *f* orthonormale	ортонормированная система, ортогональная [и] нормированная система, нормированная ортогональная система, ортонормальная система
O 496	**orthopolar line** <of a line with respect to a quadrilateral> <EG>	orthopolare Gerade *f*	droite *f* orthopolaire	ортополярная прямая
O 497	**orthopole** <of a triangle> <EG>	Orthopol *m*, Lotpunkt *m*	orthopôle *m*	ортополюс
O 498	**orthoptic circle,** director circle, director <of a conic> <AY>	Hauptkreis *m*, Direktorkreis *m*, Leitkreis *m*, orthoptischer Kreis *m*, Kreis von Monge, Mongescher Kreis	cercle *m* orthoptique, cercle directeur, cercle de Monge, cercle diagonal	направляющая окружность, направляющий круг, круг Монжа
O 499	**orthoptic sphere** <of a quadric> <AY>	orthoptische Kugel *f*, Mongesche Kugel	sphère *f* orthoptique (de Monge), sphère orthogone	сфера Монжа
O 500	**orthoptic triangle** <of a triangle> <EG>	Höhenfußpunktdreieck *n*	triangle *m* orthoptique	ортотреугольник
O 501	**orthosurface** <DG>	Orthofläche *f*	orthosurface *f*	ортоповерхность
	orthosymmetric determinant <MD, NT>	*s.* P 524		

O 502	**orthotetrahedral quartic,** Schröter['s] quartic <GE>	orthotetraedrische Quartik *f*, Schrötersche Raumkurve *f* vierter Ordnung	quartique *f* orthotétraédrique (de Schröter)	ортотетраэдральная квартика, кривая четвертого порядка Шретера
	orthotetrahedron <EG>	*s.* O 434		
O 503	**oscillating continued fraction** <NT>	oszillierender Kettenbruch *m*	fraction *f* continue oscillante	осциллирующая цепная дробь
O 504	**oscillating divergent series,** improperly divergent series, oscillating series, series approaching no [finite or infinite] limit <SS>	unbestimmt (uneigentlich) divergente Reihe *f*	série *f* discrépante (indéterminée, oscillante, improprement divergente)	несобственно расходящийся ряд
O 505	**oscillating geometric progression** <AR>	oszillierende geometrische Progression *f*	progression *f* [géométrique] oscillante	знакочередующаяся геометрическая прогрессия
O 506	**oscillating infinite determinant** <MD>	oszillierende unendliche Determinante *f*	déterminant *m* infini oscillant	осциллирующий бесконечный определитель
	oscillating integral <DE>	*s.* O 514		
	oscillating sequence <SS>	*s.* I 174		
O 507	**oscillating series** <SS>	oszillierende Reihe *f*	série *f* oscillante	осциллирующий ряд
	oscillating series <SS>	*s.* O 504		
	oscillating solution <DE>	*s.* O 514		
O 508	**oscillation,** fluctuation <of a function in a point> <RF>	Schwankung *f* <in einem Punkt>	oscillation *f* <dans un point, en un point>	колебание <в точке>
O 509	**oscillation** <of a real-valued function in a set> <RF>	Schwankung *f*, Oszillation *f*	oscillation *f*	колебание
O 510	**oscillation** <of a time series> <SP>	Oszillation *f*	oscillation *f*	осцилляция
O 511	**oscillation** <of a number sequence *or* function sequence> <SS>	Oszillation *f*	oscillation *f*	колебание
O 512	**oscillation matrix** <MD>	Oszillationsmatrix *f*	matrice *f* oscillatoire	осцилляционная матрица
O 513	**oscillation theorem** <DE>	Oszillationssatz *m*	théorème *m* d'oscillation[s]	теорема колебаний
O 514	**oscillatory integral (solution),** oscillating integral (solution) <DE>	oszillatorisches Integral *n*, oszillatorische Lösung *f*, oszillierendes Integral, oszillierende Lösung	intégrale (solution) *f* oscillatoire (oscillante)	колеблющееся (осциллирующее) решение, колеблющийся (осциллирующий) интеграл
	osculant <DG>	*s.* I 872		
O 515	**osculating asymptote** <DG>	Schmiegasymptote *f*, oskulierende Asymptote *f*	asymptote *f* osculatrice	оскулирующая асимптота
	osculating circle <DG>	*s.* C 687		
O 516	**osculating complex** <of a ruled surface> <DG>	Schmieggewinde *n*, Schmiegkomplex *m*	complexe *m* osculateur	соприкасающийся комплекс
O 517	**osculating cone** <DG>	Schmiegkegel *m*, Schmiegungskegel *m*	cône *m* osculateur	соприкасающийся конус
O 518	**osculating cone of revolution** <AY>	Berührungsdrehkegel *m*	cône *m* de révolution osculatrice	соприкасающийся конус вращения
O 519	**osculating conic** <DG>	Schmiegkegelschnitt *m*, Schmiegungskegelschnitt *m*, oskulierender Kegelschnitt *m*	conique *f* osculatrice, section *f* conique osculatrice	соприкасающееся коническое сечение
O 520	**osculating curve** <of a curve> <DG>	oskulierende Kurve *f*	courbe *f* osculatrice	соприкасающаяся (оскулирующая) кривая
O 521	**osculating figure** <DG>	Schmiegfigur *f*, Begleitfigur *f*	figure *f* osculatrice	соприкасающаяся фигура
O 522	**osculating helix** <DG>	Schmiegschraubenlinie *f*	hélice *f* osculatrice	соприкасающаяся винтовая линия
O 523	**osculating parabola** <of a curve> <DG>	Schmiegparabel *f*, Schmiegungsparabel *f*	parabole *f* osculatrice	соприкасающаяся парабола
O 524	**osculating paraboloid** <DG>	Schmiegparaboloid *n*, Schmiegungsparaboloid *n*	paraboloïde *m* osculateur	соприкасающийся параболоид
O 525	**osculating plane,** plane of curvature <DG>	Schmiegebene *f*, Schmiegungsebene *f*, Oskulationsebene *f*	plan *m* osculateur	соприкасающаяся плоскость
O 526	**osculating quadric** <of a surface> <DG>	Schmiegquadrik *f*	quadrique *f* osculatrice	соприкасающаяся квадрика
O 527	**osculating regulus** <of a ruled surface> <DG>	Schmiegregulus *m*, Schmiegfläche *f* zweiten (II.) Grades, Schmieg-F_2 *f*	demi-quadrique *f* osculatrice	соприкасающаяся полуквадрика
O 528	**osculating space** <DG>	Schmiegraum *m*	espace *m* osculateur	соприкасающееся пространство
O 529	**osculating sphere,** sphere of curvature <DG>	Schmiegkugel *f*	sphère *f* osculatrice	соприкасающаяся сфера
O 530	**osculating strip,** osculation strip, asymptotic strip <DG>	Schmiegstreifen *m*, asymptotischer Streifen *m*	bande *f* osculatrice (d'osculation, asymptotique)	полоса (полоска) соприкосновения, полоса (полоска) прикосновения, асимптотическая полоса (полоска)
O 531	**osculating surface** <of a surface> <DG>	oskulierende Fläche *f*	surface *f* osculatrice	соприкасающаяся (оскулирующая) поверхность
O 532	**osculating tangent** <of a curve> <DG>	Schmiegtangente *f*, oskulierende Tangente *f*	tangente *f* osculatrice	соприкасающаяся касательная
O 533	**osculating tetrahedron** <DG>	Schmiegtetraeder *n*, Schmiegungstetraeder *n*	tétraèdre *m* osculateur	соприкасающийся четырехгранник (тетраэдр)
O 534	**osculation** <contact of higher [than first] order> <DG>	Oskulation *f*, Schmiegung *f* <Berührung von höherer als erster Ordnung>	osculation *f*	соприкосновение <выше первого порядка>, оскуляция

	osculation point <GE>	*s.* T 19		
	osculation strip <DG>	*s.* O 530		
O 535	**Osgood['s] theorem** <DE, FA, FT>	Satz *m* von [W. F.] Osgood, Osgoodscher Satz	théorème *m* d'Osgood, théorème de W. F. Osgood	теорема Осгуда
O 536	**Ostrogradsky['s] formula,** Hermite-Ostrogradsky formula <of integration> <DI>	Formel *f* von Hermite-Ostrogradski (Ostrogradski), [Hermite-] Ostrogradskische Formel, Ostrogradski-Hermitesche Formel	formule *f* d'Ostrogradsky, formule de Hermite-Ostrogradsky	формула Эрмита-Остроградского, формула Остроградского
O 537	**Ostrogradsky-Hermite method, Ostrogradsky['s] method** <of integration> <DI>	Methode *f* von Ostrogradski, Ostrogradski [-Hermite]sche Methode	méthode *f* d'Ostrogradsky, méthode de Hermite-Ostrogradsky	метод Остроградского, метод Эрмита-Остроградского, метод Остроградского-Эрмита
	Ostrogradsky['s] theorem <DI, VT>	*s.* G 427		
O 538	**Ostrowski['s] ring** <AL>	Ostrowskischer Ring *m*	anneau *m* d'Ostrowski	кольцо Островского
O 539	**O-symmetric,** symmetric with respect to the origin, symmetric about O <CS, EG>	symmetrisch bezüglich des Koordinatenursprungs	symétrique par rapport à l'origine des coordonnées	симметричный относительно начала координат
O 540	**other side,** leg <of the right angle>, small side, side <of a rectangular triangle> <EG>	Kathete *f*	côté *m* de l'angle droit	катет
	(o)-topology <AN, TO>	*s.* O 365		
O 541	**Ottajano['s] problem** <EG>	Ottajanosche Aufgabe *f*, Ottajanosches Problem *n*, Aufgabe von Annibale Giordano aus Ottajano, Ottajanische Aufgabe	problème *m* ottajanien (d'Ottajano)	задача Аннибале Джордано, задача Оттаяно
O 542	**out[-]degree,** demi-degree outward, out-valence, outer demidegree <of a vertex> <GP>	Ausgangsvalenz *f*, Ausgangsgrad *m*, positiver Grad *m*	degré (demi-degré) *m* extérieur	положительная степень, полустепень исхода
O 543	**outer automorphism,** contragredient automorphism <of a group> <GR>	äußerer Automorphismus *m*, kontragredienter Isomorphismus *m*	automorphisme *m* extérieur, automorphisme *m* contragrédient, automorphisme externe	внешний автоморфизм
O 544	**outer boundary** <of a star> <AT>	Außenrand *m*, Rand *m*, Begrenzungskomplex *m*, Umgebungskomplex *m*	bord *m*	край, граничный комплекс
O 545	**outer capacity** <of a point set> <PO>	äußere Kapazität *f*	capacité *f* extérieure	внешняя емкость
	outer content <ME>	*s.* E 831		
	outer demidegree <GP>	*s.* O 542		
O 546	**outer direct product,** external direct product group <of groups> <GR>	äußeres (externes) direktes Produkt *n*	produit *m* de groupes, groupe *m* produit, produit cartésien	внешнее прямое произведение
	outer Jordan content <ME>	*s.* E 831		
O 547	**outer Lebesgue measure,** Lebesgue['s] outer measure <ME>	äußeres Lebesguesches Maß *n*	mesure *f* de Lebesgue extérieure	верхняя мера [в смысле Лебега], внешняя мера [в смысле Лебега]
O 548	**outer measure,** exterior measure, upper measure <ME>	äußeres Maß *n*, Maßfunktion *f* (Maß) im Sinne von Carathéodory, Carathéodorysches Maß, Maß, gewöhnliches [äußeres] Maß	mesure *f* extérieure	внешняя мера, внешняя мера Каратеодори
O 549	**outermost parentheses** <LO>	äußere Klammern *fpl*, Außenklammern *fpl*	parenthèses *fpl* extérieures	внешние скобки, внешняя пара скобок
	outer multiplication ⌐<VT>	*s.* T 152		
O 550	**outer product,** exterior (Grassmann, wedge, alternating) product <of multivectors> <AL>	äußeres (alternierendes, progressives) Produkt *n* <Graßmann>	produit *m* extérieur (alterné, progressif) <Grassmann>	внешнее (знакопеременное, альтернированное) произведение
	outer product <SE>	*s.* C 173		
	outer product <VT>	*s.* 1. P 1596; 2. V 121		
	outer product ring <AL>	*s.* O 234		
O 551	**outer semidirect product** <of groups> <AL>	äußeres semidirektes Produkt *n*	produit *m* semi-direct externe	внешнее полупрямое произведение
O 552	**outgoing edge** <from>, edge issuing <from>, arc incident out <of> <GP>	nach außen inzidenter Bogen *m* <mit>; gerichtete Kante *f*, mit der der Knotenpunkt positiv inzident ist	arc *m* incident vers l'extérieur <de>	дуга, которая положительно инцидентна вершине
O 553	**outlier,** freak value <ST>	Ausreißer *m*	observation *f* extrême aberrante	выбраковка, резко выделяющееся наблюдение (значение), выброс
O 554	**outlier problem** <ST>	Ausreißerproblem *n*	problème *m* des observations extrêmes aberrantes	проблема выбраковки
O 555	**outlier test** <ST>	Ausreißertest *m*	test *m* des observations extrêmes aberrantes	критерий выбраковки, критерий для обнаруживания резко выделяющихся значений
O 556	**out-of-straightness,** non-straightness <GN>	Ungeradlinigkeit *f*, Ungeradheit *f*, Krummlinigkeit *f*	curvilinéarité *f*	нелинейность, криволинейность
	output <CA>	*s.* C 1130		
O 557	**output alphabet** <TA>	Ausgabealphabet *n*, Ausgangsalphabet *n*	alphabet *m* de sortie, alphabet d'émission	выходной алфавит, алфавит результатов

No.	English	German	French	Russian
O 558	**output flow** <of a network> <GP>	Flußoutput *m*	flux *m* de sortie	выходной поток
O 559	**output function** <TA>	Ergebnisfunktion *f*, Ausgabefunktion *f*, Ausgangsfunktion *f*	fonction *f* de sortie	функция выходов, функция выхода
O 560	**output signal** <TA>	Ausgabesignal *n*	signal *m* de sortie	выходной сигнал
O 561	**output state** <PG>	Ausgangszustand *m*	état *m* de sortie	выходное состояние
	out-valence <GP>	*s.* O 542		
	outward normal <DG>	*s.* E 842		
O 562	**oval,** closed convex curve <GE>	geschlossene konvexe Kurve *f*, Eikurve *f*, Eilinie *f*, nirgends konkave geschlossene Kurve	courbe *f* convexe fermée, contour *m* fermé non concave	овал, овальная линия, выпуклая замкнутая линия, замкнутая выпуклая линия
O 563	**oval of Cassini,** Cassini['s] oval, Cassinian oval, Cassinian ellipse, Cassinian curve <AG>	Cassinische Kurve (Linie, Ellipse) *f*, Cassinisches Oval *n*, Cassinoide *f*, Kassinoide *f*	ovale *f* de Cassini, cassinoïde *f*, ellipse (courbe, ligne) *f* de Cassini, ligne (ellipse) cassinienne, cassinienne *f*	овал Кассини, кассиниев овал
O 564	**oval surface** <common name of ellipsoid, hyperboloid of two sheets, and elliptic paraboloid> <AY>	ovale Fläche *f*	surface *f* ovale	овальная поверхность
	ovary ellipsoid <EG>	*s.* P 1742		
O 565	**overall correlation,** total correlation <ST>	Gesamtkorrelation *f*	corrélation *f* totale	полная корреляция
O 566	**overall estimate,** omnibus estimate <ST>	Gesamtschätzwert *m*	estimation *f* d'ensemble	полная оценка; оценка, использующая все имеющиеся данные
	overall test <ST>	*s.* O 72		
	χ^2 overall test <ST>	*s.* O 73		
O 567	**overbar,** overline, bar, vinculum, ¯ <over a quantity> <as a mathematical symbol> <GN>	Strich *m*, ¯ <über einer Größe>	ligne *f*, ¯ <sur une grandeur>	черта [сверху], черточка сверху, штрих, ¯ <над величиной>
O 568	**overbarred quantity,** overlined quantity <*e.g.:* $\bar{x}$, *read:* x overbar> <GN>	überstrichene Größe *f* <*z. B.:* $\bar{x}$, *lies:* x quer, x überstrichen>	grandeur *f* surlignée <*par exemple:* $\bar{x}$, *se lit:* x barre, x barré>	величина с чертой [сверху], величина со штрихом [сверху] <*например:* $\bar{x}$, *читается:* x с чертой>
O 569	**overconvergence** <FT>	Überkonvergenz *f*, Hyperkonvergenz *f*	ultraconvergence *f*, hyperconvergence *f*	сверхсходимость
O 570	**overconvergent sequence** <FT>	überkonvergente (hyperkonvergente) Folge *f*	suite *f* hyperconvergente	сверхсходящаяся последовательность
O 571	**overcrossing** <TO>	Überkreuzungsstelle *f*, Überkreuzung *f*		переходящая точка
	overdeterminate system of partial differential equations <DE>	*s.* O 574		
O 572	**overdetermination** <AL, AN>	Überbestimmtheit *f*	surdétermination *f*	переопределенность
O 573	**overdetermined problem** <AL, AN>	überbestimmte Aufgabe *f*	problème *m* plus que déterminé	переопределенная задача
O 574	**overdetermined system of partial differential equations,** overdeterminate system of partial differential equations <DE>	überbestimmtes System *n* von partiellen Differentialgleichungen	système *m* surdéterminé d'équations [différentielles] aux dérivées partielles	переопределенная система [дифференциальных уравнений] в частных производных
O 575	**overfield,** extension field <of a field> <AL>	Oberkörper *m*, Körpererweiterung *f*, Erweiterungskörper *m*, // Vielfaches *n*, Multiplum *n*	sur[-]corps *m*, extension *f* du sous-corps, // corps *m* supérieur, multiple *m*	надполе
	over-ideal <AL>	*s.* E 800		
O 576	**overidentification** <ST>	Überbestimmtheit *f*	suridentification *f*, surdétermination *f*	переопределенность
O 577	**overidentification** <process> <ST>	Überbestimmung *f*	surdétermination *f*, suridentification *f*	избыточное определение, переопределение
O 578	**overlap / to** <TO>	sich überlappen	avoir des points intérieurs communs	иметь общую внутреннюю часть
O 579	**overlap** <of distributions> <ST>	Überlappung *f*	recouvrement *m* partiel	перекрытие
	overlapping <SE>	*s.* N 375		
	overlapping <SE, TO>	*s.* C 2620		
O 580	**overlapping domains** <TO>	überlappende Gebiete *npl*	domaines *mpl* intersecants	сцепленные области
	overlapping mean <ST>	*s.* M 930		
O 581	**overlapping sets** <TO>	überlappende Mengen *fpl*	ensembles *mpl* ayant des points intérieurs communs	множества с общими внутренними точками, взаимно налегающие множества
	overlapping sets <SE>	*s.* N 376		
O 582	**overlap zone,** zone of overlap <ST>	Überlappungszone *f*	zone *f* de recouvrement	зона перекрытия
	overline <GN>	*s.* O 567		
	overlined quantity <GN>	*s.* O 568		
	overlining <GN>	*s.* V 187		
O 583	**overmodule,** extension module <of a module> <AL>	Obermodul *m*, Teiler *m*	sur-module *m*	надмодуль
O 584	**overrelaxation,** superrelaxation <NU>	Überrelaxation *f*	surrelaxation *f*	перерелаксация, верхняя релаксация
O 585	**overring,** extension ring <AL>	Oberring *m*, Erweiterungsring *m*	extension *f* d'un anneau, sur-anneau *m*	надкольцо
	ovoid [body] <CS, GE>	*s.* C 2384		

P

No.	English	German	French	Russian
P 1	**packing** <GE>	Packung *f*, Lagerung *f*	empilement *m*	расположение, укладка, упаковка
	packing <GP>	*s.* O 157		
P 2	**packing coefficient** <GE>	Packungskoeffizient *m*	coefficient *m* d'empilement	коэффициент упаковки
P 3	**packing density,** density of packing, density <of a packing> <GE>	Packungsdichte *f*, Lagerungsdichte *f*	densité *f* d'empilement, densité d'arrangement, densité <de l'empilement>	плотность упаковки (расположения)
	packing of spheres <GE>	*s.* S 1437		
P 4	**packing problem** <GE>	Lagerungsproblem *n*, Packungsproblem *n*	problème *m* d'empilement	проблема расположения
P 5	**Padé approximant (approximation)** <NT>	Padéscher Näherungsbruch *m*, Padésche Näherung *f*	approximant *m* de Padé	приближение Паде
P 6	**Padé['s] approximation** <NT>	Padé-Approximation *f*, Padé-Näherung *f*	approximation *f* de Padé	аппроксимация Паде
P 7	**Padé['s] table** <NT>	Padésche Tafel *f*	table *f* de Padé	таблица Паде
	p-adic absolute value	*s.* P 15		
P 8	**p-adic algebra** <AL>	p-adische Algebra *f*	algèbre *f* p-adique	p-адическая алгебра, алгебра над полем p-адических чисел
P 9	**p-adic convergence** <AL, NT>	p-adische Konvergenz *f*	convergence *f* p-adique	p-адическая сходимость
P 10	**p-adic fraction** <NT>	p-adischer Bruch *m*	fraction *f* p-adique	p-адическая дробь, p-адическое дробное число
P 11	**p-adic integer** <AL>	ganze p-adische Zahl *f*, p-adische ganze Zahl	entier *m* p-adique, nombre *m* p-adique entier	целое p-адическое число
P 12	**p-adic L-function** <NT>	p-adische L-Funktion *f*	fonction *f* L p-adique	p-адическая L-функция Жаке-Ленглендса
P 13	**p-adic number theory,** theory of p-adic numbers <NT>	p-adische Zahlentheorie (Arithmetik) *f*	arithmétique *f* p-adique	p-адическая арифметика
P 14	**p-adic topology** <AL, TO>	p-adische Topologie *f*	topologie *f* p-adique	p-адическая топология
P 15	**p-adic valuation,** p-adic absolute value <AL>	p-adische Bewertung *f*	valuation *f* p-adique, valeur *f* absolue p-adique	p-адическое нормирование (абсолютное значение), p-адическая норма, p-показатель
P 16	**Painlevé['s] theorem** <DE>	Satz *m* von Painlevé, Painlevéscher Satz	théorème *m* de Painlevé	теорема Пэнлеве
P 17	**Painlevé['s] transcendental function** <DE>	Painlevésche Transzendente (transzendente Funktion) *f*	fonction *f* transcendante de Painlevé	трансцендентная функция Пэнлеве
P 18	**Painvin['s] complex** <GE>	Painvinscher Komplex *m*, Painvins Strahlenkomplex *m*	complexe *m* de Painvin	комплекс Пэнвэна
P 19	**paired comparison** <ST>	paarweiser Vergleich *m*	comparaison *f* par paires, comparaison deux à deux	парное сравнение
P 20	**paired comparison method,** difference method <ST>	Differenzmethode *f*, Paarvergleichsmethode *f*, Methode *f* des paarweisen Vergleichs	méthode *f* de comparaison par paires, méthode d'appariement	метод парного сравнения
P 21	**paired groups** <AL>	gepaarte Gruppen *fpl*	groupes *mpl* associés	спаренные группы
P 22	**paired samples** <ST>	gepaarte Stichproben *fpl*	échantillons *mpl* appariés	парные выборки, выборки с взаимно сопоставляемыми членами
	pairing <GR>	*s.* B 345		
	pairing axiom <SE>	*s.* A 1288		
	pair of anti-involutory points <PJ>	*s.* A 728		
P 22a	**pair of complex conjugate roots** <AL>	Paar *n* konjugiertkomplexer Wurzeln	paire *f* conjuguée de racines	пара комплексно сопряженных корней
P 23	**pair of identified points** <TO>	verheftetes Punktepaar *n*	paire *f* de points identifiés	слипшееся двоеточие
	pair of involutory points <PJ>	*s.* I 1009		
	pair of numbers <AL>	*s.* N 834		
P 24	**pair of points** <space consisting of two points> <TO>	Punktepaar *n*	paire *f* de points	двоеточие
	pair of points <GE>	*s.* P 781		
	pair of primes <NT>	*s.* P 1325		
	pair-product <SE>	*s.* C 173		
	pair set <SE>	*s.* 1. T 1085; 2. U 371		
	pairwise almost disjoint sets <SE>	*s.* S 690		
P 25	**pairwise comaximal ideals** <AL>	paarweise teilerfremde (komaximale) Ideale *npl*	idéaux *mpl* étrangers (comaximaux) deux à deux	попарно комаксимальные (взаимно простые) идеалы
	pairwise disjoint subsets <SE>	*s.* M 1102		
P 26	**pairwise distinct elements** <SE>	paarweise verschiedene Elemente *npl*	éléments *mpl* deux à deux distincts	попарно разные элементы
	pairwise incompatible events <ST>	*s.* T 1076		
	pairwise independent events <ST>	*s.* M 1103		
	pairwise transitive group <GR>	*s.* T 1089		
P 27	**Palatini['s] variation (variational method)** <VA>	Palatinis Variationsmethode *f*, Variation *f* nach Palatini	méthode *f* variationnelle de Palatini, variation *f* de Palatini	вариационный метод Палатини, вариация Палатини
P 28	**Paley['s] theorems** <SS>	Paleysche Sätze *mpl*, Sätze von Paley	théorèmes *mpl* de Paley	теоремы Пэли
P 29	**Paley-Wiener theorem** <IT>	Paley-Wienerscher Satz *m*, Satz von Paley und Wiener, Satz von Paley-Wiener	théorème *m* de Paley et Wiener, théorème de Paley-Wiener[-Schwartz]	теорема Пэли-Винера

P 30	**palindromic number** <NT>	palindrome Zahl *f*	nombre *m* palindrome	палиндромическое число, число с симметрично расположенными цифрами
	***p*-analytic function** <FT>	*s.* P 1217		
	pandiagonal magic square <CT, NT>	*s.* P 416		
P 31	**paneled magic square** <CT>	[magisches] Quadrat *n* mit Berandungen, [magisches] Quadrat mit Einfassungen, Stifelsches Quadrat, gerändertes [magisches] Quadrat, eingerahmtes magisches Quadrat, doppeltmagisches Quadrat	carré *m* [magique] à bordure, carré bordé (encadré), carré magique à enceinte[s], carré magiquement (doublement) magique; carré magique à châssis	окаймленный квадрат
P 32	**pangeodesic curve,** hypergeodesic curve <DE>	pangeodätische (hypergeodätische) Kurve *f* <Fubini>	courbe *f* pangéodésique (hypergéodésique)	пангеодезическая (гипергеодезическая) кривая
P 33/4	**panpolar** <PJ>	Panpolare *f*	panpolaire *f*	панполяра
P 35	**pantograph** <GE, IN>	Pantograph *m*, Storchschnabel *m*	pantographe *m*	пантограф
	Papperitz['s] equation <DE>	*s.* R 994		
P 36	**Pappus['] cone** <AY>	Papposscher (Pappusscher) Kegel *m*, Kegel von Pappus	cône *m* de Pappus	конус Паппа
P 37	**Pappus['] problem** <EG>	Pappus' Problem *n*, Aufgabe *f* des Pappus	problème *m* de Pappus	задача Паппа
P 38	**Pappus['] rule (theorem),** theorem of Pappus, Guldin['s] rule, Guldin['s] theorem, centrobaric rule <for surface area *or* for volume> <DI, EG>	Guldinsche (Guldins) Regel *f*, Guldins Satz *m*, Guldinsches Theorem *n*, zentrobarische Regel	théorème *m* (règle *f*) de Guldin	правило (теорема) Гульдина
P 39	**Pappus['] theorem,** theorem of Pappus <for a degenerate conic section> <PJ>	spezieller Pascalscher Satz *m*, Satz von (des) Pascal für ein Geradenpaar, Pappus-Pascalscher Satz, Satz von (des) Pappus	théorème *m* restreint de Pappus	теорема Паппа
P 40	**Pappus['] theorem** <for a quadrilateral> <EG>	Satz *m* von Pappus, Pappusscher Satz	théorème *m* des quatre lignes, théorème de Pappus	теорема Паппа
P 41	**Pappus['] theorem** <for a triangle> <EG>	Papposscher (Pappusscher) Dreieckssatz *m*	théorème *m* de Pappus	теорема Паппа
P 42	**para-analyticity** <AN>	Paraanalytizität *f*	propriété *f* d'être paraanalytique, para-analycité *f*	парааналитичность
P 43	**parabola of degree *n*,** parabola of order *n* <AG>	Parabel *f* *n*-ten Grades	parabole *f* d'ordre *n*	парабола *n*-го порядка
	parabola of degree three <AG>	*s.* C 2732		
	parabola of Descartes <AG>	*s.* T 933		
	parabola of order *n* <AG>	*s.* P 43		
P 44	**parabolic approximation** <AX, NU>	parabolische Näherung *f*	approximation *f* parabolique	параболическое приближение, параболическая аппроксимация
	parabolic automorphism <FT>	*s.* P 66		
P 45	**parabolic bundle of circles,** spherical bundle of circles, parabolic (spherical) sheaf (star) of circles <AY>	parabolisches (sphärisches) Kreisbündel *n*	étoile (famille) *f* de cercles parabolique (sphérique)	параболическая (сферическая) связка окружностей
P 46	**parabolic bundle of rays,** parabolic sheaf (star) of rays <AY>	parabolisches Strahlenbündel (Geradenbündel) *n*	étoile (famille) *f* de droites parabolique	параболическая связка прямых
	parabolic case <FT>	*s.* L 749		
P 47	**parabolic cone** <AY>	parabolischer Kegel *m*	cône *m* parabolique	параболический конус
P 48	**parabolic congruence [of lines (rays)]** <DG>	parabolische Strahlenkongruenz (Linienkongruenz, Geradenkongruenz, Kongruenz) *f*, parabolisches Strahlensystem *n*	congruence *f* [de droites] parabolique	параболическая конгруэнция [прямых (лучей)]
P 49	**parabolic co-ordinates [in the plane]** <AY>	parabolische Koordinaten *fpl* [in der Ebene], ebene parabolische Koordinaten	coordonnées *fpl* paraboliques [dans le plan]	параболические координаты [в плоскости]
	parabolic co-ordinates <AY>	*s.* P 71		
	parabolic co-ordinates <GE>	*s.* C 2431		
	parabolic co-ordinates in the [three-dimensional] space <AY>	*s.* P 71		
P 50	**parabolic curve** <of a surface> <GE>	parabolische Kurve (Linie) *f*	courbe *f* parabolique	параболическая кривая
	parabolic curve of third order <AG>	*s.* C 2732		
P 51	**parabolic cusp** <of the fundamental region of a discontinuous group> <AL, FT>	parabolische Spitze *f*	pointe *f* parabolique [de Poincaré]	параболическое острие
P 52	**parabolic cylinder function,** function of the parabolic cylinder <FU>	Funktion *f* des parabolischen Zylinders, parabolische Zylinderfunktion *f*, Weber[-Hermite]sche Funktion	fonction *f* du cylindre parabolique, fonction de Weber-Hermite, polynôme *m* de Weber-Hermite	функция параболического цилиндра, функция Вебера-Эрмита

	English	German	French	Russian
	parabolic cylindrical co-ordinates <GE>	*s.* C 2430		
P 53	**parabolic [differential] equation,** parabolic partial differential equation, [partial] differential equation of the parabolic type <DE>	parabolische (parabolisch nichtausgeartete) Differentialgleichung (Gleichung, partielle Differentialgleichung) *f*, Differentialgleichung vom parabolischen Typ[us]	équation *f* parabolique (de type parabolique, aux dérivées partielles parabolique)	параболическое уравнение, [дифференциальное] уравнение [в частных производных] параболического типа, параболическое дифференциальное уравнение [в частных производных]
P 54	**parabolic folium** <GE>	parabolisches Blatt *n*	folium *m* parabolique	параболический лист
	parabolic formula <DI, NU>	*s.* S 1008		
	parabolic geometry <GE>	*s.* E 562		
	parabolic homology <PJ>	*s.* S 1074		
	parabolic hyperbola <AG>	*s.* C 2731		
P 55/6	**parabolic logarithm** <AN>	parabolischer Logarithmus *m* <Brendel>	logarithme *m* parabolique	параболический логарифм
P 57	**parabolic matrix** <FT>	parabolische Matrix *f*	matrice *f* parabolique	параболическая матрица
	parabolic method <DI, NU>	*s.* S 1008		
P 58	**parabolic net** <DG>	parabolisches Strahlennetz (Netz) *n*	réseau *m* parabolique	параболическая сеть
	parabolic partial differential equation <DE>	*s.* P 53		
P 59	**parabolic pencil of rays** <AY>	parabolisches Strahlenbüschel (Geradenbüschel) *n*	faisceau *m* de droites parabolique	параболический пучок прямых
	parabolic perspectivity <PJ>	*s.* S 1074		
P 60	**parabolic point** <of a plane curve *or* surface> <DG>	parabolischer Punkt *m* <auf einer Kurve *oder* Fläche>; parabolischer Flächenpunkt *m* <auf einer Fläche>	point *m* parabolique	параболическая точка
P 61	**parabolic ray** <DG>	parabolischer Strahl *m*	rayon *m* parabolique	параболический луч
P 62	**parabolic regression** <of *m*-th order>, polynomial regression <ST>	parabolische Regression *f* <vom Grade *m*>, polynomiale Regression	régression *f* parabolique <d'ordre *m*>, régression polynomiale	параболическая регрессия <*m*-го порядка>, полиномиальная регрессия
P 63	**parabolic regression** <of second order> <ST>	parabolische Regression *f* <vom zweiten Grade>, polynomiale Regression vom zweiten Grade	régression *f* parabolique <de deuxième ordre>	параболическая регрессия <второго порядка>
	parabolic rule <DI, NU>	*s.* S 1008		
P 64	**parabolic segment** <AY>	Parabelsegment *n*, Parabelabschnitt *m*	segment *m* d'une parabole	параболический сегмент
	parabolic sheaf of circles <AY>	*s.* P 45		
	parabolic sheaf of rays <AY>	*s.* P 46		
P 65	**parabolic spiral** <GE>	parabolische Spirale *f*, Helikoide *f* <Bernoulli>, Schraubenparabel *f* <Bernoulli>	spirale *f* parabolique, parabole *f* hélicoïdale	параболическая спираль
	parabolic spiral <GE>	*s. a.* F 133		
	parabolic star of circles <AY>	*s.* P 45		
	parabolic star of rays <AY>	*s.* P 46		
P 66	**parabolic substitution,** parabolic automorphism <FT>	parabolische (parabolische lineare) Transformation *f*, parabolische Abbildung (Substitution, Kreisverwandtschaft, eigentliche Möbiussche Kreisverwandtschaft) *f*	substitution *f* parabolique	параболическое дробнолинейное преобразование
P 67	**parabolic system, parabolic system of [partial] differential equations** <DE>	parabolisches (parabolisch ausgeartetes) System *n* [von partiellen Differentialgleichungen]	système *m* [d'équations aux dérivées partielles] parabolique	параболическая система [дифференциальных уравнений в частных производных]
	parabolic trend of *k*-th order <ST>	*s.* P 1013		
P 68	**parabolic type** <of a differential equation *or* Riemann surface> <DE, FT>	parabolischer Typ[us] *m*	type *m* parabolique	параболический тип
P 69	**parabolism** <of a curve> <GE>	Parabolismus *m*	parabolisme *m*	параболизм
P 70	**parabolograph** <GE, IN>	Parabolograph *m*, Parabelzeichner *m*	parabolographe *m*	параболограф
P 71	**paraboloidal co-ordinates,** confocal paraboloidal co-ordinates, parabolic co-ordinates [in the [three-dimensional] space], co-ordinates of the asymmetric paraboloid <AY>	parabolische Koordinaten *fpl* im [dreidimensionalen] Raum, [allgemeine] parabolische Koordinaten, parabolische Raumkoordinaten *fpl*	coordonnées *fpl* paraboloïdales, coordonnées paraboliques [dans l'espace [tridimensionnel]]	параболоидальные координаты, параболические координаты [в [трехмерном] пространстве]

P 72	**paraboloidal surface** <DG, VA>	Affinminimalfläche *f*, paraboloidische Fläche *f*	surface *f* paraboloïdale	параболоидная поверхность
P 73	**paraboloid cone,** cone of the second order <DE>	Paraboloidkegel *m*, Kegel (Richtungskegel) *m* zweiter Ordnung	cône *m* de second ordre	конус второго порядка
P 74	**paraboloid of revolution** <EG>	Drehparaboloid *n*, Rotationsparaboloid *n*, Umdrehungsparaboloid *n*, // Konoid *n* <Archimedes>	paraboloïde *m* de révolution	параболоид вращения
P 75	⌐<TO> **paracompactification**	Parakompaktifizierung *f*	paracompactification *f*	паракомпактификация
P 76	**paracompactifying family of supports** <TO>	parakompaktifizierende Trägerfamilie *f*	famille *f* paracompactifiante	паракомпактифицирующее семейство
P 77	**paracompactness** <TO>	Parakompaktheit *f*	paracompacité *f*	паракомпактность
P 78	**paracompact space,** fully normal space <TO>	parakompakter Raum *m*	espace *m* paracompact	паракомпактное пространство
P 79	**paraconvex set** <GE>	parakonvexe Menge *f*	ensemble *m* para-convexe	паравыпуклое множество
P 80	**paracycloid** <GE>	Parazykloide *f*	paracycloïde *f*	парациклоида
	paradox <MM>	*s.* A 748		
P 81	**paradoxicality** <LO>	Paradoxie *f*	caractère *m* paradoxal	парадоксальность
P 82	**paradoxical proposition** <LO>	paradoxe Aussage *f*	énoncé *m* paradoxal (paralogique, antinomique)	парадоксальное высказывание
P 83	**paradoxical set** <FO, SE>	paradoxe Menge *f*	ensemble *m* paradoxal	парадоксальное множество
	paradox of Berry <LO>	*s.* B 218		
	paradox of denotation <LO>	*s.* B 218		
	paradox of heterologicality <LO>	*s.* G 431		
P 84	**paradox of Russell,** Russell['s] paradox, antinomy of Russell, Russell['s] antinomy, Russell['s] contradiction <MM, SE>	Russells[che] Antinomie *f*, Russellsches Paradoxon *n*, Paradoxie *f* von Russell; Russellsche Paradoxie der Menge aller Mengen, die sich nicht selbst als Element enthalten	antinomie *f* de Russell, antinomie russellienne, paradoxe *m* de Russell, paradoxe des ensembles qui s'appartiennent	парадокс Рассела (Б. Рассела), антиномия Б. Рассела [множества всех множеств, не содержащих самых себя в качестве элемента]
	⌐<LO> **paradox of set theory**	*s.* L 1068		
	paradox of Skolem-Löwenheim <LO>	*s.* S 1191		
P 85	**paradox of the Barber,** pseudoparadox of the Barber, Russell['s] paradox of the barber in a village <LO>	Paradoxon *n* vom Barbier (Dorfbarbier)	paradoxe *m* du barbier (coiffeur du village)	псевдопарадокс парикмахера, парадокс парикмахера (деревенского цирюльника, цирюльника)
	paradox of the greatest ordinal <LO>	*s.* B 809		
	paradox of the liar <LO>	*s.* E 296		
	paradox of the lying Epimenides <LO>	*s.* E 296		
P 86	**paraelliptic surface** <AG>	paraelliptische Fläche *f*	surface *f* paraelliptique	параэллиптическая поверхность
P 87	**parafactorial local ring** <AL>	parafaktorieller lokaler Ring *m*	anneau *m* local [noethérien] parafactoriel	парафакториальное локальное кольцо
P 88	**parallel,** parallel line <GE>	Parallele *f*, parallele Gerade *f*	parallèle *f*, droite *f* parallèle	параллель, параллельная прямая
P 89	**parallel,** parallel circle, parallel (line) of latitude <of a surface *or* body of revolution> <GE>	Breitenkreis *m*, Parallelkreis *m*, Parallel *m*	parallèle *m*, cercle *m* de latitude	параллель, параллельный круг, параллельная окружность, круг параллели, широтный круг
P 90	**parallel,** || <EG>	parallel, ||	parallèle, ||	параллельный, ||
P 91	**parallel and equal,** # <EG>	parallel und gleich, #	parallèle et égal, #	параллельный и равный, #
P 92	**parallel angle,** Lobachevski['s] function <$\Pi(x)$> <in hyperbolic geometry> <GE>	Parallelwinkel *m*, [Lobatschewskischer] Parallelenwinkel, Lobatschewskische Funktion *f*	angle *m* du parallélisme, fonction *f* de Lobatchefski	угол параллельности, функция Лобачевского
P 93	**parallel[-] axiom,** axiom of parallelism <not necessarily Euclid's axiom> <GE>	Parallelenaxiom *n*	axiome *m* des parallèles, axiome de parallélisme	аксиома параллельности (параллельных)
	parallel axiom [of Euclid] <GE>	*s.* E 572		
P 94	**parallel body** <of a convex body> <CS, GE>	Parallelkörper *m*, äußerer Parallelkörper	corps *m* parallèle	параллельное тело
	parallel circle <GE>	*s.* P 89		
	parallel co-ordinates <AY>	*s.* A 350		
P 95	**parallel curve** <of a curve *or* on a surface> <AY, DG>	Parallelkurve *f*, parallele Kurve *f*	courbe *f* parallèle	параллельная кривая
P 96	**parallel displacement,** parallel propagation (shift), pseudo-parallel displacement <of vectors *or* tensors> <DG>	Parallelverschiebung *f*, Parallelübertragung *f*, lineare Übertragung *f*	transport *m* parallèle (par parallélisme)	параллельное перенесение, параллельный перенос
	parallel displacement <AY>	*s.* T 819		
	parallel displacement [in the sense] of Levi-Cività <DG>	*s.* I 479		
P 97	**parallel displacement of the system of co-ordinates,** parallel translation of the system of co-ordinates <AY>	Parallelverschiebung *f* des Koordinatensystems	déplacement *m* parallèle du système des coordonnées	параллельный перенос системы координат, параллельное перенесение системы координат

No.	English	German	French	Russian
P 98	**parallel edge** <of an oriented graph> <GP>	paralleler Bogen *m*, Parallelkante *f*, parallele gerichtete Kante *f*	arc *m* parallèle	параллельная дуга
	parallel elements <GP>	*s.* M 995		
	parallelepiped <EG>	*s.* P 102		
P 99	**parallelepipedal neighbourhood** <TO>	Quaderumgebung *f*, parallelepipedische Umgebung *f*	voisinage *m* parallélépipédique	параллелепипедальная окрестность
P 100	**parallelepipedal number** <NT>	parallelepipedische Zahl *f*	nombre *m* parallélépipède	параллелепипедическое число
P 101	**parallelepipedal product,** [s alar] triple product, triple scalar product, mixed product <of three vectors> <VT>	Spatprodukt *n*, skalares Dreierprodukt *n*, gemischtes (zusammengesetztes) Produkt *n*	produit *m* triple (scalaire triple, parallélépipède, mixte)	смешанное произведение [трех векторов], тройное произведение
P 102	**parallelepipedon,** parallelepiped, parallelopiped, parallelopipedon <EG>	Parallelepiped *n*, Parallelepipedon *n*, Parallelflach *n*, Spat *n*	parallélépipède *m*	параллелепипед
P 103	**parallelism** <EG>	Parallelität *f*	parallélisme *m*	параллельность
	parallelism of Levi-Cività <DG>	*s.* L 602		
P 104	**parallelizability** <DG>	Parallelisierbarkeit *f*	parallélisabilité *f*	параллелизуемость
P 105	**parallelizable manifold (variety)** <DG>	parallelisierbare Mannigfaltigkeit *f*	variété *f* parallélisable	параллелизуемое многообразие
P 106	**parallel knot** <TO>	Parallelknoten *m*		сопроводительный узел
	parallel line <GE>	*s.* P 88		
	parallel of latitude <GE>	*s.* P 89		
P 107	**parallelogram** <EG>	Parallelogramm *n*	parallélogramme *m*	параллелограмм
P 108	**parallelogram axiom** <in the affine space> <GE>	Parallelogrammaxiom *n*	axiome *m* du parallélogramme	аксиома параллелограмма
P 109	**parallelogram identity** <in a unitary space> <FA>	Parallelogrammgleichung *f*, Parallelogrammsatz *m*	identité *f* de la médiane, équation *f* du parallélogramme	уравнение параллелограмма
P 110	**parallelogram law** <for vectors> <VT>	Parallelogrammregel *f*, Parallelogrammgesetz *n*	règle (loi) *f* du parallélogramme	закон параллелограмма (сложения по правилу параллелограмма), правило параллелограмма
	parallelogram law <GR>	*s.* F 341		
P 111	**parallelogrammatic number** <NT>	parallelogrammische Zahl *f*	nombre *m* parallélogramme	параллелограммное число
	parallelogram of periods <FT>	*s.* P 466		
P 112	**parallelohedron** <EG>	Paralleloeder *n*	parallèloèdre *m*	параллелоэдр
	parallelohedron of Voronoï <GE>	*s.* V 220		
P 113	**parallelologic triangle** <GE>	parallelologes Dreieck *n*	triangle *m* parallélologique	параллелологический треугольник
	parallelopiped[on] <EG>	*s.* P 102		
P 114	**parallelotope** <GE>	Parallelotop *n*	parallélotope *m*	параллелотоп, гиперпараллелепипед
P 115	**parallel perspective** <DS>	Parallelperspektive *f*	perspective *f* parallèle	параллельная перспектива, параллельперспектива
	parallel postulate [of Euclid] <GE>	*s.* E 572		
P 116	**parallel product** <of functors> <CA>	Parallelprodukt *n*	produit *m* parallèle	параллельное произведение
P 117	**parallel projection,** cylindrical projection <DS>	Parallelprojektion *f*, Zylinderprojektion *f* <Prozeß, Ergebnis>; Parallelriß *m* <Ergebnis>	projection *f* parallèle (cylindrique)	параллельная (цилиндрическая) проекция
	parallel propagation <DG>	*s.* P 96		
P 118	**parallel proportional profile** <ST>	parallel-proportionales Profil *n*	profil *m* proportionnel parallèle	параллельный пропорциональный профиль
	parallel ruler <GE, IN>	*s.* R 1519		
P 119	**parallel set** <of a set> <GE>	Parallelmenge *f*	ensemble *m* parallèle	параллельное множество
	parallel shift <AY>	*s.* T 819		
	parallel shift <DG>	*s.* P 96		
P 120	**parallel slit** <FT>	Parallelschlitz *m*	fente *f* parallèle	параллельный разрез (надрез)
P 121	**parallel slit domain** <FT>	Parallelschlitzgebiet *n*, Parallelschlitzbereich *m*	plan *m* muni de fentes parallèles	область с параллельными разрезами (надрезами)
P 122	**parallel slit theorem** <FT>	Parallelschlitztheorem *n*	théorème *m* des fentes parallèles	теорема о конформном отображении многосвязной области на область с параллельными разрезами (надрезами)
P 123	**parallel strip** <DE>	Parallelstreifen *m*	bande *f* parallèle	полос[к]а, ограниченная параллелями; параллельная полос[к]а
P 124	**parallel subspace** <GE>	paralleler <linearer> Unterraum *m*	sous-espace *m* parallèle	параллельное пространство
P 125	**parallel surface** <GE>	Parallelfläche *f*, parallele Fläche *f*	surface *f* parallèle	параллельная поверхность
	parallel translation of the system of coordinates <AY>	*s.* P 97		
P 126	**paralogism,** fallacy <LO>	Paralogismus *m*, Fehlschluß *m*, Trugschluß *m*	paralogisme *m*	паралогизм, ложное умозаключение

P 127	**parameter** <of the elliptic integral of the third kind> <FU>	Parameter *m*	paramètre *m*	параметр
	parameter <FU>	*s.* M 795		
	parameter <ST>	*s.* D 762		
	parameter <VT>	*s.* P 611		
	parameter change <AN, DG>	*s.* T 780		
P 128	**parameter curve,** parametric curve <AY, DG, TO>	Parameterkurve *f*, Parameterlinie *f*	ligne *f* paramétrique	параметрическая линия
	parameter-free test <ST>	*s.* N 443		
P 129	**parameter group** <of a Lie transformation group> <GR>	Parametergruppe *f*	groupe *m* des paramètres	группа параметров
	parameter hypothesis <ST>	*s.* P 140		
	parameterization <GE>	*s.* P 149		
	3-parameter linear system <AG>	*s.* T 457		
P 130	**parameter neighbourhood** <FT, TO>	Parameterumgebung *f*	voisinage *m* paramétrique	параметрическая окрестность
P 131	**parameter of a family** <e.g.: of curves *or* bodies> <GE>	Scharparameter *m*	paramètre *m* d'un système <de courbes *ou* corps>	параметр семейства
	parameter of population <ST>	*s.* P 1044		
	parameter of position <ST>	*s.* P 1058		
	parameters of Rodrigues <GE>	*s.* E 593		
P 132	**parameter space** <AT, DG, ST>	Parameterraum *m*	espace *m* des paramètres	пространство параметров
P 133	**parameter specialization** <AG>	Parameterspezialisierung *f*	spécialisation *f* du paramètre	выбор специального значения параметра; специальное значение параметра
P 134	**parameter surface,** parametric surface <DG, TO>	Parameterfläche *f*	surface *f* paramétrique	параметрическая поверхность
	parameter transformation <AN, DG>	*s.* T 780		
P 135	**parameter variety** <AG, DG>	Parametermannigfaltigkeit *f*	variété *f* paramétrique	параметрическое многообразие
P 136	**parameter vector,** parametric vector <ST>	Parametervektor *m*	vecteur *m* paramétrique	вектор параметров
P 137	**parametric curvature** <of a surface> <DG>	Parameterkrümmung *f*	courbure *f* paramétrique	параметрическая кривизна
P 138	**parametric curve** <GE>	Kurve *f* in Parameterdarstellung	courbe *f* donnée par ses équations paramétriques	кривая, данная параметрическими уравнениями
	parametric curve <AY, DG, TO>	*s.* P 128		
	parametric equation[s] <AN, GE>	*s.* P 144		
P 139	**parametric estimation** <ST>	parametrische Schätzung *f*	estimation *f* paramétrique	параметрическое оценивание, параметрический метод оценивания
	parametric form <AN, GE>	*s.* P 144		
P 140	**parametric hypothesis,** parameter hypothesis <ST>	Parameterhypothese *f*, parametrische Hypothese *f*	hypothèse *f* paramétrique	параметрическая гипотеза
P 141	**parametric net** <DG>	Parameternetz *n*	réseau *m* paramétrique	параметрическая сеть (сетка)
P 142	**parametric optimal (optimum) solution** <PG>	parametrische optimale Lösung *f*, parametrisches optimales Programm *n*	solution *f* optimale paramétrique	параметрический оптимальный план, параметрическое оптимальное решение
P 143	**parametric programming** <PG>	parametrische Optimierung (Programmoptimierung, Programmierung) *f*, parametrisches Programmieren *n*	programmation *f* paramétrique	параметрическое программирование
P 144	**parametric representation;** parametric form; parametric equation[s] <AN, GE>	Parameterdarstellung *f*, parametrische Darstellung *f*, Darstellung in Parameterform, Parameterform *f*; Parametergleichung[en *fpl*] *f*, Gleichung[en *fpl*] *f* in Parameterform	représentation *f* paramétrique (à paramètre[s]), forme *f* paramétrique; équation *f* paramétrique; équations *fpl* paramétriques	параметрическое представление (задание), параметрическая форма, представление в параметрической форме; параметрическое уравнение; параметрические уравнения
P 145	**parametric representation** <TO>	Parameterdarstellung *f*	représentation *f* paramétrique	параметрическое представление
P 146	**parametric surface** <DG>	parametrische Fläche *f*, Fläche in Parameterdarstellung	surface *f* représentée paramétriquement	поверхность, заданная параметрическими уравнениями
	parametric surface <DG, TO>	*s.* P 134		
P 147	**parametric test** <ST>	Parametertest *m*, parametrischer Test *m*	test *m* paramétrique	параметрический критерий
P 148	**parametric variable** <DE>	parametrische Variable *f*	variable *f* paramétrique	параметрическая переменная
	parametric vector <ST>	*s.* P 136		

No.	English	German	French	Russian
P 149	**parametrix,** singularity function, Levi['s] function <DE>	Parametrix *f*, Levische Funktion *f*, Singularitätfunktion *f*, Singularitätsfunktion *f*, Singularitätenfunktion *f*, Parametrixfunktion *f*	paramétrix *f*, fonction *f* des singularités, fonction de Levi	параметрикс, функция особенностей
P 150	**parametrization,** parameterization <GE>	Parametrisierung *f*	paramétrisation *f*, paramétrage *m*	параметризация, параметрирование, введение параметра
P 151	**parametrized family** <GE>	parametrisierte Familie *f*	famille *f* paramétrée	параметризованное семейство
P 152	**paranormal operator** <FA>	paranormaler Operator *m*	opérateur *m* paranormal	паранормальный оператор
P 153	**parastrophic determinant** <MD>	parastrophe Determinante *f* <Frobenius>	déterminant *m* parastrophe	парастрофный определитель
P 154	**parastrophic matrix** <AL>	Strukturmatrix *f*	matrice *f* parastrophe	структурная матрица
P 155	**parastrophic quasigroup,** transposed quasigroup <AL>	parastrophe Quasigruppe *f*	quasi[-]groupe *m* parastrophique, parastrophique *m*	парастрофная квазигруппа
P 156	**parastrophy** <of quasigroups> <AL>	Parastrophie *f*	parastrophie *f*	парастрофия
P 157	**paratactic mapping** <DG>	parataktische Abbildung *f*	application *f* paratactique	паратактическое отображение
P 158	**paratingent** <DG, TO>	Paratingent *n*	paratingent *m*	паратингенция
P 159	**paratopological group** <AL>	paratopologische Gruppe *f*	groupe *m* paratopologique	паратопологическая группа
P 160	**paratopy** <of quasigroups> <AL>	Paratopie *f*	paratopie *f*	паратопия
P 161	**para-unitary** <AL>	paraunitär	para-unitaire	параунитарный
	parentheses closed <LO>	*s.* R 1165		
P 162	**parenthesis,** round bracket, bracket <GN>	runde Klammer *f*, Klammer	parenthèse *f*, parenthèse ronde	круглая (простая) скобка, скобка
P 163	**parenthesis-free notation,** notation without brackets, prefix notation <LO>	klammerfreie Schreibweise *f*	notation *f* sans parenthèses	бесскобочная символика
	parenthesize / to <GN>	*s.* P 2080		
P 164	**parent population,** population, universe <ST>	Grundgesamtheit *f*, Population *f*, Gesamtheit *f*	population *f* parente, population, univers *m*	генеральная совокупность, популяция, совокупность
P 165	**Pareto['s] condition** <PG>	Pareto-Bedingung *f*	condition *f* de Pareto	условие Парето
P 166	**Pareto['s] distribution** <ST>	Pareto-Verteilung *f*, Paretosche Verteilung *f*	distribution *f* de Pareto	распределение Парето
P 167	**Pareto['s] optimality** <TG>	Pareto-Optimalität *f*	optimalité *f* au sens de Pareto	оптимальность по Парето
P 168	**parexic analysis** <AX, NU>	numerische Analysis *f* mit dem Ziel der Aufstellung von Näherungsformeln		приближенный анализ с целью получения приближенных формул
P 169	**parity** <of a function *or* a number: even *or* odd> <AN, NT>	Parität *f*	parité *f*	четность
	parity <AL>	*s.* S 836		
P 170	**parity digit** <NU>	Paritätsziffer *f*	chiffre (clef) *m* de parité, digit parité	контрольный разряд для проверки на четность, разряд четности
P 171	**Parseval['s] equality,** Parseval['s] formula <AP>	Parsevalsche Gleichung *f*, Vollständigkeitsrelation *f*	égalité *f* de Parseval	равенство Парсеваля
P 172	**Parseval['s] equation** <for eigenvalue problems> <DE>	Parsevalsche Gleichung (Formel) *f*	égalité (formule) *f* de Parseval	равенство Парсеваля
P 173	**Parseval['s] equation,** completeness relation, relation of completeness, Parseval['s] theorem, Parseval['s] formula <for orthonormal systems in a Hilbert space> <FA>	Vollständigkeitsrelation *f*, Parsevalsche Gleichung *f*, Abgeschlossenheitsrelation *f*, Parsevalscher Satz *m*, Parsevalsches Theorem *n*, Parsevalsche Formel *f*, verallgemeinerte Parsevalsche Gleichung	égalité (formule) *f* de Parseval, condition (relation) *f* de complétude	условие (отношение) замкнутости Ляпунова-Стеклова, равенство Ляпунова-Стеклова, соотношение полноты, равенство Парсеваля, отношение (уравнение) замкнутости
P 174	**Parseval['s] equation** <for Fourier *or* Laplace transform> <IT>	Parsevalsche Gleichung *f*	égalité (équation) *f* de Parseval	равенство Парсеваля
P 175	**Parseval['s] equation,** completeness relation, relation of completeness, Liapunov['s] formula <for Fourier series> <SS>	Parsevalsche Gleichung *f*, Vollständigkeitsrelation *f*, Ljapunovsche Formel *f*	égalité *f* de Parseval, relation *f* de complétude, formule *f* de Liapounoff	равенство Парсеваля, отношение полноты, формула Ляпунова
P 176	**Parseval['s] equation,** generalized Parseval['s] equation, generalized relation of completeness <for Fourier series> <SS>	Parsevalsche Gleichung *f*, verallgemeinerte Parsevalsche Gleichung, verallgemeinerte Vollständigkeitsrelation *f*	égalité *f* de Parseval (Parseval généralisée), relation *f* de complétude généralisée	равенство Парсеваля, обобщенное равенство Парсеваля, обобщенное соотношение полноты
P 177	**Parseval['s] formula** <for trigonometric polynomials> <AN>	Parsevalsche Formel *f*	formule *f* de Parseval	формула Парсеваля
	Parseval['s] formula <AP>	*s.* P 171		
	Parseval['s] formula <FA>	*s.* P 173		
P 178	**Parseval['s] generalized equation,** generalized	verallgemeinerte Parsevalsche Gleichung *f*,	égalité *f* de Parseval généralisée, condition	обобщенное соотношение полноты

	English	German	French	Russian
	Parseval equation, generalized relation of completeness <for orthonormal systems in a Hilbert space> <FA>	verallgemeinerte Vollständigkeitsrelation (Abgeschlossenheitsrelation) *f*	(relation) *f* de complétude généralisée	
P 179	**Parseval['s] inequality** <DE>	Parsevalsche Ungleichung *f*	inégalité *f* de Parseval	неравенство Парсеваля
	Parseval['s] theorem <FA>	*s.* P 173		
	part <SE>	*s.* S 2177		
	parted hyperboloid <AY>	*s.* H 661		
P 180	**partial algebra,** half[-] algebra <UA>	partielle algebraische Struktur *f*, Halbalgebra *f*, unvollständige algebraische Struktur, Algebra *f* <v. Neumann>; partielle Algebra <partielle algebraische Struktur, die nicht algebraische Struktur ist>	algèbre *f* partielle, demi-algèbre *f*, semi-algèbre *f*	полуалгебра, частичная алгебра (алгебраическая система, система)
P 181	**partial algebraic operation,** partial operation, partial composition <on *A*> <AL>	partielle [algebraische] Verknüpfung *f*, partielle Operation *f* <in *A*, von *A*, auf *A*>	opération *f* [interne] partielle <sur *A*>	частичная операция <над *A*>
P 182	**partial association** <ST>	partielle Assoziation *f*	association *f* partielle	частичная зависимость между величинами, частичная ассоциация
P 183	**partial binary operation** <AL>	binäre partielle algebraische Verknüpfung *f*, partielle binäre Operation *f*	opération *f* partielle binaire	частичная бинарная операция
P 184	**partial characteristic function** <of an *n*-ary relation> <SE>	partielle charakteristische Funktion *f* <einer *n*-stelligen Relation>	fonction *f* caractéristique partielle <d'une relation *n*-aire>	частичная характеристическая функция <*n*-арного отношения>
	partial composition <AL>	*s.* P 181		
P 185	**partial confounding** <ST>	teilweises Vermengen *n*	confusion *f* partielle, « confounding » *m* partiel	неполное (частичное) смешивание
P 186	**partial conjunction,** component <of a conjunction>, conjunct <LO>	Konjunktionsglied *n*, Teilkonjunktion *f*	conjonction *f* partielle	частичная конъюнкция
P 187	**partial contingency** <ST>	partielle Kontingenz *f*	contingence *f* partielle	частичная сопряженность признаков, частичная контингенция
P 188	**partial continuity** <AN>	partielle Stetigkeit *f*	continuité *f* partielle	частичная непрерывность
P 189	**partial contraposition** <LO>	partielle Kontraposition *f*	contraposition *f* partielle	частичная контрапозиция
P 190	**partial correlation** <ST>	partielle Korrelation *f*, Teilkorrelation *f*	corrélation *f* partielle	частная корреляция
P 191	**partial correlation coefficient** <ST>	partieller Korrelationskoeffizient *m*	coefficient *m* de corrélation partielle	частный коэффициент корреляции
P 192	**partial degree** <AL>	partieller Grad *m*	degré *m* partiel	частичная степень
P 193	**partial denominator** <*n*-th> <of a continued fraction> <NT>	Teilnenner *m* <*n*-ter>	dénominateur *m* partiel <*n*-e> <d'une fraction continue>; quotient *m* incomplet <*n*-e> <d'une fraction continue régulière>	частный знаменатель <*n*-й> <цепной дроби>; неполное частное <*n*-ое> <правильной цепной дроби>
P 194	**partial derivation** <AL>	partielle Derivation *f*	dérivation *f* partielle	частичная деривация, частичное дифференцирование
P 195	**partial derivative,** partial differential coefficient <result> <DI>	partielle Ableitung *f*, partieller Differentialquotient *m*	dérivée *f* partielle	частная производная
	partial derivative of higher order <DI>	*s.* H 305		
P 196	**partial difference** <FD>	partielle Differenz *f*	différence *f* partielle	частная разность
P 197	**partial difference equation** <FD>	partielle Differenzengleichung *f*	équation *f* aux différences finies partielles	уравнение в частных конечных разностях, частное разностное уравнение
P 198	**partial difference quotient** <FD>	partieller Differenzenquotient *m*	quotient *m* des différences partiel	частная разделенная разность
P 199	**partial differential,** intermediate differential <DI>	partielles Differential *n*	différentielle *f* partielle	частный дифференциал
	partial differential coefficient <DI>	*s.* P 195		
P 200	**partial differential equation** <DE>	partielle Differentialgleichung *f*	équation *f* [différentielle] aux dérivées partielles	дифференциальное уравнение в частных производных
	partial differential equation of Hamilton-Jacobi <DE>	*s.* H 73		
P 201	**partial differential equation of mixed [elliptico-hyperbolic] type** <DE>	partielle Differentialgleichung *f* gemischten Typs	équation *f* aux dérivées partielles du type mixte	дифференциальное уравнение смешанного типа
	partial differential equation of the elliptic[al] type <DE>	*s.* E 172		

No.	English	German	French	Russian
	partial differential equation of the hyperbolic type <DE>	*s.* H 627		
	partial differential equation of the parabolic type <DE>	*s.* P 53		
P 202	**partial differential operator** <AN>	partieller Differential-operator *m*	opérateur *m* aux dérivées partielles, opérateur différentiel partiel	дифференциальный оператор с частными производными
P 203	**partial differentiation** <process> <DI>	partielle Differentiation (Ableitung) *f*	dérivation *f* partielle	частное дифференцирование, нахождение частной производной
P 204	**partial Dini derivative** <of a function> <RF>	partielle Derivierte (Hauptderivierte, extreme Derivierte, Dinische Derivierte) *f*	nombre *m* dérivé partiel, dérivée *f* partielle [au sens de Dini]	частное производное число
P 205	**partial disjunction,** component of a disjunction, disjunct <LO>	Teildisjunktion *f*	disjonction *f* partielle	частичная дизъюнкция
	partial domain <TO>	*s.* S 2098		
P 206	**partial fraction** <of a rational function> <FT>	Partialbruch *m*, Teilbruch *m*	élément *m* simple, fraction *f* simple (partielle)	элементарная (простейшая, частичная) дробь
P 207	**partial fraction** <of a rational number> <NT>	Partialbruch *m*	fraction *f* partielle	частичная дробь
P 208	**partial fraction decomposition (expansion).** expansion in (into) partial fractions, decomposition into partial fractions, expressing in partial fractions <AL, FT>; decomposition of a fraction <AL>	Partialbruchzerlegung *f* <AL, FT>; Zerlegung *f* eines Bruches <AL>	décomposition *f* en éléments (fractions) simples, décomposition en éléments simples des fractions <AL, FT>; décomposition d'une fraction <AL>	разложение на простейшие (элементарные) дроби
P 209	**partial fraction series** <FT>	Partialbruchreihe *f*	série *f* en éléments simples	ряд по простейшим (элементарным) дробям
P 210	**partial function** <AN>	Teilfunktion *f*; eingeschränkte Funktion *f*	fonction *f* partielle	частичная (ограниченная) функция
P 211	**partial function,** incompletely (partially) defined function <SE>	partielle (nicht überall definierte) Funktion *f*	fonction *f* partielle	частичная (частично определенная, не всюду определенная) функция
P 212	**partial functional** <MM>	partielles Funktional *n*	fonctionnelle *f* partielle	частичный функционал
P 213	**partial functor** <CA>	partieller Funktor *m*, Partialfunktor *m*	foncteur *m* partiel	частичный функтор
P 214	**partial graph** <GP>	Teilgraph *m*	graphe *m* partiel	частный граф, остовный подграф, суграф
P 215	**partial group** <AL>	partielle Gruppe *f*	p-groupe *m*	частичная группа
P 216	**partial groupoid,** half-groupoid, semi[-]groupoid, multiplicative system <AL>	Halbgruppoid *n*, partielles (unvollständiges) Gruppoid *n*, partielles binäres System *n*	groupoïde *m* partiel, p-groupoïde *m*, semi-groupoïde *m*	частичный группоид
P 217	**partial homomorphism** <AL, GR>	partieller Homomorphismus *m*	homomorphisme *m* partiel	частичный гомоморфизм
P 218	**partial hypergraph** <GP>	Teilhypergraph *m*	hypergraphe *m* partiel	частичный гиперграф
	partial integral <DE>	*s.* P 270		
	partial integration <DI>	*s.* I 677		
	partial isometry <FA>	*s.* P 224		
	partial latin square <CT, ST>	*s.* I 268		
P 219	**partial linear differential equation,** linear partial differential equation <DE>	lineare partielle Differentialgleichung *f*	équation *f* [différentielle] linéaire aux dérivées partielles	линейное [дифференциальное] уравнение в частных производных
P 220	**partially adjoint operator** <FA>	partiell adjungierter Operator *m*	opérateur *m* partiellement adjoint	частично сопряженный оператор
P 221	**partially computable function** <MM>	partiell berechenbare Funktion *f*	fonction *f* partiellement calculable	частично вычислимая функция
P 222	**partially contained curve** <in a linear system> <AG>	teilweise enthaltene Kurve *f*	courbe *f* partiellement contenue	частично включенная кривая
	partially defined function <SE>	*s.* P 211		
P 223	**partially differentiable function** <DI>	partiell differenzierbare Funktion *f*	fonction *f* partiellement différentiable	частно дифференцируемая функция
P 224	**partially isometric operator (transformation),** partial isometry <FA>	partiell isometrischer Operator *m*, partiell isometrische Transformation *f*, partielle Isometrie *f*	opérateur *m* (transformation *f*) partiellement isométrique, isométrie *f* partielle	частично изометрический оператор, частично изометрическое преобразование, частичная изометрия
P 225	**partially ordered by inclusion** <SE>	durch Inklusion halbgeordnet	ordonné par inclusion, partiellement ordonné par la relation d'inclusion	частично упорядоченный включением
P 226	**partially ordered class,** ordered class <CA, SE>	teilweise geordnete Klasse *f*, halbgeordnete Klasse	classe *f* partiellement ordonnée, classe ordonnée	полуупорядоченный класс
	partially ordered group <GR>	*s.* O 305		
P 227	**partially ordered groupoid** <AL>	halbgeordnetes (teilweise geordnetes) Gruppoid *n*	groupoïde *m* ordonné	частично упорядоченный группоид
	partially ordered linear space <AL, FA>	*s.* P 234		
P 228	**partially ordered monoid** <AL>	halbgeordnetes Monoid *n*	monoïde *m* ordonné	частично упорядоченный моноид
P 229	**partially ordered product** <of an ordered complex of partially ordered sets> <SE>	halbgeordnetes Produkt *n*	produit *m* direct général, produit partiellement ordonné	частично упорядоченное произведение

No.	English	German	French	Russian
	partially ordered ring <AL>	*s.* O 315		
	partially ordered semigroup <AL>	*s.* O 317		
P 230	**partially ordered semiring** <AL>	halbgeordneter Halbring *m*	demi-anneau *m* ordonné	частично упорядоченное полукольцо
P 231	**partially ordered set,** ordered set, partly ordered set, poset <SE>	halbgeordnete (teilweise geordnete, t-geordnete, partiell geordnete) Menge *f*, Verein *m*, teilweise (partielle) Ordnung *f*, geordnete Menge, Ordnung *f*, Halbordnung *f*, Halbordnungssystem *n*	ensemble *m* ordonné (partiellement ordonné, d'éléments partiellement ordonnés, d'éléments semi-ordonnés)	полуупорядоченное (частично упорядоченное, упорядоченное) множество
	partially ordered set <SE>	*s. a.* P 1230		
	partially ordered set satisfying the ascending chain condition <SE>	*s.* N 289		
P 232	**partially ordered set satisfying the descending and ascending chain condition** <SE>	längenendliche Halbordnung *f*, längenendliche halbgeordnete Menge *f*	ensemble *m* partiellement ordonné vérifiant (satisfaisant à) la condition des chaines limiteés	полуупорядоченное множество, удовлетворяющее условию обрыва убывающих и возрастающих цепей
P 233	**partially ordered set satisfying the descending chain condition** <SE>	der absteigenden Kettenbedingung genügende halbgeordnete Menge *f*	ensemble *m* ordonné d'Artin, ensemble *m* ordonné satisfaisant à la condition de chaîne descendante	частично упорядоченное множество, удовлетворяющее условию обрыва убывающих цепей
P 234	**partially ordered [vector] space,** partially ordered linear space, semi-ordered linear space, ordered vector space <AL, FA>	linearer halbgeordneter Raum *m*, halbgeordneter linearer Raum, halbgeordneter linearer Raum, geordneter linearer Raum, Raum mit Anordnung	espace *m* semi[-]ordonné linéaire, espace semi[-] ordonné, espace vectoriel ordonné	линейное упорядоченное пространство, полуупорядоченное пространство, упорядоченное векторное пространство
P 235	**partially ordering structure** <UA>	Halbordnungsstruktur *f*	structure *f* d'ordre [partiel]	структура полуупорядочения
P 236	**partially recursive attribute** <LO>	partiell rekursives Attribut *n*	attribut *m* récursif partiel	частично рекурсивный признак
	partially recursive function <FO>	*s.* P 256		
P 237	**partially representable bifunctor** <CA>	partiell darstellbarer Bifunktor *m*	bifoncteur *m* partiellement représentable	частично представимый двуместный функтор
P 238	**partially Turing-computable function** <FO>	partiell Turing-berechenbare Funktion *f*	fonction *f* partiellement Turing-calculable	функция, частично вычислимая по Тьюрингу
P 239	**partial mapping** <SE>	partielle Abbildung *f*	application *f* partielle	частичное (парциальное) отображение <из>
	partial mapping <TO>	*s.* R 936		
P 240	**partial mapping between A and B** <SE>	Abbildung *f* aus *A* in *B*	correspondance *f* univoque entre *A* et *B*	отображение из *A* в *B*
	partial matrix <MD>	*s.* S 2130		
P 241	**partial *n*-ary function** <UA>	partielle *n*-stellige Funktion *f*	fonction *f* partielle *n*-aire	частичная *n*-арная функция
P 242	**partial negation** <LO>	partielle Negation *f*	négation *f* partielle	частичное отрицание
P 243	**partial numerator** <*n*-th> <of a continued fraction> <NT>	Teilzähler *m* <*n*-ter>	numérateur *m* partiel <*n*-e>	частный числитель <*n*-й>
P 244	**partial operation** <UA>	partielle Operation *f*	opération *f* imparfaite (partielle)	частичная операция
	partial operation <AL>	*s.* P 181		
P 245	**partial operator algebra** <UA>	partielle algebraische Struktur *f* mit Operatorenbereichen (Operatoren), partielle Operatoralgebra *f*	algèbre *f* partielle à opérateurs	частичная алгебра с операторами
	partial order <SE>	*s.* 1. O 336; 2. P 246		
	partial order by first differences <SE>	*s.* L 620		
	partial order by last differences <SE>	*s.* A 736		
P 246	**partial ordering,** ordering, order-relation, partial order, quasi-ordering, semi-ordering, partial ordering relation, inclusion relation <reflexive *or* irreflexive> <SE>	Halbordnung *f*, Halbordnungsrelation *f*, Ordnung *f*, t-Ordnung *f*, teilweise Ordnung, Partialordnung *f*, schwache Ordnung, Ordnungsrelation *f* <reflexiv *oder* irreflexiv>	ordre *m*, relation *f* d'ordre partiel, ordre partiel, relation d'ordre, semi-ordre *m* <réflexif *ou* irréflexif>	частичное упорядочение, частичный упорядок, полуупорядочение, отношение порядка <рефлексивный *или* нерефлексивный>; частичная упорядоченность <свойство>
	partial ordering <SE>	*s.* O 336		
	partial ordering according to the principle of first differences <SE>	*s.* L 620		
	partial ordering according to the principle of last differences <SE>	*s.* A 736		
	partial ordering relation <SE>	*s.* 1. O 336; 2. P 246		
P 247	**partial order satisfying the ascending chain condition** <SE>	nach oben längenendliche Halbordnung *f*; Halbordnung, in der die aufsteigende Kettenbedingung gilt	ordre *m* partiel satisfaisant à la condition des chaines ascendantes	частичный упорядок, удовлетворяющий максимальному условию

P 248	**partial order satisfying the descending chain condition** <SE>	nach unten längenendliche Halbordnung *f*; Halbordnung, in der die absteigende Kettenbedingung gilt	ordre *m* partiel satisfaisant à la condition des chaînes descendantes	частичный упорядок, удовлетворяющий минимальному условию
P 249	**partial plane,** incidence structure (system) <PJ>	Inzidenzstruktur *f*	structure *f* d'incidence	система инцидентности, инцидентная структура
P 250	**partial predicate** <LO, MM>	partielles Prädikat *n*	prédicat *m* partiel	частичный предикат
P 251	**partial product,** intermediate product <in multiplication of numbers> <AR>	Teilprodukt *n* <Produkt des Multiplikanden mit einer Ziffer des Multiplikators>	produit *m* partiel	частичное произведение
P 252	**partial product** <of an infinite product> <SS>	Teilprodukt *n*, Partialprodukt *n*	produit *m* partiel	частное произведение
P 253	**partial quotient** <of a continued fraction>; term <of a regular continued fraction> <NT>	Teilbruch *m*, Partialbruch *m*, Glied *n*, // Teilquotient *m*	fraction *f* partielle (composante), terme *m*	звено
P 254	**partial range,** quasi range <ST>	partielle (gestutzte) Spannweite *f*	étendue *f* partielle	неполный (частичный) размах
P 255	**partial rank correlation coefficient** <ST>	partieller Rangkorrelationskoeffizient *m*	coefficient *m* de corrélation partielle des rangs	частный коэффициент ранговой корреляции
P 256	**partial recursive function,** partially recursive function <FO>	partiell-rekursive Funktion *f*, partiell (teilweise) rekursive Funktion	fonction *f* partielle récursive, fonction récursive partielle	частично рекурсивная функция, частично-рекурсивная функция
P 257	**partial recursive scheme** <LO>	partiell rekursives Schema *n*	schéma *m* partiellement récursif	частично рекурсивная схема
P 258	**partial recursivity** <LO>	partielle Rekursivität *f*	récursivité *f* partielle	частичная рекурсивность
P 259	**partial regression** <ST>	partielle Regression *f*, Teilregression *f*	régression *f* partielle	частная регрессия
P 260	**partial regression coefficient of the sample,** partial sample regression coefficient <ST>	partieller Stichproben-regressionskoeffizient *m*	coefficient *m* de régression partielle de l'échantillon	частный выборочный коэффициент регрессии
P 261	**partial relation** <MM>	partielle Relation *f*	relation *f* partielle	частичное отношение
P 262	**partial result** <GN>	Teilergebnis *n*	résultat *m* partiel	частичный результат
	partial sample regression coefficient <ST>	*s.* P 260		
P 263	**partial semigroup** <AL>	partielle Halbgruppe *f*	p-demi-groupe *m*	частичная полугруппа
	partial sequence <SS, TO>	*s.* S 2175		
	partial solution <DE>	*s.* P 270		
P 264	**partial subgraph** <GP>	Teiluntergraph *m*	sous-graphe *m* partiel	частичный подграф
P 265	**partial subset** <MM>	partielle Untermenge *f*	sous-ensemble *m* partiel	частичное подмножество
P 266	**partial sum,** subtotal <of a double *or* simple infinite series> <SS>	Teilsumme *f*, Partialsumme *f*, Abschnitt *m*	somme *f* partielle	частичная сумма
P 267	**partial transformation** <UA>	partielle Transformation *f*	transformation *f* partielle	частичное преобразование
P 268	**partial weight** <of a symmetric function> <AL>	Teilgewicht *n*	poids *m* partiel	частичный вес
P 269	**partial well-order[ing]** <SE>	partielle Wohlordnung *f*	bon ordre *m* partiel	частичное полное упорядочение
P 270	**particular integral,** particular solution, partial integral (solution) <DE>	partikuläres Integral *n*, partikuläre (spezielle, individuelle) Lösung *f*, Einzellösung *f*, Partiallösung *f*	intégrale (solution) *f* particulière	частное решение, частный интеграл
P 271	**particularization,** instantiation, existential generalization <LO>	Partikularisierung *f*, Existenzquantifizierung *f*	particularisation *f*, quantification *f* d'existence, quantification existentielle	применение квантора существования, подтверждение
	particular proposition <LO> ⌐<LO>	*s.* E 700		
	particular quantifier	*s.* E 699		
P 272	**particular solution** <of linear equations> <AL>	partikuläre (spezielle) Lösung *f*	solution *f* particulière	частное решение
	particular solution <DE>	*s.* P 270		
P 273/4	**particular term** <AR, SS>	spezielles Glied *n*	terme *m* spécial (particulier)	частный член
	particular value <GN>	*s.* S 1393		
P 275	**partition** <of a natural number> <NT>	Partition *f*, Zerfällung *f*, partitio *f* numerorum, Zerlegung *f*	partition *f* <des nombres>	разбиение, партиция
P 276	**partition,** decomposition, stratification, disjoint decomposition <of a set> <SE>	Zerlegung *f*, disjunkte Zerlegung, Klasseneinteilung *f*, <disjunkte und erschöpfende> Faserung *f*, Partition *f*	partition *f*, décomposition *f* en ensembles disjoints, répartition *f*	разбиение, расслоение, дизъюнктное разложение
	partition <AN>	*s.* S 2093		
	partition / to <MD>	*s.* S 529		
	χ^2 **partition** <ST>	*s.* C 642		
	partitioned form <MD>	*s.* B 506		
	partitioned matrix <MD>	*s.* H 703		
P 277	**partition function** <NT>	Partitionsfunktion *f*, Partitionsanzahlfunktion *f*	fonction *f* de partition	функция разбиения
	partition function <ST>	*s.* D 758		
	partitioning of [the] variables <DE, PG>	*s.* S 562		

No.	English	German	French	Russian
	partition into blocks / to <MD>	*s.* S 539		
P 278	**partition into classes** <SE>	Klasseneinteilung *f*, Einteilung *f* in Klassen	répartition *f* en classes, décomposition *f* en classes	разбиение (разбитие) на классы, классовое разбитие (разбиение), разбитие, разбиение, классификация
P 279	**partition** <of a set> **into** *n* **subsets** <SE>	Zerlegung *f* in *n* Untermengen	*n*-partition *f*	разбиение на *n* подмножеств
P 280	**partition into squares** <EG>	Quadrateinteilung *f*, Zerlegung *f* in Quadrate	partition *f* en carrés	разбиение на квадраты
	partition matrix <MD>	*s.* H 703		
	partition of χ^2 **(chi square)** <ST>	*s.* C 642		
P 281	**partition of unity,** decomposition of unity <subordinate to a cover> <TO>	Zerlegung *f* der Einheit (Eins) <die einer Überdeckung untergeordnet ist>	partition (décomposition) *f* de l'unité <subordonnée à un recouvrement>	разбиение (разложение) единицы <подчиненное покрытию>
P 282	**partition problem** <AB>	Partitionsproblem *n*	problème *m* de partition	проблема разбиения
P 283	**partitio numerorum** <NT>	partitio *f* numerorum, Untersuchung *f* von Kompositions- und Partitionsfunktionen	partitio *f* numerorum	теория функций разбиений
	partly open [and partly closed] interval <AN, SE>	*s.* H 27		
	partly ordered set <SE>	*s.* P 231		
P 284	**partly well-ordered set,** well-partially-ordered set, well-ordered partially ordered set <Kurepa> <SE>	teilweise (partiell) wohlgeordnete Menge *f*, wohlgeordnete Menge	ensemble *m* partiellement bien ordonné	частично вполне упорядоченное множество
	part-whole relation <SE>	*s.* I 246		
	party <TG>	*s.* P 665		
P 285	**Pascal distribution,** negative binomial [series] distribution, Pólya distribution <ST>	Pascalsche Verteilung *f*, Pascal-Verteilung *f*, negative Binomialverteilung *f*, Pólya-Verteilung *f*	distribution *f* de Pascal, distribution binomiale négative, distribution de Pólya	распределение Паскаля, отрицательное биномиальное распределение, распределение Пойа
P 286	**Pascal['s] hexagon** <SG>	Pascalsches Sechseck *n*	hexagone *m* de Pascal	шестиугольник Паскаля
P 287	**Pascal['s] hexagrammum mysticum,** hexagrammum mysticum [of Pascal] <PJ, SG>	Hexagrammum *n* mysticum, Steiner-Pascal-Konfiguration *f*, mystisches Hexagramm *n*, Pascalsches hexagrammum *n* mysticum	hexagramme *m* mystique, hexagramme *m* de Pascal	гексаграмма Паскаля
P 288	**Pascalian definition** <LO>	Pascalsche Definition *f*	définition *f* pascalienne	определение в смысле Паскаля
P 289	**pascaline** <NU>	Pascaline *f*	pascaline *f*	паскалево колесо
P 290	**Pascal['s] limaçon,** limaçon, conchoid of the circle <GE>	Pascalsche Schnecke *f*, Konchoide *f* des Kreises	limaçon *m* de Pascal, conchoïde *f* du (de) cercle	улитка Паскаля, конхоида окружности, улитка
P 291	**Pascal['s] line,** k-line <AY>	Pascalsche Gerade *f*, Pascal-Gerade *f*, Pascal-Linie *f*	droite *f* de Pascal	прямая Паскаля
P 292	**Pascal['s] theorem** <AY>	Satz *m* von (des) Pascal, Pascalscher Satz	théorème *m* de Pascal	теорема Паскаля
P 293	**Pascal['s] triangle,** binomial array, number triangle, arithmetic[al] triangle <AR, CT>	Pascalsches Zahlendreieck *n*, Zahlendreieck, Pascalsches (arithmetisches, Stifelsches) Dreieck *n*	triangle *m* arithmétique, triangle arithmétique de Pascal, triangle de Pascal	треугольник Паскаля, арифметический треугольник, треугольник Омара Хайяма, треугольник Штифеля (Тартальи)
P 294	**Pasch['s] axiom,** axiom of Pasch <GE>	Axiom *n* von Pasch	axiome *m* de Pasch	аксиома Паша
P 295	**passage to the limit,** limiting process <DI, GN>	Grenzübergang *m*	passage *m* à la limite	предельный переход, переход к пределу
P 296	**pass through the same point / to** <EG>	durch einen Punkt gehen	passer par un point	проходить через [одну и ту же] точку
	pasting together <TO>	*s.* P 598		
P 297	**pasting together of boundaries,** assembling (gluing) of boundaries, identification of boundaries <TO>	Verheftung *f* der Ränder	collage *m* (identification *f*, joint *m*) des frontières	склеивание (отождествление) границ
P 298	**pasting together of branches, pasting the branches together** <FT>	Verheftung *f* der Zweige	collage *m* des branches	слипание ветвей
P 299	**path** <as a set of arcs> <GP>	Weg *m*	ensemble *m* des arcs <d'un chemin simple>	неупорядоченный путь
P 300	**path,** simple chain progression <in an undirected graph> <GP>	Weg *m*, einfache Kettenprogression *f*	chaîne *f* élémentaire	простая цепь
P 301	**path** <TO>	Weg *m*, stetiger Weg *m*	chemin *m*, arc *m* de courbe, arc *m* paramétré	путь
	path <DE>	*s.* 1. C 518; 2. T 722		
	path <GP>	*s.* 1. D 549; 2. S 934		
	path <LO>	*s.* P 1757		
	path analysis <ST>	*s.* M 475		
P 302	**path class,** homotopy class of paths <TO>	Wegeklasse *f*, Homotopieklasse *f* von Wegen	classe *f* de chemins	класс путей
P 303	**path coefficient** <ST>	Pfadkoeffizient *m*	coefficient *m* de direction	путевой коэффициент, коэффициент пути
	path coefficient method <ST>	*s.* M 475		

P 304	**path component,** maximal path-connected subspace <TO>	Wegekomponente *f*, Wegkomponente *f*, maximale wegzusammenhängende Teilmenge *f*	sous-espace *m* maximal connexe par chemins	компонента линейной связности, максимальное линейно-связное подпространство
P 305	**path-connected space,** pathwise connected space <TO>	wegzusammenhängender Raum, wegeweise (bogenweise, linear) zusammenhängender Raum *m*	espace *m* connexe par chemins, espace *m* linéairement connexe	линейно связное пространство
P 306	**path diagram** <ST>	Pfaddiagramm *n*, Pfadkoeffizientenmodell *n*	diagramme *m* des coefficients de direction	диаграмма пути
P 307	**path lifting property** <AT>	Wegeliftungseigenschaft *f*	propriété *f* de relèvement des chemins	аксиома о накрывающем пути
P 308	**path matrix** <GP>	Wegmatrix *f*	matrice *f* des chemins	матрица путей
P 309	**path of integration,** line of integration <AN>	Integrationsweg *m*	chemin *m* d'intégration	путь интегрирования
P 310	**pathological function** <AN>	pathologische Funktion *f*	fonction *f* pathologique	патологическая функция
P 311	**path space,** set of paths <TO>	Wegeraum *m*	espace *m* de chemins	пространство путей
P 312	**pathwise connectedness** <TO>	wegeweiser Zusammenhang *m*	connexion (connexité) *f* linéaire	линейная связность
	pathwise connected space <TO>	*s.* P 305		
P 313	**path without double points** <TO>	doppelpunktfreier Weg *m*	chemin *m* simple	путь без самопересечений, простой путь
P 314	**Patnaik['s] [range] method** <ST>	Patnaiksches Spannweiteverfahren *n*	méthode *f* [d'étendue] de Patnaik	метод [размаха] Патнайка
	patterned sampling <ST>	*s.* S 2508		
P 315	**Pauli['s] matrix,** two-by-two Pauli matrix <AL>	Pauli-Matrix *f*, Paulische Matrix *f*	matrice *f* de Pauli	матрица Паули
P 316	**paving** <GE>	Pflasterung *f*, Parkettierung *f*	pavement *m*	паркетирование, паркетировка, замощение
P 317	**payoff** <TG>	Gewinn *m*, Auszahlung *f*	gain *m*, paiement *m*	выигрыш, выплата
P 318	**payoff [function],** kernel <TG>	Gewinnfunktion *f*, Auszahlungsfunktion *f*, Zielfunktion *f*	fonction *f* d'utilité, fonction de paiement, fonction du gain	функция выигрыша, платежная функция
P 319	**payoff matrix** <TG>	Gewinnmatrix *f*, Auszahlungsmatrix *f*	matrice *f* de gain (paiement)	матрица выигрыша, платежная матрица
P 320	**payoff table** <TG>	Gewinntabelle *f*, Auszahlungstabelle *f*, Spieltabelle *f*	tableau *m* de gain (paiement)	таблица выигрыша, платежная таблица
P 321/2	***p*-base, *p*-basis** <for *E*/*K*> <AL>	*p*-Basis *f* <von *E* über *K*>	*p*-base *f*, base *f* d'imperfection <de *E* sur *K*>	*p*-базис <*E* над *K*>
	P-B-W theorem <AL>	*s.* B 451		
	***p*-class** <GR>	*s.* C 801		
P 323	***p*-class group** <AB>	*p*-Klassengruppe *f*	groupe *m* de *p*-classes	группа *p*-классов
P 324	***p*-class number** <AB>	*p*-Klassenzahl *f*	nombre *m* de *p*-classes	число *p*-классов
P 325	𝔭**-component** <of an idèle *or* differential> <AB, AL>	𝔭-Komponente *f*	𝔭-composante *f*	𝔭-компонента
P 326	𝔭**-conductor** <AL>	𝔭-Führer *m*	𝔭-conducteur *m*	𝔭-кондуктор
P 327	***p*-conjugate element** <of a group> <GR>	*p*-konjugiertes Element *n*	élément *m* *p*-conjugué	*p*-сопряженный элемент
P 328	***p*-convexity** <AN>	*p*-Konvexität *f*	*p*-convexité *f*	*p*-выпуклость
P 329	𝔭**-coordinate** <of an idèle> <AB>	𝔭-Koordinate *f*	𝔭-coordonnée *f*	𝔭-координата
P 330	***p*-coprimary module** <AL>	*p*-koprimärer Modul *m*	module *m* *p*-coprimaire	*p*-копримарный модуль
P 331	***p*-cyclic complex** <AT>	*p*-zyklischer Komplex *m*	complexe *m* *p*-cyclique	*p*-циклический комплекс
P 332	***p*-dependent numbers** <AB>	*p*-abhängige Zahlen *fpl*	nombres *mpl* *p*-dépendants	*p*-зависимые числа
P 333	***p*-direction** <in a vector space> <AL, GE>	*p*-Richtung *f*	*p*-direction *f*	*p*-направление
P 334	𝔭**-discriminant** <AL>	𝔭-Diskriminante *f*	𝔭-discriminante *f*	𝔭-дискриминант
P 335	***p*-discriminant** <DE>	*p*-Diskriminante *f*	*p*-discriminante *f*	*p*-дискриминант
P 336	***p*-discriminant equation** <DE>	*p*-Diskriminantengleichung *f*	équation *f* *p*-discriminante	*p*-дискриминантное уравнение
P 337/8	***p*-discriminant locus,** discriminant curve <DE>	*p*-Diskriminantenort *m*, Diskriminantenkurve *f*	courbe *f* discriminante	дискриминантная кривая
	***p*-divisible group** <GR>	*s.* B 68		
	peaked distribution <ST>	*s.* L 579		
	peakedness <ST>	*s.* L 580		
	Peanian continuum <TO>	*s.* L 953		
	Peano['s] algebra <UA>	*s.* A 99		
P 339	**Peano['s] arithmetic** <FO>	Peano-Arithmetik *f*	arithmétique *f* de Peano	арифметика Пеано
P 340	**Peano['s] axiom system, Peano['s] axioms,** Peano['s] postulates, axioms of Dedekind-Peano <of natural numbers> <FO>	Peanosches (Peanos) Axiomensystem *n*, Peano-Axiome *npl*, Axiome *npl* Peanos (von Peano)	système *m* [d'axiomes] de Peano	аксиомы Пеано, система аксиом Пеано, система Пеано
P 341	**Peano-Baker method** <for solving linear differential equations> <DE>	Peano-Baker-Verfahren *n*	méthode *f* de Peano-Baker	метод Пеано-Бейкера
	Peano['s] continuum <TO>	*s.* C 2203		
P 342	**Peano['s] curve** <TO>	Peano-Kurve *f*, Peanosche Menge *f* im engeren Sinne	courbe *f* péanienne (de Peano)	кривая Пеано
	Peano['s] existence theorem <DE>	*s.* P 345		

No.	English	German	French	Russian
	Peano['s] postulates <FO>	*s.* P 340		
P 343	**Peano['s] remainder** <SS>	Peanosches Restglied *n*, Peanosche Form *f* des Restgliedes	reste *m* de Peano, terme *m* résiduel de Peano	остаточный член Пеано, остаток Пеано
P 344	**Peano['s] space** <TO>	Peanoscher Raum *m*	espace *m* péanien	пеаново пространство
P 345	**Peano['s] theorem,** Peano['s] existence theorem <DE>	Peanoscher Existenzsatz *m*, Existenzsatz von Peano	théorème *m* de Peano, théorème d'existence de Peano	теорема существования Пеано, теорема Пеано
P 346	**Peano['s] theorem** <IV>	Satz *m* von Peano, Peanoscher Satz	théorème *m* de Peano	теорема Пеано
P 347	**pearl of Sluse** <GE>	Perle *f* von Sluse, Perlkurve *f* <De Sluse, Pascal> <*n*-ter Ordnung>	perle *f*	жемчужная кривая <*n*-го порядка>
	Pearl-Reed curve <ST>	*s.* L 1078		
	Pearson['s] chi-squared statistic <ST>	*s.* P 357		
P 348	**Pearson['s] coefficient [of correlation],** product-moment correlation coefficient, Bravais['s] correlation coefficient, Bravais['s] coefficient [of correlation] <ST>	Maßkorrelationskoeffizient *m*, Produktmoment-Korrelationskoeffizient *m*, gewöhnlicher (Bravaisscher, Pearsonscher) Korrelationskoeffizient *m*	coefficient *m* de corrélation de Bravais (Pearson), coefficient de Bravais-Pearson, coefficient de corrélation linéaire de Bravais et Pearson	коэффициент корреляции Браве (Пирсона)
P 349	**Pearson['s] curve,** Pearson['s] distribution curve <ST>	Pearsonsche Kurve (Verteilungskurve) *f*	courbe *f* de Pearson, courbe de distribution de Pearson	кривая Пирсона
	Pearson['s] differential equation <DE>	*s.* P 351		
P 350	**Pearson['s] distribution** <ST>	Pearsonsche Verteilung *f*	distribution *f* de Pearson	распределение Пирсона
	Pearson['s] distribution curve <ST>	*s.* P 349		
P 351	**Pearson['s] equation,** Pearson['s] differential equation <DE>	Pearsonsche Differentialgleichung *f*	équation *f* (équation différentielle) de Pearson	уравнение (дифференциальное уравнение) Пирсона
P 352	**Pearson['s] factor** <ST>	Pearson-Faktor *m*	facteur *m* de Pearson	коэффициент Пирсона
P 353	**Pearson-Filon['s] formula** <ST>	Pearson-Filonsche Formel *f*	formule *f* de Pearson-Filon	формула Пирсона-Филона
P 354	**Pearson['s] function** <ST>	Pearsonsche Funktion *f*	fonction *f* de Pearson	функция Пирсона
P 355	**Pearson-Lee-Fisher function** <ST>	Pearson-Lee-Fisher-Funktion *f*	fonction *f* de Pearson-Lee-Fisher	функция Пирсона-Ли-Фишера
P 356	**Pearson['s] measure of skewness** <ST>	Pearsonsches Schiefheitsmaß *n*	coefficient *m* de dissymétrie de Pearson	мера асимметрии Пирсона
P 357	**Pearson['s] χ^2-statistic,** Pearson['s] chi-squared statistic <ST>	Pearsonsche χ^2-Stichprobenfunktion (Chi-Quadrat-Stichprobenfunktion, χ^2-Prüfzahl, Chi-Quadrat-Prüfzahl) *f*	critère *m* (statistique *f*) χ^2 de Pearson, critère (statistique) chi carré de Pearson	χ^2-статистика Пирсона, статистика хи-квадрат Пирсона
	Pearson type III <ST>	*s.* G 41		
P 358	**Peaucellier['s] cell (inversor),** cell (inversor) of Peaucellier <GE, IN>	Inversor *m* von Peaucellier, Peaucellierscher Inversor	inverseur *m* de Peaucellier	инверсор Поселье
P 359	**pedal,** pedal curve, pedal locus [line] <of a curve> <GE>	Fußpunkt[s]kurve *f*, Fußpunktenkurve *f*, Tangentenfußpunkt[en]kurve *f*	podaire *f*, courbe *f* podaire (pédale, podaire tangentielle)	подера, подерная (подэрная) кривая, подэра, подошвенная (подарная) кривая
P 360	**pedal circle** <GE>	Fußpunktkreis *m*, Umkreis *m* des Fußpunktdreiecks	cercle *m* podaire	подерная (подэрная, подошвенная) окружность
	pedal curve <GE>	*s.* P 359		
	pedal line <EG>	*s.* W 11		
	pedal locus [line] <GE>	*s.* P 359		
P 361	**pedal polygon** <of an *n*-gon> <GE>	Fußpunkt[en]vieleck *n*, Miquel-Vieleck *n*	polygone *m* podaire	подерный (подэрный, подошвенный) многоугольник
P 362	**pedal surface** <GE>	Fußpunktfläche *f*, Fußpunktenfläche *f*	surface *f* podaire, podaire *f*, surface dérivée	подерная (подэрная, подошвенная) поверхность
P 363	**pedal tetrahedron** <of a tetrahedron> <GE>	Fußpunkttetraeder *n*	tétraèdre *m* podaire	подерный четырехгранник (тетраэдр), подэрный четырехгранник (тетраэдр), подошвенный четырехгранник (тетраэдр)
P 364	**pedal transformation** <of a curve> <GE>	Fußpunkttransformation *f*	transformation *f* podaire	подерное (подэрное, подошвенное) преобразование
P 365	**pedal triangle** <GE>	Fußpunktdreieck *n*	triangle *m* podaire (pédal, orthique)	подерный (подэрный, подошвенный) треугольник
P 366	**Peirce['s] decomposition** <of a ring> <AL>	Peircesche Zerlegung *f*	décomposition *f* de Peirce	пирсовское разложение
P 367	**Peirce['s] law** <LO>	Peircesches Gesetz *n*, Peircesche Wahrform *f*, Gesetz (Satz *m*) von Peirce	loi *f* de Peirce, loi d'implication appelée « loi de Peirce », principe *m* de réduction de Peirce	закон Пирса
P 368	***p*-elementary group** <GR>	*p*-elementare Gruppe *f*	groupe *m* *p*-élémentaire	*p*-элементарная группа
	Pell['s] equation <NT>	*s.* P 370		
P 369	**Pellet['s] theorem** <on the zeros of a polynomial> <AL>	Pelletscher Satz *m*	théorème *m* de Pellet	теорема Пеллэ
P 370	**Pellian equation,** Pell['s] equation <NT>	Pellsche Gleichung *f*	équation *f* de Pell (Fermat)	уравнение Пелля

No.	English	German	French	Russian
P 371	**penalty function** <PG>	Straffunktion *f*, Penalty-funktion *f*	fonction *f* de peine	штрафная функция, штраф-функция
P 372	**penalty function method,** method of penalty functions <PG>	Methode *f* der Straffunktionen, Straffunktions-methode *f*	méthode *f* des fonctions de peines	метод штрафных функций
P 373	**pencil** <of point curves *or* point surfaces> <AG>	Punktbüschel *n*, Punktschar *f*	faisceau *m* ponctuel	пучок
	pencil <AG, AY>	*s.* L 831		
P 374	**pencil-family** <of conic sections> <AY>	Büschel-Schar *f*	faisceau-famille *f*	пучок-семейство
P 375	**pencil of circles** <AY>	Kreisbüschel *n*, Büschel *n* von Kreisen	faisceau *m* de cercles	пучок окружностей
P 376	**pencil of complexes** <PJ>	Komplexbüschel *n*	faisceau *m* de complexes	пучок комплексов
P 377	**pencil of conics** <AY>	Kegelschnittbüschel *n*, Büschel *n* von Kegelschnitten (Kurven zweiter Ordnung), [lineares] Kegelschnittsystem *n* erster (1.) Stufe	faisceau *m* ponctuel de coniques, système *m* linéaire [de coniques], système du premier degré	пучок конических сечений
P 378	**pencil of curves** <AY>	Kurvenbüschel *n*	faisceau *m* de courbes	пучок кривых
P 379	**pencil of lines,** pencil of rays <AY, DS>	Strahlenbüschel *n*, Geradenbüschel *n*	faisceau *m* de droites (rayons)	пучок прямых (лучей)
P 380	**pencil of parallel lines** <EG>	Parallelstrahlenbüschel *n*	faisceau *m* de droites parallèles	пучок параллельных прямых
P 381	**pencil of pencils** <PJ>	Büschelbüschel *n*	faisceau *m* de faisceaux	пучок пучков
P 382	**pencil of planes;** axial pencil <AY>	Ebenenbüschel *n*	faisceau *m* de plans, // ordonnance *f* de plans <Desargues>	пучок плоскостей
	pencil of points <PJ>	*s.* P 783		
	pencil of rays <AY, DS>	*s.* P 379		
P 383	**pencil of spheres** <AY>	Kugelbüschel *n*	faisceau *m* de sphères	пучок сфер
P 384	**pendant vertex** <of a tree> <GP>	Endknotenpunkt *m*, hängender Knotenpunkt *m*	sommet *m* pendant (terminal)	концевая вершина, висячая вершина
	pendant vertex <GP>	*s.* E 235		
P 385	**penosculating conic** <GE>	penoskulierender Kegelschnitt *m*	conique *f* (section *f* conique) pénosculatrice	пеноскулирующее коническое сечение
P 386	**penosculation** <DG>	Penoskulation *f*	pénosculation *f*	пеноскулирование
P 387	**pentacycle of Stephanos** <GE>	Pentazykel *m* von Stephanos	pentacycle *m* de Stephanos	пентацикл
P 388	**pentacyclic co-ordinates** <GE>	pentazyklische Koordinaten *fpl*; pentazyklisches Koordinatensystem *n*	coordonnées *fpl* pentacycliques; système *m* de coordonnées pentacycliques	пентациклические координаты; система пентациклических координат
P 389	**pentad** <CT>	Pentade *f*	pentade *f*, groupe *m* de cinq	пентада
P 390	**pentad** <as an information unit> <ST>	Pentade *f*	pentade *f*	пятиразрядное двоичное число, пятерка
P 391	**pentad criterion** <ST>	Fünffaktorkriterium *n*	critère *m* des cinq facteurs	критерий пяти факторов
	pentadic relation <LO>	*s.* F 378		
P 392	**pentagonal number** <a figurate number> <NT>	Pentagonalzahl *f*, Fünfeckzahl *f*	nombre *m* pentagonal (pentagone)	пятиугольное (пентагональное) число
P 393	**pentagram [of Pythagoras]** <EG>	Pentagramm *n*, regelmäßiges Sternfünfeck *n*, // Pentalpha *n*	pentagramme *m*, // pentalpha *m*	пентаграмма
P 394	**pentahedron** <EG>	Fünfflach *n*, Pentaeder *n*, Fünfflächner *m*	pentaèdre *m*	пятигранник, пентаэдр
P 395	**pentaspherical co-ordinates** <GE>	pentasphärische Koordinaten *fpl*, Fünfkugelkoordinaten *fpl*; pentasphärisches Koordinatensystem *n*	coordonnées *fpl* pentasphériques; système *m* de coordonnées pentasphériques	пентасферические координаты; система пентасферических координат
P 396	**pentiamond** <EG>	Pentiamant *m*	pentiamant *m*	пентиамант
P 397	**pentomino** <EG>	Pentomino *n*	pentomino *m*	пентомино
P 398	**percentage** <AR>	Prozentsatz *m*, Prozentverhältnis *n*	pourcentage *m*, pour-cent *m*, taut *m* pour-cent	процентное отношение
P 399	**percentage calculation** <AR>	Prozentrechnung *f*, Prozentrechnen *n*	calcul *m* d'intérêt, pourcentage *m*	исчисление процентов; вычисление с процентами
P 400	**percentage error,** relative error <in percents> <ER>	prozentualer Fehler *m*, relativer Fehler <in Prozent>	erreur *f* relative <en pourcents>	относительная погрешность <выраженная в процентах>
P 401	**percentage point,** tabulated significance point <ST>	Prozentpunkt *m*, Tabellenwert *m* der Prüfzahl	point *m* pourcentage, limite *f* de significance tabulée	процентная точка [статистики]
	percentage rate of interest <AR>	*s.* R 160		
P 402	**percentile,** centile <ST>	Perzentil *n*, Prozentil *n*, Zentil *n*	percentile *m*, centile *m*, pourcentile *m*	процентиль
P 403	**perfect category** <CA>	perfekte Kategorie *f*	catégorie *f* parfaite	совершенная категория
P 404	**perfect closure** <of a field> <AL>	vollkommene Hülle *f*	clôture *f* parfaite	совершенное замыкание
P 405	**perfect cube** <as an expression> <AL>	vollständige dritte Potenz *f*, vollständiger Kubus *m*	cube *m* parfait (exact)	полный (точный) куб
P 406	**perfect cube** <of a number> <NT>	Kubikzahl *f*, Kubus *m*	nombre *m* cubique (cube), cube *m* parfait	куб
P 407	**perfect curve** <AG>	perfekte Kurve *f*	courbe *f* parfaite	совершенная кривая
	perfect differential <DI>	*s.* T 624		
P 408	**perfect Euler square** <CT>	pandiagonales Eulersches Quadrat *n*	carré *m* d'Euler pandiagonal	пандиагональный эйлеров квадрат
P 409	**perfect extension** <of a field> <AL>	perfekte Erweiterung *f*	extension *f* parfaite	совершенное расширение
P 410	**perfect field** <AL>	vollkommener Körper *m*	corps *m* parfait	совершенное поле
P 411	**perfect form,** perfect positive definite quadratic form <NT>	vollkommene (vollkommene quadratische) Form *f*	forme *f* [quadratique] parfaite	совершенная квадратичная форма

No.	English	German	French	Russian
P 412	**perfect group** <GR>	perfekte (vollkommene) Gruppe *f*	groupe *m* parfait	совершенная группа
P 413	**perfect ideal** <AG, AL>	perfektes Ideal *n*	idéal *m* parfait	совершенный идеал
P 414	**perfect information,** complete information <TG>	vollständige Information *f*	information *f* complète	полная информация
P 415	**perfectly normal space** <TO>	perfekt normaler Raum *m*	espace *m* [topologique] parfaitement normal	совершенно нормальное пространство
	perfectly separable space <TO>	*s.* C 1512		
P 416	**perfect magic square,** pandiagonal magic square, diabolic magic square <CT, NT>	pandiagonales magisches Quadrat *n*, diabolisches (pan[-]diagonales, panmagisches, vollständig magisches, vollkommen magisches, gleichzeiliges magisches, zylindrisches, teuflisches) Quadrat, Teufelsquadrat *n*, parkettbildendes Quadrat	carré *m* diabolique (panmagique, pandiagonal, satanique)	пандиагональный [магический] квадрат
P 417	**perfect mapping** <TO>	perfekte Abbildung *f*	application *f* parfaite	совершенное отображение
P 418	**perfect matching,** linear factor <GP>	Linearfaktor *m*, Faktor *m* ersten Grades, perfekte Verkettung *f*, 1-Faktor *m*, linearer Faktor	couplage *m* parfait	совершенное (1-факторное) паросочетание
P 419	**perfect method of limitation** <LI>	perfektes Limitierungsverfahren *n*	méthode *f* de limitation parfaite	совершенный метод образования обобщенного предела
P 420	**perfect module** <AG, AL>	perfekter Modul *m*	module *m* parfait	совершенный модуль
P 421	**perfect, multiply perfect, abundant and deficient numbers** <NT>	abundante, defiziente und perfekte Zahlen *fpl* und ihre Verallgemeinerungen *fpl*	nombres *mpl* aliquotaires	избыточные, недостаточные и совершенные числа и их обобщения
P 422	**perfectness** <of a field> <AL>	Vollkommenheit *f*	propriété *f* d'être parfait	совершенность
P 423	**perfect *n*-th power** <AL, AR>	exakte *n*-te Potenz *f*	*n*-e puissance *f* exacte	точная *n*-я степень
P 424	**perfect number** <NT>	vollkommene (perfekte) Zahl *f*, numerus *m* perfectus	nombre *m* parfait	совершенное число
P 425	**4-perfect number** <NT>	4-perfekte Zahl *f*	nombre *m* sous-double	4-совершенное число
P 426	**6-perfect number** <NT>	6-perfekte Zahl *f*	nombre *m* sous-triple	6-совершенное число
P 427	**8-perfect number** <NT>	8-perfekte Zahl *f*	nombre *m* sous-quadruple	8-совершенное число
P 428	**10-perfect number** <NT>	10-perfekte Zahl *f*	nombre *m* sous-quintuple	10-совершенное число
P 429	**perfect number of the second kind** <NT>	vollkommene Zahl *f* zweiter Art <Lionnet>	nombre *m* parfait de seconde espèce	совершенное число второго рода
P 430	**perfect partition** <of a number> <AB>	vollkommene Teilung *f* <einer Zahl> <MacMahon>	décomposition *f* complète <d'un nombre>	совершенное разбиение <числа>
P 431	**perfect partition** <of a number> <NT>	perfekte Partition (Zerlegung) *f*	partition *f* parfaite	совершенное разбиение
	perfect positive definite quadratic form <NT>	*s.* P 411		
P 432	**perfect recall** <TG>	vollkommenes Gedächtnis *n*	mémoire *f* parfaite	полная память
	perfect relation <SE>	*s.* O 124		
P 433	**perfect set** <TO>	perfekte Menge (Punktmenge) *f*, // vollkommene Mannigfaltigkeit *f*	ensemble *m* parfait	совершенное [точечное] множество
P 434	**perfect space** <TO>	perfekter Raum *m*	espace *m* parfait	совершенное множество
	perfect space <FA, TO>	*s.* K 141		
P 435	**perfect spectrum** <FA>	perfektes Spektrum *n*	spectre *m* parfait	совершенный спектр
P 436	**perfect square** <AL>	vollständiges Quadrat *n*	carré *m* parfait (exact, complet)	точный (полный) квадрат
P 437	**perfect square,** square number <NT>	Quadratzahl *f*, Viereckszahl *f*, // gleich-gleiche (zyklische) Zahl *f*	nombre *m* carré parfait, nombre carré (quadrangulaire), tétragone *m*, // nombre cyclique	квадратичное число, квадрат
	perfect square <CT, NT>	*s.* Q 46		
P 438	**perfect trinomial square** <AL>	[vollständiges] Quadrat *n* eines Binoms	carré *m* [parfait] d'un binôme	[полный] квадрат двучлена
P 439	**perfect with respect to a valuation** <AL>	perfekt bezüglich einer Bewertung	complet pour une valuation	полный относительно нормирования
	performance function <PG>	*s.* O 6		
P 440	**perigon [angle],** round angle, full angle, angle of 360° <EG>	Vollwinkel *m*, ebener Vollwinkel, voller Winkel *m*	angle *m* plein (total, de 360°)	полный угол [в 360°], угол в 360°, угол полного оборота; плоский угол, равный 2π [радиан]
P 441	**perimeter** <of a plane figure *or* a solid> <EG>	Umfang *m*	périmètre *m*	периметр
P 442	**perimeter [of the circle]** <EG>	Kreisumfang *m*, Umfang (Perimeter) *m* des Kreises	périmètre *m* du cercle, périmètre	длина окружности
P 443	**period** <AL>	Gaußsche Periode *f*, Periode	période (« période ») *f* de Gauss, période	период
P 444	**period** <of an element of a semigroup> <AL>	Periode *f*	période *f*	показатель, период
P 445	**period** <of a cycloid> <GE>	Basis *f*, Periode *f*	période *f*	период
	period <FU>	*s.* S 2533		
	period <GR>	*s.* 1. O 271; 2. O 272		
	period characteristic <FT, FU>	*s.* T 406		
	period group <FT>	*s.* G 492		
	periodical continued fraction <NT>	*s.* R 306		

No.	English	German	French	Russian
P 446	**periodical decimal [fraction],** periodic decimal [fraction], repeating (recurring, circulating) decimal <NT>	periodischer Dezimalbruch *m*	fraction *f* décimale périodique, nombre *m* décimal périodique	периодическая [бесконечная] десятичная дробь
P 447	**periodical fluctuation,** cycle <SP>	periodische Schwankung *f*, Zyklus *m*	fluctuation *f* périodique, cycle *m*	периодическое колебание, периодическая флуктуация, цикл
P 448	**periodic continuation** <AN>	periodische Fortsetzung *f*	prolongement *m* par périodicité	продолжение периодическим образом
	periodic continued fraction <NT>	*s.* R 306		
	periodic decimal [fraction] <NT>	*s.* P 446		
P 449	**periodic distribution** <AN>	periodische Distribution *f*	distribution *f* périodique	периодическая обобщенная функция
P 450	**periodic element** <of an *R*-module> <AL>	periodisches Element *n*	élément *m* de torsion	периодический элемент
	periodic element <GR>	*s.* E 134		
P 451	**periodic free resolution** <AL>	periodische freie Auflösung *f*	résolution *f* libre périodique	периодическая свободная резольвента
P 452	**periodic group,** torsion group <GR>	periodische (ordnungsfinite) Gruppe *f*, Torsionsgruppe *f*	groupe *m* périodique, groupe avec (à, de) torsion	группа с кручением, периодическая группа
P 453	**periodicity** <of a group> <GR>	Periodizität *f*; Eigenschaft *f*, periodisch zu sein	périodicité *f*	периодичность
P 454	**periodicity interval** <AN>	Periodizitätsintervall *n*	intervalle *m* période	интервал периодичности
	periodic Laplace sequence <DG>	*s.* L 73		
P 455	**periodic Mathieu function,** Mathieu function [of the first kind]; ce; se <FU>	periodische Mathieusche Funktion *f*, Mathieusche Funktion [erster Art], Mathieusche Funktion der ersten Art; ce; se	fonction *f* de Mathieu périodique, fonction de Mathieu [de la première espèce]; ce; se	периодическая функция Матье, функция Матье [первого рода]; ce; se
P 456	**periodic module,** torsion module <AL>	periodischer Modul *m*, Torsionsmodul *m*	module *m* de torsion	модуль кручения, периодический модуль
P 457	**periodic semigroup,** torsion semigroup <AL>	periodische Halbgruppe *f*	demi-groupe *m* périodique	периодическая полугруппа
P 458	**periodic S-radical** <of a group> <GR>	periodisches S-Radikal *n*, S-Radikal	S-radical *m* périodique	периодический S-радикал, S-радикал
P 459	**periodic state** <SP>	periodischer Zustand *m*, P-Zustand *m*	état *m* périodique	периодическое состояние
P 460	**period matrix** <FT>	Periodenmatrix *f*	matrice *f* des périodes	матрица периодов
P 461	**period module,** module of periods <of a doubly periodic function> <FT>	Periodenmodul *m*	module *m* des périodes	модуль периодов
P 462	**periodogram** <AN, NU, ST>	Periodogramm *n*	périodogramme *m*	периодограмма, график спектральной функции
P 463	**periodogram analysis** <AN, NU, ST>	Periodogrammanalyse *f*, Periodogrammrechnung *f*	analyse *f* par périodogramme	анализ периодограммы, периодограммный анализ
P 464	**periodograph** <AN, IN>	Periodograph *m*	périodographe *m*	периодограф
	periodometer <AN, IN>	*s.* F 517		
P 465	**period pair** <of a doubly periodic function> <FT>	Periodenpaar *n*	couple *m* de périodes	пара период
P 466	**period[-]parallelogram,** parallelogram of periods <not necessarily primitive> <FT>	Periodenparallelogramm *n*	parallélogramme *m* des périodes	параллелограмм периодов
	period[-]parallelogram <FT>	*s. a.* P 1369		
P 467	**period parallelotope** <of an Abelian *or* theta function> <FT>	Periodenparallelotop *n*	parallélotope *m* des périodes	параллелотоп периодов
P 468	**period[s] relations** <FT>	Periodenrelationen *fpl*	relations *fpl* entre les périodes	соотношения между периодами
P 469	**period strip** <of a periodic function> <FT>	Periodenstreifen *m*	bande *f* de période	полоса (полоска) периода
	period system <FU>	*s.* S 2533		
P 470	**peripheral spectrum** <FA>	peripheres Spektrum *n*	spectre *m* périphérique	периферический спектр
	periphery of the circle <EG>	*s.* C 675		
P 471	**permanence of the functional equation,** persistence of the functional equation, principle of permanence <FT>	Permanenz *f* der Funktionalgleichung, Permanenzprinzip *n* [der Funktionalgleichung], Satz *m* der Permanenz der Funktionalgleichung	permanence *f* de l'équation fonctionnelle, principe *m* de permanence	принцип перманентности, перманентность функционального уравнения
P 472	**permanent** <MD>	Permanente *f*	permanent *m*	перманента
	permanent convergence <SS>	*s.* C 2331		
	permanently convergent power series <SS>	*s.* E 263		
P 473	**permanently convergent series** <SS>	beständig konvergente Reihe *f*	série *f* partout convergente	всюду (перманентно) сходящийся ряд
	permanently convergent series <SS>	*s. a.* E 263		
P 474	**permanent matrix,** regular matrix <in Toeplitz's limit theorem> <LI>	permanente (reguläre) Matrix *f*	matrice *f* permanente (régulière)	регулярная (перманентная) матрица

No.	English	German	French	Russian
	permanent method <LI>	*s.* R 595		
	permanent method of limitation <LI>	*s.* R 596		
	permanent method of summation <LI>	*s.* R 595		
	permanent trans-formation <LI>	*s.* R 643		
P 475	**permissible function** <of an eigenvalue problem> <DE>	zulässige Funktion *f*	fonction *f* admissible	допустимая функция
P 476/7	**permissible value** <of a variable> <AN>	zulässiger Wert *m* <einer Variablen>	valeur *f* admissible <d'une variable>	допустимое значение <переменной>
	permutability <AL, AN>	*s.* C 1273		
P 478	**permutable complexes** <GR>	vertauschbare Komplexe *mpl*	complexes *mpl* permutables	перестановочные комплексы
P 479	**permutable congruence relations** <AL>	permutierbare (vertauschbare) Kongruenzrelationen *fpl*	relations *fpl* de congruence permutables	перестановочные отношения конгруэнции
P 480	**permutable co-ordinate spaces,** permutable sequence spaces <TO>	[ineinander] permutierbare Koordinatenräume *mpl*, [ineinander] permutierbare Folgenräume *mpl*	espaces *mpl* des coordonnées (suites) permutables	перестановочные координатные пространства, перестановочные пространства последовательностей
P 481	**permutable elements,** elements commuting with each other, commutative elements <AL>	vertauschbare Elemente *npl*	éléments *mpl* permutables (échangeables, commutants, commutables)	перестановочные (коммутирующие) элементы
P 482	**permutable operators,** commuting (commutable, commutative) operators <FA>	vertauschbare (kommutierende, kommutative) Operatoren *mpl*	opérateurs *mpl* permutables (commutables)	коммутирующие (перестановочные, коммутативные) операторы
	permutable sequence spaces <TO>	*s.* P 480		
P 483	**permutable subgroups** <GR>	vertauschbare Untergruppen *fpl*	sous-groupes *mpl* commutants	перестановочные подгруппы
P 484	**permutation** <operation> <AL>	Permutation *f*, Substitution *f*, Vertauschung *f*, Umordnung *f*	substitution *f*, permutation *f*	подстановка, перестановка
P 485	**permutation** <of *n* objects (things) [taken all at a time]> <CT>	Permutation *f* <von *n* Elementen, vom Grade *n*>	permutation *f* <de *n* éléments>	подстановка <*n*-й степени, степени *n*>, перестановка <[из] *n* элементов, степени *n*>, размещение из *n* элементов по *n*
	permutation <CT>	*s.* 1. A 983; 2. A 984		
	permutation <LO>	*s.* I 701		
P 486	**permutational product** <of groups> <GR>	Permutationsprodukt *n*	produit *m* permutationnel	подстановочное произведение
P 487	**permutation character** <AL>	Permutationscharakter *m*	caractère *m* de permutations	характер перестановок
P 487 a	**permutation[-] group,** group of permutations, substitution group <of degree *n*> <GR>	Permutationsgruppe *f*, Substitutionsgruppe *f*, Gruppe *f* von Substitutionen <*n*-ten Grades>	groupe *m* de (des) permutations, groupe de (des) substitutions <de degré *n*>	группа подстановок (перестановок) <степени *n*>
P 488	**permutation homeomorphism** <TO>	Permutationshomöomorphismus *m*	homéomorphisme *m* de permutation	гомеоморфизм перестановки
	permutation of a set <SE>	*s.* O 122		
P 489	**permutation of lines, permutation of rows** <of a matrix> <MD>	Zeilenvertauschung *f*, Vertauschung (Permutation) *f* der Zeilen	permutation *f* des lignes	перестановка строк
P 490	**permutation, repetition allowed;** permutation with repetition[s] <CT>	Permutation *f* mit Wiederholung[en]	permutation *f* avec répétitions	перестановка (подстановка) с повторениями
P 491	**permutation representation** <RE>	Permutationsdarstellung *f*	représentation *f* de permutation	представление с помощью матриц перестановок
	permutation symbol <DG, VT>	*s.* A 577		
P 492	**permutation test,** randomization test, Fisher-Pitman test <ST>	Permutationstest *m*, Randomisationstest *m*, Fisher-Pitman-Test *m*	test *m* de permutation, test de randomisation, test de Fisher-Pitman	критерий перестановки (подстановки, рандомизации, Фишера-Питмана)
P 493	**permutation without repetition[s]** <CT>	Permutation *f* ohne Wiederholung[en]	permutation *f* sans répétitions	подстановка (перестановка) без повторений
	permutation with repetition[s] <CT>	*s.* P 490		
P 494	**permutation with restricted positions** <CT>	Permutation *f* mit beschränkter Stellenbesetzung	permutation *f* soumise à des conditions restrictives, permutation limitée	перестановка с ограниченными позициями; перестановка, удовлетворяющая заданным ограничениям на позиции переставляемых элементов
P 495	**permute / to** <CT>	permutieren, vertauschen, versetzen	permuter	переставлять, менять местами
P 496	**permute cyclically / to** <GN>	zyklisch vertauschen (permutieren)	permuter circulairement	переставлять циклически
P 497	**permuting relation** <SE>	injektive Relation *f* mit gleichem Definitionsbereich und Wertevorrat	relation *f* injective dont l'ensemble de définition est égal à l'ensemble des valeurs	инъективное отношение, для которого область определения равна области значений
P 498/9	**perpendicular** <EG>	Lot *n*; Senkrechte *f*	perpendiculaire *f*	перпендикуляр
	perpendicular <EG>	*s. a.* O 441		
	perpendicularity <AL, GE>	*s.* O 459		

No.	English	German	French	Russian
P 500	**perpendicular line** <EG>	senkrechte Gerade *f*	droite *f* perpendiculaire	перпендикулярная прямая
P 501	**perpendicular plane** <DS>	Lotebene *f*	plan *m* perpendiculaire	перпендикулярная плоскость
P 502	**perpetuant** <IV>	Perpetuante *f*	perpétuant *m*	перпетуанта
	Perron-integrable function <RF>	*s.* P 606		
P 503	**Perron['s] integral,** P-integral <RF>	Perronsches Integral *n*, P-Integral *n*	intégrale *f* de Perron, intégrale P	интеграл Перрона, Р-интеграл
P 504	**Perron['s] method** <DE, NU>	Perronsches Verfahren *n*	méthode *f* de Perron	метод Перрона
P 505	**Perron['s] modular function** <NT>	Perronsche Modulfunktion *f*	fonction *f* modulaire de Perron	модулярная функция Перрона
P 506	**Perron-Stieltjes['] integral** <AN>	Perron-Stieltjessches Integral *n*	intégrale *f* de Perron-Stieltjes	интеграл Перрона-Стилтьеса
P 507	**Perron['s] theorem** <for difference equations> <FD>	Satz *m* von Perron, Perronscher Satz	théorème *m* de Perron	теорема Перрона
P 508	**Perron-Wiener-Brelot method,** Brelot['s] method <PO>	Methode *f* von Perron-Wiener-Brelot, Methode von Brelot, Brelotsche Methode	méthode *f* de Perron-Wiener-Brelot, méthode de Brelot	метод Перрона-Винера-Брело, метод Брело
	persistence of the functional equation <FT>	*s.* P 471		
P 509	**personal move,** individual move <TG>	persönlicher Zug *m*	coup *m* personnel (individuel)	личный ход
	personal probability <ST>	*s.* S 2122		
	perspective <DS>	*s.* C 375		
	perspective affine correspondence <AY, DS>	*s.* P 511		
P 510	**perspective affine figure,** affine figure <DS>	perspektiv-affine Figur, affine Figur *f*	figure *f* perspective affine, figure affine	аффинно-перспективная фигура, аффинная фигура
P 511	**perspective affine relation,** perspective affine correspondence, affine relation (correspondence) <AY, DS>	perspektiv-affine Beziehung (Zuordnung) *f*, affine Beziehung (Zuordnung)	relation (correspondance) *f* perspective affine, relation (correspondance) affine	перспективно-аффинное (родственное, аффинно-перспективное, аффинное) соотношение (соответствие)
P 512	**perspective affinity** <DS>	perspektive Affinität *f*, Affinität bei perspektiver Lage	affinité *f* perspective, affinité	аффинно-перспективное преобразование
P 513	**perspective collinear figures** <DS>	perspektiv-kollineare Figuren *fpl*	figures *fpl* collinéaires perspectives	перспективно-коллинеарные фигуры
P 514	**perspective collineation,** axial collineation <DS>	perspektive Kollineation *f*	collinéation *f* perspective	перспективная коллинеация
P 515	**perspective figures,** figures in central perspective (projection) <DS, PJ>	perspektive ([zentral]perspektivische, zentralkollineare) Figuren *fpl*	figures *fpl* homologiques (perspectives, dans la perspective centrale, en projection centrale)	перспективные фигуры, фигуры в центральной перспективе, фигуры в конической проекции
P 516	**perspective having no vanishing point** <DS>	Netzhautperspektive *f*, Perspektive *f* ohne Fluchtpunkte	perspective *f* sans point de fuite	перспектива, не имеющая точки схода
	perspective image <DS>	*s.* P 518		
	perspective intervals <LA>	*s.* T 855		
P 517	**perspective involution** <PJ>	perspektive Involution *f*	involution *f* perspective	перспективная инволюция, перспективное инволюционное преобразование
P 518	**perspective picture,** perspective image, picture, image, central projection <as an image in central projection> <DS>	perspektives Bild *n*, perspektivisches Bild, Bild, Zentralprojektion *f*	image *f* perspective, image, projection *f* centrale	перспективный образ, перспективное изображение, образ, изображение
	perspective projection <DS>	*s.* C 375		
P 519	**perspective tetrahedra** <PJ>	perspektive Tetraeder *npl* <ein-, zwei- *oder* vierfach>	tétraèdres *mpl* perspectifs	перспективные четырехгранники (тетраэдры)
	perspective transformation of similitude <DS>	*s.* H 511		
P 520	**perspective triangles** <PJ>	perspektive Dreiecke *npl*	triangles *mpl* perspectifs (homologiques réciproques)	перспективные треугольники
P 521	**perspectivity** <LA>	Perspektivität *f*	perspectivité *f*	перспектива
P 522	**perspectivity,** central collineation, homology <PJ>	Perspektivität *f*, Zentralkollineation *f*, zentrale Kollineation *f*, Homologie *f*, perspektive Abbildung (Verwandlung) *f*, Perspektive *f*	perspectivité *f*, collinéation *f* centrale, homologie *f*	гомология, перспективное соответствие, центральная коллинеация, перспективитет
P 523	**perspectograph** <GE, IN>	Perspektograph *m*, Perspektivzeichner *m*	perspectographe *m*	перспектограф
P 524	**persymmetric determinant,** orthosymmetric determinant <MD, NT>	rekurrierende (einseitige, orthosymmetrische, persymmetrische) Determinante *f*	déterminant *m* orthosymétrique (récurrent, persymétrique, d'un système récurrent)	ортосимметрический определитель
P 525	**PERT,** program evaluation and review technique, program evaluation and research task <PG>	PERT-Verfahren *n*, PERT	technique *f* PERT (de révision des estimations de programmes), PERT	метод PERT, PERT

	English	German	French	Russian
	pertacticle point <AG>	*s.* C 1115		
P 526	**perturbation function,** perturbation (perturbing) term <of an inhomogeneous linear differential equation *or* a system of such equations> <DE>	Störglied *n*, Störungsglied *n*, Störfunktion *f*, Störungsfunktion *f*, Störungsterm *m*, rechte Seite *f*	fonction *f* perturbatrice, terme *m* perturbateur	функция возмущения, член возмущения, возмущающий член, свободный член
P 527	**perturbation parameter** <FA>	Störungsparameter *m*	paramètre *m* de perturbation	параметр возмущения
	perturbation term <DE>	*s.* P 526		
P 528	**perturbation theory,** theory of perturbations <in a Hilbert *or* Banach space> <DE, FA>	Störungsrechnung *f*, Störungstheorie *f*	calcul *m* (théorie *f*) des perturbations	метод (теория) возмущений
P 529	**perturbed system** <DE>	gestörtes System *n*	système *m* perturbé	возмущенная система
	perturbing term <DE>	*s.* P 526		
P 530	**perversor** <a special tensor> <VT>	Perversor *m*, Kehrversor *m* <Gibbs>	perversor *m*	перверсор
P 531	**Petersen['s] graph** <GP>	Petersenscher Graph *m*	graphe *m* de Petersen	граф Петерсена
	Petersen-Morley['s] configuration <SG>	*s.* C 1876		
P 532	**Petersen-Morley theorem** <in the hyperbolic space> <GE>	Satz *m* von Petersen und Morley, Petersen-Morleyscher Satz, Satz von Hjelmslev-Morley, Hjelmslev-Morleyscher Satz	théorème *m* de Petersen-Morley	теорема Петерсена-Морли
P 533	**Petersen['s] theorem** <GP>	Petersenscher Satz *m*, Satz von Petersen	théorème *m* de Petersen	теорема Петерсена
P 534	**Peterson-Codazzi equations** <DG>	Peterson-Codazzische Gleichungen *fpl*	équations *fpl* de Peterson-Codazzi	уравнения Петерсона-Кодацци
P 535	**Peterson['s] theorem** <DG>	Satz *m* von Peterson, Petersonscher Satz	théorème *m* de Peterson	теорема Петерсона
P 536	**Peter-Weyl theorem** <AL>	Satz *m* von Peter-Weyl, Peter-Weylscher Satz	théorème *m* de Peter-Weyl	теорема Петера-Вейля, основная аппроксимационная теорема Петера-Вейля
P 537	**Petrie['s] polygon** <GE>	Petriesches Polygon *n*	polygone *m* de Petrie	полигон Петри
P 538	**Petrowski['s] operator** <DE>	Petrowski-Operator *m*	opérateur *m* [différentiel] de Petrowski	оператор Петровского
P 539	**Petr['s] theorem** <on an *n*-gon> <EG>	Petrscher Satz *m*	théorème *m* de Petr	теорема Петра
P 540	***p*-extension** <of a field> <AL>	*p*-Erweiterung *f*	*p*-extension *f*	*p*-расширение
P 541	***p*-factor** <of Euler's product> <NT>	*p*-Faktor *m*	*p*-facteur *m*	*p*-множитель
	Pfaff['s] expression <AN>	*s.* P 546		
P 542	**pfaffian** <AL>	Pfaffian *m*, Halbdeterminante *f*, Pfaffsche Determinante *f*, Pfaffiana *f*, Pfaffsches Aggregat *n*, Pfaffiante *f*, Jacobische Funktion *f* <Cayley>	pfaffien *m*, semi-déterminant *m* <Scheibner>, déterminant *m* pfaffien	пфаффиан, полуопределитель, функция Якоби (Пфаффа)
P 543	**pfaffian** <of a form *or* matrix> <AL>	Pfaffian *m*	pfaffien *m*	пфаффиан
P 544	**pfaffian** <as a differential invariant, Cayley> <IV>	Pfaffsche Kurve *f*, Pfaffiana *f*	pfaffienne *f*	кривая Пфаффа
	Pfaffian <AN>	*s.* P 546		
P 545	**Pfaffian differential equation,** Pfaffian equation, total differential equation <DE>	Pfaffsche Gleichung *f*, Pfaffsche (totale) Differentialgleichung *f*	équation *f* de Pfaff, équation aux différentielles totales, équation différentielle de Pfaff	[дифференциальное] уравнение Пфаффа, пфаффово уравнение, уравнение в полных дифференциалах
	Pfaffian differential form <AN>	*s.* P 546		
	Pfaffian equation <DE>	*s.* P 545		
P 546	**Pfaffian form,** Pfaffian differential form, Pfaffian, Pfaff['s] expression, linear differential form (expression), differential form of order (degree) 1, 1-form <AN>	Pfaffsche Form (Differentialform) *f*, Pfaffscher Ausdruck (Differentialausdruck) *m*, lineare Differentialform, linearer Differentialausdruck, Differentialform ersten Grades	pfaffien *m*, forme *f* pfaffienne, expression *f* [différentielle] de Pfaff	пфаффова форма, пфаффиан, форма Пфаффа, [дифференциальная] 1-форма, линейная дифференциальная форма
P 547	**Pfaff['s] problem** <DE>	Pfaffsches Problem *n*	problème *m* de Pfaff	задача (проблема) Пфаффа
	Pfaff['s] problem <VA>	*s.* P 549		
P 548	**Pfaff['s] system of equations,** total differential system <DE>	Pfaffsches Differentialgleichungssystem (Gleichungssystem) *n*, totales Differentialgleichungssystem	système *m* de Pfaff, système d'équations de Pfaff	система уравнений Пфаффа (в полных дифференциалах)
P 549	**Pfaff['s] variational problem,** Pfaff['s] problem <VA>	Pfaffsches Variationsproblem *n*	problème *m* variationnel de Pfaff	вариационная задача Пфаффа
P 550	**PF-field,** field satisfying Hasse's product formula <AL>	PF-Körper *m*	PF-corps *m*	поле, удовлетворяющее формуле произведения Хассе
P 551	**Pflastersatz** <TO>	[Lebesguescher] Pflastersatz *m*, Pflastersatz von Lebesgue		теорема [Лебега] о мостовых
P 552	***p*-fold [monotonically] decreasing sequence, *p*-fold monotone sequence** <SS>	*p*-fach monotone (monoton fallende) Folge *f*	suite *f p* fois monotone, suite *p* fois [monotonement] décroissante	*p*-кратно монотонная (монотонно убывающая, убывающая) последовательность

No.	English	German	French	Russian
P 553	**p-form;** multiform <DG>	*p*-Form *f*	*p*-forme *f*	дифференциальная *p*-форма, *p*-форма
	p-form of an equation <AL>	*s.* E 344		
	p-form of the quadratic <AL>	*s.* R 357		
	p-fractile <ST>	*s.* Q 81		
P 554	**p-group** <GR>	*p*-Gruppe *f*, // primäre Gruppe *f*	*p*-groupe *m*, groupe *m* *p*-primaire	*p*-группа
P 555	**p′-group** <GR>	*p′*-Gruppe *f* <Ordnung zu *p* prim>	*p′*-groupe *m*	*p′*-группа
P 556	**P*-group** <GR>	*P**-Gruppe *f*	*P**-groupe *m*	*P**-группа
P 557	**p-harmonic function** <real part of a *p*-analytic function> <FT>	*p*-harmonische Funktion *f*	fonction *f* *p*-harmonique	*p*-гармоническая функция
	phase <AN>	*s.* A 603		
	phase <AY>	*s.* A 604		
	phase <SP>	*s.* S 1658		
P 558	**phase diagram,** phase pattern <DE>	Phasendiagramm *n*, Phasenbild *n*	diagramme (portrait) *m* de phase	фазовая диаграмма
P 559	**phase diagram method,** method of phase diagram <DE>	Methode *f* des Phasendiagramms, Phasendiagrammethode *f*	méthode *f* du diagramme de phase	метод фазовой диаграммы
	phase pattern <DE>	*s.* P 558		
P 559 a	**phase plane** <DE>	Phasenebene *f*	plan *m* de phase	фазовая плоскость
	phase space <SP>	*s.* S 1328		
P 560	**p-height** <of a group> <GR>	*p*-Höhe *f*	*p*-hauteur *f*	*p*-высота
P 561	**phi-convergent sequence,** φ-convergent sequence <AL>	φ-konvergente (phi-konvergente) Folge *f*	suite *f* φ-convergente (phi-convergente)	φ-сходящаяся (фи-сходящаяся) последовательность
	phi[ ]function <NT>	*s.* E 588		
P 562	**phoenix number** <NT>	Phönixzahl *f*	nombre *m* phénix	число феникса
	Phragmén-Lindelöf function <FT>	*s.* I 365		
P 563	**Phragmén-Lindelöf principle** <FT>	Phragmén-Lindelöfscher Satz *m*	théorème *m* de Phragmén-Lindelöf	теорема Фрагмена-Линделефа
P 564	**Phragmén['s] theorem** <for a continuous function> <FT>	Satz *m* von Phragmén, Phragménscher Satz	théorème *m* de Phragmén	теорема Фрагмена
P 565	**physical component** <of a vector> <VT>	physikalische Komponente *f*	composante *f* cartésienne (scalaire)	физическая составляющая
P 566	**PI-algebra** <algebra with a polynomial identity> <AL>	PI-Algebra *f*, Algebra *f* mit Polynomidentität	algèbre *f* à identité polynomiale, PI-algèbre *f*, algèbre qui satisfait à une identité polynomiale	PI-алгебра, алгебра с полиномиальным тождеством
P 567	**Picard-Borel theorem** <FT>	Picard-Borelscher Satz *m*	théorème *m* de Picard-Borel	теорема Пикара-Бореля
P 568	**Picard['s] congruence** <AG>	Picardsche Kongruenz *f*	congruence *f* de Picard	конгруэнция Пикара
P 569	**Picard['s] exceptional value,** Picard['s] lacunary value <FT>	Picardscher Ausnahmewert *m*	lacune *f* (valeur *f* lacunaire) de Picard	пикаровское исключительное значение, исключительное значение в смысле Пикара
	Picard['s] general (grand) theorem <FT>	*s.* G 413		
P 570	**Picard group** <as a linear group> <AB, AL>	Picardsche Gruppe *f*	groupe *m* de Picard	группа Пикара
P 571	**Picard group, picard-group** <of a ringed space> <AG>	Picardsche Gruppe *f*	groupe *m* de Picard	группа Пикара, фундаментальная группа
P 572	**Picard integral** <of the first (1st), second (2nd), *or* third (3rd) kind> <AG>	Picardsches Integral *n* <erster (1.), zweiter (2.) *oder* dritter (3.) Gattung>	intégrale *f* de Picard <de première (1-e), deuxième (2-e) *ou* troisième (3-e) espèce>	интеграл Пикара <первого (1-го), второго (2-го) *или* третьего (3-го) рода>
P 573	**Picard['s] invariant** <of an algebraic function field> <AL>	Picardsche Invariante *f*	invariant *m* de Picard	инвариант Пикара
	Picard['s] iteration <DE>	*s.* M 488		
P 574	**Picard-Julia theorem** <FT>	Satz *m* von Picard-Julia, Picard-Juliascher Satz, Satz von Julia, Juliascher Satz	théorème *m* de Picard-Julia	теорема Пикара-Жюлия
	Picard['s] lacunary value <FT>	*s.* P 569		
P 575	**Picard-Lefschetz theorem** <AG>	Picard-Lefschetzscher Satz *m*	théorème de Picard-Lefschetz	теорема Пикара-Лефшеца
	Picard-Lindelöf unique existence theorem <DE>	*s.* U 214		
P 576	**Picard['s] manifold,** Picard['s] variety, variety of Picard <AG>	Picardsche Mannigfaltigkeit *f*	variété *f* de Picard	многообразие Пикара
	Picard['s] method <DE>	*s.* M 488		
P 577	**Picard['s] prescheme** <AG>	Picardsches Präschema *n*	préschéma *m* de Picard	предсхема Пикара
P 578	**Picard['s] scheme** <AG>	Picardsches Schema *n*	schéma *m* de Picard	схема Пикара
	Picard['s] small theorem <FT>	*s.* L 905/6		
P 579	**Picard['s] surface** <AG>	Picardsche Fläche *f*	surface *f* de Picard	поверхность Пикара
P 580	**Picard['s] theorem** <FT>	Picardscher Satz *m*, Satz von Picard	théorème *m* de Picard	теорема Пикара
	Picard['s] theorem <AG>	*s.* T 325/6		
	Picard['s] variety <AG>	*s.* P 576		
P 581	**Pick['s] invariant** <DG>	Picksche Invariante *f*	invariant *m* de Pick	инвариант Пика

P 582	**pi-complete group,** Π-complete group <GR>	Π-dividierbare (pi-dividierbare) Gruppe *f*	groupe *m* Π-divisible (pi-divisible)	Π-полная (пи-полная) группа
P 583	**pictogram,** isotype <ST>	Piktogramm *n*	pictogramme *m*	пиктограмма, диаграмма в виде рисунков
	picture <DS>	*s.* P 518		
	picture plane <DS>	*s.* P 1663		
	PID <AL>	*s.* P 1429		
	piece <GP>	*s.* B 752		
P 584	**piecewise continuity** <AN>	stückweise Stetigkeit *f*	continuité *f* par morceaux	кусочная непрерывность
P 585	**piecewise continuous function,** sectionally continuous function <AN>	stückweise (abteilungsweise) stetige Funktion *f*	fonction *f* continue par morceaux (intervalles)	кусочно-непрерывная (кусочно непрерывная) функция
P 586	**piecewise continuously differentiable function** <AN>	stückweise (abteilungsweise) stetig differenzierbare Funktion *f*	fonction *f* continûment différentiable par morceaux	кусочно непрерывно дифференцируемая функция
P 587	**piecewise differentiable function** <AN>	stückweise (abteilungsweise) differenzierbare Funktion *f*	fonction *f* dérivable par morceaux	кусочно[-] дифференцируемая функция
P 588	**piecewise differentiable path** <AN, TO>	stückweise differenzierbarer Weg *m*	chemin *m* différentiable par morceaux	кусочно-гладкий путь
P 589	**piecewise linear function** <RF>	stückweise (abteilungsweise, abschnittsweise) lineare Funktion *f*	fonction *f* linéaire par morceaux, fonction polygonale	кусочно-линейная функция, кусочно линейная функция
P 590	**piecewise linearization** <PG>	stückweise Linearisierung *f*	linéarisation *f* par morceaux	кусочная линеаризация
P 591	**piecewise linear map[ping]** <TO>	stückweise lineare Abbildung *f*	application *f* linéaire par morceaux	кусочно линейное отображение
	piece-wise linear topology <AT>	*s.* C 1212		
P 592	**piecewise monotonic function** <RF>	stückweise monotone Funktion *f*	fonction *f* monotone par tranche	кусочно-монотонная функция
P 593	**piecewise regular boundary** <DE>	stückweise regulärer Rand *m*	frontière *f* régulière par morceaux	кусочно регулярная граница
P 594	**piecewise regulated function** <RF>	stückweise Regelfunktion *f*	fonction *f* réglée par morceau[x]	кусочно-линейчатая функция
P 595	**piecewise smooth contour** <AN>	stückweise glatte Randkurve *f*	contour *m* régulier par morceaux	кусочно-гладкий контур
P 596	**piecewise smooth curve,** sectionally smooth curve <AN>	stückweise glatte Kurve *f*	courbe *f* différentiable (régulière) par morceaux	кусочно-гладкая кривая
P 597	**piecing together** <functions> <AN, TO>	Zusammenstücken *n* <von Funktionen>	recollement *m* <de fonctions>	склеивание <функций>
P 598	**piecing together,** pasting together, gluing, [topological] identification <TO>	Verheften *n*, Verheftung *f*, Identifizierung *f*	collage *m*, recollement *m*	склеивание, отождествление
P 599	**piecing together of topological spaces,** piecing topological spaces together <TO>	Verheften *n* topologischer Räume	recollement *m* d'espaces topologiques	склеивание топологических пространств
	piercing point <DS>	*s.* T 711		
P 600	**pi-function,** Π-function <FU>	Π-Funktion *f*, Pi-Funktion *f*	Π-fonction *f*, pi-fonction *f*	функция Π
	pigeon-hole principle <CT>	*s.* B 705		
P 601	**Pilatte['s] theorem** <for homothetic triangles> <GE>	Pilattescher Satz *m*	théorème *m* de Pilatte	теорема Пилата
P 602	**pilot experiment** <ST>	Tastversuch *m*	expérience *f* pilote	грубый (предварительный) эксперимент
P 603	**pilot survey** <ST>	Vorerhebung *f*	enquête *f* pilote	предварительное обследование, предварительный сбор информации
	pinball board <IN, ST>	*s.* G 24		
P 604	**pinch-point, pinch point** <of a surface> <GE>	Kniffpunkt *m*, Zwickpunkt *m*, Klemmpunkt *m*, Pinch-point *m*	point-pince *m*, point *m* cuspidal	
P 605	***p*-independence** <AL>	*p*-Unabhängigkeit *f*	*p*-indépendance *f*	*p*-независимость
P 606	**P-integrable function,** Perron-integrable function <RF>	P-integrierbare (Perron-integrierbare) Funktion *f*	fonction *f* (P)-intégrable, fonction intégrable au sens de Perron	функция, интегрируемая в смысле Перрона
	P-integral <RF>	*s.* P 503		
P 607	**p-integral base** <AL>	p-Ganzheitsbasis *f*	base *f* p-entière	p-целочисленный базис
P 608	**Pippian** <of a bundle of curves> <AG>	Cayleysche Kurve *f*, Pippiana *f*, P-Kurve *f*	pipienne *f*, courbe *f* cayleyenne	кэлиана
	pippian <AG>	*s.* C 282		
	PIR <AL>	*s.* P 1430		
P 609	**PI-ring,** ring with a polynomial identity <AL>	PI-Ring *m*, Ring *m* mit Polynomidentität	PI-anneau *m*, anneau *m* à identité polynomiale, anneau qui satisfait à une identité polynomiale	PI-кольцо, кольцо с полиномиальным тождеством
	Pisano['s] series <FD, NT> ⌐<AY>	*s.* F 144		
P 610	**pitch,** lead <of a helix>	Ganghöhe *f*	pas *m* polaire	шаг
P 611	**pitch,** parameter <of a screw *or* wrench< <VT>	Parameter *m*, Pfeil *m*	flèche *f*, paramètre *m*, pas *m*	параметр <динамы>; стрелка <винта>
	pivot <AL, NU, PG>	*s.* P 613		
P 612	**pivot[al] column** <AL, NU, PG>	Pivotspalte *f*	colonne-pivot *f*	разрешающий (направляющий) столбец
P 613	**pivot[al] element,** pivot <AL, NU, PG>	Pivot *n*, Leitelement *n*, Pivotelement *n*, Stützelement *n*	pivot *m*	разрешающий (направляющий) элемент
P 614	**pivot[al] matrix** <AL, NU, PG>	Pivotmatrix *f*, Pivotblock *m*	matrice-pivot *f*	разрешающая (направляющая) матрица

P 615	**pivot[al] monomial** <AL>	Pivotmonom *n*	monôme-pivot *m*	опорный одночлен
P 616	**pivot[al] raw** <AL, NU, PG>	Pivotzeile *f*	ligne-pivot *f*	разрешающая (направляющая) строка
P 617	**pivoting** <NU, PG>	Pivotierung *f*, Austauschverfahren *n*, Austauschen *n*	pivotage *m*	метод замены базиса, замена базиса
P 618	**place** <of a field> <AL>	Stelle *f*, Ort *m*; *k*-Stelle *f*, *k*-wertige Stelle *f*	place *f*, localité *f*	место, точка
P 619	**place** <of an algebraic *or* analytic element> <FT>	Stelle *f*	place *f*	место
	place <NT>	*s.* 1. O 276; 2. P 624		
	place <SS>	*s.* I 345		
	place digit <NT>	*s.* D 481		
P 620	**place of hundreds,** hundred's place, hundreds place <NT>	Stelle *f* der Hunderter, Hunderterstelle *f*	place *f* des centaines	место сотен
P 621	**place of the first kind** <AL>	Stelle *f* erster Art	place *f* de première espèce	место первого рода
P 622	**place of the second kind** <AL>	Stelle *f* zweiter Art	place *f* de deuxième espèce	место второго рода
P 623	**place-theoretical** <AL>	stellentheoretisch	en théorie des places	в теории мест
P 624	**place value,** local value, place <of a digit in a number> <NT>	Stellenwert *m*, Stelle *f*, Positionswert *m*	valeur *f* de position	поместное значение, значение места в числе, разрядное значение
P 625	**place value system,** positional notation <NT>	Stellenwertsystem *n*, Positionssystem *n*	système *m* positionnel, arithmétique *f* de position, système *m* de position; numération *f* de position	позиционная система [счисления], поместная система счисления
	placing over a common denominator <AL, AR>	*s.* R 434		
P 626	**plaid square; plaid-square design** <ST>	Schottenquadrat *n*	carré *m* écossais	шотландский квадрат
	plain pair <SE>	*s.* U 371		
	plain quadruple <SE>	*s.* U 372		
P 627	**plain set,** unordered set <SE>	ungeordnete Menge *f*	ensemble *m* non ordonné	неупорядоченное множество
P 628	**plan,** horizontal projection, first projection <in two-plane projection> <DS>	Grundriß *m*, Horizontalprojektion *f*, erste Projektion *f*	plan *m*, plan horizontal, projection *f* horizontale; coupe *f* horizontale	план, горизонтальная проекция; горизонтальный разрез
P 629	**plan,** plan of experiment, experimental plan <ST>	Lageplan *m*, Anlageplan *m*, Versuchsplan *m*	plan *m*, plan d'expérience, plan expérimental	план, план эксперимента (опыта)
	planar body <EG>	*s.* P 965		
P 630	**planar developable [surface],** planar torse <AY, DG>	planare Torse *f*, planare abwickelbare Regelfläche (Fläche) *f*	développable *f* (surface *f* développable, torse *f*) planaire	плоская развертывающаяся поверхность, плоский торс
P 631	**planar division neoring,** planar neofield <AL>	planarer Neokörper *m*	néocorps *m* planaire	плоскостное неотело
P 632	**planar graph** <GP>	planarer (plättbarer) Graph *m*, Graph vom Geschlecht Null	graphe *m* planaire (sphérique)	плоский (уплощаемый) граф
P 633	**planar near-field** <AL>	planarer Fastkörper *m*	presque-corps *m* planaire	плоскостное почти-поле
P 634	**planar near-ring** <AL>	planarer Fastring *m*	presque-anneau *m* planaire	плоскостное почти-кольцо
	planar neofield <AL>	*s.* P 631		
P 635	**planar point** <of a Riemann manifold> <DG>	planarer Punkt *m*	point *m* planaire	плоская точка
	planar point <DG>	*s.* F 403		
	planar solid <EG>	*s.* P 965		
	planar ternary ring <AL>	*s.* T 185a		
	planar torse <AY, DG>	*s.* P 630		
P 636	**Plancherel['s] formula** <RE>	Plancherelsche Formel *f*	formule *f* de Plancherel	формула Пляншереля
P 637	**Plancherel['s] Fourier transform[ation]** <IT>	Plancherelsche Fourier-Transformation *f*	transformation *f* de Fourier-Plancherel	фурье-преобразование Пляншереля
P 638	**plane,** algebraic surface of the first order <AG, GE>	Ebene *f*, algebraische Fläche *f* erster (1.) Ordnung	plan *m*, surface *f* algébrique de premier ordre	плоскость, алгебраическая поверхность первого порядка
	plane algebraic curve of higher degree (order) <AG>	*s.* H 307		
	plane algebraic curve of second degree (order) <AG, AY>	*s.* C 1944		
	plane algebraic curve of the fifth degree (order) <AG>	*s.* Q 299		
	plane algebraic curve of the fourth degree (order) <AG>	*s.* Q 86		
	plane algebraic curve of the second degree (order) <AG, AY>	*s.* C 1944		
	plane algebraic curve of the sixth degree (order) <AG>	*s.* S 726		
	plane algebraic curve of the third degree (order) <AG>	*s.* C 2726		
P 639	**plane angle** <EG>	ebener Winkel *m*	angle *m* plan	плоский угол
	plane angle between two edges <EG>	*s.* E 14		

No.	English	German	French	Russian
P 640	**plane at infinity,** infinite (ideal, improper) plane <as an extension of the Euclidean space> <PJ>	unendlich[ ]ferne Ebene *f*, uneigentliche (ideale) Ebene, Fernebene *f*	plan *m* à (de) l'infini, plan idéal (impropre)	бесконечно удаленная плоскость, несобственная плоскость
P 641	**plane configuration,** configuration in the plane, point-line configuration <of type (m_p, n_q) or (m_p)> <SG>	ebene Konfiguration *f*, Punkt-Geraden-Konfiguration *f*, Konfiguration in der Ebene	configuration *f* plane (dans le plan, de points et droites)	конфигурация на (в) плоскости, плоскостная конфигурация, конфигурация точек и прямых
P 642	**plane contingent** <GE>	ebenes Kontingent *n*	contingent *m* plan	плоский контэнжан
P 643	**plane co-ordinates,** [homogeneous] tangential co-ordinates of the plane, Plucker (Plücker) co-ordinates of the plane <AY>	Ebenenkoordinaten *fpl*, homogene (Plückersche) Ebenenkoordinaten, [Plückersche] Koordinaten *fpl* der Ebene, Ebenenzeiger *mpl*	coordonnées *fpl* tangentielles [homogènes] du plan, coordonnées homogènes (plückériennes, pluckériennes) du plan, coordonnées du plan, coordonnées planes	[однородные] тангенциальные координаты плоскости, [плюккеровы] координаты плоскости, плоскостные координаты
P 644	**plane co-ordinates,** co-ordinates in the plane <AY>	ebene Koordinaten *fpl*, Koordinaten in der Ebene	coordonnées *fpl* planes, coordonnées dans le plan	координаты на плоскости, плоские координаты
	plane Cremona transformation <AG>	*s.* C 2661		
	plane cubic [curve] <AG>	*s.* C 2726		
	plane curve of [the] second degree (order) <AG, AY>	*s.* C 1944		
	plane cylindrical polar co-ordinates <AY>	*s.* P 849		
P 645	**plane dihedral angle** <EG>	Schnittwinkel *m* zweier Ebenen	rectiligne *m* (angle *m* rectiligne) d'un dièdre	линейный угол двугранного угла
	plane director <AY>	*s.* D 588		
P 646	**plane field of lines** <PJ>	ebenes Strahlenfeld (Geradenfeld) *n*	champ *m* plan de droites	плоское поле прямых
P 647	**plane graph** <GP>	ebener Graph *m*	graphe *m* plan	плоский граф
P 648	**plane involution,** involution of planes <AY>	Ebeneninvolution *f*	involution *f* de plans	инволюция плоскостей, инволюционное преобразование плоскостей
P 649	**plane of circular section** <of a quadric> <AY>	Kreisschnittebene *f*, Kreisebene *f*	plan *m* de section circulaire, plan cyclique	плоскость кругового сечения
	plane of complex numbers <FT>	*s.* A 937		
	plane of complex numbers with exclusion of *k* points <FT>	*s.* C 1637		
	plane of complex numbers with exclusion of one point <FT>	*s.* C 1638		
P 650	**plane of co-ordinates,** plane of reference, co-ordinate plane, reference plane <AY>	Koordinatenebene *f*, Grundebene *f*, Bezugsebene *f*	plan *m* de coordonnées (référence)	координатная плоскость, основная плоскость
	plane of curvature <DG>	*s.* O 525		
	plane of homology <AY, PJ>	*s.* P 651		
P 651	**plane of perspectivity,** plane of homology <AY, PJ>	Ebene *f* der Perspektivität, perspektivische Ebene, Perspektivitätsebene *f*	plan *m* d'homologie, plan de perspectivité, plan perspectif	плоскость гомологии (перспективы)
	plane of principal symmetry <AY>	*s.* P 1461		
	plane of projection <DS>	*s.* P 1663		
	plane of reference <AY>	*s.* P 650		
P 652	**plane of similarity,** similarity plane <GE>	Ähnlichkeitsebene *f*	plan *m* de similitude	плоскость подобия
P 653	**plane of support,** supporting plane, support[ ]plane, tac-plane <CS, GE>	Stützebene *f*	plan *m* d'appui	опорная плоскость
	plane of symmetry <AY>	*s.* P 1461		
	plane of the meridian <GE>	*s.* M 397		
P 654	**plane of the section,** section plane <EG>	Schnittebene *f*, Ebene *f* des Schnittes	plan *m* de la section	плоскость сечения
	plane polar co-ordinates <AY>	*s.* P 849		
P 655	**plane projective geometry,** projective geometry in the plane <PJ>	ebene projektive Geometrie *f*, projektive Geometrie in der Ebene	géométrie *f* plane projective, géométrie projective dans le plan	проективная геометрия на плоскости, плоская проективная геометрия
	plane quartic [curve] <AG>	*s.* Q 86		
	plane quintic [curve] <AG>	*s.* Q 299		
P 656	**plane section** <GE>	Ebenenschnitt *m*	section *f* plane	плоское сечение
	plane sextic [curve] <AG>	*s.* S 726		
	plane surface <EG>	*s.* F 7		
P 657	**plane symmetry** <EG>	Ebenensymmetrie *f*, Symmetrie *f* in bezug auf eine Ebene	symétrie *f* par rapport à un plan	симметрия относительно плоскости

No.	English	German	French	Russian
P 658	**plane trigonometry,** trigonometry in the plane <EG>	ebene Trigonometrie *f*, Trigonometrie in der Ebene	trigonométrie *f* rectiligne (plane)	плоская (прямолинейная) тригонометрия
P 659	**plane void graph** <GP>	leerer ebener Graph *m*	graphe *m* plan vide	пустой плоский граф
	plane with exclusion of *k* points <FT>	*s.* C 1637		
	plane with exclusion of one point <FT>	*s.* C 1638		
	planimeter of Amsler <GE, IN>	*s.* A 611		
P 660	**planimetry** <EG>	Planimetrie *f*	planimétrie *f*	планиметрия
	planning of experiments <ST>	*s.* D 337		
	plan of experiment <ST>	*s.* P 629		
	Plateau['s] problem <DG>	*s.* P 1568		
	platonic <EG>	*s.* R 616		
	Platonic body <EG>	*s.* R 617		
P 661	**Platonic graph** <GP>	Graph *m* eines Platonischen Körpers	graphe *m* d'un corps platonique	граф платонова тела
	Platonic regular body <EG>	*s.* R 617		
	Platonic (platonic) solid <EG>	*s.* R 617		
P 662	**platykurtic distribution,** flat distribution <ST>	flachgipflige (platykurtische) Verteilung *f*	distribution *f* platikurtique	плосковершинное распределение
P 663	**platykurtosis,** negative kurtosis (excess), flatness <ST>	Flachgipfligkeit *f*, negativer Exzeß *m*	excès *m* négatif, planitude *f*	отрицательный эксцесс, плосковершинность, настильность
P 664	**plausibility consideration** <GN>	Plausibilitätsbetrachtung *f*	considération *f* de plausibilité	наводящее рассмотрение
P 665	**play,** party <realization of a game> <TG>	Partie *f*, Spielpartie *f*, Spielablauf *m*	partie *f*	партия, исход игры, игра
P 666	**player** <TG>	Spieler *m*	joueur *m*	игрок
P 667	**Playfair['s] axiom,** Euclid['s] [parallel] axiom [in Ptolemy's form] <GE>	Parallelenaxiom *n* von Euklid in der Ptolemäischen Form, Euklidisches (euklidisches) Parallelenaxiom (Axiom *n*) [in der Ptolemäischen Form], Ptolemäische Form *f* des Euklidischen Parallelenaxioms, Playfairsches Axiom	axiome *m* des parallèles d'Euclide [en forme de Ptolemée], axiome [de parallélisme] d'Euclide [en forme de Ptolemée], axiome de Playfair	аксиома параллельности (параллельных) Евклида [в виде Птолемея], аксиома Евклида [в виде Птолемея], аксиома [параллельности (параллельных)] Плейфера
P 668	**playing** <ST>	Durchspielen *n*	jeu *m*	разыгрывание
P 669	***p*-length** <of a group> <GR>	*p*-Länge *f*	*p*-longueur *f*	*p*-длина
P 670	***p*-linear form** <AL>	*p*-fach lineare Form *f*	forme *f* *p*-linéaire	*p*-линейная форма
P 671	**pli ring,** principal left ideal ring, left principal ideal ring, left pir <AL>	Linkshauptidealring *m*	anneau *m* à idéaux principaux à gauche	кольцо главных левых идеалов, pli-кольцо
	plot <AN, NU>	*s.* D 408		
P 672	**Plücker['s] abridged notation** <GE>	Plückersche abgekürzte Bezeichnung *f*	notation *f* abrégée de Plücker	сокращенное обозначение Плюккера
P 673	**Plücker['s] characteristic** <of an algebraic curve> <AG>	Plückersche Zahl *f*, Plückers Charakteristik *f*	caractéristique *f* plückérienne (de Plücker), nombre *m* de Plücker, nombre plückérien	плюккерова характеристика
P 674	**Plücker['s] classification** <of cubics> <AG>	Plückersche Klassifikation *f*	classification *f* de Plücker	классификация Плюккера
P 675	**Plücker's conoid** <GE>	Plückersches Konoid *n*, Cayleysches Zylindroid *n*	conoïde *m* de Plücker, conoïde plückérien	плюккеров коноид, коноид Плюккера
P 676	**Plücker['s] (Plucker['s]) co-ordinates [of the line],** Plücker['s] (Plucker['s]) line co-ordinates, line co-ordinates <AY>	Plückersche Linienkoordinaten (Strahlenkoordinaten, Geradenkoordinaten) *fpl*, Plückersche Koordinaten *fpl* [der Geraden], Linienkoordinaten, Strahlenkoordinaten, Geradenkoordinaten, Koordinaten der Geraden	coordonnées *fpl* plückériennes [de la droite], coordonnées pluckériennes [de la droite], coordonnées de Plücker [de la droite], coordonnées de Plucker [de la droite], coordonnées de la droite	плюккеровы координаты [прямой], координаты прямой, линейчатые координаты
	Plucker (Plücker) co-ordinates of the plane <AY>	*s.* P 643		
P 677	**Plücker['s] equations** <AG>	Plückersche Formeln (Gleichungen) *fpl*	formules *fpl* de Plücker	формулы Плюккера
	Plücker['s] geometry <AY>	*s.* L 859		
	Plucker['s] (Plücker['s]) line co-ordinates <AY>	*s.* P 676		
P 678	**Plücker['s] mapping** <PJ>	Plückersche Abbildung *f*	application *f* de Plücker	отображение Плюккера
P 679	**Plücker['s] quadric** <PJ>	Plücker-Quadrik *f*	quadrique *f* plückérienne	квадрика Плюккера
P 680	**Plücker['s] relation** <PJ>	Plücker-Relation *f*	relation *f* de Plücker	соотношение Плюккера
P 681	**Plücker['s] singularity** <AG>	Plückersche Singularität *f*	singularité *f* plückérienne	плюккерова особенность
P 682	**Plücker['s] surface** <PJ>	Plückersche Fläche (Komplexfläche) *f*	surface *f* de Plücker	поверхность Плюккера
	pluperfect number <NT>	*s.* M 982		
P 683	**pluricanonical hypersurface** <AG>	plurikanonische Hyperfläche *f*	hypersurface *f* pluricanonique	плюриканоническая гиперповерхность
P 684	**plurigenus, pluri-genus** <AG>	Plurigeschlecht *n*, Mehrgeschlecht *n*, plurigenus *n* <*pl*: plurigenera>	plurigenre *m*, pluri-genre *m*, multi-genre *m*	плюрижанр, кратный род, обобщенный жанр
P 685	**pluriharmonic function** <FT>	pluriharmonische Funktion *f*	fonction *f* pluriharmonique	плюригармоническая функция

No.	English	German	French	Russian
P 686	**plurisubharmonic function** <FT>	plurisubharmonische Funktion *f*	fonction *f* plurisousharmonique	плюрисубгармоническая функция
P 687	**plus infinity,** + ∞ <DI>	plus Unendlich, + ∞	infini positif, plus l'infini, + ∞	плюс бесконечность, + ∞
P 688	**plus sign,** positive sign, + <as a sign of a real number> <AR>	Pluszeichen *n*, positives Zeichen *n*, +	signe *m* +, signe plus, +	знак плюс, +
	plus sign <GN>	*s.* A 239		
P 689	***p*-mean** <of convex sets> <CS>	*p*-Mittel *n*	*p*-moyenne *f*	*p*-среднее
P 690	***p*-minimal condition** <GR>	*p*-Minimalbedingung *f*	condition *f p*-minimale	условие *p*-минимальности
P 691	***p*-mixed group** <GR>	*p*-gemischte Gruppe *f*	groupe *m p*-mixte	*p*-смешанная группа
P 692	***p*-modular representation** <RE>	*p*-modulare Darstellung *f*	représentation *f p*-modulaire	*p*-модулярное представление
P 693	***p*-normal group** <GR>	*p*-normale Gruppe *f*	groupe *m p*-normal	*p*-нормальная группа
	Pochhammer-Barnes equation <DE>	*s.* C 1884		
P 694	**Pochhammer['s] [differential] equation** <DE>	Pochhammers[che] Differentialgleichung *f*	équation *f* [différentielle] de Pochhammer	[дифференциальное] уравнение Похгаммера
P 695	**Pochhammer['s] function** <FU>	Pochhammersche Funktion *f*	fonction *f* de Pochhammer	функция Похгаммера
	Pochhammer['s] symbol <FD, FU>	*s.* F 38		
	po-group <GR>	*s.* O 305		
P 696	**Pohlke['s] theorem** <DS>	Pohlkescher Satz *m*, Satz von Pohlke	théorème *m* de Pohlke	теорема Польке-Шварца (Польке)
P 697	**Poincaré['s] algebra** <AL>	Poincaré-Algebra *f*	algèbre *f* de Poincaré	алгебра Пуанкаре
	Poincaré-Birkhoff-Witt theorem <AL>	*s.* B 451		
P 698	**Poincaré['s] bundle** <AG>	Poincarésches Bündel *n*	fibré *m* de Poincaré	расслоение Пуанкаре
P 699	**Poincaré['s] conjecture** <AT>	Poincarésche Vermutung *f*	conjecture *f* de Poincaré	гипотеза Пуанкаре
P 700	**Poincaré['s] difference equation** <FD>	Poincarésche Differenzengleichung *f*	équation *f* aux différences finies de Poincaré	уравнение в конечных разностях Пуанкаре
P 701	**Poincaré['s] differential equations,** Poincaré['s] equations, Poincaré['s] system [of partial differential equations] <FT>	Poincarésche Differentialgleichungen *fpl*, System *n* der Poincaréschen Differentialgleichungen	équations *fpl* différentielles [partielles] de Poincaré, système *m* des équations de Poincaré	система дифференциальных уравнений Пуанкаре, дифференциальные уравнения Пуанкаре
P 702	**Poincaré['s] divisor** <AG>	Poincaréscher Divisor *m*	diviseur *m* de Poincaré	дивизор Пуанкаре
P 703	**Poincaré['s] duality** <AT>	Poincarésche Dualität *f*	dualité *f* de Poincaré	двойственность Пуанкаре
P 704	**Poincaré['s] duality theorem,** duality theorem of Poincaré <AT>	Poincaréscher Dualitätssatz *m*	théorème *m* de dualité de Poincaré	теорема (закон) двойственности Пуанкаре
	Poincaré['s] equations <FT>	*s.* 701		
	Poincaré['s] group <AT>	*s.* F 824		
P 705	**Poincaré group** <of a groupoid> <CA>	Poincarésche Gruppe *f*	groupe *m* de Poincaré	группа Пуанкаре
P 706	**Poincaré['s] group** <of a continuous group> <GR>	Fundamentalgruppe *f*, Poincarésche Gruppe *f*, Konnexionsgruppe *f*	groupe *m* de Poincaré	группа Пуанкаре
	Poincaré['s] group <GR>	*s.* I 520		
P 707	**Poincaré['s] groupoid** <AT>	Poincarésches Gruppoid *n*	groupoïde *m* de Poincaré	группоид Пуанкаре
P 708	**Poincaré['s] half-plane,** upper half-plane <in non-Euclidean geometry> <GE>	Poincarésche (obere) Halbebene *f*	demi-plan *m* de Poincaré	верхняя плоскость
P 709	**Poincaré['s] inequality** <DE>	Poincarésche Ungleichung *f*	inégalité *f* de Poincaré	неравенство Пуанкаре
P 710	**Poincaré['s] lemma,** converse of Poincaré's theorem <on differential forms> <DG>	Umkehrung *f* des Satzes von Poincaré	réciproque *f* du théorème de Poincaré	обратная теорема Пуанкаре
	Poincaré['s] lemma <DG>	*s.* T 328		
P 711	**Poincaré['s] manifold** <AT>	Poincarésche Mannigfaltigkeit *f*	variété *f* de Poincaré	многообразие Пуанкаре
P 712	**Poincaré['s] matrix** <AT>	Poincarésche Matrix *f*	matrice *f* de Poincaré	матрица Пуанкаре
P 713	**Poincaré['s] method [of generating solution]** <DE, NU>	Methode *f* der erzeugenden Lösung von Poincaré, Poincarésche Methode der erzeugenden Lösung	méthode *f* de Poincaré [de la solution génératrice]	метод порождающего решения Пуанкаре
P 714	**Poincaré['s] model** <of the hyperbolic plane> <GE>	Poincarésches Modell *n*, Poincaré-Modell *n*	modèle *m* de Poincaré	модель Пуанкаре
P 715	**Poincaré[s'] number** <of a discrete group> <GR>	Poincarésche Zahl *f*	nombre *m* de Poincaré	число Пуанкаре
P 716	**Poincaré['s] polarization** <AG>	Poincarésche Polarisierung *f*	polarisation *f* de Poincaré	поляризация Пуанкаре
P 717	**Poincaré['s] polynomial** <AT>	Poincarésches Polynom *n*	polynôme *m* de Poincaré	полином (многочлен) Пуанкаре
	Poincaré['s] problem <TO>	*s.* P 1569		

No.	English	German	French	Russian
	Poincaré['s] recurrence theorem <ME, ST>	*s.* R 297		
P 718	**Poincaré['s] series** <FT>	Poincarésche Thetareihe *f*, Poincaré-Reihe *f*	série *f* de Poincaré	ряд Пуанкаре
P 719	**Poincaré['s] space** <AT>	Poincaréscher Raum *m*	espace *m* de Poincaré	пространство Пуанкаре
	Poincaré['s] system [of partial differential equations] <FT>	*s.* P 701		
	Poincaré['s] theorem <DG>	*s.* T 328		
	Poincaré-Volterra theorem <TO>	*s.* T 335		
	Poincaré-Witt theorem <AL>	*s.* B 451		
P 720	**Poinsot['s] body,** regular star polyhedron <EG>	Poinsotscher Körper *m*, regelmäßiges Sternpolyeder (Sternvielflach) *n*	corps (solide) *m* de Poinsot, polyèdre *m* régulier étoilé, polyèdre étoilé régulier	тело Пуансо, правильный невыпуклый (звездчатый) многогранник, самопересекающийся (звездчатый) правильный многогранник
P 721	**point,** vector <in a vector space> <AL, FA>	Punkt *m*, Vektor *m*	point *m*, vecteur *m*	точка, вектор
	point <FA>	*s.* V 26		
	point <GE, IN>	*s.* N 77		
	point <GP>	*s.* V 156		
	point <LA>	*s.* A 1184		
	point <TG>	*s.* S 1142		
	point at finite distance <GE>	*s.* P 1819		
P 722	**point at infinity,** infinite (ideal, improper, infinitely distant) point <as an extension of the Euclidean space> <PJ>	unendlich[ ]ferner Punkt *m*, uneigentlicher (idealer) Punkt, Fernpunkt *m*	point *m* à (de) l'infini, point idéal (impropre)	бесконечно удаленная точка, несобственная точка, идеальная точка
P 723	**point at infinity,** infinity, ∞ <FT>	unendlich[ ]ferner Punkt *m*, Unendlichkeitspunkt *m*, Unendlich *n*, ∞	point *m* à l'infini, infini *m*, ∞	бесконечно удаленная точка, бесконечность, ∞
P 724	**point at which a rational function is defined** <AN>	Punkt *m*, in dem eine rationale Funktion definiert ist	élément *m* substituable dans une fraction rationnelle	точка, в которой определена рациональная функция
P 725	**point** <of a curve> **at which the highest derivative equalling zero is of even order** <DG>	Flachpunkt *m*, Undulationspunkt *m*	point *m* d'ondulation, point *m* [de] méplat	точка уплощения
P 726	**point below a graph** <RF>	Punkt *m* unterhalb eines Graphen	point *m* au-dessous d'un graphe	точка ниже графика
P 727	**point circle,** null circle <AY>	Punktkreis *m*, Nullkreis *m*	cercle-point *m*, cercle *m* réduit à un point, cercle [de rayon] nul	круг, выродившийся в точку; нулевой круг, нулевая окружность
P 728	**point complex** <GE>	Punktkomplex *m*	complexe *m* ponctuel	точечный комплекс
	point conic, point-conic <AG, AY>	*s.* C 1944		
P 729	**point co-ordinates** <AY>	Punktkoordinaten *fpl*	coordonnées *fpl* ponctuelles (de points)	точечные координаты
P 730	**point-cube** <AT>	nulldimensionaler Würfel *m*	cube *m* ponctuel	куб, который сводится к точке
P 731	**point-curve, point curve** <contrary to class curve> <AG>	Punktkurve *f*, Punktort *m*, Ortskurve *f*, Ordnungskurve *f*, Ortslinie *f*	lieu *m* de points, courbe *f* envisagée comme lieu de points, courbe ponctuel	точечная кривая
	point curve <TO>	*s.* C 2109		
P 732	**point density** <IG>	Punktdichte *f*	densité *f* des points	плотность точек
	point diagram <NU, ST>	*s.* D 894		
	point-direction equation <AY>	*s.* P 789		
P 733	**pointed bracket,** broken (angle, pointy) bracket, chevron, <. . .> <GN>	spitze Klammer *f*	chevron *m*	угловая (угольная) скобка
P 734	**pointed category,** category with zero morphisms <CA>	Kategorie *f* mit Nullmorphismen, punktierte Kategorie	catégorie *f* pointée (avec morphismes nuls)	категория с нулевыми морфизмами, пунктированная категория
P 735	**pointed complex** <AT, CA>	simpliziale Menge *f* mit Grundpunkt	ensemble *m* simplicial pointé	пунктированное симплициальное множество
P 736	**pointed cone** <includes apex> <in a linear space> <AN, GE>	spitzer Kegel *m*	cône *m* pointé	заостренный конус
P 737	**pointed groupoid** <CA>	punktiertes Gruppoid *n*	groupoïde *m* pointé	пунктированный группоид
P 738	**pointed homotopic category** <CA, TO>	punktierte Homotopiekategorie *f*	catégorie *f* homotopique d'espaces topologiques pointés	пунктированная гомотопическая категория
P 739	**pointed object** <CA>	punktiertes Objekt *n*	objet *m* pointé	пунктированный объект
P 740	**pointed set,** set with base point, based set <SE>	punktierte Menge *f*, Menge mit ausgezeichnetem Grundpunkt, Menge mit Grundpunkt	ensemble *m* pointé	множество с отмеченной точкой, пунктированное множество
P 741	**pointed simplicial complex,** simplicial complex together with a distinguished base vertex <AT>	simplizialer Komplex *m* mit ausgezeichnetem Eckpunkt	complexe *m* simplicial pointé	симплициальный комплекс с отмеченной вершиной
	pointed topological space <TO>	*s.* T 547		
	point ellipse <AY>	*s.* N 767		

No.	English	German	French	Russian
P 742	**point equation** <AY>	Punktgleichung *f*, Gleichung *f* des Punktes	équation *f* ponctuelle	уравнение точки
P 743	**point estimation** <ST>	Punktschätzung *f*	estimation *f* ponctuelle (de paramètres)	точечное оценивание, точечная оценка
P 744	**point finite cover[ing],** point finite open covering <TO>	punktal endliche Überdeckung *f*, punktendliche (punkt-endliche) Überdeckung	recouvrement *m* ponctuellement fini	точечно конечное [открытое] покрытие
P 745	**point finite family of subsets** <TO>	punktal endliches System *n* von Teilmengen	système *m* de parties ponctuellement fini	точечно конечная система подмножеств
	point finite open covering <TO>	*s.* P 744		
P 746	**point function** <contrary to set function> <AN>	Punktfunktion *f*	fonction *f* de point[s]	функция точки
	point function <GE>	*s.* P 798		
P 747	**point group,** symmetry group, group of symmetries <of a figure> <GE>	Symmetriegruppe *f*	groupe *m* de symétrie, groupe isométrique	группа симметрии
	point[-] group <AG>	*s.* G 494		
P 748	**point harmonic conic** <AG>	harmonische Kurve *f* zweiter Ordnung	conique *f* harmonique du second ordre	гармоническая кривая второго порядка
P 749	**point ideal** <ideal of the functions holomorphic in one point> <FT>	Punktideal *n*	idéal *m* ponctuel	точечный идеал
	point in space <GE>	*s.* S 1332		
P 750	**point involution,** involution of points <AY>	Punktinvolution *f*	involution *f* ponctuelle (de points)	инволюция (инволюционное преобразование) точек
	point isolated from the left <TO>	*s.* L 412		
	point isolated from the right <TO>	*s.* R 1193		
P 751	**point lattice** <AL, GE>	Punktgitter *n*	réseau *m* à points, grillage *m* de points	точечная решетка
P 752	**point lattice** <NT>	Zahlengitter *n*, Punktgitter *n*, Parallelgitter *n*, // Zahlennetz *n*	réseau *m* des nombres (points entiers)	числовая решетка
	point lattice <LA>	*s.* A 1194		
	pointlike discontinuous function <RF>	*s.* P 810		
	pointlike set <TO>	*s.* T 648		
	point-line configuration <SG>	*s.* P 641		
	point-line-plane-configuration <SG>	*s.* C 1869		
	point mapping <GE>	*s.* P 798		
P 753	**point mass,** concentrated mass <ME>	Punktmasse *f*, konzentrierte Masse *f*	masse *f* ponctuelle	сосредоточенная масса
P 754	**point measure** <ME>	Punktmaß *n*	mesure *f* ponctuelle	точечная мера
	point of accumulation <TO>	*s.* A 188		
P 755	**point of adherence** <of a filter> <TO>	Berührungspunkt *m*, Häufungspunkt *m*, Adhärenzpunkt *m*	point *m* d'adhérence	предельная точка, точка прикосновения, точка накопления
	point of application <VT>	*s.* I 535		
	point of attraction <NU>	*s.* A 1202		
	point of Brianchon <AY>	*s.* B 750		
P 756	**point of closure,** adherent point <of a set> <TO>	Berührungspunkt *m*, adhärenter Punkt *m*, // Limespunkt *m*	point *m* adhérent (d'adhérence), valeur *f* d'adhérence	точка прикосновения
P 757	**point of condensation,** condensation point <TO>	Verdichtungspunkt *m*, Kondensationspunkt *m*, verdichteter Punkt *m*	point *m* de condensation (densité), élément *m* de condensation	точка сгущения (конденсации, накопления), // предельная точка
	point of contact <GE>	*s.* P 777		
P 758	**point of continuity** <AN>	Stetigkeitspunkt, Stetigkeitsstelle *f*	point *m* de continuité	точка непрерывности
P 759	**point of control** <ST>	Kontrollpunkt *m*	point *m* de contrôle	контрольная точка
P 760	**point of convergence** <of a sequence *or* series> <SS>	Konvergenzpunkt *m*	point *m* de convergence	точка сходимости
P 761	**point of determinacy** <FT>	Bestimmtheitsstelle *f*	point *m* de détermination	точка определенности
	point of determinacy <DE>	*s.* R 630		
	point of determination <DE>	*s.* R 630		
P 762	**point of discontinuity** <of the first *or* second kind> <DI>	Unstetigkeitspunkt *m*, Unstetigkeitsstelle *f* <erster *oder* zweiter Art>	point (lieu) *m* de discontinuité <de première *ou* seconde (deuxième) espèce, régulier *ou* irrégulier>	точка разрыва <первого *или* второго рода>
P 763	**point of divergence** <of a series> <SS>	Divergenzpunkt *m*, Divergenzstelle *f*	point *m* de divergence	точка расходимости
P 764	**point of division** <EG>	Teilungspunkt *m*, Teilpunkt *m*	point *m* de division	точка деления
P 765	**point of double inflexion** <of a curve> <GE>	Schlangenpunkt *m*, Punkt *m* doppelter Inflexion	point *m* de serpentement, point d'inflexion double, serpentant *m*	точка двойного перегиба
	point of Gergonne <EG>	*s.* G 282		
	point of indeterminacy <FT>	*s.* A 594		

	point of indetermination <DE>	s. I 1069		
P 766	**point of infinity** <DI>	Unendlichkeitsstelle *f*	point *m* où la fonction devient infinie	точка обращения в бесконечность, полюс
P 767	**point of inflection (inflexion),** inflexion (inflection) point, flex [point] <of a curve> <DG, DI>	Wendepunkt *m*, Inflexionspunkt *m* erster Ordnung, Inflexionspunkt, // Beugungspunkt *m*	point *m* d'inflexion <d'une courbe>	точка перегиба <на кривой>
P 768	**point of inflection (inflexion),** inflexion (inflection) point <of order *p*> <DG>	Inflexionspunkt *m* <in der Ordnung *p*>	point *m* d'inflexion <d'ordre *p*>	точка перегиба <порядка *p*>
	point of intersection <EG>	s. I 814		
P 769	**point of irreducibility** <TO>	Irreduzibilitätspunkt *m*	point *m* d'irréductibilité	точка неприводимости
	point of jump discontinuity <DI>	s. J 115		
	point of lattice <NT>	s. P 771		
P 770	**point of local connectivity** <TO>	Punkt *m* lokalen Zusammenhangs	point *m* de connexité locale	точка локальной связности
	point of maximum <DI>	s. M 269		
	point of minimum <DI>	s. M 613		
P 771	**point of net,** point of lattice, lattice point <NT>	Gitterpunkt *m*	sommet *m*	целая точка, точка решетки, узел решетки, узел
	point of non-removable discontinuity <DI>	s. N 468		
P 772	**point of order 2** <of a curve in Menger's theory> <TO>	gewöhnlicher Kurvenpunkt (Punkt) *m*, Punkt der Ordnung 2, Punkt von zweiter Ordnung	point *m* d'ordre 2	обыкновенная точка
	point of osculation <GE>	s. T 19		
	point of ramification <FT>	s. B 733		
P 773	**point of regular type** <of a linear operator> <FA>	Punkt *m* regulären Typus	point *m* de type régulier	точка регулярного типа
	point of removable discontinuity <DI>	s. R 798		
	point of self-intersection <DS, GE>	s. S 293		
P 774	**point of semi[-]continuity** <of a function> <AN>	Halbstetigkeitspunkt *m*	point *m* de semi-continuité	точка полунепрерывности
	point of sight <DS>	s. C 422		
	point of spectrum <FA>	s. S 1409		
P 775	**point of strong convexity** <GE>	Punkt *m* strenger Konvexität	point *m* de stricte convexité	точка строгой выпуклости
P 776	**point of support,** supporting point <DG>	Stützpunkt *m*	point *m* d'appui	опорная точка
P 777	**point of tangency,** point of contact <GE>	Berührungspunkt *m*	point *m* de contact (tangence)	точка касания (соприкосновения)
P 778	**point of the dummy scale** <NO>	Zapfenpunkt *m*	point *m* de la ligne de correspondance	точка немой шкалы
P 779	**point of uniform convergence** <for a sequence> <SS, TO>	Punkt *m* der gleichmäßigen Konvergenz <für eine Folge>	point *m* de convergence uniforme <pour une suite>	точка равномерной сходимости <для последовательности>
P 780	**point of view,** interpretation <LO>	Auffassung *f*, Deutung *f*	point *m* de vue, interprétation *f*	точка зрения, интерпретация
P 781	**point pair,** pair of points, two points <GE>	Punktepaar *n*	couple *m* de points	пара точек
P 782	**point process** <SP>	Punktprozeß *m*, zufällige Punktfolge *f*	processus *m* ponctuel	точечный процесс
P 783	**point range,** range (series, row, pencil) of points <PJ>	Punktreihe *f* <auch im Sinne von Reye>, Punkt[e]büschel *n*	ponctuelle *f*, division *f* rectiligne	ряд точек
	point ranges having (on) the same base <PJ>	s. C 1959		
P 784	**points connected in the space,** points which can be connected by a connected subset <TO>	verbindbare Punkte *mpl*	points *mpl* qui se laissent unir par un ensemble connexe	связанные в пространстве точки; точки, которые могут соединяться связным множеством
P 785	**point set,** set (assemblage) of points <SE, TO>	Punktmenge *f*, Punktmannigfaltigkeit *f* <Cantor>	ensemble *m* de points, ensemble ponctuel	точечное множество, множество точек
P 786	**point set boundary,** frontier <of a simplex> <AT>	mengentheoretischer Rand *m*	frontière *f* ensembliste	граница
P 787	**point set uniformly connected im kleinen,** uniformly connected im kleinen point set <TO>	gleichmäßig im Kleinen zusammenhängende Punktmenge *f*	ensemble *m* uniformément localement connexe	равномерно локально связное [точечное] множество
	point set union <SE>	s. U 202		
P 788	**point singularity** <of a curve> <GE>	Punktsingularität *f*	singularité *f* ponctuelle	точечная особенность
P 789	**point-slope form** <of the equation of a straight line>, point-direction equation <AY>	Gleichung *f* der Geraden durch einen gegebenen Punkt in einer gegebenen Richtung, Punktrichtungsgleichung *f* der Geraden	équation *f* de la droite passant par un point donné et ayant une direction donnée	уравнение прямой, проходящей через данную точку в данном направлении
	point slope method <DE>	s. P 935		

No.	English	German	French	Russian
P 790	**point space** <AY, TO>	Punktraum *m*	espace *m* ponctuel	точечное пространство
P 791	**point spectrum** <FA, IE>; discrete spectrum <FA>	Punktspektrum *n*; diskretes Spektrum *n*	spectre *m* ponctuel; spectre discret	точечный спектр; дискретный спектр
P 792	**point sphere,** null sphere <AY>	Punktkugel *f*, Nullkugel *f*, Kugel *f* vom Radius Null	sphère-point *f*; sphère *f* de rayon nul, sphère nulle	шар, выродившийся в точку; нулевой шар, нулевая сфера
P 793	**point strictly above a graph** <RF>	eigentlich oberhalb eines Graphen gelegener Punkt *m*, Punkt oberhalb eines Graphen im engeren Sinne	point *m* strictement au-dessus d'un graphe	точка строго выше графика
P 794	**point strictly below a graph** <RF>	eigentlich unterhalb eines Graphen gelegener Punkt *m*, Punkt unterhalb eines Graphen im engeren Sinne	point *m* strictement au-dessous d'un graphe	точка строго ниже графика
P 795	**points which are at a distance less than *V*** <TO>	von der Ordnung *V* benachbarte Punkte *mpl*	points *mpl* voisins d'ordre *V*	точки, близкие порядка *V*
P 796	**points** <of a set> **which are not condensation points** <TO>	unverdichteter Teil *m*	ensemble *m* des points qui ne sont pas des points de condensation	множество всех точек множества, не являющихся его точками конденсации
	points which can be connected by a connected subset <TO>	*s.* P 784		
P 797	**point symmetry** <EG>	Punktsymmetrie *f*, Punktspiegelung *f*, Symmetrie *f* in bezug auf einen Punkt	symétrie *f* par rapport à un point, symétrie ponctuelle	центральная симметрия
P 798	**point-to-point function (mapping), point transformation,** point mapping (function) <GE>	Punkttransformation *f*, Punktabbildung *f*	correspondance *f* point par point, transformation (application) *f* ponctuelle	точечное отображение (преобразование)
P 799	**point under consideration** <AN>	Aufpunkt *m*, betrachteter Punkt *m*	point *m* d'observation	точка наблюдения, рассматриваемая точка
P 800	**point** <of a set> **which is no condensation point** <TO>	unverdichteter Punkt *m*	point *m* qui n'est pas point de condensation	точка множества, не являющаяся точкой конденсации
P 801	**pointwise bounded sequence** <of functions> <SS>	punktweise beschränkte Folge *f*	suite *f* ponctuellement bornée	поточечно ограниченная последовательность
P 802	**pointwise continuity** <RF>	punktweise Stetigkeit *f*	continuité *f* ponctuelle	точечная непрерывность
P 803	**pointwise continuous function** <RF>	punktweise stetige Funktion *f*	fonction *f* ponctuellement continue	[по]точечно непрерывная функция
P 804	**pointwise convergence,** simple convergence <of a sequence *or* series> <SS>	punktweise (einfache, gewöhnliche) Konvergenz *f*	convergence *f* ponctuelle (simple)	поточечная (простая) сходимость
	pointwise convergence <FA, TO>	*s.* C 1669		
P 805	**pointwise convergent family** <TO>	einfach konvergente Familie *f* <nach einem Filter>	famille *f* simplement convergente	семейство, просто сходящееся <по фильтру>
P 806	**pointwise convergent sequence,** simply convergent sequence <SS>	punktweise (einfach) konvergente Folge *f*	suite *f* simplement (ponctuellement) convergente	поточечно (просто) сходящаяся последовательность
P 807	**pointwise convergent sequence** <of functions> <TO>	einfach konvergente Folge *f*	suite *f* simplement convergente	просто сходящаяся последовательность
P 808	**pointwise convergent series,** simply convergent series <SS>	punktweise (einfach) konvergente Reihe *f*	série *f* simplement (ponctuellement) convergente	поточечно (просто) сходящийся ряд
P 809	**pointwise discontinuity** <RF>	punktierte (punktweise) Unstetigkeit *f* <Hankel>	discontinuité *f* ponctuée	точечная разрывность
P 810	**pointwise discontinuous function,** pointlike discontinuous function <RF>	punktweise (punktiert) unstetige Funktion *f*	fonction *f* ponctuellement discontinue, fonction pantachiquement continue	точечно-разрывная (точечно разрывная) функция, функция с тощим множеством точек разрыва
P 811	**pointwise monomorphism** <in a natural transformation> <CA>	punktweiser Monomorphismus *m*	monomorphisme *m* ponctuel	точечный мономорфизм
	pointwise topology <FA, TO>	*s.* T 567		
P 812	**pointwise transitive** <AL>	punktweise transitiv	transitif par points	точечнотранзитивный
P 813	**point with height,** coted height <in topographic projection> <DS>	kotierter Punkt *m*	point *m* coté	точка с численной отметкой
	pointy bracket <GN>	*s.* P 733		
P 814	**Poisson['s] birth process** <SP>	Poissonscher Geburtsprozeß *m*	processus *m* de prolifération (naissance) poissonnien	пуассоновский процесс размножения
P 815	**Poisson['s] bracket[s],** classical Poisson bracket[s] <DE>	Poisson-Klammer *f*, Poissonsche Klammer *f*, Poissonscher Klammerausdruck *m*, Poissonsches Klammersymbol *n*, klassische Poisson-Klammer *f*	parenthèse *f* de Poisson (Poisson classique)	скобка (скобки, классические скобки) Пуассона
	Poisson-Charlier polynomial <FU, ST>	*s.* C 592		
	Poisson chart <IN, ST>	*s.* P 829		
P 816	**Poisson['s] death process** <SP>	Poissonscher Todesprozeß *m*	processus *m* de morbidité poissonnien	пуассоновский процесс гибели
	Poisson['s] differential equation <DE, PO>	*s.* P 819		

P 817	**Poisson['s] distribution [law]** <ST>	Poisson-Verteilung *f*, Poissonsche Verteilung *f*, Verteilung von Poisson	distribution *f* de Poisson, distribution poissonnienne, loi *f* de Poisson	распределение Пуассона, пуассоновское распределение, закон распределения Пуассона
P 818	**Poisson['s] elimination method** <AL>	Poissonsche Eliminationsmethode *f*	méthode *f* d'élimination de Poisson, méthode des fonctions symétriques	метод исключения Пуассона
P 819	**Poisson['s] equation,** Poisson['s] differential equation <DE, PO>	Poissonsche Differentialgleichung (Gleichung) *f*	équation *f* (équation différentielle) de Poisson	уравнение (дифференциальное уравнение) Пуассона
P 820	**Poisson['s] formula** <on the Haar measure> <GR, ME>	Poissonsche Formel *f*	formule *f* de Poisson	формула Пуассона
P 821	**Poisson['s] global theorem** <ST>	globaler Poissonscher Satz *m*	théorème *m* global de Poisson	глобальная теорема Пуассона
P 822	**Poisson['s] integral,** Poisson['s] integral equation <of the Bessel functions> <FU>	Poissonsche Integraldarstellung *f*	intégrale *f* de Poisson	интеграл Пуассона
P 823	**Poisson['s] integral** <PO>	Poissonsches Integral *n*, Poisson-Integral *n*	intégrale *f* de Poisson	интеграл Пуассона
	Poisson['s] integral equation <FU>	*s.* P 822		
P 824	**Poisson['s] integral formula** <PO>	Poissonsche Integralformel *f*	formule *f* intégrale de Poisson	интегральная формула Пуассона
P 825	**Poisson-Jacobi theorem,** theorem of Poisson-Jacobi <DE>	Poisson-Jacobischer Satz *m*, Satz von Poisson-Jacobi	théorème *m* de Poisson-Jacobi	теорема Пуассона-Якоби
P 826	**Poisson-Jensen formula** <FT>	Formel *f* von Jensen-Nevanlinna, Poisson-Jensensche (Jensen-Nevanlinnasche) Formel	formule *f* de Poisson-Jensen	формула Иенсена
P 827	**Poisson['s] kernel** <LI>	Poissonscher Kern *m*	noyau *m* de Poisson	ядро Пуассона
P 828	**Poisson['s] law of large numbers** <ST>	Poissonsches Gesetz *n* [der großen Zahlen]	loi *f* des grands nombres de Poisson	закон больших чисел Пуассона
	Poisson['s] limit theorem <ST>	*s.* P 833		
	Poisson['s] method [of summation] <SS>	*s.* A 37		
P 829	**Poisson [probability] paper,** Poisson chart <IN, ST>	Poisson-Papier *n*, Poisson-Netz *n*	abaque *m* de la loi de Poisson	пуассоновская вероятностная бумага
P 830	**Poisson['s] process** <SP>	Poissonscher Prozeß *m*, Poisson-Prozeß *m*	processus *m* de Poisson, processus poissonnien	пуассоновский процесс, процесс Пуассона; пуассоновский поток <в теории массового обслуживания>
P 831	**Poisson['s] random variable** <ST>	Poissonsche Zufallsvariable *f*, Poisson-Stochastik *f*	variable *f* aléatoire de Poisson	случайная величина Пуассона
	Poisson['s] sum formula <AN, NT>	*s.* P 832		
	Poisson['s] summation <SS>	*s.* A 37		
P 832	**Poisson['s] summation formula,** Poisson['s] sum formula <AN, NT>	Poissonsche Summationsformel (Summenformel) *f*	formule *f* sommatoire de Poisson	формула суммирования Пуассона, формула Пуассона
	Poisson['s] summation method <SS>	*s.* A 37		
P 833	**Poisson['s] theorem,** Poisson['s] limit theorem, limit theorem of Poisson, law of small numbers, law of rare events, Bortkiewicz['s] law <ST>	Poissonscher Grenzverteilungssatz (Grenzwertsatz) *m*, Grenzwertsatz (Grenzverteilungssatz) von Poisson, Gesetz *n* der kleinen Zahlen, Gesetz der seltenen Ereignisse, Poissonscher (lokaler Poissonscher) Satz *m*	théorème *m* de Poisson, théorème limite de Poisson, loi *f* des petits nombres, loi des événements rares	теорема Пуассона, предельная теорема Пуассона, закон малых чисел, закон редких событий
P 834	**Poisson['s] transform[ation],** potential transform <IT>	Poissonsche Transformation *f*	transformation *f* de Poisson	преобразование Пуассона
P 835	**Poisson['s] trials** <ST>	Poisson-Schema *n*, Poissonsches Versuchsschema *n*, Poissonsche Versuchsfolge *f*	schéma *m* de Poisson	схема Пуассона
P 836	**Poisson['s] variation** <ST>	Poissonsche Variation *f*	variation *f* (schéma *m*) de Poisson	дисперсия Пуассона
P 837	**polar** <*n*-th, *also* of *n*-th order> <of an algebraic curve *or* surface> <AG, IV>	Polare *f* <*n*-te, *auch* von *n*-ter Ordnung>	polaire *f* <*n*-ième, *aussi* d'ordre *n*, du *n*-e ordre>	поляра <*n*-ая, *также* *n*-го порядка>
P 838	**polar** <of a linear topological space> <FA>	polare Menge *f*	ensemble *m* polaire, polaire *f* <d'un ensemble>	полярное множество, поляра (множества)
	polar <AY>	*s.* P 872a		
	polar <LA>	*s.* P 843		
	polar angle <AN>	*s.* A 603		
	polar angle <AY>	*s.* A 604		
	polar angle <DS, PJ>	*s.* P 891		
P 839	**polar arm** <of a planimeter> <GE, IN>	Polarm *m*	bras *m* polaire	полярный рычаг
P 840	**polar axis,** zero direction, axis <of polar coordinates> <AY>	Polarachse *f*, Nullstrahl *m*	axe *m* polaire	полярная ось
P 841	**polar bundle,** polar sheaf <AY>	Polarbündel *n*	gerbe (étoile) *f* polaire	полярная связка

	English	German	French	Russian
P 842	**polar circle** <of a triangle> <AY>	Polkreis *m*	cercle *m* polaire	полярная окружность
P 843	**polar complement,** orthogonal complement, polar, orthocomplement <LA>	orthogonales Komplement *n*, Orthokomplement *n*	orthocomplément *m*	ортодополнение
P 844	**polar cone** <of a convex cone> <GE>	Polarkegel *m*	cône *m* polaire	полярный конус
P 845	**polar conic,** (n — 2)-th polar <of a point with regard to an algebraic curve of degree n> <AG>	Polarkegelschnitt *m*, konische Polare *f*, (n — 2)-te Polare <eines Punktes bezüglich einer Kurve n-ter Ordnung>	conique *f* polaire, polaire *f* conique, (n — 2)-e polaire <d'un point par rapport à une courbe du n-e degré>	коническая поляра <точки относительно кривой n-го порядка>
P 846	**polar conic** <of a triangle *or* trilateral> <AY>	Polkegelschnitt *m*	conique *f* polaire	полярное коническое сечение
P 847	**polar conic,** poloconic <of a line with respect to a cubic> <PJ>	Polokonik *f*, Polkegelschnitt *m* <einer Geraden bezüglich einer Kurve dritter Ordnung>, // Lineopolarenveloppe *f*	poloconique *f*, conique *f* polaire <d'une droite par rapport à une cubique>, // enveloppe *f* linéopolaire	полоконика <прямой относительно K_3>
P 848	**polar co-ordinate chart (paper)** <IN, NU>	Polarkoordinatenpapier *n*, Polarkoordinatennetz *n*	diagramme (papier) *m* en coordonnées polaires	сетка в полярных координатах
P 849	**polar co-ordinates,** polar co-ordinates in the plane, plane [cylindrical] polar co-ordinates, two-dimensional polar co-ordinates <AY>	Polarkoordinaten *fpl*, ebene Polarkoordinaten, Polarkoordinaten in der Ebene	coordonnées *fpl* polaires (polaires dans le plan, polaires planes)	полярные координаты, полярные координаты на плоскости, плоские полярные координаты
	polar co-ordinates [in space] <AY>	*s.* S 1479		
	polar co-ordinates in the plane <AY>	*s.* P 849		
P 850	**polar curve** <AG>	Polarkurve *f*	courbe *f* polaire	полярная кривая, поляра
P 851	**polar curve** <of a rational function> <AG>	Polstellenkurve *f*	courbe *f* des pôles	кривая полюсов
P 852	**polar curve** <of a space curve> <DG>	Polarkurve *f*, Polkurve *f*	courbe *f* polaire	полярная кривая
P 853	**polar cycle** <of a polar divisor> <AG, FT>	Polzyklus *m*	cycle *m* polaire	цикл полюсов
P 854	**polar decomposition** <of a matrix, a Lie group, *or* an operator> <FA, GR, MD>	polare Zerlegung *f*	décomposition *f* polaire	полярное разложение
P 855	**polar determinant** <AL>	Polardeterminante *f* <Clebsch>	déterminant *m* polaire	полярный определитель
P 856	**polar developable** <of a space curve> <DG>	Evolutenfläche *f*, Polarfläche *f*	surface *f* polaire	полярная поверхность, огибающая нормальных плоскостей
P 857	**polar discontinuity** <AN>	polare Unstetigkeit *f*	discontinuité *f* polaire	полярная непрерывность
P 858	**polar divisor** <in a function field> <AL>	Poldivisor *m*, Nennerdivisor *m*	diviseur *m* des pôles	дивизор полюсов
P 859	**polar equation,** equation in polar co-ordinates <of a conic section> <AY>	Polargleichung *f*, Gleichung *f* in Polarkoordinaten	équation *f* polaire (en coordonnées polaires)	полярное уравнение, уравнение в полярных координатах
P 860	**polar equation** <of a polar system> <AY, PJ>	Polargleichung *f*	équation *f* polaire	полярное уравнение
P 861	**polar form** <of a quadratic form> <AL>	Polarform *f*	forme *f* polaire	полярная (полярная билинейная) форма
P 862	**polar form,** trigonometric form, trigonometric representation <of a complex number> <AN, FT>	trigonometrische Form *f*	forme *f* trigonométrique	тригонометрическая форма
	polar function <AN>	*s.* C 1972		
P 863	**polar group** <of a group> <DE>	Polargruppe *f* <Lie>	groupe *m* polaire	полярная группа
P 864	**polar hyperbola** <of a triangle> <AY>	[gleichseitige] Polhyperbel *f*	hyperbole *f* polaire	полярная гипербола
P 865	**polar integral equation** <IE>	polare Integralgleichung *f*	équation *f* intégrale polaire	полярное интегральное уравнение
P 866	**polarity,** polar system <AY, PJ>	Polarsystem *n*, Polarität *f*	polarité *f*, système *m* polaire	полярная система, поляритет
P 867	**polarity,** polar reciprocation, dualizing <as a relation> <AY, PJ>	Polarität *f*, Polarverwandtschaft *f*, Polarsystem *n*, Polarenverwandtschaft *f*	polarité *f*, corrélation *f* involutive, réciprocité *f* polaire, conjugaison *f*	полярное преобразование (соответствие), полярная корреляция
P 868	**polarization** <*e.g.:* of an Abelian variety *or* a bilinear functional> <AG, FA, GE>	Polarisation *f*; Polarisierung *f* <GE>	polarisation *f*	поляризация
P 869	**polarization** <of homogeneous spaces, Lie algebras, *or* Lie groups> <AL, GR>	Polarisation *f*	polarisation *f*	поляризация
P 870	**polarization identity** <for a bilinear functional> <AL, FA>	Polarisationsgleichung *f*	identité *f* de polarisation	поляризационное тождество
P 871	**polarized abelian variety** <AG>	polarisierte abelsche Mannigfaltigkeit *f*	variété *f* abélienne polarisée	поляризированное абелево многообразие
	polarizing operator <IT>	*s.* P 878		
P 872	**polar kernel** <IE>	polarer Kern *m*	noyau *m* polaire	полярное ядро
P 872 a	**polar line,** polar <AY>	Polare *f*	polaire *f*	поляра
	polar line <DG>	*s.* A 1312		
P 873	**polar manifold** <of a function> <AG>	Polstellenmannigfaltigkeit *f*	variété *f* des pôles, variété polaire	многообразие полюсов

	polar matrix <AL>	*s.* M 722		
P 874	**polar net** <PJ>	Polarnetz *n*	réseau *m* polaire	полярная сеть
P 875	**polar normal** <GE>	Polarnormale *f*	normale *f* polaire	полярная нормаль
P 876	**polar operation** <for algebraic forms> <AL>	Polaroperation *f*	opération *f* polaire	операция поляризации
P 877	**polar operation** <in an algebraic system> <UA>	polare Operation *f*	opération *f* polaire	полярная (опорная) операция
P 878	**polar operator,** polarizing operator <IT>	Polarenoperator *m*	opérateur *m* polaire	оператор поляризирования
P 879	**polar parabola** <of a triangle> <AY>	Polparabel *f*	parabole *f* polaire	полярная парабола
P 880	**polar part** <of a function> <FT>	Polbestandteil *m*	partie *f* polaire	полярная часть
P 881	**polar period** <AG, FT>	polare Periode *f*	période *f* polaire	полярный период
P 882	**polar plane** <AY, PJ>	Polarebene *f*; Harmonikalebene *f* <bei Tetraederkoordinaten>	plan *m* polaire	полярная плоскость
P 883	**polar planimeter** <GE, IN>	Polarplanimeter *n*	planimètre *m* polaire	полярный планиметр
	polar point <AY, PJ>	*s.* P 903		
P 884	**polar process** <for a polar form> <AL>	Polarenprozeß *m*	procédé *m* polaire	полярный процесс
P 885	**polar quadric** <AG>	Polarquadrik *f*	quadrique *f* polaire	полярная квадрика
P 886	**polar quadrilateral** <GE>	Polvierseit *n* <Reye>	quadrilatère *f* polaire	полярный четырехсторонник
P 887	**polar radius,** radius, length of radius vector, radius vector <AY>	Polarradius *m*, Länge *f* des Radiusvektors, Radiusvektor *m*, Radius *m*	rayon *m* vecteur, rayon-vecteur *m*, rayon *m*	полярный радиус, радиус
P 888	**polar reciprocal [convex] body** <CS, GE>	polarer [konvexer] Körper *m*, polarreziproker Körper	corps *m* polaire	полярное тело
P 889	**polar reciprocation,** dualizing <AY, PJ>	Polarreziprozität *f*, polare Reziprozität *f*	réciprocité *f* polaire	полярная взаимность
	polar reciprocation <AY, PJ>	*s. a.* P 867		
P 890	**polar set** <PO>	polare Menge *f*	ensemble *m* polaire	полярное множество
	polar sheaf <AY>	*s.* P 841		
	polar simplex <PJ>	*s.* S 300		
P 891	**polar solid angle,** polar angle <DS, PJ>	supplementäres Trieder *n*, Polardreikant *n*, Supplementärdreikant *n*, supplementäre dreiseitige Ecke *f*, Polarecke *f*	trièdre *m* supplémentaire (polaire), angle *m* solide polaire, coin *m* polaire	полярный угол
	polar space <FA, TO>	*s.* A 307		
	polar space <PJ>	*s.* E 188		
P 892	**polar subtangent** <DG>	Polarsubtangente *f*	soustangente *f* polaire	полярная подкасательная
P 893	**polar surface** <of a surface> <AG>	Polarfläche *f*, polare Fläche *f*	surface *f* polaire	полярная поверхность
P 894	**polar system** <in exterior differential calculus> <DG>	Polarsystem *n*	système *m* polaire	полярная система
	polar system <AY, PJ>	*s.* P 866		
P 895	**polar system of functions** <with respect to a function> <AN>	polares Funktionensystem *n*	système *m* polaire de fonctions	полярная система функций
P 896	**polar tetrahedron** <of a tetrahedron> <EG>	Polartetraeder *n*, polares Tetraeder *n*	tétraèdre *m* polaire	полярный тетраэдр
P 897	**polar theory** <AY, PJ>	Polarentheorie *f*	théorie *f* polaire	полярная теория
P 898	**polar triangle** <PJ>	polares Dreieck *n*	triangle *m* polaire	полярный треугольник
P 899	**polar triangle** <of a spherical triangle> <EG>	Polardreieck *n*, Supplementardreieck *n*	triangle *m* polaire (supplémentaire)	полярный треугольник (сферический треугольник)
P 900	**polar trihedral** <PJ>	Poldreikant *n*, Poldreiflach *n*	trièdre *m* polaire	полярный трехгранник
P 901	**polar vector** <VT>	polarer (translatorischer) Vektor *m*, Schubvektor *m*, Richtungsvektor *m*	vecteur *m* polaire (pur)	полярный вектор
P 902	**pole** <of a quaternion function> <AL, AN>	Pol *m*, unwesentlich singulärer Punkt *m* nullter Dimension	pôle *m*	полюс
P 903	**pole,** origin <of polar *or* bipolar co-ordinates> <AY>	Pol *m*, Anfangspunkt *m*	pôle *m*, foyer *m*	полюс
P 904	**pole,** polar point <of a polar system> <AY, PJ>	Pol *m*	pôle *m*	полюс
P 905	**pole** <of a differential equation $w' = f(z, w)$> <DE>	Pol *m*, außerwesentlich[e] singuläre Stelle *f* erster (1.) Art	pôle *m*	полюс
P 906	**pole** <of order *n*, with order of multiplicity *n*> <of an analytic function> <FT>	Pol *m*, Polstelle *f*, außerwesentlich singuläre Stelle *f*, außerwesentliche singuläre Stelle <Weierstraß> <der Ordnung *n*>	pôle *m*, singularité *f* polaire <d'ordre *n*>	полюс, несущественная особая точка, полярная особенность <порядка *n*>
	pole <AG>	*s.* S 1449		
	pole <FT>	*s.* P 909		
	pole <MD>	*s.* E 65		
P 907	**pole of first order,** first-order pole, simple pole <FT>	Pol *m* erster Ordnung, einfacher Pol, Pol der Ordnung 1	pôle *m* simple (de premier ordre)	полюс первого порядка, простой полюс, полярная особенность первого порядка
P 908	**pole of rotation** <GE>	Drehpol *m*, Pol *m*	pôle *m* [de rotation]	полюс [вращения]
P 909	**pole-type singularity,** pole <an algebraic singularity> <FT>	Verzweigungspol *m*, Verzweigungspunkt *m* vom polaren Typ	point *m* critique (singulier) du type d'un pôle, singularité *f* du type d'un pôle	критический полюс, точка разветвления (ветвления) полярного типа, точка разветвления (ветвления) типа полюса

No.	English	German	French	Russian
P 910	**policy,** strategy <in dynamic programming> <PG>	Strategie *f*, Politik *f*, Entscheidungsfolge *f*, Steuerfolge *f*	stratégie *f*, politique *f*	стратегия, последовательность решений
	policy <TG>	*s.* S 1839		
P 911	**policy iteration** <PG>	Strategieiteration *f*	itération *f* de stratégie	итерация стратегии
	Polish notation <LO>	*s.* L 1187		
	Polish parenthesis-free notation <LO>	*s.* L 1187		
P 912	**Polish space** <TO>	polnischer Raum *m*	espace *m* [topologique] polonais	польское пространство
	poll <ST>	*s.* I 573		
P 913	**Pollaczek['s] polynomial** <FU>	Polynom *n* von Pollaczek, Pollaczeksches Polynom	polynôme *m* de Pollaczek	многочлен Полачека
P 914	**poloconic** <of a conic with respect to a cubic> <PJ>	Polokonik *f* <eines Kegelschnitts bezüglich einer Kubik>	poloconique *f* <d'une conique par rapport à une cubique>	полоконика <конического сечения относительно кривой K_3>
	poloconic <PJ>	*s.* P 847		
P 915	**polyadic algebra,** polyadic Boolean algebra <AL>	polyadische Algebra *f*	algèbre *f* polyadique	полиадическая алгебра
P 916	**polyadic analysis** <NT>	polyadische Analysis *f*	analyse *f* polyadique	полиадический анализ
	polyadic Boolean algebra <AL>	*s.* P 915		
P 917	**polyadic group;** *n*-group, *n*-adic group <GR>	polyadische Gruppe *f*; *n*-Gruppe *f*	groupe *m* polyadique; *n*-groupe *m*	полиадическая группа; *n*-группа
P 918	**polyadic number** <NT>	polyadische (Prüfersche ideale) Zahl *f*	nombre *m* polyadique	полиадическое число
P 919	**polyadic relation** <AL, LO>	mehrstellige Relation *f*	multirelation *f*	полиадическое (многоместное, многочленное) отношение
P 920	**Pólya['s] distribution,** Markov['s] distribution; contagious distribution <ST>	Pólya-Verteilung *f*, Markovsche Verteilung *f*; Ansteckungsverteilung *f*	distribution *f* de Pólya (Markov); distribution contagieuse	распределение Пойа (Маркова)
	Pólya distribution <ST>	*s. a.* P 285		
P 921	**Pólya['s] function** <FA>	Pólyasche Funktion *f*	fonction *f* de Pólya	функция Пойа
P 922	**Pólya[-Lundberg] process** <SP>	Pólya[-Lundberg]-Prozeß *m*, Pólya-Lundbergscher Prozeß *m*, Pólyascher Prozeß	processus *m* de Pólya [-Lundberg]	процесс Пойа-Лундберга, процесс Пойа
P 923	**Pólya['s] theorem** <DI, FT, NU>	Satz *m* von Pólya, Pólyascher Satz	théorème *m* de Pólya	теорема Пойа
P 924	**Pólya['s]trials** <ST>	Pólya-Schema *n*, Pólyasches Schema (Versuchsschema) *n*	schéma *m* de Pólya	схема Пойа
P 925	**poly-automorphism** <AL>	Polyautomorphismus *m*	poly-automorphisme *m*	полиавтоморфизм
P 926	**polycyclic group** <GR>	polyzyklische (Noethersche auflösbare) Gruppe *f*, auflösbare A_5-Gruppe *f*	groupe *m* polycyclique	полициклическая группа, разрешимая A_5-группа
P 927	**polycyclicity** <of a group> <GR>	Polyzyklischsein *n*	polycyclicité *f*	полицикличность
P 928	**polycylinder, polydisk** <FT>	Polyzylinder *m*	polydisque *m*, polycylindre *m*	полидиск, полицилиндр, круговой полицилиндр
P 929	**polyeder** <AT>	Polyeder *n*	polyèdre *m*	полиэдр
P 930	**polygamma function, polygamma-function** <FU>	Polygammafunktion *f*	fonction *f* polygamma	полигамма-функция
P 931	**polygenic function** <FT>	polygene Funktion *f*	fonction *f* polygène	полигенная функция
P 932	**polygon** <EG>	Vieleck *n*, Polygon *n*	polygone *m*	многоугольник, полигон; многовершинник
	polygon <GE>	*s.* B 775		
P 933	**polygonal body of revolution,** polygonal solid of revolution <GE>	polygonaler Drehkörper (Rotationskörper, Umdrehungskörper) *m*	corps *m* de révolution polygonal	полигональное (многоугольное) тело вращения
P 934	**polygonal domain,** domain of a polygon <GE, TO>	Polygonbereich *m*, Polygon *n*	domaine *m* polygonal	многоугольная область, область полигона
P 935	**polygonal method,** point slope method, Euler['s] method <DE>	Polygonzugverfahren *n*, Polygonzugmethode *f*, Methode *f* der Polygonzüge, Verfahren *n* von Euler-Cauchy, Euler-Cauchysches Verfahren (Polygonzugverfahren)	méthode *f* d'Euler, méthode des lignes brisées (polygonales)	метод ломаных [Эйлера], метод Эйлера, метод Коши-Липшица
P 936	**polygonal net** <TO>	Polygonnetz *n*	réseau *m* de polygones	сетка полигонов
P 937	**polygonal number** <as a figurate number> <NT>	Polygonalzahl *f*, Vieleckszahl *f*	nombre *m* polygone (polygonal)	многоугольное (полигональное) число
	polygonal number with *n* sides <NT>	*s.* N 226		
	polygonal solid of revolution <GE>	*s.* P 933		
P 938	**polygon equivalent by dissection** <GE>	zerlegungsgleiches Polygon *n*	polygone *m* égal par somme	равносоставленный многоугольник
	polygon formed by the mid-points <EG>	*s.* C 1384		
	polygon in which two nonconsecutive sides have a common point <EG>	*s.* R 477		
P 939	**polygon mapping,** Schwarz-Christoffel polygon mapping, Schwarz-Christoffel transformation <FT>	Polygonabbildung *f*, Schwarz-Christoffelsche Abbildung (Polygonabbildung) *f*	représentation *f* de Schwarz-Christoffel	отображение Шварца-Кристоффеля, полигональное отображение

P 940	**polygon of seventeen sides** <EG>	Siebzehneck *n*, 17-Eck *n*	polygone *m* de dix-sept côtés	семнадцатиугольник, 17-угольник, многоугольник с семнадцатью сторонами
	polygon of vectors <GE>	*s.* V 120		
P 941	**polygonometry** <EG>	Polygonometrie *f*	polygonométrie *f*	полигонометрия, геометрия (измерение) многоугольников
P 942	**polygons equivalent by completion** <GE>	ergänzungsgleiche Polygone *npl*	polygones *mpl* égaux par différence, polygones équivalents par adjonction	равные по дополнительности многогранники
	polygon with sides cutting each other <EG>	*s.* R 477		
P 943	**polyharmonic [differential] equation** <DE>	polyharmonische Differentialgleichung *f*	équation *f* [différentielle] polyharmonique	полигармоническое [дифференциальное] уравнение
P 944	**polyharmonic function** <FU>	polyharmonische Funktion *f*	fonction *f* polyharmonique	полигармоническая функция
P 945	**polyhedral angle,** corner, angle <EG>	*n*-seitige (körperliche) Ecke *f*, Ecke, Vielkant *n*, Vielflach *n*, räumliche Ecke	angle *m* polyédrique (polyèdre), coin *m*	многогранный угол
P 946	**polyhedral angle** <GE, TO>	Polyederecke *f*	angle *m* polyèdre (polyédrique)	многогранный угол
P 947	**polyhedral complex,** cell complex <AT>	Zellenkomplex *m*, Zellkomplex *m*, polyedraler Komplex *m*	complexe *m* cellulaire (polyédral)	полиэдральный (клеточный) комплекс
P 948	**polyhedral configuration** <SG, TO>	Polyederkonfiguration *f*, polyedrale Konfiguration *f*	configuration *f* polyédrale	полиэдральная конфигурация
P 949	**polyhedral co-ordinates** <AY, GE>	Polyederkoordinaten *fpl*	coordonnées *fpl* polyédriques <Serret>	полиэдрические координаты
P 950	**polyhedral domain** <CS, TO>	Polyederbereich *m*	domaine *m* polyédral	многогранная область
P 951	**polyhedral form** <AL>	Polyederform *f*, algebraische Primform *f*, Form *f* der regulären Polyeder	forme *f* polyédrique	полиэдрическая форма
P 952	**polyhedral game** <TG>	polyedrisches Spiel *n*	jeu *m* polyédral	полиэдральная игра
P 953	**polyhedral graph** <GP>	vielflächiger Graph *m*	graphe *m* polyédrique	многогранный граф
P 954	**polyhedral group** <GR>	Polyedergruppe *f*	groupe *m* polyédral (polyédrique, d'un polyèdre)	полиэдрическая группа, группа многогранника
P 955	**polyhedral manifold,** manifold <AT>	Polyedermannigfaltigkeit *f*, Mannigfaltigkeit *f*	variété *f* polyédrale, variété	полиэдральное многообразие, многообразие
P 956	**polyhedral metric** <TO>	polyedrische Metrik *f*	métrique *f* polyédrique	многогранная метрика
P 957	**polyhedral neighbourhood** <TO>	Polyederumgebung *f*	entourage *m* polyédral	полиэдральная окрестность
P 958	**polyhedral number** <as a figurate number> <NT>	Polyedralzahl *f*, Vielflachzahl *f*	nombre *m* polyédral	полиэдральное число
P 959	**polyhedral set** <PG>	Polyedermenge *f*	ensemble *m* polyédral	полиэдральное множество
P 960	**polyhedral subdivision** <TO>	polyedrische Unterteilung *f*	subdivision *f* polyédrale	полиэдральное подразделение
P 961	**polyhedral surface** <TO>	Polyederfläche *f*, polygonal zerlegte Fläche *f*	surface *f* polyédrique (polyédrale)	многогранная поверхность
P 962	**polyhedral theory** <PG>	Polyedertheorie *f*	théorie *f* polyédrale (des polyèdres)	теория полиэдров (многогранников)
P 963	**polyhedral topology** <TO>	Polyedertopologie *f*	topologie *f* polyhédrale	топология полиэдров
P 964	**polyhedrometry** <EG>	Polyedrometrie *f*	polyédrométrie *f*	полиэдрометрия
P 965	**polyhedron,** planar solid, planar body <EG>	Polyeder *n*, Vielflach *n*, Vielflächner *m*	polyèdre *m*	многогранник, полиэдр
	polyhedron <AT>	*s.* S 1304		
P 966	**polyhedron of *n* faces,** *n*-hedron <EG>	*n*-Flach *n*, *n*-seitiges Polyeder *n*, *n*-Flächner *m*	polyèdre *m* à *n* faces, *n*-èdre *m*	многогранник с *n* гранями, *n*-гранник
P 967	**polyhedron of reference** <of polyhedral co-ordinates> <GE>	Fundamentalpolyeder *n*	polyèdre *m* de référence	основной многогранник
	polyhedron with faces cutting each other <EG>	*s.* S 288		
P 968	**polyhex** <figure formed by joining regular hexagons> <GE>	Polyhex *n*	polyhexe *m*	полигекс
P 969	**polyiamond** <figure formed by joining congruent equilateral triangles> <GE>	Polyiamant *m*	polyiamant *m*	полииамант
P 970	**polyisomorphism** <AL>	Polyisomorphismus *m*	poly-isomorphisme *m*	полиизоморфизм
	polylateral <GE>	*s.* M 967		
	polyminimax group <AL>	*s.* S 1259		
P 971	**polymorphic function** <FT>	polymorphe (lineare polymorphe) Funktion *f*	fonction *f* polymorphe	линейно-полиморфная функция
P 972	**polynilpotent group** <GR>	polynilpotente Gruppe *f*	fonction *f* polynilpotent	полинильпотентная группа
P 973	**polynomial,** polynomial form <AL>	Polynom *n*	polynôme *m*	многочлен, полином
P 974	**polynomial** <as a sum of monoms> <GN>	mehrgliedriger Ausdruck *m*	polynôme *m*	многочлен

No.	English	German	French	Russian
P 975	**polynomial,** word, term function <of a polynomial algebra> <UA>	Polynom *n*, Wort *n*, Term *m*	polynôme *m*	слово
	polynomial <AN>	*s.* E 262		
P 976	**polynomial algebra,** free commutative algebra <in one (1), . . ., *n* indeterminate[s]> <AL>	Polynomalgebra *f*, freie kommutative Algebra *f* <in einer (1), . . ., *n* Unbestimmten>	algèbre *f* de (des) polynômes, algèbre polynomiale <à une (1), . . ., *n* indéterminée[s]>	алгебра полиномов (многочленов), свободная коммутативная алгебра <относительно (от) одного (1-го) неизвестного, от одной переменной, . . ., от *n* неизвестных (переменных)>
P 977	**polynomial algebra,** algebra of words <UA>	Polynomalgebra *f*, Wörteralgebra *f*	algèbre *f* de[s] polynômes	алгебра слов
P 978	**polynomial approximation,** approximation by polynomials <AX>	Approximation *f* durch Polynome, Approximation mittels Polynomen	approximation *f* polynomiale	аппроксимация (приближение) полиномами, полиномиальная аппроксимация, полиномиальное приближение
P 979	**polynomial arranged in descending powers** <AL>	nach fallenden (abnehmenden) Potenzen geordnetes Polynom *n*	polynôme *m* ordonné par rapport aux puissances décroissantes, polynôme ordonné suivant les puissances décroissantes	многочлен, упорядоченный по убывающим степеням
P 980	**polynomial convexity** <FT>	Polynomkonvexität *f*	convexité *f* polynomiale	полиномиальная выпуклость
P 981	**polynomial distribution,** multinomial distribution <ST>	[Bernoullische] Polynomialverteilung *f*, polynomiale (multinomiale, polynomische) Verteilung *f*, Multinomialverteilung *f*	distribution *f* multinomiale (polynomiale)	полиномиальное (мультиномиальное) распределение
P 982	**polynomial divisor** <AL>	Polynomteiler *m*	diviseur *m* polynomial	многочленный делитель
	polynomial domain <AL>	*s.* P 1009		
P 983	**polynomial equation** <AL>	polynomische (mehrgliedrige) Gleichung *f*	équation *f* polynomiale (polynôme)	многочленное уравнение
	polynomial equation <AL>	*s. a.* A 433		
	polynomial expansion <AL, DI>	*s.* M 976		
P 984	**polynomial factorization** <AL>	Faktorzerlegung *f* von Polynomen	décomposition *f* de polynômes	разложение многочленов на множители
	polynomial form <AL>	*s.* P 973		
P 985	**polynomial function** <AL>	Polynomfunktion *f*, ganze rationale Funktion *f*, ganz[-]rationale Funktion, Polynom *n*	fonction *f* polynomiale (polynôme), fonction-polynôme *f*	полиномиальная функция, полином
P 986	**polynomial game** <TG>	Polynomialspiel *n*	jeu *m* polynomial	полиномиальная игра
P 987	**polynomial homomorphism** <of a subgroup of $GL(n)$> <AL>	Polynomhomomorphismus *m*	homomorphisme *m* polynomial	многочленный гомоморфизм
P 988	**polynomial ideal,** ideal of polynomials <AL>	Polynomideal *n*, // Modul *m*	idéal *m* de polynômes, idéal polynomial	многочленный (полиномиальный) идеал
P 989	**polynomial identity** <AL>	Polynomidentität *f*	identité *f* polynomiale	полиномиальное тождество
	polynomial indecomposable into factors <AL>	*s.* I 1042		
P 990	**polynomial indecomposable into factors with integral coefficients** <AL>	ganzzahlig unzerlegbares Polynom *n*	polynôme *m* intégralement indécomposable	целочисленно неразложимый многочлен
P 991	**polynomial indecomposable into factors with rational coefficients** <AL>	rationalzahlig unzerlegbares Polynom *n*	polynôme *m* rationnellement irréductible	рационально неприводимый многочлен
P 992	**polynomial in several indeterminates** <AL>	Polynom *n* in mehreren Unbestimmten	polynôme *m* à plusieurs indéterminées	многочлен от многих переменных (неизвестных)
P 993	**polynomial invariant** <AL>	Polynominvariante *f*	invariant *m* polynomial	полиномиальный инвариант
P 994	**polynomial in *x* with coefficients in *A*** <AL>	Polynom *n* in *x* mit Koeffizienten in *A*	expression *f* polynomiale en *x* à coefficients dans *A*	полином от *x* с коэффициентами в *A*
P 995	**polynomial kernel** <IE>	Polynomkern *m*	noyau *m* polynomial	многочленное (полиномиальное) ядро
P 996	**polynomially convex hull** <FT>	polynomkonvexe Hülle *f*	enveloppe *f* polynomialement convexe	полиномиально выпуклая оболочка
P 997	**polynomially convex set** <FT>	polynomkonvexe Menge *f*	ensemble *m* polynomialement convexe	полиномиально выпуклое множество
P 998	**polynomial map** <AL>	Polynomabbildung *f*, polynomiale Abbildung *f*	application *f* polynomiale	полиномиальное отображение (преобразование)
P 999	**polynomial matrix,** polynomial with matrix coefficients; lambda-matrix, λ-matrix <AL>	Polynommatrix *f*; λ-Matrix *f*, Lambda-Matrix *f* <über *K*>	matrice *f* polynomiale (polynôme); λ-matrice *f*, lambda-matrice *f*	многочленная матрица; λ-матрица, ламбда-матрица
P 1000	**polynomial model** <ST>	Polynommodell *n*	modèle *m* polynomial	полиномиальная модель
P 1001	**polynomial module,** module over a polynomial ring <AL>	Modul *m* über einem Polynomring	module *m* sur un anneau de polynômes	модуль над кольцом многочленов
P 1002	**polynomial of best approximation,** poly-	Polynom *n* bester Approximation, Polynom	polynôme *m* de meilleure approximation	[алгебраический] многочлен наилучшего при-

and still: P 1002	nomial of least deviation <AX>	kleinster Abweichung (Nullabweichung)		ближения, многочлен наименьшего отклонения
P 1003	**polynomial of Cayley-Hamilton,** Cayley-Hamilton polynomial <MD>	Hamilton-Cayleysches Polynom *n*	polynôme *m* de Hamilton-Cayley	многочлен Гамильтона-Кэли
	polynomial of least deviation <AX>	*s.* P 1002		
P 1004	**polynomial operation** <of an algebra> <UA>	Polynomoperation *f*	opération *f* polynôme	полиномиальная операция
P 1005	**polynomial operator** <AL>	Polynomoperator *m*	opérateur *m* polynôme	многочленный оператор
P 1006	**polynomial over *R*,** polynomial with coefficients in *R* <AL>	Polynom *n* über *R*	polynôme *m* à coefficients dans *R*	многочлен над кольцом *R*
P 1007	**polynomial polyhedron** <FT>	Polynompolyeder *n*	polyèdre *m* polynomial	полиномиальный полиэдр
	polynomial regression <ST>	*s.* P 62		
P 1008	**polynomial representation** <AL, AN>	Polynomdarstellung *f*	représentation *f* polynomiale	полиномиальное представление
P 1009	**polynomial ring,** ring of polynomials; polynomial domain <over *K*> <AL>	Polynomring *m*, Polynombereich *m*	anneau *m* des (de) polynômes	кольцо многочленов (полиномов)
P 1010	**polynomial ring over a field** <in one, . . ., *n* indeterminate[s]> <AL>	Polynomring *m* <in einer, . . ., *n* Unbestimmten> über einem Körper	anneau *m* de polynômes <à une (1), . . ., *n* indéterminée[s]> à coefficients dans un corps	кольцо многочленов <относительно (от) одного (1-го) неизвестного, . . ., *n* неизвестных> над полем
P 1011	**polynomial solution** <DE, FD, GN>	Polynomlösung *f*	solution *f* polynomiale	полиномиальное решение
P 1012	**polynomial symbol** <UA>	Polynomsymbol *n*	symbole *m* polynomial	полиномиальный символ
P 1013	**polynomial trend,** parabolic trend of *k*-th order <ST>	polynomialer Trend *m*, parabolischer Trend *k*-ten Grades	tendance *f* polynomiale (parabolique d'ordre *k*)	полиномиальный тренд, параболический тренд порядка *k*
P 1014	**polynomial valuation** <AL>	Polynomialbewertung *f*	valuation *f* polynomiale	полиномиальная норма
P 1015	**polynomial-valued** <AL, AN>	polynomwertig	à valeurs polynomiales	полиномиальнозначный
P 1016	**polynomial which has a unit as highest coefficient** <AL>	Polynom *n* mit einer Einheit als höchstem Koeffizienten	polynôme *m* unitaire	унитарный многочлен; многочлен, который имеет в качестве старшего коэффициента обратимый элемент
	polynomial with coefficients in R <AL>	*s.* P 1006		
	polynomial with matrix coefficients <AL>	*s.* P 999		
P 1017	**polynomial without affect,** affectless polynomial <AL>	affektloses (affektfreies) Polynom *n*, Polynom ohne Affekt	polynôme *m* sans affect	полином без аффекта
P 1018	**polynomial without constant term** <AL>	Polynom *n* ohne Absolutglied	polynome *m* sans terme constant	многочлен без свободного члена
P 1019	**polyomino** <figure consisting of a number of squares> <GE>	Polyomino *n*	polyomino *m*	полиомино
P 1020	**polyradius** <FT>	Polyradius *m*	polyrayon *m*	полирадиус
	polytrope <GE>	*s.* P 1021		
P 1021	**polytropic curve (line),** polytrope <GE>	polytropische Kurve (Linie) *f*, Polytrope *f*	courbe (ligne) *f* polytropique, polytrope *f*	политропическая кривая (линия), политропная кривая (линия), политропа
P 1022	**polyword** <GR>	Polywort *n*	poly-mot *m*	полислово
P 1023	**polyzonal curve** <GE>	Polyzonalkurve *f*, Vielgürtelkurve *f* <Cayley>	courbe *f* polyzonale	полизональная кривая
P 1024	**Pompey['s] theorem** <on the triangle> <EG>	Pompeiusscher Satz *m*	théorème *m* de Pompée	теорема Помпея
P 1025	**Poncelet['s] formula** <DI, NU>	Formel *f* von Poncelet, Ponceletsche Formel	formule *f* de Poncelet	формула Понселе
P 1026	**Poncelet['s] polygon** <GE>	Ponceletsches Polygon *n*	polygone *m* de Poncelet	многогранник Понселе
	Poncelet['s] principle of continuity >GE>	*s.* C 2196		
	Poncelet-Steiner construction <GE>	*s.* S 1713		
P 1027	**Poncelet['s] theorem** <for a cubic> <AG, PJ>	Satz *m* von Poncelet, Poncelets Satz	théorème *m* de Poncelet	теорема Понселе
P 1028	**Poncelet['s] theorem** <for a conic> <AY>	Ponceletscher Schließungssatz *m*, Poncelets Satz *m*	théorème *m* de Poncelet, théorème dit « de fermeture » de Poncelet	теорема Понселе
P 1029	**pontoon** <EG>	Keilstumpf *m*, Ponton *m*	ponton *m*, coin *m* tronqué	усеченный клин
P 1030	**Pontryagin['s] class** <AT>	Pontrjaginsche Klasse *f*	classe *f* caractéristique de Pontrjagin, classe de Pontrjagin	класс Понтрягина
P 1031	**Pontryagin['s] duality** <AL>	Pontrjagin-Dualität *f*	dualité *f* de Pontrjagin	двойственность Понтрягина
P 1032	**Pontryagin['s] duality theorem,** duality theorem <for topological groups> <AL>	Pontrjaginscher (Pontrjagins) Dualitätssatz *m*, Dualitätssatz	théorème *m* de Pontrjagin	теорема двойственности Понтрягина
P 1033	**Pontryagin['s] duality theory** <of topological groups> <AL>	Pontrjaginsche Dualitätstheorie *f*, Dualitätstheorie	théorie *f* de la dualité de Pontrjagin	теория двойственности Понтрягина
P 1034	**Pontryagin['s] maximum principle** <PG>	Pontrjaginsches Maximumprinzip *n*	principe *m* [du] maximum de Pontrjagin	принцип максимума Понтрягина

P 1035	**Pontryagin['s] number** <AT>	Pontrjaginsche Zahl *f*	nombre *m* caractéristique de Pontrjagin, nombre de Pontrjagin	число Понтрягина
P 1036	**Pontryagin['s] polynomial** <AT>	Pontrjaginsches Polynom *n*	polynôme *m* de Pontrjagin	многочлен Понтрягина
P 1037	**Pontryagin['s] product** <AT>	Pontrjaginsches Produkt *n*	produit *m* de Pontrjagin	понтрягинское произведение, произведение Понтрягина
P 1038	**Pontryagin['s] ring** <AT>	Pontrjaginscher Ring *m*	anneau *m* de Pontrjagin	кольцо Понтрягина
P 1039	**Pontryagin['s] square** <AT>	Pontrjaginsches Quadrat *n*	carré *m* de Pontrjagin	понтрягинский квадрат
P 1040	**pooled error** <ER, ST>	zusammengefaßter Fehler *m*	erreur *f* combinée	объединенная ошибка, ошибка группировки
	pooled sum of squares <ST>	*s.* D 364		
P 1041	**pooling** <of data> <ST>	Zusammenfassen *n* <von Daten>	réunion *f* <de données>	группировка <данных>
	population <ST>	*s.* P 164		
	population game <TG>	*s.* C 2415		
P 1042	**population genetics** <ST>	Populationsgenetik *f*, Bevölkerungsgenetik *f*	génétique *f* démographique	генетика популяции (населения)
P 1043	**population mean,** true mean <ST>	Mittelwert *m* der Grundgesamtheit, wahrer Mittelwert, wahres Mittel *n*	moyenne *f* de la population, moyenne de l'univers, moyenne vraie	среднее значение совокупности (популяции), истинное среднее [значение]
P 1044	**population parameter,** parameter of population <ST>	Populationsparameter *m*, Parameter *m* der Grundgesamtheit, Gesamtheitsparameter *m*	paramètre *m* de la population	параметр [генеральной] совокупности, параметр популяции
P 1045	**population statistics** <concerned with human population> <ST>	Bevölkerungsstatistik *f*	statistique *f* démographique	статистика народонаселения (населения), демографическая статисика
P 1046	**population statistics** <ST>	Populationsstatistik *f*	statistique *f* des populations	статистика популяций
P 1047	**porism** <LO>	Porisma *n*	porisme *m*	поризма
P 1048	**porism[at]ic equation** <AL, NU>	porismatische Gleichung *f*	équation *f* porismatique	поризматическое уравнение
	poset <SE>	*s.* 1. P 231; 2. P 1230		
P 1049	**posing of a problem,** formulation of a problem; formulation of the question <GN>	Problemstellung *f*, Aufgabenstellung *f*; Fragestellung *f*	position *f* d'un problème, problème *m*; formulation *f* de la question	постановка задачи; постановка вопроса
P 1050	**position,** line of application <of a vector> <VT>	Trägergerade *f*	droite *f* portante, support *m*	прямая-носитель, несущая прямая, линия действия
P 1051	**positional game,** extensive game, game in extensive form <TG>	Positionsspiel *n*, Spiel *n* in extensiver (erweiterter) Form	jeu *m* de position, jeu positionnel (extensif, en forme extensive)	позиционная игра, игра в развернутой форме, развернутая игра
P 1052	**positional notation** <of a number> <NT>	Darstellung *f* im Stellenwertsystem (Positionssystem)	notation *f* dans le système de position	позиционное представление, представление в позиционной системе счисления
	positional notation <NT>	*s.* P 625		
	positional numeration system to basis (radix) 60 <AR, NT>	*s.* S 721		
P 1053	**position function,** function of the position [of the point], local function <AN>	Ortsfunktion *f*, Koordinatenfunktion *f*	fonction *f* de lieu (position), fonction des coordonnées	функция точки (координат, места)
P 1054	**position line** <in central perspective> <DS>	Standlinie *f*	ligne *f* de position	
	position of a local maximum <DI>	*s.* P 1056		
	position of a local minimum <DI>	*s.* P 1057		
P 1055	**position of an extremum** <of a function> <DI>	Extremalstelle *f*, Extremstelle *f*	point *m* où la fonction admet un extrémum	точка, в которой функция принимает экстремум
P 1056	**position of a relative maximum,** position of a local maximum <DI>	relative (lokale) Maximalstelle *f*	point *m* (position *f*) où la fonction admet un maximum relatif (local)	точка, в которой функция принимает относительный (локальный) максимум
P 1057	**position of a relative minimum,** position of a local minimum <DI>	relative (lokale) Minimalstelle *f*	point *m* (position *f*) où la fonction admet un minimum relatif (local)	точка, в которой функция принимает относительный (локальный) минимум
	position of maximum <DI>	*s.* M 269		
	position of minimum <DI>	*s.* M 613		
P 1058	**position parameter,** location parameter, parameter of position <ST>	Lageparameter *m*, Stellungsparameter *m*	paramètre *m* de position	параметр положения
P 1059	**position plane** <in central perspective> <DS>	Grundrißebene *f*, Standebene *f*	plan *m* de position	предметная плоскость
P 1060	**position point,** standpoint <in central perspective> <DS>	Standpunkt *m*		основание центра проекций, основание глаза
	position rank <NT>	*s.* O 276		
	position vector <GE>	*s.* R 42		
P 1061	**positive affine mapping,** direct affine transformation <AY>	affine Abbildung *f* mit positiver Determinante	affinité *f* à déterminante positive	положительное аффинное отображение

P 1062	**positive analytic function** <SE>	positiv-analytische Mengenfunktion (Funktion) *f*	fonction *f* analytique positive <d'une famille infinie d'ensembles>	положительная аналитическая функция множеств
P 1063	**positive complex,** cochain complex <HA>	positiver Komplex *m*, Kokettenkomplex *m*, Cokettenkomplex *m*	complexe *m* positif	положительной (коцепной) комплекс
P 1064	**positive component** <AL>	Positivitätskomponente *f*	composante *f* positive	компонента положительности
P 1065	**positive cone** <in a linear space> <FA>	Positivitätskegel *m*	cône *m* positif	конус положительности
P 1066	**positive correlation,** direct correlation <ST>	positive Korrelation *f*	corrélation *f* positive (directe)	положительная корреляция
	positive cycle <AG>	*s.* E 33		
P 1067	**positive definite eigenvalue problem** <MD>	positiv definite Eigenwertaufgabe *f*	problème *m* aux valeurs propres défini positif	положительно определенная задача на собственные значения
	positive definite Hermitian form <AL>	*s.* P 1078		
P 1068	**positive definite inner product space** <AL>	Raum *m* mit positiv definitem innerem Produkt	espace *m* à produit scalaire défini positif	пространство с положительно определенным внутренним произведением
P 1069	**positive definite matrix,** positively definite matrix <MD>	positiv definite Matrix *f*	matrice *f* définie positive	положительно определенная матрица
P 1070	**positive definiteness** <AL, AN>	positive Definitheit *f*	propriété *f* d'être défini positif	положительная определенность
	positive definite quadratic form <AL>	*s.* P 1080		
	positive direction <GE, GN>	*s.* C 2575		
	positive element <AL, GR>	*s.* S 1893		
	positive excess <ST>	*s.* L 580		
P 1071	**positive existential sentence,** positive particular proposition <LO>	positives partikuläres Urteil *n*, partikulär bejahendes Urteil, bejahendes partikuläres Urteil	proposition *f* particulière positive	частноутвердительное суждение
	positive existential sentence <LO>	*s.* a. P 1095		
P 1072	**positive function,** strictly positive function <> 0> <AL, AN>	positive (strikt positive, echt positive, streng positive) Funktion *f*	fonction *f* positive (strictement positive)	положительная (строго положительная, существенно положительная, позитивная) функция
	positive homothety <GE>	*s.* D 557		
	positive integer <NT>	*s.* N 33		
P 1073	**positive integral power of a prime** <NT>	primäre Zahl *f*, Primzahlpotenz *f* mit positivem Exponenten	nombre *m* primaire	степень простого числа с положительным показателем
	positive kernel <IE>	*s.* P 1079		
	positive kurtosis <ST>	*s.* L 580		
P 1074	**positive linear operator,** positive operator <of a partially ordered linear space> <AL>	Ordnungshomomorphismus *m*, positive lineare Abbildung *f*	opérateur *m* linéaire positif	положительный [линейный] оператор
P 1075	**positive logic** <LO>	positive Logik *f*	logique *f* positive	положительная логика, логика без отрицания
P 1076	**positively definite eigenvalue problem** <DE>	positiv definite Eigenwertaufgabe *f*, positiv definites Eigenwertproblem *n*	problème *m* aux valeurs singulières (caractéristiques, critiques, propres) défini positif	положительно определенная задача на собственные значения
P 1077	**positively definite Hermitian endomorphism** <AL>	positiv definiter hermitescher Endomorphismus *m*	endomorphisme *m* hermitien positif et non dégénéré	невырожденный положительный эндоморфизм
P 1078	**positively definite Hermitian form,** positive definite Hermitian form <AL>	positiv definite hermitesche Form *f*	forme *f* hermitienne positive non dégénérée, forme hermitienne définie positive	положительная невырожденная эрмитова форма
P 1079	**positively definite kernel,** positive kernel <IE>	positiv definiter Kern *m*	noyau *m* défini positif	положительно определенное ядро
	positively definite matrix <MD>	*s.* P 1069		
P 1080	**positively definite quadratic form,** positive definite quadratic form <AL>	positiv definite quadratische Form *f*	forme *f* quadratique strictement (définie) positive	положительно определенная квадратичная форма
P 1081	**positively definite sequence of numbers** <SS>	positiv definite Zahlenfolge *f*	suite *f* de nombres définie positive	положительно определенная последовательность чисел
P 1082	**positively definite variational problem** <VA>	positiv definites Variationsproblem *n*	problème *m* variationnel défini positif	положительно определенная вариационная задача
P 1083	**positively homogeneous functional** <on a linear space> <FA>	positiv homogenes Funktional *n*	fonctionnelle *f* positivement homogène	положительно однородный функционал
P 1084	**positively oriented base** <of a vector space> <AG, GE>	positiv orientierte Basis *f*, Rechtssystem *n*	base *f* positive (directe, orientée positivement, positivement orientée)	правый упорядоченный базис
P 1085	**positively related** <simplex and a face> <AT>	mit Inzidenzzahl +1	à coefficient d'incidence +1	с коэффициентом инцидентности +1
P 1086	**positively related base** <AL, GE>	gleich[ ]orientierte Basis *f*	base *f* de sens direct	базис одной ориентации, эквивалентный (одноименный, одинаково ориентированный) базис

No.	English	German	French	Russian
P 1087	**positively related system of coordinates** <GE>	gleichsinnig orientiertes Koordinatensystem *n*	système *m* de coordonnées de sens direct	система координат одной ориентации
P 1088	**positively semi[-] definite eigenvalue problem** <DE>	positiv semidefinite Eigenwertaufgabe *f*, positiv semidefinites Eigenwertproblem *n*	problème *m* aux valeurs singulières (caractéristiques, critiques, propres) semi-défini positif	положительно полуопределенная задача на собственные значения
P 1089	**positively semi-definite variational problem** <VA>	positiv semidefinites Variationsproblem *n*	problème *m* variationnel semi-défini positif	положительно полуопределенная вариационная задача
P 1090	**positively stable solution** <DE>	positiv stabile Lösung *f*	solution *f* positivement stable	положительно устойчивое решение
	positive matrix <MD>	*s.* N 424/5		
	positive operator <AL>	*s.* P 1074		
P 1091	**positive ordering** <of a simplex> <TO>	positive Umlaufung *f*	ordre *m* positif	положительный обход
P 1092	**positive part,** set of positive elements, positivity domain <of an ordered group *or* ring> <AL>	Positivbereich *m*	ensemble *m* des éléments positifs, partie *f* positive	область положительных (позитивных) элементов, положительный конус
P 1093	**positive part** <of an element in an l-group *or* space> <AL, FA>	positiver Teil *m*, Positivteil *m*	partie *f* positive	положительная часть, компонента положительности
P 1094	**positive part** <of a Hermitian operator> <FA>	Positivteil *m*	partie *f* positive	положительная часть
P 1095	**positive particular proposition,** affirmative particular proposition, positive existential sentence <LO>	partikulär bejahendes Urteil *n*, affirmative Existentialaussage *f*	proposition *f* particulière affirmative	частное утвердительное суждение
	positive particular proposition <LO>	*s. a.* P 1071		
	positive proposition <LO>	*s.* A 381		
	positive real number <NT>	*s.* A 962		
P 1096	**positive recurrent state** <SP>	positiv-rekurrenter Zustand *m*	état *m* récurrent positif	положительное возвратное состояние
P 1097	**positive root** <AL>	positive Wurzel *f*, // wahre Wurzel	racine *f* positive, // racine vraie	положительный корень
	positive rotation <EG>	*s.* R 1157		
P 1098	**positive semi[-]definite form** <AL>	positiv semidefinite Form *f*	forme *f* positive (semi-définie positive)	положительная форма, неотрицательная (неотрицательно определенная) форма
P 1099	**positive semi[-]definite Hermitian endomorphism** <AL>	positiv semidefiniter hermitescher Endomorphismus *m*	endomorphisme *m* hermitien positif	положительный эндоморфизм
	positive semi[-]definite matrix <MD>	*s.* N 424/5		
	positive sense <GE, GN>	*s.* C 2575		
P 1100	**positive series,** series of positive terms <SS>	Reihe *f* mit positiven (nur positiven) Gliedern	série *f* à termes positifs, série positive	знакоположительный ряд, ряд с положительными членами
	positive sign <AR>	*s.* P 688		
	positive similitude <GE>	*s.* D 557		
P 1101	**positive variation,** upper variation <of a function *or* set function> <AN>	obere (positive) Variation *f*	variation *f* positive	положительная (верхняя) вариация
	positivity domain <AL>	*s.* P 1092		
P 1102	**Post['s] algebra, Post-algebra** <UA>	Post-Algebra *f*, Postsche Algebra *f*, Postalgebra *f*	algèbre *f* de Post	алгебра Поста
P 1103	**Post['s] completeness theorem** <LO>	Postscher Vollständigkeitssatz *m*	théorème *m* de complétude de Post	теорема полноты Поста
P 1104	**posterior defect** <of a kernel> <IE>	hinterer Defekt *m*	défaut *m* postérieur	задний дефект
P 1105	**posterior distribution,** a posteriori distribution, distribution a posteriori <ST>	A-posteriori-Verteilung *f*, Aposterioriverteilung *f*	distribution *f* à postériori, distribution a posteriori	апостериорное распределение
P 1106	**posterior null solution** <IE>	hintere Nullösung *f*	solution *f* nulle postérieure	заднее нулевое решение
P 1107	**posterior probability,** a posteriori probability, inverse probability, probability a posteriori <ST>	A-posteriori-Wahrscheinlichkeit *f*, Aposterioriwahrscheinlichkeit *f*, inverse (umgekehrte, aposteriorische) Wahrscheinlichkeit *f*, Rückschlußwahrscheinlichkeit *f*, Wahrscheinlichkeit a posteriori, Endwahrscheinlichkeit *f*	probabilité *f* à postériori, probabilité a posteriori	апостериорная вероятность, вероятность a posteriori
P 1108	**postliminal Banach algebra** <AL>	nachbegrenzte Banachsche Algebra *f*	algèbre *f* de Banach postliminaire	
P 1109	**postliminal operator** <FA>	nachbegrenzter Operator *m*	opérateur *m* postliminaire	
P 1110	**post-multiplication** <NT>	Multiplikation *f* von rechts nach links	multiplication *f* <de nombres> en commençant par le chiffre des unités	умножение начиная справа <с низшего разряда>
	post[-]multiplication <AL>	*s.* R 1211		
	post[-]multiplying <AL>	*s.* R 1211		
P 1111	**Postnikov['s] base** <CA, TO>	Postnikov-Basis *f*, Postnikovbasis *f*	base *f* de Postnikov	база Постникова
P 1112	**Postnikov['s] invariant** <TO>	Postnikov-Invariante *f*	invariant *m* de Postnikov	инвариант Постникова

No.	English	German	French	Russian
P 1113	**Postnikov['s] system** <AL>	Postnikov-System *n*	système *m* de Postnikov	система Постникова
P 1114	**Post['s] normal system** <FO>	Postscher Algorithmus *m*, Algorithmus im Sinne von Post, normales System *n*	algorithme (système) *m* de Post, algorithme normal [dans le sens de Post]	исчисление Поста, нормальная система Поста
P 1115	**post-optimal [optimization] problem** <PG>	postoptimales Optimierungsproblem *n*, postoptimale Aufgabe *f*, po-Aufgabe *f*	problème *m* [d'optimisation] post-optimal	
P 1116	**Post['s] problem** <FO>	Postsches Problem *n*	problème *m* de Post	проблема Поста
P 1117	**post-subscript** <GN>	rechter unterer Index *m*	indice *m* inférieur droit	правый нижний индекс
P 1118	**post-superscript** <GN>	rechter oberer Index *m*	indice *m* supérieur droit	правый верхний индекс
P 1119	**postulate** <GN>	Postulat *n*, Forderung *f*	postulat *m*, demande *f*	постулат
	postulate of Bertrand <NT>	*s.* B 223		
P 1120	**postulate of infinity,** axiom of infinity, infinity postulate (axiom) <GE>	Unendlichkeitspostulat *n*, Abtragbarkeitspostulat *n*, Unendlichkeitsaxiom *n*, Abtragbarkeitsaxiom *n*	postulat (axiome) *m* de l'infini	постулат (аксиома) бесконечности
	postulates independent as to consequence <FO>	*s.* I 309		
P 1121	**postulation** <*also* of a curve *or* variety> <AG, LO>	Postulation *f*	postulation *f*	постулирование
	postulational method <MM>	*s.* A 1272		
	postulation formula <AG, AL>	*s.* C 550		
	potency <SE>	*s.* C 123		
P 1122	**potency class,** exponential, class of all subsets <of a class> <SE>	Potenzklasse *f*	classe *f* de toutes les parties	класс всех подмножеств, булеан
P 1123	**potential** <in transport programming> <GP, PG>	Potential *n* <der Basis *B*>	potentiel *m*	потенциал
	potential <FT, PO>	*s.* H 99		
	potential difference <GP>	*s.* T 130		
	potential equation <PO>	*s.* L 75		
	potential field <VT>	*s.* I 1070		
	potential function <FT, PO>	*s.* H 99		
P 1124	**potential infinity,** virtual infinity, constructive infinity <FO, SE>	potentielles Unendliches (Unendlich) *n*, uneigentliches (synkategorematisches) Unendlich	infinité *f* potentielle, infini *m* improprement dit, infini potentiel, infinitude *f* constructive	потенциальная (конструктивная) бесконечность
	potential kernel <PO>	*s.* N 210		
P 1125	**potentially infinite** <FO>	potentiell unendlich	potentiellement infini	потенциально бесконечный
	potential range <SE, TO>	*s.* R 123		
P 1126	**potential-theoretical** <PO>	potentialtheoretisch	en (de, au sens de) théorie du potentiel	теоретико-потенциальный
P 1127	**potential theory** <PO>	Potentialtheorie *f*	théorie *f* du potentiel	теория потенциала
	potential transform <IT>	*s.* P 834		
P 1128	**Pothenot['s] problem** <EG>	Pothenotsche Aufgabe *f*, Pothenotsches Problem *n*	problème *m* de Pothenot	задача Потенота (Потенота-Снеллиуса)
P 1129	**power** <*a* [raised] to the power *n*, *a* to the *n*-th power> <AR>	Potenz *f* <*a* hoch *n*>	puissance *f* <*a* puissance *n*, *a* à la puissance *n*, puissance ennième (*n*-e) de *a*>	степень
P 1130	**power** <of a line with respect to a circle> <AY>	Potenz *f* <einer Geraden bezüglich eines Kreises>	puissance *f* <d'une droite par rapport à un cercle>	степень <прямой относительно окружности>
P 1131	**power** <of a point with respect to a circle *or* sphere> <AY>	Potenz *f* <eines Punktes bezüglich eines Kreises *oder* einer Kugel>	puissance *f* <d'un point par rapport à un cercle *ou* à une sphère>	степень <точки относительно окружности *или* сферы>
P 1132	**power,** strength <of a test> <ST>	Trennschärfe *f*, Macht *f*, Güte *f*, Stärke *f*, Strenge *f* <eines Tests>, Teststärke *f*	puissance *f* <d'un test>	мощность <критерия>
	power <AL, AR>	*s.* E 730		
	power <AY>	*s.* P 1146		
	power <FU>	*s.* P 1142		
	power <SE>	*s.* C 123		
	power <ST>	*s.* P 1140		
P 1133	**power-associative algebra** <AL>	potenzassoziative Algebra *f*	algèbre *f* à puissances associatives	алгебра с ассоциативными степенями
P 1134	**power-associative loop** <AL>	potenzassoziative Loop *f*	loop *m* à puissances associatives	лупа с ассоциативными степенями
	power axiom <SE>	*s.* A 1289		
P 1135	**power character** <AB>	Potenzcharakter *m*	caractère *m* de puissance	степенной характер
P 1136	**power chart,** power scale <NO>	Potenzleiter *f*; Potenzskala *f*	échelle *f* en puissance	степенная шкала
	power density <SP>	*s.* S 1396		
P 1137	**power efficiency** <ST>	Testeffizienz *f*	efficacité *f* du test	эффективность критерия
	power exponent <AL, AR>	*s.* E 730		
P 1138	**powerful test** <ST>	trennscharfer Test *m*	test *m* puissant	мощный критерий
P 1139	**power function** <AN>	Potenzfunktion *f*	fonction *f* puissance	степенная функция
P 1140	**power function,** power <ST>	Machtfunktion *f*, Gütefunktion *f*, Schärfefunktion *f*, Powerfunktion *f*, Macht *f*, Schärfe *f*	fonction *f* puissance, puissance *f*	функция мощности, мощность
	power function <SP>	*s.* S 1401		

No.	English	German	French	Russian
P 1141	**power function with exponent *n*** <AL, AN>	Funktion *f* der *n*-ten Potenz, Funktion *n*-te Potenz	fonction *f* puissance d'exposant *n*, fonction puissance *n*-e	степенная функция с показателем *n*
P 1142	**power index,** power <of a factorial function, *y*> <FU>	Exponent *m*, Faktoriellenexponent *m*	exposant *m*	показатель
P 1143	**power mean** <ST>	Potenzmittel *n*	moyenne *f* puissance	степенное среднее, среднее степенное
P 1144	**power nonresidue** <NT>	Potenznichtrest *m*	non-résidu *m*, non-reste *m*	степенной невычет
	power of a prime number <NT>	*s.* P 1330		
	power of a relation <SE>	*s.* R 765		
P 1145	**power of the continuum,** cardinal of the continuum, continuum power <SE>	Mächtigkeit *f* des Kontinuums	puissance *f* (cardinal *m*) du continu	мощность континуума
P 1146	**power of the inversion,** power <AY>	Potenz *f* [der Inversion]	puissance *f* [de l'inversion]	коэффициент [инверсии], степень [инверсии]
P 1147	**power of the set of natural numbers** <SE>	Mächtigkeit *f* der Menge der natürlichen Zahlen	puissance *f* du dénombrable	мощность множества натуральных чисел
P 1148	**power remainder (residue)** <NT>	Potenzrest *m*	résidu *m* de puissance	степенной вычет
	power residue of *m* of the *n*-th order <NT>	*s.* N 233		
	power residue symbol of the *n*-th order <NT>	*s.* N 746		
	power residue of the second order of *p* <NT>	*s.* Q 43		
P 1149	**power residue symbol** <NT>	Potenzrestsymbol *n*	symbole *m* de puissance	символ степенного вычета
	power scale <NO>	*s.* P 1136		
P 1150	**power series,** ascending power series <SS>	Potenzreihe *f*	série *f* entière, série de (en) puissances	степенной ряд
P 1151	**power series expansion** <AN>	Potenzreihenentwicklung *f*, Entwicklung *f* in eine Potenzreihe	développement *m* en série entière	разложение в степенной ряд
P 1152	**power series method** <AN>	Methode *f* des Potenzreihenansatzes, Potenzreihenansatz *m*	méthode *f* des séries entières	метод степенных рядов
P 1153	**power series representation** <AN>	Potenzreihendarstellung *f*	représentation *f* en forme d'une série entière	представление в виде степенного ряда
P 1154	**power series ring,** ring of power series <AL>	Potenzreihenring *m*	anneau *m* de séries de puissances	кольцо степенных рядов
P 1155	**power series statement** <AN>	Potenzreihenansatz *m*	expression *f* en série entière	выражение в виде степенного ряда
P 1156	**power set,** power-set, set of all subsets <SE>	Potenzmenge *f*	ensemble *m* des parties, ensemble de tous les sous-ensembles, ensemble de toutes les parties, booléin *m*, simplexe *m*, famille *f* de parties <d'un ensemble>	совокупность подмножеств, булеан множества, множество-степень, множество всех подмножеств, степень множества, семейство частей множества
	power-set axiom <SE>	*s.* A 1289		
P 1157	**power set functor** <CA>	Potenzmengenfunktor *m*	foncteur *m* ensemble des parties	функтор «степень множества»
P 1158	**power spectrum** <ST>	Potenzspektrum *n*	spectre *m* exponentiel	степенной спектр
	power spectrum <SP>	*s.* S 1401		
P 1159	**power with a natural exponent** <AL>	natürliche Potenz *f*, Potenz mit ganzem positivem Exponenten	puissance *f* naturelle	степень с целым положительным показателем
P 1160	**power with an integral exponent** <AL, AR>	ganzzahlige (ganze) Potenz *f*, Potenz mit ganzzahligem Exponenten	puissance *f* entière	степень с целым показателем
P 1161	***p*-primary component** <of a group> <GR, NT>	*p*-primäre Komponente *f*	composante *f p*-primaire, *p*-composant *m*	*p*-примарная компонента, *p*-компонента, примарная по *p* компонента
P 1162	**p-primary ideal** <AL>	p-primäres Ideal *n*	idéal *m* p-primaire	p-примарный идеал
P 1163	***P*-primary object** <CA>	*P*-primäres Objekt *n*	objet *m P*-primaire	*P*-примарный объект
P 1164	**p-primary submodule** <AL>	p-primärer (zu dem Primideal p gehöriger primärer) Untermodul *m*	sous-module *m* p-primaire	p-примарный подмодуль; примарный подмодуль, принадлежащий простому идеалу p
P 1165	***p*-pure subgroup** <GR>	*p*-Servanzuntergruppe *f*	sous-groupe *m p*-pur	*p*-сервантная подгруппа
	***p*-quantile** <ST>	*s.* Q 81		
P 1166	***p*-rank** <of a group> <GR>	*p*-Rang *m*	*p*-rang *m*	*p*-ранг
P 1167	**preabelian category** <CA>	präabelsche Kategorie *f*	catégorie *f* préabélienne	предабелева категория
P 1168	**preabelian representation** <of a group> <RE>	präabelsche Darstellung *f*	représentation *f* préabélienne	предабелево представление
P 1169	**preadditive category,** Ab-category <CA>	präadditive Kategorie *f*, Ab-Kategorie *f*	catégorie *f* préadditive	преаддитивная категория
P 1170	**preaxiomatic** <FO>	präaxiomatisch	préaxiomatique	доаксиоматический
	precategory <CA>	*s.* D 412		
P 1171	**precede / to,** to be less <than>, to be under, to be included <in>, to be subelement <of>, to be contained <in> <$x \leqq y$> <SE>	vorangehen, enthalten sein <in>, kleiner oder gleich sein	être plus petit que ou au plus égal <à>, être avant [ou égal] <à>, être inférieur [ou égal] <à>, précéder	содержаться <в>, предшествовать, быть меньше или равно
P 1172	**precede / to,** to be smaller <$x < y$> <in an order relation> <SE>	vorangehen, kleiner sein <als>	être inférieur	подчиняться, быть меньше
	preceding <SE>	*s.* L 585		
	preceding element <SE>	*s.* E 2		
	precise tripleability theorem <CA>	*s.* B 160		

	precising <GN>	*s.* S 1850		
P 1173	**precision** <ST>	Wiederholungsgenauigkeit *f*, Präzision *f*	fidélité *f*, // précision *f*	точность, прецизионность
	pre-closed linear operator <FA>	*s.* C 839		
P 1174	**precompact linear mapping,** precompact mapping <FA>	präkompakte [lineare] Abbildung *f*	application *f* [linéaire] précompacte	предкомпактное [линейное] отображение
	precompact mapping <FA>	*s.* P 1174		
P 1175	**precompactness,** total boundedness <FA, TO>	Präkompaktheit *f*, Totalbeschränktheit *f*	précompacité *f*	предкомпактность, полная ограниченность
P 1176	**precompact set,** totally bounded set <of a topological linear space> <FA, TO>	präkompakte (totalbeschränkte) Menge *f*	ensemble *m* précompact (totalement borné)	предкомпактное (вполне ограниченное) множество
P 1177	**precompact space,** totally bounded space <FA, TO>	präkompakter (totalbeschränkter) Raum *m*	espace *m* précompact (totalement borné)	предкомпактное (вполне ограниченное) пространство
P 1178	**precongruence** <CA, UA>	Präkongruenz *f*	précongruence *f*	предконгруэнция
P 1179	**predecessor,** antecedent <FO, NT>	Vorgänger *m*	prédécesseur *m*, antécédent *m*	предшествующий элемент, предшественник
P 1180	**predecessor** <of a vertex> <GP>	Vorgänger *m*	précédent *m*, prédécesseur *m*	предшественник
P 1181	**predecessor function** <FO>	Vorgängerfunktion *f*	fonction *f* de prédécesseur	функция предшественника
	predicable property <LO>	*s.* P 1194		
P 1182	**predicate,** sentential function <LO>	Prädikat *n*, logische Funktion *f*, Attribut *n*	prédicat *m*, symbole *m* relationnel	предикат, логическая функция, сказуемое <суждения>
	predicate <LO>	*s. a.* P 1192		
P 1183	**predicate calculus,** functional calculus, quantification theory, predicate logic, quantificational logic, quantifier logic, calculus (logic) of quantifiers <LO>	Prädikatenkalkül *m*, Prädikatenlogik *f*, Funktionenkalkül *m*, Quantorenlogik *f*, Attributenkalkül *m*, Relationenkalkül *m*, PK, // Relativkalkül *m*, Kalkül *m* der Relative	calcul *m* des relations (prédicats), logique *f* fonctionnelle (des prédicats), calcul fonctionnel, logique des fonctions (fonctions propositionnelles)	исчисление предикатов, функциональное исчисление, логика предикатов, теория кванторов
P 1184	**predicate calculus of the third order,** functional calculus of the third order <LO>	Prädikatenkalkül *m* dritter Stufe	logique *f* du troisième ordre	исчисление предикатов третьего порядка
P 1851	**predicate calculus with identity** <LO>	Prädikatenkalkül *m* mit Identität, I-Kalkül *m*, Gleichungskalkül *m*	calcul *m* des prédicats avec identité	исчисление предикатов с равенством
	predicate calculus without identity <LO>	*s.* L 1076		
P 1186	**predicate constant** <LO>	Prädikatenkonstante *f*, individuelles Prädikat *n*	constante *f* de prédicat	индивидуальный предикат
P 1187	**predicate constant of second level,** second-level predicate constant <LO>	Prädikatenkonstante *f* zweiter Stufe, individuelles Prädikatenprädikat *n*	constante *f* de prédicat d'ordre deux (2)	индивидуальный предикат второго (2-го) порядка
	predicated variable <ST>	*s.* R 506		
	predicate logic <LO>	*s.* 1. F 349; 2. P 1183		
P 1188	**predicate of first level** <LO>	Prädikat *n* erster (der ersten) Stufe, Attribut *n* erster Stufe	prédicat *m* d'ordre un (1), prédicat de premier ordre	предикат первого (1-го) порядка
P 1189	**predicate of *n* arguments,** *n*-ary predicate, *n*-place predicate, *n*-adic predicate <LO>	*n*-stelliges Prädikat (Attribut) *n*	prédicat *m* à *n* arguments (variables, places), ion *m* à *n* places <Kleene>	*n*-арный (*n*-й) предикат, предикат от *n* переменных
	predicate of one argument <LO>	*s.* O 94		
	predicate of predicates (second level) <LO>	*s.* F 797		
P 1190	**predicate of three arguments,** triadic predicate, three-place predicate, three-term relation <LO>	dreistelliges Prädikat (Attribut) *n*, ternäre Relation *f*	prédicat *m* triadique, relation *f* ternaire	триадическое отношение
	predicate of two arguments <LO>	*s.* T 1096		
P 1191	**predicate symbol** <LO>	Prädikatzeichen *n*, Attributensymbol *n*, Prädikatensymbol *n*	symbole *m* de prédicat, symbole relationnel, prédicat *m*	предикатный символ, предикатная буква
P 1192	**predicate variable,** variable representing predicates, relation symbol, predicate <LO>	Prädikatenvariable *f*, P-Variable *f*	variable *f* de prédicat[s], proposition *f* variable, fonction (variable, expression) *f* prédicative, prédicat *m*	предикатное переменное, переменный символ для предикатов, предикатная переменная
	predicate with many argument places <LO>	*s.* M 891		
P 1193	**predicative definition** <LO>	prädikative Definition *f*	définition *f* prédicative	предикативное определение
P 1194	**predicative property,** predicable property <LO>	prädikative (prädikable) Eigenschaft *f*	propriété *f* prédicable	предикативное свойство
P 1195	**predicative proposition** <LO>	prädikative Aussage *f*	proposition *f* prédicative (attributive, d'inhérence)	предикативное высказывание
	predictand <ST>	*s.* R 487		
	prediction <SP>	*s.* F 458a		

P 1196	**prediction equation** <SP>	Vorhersagegleichung *f*	équation *f* de prévision	уравнение предсказания
P 1197	**prediction formula** <SP>	Vorhersageformel *f*	formule *f* de prévision	формула предсказания
	prediction function <SP>	*s.* P 1201		
P 1198	**prediction interval** <SP>	Vorhersageintervall *n*	intervalle *m* de prévision	интервал предсказания
P 1199	**prediction theorem** <SP>	Vorhersagesatz *m*, „prediction"-Satz *m*	théorème *m* de prédiction statistique	теорема прогнозирования
P 1200	**prediction theory** <SP>	Vorhersagetheorie *f*	théorie *f* de la prédiction statistique, théorie de la prédiction (prévision)	теория прогнозирования (прогнозов, предсказания)
P 1201	**predictor,** prediction function <SP>	Vorhersagefunktion *f*, Prädiktor *m*	fonction *f* de prévision (prédiction), prédicteur *m*	функция предсказания
P 1202	**predictor-corrector method,** mixed extrapolation and interpolation method <DE, NU>	gemischtes Extra-Interpolationsverfahren *n*, Prädiktor-Korrektor-Verfahren *n*, Prediktor-Korrektor-Verfahren *n*	méthode *f* de prédiction-correction, méthode « prédicteur-correcteur », méthode à deux pas	процесс (метод) численного интегрирования типа прогноза и коррекции
	predictor formula of the Adams-Moulton method <DE, NU>	*s.* A 221		
P 1203	**predictor variable** <SP>	Prädiktorvariable *f*, Vorhersagevariable *f*	variable *f* explicative	переменная предсказания
P 1204	**predual** <FA>	Prädual *m*	prédual *m*	преддвойственное (предсопряженное) пространство
P 1205	***p*-reduced group** <GR>	*p*-reduzierte Gruppe *f*	groupe *m* *p*-réduit	*p*-приведенная группа
P 1206	**pre-equivalence relation** <CA>	Gruppoid *n*, Prääquivalenzrelation *f*	pré-relation *f* d'équivalence	предотношение эквивалентности
P 1207	**preference** <ST, TG>	Präferenz *f*	préférence *f*	предпочтение, преферанс
	preference function <PG>	*s.* O 6		
P 1208	**preference region** <ST>	Entscheidungsbereich *m*	région *f* de décision, région de préférence	область, в которой принимается окончательное решение
P 1209	**preference relation** <ST, TG>	Präferenzbeziehung *f*, Vorzugsrelation *f*	relation *f* de préférence	предпочтительное соотношение, отношение предпочтения
P 1210	**preference set** <ST, TG>	Präferenzmenge *f*	ensemble *m* de préférence	предпочтительное множество
P 1211	**preference testing** <ST, TG>	Präferenzprüfung *f*	test *m* de préférence	проверка предпочтения
	preference zone <ST>	*s.* Z 81		
P 1212	**prefilter** <SE, TO>	Präfilter *m*	préfiltre *m*	предфильтр
P 1213	**prefix** <LO>	Präfix *n*	préfixe *m*	приставка, префикс
	prefix notation <LO>	*s.* P 163		
	pregeometry <LA>	*s.* E 677		
P 1214	***p*-regular class [of conjugate elements]** <of a group> <GR>	*p*-reguläre Klasse *f* [konjugierter Elemente]	classe *f* de conjugaison *p*-régulière	*p*-регулярный класс [сопряженных элементов]
P 1215	***p*-regular extension** <of a local field> <AL>	*p*-reguläre Erweiterung *f*	extension *f* *p*-régulière	*p*-регулярное расширение
P 1216	***p*-regular factor** <of a group element> <GR>	*p*-regulärer Faktor *m*	facteur *m* *p*-régulier	*p*-регулярный множитель
P 1217	***p*-regular function,** *p*-analytic function <FT>	*p*-analytische Funktion *f*	fonction *f* *p*-analytique	*p*-аналитическая функция
P 1218	**pre-Hilbert norm** <FA>	prähilbertsche Norm *f*	norme *f* pré-hilbertienne	предгильбертова норма
	prehilbert (pre-Hilbert) space <FA>	*s.* U 260		
	prehistory <PG>	*s.* H 374		
	pre[-]image <AN>	*s.* I 912		
P 1219	**pre[-]inductive class** <CA>	präinduktive Klasse *f*	classe *f* préinductive	предындуктивный (прединдуктивный) класс
P 1220	***p*-relations** <IV>	*p*-Relationen *fpl*	*p*-relations *fpl*	*p*-соотношения
P 1221	**prelogical** <LO>	prälogisch	prélogique	дологический
P 1222	**premise,** premiss, premisse, antecedent, hypothesis <LO>	Prämisse *f*, Voraussetzung *f*	prémisse *f*, antécédent *m*, hypothèse *f*	посылка, исходная (верхняя) формула <фигуры заключения>, гипотеза <вывода>
	premise <GN, LO>	*s.* A 1130		
	premise <LO>	*s.* A 695		
	premiss <LO>	*s.* P 1222		
	premisse <LO>	*s.* 1. A 695; 2. P 1222		
P 1223	**pre-module** <AL>	Prämodul *m*	prémodule *m*	премодуль
P 1224	**premultiplication** <NT>	Multiplikation *f* von links nach rechts	multiplication *f* <de nombres> en commençant de gauche	умножение начиная слева <со старшего разряда>
	pre[-]multiplication <AL>	*s.* L 433		
	pre[-]multiplying <AL>	*s.* L 433		
P 1225	**prenex formula,** formula in [the] prenex normal form, formula of (having) a normal form <LO>	Ausdruck *m* in pränexer Normalform, pränexer Ausdruck (P-Ausdruck *m*)	formule *f* mise sous forme prénexe, formule normale	предваренная формула, пренексное предложение, предложение в пренексной нормальной форме
P 1226	**prenex normal form,** normal form <LO>	pränexe Normalform *f*	forme *f* prénexe (normale), formule *f* normale	пренексная (предваренная) нормальная форма
P 1227	**prenex normal form theorem** <LO>	pränexer Normalformsatz *m*, Theorem *n* der pränexen Normalformen	théorème *m* de la forme prénexe	теорема предваренных нормальных формул
P 1228	**prenorm** <TO>	Pränorm *f*	prénorme *f*	преднорма
P 1229	**preorder** <SE>	Vorgeordnetheit *f*	propriété *f* d'être préordonné	квазиупорядоченность, предупорядоченность
	preorder <SE>	*s.* Q 214		
P 1230	**preordered set,** quasi-ordered set, reflexively quasi-ordered set,	reflexiv quasigeordnete Menge *f*, vorgeordnete (quasigeordnete, schwach	ensemble *m* préordonné	предупорядоченное (частично предупорядоченное, квазиупоря-

No.	English	German	French	Russian
and still: P 1230	partially ordered set, poset <SE>	halbgeordnete) Menge, Quasiordnung *f*, prägeordnete Menge		доченное) множество
P 1231	**preparating lemma** <GN>	vorbereitendes Lemma *n*	lemme *m* préliminaire	предварительная лемма
P 1232	**prepared form** <IV>	präparierte Form *f* <Sylvester>	forme *f* préparée	препарированная форма
P 1233	**pre-*p*-ring** <AL>	Prä-*p*-Ring *m*	pré-*p*-anneau *m*	pre-*p*-кольцо
P 1234	**preradical,** subfunctor of the identity <CA>	Präradikal *n*, Subfunktor *m* der Identität	préradical *m*, sous-foncteur *m* du foncteur identique	предрадикал, подфунктор тождественного функтора
P 1235	**prescheme** <AG>	Präschema *n*	schéma *m*, // préschéma *m*	предсхема
P 1236	**presentation** <of a module> <AL>	Darstellung *f*, Präsentation *f*	présentation *f*, présentation de longueur 1	представление [длины 1]
P 1237	**presentation of length *n*** <of a module> <AL>	Darstellung *f* der Länge *n*	*n*-présentation *f*, présentation *f* de longueur *n*	*n*-представление, представление длины *n*
P 1238	**presentation of the pair (*G*,*P*)** <AL>	Darstellung *f* des Paares (*G*,*P*)	présentation *f* de la paire (*G*,*P*)	задание пары (*G*,*P*)
P 1239	**preservation** <*e.g.:* of limits> <CA>	Respektierung *f* <*z. B.:* von Limiten>	préservation *f* <*par exemple:* de limites>	сохранение <*например:* пределов>
P 1240	**preservation of angles,** isogonality, conformity <of a map> <FT, GE>	Winkeltreue *f*, Konformität *f*, Isogonalität *f*	isogonalité *f*, conformité *f*, conservation *f* des angles	сохранение углов, равноугольность, изогональность, неискаженность угловых соотношений
P 1241	**preservation of area** <by a map> <AY>	Flächentreue *f*	conservation *f* des aires	сохранение площадей
P 1242	**preservation of length** <by a map> <TO>	Längentreue *f*	conservation *f* de la longueur	сохранение длины
P 1243	**pre[-]sheaf,** stack <AT>	Prägarbe *f*, Garbendatum *n*, projektives System *n*	préfaisceau *m*	предпучок, стек
P 1244	**presheaf of abelian groups** <AL, TO>	Prägarbe *f* abelscher Gruppen	préfaisceau *m* de groupes abéliens	предпучок абелевых групп, абелев предпучок
P 1245	**presheaf of sets** <CA>	mengenwertige Prägarbe *f*	préfaisceau *m* d'ensembles	предпучок множеств
P 1246	**presheaf structure** <AL, TO>	Prägruppenstruktur *f*	structure *f* de prégroupe	структура предпучка
P 1247	**prestructure** <UA>	Prästruktur *f*	préstructure *f*	предструктура
P 1248	**pre-subscript** <GN>	linker unterer Index *m*	indice *m* inférieur gauche	левый нижний индекс
P 1249	**pre-superscript** <GN>	linker oberer Index *m*	indice *m* supérieur gauche	левый верхний индекс
P 1250	**pretopological** <CA, TO>	prätopologisch	prétopologique	предтопологический
P 1251	**pre-topology** <CA, TO>	Prätopologie *f*	prétopologie *f*	предтопология
P 1252	**pre[-]torsion** <AL>	Prätorsion *f*	prétorsion *f*	предкручение
P 1253	**pre-torsion theory** <AL>	Prätorsionstheorie *f*	théorie *f* de pré-torsion	теория предкручения
P 1254	**pretzel** <GE>	Brezelfläche *f*, Doppelringfläche *f*	bretzel *m*	крендель
P 1255	**primal algebra,** functionally [strictly] complete algebra <UA>	primale (funktional vollständige) Algebra *f*	algèbre *f* fonctionnellement complète, algèbre primale	функционально полная алгебра, примальная алгебра
P 1256	**primal ideal** <AL>	primales Ideal *n*	idéal *m* primal	примальный идеал
P 1257	**primal problem** <of optimization> <PG>	primales (ursprüngliches) Problem *n*.	problème primal (primordial, primitif)	основная (прямая) задача
P 1258	**primal radical,** adjoint ideal <AL>	zugehöriges Ideal *n*	radical *m* primal, idéal *m* adjoint	сопряженный идеал
P 1259	**primal simplex method** <PG>	primales Simplexverfahren (Verfahren) *n*	méthode *f* simpliciale (du simplexe) primale (primordiale, primitive)	прямой (основной) симплекс-метод
P 1260	**primal solution,** solution of a primal problem <PG>	primale Lösung *f*, Lösung des primalen Problems	solution *f* primale, solution du problème primal	решение прямой (основной) задачи
P 1261	**primal variable** <PG>	primale (ursprüngliche) Variable *f*	variable *f* primale (primordiale, primitive)	первоначальная (основная) переменная
P 1262	**primary abelian group** <to the prime number *p*> <GR>	abelsche *p*-Gruppe *f*, primäre abelsche Gruppe *f*, primäre Gruppe <zur Primzahl *p*>	groupe *m* primaire (abélien primaire)	примарная группа <по простому числу *p*>
P 1263	**primary component** <of an ideal> <AL>	Primärkomponente *f*, primäres Komponentenideal *n*	composante *f* primaire	примарная компонента
P 1264	**primary covariant** <AL>	primäre Kovariante *f* <Deruyts>	covariant *m* primaire	первичный ковариант
P 1265	**primary decomposition** <AL>	Primärzerlegung *f*	décomposition *f* primaire	примарное разложение
P 1266	**primary difference** <of cross-sections> <AT>	erste Differenz *f*	première classe *f* différence	первый разностный класс
P 1267	**primary domain of integrity** <AL>	primärer Integritätsbereich *m*	anneau *m* d'intégrité primaire	примарная область целостности
P 1268	**primary element** <AL>	primäres Element *n*	élément *m* primaire	примарный элемент
P 1269	**primary extension** <of a field> <AL>	primäre Erweiterung *f*	extension *f* primaire	примарное расширение
	primary factor <FT>	*s.* P 1270		
P 1270	**primary factor of Weierstrass,** primary factor <FT>	Weierstraßscher Primfaktor *m*, Primfaktor *m* von Weierstraß, Primfaktor *m*	facteur *m* primaire <de Weierstrass>	первичный (примарный) множитель Вейерштрасса
P 1271	**primary ideal** <AL, NT>	Primärideal *n*, primäres Ideal *n*	idéal *m* primaire	примарный идеал
P 1272	**primary ideal belonging to the prime ideal $\mathfrak{P}$, primary ideal for $\mathfrak{P}$** <AL>	zu dem Primideal $\mathfrak{P}$ gehöriges Primärideal *n*	idéal *m* primaire ayant l'idéal premier $\mathfrak{P}$ pour idéal premier associé	примарный идеал, которому соответствует простой идеал $\mathfrak{P}$
P 1273	**primary module** <AL>	Primärmodul *m*	module *m* primaire	примарный модуль
P 1274	**primary normal divisor** <GR>	primärer Normalteiler *m*	sous-groupe *m* invariant primaire	первичный нормальный делитель

No.	English	German	French	Russian
P 1275	**primary normal simple algebra** <AL>	primäre zentrale einfache Algebra *f*	algèbre *f* simple centrale primaire	примарная центральная простая алгебра
	primary obstruction <AT>	*s.* F 344		
P 1276	**primary radical** <AL>	primäres Radikal *n*	radical *m* primaire	примарный радикал
	primary radical <AL>	*s. a.* A 1089		
P 1277	**primary representation** <of an ideal>, representation <of an ideal> as an intersection of primary ideals <AL>	Primärkomponentenzerlegung *f* <eines Ideals>	décomposition *f* primaire <d'un idéal>	примарное разложение <идеала>
P 1278	**primary representation** <RE>	primäre Darstellung *f*	représentation *f* isotypique (primaire, factorielle)	изотипное представление
P 1279	**primary ring** <AL>	primärer Ring (Nullteilerring) *m*	anneau *m* primaire	примарное кольцо
P 1280	**primary submodule** <AL>	primärer Untermodul *m*	sous-module *m* primaire	примарный подмодуль
P 1281	**primary unit** <ST>	Primäreinheit *f*	unité *f* primaire	первичный неделимый элемент
P 1282	**prime,** dash, accent, ′ <at a quantity> <as a mathematical symbol, *e.g.* a'> <GN>	Strich *m*, ′ <an einer Größe>	prime *f*, ′	прим, штрих, ′ <у величины>
	prime <AB>	*s.* P 1342		
	prime <AL>	*s.* P 1293		
	prime <NT>	*s.* P 1318		
	prime at infinity <AB, AL>	*s.* I 467		
P 1283	**prime base** <of a prime ideal> <AL>	Primbasis *f*	base *f* première	простой базис
P 1284	**prime characteristic** <AL>	Primzahlcharakteristik *f*	caractéristique *f* première	простая характеристика
P 1285	**prime component,** number indecomposable with respect to addition <SE>	unzerlegbare (additiv unzerlegbare) Ordnungszahl *f*	nombre *m* ordinal indécomposable (indécomposable par rapport à l'addition)	аддитивно неразложимое порядковое число
P 1286	**prime cycle,** rational prime cycle <AG>	Primzyklus *m*	cycle *m* premier	простой цикл
	prime decomposition <AL, NT>	*s.* F 44		
P 1287	**prime degree** <AL>	Primzahlgrad *m*	degré *m* premier	простая степень
P 1288	**prime divisor** <of the first (1st) *or* second (2nd) kind> <AL, FT>	Primdivisor *m*, Primteiler *m* <[von] erster (1.) *oder* zweiter (2.) Art>	diviseur *m* premier (algébrique premier) <de première (1e) *ou* seconde (2e) espèce>	простой дивизор <первого (1-го) *или* второго (2-го) рода>
P 1289	**prime divisor** <NT>	Primteiler *m*	diviseur *m* premier (primaire)	простой делитель
P 1290	**primed quantity,** accented quantity <GN>	gestrichene Größe *f*	quantité *f* primée	величина со штрихом, величина с примом
P 1291	**prime dual ideal,** ultrafilter <of a lattice> <LA>	duales Primideal *n*, $\cap$-Primideal *n*	$\cap$-idéal *m* premier	простой фильтр
P 1292	**prime element,** irreducible element <of a groupoid> <AL>	unzerlegbares Element *n*	élément *m* indécomposable	неприводимый элемент
P 1293	**prime element,** prime <of a ring, semigroup, *or* in a field with discrete valuation> <AL>	Primelement *n*	élément *m* premier	простой элемент
P 1294	**prime element,** relatively prime element <to> <AL>	primes (relativ primes) Element *n* <zu>	élément *m* premier <à>	простой элемент <к>
	prime element <LA>	*s.* A 1184		
P 1295	**prime end** <TO>	Primende *n*	bout *m* premier	простой конец, простой (граничный) элемент области
P 1296	**prime factor** <AL, NT>	Primfaktor *m*	facteur (diviseur) *m* premier	простой множитель
	prime factor <SE>	*s.* P 1319		
P 1297	**prime factorization** <of an ideal> <AB, AL>	Primfaktorzerlegung *f*, Primidealzerlegung *f*	décomposition *f* en facteurs premiers	разложение на простые множители (идеалы)
	prime factorization <AL, NT>	*s.* F 44		
P 1298	**prime Fermat number,** Fermat['s] prime <NT>	Fermatsche (Gaußsche) Primzahl *f*	nombre *m* premier de Fermat	простое число Ферма
P 1299	**prime field**; prime subfield <AL>	Primkörper *m*	corps *m* premier; sous-corps *m* premier	простое поле; простое подполе
P 1300	**prime field type** <AL>	Primkörpertypus *m*	type *m* de corps premier	тип простого поля
P 1301	**prime filter** <of a lattice> <LA>	Primfilter *m*	filtre *m* premier	простой фильтр
P 1302	**prime form,** irreducible form <AB>	Primform *f*, irreduktible Form *f*, Primdivisor *m*	forme *f* primaire	неприводимая форма
P 1303	**prime form** <FT>	Primform *f*	forme *f* primaire	простая форма
P 1304	**prime form** <Klein> <FT>	Primform *f* <Klein>, Kleinsche transzendente Primform	forme *f* première	простая форма <по Клейну>
	prime formula <LO>	*s.* E 107		
P 1305	**prime function,** irreducible function <of a polynomial> <AL>	Primfunktion *f*, irreduktible Funktion *f*	fonction *f* irréductible (première), fonction-première *f*	неприводимая функция
P 1306	**prime Goldie ring** <AL>	primer Goldie-Ring *m*	anneau *m* de Goldie premier	первичное кольцо Голди
P 1307	**prime graph** <GP>	Primgraph *m*, primer Graph *m*	graphe *m* premier	простой граф
P 1308	**prime ideal** <of a ring> <AL>	Primideal *n*, Ringprimideal *n*	idéal *m* premier <d'un anneau>	простой идеал <кольца>

No.	English	German	French	Russian
P 1309	**prime ideal** <of a semigroup> <AL>	Primideal *n*	partie *f* première	вполне изолированный идеал
P 1310	**prime ideal** <of a lattice> <LA>	Primideal *n*, ∪-Primideal *n*	idéal (∪-idéal) *m* premier	простой идеал
P 1311	**prime ideal** <*e.g.:* over p> <NT>	Primideal *n* <*z. B.:* über p>	idéal *m* premier <*par exemple:* au-dessus de p>	простой идеал <*например:* над p>
	prime ideal <AL>	*s.* A 1087		
P 1312	**prime ideal theorem** <NT>	Primidealsatz *m*	théorème *m* des idéaux premiers	теорема о простых идеалах
P 1313	**prime model, prime-model,** prime system <UA>	Primmodell *n*	modèle *m* premier	первичная система (модель), простая модель
P 1314	**prime module** <AL>	Primmodul *m*	module *m* premier	простой модуль
	prime module <NT>	*s.* P 1320		
P 1315	**prime module system,** ideal which cannot be decomposed into a product <NT>	Primmodulsystem *n* <Kronecker>, nicht in ein Produkt zerlegbares Ideal *n*, irreduktibles System *n*	système *m* modulaire premier, « Primmodulsystem » *m* <Kronecker>, idéal *m* indécomposable en produit de deux autres	простая система модулей, «Primmodulsystem» <Кронекер>; идеал, неразложимый в произведение двух других
	prime natural number <NT>	*s.* P 1318		
P 1316	**prime notation** <ST>	Urliste *f*	liste *f* des observations originales	таблица необработанных наблюденных значений
P 1317	**prime null divisor** <AL>	Nullstellenprimdivisor *m*	diviseur *m* des zéros premier	простой дивизор нулей
P 1318	**prime number,** prime [natural number] <NT>	Primzahl *f*, // einfache Zahl *f*	nombre *m* premier [rationnel], // nombre simple	простое (простое рациональное) число
P 1319	**prime number,** prime ordinal (factor) <SE>	multiplikative Primzahl *f*, Primzahl, Primfaktor *m*	facteur *m* premier	мультипликативное простое число
P 1320	**prime number modulus,** prime module <NT>	Primzahlmodul *m*, Primmodul *m*	module *m* premier	простой модуль
P 1321	**prime-number problem** <NT>	Primzahlproblem *n*	problème *m* des nombres premiers	проблема простых чисел
P 1322	**prime number theorem,** prime-number theorem <NT>	Primzahlsatz *m*	théorème *m* [fondamental] des nombres premiers, théorème sur la distribution des nombres premiers, loi *f* des nombres premiers	закон простых чисел
P 1323	**prime number theory** <NT>	Primzahltheorie *f*, Primzahllehre *f*	théorie *f* des nombres premiers	теория простых чисел
P 1324	**prime order** <AL, GR>	Primzahlordnung *f*	ordre *m* premier	простой порядок
	prime ordinal <SE>	*s.* P 1319		
P 1325	**prime pair, prime-pair,** [prime] twins, twin primes, pair of primes, Gemini <NT>	Primzahlzwillinge *mpl*, Primzahlpaar *n*	couple *m* de nombres premiers jumeaux, nombres *mpl* premiers jumeaux, jumeaux *pl*, doublets *mpl*	близнецы-пары, пара простых чисел, пары-близнецы, простые числа-близнецы, «близнецы»
P 1326	**prime part,** complete oscillatory set <of a continuum> <TO>	Primteil *m*, Schicht *f*	constituant *m* premier, tranche *f*	простая составляющая, слой
P 1327	**prime polar divisor** <AL>	Polprimdivisor *m*	diviseur *m* des pôles premier	простой дивизор полюсов
P 1328	**prime polynomial** <AL>	Primpolynom *n*, irreduzibles Polynom *n*	polynôme *m* premier	простой полином
P 1329	**prime polynomial ideal** <AL>	Primideal *n* in einem Polynomring	idéal *m* premier de polynômes	простой многочленный идеал
P 1330	**prime power,** power of a prime <NT>	Primzahlpotenz *f*	puissance *f* de [nombres] premiers	степень простого числа
P 1331	**prime power,** ultra power <UA>	Ultrapotenz *f*	ultra-puissance *f*	ультрастепень
P 1332	**prime-power group,** finite *p*-group <GR>	Primzahlpotenzgruppe *f*, endliche *p*-Gruppe *f*	*p*-groupe *m* fini	конечная *p*-группа
P 1333	**prime-power order** <of a group> <GR>	Primzahlpotenzordnung *f*	ordre *m* qui est puissance d'un nombre premier	порядок, который является степенью простого числа
P 1334	**prime prefilter** <AL>	Primpräfilter *m*	préfiltre *m* premier	простой предфильтр
	prime product <UA>	*s.* U 22		
P 1335	**prime quadruplet, prime-quadruplet** <NT>	Primzahlvierlinge *mpl*	quadruplet *m* de nombres premiers	четверки-близнецы, близнецы-четверки, четверка простых чисел
P 1336	**prime quaternion** <AL>	Primquaternion *f*	quaternion *m* premier	простой кватернион
P 1337	**prime radical** <AL>	Primradikal *n*	radical *m* premier	простой радикал
	prime rational cycle over *k* <AG>	*s.* I 1038		
P 1338	**prime ring** <AL>	Primring *m*	anneau *m* premier	простое кольцо
P 1339	**prime ring** <$aRb = 0 \to a = 0 \vee b = 0$> <AL>	primer Ring *m*	anneau *m* premier	первичное кольцо
P 1340	**prime ring of an integral domain** <AL>	Primring *m* eines Integritätsbereichs	domaine *m* d'intégrité premier	простое кольцо области целостности
P 1341	**prime sequence,** *R*-sequence <AL>	*R*-Sequenz *f*, Primsequenz *f*	*R*-suite *f*	*R*-последовательность
P 1342	**prime spot,** prime <of an algebraic number field> <AB>	Primstelle *f*	place *f*	простой элемент
	prime subfield <AL>	*s.* P 1299		
	prime system <UA>	*s.* P 1313		
P 1343	**prime-triplet,** triplet of primes <NT>	Primzahltripel *n*	triplet *m* de nombres premiers	тройка простых чисел, тройки-близнецы
	prime twins <NT>	*s.* P 1325		

No.	English	German	French	Russian
P 1344	**primitive,** antiderivative, [Newton['s]] indefinite integral <DI>	Stammfunktion *f*, primitive Funktion *f*, Newtonsches (unbestimmtes Newtonsches, unbestimmtes) Integral *n*	primitive *f* stricte, primitive, fonction *f* primitive, antidérivée *f*, intégrale *f* indéfinie de Newton, intégrale indéfinie	первообразная (примитивная) функция, первообразная, неопределенный интеграл Ньютона, неопределенный интеграл
	primitive <AN>	*s.* I 912		
P 1345	**primitive adjacency matrix** <GP>	primitive Knotenmatrix *f*	matrice *f* associée primitive	примитивная матрица смежности
P 1436	**primitive adjoint,** primitive contravariant <of a quadratic form> <NT> ┌<AL>	primitive Adjungierte *f* <Meyer>, primitive Kontravariante *f* <Smith>, Reziproke *f*, // Reciproke *f* <Bachmann>	primitive adjointe (contravariante) *f*, réciproque *f*	примитивная присоединенная форма
P 1347	**primitive adjunction**	primitive Adjunktion *f*	adjonction *f* primitive	примитивное присоединение
	primitive atomic formula <LO>	*s.* A 1189		
	primitive binary quadratic form <NT>	*s.* P 1356		
P 1348	**primitive class** <of binary forms> <NT>	primitive (ursprüngliche) Klasse *f* <erster (1.) *oder* zweiter (2.) Art>	classe *f* primitive	примитивный класс
	primitive class <UA>	*s.* E 337		
P 1349	**primitive cohomology** <AT>	primitive Kohomologie *f*	cohomologie *f* primitive	примитивная когомология
P 1350	**primitive cohomology class** <AT>	primitive Kohomologieklasse *f*	classe *f* de cohomologie primitive	примитивный когомологический класс
	primitive contravariant <NT>	*s.* P 1346		
P 1351	**primitive divisor class** <AL>	primitive Divisorenklasse (Klasse) *f*	classe *f* de diviseurs primitive	примитивный класс дивизоров
P 1352	**primitive element** <Zermelo>, proper class <SE>	Unmenge *f*, eigentliche Klasse *f*, Menge *f* zweiter Art <Klasse, die nicht Menge ist>	classe *f* pure, non-ensemble *m*	собственный класс
P 1353	**primitive equation** <in Galois' theory> <AL>	primitive Gleichung *f*	équation *f* primitive	примитивное уравнение
P 1354	**primitive [field] extension** <AL>	primitive Erweiterung (Körpererweiterung) *f*	extension *f* primitive	примитивное расширение (расширение поля)
P 1355	**primitive form** <AL>	primitive Form *f*, Einheitsform *f*	forme *f* primitive, forme-unité *f*, forme unité	примитивная форма
P 1356	**primitive form,** primitive binary quadratic form <NT>	primitive (ursprüngliche quadratische, ursprüngliche, primitive quadratische) Form *f* <nicht notwendig eigentlich>	forme *f* primitive (quadratique primitive)	примитивная форма
P 1357	**primitive formula** <LO>	formaler Ausdruck *m*	expression *f* formale	формальное выражение
P 1358	**primitive formula** <without quantifiers> <LO>	primitive Formel *f*	formule *f* primitive	примитивная формула
	primitive formula <LO>	*s.* A 1189		
P 1359	**primitive group** <GR>	primitive Gruppe *f*	groupe *m* primitif, permutation *f* composée du troisième genre <Ruffini>, // équation *f* primitive <Galois>	примитивная группа
P 1360	**primitive idempotent [element]** <AL>	primitives (unzerlegbares) Idempotent *n*	idempotent *m* indécomposable (primitif)	примитивный (неразложимый) идемпотент
P 1361	**primitive *k*-abundant number** <NT>	primitive (erzeugende) *k*-abundante Zahl *f*	nombre *m* *k*-abondant primitif	примитивное *k*-избыточное число
P 1362	**primitive Lie group of transformations** <AL>	primitive Liesche Transformationsgruppe *f*	groupe *m* de transformations de Lie primitif	примитивная лиева группа преобразований
	primitively elementary subsystem <UA>	*s.* P 1381		
P 1363	**primitively false formula** <LO>	primitiv falsche Formel *f*	formule *f* primitivement fausse	примитивно сложная формула
P 1364	**primitively true formula** <LO>	primitiv wahre Formel *f*	formule primitivement vraie	примитивно истинная формула
P 1365	**primitive matrix** <AL, MD>	primitive Matrix (unzerlegbare Matrix) *f*	matrice *f* primitive	примитивная матрица
P 1366	**primitive *n*-th root of unity** <AL>	primitive *n*-te Einheitswurzel *f*	racine *f* primitive *n*-e de l'unité, racine *n*-e de l'unité	примитивный (первообразный) корень *n*-ой степени из единицы
P 1367	**primitive number** <NT>	primitive Zahl *f*	nombre *m* primitif	примитивное число
P 1368	**primitive period,** fundamental period <AN, FU>	primitive Periode *f*, Grundperiode *f*, // index *m* proprius <Jacobi>	période *f* fondamentale (primitive, principale)	основной (простой) период
P 1369	**primitive period parallelogram,** [fundamental] period parallelogram <FT>	Fundamentalparallelogramm *n*, Elementarparallelogramm *n*, Periodenparallelogramm *n* für ein primitives Periodenpaar, Periodenparallelogramm	parallélogramme *m* des périodes fondamentales, parallélogramme élémentaire, parallélogramme des périodes	основной параллелограмм периодов, параллелограмм периодов
P 1370	**primitive periods (period system),** principal system of periods <of a *q*-fold periodic function> <FT>	primitives Periodensystem *n*, System *n* primitiver Perioden, Basis *f* des Periodenmoduls, Periodenmodulbasis *f*	système *m* principal de périodes	главная система периодов, основная система периодов
P 1371	**primitive polynomial** <content = 1> <AL>	primitives Polynom *n*	polynôme *m* primitif	примитивная функция, примитивный многочлен
P 1372	**primitive polynomial** <in Galois' theory> <AL>	primitives Polynom *n*	polynôme *m* primitif	примитивный многочлен
P 1373	**primitive recursive attribute** <LO>	primitiv-rekursives Attribut *n*	attribut *m* récursif primitif	примитивно-рекурсивный признак

P 1374	**primitive recursive function,** primitive recursive numerical function <MM>	primitiv-rekursive [zahlentheoretische] Funktion *f*	fonction *f* récursive (récurrente) primitive, fonction primitive récursive	примитивно-рекурсивная функция, примитивно рекурсивная функция
P 1375	**primitive recursive isomorphism** <MM>	primitiv-rekursiver Isomorphismus *m*	isomorphisme *m* récursif primitif	примитивно-рекурсивный изоморфизм
P 1376	**primitive recursively enumerable set** <FO>	primitiv-rekursiv aufzählbare Menge *f*	ensemble *m* primitivement récursivement énumérable	примитивно-рекурсивно перечислимое множество
	primitive recursive numerical function <MM>	*s.* P 1374		
P 1377	**primitive recursive predicate** <LO>	primitiv-rekursives Prädikat *n*	prédicat *m* primitif récursif	примитивно-рекурсивный предикат, примитивно рекурсивный предикат
P 1378	**primitive root** <AL>	Primitivwurzel *f*, primitive Wurzel *f*, Primitivzahl *f*, primitive Kongruenzwurzel	racine *f* primitive	первообразный (примитивный) корен
P 1379	**primitive root of *m*** <NT>	primitive Wurzel *f* modulo *m*, Primitivwurzel *f* modulo *m*	racine *f* primitive modulo *m*	первообразный корень по модулю *m*
P 1380	**primitive set** <of integers> <AB>	primitive (irreduzible) Menge *f*	ensemble *m* primitif	примитивное множество
P 1381	**primitive subsystem,** primitively elementary subsystem <of an algebraic system> <UA>	primitives Untersystem *n*	sous-système *m* primitif	примитивная (примитивно элементарная) подсистема
	primitive term <GN>	*s.* T 113		
P 1382	**primitivity** <AL, NT>	Primitivität *f*	primitivité *f*	примитивность
P 1383	**primordial vector** <of a module with respect to a basis> <AL>	primordialer Vektor *m*	vecteur *m* primordial	
P 1384	**principal** <in simple *or* compound interest> <AR>	Grundwert *m*, Grundkapital *n*, Kapital *n*	capital *m*	основная сумма, капитал, ссуда
P 1385	**principal adele** <AB>	Hauptadel *n*	adèle *m* principal	главный адель
P 1386	**principal anti-automorphism** <of a Clifford algebra> <AL>	Haupt-Antiautomorphismus *m*	antiautomorphisme *m* principal	главный антиавтоморфизм
P 1387	**principal approximate value** <of a Farey series> <NT>	Hauptnäherungswert *m*	valeur *f* approchée principale	главное приближенное значение
P 1388	**principal argument** <of a complex number> <FT>	Hauptargument *n*	argument *m* principal, valeur *f* principale	главное значение
	principal axes theorem <AL, AY>	*s.* T 336		
	principal axes transformation <AL, AY>	*s.* T 784		
P 1389	**principal axis** <of a conic *or* quadric *or* quadratic form> <AY>	Hauptachse *f*	axe *m* principal	главная ось
P 1390	**principal axis solution** <ST>	Hauptachsenlösung *f*	solution *f* par la méthode des axes principaux	решение методом главных осей
	principal axis theorem <AL, AY>	*s.* T 336		
	principal axis transformation, principal-axis transformation <AL, AY>	*s.* T 784		
P 1391	**principal branch** <of a cubic> <AG>	Hauptast *m*, Hauptzug *m*	branche *f* principale, trait *m* principal	главная ветвь
	principal branch <FT>	*s.* P 1488		
P 1392	**principal bundle,** principal fibre bundle <AT>	Prinzipal[faser]bündel *n*, Hauptfaserbündel *n*, Hauptfaserraum *m*	fibré *m* principal, espace *m* fibré principal	главное расслоение (расслоенное пространство), главное косое произведение
P 1393	**principal character** <mod *m*> <NT>	Hauptcharakter *m* <mod *m*>	caractère *m* principal <mod *m*>	главный характер <по модулю *m*>
P 1394	**principal circle** <of a Fuchsian group> <FT>	Hauptkreis *m*	cercle *m* principal	основной круг
P 1395	**principal coefficient of contraction** <of a transformation> <GE>	Hauptkontraktionskoeffizient *m*	coefficient *m* principal de contraction	главный коэффициент сжатия
P 1396	**principal cohomology class** <AB>	Hauptkohomologieklasse *f*	classe *f* principale de cohomologie	главный класс когомологии
P 1397	**principal coincidence curve** <DG>	Hauptkoinzidenzkurve *f* <Clebsch>	courbe *f* des coïncidences principales	главная прилегающая кривая
P 1398	**principal combinant** <of *n* binary forms> <IV>	Hauptkombinante *f*	combinant *m* principal	главный комбинант
P 1399	**principal component** <of an ideal> <AL>	Hauptkomponente *f*	composante *f* principale	главная (основная) компонента
P 1400	**principal congruence relation,** minimal congruence relation <induced by $a \equiv b$> <UA>	minimale Kongruenzrelation *f*	relation *f* de congruence minimale	наименьшее отношение конгруэнций
P 1401	**principal congruence subgroup** <of level *n*> <AB>	Hauptkongruenzgruppe *f* <vom Grade *n*>	groupe *m* de congruences principal, Hauptkongruenzgruppe *m*, sous-groupe *m* principal de congruence <de niveau *n*>	главная конгруэнц-подгруппа <уровня *n*>
P 1402	**principal conjunctive normal form,** distinguished conjunctive normal form, full conjunctive normal form <LO>	kanonische (ausgezeichnete) konjunktive Normalform *f*	forme *f* normale conjonctive parfaite (complète), forme conjonctive canonique	совершенная конъюнктивная нормальная форма

P 1403	**principal crossed homomorphism,** principal homomorphism <AL>	[zerfallender] verschränkter Homomorphismus *m*	homomorphisme *m* croisé principal	главный скрещенный гомоморфизм
P 1404	**principal curvature** <of a surface> <DG>	Hauptkrümmung *f*	courbure *f* principale	главная кривизна
P 1405	**principal curve [of dilatation]** <of a differentiable mapping of surfaces> <GE>	Hauptverzerrungskurve *f*, Hauptkurve *f*	courbe *f* principale de dilatation	главная кривая деформации
P 1406	**principal determinant** <of a matrix> <MD>	Hauptdeterminante *f*	déterminant *m* principal	главный определитель
	principal diagonal <MD>	*s.* M 34		
P 1407	**principal direction,** principal direction of dilatation <of a differentiable mapping of surfaces> <GE>	Hauptverzerrungsrichtung *f*, Hauptrichtung *f*	direction *f* principale de dilatation	главное направление деформации
P 1408	**principal direction [of curvature],** direction of principal curvature <DG>	Hauptkrümmungsrichtung *f*, Hauptrichtung *f*	direction *f* principale [de courbure]	главное направление [кривизны], направление главной кривизны
	principal direction of dilatation <GE>	*s.* P 1407		
P 1409	**principal disjunctive normal form,** full disjunctive normal form, distinguished disjunctive normal form <LO>	kanonische alternative Normalform *f*, ausgezeichnete disjunktive (alternative) Normalform, alternative kanonische Normalform, kanonisch-alternative Normalform, kanonische disjunktive Normalform	forme *f* normale disjonctive parfaite (complète), forme disjonctive canonique	совершенная дизъюнктивная нормальная форма
P 1410	**principal distribution parameter** <of a complex *or* congruence of lines> <DG>	Hauptdrall *m*, Hauptverteilungsparameter *m*	paramètre *m* de distribution principal	главный параметр распределения
P 1411	**principal divisor** <AG, AL>	Hauptdivisor *m*	diviseur *m* principal	главный дивизор
P 1412	**principal equation** <AL>	Hauptgleichung *f* <*n*-ten Grades>	équation *f* principale	главное уравнение
P 1413	**principal factor** <ST>	Hauptfaktor *m*	facteur *m* principal	основной фактор
	principal factor <AL>	*s.* F 13		
P 1414	**principal fibration** <AT>	Prinzipalfaserung *f*	fibration *f* principale	главное расслоение
	principal fibre bundle <AT>	*s.* P 1392		
P 1415	**principal filter,** dual principal ideal <generated by *x*> <AL, SE>	Hauptfilter *m* <von *x* erzeugter>	filtre *m* principal, section *f* finissante <de base *x*>	главный фильтр <порождаемый элементом *x*>
P 1416	**principal form** <as a binary quadratic form *or* of a continued fraction> <NT>	Hauptform *f*	forme *f* principale	главная форма
P 1417	**principal formula** <LO>	Hauptformel *f*	formule *f* principale	главная формула
P 1418	**principal fractionary ideal** <AL>	gebrochenes Hauptideal *n*	idéal *m* principal fractionnaire	дробный главный идеал
P 1419	**principal function** <of an element of an algebra> <AL>	Hauptpolynom *n*	polynôme *m* principal	главный многочлен
P 1420	**principal function** <of an integral equation> <IE>	Hauptfunktion *f*	fonction *f* principale	присоединенная функция
P 1421	**principal function [of Hamilton],** Hamilton['s] principal function, action integral <VA>	[Hamiltonsche] Prinzipalfunktion *f*, extremaler Abstand *m*, geodätische Distanz *f*, [zeitabhängige] Wirkungsfunktion *f*, Wirkungsintegral *n*, Hamiltons Hauptfunktion *f*	fonction *f* principale [de Hamilton], intégrale *f* d'action	главная функция [Гамильтона], функция действия, интеграл действия, действие по Гамильтону
	principal functor <CA, HA>	*s.* F 790		
P 1422	**principal genus** <of quadratic forms *or* groups *or* in algebraic number theory> <AL, NT>	Hauptgeschlecht *n*	genre *m* principal	главный род
P 1423	**principal group** <AY>	Hauptgruppe *f*	groupe *m* fondamental	главная группа
P 1424	**principal group,** Frattini['s] subgroup <GR>	Frattini-Gruppe *f*, Hauptgruppe *f*, Φ-Untergruppe *f*, Frattinische Untergruppe *f*	groupe *m* principal, sous-groupe *m* principal	главная группа, подгруппа Фраттини, Φ-подгруппа
P 1425	**principal homogeneous space** <AG, AL>	prinzipaler homogener Raum *m*	espace *m* homogène principal	главное однородное пространство
P 1426	**principal homomorphism** <AL>	Haupthomomorphismus *m*	homomorphisme *m* principal	главный гомоморфизм
	principal homomorphism <AL>	*s. a.* P 1403		
P 1427	**principal ideal** <AL>	Hauptideal *n*	idéal *m* principal (monogène)	главный (моногенный) идеал
P 1428	**principal ideal** <generated by *x*> <of a lattice> <LA>	Hauptideal *n*, ∪-Hauptideal *n* <von *x* erzeugtes>	idéal *m* principal, section *f* commençante <de base *x*>	главный идеал <порожденный элементом *x*>
P 1429	**principal ideal domain,** PID <AL>	nullteilerfreier Hauptidealring *m*, Hauptidealring	domaine *m* d'idéaux principaux, anneau *m* principal sans diviseurs de zéro	область главных идеалов
P 1430	**principal ideal ring,** PIR <AL>	Hauptidealring *m* <nicht notwendig nullteilerfrei>	anneau *m* principal (à idéaux principaux)	кольцо главных идеалов
P 1431	**principal ideal ring** <with unit element> <AL>	Quasihauptidealring *m*	anneau *m* quasi-principal	квазиглавное кольцо, квазикольцо главных идеалов

P 1432	**principal ideal theorem** <AL>	Hauptidealsatz *m*	théorème *m* de l'idéal principal, «Hauptidealsatz» *m*	теорема о главном идеале, теорема главных идеалов
	⌐<AL> **principal ideal theorem**	*s. a.* K 173		
P 1433	**principal idele** <AB>	Hauptidel *n*	idèle *m* principal	главный идель
P 1434	**principal idempotent** <of a ring> <AL>	Hauptidempotent *n*, ausgezeichnetes Idempotent *n*	idempotent *m* principal	главный идемпотент
P 1435	**principal identity,** unity quantity <of an algebra> <AL>	Haupteinheit *f*, Zahl *f* Eins, Modul *m*, Einselement *n*	module *m*, nombre *m* indifférent, unité *f* principale	единичный элемент, единица, главная единица
	principal integral <DE>	*s.* P 1474		
P 1436	**principal invariant** <of a tensor> <VT>	Hauptinvariante *f*	invariant *m* principal	основной инвариант, главный инвариант
P 1437	**principal isotope** <of a groupoid *or* quasifield> <AL>	Hauptisotop *n*	isotope *m* principal	главный изотоп
P 1438	**principal isotopy** <AL>	Hauptisotopie *f*	isotopie *f* principale	главная изотопия
P 1439	**principal left ideal** <AL>	Linkshauptideal *n*, Links-Hauptideal *n*	idéal *m* principal à gauche	главный левый идеал
P 1440	**principal left ideal domain,** left PID <AL>	nullteilerfreier Linkshauptidealring *m*	domaine *m* d'idéaux principaux à gauche	область главных левых идеалов, pli-область
	principal left ideal ring <AL>	*s.* P 671		
P 1441	**principal line,** trace parallel <in two-plane projection> <DS>	Hauptlinie *f*, Tafellinie *f*, Streichlinie *f*	ligne *f* principale	главная (основная) линия; линия, параллельная плоскости проекций
P 1442	**principal map** <of fibre bundles><AT>	Prinzipalabbildung *f*, Hauptabbildung *f*	application *f* principale	главное отображение
P 1443/4	**principal matrix** <of a Riemann matrix> <FT>	Prinzipalmatrix *f*	matrice *f* principale	главная матрица
	principal matrix <MD>	*s.* P 1447		
P 1445	**principal measure** <of the angle between half-lines> <GE>	Hauptwert *m*	mesure *f* principale	главная мера
P 1446	**principal minor,** principal minor determinant <MD>	Hauptunterdeterminante *f*, Hauptminor *m*, Hauptsubdeterminante *f*	mineur *m* principal, sous-déterminant *m* principal	главный минор, диагональный минор, главный диагональный минор
P 1447	**principal minor array,** principal matrix <of a matrix> <MD>	Hauptuntermatrix *f*, Hauptmatrix *f*	sous-matrice *f* principale, matrice *f* principale	главная подматрица, главная матрица
	principal minor determinant <MD>	*s.* P 1446		
	principal module <AL>	*s.* C 2862		
P 1448	**principal neutral point** <DS>	Hauptverschwindungspunkt *m*	point *m* neutre principal	главная нейтральная точка
P 1449	**principal normal,** first normal <DG>	Hauptnormale *f*	normale *f* principale	главная нормаль
P 1450	**principal normal bundle** <AT>	Prinzipalnormalenbündel *n*	fibré *m* normal principal	главное нормальное расслоение
P 1451	**principal normal complex,** complex of principal normals <DG>	Hauptnormalenkomplex *m*	complexe *m* des normales principales	комплекс главных нормалей
P 1452	**principal** <conjunctive *or* disjunctive> **normal form,** distinguished normal form <LO>	Boolesche Normalform *f*, ausgezeichnete <konjunktive *oder* alternative> Normalform, kanonische (vollkommene) Normalform	forme *f* normale <conjonctive *ou* disjonctive> parfaite, forme normale complète	совершенная <конъюнктивная *или* дизъюнктивная> нормальная форма
P 1453	**principal normal plane** <DG>	Hauptnormalebene *f*, Hauptkrümmungsebene *f*	plan *m* normal principal	плоскость главной нормали, плоскость главной кривизны
P 1453a	**principal normal section** <DG>	Hauptnormalschnitt *m*, Hauptkrümmungsschnitt *m*, Hauptschnitt *m*	section *f* normale principale	главное нормальное сечение, сечение нормальной (главной) кривизны
P 1454	**principal normal surface** <DG>	Hauptnormalenfläche *f*	normalie *f*	главная поверхность нормалей
P 1455	**principal normal [unit] vector,** first normal [unit] vector, unit principal normal [vector], unit first normal [vector], [unit] vector of principal (first) normal <DG>	Hauptnormalenvektor *m*, Hauptnormaleneinheitsvektor *m*	vecteur *m* de la normale principale, vecteur unitaire (unité) de la normale principale, vecteur [unitaire] normal principal	единичный вектор главной нормали, вектор главной нормали
P 1456	**principal number,** principal ordinal <SE>	Hauptzahl *f*	nombre *m* principal	главное число
	principal number of addition <SE>	*s.* G 43		
	principal number of exponentiation <SE>	*s.* E 315		
	principal number of multiplication <SE>	*s.* D 212		
P 1457	**principal order** <of a ring> <AB>	Hauptordnung *f*, Hauptart *f*	espèce *f* principale, ordre *m* principal	главный порядок
	principal ordinal <SE>	*s.* P 1456		
	principal ordinal for (of) addition <SE>	*s.* G 43		
	principal ordinal for (of) exponentiation <SE>	*s.* E 315		
	principal ordinal for (of) multiplication <SE>	*s.* D 212		

	English	Deutsch	Français	Русский
P 1458	**principal part** <of the first *or* higher degree> <of an Artinian ring> <AL>	Hauptteil *m* <ersten *oder* höheren Grades>	partie *f* principale <du premier degré *ou* de degré supérieur>	главная часть <первой *или* высшей степени>
P 1459	**principal part** <of a linear partial differential equation *or* a differential operator> <DE, FA>	Hauptteil *m*	partie *f* principale	главная часть
P 1460	**principal part,** meromorphic part <of Laurent expansion> <FT>	Hauptteil *m*, meromorpher Teil *m*	partie *f* principale (irrégulière, de gauche, infinie, singulière)	главная часть, мероморфная часть
P 1461	**principal plane,** plane of [principal] symmetry <of a surface> <AY>	Symmetrieebene *f*, Hauptebene *f*, Hauptsymmetrieebene *f*	plan *m* principal	плоскость главной симметрии
P 1462	**principal plane** <in two-plane projection> <DS>	Hauptebene *f*	plan *m* principal	главная плоскость
P 1463	**principal point,** principal vanishing point <in central perspective> <DS>	zentraler Augenpunkt (Hauptpunkt, Fluchtpunkt) *m*, Hauptfluchtpunkt *m*	point *m* principal, point de fuite principal	главная точка [схода]
P 1464	**principal point** <of a prime end> <TO>	Hauptpunkt *m*	point *m* principal	главная точка
	principal radius of curvature <DG>	*s.* R 39		
P 1465	**principal ray** <in central perspective> <DS>	Hauptstrahl *m*	rayon *m* principal	главный луч
P 1466	**principal reduced form** <of a quadratic form> <NT>	Hauptreduzierte *f*	réduite *f* principale	главная приведенная форма
P 1467	**principal remainder,** least [non-negative] residue <modulo *m*> <NT>	kleinster [nichtnegativer] Rest *m* <mod *m*>	reste (résidu) *m* minimé, le moindre résidu <mod. *m*> <DG>	наименьший вычет <mod. *m*>
P 1468	**principal representative** <of a class of quadratic forms> <NT>	Hauptrepräsentant *m*	représentant *m* principal	главный представитель
P 1469	**principal right ideal** <AL>	Rechtshauptideal *n*, Rechts-Hauptideal *n*	idéal *m* principal à droite	главный правый идеал
P 1470	**principal right ideal domain,** right PID <AL>	nullteilerfreier Rechtshauptidealring *m*	domaine *m* d'idéaux principaux à droite	область главных правых идеалов
	principal right ideal ring <AL>	*s.* P 1526		
	principal ruled surface <DG>	*s.* P 1477		
P 1471	**principal series** <of a semigroup> <AL>	Hauptreihe *f*	série *f* principale	главный ряд
P 1472	**principal series,** chief series, chief-series, maximal invariant series, chief-composition series <of a group> <GR>	Hauptreihe *f*, Grundreihe *f*, // Hauptreihe der Zusammensetzung	série *f* [de composition] principale, série fondamentale, suite *f* principale [de composition], chaîne *f* principale	главный ряд, основной ряд
P 1473	**principal series** <of representations> <RE>	Hauptreihe *f*	série *f* principale [de Bargmann]	главный ряд
P 1474	**principal solution,** principal integral <DE>	Hauptintegral *n*, Hauptlösung *f*	solution (intégrale) *f* principale	главное решение
P 1475	**principal solution matrix** <first *or* second> <FD>	Hauptlösungsmatrix *f* <erste *oder* zweite>	matrice *f* de solutions principale <première *ou* deuxième>	главная матрица решений <первая *или* вторая>
P 1476	**principal sphere [of curvature** <of a surface> <DG>	Hauptkrümmungskugel *f*, Hauptkugel *f*	sphère *f* principale [de courbure]	главная сфера [кривизны]
P 1477	**principal surface,** principal ruled surface <of a congruence of lines> <DG>	Hauptfläche *f*, Hauptregelfläche *f*	surface *f* principale, surface réglée principale	главная поверхность, главная линейчатая поверхность
	principal system <GR>	*s.* C 631		
	principal system of periods	*s.* P 1370		
P 1478/9	**principal tangent** <of a space curve> <AG>	Haupttangente *f*	tangente *f* principale	главная касательная
	principal tangent <DG>	*s.* A 1137		
P 1480	**principal tangent bundle** <AT>	tangentielles Prinzipal-Faserbündel *n*	fibré *m* tangent principal	главное касательное расслоение
P 1481	**principal term** <of an asymptotic expansion> <AX>	Hauptglied *n*	terme *m* principal, terme fondamental	главный член, основной член
P 1482	**principal term** <of a determinant> <MD>	Hauptglied *n*, Hauptprodukt *n*	terme *m* principal, produit *m* principal	главный член
P 1483	**principal trace** <of an element of algebra> <AL>	Hauptspur *f*, reduzierte Spur *f*	trace *f* principale	главный след
P 1484	**principal trace** <DS>	Hauptspurpunkt *m*	trace *f* principale	главный след
P 1485	**principal two-sided ideal** <AL>	zweiseitiges Hauptideal *n*	idéal *m* bilatère principal	главный двусторонний идеал
P 1486	**principal uniformization** <FT>	Hauptuniformisierung *f*	uniformisation *f* principale	главная униформизация
P 1487	**principal uniformizing function** <FT>	Hauptuniformisierende *f*	fonction *f* uniformisante principale	главная униформизирующая функция
P 1488	**principal value,** principal branch <of an analytic function> <FT>	Hauptwert *m*, Hauptzweig *m*	détermination (branche) *f* principale	главное значение, главная ветвь
P 1489	**principal value** <of a logarithm> <AN>	Hauptwert *m*	valeur (détermination) *f* principale *f*	главное значение
	principal value <AN>	*s. a.* C 260		

	principal value <DE>	*s.* E 59		
	principal vanishing point <DS>	*s.* P 1463		
P 1490	**principal variable** <DE>	prinzipale Variable *f*	variable *f* principale	главная переменная
P 1491	**principal vector** <MD>	Hauptvektor *m* <von der Stufe *r*>	vecteur *m* principal	корневой вектор, присоединенный [собственный] вектор, главный вектор <высоты *r*>
P 1492	**principiant** <of general forms> <AL>	Prinzipiante *f* <allgemeine Reziprokante, Sylvester>	principiant *m*	принципиант
P 1493	**principle of abstraction,** principle of definition <of equivalence relations> by means of abstraction <FO>	Abstraktionsprinzip *n*, Prinzip *n* der Definition durch Abstraktion	principe *m* d'abstraction, axiome *m* du partage <Lusin>	принцип абстракции (свертывания)
	principle of addition <LO>	*s.* L 165		
	principle of argument <FT>	*s.* A 941		
P 1494	**principle of balayage** <PO>	Balayage-Prinzip *n*	principe *m* de balayage, extrémisation *f* <Brelot>	принцип выметания
P 1495	**principle of bivalence,** principle of two-valued propositions <LO>	Prinzip *n* der Zweiwertigkeit <der Logik>, Satz *m* der Zweiwertigkeit	principe *m* de deux valeurs	принцип двузначности
	principle of choice <SE>	*s.* A 1280		
	principle of Clebsch <AG>	*s.* C 816		
P 1496	**principle of comparison** <of the series> <AN, SS>	Prinzip *n* der Reihenvergleichung	principe *m* de comparaison (comparaison des séries)	принцип сравнения
	principle of complete induction <FO, LO>	*s.* P 1510		
	principle of continuity <AG>	*s.* P 1518		
	principle of contradiction <LO>	*s.* L 175		
P 1497	**principle of convergent intervals** <AN>	Schachtelungsprinzip *n*, Satz *m* von der Intervallschachtelung, Prinzip *n* der Intervallschachtelung	principe *m* des segments emboîtés, principe *m* de Cantor, principe des intervalles intercalés	принцип Кантора (стягивающихся отрезков, вложенных промежутков)
P 1498	**principle of correspondence** <AG>	Korrespondenzprinzip *n*	principe *m* de correspondance	принцип соответствия
P 1499	**principle of correspondence of Zeuthen-Severi** <AG>	Zeuthen-Severisches Korrespondenzprinzip *n*	principe *m* de correspondance de Zeuthen-Severi	принцип соответствия Цейтена-Севери
P 1500	**principle of counting constants** <AG>	Prinzip *n* der Konstantenzählung (Abzählung der Konstanten)	principe *m* de décompte des constantes, principe de l'énumération	принцип пересчета констант
	principle of definition by means of abstraction <FO>	*s.* P 1493		
	principle of definition by transfinite induction <FO>	*s.* T 749		
	principle of degeneration <AG>	*s.* E 255		
	principle of domain extension <FT>	*s.* C 134		
P 1501	**principle of domination,** domination principle <PO>	Dominationsprinzip *n*, zweites Maximumprinzip *n*, Maximumprinzip von H. Cartan	principe *m* de (de la) domination	принцип мажорирования
	principle of duality <PJ>	*s.* D 1002		
P 1502	**principle of energy,** energy principle <PO>	Energieprinzip *n*	principe *m* d'énergie	принцип энергии
P 1503	**principle of equilibrium,** equilibrium principle <PO>	Gleichgewichtsprinzip *n*	principe *m* d'équilibre	принцип равновесия
P 1504	**principle of exchange,** exchange axiom <for dependencies> <AL>	Austauschaxiom *n*	axiome *m* d'échange	аксиома замены
	principle of extension <AL>	*s.* P 1512		
P 1505	**principle of extensionality** <LO>	Extensionalitätsprinzip *n*, Extensionalitätsthese *f*	principe *m* d'extensionalité	принцип экстенсиональности
	principle of extensionality <SE>	*s.* A 1286		
P 1506	**principle of first differences** <SE>	Prinzip *n* der lexikographischen Anordnung	principe *m* des premières différences	принцип лексикографического упорядочения
P 1507	**principle of harmonic measure** <FT>	Prinzip *n* vom harmonischen Maß	principe *m* de la mesure harmonique	принцип гармонической меры
P 1508	**principle of Hermitian continual reduction** <of quadratic forms> <NT>	Hermitesche Reduktionsvorschrift (Vorschrift) *f*	principe *m* de la réduction continuelle d'Hermite	принцип эрмитова приведения
P 1509	**principle of hyperbolic measure** <FT>	Prinzip *n* des hyperbolischen Maßes	principe *m* de mesure hyperbolique	принцип гиперболической меры
	principle of induction <FO, LO>	*s.* P 1510		
	principle of infinity <SE>	*s.* A 1287		
	principle of least squares <ER, NU>	*s.* L 250		
P 1510	**principle of mathematical induction,**	Induktionsprinzip *n*, Prinzip *n* der vollstän-	principe *m* d'induction [mathématique], prin-	принцип математической (полной) индукции,

	English	German	French	Russian
	principle of [complete] induction, induction principle <FO, LO>	digen Induktion	cipe de l'induction [complète], principe d'induction complète	принцип индукции, аксиома [математической] индукции
	principle of maximum <PO>	*s.* M 270		
	principle of maximum likelihood <ST>	*s.* M 261		
	principle of minimum <DE>	*s.* M 614		
	principle of monodromy <FT>	*s.* M 837		
	principle of noetherian induction <AL>	*s.* G 143		
P 1511	**principle of optimality,** optimality principle <PG, ST, TG>	Optimalitätsprinzip *n*	principe *m* d'optimalité	принцип оптимальности
	principle of optimality <PG>	*s.* B 175		
	principle of pairing <SE>	*s.* A 1288		
P 1512	**principle of permanence,** principle of permanence of formal laws, principle of permanence of the formal laws [of operation], principle of permanence of the formal calculating rules, principle of extension <AL>	Permanenzprinzip *n*, Prinzip *n* der Permanenz (Permanenz der formalen Rechengesetze), Erweiterungsprinzip *n*; Prinzip der Permanenz der Grundrechnungsarten	principe *m* de permanence, principe d'extension, principe des relations permanentes, théorème *m* de permanence, principe de prolongement des identités algébriques	принцип перманентности (расширения, продолжения тождеств)
	principle of permanence <FT>	*s.* P 471		
	principle of permanence of formal laws <AL>	*s.* P 1512		
	principle of permanence of the formal calculating rules <AL>	*s.* P 1512		
	principle of permanence of the formal laws of operation <AL>	*s.* P 1512		
P 1513	**principle of permutation,** commutative law <for disjunction and conjunction> <LO>	Kommutativgesetz *n*	loi *f* de commutativité (permutation)	закон коммутативности, переместительный закон
	principle of permutation for the conjunction <LO>	*s.* C 1253		
P 1514	**principle of position** <for a number system> <NT>	Stellenwertprinzip *n*, Positionsprinzip *n*, Prinzip *n* der Position	principe *m* de position [de la numération], règle *f* de position	позиционный принцип
	principle of power-set <SE>	*s.* A 1289		
P 1515	**principle of realizability of goal** <TG>	Prinzip *n* der Zielrealisierbarkeit		принцип осуществимости цели
	principle of recurrence (recursion) <FO, SE>	*s.* P 1519		
P 1516	**principle of recursive construction,** recursion theorem <FO>	Rechtfertigungssatz *m* für die Definition durch vollständige Induktion	théorème *m* de légitimation de la définition par récurrence	теорема узаконения индуктивного определения
	principle of reflection <FT>	*s.* S 172		
P 1517	**principle of relativization** <TO>	Relativierungsprinzip *n*	principe *m* de relativisation	принцип релятивизации
	principle of similarity <FT>	*s.* S 874		
	principle of subsets <LO, SE>	*s.* A 1293		
	principle of summation <LO>	*s.* L 167		
	principle of sum-set <SE>	*s.* A 1295		
	principle of superposition <DE>	*s.* S 2329		
	principle of the argument <FT>	*s.* A 941		
P 1518	**principle of the conservation of the number,** principle of continuity <AG>	Prinzip *n* [von] der Erhaltung der Anzahl, Kontinuitätsprinzip *n*, Stetigkeitsprinzip *n*, Prinzip *n* der Kontinuität (Stetigkeit)	principe *m* de [la] conservation du nombre, principe *m* de continuité (permanence)	принцип непрерывности
	principle of the excluded middle (third) <LO>	*s.* L 184		
	principle of the maximum <FT>	*s.* M 267		
	principle of the smallest number <AN, FO>	*s.* L 247		
	principle of transfer <PJ>	*s.* T 740		
P 1519	**principle of transfinite induction,** principle of recurrence (recursion) <FO, SE>	Prinzip *n* der transfiniten Induktion	principe *m* de l'induction transfinie, principe de récurrence [transfinie]	принцип трансфинитной индукции
P 1520	**principle of trivalence** <LO>	Prinzip *n* (Satz *m*) der Dreiwertigkeit	principe *m* de trois valeurs	принцип трехзначности

	principle of two-valued propositions <LO>	*s.* P 1495		
	principle of uniform boundedness <FA>	*s.* U 120		
	principle of Zorn <SE>	*s.* Z 83		
	principles of continuity <GE>	*s.* A 1300		
P 1521	**Pringsheim['s] definition of convergence** <of a double sequence> <SS>	Pringsheimsche Konvergenzdefinition *f*	définition *f* de la convergence de Pringsheim	определение сходимости Прингсгейма
P 1522	**Pringsheim['s] theorem,** theorem of Pringsheim <FT, SS>	Satz *m* von Pringsheim (Dienes), Pringsheimscher (Dienesscher) Satz	théorème *m* de Pringsheim	теорема Прингсгейма
P 1523	**prior distribution,** a priori distribution <ST>	A-priori-Verteilung *f*, Aprioriverteilung *f*	distribution *f* a (à) priori	априорное распределение [вероятностей]
P 1524	**priority rule for operations** <AL, SE>	Regel *f* für die Bindungsstärke von Operationen	règle *f* de priorité pour les opérations	правило силы операции
P 1525	**prior probability,** a priori probability, probability a priori <ST>	A-priori-Wahrscheinlichkeit *f*, Aprioriwahrscheinlichkeit *f*, Anfangswahrscheinlichkeit *f*, Wahrscheinlichkeit *f* a priori	probabilité *f* a (à) priori	априорная вероятность, вероятность a priori
P 1526	**pri ring,** principal right ideal ring, right principal ideal ring, right pir <AL>	Rechtshauptidealring *m*	anneau *m* à idéaux principaux à droite	кольцо главных правых идеалов, pri-кольцо
P 1527	**prism** <over a complex> <AT>	Prisma *n*, Zylinder *m* <über einem Komplex>	prisme *m* <sur un complexe>	призма <над комплексом>
P 1528	**prismatic surface** <EG>	Prismenfläche *f*	surface *f* prismatique	призматическая поверхность
	prismatic ungula <EG>	*s.* U 103		
P 1529	**prismatoid** <EG>	Prismatoid *n*, Trapezoidalkörper *m*, Körperstumpf *m*	prismatoïde *m*	призматоид
P 1530	**prismoid** <prismatoid the base and covering surface of which having equal number of sides> <EG>	Prismoid *n*	prismoïde *m*	призмоид
	prismoidal formula <DI, NU>	*s.* S 1008		
	prismoidal formula <EG, NU>	*s.* K 43		
P 1531	**Privalov['s] theorem** <FT, PO>	Satz *m* von Priwalow, Priwalowscher Satz	théorème *m* de Privalov	теорема Привалова
P 1532	**proalgebraic group** <AL>	proalgebraische Gruppe *f*	groupe *m* proalgébrique	проалгебраическая группа
P 1533	**probability algebra** <ST>	Wahrscheinlichkeitsalgebra *f*	algèbre *f* de probabilités	алгебра вероятностей
	probability a posteriori <ST>	*s.* P 1107		
	probability a priori <ST>	*s.* P 1525		
	probability calculus <ST>	*s.* P 1547		
	probability chart <IN, ST>	*s.* P 1543		
	probability convergence <ST>	*s.* C 2338		
	probability curve <ST>	*s.* E 471		
P 1534	**probability density [function],** distribution density, density of probability, density, density function, probability function, relative frequency function <ST>	Wahrscheinlichkeitsdichte *f*, Verteilungsdichte *f*, Dichte *f* der Wahrscheinlichkeit[sverteilung], Dichte, Dichtefunktion *f*, Wahrscheinlichkeitsdichtefunktion *f*	densité *f* de probabilité (distribution, répartition), densité, probabilité *f* différentielle, fonction *f* des densités, fonction de densité, fonction des probabilités élémentaires, loi *f* de probabilité, loi élémentaire de probabilité	плотность вероятности, плотность распределения [вероятностей], плотность математического ожидания, плотность, дифференциальный закон распределения, закон распределения, функция плотности
P 1535	**probability distribution,** distribution, distribution law, random distribution <ST>	Wahrscheinlichkeitsverteilung *f*, Verteilung *f*, Verteilungsgesetz *n*, Zufallsverteilung *f*, zufällige Verteilung	distribution *f* des (de) probabilités, distribution, loi *f* de distribution, distribution aléatoire	распределение вероятностей, распределение, закон распределения, случайное распределение
	probability distribution function <ST>	*s.* D 758		
P 1536	**probability element** <ST>	Wahrscheinlichkeitselement *n*	élément *m* de probabilité	элемент вероятности, дифференциал функции распределения
	probability field <ST>	*s.* P 1545		
P 1537	**probability for exceeding,** exceeding probability <ST>	Überschreitungswahrscheinlichkeit *f*	probabilité *f* de dépassage	вероятность превышения [уровня]
	probability for exceeding <ST>	*s. a.* S 842		
	probability frequency function <ST>	*s.* F 649		
P 1538	**probability function** <ST>	Wahrscheinlichkeitsfunktion *f*	fonction *f* de probabilité	функция вероятности
	probability function <ST>	*s. a.* 1. D 758; 2. P 1534		
P 1539	**probability generating function,** generating function <ST>	wahrscheinlichkeitserzeugende Funktion *f*, Wahrscheinlichkeitserzeugende *f*, erzeugende Funktion, Erzeugende *f*	fonction *f* génératrice des probabilités, fonction génératrice	производящая функция вероятностей, производящая функция

No.	English	German	French	Russian
P 1540	**probability integral** <ST>	Wahrscheinlichkeits-integral *n*	intégrale *f* de probabilité	интеграл вероятности
	probability matrix <MD, ST>	*s.* S 1797		
P 1541	**probability measure,** normalized measure <ME, ST>	Wahrscheinlichkeitsmaß *n*, normiertes Maß *n*	mesure *f* de probabilité, mesure normée	вероятностная мера, мера вероятности, нормализованная мера
	probability model <ST>	*s.* S 1799		
P 1542	**probability of death** <ST>	Sterbenswahrscheinlichkeit *f*	probabilité *f* de mort	вероятность смерти (смертности)
P 1543	**probability paper,** probability chart <IN, ST>	Wahrscheinlichkeitspapier *n*, Wahrscheinlichkeitsnetz *n*	papier *m* à échelle fonctionnelle de probabilité [cumulée], diagramme *m* à échelle fonctionnelle de probabilité [cumulée]	вероятностная бумага (сетка)
	probability ratio test <ST>	*s.* L 692		
P 1544	**probability sampling** <ST>	Wahrscheinlichkeitsstichprobenverfahren *n*, Zufallsauswahl *f*	échantillonnage (sondage) *m* probabiliste	вероятностный выбор
P 1545	**probability space,** probability field <ST>	Wahrscheinlichkeitsraum *m*, Wahrscheinlichkeitsfeld *n*	espace *m* probabilisé (de probabilité), champ *m* de probabilité, champ des probabilités	вероятностное пространство, поле вероятностей, случайное поле
P 1546	**probability statement** <ST>	Wahrscheinlichkeitsaussage *f*	jugement *m* de probabilité	вероятностное утверждение
P 1547	**probability theory,** theory of probabilities, probability calculus, calculus of probability (probabilities), theory of chance[s] <ST>	Wahrscheinlichkeitsrechnung *f*, Wahrscheinlichkeitstheorie *f*	calcul *m* des probabilités, // règle *f* des partis	теория вероятностей (вероятности), исчисление вероятностей, расчет вероятности
	probability unit <ST>	*s.* P 1552		
P 1548	**probability vector** <ST>	Wahrscheinlichkeitsvektor *m*	vecteur *m* de probabilités	вектор вероятностей
P 1549	**probable deviation,** probable error <ER, ST>	wahrscheinliche Abweichung *f*, wahrscheinlicher Fehler *m*	écart *m* (erreur *f*) probable	вероятное отклонение, вероятная погрешность (ошибка)
P 1550	**probable ellipse** <ST>	wahrscheinliche Ellipse *f*	ellipse *f* probable	вероятностный эллипс
P 1551	**probable ellipsoid** <ST>	wahrscheinliches Ellipsoid *n*	ellipsoïde *m* probable	вероятностный эллипсоид
	probable error <ER, ST>	*s.* D 1549		
P 1552	**probit,** probability unit <ST>	Probit *m*	probit *m*	пробит
P 1553	**probit analysis** <ST>	Probitanalyse *f*	analyse *f* par la méthode des probits	пробит-анализ, анализ пробитов
P 1554	**probit regression line** <ST>	Probitregressionsgerade *f*	ligne *f* de régression des probits	прямая регрессии, построенная пробит-методом
P 1555	**probit transformation** <ST>	Probittransformation *f*	transformation *f* en probits	пробит-преобразование
	problem <AR, GN>	*s.* E 689		
P 1556	**"problème des rencontres"** <CT>	Problem *n* der Begegnungen	problème *m* des rencontres	задача о встречах
	problem of allocation <PG>	*s.* A 1056		
P 1557	**problem of Apollonius,** Apollonius['s] problem <EG>	Berührungsaufgabe *f* von Apollonios, Berührungsproblem *n* des Apollonios (Apollonius), Taktionsproblem *n* des Apollonios (Apollonius), Apollonisches Berührungsproblem	problème *m* d'Apollonius, problème apollonien (de tangence), problème de contact d'Apollonius	задача о касании Аполлония, задача Аполлония [о касании]
	problem of assignment <PG>	*s.* A 1056		
P 1558	**problem of Bolza,** Bolza['s] problem <with separate *or* mixed final conditions> <VA>	Bolza-Problem *n* <mit getrennten *oder* gemischten Endbedingungen>	problème *m* de Bolza <aux conditions finales séparées *ou* mixtes>	задача Больца <с разделенными *или* смешанными конечными условиями>
P 1559	**problem of characteristics** <GE>	Charakteristikenproblem *n* <Chasles>	problème *m* des caractéristiques	проблема характеристик
	problem of colouring maps in four colours <GP>	*s.* F 506		
P 1560	**problem of contact** <of circles *or* spheres> <EG>	Berührungsproblem *n*, Berührungsaufgabe *f*	problème *m* de contact (tangence)	задача о касании
	problem of coordination <PG>	*s.* C 2438		
P 1561	**problem of Douglas,** Douglas['] problem <AN>	Problem *n* von Douglas, verallgemeinertes Plateausches Problem, Douglassches Problem	problème *m* de Douglas	обобщенная задача Плато, задача Дугласа
P 1562	**problem of fixed points** <AT>	Fixpunktproblem *n*	problème *m* des points invariants	задача о неподвижных точках
P 1563	**problem of Goldbach-Waring,** Goldbach-Waring problem <NT>	Goldbach-Waringsches Problem *n*, Waring-Goldbachsches Problem *n*	problème *m* de Waring-Goldbach	проблема Гольдбаха-Варинга
P 1564	**problem of Hopf,** Hopf['s] problem <for groups> <GR>	Hopfsches Problem *n*	problème *m* de Hopf	проблема Хопфа
	problem of interpolation <AX, FD, NU>	*s.* I 782		
	problem of *k* samples <ST>	*s.* K 180		

	English	German	French	Russian
	problem of Lagrange <VA>	*s.* L 29		
P 1565	**problem of Lucas** <CT, GP>	Problem *n* der Ehepaare	problème *m* des ménages, problème de Lucas	задача о супружеских парах, задача о гостях, задача Люка
P 1566	**problem of Mayer** <in the calculus of variations> <VA>	Mayersches Variationsproblem *n*	problème *m* de Mayer	задача Майера, вариационная задача Майера
	problem of moduli <AL, FT>	*s.* M 784		
P 1567	**problem of moments,** moment problem <AN, ST>	Momentenproblem *n*	problème *m* des moments	проблема (задача) моментов
P 1568	**problem of Plateau,** Plateau['s] problem <DG>	Plateausches Problem *n*	problème *m* de Plateau	задача Плато
P 1569	**problem of Poincaré** <FT>; Poincaré['s] problem <TO>	Problem *n* von Poincaré <FT>; Poincarésches Problem <TO>	problème *m* de Poincaré	проблема Пуанкаре
P 1570	**problem of prime twins** <NT>	Problem *n* der Primzahlzwillinge	problème *m* des jumeaux	проблема близнецов
P 1571	**problem of projectivity** <in the plane *or* in the space> <PJ>	Problem *n* der Projektivität <ebenes *oder* räumliches>	problème *m* de projectivité <dans le plan *ou* dans l'espace>	задача проективности <в плоскости *или* в пространстве>
P 1572	**problem of pursuit** <DE>	Verfolgungsaufgabe *f*	problème *m* de poursuite	задача погони
	problem of random walk <SP>	*s.* R 117		
P 1573	**problem of semantical completeness** <LO>	Vollständigkeitsproblem *n* im weiteren Sinne	problème *m* de la complétude au sens large	проблема полноты в широком смысле
P 1574	**problem of Souslin,** Souslin['s] problem, problem of Suslin <SE>	Suslinsches Problem *n*	problème *m* de Souslin	проблема Суслина
	problem of Suslin <SE>	*s.* P 1574		
P 1575	**problem of testing** <ST>	Testproblem *n*, statistisches Testproblem	problème *m* du test [statistique]	задача проверки статистической гипотезы
	problem of the Königsberg bridges <GP>	*s.* K 134		
P 1576	**problem of the queens** <CT>	Achtköniginnenproblem *n*	problème *m* des 8 reines [du jeu d'échecs]	задача восьми ферзей
	problem of the seven bridges of Königsberg <GP>	*s.* K 134		
P 1577	**problem of the sphere** <GU>	Kugelproblem *n*	problème *m* de la sphère	проблема шара
P 1578	**problem of three factories and three utilities,** three houses problem <GP>	Problem *n* der zänkischen Nachbarn, dreifaches Versorgungsproblem *n* von drei Häusern		задача о трех домах и трех колодцах, задача о трех пунктах обслуживания и трех домах
	problem of trigonometric moments <AN, ST>	*s.* T 945		
P 1579	**problem of triple systems** <CT>	Problem *n* der dreifachen Systeme, Problem der Tripelsysteme <Steiner>	problème *m* des systèmes triples	задача систем троек
P 1580	**problem of trisection** <of an angle> <AL, EG>	Trisektionsproblem *n*, Problem *n* der Dreiteilung des Winkels	problème *m* de la trisection <d'un angle>	проблема трисекции <угла>
P 1581	**problem on the knight's moves** <CT>	Rösselsprungproblem *n*, Rösselsprungaufgabe *f*	problème *m* de cavalier	задача о ходе конем
P 1582	**procedural bias,** error of procedure, error of approximation <ER, NU>	Verfahrensfehler *m*	biais *m* dû au procédé, erreur *f* systématique due au procédé, distorsion *f* due au procédé, erreur du procédé, erreur de (due à) la méthode, erreur d'approximation	смещение, обусловленное методом обработки; погрешность, обусловленная методом обработки; погрешность метода, ошибка приближения
	σ-process <AG>	*s.* B 510		
P 1583/4	**process average** <SP>	Prozeßmittelwert *m*	moyenne *f* du processus	среднее значение процесса
	process of rationalizing <AL, AN>	*s.* R 801		
	process with aftereffect <SP>	*s.* S 1806		
	process with continuous time <SP>	*s.* S 1807		
	process with independent increments <SP>	*s.* S 1808		
	process with orthogonal increments <SP>	*s.* O 481		
P 1585	**proconstructible set** <AG>	pro-konstruierbare Menge *f*	ensemble *m* pro-constructible	проконструируемое множество
P 1586	**producer's risk** <ST>	Produzentenrisiko *n*, Risiko *n* des Produzenten	risque *m* du producteur	риск производства (производителя)
P 1587	**product** <of correspondences> <AG>	Produkt *n* <von Korrespondenzen>	composé *m* <des correspondances>	композиция <соответствий>
P 1588	**○-product** <in a ring> <AL>	Kreisprodukt *n*	○-produit *m*	«круговое» произведение <вида $a \circ b = a + b - ab$>
P 1589	**product** <of numbers> <AR>	Produkt *n*	produit *m*	произведение
P 1590	**product** <of inversions> <AY>	Produkt *n* <von Inversionen>	anallagmatie *f*, produit *m* <d'inversions>	произведение <инверсий>
P 1591	**product,** direct join <CA>	Produkt *n*, direktes Produkt	produit *m* direct, produit	произведение, прямое произведение
P 1592	**product,** group product <of group elements> <GR>	Produkt *n*	produit *m*	произведение

No.	English	Deutsch	Français	Русский
P 1593	**product** <of filters> <SE>	Filterprodukt *n*, Produktfilter *m*, Produkt *n*	filtre *m* produit, produit *m* <de filtres>	фильтр-произведение, произведение <фильтров>
P 1594	**product** <of uniform spaces> <TO>	Produkt *n* <uniformer Räume>	espace *m* uniforme produit	произведение <равномерных пространств>
P 1595	**product,** iterate, composition, resultant, composite, composition product <of mappings, functions>; composite mapping, product mapping, composite function, composition mapping <AN, SE, TO>	Produkt *n*, Zusammensetzung *f*, Verkettung *f*, Kompositum *n*, kategorisches Produkt <von Abbildungen, Funktionen>; zusammengesetzte Abbildung *f*, Produktabbildung *f*	produit *m*, composé *m*, résultant *m* <d'applications>; application *f* composée, application-composition *f*, application produit	произведение, композиция, суперпозиция <отображений, функций>; составное (сложное) отображение
P 1596	**product,** tensor product, outer product, general product <of tensors> <VT>	allgemeines Produkt (Tensorprodukt) *n*, Tensorprodukt *n*, direktes Produkt	produit *m* tensoriel, produit général	тензорное (общее) произведение
	product <AL>	*s.* 1. B 556; 2. C 1692; 3. C 1694		
	product <AN>	*s.* M 1049		
	product <CA>	*s.* 1. C 1673; 2. P 1629		
	product <LA>	*s.* M 362		
	product <SE>	*s.* 1. C 128; 2. C 173; 3. I 802; 4. O 311		
	product <SE, UA>	*s.* R 767		
	product <TO>	*s.* 1. P 1627; 2. P 1633		
	⌒ **product** <AT>	*s.* C 106		
	product-aggregate <SE>	*s.* C 173		
P 1597	**product algebra** <AL>	Produktalgebra *f*	algèbre *f* produit	произведение алгебр
P 1598	**product bundle** <TO>	Produktbündel *n*	fibré *m* produit	расслоение-произведение, прямое произведение
P 1599	**product category,** product of categories <CA>	Produktkategorie *f*	catégorie *f* produit	произведение категорий
P 1600	**product chain complex** <HA>	Produkt *n* <von Kettenkomplexen>	complexe *m* <de chaînes> produit	произведение <цепных комплексов>
P 1601	**product class** <SE>	Produktklasse *f*	classe *f* produit	класс-произведение
	product-complete category <CA>	*s.* C 223		
P 1602	**product complex** <AT>	Produktkomplex *m*	complexe-produit *m*	произведение комплексов, комплекс-произведение
P 1603	**product cycle** <AG>	Produktzyklus *m*	cycle *m* produit	цикл-произведение
P 1604	**product deviation** <ST>	Produktabweichung *f*	produit *m* des écarts	отклонение произведения, произведение отклонений
P 1605	**product diagram** <CA>	Produktdiagramm *n*	diagramme *m* produit	произведение диаграмм
P 1606	**product directed set** <SE>	gerichtete Produktmenge *f*	ensemble *m* filtrant produit	фильтрующее множество-произведение
P 1607	**product equation** <for the terms of a proportion> <AR>	Produktgleichung *f*	égalité *f* du produit des extrêmes au produit des moyennes	равенство произведений <пропорции>
P 1608	**product filtration** <AL>	Produktfiltration *f*	filtration *f* produit	произведение фильтраций
P 1609	**product formula** <for a valuation> <AB>	Produktformel *f* <der Bewertungstheorie>	formule *f* [dite] du produit, formule [du produit] d'Artin-Whaples	формула для произведения нормирований
P 1610	**product formula** <for the norm residue symbol> <AB>	Produktformel *f*	formule *f* du produit	формула произведения
P 1611	**product formulas** <for the trigonometric functions> <EG>	Produktformeln *fpl*	formules *fpl* pour les produits des fonctions trigonométriques	[тригонометрические] формулы приведения к виду, удобному для логарифмирования
	product function <AN>	*s.* C 1678		
	product ideal <LA>	*s.* D 995		
P 1612	**product integral** <DE, MD>	Produktintegral *n*	intégrale *f* de produit	мультипликативный интеграл
P 1613	**production,** rewriting rule <for Post's algorithm> <MM>	Produktion *f*, Substitutionsregel *f*	règle *f*	правило вывода
P 1614	**productive set** <MM>	produktive Menge *f*	ensemble *m* productif	продуктивное множество
P 1615	**product kernel** <IE>	Produktkern *m*	noyau *m* produit	ядро-произведение
P 1616	**product mapping** <in the product space> <TO>	Produktabbildung *f*	application *f* produit	отображение-произведение, составное отображение
	product mapping <AN, SE, TO>	*s.* P 1595		
P 1617	**product measure** <ME>	Produktmaß *n*	mesure *f* produit	мера произведения, мера-произведение
P 1618	**product metric** <TO>	Produktmetrik *f*	métrique *f* produit	метрика произведения
P 1619	**product module** <AL>	Produktmodul *m*	module *m* produit	модуль-произведение
P 1620	**product moment,** bilinear moment <ST>	Produktmoment *n*	moment *m* mixte	смешанный момент
P 1621	**product-moment correlation** <ST>	Produktmomentkorrelation *f*, Korrelation *f* [im engsten Sinne]	corrélation *f* des moments mixtes	корреляция смешанных моментов
	product-moment correlation coefficient <ST>	*s.* P 348		
P 1622	**product object** <CA>	Produktobjekt *n*	objet *m* produit	объект-произведение
	product of a scalar and a matrix <MD>	*s.* S 85		
	product of categories <CA>	*s.* P 1599		
P 1623	**product of differences,** difference-product <FD>	Differenzenprodukt *n*	produit *m* des différences	произведение разностей

	English	German	French	Russian
P 1624	**product of rings** <AL>	Produktring *m*	anneau *m* produit, anneau-produit *m*	произведение колец
P 1625	**product order** <SE>	Produktordnung *f*, Produkthalbordnung *f*	ordre *m* produit	произведение порядков
P 1626	**product orientation** <AL, GE>	Produktorientierung *f*	orientation *f* produit	произведение ориентирований
	product over an object <CA>	*s.* P 2028		
P 1627	**product path,** product, composition <of paths> <TO>	zusammengesetzter Weg *m*, Zusammensetzung *f* <von Wegen>, Produktweg *m*	chemin *m* composé	произведение путей, сложный путь
P 1628	**product preserving functor** <CA>	produkterhaltender Funktor *m*	foncteur *m* préservant les produits	функтор, сохраняющий произведения
P 1629	**product scheme,** product <of diagram schemes> <CA>	Produkt *n* <von Diagrammschemata>	schéma *m* <de diagrammes> produit	произведение <схем диаграмм>
P 1630	**product series** <of power series> <SS>	Produktreihe *f*, Produkt *n* <von Reihen>	série *f* produit	ряд-произведение
P 1631	**product set** <SE>	Produktmenge *f*	ensemble *m* produit	множество-произведение
P 1632	**product sign,** Π <GN>	Produktzeichen *n*, Π	signe *f* de produit, Π	знак произведения, Π
P 1633	**product space;** product <of spaces> <TO>	Produktraum *m*; Produkt *n* <von Räumen>	espace *m* produit; produit *m* d'espaces	пространство-произведение; произведение пространств
P 1634	**product star** <FT>	Produktstern *m*	étoile *f* produit	звезда-произведение
P 1635	**product structure** <AL, TO>	Produktstruktur *f*	structure *f* produit	произведение структур
P 1636	**product theorem** <for the different> <AL>	Produktsatz *m*	théorème *m* de produit	теорема о произведении
	product theorem for norm residue symbols <AB>	*s.* H 128		
P 1637	**product topology,** Tychonoff['s] topology <TO>	Produkttopologie *f*, Tychonoffsche (schwache) Topologie *f*	topologie *f* produit (de Tychonoff, faible)	тихоновская топология, произведение топологий
P 1638	**product transformation** <AL, GE, SE>	Produkttransformation *f*, Produkt *n* <von Transformationen>	transformation *f* produit, produit *m* de [deux] transformations, transformation résultante	произведение преобразований
P 1639	**product uniformity** <of uniform structures> <TO>	Produktstruktur *f*, Produkt *n* <uniformer Strukturen>	structure *f* [uniforme] produit	произведение <равномерных структур>
P 1640	**product variety, product-variety** <AG, GE, TO>	Produktmannigfaltigkeit *f*	variété *f* produit	произведение многообразий, многообразие-произведение
	profile <DS>	*s.* C 2702		
	profile line <DS>	*s.* T 426		
P 1641	**pro-finite completion** <GR>	proendliche Vervollständigung *f*	complété *m* profini	проконечное пополнение
P 1642	**pro-finite group** <GR>	proendliche Gruppe *f*	groupe *m* profini	проконечная группа
	prognosis <SP>	*s.* F 458a		
	program <PG>	*s.* S 1265		
	program evaluation and research task <PG>	*s.* P 525		
	program evaluation and review technique <PG>	*s.* P 525		
	programme <PG>	*s.* S 1265		
	programming <PG>	*s.* M 170		
	0—1 programming <PG>	*s.* Z 50		
P 1643	**progression** <AR>	Progression *f*, // fortschreitende Reihe *f*	progression *f*, // suite *f* progressive	прогрессия
P 1644	**progressive multiplication** <AL>	progressive Multiplikation *f*	multiplication *f* progressive <Grassmann>	прогрессивное умножение
	projecting <DS>	*s.* P 1650		
P 1645	**projecting cone** <DS>	projizierender Kegel *m*, Strahlenkegel *m*	cône *m* projetant	проектирующий конус
	projecting line <DS>	*s.* P 1736		
P 1646	**projecting plane** <DS>	projizierende Ebene *f*, Sehebene *f*	plan *m* projetant	проектирующая плоскость
	projecting ray <DS>	*s.* P 1736		
P 1647	**projection** <of a correspondence> <AG>	Projektion *f*	projection *f*	проекция
P 1648	**projection,** evaluation, evaluation map, coordinate function <of a cartesian product> <AL, SE>	Projektionsabbildung *f*, Projektion *f*	projection *f*, fonction *f* coordonnée (projection)	проектирование, проектирующая функция
P 1649	**projection,** bundle (fibre) projection, fibration <of a fibre bundle> <AT>	Projektion *f* <eines Faserbündels>	projection *f* <d'un espace fibré>	проекция <расслоенного пространства>, расслаивающее отображение
P 1650	**projection,** projecting <as an operation> <DS>	Projizieren *n*, Projektion *f*	projection *f*	проектирование, проецирование, операция проектирования (проецирования)
P 1651	**projection** <as an image> <DS>	Projektion *f*, projektives Bild *n*	projection *f*	проекция
P 1652	**projection,** covering [projection] <of a covering space *or* surface> <GE, TO>	Spurabbildung *f*	projection *f*	проекция, проектирование, накрывающее отображение
P 1653	**projection** <of a point of a covering space> <TO>	Spurpunkt *m* <eines Punktes>	trace *f* <d'un point>	проекция, след <точки>
	projection <AL>	*s.* C 70		
	projection <CA>	*s.* P 1659		
	projection <FA>	*s.* 1. P 1737; 2. P 1738		

No.	English	German	French	Russian
	projection <FA, VT>	*s.* C 2419		
	projection <PJ>	*s.* D 154		
	projection <SE>	*s.* N 32		
	projection <ST>	*s.* C 1813		
P 1654	**projection chain map** <HA>	natürliche Kettentransformation *f* eines Kettenkomplexes auf einen Faktorkomplex	chaine-homomorphisme *m* naturel d'un complexe de chaîne sur un complexe quotient	цепная проекция
P 1655	**projection cone** <of a convex body> <CS, GE>	Projektionskegel *m*, Kontingens *m* <Bouligand>	cône *m* de projection	опорный конус
P 1656	**projection functor** <CA>	Projektion *f* <Faktorkategorie>; Projektionsfunktor *m* <Produktkategorie>	foncteur *m* de projection	функтор проекции
P 1657	**projection into the *n*-th co-ordinate set,** evaluation at *n*, *n*-th projection <of a cartesian product> <AL, SE>	zum Index *n* gehörige Projektionsabbildung *f*, *n*-te Projektionsabbildung (Projektion *f*), Projektion auf die *n*-te Achse	projection *f* d'indice *n*	проектирование на *n*-ю ось, проектирование на *n*-е множество, *n*-я проектирующая функция
	projection map <SE>	*s.* N 32		
P 1658	**projection matrix** <AL, MD>	Projektionsmatrix *f*	matrice-projection *f*	проекционная матрица
P 1659	**projection morphism,** [canonical] projection <of products *or* limits> <CA>	Projektion *f*, kanonische Projektion	projection *f* canonique, projection	каноническая проекция, проекция
P 1660	**projection of the knot** <AT>	Knotenprojektion *f*	projection *f* du nœud	проекция узла
P 1661	**projection on axis** <DS>	Achsenprojektion *f*, Projektion *f* auf die Achse	projection *f* sur l'axe	проекция на ось
P 1662	**projection operator** <AL>	Projektionsoperator *m*	projecteur *m*, opérateur *m* de projection	оператор проектирования
	projection operator <FA>	*s.* 1. P 1737; 2. P 1738		
P 1663	**projection plane,** plane of projection, picture plane <DS>	Bildtafel *f*, Projektionsebene *f*, Bildebene *f*	plan *m* de projection, plan image	плоскость проекций, картинная плоскость
	projection with elevations <DS>	*s.* T 501		
	projection with heights <DS>	*s.* T 501		
	projective <CA>	*s.* P 1715		
P 1664	**projective algebraic variety** <AG>	projektive algebraische Menge (Mannigfaltigkeit) *f*, algebraische Mannigfaltigkeit; projektive Menge des $\mathbf{P}^m(C)$	ensemble *m* algébrique projectif, variété *f* algébrique projective	проективное алгебраическое многообразие
P 1665	**projective algebraic variety,** algebraic variety, projective variety <FT>	projektiv-algebraische (projektive algebraische, algebraische, projektive) Mannigfaltigkeit *f*	variété *f* algébrique projective, variété algébrique (projective)	проективно-алгебраическое (алгебраическое, проективное) многообразие
P 1666	**projective arc length** <DG>	Projektivbogenlänge *f*	arc *m* projectif	проективная дуга (длина дуги)
P 1667	**projective assembly,** projective group <e.g. of points> <PJ>	projektive Gruppe *f*	assemblage (groupe) *m* projectif	проективная группа
	projective axioms of incidence <PJ>	*s.* A 1304		
P 1668	**projective base** <PJ>	projektive Basis *f*	base *f* projective, repère *m* projectif	проективная база
P 1669	**projective binormal** <DG>	Projektivbinormale *f*	binormale *f* projective	проективная бинормаль
	projective chart <NO>	*s.* H 450		
P 1670	**projective closure,** projective extension <of a *k*-set> <AG>	projektive Erweiterung *f*	fermeture *f* projective	проективизация
P 1671	**projective closure** <of an affine space *or* a vector bundle> <AT, GE>	projektive Abschließung *f*	complétion *f* projective	проективизация
P 1672	**projective collineation** <AY, PJ>	projektive Kollineation *f*	collinéation *f* projective	проективная коллинеация
P 1673	**projective cone,** inverse cone <with domain vertex *A* and base *d*> <CA>	Pinsel *m* <von Morphismen mit Quelle *A*>	cône *m* projectif <à sommet *A*>	конус <с вершиной *A*>, обратный конус <с начальной вершиной *A*>, проективный конус <с начальной вершиной *A* и базой *d*>
P 1674	**projective conic,** conic section in projective geometry <PJ>	projektiver Kegelschnitt *m*	conique *f* (section *f* conique) projective	проективное коническое сечение, проективная коника
	projective connected manifold <DG>	*s.* P 1701		
	projective connected space <DG>	*s.* P 1702		
P 1675	**projective connection,** projective transfer <DG>	projektive Übertragung *f*, projektiver Zusammenhang *m*	connexion *f* projective, transfert *m* projectif	проективная связность, проективное перенесение
	projective connection component <DG>	*s.* C 1666		
P 1676	**projective co-ordinates; projective co-ordinate system,** set (system) of projective co-ordinates, projective system (set) [of co-ordinates] <AG, AY, PJ>	projektive Koordinaten *fpl*; projektives Koordinatensystem *n*	coordonnées *fpl* projectives; système *m* de coordonnées projectives, système projectif [de coordonnées]	проективные координаты; система проективных координат, проективная система [координат]

	English	German	French	Russian
P 1677	**projective cover** <of a module *or* object> <AL, CA>	projektive Hülle *f*	enveloppe *f* projective	проективное покрытие <модуля>; проективная оболочка <объекта>
P 1678	**projective curvature** <DG>	Projektivkrümmung *f*	courbure *f* projective	проективная кривизна
P 1679	**projective curvature tensor,** Weyl['s] curvature tensor <DG>	projektiver Krümmungstensor *m*, Projektivkrümmungstensor *m*, Weylscher Tensor *m*	tenseur *m* de courbure projective	тензор проективной кривизны
	projective deformation <PJ>	*s.* P 1680		
P 1680	**projective development,** projective deformation <PJ>	projektive Abwicklung (Deformation) *f*	développement *m* projectif, déformation *f* projective	проективная развертка, проективное развертывание (деформирование)
P 1681	**projective differential geometry** <DG>	projektive Differentialgeometrie *f*	géométrie *f* différentielle projective	проективно-дифференциальная геометрия, проективная дифференциальная геометрия
P 1682	**projective differential of arc,** projective line element <DG>	Projektivbogenelement *n*, Projektivlinienelement *n*, projektives Bogenelement (Linienelement) *n*	différentielle *f* de l'arc projective, élément *m* d'arc (linéaire) projectif	проективный дифференциал дуги, проективный линейный элемент
P 1683	**projective dimension,** homogeneous dimension <AG>	homogene Dimension *f*	dimension *f* homogène	однородная размерность
P 1684	**projective dimension** <CA, PJ>	projektive Dimension *f*	dimension *f* projective	проективная размерность
	projective dimension <AL, AT, CA>	*s.* H 456/7		
P 1685	**projective displacement,** projective transfer <PJ>	projektive Verschiebung (Übertragung) *f*	transport (transfert) *m* projectif	проективное перенесение
	projective division <PJ>	*s.* H 452		
P 1686	**projective duality theorem** <PJ>	projektiver Dualitätssatz *m*	théorème *m* de dualité projective	теорема проективной двойственности
	projective extension <AG>	*s.* P 1670		
	projective family of mappings <TO>	*s.* C 1120		
P 1687	**projective general linear group,** projective group <of *n* variables over *K*> <AY, GR, PJ>	allgemeine projektive Gruppe *f* <für *n* Variable über *K*>, *n*-äre projektive Gruppe, Gruppe der linearen projektiven Abbildungen von $P_{n-1}(K)$ auf sich, projektive Gruppe PGL (*n*,*K*)	groupe *m* projectif général, groupe projectif <à *n* variables sur *K*>	общая проективная группа, проективная группа <от *n* переменных над *K*>
P 1688	**projective generation,** Steiner['s] generation <of conics> <PJ, SG>	projektive Erzeugung *f*, Steinersche Erzeugung	génération *f* projective, génération de Steiner	проективное порождение, порождение Штейнера
P 1689	**projective generator** <CA>	projektiver Generator *m*	générateur *m* projectif	проективный образующий
P 1690	**projective-geometric** <PJ>	projektiv-geometrisch, projektiv geometrisch	de (en, à, par) géométrie projective	проективно-геометрический
P 1691	**projective geometry** <*n*-dimensional> <as a lattice> <LA>	projektive Geometrie *f* <*n*-dimensionale>	treillis *m* projectif, géométrie *f* projective <de dimension *n*>	проективная геометрия <*n*-мерная>
P 1692	**projective geometry** <PJ>	projektive Geometrie *f*, // projectivische Geometrie	géométrie *f* projective	проективная геометрия, // геометрия положения
	projective geometry in the plane <PJ>	*s.* P 655		
P 1693	**projective group** <AY, GR, PJ>	projektive Gruppe *f*	groupe *m* projectif	проективная группа
	projective group <AY, GR, PJ>	*s. a.* P 1687		
	projective group <PJ>	*s.* P 1667		
P 1694	**projective Hjelmslev plane** <PJ>	projektive Hjelmslev-Ebene *f*, PH-Ebene	plan *m* de Hjelmslev (Petersen) projectif	проективная плоскость Петерсена
P 1695	**projective *k*-set** <AG>	projektive *k*-Menge *f* (Mannigfaltigkeit *f* über *k*) <nicht notwendig irreduzibel>	ensemble *m* algébrique projectif sur *k*, *k*-ensemble *m* projectif	проективное *k*-множество, проективное алгебраическое множество над *k*
P 1696	**projective *k*-variety,** irreducible projective *k*-set <AG>	projektive Varietät *f* über *k*, projektive *k*-Varietät *f*	*k*-variété *f* projective, variété *f* projective irréductible sur *k*	неприводимое проективное *k*-многообразие
	projective *k*-variety projectively normal over *k* <AG>	*s.* A 947		
P 1697	**projective limit,** inverse limit <of an inverse system> <AL, TO>	projektiver (inverser) Limes *m* <eines inversen Systems>	limite *f* projective (inverse, gauche) <d'un système projectif>	проективный (обратный) предел, предел <обратного спектра>
P 1698	**projective limit** <of topological spaces> <TO>	projektiver Limes *m* <von Räumen>	espace *m* limite projectif	проективный предел <топологических пространств>
	projective limit <CA>	*s.* 1. L 697; 2. L 736		
P 1699	**projective line** <PJ>	projektive Gerade *f*	droite *f* projective	проективная прямая
	projective line element <DG>	*s.* P 1682		
P 1700	**projective line geometry** <DG>	projektive Liniengeometrie *f*	géométrie *f* réglée projective	проективная линейчатая геометрия
P 1701	**projectively connected manifold,** projective connected manifold <DG>	projektiv zusammenhängende Mannigfaltigkeit *f*, Mannigfaltigkeit mit projektiver Übertragung	variété *f* à connexion projective	многообразие проективной связности

P 1702	**projectively connected space,** projective connected space <DG>	projektiv[-]zusammenhängender Raum *m*	espace *m* à connexion projective	пространство проективной связности
P 1703	**projectively deformable surface, projectively developable surface** <PJ>	projektiv abwickelbare Fläche *f*, projektiv deformierbare Fläche	surface *f* projectivement déformable (développable)	проективно деформируемая (развертывающаяся) поверхность
P 1704	**projectively flat space** <DG>	projektiv-ebener (projektiv-euklidischer) Raum *m*	espace *m* projectivement plat	проективно плоское (евклидово) пространство
P 1705	**projectively independent points** <PJ>	projektiv unabhängige Punkte *mpl*	famille *f* de points [projectivement] libre, points *mpl* projectivement indépendants	проективно независимые точки
	projectively normal *k*-variety <AG>	*s.* A 947		
P 1706	**projective mapping** <of an object> <CA>	projektive Abbildung *f*	application *f* projective	проективное отображение
P 1707	**projective mapping,** projective transformation (relation), projectivity <not necessarily linear> <PJ>	Projektivität *f*, projektive Abbildung (Verwandtschaft) *f*, Kollineation *f*	application (transformation, relation) *f* projective, projectivité *f*	проективное преобразование (отображение, соответствие), проективность
	projective mapping <AY, PJ>	*s.* C 1147		
	projective mensuration <PJ>	*s.* P 1708		
P 1708	**projective metric [determination],** Cayley[-Klein] metric, projective mensuration <PJ>	projektive (Cayley[-Klein]-sche) Maßbestimmung *f*, projektive Metrik *f*	métrique *f* projective (de Cayley[-Klein]), détermination *f* métrique projective	проективная метрика, метрика Кэли (Кэли-Клейна), мероопределение Кэли[-Клейна], проективное мероопределение
P 1709	**projective minimal surface** <DG>	Projektivminimalfläche *f*	surface *f* minimale projective	проективная минимальная поверхность
P 1710	**projective module** <AL>	projektiver Modul *m*	module *m* projectif, projectif *m*	проективный модуль
P 1711	**projective normal** <DG>	Projektivnormale *f*	normale *f* projective	проективная нормаль
P 1712	**projective normalization** <AG>	projektive Normalisierung *f*	normalisation *f* projective	проективная нормализация
P 1713	**projective *n*-space,** *n*-dimensional projective space <PJ>	*n*-dimensionaler projektiver Raum *m*	espace *m* projectif à *n* dimensions	*n*-мерное проективное пространство
P 1714	**projective Nullstellensatz,** projective theorem of zeros <AG>	projektiver Nullstellensatz *m*	Nullstellensatz *m* projectif, théorème *m* des zéros projectif	проективная теорема о нулях
P 1715	**projective object,** projective <CA>	projektives Objekt *n*	objet *m* projectif	проективный объект
P 1716	**projective parameter** <PJ>	projektiver Parameter *m*	paramètre *m* projectif	проективный параметр
P 1717	**projective pencil of lines** <AY, PJ>	projektives Geradenbüschel (Strahlenbüschel) *n*	faisceau *m* de rayons homographiques	проективный пучок прямых (лучей)
P 1718	**projective plane** <LA, PJ>	projektive Ebene *f*	plan *m* projectif	проективная плоскость
P 1719	**projective point ranges** <PJ>	projektive Punktreihen *fpl*	ponctuelles *fpl* projectives (homographiques)	проективные ряды точек
	projective point ranges having (on) the same base <PJ>	*s.* C 1959		
	projective point set <TO>	*s.* P 1723		
P 1720	**projective principal normal** <DG>	Projektivhauptnormale *f*	normale *f* principale projective	проективная главная нормаль
P 1721	**projective property** <PJ>	projektive Eigenschaft *f*	propriété *f* projective	проективное свойство
P 1722	**projective quadric,** quadric in projective geometry <PJ>	projektive Quadrik *f*	quadrique *f* projective	проективная квадрика
	projective relation <AY, PJ>	*s.* C 1147		
	projective relation <PJ>	*s.* P 1707		
	projective representation <RE>	*s.* R 205		
	projective scale <NO>	*s.* H 450		
P 1723	**projective set,** projective point set <of class *n*> <TO>	projektive Menge *f*, L-Menge *f* <*n*-ter Klasse>	ensemble *m* projectif <de classe *n*>	проективное множество <класса *n*>
	projective set <AG, AY, PJ>	*s.* P 1676		
	projective set of class 1 <TO>	*s.* A 645		
	projective set of co-ordinates <AG, AY, PJ>	*s.* P 1676		
P 1724	**projective space** <PJ>	projektiver Raum *m*	espace *m* projectif	проективное пространство
P 1725	**projective subcone** <CA>	Unterpinsel *m*	sous-cône *m* projectif	подконус
P 1726	**projective surface** <DG>	Projektivoberfläche *f*	surface *f* projective	проективная поверхность
	projective system [of co-ordinates] <AG, AY, PJ>	*s.* P 1676		
P 1727	**projective tensor** <PJ>	Projektor *m*, projektiver Tensor *m*	tenseur *m* projectif	проективный тензор
P 1728	**projective theorem** <PJ>	projektiver Satz *m*	théorème *m* projectif	проективная теорема
	projective theorem of zeros <AG>	*s.* P 1714		
P 1729	**projective torsion tensor** <DG>	projektiver Torsionstensor *m*, Projektivtorsionstensor *m*	tenseur *m* de torsion projective	тензор проективного кручения

No.	English	German	French	Russian
	projective transfer <DG>	*s.* P 1675		
	projective transfer <PJ>	*s.* P 1685		
P 1730	**projective transformation** <of a symmetric linear affine connection> <PJ>	projektive Transformation *f*	transformation *f* projective	проективное преобразование
	projective transformation <AY, PJ>	*s.* C 1147		
	projective transformation <PJ>	*s.* P 1707		
P 1731	**projective variety** <GE>	projektive Mannigfaltigkeit *f*	variété *f* projective	проективное многообразие
	projective variety <FT>	*s.* P 1665		
P 1732	**projective vector** <PJ>	projektiver Vektor *m*, Projektor *m*	vecteur *m* projectif	проективный вектор
P 1733	**projective zero** <of an H-ideal *or* a system of equations> <AG>	Lösungsstrahl *m*, projektive Nullstelle *f*	zéro *m* projectif	луч (полупрямая) решений
P 1734	**projectivity** <of modules *or* objects> <AL, CA>	Projektivität *f*	projectivité *f*	проективность
P 1735	**projectivity**, structural (lattice) isomorphism, L-isomorphism, lattice-isomorphism <of a subgroup lattice> <GR, LA>	Projektivität *f*, Strukturisomorphismus *m*, L-Isomorphismus *m*, Verbandsisomorphismus *m*, verbandsisomorphe Abbildung *f*	isomorphisme *m* structural	структурный изоморфизм, структурно изоморфное отображение
	projectivity <AY, PJ>	*s.* C 1147		
	projectivity <PJ>	*s.* P 1707		
P 1736	**projector**, projecting ray, projecting line <DS>	Projektionsstrahl *m*, projizierender Strahl *m*, projizierende Gerade *f*, Projektionsgerade *f*, Sehstrahl *m*; Perspektivitätsstrahl *m*, Kollineationsstrahl *m* <bei der Perspektive>; Affinitätsstrahl *m* <bei der Affinität>	rayon *m* projetant (de projection), droite *f* projetante (de projection)	проектирующий луч, проектирующая прямая, прямая проекций, луч зрения
P 1737	**projector**, projection operator, projection, orthogonal projector (projection) <in a Hilbert space> <FA>	Projektor *m*, Projektionsoperator *m*, Projektion *f*, Orthogonalprojektor *m*, orthogonaler Projektor, orthogonale Projektion	projecteur *m*, opérateur *m* de projection, projection *f*, projecteur orthogonal, projection orthogonale	проектор, оператор проектирования (ортогонального проектирования), проекция, ортогональный проектор, ортогональная проекция
P 1738	**projector**, projection operator, projection <of a linear space onto a subspace along its complementary subspace> <FA>	Projektor *m*, Projektionsoperator *m*, Projektion *f* <von einem linearen Raum auf einen Teilraum längs dessen Komplementärraum>	projecteur *m*, opérateur *m* de projection, projection *f*, opérateur projectif <d'un espace linéaire sur un sous-espace le long de son sous-espace complémentaire>	оператор проектирования, проектор, проекционный оператор, проекция <линейного пространства на подпространство вдоль дополнительного подпространства>
P 1739	**Prokhorov['s] theorem** <ST>	Satz *m* von Prochorow, Prochorowscher Satz	théorème *m* de Prokhorov	теорема Прохорова
P 1740	**prolate cissoid** <GE>	verlängerte Kissoide *f*	cissoïde *f* allongée	удлиненная циссоида
P 1741	**prolate cycloid** <GE>	verlängerte (verschlungene, geschlungene, verlängerte gemeine, verschlungene gemeine, geschlungene gemeine) Zykloide *f*	cycloïde *f* allongée	удлиненная циклоида
P 1742	**prolate ellipsoid [of revolution]**, prolate spheroid, ovary ellipsoid <EG>	verlängertes (gestrecktes, langgestrecktes) Drehellipsoid (Rotationsellipsoid, Ellipsoid) *n*	ellipsoïde *m* [de révolution] allongé	вытянутый эллипсоид [вращения]
P 1743	**prolate epicycloid (epitrochoid)** <GE>	verlängerte (verschlungene, geschlungene) Epizykloide (Epitrochoide) *f*	épicycloïde (épitrochoïde) *f* allongée	удлиненная эпициклоида (эпитрохоида)
P 1744	**prolate hypocycloid (hypotrochoid)** <GE>	verlängerte (verschlungene, geschlungene) Hypozykloide (Hypotrochoide) *f*	hypocycloïde (hypotrochoïde) *f* allongée	удлиненная гипоциклоида (гипотрохоида)
	prolate spheroid <EG>	*s.* P 1742		
P 1745	**prolate trochoid** <common name of prolate epitrochoid and prolate hypotrochoid> <GE>	verlängerte (verschlungene, geschlungene) Trochoide (Rollkurve) *f*	trochoïde *f* allongée	удлиненная трохоида
P 1746	**prolongability** <of a Riemann surface> <FT>	Fortsetzbarkeit *f*	prolongeabilité *f*	продолжаемость
P 1747	**prolongable Riemann surface** <FT>	fortsetzbare Riemannsche Fläche *f*	surface *f* de Riemann prolongeable	продолжаемая риманова поверхность
P 1748	**prolongation** <of a Riemann surface> <FT>	Fortsetzung *f*, eigentliche Fortsetzung	prolongement *m*	продолжение
	prolongation <AN, FA>	*s.* E 780		
P 1749	**pronormal subgroup** <GR>	pronormale Untergruppe *f*	sous-groupe *m* pronormal	пронормальная подгруппа
P 1750	**pro-object** <CA>	Proobjekt *n*	pro-objet *m*	прообъект
P 1751	**proof**, argumentation, argument <FO>	Beweisführung *f*	argumentation *f*	аргументация
P 1752	**proof** <FO, LO>	Beweis *m*	démonstration *f*	доказательство, демонстрация
	proof by analysis <GN>	*s.* A 641		
P 1753	**proof by cases**, case-by-case proof <FO, LO>	Beweis *m* durch Fallunterscheidung	démonstration *f* par cas (énumération)	доказательство разбором случаев
P 1754/5	**proof by induction, proof by mathematical induction, proof by recursion,** inductive	Beweis *m* durch vollständige Induktion, Induktionsbeweis *m*, induktiver Beweis *m*	démonstration *f* par récurrence, démonstration par induction mathématique (complète), démonstra-	доказательство математической индукцией, доказательство индукцией (по индукции,

	English	German	French	Russian
	(induction) proof <FO>		tion *f* par induction, raisonnement *m* par récurrence, démonstration inductive	методом индукции), индуктивное доказательство
	proof by reductio ad absurdum <LO>	*s.* I 378		
P 1756	**proof by transfinite induction (recursion)** <FO, LO>	Beweis *m* durch transfinite Induktion	démonstration *f* par induction transfinie	доказательство трансфинитной индукцией
P 1757	**proof line,** proof thread, derivation filament, path <LO>	Beweisfaden *m*	fil *m* de démonstration	нить (идея) доказательства
P 1758	**proof of deducibility** <LO>	Ableitbarkeitsbeweis *m*	démonstration *f* de la déductibilité	доказательство выводимости
P 1759	**proof of existence,** existence proof <DE, FO, GN>	Existenzbeweis *m*	démonstration *f* d'existence	доказательство существования
P 1760	**proof scheme,** scheme of proof <FO>	Beweisschema *n*	schéma *m* de la démonstration	схема доказательства
P 1761	**proof theory,** "Beweistheorie" <MM>	Beweistheorie *f*	théorie *f* [hilbertienne] de la démonstration, « Beweistheorie » *f*, théorie des démonstrations	теория доказательств (доказательства)
	proof thread <LO>	*s.* P 1757		
P 1762	**propagate parallely / to** <DG>	parallel verschieben (übertragen)	transporter par équipollence (parallélisme)	параллельно переносить
P 1763	**propagation of errors,** error propagation <ER>	Fehlerfortpflanzung *f*	propagation *f* des erreurs	распространение [случайных] ошибок, преобразование ошибок
P 1764	**propagation theorem,** error propagation theorem (law), law of the propagation of errors <ER>	Fehlerfortpflanzungsgesetz *n*	loi *f* de propagation des erreurs	закон распространения случайных ошибок, формула распространения случайных ошибок
P 1765	**proper additive character** <AL>	echter Additivcharakter *m*	caractère *m* additif propre	истинный аддитивный характер
P 1766	**proper automorph[ic transformation],** proper transformation into itself <of a form> <NT>	eigentliche automorphe Substitution *f*	transformation *f* automorphe propre, substitution *f* automorphe propre	собственно автоморфное преобразование
	proper bisecant <GE>	*s.* P 1768		
P 1767	**proper characteristic element** <of a lattice> <LA>	Element *n* $\neq 0, 1$	élément *m* $\neq 0, 1$	элемент $\neq 0, 1$
P 1768	**proper chord,** proper bisecant <GE>	eigentliche Sehne (Sekante, Bisekante) *f*	corde (bisécante) *f* propre	собственная хорда
P 1769	**proper circular domain** <FT>	eigentlicher Kreiskörper *m*	domaine *m* cerclé propre	собственная круговая область
	proper class <SE>	*s.* P 1352		
	proper comprehending set <SE>	*s.* P 1789		
P 1770	**proper congruence** <on an algebra> <UA>	eigentliche Kongruenz *f*	congruence *f* propre	собственная конгруэнция
P 1771	**proper continuum** <TO>	eigentliches Kontinuum *n*	continu *m* propre	собственный континуум
P 1772	**proper convex body** <CS, GE>	eigentlicher konvexer Körper *m*	corps *m* convexe propre	собственное выпуклое тело
P 1773	**proper curve of the second order** <AY>	eigentliche Kurve *f* zweiter (2.) Ordnung	courbe *f* de deuxième ordre propre[ment dite]	невырожденная кривая второго порядка
P 1774	**proper cut-set, proper cut set** <GP>	echte Schnittmenge *f*		простой разрез
	proper derivative <DI>	*s.* F 264		
P 1775	**proper differentiability** <DI>	eigentliche Differenzierbarkeit *f*	dérivabilité *f* propre[ment dite]	собственная дифференцируемость
P 1776	**proper direction** <of a matrix *or* linear mapping>; characteristic direction <of a linear mapping> <AL, GE>	Eigenrichtung *f*	direction *f* propre	собственное направление
P 1777	**proper divergence,** definite divergence, divergence to $+\infty$ or $-\infty$ <SS>	eigentliche Divergenz *f*, bestimmte Divergenz	divergence *f* propre, divergence simple	собственная расходимость
	proper divisor <NT>	*s.* A 495		
P 1778	**proper dual ideal** <of a lattice> <LA>	eigentliches duales Ideal *n*	idéal *m* dual propre	собственный дуальный идеал
P 1779	**proper equivalence** <of forms> <AL, NT>	eigentliche Äquivalenz *f*	équivalence *f* propre	собственная эквивалентность
P 1780	**proper extension** <of a module> <AL>	echter Obermodul *m*	extension *f* propre d'un module	собственный надмодуль
P 1781	**proper extension field** <AL>	echte Erweiterung (Körpererweiterung) *f*, echter Oberkörper (Erweiterungskörper) *m*	véritable extension *f* du corps	собственное расширение поля
P 1782	**proper extension ring** <AL>	echter Oberring (Erweiterungsring) *m*	extension *f* propre d'anneau	собственное надкольцо
P 1783	**proper face** <of a simplex> <AT>	eigentliche Seite *f*	face *f* propre	собственная грань
P 1784	**proper factor** <no unit, no associate> <AL>	eigentlicher (nichttrivialer, echter) Teiler *m*	véritable diviseur *m*	собственный делитель
P 1785	**proper factor group** <GR>	echte Faktorgruppe *f*	groupe *m* quotient propre	истинная фактор-группа
P 1786	**proper filter,** filter <AL, SE, TO>	eigentlicher Filter *m*, Filter	filtre *m* propre (non impropre), filtre	собственный (центрированный) фильтр

No.	English	German	French	Russian
P 1787	**proper fraction** <AL, NU>	echter (eigentlicher) Bruch *m*, fractio *f* vera	fraction *f* propre (proprement dite, pure)	правильная дробь
P 1787 a	**proper function** <from a topological space> <TO>	eigentliche Abbildung *f*	application *f* propre	собственное отображение
	proper function <DE, IE>	*s.* E 57		
P 1788	**proper game** <TG>	Eigenspiel *n*	jeu *m* propre	собственная игра
P 1789	**proper including set,** proper comprehending set <SE>	echte Obermenge *f*, eigentliche Obermenge *f*	sur-ensemble *m* propre	собственное надмножество, истинное надмножество
P 1790	**proper inclusion** <SE>	echte Inklusion (Enthaltenseinsbeziehung) *f*; Inklusion als echte Teilmenge	inclusion *f* stricte (au sens strict), inclusion propre	собственное (строгое) включение
	proper infinity <LO>	*s.* A 208		
P 1791	**proper intersection** <AG>	eigentlicher Schnitt *m*	intersection *f* propre	собственное пересечение
P 1792	**proper left divisor** <AL>	echter Linksteiler *m*	diviseur *m* propre à gauche	собственный левый делитель
P 1793	**proper Lorentz group,** group of restricted homogeneous Lorentz transformations <AL>	eigentliche Lorentz-Gruppe *f*, homogene orthochrone Lorentz-Gruppe ohne Spiegelungen	groupe *m* propre de Lorentz, groupe homogène propre de Lorentz	собственная лоренцова группа, собственная группа Лоренца
P 1794	**proper Lorentz transformation** <AL>	eigentliche Lorentz-Transformation *f*	transformation *f* de Lorentz propre	собственное лоренцово преобразование
P 1795	**properly almost periodic function** <AP>	gewöhnliche (eigentlich[-]) fastperiodische Funktion *f*	fonction *f* proprement presque périodique	собственно почти периодическая функция
P 1796	**properly contained filter** <SE, TO>	echt feinerer Filter *m*	filtre *m* strictement plus fin	фильтр сильнее <другого>
P 1797	**properly contained** <in> / **to be,** to be strictly contained <in>, to be proper subset <of a set> <said of **a** set> <SE>	echt enthalten sein <in>	être strictement inclus <dans>, faire partie stricte <de>, être strictement contenu <dans>	быть собственным подмножеством, быть <заключеным> строго <внутри>
P 1798	**properly containing filter** <SE, TO>	echt gröberer Filter *m*	filtre *m* strictement moins fin	фильтр слабее <другого>
P 1799	**properly differentiable function** <DI>	eigentlich differenzierbare Funktion *f*	fonction *f* proprement dérivable	собственно дифференцируемая функция
P 1800	**properly discontinuous group** <of homeomorphisms of a topological space> <GR, TO>	eigentlich diskontinuierliche Gruppe *f*	groupe *m* proprement discontinu	вполне разрывная группа; группа, которая действует дискретно
P 1801	**properly discontinuous group of linear transformations** <AL, FT>	Polygongruppe *f*, eigentlich diskontinuierliche Gruppe von linearen Transformationen	groupe *m* de transformations linéaires proprement discontinu	вполне разрывная группа линейных преобразований
P 1802	**properly discontinuous subgroup** <of a continuous group> <GR>	diskrete Untergruppe *f*, eigentlich diskontinuierliche Untergruppe	sous-groupe *m* discret	дискретная подгруппа
P 1803	**properly divergent [infinite] continued fraction,** inessentially divergent [infinite] continued fraction <NT>	eigentlich divergenter unendlicher Kettenbruch *m*, unwesentlich divergenter Kettenbruch	fraction *f* continue infinie simplement divergente	собственно (несущественно) расходящаяся цепная дробь
P 1804	**properly divergent sequence,** definitely divergent sequence, sequence diverging to + ∞ or — ∞ <SS>	eigentlich divergente Zahlenfolge *f*, bestimmt divergente Folge *f*, eigentlich divergente Folge	suite *f* simplement (proprement) divergente, suite tendant vers une limite infinie	собственно расходящаяся [численная] последовательность
P 1805	**properly divergent series,** unconditionally divergent series <SS>	unbedingt (bestimmt, eigentlich) divergente Reihe *f*	série *f* proprement divergente	безусловно (собственно) расходящийся ряд
P 1806	**properly elliptic[al] operator** <DE>	eigentlich elliptischer Operator *m*	opérateur *m* proprement elliptique	собственно эллиптический оператор
P 1807	**properly equivalent form, properly equivalent quadratic form** <AL>	eigentlich äquivalente [quadratische] Form *f*, äquivalente Form	forme *f* proprement équivalente, forme de même classe	собственно эквивалентная форма
P 1808	**properly Euclidean space** <GE>	eigentlich euklidischer Raum *m*	espace *m* proprement euclidien	собственно евклидово пространство
	properly infinite type II algebra <FA>	*s.* W 9		
P 1809	**properly nilpotent element,** root element, proper nilpotent element <AL>	eigentlich nilpotentes Element *n*, Wurzelgröße *f*	élément *m* proprement nilpotent	собственно нильпотентный элемент
	properly posed problem <DE>	*s.* W 217		
P 1810	**properly primitive [binary quadratic] form** <NT>	primitive [quadratische] Form *f*, eigentlich primitive [quadratische] Form, quadratische Form [von] erster (1.) Art, ungerade quadratische Form	forme *f* quadratique proprement primitive, forme proprement (quadratique) primitive	собственно примитивная форма
P 1811	**properly triangular matrix,** strictly triangular matrix <with zeros in the diagonal> <MD>	eigentliche Dreiecksmatrix *f*	matrice *f* proprement triangulaire	собственно треугольная матрица
	properly triangular matrix <MD>	*s.* U 300		
P 1812	**proper morphism** <AG>	eigentlicher Morphismus *m*	morphisme *m* propre	собственный морфизм
P 1813	**proper motion (movement),** motion, movement <GE>	eigentliche Bewegung *f*, Bewegung	isométrie *f* positive, déplacement *m* direct, déplacement, mouvement *m* propre, mouvement	собственное движение, движение

No.	English	German	French	Russian
P 1814	**proper multiplicative character** <AL>	eigentlicher Multiplikativcharakter *m*	caractère *m* multiplicatif propre	истинный мультипликативный характер
	proper name of a function <LO>	*s.* F 757		
	proper nilpotent element <AL>	*s.* P 1809		
P 1815	**proper nonvoid subset** <SE>	echte nichtleere Untermenge *f*	partie *f* stricte non vide	непустое собственное подмножество
	proper number <MD>	*s.* E 61		
P 1816	**proper open covering** <TO>	eigentliche [offene] Überdeckung *f*	recouvrement *m* ouvert propre	собственное открытое покрытие
	proper orthogonal group <AY, GR>	*s.* R 1404		
	proper orthogonal group <GR>	*s.* S 1378		
P 1817	**proper orthogonal mapping,** proper orthogonal transformation <AL, AN>	eigentlich orthogonale Abbildung (Transformation) *f*	transformation *f* proprement orthogonale	собственно[-] ортогональное преобразование
P 1818	**proper orthogonal matrix,** rotation matrix <AL, MD>	eigentlich orthogonale Matrix *f*, Drehungsmatrix *f*, Rotationsmatrix *f*	matrice *f* orthogonale droite, matrice de rotation, matrice rotationnelle	собственно ортогональная матрица, вращательная матрица
	proper orthogonal transformation <AL, AN>	*s.* P 1817		
P 1819	**proper point,** point at finite distance <GE>	eigentlicher Punkt *m*	point *m* à distance finie	собственная точка
P 1820	**proper point of inflection** <DG, DI>	Wendepunkt *m* im eigentlichen Sinne	point *m* d'inflexion propre	собственная точка перегиба
P 1821	**proper quadric,** conicoid <ellipsoid, hyperboloid, *or* paraboloid> <AY>	eigentliche Fläche *f* zweiter (2.) Ordnung, ordinäre Fläche zweiter (2.) Ordnung, Fläche zweiter (2.) Ordnung ohne singuläre Punkte, nichtausgeartete Quadrik *f*	quadrique *f* proprement dite, quadrique propre, quadrique	невырожденная квадрика, невырождающаяся поверхность второго порядка
	proper quasi-order <SE>	*s.* O 336		
P 1822	**proper quasi-rotation** <DG>	eigentliche Quasidrehung *f*	quasi-rotation *f* propre	собственное квазивращение
P 1823	**proper rational fraction,** rational function <the nominator polynomial of which having a degree less than that of the denominator polynomial> <AL, FT>	echt gebrochene rationale Funktion *f*, echte gebrochen[-]rationale Funktion	fraction *f* rationnelle propre (proprement fractionnaire)	правильная дробно-рациональная функция
P 1824	**proper refinement** <GR>	echte Verfeinerung *f*	raffinement *m* propre	собственное уплотнение
P 1825	**proper Reinhardt domain** <FT>	eigentlicher Reinhardtscher Körper *m*	domaine *m* [cerclé] de Reinhardt propre	собственная кратнокруговая область
P 1826	**proper representation** <of a number by a quadratic form> <NT>	eigentliche Darstellung *f*	représentation *f* propre	собственное представление
P 1827	**proper right divisor** <AL>	echter Rechtsteiler *m*	diviseur *m* propre à droite	собственный правый делитель
	proper rotation <GE>	*s.* R 1398		
P 1828	**proper segment,** segment in the proper sense <CS, TO>	echte Strecke *f*	segment *m* propre	истинный (собственный) отрезок
	proper solution <DE, IE>	*s.* E 57		
	proper state <FA>	*s.* C 578		
	proper state <MD>	*s.* E 65		
P 1829	**proper subalgebra** <AL>	eigentliche Unteralgebra (Teilalgebra) *f*	sous-algèbre *f* propre	собственная подалгебра
P 1830	**proper subcategory,** non-trivial subcategory <CA>	nichttriviale (eigentliche) Teilkategorie *f*	sous-catégorie *f* propre	нетривиальная (собственная) подкатегория
P 1831	**proper subfield** <AL>	echter Unterkörper *m*	sous-corps *m* proprement dit	собственное подполе
P 1832	**proper subgraph** <GP>	echter (eigentlicher) Teilgraph *m*	sous-graphe *m* propre	собственный подграф
P 1833	**proper subgroup** <GR>	eigentliche (nichttriviale) Untergruppe *f*	sous-groupe *m* propre (véritable)	собственная (истинная) подгруппа
P 1834	**proper submodule** <AL>	echter Teilmodul *m*	sous-module *m* propre	собственный подмодуль
P 1835	**proper subset,** subset contained properly <in> <SE>	echte Untermenge (Teilmenge) *f*, eigentliche Untermenge	partie *f* stricte (propre), vraie partie *f*, sous-enesmble *m* propre, partie aliquote, vrai sous-ensemble *m*, sous-ensemble *m* strict	собственное подмножество, истинное подмножество
	proper subset / to be <SE>	*s.* P 1797		
P 1836	**proper subspace** <GE>	echter Unterraum *m*	sous-espace *m* propre	собственное подпространство
P 1837	**proper topology** <FA>	Eigentopologie *f*	topologie *f* propre	собственная топология
	proper transformation into itself <NT>	*s.* P 1766		
	property of Baire <TO>	*s.* C 1832		
P 1838	**property of being a Dedekind ring** <AL>	Eigenschaft *f*, Dedekindscher Ring zu sein	propriété *f* d'être un anneau de Dedekind	дедекиндовость
P 1839	**property of being a Frobenius algebra** <AL>	Eigenschaft *f*, Frobenius-Algebra zu sein	propriété *f* d'être une algèbre frobeniusienne	фробениусовость
P 1840	**property of being a Lindelöf space** <TO>	Eigenschaft *f*, lindelöfsch zu sein	propriété *f* d'être un espace de Lindelöf	линделефовость
P 1841	**property** <of a ring> **of being Artinian** <AL>	Eigenschaft *f*, artinsch zu sein	propriété *f* d'être artinien	артиновость

No.	English	German	French	Russian
	property of being dissimilar <AL, AR>	*s.* P 1846		
P 1842	**property of being in perspective** <DS>	Homothetie *f*	homothétie *f*	гомотетия
P 1843	**property of being left associated,** left-associatedness <of elements of a ring> <AL>	Linksassoziiertheit *f*	propriété *f* d'être associé à gauche	левая ассоциированность
P 1844	**property of being right associated,** right-associatedness <of elements of a ring> <AL>	Rechtsassoziiertheit *f*	propriété *f* d'être associé à droite	правая ассоциированность
P 1845	**property of being separated,** separatedness <of a topological space> <TO>	Separiertheit *f*	séparation *f*	отделимость, хаусдорфовость
P 1846	**property of being unlike,** property of being dissimilar <AL, AR>	Ungleichnamigkeit *f*	propriété *f* d'être non semblable	разноименность
P 1847	**property of flatness** <AL>	Flachheitseigenschaft *f*	propriété *f* de platitude	плоскостное свойство
	property of satisfying a Hölder condition <AN>	*s.* H 386		
	property of satisfying a Lipschitz condition <DE>	*s.* L 894		
	property to be elliptic[al] <DE>	*s.* E 182		
P 1848	**property to form a net** <GE>	Netzeigenschaft *f*	propriété *f* d'être un réseau	свойство быть сетью
	proper value <DE>	*s.* E 59		
	proper value <MD>	*s.* E 61		
	proper value problem <DE>	*s.* E 62		
	proper value problem <MD>	*s.* E 63		
	proper vector <MD>	*s.* E 65		
P 1849	**proper zero divisor,** non-zero zero divisor <GR>	eigentlicher Nullteiler *m*	diviseur *m* de zéro propre, véritable diviseur *m* de zéro, diviseur propre de zéro	собственный делитель нуля, истинный делитель нуля
P 1850	**pro-*p*-group** <GR>	Pro-*p*-Gruppe *f*	pro-*p*-groupe *m*	про-*p*-группа
P 1851	**proportion** <AR>	Proportion *f*, Verhältnis *n*, Verhältnisgleichung *f*	proportion *f*, analogie *f*	пропорция, тройное правило
P 1852	**proportional** <AR>	Proportionale *f*	proportionnelle *f*	член пропорции, пропорциональная, пропорциональная величина
P 1853	**proportional** <to>, $\sim$, $\propto$; directly proportional <GN>	proportional, verhältnisgleich, $\sim$, $\propto$; direkt proportional	proportionnel <à>, $\sim$, $\propto$; directement proportionnel	пропорциональный, $\sim$, $\propto$; прямо пропорциональный
P 1854	**proportional allocation,** selection with a uniform sampling fraction, uniform sample fraction <ST>	proportionale Stichprobenaufteilung (Aufteilung) *f*, einheitlicher Auswahlsatz *m*	répartition *f* proportionnelle de l'échantillon, sélection *f* à fraction de sondage uniforme, fraction *f* de sondage uniforme	пропорциональный отбор, пропорциональное размещение, пропорциональное распределение <объектов> в выборке, однородная выборочная доля
P 1855	**proportional compasses, proportional dividers** <US>, graduated dividers <GE, IN>	Proportionalzirkel *m*, Reduktionszirkel *m*	compas *m* de réduction, compas de proportion[s]	пропорциональный циркуль, делительный циркуль
P 1856	**proportional division** <of a number *or* line segment> <AR, EG>	proportionale Teilung *f*	partage *m* proportionnel (en parties proportionnelles)	пропорциональное деление
	proportional frequency <ST>	*s.* R 709		
	proportionality coefficient (factor) <GN>	*s.* F 51		
P 1857	**proportional part** <NT>	proportionaler Teil *m*	partie *f* proportionnelle	пропорциональная часть
	proportional part <NU>	*s.* T 2		
P 1858	**proportional sampling** <ST>	proportionale Stichprobennahme *f*	échantillonnage (sondage) *m* à fraction sondée constante	пропорциональный выбор
P 1859	**proportional stratified sampling (selection)** <ST>	proportionale geschichtete Stichprobennahme (Auswahl, Stichprobenerhebung) *f*	échantillonnage (sondage) *m* stratifié à fraction sondée constante	пропорциональный расслоенный выбор
P 1860	**proportional subclass numbers** <ST>	proportionale Klassenbesetzung (Klassenhäufigkeit) *f*	effectif *m* proportionnel des sous-classes	пропорциональная численность подкласса
	proportion by addition <AR>	*s.* P 1861		
	proportion by addition and subtraction <AR>	*s.* P 1862		
	proportion by extreme and mean ratio <AR>	*s.* P 1864		
	proportion by subtraction <AR>	*s.* P 1863		
P 1861	**proportion derived by addition,** proportion by addition <AR>	durch korrespondierende Addition erhaltene Proportion *f*	proportion *f* $(a+b):b=(c+d):d$ <dérivée de la proportion $a:b=c:d$>	производная пропорция $(a+b):b=(c+d):d$ <основная $a:b=c:d$>
P 1862	**proportion derived by addition and subtraction,** proportion by	durch korrespondierende Addition und Subtraktion erhaltene Proportion *f*	proportion *f* dérivée	производная пропорция $(a+b):(a-b)$ $=(c+d):(c-d)$

	addition and subtraction, proportion obtained by corresponding addition and subtraction <AR>			
P 1863	**proportion derived by subtraction, proportion obtained by corresponding subtraction,** proportion by subtraction <AR>	durch korrespondierende Subtraktion erhaltene Proportion *f*	proportion *f* $(a-b):b=(c-d):d$ <dérivée de la proportion $a:b=c:d$>	производная пропорция $(a-b):b=(c-d):d$
	proportion obtained by corresponding addition and subtraction <AR>	*s.* P 1862		
P 1864	**proportion with equal means,** proportion by extreme and mean ratio <$a:b=b:c$> <AR>	stetige (kontinuierliche) Proportion *f*, Medietät *f*, medietas *f*, Mesotät *f*	proportion *f* continue, médiété *f*	непрерывная пропорция
P 1865	**proposition,** sentence, statement, closed statement, judg[e]ment <LO>	Aussage *f*, Urteil *n*	proposition *f*, jugement *m*	высказывание, суждение, утверждение, пропозиция, предложение, элементарное предложение
	proposition <GN>	*s.* 1. A 1048; 2. T 253		
P 1866	**propositional algebra** <LO>	Aussagenalgebra *f*	algèbre *f* des propositions	алгебра высказываний
P 1867	**propositional axiom** <LO>	Axiom *n* des ausgeschlossenen Dritten	axiome *m* du tiers exclu	аксиома исключенного третьего, пропозициональная аксиома
P 1868	**propositional calculus,** sentential calculus; propositional (sentential) logic, logic of propositions, theory of propositions (truth-functions, deduction), // calculus of equivalent statements <LO>	Aussagenkalkül *m*, formale Aussagenlogik *f*; Aussagenlogik, Aussagentheorie *f*	calcul *m* des propositions, logistique *f*, calcul propositionnel; logique *f* des propositions	исчисление высказываний (суждений); логика высказываний, пропозициональная логика, логика предложений (суждений), теория высказываний
P 1869	**propositional calculus of Łukasiewicz** <LO>	Łukasiewiczscher Aussagenkalkül *m*	calcul *m* propositionnel de Łukasiewicz	исчисление высказываний Лукасевича
	propositional connective <LO>	*s.* S 498		
	propositional expression <LO>	*s.* S 499		
	propositional form <LO>	*s.* S 497		
P 1870	**propositional function,** sentential function, statement function <LO>	Aussagenfunktion *f*	fonction *f* propositionnelle	функция-высказывание, высказательная функция, функция утверждений
P 1871	**propositional inference** <LO>	aussagenlogischer (junktorenlogischer) Schluß *m*	inférence *f* propositionnelle	пропозициональный вывод
	propositional logic <LO>	*s.* P 1868		
P 1872	**propositional variable,** sentential variable, atom, atomic formula <of the propositional calculus> <LO>	Aussagenvariable *f*, Aussagevariable *f*, Aussagenveränderliche *f*, A-Variable *f*, Wahrheitswertvariable *f*, Aussagesymbol *n*, Variable *f*	variable *f* propositionnelle (de proposition), symbole *m* des propositions, proposition *f* variable	переменное высказывание, переменная высказывания, пропозициональная переменная, ПП, переменный символ для высказываний, переменная для высказываний
	proposition without sense <LO>	*s.* M 309		
P 1873	**prorepresentability** <of functors> <CA>	Prodarstellbarkeit *f*	pro-représentabilité *f*	пропредставимость
P 1874	**prorepresentable functor** <CA>	prodarstellbarer Funktor *m*	foncteur *m* pro-représentable	пропредставимый функтор
P 1875	**prorepresenting system** <for a functor> <CA>	prodarstellendes System *n*	système *m* pro-représentant	пропредставляющая система
P 1876	**prosequence** <LO>	endliche Folge *f* von Aussagen		просеквенция
P 1877	**prospective equation** <SP>	prospektive Gleichung *f*, Vorwärtsgleichung *f*	équation *f* prospective	уравнение для случайного процесса в будущем
P 1878	**prostapheresis** <method for multiplying sines and cosines> <EG>	Prosthaphärese *f*, prosthaphairetische Methode *f*, Prostaphäresis *f*	prostaphérèse *f*	простаферезис
	prototype <AN>	*s.* I 912		
	protractor <GE, IN>	*s.* S 341		
	Prouhet['s] problem <NT>	*s.* T 80		
P 1879	**provability,** demonstrability <LO>	Beweisbarkeit *f*	démontrabilité *f*	доказуемость
P 1880	**provable,** demonstrable <LO>	beweisbar	démontrable, prouvable	доказуемый
P 1881	**provable formula,** thesis <LO>	beweisbare Formel *f*	formule *f* démontrable, thèse *f*, théorème *m*	доказуемая формула
P 1882	**prove / to,** to demonstrate, to verify <FO, LO>	beweisen	démontrer	доказывать
	provisional mean <ST>	*s.* W 294		
P 1883	**proximal,** close <in a proximity space> <TO>	benachbart	proximal	близкий
P 1884	**proximal continuity** <TO>	δ-Stetigkeit *f*, Delta-Stetigkeit *f*, Nachbarschaftsstetigkeit *f*	δ-continuité *f*, delta-continuité *f*	δ-непрерывность, дельта-непрерывность
P 1885	**proximal homeomorph** <of a proximity space> <TO>	äquimorphes Bild *n*	image *f* équimorphe	эквиморфный образ

No.	English	German	French	Russian
	proximal homeomorphism <TO>	*s.* E 397		
P 1886	**proximally continuous mapping,** proximity preserving mapping (function) <TO>	nachbarschaftsstetige (infinitesimal stetige, δ-stetige, delta-stetige) Abbildung *f*	application *f* δ-continue (delta-continue)	δ-непрерывное (дельта-непрерывное, близостное) отображение
	proximity <TO>	*s.* P 1888		
P 1887	**proximity geometry** <GE>	Nachbarschaftsgeometrie *f*	géométrie *f* de proximité	геометрия близости
	proximity preserving fonction (mapping) <TO>	*s.* P 1886		
P 1888	**proximity relation,** proximity <in a proximity space> <TO>	Nachbarschaftsrelation *f*, Nachbarrelation *f*	relation *f* de proximité	соотношение (отношение) близости, соотношение (отношение) соседства
P 1889	**proximity space** <TO>	Nachbarschaftsraum *m*, infinitesimaler Raum *m*, δ-Raum *m*, Delta-Raum *m*	espace *m* de proximité	пространство близости, плесиопространство, // соседнее пространство
P 1890	**proximity structure** <on a set> <TO>	Nachbarschaftsstruktur *f*, infinitesimale Struktur *f*, δ-Struktur *f*, Delta-struktur *f*	structure *f* de proximité	близостная (инфинитезимальная) структура, структура близости
	Prüfer['s] domain <AL>	*s.* P 1893		
P 1891	**Prufer p^∞-group (p-group),** quasi-cyclic group <AL>	[Prüfersche] Gruppe *f* vom Typ p^∞, quasizyklische Gruppe	groupe *m* quasi-cyclique, groupe de type p^∞	группа типа p^∞, квазициклическая группа
P 1892	**Prüfer['s] rank** <of a group> <GR>	Prüferscher Rang *m*	rang *m* prüférien	прюферов ранг
P 1893	**Prüfer['s] ring,** Prüfer['s] domain, commutative semihereditary entire ring, commutative semihereditary domain <AL>	Prüferscher Ring *m*	anneau *m* de Prüfer (multiplication), anneau prüférien	прюферово кольцо, кольцо Прюфера, прюфферово кольцо
P 1894	**Prüfer['s] theorem** <GR>	Satz *m* von Prüfer, Prüferscher Satz	théorème *m* de Prüfer	теорема Прюфера
P 1895	**Prym['s] function** <FT, FU>	Prymsche Funktion *f*	fonction *f* de Prym	функция Прима
P 1896	***p*-saturated filtred group** <GR>	*p*-saturierte gefilterte Gruppe *f*	groupe *m* filtré *p*-saturé	*p*-насыщенная фильтрованная группа
P 1897	***p* series / the** <SS>	Reihe *f* $1 + (\frac{1}{2})^p + (\frac{1}{3})^p + \ldots$	série *f* $1 + (\frac{1}{2})^p + (\frac{1}{3})p + \ldots$	ряд вида $1 + (\frac{1}{2})^p + (\frac{1}{3})p + \ldots$
P 1898	**pseudo-abelian category,** karoubian category <CA>	pseudoabelsche Kategorie *f*	catégorie *f* pseudo-abélienne (karoubienne)	псевдоабелева категория
P 1899	**pseudo-Abelian variety** <AG>	pseudoabelsche Mannigfaltigkeit *f*	variété *f* pseudo-abélienne	псевдоабелево многообразие
P 1900	**pseudo-addition** <GR>	Pseudoaddition *f*	pseudo-addition *f*	псевдосложение
P 1901	**pseudoalgebraic subgroup** <GR>	pseudoalgebraische Untergruppe *f*	sous-groupe *m* pseudo-algébrique	псевдоалгебраическая подгруппа
P 1902	**pseudo[-]analytic function** <FT>	pseudoanalytische Funktion *f*; pseudoanalytische Funktion zweiter Art <im Sinne von L. Bers>	fonction *f* pseudo-analytique	псевдоаналитическая функция
P 1903	**pseudo[-]analytic function of the first kind** <in the sense of Bers> <FT>	pseudoanalytische Funktion *f* erster Art	fonction *f* pseudo-analytique de première espèce <au sens de Bers>	псевдоаналитическая функция первого рода <в смысле Берса>
P 1904	**pseudo-arc** <TO>	Pseudobogen *m*	pseudo-arc *m*	псевдодуга
P 1905	**pseudo-automorphism** <of a loop> <AL>	Pseudoautomorphismus *m*	pseudo-automorphisme *m*	псевдоавтоморфизм
P 1906	**pseudo-axiomatic class** <UA>	pseudoaxiomatische Klasse *f*	classe *f* pseudo-axiomatique	псевдоаксиоматизируемый класс
	pseudobase <TO>	*s.* P 1907		
P 1907	**pseudo-basis,** pseudobase <TO>	Pseudobasis *f*	pseudo-base *f*	псевдобазис, псевдобаза
	pseudo-bijective homomorphism <AL>	*s.* P 1948		
P 1908	**pseudo-catenary** <GE>	Pseudokatenarie *f*	pseudo-caténaire *f*	псевдоцепная линия
P 1909	**pseudochordal distance** <FT>	pseudochordale Entfernung *f*	distance *f* pseudocordale	псевдохордальное расстояние
P 1910	**pseudocoherent sheaf** <AL, TO>	pseudokohärente Garbe *f*	faisceau *m* pseudo-cohérent	псевдокогерентный пучок
	pseudo-combination <ST>	*s.* D 1048		
P 1911	**pseudo-commutativity** <AL>	Pseudokommutativität *f*	pseudo-commutativité *f*	псевдокоммутативность
P 1912	**pseudocompact module** <AL>	pseudokompakter Modul *m*	module *m* pseudo-compact	псевдокомпактный модуль
P 1913	**pseudo-compactness** <AL>	Pseudokompaktheit *f*	pseudo-compacité *f*	псевдокомпактность
P 1914	**pseudo-complement** <relative to an element *b*> <LA>	Pseudokomplement *n* <bezüglich eines Elements *b*>	pseudo-complément *m* <relatif à un élément *b*>	псевдодополнение <относительно элемента *b*>
P 1915	**pseudo-complementation** <LA>	Pseudokomplementbildung *f*	pseudo-complémentation *f*	переход к псевдодополнению
P 1916	**pseudo-complemented lattice** <LA>	pseudokomplementärer Verband *m*	treillis *m* pseudo-complémenté	структура с псевдодополнениями
P 1917	**pseudocomplex manifold** <FT, GE>	pseudokomplexe Mannigfaltigkeit *f*	variété *f* pseudo-complexe	псевдокомплексное многообразие
P 1918	**pseudoconformal mapping,** biholomorphic map <of a complex variety> <AN>	pseudokonforme (analytische, biholomorphe) Abbildung *f*	représentation (application) *f* pseudo-conforme	псевдоконформное отображение, голоморфный изоморфизм, биголоморфное отображение
P 1919	**pseudoconjugate function** <FT>	pseudokonjugierte Funktion *f*	fonction *f* pseudo-conjuguée	псевдосопряженная функция

	pseudo-conjugation <AL>	*s.* P 2004		
P 1920	**pseudoconvergence** <with respect to a valuation> <AL>	Pseudokonvergenz *f* <bezüglich einer Bewertung>	pseudo-convergence *f* <par rapport à une valuation>	псевдосходимость <относительно нормирования>
P 1921	**pseudo-convergent well-ordered sequence** <AL>	pseudokonvergente wohlgeordnete Folge *f*	suite *f* bien ordonnée pseudo-convergente	псевдосходящаяся вполне-упорядоченная последовательность
P 1922	**pseudoconvex domain** <FT>	pseudokonvexes Gebiet *n*	domaine *m* pseudoconvexe	псевдовыпуклая область
P 1923	**pseudoconvexity** <DG, FT>	Pseudokonvexität *f*	pseudo-convexité *f*	псевдовыпуклость
	pseudo co-ordinates <GE>	*s.* Q 134		
P 1924	**pseudo-creative set** <SE>	pseudokreative Menge *f*	ensemble *m* pseudo-créatif	псевдокреативное множество
P 1925	**pseudocycle** <AT, GP>	Pseudozyklus *m*	pseudo-cycle *m*	псевдоцикл
P 1926	**pseudo-cycloid** <GE>	Pseudozykloide *f*	pseudo-cycloïde *f*	псевдоциклоида
P 1927	**pseudodifferential operator** <DE, FA>	Pseudodifferentialoperator *m*	opérateur *m* pseudo-différentiel	псевдодифференциальный оператор
P 1928	**pseudodiscriminant** <AL>	Pseudodiskriminante *f*	pseudo-discriminant *m*	псевдодискриминант
P 1929	**pseudo-distance** <TO>	Pseudoabstand *m*	pseudo-distance *f*	псевдорасстояние
	pseudo-distance <TO>	*s. a.* Q 143		
P 1930	**pseudo-effect** <ST>	Scheinwirkung *f*	pseudo-effet *m*	псевдо-эффект
P 1931	**pseudo-elementary class** <FO>	pseudoelementare Klasse *f*	classe *f* pseudo-élémentaire	псевдоэлементарный класс
P 1932	**pseudoelliptic function,** quasielliptic function <FT, FU>	pseudoelliptische Funktion *f*	fonction *f* pseudo-elliptique	псевдоэллиптическая функция
P 1932a	**pseudoelliptic integral** <FT>	pseudoelliptisches Integral *n*	intégrale *f* pseudo-elliptique	псевдоэллиптический интеграл
P 1933	**pseudo-equivalence,** reflexive symmetric relation <SE>	Pseudoäquivalenzrelation *f*, reflexive und symmetrische Relation *f*	pseudo-équivalence *f*, relation *f* réflexive et symétrique	псевдоэквивалентность, рефлексивное и симметричное отношение
P 1934	**pseudo-Euclidean geometry** <GE>	pseudoeuklidische Geometrie *f*	géométrie *f* pseudo-euclidienne	псевдоевклидова геометрия
P 1935	**pseudo-Euclidean metric** <GE>	pseudoeuklidische Metrik *f*	métrique *f* pseudo-euclidienne	псевдоевклидова метрика
P 1936	**pseudo-Euclidean space** <DG, GE, TO>	pseudoeuklidischer Raum *m*	espace *m* pseudo-euclidien	псевдоевклидово пространство
P 1937	**pseudo-extremal** <VA>	Pseudoextremale *f*	pseudo-extrémale *f*	псевдоэкстремаль
P 1938	**pseudo-extremaloid** <VA>	Pseudoextremaloide *f*	pseudo-extrémaloïde *f*	псевдоэкстремалоида
	pseudo-filtered category <CA>	*s.* Q 155		
P 1939	**pseudo-filtered limit** <CA>	pseudofiltrierender Limes *m*	limite *f* pseudo-filtrante	квазифильтрующийся проективный предел
P 1940	**pseudo-free group** <GR>	pseudofreie Gruppe *f*	groupe *m* pseudo-libre	псевдосвободная группа
P 1941	**pseudo-functor** <CA>	Pseudofunktor *m*	pseudo-foncteur *m*	псевдофунктор
P 1942	**pseudogroup of transformations** <AL>	Pseudotransformationsgruppe *f*	pseudo-groupe *m* de transformations	псевдогруппа преобразований
P 1943	**pseudoharmonic function** <FT>	pseudoharmonische Funktion *f*	fonction *f* pseudoharmonique	псевдогармоническая функция
P 1944	**pseudoholomorphic form** <FT>	pseudoholomorphe Form *f*	forme *f* pseudo-holomorphe	псевдоголоморфная форма
P 1945	**pseudohomogeneous co-ordinates,** Study['s] normal co-ordinates <PJ>	pseudohomogene Koordinaten *fpl*, Studysche Normalkoordinaten *fpl*	coordonnées *fpl* pseudo-homogènes (normales de Study)	псевдооднородные координаты, нормальные координаты Штуди
P 1946	**pseudo-independent elements** <of a module> <AL>	pseudo-unabhängige Elemente *npl*	famille *f* d'éléments pseudo-libre	псевдосвободное семейство элементов
P 1947	**pseudoinjective homomorphism** <AL>	pseudoinjektiver Homomorphismus *m*	homomorphisme *m* pseudo-injectif	псевдоинъективный гомоморфизм
	pseudoinverse <AL>	*s.* G 144		
	pseudo[-]inverse <AL>	*s.* G 176		
	pseudo-inverse <FA>	*s.* R 1190		
P 1948	**pseudo-isomorphism,** pseudo-bijective homomorphism <of modules> <AL>	Pseudoisomorphismus *m*, pseudobijektiver Homomorphismus *m*	pseudo-isomorphisme *m*, homomorphisme *m* pseudo-bijectif	псевдоизоморфизм, псевдобиективный гомоморфизм
P 1949	**pseudo-kählerian manifold** <DG>	pseudokählersche Mannigfaltigkeit *f*	variété *f* pseudo-kählérienne	псевдокэлерово многообразие
P 1950	**pseudo laplacian** <FA>	Pseudo-Laplace-Operator *m*	pseudo-laplacien *m* <associé à la forme *D*>	псевдолапласиан
P 1951	**pseudo-lattice,** pseudo-structure <AL>	Pseudoverband *m*, Pseudostruktur *f*	semi-structure *f*	псевдоструктура
P 1952	**pseudolimit** <in a field with valuation> <AL>	Pseudolimes *m*	pseudo-limite *f*	псевдопредел
P 1953	**pseudomanifold** <AT>	Pseudomannigfaltigkeit *f*	pseudo-variété *f*	псевдомногообразие
P 1954	**pseudo-measure** <ME>	Pseudomaß *n*	pseudo-mesure *f*	псевдомера
P 1955	**pseudo-metric,** semi-metric, écart, almost-metric <TO>	Pseudometrik *f* <$\rho(x,y) = 0$ für $x \neq y$ möglich>	pseudo-métrique *f*, écart *m*, distance *f*	псевдометрика
P 1956	**pseudometric lattice,** quasi metric lattice <LA>	quasimetrischer Verband *m*	treillis *m* quasi-métrique, treillis écarté, treillis à valuation isotone	квазиметрическая структура
P 1957	**pseudometric space,** semi-metric space <TO>	pseudometrischer (quasimetrischer) Raum *m*	espace *m* pseudo-métrique	псевдометрическое пространство
P 1958	**pseudo-metric uniformity,** uniformity generated by a pseudo-metric <TO>	pseudometrische uniforme Struktur *f*	structure *f* uniforme pseudo-métrique	псевдометрическая равномерная структура
P 1959	**pseudo[-]metrizable uniform space** <TO>	[uniform] pseudometrisierbarer uniformer Raum *m*	espace *m* uniforme pseudo-métrisable	псевдометризуемое равномерное пространство

P 1960	**pseudonorm** <FA>	Pseudonorm *f*	pseudo-norme *f*	псевдонорма
	pseudonorm <FA, TO>	*s.* S 425		
P 1961	**pseudo-normed space, pseudo-normalized space** <FA>	pseudonormierter Raum *f*	espace *m* pseudo-normé	псевдонормированное пространство
P 1962	**pseudo-operation** <SE>	Pseudooperation *f*	pseudo-opération *f*	псевдооперация
P 1963	**pseudo-orthogonality** <GE>	Pseudoorthogonalität *f*	pseudo-orthogonalité *f*	псевдоортогональность
P 1964	**pseudo-orthonormal matrix** <DG>	pseudoorthonormale (pseudoorthonormierte) Matrix *f*	matrice *f* pseudo-orthonormale (pseudo-orthonormée)	псевдоортонормированная матрица
P 1965	**pseudo-orthonormal transformation** <DG>	pseudoorthonormale (pseudoorthonormierte) Transformation *f*	transformation *f* pseudo-orthonormale (pseudo-orthonormée)	псевдоортонормированное преобразование
P 1966	**pseudoparadox** <LO>	Pseudoparadoxon *n*	pseudo-paradoxe *m*	псевдопарадокс
	pseudoparadox of the Barber <LO>	*s.* P 85		
P 1967	**pseudoparadox of the catalogue** <LO>	Katalogparadoxon *n*	paradoxe *m* (antinomie *f*) du catalogue	псевдопарадокс каталога, парадокс каталога
	pseudo-parallel displacement <DG>	*s.* P 96		
	pseudo-parallelism <GE>	*s.* L 789		
P 1968	**pseudo-parallel tetrahedra** <EG>	pseudoparallele Tetraeder *npl*	tétraèdres *mpl* pseudo-parallèles	псевдопараллельные четырехгранники
P 1969	**pseudo-period** <AN>	Pseudoperiode *f*	pseudo-période *f*	псевдопериод
P 1970	**pseudoperiodic function** <AN>	pseudoperiodische Funktion *f*	fonction *f* pseudopériodique	псевдопериодическая функция
P 1971	**pseudo-point** <AG>	Pseudopunkt *m*	pseudo-point *m*	псевдоточка
P 1972	**pseudo-polynomial** <FT>	Pseudopolynom *n*	pseudo-polynôme *m*	псевдомногочлен
P 1973	**pseudo-power** <of types> <SE>	Ersatzpotenz *f* <Hausdorff>	pseudo-puissance *f*	псевдостепень
P 1974	**pseudoprime number** <NT>	Pseudoprimzahl *f*, Carmichaelsche Zahl *f*, C_1-Zahl *f*	nombre *m* pseudo-premier	псевдопростое число
P 1975	**pseudoproduct** <TO>	Pseudoprodukt *n*	pseudoproduit *m*	псевдопроизведение
P 1976	**pseudoprojective space** <TO>	pseudoprojektiver Raum *m*	espace *m* pseudo-projectif	псевдопроективное пространство
P 1977	**pseudo-Prüfer ring** <AL>	pseudo-Prüferscher Ring *m*	anneau *m* pseudo-prüférien	псевдопрюферово кольцо
P 1978	**pseudoradius** <of the pseudosphere> <DG>	Pseudoradius *m*	pseudo-rayon *m*	псевдорадиус
P 1979	**pseudorandom (pseudo random) function** <ST>	Pseudozufallsfunktion *f*	fonction *f* pseudo-aléatoire	псевдослучайная функция
P 1980	**pseudorandom (pseudo random) number** <ST>	Pseudozufallszahl *f*	nombre *m* pseudo-aléatoire	псевдослучайное число
P 1981	**pseudo-rational set** <of integers> <NT>	pseudorationale Menge *f*	ensemble *m* pseudo-rationnel	псевдорациональное множество
P 1982	**pseudo-recurrence** <FO>	Pseudorekursivität *f*	pseudo-récurrence *f*	псевдорекуррентность
P 1983	**pseudoresolvent** <IE>	Pseudoresolvente *f*	pseudo-résolvante *f*, noyau *m* pseudo-résolvant	псевдорезольвента
P 1984	**pseudo-Riemannian space** <DG>	pseudoriemannscher Raum *m*	espace *m* pseudo-riemannien	псевдориманово пространство
P 1985	**pseudoscalar,** pseudoscalar quantity <AL, DG, VT>	Pseudoskalar *m*, pseudoskalare Größe *f*	pseudo-scalaire *m*, grandeur *f* pseudo-scalaire, scalaire *m* de deuxième espèce	псевдоскаляр, псевдоскалярная величина
P 1986	**pseudoscalar covariant** <AL>	pseudoskalare Kovariante *f*	covariant *m* pseudo-scalaire	псевдоскалярная ковариантная величина
	pseudoscalar quantity <AL, DG, VT>	*s.* P 1985		
P 1987	**pseudo-skewsymmetric** <AL>	pseudo-schiefsymmetrisch	pseudo-antisymétrique	псевдокососимметрический
P 1988	**pseudosphere** <DG>	Pseudosphäre *f*	pseudosphère *f*	псевдосфера
P 1989	**pseudosphere** <with respect to a pseudometric> <GE>	Pseudokugel *f*	pseudosphère *f*	псевдошар
P 1990	**pseudospherical congruence, pseudospherical congruence of lines (rays)** <DG>	pseudosphärische Strahlenkongruenz (Linienkongruenz, Geradenkongruenz, Kongruenz) *f*, pseudosphärisches Strahlensystem *n*	congruence *f* [de droites] pseudosphérique	псевдосферическая конгруэнция [прямых (лучей)]
P 1991	**pseudospherical geometry** <GE>	pseudosphärische Geometrie *f*	géométrie *f* pseudo-sphérique	псевдосферическая геометрия
P 1992	**pseudospherical space** <DG>	pseudosphärischer Raum *m*	espace *m* pseudo-sphérique	псевдосферическое пространство
P 1993	**pseudospherical surface,** surface of constant negative curvature <of elliptic, hyperbolic, *or* parabolic type> <DG>	pseudosphärische Fläche *f*, Fläche konstanter negativer Krümmung	surface *f* pseudo-sphérique, surface à courbure constante négative	псевдосферическая поверхность, поверхность постоянной отрицательной кривизны, псевдосфера
P 1994	**pseudospiral** <GE>	Pseudospirale *f*	pseudospirale *f*	псевдоспираль
P 1995	**pseudosquare** <EG>	Pseudoquadrat *n*	pseudocarré *m*	псевдоквадрат
	pseudo-structure <AL>	*s.* P 1951		
P 1996	**pseudosurjective homomorphism** <AL>	pseudosurjektiver Homomorphismus *m*	homomorphisme *m* pseudo-surjectif	псевдосюръективный гомоморфизм
P 1997	**pseudo[-]symmetric graph** <GP>	pseudosymmetrischer (gerichteter Eulerscher) Graph *m*	graphe *m* pseudo-symétrique	равновесный граф по всем вершинам, псевдосимметрический (ориентированный эйлеров) граф
P 1998	**pseudo-symmetric graph in v** <GP>	pseudosymmetrischer Graph *m* im Knoten *v*	graphe *m* pseudo-symétrique en *v*	равновесный граф по вершине *v*
P 1999	**pseudo[-]symmetric number** <NT>	pseudosymmetrische Zahl *f* <Lemoine>	nombre *m* pseudo-symétrique	псевдосимметрическое число
P 2000	**pseudotangent** <DG>	Pseudotangente *f*	pseudo-tangente *f*	псевдокасательная

No.	English	German	French	Russian
P 2001	**pseudotensor** <DG, VT>	Pseudotensor *m*	pseudo-tenseur *m*	псевдотензор
P 2002	**pseudo tensor density** <DG, VT>	Pseudotensordichte *f*	densité *f* quasi tensorielle	псевдотензорная плотность
P 2003	**pseudotractrix** <GE>	Pseudotraktrix *f*	pseudo-tractrice *f*	псевдотрактриса
P 2004	**pseudo-transposition,** pseudo-conjugation <AL>	Pseudotransposition *f*	pseudo-transposition *f*	псевдотранспонирование
P 2005	**pseudo-triangle** <GE>	Pseudodreieck *n*	pseudo-triangle *m*	псевдотреугольник
P 2006	**pseudo-unitary** <AL>	pseudounitär	pseudo-unitaire	псевдоунитарный
P 2007	**pseudo[-]valuation** <AL>	Pseudobewertung *f*	pseudo-valuation *f*	псевдооценка, псевдометрика
P 2008	**pseudovector** <DG, VT>	Pseudovektor *m*	pseudovecteur *m*	псевдовектор
	pseudovector <VT>	*s.* A 1269		
P 2009	**pseudo-versiera** <GE>	Pseudoversiera *f*, geometrische Quadratrix *f* [von Ozanam]	pseudoversiéra *f*	псевдоверзиера
P 2010	**pseudo-zero homomorphism** <AL>	Pseudonullhomomorphismus *m*	homomorphisme *m* pseudo-nul	псевдонулевой гомоморфизм
P 2011	**pseudo-zero module** <AL>	Pseudo-Nullmodul *m*	module *m* pseudo-nul	псевдонулевой модуль
	psi-function, Psi function, Ψ-function <FU>	*s.* D 480		
P 2012	***p*-singular factor** <of a group element> <GR>	*p*-singulärer Faktor *m*	facteur *m* *p*-singulier	*p*-сингулярный множитель
P 2013	***p*-soluble group** <GR>	*p*-auflösbare Gruppe *f*	groupe *m* *p*-résoluble	*p*-разрешимая группа
P 2014	***p*-subgroup** <GR>	*p*-Untergruppe *f*	*p*-sous-groupe *m*	*p*-подгруппа
P 2015	***p*-sum** <of convex sets> <CS>	*p*-Summe *f*	*p*-somme *f*	*p*-сумма
P 2016	***p*-surjection** <CA>	*p*-Surjektion *f*	*p*-surjection *f*	*p*-сюръекция
P 2017	***p*-th adjugate [matrix], *p*-th compound (derived) matrix,** matrix of $p \times p$ minors, derived matrix, adjugate matrix <of order *p*> <of a matrix> <MD>	*p*-te abgeleitete (assoziierte) Matrix *f*, Matrix der *p*-reihigen Unterdeterminanten, *p*-te Ableitung *f*	matrice *f* des mineurs d'ordre *p*	матрица миноров порядка *p*, *p*-я ассоциированная матрица
	***p*-times contravariant tensor** <AL, VT>	*s.* C 2304		
	***p*-times covariant tensor** <VT>	*s.* C 2612		
P 2018	**ptolemaic inequality** <for a metric space> <TO>	Ptolemäische Ungleichung *f*	inégalité *f* ptolémaïque	неравенство Птолемея
P 2019	**Ptolemaic (ptolemaic) space** <GE>	Ptolemäischer (ptolemäischer) Raum *m*	espace *m* ptolémaïque	пространство Птолемея
P 2020	**Ptolemy['s] theorem** <EG>	Ptolemäischer Satz, ptolemäischer Lehrsatz *m*, Gegensehnensatz *m*, Satz des (von) Ptolemäus	théorème *m* de Ptolémée	теорема Птолемея
P 2021	***p*-topology** <of a group> <AB>	*p*-Topologie *f*	*p*-topologie *f*	*p*-топология
P 2022	***p*-torsion** <of a group> <GR>	*p*-Torsion *f*	*p*-torsion *f*	*p*-кручение
P 2023	***p*-trivial field** <AL>	*p*-trivialer Körper *m*	corps *m* *p*-trivial	*p*-тривиальное поле
	Puiseux['] method <FT>	*s.* M 479		
	Puiseux['] rule <FT>	*s.* N 212		
P 2024	**Puiseux['] series** <AL, FT>	Puiseux-Reihe *f*	série *f* de Puiseux	ряд Пюизе, обобщенный степенной ряд
	Puiseux['] series expansion <FT>	*s.* N 211		
P 2025	**Puiseux['] theorem** <FT>	Puiseuxscher (Puiseux') Satz *m*	théorème *m* de Puiseux	теорема Пюизе
P 2026	**pull-back** <in a fibration> <AT>	Pullback *n*	rétrotirette *f*	расслоенное произведение
P 2027	**pullback,** pull-back, cartesian square, fibred product, comeet <of morphisms, of maps> <CA>	Pullback *n*, Faserprodukt *n*, kartesisches (cartesisches) Quadrat *n*	produit *m* fibré, « pull back » *m*	расслоенное произведение, коуниверсальный (декартов) квадрат, левое пересечение пар морфизмов с общим концом, pull back
P 2028	**pullback,** fibred product, product <of objects *A* and *B*> over an object <*C*> <as an object> <CA>	Pullback *n*, Faserprodukt *n*, Produkt *n* <der Objekte *A* und *B*> über einem Objekt <*C*>	produit *m* fibré <des objets *A* et *B* sur un objet *C*>	расслоенное произведение, коамальгама объектов *A* и *B* над объектом *C*
P 2029	**pull[-]back [diagram], pull[-]back square,** cartesian square, upper complete square <as a diagram> <CA>	Pullbackdiagramm *n*, Pullbackquadrat *n*, Pullback *n*, kartesisches (cartesisches) Quadrat *n*	diagramme *m* de morphismes cartésien, carré *m* cartésien	декартов квадрат
	pulse response <AN>	*s.* I 203		
	punctual Lipschitz condition <AN>	*s.* L 893		
P 2030	**punctuation symbol,** grouping symbol, sign of aggregation <FO>	technisches Zeichen *n* <Klammer auf, Klammer zu>	symbole *m* de ponctuation, signe *m* de ponctuation	вспомогательный знак (символ), несобственный (разделительный) символ, знак объединения членов алгебраического выражения
	punctured complex plane <FT>	*s.* C 1638		
P 2031	**punctured disk** <FT>	punktierte Kreisscheibe *f*	disque *m* pointé (privé d'un point)	проколотый диск (круг), диск с выкинутой точкой
	punctured plane <FT>	*s.* C 1638		
P 2032	**punctured projective line** <PJ>	punktierte projektive Gerade *f*	droite *f* projective privée d'un point	проективная прямая с выкинутой точкой
P 2033	**punctured space** <GE>	punktierter (gelöcherter) Raum *m*	espace *m* troué	проколотое пространство, пространство с дыркой
	punctured sphere <FT>	*s.* C 1645		

No.	English	German	French	Russian
P 2034	**p-unipotent element** <AL>	*p*-unipotentes Element *n*	élément *m* *p*-unipotent	*p*-унипотентный элемент
P 2035	**Puppe['s] exact sequence** <AT>	Puppesche Sequenz *f*	suite *f* de Puppe	последовательность Пуппе
P 2036	**Puppe['s] sequence** <TO>	Abbildungsfolge *f*, Puppe-Folge *f*	suite *f* de Puppe	последовательность Пуппе
P 2037	**pure complex** <AT>	homogen-dimensionaler (reiner) Komplex *m*	complexe *m* pur	размерно[-] однородный комплекс, чистый комплекс
P 2038	**pure complex** <Reidemeister> <AT>	reiner Komplex *m*	complexe *m* pur	чистый комплекс
P 2039	**pure continuous spectrum,** purely continuous spectrum <FA, IE>	reines Streckenspektrum *n*, rein kontinuierliches Spektrum *n*	spectre *m* purement continu	чисто непрерывный спектр
P 2040	**pure cubic equation** <AL>	reinkubische (rein kubische) Gleichung *f*	équation *f* cubique pure	уравнение вида $x^3 + a = 0$
	pure equation <AL>	*s.* B 394		
	pure functional calculus <LO>	*s.* R 927		
	pure functional calculus of first order <LO>	*s.* P 2060		
	pure geometry <SG>	*s.* S 2502		
	pure imaginary number <AL, FT, NT>	*s.* I 97		
P 2041	**pure infinitesimal geometry** <DG>	reine Infinitesimalgeometrie *f*, Geometrie *f* einer affinzusammenhängenden Mannigfaltigkeit <Weyl>	géométrie *f* infinitésimale pure	чисто инфинитезимальная геометрия
P 2042	**purely arithmetical quantity** <NT>	Zahlengröße *f* <Graßmann>	quantité *f* purement arithmétique	чисто арифметическая величина
P 2043	**purely atomic measure** <ME>	atomistisches Maß *n*	mesure *f* atomique	атомическая мера
P 2044	**purely binary number** <AL>	rein duale (binäre) Zahl *f*	nombre *m* purement binaire	просто двоичное число
	purely continuous spectrum <FA, IE>	*s.* P 2039		
P 2045	**purely discontinuous Markov process** <SP>	rein unstetiger Markovscher Prozeß *m*	processus *m* markovien purement discontinu	чисто разрывный марковский процесс
P 2046	**purely discrete spectrum,** pure point spectrum <FA, IE>	reines Punktspektrum *n*, rein diskretes Spektrum *n*	spectre *m* purement ponctuel	чисто точечный спектр
P 2047	**purely imaginary expression** <AL>	rein imaginärer Ausdruck *m*	expression *f* purement imaginaire	чисто мнимое выражение
	purely imaginary number <AL, FT, NT>	*s.* I 97		
P 2048	**purely imaginary quaternion,** imaginary quaternion <AL>	rein imaginäre Quaternion *f*, imaginäre Quaternion	quaternion *m* imaginaire	мнимый (чисто мнимый) кватернион
P 2049	**purely indecomposable group** <GR>	servanzunzerlegbare Gruppe *f*		сервантно неразложимая группа
P 2050	**purely inseparable element** <AL>	rein inseparables Element *n*	élément *m* radical	радикальный элемент
P 2051	**purely inseparable extension [field], purely inseparable field [extension];** purely unseparable extension <AL>	rein inseparable Körpererweiterung (Erweiterung) *f*	extension *f* inséparable pure	чисто (вполне) несепарабельное расширение <поля>
P 2052	**purely inseparable isogeny** <of algebraic groups> <AG>	rein inseparable Isogenie *f*	isogénie *f* purement inséparable	чисто несепарабельная изогения
P 2053	**purely periodic continuous fraction** <NT>	rein[ ]periodischer Kettenbruch *m*	fraction *f* continue périodique simple, fraction continue immédiatement périodique	чисто периодическая цепная дробь
P 2054	**purely periodic decimal fraction** <NT>	rein[ ]periodischer Dezimalbruch *m*	fraction *f* décimale périodique simple (pure)	чистая бесконечная (периодическая) десятичная дробь
P 2055	**purely quadratic function** <AN, PG>	rein[ ]quadratische Funktion *f*	fonction *f* purement quadratique, fonction quadratique pure	чисто квадратная функция
P 2056	**purely transcendental extension,** pure transcendental extension; purely transcendental extension field <AL>	rein transzendente Körpererweiterung (Erweiterung) *f*	extension *f* transcendante pure, extension purement transcendante, extension pure	чисто трансцендентное расширение, чистое расширение
	purely transcendental extension field <AL>	*s.* P 2056		
	purely unseparable extension <AL>	*s.* P 2051		
P 2057	**pure mathematics,** abstract mathematics <GN>	reine Mathematik *f*	mathématiques *fpl* pures	чистая математика
P 2058	**pure *n*-dimensional complex, pure *n*-complex,** homogeneously *n*-dimensional complex <AT>	homogen (reiner) *n*-dimensionaler Komplex *m*	complexe *m* pur de dimension *n*	*n*-мерно-однородный комплекс, однородно *n*-мерный компекс
	pure point spectrum <FA, IE>	*s.* P 2046		
P 2059	**pure polynomial** <AL>	reines Polynom *n*, Polynom der Gestalt $x^n - a$	polynôme *m* de la forme $x^n - a$	полином вида $x^n - a$, двучленный полином
	pure predicate calculus <LO>	*s.* R 927		

No.	English	German	French	Russian
P 2060	**pure predicate calculus of first order,** pure functional calculus of first order <LO>	reiner Prädikatenkalkül (Funktionalkalkül) *m* erster Stufe	calcul *m* des prédicats pur du premier ordre	чистое исчисление предикатов первого порядка
P 2061	**pure projective algebraic variety** <AG>	ungemischte (reine) projektive algebraische Mannigfaltigkeit *f*	variété *f* algébrique projective pure (équidimensionnelle)	чистое (несмешанное) проективное алгебраическое многообразие
P 2062	**pure quadratic** <AL>	rein[ ]quadratische Gleichung *f*	équation *f* binôme quadratique	неполное квадратное уравнение, квадратное уравнение вида $ax^2 + q = 0$
P 2063	**pure quaternion** <AL>	reine (vektorielle) Quaternion *f*	quaternion *m* pur	чистый кватернион
P 2064	**pure set** <SE>	reine Menge *f*	ensemble *m* pur	чистое множество
	pure set theory <SE>	*s.* G 183		
P 2065	**pure state** <extreme state on a C^*-algebra> <FA>	reiner Zustand *m*	état *m* pur	чистое состояние
P 2066	**pure strategy** <PG, TG>	reine Strategie *f*	stratégie *f* pure	чистая стратегия
P 2067	**pure subgroup,** isolated subgroup <of an *R*-group> <GR>	isolierte Untergruppe *f*, Servanzuntergruppe *f*	sous-groupe *m* pur (isolé)	изолированная (сервантная) подгруппа
	pure subgroup <GR>	*s.* S 633		
P 2068	**pure submodule** <AL>	reiner Untermodul *m*	sous-module *m* pur	чистый подмодуль
P 2069	**pure surd** <AL>	irrationaler Ausdruck *m*, dessen Glieder irrational sind	expression *f* irrationnelle dont tous les termes sont irrationnells	иррациональное выражение, все члены которого иррациональны
	pure transcendental extension <AL>	*s.* P 2056		
P 2070	**pure value,** value <of a game> <TG>	reiner Wert *m*, Wert <eines Spiels>, Spielwert *m*	valeur *f* pure, valeur <d'un jeu>	чистая цена, цена, чистое значение, значение <игры>
P 2071	**pure variety** <AG>	reine Varietät *f*	variété *f* pure	чистое (несмешанное) многообразие
P 2072	**pure variety** <over *k*> <AG>	reine algebraische Mannigfaltigkeit *f*, reine (ungemischte) Mannigfaltigkeit <über *k*>	variété *f* pure <sur *k*>, *k*-ensemble *m* équidimensionnel (pur)	чистое (несмешанное) многообразие <над *k*>
P 2073	**purity theorem of Zariski-Nagata** <AG, AL>	Ungemischtheitssatz *m* von Zariski und Nagata, Zariski-Nagatascher Ungemischtheitssatz	théorème *m* de pureté de Nagata-Zariski (Zariski-Nagata>	теорема чистоты Зариского-Нагаты
P 2074	**purposive sample** <ST>	bewußt ausgewähltes Stichprobenelement *n*	échantillon *m* choisi à dessein	пристрастная выборка
P 2075	**purposive sampling,** judgement sampling, judgment sampling <ST>	bewußte (subjektive) Auswahl *f*	choix *m* à dessein, choix au jugé, sélection *f* au jugé, échantillonnage *m* au jugé, sondage *m* au jugé	пристрастный выбор, не вполне случайный выбор
	push-me-pull-you <CA>	*s.* B 276		
P 2076	**push[-]out,** cocartesian square, amalgamized sum, union, universal square, amalgamated sum, fibred sum, cofibred sum <of morphisms> <CA>	Pushout *m*, verschmolzene (amalgamierte) Summe *f*, Fasersumme *f*, Kofaserprodukt *n*, kokartesisches (cocartesisches) Quadrat *n*, „universal square" *n*	somme *f* fibrée (amalgamée), union *f*, push-out *m*	универсальный квадрат, правое пересечение пар морфизмов с общим началом, push-out, кодекартов квадрат, корасслоенная (расслоенная) сумма
	pushout <CA>	*s.* F 155		
	push-out <CA>	*s.* P 2077		
P 2077	**push-out diagram,** universal square, cocartesian square, lower complete square, push-out <as a diagram> <CA>	Pushout-Diagramm *n*, Pushout *n*, kokartesisches (cocartesisches) Quadrat *n*, Pushout-Quadrat *n*	carré *m* cocartésien, pushout *m*, diagramme *m* de morphismes co-cartésien	кодекартов (универсальный) квадрат
	put before the brackets / to <GN>	*s.* F 52		
P 2078	**put in braces / to,** to collect in braces, to enclose (aggregate) in braces, to brace <GN>	einklammern <in geschweifte Klammern>, in geschweifte Klammern einschließen (setzen), beklammern	enfermer entre accolades, mettre en accolades	заключать (взять, брать) в фигурные скобки
P 2079	**put in brackets / to,** to collect in brackets, to enclose (aggregate) in brackets, to bracket <GN>	einklammern <in eckige Klammern>, in eckige Klammern einschließen (setzen), beklammern	enfermer entre crochets, mettre en crochets	заключать в квадратные скобки, взять в квадратные скобки, брать в квадратные скобки
P 2080	**put in parentheses / to,** to collect in parentheses, to enclose (aggregate) in parentheses, to parenthesize <GN>	einklammern <in runde Klammern>, in runde Klammern einschließen (setzen), beklammern	enfermer entre parenthèses, mettre en parenthèses	заключать в [круглые] скобки, взять в [круглые] скобки, брать в [круглые] скобки
	putting equal <GN>	*s.* E 335/6		
	putting over a common denominator <AL, AR>	*s.* R 434		
	15 Puzzle <CT>	*s.* B 620		
P 2081	***p*-valuation** <AL>	*p*-Bewertung *f*	*p*-valuation *f*	*p*-нормирование
P 2082	**$\mathfrak{P}$-value of *x*,** value of *x* at the place $\mathfrak{P}$ <AL>	Wert *m* von *x* an der Stelle $\mathfrak{P}$	valeur *f* de *x* en $\mathfrak{P}$	значение *x* в $\mathfrak{P}$
	***p*-vector** <AL, GE, VT>	*s.* M 1091		
	pyramidal ungula <EG>	*s.* U 104		
P 2083	**Pythagoras['s] theorem,** Pythagorean theorem, theorem of Pythagoras <EG>	pythagoreischer Lehrsatz (Satz) *m*, Lehrsatz des Pythagoras, Satz des (von) Pythagoras, Pythagoras *m*, Pythagoras-Satz *m*, Pythagoräischer Lehrsatz (Satz), Magister *m* mathesos	théorème *m* de Pythagoras, théorème pythagoricien	пифагорова теорема, теорема Пифагора

No.	English	German	French	Russian
P 2084	**Pythagorean equation** <AL>	pythagoreische (Pythagoreische, Pythagoräische) Gleichung *f*	equation *f* pythagoricienne (pythagoréenne)	пифагорейское (пифагорово) уравнение
P 2085	**pythagorean field;** ordered pythagorean field <AL> ┌<GE>	Pythagoreischer Körper *m*	corps *m* pythagoricien	пифагорово поле
	Pythagorean metric	*s.* E 563		
P 2086	**Pythagorean numbers, pythagorean numbers,** pythagorean triple <NT>	pythagoreische (Pythagoreische) [ganze] Zahlen *fpl*, pythagoreisches Zahlentripel *n*, // Pythagoräische [ganze] Zahlen	nombres *mpl* pythagoriques (pythagoriciens)	пифагоровы числа
P 2087	**pythagorean quadruple** <NT>	pythagoreisches Zahlenquadrupel *n*	quadruple *m* de nombres pythagorique	пифагорова четверка чисел
P 2088	**Pythagorean relation** <between direction cosines> <AY>	Pythagoreische Relation *f* <zwischen den Richtungskosinussen>	rélation *f* exprimant que la somme des carrés des cosinus directeurs est égale à l'unité	теорема о том, что сумма квадратов направляющих косинусов равна единице
	Pythagorean theorem <EG>	*s.* P 2083		
P 2089	**pythagorean triangle, Pythagorean triangle** <EG>	pythagoreisches (Pythagoreisches, pythagoräisches) Dreieck *n*	triangle *m* rectangle en nombres, triangle pythagorique (pythagoricien)	пифагоров (пифагорейский) треугольник
	pythagorean triple <NT>	*s.* P 2086		

Q

No.	English	German	French	Russian
Q 1	**Q-closed set** <LO>	Q-abgeschlossene Menge *f*	ensemble *m* Q-fermé	Q-замкнутое множество
	Q-complete collection of identities <UA>	*s.* Q 148		
Q 2	**q-complete space** <FT>	*q*-vollständiger Raum *m*	espace *m* *q*-complet	*q*-полное пространство
Q 3	**q-convex domain** <FT>	*q*-konvexes Gebiet *n*	domaine *m* *q*-convexe	*q*-выпуклая область
Q 4	**q-convexity** <FT>	*q*-Konvexität *f*	*q*-convexité *f*, (*n* — *q*)-pseudoconvexité *f*	*q*-выпуклость
Q 5	**q-critical level** <in Morse's theory> <VA>	*q*-kritischer Wert *m*	valeur *f* *q*-critique	*q*-критическое значение
	q.e.d. <GN>	*s.* Q 308		
	QF ring <AL>	*s.* Q 160		
Q 6	**QF-3 ring** <contains a faithful projective injective left ideal> <AL>	QF-3-Ring *m*	QF-3 anneau *m*	QF-3 кольцо
Q 7	**q-function** <as a quaternion function> <AN>	*q*-Funktion *f*	*q*-fonction *f*	*q*-функция
Q 8	**q-linear form** <AL>	*q*-Linearform *f*	forme *f* *q*-linéaire	*q*-линейная форма
Q 9	**q-polyhedron** <FT>	*q*-Polyeder *n*	*q*-polyèdre *m*	*q*-многогранник
Q 10	**q-pseudoconcave space** <FT>	*q*-pseudokonkaver Raum *m*	espace *m* *q*-pseudoconcave	*q*-псевдовогнутое пространство
Q 11	**q-pseudoconvex space** <FT>	*q*-pseudokonvexer Raum *m*	espace *m* *q*-pseudoconvexe	*q*-псевдовыпуклое пространство
	Q-space <TO>	*s.* H 284		
Q 12	**q-subharmonic function** <FT>	*q*-subharmonische Funktion *f*	fonction *f* *q*-sous harmonique, fonction *q*-sous-harmonique	*q*-субгармоническая функция
Q 13	**QT-graph** <GP>	Quasiturnier *n*	quasi-tournament *m*	квазитурнир
Q 14	**quadrangle** <of general shape> <EG>	Viereck *n*, // Trapez *n* <Euklid>	quadrangle *m*	четырехугольник
Q 15	**quadrangle circumscribing** <e.g.: a circle> <EG>	Tangentenviereck *n*, umschriebenes Viereck *n*	quadrangle *m* circonscriptible (circonscrit, tangentiel)	описанный четырехгранник
Q 16	**quadrangle with three right angles** <in hyperbolic geometry> <GE>	Spitzeck *n*	quadrangle *m* à trois angles droits	четырехугольник с тремя прямыми углами
Q 17	**quadrangular prism** <EG>	vierseitiges Prisma *n*	prisme *m* quadrangulaire	четырехугольная призма
Q 18	**quadrant** <AY, GN>	Viertelebene *f*, Quadrant *m*	quadrant *m*	квадрант
	quadrant I <AY>	*s.* F 351		
Q 19	**quadrant relations,** reduction formulas <for the trigonometric functions> <EG>	Quadrantenrelationen *fpl*, Reduktionsformeln *fpl*	formules *fpl* de réduction, formules relatives aux angles associés	формулы приведения
	quadratic <AL>	*s.* Q 25		
	quadratically convergent Newton-Raphson process <AX, NU>	*s.* N 206		
	quadratically integrable function <AN>	*s.* S 1557		
	quadratically integrable kernel <FA, IE>	*s.* H 356		
	quadratically summable function <AN>	*s.* S 1568		
Q 20	**quadratic component,** second-order component, component of the second degree (order) <of regression> <ST>	quadratische Komponente *f*, Komponente zweiten Grades, Komponente zweiter Ordnung	composante *f* quadratique (de deuxième ordre)	квадратическая компонента, компонента второго порядка
Q 21	**quadratic convergence** <AX, NU>	quadratische Konvergenz *f*	convergence *f* quadratique	квадратическая сходимость
Q 22	**quadratic cosine,** cp <EG>	quadratischer Kosinus *m*, cp	cosinus *m* quadratique, cp	квадратический косинус, cp
	quadratic curve <AG, AY>	*s.* C 1944		
Q 23	**quadratic diameter** <of a cubic> <GE>	quadratischer Durchmesser *m*	diamètre *m* quadratique	квадратический диаметр

No.	English	German	French	Russian
Q 24	**quadratic discriminatory analysis,** Welch analysis <ST>	quadratische Diskriminanzanalyse *f*, Welch-Analyse *f*	analyse *f* discriminatoire quadratique, analyse de Welch	квадратичный дискриминантный анализ, анализ Уэлча
Q 25	**quadratic equation,** second-degree equation, equation of the second degree, quadratic, quadric <AL>	quadratische Gleichung *f*, Gleichung zweiten Grades	équation *f* quadratique, équation du second degré, équation du deuxième degré	квадратичное уравнение, квадратное уравнение, уравнение второй (2-ой) степени
Q 26	**quadratic extension,** quadratic field extension <AL>	quadratische Erweiterung (Körpererweiterung) *f*	extension *f* quadratique	квадратичное расширение [поля], квадратическое расширение [поля]
Q 27	**quadratic field extension** <AL>	relativquadratischer Körper *m*	corps *m* quadratique relatif	квадратичное расширение поля
	quadratic field extension ┌<AL>	*s. a.* Q 26		
Q 28	**quadratic form,** quadric quantic, quadric <AL>	quadratische Form *f*	forme *f* quadratique, quadrique *f*	квадратичная форма
Q 29	**quadratic form reduced to a sum of squares** <linear combination of squares> <AL>	auf eine Summe von Quadraten transformierte quadratische Form *f*	forme *f* réduite <d'une forme quadratique>	квадратичная форма, преобразованная в сумму квадратов
Q 30	**quadratic formula** <AL>	Auflösungsformel *f* für quadratische Gleichungen	formule *f* de résolution des équations quadratiques	формула корней квадратного уравнения
Q 31	**quadratic form which is the sum of two forms with separated sets of variables** <AL, NT>	in die Summe zweier Formen in disjunkten Mengen von Variablen zerlegbare quadratische Form *f*	forme *f* décomposable	квадратичная форма, разложимая в сумму двух форм в дизъюнктных множествах переменных
Q 32	**quadratic form with integral coefficients** <NT>	ganzzahlige quadratische Form *f*	forme *f* quadratique à coefficients entiers	целочисленная квадратичная форма
	quadratic form without mixed terms <AL>	*s.* D 399		
Q 33	**quadratic fundamental form** <DG>	quadratische Grundform (Fundamentalform) *f*	forme *f* fondamentale quadratique	квадратическая фундаментальная форма
	quadratic group <GR>	*s.* K 90		
Q 34	**quadratic inversion** <of a transformation> <AL, GE>	quadratische Umkehrung *f*	inversion *f* quadratique	квадратичное обращение
Q 35	**quadratic irrationality** <NT>	quadratische Irrationalität *f*, quadratische irrationale Zahl *f*	irrationnelle *f* quadratique	квадратическая иррациональность, квадратная иррациональность
Q 36	**quadratic lattice** <AX, ┌DE, NU>	quadratisches Gitter *n*	réseau *m* quadratique	квадратная решетка
Q 37	**quadratic logarithm** <FU>	quadratischer Logarithmus *m* <Prampero>	logarithme *m* quadratique	квадратический логарифм
Q 38	**quadratic mapping** <AL, GE>	quadratische Abbildung *f*	application *f* quadratique	квадратичное отображение, квадратическое отображение
	quadratic matrix <MD>	*s.* S 1558		
	quadratic mean <ST>	*s.* R 1378		
Q 39	**quadratic nonresidue, quadratic non-residue** <modulo *m*> <NT>	quadratischer Nichtrest *m* <modulo *m*>	non-résidu *m* quadratique <modulo *m*>	квадратический невычет, квадратичный невычет <по модулю *m*>
Q 40	**quadratic optimization (programming)** <PG>	quadratische Optimierung (Programmoptimierung, Programmierung) *f*, quadratisches Programmieren *n*	programmation (optimisation) *f* quadratique	квадратичное программирование
Q 41	**quadratic reciprocity** <NT>	quadratische Reziprozität *f*	réciprocité *f* quadratique	квадратичная взаимность
Q 42	**quadratic reciprocity law,** law of quadratic reciprocity, Gauss['s] law of reciprocity <NT>	quadratisches (Gaußsches) Reziprozitätsgesetz *n*, Reziprozitätsgesetz, theorema *n* fundamentale <Gauß>, theorema fundamentale theoriae residuorum quadraticorum, Gauß' Fundamentalsatz *m* der Zahlentheorie, verallgemeinertes (Legendresches, allgemeines, Legendres) Reziprozitätsgesetz	loi *f* de réciprocité quadratique, théorème *m* de réciprocité (Legendre), loi de réciprocité des résidus quadratiques, theorema *m* fundamentale, loi de réciprocité de Legendre	квадратический закон взаимности, закон квадратичной взаимности, закон взаимности квадратичных вычетов, закон взаимности Гаусса
Q 43	**quadratic residue of *p*,** residue of *p*, power residue of the second order of *p* <NT>	quadratischer Rest *m* modulo *p*, quadratischer Rest von *p*	résidu (reste) *m* quadratique modulo *p*	квадратический (квадратичный) вычет по модулю *p*
Q 44	**quadratic residue symbol** <AB>	quadratisches Restsymbol *n*	symbole *m* de deuxième puissance	символ вычета второй степени
Q 45	**quadratic sine,** sp <EG>	quadratischer Sinus *m*, sp	sinus *m* quadratique, sp	квадратический синус, sp
Q 46	**quadratic square,** perfect square <CT, NT>	quadratisches Quadrat *n*, vollkommenes Quadrat	carré *m* quadratique, carré parfait	совершенный квадрат, квадратический квадрат
	quadratic supplement <AL>	*s.* C 1595		
Q 47	**quadratic trigonometry** <EG>	quadratische Trigonometrie *f*	trigonométrie *f* quadratique	квадратическая тригонометрия
Q 48	**quadratrix** <GE>	Quadratrix *f*	quadratrice *f*	квадратриса
Q 49	**quadrature,** integration <of a differential equation> <DE>	Quadratur *f*, Integration *f*	quadrature *f*, intégration *f*	квадратура, интегрирование
Q 50	**quadrature,** squaring, complanation <of surfaces> <DI, DG>	Quadratur *f*, Komplanation *f*	quadrature *f*	квадратура
Q 51	**quadrature formula,** mechanical quadrature formula <AX, DI, NU>	Quadraturformel *f*, mechanische Quadraturformel	formule *f* de quadrature, formule de quadrature mécanique, formule pour l'intégration numérique	квадратурная формула, формула механических (численных) квадратур

No.	English	German	French	Russian
Q 52	**quadrature formula of best approximation** <AX, DI, NU>	Quadraturformel (Formel) *f* bester Annäherung	formule *f* [pour l'intégration numérique] de la meilleure approximation, formule de quadrature de la meilleure approximation	[квадратурная] формула наилучшего приближения
Q 53	**quadrature method** <AX, DI, NU>	Quadraturverfahren *n*	procédé *m* de quadrature	метод квадратур
Q 54	**quadrature of the circle,** squaring the circle <EG>	Quadratur *f* des Kreises (Zirkels)	quadrature *f* du cercle	квадратура круга
Q 55	**quadric,** quadric surface, surface of second order, quadric-locus <AG>	Fläche *f* zweiter (2.) Ordnung, Fläche zweiten (2.) Grades, Ordnungsquadrik *f*, Quadrik *f*, // Quadrifläche *f*	quadrique *f*, surface *f* du second ordre (degré)	поверхность второго порядка, квадрика
	quadric <AL>	*s.* 1. Q 25; 2. Q 28		
	quadric <GE>	*s.* H 716		
	quadric curve <AG, AY>	*s.* C 1944		
	quadric-envelope <AG>	*s.* S 2373		
	quadric in projective geometry <PJ>	*s.* P 1722		
	quadric-locus <AG>	*s.* Q 55		
	quadric quantic <AL>	*s.* Q 28		
	quadric surface <AG>	*s.* Q 55		
	quadric surface <GE>	*s.* H 716		
	quadrifolium <GE>	*s.* F 543		
Q 56	**quadrilateral** <EG>	Vierseit *n*	quadrilatère *m*	четырехсторонник; четырехвершинник
Q 57	**quadrilateral** <GP>	Vierkreis *m*	quadrilatère *m*, cycle *m* élémentaire de longueur 4	простой цикл длины 4
Q 58	**quadrilateral circumscribing** <*e.g.:* a circle> <EG>	Tangentenvierseit *n*	quadrilatère *m* circonscriptible	четырехсторонник, имеющий вписанную окружность; описываемый (описанный) четырехсторонник
	quadrilateral inscribed <EG>	*s.* I 579		
Q 59	**quadrilinear form** <AL>	quadrilineare (vierfach lineare) Form *f*	forme *f* quadrilinéaire	четырехкратно линейная форма
Q 60	**quadrinomial** <AL>	Quadrinom *n*, viergliedriger Ausdruck *m*	quadrinôme *m*	четырехчлен
Q 61	**quadrinomial equation,** four-termed equation <AL>	quartinomische (viergliedrige) Gleichung *f*	équation *f* quartinôme (tétranôme, quadrinôme)	четырехчленное уравнение
Q 62	**quadripartite curve** <AY>	vierteilige Kurve *f*	courbe *f* quadripartite, courbe ayant (possédant) quatre branches distinctes	четырехдольная кривая
Q 63	**quadripartition** <AR, EG>	Vierteilung *f*	quadripartition *f*, quadrisection *f*	деление на четыре части
Q 64	**quadripolar surface** <AG>	Quadripolarfläche *f*, (*n* — 2)-te Polarfläche *f*	surface *f* quadripolaire	(*n* — 2)-я полярная поверхность, квадриполярная поверхность
Q 65	**quadruple,** 4-uple <CT, SE>	Quadrupel *n*, 4-Tupel *n*, Vierling *m*, Viersatz *m*	quadruplet *m*, 4-tuple *m*, quaterne *m*	четверка
Q 66	**quadruple of points** <GE>	Punktequadrupel *n*, Punktquadrupel *n*	quadruplet (quadruple) *m* de points	четверка точек
Q 67	**quadruple point** <GE>	vierfacher Punkt *m*	point *m* quadruple	четверная точка
Q 68	**quadruple product** <of vectors> <VT>	vierfaches Produkt *n*	produit *m* quadruple	четырехкратное произведение
Q 69	**quadruple root** <AL>	vierfache Nullstelle (Wurzel) *f*	racine *f* quadruple (de multiplicité 4)	нуль кратности четыре, корень четвертой кратности
	quadruplicity <AN, LO>	*s.* F 551		
Q 70	**quadruply periodic function** <AN>	vierfach periodische Funktion *f*	fonction *f* quadruplement périodique	четырехкратно периодическая функция
Q 71	**quadruply perspective tetrahedra** <PJ>	vierfach perspektive Tetraeder *npl*	tétraèdres *mpl* quadruplement perspectifs	четырехкратно перспективные тетраэдры
Q 72	**qualitative character,** attribute <ST>	qualitatives Merkmal *n*, Attribut *n*	caractère *m* qualitatif, attribut *m*	характерный признак, качественный признак, качественное свойство
	qualitative variability <ST>	*s.* A 576		
Q 73	**quantal response,** all or none <ST>	Alternativreaktion *f*, Alles *n* oder Nichts *n*	réponse *f* par tout ou rien, tout *m* ou rien *m*	альтернативный исход, данные типа «да или нет»
	quantic <AL>	*s.* F 461		
	quantic of the fifth degree <AL>	*s.* Q 303		
	quantic of the fourth degree <AL>	*s.* Q 90		
	quantic of the sixth degree <AL>	*s.* S 729		
	quantic of the third degree <AL>	*s.* C 2743		
Q 74	**quantifiable propositional form** <LO>	quantifizierbare Aussageform *f*	forme *f* propositionnelle quantifiable	квантифицируемая форма высказывания
Q 75	**quantification** <LO>	Quantifizierung *f*	quantification *f*, préfixation *f* de quantificateurs, généralisation *f*	квантификация, навешивание кванторов
	quantificational logic <LO>	*s.* P 1183		
	quantification theory <LO>	*s.* 1. F 347; 2. P 1183		
Q 76	**quantified propositional form** <LO>	quantifizierte Aussageform *f*	forme *f* propositionnelle quantifiée	квантифицированная форма высказывания
Q 77	**quantifier,** operator <LO>	Quantifikator *m*, Quantor *m*, prädikatenlogischer Funktor *m*, Klammerzeichen *n*	quantificateur *m*, quantificateur logique, quantifieur *m*, quanteur *m*	квантор

No.	English	German	French	Russian
Q 78	**quantifier-free formula,** formula free of quantifiers <LO>	quantifikatorenfreier (quantorenfreier) Ausdruck *m*	formule *f* sans quantificateurs	бесканторная формула, формула без кванторов
	quantifier-free portion <LO>	*s.* M 181		
	quantifier logic <LO>	*s.* P 1183		
Q 79	**quantifier rule** <LO>	Quantifizierungsregel *f*	règle *f* de liaison par quantificateur	правило связывания квантором
	quantifier with a limited range <LO>	*s.* B 682		
Q 80	**quantify existentially / to** <LO>	partikularisieren	particulariser	связывать квантором существования
Q 81	**quantile of order *p*,** *p*-quantile, fractile of order *p*, *p*-fractile <ST>	Quantil *n* der Ordnung *p*, Quantil *p*-ter Ordnung, *p*-Quantil *n*, Fraktil *n* der Ordnung *p*, *p*-Fraktil *n*	quantile *m* de l'ordre *p*, fractile *m* de l'ordre *p*	квантиль *p*-го порядка, квантиль порядка *p*, *p*-квантиль
	quantities prime to each other <AL>	*s.* R 751		
Q 82	**quantity** <for a group> <GR, IV>	Größe *f* <für eine Gruppe>	grandeur *f* <pour un groupe>	групповая величина
Q 83	**quantity obeying the same transformation law** <AL, GE>	gleichtransformierte Größe *f*	grandeur *f* obéissant à la même loi de transformation	одинаково преобразовае-мая величина
	quantity of information <ST>	*s.* I 506		
Q 84	**quantity of the same kind** <GN>	Größe *f* gleicher Art	grandeur *f* de même espèce	величина одинакового рода
Q 85	**quarter-square** <NT>	Viertelquadrat *n*	quart *m* de carré	четверть квадрата
Q 86	**quartic,** plane quartic [curve], plane algebraic curve of the fourth degree (order), algebraic plane curve of the fourth degree (order) <AG>	algebraische ebene Kurve *f* vierter (4.) Ordnung, [ebene] algebraische Kurve vierter (4.) Ordnung, ebene Kurve vierter (4.) Ordnung, ebene Quartik *f*	courbe *f* [algébrique] plane d'ordre quatre (4), courbe quartique plane, quartique *f* plane	плоская [алгебраическая] кривая четвертого (4-го) порядка
	quartic <AG>	*s. a.* 1. Q 89; 2. Q 91		
	quartic <AL>	*s.* 1. Q 88; 2. Q 90		
Q 87	**quartic [curve],** [algebraic] curve of the fourth order (degree) <AG>	Kurve *f* vierter (4.) Ordnung, Quartik *f*, algebraische Kurve vierter (4.) Ordnung, Kurve vierten (4.) Grades	courbe *f* quartique, quartique *f*, courbe [algébrique] du quatrième (4-me) ordre, courbe biquadratique, courbe d'ordre 4	алгебраическая кривая четвертого (4-го) порядка, кривая четвертого (4-го) порядка, квартика
	quartic curve in space <AG>	*s.* S 1308		
Q 88	**quartic equation,** quartic, [algebraic] equation of [the] fourth degree, fourth-degree polynomial equation <AL>	Gleichung *f* vierten (4.) Grades, algebraische [allgemeine] Gleichung vierten (4.) Grades, biquadratische Gleichung	équation *f* quartique, équation du (de) quatrième (4-me) degré (ordre), équation bicarrée (biquadratique), quartique *f*	уравнение четвертой (4-ой) степени, уравнение четвертого (4-го) порядка, биквадратное уравнение
Q 89	**quartic manifold,** quartic <AG>	Mannigfaltigkeit *f* vierter Ordnung	variété *f* quartique	многообразие четвертого порядка
Q 90	**quartic quantic,** quartic, quantic (form) of the fourth degree <AL>	biquadratische Form *f*, Form vierten Grades, Quartik *f*	forme *f* biquadratique, quartique *f*, forme quartique	биквадратическая форма, форма четвертой степени
	quartic space curve <AG>	*s.* S 1308		
Q 91	**quartic surface,** quartic, surface of fourth order <AG>	Fläche *f* vierter Ordnung, Fläche vierten Grades	surface *f* quartique, surface du quatrième ordre	поверхность четвертого порядка
Q 92	**quartic symmetry,** four-fold symmetry, tetragonal symmetry, tetrad symmetry <EG>	vierzählige Symmetrie *f*	symétrie *f* d'ordre 4	симметрия четвертого порядка
Q 93	**quartile** <ST>	Quartil *n*	quartile *m*	квартиль
	quartile deviation <ST>	*s.* S 392		
	quartile range <ST>	*s.* I 791		
Q 94	**quasi-Abelian function** <FT>	quasiabelsche Funktion *f*	fonction *f* quasi-abélienne	квазиабелева функция
Q 95	**quasi-affine group** <DG>	quasiaffine Gruppe *f*	groupe *m* quasi[-] affine	квазиаффинная группа
Q 96	**quasi-affine mapping (transformation)** <DG>	quasiaffine Abbildung (Transformation) *f*	application (transformation) *f* quasi-affine (quasi affine)	квазиаффинное отображение (преобразование)
Q 97	**quasi-algebraically closed field** <AL>	quasi-algebraisch abgeschlossener Körper *m*	corps *m* quasi-algébriquement clos	квазиалгебраически замкнутое поле
Q 98	**quasi-algebraic group** <GR>	quasialgebraische Gruppe *f*	groupe *m* quasi-algébrique	квазиалгебраическая группа
Q 99	**quasi-alternating permutation** <AL>	quasialternierende Permutation *f*	permutation *f* quasi-alternée, permutation quasialternée <André>	
Q 100	**quasi-analytic class** <AN>	quasianalytische Klasse *f*	classe *f* quasi analytique	квазианалитический класс
Q 101	**quasi-analytic function** <in Bernstein's sense with respect to a sequence of natural numbers> <AN>	quasianalytische Funktion *f* <in bezug auf eine Folge natürlicher Zahlen im Bernsteinschen Sinne>, (*P*)-quasianalytische Funktion	fonction *f* quasi analytique <par rapport à une suite de nombres naturels au sens de Bernstein>	квазианалитическая функция <по последовательности натуральных чисел в смысле Бернштейна>
Q 102	**quasi-analytic function** <in the sense of the corresponding class> <AN>	quasianalytische Funktion *f*	fonction *f* quasi analytique	квазианалитическая функция
Q 103	**quasi-analyticity** <AN>	Quasianalytizität *f*	quasi-analyticité *f*	квазианалитичность
Q 104	**quasi-asymptotic curve** <DG>	Quasiasymptotenlinie *f*	ligne *f* quasi[-] asymptotique	квазиасимптотическая линия

No.	English	German	French	Russian
Q 105	**quasiatomic formula** <UA>	quasiatomarer Ausdruck *m*	formule *f* quasi-atomique	квазиатомарная формула
Q 106	**quasi-axiomatic class** <MM>	quasiaxiomatische Klasse *f*	classe *f* quasi-axiomatique	квазиаксиоматизируемый класс
Q 107	**quasi-bilinear function** <AL>	quasibilineare Funktion *f*	fonction *f* quasi-bilinéaire	квазибилинейная функция
Q 108	**quasibounded function,** weakly bounded function <AN> ⌐<GR>	quasibeschränkte Funktion *f*	fonction *f* quasi-bornée	квазиограниченная функция
Q 109	**quasi-centre** <of a group>	Quasizentrum *n*	quasi-centre *m*	квазицентр
Q 110	**quasi centred affine map[ping] (transformation)** <DG>	quasizentroaffine Abbildung (Transformation) *f*	application (transformation) *f* affine quasi centrée	квази-центроаффинное отображение (преобразование)
Q 111	**quasi-character** <AL>	Quasicharakter *m*	quasi-caractère *m*	квазихарактер
	"quasi-clairsemé" set <TO>	*s.* Q 142		
Q 112	**quasi-closed group** <GR>	quasiabgeschlossene Gruppe ⌐*f*	groupe *m* quasi-fermé	квазизамкнутая группа
Q 113	**quasicoherent sheaf** <AL>	quasikohärente Garbe *f*	faisceau *m* quasi-cohérent	квазикогерентный пучок
Q 114	**quasi[-]compact space,** bicompact space, compact space <TO>	quasikompakter Raum *m*, bikompakter [topologischer] Raum, kompakter Raum	espace *m* quasi-compact <Bourbaki>, espace bicompact (compact)	квазикомпактное пространство, бикомпактное пространство; пространство, компактное в смысле Лефшеца
Q 115	**quasi-compactum** <TO>	Quasikompaktum *n*	quasi-compact *m*	квазикомпакт
Q 116	**quasi-complement** <in a lattice> <LA>	Quasikomplement *n*	quasicomplément *m*	квазидополнение
Q 117	**quasi-complemented lattice** <LA> ⌐<TO>	quasikomplementärer Verband *m*	treillis *m* quasi-complémenté	структура с квазидополнениями
Q 118	**quasicompleteness** <FA,	Quasivollständigkeit *f*	quasi-complétude *f*	квазиполнота
Q 119	**quasi-complete space** <FA, TO>	quasivollständiger Raum *m*	espace *m* [vectoriel topologique] quasi[-] complet	квазиполное [топологическое векторное] пространство
Q 120	**quasi-complete topology** <FA, TO>	quasivollständige Topologie *f*	topologie *f* quasi[-] complète	квазиполная топология
Q 121	**quasicomplex,** weak semi-complex <AT>	Quasikomplex *m*	semi-complexe *m* faible <Thomson>, quasi-complexe *m* <Lefschetz>	квазикомплекс
Q 122	**quasi-complex manifold** <GE>	quasikomplexe Mannigfaltigkeit *f*	variété *f* quasi[-] complexe	квазикомплексное многообразие
Q 123	**quasi-component** <of a point> <TO>	Konstituante *f*	constituant *m*	конституанта <точки>; квазикомпонента, составляющая <пространства>
Q 124	**quasi-component** <of a space> <TO>	Quasikomponente *f*	quasi-composante *f*	квазикомпонента
Q 125	**quasi-concave function** <AN>	quasikonkave Funktion *f*	fonction *f* quasi concave	квазивогнутая функция
Q 126	**quasi-concavity** <AN>	Quasikonkavität *f*	quasi-concavité *f*	квазивогнутость
Q 127	**quasi-conformality** <FT>	Quasikonformität *f*	quasi-conformité *f*	квазиконформность
Q 128	**quasi[-]conformal mapping** <FT>	quasikonforme Abbildung *f*, pseudoanalytische Funktion *f*	application (représentation) *f* quasi[-] conforme	квазиконформное отображение
Q 129	**quasi-continuity** <AN>	Quasistetigkeit *f*	quasi-continuité *f*	квазинепрерывность
Q 130	**quasi-continuous function** <AN>	quasistetige Funktion *f*, nahezu stetige Funktion	fonction *f* quasi continue	квазинепрерывная функция
Q 131	**quasi-convergence** <SS>	Fastkonvergenz *f*	quasi-convergence *f*	почти-сходимость
Q 132	**quasi-convex function** <AN>	quasikonvexe Funktion *f*	fonction *f* quasi convexe, fonction quasi-convexe	квазивыпуклая функция
Q 133	**quasi-convexity** <AN>	Quasikonvexität *f*	quasi-convexité *f*	квазивыпуклость
Q 134	**quasi-coordinates,** nonholonomic co-ordinates, pseudo co-ordinates <GE>	Quasikoordinaten *fpl*, nichtholonome Koordinaten *fpl*, Pseudokoordinaten *fpl*	quasi-coordonnées *fpl*, coordonnées *fpl* non holonomiques, pseudo-coordonnées *fpl*	квазикоординаты, неголономные координаты, псевдокоординаты
	quasi-cyclic group <AL>	*s.* P 1891		
Q 135	**quasi-decomposition** <of groups> <GR>	Quasizerlegung *f*	quasi-décomposition *f*	квазиразложение
Q 136	**quasi[-] derivative** <AN>	Quasiableitung *f*	quasi-dérivée *f*	квазипроизводная
	quasi-diagonal matrix <MD>	*s.* M 187		
Q 137	**quasi-different** <AL>	Quasidifferente *f*	quasi-différente *f*	квазидифферент
Q 138	**quasidifferential equation** <AN, DE>	Quasidifferentialgleichung *f*, Quasi-Differentialgleichung *f*	équation *f* quasi différentielle	квазидифференциальное уравнение
Q 139	**quasidifferential expression** <AN>	Quasidifferentialausdruck *m*, Quasi-Differentialausdruck *m*	expression *f* quasi différentielle	квазидифференциальное выражение
Q 140	**quasidirected set,** filtrant pre-ordered set, right direction, right[-] directed quasi-order, directed set, filtered set, directed pre-order, directed upward set, directed system, directed preordered set, directed quasi-ordered set <preordered> <SE>	nach oben quasigerichtete Menge *f*, quasigerichtete Menge, gerichtete Menge, gerichtete Vorordnung *f*, filtrierende Menge, nach oben gerichtete Menge, nach rechts gefilterte Menge, aufsteigend filtrierende Menge	ensemble *m* quasi-filtrant, ensemble filtrant supérieurement, ensemble filtrant à droite, ensemble filtrant, ensemble filtré, ensemble [pré]ordonné filtrant, ensemble dirigé, ensemble préordonné filtrant à droite	квазинаправленное множество, направленное множество, фильтрующееся множество, фильтрующееся вправо множество, фильтрующееся возрастающее семейство; множество, фильтрующееся вверх; множество, фильтрующееся вправо, направление, сеть, направленное упорядоченное множество, возрастающее направленное семейство; квазиупорядоченное множество, направленное вверх

No.	English	German	French	Russian
Q 141	**quasi-discrete space** <TO>	quasidiskreter Raum *m*	espace *m* quasi discret	квазидискретное пространство
Q 142	**quasi-dispersed set,** "quasi-clairsemé" set <TO>	quasi-zerstreute Menge *f*	ensemble *m* quasi-clairsemé	квазирассеянное множество
Q 143	**quasi-distance,** pseudo-distance <TO>	Quasiabstand *m*, Spanne *f*, Quasimetrik *f*	quasi-écart *m*, quasi-distance *f*, écart *m*	квазирасстояние
Q 144	**quasi-divisibility** <AL>	Quasiteilbarkeit *f*	quasi-divisibilité *f*	квазиделимость
Q 145	**quasi-divisor** <of an ideal *or* in an l-semigroup> <AL>	Quasiteiler *m*	quasi-diviseur *m*	квазиделитель
	quasi-elliptic function <FT, FU>	*s.* P 1932		
Q 146	**quasi-equal ideal** <AL>	quasigleiches Ideal *n*	idéal *m* quasi-égal	квазиравный идеал
Q 147	**quasi-equality** <of ideals> <AL>	Quasigleichheit *f*, „quasi"-Identität *f*	quasigleichheit *m*	квазиравенство
Q 148	**quasi-equationally complete collection of identities,** Q-complete collection of identities <UA>	Q-vollständige Menge *f* von Identitäten, quasigleichungsmäßig vollständige Menge von Identitäten		квазиэквационально полная совокупность тождеств, Q-полная совокупность тождеств
Q 149	**quasi-equivalent function** <AG>	quasiäquivalente Funktion *f*	fonction *f* quasi-équivalente	квазиэквивалентная функция
Q 150	**quasi everywhere** <PO>	quasi überall	quasi partout	квази всюду, с точностью до множества внешней емкости нуль, почти всюду
Q 151	**quasi-exact category** <CA>	quasiexakte Kategorie *f*	catégorie *f* quasi-exacte	квазиточная категория
Q 152	**quasifactor,** quasimultiple <of an ideal> <AL>	Quasivielfaches *n*	quasi-multiple *m*	квазикратный
Q 153	**quasifibration** <AT>	Quasifaserung *f*	quasi-fibration *f*	квазирасслоение
Q 154	**quasi-field,** Veblen-Wedderburn number system <AL>	Quasikörper *m*, Klein-Desarguessches Zahlsystem *n*, <rechts- bzw. linksdistributive> kartesische (cartesische) Gruppe *f*, Veblen-Wedderburn-System *n*, V-W-System *n*	système *m* de Veblen-Wedderburn, quasi-corps *m*	квазиполе
Q 155	**quasi filtering category,** right-quasi filtering category, pseudo-filtered category <CA>	pseudofiltrierende Kategorie *f*, quasifiltrierende Kategorie	catégorie *f* pseudo-filtrante	квазифильтрующаяся категория, квазифильтрующаяся справа категория
Q 156	**quasi-finite extension** <of a local ring> <AL>	quasiendliche Ringerweiterung *f* <eines Stellenrings>, quasiendlicher Stellenring *m* <über einem Teilstellenring>	extension *f* quasi-finie <d'un anneau local>	квазиконечное расширение <локального кольца>
Q 157	**quasi-free basis** <of a group> <GR>	quasifreie Basis *f*	base *f* quasi libre	квазисвободная база
Q 158	**quasi-free group** <GR>	quasifreie Gruppe *f*	groupe *m* quasi-libre, groupe quasi libre	квазисвободная группа
Q 159	**quasi-Frobenius extension** <AL>	Quasi-Frobenius-Erweiterung *f*	extension *f* quasi-frobeniusienne	квазифробениусово расширение
Q 160	**quasi-Frobenius ring, quasifrobenius ring,** QF ring, zero Gorenstein ring, Artinian Gorenstein ring, self-injective Artin ring <AL>	Quasi-Frobenius-Ring *m*, Quasifrobeniusring *m*, Artinscher Gorenstein-Ring *m*	anneau *m* quasi-frobeniusien	квазифробениусово кольцо, QF-кольцо
Q 161	**quasifunction** <AG>	Quasifunktion *f*	quasi-fonction *f*	квазифункция
Q 162	**quasi-geodesic [line]** <DG>	Quasigeodätische *f*	quasi-géodésique *f*	квазигеодезическая [линия]
Q 163	**quasi[-]group** <AL>	Quasigruppe *f*, Divisionsgruppoid *n* mit eindeutiger Division	quasi-groupe *m*	квазигруппа
	quasi-harmonic autonomous system <DE>	*s.* Q 165		
Q 164	**quasi-harmonic differential equation** <DE>	quasiharmonische Differentialgleichung *f*	équation *f* différentielle quasi-harmonique	квазигармоническое дифференциальное уравнение
Q 165	**quasi-harmonic [dynamical] system,** quasi-harmonic autonomous system <DE>	quasiharmonisches dynamisches System *n*, quasiharmonisches [autonomes] System	système *m* dynamique quasi-harmonique, système [autonome] quasi-harmonique	квазигармоническая автономная система, квазигармоническая [динамическая] система
Q 166	**quasi-Hermitian matrix** <MD>	quasihermitesche Matrix *f*	matrice *f* quasi hermitienne	квазиэрмитова матрица
Q 167	**quasi-homeomorphic space** <TO>	quasihomöomorpher Raum *m*	espace *m* quasi-homéomorphe	квазигомеоморфное пространство
Q 168	**quasi-homeomorphism** <TO>	Quasihomöomorphismus *m*	quasi-homéomorphisme *m*	квазигомеоморфизм
Q 169	**quasi-homogeneous affine surface** <AG>	quasihomogene affine Fläche *f*	surface *f* affine quasi[ ] homogène	квазиоднородная аффинная поверхность
Q 170	**quasihyperbolic differential geometry** <DG>	quasihyperbolische Differentialgeometrie *f*	géométrie *f* différentielle quasi[ ]hyperbolique	квазигиперболическая дифференциальная геометрия
Q 171	**quasi-hyperelliptic curve** <AG>	quasi-hyperelliptische Kurve *f*	courbe *f* quasi-hyperelliptique	квазигиперэллиптическая кривая
Q 172	**quasi-ideal** <of a semigroup> <AL>	Quasiideal *n*	quasi-idéal *m*	квазиидеал
Q 173	**quasi-idempotency** <AL>	Quasiidempotenz *f*	quasi-idempotence *f*	квазиидемпотентность
Q 174	**quasi-identity,** universal Horn sequence <LO, UA>	Quasiidentität *f*, bedingte Identität *f*	quasi-identité *f*	квазитождество, условное тождество, универсальное хорновское предложение

Q 175	**quasi-injective hull** <AL>	quasiinjektive Hülle *f*	enveloppe *m* quasi-injective	квазиинъективная оболочка
Q 176	**quasi-injective module** <AL>	quasiinjektiver Modul *m*	module *m* quasi-injectif	квазиинъективный модуль
Q 177	**quasi-injectivity** <AL>	Quasiinjektivität *f*	quasi-injectivité *f*	квазиинъективность
Q 178	**quasi-integrable function** <AN>	quasiintegrierbare Funktion *f*	fonction *f* quasi intégrable	квазиинтегрируемая функция
Q 179	**quasi-interior point** <TO>	quasiinnerer Punkt *m*	point *m* quasi-intérieur	квазивнутренняя точка
Q 180	**quasi-invariant measure** <on a locally compact space> <ME>	quasiinvariantes Maß *n*	mesure *f* quasi-invariante	квазиинвариантная мера
Q 181	**quasi-inverse** <of an element of a ring> <AL>	Quasiinverses *n*	adverse *m*	квазиобратный элемент
Q 182	**quasi inverse functor** <CA>	äquivalenzinverser Funktor *m*, Äquivalenzinverser *m*	foncteur *m* quasi-inverse	квазиобратный функтор
Q 183	**quasi[-]inverse matrix** <MD> ┌<AL>	quasiinverse Matrix *f*	matrice *f* quasi-inverse	квазиобратная матрица
	quasi-invertible element	*s.* Q 239		
Q 184	**quasi-isomorphic group** <GR>	quasiisomorphe Gruppe *f*	groupe *m* quasi-isomorphe	квазиизоморфная группа
Q 185	**quasi-isomorphism** <of groups> <mapping> <GR>	Quasiisomorphismus *m*	quasi-isomorphisme *m*	квазиизоморфизм
Q 186	**quasi-isomorphism** <of groups> <property> <GR>	Quasiisomorphie *f*	quasi-isomorphie *f*	квазиизоморфизм
Q 187	**quasi latin-square** <CT, ST>	quasilateinisches Quadrat *n*	carré *m* quasi latin	квазилатинский квадрат
Q 188	**quasi[-]length** <VA>	Quasilänge *f*, J-Länge *f*	quasi-longueur *f*	квазидлина
Q 189	**quasi[-]linear autonomous system,** quasi[-]linear dynamic system <DE>	quasilineares dynamisches (autonomes) System *n*	système *m* autonome (dynamique) quasi (presque) linéaire	квазилинейная автономная (динамическая) система
	quasi[-]linear differential equation <DE>	*s.* Q 190		
	quasi[-]linear dynamic system <DE>	*s.* Q 189		
Q 190	**quasi[-]linear equation,** quasi[-]linear <partial> differential equation <DE>	quasilineare [partielle] Differentialgleichung *f*, quasilineare Gleichung *f*	équation *f* [différentielle] quasi (presque) linéaire	квазилинейное [дифференциальное] уравнение
Q 191	**quasi[-]linear function** <AL> ┌<GR>	quasilineare Funktion *f*	fonction *f* quasi-linéaire	квазилинейная функция
Q 192	**quasi[-]linear group**	quasilineare Gruppe *f*	groupe *m* quasi-linéaire	квазилинейная группа
Q 193	**quasilinear system** <of ordinary differential equations> <DE>	quasilineares System *n* von gewöhnlichen Differentialgleichungen	système *m* quasi (presque) linéaire <d'équations différentielles ordinaires>	квазилинейная система <обыкновенных дифференциальных уравнений>
	quasi[-]linear transformation <FT>	*s.* I 376		
Q 194	**quasi-local ring** <AL>	quasilokaler Ring *m*	anneau *m* quasi-local	квазилокальное кольцо
Q 195	**quasi-maximal topology** <TO>	quasimaximale Topologie *f*	topologie *f* quasi-maximale	квазимаксимальная топология
Q 196	**quasi-measure** <ME>	Quasimaß *n*	quasi-mesure *f*	квазимера
Q 197	**quasi-metric** <TO>	Quasimetrik *f*	quasi-métrique *f*	квазиметрика
	quasi metric lattice <LA>	*s.* P 1956		
Q 198	**quasi-metric space** <TO>	quasimetrischer Raum *m*	espace *m* muni d'une distance non symétrique, espace quasi[-] métrique	квазиметрическое пространство
Q 199	**quasi-monotone transformation** <TO>	quasimonotone Transformation *f*	transformation *f* quasi monotone	квазимонотонное преобразование
Q 200	**quasimorphism** <CA>	Quasimorphismus *m*	quasi-morphisme *m*	квазиморфизм
Q 201	**quasi-motion** <DG>	Quasibewegung *f*	quasi-mouvement *m*	квазидвижение
	quasimultiple <AL>	*s.* Q 152		
Q 202	**quasi-multiplication,** weak multiplication <AL>	Quasimultiplikation *f*	quasi-multiplication *f*	квазиумножение
Q 203	**quasi[-]nilpotent group** <GR>	quasinilpotente Gruppe *f*	groupe *m* quasi[-] nilpotent	квазинильпотентная группа
Q 204	**quasi[-]nilpotent operator** <FA>	eigenwertfreier Operator *m*, quasinilpotenter Operator	opérateur *m* quasi[-] nilpotent	квазинильпотентный оператор
Q 205	**quasi-norm** <of a polynomial> <AL>	Quasinorm *f*	quasi-norme *f*	квазинорма
Q 206	**quasinormal** <GE>	Quasi-Normale *f* <Fiedler>	quasi-normale *f*	квазинормаль
Q 207	**quasi-normal family [of functions],** weakly normal family [of functions] <AN>	quasi-normale Funktionenschar (Schar) *f*	famille *f* quasi normale [de fonctions]	квазинормальное семейство [функций]
Q 208	**quasi-normal group** <GR>	quasinormale Gruppe *f*	groupe *m* quasi normal	квазинормальная группа
Q 209	**quasi-normal vectors** <FA, TO>	[zueinander] quasinormale Vektoren *mpl*	vecteurs *mpl* quasi-normaux	квазинормальные векторы
Q 210	**quasi-normed space** <TO>	quasinormierter Raum *m*	espace *m* quasi-normé	квазинормированное (квазинормируемое) пространство <Гротендик>
Q 211	**quasi-open mapping, quasi-open transformation** <TO>	quasioffene Abbildung *f*	application *f* quasi-ouverte (quasi ouverte)	квазиоткрытое отображение <отображение, при котором всякая точка образа является внутренней для образа всякого открытого множества, содержащего хотя бы одну компактную компоненту прообраза рассматриваемой точки>

Q 212	**quasi-optimum strategy,** ε-optimal strategy <SP, TG>	quasioptimale Strategie *f*, ε-optimale Strategie, epsilon-optimale Strategie	stratégie *f* quasi optimale, stratégie ε-optimale, stratégie epsilon-optimale	квазиоптимальная стратегия, ε-оптимальная стратегия, эпсилон-оптимальная стратегия
Q 213	**quasi-order / to** <SE>	vorordnen	préordonner	предупорядочивать
Q 214	**quasi-order,** reflexive quasi-order, quasi-ordering, weak ordering, preorder, reflexive and transitive relation <SE>	reflexive Quasiordnung *f*, Quasiordnung, Präordnung *f*, schwache Ordnung (Halbordnung) *f*, Vorordnung *f*	préordre *m* partiel, préordre, quasi-ordre *m*, ordre *m* partiel, relation *f* de quasi-ordre (préordre)	квазиупорядок, отношение квазиупорядоченности, предупорядок, отношение предпорядка, частичный упорядок
Q 215	**quasi-order** <not necessarily reflexive> <SE>	Quasiordnung *f*	quasi-ordre *m*	квазиупорядок
	quasi-order <SE>	*s.* T 808		
Q 216	**quasi-ordered group** <GR>	quasigeordnete (vorgeordnete) Gruppe *f*	groupe *m* préordonné	квазичастично упорядоченная группа, пре[д]упорядоченная группа
Q 217	**quasi-ordered semigroup** <AL>	vorgeordnete (quasigeordnete) Halbgruppe *f*	monoïde (demi-groupe) *m* préordonné	предупорядоченная (квазичастично упорядоченная) полугруппа
Q 218/9	**quasi-ordered set** <not necessarily reflexively> <SE>	quasigeordnete Menge *f*	ensemble *m* quasi-ordonné	квазиупорядоченное множество
	quasi-ordered set <SE>	*s.* P 1230		
	quasi-ordering <SE>	*s.* 1. P 246; 2. Q 214		
Q 220	**quasi-ordering structure** <UA>	Vorordnungsstruktur *f*	structure *f* de préordre	структура предупорядка
Q 221	**quasi-orthogonal system** <AN>	quasiorthogonales System *n*	système *m* quasi orthogonal	квазиортогональная система
Q 222	**quasi-periodic function** <AP>	quasiperiodische Funktion *f*	fonction *f* quasi[-] périodique	квазипериодическая функция
Q 223	**quasi-periodicity** <AP, NT>	Quasiperiodizität *f*	quasi-périodicité *f*	квазипериодичность
Q 224	**quasi-periodic *q*-adic fraction** <NT>	quasiperiodischer *q*-adischer Bruch *m*	fraction *f* *q*-imale quasi[-] périodique <Maillet>	квазипериодическая *q*-адическая дробь
Q 225	**quasi-periodic sequence** <SS>	quasiperiodische Folge *f* <Maillet>	suite *f* quasi[-] périodique	квазипериодическая последовательность
Q 226	**quasi-periodic set** <NT, SE>	quasiperiodische Menge *f*	ensemble *m* quasi[-] périodique	квазипериодическое множество
Q 227	**quasi-plane curve** <GE>	quasiebene Kurve *f*	courbe *f* quasi[-] planaire	квазиплоская кривая
Q 228	**quasi-polynomial** <AN>	Quasipolynom *n*	quasipolynôme *m*	квазиполином
Q 229	**quasi-primary element** <AL>	quasiprimäres Element *n*	élément *m* quasi[-] primaire	квазипримарный элемент
Q 230	**quasi-prime ideal** <AL>	Quasiprimideal *n*	idéal *m* quasi-premier	квазипростой идеал
Q 231	**quasi-prime ring** <AL>	quasiprimer Ring *m*	anneau *m* quasi-premier	квазипростое кольцо
Q 232	**quasiprimitive class,** implicationally defined class, quasivariety <UA>	Quasivarietät *f*, quasiprimitive Klasse *f*	quasi-variété *f*, classe *f* quasi-primitive	квазимногообразие, квазипримитивный класс
Q 233	**quasi-projective cover** <of a module> <AL>	quasiprojektive Hülle *f*	enveloppe *f* quasi-projective	квазипроективное покрытие
Q 234	**quasi-quadratic function** <having a quasibilinear derivative> <AL>	quasiquadratische Funktion *f*	fonction *f* quasi-quadratique	квазиквадратическая функция
Q 235	**quasi random sampling** <ST>	bedingte Zufallsauswahl *f*	échantillonnage *m* quasi probabiliste	квазислучайный (псевдослучайный) выбор
	quasi range <ST>	*s.* P 254		
Q 236	**quasi-rank** <AL>	Quasirang *m*	quasirang *m*	квазиранг
Q 237	**quasi-rational number** <NT>	quasirationale Zahl *f*	nombre *m* quasi-rationnel <Maillet>	квазирациональное число
Q 238	**quasiregular differential operator** <FA>	quasiregulärer Differentialoperator *m*	opérateur *m* différentiel quasi[-] régulier	квазирегулярный дифференциальный оператор
Q 239	**quasi-regular element,** quasi-invertible element <of a ring> <AL>	quasireguläres Element *n*	élément *m* quasi régulier, élément quasi-régulier	квазирегулярный элемент, радикальный элемент
Q 240	**quasi-regularity** <of a semigroup> <AL>	Quasiregularität *f*	quasi-simplifiabilité *f*	квазирегулярность
Q 241	**quasi-regular left ideal** <AL>	quasireguläres Linksideal *n*	idéal *m* à gauche quasi[-] régulier, idéal à gauche dont tous les éléments sont quasi réguliers à gauche	лево-квазирегулярный [левый] идеал, левый лево-квазирегулярный идеал
Q 242	**quasi-regular right ideal** <AL>	quasireguläres Rechtsideal *n*	idéal *m* à droite quasi[-] régulier, idéal à droite dont tous les éléments sont quasi réguliers à droite	право-квазирегулярный [правый] идеал, правый право-квазирегулярный идеал
Q 243	**quasi-regular variational problem,** semi-regular variational problem <positive *or* negative> <VA>	quasireguläres Variationsproblem *n* <positiv *oder* negativ>	problème *m* variationnel quasi[-]régulier, problème variationnel semi-régulier <positif *ou* négatif>	квазирегулярная (полурегулярная) вариационная задача <положительно *или* отрицательно>
Q 244	**quasi-representable functor** <CA>	quasidarstellbarer Funktor *m*	foncteur *m* quasi-représentable	квазипредставимый функтор
Q 245	**quasi-rotation** <DG>	Quasidrehung *f*	quasi-rotation *f*	квазивращение
Q 246	**quasi-rotation group** <DG>	Gruppe *f* der Quasidrehungen	groupe *m* des quasi-rotations	группа квазивращений
Q 247	**quasi self adjoint operator** <FA>	quasiselbstadjungierter Operator *m*	opérateur *m* quasi-auto-adjoint	квазисамосопряженный оператор
Q 248	**quasisimple module** <AL>	quasieinfacher Modul *m*	module *m* quasisimple	квазипростой модуль
Q 249	**quasi skew field** <AL>	Quasischiefkörper *m*	quasi-corps *m* gauche	тело, квазитело
Q 250	**quasisphere** <VA>	Quasikugel *f*	quasi-sphère *f*	квазисфера
Q 251	**quasispherical curve** <DG>	quasisphärische Kurve *f*	courbe *f* quasi sphérique	квазисферическая кривая

Q 252	**quasispinorial map[ping]** <DG>	quasispinorielle Abbildung *f*	application *f* quasi spinorielle	квазиспинорное отображение
Q 253	**quasistochastic matrix** <ST>	quasistochastische Matrix *f*	matrice *f* quasi stochastique	квазистохастическая матрица
Q 254	**quasi-strong connectedness** <of a graph> <GP>	quasistarker Zusammenhang *m*	connexité *f* quasi-forte, q. f.-connexité *f*	квазисильная связность
Q 255	**quasi-strongly connected graph** <GP>	quasi-stark zusammenhängender Graph *m*	graphe *m* quasi-fortement connexe	квазисильно связный граф
Q 256	**quasi-subvariety** <TO>	Quasiuntermannigfaltigkeit *f*	quasi-sous-variété *f*	квазиподмногообразие
Q 257	**quasi superharmonic function** <PO>	quasi-superharmonische Funktion *f*	fonction *f* quasi superharmonique	квазисупергармоническая функция
Q 258	**quasisymmetry** <for a unitary group> <GR>	Quasispiegelung *f*	quasi-symétrie *f*	квазисимметрия
Q 259	**quasi-topological group** <AL>	quasitopologische Gruppe *f*	groupe *m* quasi-topologique	квазитопологическая группа
Q 260	**quasi-translation** <GE>	Quasi-Translation *f*	quasi-translation *f*	квазиперенос
Q 261	**quasi[-]uniform convergence,** almost uniform convergence, essentially uniform convergence <of a sequence of measurable functions in a measure space> <FA>	nahezu gleichmäßige Konvergenz *f*, quasigleichmäßige Konvergenz, wesentlich gleichmäßige Konvergenz	convergence *f* uniforme essentielle, convergence quasi-uniforme (presque uniforme, uniforme à traits), convergence quasi uniforme	квазиравномерная сходимость, почти (существенно) равномерная сходимость
Q 262	**quasi[-]uniform convergence** <of a sequence of real functions on an interval> <RF>	quasigleichmäßige (streckenweise gleichmäßige) Konvergenz *f*	convergence *f* quasi[-] uniforme	квазиравномерная сходимость
Q 263	**quasi[-]uniformly convergent sequence,** almost uniformly convergent sequence, essentially uniformly convergent sequence <of measurable functions> <FA>	nahezu gleichmäßig konvergente Folge *f*, quasigleichmäßig konvergente Folge, wesentlich gleichmäßig konvergente Folge	suite *f* quasi[-] uniformément convergente, suite presque uniformément convergente	квазиравномерно (почти равномерно) сходящаяся последовательность, существенно равномерно сходящаяся последовательность
Q 264	**quasi-unitary matrix** <AL>	quasiunitäre Matrix *f*	matrice *f* quasi-unitaire	квазиунитарная матрица
Q 265	**quasivariety** <CA>	Quasimannigfaltigkeit *f*	quasi-variété *f*	квазимногообразие
	quasivariety <UA>	*s.* Q 232		
Q 266	**quaternariant** <as a comitant> <IV>	Quaternariante *f*	quaternariant *m*	кватернариант
	quaternary <CT>	*s.* F 508		
Q 267	**quaternary domain** <PJ>	quaternäres Gebiet *n*, Gebiet vierter (4.) Stufe	domaine *m* quaternaire	кватернарная область, область четвертой ступени
Q 268	**quaternary form,** quaternary (4-ary) quantic <AL>	quaternäre (4-äre) Form *f*, Quaternärform *f*, Form von vier Variablen, algebraische Form mit vier homogenen Variablen	forme *f* quaternaire (4-aire), forme de quatre variables, forme algébrique quaternaire	форма от четырех переменных, кватернарная (4-арная) форма
Q 269	**quaternary group** <GR>	quaternäre Gruppe *f*	groupe *m* quaternaire	кватернарная группа
Q 270	**quaternary notation** <NT>	quaternäre Zahlendarstellung (Schreibweise) *f*	notation *f* quaternaire	представление чисел в четверичной системе
Q 271	**quaternary number system,** quaternary system <NT>	Quaternärsystem *n*, quaternäres Zahlensystem *n*	système *m* quaternaire, système de numération à base 4, numération *f* quaternaire	четверичная система
Q 272	**quaternary quadratic form** <AL>	quaternäre quadratische Form *f*	forme *f* quadratique quaternaire	кватернарная квадратичная форма
	quaternary quantic <AL>	*s.* Q 268		
Q 273	**quaternary substitution** <having four indices> <AL>	quaternäre Substitution *f*	substitution *f* quaternaire	кватернарная подстановка
	quaternary system <NT>	*s.* Q 271		
Q 274	**quaternion** <of a quaternion algebra> <AL>	Quaternion *f*	quaternion *m*	кватернион
	quaternion <AL>	*s.* R 228		
	quaternion <CT>	*s.* F 508		
Q 275	**quaternion algebra,** algebra of quaternions, ring of quaternions <AL>	Quaternionenalgebra *f*	algèbre *f* des quaternions	алгебра кватернионов
Q 276	**quaternion elliptic space** <GE>	elliptischer Quaternionenraum *m*	espace *m* elliptique de quaternions	кватернионное эллиптическое пространство
	quaternion field <AL>	*s.* D 814		
Q 277	**quaternion function** <FT>	Quaternionenfunktion *f*	fonction *f* quaternionienne	кватернионная функция
Q 278	**quaternion group** <AL>	Quaternionengruppe *f*, Hamiltonsche Quaternionengruppe	groupe *m* quaternionien (des quaternions), groupe quaternionique	группа кватернионов
Q 279	**quaternionic equation** <AL>	Quaternionengleichung *f*	équation *f* en quaternions	кватернионное уравнение
Q 280	**quaternionic extension** <AL>	Quaternionenerweiterung *f*	extension *f* quaternionienne	кватернионное расширение
Q 281	**quaternionic matrix** <AL>	Quaternionenmatrix *f*	matrice *f* quaternionienne	кватернионная матрица
Q 282	**quaternionic system** <as a hypercomplex system> <AL>	Quaternionensystem *n*, Quaternionsystem *n* <Scheffers>	système *m* de la seconde catégorie, « Quaternionsystem » *m*, système quaternionien	кватернионная система
Q 283	**quaternionic variable** <AL, FT>	Quaternionenvariable *f*	variable *f* quaternionienne	кватернионная переменная
Q 284/5	**quaternionic vector** <AL, GE>	Quaternionenvektor *m*	vecteur *m* quaternion	кватернионный вектор
	quaternion of norm 1 <AL>	*s.* N 612		
Q 286	**quaternion ring** <AL>	Quaternionenring *m*	anneau *m* des quaternions	кольцо кватернионов

No.	English	German	French	Russian
	quaternion space <GE>	*s.* S 1325		
	Quermass-integral <CS, GE>	*s.* M 300		
Q 287	**questionnaire, questionaire** <US>, **questionary** <US> <CT, ST>	Fragebogen *m*	questionnaire *m*	анкета
Q 288	**Quételet-Raabe theorem** <GE>	Quételet-Raabescher Satz *m*	théorème *m* de Quételet-Raabe	теорема Кветеле-Раабе
Q 289	**queue,** waiting line <ST>	Warteschlange *f*	file *f* d'attente, queue *f*	очередь
Q 290	**queueing problem** <ST>	Warteproblem *n*	problème *m* d'attente	проблема очереди, задача очереди
Q 291	**queueing process** <SP, ST>	Wartezeitprozeß *m*	processus *m* d'attente	процесс очереди
Q 292	**queu[e]ing theory,** theory of queues; waiting line theory <ST>	Bedienungstheorie *f*, Massenbedienungstheorie *f*; Warteschlangentheorie *f*, Theorie *f* der Warteschlangen	théorie *f* des files (phénomènes) d'attente	теория массового обслуживания, теория обслуживания; теория очередей
Q 293	**quinary digit** <NT>	Quinärziffer *f*, Quinärzahl *f*	chiffre *m* quinaire	пятеричный разряд
Q 294	**quinary notation (number notation)** <NT>	quinäre Zahlendarstellung *f*, quinäre Schreibweise *f*	notation *f* quinaire, notation quinaire des nombres	представление чисел в пятеричной системе
Q 295	**quinary [number] system** <NT>	Quinärsystem *n*, Quinarsystem *n*, Fünfzahlsystem *n*	système *m* quinaire (quinquénaire)	пятеричная система
Q 296	**quindecagon,** fifteen-cornered polygon <EG>	Fünfzehneck *n*, Quindekagon *n*	pentédécagone *m*, pentadécagone *m*, quindécagone *m*	пятнадцатиугольник
Q 297	**Quine['s] set theories** <SE>	Quinesche Mengentheorien *fpl*	théories *fpl* des ensembles de Quine	теории множеств Куайна
Q 298	**quinternion** <AL>	Quinternion *f*, Quinion *f*	quinternion *m*	квинтернион
Q 299	**quintic,** plane quintic [curve], plane algebraic curve of the fifth degree (order), algebraic plane curve of the fifth degree (order) <AG>	algebraische ebene Kurve *f* fünfter (5.) Ordnung, [ebene] algebraische Kurve fünfter (5.) Ordnung, ebene Kurve fünfter (5.) Ordnung, ebene Quintik *f*	courbe *f* [algébrique] plane d'ordre cinq (5), courbe quintique plane, quintique *f* plane	плоская алгебраическая кривая пятого (5-го) порядка, плоская кривая пятого (5-го) порядка
Q 300	**quintic,** algebraic function of the fifth degree <AL>	algebraische Funktion *f* fünften Grades	fonction *f* algébrique de degré 5	алгебраическая функция степени 5
	quintic <AG>	*s.* 1. Q 301; 2. Q 304		
	quintic <AL>	*s.* 1. Q 302; 2. Q 303		
Q 301	**quintic curve,** quintic, [algebraic] curve of the fifth degree (order) <AG>	Kurve *f* fünfter (5.) Ordnung, Quintik *f*, algebraische Kurve fünfter (5.) Ordnung, Kurve fünften (5.) Grades	courbe *f* quintique, quintique *f*, courbe [algébrique] du cinquième (5ème) ordre	алгебраическая кривая пятого (5-го) порядка, кривая пятого (5-го) порядка
Q 302	**quintic equation,** quintic, algebraic equation of [the] fifth degree, fifth-degree polynomial equation <AL>	Gleichung *f* fünften Grades, algebraische Gleichung fünften Grades	équation *f* quintique, équation du cinquième (5ème) degré (ordre)	уравнение пятой (5-ой) степени, уравнение пятого (5-го) порядка
Q 303	**quintic quantic,** quintic, quantic (form) of the fifth degree <AL>	Form *f* fünften Grades, Quintik *f*	quintique *f*, forme *f* quintique	форма пятой степени
Q 304	**quintic surface,** quintic, surface of fifth order <AG>	Fläche *f* fünfter Ordnung	surface *f* quintique, surface du cinquième ordre	поверхность пятого порядка
Q 305	**quintile** <ST>	Quintil *n*	quintile *m*	квинтиль
Q 306	**quintuple,** 5-uple <SE>	Quintupel *n*, 5-Tupel *n*	quintuple[t] *m*, 5-tuple *m*	пятерка
Q 307	**quintuple point** <GE>	fünffacher Punkt *m*	point *m* quintuple	пятикратная точка
Q 308	**quod erat demonstrandum,** q.e.d. <GN>	quod erat demonstrandum, was zu beweisen war, q. e. d., w. z. b. w.	ce qu'il fallait démontrer, c. q. f. d.	что и требовалось доказать, ч. и т. д.
Q 309	**quota game** <TG>	Quotenspiel *n*	jeu *m* à quota	игра с квотой
Q 310	**quotal ring** <AL>	Quotalring *m*	anneau *m* quotal	квотальное кольцо
Q 311	**quota sample** <ST>	Quotenstichprobe *f*	échantillon *m* par la méthode des quota	выборка по группам
Q 312	**quota sampling** <ST>	Quotenstichprobenverfahren *n*	échantillonnage (sondage) *m* par la méthode des quota	выбор по группам
Q 313	**quotient** <in a division algorithm> <AL>	Quotient *m* <beim euklidischen Algorithmus>	quotient *m* [euclidien], quotient entier, quotient incomplet	неполное частное <при делении с остатком>
Q 314	**quotient** <AR>	Quotient *m*	quotient *m*	частное
Q 315	**quotient** <of a simplicial set> <AT>	Faktorkomplex *m*	ensemble *m* simplicial quotient	симплициальное фактор-множество
	quotient <TO>	*s.* Q 328		
Q 316	**quotient algebra** <FA>	Quotientenalgebra *f*	algèbre *f* des fractions (quotients)	алгебра отношений (частных)
Q 317	**quotient algebra** <UA>	Faktoralgebra *f*, Restklassenalgebra *f*	algèbre *f* quotient	фактор-алгебра, фактор, алгебра классов вычетов, фактор-система
Q 318	**quotient bundle** <AT>	Quotientenbündel *n*	fibré *m* quotient	факторрасслоение
Q 319	**quotient category** <CA>	Faktorkategorie *f*, Quotient *m* <einer Kategorie>	catégorie *f* quotient	фактор[-]категория
Q 320	**quotient chain complex** <of a chain complex> <HA>	Faktorkomplex *m*	complexe *m* quotient de chaînes	цепной фактор[-]комплекс
Q 321	**quotient field,** quotient-field, fraction field, field of quotients <AL>	Quotientenkörper *m*	corps *m* des fractions (quotients)	поле частных (отношений, дробей)
Q 322	**quotient filtration** <AL>	Faktorfiltration *f*	filtration *f* quotient <par un sous-groupe distingué>	фактор[-]фильтрация

No.	English	German	French	Russian
Q 323	**quotient full ring** <AL>	QFL-Ring *m*	QFL-anneau *m*	QFL-кольцо
Q 324	**quotient function** <AL>	Quotientenfunktion *f*	fonction *f* quotient	функция частного; функция, выражающая частное
Q 325	**quotient functor** <AL, CA>	Quotientenfunktor *m*	foncteur-quotient *m*	факторфунктор
	quotient group <AL>	*s.* G 495		
	quotient group <GR>	*s.* F 27		
	quotient groupoid <AL>	*s.* F 30		
Q 326	**quotient ideal,** residual module <AL>	Idealquotient *m*, Quotient *m* <von Idealen>	quotient *m* d'idéaux	частное идеалов
Q 327	**quotient loop** <AL>	Faktorloop *f*	loop *m* quotient	фактор-лупа, факторлупа
Q 328	**quotient manifold,** quotient <TO>	Faktormannigfaltigkeit *f*	variété *f* quotient, variété-quotient *f*	фактор-многообразие, фактормногообразие
	quotient map <SE>	*s.* N 32		
	quotient mapping <TO>	*s.* I 51		
Q 329	**quotient measure** <ME>	Faktormaß *n*	mesure-quotient *f*	фактор-мера
	quotient module <AL>	*s.* F 50		
Q 330	**quotient norm** <FA>	Quotientennorm *f*	norme *f* quotient	фактор-норма
Q 331	**quotient object** <CA>	Quotientenobjekt *n*, Faktorobjekt *n*	objet *m* quotient, quotient *m* <d'un objet>	фактор-объект
	quotient of Herbrand <AL>	*s.* H 204		
Q 332	**quotient orientation** <of a vector space> <AL, GE>	Faktororientierung *f*	orientation *f* quotient	фактор-ориентировка
Q 333	**quotient partial algebra** <UA>	Faktoralgebra *f* einer partiellen Algebra	algèbre *f* partielle quotient	фактор-алгебра частичной алгебры
Q 334	**quotient presheaf** <AL, TO>	Quotientengarbendatum *n*	préfaisceau *m* quotient	факторпредпучок
	quotient programming <PG>	*s.* R 194		
Q 335	**quotient relation** <SE, UA>	Faktorrelation *f*	relation *f* quotient	фактор-соотношение
Q 336	**quotient representation** <AL>	Faktordarstellung *f*	représentation *f* quotient	фактор[-]представление
Q 337	**quotient ring,** ring of quotients <AL>	Quotientenring *m*	anneau *m* des fractions (quotients)	кольцо отношений (частных)
	quotient[-]ring <AG, AL>	*s.* S 1368		
	quotient ring <AL>	*s.* R 897		
Q 338	**quotient ring with respect to a multiplicatively closed set** <AL>	[verallgemeinerter] Quotientenring *m* bezüglich eines multiplikativ abgeschlossenen Systems, verallgemeinerter Quotientenring	anneau *m* complet des fractions ayant leurs dénominateurs dans une partie multiplicative	кольцо частных по мультипликативному подмножеству, кольцо отношений по мультипликативному множеству
Q 339	**quotient rule** <DI>	Quotientenregel *f*	règle *f* pour la dérivation d'un quotient	правило дифференцирования частного
Q 340	**quotient semigroup** <relative to an equivalence relation> <AL>	Quotientenhalbgruppe *f*, Differenzenhalbgruppe *f*	demi-groupe *m* quotient	факторполугруппа
	quotient semigroup <AL>	*s.* S 379		
Q 341	**quotient semi-norm** <FA>	Quotientenhalbnorm *f*	semi-norme *f* quotient	фактор-полунорма
Q 342	**quotient sequence** <HA>	Faktorsequenz *f*	séquence *f* quotient	факторпоследовательность
Q 343	**quotient set,** factor set, quotient space <*e.g.:* of *M* by *R*, of *M* modulo *R*> <SE>	Quotientenmenge *f*, Restklassenmenge *f*, Faktormenge *f* <*z. B.:* von *M* nach (modulo) *R*>	ensemble *m* quotient, quotient *m*, espace-quotient *m* <*par exemple:* de *M* par *R*>	множество классов вычетов, фактор-множество, фактормножество <*например:* множества (от) *M* по *R*>
Q 344	**quotient sheaf** <AL, TO>	Quotientengarbe *f*	faisceau *m* quotient	фактор-пучок
Q 345	**quotient skew field** <AL>	Quotientenschiefkörper *m*	corps *m* des fractions (quotients)	тело отношений (частных)
Q 346	**quotient space** <of a vector space> <AL>	Faktorvektorraum *m*	espace *m* vectoriel quotient, espace quotient	факторное пространство
Q 347	**quotient space,** identification space, factor space, decomposition space, hyperspace <of a decomposition>, topological quotient <of a space> <TO>	Quotientenraum *m*, Zerlegungsraum *m*, Identifikationsraum *m*, Raum *m* der Zerlegung, konjugierter Raum <zu einer Zerlegung>	espace *m* quotient, espace-quotient *m*, espace topologique quotient, hyper-espace *m* <d'une décomposition>	факторпространство, пространство [данного] разложения, пространство разбиения
Q 348	**quotient space,** orbit space, trajectory space <with respect to a group *G*> <TO>	Quotientenraum *m*, Raum *m* der Orbits <bezüglich einer Gruppe *G*, bezüglich *G*>	espace *m* des orbites, espace des trajectoires <du groupe *G*>, espace quotient <par le groupe *G*>	пространство орбит, пространство траекторий <относительно группы *G*>
	quotient space <AL>	*s.* F 56		
	quotient space <SE>	*s.* Q 343		
Q 349	**quotient structure** <AL>	Restklassenstruktur *f*, Quotientenstruktur *f*, Faktorstruktur *f*	structure *f* quotient, structure-quotient *m*	фактор-структура, факторструктура
Q 350	**quotient-symbol** <AL>	Quotientensymbol *n*	symbole-quotient *m*	символ частного
Q 351	**quotient topology,** identification topology, induced topology <by a mapping> <TO>	Quotiententopologie *f*, Identifizierungstopologie *f* induzierte Topologie *f* <bezüglich einer Abbildung>	topologie *f* quotient (induite) <par une fonction>	индуцированная топология, фактор[-]топология, топология отождествления <отображением>
Q 352	**quotient topology,** identification topology <with respect to an equivalence relation> <TO>	Quotiententopologie *f*, Identifizierungstopologie *f*	topologie *f* quotient	фактортопология, фактор-топология

	English	German	French	Russian
Q 353	**quotity** <of *n* with respect to *a*, *b*, . . . , *l*> <AB>	Quotity *f* <von *n* mit Bezug auf *a*, *b*, . . . , *l*>, Denumerant *m* < $\frac{n;}{a, b, \ldots, l;}$ der Gleichung $ax + by + \ldots + lt = n$ >	quotity *f* <de *n* par rapport aux éléments *a*, *b*, . . . , *l*>, denumérant *m* < $\frac{n;}{a, b, \ldots, l;}$ de l'équation $ax + by + \ldots + lt = n$ >	

R

	English	German	French	Russian
	Raabe['s] convergence test <SS>	*s.* R 2		
R 1	**Raabe['s] integral** <for the Γ-function> <FU>	Raabesche Integraldarstellung *f*, Raabesches Integral *n*	intégrale *f* de Raabe	интеграл Раабе
R 2	**Raabe['s] ratio test, Raabe['s] test** <for convergence>, Raabe['s] convergence test <SS>	Raabesches Kriterium *n*, Raabesches Konvergenzkriterium *n*, Raabe-Kriterium *n*	critère *m* (règle *f*) de Raabe, critère *m* de Raabe-Darboux-Duhamel, règle *f* de Duhamel	признак (критерий) [сходимости] Раабе
	rad <AL>	*s.* R 16		
	rad <GE>	*s.* R 11		
R 3	**Rademacher-Menshov theorem** <for orthogonal series> <AN>	Satz *m* von Rademacher-Menschow, Rademacher-Menschowscher Satz	théorème *m* de Rademacher-Menshov	теорема Радемахера-Меншова
R 4	**Rademacher['s] system** <AN>	System (Funktionensystem) *n* von Rademacher, Rademacher-System *n*	système *m* de Rademacher	система Радемахера
R 5	**Rademacher['s] theorem** <RF>	Rademacherscher Satz *m*, Satz von Rademacher	théorème *m* de Rademacher	теорема Радемахера
R 6	**radial [curve]** <of a curve> <GE>	Radiale *f*	radiale *f*	радиала
	radially related figure <GE>	*s.* F 218		
	radial nomogram <NO>	*s.* R 13		
R 7	**radial planimeter** <GE, IN>	Radialplanimeter *n*	planimètre *m* radial	радиальный планиметр
R 8	**radial slit domain** <FT>	Radialschlitzgebiet *n*, Radialschlitzbereich *m*	plan *m* muni de fentes radiales	область с радиальными разрезами
R 9	**radial symmetry in three dimensions,** spherical symmetry <EG>	Kugelsymmetrie *f*, sphärische Symmetrie *f*	symétrie *f* sphérique	сферическая симметрия
R 10	**radial symmetry in two dimensions,** circular symmetry <EG>	Kreissymmetrie *f*	symétrie *f* du cercle, symétrie circulaire, symétrie par rapport au cercle	симметрия относительно окружности, кругообразная симметрия
R 11	**radian,** rad <GE>	Radiant *m*, rad	radian *m*, rad	радиан, rad
R 12	**radian measure,** circular measure, arc <of an angle>, measure of angle in radians <GE>	Bogenmaß *n* [des Winkels], analytisches Maß *n*, arc	mesure *f* d'arc, arc, mesure d'angle en radians	дуговая мера [угла], радианная мера [угла]
R 13	**radiant nomogram,** radial nomogram <NO>	Strahlentafel *f*, Radiantentafel *f*, Strahlennomogramm *n*, Radiantennomogramm *n*	nomogramme *m* radiaire (radial, en rayons)	лучистая номограмма, радиальная номограмма
R 14	**π-radicable group,** π-complete group; π-divisible group <for additive groups> <GR>	π-vollständige Gruppe *f*	groupe *m* π-divisible	π-полная группа
	radicable group <GR>	*s.* C 1438		
R 15	**radical** <over a field> <AL>	Radikal *n*, Wurzelausdruck *m* <über einem Körper>	radical *m*, expression *f* radicale <sur un corps>	радикал, подкоренное выражение <над полем>
R 16	**radical,** rad <of an algebra> <AL>	Radikal *n*, rad	radical *m*, rad	радикал, rad
R 17	**radical** <of a group, an ideal, *or* a ring> <AL, GR>	Radikal *n*	radical *m*	радикал <группы, идеала *или* кольца>; корень <идеала>
R 18	**radical** <of the *n*-th degree> <AR>	Radikal *n* <*n*-ten Grades>	radical *m* <du *n*-e degré>	радикал <*n*-ой степени>
	radical <AL>	*s.* 1. A 1089; 2. S 2352		
	radical <AL, AR>	*s.* 1. R 29; 2. R 1370		
R 19	**radical axis** <of two circles> <AY>	Potenzlinie *f*, Chordale *f*, Radikalachse *f*, Linie *f* gleicher Potenzen, // Radikalaxe *f*	axe *m* radical, ligne *f* d'égale puissance, cordale *f*	радикальная ось
R 20	**radical axis** <of three spheres> <AY>	Potenzachse *f*	axe *m* radical	радикальная ось
R 21	**radical centre** <of three circles *or* four spheres> <AY>	Potenzpunkt *m*, Potenzzentrum *n*, Radikalpunkt *m*, Radikalzentrum *n*, Chordalpunkt *m*, Potenzmittelpunkt *m*	centre *m* radical	радикальный центр
R 22	**radical class** <CA, GR>	Radikalklasse *f*, radikale Klasse *f*	classe *f* radicale	радикальный класс
	radical element <AL>	*s.* R 1374		
	radical equation <AL, AN>	*s.* I 1015		
R 23	**radical extension** <of a field> <AL>	Radikalerweiterung *f*	extension *f* radicielle <d'un corps>, corps *m* radical <relativement à un sous-corps>	радикальное расширение
R 24	**radical group** <AL>	Radikalgruppe *f*	groupe *m* radical	радикальная группа
R 25	**radical ideal** <AL>	Radikalideal *n*	idéal *m* radical	радикальный идеал
R 26	**radical invariant subgroup** <GR>	radikaler Normalteiler *m*	sous-groupe *m* invariant radical	радикальный нормальный делитель

R 27	**radical number** <NT>	Wurzelzahl *f* <Hilbert>	nombre *m* radical	радикальное число
R 28	**radical plane** <of two spheres> <AY>	Potenzebene *f*, Radikalebene *f*	plan *m* radical	радикальная плоскость
R 29	**radical sign,** radical, root sign, $\sqrt{}$ <AL, AR>	Wurzelzeichen *n*, $\sqrt{}$	signe *m* radical, radical *m*, $\sqrt{}$	знак корня, радикал, знак радикала, корневой знак, $\sqrt{}$
R 30	**radical theory** <AL>	Radikaltheorie *f*	théorie *f* du radical	теория радикала
R 31	**radicand** <AL>	Radikand *m*	quantité *f* sous le signe radical, quantité *f* sous le radical, expression *f* sous le [signe] radical, radicand *m*, radicande *m*; nombre *m* placé sous le radical, nombre *m* sous le radical, nombre *m* sous le signe radical; fonction *f* sous le radical	подкоренная величина, подкоренное выражение, подрадикальное выражение; подкоренное число; подкоренная функция
R 32	**radius** <of a circle *or* a sphere> <EG>	Radius *m*, Halbmesser *m*	rayon *m*	радиус
R 33	**radius** <of a graph> <GP>	Radius *m*, Breite *f*	rayon *m*, largeur *f*	радиус
	radius <AY>	*s.* P 887		
	radius at bend <DG>	*s.* R 36		
R 34	**radius of affine curvature** <DG>	Affinkrümmungsradius *m*	rayon *m* de courbure affine	радиус аффинной кривизны
R 35	**radius of convergence** <FT, SS>	Konvergenzradius *m*	rayon *m* de convergence	радиус сходимости
R 36	**radius of curvature,** radius at bend <DG>	Krümmungsradius *m*, Krümmungshalbmesser *m*, Radius *m* der ersten Krümmung, Biegungsradius *m*	rayon *m* de courbure	радиус кривизны
R 37	**radius of holomorphy** <FT>	Holomorphieradius *m*	rayon *m* d'holomorphie	радиус голоморфности
R 38	**radius of inversion** <AY>	Radius *m* des Grundkreises <einer Inversion>	rayon *m* du cercle d'inversion	радиус окружности инверсии
R 39	**radius of principal curvature,** principal radius of curvature <DG>	Hauptkrümmungsradius *m*	rayon *m* de courbure principal	радиус главной кривизны, главный радиус кривизны
	radius of second curvature <DG>	*s.* R 40		
	radius of the circumscribed circle <EG>	*s.* C 738		
	radius of the circumsphere <EG>	*s.* C 739		
	radius of the escribed circle <EG>	*s.* E 756		
	radius of the escribed sphere <EG>	*s.* E 757		
	radius of the inscribed circle <EG>	*s.* 1. A 809; 2. I 575		
	radius of the inscribed sphere <EG>	*s.* I 574		
R 40	**radius of torsion,** radius of second curvature, torsion radius <DG>	Windungsradius *m*, Torsionsradius *m*, Schmiegungsradius *m*, Radius *m* der zweiten Krümmung, zweiter Krümmungsradius *m*	rayon *m* de torsion (la deuxième courbure)	радиус кручения (второй кривизны)
R 41	**radius vector** <*pl.*: radii vectores> <of a point> <AY>	Radiusvektor *m* <*pl.*: Radiivektoren>, Fahrstrahl *m*	rayon *m* vecteur, rayon-vecteur *m* <*pl.*: rayons-vecteurs>	радиус-вектор <*pl.*: радиус-векторы>
R 42	**radius vector,** position vector <in an affine space> <GE>	Ortsvektor *m*, Radiusvektor *m*	rayon *m* vecteur, rayon-vecteur *m*, vecteur *m* de position	радиус-вектор, вектор-радиус
	radius vector <AY>	*s.* P 887		
R 43	**radix,** base <of a system of logarithms> <AR>	Basis *f*, Logarithmenbasis *f*	base *f* <d'un système de logarithmes>	основание, базис <системы логарифмов>
	radix <AL>	*s.* B 83		
	radix <AL, AR>	*s.* R 1370		
	radix <NT>	*s.* B 88		
R 44	**radix fraction** <NT>	Bruch *m* der Form $a/r + b/r^2 + c/r^3 + \ldots$ <Darstellung in einem beliebigen Zahlensystem>	fraction *f* de forme $a/r + b/r^2 + c/r^3 + \ldots$	дробь вида $a/r + b/r^2 + c/r^3 + \ldots$
R 45	**radix point** <NT>	Basiskomma *n*, Komma *n* <in einem Stellenwertsystem>	virgule *f* de base	запятая <в позиционном представлении числа>
	Radon['s] integral <AN>	*s.* L 273		
R 46	**Radon['s] measure** <ME>	Radonsches Maß *n*	mesure *f* de Radon	мера Радона
	Radon['s] measure <ME>	*s. a.* R 516		
R 47	**Radon-Nikodým theorem** <ME>	Satz *m* von Radon-Nikodým, Radon-Nikodýmscher Satz, Lebesgue-Nikodýmscher Satz	théorème *m* de Radon-Nikodým	теорема Радона-Никодима
	Radon-Stieltjes integral <AN>	*s.* L 273		
R 48	**Radon['s] transform** <of a function> <AN>	Radon-Transformierte *f*	transformée *f* de Radon	изображение Радона
R 49	**Raikov['s] theorem** <ST>	Satz *m* von Raikow, Raikowscher Satz	théorème *m* de Raikov	теорема Райкова
	rainbow integral of Airy <FU>	*s.* A 389		
R 50	**Rainville['s] polynomial** <FU>	Rainvillesches Polynom *n*	polynôme *m* de Rainville	многочлен Ренвилля

No.	English	German	French	Russian
	raised figure <GN>	*s.* S 2330		
	raise to the second power / to <AL>	*s.* S 1550		
R 51	**raising** <of indices> <VT>	Heraufziehen *n*	faire *m* ascendre, faire passer de bas en haut	поднятие
R 52	**raising and/or lowering** <of indices> <VT>	Herauf- und/oder Herunterziehen *n* <von Indizes>	déplacement *m* <des indices>	жонглирование <индексами>
R 53	**raising into a symbolic power** <AL>	symbolische Potenzierung *f*	élévation *f* symbolique à une puissance	возведение в символическую степень
R 54	**raising to a power,** exponentiation, involution <AR>	Potenzieren *n*, Potenzierung *f*, Erhebung *f* in eine Potenz, Potenzerhebung *f*	élévation *f* (élèvement *m*) à une puissance, exponentiation *f*	возведение в степень, потенцирование
	raising to the third power <AL, AR>	*s.* C 2746		
	R-algebra <AL>	*s.* A 406		
	R-algebra of finite order <AL>	*s.* A 474		
R 55	**R-algebra with identity [element]** <AL>	*R*-Algebra *f* mit Einselement	*R*-algèbre *f* unitaire	*R*-алгебра с единицей, унитарная *R*-алгебра
R 56	**Ramanujan['s] congruence** <NT>	Ramanujan-Kongruenz *f*	congruence *f* de Ramanujan	сравнение Рамануджана
R 57	**Ramanujan['s] conjecture** <NT>	Ramanujan-Hypothese *f* <Abschätzung für $\tau(p)$, *p* Primzahl>; Ramanujansche Vermutung *f* <über die Größenordnung von $\tau(n)$>	hypothèse *f* de Ramanujan	гипотеза Рамануджана
R 58	**Ramanujan['s] continued fraction** <NT>	Ramanujanscher Kettenbruch *m*	fraction *f* continue de Ramanujan	цепная дробь Рамануджана
R 59	**Ramanujan['s] expansion** <NT>	Ramanujan-Entwicklung *f*, Ramanujansche Entwicklung *f*	développement *m* de Ramanujan	разложение Рамануджана
R 60	**Ramanujan['s] function** <NT>	Ramanujan-Funktion *f*, Ramanujansche Funktion *f*	fonction *f* de Ramanujan	τ-функция Рамануджана
R 61	**Ramanujan['s] identity,** Rogers-Ramanujan identity <NT>	Ramanujansche Identität *f*, Rogers-Ramanujan-Identität *f*	identité *f* de Ramanujan	тождество Рамануджана
R 62	**Ramanujan['s] sum** <NT>	Ramanujansche Summe *f*	somme *f* de Ramanujan	сумма Рамануджана
R 63	**ramification** <AL, FT, TO>; branching <FT>	Verzweigung *f*	ramification *f*	разветвление, ветвление
R 64	**ramification** <AL, TO>	Verzweigtheit *f*	ramification *f*	разветвленность
	ramification <GN>	*s.* B 725		
	ramification <GP>	*s.* T 885		
	ramification exponent <AB>	*s.* R 68		
	ramification exponent <AL>	*s.* R 69		
	ramification field of higher order <AB>	*s.* H 308		
R 65	**ramification function** <AB>	Verzweigungsfunktion *f*	fonction *f* de ramification	функция разветвления
R 66	**ramification group** <AB, RE>	Verzweigungsgruppe *f*	groupe *m* de ramification	группа ветвления <AB, RE>; группа разветвления <AB>
	ramification group of higher degree <AB>	*s.* H 306		
R 67	**ramification ideal** <of a valuation> <AL>	Verzweigungsideal *n*	idéal *m* de ramification	идеал разветвления
R 68	**ramification index,** ramification exponent <AB>	Verzweigungsindex *m*, Verzweigungsordnung *f*	ordre (indice) *m* de ramification	индекс ветвления, степень разветвления
R 69	**ramification index,** ramification exponent <of a valuation> <AL>	Verzweigungsordnung *f* <einer Bewertung>	ordre *m* de ramification, indice *m*, indice (nombre *m*) de ramification <d'une valuation>	индекс ветвления <относительно нормирования>
R 70	**ramification manifold** <DG>	Verzweigungsmannigfaltigkeit *f*	sous-variété *f* de ramification	многообразие разветвления
R 71	**ramification number** <AB, AL>	Verzweigungszahl *f*	nombre *m* de ramification	число ветвления
	ramification point <AG, TO>	*s.* B 732		
	ramification point <FT>	*s.* B 733		
	ramification point <TO>	*s.* B 734		
	ramification point of order *k* — 1 <FT>	*s.* B 735		
R 72	**ramification prime divisor** <of order $\alpha - 1$> <AL>	Verzweigungsprimdivisor *m* <der Ordnung $\alpha - 1$>	diviseur *m* premier de ramification <d'ordre $\alpha - 1$>	простой дивизор ветвления <порядка $\alpha - 1$>
R 73	**ramification prime ideal** <AL>	Verzweigungsprimideal *n*	idéal *m* premier de ramification	простой идеал ветвления
R 74	**ramification theory** <of prime ideals> <AL>	Verzweigungstheorie *f*	théorie *f* de la ramification	теория разветвления
R 75	**ramified algebraic function element** <FT>	verzweigtes algebraisches Funktionselement *n*	élément *m* de fonction algébrique ramifié	разветвленный алгебраический элемент функции
R 76	**ramified algorithm** <FO>	verzweigter Algorithmus *m*	algorithme *m* ramifié	разветвленный алгоритм
R 77	**ramified covering** <TO>	verzweigte Überlagerung *f*	revêtement *m* ramifié	разветвленное накрытие
R 78	**ramified covering surface** <FT, TO>	[relativ] verzweigte Überlagerungsfläche *f*	surface *f* de recouvrement ramifiée	разветвленная накрывающая поверхность, разветвленная поверхность наложения
R 79	**ramified curve** <GE>	verzweigte Kurve *f*	courbe *f* ramifiée	ветвящаяся кривая

No.	English	German	French	Russian
R 80	**ramified differential** <of a number field> <AB>	verzweigtes Differential *n*	différentielle *f* ramifiée	разветвленный дифференциал
R 81	**ramified domain** <TO>	verzweigtes Gebiet *n*	domaine *m* ramifié	разветвленная область
R 82	**ramified extension** <AL>	verzweigte Erweiterung *f*	extension *f* ramifiée	разветвленное расширение
	ramified function <FT>	*s.* M 1083		
R 83	**ramified manifold** <GE>	verzweigte Mannigfaltigkeit *f*	variété *f* ramifiée	разветвленное многообразие
R 84	**ramified place** <AL>	verzweigte Stelle *f*	place *f* ramifiée	разветвленная точка
R 85	**ramified prime divisor** <AL>	verzweigter Primdivisor *m*	diviseur *m* premier ramifié	разветвленный простой дивизор
R 86	**ramified prime ideal** <AL>	verzweigtes Primideal *n*	idéal *m* premier ramifié	разветвленный простой идеал
R 87	**ramified prime number** <NT>	verzweigte Primzahl *f*	nombre *m* premier ramifié	ветвящееся простое число
R 88	**ramified proof** <FO, LO>	verzweigter Beweis *m*	démonstration *f* ramifiée	разветвленное доказательство
R 89	**ramified theory of types, ramified type theory** <SE>	verzweigte Typentheorie (Typenlehre) *f*, verzweigter Stufenkalkül *m*	théorie *f* des types ramifiée	разветвленная теория типов
R 90	**ramified valuation** <AL>	verzweigte Bewertung *f*	valuation *f* ramifiée	разветвленное нормирование
	ramified value <FT>	*s.* B 723		
	ramphoid cusp <GE>	*s.* C 2811		
R 91	**Ramsey['s] cardinal** <SE>	Ramseysche Kardinalzahl *f*	cardinal *m* de Ramsey	кардинальное число Рамсея
R 92	**Ramsey['s] number** <GP>	Ramsey-Zahl *f*	nombre *m* de Ramsey	число Рамсея
R 93	**random component,** random element, residual component <of a time series> <SP>	Zufallskomponente *f*, Restkomponente *f*	composante *f* aléatoire (résiduelle)	случайный элемент, случайная (остаточная) компонента
R 94	**random component** <ST>	Zufallskomponente *f*	composante *f* aléatoire	случайная компонента
R 95	**random deviation,** deviate <ST>	Zufallsabweichung *f*, zufällige Abweichung *f*	écart *m* aléatoire	случайное отклонение
R 96	**random digit,** random figure <ST>	Zufallsziffer *f*, Zufallszahl *f* schlechthin	chiffre *m* aléatoire (au hasard, tiré au hasard)	случайная цифра
	random distribution <ST> ⌐<ST>	*s.* P 1535		
	random effects model	*s.* M 731		
	random element <SP>	*s.* R 93		
R 97	**random ergodic theorem** <Ulam and J. von Neumann>, Ulam-von Neumann ergodic theorem <SP>	zufälliger Ergodensatz *m* <Ulam und J. von Neumann>, Ergodensatz von Ulam und von Neumann	théorème *m* ergodique aléatoire <Ulam et J. von Neumann>, théorème ergodique d'Ulam-von Neumann	случайная эргодическая теорема <Улама и Неймана>
R 98	**random error,** error variable <ST>	Zufallsfehler *m*, Fehlervariable *f*, zufälliger Fehler *m*	erreur *f* aléatoire (accidentelle, fortuite), variable *f* de l'erreur	случайная ошибка
R 99	**random event,** chance event, event <ST>	zufälliges (stochastisches, statistisches) Ereignis *n*, Ereignis	événement *m* aléatoire (fortuit), événement	случайное событие, событие
R 100	**random field** <SP>	zufälliges Feld *n*	champ *m* aléatoire	случайное поле
	random figure <ST>	*s.* R 96		
R 100a	**random function** <ST>	Zufallsfunktion *f*, zufällige (stochastische, statistische) Funktion *f*	fonction *f* aléatoire, fonction éventuelle	случайная функция, стохастическая функция
	random function <SP>	*s.* S 1800		
R 101	**random graph** <GP, ST>	stochastischer Graph *m*	graphe *m* stochastique	стохастический граф
R 102	**randomization,** randomizing <ST>	Randomisation *f*, Randomisierung *f*, zufällige Anordnung (Zuordnung) *f*; Chaotisierung *f*	arrangement *m* (disposition *f*, répartition *f*) au hasard, randomisation *f*; chaotisation *f*	рандомизация, разупорядочение; хаотизация
R 103	**randomization model,** finite model <ST>	Randomisationsmodell *n*, endliches Modell *n*	modèle *m* de randomisation, modèle fini	модель рандомизации, конечная модель
	randomization test <ST>	*s.* P 492		
R 104	**randomized decision function; randomized [statistical] decision rule** <ST>	randomisierte Entscheidungsfunktion *f*; randomisierte [statistische] Entscheidungsregel *f*	fonction *f* de décision randomisée; règle *f* de décision [statistique] randomisée	рандомизированная решающая функция; рандомизированное [статистическое] правило решения
	randomized strategy <PG, TG>	*s.* M 699		
R 105	**randomized test** <ST>	randomisierter Test *m*	test *m* randomisé	рандомизированный критерий
	randomizing <ST>	*s.* R 102		
	random measure <ME, ST>	*s.* O 473		
	random model <ST>	*s.* M 731		
R 106	**randomness** <ST>	Zufälligkeit *f*	aléa *m*, hasard *m*, propriété *f* d'être aléatoire, caractère *m* aléatoire	случайность
R 107	**random number** <ST>	Zufallszahl *f*	nombre *m* aléatoire (au hasard, tiré au hasard)	случайное число
R 108	**random number generator** <ST>	Zufallsgenerator *m*	générateur *m* de nombres aléatoires	генератор случайных чисел
R 109	**random order** <ST>	zufällige Reihenfolge *f*	ordre *m* aléatoire	случайный порядок
	random process <SP>	*s.* S 1800		
R 110	**random sample** <ST>	mathematische (zufällige) Stichprobe *f*, Zufallsstichprobe *f*	échantillon *m* aléatoire (probabiliste)	случайная выборка
R 111	**random sampling,** random selection <ST>	Zufallsauswahl *f*, zufällige Auswahl (Stichprobenerhebung) *f*	échantillonnage *m* (sondage *m*, choix *m*, sélection *f*) probabiliste (au hasard)	случайный выбор (отбор), случайная селекция
R 112	**random search [procedure]** <ST>	stochastisches (zufälliges) Suchverfahren *n*	exploration *f* aléatoire	случайный поиск
	random selection <ST>	*s.* R 111		
R 113	**random sequence,** stochastic sequence,	zufällige (stochastische) Folge *f*, Zufallsfolge *f*,	suite (séquence) *f* aléatoire, processus *m* stochastique à	случайная (стохастическая) последователь-

No.	English	German	French	Russian
	stochastic process with discrete time, random series <SP>	stochastischer Prozeß m mit diskreter (diskontinuierlicher) Zeit	temps discret, série f aléatoire	ность, случайный процесс с дискретным временем, случайный ряд
	random series <SP>	s. R 113		
R 114	**random spectral measure** <ST>	zufälliges Spektralmaß n	mesure f spectrale aléatoire	случайная спектральная мера
	random variable <ST>	s. V 67		
	random variable having the same distribution <ST>	s. E 329		
R 115	**random vector,** vector variate, multidimensional [random] variate <ST>	zufälliger Vektor m, Zufallsvektor m, mehrdimensionale Zufallsvariable f	vecteur m aléatoire (stochastique), variable f aléatoire multidimensionnelle (à plusieurs dimensions)	случайный вектор, многомерная случайная переменная (величина)
R 116	**random walk,** walk <r-dimensional> <SP>	Irrfahrt f, zufällige (stochastische) Irrfahrt, zufällige Schrittfolge f, Zufallsbewegung f <r-dimensionale>	marche f (trajet m, cheminement m) aléatoire, marche au hasard, proménade f aléatoire, errance f, errance aléatoire, va-et-vient m <r-dimensionnel[le], de dimension r>	случайное блуждание, блуждание <r-мерное>
R 117	**random walk problem,** problem of random walk <SP>	Irrfahrt[s]problem n	problème m de marche aléatoire	задача случайного блуждания
R 118	**random walk process** <SP>	Irrfahrt[s]prozeß m	processus m de marche (trajet) aléatoire, processus de marche au hasard, processus de cheminement aléatoire	процесс случайного блуждания
R 119	**range,** tangential pencil <of conics> <AY>	Kegelschnittschar f	faisceau m tangentiel <de coniques>	пучок кривых второго (2-го) класса
R 120	**range,** codomain, target, range-object, end-object, range carrier <of a morphism> <CA>	Ziel n, Wertbereich m	but m	цель, конец, область значений, кообласть, «конечный» объект
R 121	**range** <of an ordered set> <SE>	unterliegende Menge f, Trägermenge f	ensemble m sous-jacent	носитель
R 122	**range,** counterdomain, counter-domain, counter domain, converse (right) domain <of a relation> <SE>	Nachbereich m, Wertebereich m, Wertevorrat m, Bildbereich m, Wertbereich m, Gegenbereich m	codomaine m, ensemble m des images, ensemble m des coupes, contre-domaine m, domaine m converse, ensemble m des valeurs, seconde projection f	множество значений, область значения, противоположная область
R 123	**range,** latent (potential) range, codomain, target <of a mapping> <SE, TO>	Zielbereich m <es braucht nicht alles Bild zu sein>	ensemble m d'arrivée, ensemble cible	множество прибытия
R 124	**range,** range of variation <of a sample> <ST>	Spannweite f, Variationsbreite f der Stichprobe, Stichprobenvariationsbreite f, Stichprobenbreite f	étendue f, amplitude f [de variation], intervalle m de variation, marge f	размах [вариации], размах варьирования
	range <AG>	s. T 59		
	range <AN>	s. 1. C 1015; 2. D 850		
	range <SE>	s. 1. A 210; 2. I 86		
	range <ST>	s. R 129		
	range carrier <CA>	s. R 120		
	range carrier <SE>	s. L 106		
R 125	**range[-] extension** <of a mapping> <SE>	Erweiterung f des Bildbereichs (Nachbereichs)	extension f de l'ensemble d'arrivée	расширение области значений
R 126	**range method** <ST>	Spannweiteverfahren n	méthode f d'amplitude, méthode d'étendue	метод размаха
	range-object <CA>	s. R 120		
	range of arguments <AN>	s. D 850		
	range of definition <AN>	s. D 850		
	range of points <PJ>	s. P 783		
R 127	**range of summation** <GN>	Summationsbereich m	domaine m de sommation	область суммирования
	range of the independent variable <AN>	s. D 850		
R 128	**range of validity** <of an expansion> <SS>	Gültigkeitsbereich m	domaine m de validité	область задания (определения)
	range of validity <AN>	s. D 850		
	range of values <AN>	s. C 1015		
R 129	**range of variation,** range <of a population>, scatter, spread <of a distribution> <ST>	Variationsbreite f, Streubreite f, Schwankungsbreite f	amplitude f [de variation], étendue f [de variation]	размах [вариации], разброс, широта распределения
	range of variation <ST>	s. R 124		
R 130	**range[-] restriction** <of a mapping> <AN>	Einschränkung f des Bildbereichs (Nachbereichs)	restriction f du contre-domaine	сужение области значений
R 131	**range test** <ST>	Spannweitetest m	test m d'étendue, test d'amplitude	критерий размаха
	range unit <AL>	s. L 517		
R 132	**rank,** dimension <of a free R-module or free abelian group> <AL, GR>	Rang m	rang m	ранг
R 133	**rank,** order, degree, valence <of a tensor> <AL, VT>	Stufe f, Ordnung f, Valenz f, Stufenzahl f	ordre m, valence f	ранг, валентность
R 134	**rank** <of a linear operator> <FA>	Rang m	rang m	ранг
R 135	**rank** <of a derivation> <LO>	Rang m, Rangzahl f <eines Beweises>	rang m <d'une dérivation>	ранг <вывода>

R 136	**rank,** grade <of a matrix>; determinant rank <MD>	Rang *m* <einer Matrix>, Matrizenrang *m*	rang *m* <d'une matrice>	ранг <матрицы>
R 137	**rank** <in a classification> <SE>	Rang *m*	rang *m*, ordre *m*	порядковое число
R 138	**rank,** ranking <ST>	Rangzahl *f*, Rang *m*	rang *m*	ранг, ранговое число
R 139	**rank,** axiomatic rank <of a variety> <UA>	Rang *m*, axiomatischer Rang *m*	rang *m*	[аксиоматический] ранг
	rank <AL>	*s.* 1. H 168; 2. R 1245		
	rank <AL, SE>	*s.* I 333		
	rank <GP>	*s.* G 390		
	rank <LA, SE>	*s.* D 510		
	rank <LO, UA>	*s.* A 973		
R 140	**rank analysis of variance** <ST>	Rangvarianzanalyse *f*	analyse *f* dispersionnelle des rangs	ранговый дисперсионный анализ
	rank concordance coefficient <ST>	*s.* K 41		
R 141	**rank correlation,** grade correlation <ST>	Rangkorrelation *f*	corrélation *f* des rangs, corrélation de classement	ранговая корреляция
R 142	**rank correlation analysis** <ST>	Rangkorrelationsanalyse *f*	analyse *f* de corrélation des rangs	анализ ранговой корреляции
R 143	**rank correlation coefficient,** coefficient of rank correlation <ST>	Rangkorrelationskoeffizient *m*, Koeffizient *m* der Rangkorrelation	coefficient *m* de corrélation de[s] rangs	коэффициент ранговой корреляции, коэффициент корреляции рангов, ранговый коэффициент корреляции
	rank correlation coefficient <ST>	*s.* S 1350		
R 144	**rank correlation method** <ST>	Rangkorrelationsverfahren *n*	méthode *f* de corrélation des rangs	метод ранговой корреляции
R 145	**ranked data** <ST>	ranggeordnete Daten *pl*	données *fpl* rangées (ordonnées)	упорядоченные данные
R 146	**rank function** <GP, SE>	Rangfunktion *f*	fonction *f* de rang	функция ранга
R 147	**rank function** <LA>	Dimensionsfunktion *f*	fonction *f* de rang, graduation *f*	функция размерности
	ranking <ST>	*s.* R 138		
R 148	**rank invariant** <AL>	Ranginvariante *f*	invariant *m* de rang	инвариант ранга
R 149	**rank of the group of units** <AB>	Einheitenrang *m*	rang *m* du groupe des unités	ранг группы единиц
R 150	**rank of the matrix of coefficients** <AL>	Rang *m* der Koeffizientenmatrix, Rang des [linearen] Gleichungssystems	rang *m* du système	ранг матрицы системы, ранг основной матрицы
R 151	**rank order statistic,** rank statistic <ST>	Rangmaßzahl *f*, Rangordnungsmaßzahl *f*	fonction *f* des rangs des observations	ранговая статистика <статистика, зависящая лишь от ранговых соотношений в выборке>
R 152	**rank order test,** order test <ST>	Rangtest *m*, Rangverfahren *n*, Anordnungstest *m*	test *m* des rangs	критерий ранга, порядковый критерий, порядковый тест, тест на расположение, ранговый критерий
	rank statistic <ST>	*s.* R 151		
R 153	**rank sum test** <ST>	Rangsummentest *m*	test *m* de somme des rangs	критерий суммы рангов
R 154	**Rao-Cramér[-Fréchet-Darmois] inequality** <ST>	Ungleichung *f* von Rao-Cramér-Fréchet-Darmois, Rao-Cramér[-Fréchet-Darmois]sche Ungleichung	inégalité *f* de Rao-Cramér-Fréchet-Darmois, inégalité de Rao-Cramér	неравенство Рао-Крамера-Фреше-Дармуа, неравенство Рао-Крамера
R 155	**rapid convergence** <AN, NU>	schnelle Konvergenz *f*	convergence *f* rapide	быстрая сходимость
	rapidity of convergence <AX, NU, SS>	*s.* R 158		
	rapidly mixing transformation <ME>	*s.* S 1978		
	rapid method <ST>	*s.* S 768		
	rapid test <ST>	*s.* S 769		
R 156	**rare event** <ST>	seltenes Ereignis *n*	événement *m* rare	редкое событие
R 157	**rarified set of points** <TO>	verdünnte Punktmenge *f*	ensemble *m* de points effilé	разреженное множество точек
	raster <SE>	*s.* F 224		
	rate of change <AN, DI, FD>	*s.* D 789		
	rate of change <DI, NU>	*s.* G 361		
R 158	**rate of convergence,** speed of convergence, rapidity of convergence <AX, NU, SS>	Konvergenzgeschwindigkeit *f*, Güte *f* der Konvergenz	rapidité *f* de convergence, rapidité *f* de la convergence, vitesse *f* de convergence	быстрота (скорость, порядок) сходимости
R 159	**rate of growth,** growth rate <of a function> <FT, RF>	Wachstumsgeschwindigkeit *f*	taux *m* d'accroissement, taux de croissance	скорость возрастания (приращения)
R 160	**rate of interest,** percentage rate of interest <AR>	Zinssatz *m*, Zinsfuß *m* <*p*>; Zinsrate *f* <*p*/100>	taux *m* d'intérêt	простые проценты [годовых], % годовых
	ratio <AR>	*s.* C 1241		
R 161	**ratio estimate (estimation)** <procedure> <ST>	Verhältnisschätzung *f*	estimation *f* par quotient	оценка в виде отношения
R 162	**ratio estimator** <ST>	Verhältnisschätzung *f*, Quotientenschätzung *f*, Verhältnisschätzfunktion *f*	estimateur *m* par quotient	оценка в виде отношения
	rational <NT>	*s.* R 182		
R 163	**rational basis** <of a group> <GR>	Rationalbasis *f*	base *f* rationnelle	рациональный базис
	rational canonical form <MD>	*s.* F 669		
R 164	**rational chain,** chain over $\mathfrak{R}$ <AT>	rationale Kette *f*	chaine *f* rationnelle, chaine sur $\mathfrak{R}$	рациональная цепь

R 165	**rational circle** <AY>	rationaler Kreis *m*	cercle *m* rationnel	рациональный круг; рациональная окружность
R 166	**rational convexity** <FT>	Rationalkonvexität *f*	convexité *f* rationnelle	рациональная выпуклость
R 167	**rational curve** <consisting of rational points only> <TO>	rationale Kurve *f*	courbe *f* rationnelle	рациональная кривая
	rational curve <AG>	*s.* U 111		
R 168	**rational equivalence class** <of modules> <AL>	rationale Äquivalenzklasse *f*	classe *f* d'équivalence rationnelle	класс рациональной эквивалентности
R 169	**rational field,** field of polynomial quotients <AL>	rationaler Körper *m*	corps *m* rationnel	рациональное поле, поле рациональных дробей
R 170	**rational fraction,** commensurable fraction <AR>	rationaler Bruch *m*, kommensurabler Bruch	fraction *f* rationnelle, fraction commensurable	рациональная (соизмеримая) дробь
	rational fraction <AL, FT>	*s.* R 171		
R 171	**rational function,** rational fraction <as a fraction of two polynomials> <AL, FT>	rationale Funktion *f*, gebrochen[-]rationale Funktion	fonction *f* rationnelle, expression *f* rationnelle, fraction *f* rationnelle	[дробно-] рациональная функция, дробно рациональная функция, рациональная дробь, рациональное выражение
	rational function <AL, FT>	*s. a.* 1. I 189; 2. P 1823		
	rational integer <NT>	*s.* I 596		
	rational integral function <AN>	*s.* E 262		
	rational involution <GE>	*s.* U 113		
R 172	**rationality** <AG>	Unikursalität *f*, Rationalität *f*	rationalité *f*, propriété *f* d'être unicursal	уникурсальность, рациональность
R 173	**rationality rank** <of a system of linear equations> <NT>	Rationalitätsrang *m*	rang *m* de rationalité	ранг рациональности
	rationalization <AL, AN>	*s.* R 801		
R 174	**rationalize / to** <AL>	rational machen	rendre rationnel, rationaliser	представлять в рациональном виде, избавляться от иррациональности, освобождаться от иррациональностей, рационализировать, приводить к рациональному виду
	rationalizing <AL, AN>	*s.* R 801		
R 175	**rationally dependent** <AL, NT>	rational abhängig, rationalzahlig linear abhängig, in bezug auf den rationalen Zahlkörper linear abhängig	rationnellement dépendant	рационально зависимый
R 176	**rationally equivalent cycle** <AG>	rational äquivalenter Zyklus *m*	cycle *m* rationnellement équivalent	рационально эквивалентный цикл
R 177	**rationally equivalent module** <AL>	rational[-] äquivalenter Modul *m*	module *m* rationnellement équivalent	рационально эквивалентный модуль
R 178	**rationally irreducible representation** <RE>	rational-irreduzible Darstellung *f*	représentation *f* rationnellement irréductible	рационально неприводимое представление
R 179	**rational map[ping],** rational transformation <AG>	rationale Transformation *f*, rationale Abbildung *f*	application *f* rationnelle	рациональное отображение
R 180	**rational metamathematics** <Chwistek> <FO>	rationale Metamathematik *f*	métamathématique *f* rationnelle	рациональная метаматематика
R 181	**rational normal curve** <AG>	rationale Normkurve *f*	courbe *f* normale rationnelle	рациональная нормальная кривая
R 182	**rational number,** rational <NT>	rationale Zahl *f*, Rationalzahl *f*, Bruch *m*	nombre *m* rationnel, rationnel *m*	рациональное число
R 183	**rational number sequence,** sequence of rational numbers <SS>	rationale Zahlenfolge *f*	suite *f* de nombres rationnels, // variante *f*, variable *f* progressive <Méray>	последовательность рациональных чисел
	rational prime cycle <AG>	*s.* P 1286		
	rational quadrangle <EG>	*s.* H 259		
R 184	**rational quartic curve [in space]** <AG>	Raumkurve *f* vierter (4.) Ordnung zweiter (II.) Spezies (Art), k_4 *f* zweiter Art	quartique *f* de seconde espèce, courbe *f* gauche du quatrième ordre de seconde espèce, quartique <Laguerre>	пространственная кривая четвертого порядка второго рода
R 185	**rational quaternion** <AL>	rationalzahlige Quaternion *f*	quaternion *m* rationnel	рациональный кватернион
R 186	**rational space** <as a space of rational points> <TO>	rationaler Raum *m*	espace *m* rationnel	рациональное пространство <в смысле теории порядка>
R 187	**rational space curve,** unicursal space curve <AG>	rationale (unikursale) Raumkurve *f*	courbe *f* gauche unicursale (rationnelle)	уникурсальная (рациональная) пространственная кривая
R 188	**rational tetrahedron** <EG>	rationales Vierflach *n*	tétraèdre *m* rationnel	рациональный четырехгранник
R 189	**rational transform** <of an algebraic variety> <AG>	rationale Transformierte *f*	image *f* par une application rationnelle	образ при рациональном отображении
	rational transformation <AG>	*s.* R 179		
	rational triangle <EG>	*s.* H 260		
R 190	**rational variety** <AG>	rationale (unikursale) Mannigfaltigkeit *f*	variété *f* rationnelle (unicursale)	рациональное многообразие
	ratio of division <AY, EG>	*s.* A 370		

No.	English	German	French	Russian
	ratio of foreshortening <DS>	*s.* R 424		
R 191	**ratio of magnification,** linear deformation ratio <of a conformal mapping> <GE>	Vergrößerungsverhältnis *n*	coefficient *m* d'agrandissement	коэффициент увеличения
R 192	**ratio of similitude,** ray ratio, homothetic ratio <in homothety> <GE>	Ähnlichkeitsverhältnis *n*, Verhältnis *n* der Homothetie, Streckungsfaktor *m*	rapport *m* d'homothétie, rapport de similitude, rapport	коэффициент подобия (гомотетии), коэффициент, отношение гомотетии
R 193	**ratio of two geometric quantities** <EG>	Verhältnis *n* zweier geometrischer Größen	raison *m*, rapport *m* géométrique <entre deux grandeurs géométrique>	отношение двух геометрических величин
	ratio paper <IN, NU>	*s.* S 408		
R 194	**ratio programming,** quotient programming <PG>	Quotientenoptimierung *f*, Quotientenprogrammoptimierung *f*, Quotientenprogrammierung *f*	programmation (optimisation) *f* d'un rapport	программирование отношения
	ratio test <SS>	*s.* 1. D 4; 2. S 205		
R 195	**R-automorphism** <AL>	*R*-Automorphismus *m*	*R*-automorphisme *m*	*R*-автоморфизм
R 196	**raw estimate,** coarse estimate <ST>	rohe (grobe) Schätzung *f*	estimation *f* (valeur *f* estimée) brute	грубая оценка
	raw [sample] moment <ST>	*s.* U 30		
R 197	**ray** <modulo m> <in number field theory> <AB>	Zahlstrahl *m*, Strahl *m* <mod m>	rayon *m* [de nombres] <modulo m>	числовой луч <по модулю m>
R 198	**ray,** closed half-line, half-line <GE>	Strahl *m*, abgeschlossene Halbgerade *f*, Halbgerade, Halbstrahl *m*	rayon *m*, demi-droite *f* fermée, demi-droite, semi-droite *f* [fermée]	луч, замкнутая полупрямая, полупрямая
	ray <DG>	*s.* L 772		
	ray centre <GE>	*s.* C 429		
	ray centre <PJ>	*s.* C 423		
R 199	**ray class** <mod m> <AB>	Strahlklasse *f* <mod m>	classe *f* de rayon <mod. m>	лучевой класс <по модулю m>
	ray congruence <AY, DG>	*s.* C 1923		
R 200	**Rayleigh['s] distribution** <ST>	Rayleigh-Verteilung *f*, RayleighscheVerteilung *f*	distribution *f* de Rayleigh	распределение Рэлея, рэлеевское распределение
R 201	**Rayleigh['s] principle** <DE, FA>	Prinzip *n* von Rayleigh, Rayleighs[ches] Prinzip	principe *m* de Rayleigh	принцип Рэлея
R 202	**Rayleigh['s] problem** <VA>	Problem *n* von Rayleigh, Rayleighsches Problem	problème *m* de Lord Rayleigh	проблема Рэлея
R 203	**Rayleigh['s] quotient** <DE, FA, NU>	Rayleighscher Quotient *m*	quotient *m* de Rayleigh	отношение Рэлея
R 204	**Rayleigh-Ritz method,** Rayleigh-Ritz-Weinstein method <FA>	Rayleigh-Ritz-Weinstein-Methode *f*, Methode *f* von Rayleigh-Ritz, Rayleigh-Ritzsche Methode	méthode *f* de Rayleigh-Ritz[-Weinstein]	метод Рэлея-Ритца [-Вайнштейна]
	Rayleigh-Ritz method <NU, VA>	*s.* R 1347		
	Rayleigh-Ritz-Weinstein method <FA>	*s.* R 204		
	ray of similarity <DS>	*s.* S 875		
	ray of striction <DG>	*s.* C 390		
	ray ratio <GE>	*s.* R 192		
R 205	**ray representation,** projective representation <of groups> <RE>	projektive Darstellung *f*, Darstellung durch projektive Transformationen, Strahldarstellung *f*	représentation *f* projective	проективное представление
	ray system <AY, DG>	*s.* C 1923		
R 206	**ℜ-class,** equivalence class mod ℜ <in a semigroup> <AL>	ℜ-Äquivalenzklasse *f*	classe *f* d'é quivalence mod. ℜ	ℜ-класс, класс эквивалентности по модулю ℜ
R 207	**r-cycle on V,** homogeneous *r*-cycle on <a variety> *V*, *V*-cycle of dimension *r* <AG>	*r*-Zyklus *m* auf *V*	*r*-cycle *m* sur *V*	*r*-цикл над *V*
	RD <LO>	*s.* R 1467		
	R-derivation <AL>	*s.* D 272		
	Re <FT, NT>	*s.* R 226		
	reach / to <GN>	*s.* A 1199		
R 208	**read[ing] head** <of a Turing machine> <TA>	Lesekopf *m*	tête *f* de lecture	читающая (считывающая) головка
R 209	**ready reckoner** <AR>	Rechenknecht *m*, Rechentabelle *f*	livre *m* de comptes faits, comptes *mpl* faits, barème *m*	сборник решенных задач
	real <NT>	*s.* R 223		
R 210	**real-analytic manifold** <GE>	reell-analytische Mannigfaltigkeit *f*	variété *f* analytique réelle	вещественно-аналитическое многообразие
	real axis <AN, SE>	*s.* N 872		
	real axis <FT>	*s.* A 1318		
R 211	**real-closed field** <AL>	reell-abgeschlossener Körper *m*	corps *m* ordonné maximal	вещественно замкнутое поле, действительно[-] замкнутое поле
R 212	**real closure** <of a field> <AL>	reell-abgeschlossene Hülle *f*	clôture *f* réelle	вещественное замыкание
R 213	**real compactification** <of a space> <TO>	Hewittsche Reellkompaktifizierung *f*, Reellkompaktifizierung *f*	réplétion *f*	вещественное пополнение
	real[-] compact space <TO> <TO>	*s.* H 284		
	real[-] complete space	*s.* H 284		

R 214	**real domain / in the** <GN>	im Reellen	dans le réel	в действительной области
R 215	**real figure** <of complex geometry> <GE>	reelle Figur *f*	figure *f* réelle	действительная фигура
	real function <RF>	*s.* R 234		
R 216	**reality** <AL, AN>	Realität *f*	réalité *f*	действительность, вещественность
R 217	**realizability;** feasibility <AL>	Realisierbarkeit *f*	réalisabilité *f*	осуществимость
R 218	**realization** <e.g. of a group, an ordered group, *or* a simplicial complex> <AL, AT, GR>	Realisierung *f*	réalisation *f*	реализация, осуществление
R 219	**realization,** trajectory <of a stochastic process> <SP>	Realisierung *f*, Trajektorie *f*	réalisation *f*, trajectoire *f*	реализация, траектория
R 220	**realization** <of a random function> <ST>	Realisierung *f* <einer Zufallsfunktion>	épreuve *f* <sur une fonction aléatoire>	реализация <случайной функции>
R 221	**realization** <of a random variable> <ST>	Realisierung *f*, Realisation *f*	réalisation *f*	реализация, осуществление
	real line <AN, SE>	*s.* N 872		
R 222	**real-linearly independent** <AL>	reell-linear-unabhängig, reellzahlig linear unabhängig, in bezug auf den reellen Zahlkörper linear unabhängig	linéairement indépendant sur le corps réel	вещественно-линейно независимый
R 223	**real number,** real <NT>	reelle Zahl *f*	nombre *m* réel, réel *m*	действительное число, вещественное число
R 224	**real number system** <NT>	reelles Zahlensystem *n*	système *m* de nombres réels	действительная числовая система
R 225	**real orthogonal group,** real unitary group <GR>	reelle orthogonale Gruppe *f*, reelle unitäre Gruppe	groupe *m* orthogonal réel, groupe unitaire réel, groupe unitaire orthogonal	вещественная ортогональная группа, вещественная унитарная группа
R 226	**real part,** Re <of a complex number *or* function> <FT, NT>	Realteil *m*, Re, // reeller Bestandteil *m*, $\mathfrak{Re}$, $\mathfrak{R}$	partie *f* réelle, Re	действительная часть, вещественная часть, Re
R 227	**real quadratic number field** <NT>	reell-quadratischer Zahlkörper *m*	corps *m* quadratique réel	действительное квадратичное поле
R 228	**real quaternion,** Hamilton['s] quaternion, quaternion <AL>	Hamiltonsche Quaternion *f*, reelle Quaternion, klassische Hamiltonsche Quaternion, Quaternion	quaternion *m* réel, quaternion *m*	вещественный кватернион, кватернион
	real reflection group <AL>	*s.* C 2641		
R 229	**real rotation group,** rotation group <GR>	reelle Drehgruppe *f*, Drehgruppe *f*	groupe *m* des rotations réel, groupe orthogonal réel unimodulaire, groupe des rotations	вещественная группа вращений
R 230	**real unimodular group** <GR>	reelle unimodulare Gruppe *f*	groupe *m* unimodulaire réel	вещественная унимодулярная группа
R 231/2	**real unit** <of complex numbers> <AL>	reelle Einheit *f*	unité *f* réelle, unité primaire <Hamilton>	вещественная единица
	real unitary group <GR>	*s.* R 225		
R 233	**real unitary space,** Euclidean space <FA>	reeller unitärer Raum *m*, reeller prä-hilbertscher Raum, euklidischer Raum *m*	espace *m* unitaire réel, espace euclidien	вещественное унитарное пространство, евклидово пространство
	real valuation <AL>	*s.* V 23		
R 234	**real-valued function,** real function <RF>	reelle Funktion *f*, reellwertige Funktion	fonction *f* réelle, fonction à valeurs réelles	вещественная функция, действительная функция, вещественнозначная (действительнозначная) функция
	real variable <LO>	*s.* F 637		
R 235	**rearrangement,** shuffling, regrouping <e.g. of terms, also in a sequence *or* series> <GN, SS>	Umordnung *f*, Umstellung *f*, Umgruppierung *f*	réarrangement *m*, interversion *f*, modification *f* de l'ordre <par exemple des termes>	перестановка, перегруппировка, переставление, перегруппирование, переупорядочение, изменение порядка
R 236	**rearrangement of a power series** <with respect to a new centre> <FT, SS>	Umordnung *f* einer Potenzreihe	réarrangement *m* d'une série entière	преобразование степенного ряда к новому центру
R 237	**reason by induction / to** <LO>	induktiv schließen	induire	делать индуктивный вывод
R 238	**reasoning by induction,** inductive inference <LO>	Induktionsschluß *m*	raisonnement *m* par récurrence, conclusion *f* totalisante	заключение по индукции, индуктивный вывод
	reasons <GN>	*s.* F 502		
	reasons of symmetry / by <GN>	*s.* S 2471		
R 239	**recalculate / to,** to check a calculation <AR>	nachrechnen	vérifier un calcul	пересчитывать, проверять вычисление
R 240	**receiving category,** codomain category, codomain <of a functor, for a functor> <CA>	Zielkategorie *f* <eines Funktors>	catégorie-but *f* <d'un foncteur>	цель <функтора>
	reciprocal <NT>	*s.* I 929		
	reciprocal algebra <AL>	*s.* O 208		
	reciprocal basis <AL>	*s.* I 895		
	reciprocal chart <IN, NU>	*s.* R 252		
	reciprocal complex <AT>	*s.* B 72		
R 241	**reciprocal correspondence** <GE>	reziproke Korrespondenz *f*	correspondance *f* réciproque	взаимно обратное соответствие

	reciprocal correspondence <SE>	*s.* O 121		
R 242	**reciprocal determinant** <MD>	reziproke Determinante *f*, Reziprokaldeterminante *f*	déterminant *m* réciproque	обратный определитель
R 243	**reciprocal difference** <of a function> <FD>	reziproke Differenz *f* <*n*-ter Ordnung>	différence *f* réciproque	обратная разность
R 244	**reciprocal division** <NO>	reziproke Teilung *f*, Kehrwertteilung *f*	division *f* réciproque	обратное деление
	reciprocal divisor <NT>	*s.* R 256		
	reciprocal element <AL>	*s.* 1. I 890; 2. R 723		
R 245	**reciprocal equation** <AL>	reziproke Gleichung *f*	équation *f* réciproque	возвратное уравнение <*n*-ой степени>
R 246	**reciprocal factorial,** negative factorial function <FU>	reziproke Faktorielle *f*	factorielle *f* réciproque	обратный факториал
R 247	**reciprocal figures** <EG>	reziproke Figuren *fpl*	figures *fpl* réciproques (inverses)	взаимно обратные фигуры
R 248	**reciprocal function** <different from the inverse function> <FA>	reziproke Funktion *f*	fonction *f* réciproque	возвратная функция
R 249	**reciprocal ideal class** <AB>	reziproke Idealklasse *f*	classe *f* réciproque (opposée)	обратный класс идеалов
R 250	**reciprocal integral equations** <IE>	[zueinander] reziproke Integralgleichungen *fpl*	équations *fpl* intégrales réciproques	взаимные интегральные уравнения
	reciprocal kernel <IE>	*s.* R 911		
	reciprocally proportional <AR>	*s.* I 923		
	reciprocal map <SE>	*s.* I 926		
	reciprocal mapping <AY>	*s.* R 260		
	reciprocal mapping <GE>	*s.* I 972		
	reciprocal mapping <SE>	*s.* I 926		
R 251	**reciprocal matrix,** inverse matrix, inverse <of a matrix>, // adjugate matrix <MD>	inverse Matrix *f*, Kehrmatrix *f*, reziproke Matrix, Inverse *f*, Inverses *n*, Reziproke *f*	matrice *f* inverse, inverse *f*, matrice réciproque, // système *m* réciproque	обратная матрица
	reciprocal operator <AL, FA>	*s.* I 931		
R 252	**reciprocal paper,** reciprocal chart <IN, NU>	Reziprokpapier *n*, Reziproknetz *n*	papier *m* à échelle fonctionnelle réciproque, diagramme *m* réciproque	обратная бумага (диаграмма)
R 253	**reciprocal points** <with respect to a triangle> <EG>	isotom verwandte Punkte *mpl*, reziproke Punkte, Seitengegenpunkte *mpl* <bezüglich eines Dreiecks>	points *mpl* opposés à un côté <d'un triangle>	изогонально (изотомически) сопряженные точки, взаимные точки <относительно треугольника>
R 254	**reciprocal polar** <AY>	reziproke Polare *f*, konjugierte Gerade *f*	polaire *f* réciproque (conjuguée)	сопряженная поляра
R 255	**reciprocal polar curve** <with respect to a conic> <AY>	reziproke Polarkurve *f*	courbe *f* polaire réciproque	сопряженная полярная кривая
	reciprocal proposition <PJ>	*s.* D 1036		
R 256	**reciprocal quadratic divisor,** reciprocal divisor <of a quadratic form> <NT>	reziproker Teiler (Divisor) *m*	diviseur *m* réciproque	взаимный делитель
R 257	**reciprocal quadric** <of a tensor> <VT>	reziproke quadratische Form *f*	quadrique *f* réciproque	обратная квадратичная форма
R 258	**reciprocal ratio,** inverse ratio <AR>	umgekehrtes (inverses, reziprokes) Verhältnis *n*, reziproker Wert *m* des Verhältnisses	raison *f* inverse, rapport *m* inverse (réciproque)	обратное отношение, отношение обратных величин
	reciprocal ratio <NT>	*s.* I 940		
	reciprocal sentence <LO>	*s.* D 1030		
	reciprocal spiral <GE>	*s.* H 651		
R 259	**reciprocal submodule** <AL>	reziproker Untermodul *m*	sous-module *m* réciproque	обратный подмодуль
	reciprocal theorem <PJ>	*s.* D 1036		
R 260	**reciprocal transformation,** correlative transformation, reciprocal (correlative) mapping <in polar theory> <AY>	reziproke (korrelative) Abbildung *f*, reziproke (korrelative, inverse) Transformation *f*, Reziprokaltransformation *f*	transformation *f* réciproque (corrélative)	коррелятивное (обратное) преобразование
	reciprocal value <NT>	*s.* I 929		
R 261	**reciprocant** <of an algebraic form> <IV>	Reziprokante *f*, // Reciprokante *f* <Sylvester>	réciprocant *m*	реципрокант
	reciprocation <PJ>	*s.* R 263		
R 262	**reciprocity** <e.g. of a semigroup *or* Green's function> <AL, DE, NT>	Reziprozität *f*	réciprocité *f*	взаимность
R 263	**reciprocity,** reciprocation, duality <PJ>	Reziprozität *f*, Dualität *f*	réciprocité *f*, dualité *f*	двойственность, взаимность
	reciprocity <AY, PJ>	*s.* C 2485		
R 264	**reciprocity law for Dedekind sums** <NT>	Reziprozitätsgesetz *n* der Dedekindschen Summen, Reziprozitätsgesetz für Dedekindsche Summen	loi *f* de réciprocité pour les sommes de Dedekind	закон взаимности для сумм Дедекинда
R 265	**reciprocity law for [the *n*-th] power residues** <AB>	Reziprozitätsgesetz *n* der *n*-ten Potenzreste	loi *f* de réciprocité des résidus de puissance	общий закон степенной взаимности, закон взаимности вычетов

	English	German	French	Russian
	reckonable function <MM>	*s.* C 1753		
R 266	**re-conversion** <NT>	Rekonvertierung *f*, Rückkonvertierung *f*, Rückführung *f* aus dem Dual- ins Dezimalsystem	réconversion *f*	обратный перевод (пересчет)
R 267	**rectangle function** <AN>	Rechteckfunktion *f*, Rechtecksfunktion *f*	fonction *f* de rectangle	функция прямоугольника
R 268	**rectangle of deformation** <in homotopy> <TO>	Deformationsrechteck *n*	rectangle *m* de déformation	прямоугольник деформации
	rectangular array <MD>	*s.* R 277		
R 269	**rectangular band** <on $X \times Y$> <of a semigroup> <AL>	rechtwinkliges Band *n*	bande *f* rectangulaire	прямоугольная (матричная) связка
	rectangular Cartesian co-ordinates <AY>	*s.* C 161		
R 270	**rectangular Cartesian co-ordinate system** <AY>	rechtwinkliges kartesisches (cartesisches) Koordinatensystem *n*, orthonormiertes Koordinatensystem, kartesisches (cartesisches) Koordinatensystem; rechtwinkliges Raumkreuz *n* <im E^n>	système *m* de coordonnées cartésiennes en axes rectangulaires	декартова прямоугольная система координат, прямоугольная декартова система координат, декартова система координат
	rectangular co-ordinates <AY>	*s.* 1. C 161; 2. R 279		
	rectangular distribution <ST>	*s.* C 2245		
	rectangular equation <AG, AY>	*s.* C 163		
	rectangular form <AL, AN>	*s.* A 437		
R 271	**rectangular formula,** rectangular rule, rectangular method <AX, DI, NU>	Rechteckformel *f*, Rechteckregel *f*, Rechteckmethode *f*, mittlere Rechteckformel	formule (règle, méthode) *f* des rectangles	формула прямоугольников, правило прямоугольников, метод прямоугольников, формула средних ординат
R 272	**rectangular formula by deficiency** <DI, NU>	Formel *f* der linken Rechtecke, unterschreitende Rechteckformel *f*	formule *f* des rectangles par défaut	формула прямоугольников по недостатку
R 273	**rectangular formula by excess** <DI, NU>	Formel *f* der rechten Rechtecke, überschreitende Rechteckformel *f*	formule *f* des rectangles par excès	формула прямоугольников по избытку
	rectangular hyperbola <AY>	*s.* E 389		
R 274	**rectangular inequality** <FA>	Viereckungleichung *f*	inégalité *f* rectangulaire	неравенство четырехугольника
R 275	**rectangularity** <EG>	Rechtwinkligkeit *f*	rectangularité *f*	прямоугольность, свойство быть прямоугольным
R 276	**rectangular mapping** <GE>	rektanguläre Abbildung *f* <Tissot>	application *f* rectangulaire	прямоугольное отображение
R 277	**rectangular matrix,** rectangular array <MD>	rechteckige Matrix *f*, Rechteckmatrix *f*	matrice *f* rectangulaire	прямоугольная матрица, прямоугольная таблица
	rectangular method <AX, DI, NU>	*s.* R 271		
R 278	**rectangular neighbourhood** <TO>	Rechteckumgebung *f*	voisinage *m* rectangulaire	прямоугольная окрестность
R 279	**rectangular parallel co-ordinates,** rectangular co-ordinates, orthogonal co-ordinates <AY>	rechtwinklige (orthogonale) Parallelkoordinaten (Koordinaten) *fpl*	coordonnées *fpl* orthogonales (en axes rectangulaires, rectangulaires)	прямоугольные координаты
R 280	**rectangular parallelepipedon,** rectangular solid, cuboid, block <EG>	Quader *m*, rechtwinkliges Parallelepipedon *n*, rechtwinkliges Parallelepiped *n*	parallélépipède *m* rectangle, cuboïde *m*, pavé *m*, bloc *m*	прямоугольный параллелепипед, трипрямоугольник, кубоид, кирпич, брус
	rectangular partition <ST>	*s.* C 2245		
	rectangular rule <AX, DI, NU>	*s.* R 271		
R 281	**rectangular semigroup** <AL>	rechtwinklige Halbgruppe *f*	demi-groupe *m* rectangulaire	прямоугольная полугруппа
	rectangular solid <EG>	*s.* R 280		
R 282	**rectifiability** <DG>	Rektifizierbarkeit *f*	rectifiabilité *f*	спрямляемость
R 283	**rectifiable arc** <DG>	rektifizierbarer (streckbarer) Bogen *m*	arc *m* rectifiable	спрямляемая дуга
R 284	**rectifiable curve** <DG>	rektifizierbare (streckbare) Kurve *f*	courbe *f* rectifiable	спрямляемая кривая
R 285	**rectifiable function** <AN>	rektifizierbare Funktion *f*	fonction *f* rectifiable	спрямляемая функция
R 286	**rectification** <of a curve> <DG>	Rektifikation *f*, Rektifizierung *f*	rectification *f*	спрямление
	rectified value <ER, NU>	*s.* A 1253		
R 287	**rectifying developable,** rectifying surface <DG>	rektifizierende Fläche *f*	surface *f* rectifiante	спрямляющая поверхность
R 288	**rectifying inspection,** screening inspection <ST>	verbessernde Prüfung *f*	inspection *f* rectifiante (rectificative)	обследование с заменой всех дефектных изделий годными, сплошная проверка с отбрасыванием дефектных экземпляров, отсеивающая проверка
R 289	**rectifying line** <at a point of a twisted curve> <generator of the rectifying developable> <DG>	rektifizierende Gerade *f*	droite *f* rectifiante	спрямляющая прямая

	English	German	French	Russian
R 290	**rectifying plane** <DG>	rektifizierende Ebene *f*	plan *m* rectifiant	спрямляющая плоскость
	rectifying surface <DG>	*s.* R 287		
	rectilinear asymptote <AG, RF>	*s.* A 1136		
	rectilinear complex <GE>	*s.* C 1635		
	rectilinear congruence <AY, DG>	*s.* C 1923		
R 291	**rectilinear figure,** straight-sided figure <EG>	geradlinige Figur *f* <aus Geraden zusammengesetzt>	figure *f* rectiligne	прямолинейная фигура
	rectilinear generator <EG>	*s.* G 205		
R 292	**rectilinearly accessible point** <of the R^n> <TO>	geradlinig erreichbarer Punkt *m*	point *m* linéairement accessible	прямолинейно достижимая точка
R 293	**rectilinear range of points** <PJ>	gerade Punktreihe *f*	ponctuelle *f* rectiligne (rectilinéaire)	прямолинейный ряд точек
R 294	**recurrence,** recursion <FO, GN>	Rekursion *f*, Rekurrenz *f*	récurrence *f*, récursion *f*	рекуррентность, рекурсия
R 295	**recurrence** <ME, ST>	Wiederkehr *f*, Rekurrenz *f*	récurrence *f*, retour *m*	возвращение, возврат
	recurrence <GN, MM>	*s.* T 744		
	recurrence formula <FO, GN>	*s.* R 312		
R 296	**recurrence point** <ME, ST>	Wiederkehrpunkt *m*, Rekurrenzpunkt *m*	point *m* de récurrence (retour)	точка возврата (возвращения)
	recurrence relation <FO, GN>	*s.* R 312		
R 297	**recurrence theorem [of Poincaré],** Poincaré['s] recurrence theorem <for a measurable transformation> <ME, ST>	Poincaréscher Wiederkehrsatz (Rekurrenzsatz) *m*, Wiederkehrsatz von Poincaré, Wiederkehrsatz, Rekurrenzsatz von Poincaré, Rekurrenzsatz	théorème *m* du (de) retour, théorème de retour de Poincaré, théorème de Poincaré	теорема Пуанкаре, теорема Пуанкаре-Каратеодори о возвращении, теорема возвращения Пуанкаре, теорема возвращения
R 298	**recurrence time** <SP>	Wiederkehrzeit *f*, Rekurrenzzeit *f*	temps *m* de récurrence (retour)	время возврата (возвращения) <в исходное положение>
	recurrent continued fraction <NT>	*s.* R 306		
R 299	**recurrent event** <ME, ST>	wiederkehrendes (rekurrentes) Ereignis *n*	événement *m* récurrent	рекуррентное (возвратное) событие
R 300	**recurrent measurable transformation** <ME>	rekurrente meßbare Transformation *f*	transformation *f* mesurable récurrente	возвратное измеримое преобразование
R 301	**recurrent process,** simple renewal process <SP>	rekurrenter Prozeß *m*, einfacher Erneuerungsprozeß *m*	processus *m* récurrent (simple du renouvellement)	возвратный (рекуррентный) процесс, простой процесс восстановления
R 302	**recurrent sequence,** recursive sequence <FO>	rekursive Folge *f*	suite *f* récurrente	рекурсивная последовательность
R 303	**recurrent sequence** <GN>	rekurrente Folge *f*	suite *f* récurrente	рекуррентная последовательность
R 304	**recurrent sequence,** recurring series, linear recurrent series, linear recurring sequence <of order *r*, with *n* indices> <NT>	rekurrente Zahlenreihe (Reihe) *f*, rekurrierende Reihe *f* <der Ordnung *r*, mit *n* Indizes>	série (suite) *f* récurrente <d'ordre *r*, à *n* indices>	возвратная (рекуррентная, повторяющаяся) последовательность, повторяющийся числовой ряд <порядка *r*, с *n* индексами>
R 305	**recurrent state** <SP>	rekurrenter (wiederkehrender) Zustand *m*, R-Zustand *m*	état *m* récurrent	возвратное (рекуррентное) состояние
R 306	**recurring chain (continued) fraction,** recurrent continued fraction, periodic continued fraction, periodical continued fraction <NT>	periodischer Kettenbruch *m*	fraction *f* continue périodique	периодическая непрерывная дробь
	recurring decimal <NT>	*s.* P 446		
R 307	**recurring principle** <PG>	Rekursionsprinzip *n*	principe *m* récurrent	рекуррентный принцип
R 308	**recurring problem** <FO, GN>	Rekursionsproblem *n*, rekursives Problem *n*	problème *m* récurrent	рекуррентная задача, рекурсивная проблема
R 309	**recurring relation of order *k*,** law of recurrence of order *k* <FD, NT>	Rekursionsgleichung *f* der Ordnung *k*	relation (loi) *f* de récurrence d'ordre *k*	возвратное уравнение порядка *k*
R 310	**recurring series** <a power series whose coefficients form a recurrent sequence> <SS>	rekurrierende (rekurrente) Reihe *f*	série *f* récurrente	возвратный ряд
	recurring series <NT>	*s.* R 304		
	recursion <FO, GN>	*s.* R 294		
	recursion <GN, MM>	*s.* T 744		
	recursion definition <FO>	*s.* D 140		
R 311	**recursion equation** <LO>	Rekursionsgleichung *f*	égalité *f* récurrente	рекурсивное равенство
R 312	**recursion formula,** recurrence formula, recurrence relation, recursion relation <FO, GN>	Rekursionsformel *f*, rekurrente Beziehung (Formel) *f*, Rekursionsgleichung *f*, rekursive Bestimmungsrelation *f*	relation (formule) *f* de récurrence	рекуррентная (рекурсивная) формула, возвратное уравнение, рекуррентное соотношение, формула приведения
R 313	**recursion of order *p*** <GN, NT>	Rekursion *f* der Ordnung *p*	récurrence *f* d'ordre *p*	рекурсия порядка *p*
	recursion relation <FO, GN>	*s.* R 312		
R 314	**recursion scheme (schema)** <FO>	Rekursionsschema *n*	schéma *m* de récurrence	рекуррентная схема
R 315	**recursion theorem** <Kleene> <MM, SE>	Rekursionstheorem *n*	théorème *m* de récurrence	теорема о рекурсии

	recursion theorem <FO>	*s.* P 1516		
R 316	**recursion theory** <MM>	Rekursionstheorie *f*	théorie *f* de la récursivité	теория рекурсивности
	recursion with respect to a course of values <FO>	*s.* C 2591		
	recursion with respect to a single variable <FO>	*s.* S 943		
R 317	**recursive algorithm** <FO>	rekursiver Algorithmus *m*	algorithme *m* récursif	рекурсивный алгоритм
	recursive computation <GN, MM>	*s.* F 462		
R 318	**recursive convergent sequence** <FO>	rekursiv (berechenbar) konvergente Folge *f*	suite *f* récursivement convergente	рекурсивно сходящаяся (конвергентная) последовательность
	recursive definition <FO>	*s.* D 140		
R 319	**recursive equivalence** <MM>	rekursive Äquivalenz *f*	équivalence *f* récursive	рекурсивная эквивалентность
R 320	**recursive function** <FO>	rekursive Funktion *f*	fonction *f* récurrente (récursive)	рекурсивная (возвратная) функция
R 321	**recursive functional** <FO>	rekursives Funktional *n*	fonctionnelle *f* récursive	рекурсивный функционал
R 322	**recursive function theory,** computability theory, theory of algorithms <FO>	Theorie *f* der rekursiven Funktionen	théorie *f* des fonctions récursives	теория рекурсивных функций
	recursive interpolation process due to Aitken <AX, FD, NU>	*s.* A 390		
R 323	**recursive isomorphism** <FO>	rekursiver Isomorphismus *m*	isomorphisme *m* récursif	рекурсивный изоморфизм
R 324	**recursively definable group** <GR>	rekursiv definierbare Gruppe *f*	groupe *m* récursivement définissable	рекурсивно определимая группа
R 325	**recursively enumerable set** <FO>	rekursiv aufzählbare (abzählbare) Menge *f*, allgemeinrekursiv aufzählbare Menge	ensemble *m* récursivement énumerable, ensemble positivement décidable	рекурсивно перечислимое множество
R 326	**recursively inseparable sets** <FO>	rekursiv untrennbare Mengen *fpl*	ensembles *mpl* récursivement inséparables	рекурсивно неотделимые множества
R 327	**recursively presentable group** <GR, MM>	rekursiv präsentierbare Gruppe *f*	groupe *m* récursivement présentable	рекурсивно определяемая группа
R 328	**recursively presented group** <GR, MM>	rekursiv präsentierte Gruppe *f*	groupe *m* récursivement présenté	рекурсивно определенная группа
R 329	**recursively representable mapping** <FO>	rekursiv darstellbare Abbildung *f*	application *f* récursivement représentable	рекурсивно представляемое отображение
R 330	**recursively unsolvable word problem** <FO, GR>	rekursiv unlösbares Wortproblem *n*	problème *m* des mots récursivement irrésoluble	рекурсивно неразрешимая проблема тождества [слов]
R 331	**recursiveness** <FO>	Rekursivität *f*	récursivité *f*	рекурсивность
R 332	**recursive number theory** <MM>	rekursive Zahlentheorie (Arithmetik) *f*	arithmétique *f* récursive	рекурсивная теория чисел, рекурсивная арифметика
	recursive predicate <MM>	*s.* G 178		
R 333	**recursive relation** <FO>	rekursive Relation *f*	relation *f* récursive	рекуррентное соотношение
	recursive sequence <FO>	*s.* R 302		
R 334	**recursive set** <FO>	rekursive Menge *f*	ensemble *m* récursif	рекурсивное множество
R 335	**recursive undecidability** <MM>	rekursive Unentscheidbarkeit *f*	indécidabilité *f* récursive	рекурсивная неразрешимость
R 336	**recursive unsolvability** <FO>	rekursive Unlösbarkeit *f*	irrésolubilité *f* récursive	рекурсивная неразрешимость
	Rédeian skew product <GR>	*s.* S 1178		
R 337	**redesignating of variables,** relettering of variables, rewriting of (the) variables <LO>	Variablenumbenennung *f*, Umbenennung *f* von Variablen	changement *m* de nom (désignation) de variables	замена (переименование) переменных
R 338	**reduce / to** <the structure group> <AT>	reduzieren <die Strukturgruppe>	réduire <le groupe structural>	редуцировать <структурную группу>
R 339	**reduced algebra** <AL>	reduzierte Algebra *f*	algèbre *f* réduite	приведенная алгебра
R 340	**reduced base** <of an abelian group> <GR>	Fundamentalsystem *n* von Erzeugenden	système *m* fondamental, base *f* réduite <Heffter>, base *f* normale	приведенный базис
R 341	**reduced chain complex** <of an augmented chain complex> <HA>	reduzierter Kettenkomplex *m*	complexe *m* de chaînes réduit	приведенный цепной комплекс
R 342	**reduced characteristic equation,** minimum equation <of a matrix *or* form> <AL, MD>	Minimumgleichung *f*, Minimalgleichung *f*, Grundgleichung *f*, reduzierte charakteristische Gleichung *f*	équation *f* minimale, équation fondamentale, équation caractéristique réduite, équation minimum, équation minima	минимальное уравнение
	reduced characteristic function <MD>	*s.* M 567		
R 343	**reduced characteristic polynomial** <AL>	reduziertes charakteristisches Polynom *n*	polynôme *m* caractéristique réduit	приведенный многочлен
R 344	**reduced Clifford group,** spin group <AL>	reduzierte Cliffordsche Gruppe *f*	groupe *m* de Clifford réduit, groupe *m* spinoriel	приведенная группа Клиффорда
R 345	**reduced cofactor** <MD>	reduzierter Kofaktor *m*; Kofaktor *m*, dividiert durch die Determinante	cofacteur *m* réduit	приведенное алгебраическое дополнение
R 346	**reduced cohomology group** <HA>	reduzierte Kohomologiegruppe *f*	groupe *m* de cohomologie réduit	приведенная группа когомологий
R 347	**reduced cone over X** <AT>	reduzierter Kegel *m* über *X*	cône *m* réduit sur *X*	приведенный конус над пространством *X*
R 348	**reduced continued fraction** <NT>	reduzierter Kettenbruch *m* <Stern>	fraction *f* continue réduite	приведенная цепная дробь

	English	German	French	Russian
	reduced cost function <PG>	*s.* R 369		
R 349	**reduced cost matrix** <PG>	reduzierte Kostenmatrix *f*	matrice *f* [de] coût réduite	приведенная матрица стоимости
R 350	**reduced cubic [equation],** reduced form of the cubic equation <AL>	reduzierte kubische Gleichung *f*, reduzierte Form *f* der kubischen Gleichung	équation *f* cubique réduite	приведенное кубическое уравнение
R 351	**reduced cycle** <AG>	reduzierter Zyklus *m*	cycle *m* réduit	редуцированный цикл
R 352	**reduced degree,** degree of separability <of an inseparable polynomial> <AL>	reduzierter Grad *m*	degré *m* réduit	степень сепарабельности
R 353	**reduced degree,** degree of separability, separable degree, separable factor of the degree <$[K:k]$> <AL>	reduzierter Grad *m*, reduzierter Körpergrad *m* <von *K* über *k*>	degré *m* réduit <de l'extension *K* du corps *k*>, facteur *m* séparable du degré <de *K* sur *k*>	сепарабельная степень, степень сепарабельности <*K* над *k*>
R 354	**reduced discriminant** <AL>	reduzierte Diskriminante *f*	discriminant *m* réduit	дискриминант $b^2 - ac$ <уравнения $ax^2 + 2bx + c = 0$>
	reduced distribution function <ST>	*s.* M 118		
R 355	**reduced equation, reduced form** <of an equation> <AL>	reduzierte Gleichung *f*, Reduzierte *f*, reduzierte Form *f* <einer Gleichung>	équation *f* réduite, réduite *f*, forme *f* réduite <d'une équation>	приведенное уравнение, приведенная форма <уравнения>
R 356	**reduced form** <of a quadratic *or* higher-order form> <NT>	reduzierte Form *f*	forme *f* réduite	приведенная форма
	reduced form <NT>	*s.* R 371		
	reduced form of the cubic equation <AL>	*s.* R 350		
R 357	**reduced form of the quadratic,** *p*-form of the quadratic <AL>	reduzierte quadratische Gleichung *f*, reduzierte Form *f* der quadratischen Gleichung	équation *f* quadratique réduite	приведенное квадратное уравнение
R 358	**reduced formula** <LO>	reduzierte Formel *f*, reduzierte Form *f* <einer Formel>	forme *f* réduite, formule *f* réduite	приведенная формула, приведенная форма <формулы>
	reduced fraction <AL, NT>	*s.* F 572		
	reduced free group <AL>	*s.* R 743		
R 359	**reduced game** <TG>	reduziertes Spiel *n*	jeu *m* réduit	приведенная (редуцированная) игра
R 360	**reduced *G*-bundle** <AT>	reduziertes *G*-Bündel *n*	*G*-fibré *m* réduit	редуцированное *G*-расслоение
R 361	**reduced gradient** <PG>	reduzierter Gradient *m*	gradient *m* réduit	приведенный градиент
R 362	**reduced gradient method,** Wolfe['s] method (algorithm) <PG>	Verfahren *n* der reduzierten Gradienten <von Wolfe>, reduziertes Gradientenverfahren *n*, Wolfesches Verfahren der reduzierten Gradienten, Wolfe-Verfahren *n*	méthode *f* des gradients réduits	метод приведенных градиентов
R 363	**π-reduced group** <GR>	π-reduzierte Gruppe *f*	groupe *m* π-réduit	π-редуцированная группа
	reduced homogeneous equation <DE>	*s.* A 1070		
R 364	**reduced homology sequence** <HA>	reduzierte Homologiesequenz *f*	suite *f* d'homologie réduite	приведенная гомологическая последовательность
R 365	**reduced join** <of spaces> <TO>	reduzierte Vereinigung *f*, „reduced join" *m*	union *f* réduite	приведенное соединение
	reduced latin square <CT, ST>	*s.* S 1634		
R 366	**reduced matrix** <AL, NU>	reduzierte Matrix *f*	matrice *f* réduite	приведенная матрица
	reduced matrix <AL>	*s.* J 94		
R 367	**reduced minimum polynomial** <AL>	reduziertes Minimalpolynom *n*	polynôme *m* minimal réduit	приведенный минимальный многочлен
R 368	**reduced norm** <in an algebra> <AL>	reduzierte Norm *f*, Hauptnorm *f*	norme *f* réduite	приведенная норма
R 369	**reduced objective function,** reduced cost function <PG>	reduzierte Zielfunktion *f*	fonction *f* économique réduite	приведенная целевая функция
R 370	**reduced polynomial** <AL>	reduziertes Polynom *n*	polynôme *m* réduit	редуцированный многочлен, приведенный многочлен, приведенный полином
	reduced power <AT>	*s.* S 1705		
	reduced primary representation <AL>	*s.* I 1052		
	reduced product <TO>	*s.* S 1229		
	reduced product <UA>	*s.* L 1177		
R 371	**reduced quadratic form,** reduced form <NT>	Gaußsche reduzierte Form *f*, reduzierte [quadratische] Form *f*	forme *f* réduite [de Gauss], forme quadratique réduite	приведенная [квадратичная] форма
R 372	**reduced rank** <of a group> <GR>	reduzierter Rang *m*	rang *m* réduit	редуцированный ранг
R 373	**reduced relative degree** <of a prime ideal> <AL>	reduzierter Relativgrad *m*	degré *m* relatif réduit	приведенная относительная степень
R 374	**reduced representation** <AL>	reduzierte Darstellung *f*	représentation *f* réduite	представление в приведенной форме
R 375	**reduced residue system,** reduced set of residues <mod. *n*>, complete set of residues <prime to *n*> <NT>	reduziertes (vollständiges primes, volles primes) Restsystem *n* <mod *n*>	système *m* réduit de résidus (restes), système résiduel réduit <mod. *n*>	приведенная система вычетов <по модулю *n*>
	reduced resultant <AL>	*s.* S 1382		

R 376	**reduced scheme** <AG>	reduziertes Schema *n*	schéma *m* réduit	приведенная схема, многообразие
	reduced set of residues <NT>	*s.* R 375		
R 377	**reduced sheaf** <of rings> <AL, TO>	reduzierte Garbe *f* <von Ringen>	faisceau *m* <d'anneaux> réduit	приведенный пучок <колец>
	reduced square <AT>	*s.* S 1706		
R 378	**reduced suspension,** suspension <of pointed spaces> <TO>	reduzierte Einhängung *f*	suspension *f* réduite	приведенная надстройка, надстройка
R 379	**reduced tensor product** <AT>	reduziertes Tensorprodukt *n*	produit *m* tensoriel réduit	приведенное тензорное произведение
R 380	**reduced Whitehead group** <AL>	reduzierte Whitehead-Gruppe *f*	groupe *m* de Whitehead réduit	приведенная группа Уайтхеда
R 381	**reduced word** <AL>	Kurzwort *n*, zyklisch reduziertes Wort *n*	mot *m* réduit	циклически несократимое слово
R 382	**reduced word** <GR>	reduziertes Wort *n*	mot *m* réduit, réduit *m* <d'un mot>	несократимое слово
R 383	**reduce** <a matrix> **to a triangular matrix / to** <MD>	auf Dreiecksform bringen, auf Dreiecksform transformieren	trigonaliser	приводить к треугольному виду
R 384	**reduce to canonical form / to;** to transform to canonical form <AL, AY, DE, VA>	auf kanonische Form bringen; in die kanonische Gestalt transformieren	canoniser; transformer en forme canonique	приводить к каноническому виду, [про-] канонизировать; преобразовать в канонический вид
R 385	**reduce** <a fraction> **to its lowest terms / to** <AR>	<einen Bruch> kürzen, vollständig kürzen, auf die einfachste Form bringen (zurückführen, reduzieren)	réduire <une fraction> à sa plus simple expression, simplifier <une fraction>	приводить <дробь> к несократимому виду, представить <дробь> посредством сокращения в виде несократимой, придавать <дроби> самую простую форму
	reducibility axiom <LO>	*s.* A 1290		
R 386	**reducibility criterion** <AL>	Reduzibilitätskriterium *n*	critère *m* de réductibilité	критерий приводимости, признак приводимости
R 387	**reducible Abelian integral** <of the first kind> <AN>	reduzibles Abelsches Integral <erster (1.) Gattung>	intégrale *f* abélienne réductible	приводимый интеграл Абеля
R 388	**reducible affine algebraic *k*-variety** <AG>	reduzible (zusammengesetzte) affine algebraische *k*-Mannigfaltigkeit *f*, affine algebraische *k*-Menge *f*	*k*-variété *f* algébrique affine réductible	приводимое аффинное алгебраическое *k*-множество
R 389	**reducible algebra** <AL>	reduzible Algebra *f*	algèbre *f* réductible	приводимая алгебра
R 390	**reducible algebraic curve,** reducible curve <AG>	reduzible algebraische Kurve *f*	courbe *f* algébrique réductible, courbe algébrique décomposée, courbe décomposée	приводимая алгебраическая кривая, распадающаяся [алгебраическая] кривая
R 391	**reducible algebraic equation** <AL>	reduzible algebraische Gleichung *f*, reduzible Gleichung	équation *f* algébrique réductible	приводимое алгебраическое уравнение, приводимое уравнение
R 392	**reducible algebraic surface,** reducible surface <AG>	reduzible algebraische Fläche *f*, zerfallende [algebraische] Fläche	surface *f* algébrique réductible (décomposée)	распадающаяся [алгебраическая] поверхность, приводимая алгебраическая поверхность
	reducible chain <SP>	*s.* R 402		
R 393	**reducible character** <of a representation> <RE>	zusammengesetzter Charakter *m*	caractère *m* composé	характер приводимого представления
R 394	**reducible curve,** decomposed curve <GE>	zerfallende Kurve *f*	courbe *f* à plusieurs branches	распадающаяся кривая (линия)
R 395	**reducible curve** <in the direct infinitesimal geometry> <DG>	reduzible Kurve *f*	courbe *f* réductible	приводимая кривая
	reducible curve <AG>	*s.* R 390		
R 396	**reducible differential equation** <DE>	reduzible Differentialgleichung *f*	équation *f* différentielle réductible	приводимое дифференциальное уравнение
R 397	**reducible element** <of a ring> <AL>	zerlegbares Element *n*	élément *m* réductible	приводимый элемент
R 398	**reducible element** <of a lattice> <LA>	reduzibles Verbandselement *n*, reduzibles Element *n* <eines Verbandes>	élément *m* décomposable <d'un treillis>	приводимый элемент <структуры>
	reducible element <LA>	*s.* M 373		
	reducible form <AL>	*s.* R 407		
R 399	**reducible generating set** <of a group> <GR>	reduzibles Erzeugendensystem *n*	système *m* générateur réductible	приводимая система образующих
R 400	**reducible ideal** <AL>	reduzibles Ideal *n*	idéal *m* réductible	приводимый идеал
R 401	**reducible integer** <NT>	reduzible Zahl *f*	entier *m* réductible	приводимое целое число
R 402	**reducible Markov chain,** reducible chain <SP>	reduzible [Markovsche] Kette *f*, zerlegbare [Markovsche] Kette	chaîne *f* [markovienne] réductible	приводимая цепь [Маркова]
R 403	**reducible matrix** <MD>	reduzible Matrix *f*	matrice *f* réductible	приводимая матрица, редуцируемая матрица
R 404	**reducible matrix representation** <RE>	reduzible Matrizendarstellung *f*	représentation *f* matricielle réductible	приводимое матричное представление
R 405	**reducible polynomial,** factorable polynomial <AL>	reduzibles (zerlegbares) Polynom *n*	polynôme *m* réductible, fonction *f* rationnelle entière décomposable (réductible)	приводимый многочлен (полином)
R 406	**reducible projective algebraic variety** <AG>	reduzible (zerfallende, zusammengesetzte) projektive algebraische Mannigfaltigkeit *f*	variété *f* algébrique projective réductible (décomposée)	приводимое (распадающееся) проективное алгебраическое множество
R 407	**reducible quadratic form,** reducible form <AL>	reduzible quadratische Form *f*, reduzible Form	forme *f* quadratique réductible, forme réductible	приводимая квадратичная форма, приводимая форма

R 408	**reducible representation,** semi-reducible representation <of a group *or* ring> <AL, RE>	reduzible Darstellung *f*, halbreduzible Darstellung	représentation *f* réductible, représentation semi-réductible	приводимое представление, полуприводимое представление
	reducible space <TO>	*s.* 1. C 2265; 2. R 412		
R 409	**reducible star body** <GU>	reduzibler Sternkörper *m*	corps *m* étoilé réductible	приводимое звездное тело
R 410	**reducible surface,** decomposable surface <GE>	zerfallende Fläche *f*	surface *f* à plusieurs branches	распадающаяся поверхность
	reducible surface <AG>	*s.* R 392		
R 411	**reducible term** <LO>	reduzibler Term *m*		сводимый терм
R 412	**reducible topological space,** reducible space <TO>	zerlegbarer (zerlegbarer topologischer, reduzibler) Raum *m*	espace *m* réductible	приводимое пространство; пространство, являющееся объединением двух отличных от него замкнутых подмножеств
	reducible topological space <TO>	*s. a.* C 2265		
R 413	**reducible variety** <DG>	reduzible (zerfallende) Mannigfaltigkeit *f*	variété *f* décomposée	приводимое многообразие
R 414	**reducing the group of a bundle,** reduction of the group of the bundle <AT>	Reduktion *f* der Strukturgruppe	réduction *f* du groupe structural	редукция структурной группы
R 415	**reductant** <IV>	Reduzent *m*	réduisant *m*	приводящий множитель
	reductio ad absurdum <GN>	*s.* R 481		
	reductio ad absurdum <LO> ⌐<LO>	*s.* 1. I 378; 2. R 442		
	reductio ad impossibile	*s.* I 378		
R 416	**reduction** <of a matroid> <CT>	Reduktion *f*	réduction *f*	редукция
R 417	**reduction,** foreshortening <e.g. in axonometry> <DS>	Verkürzung *f*	réduction *f*	укорочение
R 418	**reduction** <of an operator by a closed linear subspace> <FA>	Reduzieren *n* <eines Operators durch einen abgeschlossenen linearen Teilraum>	réduction *f* <d'un opérateur par un sous-espace linéaire fermé>	приведение <оператора замкнутым линейным подпространством>
R 419	**reduction** <GR, LO>	Kürzung *f*	réduction *f*	сокращение
R 420	**reduction** <mod *p*> <NT>	Reduktion *f*, Restklassenabbildung *f* <mod *p*>	réduction *f* <modulo *p*>	редукция, приведение <по модулю *p*>
	reduction <AR, GN>	*s.* C 43		
	reduction <RE>	*s.* U 8		
	reduction ad absurdum proof <LO>	*s.* I 378		
R 421	**reduction ascending** <of a denominate number> <NU>	Umwandlung *f* in eine größere Einheit		превращение в более крупную именованную единицу
R 422	**reduction condition** <for quadratic forms> <NT>	Reduktionsbedingung *f*	condition *f* de réduction	условие редукции
R 423	**reduction descending** <of a denominate number> <NU>	Umwandlung *f* in eine kleinere (niedrigere) Einheit		превращение в более мелкую единицу
R 424	**reduction factor,** scale ratio, ratio of foreshortening <in axonometry *or* oblique projection> <DS>	Verkürzungsverhältnis *n*, Verkürzungsfaktor *m*	unité *f* axonométrique	показатель искажения
	reduction formulas <EG>	*s.* Q 19		
R 425	**reduction method** <FA, IE, NT, PG>	Reduktionsmethode *f*, Reduktionsverfahren *n*	méthode *f* des réduites <FA, IE>; méthode de la réduction <NT, PG>	метод приведения
	reduction of a common fraction to a decimal fraction <NT>	*s.* T 774		
R 426	**reduction of an equation** <AL>	Reduktion *f* einer Gleichung; Vereinfachung *f* einer Gleichung	réduction *f* d'une équation	приведение уравнения
R 427	**reduction of an expression,** simplification of an expression <GN>	Vereinfachung *f* eines Ausdrucks	simplification *f* d'une expression	упрощение выражения
	reduction of a vulgar fraction to a decimal fraction <NT>	*s.* T 774		
R 428	**reduction of data** <ST>	Reduktion *f* der Daten (Beobachtungswerte)	réduction *f* des données (observations)	приведение данных, обработка данных
R 429	**reduction of holes** <of a surface> <TO>	Zukleben *n* von Löchern	réduction *f* des trous	заклеивание дыр
R 430	**reduction of order,** lowering of order, deflation <MD>	Ordnungserniedrigung *f*, Erniedrigung *f* der Ordnung, Deflation *f*	abaissement *m* (réduction *f*) de l'ordre	понижение порядка
	reduction of singularities <AG>	*s.* R 906		
	reduction of the group of the bundle <AT>	*s.* R 414		
R 431	**reduction of two holes by means of a handle** <AT>	Aufsetzen *n* eines Henkels	attachement *m* d'une anse	заклеивание двух дыр одной ручкой
R 432	**reduction principle** <FO>	Reduktionsprinzip *n*	principe *m* de réduction	принцип редукции
R 433	**reduction theorem** <AG, AL, LO, SE, TO>	Reduktionssatz *m* <AG, AL, SE, TO>; Reduktionstheorem *n* <LO>	théorème *m* de réduction	теорема редукции
R 434	**reduction** <of a fraction> **to a common denominator,** putting (placing) over a common denominator <AL, AR>	Gleichnamigmachen *n*, Zurückführen (Bringen) *n* auf gleichen Nenner, Auf-den-gleichen-Nenner-Bringen *n*	réduction *f* au même dénominateur	приведение к общему знаменателю

	English	German	French	Russian
R 435	**reduction** <of a fraction> **to a common numerator** <AL, AR>	Zurückführen *n* auf gleichen Zähler	réduction *f* au même numérateur	приведение к одинаковому числителю
R 436	**reduction to a direct product** <of an algebra> <AL>	Produktzerlegung *f*	décomposition *f* en produit tensoriel	разложение <алгебры> в тензорное произведение
R 437	**reduction** <of a quadratic form> **to a sum of squares** <AL>	Transformation *f* <einer quadratischen Form> auf eine Summe von Quadraten, Zerlegung *f* <einer quadratischen Form> in eine Summe von Quadraten	décomposition *f* <d'une forme quadratique> en carrés, décomposition <d'une forme quadratique>	преобразование <квадратичной формы> в сумму квадратов
R 438	**reduction to a triangular matrix,** triangularization <of a matrix> <MD>	Transformation *f* auf Dreiecksform, Umformung *f* auf Dreiecksgestalt	trigonalisation *f*, triangularisation *f*	приведение к треугольному виду
R 439	**reduction to canonical form** <e.g. of a matrix> <AL, MD>	Transformation *f* auf kanonische Form, Überführung *f* in die kanonische Form	réduction *f* à la forme canonique	приведение к каноническому виду
R 440/1	**reduction** <of a fraction> **to higher terms** <e.g. by *q*>**,** extension, expansion <of a fraction> <e.g. by *q*> <AR> ⌐<AR>	Erweiterung *f* <eines Bruches> <z. B. mit *q*>	multiplication *f* des deux termes <d'une fraction> <par exemple, par *q*>, multiplication du numérateur et du dénominateur <d'une fraction> <par exemple, par *q*>, action *f* de porter <une fraction> à une plus grande expression <par exemple, par *q*>	умножение числителя и знаменателя <дроби> <например, на *q*>
	reduction to lower terms	*s.* S 992		
	reduction to normal form <AL, AY>	*s.* T 784		
R 442	**reduction to the impossible,** reductio ad absurdum, law of reductio ad absurdum <LO>	Reductio (reductio) *f* ad absurdum, Deductio (deductio) *f* ad absurdum	réduction *f* à l'absurde	приведение к нелепости, приведение к невозможности, приведение к абсурду, закон приведения к абсурду, сведение к абсурду, reductio ad absurdum, reductio ad impossibile, deductio ad absurdum
R 443	**reductive algebraic group** <GR>	reduktive algebraische Gruppe *f*	groupe *m* [algébrique] réductif	редуктивная алгебраическая группа
R 444	**redundance, redundancy** <ST>	Redundanz *f*	redondance *f*	избыточность
R 445	**redundancy** <ST>	warme Reserve *f*	élément *m* redondant	облегченный резерв
R 446	**redundant axiom** <FO>	überflüssiges Axiom *n*	axiome *m* abondant	избыточная аксиома
R 447	**redundant co-ordinates** <AY>	überzählige Koordinaten *fpl*	coordonnées *fpl* surabondantes	избыточные координаты
R 448	**redundant equation** <AL>	Gleichung *f*, die mehr Wurzeln enthält als die, aus der sie gewonnen wurde	équation *f* rédondante	уравнение, содержащее посторонние корни; уравнение, содержащее избыточные корни
	redundant number <NT>	*s.* A 161		
R 449	**redundant representation** <of an ideal *or* a lattice element> <AL, LA>	verkürzbare Darstellung *f*	représentation *f* rédondante	сократимое представление
R 450	**reentrant angle** <EG>	einspringender Winkel *m*	angle *m* rentrant	угол, больший развернутого, но меньший полного
R 451	**Rees congruence** <modulo *I*> <of a semigroup> <AL>	Reessche Kongruenz <modulo *I*>	congruence *f* de Rees <modulo *I*>	конгруэнция Риса <по модулю *I*>
R 452	**Rees['s] factor semigroup,** <relative to an ideal *I*>, Rees['s] quotient <of a semigroup modulo an ideal> <AL>	Reessche Faktorhalbgruppe *f*, Differenzenhalbgruppe *f*, Quotientenhalbgruppe *f* <nach einem Ideal *I*>	demi-groupe *m* quotient de Rees <d'un demi-groupe par un ideal *I*>	факторполугруппа Риса, полугруппа разностей <полугруппы по модулю *I*>
R 453	**Rees['s] matrix semigroup without zero over the group 𝔖 with sandwich matrix *P*** <AL>	Matrizenhalbgruppe *f* über der Gruppe 𝔖 mit der definierenden Matrix *P*	demi-groupe *m* matriciel sur le groupe 𝔖 à matrice définissante *P*	рисовская полугруппа матричного типа с сэндвич-матрицей *P* над группой 𝔖
	Rees['s] quotient <AL>	*s.* R 452		
R 454	**reference period,** base period <ST>	Bezugsperiode *f*, Vergleichsperiode *f*	période *f* de référence	базовый период
	reference plane <AY>	*s.* P 650		
R 455	**refinement** <of a normal series> <GR>	Verfeinerung *f* <einer Normalreihe>	raffinement *m* <d'une série normale>, suite *f* normale plus fine	уплотнение <нормального ряда>
R 456	**refinement** <of a chain> <LA>	Verfeinerung *f* <einer Kette>	raffinement *m* <d'une chaîne>	уплотнение <цепи>
R 457	**refinement** <of a partition> <SE>	Verfeinerung *f* <einer Zerlegung *oder* Einteilung>	subdivision *f* <d'une partition>	измельчение <разбиения>
R 458	**refinement** <of a cover> <TO>	Verfeinerung *f* <einer Überdeckung>	raffinement *m* <d'un recouvrement>	вписанное покрытие, измельчение <покрытия>
	refinement <UA>	*s.* S 2082		
R 459	**refinement theorem** <for chains> <LA>	Verfeinerungssatz *m*	théorème *m* de raffinement	теорема об уплотнениях цепей
R 460	**reflected code** <NU>	reflektierter Kode (Code) *m*	code *m* réfléchi, code de réflexion	рефлексивный код

	reflected image <GE>	*s.* M 663		
R 461	**reflecting barrier** <ST>	Reflexionsschirm *m*	barrière *f* réfléchissante	отражающий экран
	reflecting curve <GE>	*s.* A 612		
R 462	**reflection** <CA>	Reflexion *f*	réflexion *f*	отражение
R 463	**reflection** <with respect to a plane> <EG>	Spiegelung *f* <an einer Ebene>	symétrie *f* par rapport à un plan, réflexion *f* <par rapport à un plan>	симметрия [в узком смысле], отображение относительно плоскости, зеркальное отображение <относительно плоскости>, симметрия относительно плоскости, отражение <относительно плоскости>
	reflection <GE>	*s.* M 663		
R 464	**reflection in the plane** <GE>	Spiegelung *f* in der Ebene	symétrie *f* plane, réflexion *f*, mirage *m*	отражение в плоскости
	reflection principle <FT>	*s.* S 172		
	reflective . . .	*s.* **reflexive . . .**		
R 465	**reflector** <CA>	Reflektor *m*	réflecteur *m*	рефлектор
	reflex angle <EG>	*s.* C 2383		
R 466	**reflexive $\mathfrak{A}$-module** <AL>	reflexiver $\mathfrak{A}$-Modul *m*	$\mathfrak{A}$-module *m* réflexif	рефлексивный $\mathfrak{A}$-модуль
	reflexive and symmetric binary relation <SE>	*s.* T 492		
	reflexive and transitive relation <SE>	*s.* Q 214		
R 467	**reflexive Banach space, reflexive B-space,** regular Banach space, regular B-space <FA>	reflexiver Banach-Raum *m*	espace *m* de Banach réflexif	рефлексивное банахово пространство
	reflexive cardinal <SE>	*s.* T 747		
R 468	**reflexive class** <SE>	reflexive Klasse *f*, D[edekind]-unendliche Klasse	classe *f* infinie au sens de Dedekind	бесконечный класс в смысле Дедекинда
R 469	**reflexive closure** <of a relation> <SE>	reflexive Hülle *f*, Reflexivitätshülle *f*	fermeture *f* réflexive	рефлексивное замыкание
	reflexive law of [material] implication <LO>	*s.* L 189		
	reflexive linear space <FA, TO>	*s.* R 473		
R 470	**reflexively partially ordered set** <SE>	reflexiv halbgeordnete Menge *f*	ensemble *m* partiellement ordonné au sens large, ensemble muni d'une relation d'ordre partiel [large]	рефлексивно полуупорядоченное множество
	reflexively quasi-ordered set <SE>	*s.* P 1230		
	reflexive quasi-order <SE>	*s.* Q 214		
R 471	**reflexive relation,** vicinity <SE>	reflexive Relation *f*	relation *f* réflexive	рефлексивное отношение, возвратное отношение
	reflexive set <SE>	*s.* D 90		
R 472	**reflexive skew-field** <AL>	reflexiver Schiefkörper *m*	corps *m* réflexif	рефлексивное тело
R 473	**reflexive space,** reflexive linear space, // regular space <FA, TO>	reflexiver (reflexiver linearer) Raum *m*, // regulärer Raum	espace *m* réflexif (linéaire réflexif), // espace régulier	рефлексивное (рефлексивное линейное) пространство, // регулярное (правильное) пространство
R 474	**reflexive subcategory** <CA>	reflexive Unterkategorie *f*, reflektive Unterkategorie	sous-catégorie *f* réflexive	рефлективная подкатегория, R-полная подкатегория
	reflexive symmetric relation <SE>	*s.* P 1933		
R 475	**reflexivity** <SE>	Reflexivität *f*	réflexivité *f*	рефлективность, рефлексивность
R 476	**reflexivity of equipollence** <of sets> <SE>	Reflexivität *f* der Äquivalenz <von Mengen>	principe *m* d'identité <d'ensembles>	рефлексивность равномощности <множеств>
	reflexotation <GE>	*s.* I 183		
R 477	**reflex polygon,** self-intersecting polygon, polygon with sides cutting each other, polygon in which two nonconsecutive sides have a common point <EG>	überschlagenes Vieleck (Polygon) *n*	polygone *m* croisé	самопересекающийся многоугольник, многоугольник с самопересечением
R 478	**reflex quadrilateral** <EG>	überschlagenes Viereck *n*	quadrangle *m* croisé	самопересекающийся четырехугольник, четырехугольник с самопересечением
	refracting curve <GE>	*s.* A 613		
R 479	**refutability** <LO>	Widerlegbarkeit *f*	réfutabilité *f*	опровержимость
R 480	**refutable formula** <LO>	widerlegbarer Ausdruck *m*, widerlegbare Formel *f*	formule *f* réfutable	опровержимая формула
R 481	**refutal, refutation,** reductio ad absurdum <GN>	Gegenbeweis *m*, Widerlegung *f*	contre-épreuve *f*, réfutation *f*	опровержение
R 482	**region** <ST>	Bereich *m*, Punktmenge *f*	région *f*	область
R 483	**region** <in a metric space> <Lefschetz> <TO>	offene Menge *f* in einem metrischen Raum	ensemble *m* ouvert dans un espace métrique	открытое множество в метрическом пространстве
	region <GP>	*s.* F 8		
	region <TO>	*s.* D 855		
	region estimate (estimation) <ST>	*s.* C 1865		
R 484	**region of analyticity** <FT>	Analytizitätsgebiet *n*	ouvert *m* d'analyticité	область аналитичности

No.	English	Deutsch	Français	Русский
	region of convergence <FT, SS>	*s.* D 864		
	region of discontinuity <FT>	*s.* F 811		
R 485	**region of regularity** <FT>	Regularitätsbereich *m*, Regularitätsgebiet *n*	domaine *m* de régularité	область регулярности; область, в которой аналитическая функция регулярна
R 486	**region of summability** <of a series> <SS>	Summabilitätsbereich *m*	région *f* de sommabilité	область суммируемости
R 487	**regressand,** predictand <ST>	Regressand *m*	variable *f* expliquée	зависимое переменное в уравнении регрессии, зависимая переменная в уравнении регрессии
R 488	⌐<ST> **regression** <of *y* on *x*>	Regression *f* <von *y* auf *x*>	régression *f* <de *y* en *x*>	регрессия <[от] *y* по *x*>
	regression <ST>	*s.* R 491		
R 489	**regression analysis** <ST>	Regressionsanalyse *f*	analyse *f* de régression	регрессионный анализ
R 490	**regression coefficient** <ST>	Regressionskoeffizient *m*	coefficient *m* de régression	коэффициент регрессии
R 491	**regression curve,** regression line, regression <ST>	Regressionskurve *f*, Regressionslinie *f*, Ausgleichskurve *f*, Ausgleichslinie *f*	ligne (courbe) *f* de régression	кривая (линия) регрессии
R 492	**regression effect** <ST>	Regressionseffekt *m*	effet *m* de régression	эффект (влияние) регрессии
R 493	**regression equation** <ST>	Regressionsgleichung *f*	équation *f* de régression, équation d'estimation	уравнение регрессии
	regression estimate <ST>	*s.* R 495		
R 494	**regression estimate (estimation)** <process> <ST>	Regressionsschätzung *f*	estimation *f* par régression	оценивание по уравнению регрессии, оценивание регрессии
R 495	**regression estimator,** regression estimate <ST>	Regressionsschätzung *f*, Regressionsschätzfunktion *f*	estimateur *m* par régression	оценка по уравнению регрессии, оценка регрессии
R 496	**regression function** <of the first *or* second kind> <ST>	Regressionsfunktion *f*, Ausgleichsfunktion *f*, // Regressionsgleichung *f* <erster *oder* zweiter Art>	fonction *f* de régression, fonction d'ajustement <de première *ou* seconde espèce>	функция регрессии, регрессивная (регрессионная) функция <первого *или* второго рода>
R 497	**regression hyperplane** <ST>	Regressionshyperebene *f* <erster *oder* zweiter Art>	hyperplan *m* de régression	гиперплоскость регрессии
R 498	**regression line,** line of regression, regression straight line <ST>	Regressionsgerade *f*, Ausgleichsgerade *f*, Beziehungsgerade *f*, ausgleichende Gerade *f* <erster *oder* zweiter Art>	droite (ligne) *f* de régression, droite de tendance, droite d'estimation, droite de longue durée	линия (прямая) регрессии, прямая выравнивания
	regression line <ST>	*s. a.* R 491		
R 499	**regression of the first kind,** general regression <ST>	Regression *f* erster (1.) Art, allgemeine Regression	régression *f* de première (1e) espèce, régression générale	регрессия первого рода, общая регрессия
R 500	**regression of the second kind,** specific regression <ST>	Regression *f* zweiter (2.) Art, spezielle Regression	régression *f* de deuxième (seconde) espèce, régression spécifique	регрессия второго рода
R 501	**regression plane** <ST>	Regressionsebene *f*	plan *m* de régression	плоскость регрессии
	regression straight line <ST>	*s.* R 498		
R 502	**regression surface** <ST>	Regressionsfläche *f* <erster *oder* zweiter Art>	surface *f* de régression	поверхность регрессии
R 503	**regressive function** <SE>	regressive Funktion *f*	fonction *f* régressive	регрессивная функция
R 504	**regressive product** <of multivectors> <AL, GE>	regressives Produkt *n*	produit *m* régressif	регрессивное произведение
R 505	**regressive set** <SE>	regressive Menge *f*	ensemble *m* régressif	регрессивное множество
R 506	**regressor,** predicated variable, determining variable <ST>	Regressor *m*	variable *f* explicative <dans l'analyse de régression>	независимое переменное в уравнении регрессии, независимая переменная в уравнении регрессии
R 507	**regret** <ST>	Regret *m*, vermeidbarer Verlust *m*	regret *m*	сожаление, разочарование
R 508	**regret function** <ST>	Regretfunktion *f*	fonction *f* de regret	функция потерь
	regrouping <GN, SS>	*s.* R 235		
	regula (Regula) falsi <AN, NU>	*s.* M 463		
R 509	**regular affinity,** non-degenerate affinity, non[-]singular affine transformation, affine transformation <AY>	reguläre (nichtausgeartete) Affinität *f*, nichtausgeartete (nichtsinguläre) affine Transformation *f*, affine Transformation	affinité *f* (transformation *f* affine) régulière, transformation affine non singulière, transformation affine	невырожденное (неособенное, регулярное) аффинное преобразование, аффинное преобразование
R 510	**regular algebra** <UA>	reguläre Algebra *f*	algèbre *f* régulière	регулярная алгебра
	regular algebraic branch[-]point (ramification point, singularity) <FT>	*s.* O 382		
R 511	**regular algebraic surface,** regular surface <AG> ⌐<FT>	reguläre algebraische Fläche *f*	surface *f* [algébrique] régulière	регулярная [алгебраическая] поверхность
	regular analytic function	*s.* H 405		
R 512	**regular anti-representation,** left regular representation <AL>	reguläre Antidarstellung (Linksdarstellung) *f*, antistrophe Darstellung *f* <einer Algebra>; reguläre Antidarstellung, linke reguläre Darstellung <einer Gruppe oder Halbgruppe>	antireprésentation *f* régulière, représentation *f* régulière gauche	левое регулярное представление, регулярное антипредставление

No.	English	German	French	Russian
R 513	**regular arc** <DG>	reguläres Kurvenstück *n*	arc *m* régulier	регулярный кусок кривой
R 514	**regular arrow** <CA>	regulärer Pfeil *m*	morphisme *m* régulier	регулярный морфизм
R 515	**regular astroid** <GE>	reguläre Astroide *f*	astroïde *f* régulière	регулярная астроида
	regular Banach space <FA>	*s.* R 467		
R 516	**regular Borel measure,** Borel-Stieltjes measure; Radon['s] measure <determined by a function *f*> <ME>	reguläres Borelsches Maß *n*, // Radonsches Maß	mesure *f* borélienne (de (Borel) régulière	регулярная мера Бореля
	regular branch <FT>	*s.* B 717		
	regular branch[-]point <FT>	*s.* O 382		
	regular B-space <FA>	*s.* R 467		
R 517	**regular cardinal** <SE>	reguläre Kardinalzahl *f*, Kardinalzahl zweiter Art	cardinal *m* régulier (régulier infini)	регулярный кардинал, регулярное кардинальное число
R 518	**regular chain** <in a complex *or* of integral elements> <AT, DE>	reguläre Kette *f*	chaîne *f* régulière	регулярная цепь
	regular chain <SP>	*s.* R 591		
R 519	**regular character** <RE>	regulärer Charakter *m*	caractère *m* régulier	регулярный характер
R 520	**regular class of divisors** <AL>	reguläre Divisorenklasse (Klasse) *f*	classe *f* de diviseurs régulière	регулярный класс дивизоров, регулярный класс
R 521	**regular closed set** <TO>	reguläre (regulär) abgeschlossene Menge *f*	ensemble *m* fermé régulier	регулярное замкнутое множество
	regular-closed space <TO>	*s.* R 639		
R 522	**regular-closed subspace** <of a locally convex space> <FA>	orthogonalabgeschlossener Teilraum *m*, orthogonal abgeschlossener Unterraum *m*, regulär-abgeschlossener Unterraum	sous-espace *m* régulièrement fermé, sous-espace du dual fermé pour la topologie faible	регулярно замкнутое подпространство
	regular complex <AT>	*s.* B 79		
R 523	**regular component** <of a regular point of an elementary curve> <TO>	gewöhnlicher Bestandteil *m*	composante *f* régulière	компонента регулярности
R 524	**regular composition** <AL>	reguläre Verknüpfung *f*	composition *f* régulière	регулярная композиция; // действие, обладающее свойством сокращаемости
R 525	**regular confidence region** <ST>	regulärer Konfidenzbereich *m*	région *f* de confiance régulière	регулярная доверительная область
R 526	**regular congruence [of lines (rays)]** <DG>	reguläre Strahlenkongruenz (Linienkongruenz, Geradenkongruenz, Kongruenz) *f*, reguläres Strahlensystem *n*	congruence *f* [de droites] régulière	регулярная (правильная) конгруэнция [прямых (лучей)]
	regular conic [section] <AY>	*s.* N 357		
R 527/8	**regular continuation** <of a linear operator> <FA>	reguläre Fortsetzung *f*	prolongement *m* régulier	регулярное продолжение
R 529	**regular continued fraction,** simple continued fraction <NT>	regelmäßiger (einfacher, gewöhnlicher) Kettenbruch *m*	fraction *f* continue régulière (simple, ordinaire), fraction continue arithmétique ordinaire	правильная цепная дробь
R 530	**regular convergence** <TO>	reguläre Konvergenz *f* <im Sinne von Curtis>	convergence *f* régulière <au sens de Curtis>	регулярная сходимость
R 531	**regular covering surface** <TO>	reguläre Überlagerungsfläche *f*	surface *f* de recouvrement régulière	регулярная поверхность наложения
R 532	**regular curve** <of class *r*> <DG>	reguläre (gewöhnliche) Kurve *f* <der Klasse *r*>	courbe *f* régulière <de classe *r*>	регулярная кривая <класса *r*>
R 533	**regular determinant** <of a quadratic form> <NT>	reguläre Determinante *f* <Frobenius>	déterminant *m* régulier	регулярный определитель
R 534	**regular distribution** <AN>	reguläre Distribution *f*	distribution *f* régulière	регулярная обобщенная функция
R 535	**regular dodecahedron,** dodecahedron <EG>	regelmäßiges Zwölfflach (Dodekaeder) *n*, Dodekaeder	dodécaèdre *m* régulier, dodécaèdre	правильный додекаэдр, додекаэдр, [правильный] двенадцатигранник
R 536	**regular domain,** regular region <GE, PO>	regulärer Bereich *m*; reguläres Gebiet *n*	domaine *m* régulier	регулярная область
R 537	**regular eigenvalue problem** <DE>	reguläre Eigenwertaufgabe *f*, reguläres Eigenwertproblem *n*	problème *m* aux valeurs propres régulier	правильная задача на собственные значения
R 538	**regular element** <of a Banach algebra, Lie group, *or* Lie algebra> <AL>	reguläres Element *n*	élément *m* régulier	регулярный элемент
R 539	**regular element,** cancellable element <of a composition> <AL>	reguläres (kürzbares) Element *n*	élément *m* régulier (simplifiable)	регулярный (сократимый) элемент
R 540	**regular element,** nonzerodivisor <of a ring> <AL>	Nichtnullteiler *m*, reguläres Element *n*	élément *m* non diviseur de zéro, élément simplifiable	неделитель нуля, сократимый элемент
	regular element <AL>	*s.* R 541		
	regular element <FA>	*s.* I 977		
R 541	**regular element in the sense of Neumann,** regular element <AL>	reguläres Element *n* [im Sinne von Neumann]	élément *m* régulier [au sens de von Neumann]	регулярный элемент [в смысле Неймана]
R 542	**regular embedding** <e.g. of categories *or* a manifold> <AL, CA, DG>	reguläre Einbettung *f*	plongement *m* régulier	регулярное вложение <AL, DG>; правильн вложение <CA>

No.	English	German	French	Russian
	regular error <ST>	*s.* B 269		
R 543	**regular estimating function, regular estimator** <ST>	reguläre Schätzung (Punktschätzung, Schätzfunktion) *f*	estimateur *m* régulier, fonction *f* estimatrice régulière	регулярная оценка
R 544	**regular extension** <of a field *or* Lie algebra> <AL>	reguläre Erweiterung *f*; reguläre Körpererweiterung *f*	extension *f* régulière	регулярное расширение
R 545	**regular exterior measure** <ME>	reguläres äußeres Maß *n*	mesure *f* extérieure régulière	регулярная внешняя мера
R 546	**regular extremal** <VA>	reguläre Extremale *f*	extrémale *f* régulière	регулярная экстремаль
R 547	**regular factor** <in a graph *or* a regular product of groups> <GP, GR>	regulärer Faktor *m*	facteur *m* régulier	регулярный множитель <в регулярном произведении групп> <GR>; регулярный фактор <графа> <GP>
R 548	**regular fibration** <TO>	regulärer Faserraum *m*	fibré *m* régulier	регулярное расслоение
R 549	**regular field** <AB>	regulärer Körper *m*	corps *m* régulier	регулярное поле
R 550	**regular filtration** <of a module> <AL>	reguläre Filtration *f*	filtration *f* régulière	регулярная фильтрация
R 551	**regular fixed point** <AT>	regulärer Fixpunkt *m*	point *m* fixe régulier	регулярная неподвижная точка
R 552	**regular form** <AL>	reguläre Form *f*, einfach transitive reguläre Darstellungsform *f*	groupe *m* régulier (normal, Ω), forme *f* régulière <d'un groupe>, groupe transitif régulier <de permutations de *r* symboles>	
R 553	**regular form** <DG>	reguläre Form *f*	forme *f* régulière	регулярная форма
R 554	**regular function** <AN>	reguläre Funktion *f*	fonction *f* régulière	регулярная функция
	regular function <FT>	*s.* H 405		
R 555	**regular function element** <FT>	reguläres Funktionselement *n*	élément *m* de fonction régulier	регулярный элемент функции
R 556	**regular generation** <of groups> <GR>	reguläre Erzeugung *f*	génération *f* régulière	правильная порождаемость
R 557	**regular graph of degree *n*,** homogeneous graph of degree *n* <GP>	regulärer Graph *m* vom Grad *n*, *n*-fach regulärer Graph, *n*-regulärer Graph	graphe *m* régulier (homogène) de degré *n*	однородный граф степени *n*, *n*-однородный граф, регулярный граф степени *n*
R 558	**regular graph of degree 0** <GP>	entarteter Graph *m*	graphe *m* régulier de degré 0	вырожденный граф, регулярный граф степени 0
	regular graph of degree 3 <GP>	*s.* C 2729		
	regular graph with the valence 3 at each vertex <GP>	*s.* C 2729		
R 559	**regular hexahedron,** cube, hexahedron <EG>	regelmäßiges Sechsflach (Hexaeder) *n*, Würfel *m*, Hexaeder, Kubus *m*	hexaèdre *m* régulier, cube *m*, hexaèdre	правильный гексаэдр, куб, гексаэдр, правильный шестигранник
R 560	**regular homomorphism** <of an algebraic group> <AG>	regulärer (algebraischer, rationaler) Homomorphismus *m*, Homomorphismus	homomorphisme *m* régulier	регулярный гомоморфизм
R 561	**regular homotopy class** <TO>	reguläre Homotopieklasse *f*	classe *f* d'homotopie régulière	регулярный гомотопический класс
R 562	**regular icosahedron,** icosahedron <EG>	regelmäßiges Zwanzigflach (Ikosaeder) *n*, Ikosaeder	icosaèdre *m* régulier, icosaèdre	правильный икосаэдр, икосаэдр, правильный двадцатигранник
R 563	**regular ideal,** modular ideal, distinguished ideal <AL>	reguläres (modulares) Ideal *n*	idéal *m* régulier	регулярный (модулярный, отмеченный) идеал
R 564	**regular ideal** <as the intersection of mutually prime irreducible ideals> <AL>	reguläres Ideal *n*	idéal *m* régulier	регулярный идеал
R 565	**Regular ideal,** von Neumann['s] regular ideal <AL>	reguläres Ideal *n* [im Sinne von von Neumann]	idéal *m* régulier [au sens de von Neumann]	регулярный идеал [в смысле фон Неймана]
R 566	**regular initial number** <SE>	reguläre Anfangszahl *f*	nombre *m* initial régulier	регулярное начальное число
R 567	**regular integral,** regular solution <DE>	reguläres Integral *n*, reguläre Lösung *f*	intégrale (solution) *f* régulière	регулярный интеграл, регулярное решение
R 568	**regular integral curve** <DE>	reguläre Integralkurve *f*	courbe *f* intégrale régulière	регулярная интегральная кривая
R 569	**regularity,** regularity in the sense of von Neumann, von Neumann['s] regularity <of a semigroup> <AL>	Regularität *f* [im Sinne von von Neumann]	régularité *f* [au sens de von Neumann]	регулярность [в смысле фон Неймана]
R 570	**regularity** <GE, TO>	Regularität *f*	régularité *f*	регулярность <GE, TO>; правильность <GE>
R 571	**regularity axiom,** T_3-separation axiom <TO>	drittes (Vietorissches) Trennungsaxiom *n*	axiome *m* de Vietoris, axiome T_3 (de régularité)	аксиома Виеториса, аксиома (O_{III}), аксиома (T_3), аксиома T_3, аксиома регулярности
	regularity axiom <SE>	*s.* A 1291		
R 572	**regularity condition** <FT, TO>	Regularitätsbedingung *f*	condition *f* de régularité	условие регулярности
	regularity in the sense of von Neumann <AL>	*s.* R 569		
R 573	**regularity on the left,** left regularity, left cancellability <of an element> <AL>	Linkskürzbarkeit *f*, Linksregularität *f*	simplifiabilité *f* à gauche, régularité *f* à gauche	сократимость слева
R 574	**regularity on the right,** right regularity, right cancellability <of an element> <AL>	Rechtskürzbarkeit *f*, Rechtsregularität *f*	simplifiabilité *f* à droite, régularité *f* à droite	сократимость справа

No.	English	German	French	Russian
R 575	**regularizable problem** <DE>	regularisierbares Problem *n*	problème *m* régularisable	регуляризуемая задача
R 576	**regularization** <*e.g.:* of a distribution> <AN, DE>	Regularisation *f*, Regularisierung *f*	régularisation *f*	регуляризация
R 577	**regularized function** <FA>	Regularisierte *f*, regularisierte Funktion *f*	fonction *f* régularisée	регуляризованная функция
R 578	**regularizing kernel** <DE, FA>	regularisierender Kern *m*	noyau *m* régularisant	регуляризующее ядро
R 579	**regularizing operator** <DE>	regularisierender Operator *m*	opérateur *m* régularisant (de régularisation)	регуляризующий (исправляющий) оператор
R 580	**regular kernel** <IE>	regulärer Kern *m*	noyau *m* régulier	регулярное ядро
R 581	**regular left ideal,** modular left ideal, left modular ideal <AL>	reguläres (modulares) Linksideal *n*	idéal *m* à gauche régulier	регулярный (модулярный) левый идеал
R 582	**regular line element** <of a first-order differential equation> <DE>	reguläres Linienelement *n*	élément *m* linéaire régulier	регулярный линейный элемент
R 583	**regular local ring** <AL>	regulärer Stellenring (lokaler Ring) *m*	anneau *m* local régulier	регулярное локальное кольцо
R 584	**regularly branched Riemann surface,** regularly ramified Riemann surface <FT>	regulär verzweigte Riemannsche Fläche *f*	surface *f* riemannienne régulièrement ramifiée	регулярно разветвленная риманова поверхность
R 585	**regularly connected complex** <AT>	regulär zusammenhängender Komplex *m*	complexe *m* régulièrement connexe	регулярно связный комплекс
R 586	**regularly convergent series** <of functions> <SS>	regulär konvergente Funktionenreihe *f*	série *f* <de fonctions> régulièrement convergente	регулярно сходящийся ряд функций
R 587	**regularly convex function** <RF>	regulär konvexe Funktion *f*	fonction *f* régulièrement convexe	регулярно выпуклая функция
R 588	**regularly integrally closed ring** <AL>	regulär ganzabgeschlossener Ring *m*	anneau *m* régulièrement intégralement clos	регулярно целозамкнутое кольцо
R 589	**regularly ramified covering surface** <FT>	regulär verzweigte Überlagerungsfläche *f*	surface *f* de recouvrement régulièrement ramifiée	регулярно разветвленная накрывающая поверхность, регулярно разветвленная поверхность наложения
	regularly ramified Riemann surface <FT>	*s.* R 584		
R 590	**regular map,** regular mapping <AT, DG>	reguläre Abbildung *f*	application (représentation) *f* regulière	регулярное отображение
	regular map of degree 3 <GP>	*s.* T 985		
	regular mapping <AT, DG>	*s.* R 590		
R 591	**regular Markov chain,** regular chain <SP>	reguläre [Markovsche] Kette *f*	chaîne *f* [markovienne] régulière	регулярная цепь [Маркова]
R 592	**regular matrix** <over a group with zero> <AL>	reguläre Matrix *f* <über einer Gruppe mit Null>	matrice *f* régulière <sur un groupe avec zéro>	регулярная матрица <над группой с нулем>
	regular matrix <LI>	*s.* P 474		
	regular matrix <MD>	*s.* N 485		
R 593	**regular matroid** <GP>	reguläres Matroid *n*	matroïde *m* régulier	регулярный матроид
R 594	**regular measure** <ME>	reguläres Maß *n*	mesure *f* régulière	регулярная мера
R 595	**regular method,** permanent (consistent) method [of summation], regular method of summation <LI>	permanentes (reguläres, konsistentes) Summierungsverfahren *n*	méthode *f* régulière (consistante, permanente) de sommation	регулярный метод суммирования
R 596	**regular method of limitation,** permanent (consistent) method of limitation <LI>	permanentes (reguläres, konsistentes) Limitierungsverfahren (*V*-Verfahren) *n*	méthode *f* régulière (consistante, permanente) de limitation	регулярный метод образования обобщенного предела
	regular method of summation <LI>	*s.* R 595		
	regular multiplet of elements <SE>	*s.* T 1061		
R 597	**regular multiplicative system,** idempotent subset <AL>	nullteilerfreies multiplikativ abgeschlossenes System *n*, multiplikativ abgeschlossenes System ohne Nullteiler	partie *f* multiplicative sans diviseurs de zéro	мультипликативно замкнутая система без делителей нуля
R 598	**regular neighbourhood** <TO>	reguläre Umgebung *f*	voisinage *m* régulier	регулярная окрестность
R 599	**regular norm** <in an algebra> <AL>	reguläre Norm *f*	norme *f* régulière	регулярная норма
R 600	**regular number field** <NT>	regulärer Zahlkörper *m*	corps *m* arithmétique régulier	регулярное числовое поле
R 601	**regular octahedron,** octahedron <EG>	regelmäßiges Achtflach *n*, regelmäßiges (reguläres) Oktaeder *n*, Oktaeder	octaèdre *m* régulier, octaèdre	правильный октаэдр, октаэдр, правильный восьмигранник
R 602	**regular open set,** open domain <TO>	reguläre offene Menge *f*, regulär-offene (regulär offene) Menge, offener Bereich *m*	ensemble *m* ouvert régulier, ouvert *m* régulier, domaine ouvert	регулярное открытое множество, открытая область
R 603	**regular operation** <GR>	reguläre Operation *f*	opération *f* régulière	правильная операция
R 604	**regular operator** <FA>	regulärer Operator *m*	opérateur *m* régulier	регулярный оператор
R 605	**regular ordinal** <SE>	reguläre Ordnungszahl *f*	ordinal *m* régulier	регулярное ординальное (порядковое) число
R 606	**regular parametric representation** <of class *r*> <of a surface> <DG>	reguläre Parameterdarstellung *f* <der Klasse *r*>	représentation *f* paramétrique régulière <de classe *r*>	регулярное параметрическое представление <класса *r*>
R 607	**regular permutation** <AL>	reguläre Substitution (Permutation) *f*	substitution *f* régulière	регулярная перестановка (подстановка)
R 608	**regular permutation group** <GR>	reguläre Permutationsgruppe *f* (Untergruppe *f* der symmetrischen Gruppe)	groupe *m* de permutations régulier	регулярная группа подстановок, регулярная подгруппа симметрической группы

R 609	**regular point** <of a system of linear equations> <AL>	regulärer Punkt *m* <eines linearen Gleichungssystems>	point *m* régulier <d'un système d'équations linéaires>	регулярная точка <системы линейных уравнений с переменными коэффициентами>
R 610	**regular point** <of a polyhedron> <AT>	regulärer Punkt *m*	point *m* régulier	правильная точка
R 611	**regular point** <of a surface> <DG>	regulärer Punkt (Flächenpunkt) *m*	point *m* régulier (ordinaire)	обыкновенная (правильная) точка
R 612	**regular point** <of a curve> <DG, TO>	regulärer Punkt (Kurvenpunkt) *m*	point *m* régulier	регулярная точка
R 613	**regular point** <of a differential equation *or* an analytic function>; ordinary point <of a differential equation in the complex domain> <DE>	regulärer Punkt *m*, reguläre Stelle *f*	point *m* régulier	регулярная точка
	regular point <AG>	*s.* S 936		
	regular point <FA>	*s.* R 646		
R 614	**regular point of the boundary** <of a convex body> <CS>	regulärer Randpunkt *m*; $(n-1)$-Kantenpunkt *m* <im R^n>	point *m* [de la frontière] de classe 1	обыкновенная точка границы
	regular point set <TO>	*s.* L 954		
R 615	**regular point system,** regular system of points <GE>	regelmäßiges (reguläres) Punkt[e]system *n*	système *m* régulier de points	правильная (регулярная) система точек
R 616	**regular polygon** <EG>	regelmäßiges Vieleck (Polygon) *n*, reguläres Polygon (Vieleck)	polygone *m* régulier	правильный многоугольник (полигон)
R 617	**regular polyhedron,** Platonic body, Platonic regular body, Platonic solid, platonic [solid] <EG>	regelmäßiges Vielflach (Polyeder) *n*, reguläres Vielflach (Polyeder), Platonischer (platonischer) Körper *m*, Platonischer regulärer Körper, Pythagoräischer Körper	polyèdre *m* régulier, corps platonique régulier, corps platonique (polyédrique régulier), solide *m* (polyèdre) platonique, corps pythagoricien, corps (solide, polyèdre) platonicien	правильный многогранник, тело Платона, платонов (правильный выпуклый) многогранник, платоново [регулярное] тело, правильный полиэдр, правильное тело
R 618	**regular prime** <AB, AL>	reguläre Primzahl *f*	nombre *m* premier régulier	регулярное простое число
R 619	**regular product** <of groups *or* algebraic systems> <GR, UA>	reguläres Produkt *n*	produit *m* régulier	регулярное произведение
R 620	**regular pyramid** <EG>	regelmäßige (reguläre) Pyramide *f*	pyramide *f* régulière	правильная пирамида
	regular ramification point <FT>	*s.* O 382		
R 621	**regular rational mapping (transformation),** holomorphic rational mapping (transformation) <AG>	reguläre (holomorphe) rationale Abbildung (Transformation) *f*	application *f* rationnelle régulière (holomorphe)	регулярное (голоморфное) рациональное отображение (преобразование)
	regular region <GE, PO>	*s.* R 536		
	regular representation <AL>	*s.* 1. A 306; 2. R 1248		
R 622	**regular right ideal,** modular right ideal, right modular ideal <AL>	reguläres (modulares) Rechtsideal *n*	idéal *m* à droite régulier	регулярный (модулярный) правый идеал
R 623	**regular ring** <AL>	regulärer Ring *m*	anneau *m* régulier	регулярное кольцо
R 624	**Regular ring,** von Neumann['s] regular ring, von Neumann['s] ring, ring regular in the sense of von Neumann <AL>	regulärer Ring *m* [im Sinne von von Neumann]	anneau *m* régulier, anneau régulier au sens de von Neumann, anneau absolument plat	регулярное кольцо [в смысле фон Неймана]
R 625	**π-regular ring** <AL>	pseudoregulärer Ring *m*	anneau *m* pseudo-régulier	псевдорегулярное кольцо
R 626	**regular semigroup** <AL>	reguläre Halbgruppe *f*	demi-groupe *m* inversif	регулярная полугруппа
	regular sequence <SS, TO>	*s.* 1. C 268; 2. C 2362		
R 627	**regular set** <SE>	reguläre Menge *f*	ensemble *m* régulier	правильное (регулярное) множество
R 628	**regular set function** <ME>	reguläre Mengenfunktion *f* <in bezug auf ein Maß>	fonction *f* d'ensemble régulière	регулярная функция множества
R 629	**regular sheaf** <*e.g.:* of rings> <AL, TO>	reguläre Garbe *f* <*z. B.:* von Ringen>	faisceau *m* <*par exemple:* d'anneaux> régulier	регулярный пучок <*например:* колец>
	regular singularity <DE>	*s.* R 630		
	regular singularity <FT>	*s.* 1. O 382; 2. R 631		
R 630	**regular singular point,** regular (inessential) singularity, point of determination (determinacy) <of a homogeneous linear differential equation> <DE>	Stelle *f* der Bestimmtheit, singuläre Stelle der Bestimmtheit, Bestimmtheitsstelle *f*, außerwesentlich (außerwesentliche, schwach) singuläre Stelle, außerwesentliche (schwache) Singularität *f*, reguläre singuläre Stelle, reguläre Singularität	point *m* singulier régulier (non essentiel), singularité *f* régulière (non essentielle), point *m* de détermination	несущественная (несущественно, регулярная, простая) особая точка, особая точка определенности, точка определенности
R 631	**regular singular point,** regular singularity, inessential singular point, inessential singularity <of an analytic function, common name of removable singularity, pole, and algebraic branch point> <FT>	außerwesentlich (außerwesentliche) singuläre Stelle *f*, reguläre singuläre Stelle, außerwesentliche (reguläre) Singularität *f*	point *m* singulier régulier, singularité *f* régulière, point singulier non essentiel, singularité non essentielle	регулярная особая точка, регулярная особенность, несущественная (несущественно) особая точка, несущественная особенность
	regular solution <DE>	*s.* R 567		

No.	English	German	French	Russian
R 632	**regular space** <in theory of curves> <TO>	regulärer Raum *m*	espace *m* régulier	регулярное пространство
	regular space <FA, TO>	*s.* R 473		
	regular space <TO>	*s.* R 637		
	regular space having a countable basis <TO>	*s.* R 638		
R 633	**regular star polygon** <EG>	regelmäßiges Sternvieleck (Sternpolygon) *n*	polygone *m* régulier étoilé, polygone étoilé régulier	правильный звездчатый (самопересекающийся) многоугольник, правильный звездный многоугольник
	regular star polyhedron <EG>	*s.* P 720		
R 634	**regular stationary process** <SP>	regulärer [stationärer] Prozeß *m*, rein indeterministischer [stationärer] Prozeß	processus *m* stationnaire régulier, processus régulier	регулярный стационарный процесс, регулярный процесс
	σ-regular subalgebra <AL>	*s.* S 830		
	regular subdivision <AT>	*s.* 1. B 78; 2. B 79		
R 635	**regular surface** <GE, PO>	reguläre Fläche *f* <GE>; reguläre Oberfläche *f* <PO>	surface *f* régulière	регулярная поверхность
	regular surface <AG>	*s.* R 511		
	regular system <AL>	*s.* C 2650		
	regular system of points <GE>	*s.* R 615		
R 636	**regular tetrahedron,** tetrahedron <EG>	regelmäßiges Vierflach (Tetraeder) *n*, Tetraeder	tétraèdre *m* régulier, tétraèdre	правильный тетраэдр, тетраэдр, правильный четырехгранник
R 637	**regular topological space,** regular space, T_3-space, T_3 topological space <TO>	regulärer [topologischer] Raum *m*, T_3-Raum *m*	espace *m* régulier (topologique régulier, T_3)	регулярное (правильное) пространство, T_3-пространство
R 638	**regular topological space having a countable basis,** regular space having a countable basis, second-countable regular [topological] space <TO>	separabler (separabler topologischer) Raum *m* <nach Menger>	espace *m* régulier à base dénombrable	регулярное пространство, имеющее счетный базис
R 639	**regular topological space whose homeomorphic image in any regular space is closed,** regular-closed space <TO>	r-abgeschlossener Raum *m*	espace *m* régulier dont l'image homéomorphe dans un espace régulier est fermé	*R*-замкнутое пространство <регуляное пространство *E* такое, что для любого его гомеоморфизма *f* в регулярное пространство множество *f* (*E*) замкнуто>
R 640	**regular topology** <TO>	reguläre Topologie *f*	topologie *f* régulière	регулярная топология
R 641	**regular trace** <of an element of an algebra> <AL>	reguläre Spur *f*	trace *f* régulière	регулярный след
R 642	**regular transformation** <AN>	reguläre Transformation *f*	transformation *f* régulière	невырожденное (неособенное, регулярное) преобразование
R 643	**regular transformation,** normal (permanent) transformation <in Toeplitz's limit theorem> <LI>	reguläre (permanente) Transformation *f*	transformation *f* régulière (permanente)	регулярное (перманентное) преобразование
	regular triangle <EG>	*s.* E 391		
R 644	**regular union** <in categories> <CA>	reguläre Vereinigung *f*	union *f* régulière	правильное объединение
R 645	**regular value** <of a differentiable map *or* an endomorphism of a vector space> <DG, FA>	regulärer Wert *m*	valeur *f* régulière	регулярное значение
R 646	**regular value,** regular point <as an element of the resolvent set> <FA>	regulärer Punkt *m*, Vollwert *m*, regulärer Wert *m*	valeur *f* régulière (résolvante)	правильная точка, правильное (резольвентное) значение
R 647	**regular variational problem** <VA>	reguläres Variationsproblem *n*	problème *m* variationnel régulier	регулярная вариационная задача
R 648	**regular variety** <DG>	reguläre (gewöhnliche) Mannigfaltigkeit *f*	variété *f* régulière	регулярное многообразие
R 649	**regular variety** <of primitive classes> <UA>	reguläre Mannigfaltigkeit (Varietät) *f*	variété *f* régulière	регулярное многообразие
R 650	**regular web** <GE>	reguläres Gewebe (3-Netz) *n*	3-tissu *m* régulier	регулярная 3-сеть
R 651	**regulated function** <RF>	Regelfunktion *f*; Funktion *f*, die höchstens Unstetigkeiten erster Art hat	fonction *f* réglée, fonction n'ayant que des discontinuités de première espèce	линейчатая функция
R 652	**regulated mapping** <RF>	Regelabbildung *f*	application *f* réglée	линейчатое отображение
R 653	**regulator** <AL, NT>	Regulator *m*	régulateur *m*	регулятор
R 654	**regulus,** generation <AY>	Regelschar *f*, Regulus *m*	série *f* réglée, famille *f* linéaire de droites à un paramètre	однопараметрическое линейное семейство прямых
R 655	**regulus** <of a quadric> <AY>	Regulus *m*, Regelschar *f*, Regelschar zweiter (2.) Ordnung	demi-quadrique *f*, système *m* de génératrices (génératrices rectilignes)	полуквадрика
R 656	**Reidemeister['s] figure** <AL, GE>	Reidemeister-Figur *f*	figure *f* de Reidemeister	фигура Рейдемейстера
R 657	**Reidemeister['s] method** <GR>	Reidemeister-Verfahren *n*	méthode *f* de Reidemeister	метод Рейдемейстера
R 658	**Reid['s] inequality** <FA>	Reidsche Ungleichung *f*	inégalité *f* de Reid	неравенство Рейда
R 659	**Reinhardt['s] domain** <FT>	Reinhardtscher Körper (Kreisbereich) *m*	domaine *m* multicirculaire (de Reinhardt, cerclé de Reinhardt)	кратнокруговая область, *n*-круговая область
	reject / to <AR, NU>	*s.* D 637		

	English	German	French	Russian
R 660	**rejection** <of a hypothesis> <ST>	Ablehnung *f*, Abweisung *f*, Rückweisung *f*, Zurückweisung *f*, Verwerfen *n*	rejet *m*	непринятие, отказ, отбрасывание, браковка
	rejection <LO>	*s.* S 2439		
R 661	**rejection boundary (limit),** significance point, critical value <ST>	Ablehnungsschwelle *f*, Ablehnungsgrenze *f*, Signifikanzgrenze *f*, Signifikanzschwelle *f*, Signifikanzpunkt *m*, kritischer Wert *m*	limite *f* de rejet (signification), valeur *f* critique	критическая (браковочная) граница, критическое значение
R 662	**rejection line** <ST>	Ablehnungslinie *f*	ligne *f* de rejet, droite *f* limite de rejet	критическая линия, браковочная линия
R 663	**rejection number** <ST>	Ablehnungszahl *f*, Rückweisezahl *f*	nombre *m* de rejet	критическое количество, браковочное число
R 664	**rejection probability** <ST>	Ablehnungswahrscheinlichkeit *f*	probabilité *f* de rejet	вероятность отказа
	rejection region <ST>	*s.* C 2681		
R 665	**rejection zone** <ST>	Ablehnungszone *f*	zone *f* de rejet	критическая зона, критическая область
	related division <PJ>	*s.* H 452		
	related homogeneous equation <DE>	*s.* A 1070		
	related homogeneous system <DE>	*s.* A 1072		
R 666	**related notion** <GN>	verwandter Begriff *m*	concept *m* apparenté	близкое (родственное) понятие
R 667	**related ring** <AL>	verwandter Ring *m*	anneau *m* apparenté	родственное кольцо
R 668	**relation** <in a group> <GR>	Relation *f* <in einer Gruppe>	relation *f* <dans un groupe>	соотношение <в группе>
R 669	**relation** <on a set> <*e.g.:* a relation holds between a pair of things, the things stand in a relation, the things bear a relation one to another; *x* is in the relation *R* to *y*, *R* relates *y* to *x*, *x* bears the relation *R* to *y*, *x*, *y* are *R*-related, the relation *R* holds between the pair (*x*, *y*), *x* and *y* stand in the relation *R*, *x* and *y* bear the relation *R* one to another> <SE, UA>	Relation *f* <in einer Menge, über einer Menge, zwischen den Elementen einer Menge> <*z. B.:* eine Relation besteht zwischen einem Paar von Dingen; *x* steht zu *y* in der Relation *R*, *y* ist vermöge *R* *x* zugeordnet, *y* entspricht *x* vermöge *R*, *x* steht in der Relation *R* zu *y*>	relation *f* <définie dans un ensemble, entre éléments d'un ensemble, dans un ensemble> <*par exemple:* une relation est vérifiée par un couple, un couple vérifie une relation; *y* corresponds à *x* par la relation *R*, le couple (*x*, *y*) vérifie la relation *R*, la relation *R* est vérifiée par le couple (*x*, *y*), *x* et *y* vérifient la relation *R*>	отношение <на множестве> <*например:* пара находится в отношение; *x* находится в отношение *R* с *y*>
	relation <GE>	*s.* M 97		
	relation <LO>	*s.* M 891		
	∈-relation <SE>	*s.* N 418		
	relational algebra <AL>	*s.* R 671		
	relational algebra of the same type <UA>	*s.* S 881		
R 670	**relational Cartesian product,** Cartesian product <of relations> <SE>	kartesisches Produkt *n* <von Relationen>	produit *m* direct <de relations>	декартово произведение <отношений>
	relational composite <SE, UA>	*s.* R 767		
R 671	**relation algebra,** relational algebra, algebra of relations <on a set> <AL>	Relationenalgebra *f* <auf einer Menge>	algèbre *f* des relations <sur un ensemble>	алгебра отношений <на множестве>
R 672	**relational proposition** <LO>	relationale Aussage *f*	proposition *f* relationnelle (de relation)	суждение отношения
R 673	**relational structure (system),** model <UA>	Relationalsystem *n*, Gebilde *n*, Relationengebilde *n*, Relativ *n*, Modell *n*	structure *f* relationnelle, relatif *m*, système *m* de relations	реляционная система, модель
R 674	**relational symbol,** relation symbol <LO, SE>	Relationszeichen *n*, Relationensymbol *n*	signe (symbole) *m* relationnel	знак отношений, реляционный знак, символ [для] отношения
	relation between the roots and coefficients of an algebraic equation <AL>	*s.* V 180		
R 675	**relation greater than,** greater than relation <SE>	„größer"-Relation *f*, „größer"-Beziehung *f*, >-Beziehung *f*	relation *f* « plus grand que », relation >	отношение «больше»
R 676	**relation less than,** less than relation <SE>	„kleiner"-Relation *f*, „kleiner"-Beziehung *f*, <-Beziehung *f*	relation *f* « plus petit que », relation *f* <	отношение «меньше чем», отношение <
R 677	**relation limited to** <the set> ***X***, confinement of the relation to <the set> *X* <SE>	Einschränkung *f* der Relation auf <die Menge> *X*, auf <die Menge> *X* eingeschränkte Relation *f*	restriction *f* de la relation à <la partie> *X*	ограничение (сужение) отношения на <множество> *X*
R 678	**relation of between[-ness],** betweenness relation, betweenness, between relation, intermediacy <GE, SE>	„zwischen"-Beziehung *f*, „zwischen"-Relation *f*, Zwischenrelation *f*, Beziehung (Relation) *f* „zwischen"	relation *f* « entre », relation [ternaire] d'intermédiaire, relation ternaire d'intermédiarité	отношение «лежит между», отношение (соотношение) «между», промежуточность, отношение промежуточности
R 679	**relation of comparison,** comparison relation <RF>	Vergleichungsrelation *f*, Vergleichsrelation *f*	relation *f* de comparaison	отношение сравнения
	relation of completeness <FA>	*s.* P 173		
	relation of completeness <SS>	*s.* P 175		
R 680	**relation of concatenation** <LO>	Verkettungsrelation *f*	relation *f* de concaténation	отношение сочленения

No.	English	German	French	Russian
R 681	**relation of disjointness** <of classes> <LO>	Relation *f* der Disjunktheit <von Klassen>	relation *f* de séparation (disjonction) <entre classes>	отношение непересекаемости <классов>
	relation of equality <SE>	*s.* E 326		
R 682	**relation of equipollence** <of vectors> <VT>	Relation *f* der Äquipollenz	relation *f* d'équipollence	отношение эквиполлентности
R 683	**relation of following,** successor relation <NT, SE>	Nachfolgerbeziehung *f*, Nachfolgebeziehung *f*, Nachfolgerelation *f*	relation *f* du suivant	отношение [непосредственного] следования, отношение «следования за»
	relation of identity <SE>	*s.* E 326		
R 684	**relation of implication** <LO>	Folgebeziehung *f*	relation *f* d'implication	отношение следования
	relation of inclusion <SE>	*s.* I 246		
	relation of order <SE>	*s.* O 359		
	relation of rank *n* <CA, SE>	*s.* N 17		
	relation of set-inclusion <SE>	*s.* I 246		
R 685	**relation of subordination** <AL, TO>	Unterordnungsrelation *f*	relation *f* de subordination	отношение подчиненности
	relation of subset <SE>	*s.* I 246		
	relation's domain <SE>	*s.* D 854		
R 686	**relations of Maxwell-Todd,** Maxwell-Todd relations <AG>	Maxwell-Toddsche Relationen *fpl*	relations *fpl* de Maxwell-Todd	соотношения Максвелла-Тодда
	relation symbol <LO>	*s.* P 1192		
	relation symbol <LO, SE>	*s.* R 674		
R 687	**relation[-] type** <SE>	Relationstypus *m*	type *m* relationnel	тип отношений, реляционный тип
R 688	**relative Alexander presheaf with coefficients *G*** <AT>	relative Alexandersche Prägarbe *f* mit Koeffizienten in *G*	préfaisceau *m* relatif d'Alexander à coefficients dans *G*	относительный предпучок Александера с коэффициентами в *G*
R 689	**relative boundary,** boundary mod. $\mathfrak{U}$ <AT>	Relativrand *m* bis auf $\mathfrak{U}$, Rand *m* mod $\mathfrak{U}$	bord *m* modulo $\mathfrak{U}$	граница по модулю $\mathfrak{U}$
R 690	**relative bundle** <AT>	relatives Bündel *n*	fibré *m* relatif	относительное косое произведение
R 691	**relative category,** formal category <CA>	relative Kategorie *f*	catégorie *f* relative	относительная (формальная) категория
R 692	**relative cell (class) frequency** <ST>	relative Klassenhäufigkeit *f*	fréquence *f* de classe relative	относительная частота в классе
R 693	**relative class number** <AB>	Relativklassenzahl *f*	nombre *m* de classes relatif	относительное число классов
R 694	**relative closure** <of a set> <TO>	relative abgeschlossene Hülle *f*	fermeture *f* relative <à>	относительное замыкание, замыкание относительно . . .
R 695	**relative cohomology group** <AT, HA>	relative Kohomologiegruppe *f*	groupe *m* de cohomologie relative	группа относительных когомологий, относительная группа когомологий
R 696	**relative complement** <LA>	relatives Komplement *n*, Relativkomplement *n*	complément *m* relatif	относительное дополнение, относительный комплемент
R 697	**relative complement,** complement <of a set in a set> <SE>	Relativkomplement *n*, Komplement *n* <in einer Obermenge>	complément relatif	относительное дополнение, относительный комплемент
	relative complement <SE>	*s.* D 427		
R 698	**relative curvature** <of a Riemannian manifold> <DG>	relative Krümmung *f*, Relativkrümmung *f*	courbure *f* relative	относительная кривизна
R 699	**relative curvature vector** <of a curve *or* embedded Riemannian manifold> <DG>	relativer Krümmungsvektor *m*, Relativkrümmungsvektor *m*	vecteur *m* de courbure relative	вектор относительной кривизны
R 700	**relative cycle** <mod. $\mathfrak{U}$> <AT>	Relativzyklus *m*, relativer Zyklus *m* <bis auf $\mathfrak{U}$>, Zyklus mod $\mathfrak{U}$	cycle *m* relatif <mod. $\mathfrak{U}$>	относительный цикл <по модулю $\mathfrak{U}$>
R 701	**relative defect** <Milloux> <of a meromorphic function> <FT>	relativer Defekt *m*	défaut *m* relatif	относительный дефект
R 702	**relative degree** <of a prime ideal, prime divisor, *or* valuation> <AL>	Relativgrad *m*	degré *m* relatif	относительная степень
R 703	**relative different** <of a field> <AL>	Relativdifferente *f*, Differente *f*, Verzweigungsideal *n*	différente *f* relative	относительная дифферента
R 704	**relative dimension** <*also* of a von Neumann algebra> <AL, FA>	relative Dimension *f* <AL, FA>; Relativdimension *f* <AL>	dimension *f* relative	относительная размерность
R 705	**relative discriminant** <AL>	Relativdiskriminante *f*	discriminant *m* relatif	относительный дискриминант
R 706	**relative distance** <of supporting planes> <GE>	Relativabstand *m*	distance *f* relative	относительное расстояние
	relative efficiency <ST>	*s.* E 47		
R 707	**relative error** <ER>	relativer Fehler *m*	erreur *f* relative	относительная ошибка
	relative error <ER>	*s. a.* P 400		
	relative extremum <DI>	*s.* L 930		
	relative extremum <DI, PG, VA>	*s.* E 898		
R 708	**relative field** <AL>	Relativkörper *m*	corps *m* relatif (relativement algébrique)	относительное поле

R 709	**relative frequency,** proportional frequency <ST>	relative Häufigkeit *f*	fréquence *f* relative	частость, относительная частота
	relative frequency function <ST>	*s.* P 1534		
R 710	**relative growth** <ST>	relatives Wachstum *n*, Differentialwachstum *n*	croissance *f* relative	относительный рост
R 711	**relative growth rate** <ST>	relative (spezifische) Wachstumsrate *f*	taux *m* de croissance relative	относительная скорость роста
R 712	**relative homology group** <*n*-th> <AT>	relative Homologiegruppe *f* <*n*-te>	groupe *m* d'homologie relatif <*n*-e>	относительная группа гомологий <*n*-я>
R 713	**relative homology theory** <AT>	relative Homologietheorie *f*	théorie *f* d'homologie relative	относительная теория гомологий
R 714	**relative homomorphism over R_0,** R_0-homomorphism <AL>	R_0-Homomorphismus *m*, Relativhomomorphismus (relativer Homomorphismus) *m* über R_0	R_0-homomorphisme *m*, homomorphisme *m* [relatif] sur R_0	R_0-гомоморфизм, [относительный] гомоморфизм над R_0
R 715	**relative homotopy group** <*n*-th> <AT>	relative Homotopiegruppe *f* <*n*-te>	groupe *m* d'homotopie relatif <*n*-e>	относительная гомотопическая группа <*n*-я>
R 716	**relative homotopy set** <AT>	relative Homotopiemenge *f*	ensemble *m* d'homotopie relative	относительное гомотопическое множество
R 717	**relative Hurewicz isomorphism theorem** <AT>	relativer Hurewiczscher Isomorphiesatz *m*	théorème *m* de Hurewicz relatif	относительная теорема Гуревича об изоморфизме, теорема Гуревича для относительных групп
R 718	**relative ideal series** <of an algebra> <AL>	Idealkette *f*		идеальный ряд
R 719	**relative integral base** <AB>	Relativganzheitsbasis *f*	base *f* des entiers relative	относительный целочисленный базис
R 720	**relative intersection multiplicity** <AG>	relative Schnittmultiplizität *f*	multiplicité *f* d'intersection relative	относительная кратность пересечения
R 721	**relative invariant,** density <VT>	relative Invariante *f*, Dichte *f*	invariant *m* relatif, densité *f*	относительный инвариант, плотность
R 722	**relative invariant** <of a group> <GR>	relative Invariante *f*	invariant *m* relatif	относительный инвариант
R 723	**relative inverse,** generalized inverse, inverse, reciprocal element <of an element of semigroup *or* algebra> <AL>	relativ Inverse *n*, relativ inverses Element *n*, verallgemeinerte Inverse	élément *m* inversif	регулярно сопряженный элемент, обобщенно обратный, инверсный (обобщенно обратный) элемент
	relative inverse <FA>	*s.* G 145		
	relative inverse element <AL>	*s.* G 144		
R 724	**relative isomorphism over R_0,** R_0-isomorphism, isomorphism over R_0 <AL>	Relativisomorphismus *m* bezüglich R_0, R_0-Isomorphismus *m*, Isomorphismus *m* über R_0; Relativisomorphismus, der R_0 elementweise festläßt; relativer Isomorphismus über R_0	R_0-isomorphisme *m*, isomorphisme *m* [relatif] sur R_0	R_0-изоморфизм, [относительный] изоморфизм над R_0
R 725	**relatively abelian field** <AL>	relativ abelscher Körper *m*, relativabelscher (relativ-Abelscher) Körper	corps *m* relativement abélien, corps abélien relatif	относительно абелево поле
R 726	**relatively ambiguous Borel set** <SE, TO>	relativ ambige Borel-Menge *f*	ensemble *m* relativement ambigu	относительно двустороннее множество
	relatively atomic lattice <LA>	*s.* A 1194		
R 727	**relatively Borel set** <TO>	relativ Borelsche Menge *f*	ensemble *m* relativement borélien	относительно борелевское множество
R 728	**relatively bounded space** <FA>	relativ beschränkter Raum *m*	espace *m* relativement borné	относительно ограниченное пространство
R 729	**relatively closed set** <TO>	relativ abgeschlossene Menge (Untermenge) *f*	ensemble *m* relativement fermé, partie *f* relativement fermée	относительно замкнутое множество; множество, замкнутое относительно подпространства; относительно замкнутое подмножество
R 730	**relatively compact set** <in a metric space> <TO>	relativ kompakte (folgenkompakte, halbkompakte) Menge *f*	ensemble *m* relativement compact	относительно компактное множество
R 731	**relatively compact set,** conditionally compact set <TO>	relativ kompakte Menge *f*, kompakte Menge in bezug auf den Raum	ensemble *m* relativement compact, partie *f* relativement compacte	относительно компактное множество
R 732	**relatively compact space** <TO>	relativ kompakter Raum *m*	espace *m* relativement compact	относительно компактное пространство
R 733	**relatively complemented lattice,** sectionally complemented lattice <LA>	relativ komplementärer Verband *m*, abschnittskomplementärer Verband	treillis *m* relativement (bien) complémenté	структура с относительными дополнениями
	relatively complemented semi-modular lattice <LA>	*s.* E 677		
R 734	**relatively conjugate complex** <AB>	relativkonjugierter Komplex *m*	complexe *m* conjugué relatif	относительно сопряженный комплекс
R 735	**relatively conjugate ideal** <AL>	relativkonjugiertes Ideal *n*	idéal *m* conjugué relatif	относительно сопряженный идеал
R 736	**relatively conjugate number** <AB>	relativkonjugierte Zahl *f*, Relativkonjugierte *f*	nombre *m* conjugué relatif	относительно сопряженное число
R 737	**relatively consistent** <LO>	relativ widerspruchsfrei	relativement consistant, consistant par rapport à . . .	относительно непротиворечий
R 738	**relatively convergent** <FA>	relativ konvergent	relativement convergent	относительно сходящийся

	English	German	French	Russian
	relatively convergent series <SS>	*s.* C 1818		
R 739	**relatively countably compact subset** <TO>	relativ abzählbar kompakte Teilmenge *f*	partie *f* relativement dénombrablement compacte	относительно счетно-компактное подмножество
R 740	**relatively cyclic field,** cyclic field extension <AL>	relativzyklischer Körper *m*	corps *m* cyclique relatif	относительно циклическое поле
R 741	**relatively dense set** <of real numbers> <AP>	relativ dichte Menge *f* <reeller Zahlen>	ensemble *m* relativement dense <de nombres réels>	относительно плотное множество <вещественных чисел>
R 742	**relatively free algebra** <UA>	relativ freie Algebra *f*, Hall-freie Algebra	algèbre *f* relativement libre	относительно свободная алгебра
R 743	**relatively free group,** reduced free group <of a variety> <AL>	relativ freie Gruppe *f*, Hall-freie Gruppe, reduzierte freie Gruppe	groupe *m* relativement libre, groupe libre réduit	относительно (приведенная, холловски) свободная группа
R 744	**relatively general position** <AT>	relativ allgemeine Lage *f*	position *f* relativement générale	относительно общее положение
R 745	**relatively induced module** <AL>	relativ induzierter Modul *m*	module *m* relativement induit, module induit relativement <au sous-groupe fermé>	относительно индуцированный модуль
R 746	**relatively invariant measure** <on a topological group> <GR, ME>	relativ invariantes Maß *n*	mesure *f* relativement invariante	относительно инвариантная мера
R 747	**relatively minimal model** <AG>	relatives minimales Modell *n*	modèle *m* relativement minimal	относительная (относительно) минимальная модель
R 748	**relatively open set** <TO>	relativ offene Menge *f*	ensemble *m* relativement ouvert	относительно открытое множество; множество, открытое относительно подпространства
R 749	**relatively perfect field extension** <AL>	relativ vollkommene Körpererweiterung *f*	extension *f* relativement parfaite	относительно совершенное расширение поля
R 750	**relatively perfect set** <TO> ⌐<AL>	relativ perfekte Menge *f*	ensemble *m* relativement parfait	множество, совершенное относительно подпространства
	relatively prime element	*s.* P 1294		
R 751	**relatively prime elements,** coprime elements, mutually prime elements, relatively prime quantities, quantities prime to each other <AL>	relativ prime Elemente *npl*, teilerfremde (teilerfreie) Elemente	éléments *mpl* premiers entre eux, éléments sans diviseurs communs, éléments étrangers	взаимно-простые (взаимно простые) элементы
R 752	**relatively prime functions** <AL, FT>	teilerfremde Funktionen *fpl*	fonctions *fpl* sans commun diviseur	взаимно-простые (взаимно простые) функции
	relatively prime ideals <AL>	*s.* C 1174		
	relatively prime numbers <NT>	*s.* C 2447		
R 753	**relatively prime polynomials** <AL>	teilerfremde Polynome *npl*, relativ prime Polynome	polynômes *mpl* relativement premiers, polynômes premiers entre eux	взаимно-простые (взаимно простые) многочлены
	relatively prime quantities <AL>	*s.* R 751		
R 754	**relatively pseudo-complemented lattice** <LA>	relativ pseudokomplementärer Verband *m*	treillis *m* relativement pseudo-complémenté	структура с относительными псевдодополнениями
R 755	**relatively quasicompact set** <TO>	relativ quasikompakte Menge *f*	partie *f* relativement quasi-compacte	относительное квазикомпактное множество
R 756	**relatively regular operator** <FA>	relativ regulärer Operator *m*	opérateur *m* relativement régulier	относительно регулярный оператор
R 757	**relatively strong topology** <FA>	relativ starke Topologie *f*	topologie *f* relativement forte	относительно сильная топология
R 758	**relatively unramified algebraic extension** <AL>	relativ-unverzweigte algebraische Erweiterung *f*	extension *f* algébrique relativement non ramifiée	относительно неразветвленное алгебраическое расширение
	relatively unramified covering surface <FT, TO>	*s.* U 379		
	relative manifold <TO>	*s.* O 141		
	relative maximum <DI>	*s.* L 1005		
	relative maximum <DI, PG, VA>	*s.* M 276		
R 759	**relative maximum error** <NU>	relativer Maximalfehler (Höchstfehler) *m*	erreur *f* maximale relative	относительная максимальная (наибольшая) погрешность
	relative minimal surface <DG>	*s.* A 1097		
	relative minimum <DI>	*s.* L 1006		
	relative minimum <DI, PG, VA> ⌐<SE>	*s.* M 621		
	relative multiplication	*s.* C 1702		
R 760	**relative neighbourhood** <TO>	Relativumgebung *f*, relative Umgebung *f*	voisinage *m* relatif	относительная окрестность
R 761	**relative norm** <AL>	Relativnorm *f*	norme *f* relative	относительная норма
R 762	**relative normal** <DG>	Relativnormale *f*	normale *f* relative	относительная нормаль
R 763	**relative number,** directed (signed, algebraic) number <AR>	relative Zahl *f*, Relativzahl *f*, Zahl mit Vorzeichen, mit Vorzeichen versehene Zahl, // algebraische Zahl	nombre *m* relatif (qualifié, algébrique)	относительное число
R 764	**relative oriented homology group of *K* modulo *L*** <AT>	orientierte relative Homologiegruppe *f*	groupe *m* d'homologie relative orientée	группа ориентированных гомологий комплекса *K* относительно *L*, относительная группа ориентированных гомологий

No.	English	German	French	Russian
R 765	**relative power,** power of a relation <SE>	Potenz *f* einer Relation	puissance *f* d'une relation	степень отношения
R 766	**relative precision** <ST>	relative Präzision *f*	fidélité (précision) *f* relative	относительная точность
R 767	**relative product,** product, composition, relational composite, composite <of binary relations> <SE, UA>	Produkt *n*, Produktrelation *f*, Relationenprodukt *n*, Relationsprodukt *n*, Verkettung *f*, Verkettungsrelation *f*	composée *f*, composé *m*, produit *m*, produit simple (relatif), conjonction *f* relative	произведение, композиция
R 768	**relative rate of growth** <FT, RF>	relative (spezifische) Wachstumsgeschwindigkeit *f*	taux *m* d'accroissement relatif	относительная скорость возрастания
R 769	**relative singular homology group** <of *X* modulo *A*> <AT>	singuläre relative Homologiegruppe *f* <von *X* mod *A*>	groupe *m* d'homologie singulière relative <de *X* modulo *A*>	группа сингулярных гомологий <пространства *X* относительно подпространства *A*>, относительная группа сингулярных гомологий
R 770	**relative singular presheaf with coefficients *G*** <AT>	relative singuläre Prägarbe *f* mit Koeffizienten in *G*	préfaisceau *m* singulier relatif à coefficients dans *G*	относительный сингулярный предпучок с коэффициентами в *G*
R 771	**relative sphere** <DG>	Relativsphäre *f*	sphère *f* relative	относительная сфера
R 772	**relative surface** <DG>	Relativoberfläche *f*	surface *f* relative	относительная поверхность
R 773	**relative tensor** <VT>	relativer Tensor *m*	tenseur *m* relatif	относительный тензор
	relative tensor of unit weight <VT>	*s.* T 140		
	relative tensor of weight unity <VT>	*s.* T 140		
R 774	**relative topology,** subspace topology, relativization of the topology to a subset <TO>	Relativtopologie *f*, Spurtopologie *f*, relative (induzierte) Topologie *f*, Unterraumtopologie *f*	topologie *f* relative (induite)	относительная (индуцированная, индуцированная извне, естественная, наведенная) топология
R 775	**relative trace** <AL, FA>	Relativspur *f*	trace *f* relative	относительный след
R 776	**relative uniform convergence** <AN, TO>	relative gleichmäßige Konvergenz *f* <Moore>	convergence *f* uniforme relative	относительная равномерная сходимость
R 777	**relative uniformity,** relativization <of a uniformity> <TO>	Relativstruktur *f* <einer uniformen Struktur>	relativisation *f* <d'une structure uniforme>	релятивизация <равномерной структуры>
	relative uniformity <TO>	*s.* I 396		
R 778	**relativization** <*e.g.*: of a formula> <LO, TO>	Relativierung *f* <*z. B.*: eines Ausdrucks>	relativisation *f* <*par exemple:* d'une formule>	релятивизация <*например:* формулы>
	relativization <TO>	*s.* R 777		
	relativization of the topology to a subset <TO>	*s.* R 774		
	relativization of the uniformity <TO>	*s.* I 396		
R 779	**relativized formula** <LO>	relativierter Ausdruck *m*	formule *f* relativée	релятивизованная формула
	relaxation <AN, NU>	*s.* R 780		
R 780	**relaxation method [of Southwell],** relaxation <AN, NU>	Relaxationsmethode *f* (Relaxationsverfahren *n*) von (nach) [Gauß-] Southwell, Relaxationsmethode, Relaxationsverfahren, Maschenverfahren *n*, Relaxation *f*, Southwellsche Relaxationsmethode	méthode *f* de relaxation [de Southwell], relaxation *f*	релаксационный метод (прием) [Гаусса-Саусвелла], релаксация Гаусса-Саусвелла
	relettering of variables <LO>	*s.* R 337		
	relevant prime ideal <AL>	*s.* A 1089		
R 781	**reliability** <ST>	Zuverlässigkeit *f*	fiabilité *f*	надежность
R 782	**reliability function,** survival function <ST>	Zuverlässigkeitsfunktion *f*, Überlebensfunktion *f*	fonction *f* de fiabilité (survie)	вероятность безотказной работы [за время *t*], функция надежности (выживания)
R 783	**reliable digit (figure)** <NU>	zuverlässige (gültige) Ziffer *f*		надежная цифра
R 784	**relief,** modular surface <of an analytic function> <FT>	Betragsfläche *f*, Relief *n*	relief *m*	рельеф функции, рельеф, аналитический рельеф (ландшафт), поверхность модуля (модулей)
R 785	**Rellich['s] identity** <DE>	Rellichsche Identität *f*	égalité *f* de Rellich	равенство Реллиха
R 786	**Rellich['s] theorem** <DE>	Rellichscher Satz *m*, Satz von Rellich	théorème *m* de Rellich	теорема Реллиха
R 787	**remainder** <in division> <AL, AR>	Rest *m* <bei der Division>, Divisionsrest *m*	reste *m*, résidu <de la division>	остаток <при делении>
R 788	**remainder,** remainder term <after the *n*-th term, after *n* terms> <of a series> <DI, SS>	Restglied *n*, Rest *m*, Fehler *m* <*n*-ter Ordnung>, // Reihenrest *m*	reste *m*, terme *m* résiduel (complémentaire) <de rang *n*, d'une série arrêtée au *n*-e terme>	остаточный член, остаток <порядка *n*>
R 789	**remainder,** final segment, subset closed above, I closed subset, right segment <of an ordered set> <SE>	Ende *n*, Endstück *n*	section *f* finissante, section finale, partie *f* finissante, segment *m* final	остаток, остаточный сегмент, правый отрезок, концевой сегмент, конечный отрезок
R 790	**remainder,** sequent, residue <of an element *x*, determined by *x*> <of an ordered set> <SE>	Rest *m*, Ende *n* <durch *x* bestimmt>	segment *m* final, section *f* finissante <de *x*>	концевой сегмент, остаток <отвечающий элементу *x*>
	remainder <AL, AR>	*s.* D 424		
	remainder <ER>	*s.* R 886 a		
	remainder <SE>	*s.* R 865		
	remainder <ST>	*s.* D 368		

R 791	**remainder on dividing x by m** <AR, NT>	Rest *m* bei der Division von x durch m	reste *m* de la division de x par m, résidu *m* modulo m de x	вычет числа x по модулю m, остаток от деления x на m
	remainder term <DI, SS>	*s.* R 788		
R 792	**remainder type** <of an order type> <SE>	Resttypus *m*	type-reste *m*	остаточный тип
R 793	**Remak['s] decomposition** <of a group> <GR>	Remaksche Zerlegung *f*	décomposition *f* de Remak	разложение Ремака
R 794	**remarkable curve** <GE>	bemerkenswerte Kurve *f*	courbe *f* remarquable	замечательная кривая
R 795	**remarkable line** <DS>	ausgezeichnete Gerade *f*	droite *f* remarquable	прямая, занимающая особое положение
R 796	**remarkable plane** <DS>	ausgezeichnete Ebene *f*	plan *m* remarquable	плоскость, занимающая особое положение
R 797	**remarkable point** <of the triangle> <EG>	merkwürdiger Punkt *m* <des Dreiecks>	point *m* remarquable <du triangle>	замечательная точка <треугольника>
	remote <TO>	*s.* D 742		
R 798	**removable discontinuity,** point of removable discontinuity <DI>	hebbare Unstetigkeitsstelle *f*	discontinuité *f* (point *m* de discontinuité) non essentielle	устранимый разрыв, точка устранимого разрыва
R 799	**removable discontinuity,** inessential discontinuity <RF>	hebbare Unstetigkeit *f*	discontinuité *f* qui peut être levée, discontinuité non essentielle	устранимый разрыв
R 800	**removable singularity (singular point)** <FT>	hebbare Singularität *f*, hebbare singuläre Stelle *f*	fausse singularité *f*, singularité *f* artificielle	устранимая особенность, устранимая особая точка, правильная точка
R 801	**removal of an irrationality,** rationalization; [process of] rationalizing <AL, AN>	Rationalmachen *n*	faire *m* rationnel, rendre *m* rationnel, rationalisation *f*	уничтожение иррациональности, приведение к рациональному виду, освобождение от иррациональностей, рационализация
R 802	**removal of brackets,** dissolution of brackets <GN>	Auflösung *f* (Auflösen *n*) der Klammern, Klammerauflösung *f*, Ausmultiplizieren *n* der Klammern	suppression *f* (ouvrage *m*) des parenthèses	раскрытие скобок
	removal of unknowns <AL, AN>	*s.* E 152		
R 803	**removed parentheses** <GN>	aufgelöste Klammern *fpl*	parenthèses *fpl* supprimées	раскрытые скобки
	render well-ordered / to <SE>	*s.* W 209		
R 804	**R-endomorphism** <of a module> <AL>	*R*-Endomorphismus *m*	*R*-endomorphisme *m*	*R*-эндоморфизм
R 805	**renewal density,** failure intensity <ST>	Erneuerungsdichte *f*, Ausfallintensität *f*	densité *f* de renouvellement, intensité *f* de défaillances	плотность восстановления, опасность отказа
R 806	**renewal function** <ST>	Erneuerungsfunktion *f*	fonction *f* du renouvellement	функция восстановления
R 807	**renewal theory** <ST>	Erneuerungstheorie *f*	théorie *f* du renouvellement	теория восстановления
R 808	**renormalization** <DG>	Umnormung *f*	renormalisation *f*	перенормализация, перенормирование
R 809	**renumbering** <GN>	Umnumerieren *n*	rénumération *f*, rénumérotage *m*	перенумеровка, перенумерование
	reordering <CT>	*s.* A 983		
R 810	**reorientation** <AT>	Umorientierung *f*	réorientation *f*	переориентирование
R 811	**reoriented complex** <AT>	umorientierter Komplex *m*	complexe *m* réorienté	переориентированный комплекс
R 812	**reparametrization** <ST>	Reparametrisierung *f*	réparamétrisation *f*	репараметризация
R 813	**reparametrization condition** <ST>	Reparametrisierungsbedingung *f*	condition *f* de réparamétrisation	условие репараметризации
	repartition <AB, AL>	*s.* A 264		
R 814	**repayment** <AR>	Tilgung *f*, Rückzahlung *f*	remboursement *m*	погашение
R 815	**repayment formula** <AR>	Tilgungsformel *f*	formule *f* de remboursement	формула погашения
R 816	**repeatability** <ST>	Wiederholbarkeit *f*	répétibilité *f*	повторность, повторяемость
R 817	**repeatability coefficient,** coefficient of repeatability <ST>	Wiederholbarkeitskoeffizient *m*	coefficient *m* de répétibilité	коэффициент повторности
	repeated line <AG, AY>	*s.* D 924		
	repeated root <AL>	*s.* D 940		
	repeated root <AL, AN>	*s.* M 1012		
R 818	**repeated sampling,** sampling on successive occasions <ST>	wiederholte Stichprobennahme *f*	échantillonnage *m* répété [successivement], sondage *m* répété [successivement]	повторный выбор, повторное взятие выборки
	repeated series <SS>	*s.* I 1219		
	repeating decimal <NT>	*s.* P 446		
	"repère mobile" [of Darboux] <DG>	*s.* M 933		
	repetition <LO>	*s.* L 189		
	repetition <ST>	*s.* R 823		
	replaceability <LO>	*s.* S 2205		
R 819	**replacement** <LO, SE>	Ersetzung *f* <in der Logik Oberbegriff für Einsetzung und Umsetzung>	remplacement *m*	замена
R 820	**replacement,** call-back <ST>	Zurücklegen *n*, Rückerstattung *f*	remplacement *m*, remise *f*	возвращение, возврат
	replacement <GN>	*s.* S 2196		
	replacement axiom <LO>	*s.* A 1294		
	replacement theorem <AL, LA>	*s.* E 678		
R 821	**replete class,** replica-complete class <UA>	replikvollständige Klasse *f*		реплично полный класс

No.	English	German	French	Russian
R 822	**replica** <AL, UA>	Replik *f*	réplique *f*	реплика
	replica-complete class <UA>	*s.* R 821		
R 823	**replicated experiment, replication,** repetition <ST>	Wiederholung *f*, Parallelversuch *m*, Parallele *f*, Kontrolle *f*	répétition *f*, expérience *f* répétée	повторение, репликация, повторный эксперимент, повторение опыта
R 824	**representability** <CA, LO>	Darstellbarkeit *f*	représentabilité *f*	представимость
R 825	**representable function** <LO>	darstellbare Funktion *f*	fonction *f* représentable (qui peut être représentée)	представимая функция
R 826	**representable functor** <CA>	darstellbarer Funktor *m*	foncteur *m* représentable	представимый функтор, представительный функтор, представляющийся функтор
R 827	**representation** <of a ring *or* set> <AL>	Darstellung *f*	représentation *f*	представление
R 828	**representation** <of degree *n*> <of a group> <GR, RE>	Darstellung *f*, Gruppendarstellung *f* <*n*-ten Grades>	représentation *f* <du degré *n*>	представление <размерности *n*>
	representation <AN, FA>	*s.* M 96		
	representation <GR>	*s.* H 500		
R 829	**representation as a join of ∪-irreducible (join-irreducible) elements** <LA>	vereinigungsirreduzible (∪-irreduzible) Darstellung (Zerlegung) *f*	représentation (décomposition) *f* ∨-irréductible	∪-представление с ∪-неразложимыми элементами
R 830	**representation as a meet of irreducible elements** <LA>	durchschnittsirreduzible (∩-irreduzible) Zerlegung *f*	représentation *f* ∧-irréductible	∩-представление с ∩-неразложимыми элементами
	representation as an intersection of primary ideals <AL>	*s.* P 1277		
	representation by a product <AN>	*s.* R 832		
R 831	**representation by arrows** <of a binary relation, map> <SE>	graphische Darstellung *f*, Darstellung durch Pfeile	représentation *f* sagittale (graphique, par flèches)	представление с помощью стрелок, стрелочное представление
	representation by a series <AN>	*s.* R 833		
	representation by integral[s] <AN>	*s.* I 655		
	representation by matrices <AL>	*s.* M 208		
R 832	**representation** <of a function> **by product,** representation by a product <AN>	Darstellung *f* <einer Funktion> als (durch ein) Produkt, Darstellung in Form eines Produkts, Produktdarstellung *f*	représentation *f* <d'une fonction> par [un] produit	представление <функции> произведением, представление в виде произведения
R 833	**representation** <of a function> **by series,** representation by a series <AN>	Darstellung *f* <einer Funktion> durch eine Reihe, Darstellung in Form einer Reihe, Reihendarstellung *f*	représentation *f* <d'une fonction> par [une] série	представление <функции> рядом, представление в виде ряда
R 834	**representation definable over *k*** <RE>	über *k* definierbare Darstellung *f*	représentation *f* définissable sur *k*	представление, определимое над *k*
R 835	**representation in a closed form, representation in an analytic form,** expression in an analytic form, expression in a closed form, analytic (closed) form <AN, GN>	geschlossene Darstellung *f*, Darstellung in geschlossener Form, geschlossene Form *f*	représentation (expression) *f* en forme analytique (fermée), forme *f* analytique (fermée)	представление (выражение) в аналитической (замкнутой) форме, аналитическая (замкнутая) форма
R 836	**representation in a number system** <NT>	Zahlendarstellung *f* in einem gewissen Zahlensystem	figuration *f* des nombres, numération *f*	представление <чисел> в некоторой системе счисления
R 837	**representation** <of ...> **in base *n*,** expansion <of ...> in base *n*, expression <for ...> in base *n* <NT>	Zahlendarstellung (Darstellung) *f* <von ...> bezüglich der Basis *n*	décomposition *f* <de ...> dans la base *n*	представление <чисел>, отнесенное к позиционной системе счисления с основанием *n*
R 838	**representation in components** <GN>	Komponentendarstellung *f*	représentation *f* en composantes	представление в компонентах
R 839	**representation in coordinates** <AY>	Koordinatendarstellung *f*, koordinatenmäßige Darstellung *f*	représentation *f* en coordonnées	координатное представление
R 840	**representation in ultimately reduced form** <AL>	Darstellung *f* in ausreduzierter Form	représentation *f* décomposée	представление в полностью приведенном виде
R 841	**representation module,** space of representation, representation space <of a group> <AL, RE>	Darstellungsmodul *m*, Darstellungsraum *m*	module *m* de la représentation, espace *m* de représentation, espace des représentations, espace-support *m*	модуль представления, *G*-модуль, *G*-пространство <группы *G*>
R 842	**representation of degree 1** <of a group> <GR, RE>	Darstellung *f* vom Grad 1, eindimensionale (lineare) Darstellung	représentation *f* de la degré 1	представление размерности 1
R 843	**representation of [surface] terrain, representation of topographical surfaces** <DS>	Geländedarstellung *f*	représentation *f* du terrain, représentation de surfaces topographiques	представление области (топографических поверхностей)
R 844	**representation space,** carrier space <of an algebra> <AL, RE>	Darstellungsraum *m*	espace *m* de représentation	пространство представления, несущее пространство
	representation space <AL, RE>	*s.* R 841		

No.	English	German	French	Russian
R 845	**representation sub-module** <AL>	Teildarstellungsmodul *m*	sous-module *m* de la représentation	подмодуль представления
R 846	**representation theorem** <for a normed space> <FA>	Darstellungssatz *m*	théorème *m* de représentation	теорема представления
	representation theorem <LA>	*s.* S 1819		
	representation theory <RE>	*s.* T 396		
R 847	**representative** <AL, GR, PG>	Repräsentant *m*, Vertreter *m* <AL, GR, PG>; Nebenklassenvertreter *m* <GR>	représentant *m*	представитель
R 848	**representative class** <of subobjects> <CA>	repräsentative Klasse *f*	classe *f* représentative	представительный класс
R 849	**representative cone** <AG>	repräsentativer Kegel *m*	cône *m* représentatif	представительный конус
R 850	**representative domain** <FT>	Repräsentantengebiet *n*	domaine *m* des représentants	область представителей
	representative field <AL>	*s.* F 199		
	representative graph <GP>	*s.* R 856		
R 851	**representative inquiry** <ST>	repräsentative Umfrage *f*	enquête *f* représentative	представительный опрос
R 852	**representative sample** <ST>	repräsentative Stichprobe *f*	échantillon *m* représentatif	представительная (репрезентативная) выборка
R 853	**representative-wise** <AL>	repräsentantenweise	par représentants	попредставительный
R 854	**represent explicitly / to** <GN>	explizit darstellen	rendre explicite	представлять в явном виде
R 855	**representing function** <LO>	darstellende Funktion *f*	fonction *f* représentante	представляющая функция
R 856	**representing graph,** representative graph, line graph <of a hypergraph> <GP>	entsprechender Graph *m*	graphe *m* représentatif	соответствующий граф
R 857	**representing object,** object representing a functor <CA>	darstellendes Objekt *n* <eines Funktors>	objet *m* représentant <un foncteur>, représentant *m* <d'un foncteur>	представляющий объект <функтора>
R 858	**reproducibility** <ST>	Reproduzierbarkeit *f*	reproductibilité *f*	воспроизводимость
R 859	**reproducing kernel** <FA>	reproduzierender Kern *m*	noyau *m* reproduisant	воспроизводящее ядро
R 860	**reproducing property** <FA>	reproduzierende Eigenschaft *f*	propriété *f* reproduisante	воспроизводящее качество (свойство)
	requirement of integrality <GN, PG>	*s.* I 634		
R 861	**ℜ-equivalence** <of a semigroup> <AL>	ℜ-Äquivalenz *f*	ℜ-équivalence *f*	ℜ-эквивалентность
R 862	**R-equivalence class,** abstraction class with respect to the relation *R*, equivalence class modulo *R* <SE>	Äquivalenzklasse *f* modulo (nach) *R*, Restklasse *f* modulo (nach) *R*, Faser *f* modulo (nach) *R*	classe *f* par rapport à *R*, classe modulo *R*, classe d'équivalence par rapport à *R*, classe d'équivalence modulo *R*	класс эквивалентности по модулю *R*
R 863	**ℜ-equivalent elements** <of a semigroup> <AL>	ℜ-äquivalente Elemente *npl*	éléments *mpl* ℜ-équivalents	ℜ-эквивалентные элементы
	res <FT>	*s.* R 887		
R 864	**reservation** <ST>	Reservierung *f*, Reservebildung *f*	réservation *f*	резервирование
R 865	**residual,** remainder <of an ordinal> <SE>	Rest *m* <einer Ordinalzahl>	reste *m* <d'un ordinal>	остаток <порядкового числа>
	residual <ST>	*s.* D 368		
R 866	**residual boundary condition,** dynamic boundary condition <DE>	restliche (dynamische) Randbedingung *f*	condition *f* aux limites restante (résiduelle, dynamique)	остаточное (динамическое) краевое условие
R 867	**residual category** <CA, UA>	residuale Kategorie *f*	catégorie *f* résiduelle	резидуальная категория
	residual class <AL>	*s.* S 460		
	residual class degree <AL>	*s.* R 898		
	residual component <SP>	*s.* R 93		
R 868	**residual correlation of *k*-th order** <ST>	Restkorrelation *f* *k*-ter Ordnung	corrélation *f* résiduelle de *k*-e ordre	остаточная корреляция *k*-го порядка
R 869	**residual curve** <of a linear system with respect to a curve> <AG>	residuale Kurve *f*, Restkurve *f*	courbe *f* résiduelle	резидуальная кривая
	residual dispersion <ST>	*s.* R 883		
	residual errors <ST>	*s.* R 878		
R 870	**residual finiteness** <of a group> <GR>	residuale Endlichkeit *f*, endliche Approximierbarkeit *f*	finitude *f* résiduelle	резидуальная конечность, конечная аппроксимируемость
R 871	**residual group [of points]** <AG>	residuale Punktgruppe (Gruppe) *f*, Restgruppe *f*	groupe *m* résiduel	резидуальная группа точек
R 872	**residually finite group** <AL>	endlich approximierbare Gruppe *f*, residual endliche Gruppe <Gruppe, die durch endliche Gruppen approximiert wird>	groupe *m* résiduellement fini	финитно[-] аппроксимируемая группа, резидуально (остаточно) конечная группа, конечно аппроксимируемая группа <группа, которая аппроксимируется конечными группами>
R 873	**residually finite *p*-group** <AL>	residual (residuell) endliche *p*-Gruppe *f*, endlich approximierbare *p*-Gruppe	*p*-groupe *m* résiduellement fini	финитно-аппроксимируемая *p*-группа
R 874	**residual matrix** <ST>	Restmatrix *f*	matrice *f* résiduelle	остаточная матрица

No.	English	German	French	Russian
	residual module <AL>	*s.* Q 326		
R 875	**residual part of higher degree** <of an Artinian ring> <AL>	Restteil *m* höheren Grades	partie *f* résiduelle du degré supérieur	остаточная часть высшей степени
R 876	**residual points** <of a cubic> <AG>	residuale Punkte *mpl*	points *mpl* résiduels	резидуальные точки
R 877	**residual property** <UA>	residuale Eigenschaft *f*	propriété *f* résiduelle	резидуальное свойство
R 878	**residuals,** residual errors <ST>	Restfehler *mpl*	erreurs *fpl* résiduelles	остаточные свободные члены, остаточные ошибки
	residual set <TO>	*s.* C 1218		
R 879	**residual space** <AG, TO>	Restraum *m*	espace *m* résiduel	остаточное пространство
R 880	**residual spectrum** <FA>	Residualspektrum *n*, Restspektrum *n*	spectre *m* résiduel	остаточный спектр
R 881	**residual subgroup** <AL>	residuelle Untergruppe *f*	sous-groupe *m* résiduel	остаточная подгруппа
R 882	**residual sum [of squares],** error sum [of squares] <ST>	Restsumme *f* [von Abweichungsquadraten], Fehlerquadratsumme *f*, quadratische Restsumme	somme *f* [des carrés] des résidus	остаточная сумма [квадратов]
R 883	**residual variance,** residual dispersion <ST>	Reststreuung *f*, Restvarianz *f*, Fehlervarianz *f*, Restdispersion *f*	variance *f* résiduelle (conditionnelle), dispersion *f* résiduelle	остаточная дисперсия
R 884	**residuated lattice** <LA>	Verband *m* mit Division	treillis *m* résidué	структура с делением
	residuate residuata <NT>	*s.* A 1082		
R 885	**residue** <of an algebraic curve> <AG>	Rest *m*, Residuum *n*	résidu *m*	вычет
R 886	**residue** <of a double integral *or* a point set> <AG, FT, TO>	Residuum *n*	résidu *m*	вычет
R 886 a	**residue,** remainder, apparent error, seeming error <ER>	Rest *m*, scheinbarer (plausibelster) Fehler *m*	résidu *m*, erreur *f* apparente	остаток, ожидаемая (кажущаяся, наиболее доверительная) погрешность, кажущаяся ошибка
R 887	**residue,** res <FT>	Residuum *n*, Res	résidu *m*, res	вычет, резидуум
	residue <SE>	*s.* R 790		
	residue character <NT>	*s.* R 892		
R 888	**residue character mod. *m*** <NT>	Charakter (Restcharakter) *m* mod *m*	caractère *m* mod. *m*	характер по модулю *m*
R 889	**residue class,** coset, residue system <in a ring> <AL>	Restklasse *f*	classe *f* résiduelle (latérale), classe [des résidus]	класс вычетов
R 890	**residue class** <in the ring of integers> <NT>	Restklasse *f*	classe *f*, classe de congruence, classe résiduelle	класс вычетов
	residue class <GR>	*s.* C 2523		
R 891	**residue class by an ideal** <AL>	Restklasse *f* nach einem Ideal	classe *f* résiduelle modulo (par) un idéal	класс вычетов по идеалу
R 892	**residue class character,** residue character <mod. *m*> <NT>	Restklassencharakter *m* <mod *m*>	caractère *m* de classe résiduelle, caractère de l'anneau-quotient <mod. *m*>	характер по модулю <*m*>, характер классов вычетов по модулю <*m*>
R 893	**residue[-] class field,** field of residue classes, residue field, difference field <AL>	Restklassenkörper *m*	corps *m* résiduel (des restes, quotient), champ *m* quotient	поле [классов] вычетов, фактор-поле, разностное поле
R 894	**residue class mapping** <AL>	Restklassenabbildung *f*	application *f* canonique associant à chaque élément sa classe	переход к классам вычетов, факторотображение
	residue class module <AL>	*s.* F 50		
R 895/6	**residue class modulo *m*** <NT>	Restklasse *f* modulo *m*	classe *f* résiduelle modulo *m*, entier *m* modulo *m*	класс вычетов по модулю *m*
R 897	**residue[-] class ring,** difference ring, factor[-] ring, quotient ring, residue[-] ring; difference-algebra <non-commutative> <by an ideal> <AL>	Restklassenring *m*, Faktorring *m*, Differenzring *m*, Differenzenring *m* <nach einem Ideal>	anneau *m* quotient, anneau-quotient *m*, anneau résiduaire (des classes résiduelles, résiduel, de restes) <modulo un idéal, par un idéal>	фактор-кольцо, фактор-кольцо, кольцо классов вычетов, кольцо вычетов
R 898	**residue degree,** residual class degree <AL>	Restklassengrad *m*, Restklassenkörpergrad *m*	degré *m* résiduel	степень поля вычетов, степень вычетов, степень классов вычетов
	residue field <AL>	*s.* R 893		
R 899	**residue field of a valuation** <AL>	zu einer Bewertung gehöriger Restklassenkörper *m*	corps *m* résiduel d'une valuation, corps résiduel (des restes) du corps valué	поле вычетов нормирования; тело вычетов нормирования
	residue of *p* <NT>	*s.* Q 43		
	residue[-] ring <AL>	*s.* R 897		
R 900	**residue system** <NT>	Restsystem *n*, Restklassenzahlsystem *n*, // System *n* nicht kongruenter Zahlen	système *m* résiduel (de nombres incongrus)	система вычетов (представителей классов вычетов)
	residue system <AL>	*s.* R 889		
R 901	**residue theorem,** theorem of residuation, theorem of coresiduation <for algebraic functions and curves> <AG>	Restsatz *m*	théorème *m* des résidus	теорема о вычетах
R 902	**residue theorem,** Liouville['s] residue theorem, [Liouville['s]] theorem of residues <for elliptic functions> <FU>	Residuensatz *m*, Liouvillescher Residuensatz	théorème *m* des résidus [de Liouville]	теорема о вычетах [Лиувилля]
	residue theorem <FT>	*s.* C 266		
	residuum sociatum <NT>	*s.* A 1092		

R 903	**resolution** <of a module *or* sheaf> <AL, AT, HA>	Auflösung *f*	résolution *f*	резольвента
	resolution <VT>	*s.* V 102		
	resolution into a solenoidal and irrotational vector <VT>	*s.* V 123		
R 904	**resolution of a double complex** <HA>	Auflösung *f* eines Doppelkomplexes	résolution *f* d'un double complexe	двойная резольвента
R 905	**resolution of finite type** <of a sheaf> <AT>	Auflösung *f* endlichen Typs	résolution *f* finitiste	резольвента конечного типа
R 906	**resolution of singularities,** reduction of singularities <AG>	Auflösung *f* der Singularitäten, Reduktion *f* der Singularitäten	résolution *f* des singularités	разрешение особенностей
	resolution of the identity <FA>	*s.* S 1398		
R 907	**resolved equation** <AL>	aufgelöste Gleichung *f*	équation *f* résolue	разрешенное уравнение
R 908	**resolvent** <of an algebraic equation> <AL>	Resolvente *f*, resolvierende Gleichung *f*	résolvante *f*, équation *f* résolvante	резольвента <уравнения *n*-ой степени>, разрешающее уравнение
R 909	**resolvent** <of a differential equation> <DE>	Resolvente *f* <Picard>	résolvante *f*	резольвента
R 910	**resolvent** <of a linear operator> <as a mapping> <FA>	Resolvente *f*	résolvante *f*	резольвента
R 911	**resolvent,** resolvent kernel, reciprocal kernel <IE>	Resolvente *f*, lösender Kern *m*	noyau *m* résolvant, résolvante *f*	разрешающее ядро, резольвента, ядро резольвенты
R 912	**resolvent** <of a matrix> <MD>	Resolvente *f*	matrice *f* résolvante, résolvante *f* <d'une matrice>	резольвента <матрицы>, матрица-резольвента
	resolvent <FA>	*s.* R 916		
R 913	**resolvent cubic,** cubic resolvent <AL>	kubische Resolvente *f*	résolvante *f* cubique	кубическая резольвента
R 914	**resolvent equation** <AL, FA>	Resolventengleichung *f*, Hilbert-Relation *f*, Hilbertsche Funktionalgleichung *f*	équation *f* de la résolvante	резольвентное уравнение, тождество Гильберта
	resolvent function <FA>	*s.* R 916		
	resolvent kernel <IE>	*s.* R 911		
R 915	**resolvent of Malfatti** <of an equation of fifth order> <AL>	Malfattische Resolvente *f*	résolvante *f* de Malfatti	резольвента Малфати
R 916	**resolvent operator,** resolvent function, resolvent <of a linear operator> <FA>	Resolventenoperator *m*, Resolvente *f*	opérateur *m* résolvant, transformation *f* résolvante, résolvante *f*	резольвентный (разрешающий) оператор, резольвента
R 917	**resolvent set** <of a linear operator *or* of an element of a Banach algebra> <FA>	Resolventenmenge *f*	ensemble *m* résolvant	резольвентное множество
R 918	**resolvent transformation** <IE>	lösende Transformation *f*	transformation *f* résolvante	разрешающее преобразование
	resolving <GN>	*s.* S 1283		
	resolving <VT>	*s.* V 102		
R 919	**response curve** <ST>	Wirkungskurve *f*	courbe *f* de réponse	кривая отклика
	response degree <ST>	*s.* D 186		
R 920	**response surface** <ST>	Wirkungsfläche *f*	surface *f* de réponse	поверхность отклика
R 921	**restricted adele** <AL>	eingeschränktes Adel *n*	adèle *m* restreint	ограниченный адел
R 922	**restricted Bayes solution** <ST>	eingeschränkte Bayessche Lösung *f*	solution *f* de Bayes restreinte	ограниченное бейесово решение
	restricted Burnside conjecture <GR>	*s.* R 923		
R 923	**restricted Burnside problem,** restricted Burnside conjecture <GR>	abgeschwächtes Burnsidesches Problem *n*, eingeschränktes Burnsidesches Problem, beschränkte Burnsidesche Vermutung *f*, Abschwächung *f* des Burnsideschen Problems	problème *m* restreint de Burnside	ослабленная проблема Бернсайда, ограниченная проблема Бернсайда
R 924	**restricted formal power series** <AL>	eingeschränkte formale Potenzreihe *f*	série *f* formelle restreinte	ограниченный формальный ряд
	restricted functional calculus <LO>	*s.* F 349		
R 925	**restricted holonomy group** <DG>	eingeschränkte Holonomiegruppe *f*	groupe *m* d'holonomie restreint	ограниченная группа голономий
R 926	**restricted Lie algebra** <AL>	eingeschränkte Liesche Algebra *f*	algèbre *f* de Lie restreinte	ограниченная алгебра Ли
	restricted limit <SE>	*s.* L 725		
	restrictedly convergent series <SS>	*s.* B 676		
R 927	**restricted predicate calculus,** pure predicate (functional) calculus <LO>	engerer Prädikatenkalkül *m*	calcul *m* des prédicats restreint (dans le sens restreint)	узкое (чистое) исчисление предикатов
	restricted predicate calculus <LO>	*s. a.* F 349		
R 928	**restricted randomization** <ST>	eingeschränkte Randomisation *f*	arrangement *m* au hasard restreint, répartition *f* au hasard restreint	неполная рандомизация
R 929	**restricted random sampling** <ST>	eingeschränkte Zufallsauswahl *f*	échantillonnage *m* au hasard restreint, échantillonnage au jugé	неполностью случайный выбор, не вполне случайный выбор
	restricted sense / in the <GN>	*s.* N 12		
R 930	**restricted set product** <SE>	eingeschränktes kartesisches Produkt *n*	produit *m* cartésien restreint	ограниченное декартово произведение

R 931	**restricted topological product of spaces** <TO>	eingeschränkter Produktraum *m*, eingeschränktes topologisches Produkt *n* von Räumen	produit *m* restreint d'un système restreint d'espaces, espace *m* produit restreint	ограниченное топологическое произведение пространств
R 932	**restricted universal associative algebra** <for a Lie algebra>, u-algebra <of a Lie algebra> <AL>	eingeschränkte Hüllalgebra *f*	algèbre *f* enveloppante restreinte	ограниченная универсальная обертывающая алгебра
R 933	**restriction** <of a distribution> <AN>	Einschränkung *f*	restriction *f*	сужение, ограничение
	restriction <PG>	*s.* C 2123		
R 934	**restriction homomorphism** <AL, TO>	Beschränkungshomomorphismus *m*, Einschränkungshomomorphismus *m*	homomorphisme *m* de restriction, morphisme *m* de restriction	гомоморфизм ограничения
R 935	**restriction map** <AL, TO>	Einschränkungsabbildung *f*	application *f* restriction, application de restriction	отображение ограничения
R 936	**restriction of a function (mapping),** partial mapping <TO>	Einschränkung *f* einer Abbildung	restriction *f* d'une application <à>, trace *f* d'une application <sur>	ограничение отображения, сужение отображения
	restrictive axiom <SE>	*s.* A 1291		
R 937	**Restsatz of Brill and Noether,** Brill and Noether theorem <AG>	Brill-Noetherscher Restsatz *m*, Restsatz von Brill und Noether	théorème *m* des résidus de Brill-Noether	теорема Брилля-Нетера, теорема Брилля и Нетера
R 938	**resultant,** eliminant <AL>	Resultante *f*	résultant *m*	результант
	resultant <AN>	*s.* C 2409		
	resultant <TO>	*s.* P 1595		
	resultant <VT>	*s.* G 270		
R 939	**resultant system** <AL>	Resultantensystem *n*	système *m* de résultants	система результантов
R 940	**retain / to** <in addition> <AR>	merken	retenir	запоминать
R 941	**retarded value** <of a function> <DE>	retardierter (nacheilender) Wert *m*	valeur *f* retardée	запаздывающее значение
R 942	**retopologize / to** <TO>	umtopologisieren	rétopologiser, munir d'une nouvelle topologie	перетопологизировать, наделить новой топологией
R 943	**retract** <AL, CA, GR, TO>	Retrakt *m*	rétracte *m* <*par exemple:* d'un espace topologique, d'un objet *ou* d'un groupe> <CA, GR, TO>; retour *m* <*par exemple:* d'une algèbre de Boole *ou* d'un espace topologique> <AL, TO>	ретракт
R 944	**retract homomorphism** <of a Boolean algebra *or* group> <AL, GR>	Retraktionshomomorphismus *m*	homomorphisme *m* rétractant	ретрактный гомоморфизм
R 945	**retractibility** <TO>	Retrahierbarkeit *f*	rétractilité *f*	ретрагируемость
R 946	**retractible neighbourhood** <TO>	retrahierbare Umgebung *f*	voisinage *m* rétractile	ретрагируемая окрестность
R 947	**retracting deformation** <TO>	retrahierende Deformation *f*	déformation *f* rétractante	ретрагирующая (ретракционная) деформация
	retracting function <TO>	*s.* R 950		
R 948	**retraction** <of a simplex> <AT>	Ausfegung *f*	balayage *m*	выметание
R 949	**retraction,** right semi-isomorphism <CA>	Retraktion *f*	rétraction *f*, morphisme *m* inversible à gauche	ретракция, обратимый слева морфизм
R 950	**retraction,** retracting function <TO>	Retraktion *f*, retrahierende Abbildung *f*, Retraktionsabbildung *f*	application *f* de rétraction, rétraction *f*	ретракция, ретрагирующее отображение, стягивание
R 951	**retraction theorem** <AT>	Ausfegungssatz *m*	théorème *m* de balayage	теорема о выметании
R 952	**retrosection,** cross[-] cut <FT, TO>	Rückkehrschnitt *m*	rétrosection *f*	прорез, рассечение, циклическое сечение
R 953	**retrospective equation** <SP>	retrospektive Gleichung *f*, Rückwärtsgleichung *f*	équation *f* rétrospective	уравнение для случайного процесса в прошлом
R 954	**Reuleaux['s] polygon** <CS, GE>	Reuleaux-Polygon *n*	polygone *m* de Reuleaux	многогранник Рело (Рёло́, Релло)
R 955	**Reuleaux['s] triangle** <CS, GE>	Reuleauxsches Dreieck *n*, Reuleaux-Dreieck *n*	triangle *m* de Reuleaux	треугольник Рело (Рёло́, Релло)
	reversal <GE>	*s.* I 183		
	reversal of sign <GN>	*s.* C 498		
R 956	**reversal test** <ST>	Vorzeichenwechseltest *m*	test *m* de réversibilité	критерий обратимости индекса
	reversed in order <GN>	*s.* I 975		
	reverse order / in [the] <GN>	*s.* I 975		
R 957	**reverse the order of integration / to** <DI>	die Reihenfolge der Integrationen umkehren	intervertir les intégrations	изменять порядок интегрирований
R 958	**reversion** <of a series> <SS>	Umkehrung *f* <einer Reihe>	inversion *f* <d'une série>	обращение <ряда>
	reversion <NT>	*s.* N 858		
R 959	**reversion of the arrows** <CA>	Umkehrung *f* der Pfeile	renversement *m* des flèches	обращение стрелок
R 960	**revised simplex method** <PG>	revidiertes (verkürztes) Simplexverfahren *n*, Simplexverfahren mit abgeänderter Rechenorganisation	méthode *f* simpliciale (du simplexe) révisée	переработанный симплексный метод
	revolution solid <EG>	*s.* B 529		
	reward function <PG>	*s.* Y 2		
R 961	**reward functional** <PG>	Ertragsfunktional *n*	fonctionnelle *f* de rendement	функционал выхода
R 962	**rewriting** <LO>	Umbenennung *f*	changement *m* de nom (désignation)	переименование

No.	English	German	French	Russian
	rewriting <GN>	*s.* T 761		
	rewriting of variables <LO>	*s.* R 337		
	rewriting rule <MM>	*s.* P 1613		
R 963	**rewriting the indices** <GN>	Umbenennung *f* der Indizes	changement *m* de désignation des indices	переименование индексов
	rewriting the variables <LO>	*s.* R 337		
	Reye['s] complex <PJ>	*s.* T 232		
R 964	**Reye['s] configuration** <SG>	Reyes[che] Hexaeder- und Oktaederkonfiguration *f*	configuration *f* de Reye	конфигурация Рейе
	Reye['s] configuration problem <SG>	*s.* C 1878		
R 965	**Reye['s] plane configuration** <SG>	Reyes[che] ebene Konfiguration *f*	configuration *f* plane de Reye	плоскостная конфигурация Рейе
R 966	***r*-fold eigenvalue** <DE>	*r*-facher Eigenwert *m*	valeur *f* propre *r*-uple	*r*-кратное собственное значение
R 967	***r*-fold singular quadric** <GE>	*r*-fach singuläre Quadrik *f*	quadrique *f* *r* fois singulière	*r*-кратно особая (сингулярная) квадрика
	rhodonea <GE>	*s.* R 1390		
R 968	**rhombohedron** <EG>	Rhomboeder *n*, Rautenflächner *m*	rhomboèdre *m*	ромбоэдр
R 969	**rhomboid** <EG>	Rhomboid *n*, ungleichseitig-schiefwinkliges Parallelogramm *n*	rhomboïde *m*	ромбоид
R 970	**rhombus** <EG>	Rhombus *m*, Raute *f*, gleichseitiges Parallelogramm *n*	losange *m*, rhombe *m*	ромб
R 971/2	**R-homomorphism,** *R*-linear mapping, homomorphism <of an *R*-module> <AL>	*R*-Homomorphismus *m*, *R*-lineare Abbildung *f*, *R*-Modulhomomorphismus *m*, lineare Abbildung (Funktion) *f*, Homomorphismus *m* <eines *R*-Moduls>	*R*-homomorphisme *m*, application *f* *R*-linéaire, homomorphisme *m* <d'un *R*-module>	*R*-гомоморфизм, *R*-линейное отображение, гомоморфизм <*R*-модуля>
	R_0-homomorphism <AL>	*s.* R 714		
	RHS <GN>	*s.* R 1166		
	rhumb <EG>	*s.* L 1173		
	rhumb (Rhumb) line <EG>	*s.* L 1173		
R 973	**Ribaucour['s] congruence [of lines (rays)]** <DG>	Ribaucoursche Strahlenkongruenz (Linienkongruenz, Geradenkongruenz, Kongruenz) *f*, Ribaucoursches Strahlensystem *n*, Ribaucours Kongruenz	congruence *f* [de droites] de Ribaucour	конгруэнция [прямых (лучей)] Рибокура
R 974	**Ribaucour['s] curve** <GE>	Ribaucoursche Kurve *f*	ligne (courbe) *f* de Ribaucour	кривая Рибокура
R 975	**Ribaucour['s] theorem** <DG>	Satz *m* von Ribaucour, Ribaucourscher Satz	théorème *m* de Ribaucour	теорема Рибокура
R 976	**Ribaucour['s] transformation** <DG>	Ribaucoursche Transformation *f*	transformation *f* de Ribaucour	преобразование Рибокура
R 977	**Riccati['s] [differential] equation,** general [nonlinear] Riccati equation, Riccati['s] general [differential] equation, differential equation of Riccati <DE>	Riccatische Differentialgleichung *f*, allgemeine Riccatische Differentialgleichung (Gleichung *f*)	équation *f* de Riccati, équation différentielle de Riccati, équation de Riccati générale	общее уравнение Риккати, уравнение Риккати общего вида, уравнение Риккати, // уравнение Риккати
R 978	**Riccati['s] equation,** special Riccati equation, Riccati['s] special [differential] equation <DE>	[spezielle] Riccatische Differentialgleichung (Gleichung) *f*	équation *f* de Riccati [spéciale]	уравнение Риккати, специальное уравнение Риккати
	Riccati['s] general [differential] equation <DE>	*s.* R 977		
	Riccati['s] special [differential] equation <DE>	*s.* R 978		
R 979	**Ricci calculus,** absolute differential calculus, absolute differentiation, tensor calculus <DG, VT>	Ricci-Kalkül *m*, Kalkül *m* der absoluten Differentiation [von Ricci], absolute Differentiation *f* [von Ricci], absoluter Differentialkalkül *m*, [Christoffelsche] invariante Ableitung *f*	calcul *m* de Ricci, calcul différentiel absolu, calcul tensoriel, différentiation (dérivation) *f* absolue	абсолютное дифференцирование, исчисление Риччи
	Ricci's coefficient of rotation <DG>	*s.* R 1403		
R 980	**Ricci['s] curvature** <DG>	Riccische Krümmung *f*	courbure *f* de Ricci	кривизна Риччи
R 981	**Ricci['s] curvature tensor,** Ricci['s] tensor, Einstein['s] tensor <DG>	Ricci-Tensor *m*, Riccitensor *m*, Einstein-Tensor *m*, *m*, Tensor *m* von Ricci	tenseur *m* de Ricci, tenseur d'Einstein	тензор Риччи (Эйнштейна)
R 982	**Ricci['s] equation (identity)** <VT>	Riccische Gleichung (Identität) *f*, Identität von Ricci	identité *f* de Ricci	тождество Риччи
	Ricci['s] lemma <DG>	*s.* R 985		
	Ricci['s] manifold <DG>	*s.* R 984		
R 983	**Ricci['s] scalar curvature,** scalar curvature, mean Riemannian curvature <of a Riemann manifold> <DG>	Ortsinvariante *f* der Krümmung, mittleres Riemannsches Krümmungsmaß *n*, skalare Krümmung	courbure *f* scalaire (riemannienne moyenne)	скалярная (средняя риманова) кривизна

No.	English	German	French	Russian
R 984	**Ricci['s] space,** Ricci['s] variety, Ricci['s] manifold <DG>	Ricci-Mannigfaltigkeit *f*, Ricci-Raum *m*	variété *f* (espace *m*) de Ricci	многообразие (пространство) Риччи
	Ricci['s] tensor <DG>	*s.* R 981		
R 985	**Ricci['s] theorem,** Ricci['s] lemma <DG>	Satz *m* (Lemma *n*) von Ricci, Riccischer Satz	théorème *m* de Ricci	теорема Риччи
	Ricci['s] variety <DG>	*s.* R 984		
R 986	**Richard['s] number** <in Richard's paradox> <FO>	Richardsche Zahl *f*, // Richardische Zahl	nombre *m* de Richard	число Ришара
R 987	**Richard['s] paradox** <FO>	Richardsche Antinomie *f*	antinomie *f* (paradoxe *m*) de Richard	парадокс Ришара
R 988	**rich collection** <of subsets> <TO>	reiche Menge *f*	ensemble *m* riche	изобильное множество
R 989	**Richey['s] method** <ST>	Richey-Methode *f*	méthode *f* de Richey	метод Ричи
R 990	**Richmond['s] configuration** <SG>	Richmondsche Konfiguration *f*	configuration *f* de Richmond	конфигурация Ричмонда
R 991	**ridge point** <of a convex body> <GE>	Kantenpunkt *m*	point *m* d'arête	ребристая точка
	Riemann-Christoffel curvature tensor <DG>	*s.* R 1040		
	Riemann-Christoffel symbol <DG>	*s.* R 1040		
	Riemann-Christoffel tensor [of the first kind] <DG>	*s.* R 1040		
	Riemann-Christoffel three-index symbol <DG>	*s.* C 667		
R 992	**Riemann['s] conjecture,** Riemann['s] hypothesis, Riemann['s] "Vermutung" <on the zeta-function> <FU, NT>	Riemannsche (große Riemannsche) Vermutung *f*	hypothèse *f* de Riemann	гипотеза Римана
	Riemann['s] criterion [for convergence] <SS>	*s.* R 1041		
R 993	**Riemann['s] criterion for integrability** <AN>	Riemannsches Integrabilitätskriterium *n*	critère *m* de Riemann pour l'intégrabilité	критерий интегрируемости Римана
R 994	**Riemann['s] differential equation,** Riemann-Papperitz equation, Papperitz['s] equation; Riemann['s] *P*-equation <DE>	Riemannsche (Papperitzsche) Differentialgleichung *f*, Papperitzsche Gleichung *f*; Riemannsche *P*-Gleichung *f*	équation *f* différentielle de Riemann, équation de Riemann (Riemann-Papperitz, Papperitz); équation *P* de Riemann	дифференциальное уравнение Римана, уравнение Римана; *P*-уравнение Римана
R 995	**Riemann['s] equations** <for the Riemann matrix> <FT>	Riemannsche Gleichungen *fpl*	équations *fpl* de Riemann	уравнения Римана
R 996	**Riemann['s] existence theorem** <AG>	Riemannscher Existenzsatz *m*	théorème *m* d'existence de Riemann	теорема существования Римана
R 997	**Riemann['s] form** <AG, FT>	Riemannsche Form *f*	forme *f* de Riemann, forme riemannienne	форма Римана
R 998	**Riemann['s] formula** <NT>	Primzahlformel *f* von Riemann, Riemannsche (Riemann-von Mangoldtsche, Riemann-Mangoldtsche) Primzahlformel, Riemannsche Formel *f*	formule *f* de Riemann	формула Римана
R 999	**Riemann['s] function** <DE>	Riemannsche Funktion *f*	fonction *f* de Riemann	функция Римана
	Riemann['s] ζ-function <FU, NT>	*s.* R 1046		
R 1000	**Riemann['s] functional equation** <for the zeta function> <FU>	Riemannsche Funktionalgleichung *f*	équation *f* fonctionnelle de Riemann	функциональное уравнение Римана
R 1001	**Riemann-Helmholtz problem,** Lie-Riemann-Helmholtz[-Hilbert] problem of the foundations of geometry <GE>	Riemann-Helmholtz-Liesches Raumproblem *n*	problème *m* de Helmholtz (Helmholtz-Lie)	задача Гельмгольца-Ли, задача Римана-Гельмгольца-Ли
R 1002	**Riemann-Hurwitz relation** <AG>	Riemann-Hurwitzsche Formel *f*	formule *f* de Riemann-Hurwitz	соотношение Римана-Гурвица, формула Гурвица
	Riemann['s] hypothesis <FU, NT>	*s.* R 992		
R 1003	**Riemannian class** <AG, AL>	Riemannsche Klasse *f*	classe *f* riemannienne	риманов класс, класс Римана
R 1004	**Riemannian connection,** Levi-Cività connection, Riemannian transfer <associated to the Riemannian metric> <DG>	Riemannsche Übertragung *f*, Riemannscher Zusammenhang *m*	connexion *f* riemannienne, transfert *m* riemannien	риманова связность, риманово перенесение
R 1005	**Riemannian co-ordinates** <DG>	Riemannsche Koordinaten *fpl*	coordonnées *fpl* riemanniennes	римановы координаты
R 1006	**Riemannian curvature,** sectional curvature <DG>	Riemannsches Krümmungsmaß *n*, Riemannsche Krümmung *f*, Büschelinvariante *f* der Krümmung	courbure *f* riemannienne (bidimensionnelle, sectionnelle, segmentaire, dans le plan tangent)	риманова (сегментарная) кривизна
R 1007	**Riemannian differential geometry** <DG>	Riemannsche Differentialgeometrie *f*	géométrie *f* différentielle riemannienne	риманова дифференциальная геометрия
R 1008	**Riemannian domain** <FT>	Riemannsches Gebiet *n*, Riemannscher Raum *m*	domaine *m* riemannien (de Riemann)	риманова область, область Римана
R 1009	**Riemannian field** <FT>	Riemannsches Feld *n*	champ *m* riemannien (de Riemann)	риманово поле
	⌐<GE> **Riemannian geometry**	*s.* E 176		

No.	English	German	French	Russian
	Riemannian integral <DI>	s. R 1015		
	Riemannian manifold <DG>	s. R 1012		
R 1010	**Riemannian manifold of constant curvature** <DG>	Riemannsche Mannigfaltigkeit *f* konstanter (skalarer) Krümmung	espace *m* de Riemann à courbure constante	риманово пространство постоянной кривизны
R 1011	**Riemannian metric** <DG>	Riemannsche Metrik *f*	métrique *f* riemannienne	риманова метрика, метрика Римана
R 1012	**Riemannian space,** Riemannian manifold <DG>	Riemannsche Mannigfaltigkeit *f*, Riemannscher Raum *m*	espace *m* de Riemann, espace riemannien, variété de Riemann	риманово пространство, пространство Римана, риманово многообразие
	Riemannian surface <FT>	s. R 1038		
	Riemannian transfer <DG>	s. R 1004		
R 1013	**Riemannian variety** <AG>	Riemanniana *f*, Riemannsche Mannigfaltigkeit *f*	variété *f* de Riemann	риманово многообразие
R 1014	**Riemann integrable function,** R-integrable function, function integrable in the sense of Riemann <AN>	R-integrierbare (Riemann-integrierbare, im Riemannschen Sinne integrierbare) Funktion *f*	fonction *f* intégrable au sens de Riemann	интегрируемая в смысле Римана функция; функция, интегрируемая в смысле Римана
R 1015	**Riemann['s] integral,** Riemannian integral, integral in the Riemann sense, R-integral <DI>	Riemannsches Integral *n*, Integral im Riemannschen Sinne, R-Integral *n*	intégrale *f* riemannienne (de Riemann, au sens de Riemann, (R))	интеграл Римана (в смысле Римана), R-интеграл
R 1016	**Riemann-Lebesgue lemma (theorem)** <AN, SS>	Riemann-Lebesguesches Lemma (Fundamentallemma) *n*, Satz *m* von Riemann-Lebesgue, Riemann-Lebesguescher Satz	théorème *m* de Riemann-Lebesgue	теорема Римана-Лебега
R 1017	**Riemann['s] localization theorem** <for Fourier series> <SS>	Riemannscher Lokalisationssatz *m*, Lokalisationssatz von Riemann	théorème *m* de localisation de Riemann	теорема локализации Римана
	Riemann['s] mapping theorem <FT>	s. R 1043		
R 1018	**Riemann matrix** <of genus *p*> <FT>	Riemannsche Matrix (Periodenmatrix) *f*	matrice *f* de Riemann	матрица Римана
R 1019	**Riemann['s] method,** *R*-method <of summation> <LI>	*R*-Verfahren *n*, Riemannsche Summation *f*	méthode *f* de Riemann	*R*-метод
R 1020	**Riemann['s] method [of integration]** <DE>	Riemannsche Integrationsmethode *f*	méthode *f* [d'intégration] de Riemann	метод [интегрирования] Римана
	Riemann-Papperitz equation <DE>	s. R 994		
	Riemann['s] *P*-equation <DE>	s. R 994		
R 1021	**Riemann['s] *P*-equation (*P*-form, *P*-function)** <FU>	Riemannsche *P*-Funktion *f*, Riemannsches Schema *n*, Riemannsche *P*-Gleichung *f*	schéma *m* de Riemann, schéma (équation *f*) *P* de Riemann	схема Римана (*P* Римана), *P*-уравнение Римана
R 1022	**Riemann['s] problem** <DE>	Riemannsches Problem *n*	problème *m* de Riemann	задача Римана
R 1023	**Riemann['s] rearrangement theorem** <for a non-absolutely convergent series> <SS>	Riemannscher Umordnungssatz *m*	théorème *m* de Riemann	теорема Римана
R 1024	**Riemann-Roch group** <AG>	Riemann-Rochsche Gruppe *f*	groupe *m* de Riemann-Roch	группа Римана-Роха
R 1025	**Riemann-Roch inequality** <AG>	Riemann-Rochsche Ungleichung *f*, Riemannscher Satz *m*	inégalité *f* de Riemann-Roch	неравенство Римана-Роха
R 1026	**Riemann-Roch problem** <AG, FT>	Problem *n* von Riemann-Roch, Riemann-Rochsches Problem	problème *m* de Riemann-Roch	проблема Римана-Роха
R 1027	**Riemann-Roch space** <of a divisor> <AG>	Raum *m* von Riemann-Roch, Riemann-Rochscher Raum	espace *m* de Riemann-Roch	пространство Римана-Роха; пространство, ассоциированное с дивизором
R 1028	**Riemann-Roch theorem,** theorem of Riemann-Roch <AG, FT>	Riemann-Rochscher Satz *m*, Satz von Riemann-Roch	théorème *m* de Riemann-Roch	теорема Римана-Роха
R 1029	**Riemann['s] series** <NT>	Riemannsche Reihe *f*	série *f* de Riemann	ряд Римана
R 1030	**Riemann['s] sphere,** complex sphere, Neumann]'s] sphere, sphere of complex numbers <FT>	Riemannsche Zahlenkugel *f*, Zahlenkugel *f*, Gaußsche Zahlenkugel, Gaußsche Sphäre *f*	sphère *f* de Riemann	числовая сфера, сфера Римана
R 1031	**Riemann['s] standard domain,** standard domain <FT>	Riemannsches Normalgebiet *n*, Normalgebiet	domaine *m* canonique [de Riemann]	нормальная область Римана
R 1032	**Riemann-Stieltjes integral** <AN>	Riemann-Stieltjes-Integral *n*, Riemann-Stieltjessches Integral *n*	intégrale *f* de Riemann-Stieltjes	интеграл Римана-Стилтьеса
R 1033	**Riemann-Stieltjes measure** <ME>	Riemann-Stieltjes-Maß *n*	mesure *f* de Riemann-Stieltjes	мера Римана-Стилтьеса
R 1034	**Riemann-Stieltjes sum** <AN>	Riemann-Stieltjessche Summe (Zerlegungssumme) *f*	somme *f* de Riemann-Stieltjes	сумма Римана-Стилтьеса
R 1035	**Riemann['s] sum,** integral sum <DI>	Riemannsche Summe *f*, Integralsumme *f*	somme *f* de Riemann	интегральная сумма, сумма Римана
	Riemann['s] sum <LI, SS>	s. R 1444		

R 1036	**Riemann summable series,** R-summable series <LI>	Riemann-summierbare (R-summierbare) Reihe *f*	série *f* R-sommable (sommable au sens de Riemann)	R-суммируемый (суммируемый в смысле Римана) ряд
R 1037	**Riemann['s] summation** <of trigonometric series> <SS>	Riemannsche Summation *f*	sommation *f* de Riemann	суммирование Римана
R 1038	**Riemann['s] surface,** Riemannian surface <FT>	Riemannsche (Klein-Riemannsche) Fläche *f*	surface *f* de Riemann, surface riemannienne	риманова поверхность
R 1039	**Riemann surface of infinitely many sheets** <FT, TO>	unendlichblättrige (unendlich vielblättrige) Riemannsche Fläche *f*	surface *f* de Riemann à une infinité de feuilles	бесконечнолистная поверхность Римана
R 1040	**Riemann['s] tensor,** Riemann-Christoffel curvature tensor, Riemann-Christoffel symbol, Riemann-Christoffel tensor [of the first kind], covariant curvature tensor, curvature tensor, four-index symbol <DG>	Riemannscher (Riemann-Christoffelscher) Krümmungstensor *m*, Krümmungstensor von Riemann, [kovarianter] Krümmungstensor, Riemann-Christoffelscher Tensor *m*, Vierindizessymbol *n*	tenseur *m* de Riemann-Christoffel, tenseur de courbure de Riemann-Christoffel, tenseur de courbure	тензор кривизны Римана-Кристоффеля, тензор Римана-Кристоффеля, тензор кривизны
R 1041	**Riemann['s] test [for convergence],** Riemann['s] criterion [for convergence] <SS>	Riemannsches Kriterium (Konvergenzkriterium) *n*	règle *f* de Riemann	признак [сходимости] Римана
R 1042	**Riemann['s] theorem,** Green['s] theorem for $n = 2$ <DI, VT>	Gaußsche Integralformel *f* im Fall $n = 2$, Greensche Integralformel (Formel *f*), Integralformel (Formel) von Green, Riemannsche Integralformel (Formel), Gaußscher Integralsatz *m* im Fall $n = 2$	formule *f* de Riemann (Green)	формула Римана
R 1043	**Riemann['s] theorem,** conformal mapping theorem, Riemann['s] mapping theorem <FT>	Riemannscher Abbildungssatz (Hauptsatz) *m*, Hauptsatz der konformen Abbildung, Riemannscher Fundamentalsatz *m*, Fundamentalsatz der konformen Abbildung	théorème *m* fondamental de la représentation conforme	теорема Римана, теорема Римана о конформных отображениях, основная теорема [в] теории конформных отображений
R 1044	**Riemann['s] theorem,** theorem of Riemann <for a removable singularity *or* analytic continuations> <FT>	Satz *m* von Riemann, Riemannscher Satz	théorème *m* de Riemann	теорема Римана
R 1045	**Riemann['s] theta formula** <FT>	Riemannsche Thetaformel *f*	thêta-formule *f* de Riemann	тэта-формула Римана
	Riemann['s] "Vermutung" <FU, NT>	*s.* R 992		
R 1046	**Riemann['s] zeta function,** zeta[-] function [of Riemann], [Riemann['s]] ζ-function <FU, NT>	Riemannsche Zetafunktion (ζ-Funktion) *f*, Zetafunktion (ζ-Funktion) von Riemann, Zetafunktion *f*, ζ-Funktion	fonction *f* zêta (ζ) [de Riemann], fonction de Riemann, // fonction dzéta de Riemann	дзета-функция [Римана], ζ-функция [Римана], дзета Римана
R 1047	**Riesz['s] arithmetic mean** <LI>	Rieszsches arithmetisches Mittel *n*	moyenne *f* arithmétique [de [M.] Riesz]	среднее арифметическое [M.] Риса
R 1048	**Riesz['s] convexity theorem,** convexity theorem of M. Riesz <FA>	Konvexitätssatz *m* von M. Riesz, Rieszscher Konvexitätssatz	théorème *m* de convexité de M. Riesz	теорема выпуклости M. Риса
R 1049	**Riesz['s] domain** <FA>	Riesz-Bereich *m*	domaine *m* de Riesz	область Риса
	Riesz-Fischer theorem <FA> ┌<FA>	*s.* F 361		
	Riesz-Fréchet theorem	*s.* R 1061		
R 1050/1	**Rieszian sum,** sum by Riesz's method, (R,λ,k) sum, $R_{\lambda k}$-sum <LI>	$R_{\lambda k}$-Summe *f*, (R,λ,k)-Summe *f*, Summe *f* nach dem (R,λ,k)-Verfahren	somme *f* par la méthode de Riesz, *R*-somme *f*, $R_{\lambda k}$-somme *f*	[обобщенная] сумма по методу [M.] Риса, [обобщенная] сумма по [M.] Рису
R 1052	**Rieszian summability** <LI> ┌<LI>	Rieszsche Summierbarkeit *f*, Summierbarkeit nach dem (R,λ,k)-Verfahren	sommabilité *f* par la méthode de [M.] Riesz	суммируемость по методу [M.] Риса
R 1053	**Rieszian typical sum**	Rieszsche typische Summe *f*	somme *f* typique de Riesz	типическая сумма Риса
	Riesz['s] ideal <FA>	*s.* I 10		
	Riesz['s] (λ,k) method <LI>	*s.* 1. R 1055; 2. R 1057		
R 1054	**Riesz['s] lemma** <FA>	Rieszsches Lemma *n*	lemme *m* de Riesz	лемма Риса
R 1055	**Riesz['s] limitation method,** Riesz['s] method [of limitation], Riesz['s] (λ,k) method, (R,λ,k)-method, $R_{\lambda k}$-method <for divergent sequences> <LI>	Rieszsches Limitierungsverfahren *n*, Rieszsches [(λ,k)-]Verfahren *n*, (R,λ,k)-Verfahren *n*, $R_{\lambda k}$-Verfahren *n*	méthode *f* de limitation de [M.] Riesz, méthode de [M.] Riesz	метод [образования обобщенного предела] [M.] Риса
R 1056	**Riesz['s] logarithmic mean** <LI>	Rieszsches logarithmisches Mittel *n*	moyenne *f* logarithmique de [M.] Riesz	среднее логарифмическое [M.] Риса
	Riesz['s] method [of limitation] <LI>	*s.* R 1055		
R 1057	**Riesz['s] method [of summation],** Riesz['s] summation method, Riesz['s] (λ,k)-method, (R,λ,k)-method, $R_{\lambda k}$-method <for divergent series, especially for Dirichlet series> <LI>	Rieszsches Summierungsverfahren *n*, Rieszsches [(λ,k)-]Verfahren *n*, (R,λ,k)-Verfahren *n*, $R_{\lambda k}$-Verfahren *n*	méthode *f* de [M.] Riesz, méthode de sommation de [M.] Riesz	метод [M.] Риса, метод суммирования [расходящихся рядов] [M.] Риса

R 1058	**Riesz['s] operator** <FA>	Riesz-Operator *m*, Riesz-operator *m*	opérateur *m* de Riesz	оператор Риса
R 1059	**Riesz['s] point** <FA>	Riesz-Punkt *m*	point *m* de Riesz	точка Риса
	Riesz['s] projector <FA>	*s.* S 1410		
R 1060	**Riesz['s] radius** <FA>	Riesz-Radius *m*	rayon *m* de Riesz	радиус Риса
R 1061	**Riesz['s] representation theorem,** F. Riesz's representation theorem, Fréchet-Riesz theorem, Riesz-Fréchet theorem <for functionals> <FA>	Rieszscher Darstellungssatz *m*, Satz *m* von Riesz, Rieszscher Satz, Riesz-Fréchetscher Satz, Satz von Riesz-Fréchet (Fréchet-Riesz) // Rieß-scher Satz	théorème *m* de [F.] Riesz, théorème de représentation de Riesz, théorème de Riesz-Fréchet <pour les fonctionnelles linéaires>	теорема Риса [о представлении линейного функционала], теорема представления Риса, теорема Риса-Фреше
R 1062	**Riesz['s] space** <FA, TO>	Rieszscher Raum *m*	espace *m* topologique de Riesz	пространство Риса
	Riesz['s] summation method <LI>	*s.* R 1057		
R 1063	**Riesz['s] theory** <of compact operators> <FA>	Rieszsche Theorie *f* <der kompakten Operatoren>	théorie *f* de Riesz <des opérateurs compacts>	теория Риса <компактных операторов>
R 1064	**Riesz['s] typical mean** <LI>	Rieszsches typisches Mittel *n*	moyenne *f* typique [de [M.] Riesz]	среднее типичное [M.] Риса
R 1065	**right action** <AL> ┌<CA>	rechte Wirkung *f*	action *f* droite	правое действие
R 1066	**right action** <of a monoid>	Rechtsoperation *f*	action *f* à droite	правое действие
R 1067	**right adherent point** <TO>	rechtsseitiger Berührungspunkt *m*	point *m* adhérent à droite	правая точка прикосновения
	right[-] adjoint <CA>	*s.* C 951		
R 1068	**right adjoint homomorphism** <AL>	rechtsadjungierter Homomorphismus *m*	adjoint *m* à droite <d'un homomorphisme>	сопряженный справа гомоморфизм
R 1069	**right almost periodic function,** function almost periodic on the right <on a topological group> <AP>	rechts-fastperiodische Funktion *f*	fonction *f* presque périodique à droite	почти периодическая справа функция
R 1070	**right[-] alternative algebra** <AL>	rechtsalternative Algebra *f*	algèbre *f* alternative à droite	правоальтернативная алгебра
R 1071	**right alternative division ring, right alternative field** <AL>	Rechtsalternativkörper *m*	corps *m* alternatif à droite	правоальтернативное поле
R 1072	**right alternative law** <AL>	Rechtsalternativgesetz *n*	loi *f* alternative à droite	правый альтернативный закон
R 1073	**right alternative ring** <AL>	Rechtsalternativring *m*	anneau *m* alternatif à droite	правоальтернативное кольцо
R 1074	**right amenable** <AL>	rechtsamenabel	aménable à droite, moyennable à droite	правоаменабельный, право-усреднимый
R 1075	**right[-] analytic function** <FT>	rechtsanalytische Funktion *f*	fonction *f* analytique à droite	аналитическая справа функция, правоаналитическая функция
R 1076	**right[-] analytic hypercomplex function** <AN>	rechtsanalytische hyperkomplexe Funktion *f*	fonction *f* hypercomplexe analytique à droite	аналитическая справа гиперкомплексная функция, правоаналитическая функция, праворегулярная функция гиперкомплексного переменного
R 1077	**right angle,** └ <EG>	rechter Winkel *m*, Rechte *m*, └	rangle *m* droit, └	прямой угол, └
R 1078	**right-angled triangle,** right triangle <EG>	rechtwinkliges Dreieck *n*	triangle *m* rectangle	прямоугольный треугольник
R 1079	**right[-] annihilating** <AL>	rechts[-] annullierend	annihilant à droite	правоуничтожающий
R 1080	**right[-]annihilator, right annihilator ideal** <AL>	rechter Annulator (Annullator) *m*, Rechtsannulator *m*, Rechtsannullator *m*	annulateur *m* à droite	правый аннулятор
R 1081	**right artinian ring,** ring with right DCC <AL>	rechtsartinscher Ring *m*	anneau *m* artinien à droite	артиново справа кольцо, правоартиново кольцо
R 1082	**right artinian semigroup** <AL>	rechtsartinsche Halbgruppe *f*	demi-groupe *m* artinien à droite	артинова справа полугруппа, правоартинова полугруппа
R 1083	**right associate** <of a matrix> <AL, MD>	rechtsassoziierte Matrix *f*, Rechtsassoziierte *f*	matrice *f* associée à droite	правоассоциированная матрица
R 1084	**right associate[d] element** <in a ring> <AL>	rechtsassoziiertes Element *n*	élément *m* associé à droite	ассоциированный справа элемент, правоассоциированный элемент
	right-associatedness <AL>	*s.* P 1844		
R 1085	**right balanced functor** <CA>	rechtsausgeglichener Funktor *m*	foncteur *m* balancé à droite	сбалансированный справа функтор
R 1086	**right bimodule** <AL>	Birechtsmodul *m*, Doppelrechtsmodul *m*	bimodule *m* à droite	правый бимодуль
R 1087	**right bisector,** mid[-]perpendicular <of a side of a triangle> <EG>	Mittellot *n*, Mittelsenkrechte *f*	médiatrice *f*, perpendiculaire *f* au milieu	медиатриса
	right bound <SE>	*s.* U 411		
	right-bounded ordered set <SE>	*s.* B 664		
	right-bounded set <SE>	*s.* B 672		
	right bracket <LO>	*s.* R 1165		
	right cancellability <AL>	*s.* R 574		
	right cancellable element <AL>	*s.* E 138/9		
R 1088	**right-cancellation halfgroupoid** <AL>	Halbgruppoid *n* mit Rechtskürzungsregel	p-groupoïde *m* simplifiable à droite	частичный группоид с правым сокращением
R 1089	**right[-] cancellation law,** law of right-side cancellation <AL>	Rechtskürzungsregel *f*, rechtsseitige Kürzungsregel *f*	règle *f* de simplification à droite	закон правостороннего сокращения

No.	English	German	French	Russian
R 1090	**right cancellative groupoid** <AL>	Gruppoid *n* mit Rechtskürzungsregel	groupoïde *m* vérifiant la règle de simplification à droite	группоид с правым сокращением (законом сокращения)
R 1091	**right cancellative semigroup** <AL>	Halbgruppe *f* mit Rechtskürzungsregel, rechtsreguläre Halbgruppe *f*	semi-groupe *m* à droite	полугруппа с правым сокращением, полугруппа с правым законом сокращения
R 1092	**right chain ring** <AL>	Ring *m*, dessen Rechtsideale linear geordnet sind	anneau *m* dont l'ensemble des idéaux à droite est linéairement ordonné	кольцо, для которого множество правых идеалов линейно упорядочено
R 1093	**right circular cone,** right cone, cone <EG>	gerader (senkrechter) Kreiskegel *m*, gerader (senkrechter) Kegel *m*, Kegel	cône *m* circulaire droit, cône droit, cône	прямой круглый (круговой) конус, прямой конус, конус
R 1094	**right circular cylinder,** cylinder <EG>	gerader (senkrechter) Kreiszylinder *m*, Walze *f*, Zylinder *m*	cylindre *m* circulaire droit, cylindre	прямой круговой цилиндр, цилиндр
	right cofinality <SE>	*s.* C 1880		
	right-cofinal set <SE>	*s.* C 1052		
	right-cofinal subset <SE>	*s.* C 1053		
R 1095	**right coherent ring** <AL>	rechts-kohärenter Ring *m*	anneau *m* cohérent à droite	когерентное справа кольцо
R 1096	**right comaximal elements** <AL>	rechtskomaximale Elemente *npl*	éléments *mpl* comaximaux à droite	комаксимальные справа элементы
R 1097	**right commensurable elements** <in a ring> <AL>	rechtskommensurable Elemente *npl*	éléments *mpl* possédant un multiple à droite commun	элементы, которые обладают общим правым кратным
R 1098	**right commutator** <of two elements of a group> <GR>	rechter Kommutator *m*	commutateur *m* à droite	правый коммутатор
R 1099	**right-commutator closed group** <GR>	rechtskommutatorgeschlossene Gruppe *f*		правокоммутаторно замкнутая группа
R 1100	**right compatibility,** right regularity, right homogeneity <of a relation> <UA>	rechtsseitige Kompatibilität *f*, rechtsseitige Verträglichkeit *f*	compatibilité *f* à droite, régularité *f* à droite	правая совместимость, правая стабильность, правая регулярность
R 1101	**right compatible relation,** right regular (homogeneous) relation <AL>	rechtskompatible Relation *f*	relation *f* régulière à droite, relation compatible à droite, relation permise à droite	стабильное справа отношение, регулярное справа отношение, однородное справа отношение
	right[-] complete category <CA>	*s.* C 992		
R 1102	**right completion,** right-handed completion <of a topological group> <GR, TO>	rechtsseitige Vervollständigung *f*	complété *m* à droite	правостороннее пополнение
R 1103	**right composition algebra** <AL>	Rechtskompositionsalgebra *f*	algèbre *f* de composition à droite	правокомпозиционная алгебра
	right cone <EG>	*s.* R 1093		
R 1104	**right congruence** <on a groupoid> <UA>	rechtsseitige Kongruenzrelation *f*	équivalence *f* régulière à droite, équivalence compatible à droite, congruence à droite	правая конгруэнция, стабильная справа эквивалентность
R 1105	**right congruent element** <of a group> <AL>	rechtskongruentes Element *n*, rechtskongruentes Gruppenelement *n*	élément *m* équivalent à droite	правоконгруэнтный элемент
R 1106	**right conoid** <GE>	gerades Konoid *n*	conoïde *m* droit	прямой коноид
	right-continuous function <AN>	*s.* F 758		
R 1107	**right continuous functor,** colimit preserving functor <CA>	rechtsstetiger Funktor *m*, kostetiger (costetiger) Funktor; Funktor, der Kolimiten respektiert	foncteur *m* co-continu, foncteur préservant les colimites	функтор, перестановочный с прямыми пределами; функтор, сохраняющий прямые пределы
R 1108	**right coprime elements** <AL>	rechtsteilerfremde Elemente *npl*	éléments *mpl* sans diviseurs à droite communs, éléments étrangers à droite	копростые справа элементы, взаимно простые справа элементы, правовзаимнопростые элементы
R 1109	**right coset** <of a group> <GR>	rechte Restklasse *f*, rechte Nebenklasse *f*, rechtsseitige Restklasse *f*, rechte Nebengruppe *f*, rechtsseitige Nebenklasse, Rechtsnebenklasse *f*	classe *f* à droite, complexe *m* associé à droite, classe latérale à droite	правый смежный класс, правосторонний смежный класс
R 1110	**right coset decomposition (expansion),** decomposition into right cosets <modulo, with respect to> <of a group *or* quasigroup> <AL, GR>	rechtsseitige (rechte) Restklassenzerlegung *f*, rechtsseitige Zerlegung *f*, Zerlegung in rechte Restklassen <modulo, nach>	décomposition *f* en complexes à droite, décomposition <d'un groupe> en ses complexes à droite, décomposition en classes à droite <suivant>	правостороннее (правое) разложение <по>
R 1111	**right coset relative to *H*** <GR>	rechtsseitige Nebenklasse *f* modulo *H*, rechtsseitige Restklasse *f* modulo *H*, Rechtsnebenklasse *f* modulo *H*	classe *f* à droite modulo *H*, classe à droite suivant *H*, complexe *m* associé à droite à *H*	правый класс смежности по *H*, правосторонний смежный класс по *H*
	right coset space <AL, TO>	*s.* S 1327		
R 1112	**right cylinder** <EG>	gerader Zylinder *m*	cylindre *m* droit	прямой цилиндр
	right decomposition <AL>	*s.* R 1267		
R 1113	**right-degenerate bilinear mapping** <AL>	rechtsausgeartete bilineare Abbildung *f*	application *f* bilinéaire dégénérée à droite	вырожденное справа билинейное отображение

No.	English	Deutsch	Français	Русский
R 1114	**right-degenerate semi-linear mapping** <AL>	rechtsausgeartete halblineare Abbildung *f*	application *f* sesquilinéaire dégénérée à droite	вырожденное справа полуторалинейное отображение
R 1115	**right denominator** <AL>	Rechtsnenner *m*	dénominateur *m* à droite	правый знаменатель
R 1116	**right derivation** <AL>	rechte Derivation *f*	dérivation *f* droite	правое дифференцирование
R 1117	**right derivative** <of a matrix> <DI, MD>	rechte Ableitung *f*	derivée *f* droite	правая производная
	right derivative <DI>	*s.* R 1150		
	right derivative function <RF>	*s.* R 1151		
R 1118	**right derived functor** <*n*-th> <CA>	rechtsabgeleiteter Funktor *m* <*n*-ter>	foncteur *m* dérivé droit <*n*-e>	правая производная <функтора> <*n*-я>, правый производный функтор <*n*-й>, правый производный когомологический функтор <*n*-й>
	right determinant <AL>	*s.* R 1152		
R 1119	**right difference** <of ordinals> <SE>	rechte Differenz *f*	différence *f* à droite	правая разность
R 1120	**right differentiability,** right-hand differentiability, differentiability on the right, forward differentiability <DI>	rechtsseitige (vordere) Differenzierbarkeit *f*	dérivabilité *f* à droite	дифференцируемость справа, правосторонняя (правая) дифференцируемость
R 1121	**right differential** <of a Lie group> <GR>	rechtes Differential *n*	différentielle *f* droite	правый дифференциал
	right Dini['s] derivative <RF>	*s.* R 1154		
R 1122	**right[-] directed partial order** <SE>	gerichtete Halbordnung *f*	ordre *m* filtrant [à droite]	направленный вверх частичный порядок
R 1123	**right[-] directed quasi-order,** right direction <SE>	nach oben gerichtete Quasiordnung *f*, gerichtete Quasiordnung	préordre *m* filtrant [à droite]	направленный вверх квазипорядок
	right[-] directed quasi-order <SE>	*s. a.* Q 140		
	right[-] directed set <SE>	*s.* D 552		
	right direction <SE>	*s.* 1. Q 140; 2. R 1123		
R 1124	**right direct product** <of matrices> <MD>	rechtes direktes Produkt *n*	produit *m* direct à droite	правое прямое произведение
R 1125	**right distributive** <over, with respect to> <AL, LO, SE>	rechtsdistributiv, rechtsseitig distributiv <bezüglich>	distributif à droite <par rapport à>	дистрибутивный справа <относительно>
R 1126	**right distributive composition law** <AL>	rechtsdistributives Verknüpfungsgesetz *n*	loi *f* [de composition] distributive à droite	дистрибутивный справа закон композиции
R 1127	**right distributive law,** right-side distributive law <AL>	Rechtsdistributivgesetz *n*, rechtsseitiges Distributivgesetz *n*	condition *f* de distributivité à droite, loi *f* de distributivité à droite; loi distribuée à droite <loi externe>	закон правой дистрибутивности, правый закон дистрибутивности, правый дистрибутивный закон, правосторонний распределительный закон
R 1128	**right distributivity** <AL>	rechtsseitige Distributivität *f*, Rechtsdistributivität *f*	distributivité *f* à droite	дистрибутивность справа
R 1129	**right[-]division** <AL, SE>	rechtsseitige (rechte) Division *f*	division *f* à droite	правое деление
R 1130	**right division algorithm** <AL>	rechtsseitiger Divisionsalgorithmus *m*, Rechtsdivisionsalgorithmus *m*	division *f* généralisée à gauche, algorithme *m* de la division à droite	правый алгоритм деления
R 1131	**right divisor,** right-hand divisor <AL, SE>	Rechtsteiler *m*, rechter Teiler *m*	diviseur *m* à droite	правый делитель
	right divisor of zero <AL>	*s.* R 1293		
	right domain <SE>	*s.* R 122		
R 1132	**right dual couple** <FA>	Rechtsdualsystem *n*	couple *m* d'espaces associés à droite	правая дуальная пара
R 1133	**right eigenvector** <AL>	Rechtseigenvektor *m*	vecteur *m* propre à droite	правый собственный вектор
	right end point <AN>	*s.* R 1159		
R 1134	**right Engel element** <of a group> <GR>	rechts-engelsches Element *n*	élément *m* engelien à droite	право-энгелев элемент
R 1135	**right-equivalent matrix** <AL>	rechtsäquivalente Matrix *f*	matrice *f* équivalente à droite	право-эквивалентная матрица
R 1136	**right essential extension** <of a ring> <AL>	rechte wesentliche Erweiterung *f*	extension *f* essentielle à droite	правое существенное расширение
R 1137	**right exact functor** <CA>	rechtsexakter Funktor *m*	foncteur *m* exact à droite	точный справа функтор
R 1138	**right exactness** <of a functor> <CA>	Rechtsexaktheit *f*	exactitude *f* à droite	правоточность
R 1139	**right exponent** <AL>	Rechtsexponent *m*	exposant *m* à droite	правый показатель
R 1140	**right external composition law** <AL>	rechtsseitige äußere Verknüpfung *f*	loi *f* de composition externe à droite, loi externe à gauche	правая внешняя композиция
	right extremity <AN>	*s.* R 1159		
R 1141	**right factor** <of an unknown> <AL>	Rechtsfaktor *m*	facteur *m* droite	правый множитель
R 1142	**right faithful functor** <on the object *A*> <CA>	rechtstreuer Funktor *m* <auf dem Objekt *A*>	foncteur *m* fidèle à droite <sur l'objet *A*>	унивалентный справа функтор <на объекте *A*>
R 1143	**right faithful ring** <AL>	rechtstreuer Ring *m*	anneau *m* fidèle à droite	точное справа кольцо
	right free object <CA>	*s.* C 1057		
R 1144	**right global homological (projective) dimension** <of a ring> <AL>	rechte globale homologische Dimension *f*, rechte globale projektive Dimension	dimension *f* homologique globale à droite	правая глобальная гомологическая размерность
R 1145	**right Goldie dimension** <AL>	rechte Goldie-Dimension *f*	dimension *f* de Goldie à droite	правая размерность Голди
R 1146	**right Goldie ring** <AL>	Rechts-Goldie-Ring *m*	anneau *m* de Goldie à droite	правое кольцо Голди

No.	English	German	French	Russian
R 1147	**right Haar measure,** right-invariant Haar measure <AL>	rechtes Haar-Maß *n*	mesure *f* de Haar à droite	правая мера Хаара, правоинвариантная мера Хаара
R 1148	**right Haar module** <AL>	rechter Haar-Modul *m*	module *m* de Haar à droite	правый модуль Хаара
R 1149	**right-hand cancellation,** right-side cancellation <AL>	rechtsseitige Kürzung *f*, rechtsseitiges Kürzen *n*	simplification *f* à droite	правостороннее сокращение
	right-hand continuous function <AN>	*s.* F 758		
R 1150	**right-hand derivative,** derivative on the right, right derivative, right-handed derivative, forward derivative <of a function> <DI>	rechtsseitige (vordere, rechte) Ableitung (Derivierte) *f*, Rechtsableitung *f*, Rechtsderivierte *f*, rechtsseitiger (vorderer) Differentialquotient *m*	dérivée (semi-dérivée) *f* à droite	производная справа, правосторонняя производная, [односторонняя] правая производная
R 1151	**right-hand derivative function,** right derivative function, derivative function on the right, forward derivative function <RF>	rechtsseitige (vordere) Derivierten funktion *f*	fonction *f* dérivée à droite	производная функция справа, правосторонняя (правая) производная функция
R 1152	**right-hand determinant,** right determinant <in a non-commutative ring> <AL>	rechtsseitige Determinante *f*	déterminant *m* à droite	правосторонний определитель
	right-hand differentiability <DI>	*s.* R 1120		
R 1153	**right-hand differentiable function,** function differentiable on the right <RF>	rechtsseitig (nach rechts) differenzierbare Funktion *f*	fonction *f* dérivable à droite	дифференцируемая справа функция
R 1154	**right-hand Dini['s] derivative,** right (forward) Dini['s] derivative, Dini['s] derivative on the right, D_r <RF>	rechtsseitige Derivierte (Ableitungszahl) *f*, vordere Derivierte, D_v, D_r	nombre *m* dérivé à droite	правое производное число
	right-hand divisor <AL, SE>	*s.* R 1131		
	right-handed completion <GR, TO>	*s.* R 1102		
R 1155	**right-handed co-ordinate system,** right-handed system, right system <of co-ordinates, of co-ordinate axes> <AY>	rechtshändiges Koordinatensystem *n*, Rechtssystem *n*, rechtshändiges System *n*; Rechtskreuz *n* <im E^n>	système *m* dextrogyre, système droit [des axes de coordonnées], système de rotation à droite, système direct [de coordonnées], système de coordonnées à droite, système à droite	правовращающая[ся] система [координат], правая система [координат], правая координатная система, правовинтовая система
R 1156	**right-handed curve,** dextrorse curve, dextrorsum curve <GE>	rechtswendige Kurve *f*, rechtsgewundene Kurve, rechtsgängige Kurve	courbe *f* dextrorsum	кривая правого вращения, завитая вправо кривая
	right-handed derivative <DI>	*s.* R 1150		
	right-handed helix <GE>	*s.* D 372		
R 1157	**right-handed rotation,** positive rotation, clockwise rotation <EG>	Rechtsdrehung *f*, positive Drehung *f*	rotation *f* droite, rotation positive	правое вращение, положительное вращение, вращение вправо, вращение по часовой стрелке
	right-handed ruled surface <GE>	*s.* D 373		
	right-handed screw <GE>	*s.* R 1261		
	right-handed system <AY>	*s.* R 1155		
R 1158	**right-handed trihedral** <of vectors> <GE, VT>	rechtshändiges Dreibein *n* (Tripel *n* von Vektoren), positiv orientiertes Dreibein	trièdre *m* de sens direct, trièdre direct, trièdre positivement orienté	правая упорядоченная тройка векторов
R 1159	**right-hand end-point,** right end point, right extremity <of an interval> <AN>	rechter Endpunkt *m*	extrémité *f* à droite	правый конец
	right-hand helix <GE>	*s.* D 372		
R 1160	**right-hand inclusion,** ⊃ <SE>	rechtsseitige Inklusion *f*, ⊃	inclusion *f* à droite, ⊃	правостороннее включение, ⊃
	right-hand limit <DI>	*s.* L 741		
R 1161	**right-hand lower approximate limit** <AN>	rechtsseitiger unterer approximativer Limes (Hauptlimes) *m*	limite *f* approximative inférieure à droite	правосторонний (правый) нижний аппроксимативный предел
R 1162	**right-hand lower continuous** <AN>	rechtsseitig unterhalb[ ] stetig, rechtsseitig nach unten stetig, rechtsseitig abwärts stetig	continu inférieurement à droite	справа непрерывный снизу
R 1163	**right-hand lower Dini['s] derivative,** lower Dini['s] derivative on the right <of a function> <RF>	untere rechtsseitige (vordere) Derivierte *f*, rechtsseitige (rechte) untere Derivierte (Ableitungszahl *f*), $\underline{D}_v$, $\underline{D}_r$, $\underline{D}_+$	nombre *m* dérivé inférieur à droite, nombre dérivé à droite par défaut	нижнее правое производное число, нижнее производное число справа
R 1164	**right-hand lower limit,** right lower limit, lower right-hand limit, lower limit on the right <DI>	unterer rechtsseitiger Limes (Hauptlimes) *m*	limite *f* inférieure à droite	нижний правосторонний (правый) предел, нижний предел справа
R 1165	**right-hand parenthesis,** right parenthesis, parentheses closed, end of parentheses; brackets closed, end of brackets, right bracket,) <LO>	rechte Klammer *f*, Klammer zu,)	parenthèse *f* fermante,)	правая скобка,)

	right-hand ruled surface <GE>	*s.* D 373		
	right-hand screw <GE>	*s.* R 1261		
R 1166	**right-hand side,** right hand side, right side, right member, second member, RHS <of an equation *or* inequality> <GN>	rechte Seite *f*, zweites Glied *n*	membre *m* droit, second (deuxième) membre, partie *f* droite, membre à droite, côté *m* droit	правая сторона (часть)
R 1167	**right-hand symmetrizable kernel** <FA>	rechtsseitig symmetrisierbarer Kern *m*	noyau *m* symétrisable à droite	симметризируемое справа ядро
R 1168	**right-hand system** <of linear equations> <in a non-commutative ring> <AL>	rechtsseitiges lineares Gleichungssystem *n*	système *m* d'équations linéaires à droite	правосторонняя система линейных уравнений
R 1169	**right-hand upper approximate limit** <AN>	rechtsseitiger oberer approximativer Limes (Hauptlimes) *m*	limite *f* approximative supérieure à droite	правосторонний (правый) верхний аппроксимативный предел
R 1170	**right-hand upper continuous** <AN>	rechtsseitig oberhalb[ ] stetig, rechtsseitig nach oben stetig, rechtsseitig aufwärts stetig	continu supérieurement à droite	справа непрерывный сверху
R 1171	**right-hand upper Dini['s] derivative,** upper Dini['s] derivative on the right <of a function> <RF>	obere rechtsseitige (vordere) Derivierte *f*, rechtsseitige (rechte) obere Derivierte (Ableitungszahl *f*)	nombre *m* dérivé supérieur à droite, nombre dérivé à droite par excès, dérivée *f* supérieure à droite de Dini	верхнее правое производное число
R 1172	**right-hand upper limit,** right upper limit, upper right-hand limit, upper limit on the right <DI>	oberer rechtsseitiger Limes (Hauptlimes) *m*	limite *f* supérieure à droite	правосторонний верхний предел, верхний предел справа
	right-hand zero-element <AL>	*s.* R 1294		
R 1173	**right helicoid** <AY, DG>	Wendelfläche *f*, Minimalregelfläche *f*, gemeine (flachgängige, Meusniersche) Schraubenfläche *f*, [gewöhnliche] Schraubenfläche, gemeines (gewöhnliches) Helikoid *n*	hélicoïde *m* droit, hélicoïde gauche à plan directeur	прямой геликоид, обыкновенная винтовая поверхность
R 1174	**right hereditary ring** <AL> ┌<AL>	rechtserblicher Ring *m*	anneau *m* héréditaire à droite	наследственное справа кольцо
R 1175	**right heredity** <of a ring>	Rechtserblichkeit *f*	hérédité *f* à droite	наследственность справа
R 1176	**right Hermite ring** <AL>	rechtshermitescher Ring *m*	anneau *m* hermitien à droite	правоэрмитово кольцо
	right homogeneity <UA>	*s.* R 1100		
	right homogeneous relation <AL>	*s.* R 1101		
	right homothetic (homothety) <AL, GR>	*s.* R 1212		
R 1177	**right homotopy inverse,** right inverse in the homotopy category <CA, TO>	Rechts-Homotopieinverses *n*, Rechtsinverses *n* in der Kategorie der topologischen Räume modulo Homotopie	homotopie-inverse *m* à droite	правый гомотопически обратный [элемент], гомотопически правообратное отображение, правый обратный элемент в категории гомотопических типов
R 1178	**right ideal** <AL, CA>	Rechtsideal *n*, rechtsseitiges Ideal *n*	idéal *m* à droite	правый идеал
	right identity <AL>	*s.* R 1286		
	right identity <AL, GR>	*s.* R 1179		
R 1179	**right identity element,** right unity, right unit-element, right unit, right identity; right neutral element <AL, GR>	Rechtseinselement *n*, rechtsseitiges Einselement *n*, Rechtseinheit *f*, Rechtseins *f*; rechtsneutrales Element *n*; rechtes Hauptelement *n* erster Art <in einem Gruppoid>	élément *m* unité à droite, élément-unité *m* à droite, unité *f* droite; élément neutre à droite	правый единичный элемент, правая единица, правосторонний единичный элемент; правый нейтральный элемент
R 1180	**right injective dimension** <AL>	rechte injektive Dimension *f*	dimension *f* injective à droite	правая инъективная размерность
R 1181	**right injective ring** <AL>	rechtsinjektiver Ring *m*	anneau *m* injectif à droite	правоинъективное кольцо
R 1182	**right inner product** <of *p*-forms> <AL>	rechtes inneres Produkt *n*	produit *m* intérieur droit	правое внутреннее произведение
R 1183	**right[-] invariance** <AL>	Rechtsinvarianz *f*	invariance *f* à droite	правоинвариантность
	right-invariant Haar measure <AL>	*s.* R 1147		
R 1184	**right[-] invariant infinitesimal transformation** <AL>	rechtsinvariante infinitesimale Transformation *f*	transformation *f* infinitésimale invariante à droite	правоинвариантное (инвариантное справа) инфинитезимальное преобразование
R 1185	**right[-] invariant measure** <on a group> <GR>	rechtsinvariantes Maß *n*	mesure *f* invariante par translation à droite	правоинвариантная мера
R 1186	**right inverse** <AL>	rechtsinvers	symétrique à droite <loi arbitraire>; inverse à droite <en particulier loi multiplicative>	симметричный справа <обще>; правый обратный <в частности для умножения>
R 1187	**right inverse** <of a linear mapping> <AL>	Rechtsreziproke *f*, Rechtsinverse *f* <einer linearen Abbildung>	inverse *f* à droite <d'une application linéaire>	правое обратное отображение
	right inverse <AL>	*s.* R 1188		
	right inverse <FA>	*s.* R 1190		
	right inverse <MD>	*s.* R 1189		
R 1188	**right inverse element,** right inverse <of an element> <AL>	Rechtsinverses *n*, rechtsseitiges Inverses *n*, rechtsinverses Element *n*	élément *m* inverse à droite, inverse *m* de droite, inverse *m* à droite; élément *m* symétrique à droite	правый обратный элемент, обратный справа [элемент], правосторонний обратный элемент

No.	English	German	French	Russian
	right inverse in the homotopy category <CA, TO>	*s.* R 1177		
R 1189	**right inverse matrix,** right inverse <of a[n infinite] matrix> <MD>	Rechtsinverse *f*, rechte Reziproke *f*, hintere Reziproke, rechtsinverse Matrix *f*	inverse *f* à droite <d'une matrice [infinie]>	правая обратная матрица
R 1190	**right inverse operator,** right inverse, pseudo-inverse <of a linear operator> <FA>	rechtsinverser Operator *m*	opérateur *m* inverse à droite	правый обратный оператор
R 1191	**right-invertible element** <AL>	rechtsinvertierbares Element *n*	élément *m* inversible à droite, élément symétrisable à droite	обратный справа элемент
R 1192	**right-invertible mapping** <AL>	rechtsinvertierbare Abbildung *f*	application *f* inversible à droite	обратимое справа отображение
R 1193	**right-isolated point,** point isolated from the right <in ordered spaces> <TO>	von rechts isolierter Punkt *m*	point *m* isolé à droite	изолированная справа точка
R 1194	**right isotropic line** <PJ>	Rechtsisotrope *f*	droite *f* isotrope à droite	правая изотропная прямая
R 1195	**right iteration** <of a transfinite function> <SE>	Rechtsiteration *f*	itération *f* à droite	правая итерация
R 1196	**right Kan extension** <CA>	rechtsseitige Kan-Erweiterung *f*	extension *f* de Kan à droite	правостороннее расширение Кана
R 1197	**right kernel** <of a bilinear mapping> <GR>	rechtsseitiger Kern *m*	noyau *m* à droite	ядро справа
R 1198	**right *K*-module** <AL>	*K*-Rechtsmodul *m*, Rechtsvektorraum *m* über *K*	*K*-module *m* à droite, espace *m* vectoriel à droite sur *K*	правый *K*-модуль
R 1199	**right Krull dimension** <of a ring> <AL>	rechte Krullsche Dimension *f*	dimension *f* de Krull à droite	правая размерность Крулля
R 1200	**right length** <of a module *or* ring> <AL>	rechte Länge *f*	longueur *f* à droite	правая длина
	right liberty <CA>	*s.* C 1129		
	right limit <DI>	*s.* L 741		
R 1201	**right linearly dependent over *K*, right linearly *K*-dependent** <AL>	rechtsseitig linear abhängig über *K*	linéairement dépendant sur *K* à droite	линейно зависимый справа над *K*, линейно *K*-зависимый справа
R 1202	**right linear topology** <on a ring> <AL>	rechtslineare Topologie *f*	topologie *f* linéaire à droite	линейная справа топология
R 1203	**right localization** <of a ring> <AL>	rechtsseitige Lokalisierung *f*	localisation *f* à droite	правая локализация
	right lower limit <DI>	*s.* R 1164		
R 1204	**right mean** <of a function on a topological group> <AL>	rechter Mittelwert *m*	moyenne *f* à droite	правое среднее
	right member <GN>	*s.* R 1166		
	right modular ideal <AL>	*s.* R 622		
R 1205	**right module** <AL>	Rechtsmodul *m*	module *m* à droite	правый модуль
	right module over *R* <AL>	*s.* R 1259		
R 1206	**right[-] monotonicity** <AL, SE>	rechtsseitige Monotonie *f*	monotonie *f* à droite	монотонность справа
R 1207	**right-monotonic law** <AL, SE>	rechtsseitiges Monotoniegesetz *n*	loi *f* de monotonie à droite	закон монотонности справа
R 1208	**right-monotonic operation** <AL, SE>	rechtsmonotone Operation *f*	opération *f* monotone à droite	монотонная справа операция
R 1209	**right multimodule** <AL>	Multirechtsmodul *m*	multimodule *m* à droite	правый мультимодуль
R 1210	**right multiple** <AL, SE>	rechtsseitiges Vielfaches *n*, Rechtsvielfaches *n*	multiple *m* à droite	правое кратное
R 1211	**right[-] multiplication,** post[-] multiplication, post[-] multiplying, multiplication on the right <AL>	Multiplikation *f* von rechts, Rechtsmultiplikation *f*, rechtsseitige Multiplikation *f*	multiplication *f* à droite, postmultiplication *f*, post-multiplication *f*	умножение справа, умножение начиная справа, умножение с обычным порядком
R 1212	**right multiplication,** right translation, right homothety, right homothetic <by *a*> <AL, GR>	rechte Translation *f*, Rechtstranslation *f*, rechte Homothetie *f*, rechte Multiplikation *f*, rechtsseitige Multiplikation, rechtsseitige Translation <durch *a*>	homothétie *f* à droite, translation *f* à droite (correspondant à *a*, par rapport à *a*, d'amplitude *a*>	правая гомотетия, сдвиг справа, правый сдвиг, правый перенос <соответствующий элементу *a*>
	right[-] multiplication <AL>	*s.* I 564		
R 1213	**right multiplication group** <of a quasigroup> <AL>	Gruppe *f* der Rechtsmultiplikationen	groupe *m* des multiplications à droite	группа правых умножений
R 1214	**right multiplicative domain,** right operator domain <AL>	Rechtsoperatorenbereich *m*, Rechtsmultiplikatorenbereich *m*, Rechtsoperatorenmenge *f*	ensemble *m* des opérateurs à droite, domaine *m* d'opérateurs à droite	область правых операторов
R 1215	**right *n*-Engel element,** bounded right Engel element <of a group> <GR>	beschränkt rechts-Engelsches Element *n*, *n*-rechts-Engelsches Element	élément *m* engelien à droite borné	ограниченный правоэнгелев элемент, *n*-право-энгелев элемент
	right neutral element <AL, GR>	*s.* R 1179		
R 1216	**right Noetherian (noetherian) ring** <AL>	rechtsnoetherscher Ring *m*	anneau *m* noethérien à droite	нетерово справа кольцо, правонетерово кольцо
R 1217	**right-nondegenerate bilinear form** <AL>	rechtsnichtausgeartete Bilinearform *f*	forme *f* bilinéaire non dégénérée à droite	невырожденная справа [билинейная] форма
R 1218	**right nonsingular form** <AL>	rechtsnichtsinguläre Form *f*	forme *f* [bilinéaire] non singulière à droite	неособая справа форма

No.	English	German	French	Russian
R 1219	**right non-zerodivisor,** right regular element <of a ring> <AL>	Rechtsnichtnullteiler *m*, Nichtrechtsnullteiler *m*, rechtsreguläres Element *n*	élément *m* non diviseur de zéro à droite, élément simplifiable à droite	правый неделитель нуля, сократимый справа элемент, правый регулярный элемент
R 1220	**right operator** <AL>	Rechtsoperator *m*, hinterer Operator *m*	opérateur *m* à droite, multiplicateur *m* à droite	правый оператор
	right operator domain <AL>	*s.* R 1214		
R 1221	**right order** <of a ring> <AL>	rechte Ordnung *f*	ordre *m* à droite	правый порядок
	right order <CT>	*s.* N 635		
R 1222	**right-ordered group** <GR>	rechts halbgeordnete Gruppe *f*	groupe *m* ordonné à droite	правая частично упорядоченная группа, правоупорядоченная группа
R 1223	**right Ore condition** <for a non-commutative ring> <AL>	rechte Ore-Bedingung *f*	condition *f* de Ore à droite	правое условие Оре
R 1224	**right Ore domain (ring)** <AL>	rechter Ore-Ring *m*	anneau *m* de Ore à droite	правое кольцо Оре, правое кольцо Орэ
R 1225	**right Ore set** <AL>	rechte Ore-Menge *f*	ensemble *m* de Ore à droite	правое множество Оре
R 1226	**right parallelepipedon** <EG>	gerades (senkrechtes) Parallelepiped *n*	parallélépipède *m* droit	прямой параллелепипед
	right parenthesis <LO>	*s.* R 1165		
R 1227	**right periodic group** <GR>	rechtsperiodische Gruppe *f*	groupe *m* périodique à droite	периодическая справа группа
	right PID <AL>	*s.* P 1470		
	right pir <AL>	*s.* P 1526		
R 1228	**right primary element** <of an ordered semigroup> <AL>	rechtsprimäres Element *n*	élément *m* primaire (premier) à droite	примарный справа элемент
R 1229	**right primitive ideal** <AL>	rechtsprimitives Ideal *n*	idéal *m* primitif à droite	примитивный справа идеал
R 1230	**right principal fibration** <AT>	rechtsseitiges Prinzipalfaserbündel *n*	fibration *f* principale à droite, faisceau *m* principal à droite	правое главное расслоение
	right principal ideal ring <AL>	*s.* P 1526		
R 1231	**right projective space** <AL>	rechtsprojektiver Raum *m*	espace *m* projectif à droite	проективное справа пространство
R 1232	**right pseudo-compact ring** <AL>	rechts-pseudokompakter Ring *m*	anneau *m* pseudo-compact à droite	псевдокомпактное справа кольцо
R 1233	**right pyramid** <EG>	gerade (senkrechte) Pyramide *f*	pyramide *f* droite	прямая пирамида
R 1234	**right quasi-field** <AL>	Rechtsquasikörper *m*, rechtsdistributive kartesische Gruppe *f*	quasi-corps *m* à droite	правое квазиполе
	right-quasi filtering category <CA>	*s.* Q 155		
R 1235	**right quasigroup** <AL>	Rechtsquasigruppe *f*	quasi-groupe *m* à droite	правая квазигруппа
R 1236	**right quasi inverse** <of an element of a ring> <AL>	rechtes Quasiinverses *n*	adverse *m* à droite	правый квазиобратный [элемент] <для>
R 1237	**right-quasi-invertible element, right[-] quasi-regular element** <of a ring> <AL>	rechts quasireguläres Element *n*	élément *m* quasi régulier à droite	право-квазирегулярный элемент
R 1238	**right[-] quasi-regularity** <AL>	Rechtsquasiregularität *f*	quasi-régularité *f* à droite	правая квазирегулярность
R 1239	**right quasi-simple ring,** ring quasi-simple from the right <AL>	rechts-quasieinfacher Ring *m*	anneau *m* quasi-simple à droite	квазипростое справа кольцо
R 1240	**right quotient** <AL>	Rechtsquotient *m*	quotient *m* à droite	правое частное
R 1241	**right quotient** <of a division algorithm> <AL>	rechtsseitiger Quotient *m*	quotient *m* à droite	правое неполное частное
R 1242	**right quotient field** <AL>	Rechtsquotientenschiefkörper *m*	corps *m* des quotients à droite	правое тело частных
R 1243	**right quotient ring,** ring of right quotients <with respect to a right Ore set> <AL>	rechter Quotientenring *m*, Rechtsquotientenring *m* <bezüglich einer rechten Ore-Menge>	anneau *m* des fractions à droite, anneau de fractions à droite <de *A* pour *S*>	правое кольцо частных
R 1244	**right radical** <AL>	rechtes Radikal *n*	radical *m* à droite	правый радикал
R 1245	**right rank,** rank <of a ring> <AL>	Rechtsrang *m*	rang *m* à droite	правый ранг
R 1246	**right regular element** <of a ring *or* semigroup> <AL>	rechtsreguläres Element *n*	élément *m* régulier à droite	регулярный справа элемент
	right regular element <AL>	*s.* 1. E 138/9; 2. R 1219		
R 1247	**right regularity** <of a semigroup> <AL>	Rechtsregularität *f*	régularité *f* à droite	правая регулярность
	right regularity <AL>	*s. a.* R 574		
	right regularity <UA>	*s.* R 1100		
	right regular matrix representation <AL>	*s.* R 1249		
	right regular relation <AL>	*s.* R 1101		
R 1248	**right regular representation,** regular representation <AL>	rechte reguläre Darstellung *f*, reguläre Darstellung	représentation *f* régulière droite, représentation régulière	правое регулярное представление, регулярное представление
R 1249	**right regular representation,** right regular matrix representation, first regular [matrix] representation <of an algebra> <AL>	rechte reguläre Matrizendarstellung *f*, reguläre (erste reguläre) Matrizendarstellung	représentation *f* matricielle régulière à droite	правое регулярное матричное представление

No.	English	German	French	Russian
R 1250	**right regular ring** <AL>	rechtsregulärer Ring *m*	anneau *m* régulier à droite	регулярное справа кольцо
R 1251	**right regular semigroup** <AL>	rechtsreguläre Halbgruppe *f*	demi-groupe *m* inversif à droite, semi-groupe *m* régulier à droite	регулярная справа полугруппа
R 1252	**right remainder** <in a division algorithm> <AL>	rechtsseitiger Rest *m*	reste *f* à droite	правый остаток
R 1253	**right representation** <of a category> <CA>	rechte Darstellung *f*	représentation *f* droite	правое представление
R 1254	**right representative** <AL>	Rechtsrepräsentant *m*	représentant *m* à droite	правый представитель
R 1255	**right representative system** <AL>	Rechtsrepräsentantensystem *n*, Rechtsvertretersystem *n*	système *m* de représentants à droite	правая система представителей
R 1256	**right resolution** <of an object> <CA>	rechte Auflösung *f*	résolution *f* à droite	правая резольвента
R 1257	**right reversible semigroup** <AL>	rechtsreversible Halbgruppe *f*	semi-groupe *m* réversible à droite	реверсивная справа полугруппа, полугруппа с общими справа кратными
R 1258	**right Riemann integral** <of a matrix> <AN>	rechtes Riemannsches Integral *n*	intégrale *f* de Riemann à droite	правый интеграл Римана
R 1259	**right R-module,** right module over *R* <AL>	*R*-Rechtsmodul *m*, Rechtsmodul *m* über *R*, Rechtsmodul mit *R* als Operatorenbereich	module *m* à droite sur *R*, *R*-module *m* à droite	правый *R*-модуль (модуль над *R*)
	right root <CA>	*s.* C 1130		
R 1260	**right satellite** <of a functor> <CA>	rechter Satellit *m*	satellite *m* droit	правый сателлит
R 1261	**right screw,** right-hand[ed] screw, right-twisted screw, dextrorse screw <GE>	Rechtsschraube *f*	vis *f* à droite, vis dextrorsum, vis à torsion droite (dextre)	правый винт
R 1262	**right secondary element** <AL>	rechtssekundäres Element *n*	élément *m* secondaire à droite	вторичный справа элемент
R 1263	**right secondary radical** <AL>	rechtes sekundäres Radikal *n*	radical *m* secondaire à droite	правый вторичный радикал
	right segment <SE>	*s.* R 789		
R 1264	**right self-injective ring** <AL>	rechtsseitig selbstinjektiver Ring *m*	anneau *m* self-injectif à droite	самоинъективное справа кольцо
R 1265	**right semi-hereditary ring** <AL>	rechts-halberblicher Ring *m*	anneau *m* semi-héréditaire à droite	полунаследственное справа кольцо
	right semi-isomorphism <CA>	*s.* R 949		
R 1266	**right semilinear mapping** <AL>	rechtshalblineare Abbildung *f*	application *f* sesquilinéaire à droite	полуторалинейное справа отображение
	right side <GN>	*s.* R 1166		
	right-side cancellation <AL>	*s.* R 1149		
R 1267	**right-sided decomposition,** right decomposition <AL>	rechtsseitige Zerlegung *f*, Rechtszerlegung *f*	décomposition *f* à droite	правостороннее разложение, правое разложение
	right-side distributive law <AL>	*s.* R 1127		
R 1268	**right-sided Peirce decomposition** <of a ring> <AL>	rechtsseitige Peircesche Zerlegung *f*	décomposition *f* de Peirce à droite	правостороннее пирсовское разложение
R 1269	**right simple semigroup** <AL>	rechtseinfache Halbgruppe *f*	demi-groupe *m* simple à droite	простая справа полугруппа
R 1270	**right singular ideal** <AL>	singuläres Rechtsideal *n*	idéal *m* singulier à droite	сингулярный правый идеал
R 1271	**right socle** <of a ring> <AL>	Rechtssockel *m*, rechtsseitiges Antiradikal *n*	socle *m* droit	правый цоколь
R 1272	**right solvable** <AL>	rechtsseitig lösbar	résoluble à droite	праворазрешимый
	right strophoid <AG>	*s.* S 2007		
R 1273	**right structure** <of a ring> <AL>	Rechtsstruktur *f*	structure *f* à droite	правая структура
R 1274	**right symbolic power** <in a non-commutative ring> <AL>	rechte symbolische Potenz *f*	puissance *f* symbolique à droite	правая символическая степень
	right system <AY>	*s.* R 1155		
R 1275	**right tangent** <DG>	rechte (rechtsseitige, vordere) Tangente *f*	tangente *f* à droite	правая касательная
R 1276	**right tensor product** <AL>	rechtsseitiges Tensorprodukt *n*	produit *m* tensoriel droite	правое тензорное произведение
R 1277	**right three-leafed rose** <GE>	gerades Dreiblatt *n*	rose *f* à trois branches droite	прямая трехлепестковая роза
R 1278	**right topological divisor of zero** <in a Banach algebra> <FA>	Rechtsnullteiler *m* im verallgemeinerten Sinn	diviseur *m* de zéro topologique à droite	правый топологический делитель нуля
R 1279	**right topological module** <AL>	topologischer Rechtsmodul *m*	module *m* topologique à droite	правый топологический модуль
R 1280	**right topological vector space** <AL>	topologischer Rechtsvektorraum *m*	espace *m* vectoriel topologique à droite	правое топологическое векторное пространство
R 1281	**right topology** <on an ordered set> <TO>	Rechtstopologie *f*	topologie *f* droite	правая топология
R 1282	**right translate** <of a function on a group> <AL>	durch Rechtstranslation aus einer Funktion hervorgehende Funktion *f*	fonction *f* translatée à droite	правый сдвиг <функции>
R 1283	**right translation** <of a function> <AL>	rechtsseitige Translation *f*	translation *f* à droite	правый сдвиг
R 1284	**right translation** <of a groupoid *or* ring> <AL>	Rechtstranslation *f*	homothétie *f* externe à droite	сдвиг справа, правый сдвиг
	right translation <AL, GR>	*s.* R 1212		
	right triangle <EG>	*s.* R 1078		

No.	English	German	French	Russian
	right-twisted helix <GE>	*s.* D 372		
	right-twisted screw <GE>	*s.* R 1261		
R 1285	**right uniformity** <of a topological group> <AL, TO>	rechts-uniforme Struktur *f*, Rechtsuniformität *f*, rechtsseitige uniforme Struktur	structure *f* uniforme droite	правая равномерная структура
	right-unique relation <SE>	*s.* S 1042		
R 1286	**right unit,** right identity <modulo 𝔞> <AL>	Rechtseinselement *n*, Rechtseinheit *f* <modulo 𝔞>	unité *f* à droite, élément *m* unité à droite <modulo 𝔞>	правая единица <по модулю 𝔞>
R 1287	**right unit,** domain unit <of an element, for an element> <AL>	Rechtseins *f* <eines Elements>	unité *f* droite <d'un élément>	правая единица <элемента>
R 1288	**right unit** <of a semigroup> <AL>	Rechtseinheit *f*	élément *m* inversible à droite	обратимый справа элемент
	right unit <AL, GR>	*s.* R 1179		
R 1289	**right-unitary kernel,** unitary kernel on the right <IE>	rechtsunitärer Kern *m*	noyau *m* unitaire à droite	унитарное справа ядро
	right unit-element <AL, GR>	*s.* R 1179		
R 1290	**right unit subsemigroup** <of a semigroup> <AL>	Unterhalbgruppe *f* der Rechtseinheiten	sous-demigroupe *m* des éléments inversibles à droite	подполугруппа [всех] обратимых справа элементов
	right unity <AL, GR>	*s.* R 1179		
R 1291	**right universal solution** <CA>	rechte universelle Lösung *f*	solution *f* universelle à droite	правое универсальное решение
	right upper limit <DI>	*s.* R 1172		
R 1292	**right vector space** <AL>	Rechtsvektorraum *m*	espace *m* vectoriel à droite	правое векторное пространство
R 1293	**right zero divisor,** right divisor of zero <AL>	rechter Nullteiler *m*	diviseur *m* de zéro à droite, diviseur droit de zéro, diviseur de zéro de seconde espèce	правый делитель нуля
R 1294	**right zero element,** right-hand zero-element <of a groupoid> <AL>	rechtes Nullelement *n*, Rechtsnullelement *n*, rechtes Hauptelement *n* zweiter Art, rechtsseitiges absorbierendes Element *n*	élément *m* permis à droite	правый нуль, правый нулевой элемент
R 1295	**right zeroid [element]** <of a semigroup> <AL>	rechtsseitiges Zeroidelement *n*, Rechtszeroid *n*	élément *m* zéroïde à droite	правый цероид
R 1296	**right zero morphism** <CA>	Rechts-Nullmorphismus *m*	morphisme *m* nul à droite	правый нулевой морфизм
	rigid complex space <FT, TO>	*s.* R 1302		
R 1297	**rigid curve** <in the isoperimetric problem> <VA>	starre Kurve *f*	courbe *f* rigide	жесткая кривая
R 1298	**rigidity** <of surfaces> <DG>	Nichtverbiegbarkeit *f*, Unverbiegbarkeit *f*, Starrheit *f*	rigidité *f*, non-flexibilité *f*	неизгибаемость, жесткость
R 1299	**rigidity** <of a metric space> <TO>	Starrheit *f*	rigidité *f*	жесткость
R 1300	**rigidity theorem** <DG>	Starrheitssatz *m*	théorème *m* de la rigidité	теорема о жесткости
	rigid motion <TO>	*s.* E 560		
R 1301	**rigid solution** <of the isoperimetric problem> <VA>	starre Lösung *f*	solution *f* rigide	жесткое решение
R 1302	**rigid space,** rigid complex space <FT, TO>	starrer Raum *m*, starrer komplexer Raum	espace *m* rigide, espace complexe rigide	жесткое пространство, жесткое комплексное пространство
R 1303	**rigid structure** <UA>	starre Struktur *f*	structure *f* rigide	жесткая структура
R 1304	**rigid surface** <DG>	starre Fläche *f*, infinitesimal unverbiegbare Fläche	surface *f* rigide	жесткая поверхность, [инфинитезимально] неизгибаемая поверхность
	rigor <GN>	*s.* M 171		
R 1305	**rigorous proof** <GN>	strenger Beweis *m*	démonstration *f* rigoureuse	строгое доказательство
R 1306	**rigorous solution** <GN>	strenge Lösung *f*	solution *f* rigoureuse	строгое решение
R 1307	**rim compact** <TO>	peripheres Kompaktum *n*		периферический бикомпакт (компакт)
R 1308	**ring** <AL>	Ring *m*	anneau *m*	кольцо
	δ-ring <SE>	*s.* D 213		
	Λ-ring <AL>	*s.* L 50		
	σ-ring <ME, SE>	*s.* S 831		
R 1309	**ring adjunction** <AL>	Ringadjunktion *f*	adjonction *f* d'anneau	кольцевое присоединение
R 1310	**ring axioms** <AL>	Ringaxiome *npl*	axiomes *mpl* d'anneaux	кольцевые аксиомы
R 1311	**ring completely reducible from the left of finite length** <AL>	linksseitig vollständig reduzibler Ring *m* endlicher Länge	anneau *m* complètement réductible à gauche de longueur finie	вполне приводимое кольцо слева конечной длины
R 1312	**ring completely reducible from the right** <AL>	rechtsseitig vollständig reduzibler Ring *m*	anneau *m* complètement réductible à droite	вполне приводимое кольцо справа
R 1313	**ring direct sum,** direct sum <of rings> <AL>	direkte Summe (Ringsumme) *f*, ringtheoretische direkte Summe	composé *m* direct <d'anneaux>	прямая сумма <колец>
R 1314	**ringed space** <AL>	geringter Raum *m*	espace *m* annelé (topologique muni d'un faisceau d'anneaux)	кольцованное (окольцованное) пространство
R 1315	**ring element not divisible by any power greater than**	quadratfreies Element *n*	élément *m* sans facteur multiple	элемент без квадратных множителей

No.	English	German	French	Russian
	one of an irreducible element <AL>			
R 1316	**ring extension** <AL>	Ringerweiterung *f*	extension *f* d'anneau	расширение кольца
	ring[-] function <FU>	*s.* T 577		
R 1317	**ring generator** <AL>	Ringerzeugende *f*	générateur *m* d'un anneau	кольцевой образующий
R 1318	**ring homomorphism,** homomorphism of rings, homomorphism, homomorphic mapping, ring representation, // meroedric isomorphism <of rings> <AL>	Ringhomomorphismus *m*, ringhomomorphe Abbildung *f*	morphisme *m* d'anneau	кольцевой гомоморфизм, гомоморфизм колец
R 1319	**ring module** <AL>	Modul *m* über einem Ring	module *m* sur un anneau	модуль над кольцом
R 1320	**ring morphism** <AL, CA>	Ringmorphismus *m*	morphisme *m* d'anneau	кольцевой морфизм
R 1321	**ring of algebraic integers** <NT>	Ring *m* der ganzen algebraischen Zahlen	domaine *m* algébrique, anneau *m* des entiers algébriques	кольцо целых алгебраических чисел
R 1322	**ring of constants** <of a polynomial ring> <AL>	Konstantenring *m*	anneau *m* des constantes	кольцо констант
R 1323	**ring of endomorphisms** <AL>	Endomorphismenring *m*, Ring *m* von Endomorphismen <nicht notwendig alle>	anneau *m* d'endomorphismes	кольцо эндоморфизмов
R 1324	**ring of formal power series,** formal power series ring <in *n* indeterminates> <AL>	Ring *m* der formalen Potenzreihen, formaler Potenzreihenring *m* <in *n* Unbestimmten>	anneau *m* de séries formelles <à *n* indéterminées>	кольцо формальных степенных рядов <от *n* переменных>
R 1325	**ring of infinite matrices** <FA>	Matrizenring *m*, Ring *m* unendlicher Matrizen	anneau *m* de matrices infinies	кольцо бесконечных матриц
R 1326	**ring of integers** <AL, NT>	Ring *m* der ganzen [rationalen] Zahlen	anneau *m* des entiers [relatifs]	кольцо целых (целых рациональных) чисел
	ring of left quotients <AL>	*s.* L 470		
R 1327	**ring of matrices,** matrix ring <AL>	Matrixring *m*, Matrizenring *m*, Matricesring *m*	anneau *m* de matrices, anneau matriciel	кольцо матриц
R 1328	**ring of numbers,** number ring <NT>	Zahlenring *m*	anneau *m* de nombres	числовое кольцо
R 1329	**ring of operators** <FA>	Operatorring *m*, Ring *m* von Operatoren	anneau *m* d'opérateurs	кольцо операторов
	ring of polynomials <AL>	*s.* P 1009		
	ring of power series <AL>	*s.* P 1154		
	ring of quaternions <AL>	*s.* Q 275		
	ring of quotients <AL>	*s.* Q 337		
R 1330	**ring of real character** <AL>	Ring *m* reellen Typs	anneau *m* de type réel	кольцо вещественного типа
	ring of right quotients <AL>	*s.* R 1243		
	ring of scalars <AL>	*s.* B 123		
	ring of sets <SE>	*s.* 1. F 200; 2. S 689		
	σ-ring of sets <ME, SE>	*s.* S 831		
	σ-ring of sets <SE>	*s.* S 823		
	ring of the affine co-ordinates <AG>	*s.* C 2427		
	ring of the polynomials <AG>	*s.* C 2427		
	ring of Zariski <AL>	*s.* Z 4		
R 1331	**ringoid** <AL>	Ringoid *n*	annéloïde *m*	кольцоид
	ring quasi-simple from the left <AL>	*s.* L 465		
	ring quasi-simple from the right <AL>	*s.* R 1239		
	ring regular in the sense of von Neumann <AL>	*s.* R 624		
	ring representation <AL>	*s.* R 1318		
R 1332	**ring structure** <AL>	Ringstruktur *f*	structure *f* d'anneau	кольцевая структура
	ring surface <EG>	*s.* T 613		
R 1333	**ring-theoretic** <AL>	ringtheoretisch	en théorie des anneaux	теоретико-кольцевой
R 1334	**ring topology** <AL>	Ringtopologie *f*	topologie *f* d'anneau	кольцевая топология
R 1335	**ring with a discrete valuation** <AL>	diskret bewerteter Ring *m*	anneau *m* à valuation discrète	дискретно[-] нормированное кольцо
	ring with a polynomial identity <AL>	*s.* P 609		
R 1336	**ring with identity [element],** ring with unit element <AL>	Ring *m* mit Eins[element]	anneau *m* unitaire (unifère, avec élément-unité, à élément unité, unital)	кольцо с единицей (единичным элементом), унитарное кольцо
R 1337	**ring with identity of characteristic zero** <AL>	Ring *m* mit Einselement der Charakteristik 0	anneau *m* unitaire de caractéristique nulle, domaine *m* orthoïde <König>	унитарное кольцо нулевой характеристики
	ring with left DCC <AL>	*s.* L 302		
R 1338	**ring with operators** <AL>	Ring *m* mit Operatoren	anneau *m* à opérateurs	кольцо с операторами, операторное кольцо
R 1339	**ring without identity** <AL>	Ring *m* ohne Eins	anneau *m* sans unité, pseudo-anneau *m*	кольцо без единицы
	ring without zero divisors <AL>	*s.* I 620		
	ring with right DCC <AL>	*s.* R 1081		
	ring with unit element <AL>	*s.* R 1336		
	R-integrable function <AN>	*s.* R 1014		
	R-integral <DI>	*s.* R 1015		
	R-integral element <AL>	*s.* I 622		

R 1340	**rise,** ordinate difference <of two points> <AY>	Ordinatenabstand *m*, Ordinatendifferenz *f*	différence *f* des ordonnées	разность ординат, разность высот
	rising branch <FT, GN>	*s.* A 1029		
	α-risk <ST>	*s.* R 1342		
	β-risk <ST>	*s.* R 1343		
R 1341	**risk function** <ST>	Risikofunktion *f*, Wagnisfunktion *f*	fonction *f* de risque	функция риска
R 1342	**risk of the first kind,** I type risk, type I risk, α-risk, alpha-risk <ST>	Risiko (Wagnis) *n* erster (1.) Art	risque (aléa) *m* de première espèce	риск первого рода
R 1343	**risk of the second kind,** II type risk, type II risk, β-risk, beta-risk <ST>	Risiko (Wagnis) *n* zweiter (2.) Art	risque (aléa) *m* de deuxième espèce	риск второго рода
R 1344	**risk of the third kind,** III type risk, type III risk <ST>	Risiko (Wagnis) *n* dritter (3.) Art	risque (aléa) *m* de troisième espèce	риск третьего рода
R 1345	**risk point** <ST>	Risikopunkt *m*, Wagnispunkt *m*	point *m* de risque	точка риска
R 1346	***R*-isomorphism** <AL>	*R*-Isomorphismus *m*	*R*-isomorphisme *m*	*R*-изоморфизм
	R_0-isomorphism <AL>	*s.* R 724		
R 1347	**Ritz['s] method,** Rayleigh-Ritz method <NU, VA>	Ritzsches Verfahren *n*, Ritzsche Variationsmethode *f*, Verfahren (Methode *f*, Variationsmethode) von Ritz	méthode *f* de Ritz (Rayleigh), méthode d'approximation variationnelle	метод Ритца
R 1348	**(R,λ,k) lim[it], $R_{\lambda k}$-lim[it],** limit by Riesz's method <LI>	(R,λ,k)-Limes *m*, $R_{\lambda k}$-Limes *m*, Limes *m* nach dem (R,λ,k)-Verfahren, (R,λ,k)-lim, $R_{\lambda k}$-lim	limite *f* par la méthode de [M.] Riesz, $R_{\lambda k}$-limite *f*, $R_{\lambda k}$-lim	[обобщенный] предел по методу [М.] Риса, [обобщенный] предел по [М.] Рису
R 1349	**(R,λ,k) limitable sequence, $R_{\lambda k}$-limitable sequence,** sequence limitable by Riesz's method <LI>	$R_{\lambda k}$-limitierbare ((R,λ,k)-limitierbare, nach dem (R,λ,k)-Verfahren limitierbare) Folge *f*	suite *f* limitable par la méthode de [M.] Riesz	последовательность, лимитируемая методом [М.] Риса
	(R,λ,k)-method, $R_{\lambda k}$-method <LI>	*s.* 1. R 1055; 2. R 1057		
	(R,λ,k) sum, $R_{\lambda k}$-sum <LI>	*s.* R 1050/1		
R 1350	**(R,λ,k) summable series, $R_{\lambda k}$-summable series,** series summable by Riesz's method <LI>	$R_{\lambda k}$-summierbare ((R,λ,k)-summierbare, nach dem (R,λ,k)-Verfahren summierbare) Reihe *f*	série *f* sommable par la méthode de [M.] Riesz, série $R_{\lambda k}$-sommable	ряд, суммируемый методом [М.] Риса
	***R*-linear mapping** <AL>	*s.* R 971/2		
	***R*-method** <LI>	*s.* R 1019		
R 1351	***R*-module,** module over <the ring> *R* <AL>	*R*-Modul *m*, Modul *m* über <dem Ring> *R*, Modul mit *R* als Operatorenbereich	*R*-module *m*, module *m* sur <l'anneau> *R*	*R*-модуль, модуль над <кольцом> *R*
	***R*-module of finite type** <AL>	*s.* F 291		
	r. m. s. [value] <ST>	*s.* R 1378		
R 1352	**Robbins-Monro process** <SP>	Robbins-Monro-Prozeß *m*	processus *m* de Robbins-Monro	процесс Роббинса-Монро
R 1353	**Robert['s] circle** <EG>	Robertscher Kreis *m*	cercle *m* de Robert	окружность Робера
R 1354	**Robert['s] curve** <GE>	Robertsche Kurve *f*	courbe *f* de Robert	кривая Робера
	Robertson['s] growth function <ST>	*s.* L 1080		
R 1355	**Roberval['s] curve** <GE>	Robervalsche Kurve *f*	courbe *f* de Roberval, robervalienne *f*	кривая Роберваля
R 1356	**Robin['s] constant** <PO>	Robinsche Konstante *f*	constante *f* de Robin	постоянная Робина, винеровская емкость
R 1357	**Robin['s] problem,** third boundary value problem <of the Laplace equation> <PO>	Robinsches Problem *n*, Robin-Problem *n*	problème *m* de Robin	задача Робина
R 1358	**robustness** <of a test> <ST>	Widerstandsfähigkeit *f*, Robustheit *f*	robustesse *f*	устойчивость
R 1359	**robust test** <ST>	widerstandsfähiger (robuster) Test *m*	test *m* robuste	устойчивый критерий
R 1360	**Rodrigues['s] formula,** Rodrigues['s] theorem <for surfaces> <DG>	Rodriguessche Formel[n *fpl*] *f*, Formel[n] von [Olinde] Rodrigues	formule[s *fpl*] *f* de Rodrigues, formule[s] d'Olinde Rodrigues	формула (формулы) Родрига
R 1361	**Rodrigues['s] formula,** Rodriguez['s] formula <for Legendre functions> <FU>	Rodriguessche Formel *f*	formule *f* de Rodrigues, formule d'Olinde Rodrigues	формула Родрига
	Rodrigues['s] theorem <DG> ⌐<FU>	*s.* R 1360		
	Rodriguez['s] formula	*s.* R 1361		
	Rogers-Ramanujan identity <NT>	*s.* R 61		
R 1362	**Rogosinski-Bernstein theorem** <for Fourier series> <SS>	Satz *m* von Rogosinski-Bernstein, Rogosinski-Bernsteinscher Satz	théorème *m* de Rogosinski-Bernstein	теорема Рогозинского-Бернштейна
	Rogosinski['s] method [of summation] <SS>	*s.* B 214		
R 1363	**Rogosinski['s] sum,** Bernstein-Rogosinski sum <SS>	Rogosinski-Summe *f*, Bernstein-Rogosinski-Summe *f*	somme *f* de Rogosinski (Bernstein-Rogosinski)	[обобщенная] сумма по методу Бернштейна-Рогозинского, [обобщенная] сумма по Бернштейну-Рогозинскому
	Rogosinski['s] summation method <SS>	*s.* B 214		
R 1364	**Rolle['s] curve** <of the third order> <GE>	Rolles (Rollesche) Kurve *f*	courbe *f* de Rolle	кривая Ролля

R 1365	**Rolle['s] method** <of cascades for solving algebraic equations> <AL>	Rolles Methode *f*	méthode *f* de Rolle	метод Ролля
R 1366	**Rolles['s] theorem** <for the roots of an equation> <AL>	Rolles Satz *m* <über Grenzen und Anzahl der Wurzeln einer Gleichung>	théorème *m* de Rolle	теорема Ролля
R 1367	**Rolle['s] theorem** <DI>	Satz *m* von Rolle, Rollescher Satz (Mittelwertsatz *m*)	théorème *m* de Rolle	теорема Ролля (о корнях производной)
R 1368	**Romanovsky['s] theorem** <on singular integrals> <AN>	Satz *m* von Romanowski, Romanowskischer Satz	théorème *m* de Romanovsky	теорема Романовского
	roof <GN>	*s.* H 131		
R 1369	**root** <of a congruence> <AL>	Kongruenzwurzel *f*, Wurzel *f* <einer Kongruenz>	racine *f* de congruence, racine <d'une congruence>	корень сравнения
R 1370	**root,** radical, radix <*e.g.:* of a number> <AL, AR>	Wurzel *f* <*z. B.:* aus einer Zahl>	racine *f* <*par exemple:* d'un nombre>	корень <*например:* числа>
R 1371	**root** <of a Lie group> <GR>	Wurzel *f*	racine *f*	корень
	root <AL>	*s.* S 1261		
	root <GP>	*s.* S 1135		
	root <MD>	*s.* E 61		
R 1372	**root condition** <FT>	Wurzelbedingung *f*	condition *f* aux racines	условие на корнях
	root deviation <ST>	*s.* S 1606		
	root diagram <AL>	*s.* D 1079		
R 1373	**rooted graph** <GP>	Wurzelgraph *m*	graphe *m* à racine	корневой граф
	rooted tree <GP>	*s.* A 881		
	rooted tree with root e <GP>	*s.* T 886		
R 1374	**root element,** radical element <of a field> <AL>	Wurzelgröße *f* <über einem Körper>	élément *m* radiciel (radical) <sur un corps>	радикальный элемент <поля>
	root element <AL>	*s.* P 1809		
R 1375	**root field** <of an algebraic equation> <AL>	Wurzelkörper *m*	corps *m* des racines	поле разложения
	root field <AL>	*s.* S 1544		
R 1376	**root function** <AN>	Wurzelfunktion *f*	fonction *f* de racines	степенная функция с дробным показателем
R 1377	**root function** $y = \sqrt[n]{x}$ <AL, AN>	Funktion *f* der *n*-ten Wurzel, Funktion *n*-te Wurzel	fonction *f* racine *n*-e (ennième)	степенная функция с показателем 1/*n*
R 1378	**root[-] mean[-] square,** root-mean-square value, root-sum-square [value], r.m.s. [value], r.s.s. value, quadratic mean <ST>	quadratisches Mittel *n*, Quadratmittel *n*, quadratischer Mittelwert *m*; Effektivwert *m* <einer periodischen Größe>	moyenne *f* quadratique, valeur *f* moyenne quadratique; valeur efficace <d'une grandeur périodique>	квадратичное среднее, среднее квадратичное [значение], среднеквадратичное [значение]; действующее (эффективное) значение <периодической величины>
	root-mean-square deviation <ST>	*s.* S 1606		
R 1379	**root-mean-square error,** standard error, least mean square error, mean error, mean square error <US> <ER, ST>	mittlerer (mittlerer quadratischer, quadratischer) Fehler *m*, Standardfehler *m*, Normalfehler *m*, Unsicherheitsmaß *n*, Quadratfehler *m*	erreur *f* type (quadratique moyenne, moyenne, standard), incertitude *f* quadratique moyenne	среднеквадратичная ошибка (погрешность), [средняя] квадратичная ошибка, [средняя] квадратичная погрешность, средняя погрешность (ошибка)
	root-mean-square of the deviation <ST>	*s.* S 1606		
	root-mean-square property <ST>	*s.* S 220		
	root-mean-square value <ST>	*s.* R 1378		
	root of multiplicity two <AL>	*s.* D 940		
	root of the absolute value <AL, FO>	*s.* A 967		
R 1380/1	**root of unity** <AL>	Einheitswurzel *f*	racine *f* de l'unité	корень из единицы
R 1382	**root shift method** <MD, NU>	Methode *f* der Wurzelverschiebung *f*, Wurzelverschiebungsmethode *f*	méthode *f* de la translation de racine	метод сдвига корня
	root sign <AL, AR>	*s.* R 29		
R 1383	**root solver** <AR, IN>	Wurzellöser *m*		устройство для нахождения корней
R 1384	**root space** <of a Lie algebra> <AL>	Wurzelraum *m*	espace *m* des racines	корневое пространство
	root-squaring method <AL, AX, NU>	*s.* G 369		
	root-sum-square [value] <ST>	*s.* R 1378		
R 1385	**root system,** system of roots <of a Lie algebra> <AL>	Wurzelsystem *n*	système *m* des racines	корневая система, система корней
R 1386	**root table** <AR, NU>	Wurzeltafel *f*	table *f* des racines	таблица корней
	root test <SS>	*s.* C 259		
	root-tree with root e <GP>	*s.* T 886		
R 1387	**root with unequal exponent** <AL>	ungleichnamige Wurzel *f*, Wurzel mit verschiedenem Exponenten	racine *f* à exposant différent	корень с неравным показателем
R 1388	**R-order** <of an algebra *or* field> <AL>	*R*-Ordnung *f*	*R*-ordre *m*	*R*-порядок
R 1389	**Rosati['s] involution** <AG>	Rosati-Involution *f*	involution *f* de Rosati	инволюция Розати

No.	English	German	French	Russian
R 1390	**rose,** rhodonea <GE>	Rosenkurve *f*, Rhodonee *f*	rose *f*, rosace *f*	роза, кривая Гвидо Гранди
R 1391	**Rosenhain['s] group** <for theta-functions> <FT, FU>	Rosenhainsche Gruppe *f*	groupe *m* de Rosenhain	группа Розенгайна
R 1392	**Rosenhain['s] normal form** <for a hyper-elliptic curve> <AG, FT>	Rosenhainsche Normal-form *f*	forme *f* [normale] de Rosenhain	нормальная форма Розенгайна
R 1393	**Rosenhain['s] system** <of theta characteristics> <FT, FU>	Rosenhainsches System *n*	système *m* de Rosenhain	система Розенгайна
R 1394	**rosette** <GE>	Rosette *f*	rosace *f*, rosette *f*	розетка
	rotary reflection <GE>	*s.* I 183		
R 1395	**rotating-disk linear planimeter** <GE, IN>	Linearscheibenplanimeter *n*	planimètre *m* linéaire à disque tournant	линейный планиметр с вращающимся диском
R 1396	**rotating-disk polar planimeter** <GE, IN>	Polarscheibenrollplani-meter *n*	planimètre *m* polaire à disque tournant	полярный планиметр с вращающимся диском
R 1397	**rotating-disk precision polar planimeter** <GE, IN>	Polarplanimeter *n* mit Gonellaschem Integrier-mechanismus, Präzisions-scheibenpolarplanimeter *n*	planimètre *m* polaire de précision à disque tournant	прецизионный дисковый полярный планиметр
	rotating tensor <DG, VT>	*s.* R 1408		
R 1398	**rotation,** proper rotation <GE>	Drehung *f*, eigentliche Drehung	rotation *f*, rotation propre	вращение, поворот первого рода
R 1399	**rotation** <of a plane figure into one of the planes of projection> <DS>	Umlegung *f*, Umklappung *f* <einer ebenen Figur in eine Projektionsebene>	rotation *f* <d'une figure plane dans un des plans de projection>	вращение, перегибание <плоской фигуры в одную из плоскостей проекции>
	rotation <VT>	*s.* C 2758		
R 1400	**rotation about a point,** rotation around a point, spherical rotation <in a metric space> <GE, TO>	Rotation (Drehung) *f* um einen Punkt, sphärische Rotation	rotation *f* autour d'un point, rotation sphérique	вращение вокруг (около) точки, сферическое вращение
	rotational axis <EG>	*s.* A 1319		
	rotationally symmetric body (solid) <EG>	*s.* B 529		
	rotationally symmetric surface <EG>	*s.* S 2370		
R 1401	**rotational symmetry** <EG>	Rotationssymmetrie *f*, Drehsymmetrie *f*, Drehungssymmetrie *f*	symétrie *f* de révolution	симметрия вращения
R 1402	**rotation and stretching,** rotation-stretching <EG>	Drehstreckung *f*	rotation *f* et dilatation *f* (allongement *m*), rotation-allongement *f*	растяжение с поворотом (вращением)
	rotation around a point <GE, TO>	*s.* R 1400		
	rotation axis <EG>	*s.* A 1319		
R 1403	**rotation coefficient,** coefficient of rotation, Ricci['s] coefficient of rotation <DG>	Rotationskoeffizient *m* [von Ricci], Riccischer Rotationskoeffizient	coefficient *m* de rotation [de Ricci], coefficient de Ricci	коэффициент вращения [Риччи]
R 1404	**rotation group,** proper orthogonal group, special orthogonal group, rotations group <AY, GR>	Drehgruppe *f*, Drehungs-gruppe *f*, eigentliche (engere, spezielle) orthogonale Gruppe *f*	groupe *m* des rotations, groupe de rotation[s], groupe spécial ortho-gonal, groupe ortho-gonal direct (propre, spécial)	группа вращений (вра-щения), собственно[-] ортогональная группа, прямая ортогональная группа
	rotation group <GR>	*s.* R 229		
	rotation matrix <AL, MD>	*s.* P 1818		
R 1405	**rotation of axes (co-ordinate system)** <GN>	Drehung *f* des Koordi-natensystems, Koordi-natendrehung *f*	rotation *f* des axes [de coordonnées]	поворот координатных осей, поворот осей
R 1406	**rotation of the circle** <GN>	Kreisdrehung *f*	rotation *f* du cercle	круговое вращение
R 1407	**rotation sampling** <ST>	Stichprobennahme *f* mit mehrfacher Erfassung derselben Einheiten	échantillonnage (sondage) *m* avec répétition périodique	выбор с периодическим повторением
	rotations group <AY, GR>	*s.* R 1404		
	rotation-stretching <EG>	*s.* R 1402		
	rotation-symmetric body (solid) <EG>	*s.* B 529		
	rotation-symmetric surface <EG>	*s.* S 2370		
R 1408	**rotation tensor,** rotating tensor <DG, VT>	Versor *m*, Drehungs-affinor *m*, Rotator *m*, Drehtensor *m*, Drehungstensor *m*	tenseur *m* de rotation	тензор вращения
R 1409	**rotation theorem** <of Bieberbach> <FT>	Drehungssatz *m* [von Bieber-bach und Golusin], Bie-berbachscher Drehungs-satz, Bieberbachs Drehungssatz	théorème *m* de Bieber-bach	теорема Бибербаха
R 1410	**rotatory affinity** <AY>	rotatorische Affinität *f*	affinité *f* rotatoire	вращательная аффин-ность, вращательное аффинное преобразо-вание
R 1411	**rotatory collineation** <AY>	rotatorische Kollineation *f*	collinéation *f* rotatoire	вращательная колли-неация

No.	English	German	French	Russian
R 1412	**Roth['s] theorem** <AX, NU>	Satz *m* von Roth, Rothscher Satz	théorème *m* de Roth	теорема Рота
	rotor <VT>	*s.* C 2758		
R 1413	**Rouché['s] theorem** <AT, FT>	Satz *m* von Rouché, Rouchéscher Satz	théorème *m* de Rouché	теорема Руше
	rough-and-ready rule <GN, NU>	*s.* R 1514		
R 1414	**rough approximation,** crude approximation <AX, NU>	rohe Annäherung (Näherung) *f*	approximation *f* grossière	грубое приближение
	rough calculation <NU>	*s.* R 1416		
R 1415	**rough estimate,** rough value <NU>	Überschlagswert *m*, Überschlag *m*, ungefährer (grober) Schätzwert *m*	montant *m* d'une estimation approximative, estimation *f* approximative, valeur *f* estimative approchée	приблизительное значение
R 1416	**rough estimate (estimation),** rough calculation <NU>	Überschlagsrechnung *f*, Überschlag *m*, ungefähre (grobe) Schätzung *f*	supputation *f*, estimation (évaluation) *f* approximative, calcul *m* approché	примерный (приблизительный) расчет, прикидка
	rough number <NT, NU>	*s.* R 1418		
	rough rule <GN, NU>	*s.* R 1514		
	rough sum <AR, NU>	*s.* R 1423		
	rough value <NU>	*s.* R 1415		
R 1417	**roulette** <GE>	Rollkurve *f*, Roulette *f*	roulette *f*	рулетта, рулета
	round angle <EG>	*s.* P 440		
	round bracket <GN>	*s.* P 162		
	round-down <NU>	*s.* R 1420		
R 1418	**round figure;** rough number <NT, NU>	runde Zahl *f* <mit 0 am Ende>	nombre *m* rond	круглое число; округленное число
R 1419	**rounding,** rounding off, round[-]off <NU>	Rundung *f*, Runden *n*, Abrundung *f*, Abrunden *n*	arrondissement *m*, arrondi *m*	округление
R 1420	**rounding down,** round-down, rounding-off downward, rounding-off to a lower number, flooring <NU>	Abrundung *f*, Rundung *f* (Abrundung) nach unten, Abrunden *n*	arrondissement *m* au nombre inférieur, arrondissement par défaut, arrondissement vers le bas	округление с недостатком, округление снизу
R 1421	**rounding error,** round-off error, round[-]off <NU>	Rundungsfehler *m*	erreur *f* d'arrondi	погрешность (ошибка) округления, погрешность за счет округлений
	rounding off <NU>	*s.* R 1419		
	rounding-off downward <NU>	*s.* R 1420		
	rounding-off to a higher number <NU>	*s.* R 1422		
	rounding-off to a lower number <NU>	*s.* R 1420		
	rounding-off upward <NU>	*s.* R 1422		
	rounding rule <NU>	*s.* R 1503		
R 1422	**rounding up,** round-up, rounding-off upward, rounding-off to a higher number, ceiling <NU>	Aufrundung *f*, Rundung *f* nach oben, Aufrunden *n*	arrondissement *m* au nombre supérieur, arrondissement par excès, arrondissement vers le haut	округление с избытком, округление сверху
	round[-]off <NU>	*s.* 1. R 1419; 2. R 1421		
	round-off error <NU>	*s.* R 1421		
	round-robin tournament <GP>	*s.* T 705		
R 1423	**round sum;** rough sum <of numbers> <AR, NU>	runde Summe *f*	somme *f* ronde	круглая сумма; округленная сумма
	round-up <NU>	*s.* R 1422		
R 1424	**row** <horizontal *or* vertical> <of a matrix> <MD>	Reihe *f* <Zeile *oder* Spalte>	rangée *f*, ligne *f* <horizontale *ou* verticale>	ряд <строка *или* столбец>
R 1425	**row,** horizontal row, line <*n*-th> <of a matrix *or* determinant> <MD>	Zeile *f*, Horizontalreihe *f*, Reihe *f* <*n*-te, vom Index *n*>	ligne *f*, ligne horizontale, ligne rangée, rangée *f* horizontale <*n*-e, de rang *n*, d'indice *n*>	строка <*n*-я>, горизонтальный ряд <*n*-й>
R 1426	**row exact diagram** <HA>	Diagramm *n* mit exakten Zeilen	diagramme *m* à lignes exactes	диаграмма с точными строками
R 1427	**row-finite matrix** <MD>	zeilenfinite Matrix *f*	matrice *f* dont les lignes ne contiennent qu'un nombre fini d'éléments non nuls	конечно[-]строчная матрица
R 1428	**row-finite method** <LI>	zeilenfinites Verfahren (Matrixverfahren, *A*-Verfahren) *n*	méthode *f* finie par rapport aux lignes	конечно-строчный метод
R 1429	**row index,** line index <MD>	Zeilenindex *m*	indice *m* de la ligne, rang *m* des lignes	индекс строки
R 1430	**row-infinite matrix** <MD>	zeileninfinite Matrix *f*	matrice *f* dont certaines lignes contiennent une infinité d'éléments non nuls	бесконечно-строчная матрица
R 1431	**row-infinite method** <LI>	zeileninfinites Verfahren (Matrixverfahren, *A*-Verfahren) *n*	méthode *f* infinie par rapport au lignes	бесконечно-строчный метод
	row limit <SS>	*s.* L 714		
R 1432	**row matrix,** single-row matrix, row vector <MD, VT>	Zeilenmatrix *f*, einzeilige (einreihige) Matrix *f*, Zeilenvektor *m*	matrice *f* ligne, matrice-ligne *f*, matrice à une ligne, matrice uniligne, vecteur-ligne *m*, vecteur *m* ligne	матрица-строка, строчная матрица, вектор-строка, строчный вектор
	row mean <ST>	*s.* M 315		

R 1433	**row[-] monomiality** <of a matrix> <MD>	Zeilenmonomialität *f*	monomialité *f* par rapport aux lignes	мономиальность по строкам
R 1434	**row-monomial matrix** <MD>	zeilenmonomiale Matrix *f*	matrice *f* monomiale par rapport aux lignes	мономиальная по строкам матрица
R 1435	**row[-] nullity** <of a matrix> <MD>	Zeilenrangdefekt *m*	nullité *f* pour les lignes	строчный дефект
	row of points <PJ>	*s.* P 783		
R 1436	**row of the co-ordinates** <GE>	Koordinatenzeile *f*	ligne *f* des coordonnées	строка координат
R 1437	**row operation** <on a matrix> <MD>	Operation *f* mit den Zeilen	opération *f* sur les lignes	операция над строками
R 1438	**row rank** <of a matrix> <MD>	Zeilenrang *m*	rang *m* défini par les lignes de la matrice, rang des vecteurs lignes, rang à gauche pour les lignes	строчный ранг, ранг по строкам
R 1439	**row space,** row vector space <of a matrix> <AL>	Zeilenraum *m* <von den Zeilen einer Matrix aufgespannter Vektorraum>	espace *m* vectoriel engendré par les lignes <d'une matrice>	пространство строк <матрицы>
R 1440	**row sum,** magic sum <of a magic square> <CT>	magische Konstante *f*, Konstante, Reihensumme *f* <eines magischen Quadrats>	constante *f* du carré <magique>	сумма чисел по строкам <магического квадрата>
	row sum <MD, SS>	*s.* S 2266		
R 1441	**row total** <of a table> <ST>	Zeilensumme *f*	total *m* de la ligne	сумма по строке
	row vector <MD>	*s.* R 1432		
	row vector space <AL>	*s.* R 1439		
R 1442	***r*-parameter local continuous group** <GR>	lokale kontinuierliche Gruppe *f* von *r* Parametern, *r*-parametriger Gruppenkeim *m*	groupuscule *m* à *r* paramètres	*r*-параметрическая локальная непрерывная группа
R 1443	***r*-ple model** <AG>	*r*-faches Modell *n*	modèle *m* *r*-uple	*r*-кратная модель
	***R*-sequence** <AL>	*s.* P 1341		
	r.s.s. value <ST>	*s.* R 1378		
R 1444	***R*-sum,** Riemann['s] sum <of a series> <LI, SS>	*R*-Summe *f*	*R*-somme *f*	*R*-сумма
	***R*-summable series** <LI>	*s.* R 1036		
R 1445	***R*-surface** <PJ>	*R*-Fläche *f*	surface *f* (*R*), *R*-surface *f*	*R*-поверхность
	rudiment <FO>	*s.* E 82		
R 1446	**ruin [of player]** <TG>	Ruin *m* [des Spielers]	ruine *f* [du joueur]	разорение [игрока]
R 1447	**ruin problem** <TG>	Ruinproblem *n*	problème *m* de la ruine [du joueur]	задача о разорении [игрока]
	rule <GE, IN>	*s.* M 348		
	3/8 rule <DI, NU>	*s.* T 450		
	3σ-rule <ST>	*s.* T 465		
R 1448	**ruled quadric** <AY>	Regelfläche *f* zweiter Ordnung, Regelquadrik *f*	surface *f* réglée du second degré	линейчатая квадрика
R 1449	**ruled surface** <GE>	Regelfläche *f*, geradlinige Fläche *f*, Linienfläche *f*	surface *f* réglée, réglée *f*	линейчатая поверхность
	rule EG <LO>	*s.* R 1472		
	rule for joining the existential quantifier <LO>	*s.* R 1472		
R 1450	**rule for joining the existential quantifier to the antecedent of an implication,** rule of preceding the antecedent of an implication with the existential quantifier, rule of ∃-introduction <LO>	Regel *f* der vorderen Partikularisierung, Partikularisierungsregel *f*, Prinzip *n* der zulässigen vorderen Partikularisierung	règle *f* d'introduction du quantificateur particulier dans l'antécédens, règle du quantificateur existentiel (« il existe à gauche »), règle de liaison par le quantificateur particulier	правило ∃-введения в антецеденте, второе правило связывания квантором, правило ∃-введения, правило конкретизации
R 1451	**rule for joining the existential quantifier to the consequent of an implication** <LO>	Regel *f* der hinteren Partikularisierung, hintere Partikularisierung *f*	règle *f* d'introduction du quantificateur particulier dans le conséquent, il existe à droite	правило ∃-введения в сукцеденте, ∃-введение, введение квантора существования
R 1452	**rule for joining the universal quantifier,** law of joining a superfluous universal quantifier, rule of generalization <LO>	abgeleitete Quantifizierungsregel *f*, Regel *f* der Alleinführung, Alleinführung *f*	règle *f* dérivée de liaison par quantificateur	производное правило связывания квантором, ∀-введение, введение квантора общности
	rule for joining the universal quantifier in the antecedent <LO>	*s.* R 1486		
	rule for joining the universal quantifier in the succedent <LO>	*s.* R 1500		
	rule for joining the universal quantifier to the consequent of an implication <LO>	*s.* R 1500		
	rule for modus ponens <LO>	*s.* R 1467		
R 1453	**rule for omitting the bounded existential quantifier,** rule of existential elimination under limitation <LO>	Regel *f* der Beseitigung des Existenzquantifikators mit begrenztem Bereich	règle *f* d'exclusion du quantificateur existentiel limité	правило удаления ограниченного квантора существования
R 1454	**rule for omitting the bounded universal**	Regel *f* der Beseitigung des Allquantifikators	règle *f* d'exclusion du quantificateur universel	правило удаления ограниченного квантора

No.	English	German	French	Russian
	quantifier, rule of universal elimination under limitation <LO>	mit begrenztem Bereich	limité	всеобщности
R 1455	**rule for omitting the existential quantifier,** rule of existential elimination <LO>	Regel *f* der Existenzbeseitigung, Existenzbeseitigung *f*, Beseitigungsregel *f* des Existenzquantifikators, Regel der Beseitigung des Existenzquantifikators	règle *f* d'exclusion du quantificateur existentiel	правило ∃-удаления
R 1456	**rule for omitting the universal quantifier,** rule of universal elimination, universal specification, universal quantification elimination <LO>	Regel *f* der Allbeseitigung, Allbeseitigung *f*, Regel der Beseitigung des Allquantifikators, Beseitigung des Allquantifikators	règle *f* d'exclusion du quantificateur universel	правило ∀-удаления
	rule for omitting the universal quantifier <LO>	*s. a.* L 209		
R 1457	**rule for omitting the universal quantifier in the consequent of an implication** <LO>	Allbeseitigung *f* im Sukzedens	élimination *f* du quantificateur universel dans le conséquent	∀-удаление, удаление квантора общности, ∀-удаление в сукцеденте
R 1458	**rule for relettering free object variables** <LO>	Umbenennungsregel *f* für freie Individuenvariable (Gegenstandsvariable)	règle *f* du changement de nom des variables d'objets libres	правило замены свободных предметных переменных
R 1459	**rule for relettering variables,** rule for rewriting [bound variables] <LO>	Umbenennungsregel *f* <für gebundene Variable>	règle *f* du changement de nom <de variables liées>	правило переименования <связанных переменных>
	rule for rewriting [bound variables] <LO>	*s.* R 1459		
R 1460	**rule for simplification in interpunction** <GN, LO>	Klammereinsparungsregel *f*, Klammerersparungsregel *f*, Regel *f* der Klammersparung	règle *f* de suppression des parenthèses	способ сокращенной записи; соглашения, по которым можно опускать скобки; правило экономии скобок
	rule modus tollendo tollens <LO>	*s.* M 802		
	rule of alligation <NU>	*s.* A 496		
	rule of arithmetic <GN>	*s.* C 12		
R 1461	**rule of assignment** <GN, SE>	Zuordnungsvorschrift *f*	loi *f* de correspondance	правило сопоставления
	rule of calculation <GN>	*s.* C 12		
	rule of combination <AL>	*s.* M 1028		
R 1462	**rule of commutativity** <LO>	Regel *f* der Prämissenvertauschung, Umstellungsregel *f*	règle *f* de permutation des prémisses	правило перестановки посылок
R 1463	**rule of commutativity of equivalence** <LO>	Regel *f* der Kommutativität der Äquivalenz, Regel der Symmetrie der Äquivalenz	règle *f* de la commutativité d'équivalence	правило коммутативности эквивалентности
R 1464	**rule of compound constructive dilemma** <LO>	Regel *f* des zusammengesetzten konstruktiven Dilemmas	règle *f* du dilemme constructif composé	схема сложной конструктивной дилеммы
R 1465	**rule of compound destructive dilemma** <LO>	Regel *f* des zusammengesetzten destruktiven Dilemmas	règle *f* du dilemme composé destructif	схема сложной деструктивной дилеммы, сложная деструктивная дилемма
R 1466	**rule of compound transposition** <LO>	Regel *f* der zusammengesetzten Transposition	règle *f* de transposition composée	правило сложной контрапозиции
	rule of conditional syllogism <LO>	*s.* R 1476		
	rule of conjunction <LO>	*s.* R 1482		
	rule of consequence <LO>	*s.* R 1478		
	rule of derivation <LO>	*s.* D 278		
	rule of Descartes <AL>	*s.* D 304		
R 1467	**rule of detachment,** rule for modus ponens, rule of modus ponens, modus ponens rule, modus ponens, modus ponendo ponens, rule T, hypothetical syllogism, RD <LO>	Abtrennungsregel *f*, Abtrennungsregel für die Allgemeingültigkeit, hypothetischer Syllogismus *m*, Wahrheitsvorwärtsschluß *m*, Grundschlußregel *f*, Schlußschema *n*, Modus (modus) *m* ponens	règle *f* de détachement (séparation, conclusion, dérivation), règle du Modus ponens, modus *m* ponens, schéma *m* d'inférence; principe *m* d'inférence, principe de séparation, loi *f* du syllogisme	схема (правило) заключения, правило modus ponens, modus ponens, modus ponens условно-категорического силлогизма, правило отделения (отрывания), положительный способ гипотетического силлогизма, первая форма гипотетического силлогизма, схема условно-категорического силлогизма, правило силлогизма, утверждение по посылке, правило удаления импликации, исключение импликации, принцип гипотетического силлогизма
R 1468	**rule of detachment for the equivalence** <LO>	Abtrennungsregel *f* für die Äquivalenz	règle *f* de détachement pour l'équivalence	правило отделения для эквивалентности

No.	English	Deutsch	Français	Русский
R 1469	**rule of distributivity of the existential quantifier with respect to a conjunction** <LO>	Regel *f* der Verteilung des Existenzquantifikators auf eine Konjunktion	règle *f* de quantification existentielle d'une conjonction	правило дистрибутивности квантора существования относительно конъюнкции
R 1470	**rule of distributivity of the universal quantifier with respect to an equivalence** <LO>	Regel *f* der Verteilung des Allquantifikators auf eine Äquivalenz	règle *f* de quantification universelle d'une équivalence	правило дистрибутивности квантора всеобщности относительно эквиваленции
R 1471	**rule of elimination** <in natural deduction> <LO>	Beseitigungsregel *f*	règle *f* d'exclusion	правило удаления (исключения), Е-правило
	rule of existential elimination <LO>	*s.* R 1455		
	rule of existential elimination under limitation <LO>	*s.* R 1453		
R 1472	**rule of existential generalization,** existential generalization, rule of existential introduction, existential quantifier introduction, rule for joining the existential quantifier, rule EG <LO>	Regel *f* der Einführung des Existenzquantifikators, Einführungsregel *f* des Existenzquantifikators, Existenzeinführung *f*	loi *f* de vérification relationnelle, règle *f* d'introduction du quantificateur particulier	правило ∃-введения, ∃-введение, введение квантора существования; аксиома для «существует»
	rule of existential generalization under limitation <LO>	*s.* R 1479		
	rule of existential introduction <LO>	*s.* R 1472		
R 1473	**rule of exportation** <LO>	Exportationsregel *f*, Regel *f* des Übergangs zur Prämissenzerlegung, Regel der Prämissentrennung, entgegengesetzte Regel zur Regel der Prämissenverschmelzung	règle *f* de séparation des prémisses, règle d'expédition, règle d'exportation	правило разъединения посылок, правило экспортации
	rule of false position <AN, NU>	*s.* M 463		
R 1474	**rule of generalization,** law of joining a superfluous quantifier, generalization rule <LO>	Generalisierungsregel *f*	règle *f* de généralisation	правило обобщения, правило связывания квантором всеобщности
R 1475	**rule of generalization,** rule of universal introduction, universal generalization, universal quantification introduction <LO>	Regel *f* der Einführung des Allquantifikators, Einführung *f* des Allquantifikators, Alleinführung *f*	règle *f* d'introduction du quantificateur universel	правило ∀-введения, правило обобщения, ∀-введение
	rule of generalization <LO>	*s.* R 1452		
R 1476	**rule of hypothetical syllogism,** rule of conditional syllogism <LO>	Kettenschlußregel *f*, Regel *f* des Kettenschlusses, Regel des hypothetischen Syllogismus, Regel des bedingten Syllogismus, Regel der Transitivität, implikativer Kettenschluß *m*	double syllogisme *m*	цепное правило, правило силлогизма, цепное заключение
	rule of implication <LO>	*s.* I 128		
R 1477	**rule of importation** <LO>	Regel *f* der Prämissenverschmelzung, Regel des Übergangs zur Prämissenverbindung, Importationsregel *f*, Verstärkungsregel *f*	règle *f* de réunion des prémisses	правило соединения посылок, правило импортации (сокращения)
	rule of induction <LO>	*s.* I 400		
R 1478	**rule of inference,** rule of consequence, rule of proof, rule of procedure, inference rule, transformation rule <LO>	Schlußregel *f*, Regel *f* des Schließens	règle *f* de conclusion (séparation, raisonnement)	правило вывода (вывода заключений, заключения, преобразования), дедуктивное правило
	rule of ∃-introduction <LO> ⌐<LO>	*s.* R 1450		
	rule of ∀-introduction	*s.* R 1500		
R 1479	**rule of introduction of the bounded existential quantifier,** rule of existential generalization under limitation <LO>	Regel *f* der Einführung des Existenzquantifikators mit begrenztem Bereich	règle *f* d'introduction du quantificateur existentiel limité	правило введения ограниченного квантора существования
R 1480	**rule of introduction of the bounded universal quantifier,** universal generalization under limitation <LO>	Regel *f* der Einführung des Allquantifikators mit begrenztem Bereich	règle *f* d'introduction du quantificateur universel limité	правило введения ограниченного квантора всеобщности
R 1481	**rule of introduction of the implication in the succedent** <LO>	Regel *f* der hinteren Einführung der Implikation	règle *f* de l'introduction de l'implication dans le conséquent	правило введения импликации в сукцеденте
R 1482	**rule of joining a conjunction,** adjunction, rule of conjunction <LO>	Konjunktionseinführung *f*, Konjunktionsschlußregel *f*, Regel *f* der Einführung der Konjunktion	règle *f* d'adjonction	∧-введение, введение конъюнкции, правило введения конъюнкции

No.	English	German	French	Russian
R 1483	**rule of joining a disjunction,** addition, expansion rule <LO>	Adjunktionseinführung *f*, Disjunktionsschlußregel *f*, Verdünnungsregel *f* für $\vee$	règle *f* de simplification <pour $\vee$>	правило введения дизъюнкции, введение дизъюнкции, $\vee$-введение, правило расширения <для $\vee$>
R 1484	**rule of joining an equivalence,** conditional — biconditional <LO>	Äquivalenzeinführung *f*	introduction *f* de la biconditionnelle	правило введения эквивалентности
R 1485	**rule of joining double negation** <LO>	erste Regel *f* der doppelten Verneinung, introductio *f* inabsurdi, Stabilitätsprinzip *n*, Negationseinführung *f*	règle *f* d'introduction de la négation	правило навешивания двойного отрицания
R 1486	**rule of joining the universal quantifier to the antecedent of an implication,** rule for joining the universal quantifier in the antecedent <LO>	Regel *f* der vorderen Generalisierung, metasprachliches Dictum *n* de omni	règle *f* d'introduction du quantificateur universel dans l'antécédent, pour tout *m* à gauche	правило $\forall$-введения в антецеденте
R 1487	**rule of Minding,** Minding['s] rule <in elimination> <AL>	Mindingsche Regel *f*	règle *f* de Minding	правило Миндинга
	rule of modus ponens <LO>	*s.* R 1467		
R 1488	**rule of multiplication of determinants,** multiplication rule <for determinants> <MD>	Multiplikationssatz *m* <für Determinanten>, Determinantenmultiplikationssatz *m*	théorème *m* de multiplication <des déterminants>	теорема об умножении <определителей>
R 1489	**rule of negating an equivalence** <LO>	Regel *f* der Negation der Äquivalenzglieder, Negationsregel *f* der Äquivalenzglieder	règle *f* de négation de l'équivalence	правило отрицания эквивалентности
R 1490	**rule of negating the existential quantifier** <LO>	Regel *f* der Negation des Partikularisators	règle *f* de la négation des existentielles	правило отрицания квантора общности
R 1491	**rule of negating the universal quantifier** <LO>	Regel *f* der Negation des Generalisators	règle *f* de la négation des universelles	правило отрицания квантора всеобщности
R 1492	**rule of omitting a conjunction,** simplification <LO>	Konjunktionsbeseitigung *f*, Regel *f* der Beseitigung der Konjunktion	règle *f* de simplification pour $\wedge$, élimination *f* de la conjonction	$\wedge$-удаление, удаление конъюнкции, правило удаления конъюнкции, исключение знака конъюнкции, удаление &
R 1493	**rule of omitting a disjunction** <LO>	Regel *f* der Beseitigung der Alternative, oder-Beseitigung *f*	élimination *f* de la disjonction	удаление $\vee$, правило удаления дизъюнкции
R 1494	**rule of omitting a disjunction,** modus tollendo ponens <LO>	Adjunktionsbeseitigung *f*, adjunktiver Syllogismus *m*, Modus *m* tollendo ponens	règle *f* d'élimination d'une disjonction, disjonctif *m* modus tollendo ponens, modus *m* tollendo ponens	правило удаления дизъюнкции, удаление дизъюнкции, $\vee$-удаление, отрицающе-утверждающий модус, modus tollendo ponens
R 1495	**rule of omitting an equivalence,** biconditional — conditional <LO>	Äquivalenzbeseitigung *f*	élimination *f* de la biconditionnelle	правило удаления эквивалентности
R 1496	**rule of omitting an implication** <LO>	Regel *f* der Beseitigung der Implikation	élimination *f* de l'implication	$\supset$-удаление, удаление импликации, удаление $\supset$
R 1497	**rule of omitting double negation** <LO>	zweite Regel *f* der doppelten Verneinung, Negationsbeseitigung *f*, Regel (Grundregel *f*) der Negationsbeseitigung, Regel der duplex negatio affirmat, drittes Verneinungsgesetz *n*, reductio *f* inabsurdi	loi *f* de double négation	закон двойного (снятия двойного) отрицания, устранение двойного отрицания, исключение отрицания, правило удаления двойного отрицания, удаление $\neg$
R 1498	**rule of operation,** law of operation, computing law, operation of arithmetic, calculating rule <AR>	Rechengesetz *n*	loi *f* de calcul	арифметический закон
R 1499	**rule of permutation** <in natural deduction> <LO>	Vertauschungsregel *f*	règle *f* de permutation	правило перестановки, разрешение переставлять посылки
	rule of preceding the antecedent of an implication with the existential quantifier <LO>	*s.* R 1450		
R 1500	**rule of preceding the consequent of an implication with the universal quantifier,** rule of $\forall$-introduction, rule for joining the universal quantifier to the consequent of an implication, rule for	Regel *f* der hinteren Generalisierung, Generalisierungsregel *f*	règle *f* du quantificateur universel, pour tout *m* à droite, règle de liaison par le quantificateur universel, règle de généralisation, règle d'introduction du quantificateur universel dans le conséquent	первое правило связывания квантором, правило $\forall$-введения, $\forall$-введение, введение квантора общности, правило обобщения, правило $\forall$-введения в сукцеденте

and still: R 1500	joining the universal quantifier in the succedent <LO>			
	rule of procedure (proof) <LO>	*s.* R 1478		
	rule of proportion <AR>	*s.* R 1512		
R 1501	**rule of reductio ad absurdum** <LO>	Regel *f* Reductio ad absurdum, Regel der reductio ad absurdum	réfutation *f* par l'absurde	правило сведения к абсурду
R 1502	**rule of risk** <PG>	Risikoregel *f*	règle *f* du risque	правило риска
R 1503	**rule of rounding,** rounding rule <NU>	Rundungsregel *f*, Rundungsprinzip *n*	règle *f* d'arrondi[ssement]	правило округления
R 1504	**rule of signs** <for the roots of an equation> <AL>	Zeichenregel *f*	règle *f* des signes, méthode *f* des variations <de Descartes>	правило знаков
R 1505	**rule of signs,** law of signs <AL, AR>	Vorzeichenregel *f*	règle (convention) *f* des signes	правило знаков
	rule of signs <AL>	*s.* D 304		
R 1506	**rule of simple constructive dilemma** <LO>	Schlußregel *f* des Dilemmas, Regel *f* des einfachen konstruktiven Dilemmas	règle *f* du dilemme constructif simple	простая конструктивная (созидательная) дилемма, схема простой конструктивной дилеммы
R 1507	**rule of simple destructive dilemma** <LO>	Regel *f* des einfachen destruktiven Dilemmas	règle *f* du dilemme destructif simple	схема простой деструктивной дилеммы, простая деструктивная дилемма
R 1508	**rule of simplification** <LO>	Abschwächungsregel *f*, Regel *f* der Prämissenbelastung, Schluß *m* „verum ex quodlibet", Vorschaltung *f* eines Vordergliedes	règle *f* de simplification	добавление антецедента, verum ex quodlibet
R 1509	**rule of simultaneous substitution** <LO>	Regel *f* der simultanen Einsetzung	règle *f* de substitution simultanée	правило одновременной подстановки
R 1510	**rule of substitution** <LO>	Ersetzungsregel *f*	règle *f* de remplacement	правило замены переменных
	rule of substitution <DI>	*s.* S 2199		
	rule of substitution <LO>	*s.* S 2204		
R 1511	**rule of syllogism** <LO>	Regel *f* des Syllogismus	règle *f* du syllogisme	правило силлогизма
	rule of the game <TG>	*s.* G 36		
R 1512	**rule of three,** rule of proportion, golden rule <AR>	Regeldetri *f*, Dreisatz *m*, Dreisatzrechnung *f*, Regel *f* de tri, goldene Regel, regula *f* aurea (marcatorum)	règle *f* de trois, règle d'or	тройное правило; правило (прием) решения арифметических задач, содержащих прямо или обратно пропорциональные величины
R 1513	**rule of three** <for a proportion> <AR>	Produktsatz *m* <Produkt der Mittelglieder = Produkt der Außenglieder>	théorème *m* de l'égalité du produit des extrêmes au produit des moyennes	основое свойство пропорций
R 1514	**rule of thumb,** rough rule, rough-and-ready rule, snap regula <GN, NU>	Faustformel *f*, Faustregel *f*	formule *f* approximative, formule approchée	упрощенная формула для приблизительного подсчета, приближенная формула, эмпирическое правило, практическое правило
R 1515	**rule of transitivity of equivalence** <LO>	Regel *f* der Transitivität der Äquivalenz	règle *f* de la transitivité de l'équivalence	правило транзитивности эквивалентности
R 1516	**rule of transposition** <LO>	Regel *f* der Transposition, Transpositionsregel *f*, Regel der Kontraposition	règle *f* de contraposition	введение отрицания, правило контрапозиции
R 1517	**rule of transposition [in the form of an implication],** first rule of transposition <LO>	erste Regel *f* der Kontraposition, Regel der schwachen Kontraposition, Gesetz *n* der Wendung	[première] règle *f* de contraposition	инверсия высказывания, первое правило контрапозиции
	rule of universal elimination <LO>	*s.* R 1456		
	rule of universal elimination under limitation <LO>	*s.* R 1454		
	rule of universal introduction <LO>	*s.* R 1475		
	rule of weakening <LO>	*s.* T 418		
R 1518	**ruler,** mathematical ruler <GE, IN>	Lineal *n*	règle *f*, règle mathématique	линейка, математическая односторонняя линейка, односторонняя линейка
	ruler and compass construction <EG>	*s.* S 1833		
R 1519	**ruler with parallel edges,** parallel ruler, bilateral ruler <GE, IN>	Parallellineal *n*, Zweikantenlineal *n*, Bilineal *n*, Parallelenlineal *n*	règle *f* à arêtes (deux bords) parallèles, règle bilatérale (à parallèles), règles *fpl* parallèles, parallèle *f* à vis	линейка с параллельными краями, двусторонняя (параллельная) линейка
	rules of punctuation <LO>	*s.* S 2535		
	rule T <LO>	*s.* R 1467		
	ruling element <EG>	*s.* G 205		

No.	English	German	French	Russian
R 1520	**run** <of two points> <GN>	Abszissendifferenz *f*	différence *f* des abscisses	разность абсцисс
R 1521	**run,** iteration <of length *r*> <of events> <ST>	Iteration *f*, Lauf *m* <der Länge *r*>	itération *f*, suite *f* <de longueur *r*>	итерация <длины *r*>
R 1522	**Runge['s] domain** <FT>	Rungesches Gebiet *n*	domaine *m* (ouvert *m* finiment) de Runge	область Рунге
R 1523	**Runge-Kutta formulae** <DE, NU>	Runge-Kuttasche Formeln *fpl*	formules *fpl* de Runge-Kutta	формулы Рунге-Кутта
R 1524	**Runge-Kutta method,** method of Runge and Kutta <DE, NU>	Runge-Kuttasches Verfahren *n*, Runge-Kuttasche Methode *f*, Runge-Kutta-Verfahren *n*, Verfahren von Runge-Kutta (Runge und Kutta), Runge-Kutta-Methode *f*	méthode *f* de Runge-Kutta (Runge et Kutta)	метод Рунге-Кутта
R 1525	**Runge['s] method** <NU>	Methode *f* von Runge, Rungesche Methode	méthode *f* de Runge	метод Рунге
R 1526	**Runge['s] scheme** <AX, NU>	Runge-Schema *n*	schéma *m* de Runge	схема Рунге
R 1527	**Runge['s] theorem** <on a polyhedron> <AT>	Satz *m* von Runge, Rungescher Satz	théorème *m* de Runge	теорема Рунге
R 1528	**Runge['s] theorem** <for approximation of an analytic function> <AX>	Approximationssatz *m* von Runge, Rungescher Satz *m*, Satz von Runge	théorème *m* de Runge	теорема Рунге
R 1529	**Runge['s] theorem** <on expansion of a meromorphic function> <FT>	Satz *m* von Runge, Rungescher Satz	théorème *m* de Runge	теорема Рунге
R 1530	**running co-ordinate,** variable co-ordinate <AY>	laufende Koordinate *f*	coordonnée *f* courante (variable)	текущая координата
R 1531	**running index,** variable index <GN>	Laufindex *m*, laufender (variabler) Index *m*	indice *m* variable (courant, parcourant)	переменный (текущий, пробегающий) индекс
	running mean <ST>	*s.* M 930		
R 1531a	**running point** <GE>	laufender Punkt *m*	point *m* courant	текущая точка
R 1532	**running through all indices** <GN>	Durchlaufung *f* aller Indizes	parcours *m* de tous les indices	последовательное принимание всех индексов
R 1533	**run test** <ST>	Iterationstest *m*	test *m* des suites	проверка итераций
	Russell['s] antinomy <MM, SE>	*s.* P 84		
	Russell['s] axiom of reducibility <LO>	*s.* A 1290		
	Russell['s] contradiction <MM, SE>	*s.* P 84		
	Russell['s] paradox <MM, SE>	*s.* P 84		
	Russell['s] paradox of the barber in a village <LO>	*s.* P 85		
R 1534	**Russell['s] set** <MM>	Russell-Menge *f*	ensemble *m* de Russell	множество Рассела
	Russell['s] vicious-circle principle <LO>	*s.* V 177		
R 1535	**Ryshik['s] function** <FU>	Ryshiksche Funktion *f*	fonction *f* de Ryshik	функция Рыжика
R 1536	**Rytz['s] construction** <of the axes of an ellipse> <DS>	Rytzsche Achsenkonstruktion (Konstruktion) *f*	construction *f* de Rytz	построение Рыца <осей эллипса>

S

No.	English	German	French	Russian
S 1	**Saalschütz['s] series** <SS>	Saalschützsche Reihe *f*	série *f* de Saalschütz	ряд Заальшютца
S 2	**saddle point,** saddle point singularity <DE>	Sattelpunkt *m*, Sattel *m*, neutraler Punkt *m*	col *m*	седло, нейтральная точка
S 3	**saddle point** <DS>	Sattelpunkt *m*, Jochpunkt *m*, Paßpunkt *m*	point *m* [de] col	точка перевала
S 4	**saddle point** <PG>	Sattelpunkt *m*	col *m*, point *m* [de] col	седловая точка, седло
S 5	**saddle point** <TG>	Sattelpunkt *m*, Sattellage *f*	point *m* d'équilibre, point selle, point-selle *m*	седловая точка
	saddle point <DG>	*s.* H 640		
	saddle point approximation <DI>	*s.* M 486		
S 6	**saddle-point game** <TG>	Sattelpunktspiel *n*	jeu *m* à col	игра с седловой точкой
	saddle-point method <DI>	*s.* M 486		
	saddle point singularity <DE>	*s.* S 2		
	saddle-point theorem <PG>	*s.* K 200		
S 7	**saddle surface** <GE>	Sattelfläche *f*, sattelähnliche Fläche *f*	surface *f* à courbures opposées	седловая поверхность
S 8	***S*-admissible lattice** <GU>	*S*-zulässiges Gitter *n*	réseau *m* *S*-admissible	*S*-допустимая решетка
S 9	**sagitta** <of an arc of circle *or* a spherical segment> <GE>	Pfeil *m*	flèche *f*	стрелка
	sake of symmetry / for <GN>	*s.* S 2471		
S 10/1	**salient angle** <in a closed figure> <EG>	ausspringender Winkel *m*	angle *m* saillant	выступающий угол; угол, меньший развернутого

S 12	**salient point,** corner point, angular point <of a curve> <GE>	Eckpunkt *m*	point *m* anguleux	угловая точка
S 13	**Salmon plane, I-plane** <SG>	Salmonsche Ebene *f*	plan *m* de Salmon	плоскость Сальмона
S 14	**Salmon['s] point** <GE>	Salmon-Punkt *m*, Salmonscher Punkt *m*	point *m* de Salmon	точка Сальмона
S 15	**saltus[-] function, saltus[-] part** <as part of a function with bounded variation> <RF>	Funktion *f* der Sprünge, Sprunganteil *m*, Sprungfunktion *f*	fonction (partie) *f* des sauts	функция (часть) скачков
	same magnitude, but oppositely directed / of the <GN>	*s.* O 209		
	same order [infinite] / of the <AN>	*s.* I 466		
S 16	**sample,** concrete sample <ST>	Stichprobe *f*, konkrete Stichprobe, Probe *f*	échantillon *m*, échantillon concret	выборка, конкретная выборка
S 17	**sample correlation coefficient** <ST>	Stichprobenkorrelationskoeffizient *m*	coefficient *m* de corrélation de l'échantillon	коэффициент корреляции выборки, выборочный коэффициент корреляции
S 18	**sample covariance** <ST>	Stichprobenkovarianz *f*	covariance *f* de l'échantillon	выборочная ковариация
S 19	**sample covariance matrix** <ST>	Stichprobenkovarianzmatrix *f*	matrice *f* des covariances de l'échantillon	выборочная ковариационная матрица, ковариационная матрица выборки
	sample design <ST>	*s.* S 35		
	sample dispersion <ST>	*s.* S 33		
	sample function <ST>	*s.* S 1686		
S 20	**sample mean,** mean of sample <ST>	Stichprobenmittel *n*, Stichprobenmittelwert *m*, Mittelwert *m* der Stichprobe	moyenne *f* de l'échantillon, moyenne d'échantillon	среднее выборочное, выборочное среднее, среднее выборочное значение
S 21	**sample median** <ST>	Stichprobenmedian *m*, Stichprobenmediane *f*	médiane *f* de l'échantillon	выборочная медиана, медиана выборки
S 22	**sample moment,** sampling moment <ST>	Stichprobenmoment *n*	moment *m* de l'échantillon, moment mesuré sur l'échantillon	выборочный момент
	sample of *k* elements without regard to order <CT>	*s.* K 29		
S 23	**sample point** <ST>	Stichprobenpunkt *m*	point *m* échantillon	выборка как *n*-мерный вектор
S 24	**sample quantile** <ST>	Stichprobenquantil *n*	quantile *m* d'échantillon	квантиль выборки, выборочный квантиль
S 25	**sample quartile** <ST>	Stichprobenquartil *n*	quartile *m* d'échantillon	квартиль выборки, выборочный квартиль
S 26	**sample regression coefficient** <ST>	Stichprobenregressionskoeffizient *m*	coefficient *m* de régression de l'échantillon	коэффициент регрессии выборки, выборочный коэффициент регрессии
S 27	**sample residual dispersion (variance)** <ST>	Stichprobenreststreuung *f*, Stichprobenrestvarianz *f*	variance (dispersion) *f* résiduelle de l'échantillon	остаточная дисперсия выборки, выборочная остаточная дисперсия
S 28	**sample size,** size <of a sample> <ST>	Stichprobenumfang *m*, Umfang *m* <einer Stichprobe>	taille *f*, effectif *m* <d'une échantillon>	объем выборки
S 29	**sample space** <ST>	Stichprobenraum *m*	espace *m* des échantillons, espace échantillon	выборочное пространство, пространство выборок
	sample statistic <ST>	*s.* S 1686		
S 30	**sample survey** <collection of existing statistical data following a prepared plan> <ST>	Stichprobenerhebung *f*, Erhebung *f*	enquête *f* par sondage	выборочное обследование
S 31	**sample unit,** sampling unit, item, individual <ST>	Stichprobeneinheit *f*, Stichprobenelement *n*; Erhebungseinheit *f*	unité *f* de sondage, unité d'échantillonnage, individu *m*	элемент выборки
S 32	**sample variable** <ST>	Stichprobenvariable *f*	variable *f* d'échantillon	компонента случайной выборки, компонента выборки
S 33	**sample variance,** sample dispersion <ST>	Stichprobenstreuung *f*, Stichprobenvarianz *f*	variance *f* de l'échantillon, dispersion *f* de l'échantillon	дисперсия выборки, выборочная дисперсия
S 34	**sampling,** selection, drawing <of a sample> <ST>	Stichprobennahme *f*, Stichprobenentnahme *f*, Stichprobenauswahl *f*, Stichprobenerhebung *f*, Auswahl *f*, Erhebung *f*, Ziehen *n* <einer Stichprobe>	sondage *m*, échantillonnage *m*, sélection *f*, choix *m*, tirage *m* <d'un échantillon>	выбор, процесс выборки, выборка, селекция, отбор, извлечение
	sampling <ST>	*s.* S 40/2		
S 35	**sampling design,** sample design, sampling plan <ST>	Stichprobenplan *m*, Stichprobenerhebungsschema *n*, Erhebungsschema *n*	plan *m* d'échantillonnage, plan de sondage	выборочный план
S 36	**sampling distribution** <ST>	Stichprobenverteilung *f*; Prüfverteilung *f*	distribution *f* d'échantillonnage	выборочное распределение
S 37	**sampling error** <ST>	Stichprobenfehler *m*, Fehler *m* der Stichprobennahme	erreur *f* d'échantillonnage, erreur de sondage	ошибка выборочного обследования, выборочная ошибка
S 38	**sampling fraction,** sampling ratio <ST>	Stichprobenanteil *m*, Auswahlsatz *m*, Stichprobenquote *f*	fraction *f* de sondage, fraction d'échantillonnage, taux *m* de sondage, taux d'échantillonnage	выборочная доля, выборочное отношение

S 39	**sampling inspection** <ST>	Teilprüfung *f*, Stichprobenprüfung *f*	inspection *f* sur échantillon	выборочная проверка
S 40/2	**sampling method,** sampling <ST>	Stichprobenverfahren *n*	méthode *f* d'échantillonnage, méthode de sondage	выборочный метод
	sampling moment <ST>	*s.* S 22		
	sampling on successive occasions <ST>	*s.* R 818		
	sampling plan <ST>	*s.* S 35		
	sampling ratio <ST>	*s.* S 38		
	sampling unit <ST>	*s.* S 31		
	sampling with arbitrary probability <ST>	*s.* S 258		
	sampling with equal probability <ST>	*s.* S 259		
	sampling without replacement <ST>	*s.* D 965		
	sampling with replacement <ST>	*s.* D 966		
S 43	**Samuel['s] compactification** <TO>	Samuel-Kompaktifizierung *f*	compactifié *m* de Samuel	компактификация Самуэля
S 44	**Samuel['s] polynomial** <AG, AL>	Hilbert-Samuel-Polynom *n*	polynôme *m* de Hilbert-Samuel	многочлен Гильберта-Самуэля
S 44a	**s-analytic function** <FT>	s-analytische Funktion *f*, analytische hyperkomplexe Funktion nach Scheffers	fonction *f* s-analytique	аналитическая по Шефферсу функция гиперкомплексного переменного
S 45	**sand reckoning** <GN>	Sandrechnung *f*, Arenarius *m*	calcul *m* arénaire	исчисление песчинок
S 46	**sandwich matrix** <of a semigroup> <AL>	definierende Matrix *f*	matrice *f* définissante	«сэндвич»-матрица
S 47	**Sard['s] lemma** <ME, TO>	Satz *m* von Sard, Sardscher Satz	théorème *m* de Sard	теорема Сарда
	saroban <IN>	*s.* C 10		
S 48	**Sarrus['] rule** <for a determinant> <MD>	Sarrussche Regel *f*, Regel von Sarrus	règle *f* de Sarrus	правило Саррюса (диагоналей и треугольников, вычисления определителя третьего порядка)
S 49	**Sartiaux['s] surface** <GE>	Sartiauxsche Fläche *f*	surface *f* de Sartiaux	поверхность Сартьо
	Satake['s] compactification <TO>	*s.* C 1294		
S 50	**satellite** <AG>	Satellit *m*	satellite *m*	сателлит, спутник
S 51	**satellite** <of a functor> <CA>	Satellit *m* <eines Funktors>	foncteur *m* satellite, satellite *m* <d'un foncteur>	сателлит <функтора>
S 52	**satellite conic** <AG>	begleitender Kegelschnitt *m*, Satellitenkegelschnitt *m*	conique *f* (section *f* conique) satellite	сателлитное коническое сечение
S 53	**satellite line** <AG>	begleitende Gerade *f*, Begleitgerade *f*	droite *f* satellite	сателлитная прямая
S 54	**satellite point** <AG>	Begleitpunkt *m*	point *m* satellite	сателлитная точка
S 55	**satisfaction,** fulfilment, satisfying <LO>	Erfüllung *f*, Erfülltsein *n*	satisfaction *f*	выполнение
S 56	**satisfaction-theoretic normal form,** Skolem['s] normal form for satisfiability <LO>	erfüllbarkeitstheoretische Skolemsche Normalform *f*	forme *f* normale de Skolem <∀∃-formule>	нормальный вид Сколема <∀∃-формула>
S 57	**satisfiability** <LO>	Erfüllbarkeit *f*	satisfiabilité *f*	выполнимость
S 58	**satisfiable formula** <in> <of predicate calculus> <LO>	erfüllbarer Ausdruck *m*, erfüllbare Formel *f* <in>	formule *f* réalisable <dans>	выполнимая формула <на классе>
S 59	**satisfiable formula** <of propositional calculus> <LO>	erfüllbarer A-Ausdruck *m*, aussagenlogisch erfüllbarer Ausdruck *m*, erfüllbarer Ausdruck, erfüllbare Formel *f*	expression *f* satisfiable, proposition *f* satisfiable	выполнимая формула
	satisfiable system <LO>	*s.* S 2509		
S 60	**satisfy / to,** to fulfil <an equation> <AL, AN>	erfüllen, befriedigen <eine Gleichung>, genügen <einer Gleichung>	vérifier <une équation>, satisfaire <[à] une équation>	удовлетворять <уравнению>
S 61	**satisfy / to** <an expression> <LO>	verifizieren, erfüllen <einen Ausdruck>	satisfier <[à] une expression>	удовлетворять <выражению>
	satisfy / to <GN>	*s.* F 701		
	satisfying <LO>	*s.* S 55		
S 62	**saturated algebra** <FA>	saturierte Algebra (Operatorenalgebra) *f*	algèbre *f* saturée	насыщенная алгебра
S 63	**saturated chain** <AL>	saturierte Kette *f*	chaîne *f* saturée	насыщенная цепь
S 64	**saturated chain of prime ideals** <AL>	geschlossene Primidealkette *f* <nicht verfeinerbar, unverkürzbar>	chaîne *f* d'idéaux premiers saturée	насыщенная цепь простых идеалов
S 65	**saturated class** <of morphisms> <CA>	saturierte Klasse *f* <von Morphismen>	classe *f* saturée <de morphismes>	насыщенный класс <морфизмов>
	saturated index <VT>	*s.* D 1049		
S 66	**saturated set** <with respect to a property> <SE>	gesättigte (saturierte) Menge *f* <bezüglich einer Eigenschaft>	ensemble *m* saturé <par rapport à une propriété>	насыщенное множество <относительно свойства>
	saturated space <TO>	*s.* H 284		
S 67	**saturated subset** <with respect to an equivalence relation> <SE>	gesättigte Teilmenge (Untermenge) *f* <bezüglich einer Äquivalenzrelation>	partie *f* saturée <pour une relation d'équivalence>	насыщенное множество <относительно отношения эквивалентности>
	saturated under a relation <SE>	*s.* C 925		

No.	English	German	French	Russian
S 68	**saturated vertex** <by a matching> <GP>	gesättigte Ecke *f*	sommet *m* saturé	покрытая вершина <относительно паросочетания>
S 69	**saturation** <of a subset of a topological space by a topological group> <AL, TO>	gesättigte Hülle *f* <einer Untermenge eines topologischen Raumes durch eine topologische Gruppe>	saturé *m* <d'une partie d'un espace topologique par un groupe topologique>, sous-espace *m* saturé <pour la relation d'équivalence définie par le groupe topologique>	насыщение <подмножества топологического пространства по топологической группе>
S 70	**saturation** <CA>	Saturation *f*	saturation *f*	насыщение
	saturation <ST>	*s.* L 911		
S 71	**saturation condition** <of a transport problem> <PG>	Sättigungsbedingung *f*	condition *f* de saturation	условие насыщения
S 72	**Savary['s] equation** <GE>	Savarysche Gleichung *f*	équation *f* de Savary	уравнение Савари
	sc <FU>	*s.* A 610		
	scaffolding <GP>	*s.* M 244		
S 73	**scalar,** scalar quantity (tensor, invariant), invariant, tensor of zero order <VT>	Skalar *m*, skalare Größe *f*, Tensor *m* nullter Stufe, skalarer Tensor, skalare Invariante *f*	scalaire *m*, grandeur *f* (tenseur *m*) scalaire, scalaire de première espèce	скаляр, скалярная величина, скалярный тензор
S 74	**scalar calculus** <NU>	skalare Berechnung *f*	calcul *m* scalaire	скалярное вычисление
	scalar curvature <DG>	*s.* R 983		
S 75	**scalar density** <of weight *k*> <VT>	skalare Dichte *f* <vom Gewicht *k*>	densité *f* scalaire <de poids *k*>	скалярная плотность <веса *k*>
S 76	**scalar density of weight —1** <VT>	skalare Dichte *f* vom Gewicht —1	capacité *f* scalaire	скалярная плотность веса —1
S 77	**scalar equation** <AL>	skalare Gleichung *f*	équation *f* scalaire, densité *f* scalaire de poids —1	скалярное уравнение, уравнение в скалярной форме
S 78	**scalar field** <DG, VT>	Skalarfeld *n*, skalares Feld *n*, Tensorfeld *n* nullter Stufe	champ *m* scalaire	скалярное поле
	scalar field <AL>	*s.* G 441		
	scalar invariant <VT>	*s.* S 73		
S 79	**scalar matrix** <MD>	skalare Matrix *f*, Skalarmatrix *f*	matrice *f* scalaire, matrice-homothétie *f*	скалярная матрица, диагональная матрица с равными диагональными элементами
S 80	**scalar multiplication,** multiplication by numbers <of matrices> <MD>	Skalarmultiplikation *f*, Multiplikation *f* mit einer Zahl	multiplication *f* par un scalaire	умножение на число
S 81	**scalar multiplication** <VT>	sklarare Multiplikation *f*, S-Multiplikation *f*	multiplication *f* scalaire	скалярное умножение
S 82	**scalar part** <of a dual number> <AL>	Realteil *m*	partie *f* scalaire	скалярная часть
S 83	**scalar part** <of a quaternion *or* biquaternion> <AL>	Skalarteil *m*, Skalar *m*, skalarer Bestandteil *m*	partie *f* scalaire	скалярная часть
S 84	**scalar product,** inner product <in a pre-Hilbert space> <FA>	inneres Produkt *n*, Innenprodukt *n*, Skalarprodukt *n*, skalares Produkt	produit *m* scalaire (intérieur)	скалярное (внутреннее) произведение
S 85	**scalar product** <of a matrix>, product of a scalar and a matrix <MD>	Produkt *n* einer Matrix mit einer Zahl	produit *m* d'une matrice par un scalaire	произведение матрицы на число
S 86	**scalar product,** inner product, dot[-] product <of vectors> <VT>	Skalarprodukt *n*, skalares (inneres) Produkt *n*	produit *m* scalaire (intérieur, contracté, direct) <selon Gibbs>, produit algébrique <selon Carvallo>	скалярное произведение
	scalar quantity <VT>	*s.* S 73		
S 87	**scalar system of equations** <AL, AY>	skalares Gleichungssystem *n*	système *m* scalaire	скалярная система уравнений
	scalar tensor <VT>	*s.* S 73		
	scalar triple product <VT>	*s.* P 101		
S 88	**scalar-valued function** <GN>	skalarwertige Funktion *f*	fonction *f* à valeurs scalaires	скалярнозначная функция
S 89	**scalar-valued map[ping]** <AL, FA>	skalarwertige Abbildung *f*	application *f* à valeurs scalaires	скалярнозначное отображение
	scale <GN>	*s.* N 837		
	scale <NO>	*s.* 1. C 2779; 2. L 11		
S 90	**scale carrier,** carrier <of a scale> <NO>	Skalenträger *m*, Träger *m* <einer Skala>	support *m* d'échelle	носитель шкалы
S 91	**scale division,** division <of a scale> <NO, NU>	Skalenteilung *f*, Teilung *f* <einer Skala>	échelle *f*	деление шкалы
S 92	**scale invariant function** <AN, ST>	maßstab[s]invariante Funktion *f*	fonction *f* invariante en changement d'échelle	инвариантная к изменению масштаба функция
	scale measure <ST>	*s.* S 98		
S 93	**scalene (scalenous) triangle** <EG>	ungleichseitiges (allgemeines) Dreieck *n*	triangle *m* scalène	разносторонний треугольник
S 94	**scale of infinity** <RF, SS>	Vergleichsskala *f*	échelle *f* de comparaison	шкала сравнения
S 95	**scale parameter** <ST>	Skalenparameter *m*	paramètre *m* d'échelle, paramètre d'étalement	масштабный параметр
S 96	**scale-preserving mapping (transformation)** <of a surface> <GE>	streckentreue (maßstabtreue, maßstabstreue) Abbildung *f*	transformation *f* conservant l'échelle	отображение с сохранением отрезков; отображение, сохраняющее отрезки
	scale ratio <DS>	*s.* R 424		
S 97	**scales method** <for algebraic equations> <AL>	Waageschalenmethode *f*	méthode *f* des plateaux d'une balance	метод весов

No.	English	German	French	Russian
S 98	**scale statistic,** scale measure <ST>	Skalenmaßzahl *f*	mesure *f* d'échelle, mesure d'étalement	масштабная статистика
S 99	**scale transformation** <NU, ST>	Maßstabtransformation *f*	transformation *f* d'échelle	преобразование масштаба (размера)
S 100	**S-category** <CA>	Scategorie *f*	S-catégorie *f*	S-категория
S 101	**scatter,** [statistical] straggling, dispersion, variability <ST>	Streuung *f*, zufällige (statistische) Streuung, Variabilität *f*, Dispersion *f*	dispersion *f*, dispersion statistique (au hasard)	рассеивание, разброс, изменчивость, дисперсия, рассеяние
	scatter <ST>	*s. a.* R 129		
S 102	**scatter diagram,** dispersion diagram, aggregate (collection) of points, bivariate point distribution, correlation diagram <ST>	Punktwolke *f*, Punkthaufen *m*, Punktgruppe *f*, Streubild *n*, Streuungsdiagramm *n*	nuage *m* de points, nuage statistique, diagramme *m* de dispersion	корреляционное поле, диаграмма разброса, диаграмма рассеивания, группа (скопление) точек, [негруппированная] корреляционная таблица
S 103	**scattered set,** thin set <TO>	separierte Menge (Punktmenge) *f*	ensemble *m* clairsemé	нигде не плотное в себе множество, разреженное множество
S 104	**scedastic equation** <ST>	skedastische Gleichung *f*	équation *f* scédastique	скедастичное уравнение
S 105	**scedasticity** <ST>	Skedastizität *f*, Streuungsverhalten *n*	scédasticité *f*	скедастичность
S 106	**scedastic line** <ST>	skedastische Linie *f*	ligne *f* scédastique	скедастичная линия
S 107	**scedastic transformation** <ST>	skedastische Transformation *f*	transformation *f* scédastique	скедастичное преобразование
	sch <FU>	*s.* H 645		
S 108	**Schanuel lemma** <AL>	Schanuel-Lemma *n*, Schanuelsches Lemma *n*	lemme *m* de Schanuel	лемма Шануэля
S 109	**Schauder['s] [fixed point] theorem** <FA, TO>	Schauderscher Fixpunktsatz *m* <erster *oder* zweiter>	principe *m* de Schauder	теорема Шаудера [о неподвижной точке], принцип Шаудера
S 110	**Schauder['s] theorem** <for a compact operator> <FA>	Schauderscher Satz *m*, Satz von Schauder	théorème *m* de Schauder	теорема Шаудера
S 111	**scheduling problem** <GP>	Reihenfolgeproblem *n*	problème *m* d'ordonnancement	задача о временном упорядочении, задача о составлении расписаний, задача теории расписаний, задача выбора оптимальной последовательности
S 112	**Scheeffer['s] theorem** <for Dini derivatives> <RF>	Scheefferscher Satz *m*	théorème *m* de Scheeffer	теорема Шеффера
S 113	**Scheffé['s] test;** S-method <ST>	Scheffé-Test *m*; S-Methode *f*	test *m* de Scheffé; méthode *f* S	критерий Шеффе; S-метод
	schema <AG>	*s.* S 115		
S 114	**schematically equal word** <AL>	für das Auge gleiches Wort *n*, gleiches Wort für das Auge	mot *m* formellement égal	графически равное слово
S 115	**scheme,** schema <AG>	Schema *n*	schéma *m* séparé, // schéma	схема
S 116	**scheme** <of a simplicial complex> <AT>	Schema *n* <eines simplizialen Komplexes>	schéma *m* <d'un complexe simplicial>	схема <симплициального комплекса>
S 117	**scheme of coefficients** <NU>	Koeffizientenschema *n*	schéma *m* des coefficients	схема (матрица) коэффициентов
	scheme of comprehension <SE>	*s.* A 1283		
S 118	**scheme of finite type** <AG>	Schema *n* endlichen Typs	schéma *m* fini	схема конечного типа
	scheme of proof <FO>	*s.* P 1760		
S 119	**scheme of the design,** layout scheme <ST>	Anlageschema *n*, Versuchsschema *n*	schéma *m* de l'arrangement, schéma de l'expérience	схема эксперимента (опыта)
S 120	**scheme-theoretic** <AG>	schematheoretisch	en théorie des schémas	как схема
S 121	**Scherk['s] minimal surface** <DG>	Scherksche Minimalfläche *f*	surface *f* minimale de Scherk	поверхность Шерка
	schety <IN>	*s.* C 10		
S 122	**Schilling['s] hexalateral** <GE> ⌐<AL>	Schillings Sechsseit *n*	hexalatère *m* de Schilling	шестисторонник Шиллинга
	Schläfli['s] diagram	*s.* D 1079		
S 123	**Schläfli['s] formula** <for the Legendre functions> <FU>	Schläflische Formel (Integraldarstellung) *f*, Integral *n* von Schläfli <der Kugelfunktionen>	formule *f* de Schlaefli	формула Шлефли
S 124	**Schläfli['s] integral [equation]** <of the Bessel functions> <FU>	Schläflische Integraldarstellung *f* <der Zylinderfunktionen>	intégrale *f* de Schlaefli	интеграл Шлефли
S 125	**Schläfli['s] polynomial** <FU>	Schläflisches Polynom *n*	polynôme *m* de Schlaefli	многочлен Шлефли
S 126	**Schläfli['s] sixfold,** double-six of lines <PJ>	Schläflische Doppelsechs *f*, Doppelsechs [von Schläfli]	double six *m* [de Schlaefli]	шестерки Шлефли, двойной шестисторонник Шлефли
	Schlauchknot <TO>	*s.* T 1054		
S 127	**schlichtartig domain** <TO> ⌐<TO>	schlichtartiges Gebiet *n*		область, подобная однолистной
	schlichtartig surface	*s.* S 958		
	schlicht domain <FT, TO>	*s.* S 903		
	schlicht function <FT>	*s.* S 915		
S 128	**schlicht mapping** <FT>	schlichte Abbildung *f*	application *f* univalente	однолистное отображение
S 129	**schlicht surface** <FT, TO>	einblättrige (schlichte) Fläche *f*	surface *f* à un feuillet	однолистная поверхность
S 130	**Schloemilch['s] expansion,** Schloemilch['s] series <FU>	Schlömilchsche Reihe *f*	série *f* de Schlœmilch	ряд Шлемильха

No.	English	German	French	Russian
S 131	**Schloemilch['s] form [of the remainder], Schloemilch['s] remainder** <in Taylor's formula> <DI>	Schlömilchsches Restglied *n*, Restglied der Taylorschen Formel in der Form von Schlömilch	reste *m* (terme *m* résiduel) de Schlœmilch	остаточный член Шлемильха, остаток Шлемильха, остаточный член [формулы Тейлора] в форме Шлемильха
	Schloemilch['s] series <FU> ⌐<IE>	*s.* S 130		
S 132	**Schmidt['s] functions**	Schmidtsche Funktionen *fpl*	fonctions *fpl* de Schmidt	функции Шмидта
S 133	**Schmidt['s] fundamental formula,** Hilbert-Schmidt fundamental formula <IE>	Schmidtsche (Hilbert-Schmidtsche) Fundamentalformel *f*	formule *f* fondamentale de [Hilbert-]Schmidt	фундаментальная (основная) формула [Гильберта-]Шмидта
	Schmidt['s] orthogonalization [process] <AL>	*s.* G 374		
	Schmidt['s] process <AL>	*s.* G 374		
	Schmidt-Remak theorem <GR>	*s.* K 175		
S 134	**Schnirelmann['s] density** <of a number set> <AB>	Dichte *f*, Schnirelmann-Dichte *f*	densité *f* globale inférieure	плотность в смысле Шнирельмана, плотность [Шнирельмана]
S 135	**Schnirelmann-Goldbach theorem** <NT>	Schnirelmann-Goldbachscher Satz *m*	théorème *m* de Schnirelmann-Goldbach	теорема Шнирельмана-Гольдбаха
S 136	**scholion, scholium** <GN>	Scholion *n*, Scholie *f*, Anmerkung *f* <zu einem Theorem>	scolie *f*	схолия
S 137	**Schottky['s] theorem** <FT>	Schottkyscher Satz *m*	théorème *m* de Schottky	теорема Шотки
S 138	**Schottky['s] uniformization** <FT>	Schottkysche Uniformisierung *f*	uniformisation *f* de Schottky	униформизация Шотки
S 139	**Schoute['s] circle** <GE>	Schoutescher (Schoutes) Kreis *m*	cercle *m* de Schoute	
S 140	**Schouten['s] invariant** <DG>	Schouten-Invariante *f*	invariant *m* de Schouten	инвариант Схоутена (Схаутена)
S 141	**Schreier['s] extension** <of groups> <GR>	Schreiersche Erweiterung *f*	extension *f* de Schreier	шрейерово расширение
S 142	**Schreier['s] refinement theorem** <for normal series> <AL>	Schreierscher Verfeinerungssatz *m*, Verfeinerungssatz	théorème *m* de Schreier	теорема Шрейера
S 143	**Schreier['s] subgroup** <GR>	Schreiersche Untergruppe *f*	sous-groupe *m* schreierien	шрейерова подгруппа
S 144	**Schreier['s] theory** <of group extensions> <GR>	Schreiersche Erweiterungstheorie *f*, Theorie *f* von Schreier, Schreiersche Theorie <der Gruppenerweiterungen>	théorie *f* de Schreier <des extensions de groupes>	шрейеровская теория <групповых расширений>, теория Шрейера
S 145	**Schreier['s] variety** <of groups> <GR>	Schreiersche Varietät *f*	variété *f* de Schreier	шрейерово многообразие
	Schröder-Bernstein theorem <SE>	*s.* E 425		
	Schroeder-Bernstein theorem <SE>	*s.* E 425		
	Schröter['s] quartic <GE> ⌐<AG>	*s.* O 502		
S 146	**Schubert['s] scheme**	Schubertsches Schema *n*	schéma *m* de Schubert	схема Шуберта
S 147	**Schubert['s] symbol** <GE>	Schubertsches Symbol *n*	symbole *m* de Schubert	символ Шуберта
S 148	**Schubert variety** <AG>	Schubertsche Mannigfaltigkeit *f*	variété *f* de Schubert	шубертово многообразие
S 149	**Schur['s] function,** S-function <AL>	charakteristische Funktion *f* von Schur, S-Funktion *f*, Schursche Funktion, Schur-Funktion *f*	fonction *f* de Schur	функция Шура
S 150	**Schur['s] index** <of a representation *or* module> <AL, RE>	Schurscher Index *m*	indice *m* de Schur	индекс Шура
S 151	**Schur['s] inequality** <IE, MD>	Schursche Ungleichung *f*	inégalité *f* de Schur	неравенство Шура
S 152	**Schur['s] lemma** <RE>	Schursches (Schurs) Lemma *n*	lemme *m* de Schur	лемма Шура
S 153	**Schur['s] multiplicator (multiplier),** multiplicator, multiplier <of a group> <GR>	Multiplikator *m*, Schurscher Multiplikator, Hopfsche Gruppe *f*	multiplicateur *m* de Schur	мультипликатор Шура, мультипликатор
S 154	**Schur['s] quadric** <GE>	Schursche Quadrik *f*, F_2 (Fläche *f* zweiter Ordnung) von Schur	quadrique *f* de Schur	квадрика Шура
S 155	**Schützenberger['s] antirepresentation** <of a semigroup> <AL>	Schützenbergersche Antidarstellung *f*	anti-représentation *f* de Schützenberger	антипредставление Шютценберже
S 156	**Schützenberger['s] group** <AL>	Schützenberger-Gruppe *f*	groupe *m* de Schützenberger	группа Шютценберже
S 157	**Schützenberger['s] representation** <of a semigroup> <AL>	Schützenbergersche Darstellung *f*	représentation *f* de Schützenberger	представление Шютценберже
S 158	**Schwartz['s] space,** (S)-space <TO>	Schwartzscher Raum *m*	espace *m* de Schwartz (Fréchet-Schwartz)	пространство Шварца
	Schwarz['s] alternating method <DE, PO>	*s.* A 551		
S 159	**Schwarz-Christoffel formula** <for a conformal mapping> <FT>	Schwarz-Christoffelsche Formel *f*, Schwarz-Christoffelsches Integral *n*	formule *f* de Schwarz-Christoffel	формула (интеграл) Шварца-Кристоффеля, формула Кристоффеля-Шварца
	Schwarz-Christoffel polygon mapping <FT>	*s.* P 939		

S 160	**Schwarz-Christoffel theorem** <FT>	Schwarz-Christoffelscher Abbildungssatz *m*	théorème *m* de Schwarz-Christoffel	теорема Шварца-Кристоффеля
	Schwarz-Christoffel transformation <FT>	*s.* P 939		
S 161	**Schwarz['s] constant** <DE, FA, NU>	Schwarzsche Konstante *f*	constante *f* de Schwarz	постоянная (константа) Шварца
S 162	**Schwarz['s] derivative** <FT>	Schwarzsche Differentialinvariante (Abgeleitete, Ableitung) *f*, Schwarzscher Differentialausdruck *m*	dérivée *f* de Schwarz, dérivée schwarzienne, schwarzien *m*	производная Шварца
S 163	**Schwarz['s] formula** <for an analytic function> <FT> ⌐<FU>	Schwarzsche Formel *f*	formule *f* de Schwarz	формула Шварца
S 164	**Schwarz['s] function**	Schwarz-Funktion *f*	fonction *f* de Schwarz	функция Шварца
S 165	**Schwarzian differential equation** <DE>	Schwarzsche Differentialgleichung *f*	équation *f* différentielle de Schwarz	[дифференциальное] уравнение Шварца
S 166	**Schwarzian triangle function** <FT>	Schwarzsche Dreiecksfunktion *f*, Dreiecksfunktion	fonction *f* du triangle schwarzienne	шварцева функция треугольника
S 167	**Schwarz['s] inequality,** Bouniakowski-Schwarz (Bouniakowsky-Schwarz) inequality, Buniakowski-Schwarz inequality <for integrals> <AN>	Schwarzsche (Bunjakowskische, Cauchy-Bunjakowskische) Ungleichung *f*, Schwarzsche Ungleichheit *f*	inégalité *f* de Schwarz (Bouniakowsky)	неравенство Буняковского (Шварца, Коши-Буняковского)
S 168	**Schwarz['s] lemma** <FT>	Schwarzsches Lemma *n*	lemme *m* de Schwarz	лемма Шварца
S 169	**Schwarz['s] minimal surface** <DG>	Schwarzsche Minimalfläche *f*	surface *f* minimale de Schwarz	минимальная поверхность Шварца
	Schwarz['s] principle of reflection <FT>	*s.* S 172		
S 170	**Schwarz['s] problem** <concerning minimal surfaces> <DG>	Schwarzsches Problem *n*	problème *m* de Schwarz	задача Шварца
S 171	**Schwarz['s] quotient** <DE, FA, MD, NU>	Schwarzscher Quotient *m*	quotient *m* de Schwarz	частное Шварца, частное Релея-Шварца
S 172	**Schwarz['s] reflection [principle],** reflection principle, Schwarz['s] principle of reflection, principle of reflection, symmetry principle, spiegelungsprinzip <FT>	Schwarzsches Spiegelungsprinzip *n*, Spiegelungsprinzip, Prinzip *n* der Symmetrie, Schwarzscher Spiegelungssatz *m*	principe *m* de la symétrie (symétrie de Schwarz), principe de symétrie de Schwarz, principe de réflexion	принцип симметрии [Шварца], принцип Римана-Шварца, принцип зеркальной симметрии, принцип аналитического продолжения, принцип отражения [Шварца]
S 173	**Schwarz['s] *S*-function** <DE>	Schwarzsche *S*-Funktion *f*	*S*-fonction *f* (fonction *f* (*S*)) de Schwarz	*S*-функция Шварца
S 174	**Schwarz['s] symmetrization** <of a convex body with respect to a line> <GE>	Schwarzsche Abrundung *f*, Abrundung	symétrisation *f* de Schwarz	симметризация Шварца
S 175	**Schwarz['s] theorem** <DI>	Satz *m* von [H. A.] Schwarz, Schwarzscher Satz	théorème *m* de Schwarz	теорема Шварца
S 176	**scope** <*e.g.:* of a logical symbol> <LO>	Geltungsbereich *m*, Wirkungsbereich *m* <*z. B.:* eines logischen Symbols>	champ *m* <*par exemple:* d'un symbole logique>	область действия <*например:* логического символа>
S 177	**scope** <of a quantifier> <LO>	Wirkungsbereich *m*	domaine *m* d'action, scope *m*, étendue *f*, champ *m*	область действия
S 178	**scope** <of a design> <ST>	Aussagebereich *m*, Reichweite *f*	étendue *f*	сфера, охватываемая опытом
	scoring <ST>	*s.* N 695		
S 179	**screening** <ST>	verbessernde Auswahl *f*, Screening *n*	sélection *f* par tri	улучшающий отбор, просеивание, отсеивание
	screening inspection <ST>	*s.* R 288		
S 180	**screw** <Ball; Hyde> <VT>	Schraube *f*	vis *f*, visseur *f*	винт
S 181	**screw displacement, screwing [motion],** helicoidal displacement, screw motion, helical motion, helicoidal motion, motion along a helix, spiralling <GE>	Schraubung *f*, Schraubenbewegung *f*, schraubenförmige Bewegung *f*	déplacement *m* hélicoïdal, vissage *f*, mouvement *m* hélicoïdal (de torsion), torsion *f*, viration *f*	винтовое движение
	screw[ ]line <GE>	*s.* H 185		
	screw motion <GE>	*s.* S 181		
	scriber <GE, IN>	*s.* T 718		
	s.c. uniformity <TO>	*s.* U 133		
	S-curve <GN>	*s.* S 835		
	Se <FU>	*s.* A 1079		
	se <FU>	*s.* P 455		
S 182	**search procedure** <PG>	Suchtechnik *f*, Suchverfahren *n*	procédé *m* de recherche	способ поиска (отыскания)
S 183	**search process** <PG>	Suchprozeß *m*	processus *m* de recherche	процесс поиска (отыскания)
S 184	**seasonal variation** <ST>	Saisonschwankung *f*, saisonale Schwankung *f*	variation *f* saisonnière	сезонное колебание (изменение)
	sec <DI>	*s.* S 186		
	sec <GE>	*s.* 1. C 341; 2. S 192		
	sec^{-1} <FU>	*s.* I 944		
S 185	**secant,** secant line <of a cercle *or* sphere, *also* of a curve> <EG>	Sekante *f*	sécante *f*, droite *f* sécante	секущая
S 186	**secant,** secant function, sec <DI>	Sekans *m*, Secans *m*, Sekansfunktion *f*, sec	sécante *f*, fonction *f* sécante, sec	секанс, функция секанс, sec
	secant <AG>	*s.* T 863		

No.	English	German	French	Russian
S 187	**secant curve,** secant line, secantoid <DI>	Sekanskurve *f*, Sekanslinie *f*, Sekansoide *f*	sécantoïde *f*, courbe (ligne) *f* sécante	секансоида, график секанса
	secant function <DI>	*s.* S 186		
S 188	**secant integral, secant-integral function,** integral secant <FU>	Integralsekans *m*, Secans *m* integralis, Sekansintegralfunktion *f*	sécante *f* intégrale	интегральный секанс
	secant line <AG>	*s.* T 863		
	secant line <DI>	*s.* S 187		
	secant line <EG>	*s.* S 185		
	secantoid <DI>	*s.* S 187		
S 189	**secantoidal curve (line)** <DI>	sekansförmige Kurve *f*, Sekanskurve *f*	ligne (courbe) *f* sécantoïdale	секансоидальная кривая (линия)
	secant plane <EG>	*s.* I 794		
S 190	**secant-tangent theorem** <EG>	Sekantentangentensatz *m*, Sekanten-Tangentensatz *m*	théorème *m* sur la sécante et la tangente	теорема о касательной и секущей
S 191	**secant theorem** <EG>	Sekantensatz *m*	théorème *m* sur les sécantes	теорема о секущих
	sech <FU>	*s.* H 645		
S 192	**second,** second of angle (arc), angular second, sexagesimal second, ″, sec <GE>	Sekunde *f*, Winkelsekunde *f*, Bogensekunde *f*, Altsekunde *f*, ″	seconde *f*, seconde de l'angle, seconde d'arc, seconde angulaire, seconde sexagésimale, ″	секунда, секунда угла (дуги), угловая секунда, ″
	second adjoint <FA>	*s.* S 194		
S 193	**second adjoint operator,** second dual operator <FA>	bidualer Operator *m*	opérateur *m* bidual	бидуальный оператор, второй сопряженный оператор
S 194	**second adjoint space,** second adjoint, second conjugate, second dual <of a linear topological space> <FA>	Bidual *m*, bidualer (zweiter adjungierter) Raum *m*	espace *m* bidual, bidual *m*	бидуальное (второе сопряженное) пространство
S 195	**second and third law for powers** <AR>	Distributionsformeln *fpl* bei gleicher Basis <ein Potenzgesetz>	formules *fpl* de distribution pour une même base	законы показателей вида $a^m \cdot a^n = a^{m+n}$, $a^m/a^n = a^{m-n}$
S 196	**secondary component** <of a Witt vector> <AL>	Nebenkomponente *f*	composante *f* fantôme	призрачная компонента
S 197	**secondary diagonal** <MD>	Nebendiagonale *f*	diagonale *f* secondaire, seconde diagonale	вторая (побочная, вторичная) диагональ
	secondary extremal <VA>	*s.* A 181		
S 198	**secondary ideal** <AL>	Sekundärideal *n*	idéal *m* secondaire	секондарный идеал
S 199	**secondary module** <AL>	Sekundärmodul *m*	sous-module *m* secondaire	вторичный модуль
S 200	**secondary obstruction** <of fibre bundles> <AT>	zweites Hindernis *n*	second (2-e) obstacle, deuxième obstruction *f*	второе препятствие
S 201	**secondary unit,** second-stage unit <ST>	Sekundäreinheit *f*	unité *f* secondaire	объект второй стадии выборки
	secondary unit <FT>	*s.* I 104		
	secondary variational problem <VA>	*s.* A 185		
S 202	**second axiom of countability,** second countability axiom, [Hausdorff['s]] second denumerability axiom, axiom of countability <TO>	zweites Abzählbarkeitsaxiom *n*	axiome *m* de la base, deuxième axiome de dénombrabilité de Hausdorff	вторая аксиома счетности
	second boundary condition <DE, PO>	*s.* N 176		
	second boundary [value] problem <DE, PO>	*s.* N 180		
S 203	**second characteristic polynomial** <of an element of an algebra> <AL>	zweites charakteristisches Polynom *n* <mit der zweiten regulären Darstellung gebildet>	deuxième polynôme *m* caractéristique	второй характеристический многочлен
S 204	**second class,** second number[-] class <SE>	zweite Zahlklasse (Zahlenklasse, ordinale Zahlklasse, Cantorsche Klasse) *f*	deuxième classe *f* <de nombres ordinaux>	второй класс (числовой класс)
S 205	**second comparison test,** comparison test of the second kind, ratio test <for convergence> <SS>	Vergleichskriterium (Konvergenzkriterium, Kriterium) *n* zweiter (2.) Art, allgemeines Vergleichskriterium zweiter (2.) Art, allgemeines Quotientenkriterium *n*, Quotientenkriterium	règle *f* (critère *m*, théorème *m*) [de convergence] de seconde (deuxième) espèce, comparaison *f* logarithmique	признак (критерий) сравнения второго рода, сравнительный признак (критерий) второго рода
S 206	**second component** <of a conjunction, disjunction, etc.> <LO>	Hinterglied *n*	second terme *m*	второй член
	second conjugate <FA>	*s.* S 194		
S 207	**second co-ordinate,** second term <of an ordered pair> <SE>	zweites Element (Glied) *n*	seconde coordonnée *f*, ordonnée *f*, seconde projection *f*	вторая координата (проекция), ордината, второй элемент
	second countability axiom <TO>	*s.* S 202		
	secound-countable regular [topological] space <TO>	*s.* R 638		
	second countable [topological] space <TO> ┌<FT>	*s.* C 1512		
	second Cousin problem	*s.* C 2595		
	second curvature <DG>	*s.* T 586		
	second-degree equation <AL>	*s.* Q 25		

No.	English	Deutsch	Français	Русский
	second denumerability axiom <TO>	*s.* S 202		
	second differential parameter [of Lamé] <DE, DG, DI, PO>	*s.* L 91		
S 208	**second distance** <DS>	zweiter Tafelabstand *m*	deuxième distance *f*	второе (вертикальное) расстояние
	second dual <FA>	*s.* S 194		
S 209	**second dual module** <of a module> <AL>	bidualer Modul *m*	bidual *m*, module *m* bidual	второй сопряженный модуль
	second dual operator <FA>	*s.* S 193		
	second equation[s] of Kolmogorov <SP>	*s.* K 122		
S 210	**second factor** <for ordinals> <SE>	Multiplikator *m*, zweiter Faktor *m*	multiplicateur *m*	второй фактор
S 211	**second fall[-] line** <DS>	zweite Fallinie *f*	seconde ligne *f* de pente	вторая линия падения
S 212	**second fundamental form** <in Euclidean surface theory> <DG>	zweite Grundform (Fundamentalform) *f*, zweite Gaußsche (quadratische) Fundamentalform	seconde (deuxième) forme *f* fondamentale	вторая основная [квадратичная] форма, вторая дифференциальная форма Гаусса
	second Green formula <DI, VT>	*s.* G 425		
	second isomorphism theorem <CA>	*s.* S 216		
	second isomorphism theorem <GR>	*s.* F 341		
	second law of the mean <DI>	*s.* B 542		
S 213	**second Lemoine circle** <of a triangle> <EG>	zweiter Lemoinescher Kreis *m*	deuxième cercle *m* de Lemoine	вторая окружность Лемуана
	second-level predicate <LO>	*s.* F 797		
	second-level predicate constant <LO>	*s.* P 1187		
S 214	**second limit theorem**	zweiter Grenzwertsatz *m*	second théorème *m* limite, seconde loi *f* de Laplace, loi de Laplace-Gauss	вторая предельная теорема
	second mean value theorem <DI>	*s.* C 240		
S 215	**second member** <in a relation> <LO>	zweites Glied *n* <in einer Relation>	successeur *m* <dans une relation>	второй член <в отношении>
	second member <GN>	*s.* R 1166		
S 216	**second Noether isomorphism theorem,** second isomorphism theorem <for categories> <CA>	zweiter Isomorphiesatz *m*	second théorème *m* d'isomorphie	вторая теорема об изоморфизмах
	second normal <DG>	*s.* B 404		
S 217	**second normal form** <of a matrix> <MD>	zweite Normalform *f*	seconde forme *f* normale	вторая нормальная форма
	second normal [unit] vector <DG>	*s.* B 407		
	second number[-] class <SE>	*s.* S 204		
	second of angle (arc) <GE>	*s.* S 192		
	second-order algebraic hypersurface <AG>	*s.* A 441		
	second order algebraic surface <AG>	*s.* T 1081		
	second-order component <ST>	*s.* Q 20		
	second-order functional calculus <LO>	*s.* S 218		
	second-order language <FO>	*s.* M 432		
S 218	**second[-] order logic,** second-order functional calculus, functional calculus of the second order, logic of second order <LO>	Prädikatenkalkül *m* (Prädikatenlogik *f*) zweiter Stufe, Quantorenlogik *f* der zweiten Stufe	calcul *m* logique du second échelon, logique *f* du second (deuxième) ordre	исчисление предикатов второго порядка, логика предикатов второго порядка, расширенное исчисление предикатов, исчисление предикатов второй ступени
	second-order Newton-Raphson process <AX, NU>	*s.* N 206		
S 219	**second order process,** stochastic process of the second order <SP>	Prozeß *m* zweiter Ordnung, stochastischer Prozeß zweiter Ordnung	processus *m* de deuxième ordre, processus stochastique de deuxième ordre	процесс второго порядка, стохастический процесс второго порядка
S 220	**second-order property,** root-mean-square property <ST>	Eigenschaft *f* zweiter Ordnung, Quadratmitteleigenschaft *f*	propriété *f* de deuxième ordre, propriété de la moyenne quadratique	свойство второго порядка
	second-order strip <DE>	*s.* S 1922		
	second-order tensor <VT>	*s.* D 949		
S 221	**second-order transformation** <GE>	Transformation *f* zweiter Ordnung <Hirst>	transformation *f* quadrique	преобразование второго порядка
S 222	**second orthogonal group** <GR>	zweite orthogonale Gruppe *f*	deuxième groupe *m* orthogonal	вторая ортогональная группа
	second plane [of projection] <DS>	*s.* V 170		
	second polar <AG>	*s.* E 638		
	second principal line <DS>	*s.* F 679		
	second principal plane <DS>	*s.* F 680		

	second problem <DE, PO>	*s.* N 180		
	second projection <DS>	*s.* E 143		
	second root <AL>	*s.* S 1565		
	second shifting theorem <IT>	*s.* T 479		
	second-stage unit <ST>	*s.* S 201		
	second system <SP>	*s.* K 122		
S 223	**second term** <of a binary operation> <AL>	passive Zahl *f*	nombre (terme) *m* passif, second (deuxième) terme	второй член
	second term <AL, AR>	*s.* A 227		
	second term <SE>	*s.* 1. A 228; 2. S 207		
	second theorem of the mean <DI>	*s.* B 542		
S 224	**second trace,** second trace point <of a line> <DS>	zweiter Spurpunkt *m*, zweite Spur *f*	deuxième trace *f* (point *m* trace)	второй (вертикальный) след <прямой>, след в вертикальной плоскости <проекций>
S 225	**second trace,** vertical trace, second (vertical) trace line <of a plane> <DS>	zweite Spurlinie (Spur) *f*, vertikale Spurlinie (Spur)	trace *f* verticale, deuxième trace	вертикальный след <плоскости>, след в вертикальной плоскости <проекций>
	second trace line <DS>	*s.* S 225		
	second trace parallel <DS>	*s.* F 679		
	second trace point <DS>	*s.* S 224		
S 226	**second variation** <VA>	zweite Variation *f*	deuxième variation *f*	вторая вариация
	second weight <DG, VT>	*s.* A 789		
S 227	**section** <of a sheaf> <AL, TO>	Schnitt *m* <einer Garbe>	section *f* <d'un faisceau>	сечение <пучка>
	section <AN, SE>	*s.* D 84		
	section <AT>	*s.* C 2711		
	section <CA>	*s.* C 2464		
	section <EG>	*s.* S 2369		
	section <SE>	*s.* S 242		
	sectional curvature <DG>	*s.* R 1006		
S 228	**sectionally analytic curve** <FT>	stückweise analytische Kurve *f*	courbe *f* analytique par morceaux	кусочно аналитическая кривая
	sectionally complemented lattice <LA>	*s.* R 733		
	sectionally continuous function <AN>	*s.* P 585		
	sectionally smooth curve <AN>	*s.* P 596		
S 229	**section functor** <CA>	Schnittfunktor *m*	foncteur *m* section	функтор образования сечений
	section graph <GP>	*s.* S 2105		
S 230	**section of a function,** function of one variable obtained by holding constant all the other variables <AN>	partielle Funktion *f* <einer Funktion mehrerer Variabler>	fonction *f* partielle	сужение <функции нескольких переменных>
S 231	**section of distributions** <of a fibred manifold> <AN, TO>	Schnitt *m* von Distributionen <einer gefaserten Mannigfaltigkeit >	section-distribution *f* <d'une variété fibré>	сечение-распределение <расслоенного многообразия>
S 232	**section of measures** <of a fibred manifold> <AN, TO>	Schnitt *m* von Maßen <einer gefaserten Mannigfaltigkeit>	section-mesure *f* <d'une variété fibrée>	сечение-мера, сечение <расслоенного многообразия>
	section plane <EG>	*s.* P 654		
S 233	**sector angle** <EG>	Sektorwinkel *m*	angle *m* du secteur, angle d'ouverture du secteur	угол сектора
S 234	**sectorial harmonic, sectorial Legendre function [of the first kind], sectorial spherical harmonic** <FU>	sektorielle Kugelfunktion *f* [erster Art], sektorielle Legendresche Funktion *f* [erster Art]	fonction *f* de Legendre sectoriale [de la première espèce], fonction harmonique sectoriale, fonction sphérique sectoriale [de la première espèce], fonction sectoriale	секториальная сферическая функция [Лежандра] первого рода, секториальная сферическая функция [Лежандра]
	sector of sphere <EG>	*s.* S 1484		
S 235	**secular constant** <AP>	mittlere Bewegung *f*, Säkularkonstante *f*	constante *f* séculaire	вековая постоянная
S 236	**secular determinant,** characteristic determinant, determinantal polynomial <of a matrix> <MD>	Säkulardeterminante *f*, charakteristische Determinante *f*, // Funktion *f* <einer Matrix>	déterminant *m* séculaire (caractéristique)	вековой (характеристический) определитель, характеристический детерминант
S 237	**secular equation** <of a conic *or* quadric> <AY>	Hauptachsengleichung *f*, Säkulargleichung *f*	équation *f* séculaire	вековое уравнение
	secular equation <AL, MD>	*s.* C 540		
	secular equation <DE>	*s.* A 1250		
	secular equation <MD>	*s.* C 544		
	security digit <NU>	*s.* G 538		
S 238	**sedenion** <AL>	Sedenion *f*		седенион
	seeming error <ER>	*s.* R 886 a		
S 239	**seesaw principle** <AG>	Schaukelsatz *m*		теорема о качелях
S 240	**segment,** one-dimensional simplex, 1-simplex; edge <of a simplex> <AT>	Strecke *f*, 1-Simplex *n*, eindimensionales Simplex *n*; Kante *f*	segment *m*, 1-simplexe *m*, simplexe *m* de dimension un; arête *f*	отрезок, одномерный симплекс, 1-симплекс; ребро
S 241	**segment** <in a linear space> <FA, TO>	Strecke *f*	segment *m*	отрезок

No.	English	German	French	Russian
S 242	**segment,** section, initial segment, segment initial <of an element *x*, determined by *x*, corresponding to the element *x*> <of an ordered set> <SE>	Hauptabschnitt *m*, Hauptanfang *m*, <durch *x* bestimmter> Abschnitt *m*, <zu *x* gehörige> Anfangsstrecke *f*, <durch ein *x* bestimmtes> Anfangsstück *n*, Abschnitt von *x*	segment *m*, section *f* commençante <déterminé(e) par *x*, de base *x*>	отрезок, начальный сегмент <отвечающий элементу *x*>
	segment <DG>	*s.* M 507		
	segment <EG>	*s.* 1. C 723; 2. L 876		
	segment <TO>	*s.* C 875		
	segment congruence <GE>	*s.* C 1924		
S 243	**segment divided in the golden section** <EG>	stetig geteilte Strecke *f*, im goldenen Schnitt geteilte Strecke	segment *m* divisé en moyenne et extrême raison	гармонически деленный отрезок
	segment initial <SE>	*s.* S 242		
	segment in the proper sense <CS, TO>	*s.* P 1828		
S 244	**segment of a curve** <GE>	Kurvenstück *n*	segment *m* d'une courbe	кусок кривой
S 245	**segment of ordinals** <SE>	Zahlenabschnitt *m*	segment *m* d'ordinaux	начальный сегмент порядковых чисел
S 246	**segment of support,** supporting segment <DG>	Stützstrecke *f*	segment *m* d'appui	опорный отрезок
	segment of the sphere <EG>	*s.* S 1486		
S 247	**segmentwise convergence,** convergence by segments <FA>	abschnittsweise Konvergenz *f*	convergence *f* par segments	сходимость по отрезкам
S 248	**segmentwise convergent,** convergent by segments <FA>	abschnittsweise konvergent	convergent par segments	сходящийся по отрезкам
S 249	**Segner['s] construction** <of the curve representing a rational function> <AN, NU>	Segnersche Konstruktion *f*	construction *f* de Segner	построение Сегнера
S 250	**Segre characteristic** <of a matrix> <MD>	Segre-Charakteristik *f*	caractéristique *f* de Segre	характеристика Сегре
S 251	**Segre['s] curve** <DG>	Segresche Kurve *f*, Segre-Kurve *f*	courbe *f* de Segre	кривая Сегре
S 252	**Segre['s] direction** <DG>	Segre-Richtung *f*, Segresche Richtung *f*	direction *f* de Segre	направление Сегре
S 253	**Segre['s] tangent** <DG>	Segresche Tangente *f*, Segre-Tangente *f*	tangente *f* de Segre	касательная Сегре
S 254	**Segre['s] variety,** variety of Segre <AG>	Segresche Mannigfaltigkeit *f*	variété *f* de Segre	многообразие Сегре
	Seidel['s] method <AL, AX, NU>	*s.* G 98		
S 255	**selection** <ST>	Selektion *f*	sélection *f*	отбор, селекция
	selection <ST>	*s. a.* S 34		
S 256	**selection set** <in axiom of choice> <SE>	Auswahlmenge *f*	ensemble *m* sélectif, partie *f* choisie <d'une fonction de choix>	множество выбора (представителей), выбирающее множество
S 257	**selection theorem of Blaschke,** Blaschke['s] selection theorem <GE>	Auswahlsatz *m* für konvexe Körper <Blaschke>, Auswahlsatz von Blaschke, Blaschkescher Auswahlsatz *m*, Auswahlsatz *m*	théorème *m* de sélection de Blaschke	теорема выбора Бляшке, принцип компактности Бляшке
	selection theorem of Mahler <GU>	*s.* M 32		
S 258	**selection with arbitrary probability,** sampling with arbitrary probability <ST>	Stichprobennahme *f* mit willkürlicher Wahrscheinlichkeit	choix *m* (sélection *f*) avec probabilité arbitraire	выбор (селекция) с произвольной вероятностью
	selection with a uniform sampling fraction <ST>	*s.* P 1854		
S 259	**selection with equal probability,** sampling with equal probability <ST>	Stichprobennahme *f* mit gleicher Wahrscheinlichkeit	choix *m* avec égale probabilité, sélection *f* avec égale probabilité	равновероятный отбор, селекция с одинаковой вероятностью
S 260	**selector** <for a relation> <SE>	Selektor *m*	sélecteur *m*	селектор
	self-adjoint algebra <FA>	*s.* A 408/9		
S 261	**self-adjoint Banach algebra,** Banach *-algebra, Banach algebra with an involution <FA>	involutive Banach-Algebra *f*	algèbre *f* de Banach involutive, algèbre de Banach avec involution	инволютивная B-алгебра
S 262	**self-adjoint boundary value problem** <DE>	selbstadjungiertes Randwertproblem *n*, selbstadjungierte Randwertaufgabe *f*	problème *m* aux limites auto-adjoint	самосопряженная краевая задача
S 263	**self-adjoint differential equation** <DE>	selbstadjungierte Differentialgleichung *f*	équation *f* différentielle auto-adjointe	самосопряженное дифференциальное уравнение
S 264	**self-adjoint eigenvalue problem** <DE>	selbstadjungiertes Eigenwertproblem *n*, selbstadjungierte Eigenwertaufgabe *f*	problème *m* aux valeurs propres auto-adjoint	самосопряженная задача на собственные значения

S 265/6	**self-adjoint element** <of a C^*-algebra> <AL, FA>	hermitesches Element *n*, selbstadjungiertes Element *n*	élément *m* hermitien, élément *m* auto-adjoint	эрмитов элемент, самосопряженный элемент
S 267	**self-adjoint graph** <GP>	selbstadjungierter Graph *m*	graphe *m* auto-adjoint	самосопряженный граф
	self-adjoint Hermitian operator <FA>	*s.* S 273		
S 268	**self-adjoint latin square** <ST>	selbstadjungiertes lateinisches Quadrat *n*	carré *m* latin auto-adjoint	самосопряженный латинский квадрат
S 269	**self-adjoint linear mapping** <AL>	selbstadjungierte lineare Abbildung *f*	application *f* linéaire auto-adjointe	самосопряженное (эрмитово) линейное отображение
S 270	**self[-]adjoint linear subspace,** self[-]adjoint subspace <FA>	selbstadjungierter [linearer] Unterraum *m*	sous-espace *m* [linéaire] auto-adjoint	самосопряженное [линейное] подпространство
	self-adjoint matrix <MD>	*s.* H 248		
S 271	**self-adjointness** <AL, FA>	Selbstadjungiertheit *f*	propriété *f* d'être auto-adjoint	самосопряженность
S 272	**self-adjoint normed algebra,** normed algebra with an involution <FA>	involutive normierte Algebra *f*	algèbre *f* normée involutive	инволютивная нормированная алгебра
S 273	**self[-]adjoint operator,** hypermaximal operator, self-adjoint Hermitian (symmetrical) operator, hypermaximal Hermitian (symmetrical) operator <FA>	selbstadjungierter (hypermaximaler) Operator *m*, selbstadjungierter hermitescher (symmetrischer) Operator, hypermaximaler hermitescher (symmetrischer) Operator, hypermaximale hermitesche Transformation *f*	opérateur *m* auto-adjoint (autoconjugué, hypermaximal), opérateur hermitien (symétrique) auto-adjoint, opérateur hermitien (symétrique) hypermaximal, opération (transformation) *f* auto-adjointe	самосопряженный (гипермаксимальный) оператор, самосопряженный эрмитов (симметричный) оператор, гипермаксимальный эрмитов (симметричный) оператор
S 274	**self-adjoint operator algebra** <FA>	selbstadjungierte Operatorenalgebra *f*	algèbre *f* auto-adjointe d'opérateurs	самосопряженная алгебра операторов
	self-adjoint operator algebra <FA>	*s. a.* A 408/9		
	self[-]adjoint subspace <FA>	*s.* S 270		
	self-adjoint symmetrical operator <FA>	*s.* S 273		
S 275	**self-complementary graph** <GP>	selbstkomplementärer (zu sich selbst komplementärer) Graph *m*	graphe *m* auto-complémentaire	самодополнительный граф
	self-computing chart <NO>	*s.* A 490		
S 276	**self-conjugacy** <AL, CT>	Selbstkonjugiertheit *f*	propriété *f* d'être auto-conjugué	самосопряженность
S 277	**self[-]conjugate latin square** <CT, ST>	selbstkonjugiertes lateinisches Quadrat *n*	carré *m* latin auto[-]conjugué	самосопряженный латинский квадрат
S 278	**self-conjugate partition** <NT>	selbstkonjugierte Partition *f*	partition *f* autoconjuguée	самосопряженное разбиение
	self-conjugate sub[-]group <GR>	*s.* I 883		
	self-contact <GE>	*s.* S 304		
	self-contradictoriness <LO>	*s.* I 279		
	self-contradictory system of axioms <FO>	*s.* I 284		
	self-corresponding point <AY, PJ>	*s.* D 935		
	self-distributive law <AL>	*s.* A 1222		
	self-distributive law of [material] implication <LO>	*s.* F 639		
S 279	**self-dual category** <CA>	selbstduale Kategorie *f*	catégorie *f* auto-duale	двойственная самой себе категория
S 280	**self-dual configuration** <GE>	selbstduale Konfiguration *f*	configuration *f* auto-duale	самодвойственная конфигурация
S 281	**self-dual element** <of a lattice> <LA>	selbstduales Element *n*	élément *m* ipsodual (plat)	самодвойственный элемент
S 282	**self-dual group** <GR>	selbstduale Gruppe *f*	groupe *m* auto-dual au sens de Pontrjagin	самодвойственная группа
S 283	**self-duality** <property> <AL, GE, LO>	Selbstdualität *f*	auto-dualité *f*, autodualité *f*, auto dualité *f*	двойственность себе, автодуальность
S 284	**self-dual lattice,** autodual lattice <LA>	selbstdualer Verband *m*	treillis *m* auto-dual (ipso[-]dual)	самодвойственная структура
S 285	**self-dual system of axioms,** system of axioms invariant under dualization <FO>	selbstduales Axiomensystem *n*	système *m* d'axiomes auto-dual (inchangé par dualité, ipso-dual)	двойственная себе система аксиом, самодвойственная система аксиом
S 286	**self equivalence** <of a fibration> <AT>	Isomorphismus *m* <eines Faserraums> auf sich	isomorphisme *m* <d'un fibré> sur lui-même	самоэквивалентность <расслоения>
	self-equivalence <AT, TO>	*s.* C 2637		
	self-injective Artin ring <AL>	*s.* Q 160		
S 287	**self[-]injective ring** <AL>	selbstinjektiver Ring *m*	anneau *m* self-injectif	самоинъективное кольцо
	self-intersecting polygon <EG>	*s.* R 477		

S 288	**self-intersecting polyhedron,** polyhedron with faces cutting each other <EG>	überschlagenes Polyeder (Vielflach) *n*	polyèdre *m* croisé	самопересекающийся многогранник, многогранник с самопересечением
S 289	**self-intersection** <AG, AT>	Selbstschnitt *m*	self-intersection *f*	самопересечение
S 290	**self-intersection** <DS, EG>	Selbstdurchdringung *f*	auto-intersection *f*	самопересечение
S 291	**self[-]intersection number** <AG, AT>	Selbstschnittzahl *f*	coefficient *m* de self-intersection	индекс самопересечения
S 292	**self[-]intersection point** <DG>	Selbstschnittpunkt *m*	point *m* de self-intersection	точка самопересечения
S 293	**self-intersection point,** point of self-intersection <DS, GE>	Selbstdurchdringungspunkt *m*	point *m* d'auto-intersection	узловая точка, точка самопересечения
S 294	**self-invariant semigroup** <AL>	selbstinvariante Halbgruppe *f*		инвариантная в себе полугруппа
	self-loop <GP>	*s.* L 1103		
S 295	**self-orthogonal submodule** <AL>	totalisotroper Untermodul *m*	sous-module *m* totalement isotrope	вполне изотропный подмодуль
S 296	**self-orthogonal subspace,** null subspace <with respect to a Hermitian form> <AL>	totalisotroper Teilraum *m* <bezüglich einer hermiteschen Form>	sous-espace *m* vectoriel totalement isotrope <pour une forme hermitienne>	вполне изотропное подпространство
	self-osculation <GE>	*s.* S 304		
S 297	**self-polar curve** <AY>	autopolare (selbstpolare) Kurve *f*	courbe *f* autopolaire	автополярная кривая
S 298	**self-polarity** <PJ>	Autopolarität *f*, Selbstpolarität *f*	autopolarité *f*	автополярность
S 299	**self-polar polygon** <of a quadric> <PJ>	Polarvieleck *n*, Polvieleck *n*, autopolares (selbstpolares) Vieleck *n*	polygone *m* autopolaire (conjugué)	автополярный полигон
S 300	**self-polar simplex,** polar simplex <PJ>	Polarsimplex *n*, Polsimplex *n*, autopolares (selbstpolares) Simplex *n*	simplexe *m* polaire (autopolaire, conjugué)	автополярный (полярный) симплекс
S 301	**self-polar tetrahedron** <of a quadric surface> <PJ>	Polartetraeder *n*, Polvierflach *n*, Poltetraeder *n*, autopolares (selbstpolares) Tetraeder *n*	tétraèdre *m* autopolaire (conjugué)	автополярный тетраэдр
S 302	**self-polar triad of lines,** self-polar trilateral <PJ>	Polardreiseit *n*, Poldreiseit *n*, autopolares (selbstpolares, sich selbst polares) Dreiseit *n*	trilatère *m* polaire (autopolaire, conjugué), triangle *m* polaire	автополярный трехсторонник (треугольник); автополярный трехвершинник
S 303	**self-polar triad of points, self-polar triangle** <for a conic> <PJ>	Polardreieck *n*, Poldreieck *n*, autopolares (selbstpolares) Dreieck *n*; drei zugeordnete harmonische Pole *mpl*, drei konjugierte Pole <Steiner>	triangle *m* autopolaire (polaire); triple *m* de points harmoniques (conjugués)	автополярный (самосопряженный) треугольник
	self-polar trilateral <PJ>	*s.* S 302		
S 304	**self-tangency,** self-contact, self-osculation <GE>	Selbstberührung *f*	auto-tangence *f*, autocontact *m*, auto-osculation *f*	самоприкосновение, самокасание, самосоприкосновение
S 305	**self-weighting sample** <ST>	selbstgewogene Stichprobe *f*	échantillon *m* auto-pondéré	самовзвешенная выборка
S 306	**semantical completeness,** semantic completeness <of an axiom system> <LO>	semantische Vollständigkeit *f*, Vollständigkeit bis auf Isomorphie	saturation *f* sémantique	содержательная полнота, полнота с точностью до изоморфизма
S 307	**semantical completeness,** [semantic] completeness <LO>	semantische (inhaltliche) Vollständigkeit *f*, Vollständigkeit im weiteren Sinne	complétude *f* au sens large, complétude sémantique	полнота в широком смысле
S 308	**semantical decision problem,** decision problem for validity <LO>	semantisches Entscheidungsproblem *n*	problème *m* de décision sémantique	семантическая проблема разрешения, проблема разрешения для истинности
S 309	**semantically complete set of formulas** <MM>	semantisch (inhaltlich) vollständige Menge *f* von Ausdrücken	collection *f* de formules sémantiquement complète	семантически полная совокупность формул
S 310	**semantically consistent set of formulas** <MM>	semantisch (inhaltlich) widerspruchsfreie Menge *f* von Ausdrücken	collection *f* de formules sémantiquement consistante	семантически непротиворечивая совокупность формул
	semantically consistent system <LO>	*s.* S 1291		
S 311	**semantically definable constant** <LO>	semantisch definierbare Konstante *f*	constante *f* sémantiquement définissable	семантически определимая константа (постоянная)
	semantically equivalent form <LO>	*s.* C 1796		
S 312	**semantical paradox,** semantic paradox, linguistic paradox, antinomy of the semantical type, epistemological paradox <FO, LO>	semantische Antinomie *f*, semantisches Paradoxon *n*	antinomie *f* sémantique	семантический парадокс
S 313	**semantical theorem** <MM>	semantischer Satz *m*	théorème *m* sémantique	семантическая теорема
	semantic completeness <LO> ⌐<LO>	*s.* 1. S 306; 2. S 307		
	semantic consistency	*s.* S 1290		
S 314	**semantic equivalence,** concurrence <LO>	Äquivalenz *f* von Aussagenverbindungen, semantische Äquivalenz, Wertverlaufsgleichheit *f*	équivalence *f* sémantique	семантическая эквивалентность

No.	English	German	French	Russian
	semantic paradox <FO, LO>	*s.* S 312		
S 315	**semantics** <LO>	Semantik *f*	sémantique *f*	семантика
S 316	**semantic tableau** <LO>	semantisches Tableau *n*, semantische Tafel *f*	tableau *m* sémantique	семантическая таблица
S 317	**semantic valuation** <LO>	semantische Belegung *f*	valuation *f* sémantique	семантическое обложение
S 318	**semantic variable** <LO>	semantische Variable *f*	variable *f* sémantique	семантическая переменная
S 319	**semi-abelian category** <CA>	semiabelsche (halbabelsche) Kategorie *f*	catégorie *f* semi-abélienne	полуабелева категория
S 320	**semi-abelian *n*-group** <AL>	semi-abelsche *n*-Gruppe *f*	*n*-groupe *m* semi-abélien	полуабелева *n*-группа
S 321	**semi-absolute invariant** <of algebraic forms> <IV>	halbabsolute Invariante *f* <Rabut>	invariant *m* semiabsolu	полуабсолютный инвариант
S 322	**semiadditive category** <CA>	semiadditive Kategorie *f*	catégorie *f* semi-additive	полуаддитивная категория
S 323	**semi[-]additive [set] function** <ME, RF>	halbadditive Funktion (Mengenfunktion) *f*	fonction *f* (fonction d'ensemble) semi-additive	полуаддитивная функция [множества]
S 324	**semi-algebra** <Peirce>, hypercomplex number system over the reals <AL>	hyperkomplexes Zahlensystem *n* über dem Körper der reellen Zahlen	système *m* [de nombres complexes] à coordonnées réelles, algèbre *f* de dimension finie sur le corps des nombres réels, semi-algèbre *f*	система гиперкомплексных чисел над полем вещественных чисел
S 325	**semialgebraic set** <AL, TO>	semialgebraische Menge *f*	ensemble *m* semi-algébrique	полуалгебраическое множество
S 326	**semi-analytic set** <TO>	semianalytische Menge *f*	ensemble *m* semi-analytique, semi-analytique *m*	полуаналитическое множество
S 327	**semi-angle, semi-apex angle,** semi-vertex angle <of a cone>, semi-cone angle, cone semi-angle <EG>	halber Öffnungswinkel *m*, Öffnungswinkel	demi-angle *m* au sommet, demi-angle d'ouverture, demi-ouverture *f*	половина угла при вершине, половинный угол раствора, угол полураствора (полуотверстия), полураствор, полуотверстие
S 328	**semiartinian module** <AL>	semiartinscher Modul *m*	module *m* semi-artinien	полуартинов модуль
S 329	**semi-automorphism** <of rings> <AL>	Semi-Automorphismus *m*	semi-automorphisme *m*	полуавтоморфизм
	semi-automorphism <AL>	*s.* J 83		
S 330	**semi-axis** <of the ellipse *or* hyperbola> <AY>	Halbachse *f*	demi-axe *m*	полуось
S 331	**semi-balanced lattice square** <ST>	halbbalanciertes (halbbalanziertes) Gitterquadrat *n*	treillis *m* carré semi-équilibré (semi-compensé)	полусбалансированный решетчатый квадрат
S 332	**semi-bilinear mapping** <AL>	semibilineare Abbildung *f*	application *f* sesquilinéaire	полубилинейное отображение
S 333	**semi-bipartite graph** <GP>	semipaarer Graph *m*	graphe *m* semi-biparti	полудвудольный граф
	semi-bounded above <FA>	*s.* B 662		
	semi-bounded from above <FA>	*s.* B 662		
S 334	**semi-boundedness,** half-boundedness, boundedness from one side <FA>	Halbbeschränktheit *f*, Beschränktheit *f* nach einer Seite	propriété *f* d'être semi-borné	полуограниченность
S 335	**semi-bounded operator,** half-bounded operator, semi-bounded transformation, half-bounded transformation <FA>	halbbeschränkter Operator *m*, halbbeschränkte Transformation *f*	opérateur *m* semi[-]borné, transformation *f* semi[-]bornée	полуограниченный оператор, полуограниченное преобразование
	semi-bounded transformation <FA>	*s.* S 335		
S 336	**semi-canonical form** <of a group> <GR>	semikanonische Form *f*	forme *f* semi-canonique	полуканонический вид
S 337	**semi-categoric set** <of formulas> <MM>	semi-kategorische Menge *f* <von Ausdrücken>	ensemble *m* <de formules> semi-catégorique	полукатегорическое множество <формул>
S 338	**semicharacter** <of a semi-group> <AL>	Halbcharakter *m*	semi-caractère *m*	полухарактер, семихарактер
S 339	**semi-characteristic,** half-characteristic <DE>	Halbcharakteristik *f*	semi-caractéristique *f*, demi-caractéristique *f*	полухарактеристика
S 340	**semi-circular domain,** Hartogs['] domain <FT>	Hartogsscher Körper *m*	domaine *m* semi-cerclé, domaine de Hartogs	полукруговая область, область Хартогса
S 341	**semicircular protractor,** protractor <GE, IN>	Transporteur *m*	rapporteur *m*, // rapport *m*	транспортир, транспортер
	semi-closed interval <AN, SE>	*s.* H 27		
S 342	**semi-combinant** <IV>	Semikombinante *f*	semi-combinant *m*	полукомбинант
S 343	**semi-comitant** <IV>	Semikomitante *f*	semi-comitant *m*	полукомитант
S 344	**semicommutative operation** <GR>	semikommutative Operation *f*	opération *f* semi-commutative	полукоммутативная операция
	semi-compactness <TO>	*s.* S 812		
	semi-compact set <TO>	*s.* S 813		
	semi-compact [topological] space <TO>	*s.* S 814		
	semicomplement <SE>	*s.* S 478		
	semi-cone angle <EG>	*s.* S 327		
S 345	**semiconjugate axis** <of a hyperbola> <AY>	imaginäre Halbachse *f*, halbe Länge *f* der Nebenachse	demi-axe *m* non traverse, demi-axe *m* non focal	мнимая полуось
S 346	**semiconnex relation** <SE>	semikonnexe Relation *f*	relation *f* semi-connexe	полусвязное отношение
S 347	**semi[-]continuity** <RF, TO>	Halbstetigkeit *f*	semi-continuité *f*	полунепрерывность
S 348	**semi[-]continuous function** <RF>	halbstetige Funktion *f*	fonction *f* semi-continue	полунепрерывная функция

No.	English	German	French	Russian
S 349	**semicontinuum** <TO>	kontinuaverknüpfter topologischer Raum *m*	semi-continu *m*	полуконтинуум
S 350	**semiconvergent series** <SS>	semikonvergente Reihe *f*; bedingt konvergente Reihe, die nicht absolut konvergiert	série *f* semi-convergente (simplement convergente)	условно сходящийся ряд
	semi-convergent series <AX, FT>	*s.* A 1165		
S 351	**semicovariant** <IV>	Semikovariante *f*, Halbkovariante *f*	semi-covariant *m*	полуковариант
S 352	**semicubical group** <of Cremona substitutions> <AG>	semikubische Gruppe *f*	groupe *m* semi-cubique	полукубическая группа
S 353	**semicubical parabola,** Neil['s] parabola <AG>	Neilsche (semikubische) Parabel *f*	parabole *f* semi[-]cubique (de Neil), semi[-]cubique *f*, seconde parabole cubique	полукубическая парабола, парабола Нейля
S 354	**semicubic set** <AT>	semikubische Menge *f*	ensemble *m* semi-cubique	полукубическое множество
S 355	**semi-definite eigenvalue problem** <DE>	semidefinite Eigenwertaufgabe *f*, semidefinites Eigenwertproblem *n*	problème *m* semi-défini aux valeurs singulières (caractéristiques, critiques, propres), problème aux valeur propres semi-défini	полуопределенная задача на собственные значения
	semidefinite in Kamke's sense <DE>	*s.* K 183		
S 356	**semi-definite kernel** <IE>	semidefiniter (definiter) Kern *m*	noyau *m* semi-défini	полуопределенное ядро
S 357	**semi-definiteness** <e.g. of an operator> <AL, FA>	Semidefinitheit *f* <AL, FA>; Definitheit *f* <FA>	propriété *f* d'être semi-défini	полуопределенность
	semidefiniteness in Kamke's sense <DE>	*s.* K 184		
S 358	**semi-definite operator** <FA>	semidefiniter (definiter) Operator *m*	opérateur *m* semi-défini	полуопределенный оператор
S 359	**semi[-]definite quadratic form** <AL>	semidefinite quadratische Form *f*	forme *f* quadratique semi-définie	полуопределенная (знакопостоянная) квадратичная форма
S 360	**semi-definite variational problem** <VA>	semidefinites Variationsproblem *n*	problème *m* variationnel semi-défini	полуопределенная вариационная задача
S 361	**semi-degree** <in-degree *or* out-degree> <of a vertex> <GP>	Halbvalenz *f* <Eingangs- *oder* Ausgangsvalenz>	demi-degré *m*	полустепень
S 362	**semi-diameter** <of a conic> <AY>	halber Durchmesser *m*	semi-diamètre *m*	полудиаметр
S 363	**semidirect factor** <GR>	semidirekter Faktor *m*	facteur *m* semi-direct	полупрямой множитель
S 364	**semidirect product** <GR>	semidirektes (halbdirektes) Produkt *n*	produit *m* semi-direct	полупрямое произведение
S 365	**semi-distributivity,** distributivity <LO>	Halbdistributivität *f*, Semidistributivität *f*	semi-distributivité *f*	полудистрибутивность
	semi-distributivity of the existential quantifier with respect to conjunction <LO>	*s.* D 780		
	semi-distributivity of the universal quantifier with respect to disjunction <LO>	*s.* D 781		
S 366	**semi-divergent series** <SS>	halbdivergente (semidivergente) Reihe *f*	série *f* semi-divergente	полурасходящийся ряд
S 367	**semi-endomorphism** <of rings> <AL>	Semi-Endomorphismus *m*	semi-endomorphisme *m*	полуэндоморфизм
S 368	**semi-exact differential of the first kind** <Severi> <AG, FT>	semiexaktes Differential *n* erster Gattung	différentielle *f* semi-exacte de première espèce	полуточный дифференциал первого рода
S 369	**semifield** <AL>	Halbkörper *m*, Semifield *n*	demi-corps *m*	полутело
S 370	**semi-finite trace** <on a C*-algebra> <FA>	halbendliche Spur *f*	trace *f* semi-finie	полуконечный след
S 371	**semifocal chord** <of a conic section> <AY>	halber Parameter *m*, Halbparameter *m*	demi-paramètre *m*, demi-corde *f* focale	фокальный параметр
S 372	**semi-Fredholm operator** <FA>	Semi-Fredholm-Operator *m*	opérateur *m* semi-Fredholm	полуфредгольмов оператор <Φ_+- или Φ_--оператор>
S 373	**semi-function** <FO>	Semifunktion *f*	semi-fonction *f*	полуфункция
S 374	**semi-functional graph** <GP>	semi-funktionaler Graph *m*	graphe *m* semi-fonctionnel (semi-univoque)	полуфункциональный граф
S 375	**semi-geodesic coordinate system** <GE>	halbgeodätisches Koordinatensystem *n*	système *m* de coordonnées semigéodésique	полугеодезическая координатная система
	semigroup <AL>	*s.* C 48		
S 376	**semigroup,** monoid, demigroup, associative groupoid, associative system, hemigroup <AL>	Halbgruppe *f*, assoziatives Gruppoid *n*, assoziatives System *n*, Assoziativ *n*, Monoid *n*, multiplikatives System, assoziatives Operativ *n*	demi-groupe *m*, monoïde *m*, semi-groupe *m*, pseudo-groupe *m*	полугруппа, моноид, ассоциативная система, ассоциативный группоид
S 377	**semigroup algebra** <AL>	Halbgruppenalgebra *f*	algèbre *f* de demi-groupe	полугрупповая алгебра, моноидная алгебра
S 378	**semigroup morphism** <CA>	Halbgruppenmorphismus *m*	morphisme *m* de demi-groupes	полугрупповой морфизм
S 379	**semigroup of quotients,** quotient semigroup <AL>	Quotientenhalbgruppe *f*	demi-groupe *m* des fractions	полугруппа частных
	semi[-]groupoid <AL>	*s.* P 216		
	semigroupoid <CA>	*s.* A 145		
S 380	**semigroup quasi-regular on the left** <AL>	links[seitig] quasireguläre Halbgruppe *f*	demi-groupe quasi-simplifiable à gauche	квазирегулярная слева полугруппа

S 381	**semigroup quasi-regular on the right** <AL>	rechts[seitig] quasireguläre Halbgruppe *f*	demi-groupe *m* quasi-simplifiable à droite	квазирегулярная справа полугруппа
S 382	**semigroup ring** <AL>	Halbgruppenring *m*	anneau *m* de demi-groupe	полугрупповое кольцо
S 383	**semigroup stationary on the left** <AL>	linksstationäre Halbgruppe *f*	demi-groupe *m* stationnaire à gauche	стационарная слева полугруппа
S 384	**semigroup stationary on the right** <AL>	rechtsstationäre Halbgruppe *f*	demi-groupe *m* stationnaire à droite	стационарная справа полугруппа
S 385	**semigroup which satisfies condition (*m, n*) with anti-reciprocity** <AL>	Halbgruppe *f* mit Antireziprozität *f*	demi-groupe *m* avec anti-réciprocité	полугруппа, удовлетворяющая условию (*m, n*) с антивзаимностью
	semi-group with cancellation <AL>	*s.* C 48		
	semigroup with identity element <AL>	*s.* M 845		
	semigroup with unit-element <AL>	*s.* M 845		
S 386	**semi-hereditary ring** <AL>	halberblicher Ring *m*	anneau *m* semi-héréditaire	полунаследственное кольцо
S 387	**semihomogeneous boundary value problem** <DE>	halbhomogenes (semihomogenes) Randwertproblem *n*, halbhomogene (semihomogene) Randwertaufgabe *f*	problème *m* aux limites semi-homogène	полуоднородная краевая задача
S 388	**semihomogeneous space** <AL>	semihomogener Raum *m*	espace *m* semi-homogène	полуоднородное пространство
S 389	**semi-homomorphism,** half-homomorphism <of a ring *or* group> <AL, GR>	Semi-Homomorphismus *m*, Semihomomorphismus *m*	semi-homomorphisme *m*	полугомоморфизм
S 390	**semi-identity** <UA>	Semiidentität *f*	semi-identité *f*	полутождество
	semi-infinite plane <AN>	*s.* I 450		
	semi-infinite space <AN, GE>	*s.* H 42		
S 391	**semi-injective module** <AL>	semiinjektiver Modul *m*	module *m* semi-injectif	полуинъективный модуль
	semi-inner product <FA>	*s.* S 457		
S 392	**semi-interquartile [range],** quartile deviation <ST>	halber Quartilsabstand *m*, Viertelwertsabstand *m*	demi-interquartile *m*, semi-interquartile *m*, déviation *f* quartile	семиинтерквартильная широта
S 393	**semi-invariant** <DG>	Halbinvariante *f*	semi-invariant *m*	полуинвариант, семиинвариант
S 394	**semi-invariant** <IV>	Semiinvariante *f*, Halbinvariante *f*, Peninvariante *f*	péninvariant *m*, semi-invariant, semi-invariant *m*	полуинвариант, семиинвариант
S 395	**semi-invariant** <Thiele>, cumulant <R. A. Fisher> <ST>	Semiinvariante *f*, Halbinvariante *f*, Kumulante *f*	semi-invariant *m*, cumulant *m*	семиинвариант, полуинвариант, кумулянт
S 396	**semi-invariant exterior derivative** <DG>	halbinvariante äußere Ableitung *f* [nach G. Reeb und G. Bol]	dérivée *f* extérieure semi-invariante	полуинвариантная (семиинвариантная) внешняя производная
S 397	**semi-involutory matrix** <MD>	halbinvolutorische Matrix *f*	matrice *f* semi-involutive	полуинволютивная матрица
S 398	**semi-isomorphism** <of a group> <GR>	Semiisomorphismus *m*	semi-isomorphisme *m*	полуизоморфизм
	semi latin square <CT, ST>	*s.* L 113		
S 399	**semi[-]lattice** <AL>	Halbverband *m*	demi-treillis *m*, ensemble *m* semi-réticulé, semi-lattice *m*, semi-structure *f*	полуструктура, полурешетка
	semi[-]lattice <AL>	*s. a.* L 1164		
S 400	**semi[-]linear mapping,** semi[-]linear substitution <AL>	halblineare Abbildung *f*, halblineare Transformation *f*	application *f* semi-linéaire	антилинейное отображение, полулинейное отображение, полулинейное преобразование
S 401	**semi-linear mapping** <AT>	semilineare Abbildung *f*	application *f* semi-linéaire	полулинейное отображение
S 402	**semi-linear substitution** <over an arbitrary field> <PJ>	Kollineation *f*	collinéation *f*	полулинейное преобразование
	semi[-]linear substitution <AL>	*s.* S 400		
S 403	**semilocal isomorphism** <AL>	semilokaler Isomorphismus *m*	isomorphisme *m* semi-local	полулокальный изоморфизм
S 404	**semi[-]locally 1-connected space** <TO>	semilokal einfachzusammenhängender Raum *m*	espace *m* semi-localement simplement connexe	полулокально односвязное пространство
S 405	**semilocal module** <AL>	semilokaler Modul *m*	module *m* semi-local	полулокальный модуль
S 406	**semilocal ring** <AL>	semilokaler Ring *m*, Halbstellenring *m*	anneau *m* semi-local	полулокальное кольцо
	semilogarithmic co-ordinate paper <IN, NU>	*s.* S 408		
S 407	**semilogarithmic diagram,** semilogarithmic plot, semilog diagram (plot), arithlog diagram <NU>	einfachlogarithmische (halblogarithmische, semilogarithmische) Darstellung *f*	diagramme *m* (graphique *f*, représentation *f*) semi[-]logarithmique, diagramme arithmético-logarithmique	полулогарифмическая диаграмма, график в полулогарифмическом масштабе
S 408	**semilogarithmic paper,** semilog paper, semilogarithmic co-ordinate paper, arithlog paper, ratio paper <IN, NU>	einfachlogarithmisches (halblogarithmisches, semilogarithmisches) Papier *n*, Exponentialpapier *n*	papier *m* semilogarithmique (semi-logarithmique)	полулогарифмическая бумага
	semilogarithmic plot <NU>	*s.* S 407		
	semilogarithmic representation <NT, NU>	*s.* F 414		

No.	English	German	French	Russian
	semilog diagram <NU>	*s.* S 407		
	semilog paper <IN, NU>	*s.* S 408		
	semilog plot <NU>	*s.* S 407		
S 409	**semi[-]magic square** <CT>	semi[-]magisches (halbmagisches) Quadrat *n*	carré *m* semi-magique	полумагический квадрат
S 410	**semi-majorant** <SS>	Quasi-Majorante *f*	semi-majorante *f*	квазисуперрешение
S 411	**semi-major axis** <of a conic section> <AY>	große Halbachse *f*, halbe Länge *f* der Hauptachse	demi-grand axe *m*, demi grand axe, demi-axe *m* focal	большая полуось
S 412	**semi-Markov process** <SP>	Semi-Markov-Prozeß *m*, semi-Markovscher (halb-Markovscher) Prozeß *m*	processus *m* semi-markovien	полумарковский процесс
S 413	**semi-martingale** <ST>	Halbmartingal *n*, Semimartingal *n*	semi-martingale *f*	полумартингал
S 414	**semi[-]mean axis** <of an ellipsoid> <AY>	halbe mittlere Achse *f* (Länge *f* der Halbachse), mittlere Halbachse *f*, halbe Länge der mittleren Halbachse	demi-axe *m* moyen	средняя полуось
S 415	**semi-metacyclic function** <AL>	halbmetazyklische (hemimetazyklische) Funktion *f*	fonction *f* semi-métacyclique	полуметациклическая функция
S 416	**semi-metric** <TO>	Halbmetrik *f*	semi-métrique *f*	полуметрика
	semi-metric <TO>	*s. a.* P 1955		
S 417	**semi-metrically connected manifold (variety)** <DG>	halbmetrisch[-] (äquiform[-]) zusammenhängende Mannigfaltigkeit *f*	variété *f* à connexion semi-métrique	многообразие полуметрической связности
S 418	**semi-metric connection,** semi-metric transfer <DG>	halbmetrische (äquiforme) Übertragung *f*, halbmetrischer (äquiformer) Zusammenhang *m*	connexion *f* (transfert *m*) semi-métrique	полуметрическая связность, полуметрическое перенесение
S 419	**semi-metric space** <TO>	halbmetrischer (semimetrischer) Raum *m*	espace *m* semi-métrique	полуметрическое пространство
	semi-metric space <TO>	*s. a.* P 1957		
	semi-metric transfer <DG>	*s.* S 418		
S 420	**semi-minorant** <SS>	Quasi-Minorante *f*	semi-minorante *f*	квазисубрешение
S 421	**semi[-]minor axis** <of an ellipse> <AY>	kleine Halbachse *f*, halbe Länge *f* der Nebenachse	demi-petit axe *m*, demi petit axe, demi-axe *m* mineur	малая полуось
S 422	**semi-modularity, semimodularity** <of a lattice> <LA>	Semimodularität *f*	semi-modularité *f*, B-modularité *f*, semi-mesurabilité *f*	полудедекиндовость, полумодулярность
S 423	**semimodular lattice** <LA>	halbmodularer (semimodularer) Verband *m*	treillis *m* (structure *f*) semi-modulaire	полумодулярная структура
	semi-modular lattice <LA>	*s. a.* B 447		
	semi-modular lattice of subgroups <AL>	*s.* U 438		
S 424	**semi-module** <AL>	Halbmodul *m*	semi-module *m*	полумодуль
S 425	**semi-norm,** pseudonorm <in a linear space> <FA, TO>	Halbnorm *f*, Quasinorm *f*, Seminorm *f*	semi-norme *f*	полунорма, семинорма
	seminormed space <FA>	*s.* S 1339		
	semi-open interval <AN, SE>	*s.* H 27		
	semi-ordered linear space <AL, FA>	*s.* P 234		
	semi-ordering <SE>	*s.* P 246		
S 426	**semiotics,** formal semantics <LO>	Semiotik *f*	sémiotique *f*, sémiologie *f*	семиотика, семиология
S 427	**semi-parabola** <AY>	Halbparabel *f*, Semiparabel *f*	semi-parabole *f*, semiparabole *f*	полупарабола
S 428	**semi-path,** undirected path <in a non-oriented graph> <GP>	Kette *f*	chaîne *f*	цепь
S 429	**semi-perfect module** <AL>	semi-perfekter Modul *m*	module *m* semi-parfait	полусовершенный модуль
S 430	**semi[-]period,** half-period, half-cycle, halfcycle <AN, DE>	Halbperiode *f*, halbe Periode *f*	demi-période *f*	полупериод
S 431	**semiperiodic solution** <of the Hill equation> <DE>	halbperiodische Lösung *f*	solution *f* demi-périodique	полупериодическое решение
S 432	**semi-permissible function** <DE>	halbzulässige Funktion *f*	fonction *f* semi-admissible	полудопустимая функция
	semi-polar co-ordinates <AY> ⌐<AB>	*s.* C 2909		
S 433	**semi-primary number**	semiprimäre Zahl *f*	nombre *m* semiprimaire	полупримарное число
S 434	**semi-primary ring** <AL>	halbprimärer Ring *m*	anneau *m* semi-primaire	полупримарное кольцо
S 435	**semi-prime ideal** <AL>	semiprimes (halbprimes) Ideal *n*; Semiprimideal *n* <im nichtkommutativen Ring>	idéal *m* semi-premier	полупростой идеал
S 436	**semiprime module** <AL>	semiprimer Modul *m*	module *m* semi-premier	полупростой модуль
S 437	**semi-prime ring** <AL>	semiprimer (halbprimer) Ring *m*	anneau *m* semi-premier	полупервичное кольцо
S 438	**semiprime subset,** closed subset <of a semigroup>, // isolated subset <AL>	isolierte Untermenge *f*	partie *f* semi-première (isolée)	изолированное (замкнутое) подмножество
S 439	**semi-primitive ring,** semi-simple ring <Jacobson> <AL>	semiprimitiver Ring *m*	anneau *m* semi-primitif	полупростое кольцо в смысле Джекобсона
S 440	**semiprimitivity** <of a ring> <AL>	Semiprimitivität *f*	semi-primitivité *f*	полупростота в смысле Джекобсона

No.	English	German	French	Russian
S 441	**semi-projectivity** <AL>	Semiprojektivität *f*	semi-projectivité	полупроективность
S 442	**semi-pseudometrization** <TO>	Semipseudometrisierung *f*	semipseudométrisation *f*	полупсевдометризация
S 443	**semi-pure variety** <AG>	halbreine Varietät *f*	variété *f* semi-pure	получистое (унирациональное) многообразие
S 444	**semi-quaternion** <AL>	Semiquaternion *f*	semi-quaternion *m*	полукватернион
	semi range <ST>	*s.* H 37		
	semi-reduced transformation <IV>	*s.* H 38		
	semi-reducible representation <AL, RE>	*s.* R 408		
S 445	**semireduction** <of Hermitian forms> <NT>	Semireduktion *f*	semi-réduction *f*	полуредукция
S 446	**semireductive algebraic group** <AG>	semireduktive algebraische Gruppe *f*	groupe *m* algébrique semi-réductif	полуредуктивная алгебраическая группа
S 447	**semi-reflexive space** <FA>	halbreflexiver (semireflexiver) Raum *m*	espace *m* semi-réflexif	полурефлексивное пространство
S 448	**semi-reflexivity** <FA, TO>	Halbreflexivität *f*, Semireflexivität *f*	semi-réflexivité *f*	полурефлексивность
S 449	**semi-regular asymptotic differential** <RF>	halbreguläres asymptotisches Differential *n*, asymptotisches halbreguläres Differential	différentielle *f* semi-régulière asymptotique	полурегулярный асимптотический дифференциал
	semiregular body <GE>	*s.* A 887		
S 450	**semi-regular continued fraction** <NT>	halbregelmäßiger Kettenbruch *m*	fraction *f* continue arithmétique	полуправильная цепная дробь
	semiregular group <GR>	*s.* S 451		
S 451	**semiregular permutation group,** semiregular group <GR>	halbreguläre Permutationsgruppe *f*	groupe *m* de substitutions semi-régulier	полурегулярная группа перестановок
	semi-regular ring <AL>	*s.* M 1		
	semiregular solid <GE>	*s.* A 887		
S 452/3	**semi-regular space** <any open set is union of regular open sets <TO>	halbregulärer topologischer Raum *m*, halbregulärer (semiregulärer) Raum	espace *m* topologique semi-régulier, espace *m* semi-régulier	полурегулярное пространство
S 454	**semiregular star polyhedron** <EG>	halbregelmäßiges Sternvielflach *n*	polyèdre *m* étoilé demi-régulier	полуправильный звездчатый многогранник
S 455	**semi-regular topology** <TO>	semireguläre Topologie *f*	topologie *f* semi-régulière	полурегулярная топология
	semi-regular variational problem <VA>	*s.* Q 243		
S 456	**semi-ring** <*e.g.*: with zero> <AL>	Semiring *m*, Halbring *m* <*z. B.*: mit Nullelement>	demi-anneau *m*, semi-anneau *m* <*par exemple:* avec zéro>	полукольцо <*например:* с нулем>
S 457	**semi-scalar product,** semi-inner product <FA>	Halbinnenprodukt *n*	produit *m* semi-scalaire (semi-intérieur)	полускалярное (полувнутреннее) произведение
S 458	**semi-secant** <of a set> <GE>	Halbsekante *f*	demi-sécante *f*	полусекущая
	semi-separated space <TO>	*s.* F 587		
S 459	**semi[-]simple algebra** <AL>	halbeinfache Algebra *f*, halbeinfaches [hyperkomplexes] System *n*, [hyperkomplexes] System ohne Radikal, // Dedekindsche Algebra	algèbre *f* semi-simple	полупростая алгебра
S 460	**semi[-]simple class,** residual class <in theory of radicals> <AL>	halbeinfache Klasse *f*, Koradikalklasse *f*, Coradikalklasse *f*	classe *f* semi-simple	полупростой класс
S 461	**semi[-]simple endomorphism** <AL>	halbeinfacher Endomorphismus *m*	endomorphisme *m* semi-simple	полупростой эндоморфизм
S 462	**semi[-]simple group** <GR>	halbeinfache Gruppe *f*	groupe *m* semi-simple	полупростая группа
S 463	**semi[-]simple module;** semi[-]simple *R*-module <AL>	halbeinfacher Modul (*R*-Modul) *m*	module (*R*-module) *m* semi-simple	полупростой модуль (*R*-модуль)
	semi-simple module <AL>	*s. a.* T 597		
S 464	**semi[-]simple part** <of an endomorphism> <AL>	halbeinfache Komponente *f*	composante *f* semi-simple	полупростая компонента
	semi-simple representation <AL>	*s.* F 726		
	semi-simple ring <AL>	*s.* S 439		
S 465	**semi[-]simple ring in the sense of Brown-McCoy** <AL>	halbeinfacher Ring *m* im Sinne von Brown-McCoy	anneau *m* semi-simple au sens de Brown-McCoy	полупростое кольцо в смысле Брауна-Маккоя
	semi[-]simple R-module <AL>	*s.* S 463		
	semi-simple subalgebra <AL>	*s.* I 428		
S 466	**semi-simplicial cochain complex** <AT>	semisimplizialer Kokettenkomplex *m*	complexe *m* de cochaînes semi-simplicial	полусимплициальный коцепной комплекс
S 467	**semi-simplicial complex** <AT>	semisimplizialer Komplex *m*, semisimpliziale (simpliziale) Menge *f*	complexe *m* semi-simplicial	полусимплициальный комплекс
S 468	**semi-simplicial group** <CA>	semisimpliziale Gruppe *f*	groupe *m* semi-simplicial	полусимплициальная группа
S 469	**semi-simplicial map** <AT>	semisimpliziale Abbildung *f*	application *f* semi-simpliciale	полусимплициальное отображение

No.	English	German	French	Russian
S 470	**semi-simplicial resolution** <AL, AT>	semisimpliziale Auflösung *f*	résolution *f* semi-simpliciale	полусимплициальная резольвента
	semi-simplicial set <AT, CA>	*s.* S 991		
S 471	**semi[-]simplicity** <AL>	Halbeinfachheit *f*	semi-simplicité *f*	полупростота
S 472	**semisingular vector** <AL>	halbsingulärer Vektor *m*	vecteur *m* semi-singulier	полусингулярный вектор
S 473	**semi-spinor** <AL>	Halbspinor *m*	semi-spineur *m*, demi-spineur *m*	полуспинор
S 474	**semi-spinor representation** <AL>	Halbspindarstellung *f*, Halb-Spindarstellung *f*	représentation *f* semi-spinorielle	полуспинорное представление
S 475	**semi-star** <AT>	Halbstern *m*	demi-étoile *f*	полузвезда
S 476	**semi-strip** <DE>	Halbstreifen *m*	demi-bande *f*	полуполоска, полуполоса
S 477	**semi-strong lineal (line) element** <VA>	halbstarkes Linienelement *n*	élément *m* linéaire semi-fort	полустрогий линейный элемент
S 478	**semisupplement,** semi-complement <SE>	Semikomplement *n*	semi-complément *m*	полудополнение
S 479	**semi-symmetric [linear affine] connection** <DG>	halbsymmetrische Übertragung *f*, halbsymmetrische lineare affine Übertragung	connexion *f* semi-symétrique	полусимметрическая связность, полусимметрическое перенесение
S 480	**semi-tangent** <also to a set> <GE, IG>	Halbtangente *f*	demi-tangente *f*	полукасательная
S 481	**semitopological group** <AL>	semitopologische Gruppe *f*	groupe *m* semi-topologique	полутопологическая группа
S 482	**semitopological loop** <AL>	semitopologische Loop *f*	loop *m* semi-topologique	полутопологическая лупа
S 483	**semi-trajectory** <DE>	Halbtrajektorie *f*	semi-trajectoire *f*	полутраектория
S 484	**semi[-]transverse axis** <of a hyperbola> <AY>	reelle Halbachse *f*	demi-axe *m* focal (transverse)	действительная полуось
S 485	**semi-uniformity** <TO>	Halbuniformität *f*	structure *f* semi-uniforme	полуравномерная структура
S 486	**semi-uniform space** <TO>	halbuniformer Raum *m*	espace *m* semi-uniforme	полуравномерное пространство
S 487	**semi-unitary kernel** <IE>	halbunitärer Kern *m*	noyau *m* semi-unitaire	полуунитарное ядро
S 488	**semivariety** <UA>	Semivarietät *f*	semi-variété *f*	полумногообразие
	semi-vertex angle <EG>	*s.* S 327		
S 489	**senary** <AL, NT>	senär	sénaire	шестеричный
S 490	**sense** <of an inequality> <GN>	Sinn *m*	sens *m*	смысл, знак
S 491	**sense** <LO>	Sinn *m*	contenu *m*, sens *m*	смысл
	sense <GE>	*s.* O 411		
	sense <LO, MM>	*s.* E 787		
	sense <MM>	*s.* I 691		
S 492	**sense[-]class,** orientation class, sense of description (revolution) <of a curve> <GE, TO>	Umlaufsinn *m*, Umlaufrichtung *f*, Durchlaufungssinn *m*, Durchlaufungsrichtung *f*	sens *m* de parcours	направление (знак) обхода, направление пути
S 493	**sense of convexity** <GE>	Richtung *f* der Konvexität	sens *m* de convexité	направление выпуклости
	sense of description (revolution) <GE, TO>	*s.* S 492		
S 494	**sense[-]preserving mapping** <AT, TO>	orientierungstreue Abbildung *f* <Abbildungsgrad positiv>	application *f* conservant le sens, application conservant l'orientation	отображение, сохраняющее направление обхода
S 495	**sensitivity analysis** <PG>	Sensitivitätsanalyse *f*	analyse *f* de sensibilité	анализ чувствительности
S 496	**sentence,** formula in which no variable has a free occurrence <LO>	Satz *m*, Formel *f* ohne freie Variable	énoncé *m*, formule *f* sans variables libres	утверждение, формула без свободных переменных
	sentence <LO>	*s. a.* P 1865		
	∃∀ sentence <LO>	*s.* E 701		
	∀∃ sentence <LO>	*s.* U 335		
S 497	**sentence[-]form,** statement form, form, function, sentential logic argument form, propositional form; argument form <LO>	Aussageform *f*, Aussagenform *f*, Aussage[n]-funktion *f*, Satzfunktion *f*	forme (fonction) *f* propositionnelle	форма высказывания, функция-высказывание, пропозициональная функция, неопределенное высказывание, пропозициональная форма
	sentence-forming functor <LO>	*s.* S 498		
	sentence of an existential character <LO>	*s.* E 700		
	sentence of a universal character <LO>	*s.* G 173		
	sentential calculus <LO>	*s.* P 1868		
	sentential combination <LO>	*s.* C 1745		
S 498	**sentential connective,** propositional connective, logical constant, connective, connective symbol, truth-functional connective, truth-functional sentential connective, truth-functional connective of propositional calculus, logical symbol, sentence-forming functor <LO>	Junktor *m*, aussagenlogischer Funktor *m*, A-Konstante *f*, aussagenerzeugender (aussagebildender, aussageerzeugender) Funktor, [aussagenlogisches] Verknüpfungszeichen *n*	connecteur *m*, opérateur *m*, connecteur (opérateur) propositionnel	пропозициональная связка, логический оператор, сентенциальная (логическая) связка, функтор, связь высказываний, пропозициональная константа, коннектор; функтор, порождающий высказывание

S 499	**sentential formula,** correct logical formula, meaningful formula, formula, propositional expression <of propositional calculus> <LO>	Ausdruck *m* des Aussagenkalküls, aussagenlogischer Ausdruck, A-Ausdruck *m*, Aussagenformel *f*, junktorenlogische Formel *f*, Formel; Aussageausdruck *m*	formule *f* du calcul propositionnel, expression *f* bien formée [du calcul des propositions]; expression propositionnelle	пропозициональная формула, ПФ
	sentential formula in the functional calculus of the first order <LO>	*s.* F 345		
	sentential function <LO>	*s.* 1. P 1182; 2. P 1870		
S 500	**sentential function of *n* free variables** <LO>	*n*-stellige Aussagenfunktion *f*, *n*-äre Aussageform *f*	fonction *f* propositionnelle *n*-adique	*n*-арная высказательная функция
S 501	**sentential function of one free variable** <LO>	unäre (einstellige) Aussageform *f*	forme (fonction) *f* propositionnelle à une variable	форма высказывания от одной переменной
	sentential inference <LO>	*s.* T 95		
S 502	**sentential logic** <LO>	Satzlogik *f*	logique *f* des théorèmes	логика предложений
	sentential logic <LO>	*s. a.* P 1868		
	sentential logic argument form <LO>	*s.* S 497		
S 503	**sentential symbol** <LO>	Aussagezeichen *n*, Aussagesymbol *n*	symbole *m* d'une proposition	пропозициональная буква, символ высказывания
	sentential variable <LO>	*s.* P 1872		
S 504	**separability** <of a field *or* space> <AL, TO>	Separabilität *f*	séparabilité *f*	сепарабельность
S 505	**separability** <*e.g.*: of sets> <AN, SE, TO>	Trennbarkeit *f*	séparabilité *f*	отделимость
	separable algebraic closure <AL>	*s.* M 242		
	separable algebraic extension <AL>	*s.* S 509		
	separable closure <AL>	*s.* M 242		
S 506	**separable covering** <TO>	separable Überlagerung *f*	revêtement *m* séparable	сепарабельное накрытие
	separable degree <AL>	*s.* R 353		
S 507	**separable element,** separably algebraic element <AL>	separables (separabel-algebraisches) Element *n*	élément *m* séparable (algébrique séparable, algébrique de première espèce)	сепарабельный элемент
S 508	**separable equation** <AL>	separable Gleichung *f*	équation *f* séparable	сепарабельное уравнение
	separable equation <DE>	*s.* S 531		
S 509	**separable extension,** separable algebraic extension <AL>	separable Körpererweiterung *f*, Erweiterung *f* (Körpererweiterung) erster Art, separabel-algebraische (separable) Erweiterung; separabler Oberkörper *m*	extension *f* séparable (algébrique de première espèce, algébrique séparable)	сепарабельное (сепарабельное алгебраическое) расширение <поля>
	separable factor of the degree <AL>	*s.* R 353		
S 510	**separable field** <AL>	separabler Körper *m*	corps *m* séparable	сепарабельное поле
S 511	**separable game** <TG>	ausgeartetes Spiel *n*	jeu *m* dégénéré	вырожденная игра
S 512	**separable graph** <GP>	einfach-knotenzusammenhängender (separabler, 1-trennbarer) Graph *m*	graphe *m* séparable	сепарабельный граф
S 513	**π-separable group** <GR>	π-separable Gruppe *f*	groupe *m* π-séparable	π-отделимая группа
S 514	**separable hull** <of *k* in *K*> <AL>	relative separable Hülle *f* <von *k* in *K*>	fermeture *f* séparable <de *k* dans *K*>	сепарабельное замыкание <*k* в *K*>
	separable hull <AL>	*s.* M 242		
S 515	**separable mapping** <AL>	separable Abbildung *f*	application *f* séparable	сепарабельное отображение
	separable normal equation <AL>	*s.* G 11		
S 516	**separable polynomial** <AL>	separables Polynom *n*, Polynom erster Art	polynôme *m* séparable, fonction *f* rationnelle entière de première espèce	сепарабельный многочлен
	separable Riemannian space <DG>	*s.* D 57		
S 517	**separable sets** <TO>	trennbare (separierbare) Mengen *fpl*	ensembles *mpl* séparables	отделимые множества
S 518	**Φ-separable sets** <TO>	Φ-trennbare Mengen *fpl*	ensembles *mpl* séparables Φ	Φ-отделимые множества
	separable space <TO>	*s.* 1. C 1512; 2. S 520		
S 519	**separable stochastic process** <SP>	separabler stochastischer Prozeß *m*	processus *m* stochastique séparable	сепарабельный случайный процесс
S 520	**separable topological space,** separable space <TO>	separabler topologischer Raum *m*, separabler Raum <nach Fréchet>	espace *m* séparable (topologique séparable, de type dénombrable, topologique de type dénombrable, topologique à caractère dénombrable)	сепарабельное (сепарабельное топологическое) пространство
S 521	**separable topology** <TO>	separable Topologie *f*	topologie *f* séparable	сепарабельная топология
S 522	**separable transcendental extension** <AL>	separabel-transzendente (separable) Erweiterung *f*; separabler (separabel-transzendenter) Erweiterungskörper *m*	extension *f* transcendante séparable	сепарабельное трансцендентное расширение
	separably algebraic element <AL>	*s.* S 507		

No.	English	German	French	Russian
S 523	**separably algebraic point** <AG>	separabel algebraischer Punkt *m*	point *m* séparablement algébrique	сепарабельно алгебраическая точка
S 524	**separably closed field** <AL>	separabel abgeschlossener Körper *m*	corps *m* séparablement clos	сепарабельно замкнутое поле
S 525	**separably closed subfield** <in a field> <AL>	relativ-separabel-abgeschlossener Teilkörper *m*	sous-corps *m* séparablement fermé <dans un surcorps>	сепарабельно замкнутое подполе <в поле>
S 526	**separably generated field** <AL>	separabel erzeugter Körper *m*, separabel erzeugbare Körpererweiterung *f*, separabel-erzeugbarer Erweiterungskörper *m*	extension *f* admettant une base de transcendance séparante	сепарабельно порожденное поле
S 527	**separably isogenous algebraic groups** <AG>	separabel isogene algebraische Gruppen *fpl*	groupes *mpl* algébriques séparablement isogènes	сепарабельно изогенные алгебраические группы
S 528	**separant** <AL>	Separante *f*	séparante *f*	сепаранта
S 529	**separate / to,** to disconnect, to decompose <a topological space by a curve *or* set> <TO>	zerlegen <einen Raum durch eine Kurve *oder* Menge>	partager <l'espace par une courbe *ou* un ensemble>	разбивать <пространство при помощи кривой *или* множества>
S 530	**separated completion** <of a topological ring> <AL>	separierte Vervollständigung *f*	séparé *m* complété	отделимое пополнение
S 531	**separated [differential] equation,** separable equation <DE>	Differentialgleichung (Gleichung) *f* mit getrennten (trennbaren, separierbaren) Variablen	équation *f* [différentielle] à variables séparées (séparables)	[дифференциальное] уравнение с разделяющимися переменными
S 532	**separated filtration** <of a group> <AL>	separierte Filtration *f*	filtration *f* séparée	отделимая фильтрация
S 533	**separated morphism** <of schemes> <AG>	separierter Morphismus *m*	morphisme *m* séparé	сепарированный морфизм
	separatedness <TO>	*s.* P 1845		
S 534	**separated presheaf** <CA, TO>	separierte Prägarbe *f*	préfaisceau *m* séparé	сепарированный предпучок
S 535	**separated sets** <TO>	getrennte (separierte, trennbare) Mengen *fpl* <keine enthält Berührungspunkt der anderen>	ensembles *mpl* séparés (séparables)	отделенные (отделимые) множества
S 536	**separated space,** Hausdorff['s] space, Hausdorff['s] topological space, T_2-space, T_2 topological space <TO>	Hausdorffscher Raum *m*, separierter [topologischer] Raum, T_2-Raum *m*, H-Raum *m*, Hausdorffscher topologischer Raum *m*, Hausdorff-Raum *m*, Hausdorffraum *m*	espace *m* séparé (de Hausdorff, Hausdorff, T_2)	отделимое [топологическое] пространство, хаусдорфово [топологическое] пространство, пространство Хаусдорфа, T_2-пространство
	separated uniformity <TO>	*s.* S 537/8		
	separated uniformizable space <TO>	*s.* C 1510		
S 537/8	**separated uniform structure,** separated uniformity <TO>	separierte uniforme Struktur *f*	structure *f* uniforme séparée	отделимая равномерная структура
S 539	**separate** <a matrix> **into blocks / to,** to partition <a matrix> into blocks <MD>	in Untermatrizen (Kästchen, Blöcke) zerlegen	partager en blocs	разбивать на клетки
S 540	**separate locally / to** <TO>	lokal trennen	séparer localement	локально разделять
S 541	**separately continuous function** <AN>	getrennt stetige Funktion *f*	fonction *f* séparément continue	отдельно непрерывная функция
S 542	**separately equicontinuous family of maps** <AN, TO>	getrennt gleichgradig stetige Familie (Menge) *f* von Abbildungen	famille *f* d'applications séparément équicontinue	отдельно равностепенно непрерывное множество (семейство) отображений
	separate points / to <AL, TO>	*s.* D 747		
S 543	**separate regression estimate** <ST>	separierte Regressionsschätzung *f*	estimation *f* par régression séparée	раздельная оценка [по уравнению] регрессии
S 544	**separate strictly / to** <convex sets> <CS>	stark trennen <konvexe Mengen>	strictement séparer <des ensembles convexes>	строго разделять <выпуклые множества>
	separating class of functions <TO>	*s.* S 546		
S 545	**separating edge,** cut edge, cut-edge, bridge, isthmus <of a graph> <GP>	Brücke *f*, Isthmus *m*	isthme *m*, chemin *m* isolant	перешеек
S 546	**separating family of functions,** separating class of functions <TO>	trennende Familie *f* von Funktionen	famille *f* de fonctions séparante	отделяющее семейство функций
S 547	**separating function algebra** <FA>	trennende Funktionenalgebra *f*	algèbre *f* de fonctions séparante	отделяющая алгебра функций
S 548	**separating plane** <of sets> <CS>	trennende Schranke (Ebene) *f*	plan *m* séparant	разделяющая плоскость
	separating point <TO>	*s.* D 793		
S 549	**separating relation** <FO>	trennende Relation *f*	relation *f* séparante	отделяющее отношение
S 550	**separating set** <TO>	separierende (trennende) Menge *f*	ensemble *m* séparant	отделяющее множество
	separating set <GP>	*s.* A 1001		
S 551	**separating tac-plane** <CS>	trennende Stützebene *f*	plan *m* d'appui séparant	разделяющая опорная плоскость

No.	English	German	French	Russian
S 552	**separating transcendence base (basis), separating transcendency base** <AL>	separierende Transzendenzbasis *f*	base *f* de transcendance séparante	сепарирующий базис трансцендентности
S 553	**separating transcendental,** separating variable <AL>	separierende Variable *f*	élément *m* transcendant séparant	сепарирующий элемент
S 554	**separating uniformizing co-ordinates** <AG>	separierende uniformisierende Koordinaten *fpl*	coordonnées *fpl* uniformisantes séparantes	сепарирующие униформизирующие координаты
	separating variable <AL>	*s.* S 553		
S 555	**separating vector** <of a *-representation of a *C**-algebra> <FA>	trennender Vektor *m*	vecteur *m* séparant	разделяющий вектор
	separating vertex <GP>	*s.* C 2828		
S 556	**separation** <of a point set> <TO>	Zerstückelung *f* <einer Punktmenge>	séparation *f* <d'un ensemble de points>	разбиение на два дизъюнктных замкнутых множества
S 557	**separation** <of a space> <TO>	Zerlegung *f* <eines Raumes, wenn nicht zusammenhängend> in zwei abgeschlossene Mengen	séparation *f* <d'un espace>	разбиение <пространства> на два замкнутых множества
	separation <AN, SE>	*s.* D 84		
S 558	**separation axiom** <TO>	Trennungsaxiom *n*	axiome *m* de séparation	аксиома отделимости
	separation of roots <AL, NU>	*s.* S 561		
S 559	**separation of the first kind** <AN, SE>	Dedekindscher Schnitt *m* mit Schnittelement	coupure *f* telle qu'il y a un élément à la coupure	дедекиндово сечение, определяющее (которое определяет) элемент
S 560	**separation of the second kind** <AN, SE>	Dedekindscher Schnitt *m* ohne Schnittelement	coupure *f* telle qu'il n'y a pas d'élément à la coupure	дедекиндово сечение, которое не определяет элемента
S 561	**separation of the zeros,** separation of roots, location of the roots, isolating of roots <of a polynomial> <AL, NU>	Separation (Trennung) *f* der Wurzeln	séparation *f* des racines	локализация (отделение) корней
S 562	**separation of variables,** partitioning of variables, partitioning the variables; method of partitioning the variables <DE, PG>	Separation *f* der Variablen (Veränderlichen), Trennung (Separierung) *f* der Variablen; Methode *f* der Trennung (Separation) der Variablen, Bernoullischer Ansatz *m*	séparation *f* des variables; méthode *f* de la séparation des variables	разделение переменных; метод разделения переменных
S 563	**separation principle** <FO, TO>	Trennungsprinzip *n*	principe *m* de séparation	прицип отделимости
	separation principle <LO, SE>	*s.* A 1293		
S 564	**separation relation** <on a set> <GE, SE>	Trennbeziehung *f* <auf einer Menge>	relation *f* de séparation <sur un ensemble>	соотношение перемежаемости <на подмножестве>
	separation scheme <LO, SE>	*s.* A 1293		
	separation sign <NU>	*s.* S 569		
S 565	**separation theorem** <CS, FO, TO>	Trennungssatz *m*	théorème *m* de séparation	теорема отделимости
S 566	**separation theorem,** Sturm['s] separation theorem <DE>	Trennungssatz *m*, Separationstheorem *n*	théorème *m* de séparation	теорема о разделении нулей
	separatively ordered set <SE>	*s.* O 318		
S 567	**separator** <between *A* and *B*> <of a space> <TO>	Separator *m* <zwischen *A* und *B*>	séparateur *m* <entre *A* et *B*>	разделитель <между множествами *A* и *B*>
S 568	**separatrix** <DE>	Separatrix *f*	séparatrice *f*	сепаратриса
S 569	**separatrix,** separation sign, division sign <for numbers> <NU>	Trennungszeichen *n*		пробел, разделяющий число на периоды
	separatrix <NT>	*s.* D 36		
S 570	**septenary** <AL, NT>	septenär	septénaire	семеричный
	seq <LO>	*s.* M 161		
S 571	**sequence** <AL, SS>	Folge *f* <AL, SS>; Sequenz *f* <AL>	suite *f*	последовательность
	sequence <FA>	*s.* V 91		
	sequence <GN, SE>	*s.* O 350		
	sequence <SE, SS>	*s.* I 472		
	α-sequence <SE>	*s.* A 537		
	sequence bounded from above <SS>	*s.* B 665		
	sequence bounded from below <SS>	*s.* B 666		
S 572	**sequence convergent almost certain[ly],** sequence convergent with probability one <of random variables> <SP>	fast sicher konvergente Folge *f*, mit Wahrscheinlichkeit Eins konvergente Folge, stark konvergente Folge	suite *f* convergente presque sûrement, suite convergente à probabilité un	почти наверное сходящаяся последовательность; последовательность, сходящаяся с вероятностью единицы
S 573	**sequence convergent almost everywhere** <SS>	fast überall konvergente Folge *f*, konvergente Folge fast überall	suite *f* convergente presque partout	сходящаяся почти всюду последовательность; последовательность, сходящаяся почти всюду
	sequence convergent everywhere <SS>	*s.* E 643		
S 574	**sequence convergent in mean,** strongly conver-	konvergente Folge *f* im Mittel, im Mittel konver-	suite *f* convergente en moyenne, suite fortement	сходящаяся последовательность в среднем,

	gent sequence <in L_p> <FA>	gente Folge, konvergente Folge bezüglich der starken Topologie, stark konvergente Folge	convergente	сильно сходящаяся последовательность
S 575	**sequence** <of random variables> **convergent in probability** <SP>	in (nach) Wahrscheinlichkeit konvergente Folge *f*, konvergente Folge in (nach) Wahrscheinlichkeit, stochastisch (schwach) konvergente Folge	suite *f* convergente en probabilité	сходящаяся по вероятности последовательность
S 576	**sequence convergent in the Mackey topology** <TO>	Mackey-konvergente (total konvergente) Folge *f*, konvergente Folge im Sinne von Mackey	suite *f* Mackey-convergente (M-convergente, bornologiquement convergente)	сходящаяся в топологии Макки последовательность
	sequence convergent with probability one <ST>	*s.* S 572		
	sequence diverging to + ∞ or — ∞ <SS>	*s.* P 1804		
S 577	**sequence left exact at *Y*** <HA>	linksexakte Sequenz *f* an der Stelle *Y*	suite *f* exacte à gauche en *Y*	последовательность, точная слева в члене *Y*
	sequence limitable by Abel's method <LI>	*s.* A 492		
	sequence limitable by arithmetic means <LI>	*s.* C 832		
	sequence limitable by Borel's method <LI>	*s.* B 590		
	sequence limitable by Borel's method of order *r* <LI>	*s.* B 762		
	sequence limitable by Cesàro's *k*-th mean <LI>	*s.* C 752		
S 578	**sequence limitable by Cesàro's method [of limitation]**, *C*-limitable sequence <LI>	*C*-limitierbare (nach dem *C*-Verfahren limitierbare) Folge *f*	suite *f* limitable par la méthode de Cesàro	последовательность, лимитируемая методом Чезаро
	sequence limitable by Cesàro's method [of limitation] of order *k* <LI>	*s.* C 752		
	sequence limitable by Euler's method <LI>	*s.* E 156		
	sequence limitable by Euler's method of *p*-th order <LI>	*s.* E 303		
	sequence limitable by Hausdorff's method <LI>	*s.* H 378		
	sequence limitable by Hölder's method <LI>	*s.* H 379		
	sequence limitable by Hölder's method of *p*-th order <LI>	*s.* H 586		
	sequence limitable by Nörlund's method <LI>	*s.* N 718		
	sequence limitable by Riesz's method <LI>	*s.* R 1349		
	sequence limitable (C,*k*) <LI>	*s.* C 752		
S 579	**sequence of arcs**, directed sequence <GP>	Bogenfolge *f*	suite *f* d'arcs	последовательность дуг
	sequence of distinct points <TO>	*s.* O 126		
	sequence of edges <GP>	*s.* E 27		
	sequence of functions <SS>	*s.* F 774		
S 580	**sequence of iterations** <AN, NU>	Iterationsfolge *f*	suite *f* des itérations	последовательность итераций
S 581	**sequence of Laplace**, Laplace['s] sequence <of surfaces> <DG>	Laplace-Folge *f*, L-Folge *f*, Laplacesche Kette *f*	suite *f* de Laplace	последовательность Лапласа, последовательность L
S 582	**sequence of** <real *or* complex> **numbers** <SS>	Zahlenfolge *f*, Folge *f* von Zahlen	suite *f* de nombres, suite numérique	последовательность чисел, числовая последовательность
	sequence of order two <CA, HA>	*s.* C 1598		
S 583	**sequence of partial sums** <of an infinite series> <SS>	Folge *f* der Partialsummen (Abschnitte), Abschnittsfolge *f*, Partialsummenfolge *f*	suite *f* des sommes partielles	последовательность частичных сумм
S 584	**sequence of points** <TO>	Punktfolge *f*	suite *f* de points	последовательность точек
	sequence of prime numbers <NT>	*s.* S 619		
	sequence of rational numbers <SS>	*s.* R 183		
S 585	**sequence of sets** <SE, TO>	Mengenfolge *f*	suite *f* d'ensembles	последовательность множеств
S 586	**sequence of signs** <for an algebraic equation> <AL>	Zeichenfolge *f*, Vorzeichenfolge *f*	suite *f* des signes	последовательность знаков
	sequence of Sturm['s] functions <AL, NU>	*s.* S 2047		
	sequence of symbols <LO>	*s.* E 754		

No.	English	German	French	Russian
	sequence of tests <ST>	*s.* T 222		
S 587	**sequence** <of numbers> **oscillating between finite limits** <SS>	zwischen endlichen Grenzen oszillierende Folge *f*, beschränkt unbestimmt divergente Folge, endlich unbestimmte Folge	suite *f* oscillant entre limites finies	последовательность, колеблющаяся между конечными пределами
S 588	**sequence right exact at *Y*** <HA>	rechtsexakte Sequenz *f* an der Stelle *Y*	suite *f* exacte à droite en *Y*	последовательность, точная справа в члене *Y*
S 589	**sequence space,** coordinate space <FA, TO>	Folgenraum *m*, Koordinatenraum *m*	espace *m* de suites, espace des coordonnées	пространство последовательностей, координатное пространство
	sequence tending to zero <SS>	*s.* N 793		
S 590	**sequence terminating to the left** <AL>	nach links abbrechende Folge *f*	suite *f* stationnaire à gauche	стабилизирующаяся слева последовательность
S 591	**sequence terminating to the right** <AL>	nach rechts abbrechende Folge *f*	suite *f* stationnaire à droite	стабилизирующаяся справа последовательность
S 592	**sequence uniformly distributed modulo *a*** <NT>	gleichverteilte Folge *f* modulo *a*	suite *f* équirépartie modulo *a*, séquence *f* équidistribuée mod. *a*, suite équidistribuée	равномерно распределенная mod. *a* последовательность
S 593	**sequence without repetitions** <CT>	Folge *f* ohne Wiederholungen	suite *f* non répétitive	последовательность без повторений
	sequence with summable majorant <FA>	*s.* M 47		
S 594	**sequent,** immediate successor <in a poset *or* lattice> <*a* covers *b*, *a* is a cover of *b*, *a* is prime over *b*> <LA, SE>	oberer Nachbar *m* <*a* ist oberer Nachbar von *b*, *b* ist unterer Nachbar von *a*>	voisin *m* supérieur <*a* couvre *b*, *b* est couvert par *b*, *a* est un élément immédiatement plus grand que *b*, *b* précède *a*, *a* succède à *b*>	верхний сосед <*a* покрывает *b*>
S 595	**sequent,** Sequenz <LO>	Sequenz *f*	énoncé *m* de conséquence	секвенция
	sequent <SE>	*s.* 1. I 117; 2. R 790		
S 596	**sequential analysis** <ST>	Sequentialanalyse *f* [von Wald], Sequenzanalyse *f*, Folgeprüfung *f*	analyse *f* séquentielle (progressive)	последовательный анализ
S 597	**sequential compactness** <TO>	Folgenkompaktheit *f*	compacité *f*, semi-compacité *f*, compacité séquentielle	счетная компактность, секвенциальная компактность; условие Больцано-Вейерштрасса
S 598	**sequential convergence** <TO>	Folgenkonvergenz *f*	convergence *f* séquentielle	секвенциальная сходимость
	sequential design <ST>	*s.* S 610		
S 599	**sequential estimation [method]** <ST>	sequentielle Schätzung *f*, sequentielles Schätzverfahren *n*	estimation *f* séquentielle (progressive), méthode *f* d'estimation séquentielle (progressive)	последовательная оценка, метод последовательной оценки
S 600	**sequential likelihood ratio test,** sequential probability ratio test <ST>	sequentieller Likelihood-verhältnistest *m*	test *m* séquentiel du rapport des vraisemblances (probabilités)	последовательный критерий отношения правдоподобия
S 601	**sequential limit; sequential limit point** <TO>	Folgenlimes *m*	limite *f* séquentielle	предел по последовательности
S 602	**sequentially closed set** <TO>	folgenabgeschlossene Menge *f*	ensemble *m* séquentiellement fermé	последовательностно (секвенциально) замкнутое множество
S 603	**sequentially compact set** <every sequence has a convergent subsequence> <TO>	eigentlich folgenkompakte Menge *f*, folgenkompakte Menge	ensemble *m* séquentiellement compact	секвенциально компактное множество
	sequentially compact space <TO>	*s.* C 1307		
S 604	**sequentially complete space** <TO>	folgenvollständiger Raum *m*	espace *m* semi-complet	секвенциально полное пространство
S 605	**sequentially continuous function (mapping, transformation)** <TO>	folgenstetige Funktion (Abbildung, Transformation) *f*	fonction (application, transformation) *f* séquentiellement continue	секвенциально (последовательностно) непрерывная функция, секвенциально (последовательностно) непрерывное отображение (преобразование)
S 606	**sequential method** <ST>	sequentielles Verfahren *n*, Sequentialverfahren *n*, Sequentialmethode *f*	méthode *f* séquentielle (progressive)	последовательный метод, метод последовательного анализа
	sequential optimization <PG>	*s.* S 607		
	sequential plan <ST>	*s.* S 610		
	sequential probability ratio test <ST>	*s.* S 600		
S 607	**sequential programming,** sequential optimization <PG>	sequentielle Optimierung *f*	programmation (optimisation) *f* séquentielle	последовательное программирование, последовательная оптимизация
S 608	**sequential ratio test** <ST>	sequentieller Verhältnistest (Quotiententest) *m*, Quotiententest	test *m* séquentiel du rapport	последовательный критерий отношения
S 609	**sequential sampling** <ST>	sequentielle Stichprobennahme *f*	échantillonnage (sondage) *m* séquentiel, échantillonnage (sondage) progressif	последовательный выбор
S 610	**sequential sampling plan,** sequential plan, sequential design <ST>	sequentieller Stichprobenplan *m*, Sequentialplan *m*	plan *m* d'échantillonnage séquentiel (progressif), plan séquentiel (progressif)	выборочный план последовательного типа, последовательный план выборки, последовательный план

S 611	**sequential scheme** <ST>	Sequentialschema *n*	schéma *m* séquentiel (progressif)	последовательная схема
S 612	**sequential test** <ST>	sequentieller Test *m*, sequentielles Testverfahren *n*, Sequentialtest *m*, Folgetest *m*	test (critère) *m* séquentiel, test progressif	последовательный критерий (тест)
	sequential unconstrained minimization technique <PG>	*s.* S 2302		
	Sequenz <LO>	*s.* S 595		
	serial correlation <ST>	*s.* A 1216		
S 613	**serial correlation coefficient** <ST>	Reihenkorrelationskoeffizient *m*, Serienkorrelationskoeffizient *m*	coefficient *m* de corrélation sériale	сериальный коэффициент корреляции
	serial correlation coefficient <ST>	*s. a.* A 1217		
	serial correlation function <ST>	*s.* A 1218		
	serially ordered set <SE>	*s.* L 822		
	serial regression <ST>	*s.* A 1239		
S 614	**serial scheme** <ST>	Serienschema *n*, Doppelfolge *f* von Zufallsgrößen	schéma *m* en série	схема серий
	ϑ series <FT>	*s.* T 411		
	series approaching no [finite or infinite] limit <SS>	*s.* O 504		
	series convergent in the mean <LI>	*s.* C 453		
	series expansion <AN>	*s.* E 709		
	series expansion in terms of eigenfunctions <DE, IE>	*s.* E 710		
S 615	**series of Fermat** <NT>	Fermatsche Zahlenreihe *f*, Fermatsche Reihe *f*	suite *f* des nombres de Fermat	ряд Ферма
	series of functions <SS>	*s.* F 775		
	series of Lamé of *n*-th order <NT>	*s.* N 748		
S 616	**series of Lucas,** Lucas['] series <NT>	Lucassche Zahlenreihe *f*	suite *f* de Lucas	последовательность Люка́
	series of matrices <SS>	*s.* M 212		
S 617	**series of observations,** set of observations <ST>	Beobachtungsreihe *f*	série *f* d'observations	серия (множество) наблюдений
S 618	**series of Pell** <NT>	Pellsche Reihe *f*	suite (série) *f* de Pell	последовательность Пелля
	series of Pisano <FD, NT>	*s.* F 144		
	series of points <PJ>	*s.* P 783		
	series of positive terms <SS>	*s.* P 1100		
S 619	**series of prime numbers,** sequence of prime numbers <NT>	Primzahlfolge *f*, Folge *f* der Primzahlen	suite *f* des nombres premiers	последовательность простых чисел
S 620	**series of series** <SS>	Reihe *f* von Reihen	série *f* de séries	ряд от рядов
S 621	**series of terms of the same sign** <SS> ┌<AR>	Reihe *f*, deren Glieder gleiches Vorzeichen haben	série *f* de seconde espèce	ряд с членами одинакового знака
S 622	**series of the reciprocals**	reziproke Reihe *f*	série *f* réciproque	ряд обратных чисел
S 623	**series solution** <DE>	Reihenlösung *f*, Lösung *f* in Reihenform	solution *f* en série	решение в виде ряда
S 624	**series statement;** expression by a series <AN>	Reihenansatz *m*; Reihenausdruck *m*	expression *f* en série	выражение в виде ряда
	series summable by Abel's method <LI>	*s.* A 1128		
	series summable by arithmetic means <LI>	*s.* C 2718		
	series summable by Borel's method <LI>	*s.* B 606		
	series summable by Borel's method of *r*-th order <LI>	*s.* B 784		
	series summable by Cesàro's *k*-th mean <LI>	*s.* C 756		
	series summable by Cesàro's method <LI>	*s.* C 453		
	series summable by Cesàro's method of order *k* <LI>	*s.* C 756		
	series summable by Cesàro's method of summation <LI>	*s.* C 453		
	series summable by Cesàro's method of summation of order *k* <LI>	*s.* C 756		
S 625	**series summable by Euler's method,** *E*-summable series <LI>	*E*-summierbare (nach dem *E*-Verfahren summierbare) Reihe *f*	série *f* sommable par la méthode d'Euler, série *E*-sommable	ряд, суммируемый методом Эйлера; *E*-суммируемый ряд
	series summable by Euler's method of *p*-th order <LI>	*s.* E 320		
	series summable by Hausdorff's method <LI>	*s.* H 594		
	series summable by Hölder's method <LI>	*s.* H 593		

No.	English	German	French	Russian
	series summable by Hölder's method of *p*-th order <LI>	*s.* H 589		
	series summable by Nörlund's method <LI>	*s.* N 720		
	series summable by Riesz's method <LI>	*s.* R 1350		
	series summable C_k <LI>	*s.* C 756		
S 626	**serpentine [curve]** <AG>	Serpentine *f*, Schlangenkurve *f*	serpentine *f*, anguinée *f*, anguinea *f*	змеевидная, серпентина, anguinea
S 627	**Serre['s] algebraic space** <AG>	Serrescher algebraischer Raum *m*	espace *m* algébrique de Serre	алгебраическое пространство Серра
S 628	**Serre['s] class** <of abelian groups> <GR>	Serresche Klasse *f*	classe *f* de Serre	класс Серра
S 629	**Serre['s] cohomology sequence** <AT>	Serresche Kohomologiesequenz *f*	suite *f* de cohomologie de Serre	когомологическая последовательность Серра
	Serre['s] fibre map (space) <AT>	*s.* W 62		
S 630	**Serre['s] homology sequence** <AT>	Serresche Homologiesequenz *f*	suite *f* d'homologie de Serre	гомологическая последовательность Серра
	Serre['s] subcategory <CA>	*s.* T 414		
S 631	**Serret['s] formulas** <of spherical trigonometry> <EG>	Serretsche Formeln *fpl*	formules *fpl* de Serret	формулы Серре
	Serret-Frenet['s] formulae <DG>	*s.* F 643		
S 632	**Serret['s] surface** <DG>	Serretsche Fläche *f*	surface *f* de Serret	поверхность Серре
S 633	**servant (serving) subgroup,** pure subgroup <GR>	Servanzuntergruppe *f*	sous-groupe *m* pur	сервантная (чистая) подгруппа
S 634	**Servois['s] formula** <for a tetrahedron> <EG>	Servoissche Formel *f*	formule *f* de Servois	формула Сервуа
S 635	**Servois['s] point** <of a tetrahedron> <EG>	Servoisscher Punkt *m*	point *m* de Servois	точка Сервуа
S 636	**sesquilinear form** <AL, FA>	Semibilinearform *f*, Sesquilinearform *f*	forme *f* sesquilinéaire	полубилинейная (полуторалинейная) форма
S 637	**set**; spread <Brouwer, intuitionist set theory>, // aggregate, ensemble, manifold <SE>	Menge *f*; Menge erster Art <keine Unmenge>, // Mannichfaltigkeit *f* <Cantor>	ensemble *m*	множество
	set <CA>	*s.* D 659		
S 638	**set algebra,** set[-] field, field of sets, algebra of sets, Boolean algebra of sets, field of subsets <closed with respect to union, meet and complementation> <SE>	Mengenalgebra *f*, Boolesche Mengenalgebra, Mengenkörper *m*, Boolescher Mengenverband *m*	algèbre *f* des ensembles, corps *m* d'ensembles, algèbre des parties <d'un référentiel>, clan *m*, algèbre de sous-ensembles	алгебра множеств, тело множеств
S 639	**set bounded from below, set bounded on the left,** bounded from below set, bounded on the left set, left-bounded set <SE>	nach unten beschränkte Menge *f*	ensemble *m* minoré (borné inférieurement)	ограниченное снизу множество, минорированное множество
S 640	**set bounded to the left** <of a topological ring> <AL>	linksseitig beschränkte Menge *f*	ensemble *m* borné à gauche	ограниченное слева множество
S 641	**set bounded to the right** <of a topological ring> <AL>	rechtsseitig beschränkte Menge *f*	ensemble *m* borné à droite	ограниченное справа множество
	set builder <LO, SE>	*s.* C 787		
	set closed in the Mackey topology <TO>	*s.* M 7		
	set cofinal from the left <SE>	*s.* C 1121		
	set cofinal from the right <SE>	*s.* C 1052		
	set conditionally compact in *R* <TO>	*s.* S 688		
	set consisting of a single element <SE>	*s.* O 86		
	set 1—1-correspondence <SE>	*s.* E 404		
S 642	**set equal to or less** <than . . .> **in power, set equal to or less pollent** <than> <SE>	höchstens so mächtige Menge *f* <wie>	ensemble *m* de puissance non supérieure <à>	множество одинаковой или меньшей мощности
	set equal to zero / to <GN>	*s.* E 334		
S 643	**set equivalent by dissection** <ME>	zerlegungsgleiche Menge *f*	ensemble *m* égal par dissection	равносоставленное множество
	set[-] field <SE>	*s.* S 638		
	set finite in the sense of Dedekind <SE>	*s.* D 88		
S 644	**set fixed elementwise** <AL, AN, SE>	elementweise (punktweise) feste Menge *f*	ensemble *m* invariant en éléments	точечно-инвариантное множество
S 645/6	**set function** <AN>	Mengenfunktion *f*	fonction *f* d'ensemble (d'ensembles)	функция множества
	set functor <CA>	*s.* S 707		
	set having less power <SE>	*s.* S 651		

No.	English	German	French	Russian
S 647	**set having the Heine-Borel property,** countably compact set <TO>	Menge *f*, die dem Borelschen Überdeckungssatz genügt; abzählbar kompakte Menge	ensemble *m* ayant la propriété de Borel, ensemble dénombrablement compact	множество со свойством Бореля <множество, всякое счетное открытое покрытие которого содержит конечное покрытие>, счетно компактное множество
S 648	**set having the Lindelöf property** <TO>	Menge *f*, die dem Lindelöfschen Überdeckungssatz genügt	ensemble *m* ayant la propriété de Lindelöf	множество со свойством Линделефа <множество, всякое открытое покрытие которого содержит счетное покрытие>
	set having the power of the continuum <SE>	*s.* S 657		
	set having the same cardinality <SE>	*s.* E 404		
S 649	**set-inclusion,** ⊂ <SE>	mengentheoretische Inklusion *f*, ⊂	inclusion *f* ensembliste, ⊂	теоретико-множественное включение, ⊂
	set in (1—1)-correspondence <SE>	*s.* E 404		
	set infinite in the sense of Dedekind <SE>	*s.* D 90		
S 650	**set in which any two elements are separated,** totally disconnected set <TO>	total zusammenhangslose Menge *f*	ensemble *m* nulle part connexe	нигде не связное множество
S 651	**set less in power,** set having less power, less pollent set <than> <SE>	weniger mächtige Menge *f* <als>	ensemble *m* ayant une puissance plus petite <que>	множество, имеющее меньшую мощность <чем>
	set linearly ordered by dictionary order <SE>	*s.* S 686		
	set-membership symbol <SE>	*s.* S 856		
	set of algebraically independent elements over *k* <AL>	*s.* T 728		
	set of all insertions of *N* into *M* <SE>	*s.* F 776		
	set of all [possible] mappings of *N* into *M* <SE>	*s.* F 776		
S 652/3	**set of all sets** <SE>	Menge *f* aller Mengen	ensemble *m* de tous les ensembles, ensemble universel	множество всех множеств
	set of all subsets <SE>	*s.* P 1156		
S 654	**set of associated prime ideals** <of a module> <AL>	Menge *f* der assoziierten Primideale	assassin *m*, ensemble *m* des idéaux premiers associés	множество ассоциированных простых идеалов
S 655	**set of associated radii of convergence** <FT>	System *n* der assoziierten (zusammengehörigen) Konvergenzradien	système *m* des rayons de convergence associés	система сопряженных радиусов сходимости
S 656	**set of condensation points** <of a point set> <TO>	verdichteter Teil *m*	ensemble *m* des points de condensation	множество точек сгущения
S 657	**set of continuum power,** continuum infinite set, set of the power of the continuum, set having the power of the continuum <SE>	kontinuumsmächtigeMenge *f*, Menge von der Mächtigkeit des Kontinuums	ensemble *m* ayant la puissance du continu, ensemble de puissance du continu	континуальное множество; множество, имеющее мощность континуума
S 658	**set of convergence,** convergence set <FT> ⌐SS>	Konvergenzmenge *f*	ensemble *m* de convergence	множество сходимости
	set of convergence <FT,	*s.* D 864		
	set of cosets <AL>	*s.* F 56		
S 659	**set of decisions** <ST>	Entscheidungsmenge *f*	ensemble *m* des décisions	множество решений
	set of definition <AN>	*s.* D 850		
S 660	**set of degrees** <in graduation> <AL>	Gradmenge *f*	ensemble *m* des degrés	множество степеней
	set of differential equations <DE>	*s.* S 1013		
S 661	**set of elements *x* of** <a ring> ***R* satisfying *x I* ⊆ *J*** <AL>	Quotient *m* <eines Ideals *J* von *R* durch ein Ideal *I*>	transporteur *m* <d'un idéal *I* d'un anneau *R* dans un idéal *J* de *R*>	множество вхех элементов *x* кольца *R*, для которых *x I* ⊆ *J*
	set of equations <AL, AN>	*s.* S 2517		
	set of first category [according to Baire] <TO>	*s.* M 293		
S 662	**set of function elements generated by analytic continuation** <FT>	analytisches Gebilde *n*, Funktionsgebilde *n*, Gebilde	ensemble *m* des éléments de fonction engendrés par prolongement analytique	аналитический образ
	set of generators <AL>	*s.* I 11		
S 663	**set of greater power** <than> <SE> ⌐<GR>	Menge *f* von größerer Mächtigkeit <als>	ensemble *m* de puissance plus grande <que>	множество большей мощности <чем>
	set of imprimitivity	*s.* S 2520		
	set of indices <SE>	*s.* 1. D 854: 2. I 361		
	set of information <ST>	*s.* I 506		
S 664	**set of less power** <than> <SE> ⌐<AN>	Menge *f* von kleinerer Mächtigkeit <als>	ensemble *m* de puissance plus petite <que>	множество меньшей мощности <чем>
	set of linear functions	*s.* S 2527		
S 665	**set of lower bounds** <AN, SE>	Menge *f* der unteren Schranken	ensemble *m* mineur, ensemble des minorants	множество минорант
S 666	**set of measure zero,** null set <ME>	Menge *f* vom Maß Null, Nullmenge *f*	ensemble *m* de mesure nulle (zéro), ensemble négligeable	множество меры нуль, множество нулевой меры, нульмерное множество, пренебрежимое (устранимое) множество

No.	English	German	French	Russian
S 667	**set of μ-measure zero** <ME>	μ-Nullmenge *f*, Nullmenge *f*	ensemble *m* μ-négligeable	множество нулевой μ-меры, μ-пренебрежимое множество
S 668	**set of multiples** <NT>	Multiplamenge *f*	ensemble *m* de multiples	множество кратных
S 669	**set of *n*! simple orderings of a set of cardinality *n*** <SE>	Menge *f* der *n*! einfachen Ordnungen auf einer Menge der Kardinalzahl *n*	permutoèdre *m* de degré *n*, taxièdre *m*	множество *n*! простых порядков на *n*-элементном множестве
S 670	**set of numbers,** number set, assemblage of numbers <NT>	Zahlenmenge *f*, Menge *f* von Zahlen	ensemble *m* de nombres	множество чисел, числовое множество
	set of observations <ST>	*s.* S 617		
	set of ordered sequences <SE>	*s.* S 684		
	set of ordinary differential equations <DE>	*s.* S 1013		
	set of partial differential equations <DE>	*s.* S 2532		
	set of paths <TO>	*s.* P 311		
	set of points <SE, TO>	*s.* P 785		
S 671	**set of points of adherence** <of a filter> <TO>	Adhärenz *f*	adhérence *f*	замыкание
S 672	**set of points of continuity** <AN>	Stetigkeitsmenge *f*, Menge *f* der Stetigkeitspunkte	ensemble *m* des points de continuité	множество точек непрерывности
	set of positive elements <AL>	*s.* P 1092		
	set of projective coordinates <AG, AY, PJ>	*s.* P 1676		
S 673	**set of projective zeros** <AG>	projektive Nullstellenmannigfaltigkeit *f*	variété *f* de zéros projectifs	многообразие проективных нулей
	set of second category <TO>	*s.* N 416		
S 674	**set of separability** <ST>	Separabilitätsmenge *f*	ensemble *m* de séparabilité	множество сепарабельности
S 675	**set of sequences of integers** <TO>	Menge *f* der Folgen ganzer Zahlen	ensemble *m* des suites d'entiers, espace *m* à zéro dimension <Baire>	множество последовательностей целых чисел
S 676	**set of sets,** system of sets <SE>	Menge *f* von Mengen, Mengensystem *n*	ensemble *m* d'ensembles, complexe *m* d'ensembles	множество множеств, система множеств
S 677	**set of sets partially ordered by inclusion** <SE>	Mengenverein *m*	ensemble *m* d'ensembles ordonné par inclusion	полуупорядоченная относительно включения система множеств
	set of simultaneous linear equations <AL>	*s.* S 2524		
S 678	**set of strategies** <TG>	Strategienmenge *f*	ensemble *m* des stratégies	множество стратегий
S 679	**set of strictly positive elements** <of an ordered group *or* ring> <AL, GR>	strenger Positivbereich *m*	cône *m* positif	область строго положительных элементов
	set of support <CS, GE>	*s.* S 2348		
S 680	**set of ternary numbers** <NT, TO>	Menge *f* von Ternärzahlen	ensemble *m* ternaire	множество троичных чисел
	set of the first category <TO>	*s.* M 293		
S 681	**set of the first category in a point** <TO>	Menge *f* [von] erster (1.) Kategorie in einem Punkt	ensemble *m* de première (I[e]) catégorie dans un point	множество первой (I-ой) категории в точке
	set of the first species <TO>	*s.* M 293		
S 682	**set of the *k*-th category** <TO>	Menge *f* von *k*-ter [Schnirelmannscher] Kategorie, Menge von der [Schnirelmannschen] Kategorie *k*	ensemble *m* de la catégorie *k*	множество, обладающее категорией [Шнирельмана-Люстерника] *k*
	set of the power of the continuum <SE>	*s.* S 657		
	set of the second category <TO>	*s.* N 416		
S 683	**set of the second category in a point** <TO>	Menge *f* [von] zweiter (2.) Kategorie in einem Punkt	ensemble *m* de deuxième (IIe) catégorie dans un point	множество второй (II-ой) категории в точке
	set of the second species <TO>	*s.* N 416		
	set of transitivity <GR>	*s.* D 874		
S 684	**set of tuples,** set of ordered sequences <SE>	Menge *f* der Tupel	ensemble *m* des séquences	совокупность наборов
S 685	**set of upper bounds** <AN, SE>	Menge *f* der oberen Schranken	ensemble *m* majeur (des majorants)	множество мажорант
	set of values <AN>	*s.* C 1015		
	set operation <SE>	*s.* S 699		
S 686	**set ordered according to the principle of first differences,** set [linearly] ordered by dictionary order <SE>	lexikographisch (nach ersten Differenzstellen) geordnete Menge *f*	ensemble *m* ordonné d'après le principe des premières différences	лексикографически упорядоченное множество
	set ordered by dictionary order <SE>	*s.* S 686		
S 687	**set product** <in a groupoid> <AL>	Komplexprodukt *n*	produit *m* des parties	произведение множеств
	set product <SE>	*s.* C 173		

No.	English	German	French	Russian
S 688	**set relatively compact in *R*,** set conditionally compact in *R* <TO>	relativ kompakte (bikompakte) Menge *f* zu *R*, kompakte Menge in bezug auf *R*, kompakte Menge in *R*	ensemble *m* relativement compact dans *R*	относительно компактное множество в *R*, компактное множество в *R*
S 689	**set[-]ring,** ring of sets <closed with respect to finite sums and products> <SE>	Mengenring *m*, *sd*-System *n*	anneau *m* d'ensembles, anneau de parties, pavage *m*, famille *f* distributive	кольцо множеств
	set satisfying the condition of Baire <RF, TO>	*s.* B 23		
S 690	**sets having pairwise only a finite number of common points,** pairwise almost disjoint sets <SE>	Mengen *fpl*, die paarweise höchstens endlich viele Punkte gemein haben	ensembles *mpl* mutuellement orthogonaux	множества, которые попарно пересекаются в не более чем конечном числе точек
S 691	**set small of the order *V*** <TO>	von der Ordnung *V* kleine Menge *f*	ensemble *m* petit d'ordre *V*	малое порядка *V* множество
	set square <GE, IN>	*s.* T 899		
S 692	**sets separated by the set *C*** <TO>	durch die Menge *C* getrennte Mengen *fpl*	ensembles *mpl* séparés par l'ensemble *C*	множества, разделенные множеством *C*
S 693	**sets strictly separated by a hyperplane** <CS>	durch eine Hyperebene stark getrennte Mengen *fpl*	ensembles *mpl* strictement séparés par un hyperplan	множества, строго разделенные гиперплоскостью
	set sum <SE>	*s.* D 704		
	sets without common elements <SE>	*s.* D 703		
S 694	**set[-]system,** hypergraph <GP>	Mengensystem *n*, verallgemeinerter Graph *m*, Hypergraph *m*	hypergraphe *m*	гиперграф
S 695	**set[-]theoretic[al],** // assemblage-theoretic <SE>	mengentheoretisch	ensembliste, en théorie des ensembles, au sens de la théorie des ensembles, d'après la théorie des ensembles	теоретико-множественный
S 696	**set-theoretic[al] addition,** union <of sets> <SE>	Vereinigungsmengenbildung *f*	opération *f* union	объединения
	set-theoretic[al] antinomy <LO>	*s.* L 1068		
	set-theoretic[al] complement <SE>	*s.* C 1358		
	set-theoretic[al] difference <SE>	*s.* D 427		
	set-theoretic[al] equivalence <SE>	*s.* E 403		
S 697	**set-theoretic[al] image** <of an algebraic set> <AG>	mengentheoretisches Bild *n*	image *f* ensembliste	теоретико-множественный образ
	set-theoretic[al] inclusion <SE>	*s.* I 242		
S 698	**set-theoretic[al] intersection** <AL, SE, TO>	mengentheoretischer Durchschnitt *m*	intersection *f* ensembliste	теоретико-множественное пересечение
	set-theoretic[al] intersection <AL>	*s.* 1. G 407/8; 2. L 240		
	set-theoretic[al] intersection <SE>	*s.* I 802		
S 699	**set-theoretic[al] operation,** operation with sets, set operation <SE>	mengentheoretische Operation *f*, Mengenoperation *f*	opération *f* sur les (des) ensembles	операция на множествах, операция над множествами, операция множеств
S 700	**set-theoretic[al] projection** <AG>	mengentheoretische Projektion *f*	projection *f* ensembliste	теоретико-множественная проекция
S 701	**set-theoretic[al] proof** <SE>	mengentheoretischer Beweis *m*	démonstration *f* ensembliste	теоретико-множественное доказательство
S 702	**set-theoretic[al] union,** ∪ <AL, SE, TO> ┌<SE>	mengentheoretische Vereinigung *f*, ∪	réunion *f* au sens de la théorie des ensembles, réunion ensembliste, ∪	теоретико-множественное объединение, ∪
	set-theoretic[al] union	*s.* U 202		
S 703	**set theory,** theory of sets, // theory of aggregates <SE>	Mengenlehre *f*, Mengentheorie *f*, allgemeine Mengenlehre	théorie *f* des ensembles	теория множеств, учение о множествах
S 704	**set theory of Zermelo and Fraenkel,** theory of Zermelo-Fraenkel, Zermelo-Fraenkel set theory, Zermelo-Fraenkel-Skolem set theory, theory of Zermelo, Zermelo['s] set theory, ZF; Zermelo-Fraenkel axiom system, Zermelo-Fraenkel system <SE>	Zermelo-Fraenkelscher Aufbau *m* der Mengentheorie, Zermelo-Fraenkelsche Begründung *f* der Mengenlehre, Zermeloscher Aufbau der Mengentheorie; Zermelo-Fraenkelsches Axiomensystem *n*	théorie *f* des ensembles de Zermelo-Fraenkel	теория (аксиоматическая теория) множеств Цермело-Френкеля, ZF; система [аксиом] Цермело-Френкеля, аксиоматическая система теории множеств Цермело-Френкеля, система ZF
	setting of (up) an equation <GN>	*s.* F 476		
S 705	**set topology,** general topology <TO>	mengentheoretische Topologie *f*, allgemeine Topologie	topologie *f* ensembliste (générale)	теоретико-множественная топология, общая топология
	set union <SE>	*s.* U 202		
S 706	**set[-]up,** arrangement, approach, statement, guess, ansatz <of an equation> <GN>	Ansatz *m*	mise *f* en équation, position *f*	составление, подход [к решению]

No.	English	German	French	Russian
S 707	**set-valued functor,** set functor <CA>	mengenwertiger Funktor *m*, Funktor in die Kategorie der Mengen	foncteur *m* dans la catégorie des ensembles, foncteur à valeurs dans la catégorie des applications	функтор в категорию множеств
S 708	**set-valued mapping** <SE>	mengenwertige Abbildung *f*	application *f* à valeurs ensembles	множество-значное отображение
S 709	**set variable** <LO>	Mengenvariable *f*	variable *f* d'ensemble	переменное множеств
	set which is complement of a null set <ME>	*s.* C 2317		
S 710	**set with an internal composition law** <AL>	Menge *f* mit innerem Verknüpfungsgesetz	ensemble *m* muni d'une loi de composition interne, magma *m*	множество, снабженное законом внутренней композиции
S 711	**set with a relation defined on it** <SE>	mit einer Relation versehene Menge *f*, geregelte Menge	ensemble *m* muni d'une relation	множество с определенным на нем отношением
	set with base point <SE>	*s.* P 740		
S 712	**set with inner points** <TO>	Menge *f* mit inneren Punkten	ensemble *m* à points intérieurs, ensemble superficiel	множество с внутренними точками
S 713	**seven cube theorem** <NT>	Waringscher Satz *m* für 7 Kuben	théorème *m* de 7 cubes	теорема о разбиении на 7 кубов
S 714	**several-sorted predicate calculus;** many-sorted elementary logic <LO>	mehrsortiger Prädikatenkalkül *m*; mehrsortige Prädikatenlogik *f*	calcul *m* des prédicats à plusieurs sortes de variables	исчисление предикатов с несколькими сортами переменных
S 715	**Severi-Brauer surface** <AG>	Severi-Brauersche Fläche *f*	surface *f* de Severi-Brauer	поверхность Севери-Брауэра
S 716	**Severi-Brauer variety** <AG>	Severi-Brauersche Mannigfaltigkeit *f*	variété *f* de Severi-Brauer	многообразие Севери-Брауэра
	Severi['s] group <AG>	*s.* D 807		
S 717	**sexadecimal notation,** hexadecimal notation <NT>	hexadezimale (sedezimale) Schreibweise *f*, hexadezimale (sedezimale) Zahlendarstellung *f*	notation *f* hexadécimale (sexadécimale)	представление чисел в шестнадцатеричной системе
S 718	**sexadecimal number system,** hexadecimal number system <NT>	Hexadezimalsystem *n*, Sedezimalsystem *n*, Hexadezimalzahlensystem *n*	système *m* de numération hexadécimal (sexadécimal), système hexadécimal (sexadécimal, hexadique)	шестнадцатеричная система счисления
S 719	**sexagesimal arithmetic** <AR, NT>	Sexagesimalarithmetik *f*, Sexagesimalrechnung *f*	arithmétique *f* sexagésimale, calcul *m* sexagésimal	исчисление в шестидесятеричной системе
	sexagesimal degree <GE>	*s.* D 174		
S 720	**sexagesimal fraction** <AR, NT>	Sexagesimalbruch *m*, sechzigteiliger (astronomischer) Bruch *m*	fraction *f* sexagésimale (systématique à base 60, astronomique)	шестидесятеричная дробь
	sexagesimal minute <GE>	*s.* M 659		
	sexagesimal second <GE>	*s.* S 192		
S 721	**sexagesimal system [of numbers],** positional numeration system to basis 60, positional numeration system to radix 60 <AR, NT>	Sexagesimalsystem *n*, sexagesimales Positionssystem *n*	système *m* sexagésimal (de numération sexagésimal, à base 60), numération *f* sexagésimale	шестидесятеричная система счисления, шестидесятеричная система
S 722	**sextactic conic** <AG>	sextaktischer Kegelschnitt *m*	conique *f* (section *f* conique) sextactique	секстактическое коническое сечение
S 723	**sextactic point** <DG>	sextaktischer Punkt *m*, sextaktische Stelle *f*, Affinscheitel *m*, konischer Scheitel *m*	point *m* sextactique, sommet *m* affine (conique)	секстактическая (шестеричная) точка, аффинная вершина
S 724	**sextactic point** <of a cubic> <GE>	sechsfacher Berührungspunkt *m*	point *m* sextactique	секстактическая точка
S 725	**sextactic tangent** <GE>	sechsfach berührende Tangente *f*	tangente *f* sextuple	секстактическая касательная
S 726	**sextic,** plane sextic, plane sextic curve, plane algebraic curve of the sixth degree (order), algebraic plane curve of the sixth degree (order) <AG>	algebraische ebene Kurve *f* sechster (6.) Ordnung, [ebene] algebraische Kurve sechster (6.) Ordnung, ebene Kurve sechster (6.) Ordnung, ebene Sextik *f*	courbe *f* [algébrique] plane d'ordre six (6), courbe sextique plane, sextique *f* plane	плоская [алгебраическая] кривая шестого (6-го) порядка
S 727	**sextic [curve],** [algebraic] curve of the sixth order, [algebraic] curve of the sixth degree <AG>	Kurve *f* sechster (6.) Ordnung, Sextik *f*, algebraische Kurve sechster (6.) Ordnung, Kurve sechsten (6.) Grades	courbe *f* sextique, sextique *f*, courbe [algébrique] du sixième (6me) ordre, courbe algébrique d'ordre 6	алгебраическая кривая шестого (6-го) порядка, кривая шестого (6-го) порядка
S 728	**sextic [equation],** algebraic equation of [the] sixth degree, sixth-degree polynomial equation <AL>	Gleichung *f* sechsten (6.) Grades, algebraische Gleichung sechsten (6.) Grades	équation *f* sextique, équation du sixième (6me) degré (ordre); équation tricarrée	уравнение шестой (6-ой) степени, уравнение шестого (6-го) порядка
S 729	**sextic [quantic],** quantic (form) of the sixth degree <AL>	Form *f* sechsten Grades, Sextik *f*	sextique *f*, forme *f* sextique	форма шестой степени
S 730	**sextile** <ST>	Sextil *n*	sextile *m*	секстиль
S 731	**sextuple[t]** <SE>	Sextupel *n*	sextuplet *m*	шестерка
	sf <FU>	*s.* H 53		
	s-field <AL>	*s.* D 813		

No.	English	German	French	Russian
	S-function <AL>	*s.* S 149		
	sg <AN>	*s.* S 861		
	sg <FU>	*s.* H 54		
	sg <NT>	*s.* S 860		
	sgn <AN>	*s.* S 861		
	sgn <NT>	*s.* S 860		
S 732	**S-group** <GR>	*S*-Gruppe *f*	*S*-groupe *m*	*S*-группа
	sh <FU>	*s.* H 648		
S 733	**shade** <DS>	Eigenschatten *m*	ombre *f* propre	собственная тень
S 734	**shadow** <general concept> <DS>	Schatten *m*	ombre *f*	тень
S 735	**shadow** <DS>	Schlagschatten *m*	ombre *f* portée, ombre	падающая (отбрасываемая, проектируемая) тень, тень
S 736	**shadow price** <PG>	Schattenpreis *m*, Effizienzpreis *m*	prix *m* d'ombre	теневая цена
S 737	**Shannon['s] entropy** <ST>	Shannonsche Entropie *f*	entropie *f* de Shannon	энтропия Шеннона
S 738	**Shannon['s] formula** <ST>	Shannonsche Formel *f*	formule *f* de Shannon	формула Шеннона
S 739	**Shannon['s] inequality** <ST>	Shannonsche Ungleichung *f*	inégalité *f* de Shannon	неравенство Шеннона
S 740	**Shannon['s] theorem** <ST>	Shannonscher Satz *m*	théorème *m* de Shannon	теорема Шеннона
S 741	**shape,** form <of a curve *or* function> <GN>	Verlauf *m*	allure *f*, tracé *m*	вид, форма, ход
S 742	**shape** <ST>	Profilmaß *n*	profil *m*	очертание
S 743	**shape parameter** <ST>	Gestaltsparameter *m*, Formparameter *m*	paramètre *m* de forme	параметр формы
S 744	**Shapley['s] function** <TG>	Shapleysche Funktion *f*	fonction *f* de Shapley	функция Шепли
S 745	**Shapley['s] value** <TG>	Shapleyscher Wertvektor *m*	vecteur *m* de Shapley	вектор Шепли
	sharpening <GN>	*s.* S 1850		
S 746	**sheaf** <*e.g.:* of finite type> <*of* groups, ideals, *K*-modules, modules, rings, or sets> <AL, AT>	Garbe *f* <*z. B.:* endlichen Typs>	faisceau *m* <*par exemple:* de type fini>	пучок <*например:* конечного типа>
S 747	**sheaf** <of complexes> <HA>	Garbe *f* <von Komplexen>	faisceau *m* différentiel, faisceau <de complexes>	дифференциальный пучок, пучок <комплексов>
	sheaf <AY>	*s.* B 796		
S 748	**sheaf concentrated on . . .** <AL, TO>	auf . . . konzentrierte Garbe *f*	faisceau *m* concentré sur . . ., faisceau nul en dehors de . . .	пучок, сосредоточенный на . . .; пучок, равен нулю вне . . .
S 749	**sheaf homomorphism** <AT>	Garbenhomomorphismus *m*	homomorphisme *m* de faisceaux	гомоморфизм пучков
S 750	**sheaf locally concentrated on *A*** <AL, TO>	lokal auf *A* konzentrierte Garbe *f*	faisceau *m* localement concentré sur *A*	локально сконцентрированный на *A* пучок
S 751	**sheaf of abelian groups** <AL>	Garbe *f* abelscher Gruppen, Garbe von abelschen Gruppen	faisceau *m* de groupes abéliens, faisceau abélien	пучок абелевых групп, абелев пучок
S 752	**sheaf of Alexander-Spanier cochains** <AT>	Garbe *f* der Keime von Alexander-Spanierschen Koketten	faisceau *m* [des germes de cochaînes] d'Alexander-Spanier	пучок [ростков коцепей] Александера-Спеньера
	sheaf of circles <AY>	*s.* B 798		
	sheaf of complexes <PJ>	*s.* B 800		
	sheaf of curves <AY>	*s.* B 801		
S 753	**sheaf of germs of divisors** <with values in *G*>, **sheaf of germs of *G*-divisors** <FT>	Garbe *f* der Keime von Divisoren <mit Werten in *G*>	faisceau *m* des germes de diviseurs <à valeurs dans *G*>, faisceau des germes de *G*-diviseurs	пучок *G*-дивизоров, пучок ростков дивизоров <со значениями в *G*>
S 754	**sheaf of germs of local complex-valued continuous functions** <AT>	Garbe *f* der Keime von lokalen stetigen komplexwertigen Funktionen	faisceau *m* des germes de fonctions continues à valeurs complexes	пучок ростков комплекснозначных непрерывных функций
	sheaf of lines <AY, DS>	*s.* B 802		
S 755	**sheaf of meromorphic functions** <FT>	Garbe *f* der Keime meromorpher Funktionen	faisceau *m* des germes de fonctions méromorphes	пучок [ростков] мероморфных функций
	sheaf of parallel lines <EG>	*s.* B 803		
	sheaf of planes <AY>	*s.* B 805		
	sheaf of rays <AY, DS>	*s.* B 802		
S 756	**sheaf of relations** <AL, TO>	Relationengarbe *f*	faisceau *m* des relations <entre>	пучок соотношений
	sheaf of spheres <AY>	*s.* B 807		
S 757	**sheaf-theoretic** <AT>	garbentheoretisch, faisceau-theoretisch	faisceautique	теоретико-пучковый
	sheaf theory <AL, AT>	*s.* T 400		
S 758	**shear,** equivalent-perspective affinity <DS>	Scherung *f*, Schiebung *f*	cisaillement *m*	сдвиг, срез
	shear [transformation] <AL>	*s.* T 862		
S 759	**sheet,** layer <of a Riemann surface> <FT>	Blatt *n*	feuillet *m*	лист
S 760	**sheet,** nappe <of a surface> <GE>	Schale *f*, Flächenschale *f*, Mantel *m*	nappe *f*, couche *f*	полость
S 761	**Sheffer['s] algebra** <AL, LO>	Sheffersche Algebra *f*	algèbre *f* de Sheffer, algèbre shefferienne	алгебра Шеффера
S 762	**Sheffer['s] stroke,** symbol of alternative negation, | <*to be read:* not both . . . and> <LO>	Shefferscher Strich *m*, Exklusionszeichen *n*, | <*lies:* nicht zugleich>	signe *m* d'incompatibilité, barre *f* de Sheffer, | <*se lit:* incompatible à . . .>	штрих Шеффера, | <*читается:* несовместный>
S 763	**Sheffer['s] stroke, Sheffer['s] stroke[-] function, Sheffer['s]**	Sheffersche Strichverknüpfung (Wahrheitsfunktion, Strichfunktion,	fonction *f* de Sheffer, incompatibilité *f*, fonction ET-NON	операция (штрих, функция) Шеффера, антиконъюнкция, отрица-

No.	English	German	French	Russian
and still: S 763	**stroke[-]operation,** stroke[-]function, stroke[-]operation, alternative denial, incompatibility, non-conjunction, alternate denial, | <AL, LO>	Funktion) *f*, Shefferscher Strich *m*, non-conjunctio *f*, Unverträglichkeit *f*, Antikonjunktion *f*, unv, |	(ET-INVERSE), opération *f* de Sheffer, fonction |, rejet *m* binaire, incompatibilité (barre *f*) de Sheffer, |	ние конъюнкции, несовместность, несовместимость, операция с чертой, |
S 764	**shell** <as a curved plate> <GE>	Schale *f*	enveloppe *f*	оболочка
S 765	**Sheppard['s] correction** <ST>	Sheppardsche Korrektur (Korrektion) *f*	correction *f* de Sheppard	поправка Шеппарда
	shift / to <GN>	*s.* T 846		
	shift <DE, MD, NU>	*s.* S 1417		
	shift <GN>	*s.* T 857		
	shifting theorem <IT>	*s.* T 479		
S 766	**shift of the graduation** <AL>	Verschiebung *f* der Graduierung	décalage *m* de la graduation	смещение градуировки
S 767	**Shilov['s] boundary,** Šilov['s] boundary, Bergman-Šilov boundary <PO>	Schilowscher (Šilovscher) Rand *m*	bord *m* de Shilov, frontière *f* de Šilov (Bergmann-Šilov)	граница в смысле Шилова
	shoe box principle <CT>	*s.* B 705		
S 768	**short cut method,** rapid method <ST>	Kurzverfahren *n*, Schnellmethode *f*	méthode *f* rapide	сокращенный (краткий, быстрый) метод
S 769	**short cut test,** short test, rapid test <ST>	Kurztest *m*	test *m* rapide	скоростное испытание, сокращенное испытание
	shorter axis <AY>	*s.* M 645		
S 770	**shortest,** shortest line <in a metric space> <GE>	Kürzeste *f*, kürzeste Linie *f*	ligne *f* la plus courte, la plus courte *f*	кратчайшая, кратчайшая линия
S 771	**shortest confidence interval,** most selective confidence interval <ST>	kürzestes (engstes) Konfidenzintervall *n*	intervalle *m* de confiance d'étendue minimale, intervalle de confiance le plus sélectif	наименьший доверительный интервал
S 772	**shortest distance** <GE>	kürzester Abstand *m*	distance *f* la plus courte	кратчайшее расстояние
	shortest line <GE>	*s.* S 770		
S 773	**shortest path (route)** <through a network> <GP, PG>	kürzester Weg (Pfad) *m*	chemin *m* le plus court, route *f* la plus courte	кратчайший маршрут, кратчайший путь
S 774	**shortest-route problem** <PG>	Problem *n* des kürzesten Weges	problème *m* du chemin le plus court	задача выбора кратчайшего маршрута
	shortest-route problem <CT, GP, PG>	*s.* T 882		
S 775	**short five lemma** <AL, CA>	kurzes Fünferlemma *n*	lemme *m* des cinq court	короткая лемма о пяти морфизмах
S 776	**short left exact sequence** <AL, CA>	kurze linksexakte Folge *f*	suite *f* courte exacte à gauche	короткая точная слева последовательность
	short multiplication <AR, NU>	*s.* A 47		
	short radius <EG>	*s.* A 809		
S 777	**short right exact sequence** <AL, CA>	kurze rechtsexakte Folge *f*	suite *f* courte exacte à droite	короткая точная справа последовательность
S 778	**short root** <of a Lie group> <GR>	kurze Wurzel *f*	racine *f* « courte »	короткий корень
	short subtraction <AR, NU>	*s.* A 48		
	short test <ST>	*s.* S 769		
S 779	**shrinkable mapping** <TO>	schrumpfbare Abbildung *f*		стягиваемое отображение
	shrinkage <GP>	*s.* C 2272		
S 780	**shrinking** <of a covering $\{U_i\}$> <TO>	Schrumpfung *f* <einer Überdeckung $\{U_i\}$>	recouvrement *m* ouvert $\{V_i\}$-tel que $V_i \subset U_i$	усечение <покрытия $\{U_i\}$>
	shrinking <GE>	*s.* C 1750		
S 781	**shrinking map** <TO>	schrumpfende Abbildung *f*		отображение стягивания
S 782	**shrinking theorem** <TO>	Schrumpfungssatz *m*		теорема сужения
	shuffling <GN, SS>	*s.* R 235		
	S_i <EG>	*s.* S 1253		
	si; Si <FU>	*s.* S 1026		
S 783	**si-ci spiral** <GE>	si-ci-Spirale *f*	spirale *f* de sinus intégral et cosinus intégral	si-ci-спираль, спираль интегрального синуса и интегрального косинуса
S 784	**side,** arm, leg <of an angle> <EG>	Schenkel *m*	côté *m*	сторона
S 785	**side** <of a polygon> <EG>	Seite *f*	côté *m*	сторона
S 786	**side** <of a triangle>; face angle <of a spherical triangle> <EG>	Seite *f*; Schenkel *m* <gleiche Seite im gleichschenkligen Dreieck>	côté *m*	сторона
	side <EG>	*s.* 1. F 7; 2. L 526; 3. O 540		
	side <GN>	*s.* M 380		
S 787	**side condition** <DE>	Nebenbedingung *f*	condition *f* latérale (supplémentaire)	дополнительное условие
S 788	**side condition,** condition, constraint <DI, VA>	Nebenbedingung *f*, Bedingung *f*	condition *f* subsidiaire, condition, contrainte *f*	дополнительное условие, условие
	side condition <PG>	*s.* C 2123		
	2-sided inverse <AL>	*s.* T 1118		
	2-sided inverse <MD>	*s.* T 1119		
S 789	**side elevation,** side projection, third projection <not necessarily orthogonal to elevation> <DS>	Seitenriß *m*, dritte Projektion *f*	élévation *f* latérale (de côté), projection *f* latérale (de côté); coupe *f* latérale	боковая (третья) проекция; боковой разрез
S 790	**side formula** <LO>	Nebenformel *f*	formule *f* secondaire	боковая формула
S 791	**side payment** <TG>	Nebenauszahlung *f*		побочный платеж

S 792	**side plane [of projection]**, side projection plane, third plane [of projection] <not necessarily orthogonal to vertical plane> <DS>	Seitenrißebene *f*, dritte Projektionsebene (Tafel) *f*, Seitenrißtafel *f*	plan *m* latéral [de projection], troisième plan [de projection]	плоскость боковой проекции
	side projection <DS>	*s.* S 789		
	side projection plane <DS>	*s.* S 792		
	side trace [line] <DS>	*s.* T 430		
S 793	**Sidon['s] theorem**, Szidon['s] theorem <SS>	Satz *m* von Sidon (Szidon), Sidonscher (Szidonscher) Satz	théorème *m* de Sidon (Szidon)	теорема Сидона
S 794	**Siebeck['s] curve** <GE>	Siebecksche Kurve *f*	courbe *f* de Siebeck	кривая Зибека
S 795	**Siegel['s] domain** <AL, FT>	Siegelsches Gebiet *n*	domaine (ouvert) *m* de Siegel	область Зигеля
S 796	**Siegel['s] modular form** <FT, NT>	Siegelsche Modulform *f*	forme *f* modulaire de Siegel	зигелева модулярная форма, модулярная форма Зигеля
S 797	**Siegel['s] modular function** <FT, NT>	Siegelsche Modulfunktion *f*	fonction *f* modulaire de Siegel	зигелева модулярная функция, модулярная функция Зигеля
S 798	**Siegel['s] upper half-space** <FT>	Siegelscher oberer Halbraum *m*	espace (demi-plan) *m* de Siegel	верхнее полупространство Зигеля
S 799	**Sierpiński['s] carpet** <TO>	Sierpińskischer Teppich *m*, zweites Kontinuum *n* von Sierpiński	courbe *f* universelle de Sierpiński, tapis *m* de Sierpiński	ковер (универсальная кривая) Серпиньского
S 800	**Sierpiński finite set** <SE>	S-endliche (im Sierpińskischen Sinne endliche) Menge *f*	ensemble *m* fini au sens de Sierpiński	конечное множество в смысле Серпиньского
S 801	**Sierpiński['s] set** <ME>	Sierpińskische Punktmenge (Menge) *f*	ensemble *m* de Sierpiński	множество Серпиньского
	Sierpiński space <TO>	*s.* C 2032		
S 802	**Sierpiński['s] triangular curve** <TO>	erstes Kontinuum *n* von Sierpiński, Sierpińskische Kurve *f*	courbe *f* triangulaire de Sierpiński	треугольная кривая Серпиньского
S 803	**sieve** <SE>	Lusinsche Sieboperation *f*	crible *m*	решето
S 804	**sieve method**, sieving process <NT>	Siebmethode *f*, Siebverfahren *n*	méthode *f* du crible	метод решета
S 805	**sieve of Eratosthenes**, crib of Eratosthenes <NT>	Sieb *n* des Eratosthenes, cribrum *n* Eratosthenis	crible *m* d'Eratosthène, procédé *m* dit d'Eratosthène, Crible d'Eratosthenês	решето Эратосфена
S 806	**sieve of Viggo Brun** <NT>	Sieb *n* von V. Brun	crible *m* de V. Brun	решето Бруна
	sieving process <NT>	*s.* S 804		
S 807	**sifted set** <by a sieve> <SE>	gesiebte Menge *f* <durch ein Lusinsches Sieb>, Kern *m* <eines Lusinschen Siebs>	noyau *m* du crible, ensemble *m* criblé <par le crible>	просеянное множество <через решето>
S 808	**sifting** <TO>	Siebung *f*	criblage *m*	просеивание
S 809	**sifting-out** <for selection of special terms> <IV>	Siebung *f* <Sylvester>	tamisage *m*	просеивание
	sigma-additive function <AN>	*s.* C 2566		
	sigma-additive measure <ME>	*s.* A 82		
	sigma-additive set function <AN>	*s.* C 2566		
	sigma-additivity <AN, SE>	*s.* C 2556		
	sigma[-] algebra <AL>	*s.* S 815		
S 810	**sigma-algebra [of sets]**, σ-algebra, σ-algebra of sets, σ-field (sigma-field) [of sets], Borel field, countably additive algebra [of sets], field of Borel sets <generated by a system of sets> <ME, SE, TO>	σ-vollständige Mengenalgebra *f*, σ-Algebra *f*, Sigma-Algebra *f*, σ-Körper *m*, Sigma-Körper *m*, Borelscher Mengenkörper (Körper) *m*, σ-Mengenalgebra *f*, Sigma-Mengenalgebra *f*, Borelscher σ-Ring (Sigma-Ring) *m*, Borelsigmaalgebra *f* <von (über) einem Mengensystem erzeugt>	corps *m* σ-complet (sigma-complet), sigma-corps *m*, σ-corps *m*, tribu *m*, tribu borélien [d'ensembles], σ-algèbre *f* [d'ensembles], clan *m* <engendré[e] par un système d'ensembles>	σ-алгебра (сигма-алгебра) [множеств], вполне аддитивная алгебра [множеств], σ-тело (сигма-тело) [множеств], борелево поле (тело) множеств <порожденная (порожденное) системой множеств>
S 811	**sigma-bounded measurable set**, σ-bounded measurable set <ME>	σ-beschränkte (sigma-beschränkte) meßbare Menge *f*	ensemble *m* mesurable σ-borné (sigma-borné)	σ-ограниченное (сигма-ограниченное) измеримое множество
S 812	**sigma-compactness**, σ-compactness, semicompactness <TO>	σ-Kompaktheit *f*, Sigma-Kompaktheit *f*, Halbkompaktheit *f*, Semikompaktheit *f*	σ-compacité *f*, sigma-compacité *f*, semi-compacité *f*	полукомпактность
S 813	**sigma-compact set**, σ-compact set, semicompact set <TO>	σ-kompakte (sigma-kompakte, halbkompakte, semikompakte) Menge *f*	ensemble *m* σ-compact (sigma-compact, semi-compact)	полукомпактное (σ-компактное, сигма-компактное) множество
	sigma-compact space <TO>	*s.* S 814		
S 814	**sigma-compact topological space**, σ-compact topological space, σ-compact (sigma-compact) space, hemicompact space, semi-	halbkompakter (halbkompakter topologischer) Raum *m*, im Unendlichen abzählbarer [topologischer] Raum, σ-kompakter (sigma-	espace *m* semi-compact (σ-compact, sigma-compact, dénombrable à l'infini)	полукомпактное [топологическое] пространство, счетное в бесконечности пространство; пространство, являющееся объеди-

and still: S 814	compact [topological] space, space which is the union of a countable number of compact subsets, hemicompact topological space <TO>	kompakter) [topologischer] Raum		нением счетного числа компактных подпространств
S 815	**sigma-complete Boolean algebra,** σ-complete Boolean algebra, σ-algebra, sigma algebra, sigma-algebra, countably additive algebra <AL>	σ-vollständige (sigma-vollständige) Boolesche Algebra *f*, σ-Algebra *f*, Sigma-Algebra *f*, Sigmaalgebra *f*	algèbre *f* de Boole σ-complète (sigma-complète), σ-algèbre, sigma-algèbre, $\aleph_0$-algèbre *f*	σ-полная (сигма-полная) [булева] алгебра, σ-алгебра, сигма-алгебра, вполне аддитивная алгебра
S 816	**sigma-complete filter,** σ-complete filter, countably complete filter <AL, SE>	σ-vollständiger (sigma-vollständiger, abzählbar vollständiger) Filter *m*	filtre *m* σ-complet (sigma-complet), σ-filtre *m*, sigma-filtre *m*	счетно полный фильтр, σ-полный (сигма-полный) фильтр
	sigma-complete ideal <AL, SE>	*s.* S 826		
S 817	**sigma-complete lower semilattice,** σ-complete lower semilattice <AL>	σ-vollständiger (sigma-vollständiger) Durchschnittshalbverband *m*	inf-demi-treillis *m* σ-complet (sigma-complet)	σ-полная (сигма-полная) [нижняя] полуструктура
S 818	**sigma[-] completeness,** σ-completeness <AL, SE>	σ-Vollständigkeit *f*, Sigma-Vollständigkeit *f*	σ-complétude *f*, sigma-complétude *f*	σ-полнота, сигма-полнота
S 819	**sigma-complete semilattice,** σ-complete semi-lattice <AL>	σ-vollständiger (sigma-vollständiger) Halbverband *m*	demi-treillis *m* σ-complet (sigma-complet)	σ-полная (сигма-полная) полуструктура
S 820	**sigma-complete upper semilattice,** σ-complete upper semilattice <AL>	σ-vollständiger (sigma-vollständiger) Vereinigungshalbverband *m*	sup-demi-treillis *m* σ-complet (sigma-complet)	σ-полная (сигма-полная) верхняя полурешетка
S 821	**sigma-discrete family of subsets,** σ-discrete family of subsets <TO>	σ-diskretes (sigma-diskretes) System *n* von Teilmengen, σ-diskretes (sigma-diskretes) Mengensystem *n*	famille *f* σ-discrète (sigma-discrète) de parties	σ-дискретное (сигма-дискретное) семейство подмножеств
S 822	**sigma-extension,** σ-extension <of a Boolean algebra> <SE>	σ-Erweiterung *f*, Sigma-Erweiterung *f*	σ-extension *f*, sigma-extension *f*	σ-расширение, сигма-расширение
	sigma-field <ME, SE, TO>	*s.* S 810		
	sigma-field of Borel sets <TO>	*s.* B 582		
S 823	**sigma[-]field of sets,** σ-field of sets, σ-ring (sigma[-]ring) of sets <as a field of sets being a sigma system> <SE>	σ-Körper *m*, Sigma-Körper *m*, σ-Mengenkörper *m*, Sigma-Mengenkörper *m*, σ-Ring *m*, Sigma-Ring *m*, σ-Mengenring *m*, Sigma-Mengenring *m*	σ-corps *m* [de parties], sigma-corps *m* [de parties]	σ-поле [множеств], сигма-поле [множеств]
	sigma-field of sets <ME, SE, TO>	*s.* S 810		
S 824	**sigma-finite measure,** σ-finite measure, weakly finite measure <ME>	σ-endliches (sigma-endliches, σ-finites, sigma-finites, schwach endliches) Maß *n*	mesure *f* σ-finie (sigma-finie, faiblement finie)	σ-конечная (сигма-конечная, слабо конечная) мера
S 825	**sigma-free group,** Σ-free group <GR>	Σ-freie (sigma-freie) Gruppe *f*	groupe *m* Σ-libre (sigma-libre)	Σ-свободная (сигма-свободная) группа
	sigma[-] function [of Weierstrass] <FT>	*s.* W 165		
S 826	**sigma[-] ideal,** σ-ideal, σ-complete (sigma-complete) ideal <AL, SE>	σ-Ideal *n*, Sigma-Ideal *n*, σ-vollständiges (sigma-vollständiges) Ideal *n*	σ-idéal *m*, sigma-idéal *m*, idéal *m* σ-complet (sigma-complet)	σ-идеал, сигма-идеал, σ-полный (сигма-полный) идеал
S 827	**sigma[-] lattice,** σ-lattice <LA>	σ-Verband *m*, Sigma-Verband *m*, σ-vollständiger (sigma-vollständiger Verband *m*	σ-treillis *m*, sigma-treillis *m*	σ-структура, сигма-структура
S 828	**sigma-locally finite family of subsets,** σ-locally finite family of subsets <TO>	σ-lokal-endliches (sigma-lokal-endliches) Mengensystem *n* (System *n* von Teilmengen)	famille *f* σ-localement (sigma-localement) finie de parties	σ-локально (сигма-локально) конечное семейство множеств
S 829	**sigma-monogenic function,** σ-monogenic function <FT>	sigma[-]monogene (σ-monogene) Funktion *f*	fonction *f* sigma-monogène (σ-monogène)	сигма-моногенная (σ-моногенная) функция
	sigma-process <AG>	*s.* B 510		
S 830	**sigma-regular subalgebra,** σ-regular subalgebra <of a Boolean algebra> <AL>	σ-reguläre (sigma-reguläre) Unteralgebra *f*	sous-algèbre *f* σ-régulière (sigma-régulière)	σ-правильная (сигма-правильная) подалгебра
S 831	**sigma[-]ring [of sets],** σ-ring of sets, σ-ring <ME, SE>	σ-Mengenring *m*, Sigma-Mengenring *m*, σ-Ring *m*, Sigma-Ring *m*, Sigmaring *m* <von Mengen>	σ-anneau *m* [d'ensembles], sigma-anneau *m* [d'ensembles]	σ-кольцо [множеств], сигма-кольцо [множеств]
	sigma[-] ring of sets <SE>	*s.* S 823		
S 832	**sigma-space,** σ-space <TO>	σ-Raum *m*, Sigma-Raum *m*	espace *m* σ (sigma)	σ-пространство, сигма-пространство
	sigma-subadditivity <RF>	*s.* C 2562		
S 833	**sigma[-]system,** σ-system <of sets> <SE>	σ-System *n*, Sigma-System *n*	σ-système *m*, sigma-système *m*	σ-система, сигма-система
	sigma-topology <FA>	*s.* W 128		
S 834	**sigma[-]torsion,** σ-torsion <AL>	σ-Torsion *f*, Sigma-Torsion *f*	σ-torsion *f*, sigma-torsion *f*	σ-скручивание, сигма-скручивание

No.	English	German	French	Russian
S 835	**sigmoid [curve],** sigmoid-shaped curve, S-shaped curve, S-curve <GN>	S-Kurve *f*, S-förmige Kurve *f*, Sigmoidkurve *f*	courbe *f* sigmoïde (en S)	сигмоидная (S-образная) кривая
	sigmoid distribution <ST>	*s.* S 1571		
	sigmoid-shaped curve <GN>	*s.* S 835		
S 836	**sign,** signum, signature, parity <of a permutation> <AL>	Signatur *f*	signature *f*, parité *f*	знак
S 837	**sign,** algebraic sign <AL, AR>	Vorzeichen *n*	signe *m*	знак
	sign <GN, LO>	*s.* S 2412		
S 838	**signature** <of an algebraic number, a quadratic form, *or* a metric> <AB, AL, GE>	Signatur *f*	signature *f*	сигнатура
	signature <AL>	*s.* S 836		
S 839	**signed distance,** algebraic distance, directed distance <GE>	vorzeichenbegabter Abstand *m*, Abstand mit Vorzeichen, mit Vorzeichen versehener Abstand	distance *f* algébrique (avec signe, affectée d'un signe)	расстояние, имеющее знак; снабженное знаком расстояние
	signed graph <GP>	*s.* L 1		
	signed minor <MD>	*s.* C 1045		
	signed number <AR>	*s.* R 763		
	signed rank test <ST>	*s.* W 256		
S 840	**signed tree** <GP>	signierter Baum *m*	arbre *m* signé	знаковое дерево
	signed value <GN>	*s.* V 38		
	sign function <AN>	*s.* S 861		
S 841	**significance,** statistical significance <ST>	Signifikanz *f*, statistische Signifikanz, statistische Sicherung *f*, Sicherung	signification *f*, signification statistique	значимость, статистическая значимость
S 842	**significance level,** level of significance, significance (error) probability, probability for exceeding, size of the [critical] region, level [of error], error rate <ST>	Signifikanzniveau *n*, Irrtumswahrscheinlichkeit *f*, Signifikanzwahrscheinlichkeit *f*, Signifikanzstufe *f*, Signifikanzgrenze *f*, Signifikanzschwelle *f*, Fehlerwahrscheinlichkeit *f*, Überschreitungswahrscheinlichkeit *f*, Größe *f* des kritischen Bereichs, Größe des Tests, Fehlerrate *f*, Grenzwahrscheinlichkeit *f*, Bedeutsamkeitsstufe *f*, Niveau *n*, Grad *m*, Sicherheitswahrscheinlichkeit *f*, kritische Wahrscheinlichkeit *f*	niveau *m* (seuil *m*, limite *f*) de signification, seuil de probabilité, probabilité *f* d'erreur, seuil de méfiance, risque *m*	уровень значимости, вероятность при испытании значимости, вероятность ошибки (превышения)
	significance point <ST>	*s.* R 661		
	significance probability <ST>	*s.* S 842		
S 843	**significance test,** test of significance <ST>	Signifikanztest *m*	test *m* (critère *m*, épreuve *f*) de signification [statistique], épreuve d'hypothèse	критерий значимости
S 844	**significant,** statistically significant <ST>	signifikant, statistisch signifikant, statistisch gesichert, gesichert	significatif, statistiquement significatif	значимый, статистический значимый
S 845	**significant difference** <ST>	signifikanter Unterschied *m*	différence *f* significative	значимое различие
S 846	**significant digit (figure),** meaningful significant figure, valid digit <of a number> <NU>	bedeutsame Ziffer (Stelle) *f*	chiffre *m* significatif (significant)	значащая цифра, значащий разряд
	significant proposition <LO>	*s.* M 308		
S 847	**signless number,** unsigned number <AR>	Zahl *f* ohne Vorzeichen, vorzeichenlose Zahl	nombre *m* sans signe, nombre arithmétique	число, не имеющее знака; арифметическое число
	sign of addition <GN>	*s.* A 239		
S 848	**sign of aggregation** <GN, LO>	Klammer *f*, Klammerzeichen *n*	parenthèse *f*	скобка
	sign of aggregation <FO>	*s.* P 2030		
S 849	**sign of definition** <LO>	Definitionszeichen *n*, Definitor *m*	signe *m* de définition	знак определения
S 850	**sign of equality,** equals sign, symbol for equality, equality symbol, equal sign, = <GN>	Gleichheitszeichen *n*, =	signe *m* d'égalité, signe de l'égalité, signe égal, =	знак равенства, символ равенства, =
S 851	**sign of falsity** <LO>	Falsch-Zeichen *n*	signe *m* du faux	тождественно-ложная постоянная, знак ложности
S 852	**sign of implication,** implication sign, symbol of implication, implication symbol, conditional, conditional ⊃ -symbol, ⇒, →, ⊃ <*to be read:* . . .	Implikationszeichen *n*, Zeichen *n* der Implikation, Folgt-Zeichen *n*, Subjugat *n*, ⇒ <*lies:* impliziert, subjungiert, bedingt>	signe *m* d'implication, flèche *f*, ⇒ <*se lit:* implique, entraîne, de . . . découle . . ., si . . . on a . . ., de . . . on conclut à . . ., de . . . on infère . . .,	знак импликации, символ импликации, знак следования, знак логического следования, ⇒ <*читается:* влечет, имплицирует, если . . .

No.	English	German	French	Russian
and still: S 852	implies ..., materially implies ..., if ... then ...> <LO>		on a *B* par suite de *A*, *B* puisque *A*, *B* résulte de *A*>	то ..., из ... следует ...>
S 853	**sign of inclusion,** $\subseteq$ <SE>	Enthaltenszeichen *n*, Enthalten-Zeichen *n*, $\subseteq$	signe *m* d'inclusion, symbole *m* de l'inclusion <au sens large>, $\subseteq$	знак включения, $\subseteq$
S 854	**sign of intersection,** $\cap$ <*to be read:* intersection> <SE>	Zeichen *n* der Durchschnittsbildung, $\cap$ <*lies:* geschnitten>	signe *m* d'intersection, $\cap$ <*se lit:* inter, intersection>	знак пересечения, $\cap$ <*читается:* пересечение, крытка, шапка>
S 855	**sign of multiplication,** ., $\cdot$, $\times$ <*to be read:* times, multiplied by, by cross dot half high> <AR>	Multiplikationszeichen *n*, Malzeichen *n*, $\cdot$, $\times$, . <*lies:* mal>	signe *m* de multiplication, $\cdot$, $\times$, . <*à lire:* multiplié par, point à mi-hauteur, croix>	знак умножения, $\cdot$, $\times$, . <*читается:* умноженное на>
	sign of subtraction <AR>	*s.* S 2216		
S 856	**sign of the membership relation,** membership relation symbol, membership sign, set-membership symbol, symbol for set-membership, epsilon, $\in$ <SE>	Zeichen *n* der (für die) Elementbeziehung, $\in$	signe *m* d'appartenance, symbole *m* d'appartenance, $\in$	знак принадлежности, знак отношения принадлежности, знак присущности элемента множеству, знак принадлежности элемента множеству, $\in$
S 857	**sign of union,** $\cup$ <SE>	Zeichen *n* der Vereinigungs[mengen]bildung, $\cup$	signe *m* de la réunion, signe de réunion, $\cup$	знак объединения множеств, $\cup$ <*читается:* чашка>
S 858	**sign** $\leqq$ **or** $\geqq$ <GN>	„kleiner-gleich"-Zeichen *n oder* „größer-gleich"-Zeichen *n*	signe *m* de comparaison	знак $\leqq$ *или* $\geqq$
	sign reversal <GN>	*s.* C 498		
S 859	**sign test,** statistical sign test <ST>	Zeichentest *m*, Vorzeichentest *m*	test *m* de signes	критерий знаков
S 860	**signum,** sgn, sg <of a real *or* complex number> <NT>	Signum *n*, sign, sgn	signe *m*, sgn	функция sgn, sgn, sign
	signum <AL>	*s.* S 836		
	signum <AN>	*s.* S 861		
S 861	**signum function,** sign function, signum, sgn, sg <AN>	Signumfunktion *f*, Vorzeichenfunktion *f*, Signum *n*, sign, sgn	fonction *f* signum (signe), signe *m*, sgn	знаковая функция, сигнум-функция, функция sgn, sgn, sign
	SI*-group <GR>	*s.* H 613		
	Sih <FU>	*s.* H 649		
S 862	**silent duel** <TG>	lautloses Duell *n*		бесшумная дуэль
S 863	**silent-noisy duel** <TG>	gemischtes Duell *n*	duel *m* mixte	смешанная дуэль
	Šilov['s] boundary <PO>	*s.* S 767		
S 864	**similar algebra,** similar simple algebra <AL>	ähnliche einfache Algebra *f*, ähnliche Algebra	algèbre *f* simple semblable	подобная простая алгебра
S 865	**similar covering** <TO>	ähnliche Überdeckung *f*	recouvrement *m* semblable aux sens combinatoire	подобное покрытие
S 866	**similar endomorphism** <AL>	ähnlicher Endomorphismus *m*	endomorphisme *m* semblable	подобный эндоморфизм
S 867	**similar form,** similar quadratic form <AL>	ähnliche Form *f*, ähnliche quadratische Form	forme *f* semblable	подобная квадратичная форма
S 868	**similar fraction,** fraction with equal denominator <AL, NT>	gleichnamiger (ähnlicher) Bruch *m*, Bruch mit gleichem Nenner	fraction *f* semblable (de même dénominateur)	подобная дробь, дробь с равным знаменателем
S 869	**similar function** <FT>	ähnliche Funktion *f*	fonction *f* semblable	подобная функция
S 870	**similar indexed systems of sets** <SE>	ähnliche Mengensysteme *npl*	systèmes *mpl* [d'ensembles] semblables au sens combinatoire	подобные между собою системы занумерованных множеств; системы множеств, подобные в комбинаторном смысле
S 871	**similarity** <e.g. of figures, matrices, *or* ordered sets> <GE, MD, SE>	Ähnlichkeit *f*	similitude *f*	подобие
	similarity <SE>	*s.* 1. E 403; 2. O 356		
	similarity axis <GE>	*s.* A 1320		
	similarity centre <GE>	*s.* C 429		
	similarity circle <GE>	*s.* C 691		
S 872	**similarity class of algebras,** species of algebras <UA>	Klasse *f* gleichartiger universeller Algebren	classe *f* d'algèbres de même type	класс однотипных универсальных алгебр
S 873	**similarity invariant** <of a matrix> <AL>	Ähnlichkeitsinvariante *f*	invariant *m* de similitude	инвариант подобия
	similarity mapping <SE>	*s.* O 356		
	similarity plane <GE>	*s.* P 652		
S 874	**similarity principle,** principle of similarity <FT>	Ähnlichkeitsprinzip *n*, Similaritätsprinzip *n*	principe *m* de similitude	принцип подобия
	similarity principle <IT>	*s.* L 204		
S 875	**similarity ray,** ray of similarity <DS>	Ähnlichkeitsstrahl *m*	rayon *m* de similitude	луч подобия
	similarity sphere <GE>	*s.* S 1435		
	similarity transformation <AY>	*s.* S 884		
	similarity transformation <DS>	*s.* T 781		
	similarity transformation <SE>	*s.* O 356		
	similarity type <UA>	*s.* T 1141		
	similarly ordered set <SE>	*s.* S 878		
S 876	**similarly oriented (sensed),** having the same sense, concordantly oriented <GE, TO>	gleichorientiert, gleichsinnig orientiert; gleichlaufend	de la même orientation, ayant la même orientation	одинаково ориентированный

No.	English	German	French	Russian
	similar mapping <SE>	*s.* O 356		
S 877	**similar matrix** <MD>	ähnliche Matrix *f*	matrice *f* semblable	подобная матрица
	similar matrix representation <AL>	*s.* E 440		
	similar one-to-one correspondence <SE>	*s.* O 356		
S 878	**similar ordered set,** similar simply ordered set, ordinally similar set, similarly ordered set, similar set <SE>	ähnliche (ähnlich) geordnete Menge *f*, Menge von gleichem Ordnungstypus, ähnlich-geordnete Menge, ähnliche Menge	ensemble *m* ordonné semblable, ensemble semblable	подобное упорядоченное множество, подобное множество
	similar partially ordered set <SE>	*s.* I 1122		
	similar permutation <CT>	*s.* C 1996		
S 879	**similar position** <GE>	ähnliche Lage *f*, Ähnlichkeitslage *f*	position *f* semblable	подобное [рас]положение
	similar quadratic form <AL>	*s.* S 867		
S 880	**similar region** <ST>	ähnlicher Bereich *m*	région *f* similaire, région semblable	подобная область
	similar relation <SE>	*s.* I 1123		
	similar relational algebra <UA>	*s.* S 881		
	similar representation <RE>	*s.* E 449		
	similar set <SE>	*s.* 1. E 404; 2. S 878		
	similar simple algebra <AL>	*s.* S 864		
	similar simply ordered set <SE>	*s.* S 878		
S 881	**similar structure,** similar relational algebra, relational algebra of the same type <UA>	gleichartiges Relationalsystem *n*	structure *f* relationnelle de même type	однотипная алгебра отношений
	similar structure <UA>	*s. a.* U 312		
	similar term <AL, AR GN>	*s.* L 695		
S 882	**similar test** <ST>	ähnlicher Test *m*	test *m* similaire, test semblable	подобный критерий
S 883	**similar triangle** <EG>	ähnliches Dreieck *n*	triangle *m* semblable	подобный треугольник
	similitude <AY>	*s.* S 884		
	similitude <DS>	*s.* T 781		
S 884	**similitude [transformation],** transformation of similitude (similarity), general similarity transformation, similarity transformation <AY>	[allgemeine] Ähnlichkeitstransformation *f*, äquiforme Transformation *f*, Ähnlichkeitsabbildung *f*, Ähnlichkeit *f*, Bewegung *f* der äquiformen Geometrie	transformation *f* par similitude, similitude *f*	преобразование подобия, подобное преобразование, подобие
S 885	**similitude with respect to a quadratic form** <AL>	Ähnlichkeitsabbildung *f* bezüglich einer quadratischen Form	similitude *f* pour une forme quadratique	подобие относительно квадратичной формы
S 886	**simple abelian variety** <AG>	einfache abelsche Mannigfaltigkeit *f*	variété *f* abélienne simple	простое абелево многообразие
S 887	**simple algebraic [field] extension** <of a field> <AL>	einfache algebraische Körpererweiterung (Erweiterung) *f*	extension *f* algébrique simple <d'un corps>	простое алгебраическое расширение <поля>
	simple arc <TO>	*s.* J 86		
S 888	**simple branch point** <of an algebraic correspondence> <AG>	einfacher Verzweigungspunkt *m*	point *m* de ramification simple	простая точка ветвления
S 889	**simple broken line** <GE>	einfacher Polygonzug *m*, einfaches Polygon *n*	ligne *f* brisée simple	простая ломаная
	simple bundle <AT>	*s.* T 993		
S 890	**simple chain** <in an oriented graph; orientation of the arcs is inessential> <GP>	Kette *f*, Kantenzug *m*	chaîne *f* simple	полумаршрут, в котором все дуги различны
S 891	**simple chain** <as a set of edges> <GP>	einfache Kette *f*	ensemble *m* des arêtes d'une chaîne élémentaire	неупорядоченная простая цепь
	simple chain <GP>	*s.* D 548		
	simple chain progression <GP>	*s.* P 300		
S 892	**simple character** <RE>	einfacher Charakter *m*	caractère *m* primitif	простой характер, неприводимый характер
S 892a	**simple circuit,** circuit, elementary cycle <GP>	Kreis *m*, geschlossene Bahn *f*, einfacher Zirkuit *m*, geschlossener Kreis *m*, einfacher geschlossener Kantenzug *m*	circuit *m* simple	простой цикл
	simple circuit <GP>	*s. a.* E 98		
	simple classical matrix <AL>	*s.* J 94		
S 893	**simple classification,** one-way classification <ST>	einfache Klassifikation *f*, Einwegklassifikation *f*	classification *f* simple (à une entrée, à un caractère)	классификация по одному признаку
S 894	**simple closed curve,** closed Jordan curve, closed simple curve, Jordan['s] curve, [topological] one-sphere <TO>	geschlossene Jordan-Kurve *f*, doppelpunktfreie (einfache) geschlossene Kurve *f*	courbe *f* simple fermée, contour *m* simple fermé, contour simple, arc *m* plan fermé sans point double	простой замкнутый контур, простая замкнутая линия (кривая), замкнутая жорданова кривая
	simple combination <CT>	*s.* C 1183		
S 895	**simple complex** <HA>	einfacher Komplex *m*	complexe *m* simple	простой комплекс

S 896	**simple component** <of an algebra *or* of a semisimple ring> <AL>	einfache Komponente *f*	composante *f* simple <d'une algèbre>; composant *m* simple <d'un anneau semi-simple>	простая компонента
S 897	**simple compression,** one-dimensional compression <in affinity> <GE>	Stauchung *f* in einer Richtung	compression *f* unidimensionnelle	одномерное сжатие
S 898	**simple connectedness (connectivity)** <TO>	einfacher Zusammenhang *m*	connexité *f* simple, simple connexité *f*	простая связность
S 899	**simple constructive dilemma** <LO>	einfaches konstruktives Dilemma *n*	dilemme *m* constructif simple	простая конструктивная дилемма
	simple continued fraction <NT>	*s.* R 529		
S 900	**simple continued fraction expansion** <AN>	Entwicklung *f* in einen regelmäßigen Kettenbruch	développement *m* en fraction continue ordinaire	разложение в простейшую цепную дробь
	simple continuous arc <TO>	*s.* J 86		
	simple convergence <SS>	*s.* P 804		
	simple convergence topology <FA, TO>	*s.* T 567		
S 901	**simple correlation coefficient,** total correlation coefficient <ST>	einfacher (totaler) Korrelationskoeffizient *m*	coefficient *m* de corrélation simple (total)	простой (полный) коэффициент корреляции
	simple cusp <GE>	*s.* C 2814		
S 902	**simple cycle** <set of arcs in a digraph> <GP>	einfacher Zyklus *m*	ensemble *m* des arcs d'un circuit élémentaire	простой неупорядоченный контур
	simple cycle <GP>	*s.* D 540		
S 903	**simple domain,** schlicht domain <FT, TO>	schlichtes Gebiet *n*	domaine *m* à un feuillet, domaine schlicht (univalent)	однолистная область
S 904	**simple edge** <GP>	einfache Kante *f*	arête *f* simple	простое ребро
S 905	**simple eigenvalue** <DE>	einfacher Eigenwert *m*	valeur *f* singulière (caractéristique, critique, propre) simple	однократное собственное значение
	simple eigenvalue <MD>	*s.* S 940		
	simple elementary divisor <AL>	*s.* E 101		
S 906	**simple elongation,** one-dimensional elongation (strain) <in affinity> <GE>	Streckung *f* in einer Richtung	élongation *f* unidimensionnelle	одномерное растяжение
S 907	**simple endomorphism** <AL>	einfacher Endomorphismus *m*	endomorphisme *m* simple	простой эндоморфизм
	simple equation <AL>	*s.* L 791		
S 908	**simple event,** elementary event <ST>	Elementarereignis *n*, elementares Ereignis *n*	événement *m* élémentaire, événement simple, épreuve *f*, tirage *m* au sort	элементарное событие
S 909	**simple extension** <of a ring> <AL>	einfache Erweiterung *f*	extension *f* simple (monogène)	простое расширение
	simple extension <AL>	*s.* S 910		
S 910	**simple extension field,** simple extension <of a field> <AL>	einfache Körpererweiterung *f*, einfacher Erweiterungskörper *m*	extension *f* monogène, extension simple <d'un corps>	простое расширение <поля>
S 911	**simple field** <AL>	ZPE-Körper *m*	corps *m* à factorisation unique	поле с однозначным разложением на множители
S 912	**simple fixed point** <TO>	einfacher Fixpunkt *m*	point *m* fixe simple	простая неподвижная точка
S 913	**simple folium** <GE>	Einblatt *n*, einfaches Blatt *n*, Unifolium *n*, „folium *n* simple"	folium *m* simple	«folium simple»
S 914	**simple fraction** <AR>	einfacher Bruch *m*	fraction *f* simple	«двухэтажная» простая дробь
	simple fraction <AR>	*s. a.* C 1234		
S 915	**simple function,** schlicht function, univalent function <FT>	schlichte (einwertige, univalente, einblättrige) Funktion *f*	fonction *f* univalente (à un feuillet)	однолистная функция
	simple function <AN>	*s.* S 1747		
S 916/7	**simple game** <TG>	einfaches Spiel *n*	jeu *m* simple, famille *f* de majorités	простая игра
S 918	**simple graph,** ordinary graph <GP>	schlichter (einfacher) Graph *m*, Graph <ohne Schlingen und Mehrfachkanten>	graphe *m* simple	обыкновенный (простой) граф
S 919	**simple group,** // non-modular group <GR>	einfache Gruppe *f*	groupe *m* simple, groupe indécomposable <Galois>, groupe premier <Betti>	простая группа
S 920	**simple groupoid** <AL>	einfaches Gruppoid *n*	groupoïde *m* simple	простой группоид
S 921	**simple hypothesis** <ST>	einfache Hypothese *f*	hypothèse *f* simple	простая гипотеза
S 922	**simple infinite sequence,** simply infinite sequence <SS>	gewöhnliche (einfache) Folge *f*	suite *f* à simple entrée	простая последовательность
S 923	**simple integral,** one-dimensional integral <DI>	einfaches Integral *n*	intégrale *f* simple	однократный (простой) интеграл
	simple interest <AR>	*s.* I 709		
	simple interest account <AR>	*s.* I 711		
S 924	**simple intersection point** <AG>	einfacher Schnittpunkt *m*, Schnittpunkt der Vielfachheit 1	point *m* d'intersection simple	простая точка пересечения
	simple isomorphism <GR>	*s.* I 1131		
	simple Jordan curve <TO>	*s.* J 86		
S 925	**simple *K*-module,** irreducible *K*-module <AL>	einfacher *K*-Modul *m*	*K*-module *m* simple, *K*-module irréductible	простой *K*-модуль

No.	English	German	French	Russian
S 926	**simple lattice** <LA>	einfacher Verband *m*	treillis *m* simple	простая решетка
S 927	**simple left ideal,** minimal left ideal <AL>	einfaches (minimales) Linksideal *n*	idéal *m* simple (minimal) à gauche	минимальный левый идеал
S 928	**simple Lie algebra** <AL>	einfache Liesche Algebra *f*	algèbre *f* de Lie simple	простая алгебра Ли
	simple limit <AN>	*s.* L 733		
S 929	**simple module** <AL>	einfacher (minimaler) Modul *m*	module *m* simple	простой модуль
S 930	**simple multivector** <VT>	einfacher Multivektor *m*, einfacher *p*-Vektor *m*, einblättriger Multivektor, einblättriger *p*-Vektor, einfache Größe *f p*-ter Stufe	multivecteur *m* simple, *p*-vecteur *m* simple, *p*-vecteur décomposable	разложимый (простой) поливектор, разложимый *p*-вектор, простой *p*-вектор
	simple *n*-gon <GE>	*s.* S 937		
S 931	**simple number** <AR>	einfach benannte Zahl *f*	nombre *m* simple	простое именованное число
S 932	**simple object** <CA>	unzerlegbares Objekt *n*	objet *m* indécomposable	неразложимый объект
	simple ordering <SE>	*s.* L 830		
S 933	**simple path** <in a digraph> <GP>	einfacher Weg *m*	chemin *m* simple	простой неупорядоченный путь
S 934	**simple path,** path, directed-edge train <in an oriented graph> <GP>	kontinuierlich gerichteter Kantenzug *m*, Wegprogression *f*, einfache Bahn *f*, Bahn <offene gerichtete Kantenprogression ohne Wiederholung von Kanten>	chemin *m* simple	путь, ориентированная цепь, орцепь
S 935	**simple path** <GP>	Bahn *f*, einfacher Weg *m*, Wegprogression *f*; kontinuierlich gerichteter Weg, in dem jede Kante dieselbe Richtung besitzt wie als Kante des Graphen	chemin *m* simple	простой путь, путь
S 936	**simple point,** ordinary point, regular point <AG>	einfacher (gewöhnlicher, regulärer) Punkt *m*	point *m* simple (régulier)	простая (обыкновенная) точка
	simple pole <FT>	*s.* P 907		
S 937	**simple polygon,** simple *n*-gon <GE>	einfaches Vieleck (Polygon) *n*, einfaches *n*-Eck *n*	polygone *m* simple	простой многоугольник, простой *n*-угольник
S 938	**simple polyhedron** <GE>	gewöhnliches (einfaches) Vielflach *n*, gewöhnliches (einfaches) Polyeder *n*	polyèdre *m* simple	простой многогранник, многогранник нулевого рода
S 939	**simple product** <SS>	einfaches Produkt *n*, Produkt mit einem Eingang	produit *m* simple (à simple entrée)	однократное (простое) произведение
S 940	**simple proper value,** simple eigenvalue <of a matrix> <MD>	einfache charakteristische Zahl *f*, einfacher Eigenwert *m*	valeur *f* propre simple	простое собственное значение
	simple proposition <LO>	*s.* A 1192		
S 941	**simple quadrilateral** <GE>	einfaches Vierseit *n*	quadrilatère *m* simple	простой четырехсторонник; простой четырехвершинник
	simple random sample <ST>	*s.* S 951		
S 942	**simple random sampling,** unrestricted random sampling <ST>	reine Zufallsauswahl *f*, Zufallsauswahl, Zufallsstichprobe *f*	échantillonnage (sondage) *m* rigoureusement au hasard	простой случайный выбор, случайный выбор без каких-либо ограничений
S 943	**simple recursion,** recursion with respect to a single variable <FO>	einfache Rekursion *f*	récurrence *f* simple	однократная рекурсия, простая рекурсия
S 944	**simple regression** <ST>	einfache Regression *f*	régression *f* simple	единичная регрессия, простая регрессия
S 945	**simple regression coefficient,** total regression coefficient <ST>	einfacher (totaler) Regressionskoeffizient *m*, Regressionskoeffizient nullter Ordnung	coefficient *m* de régression simple (total)	простой (полный) коэффициент регрессии
	simple renewal process <SP>	*s.* R 301		
	simple representation <RE>	*s.* I 1045		
S 946	**simple representation module** <AL>	einfacher (irreduzibler) Darstellungsmodul *m*	module *m* de la représentation simple	простой (неприводимый) модуль представления
S 947	**simple right ideal,** minimal right ideal <AL>	einfaches Rechtsideal *n*, minimales Rechtsideal	idéal *m* simple à droite, idéal minimal à droite	минимальный правый идеал
S 948	**simple ring** <AL>	einfacher Ring *m*	anneau *m* simple	простое кольцо
S 949	**simple root,** single root, simple zero <AL, FT>	einfache Wurzel *f*, einfache Nullstelle *f*	racine *f* simple, zéro *m* simple	простой корень, однократный корень, корень первой кратности
S 950	**simple rule of three** <AR>	einfache Regeldetri *f*, einfacher Dreisatz *m*, einfache Regel *f* de tri	règle *f* de trois simple	простое тройное правило
S 951	**simple sample,** simple random sample, unrestricted random sample <ST>	reine Zufallsstichprobe *f*, einfache (einfache zufällige, einzelne) Stichprobe *f*, unbeschränkte (uneingeschränkte) Stichprobe (Zufallsstichprobe)	échantillon *m* rigoureusement aléatoire (probabiliste), échantillon simple, échantillon aléatoire sans restriction	простая случайная выборка, простая выборка, случайная выборка без каких-либо ограничений
S 952	**simple sampling** <ST>	Einzelstichprobenverfahren *n*	échantillonnage *m* simple	однократный выбор
S 953	**simple sampling design** <ST>	einfacher (unabhängiger) Stichprobenplan *m*	plan *m* d'échantillonnage simple, plan de sondage simple	простой выборочный план
	simple sentence <LO>	*s.* A 1192		
S 954	**simple series** <SS>	einfache Reihe *f*, Reihe mit einfachem Eingang	série *f* simple (à simple entrée)	однократный (простой) ряд

No.	English	German	French	Russian
S 955	**simple set** <MM>	einfache Menge *f*	ensemble *m* simple	простре множество
	simple sheaf <AL, TO>	*s.* C 2110		
S 956	**simple spectrum** <of an operator> <FA>	einfaches Spektrum *n*	spectre *m* simple	простой спектр
S 957	**simple substitution** <LO>	einfache Einsetzung *f*	substitution *f* simple	простая подстановка
S 958	**simple surface,** schlichtartig surface <TO>	schlichtartige Fläche *f*, Fläche vom Geschlecht Null (0)	surface *f* de genre nul (0)	простая поверхность
S 959	**simple system** <AG>	einfaches lineares System *n*, einfache Linearschar *f*	système *m* simple	простая линейная система
S 960	**simple system** <a hypercomplex system ><AL>	ursprüngliches (einfaches) System *n*	système *m* simple	простая система
S 961	**simple system of sets,** system of sets, family of sets <different elements are different as sets> <SE>	Mengensystem *n*, eigentliches Mengensystem *n*	système *m* d'ensembles	система множеств, простая система множеств
S 962	**simple tangent** <of an algebraic curve *or* surface> <AG, AY, DG>	einfache Tangente *f*	tangente *f* simple	простая касательная
S 963	**simple tangential knot** <GE>	eintangentiger Knoten *m*	nœud *m* d'une seule tangente	однокасательный узел
S 964	**simple theory of types,** simple type theory <LO, SE>	einfache (einfache logische, unverzweigte) Typentheorie *f*, unverzweigte Stufentheorie *f*, unverzweigter Stufenkalkül *m*, einfache Typenlehre *f* (Theorie *f* der logischen Typen)	théorie *f* des types simple	упрощенная (простая) теория типов
S 965	**simple transcendental [field] extension** <of a field> <AL>	einfache transzendente Erweiterung (Körpererweiterung) *f*	extension *f* transcendante monogène (simple) <d'un corps>	моногенное трансцендентное расширение, простое трансцендентное расширение <поля>
S 966	**simple transitivity** <GR>	einfache Transitivität *f*	transitivité *f* simple	простая транзитивность
	simple type theory <LO, SE>	*s.* S 964		
	simple variety <AG>	*s.* K 186		
S 967	**simplex** <AT, GE, PG>	Simplex *n*	simplexe *m*	симплекс
	simplex <AT>	*s.* 1. A 156; 2. S 1154		
	1-simplex <AT>	*s.* S 240		
	simplex criterion <PG>	*s.* S 971		
S 968	**simplex method** <PG>	Simplexverfahren *n*, Simplexmethode *f* <von Dantzig>	méthode *f* simpliciale (du simplexe, de simplexes)	симплексный метод, симплекс-метод, метод симплекса
	simplex method for quadratic programming <PG>	*s.* D 8		
S 969	**simplex multiplier** <PG>	Simplexmultiplikator *m*	multiplicateur *m* simplicial	симплексный множитель
S 970	**simplex tableau** <*pl.*: -eaux>, feasible basic solution <of simplex method> <PG>	Simplextableau *n*, zulässige Basisdarstellung (Basislösung) *f*	tableau *m* simplicial (simplexe)	симплексная таблица, симплекс-таблица
S 971	**simplex theorem,** simplex criterion <PG>	Simplexkriterium *n*, Simplextheorem *n*, Hauptsatz *m* der Simplexmethode	théorème (critère) *m* du simplexe	основная теорема симплексного метода
S 972	**simplex transformation** <PG>	Simplextransformation *f*	transformation *f* simpliciale	симплексное преобразование
	simple zero <AL, FT>	*s.* S 949		
S 973	**simplicial approximation** <AT>	simpliziale Approximation *f*	approximation *f* simpliciale	симплициальное приближение, симплициальная аппроксимация
S 974	**simplicial[-] approximation theorem** <AT>	Approximationssatz *m*	théorème *m* d'approximation	теорема о симплициальной аппроксимации, аппроксимационная теорема
S 975	**simplicial cell** <AT>	simpliziale Zelle *f*	cellule *f* simpliciale	симплициальная клетка
S 976	**simplicial chain** <AT>	simpliziale Kette *f*	chaîne *f* simpliciale	симплициальная цепь
S 977	**simplicial chain complex with distinguished basis** <HA>	simplizialer Kettenkomplex *m* mit ausgezeichneter Basis	complexe *m* de chaînes simplicial basique	базисный симплициальный цепной комплекс
S 978	**simplicial chain[-] mapping** <AT>	simpliziale Kettentransformation *f*	transformation *f* de chaînes simpliciales	симплициальное цепное преобразование
S 979	**simplicial cochain complex** <AT>	simplizialer Kokettenkomplex *m*	complexe *m* de cochaînes simplicial	симплициальный коцепной комплекс
S 980	**simplicial cohomology group** <AT>	simpliziale Kohomologiegruppe *f*	groupe *m* de cohomologie simpliciale	группа симплициальных когомологий
S 981	**simplicial complex,** triangulation <AT>	simplizialer (geometrischer) Komplex *m*	complexe *m* simplicial	симплициальный комплекс, триангуляция
	simplicial complex <AT>	*s. a.* S 1157		
	simplicial complex together with a distinguished base vertex <AT>	*s.* P 741		
S 982	**simplicial homology** <AT>	simpliziale Homologie *f*	homologie *f* simpliciale	симплициальные гомологии
S 983	**simplicial image** <of a chain> <AT>	simpliziales Bild *n*	image *f* simpliciale	симплициальный образ
S 984	**simpliciality** >AT>	Simplizialität *f*	propriété *f* d'être simplicial	симплициальность
S 985	**simplicially homotopic** <AT>	simplizial homotop	simplicialement homotope	симплициально гомотопный
S 986	**simplicial map[ping],** simplicial set-transformation <AT>	simpliziale Abbildung *f*, Simplizialabbildung *f*	application *f* simpliciale, homomorphisme *m* <d'un schéma simplicial>	симплициальное отображение; гомоморфизм <симплициальной схемы>

No.	English	German	French	Russian
S 987	**simplicial mapping cylinder** <AT>	simplizialer Abbildungszylinder *m*	cylindre *m* d'application simpliciale	цилиндр симплициального отображения
S 988	**simplicial pair** <AT>	simpliziales Paar *n*	paire *f* simpliciale	симплициальная пара
S 989	**simplicial partition,** simplicial triangulation <AT>	simpliziale Zerlegung *f*, Simplizialzerlegung *f*, simpliziale Unterteilung *f*	subdivision *f* simpliciale	разложение на симплексы, симплициальное разбиение
S 990	**simplicial product** <of simplicial complexes> <AT>	simpliziales Produkt *n*	produit *m* simplicial	симплициальное произведение
S 991	**simplicial set,** // C.S.S. complex, semi-simplicial set <AT, CA>	simpliziale Menge *f*	ensemble *m* simplicial	симплициальное множество, полный полусимплициальный комплекс
	simplicial set-transformation <AT>	*s.* S 986		
	simplicial triangulation <AT>	*s.* S 989		
S 992	**simplification** <of a fraction>, reduction <of a fraction> to lower terms, cancellation <of a number out of [numerator and denominator of] a fraction> <AR>	Kürzen *n* <eines Bruchs mit einer Zahl, durch eine Zahl>	simplification *f* <d'une fraction>; réduction *f* <d'une fraction> à sa plus simple expression	сокращение <дроби на число>, отмена <дроби>
	simplification <AR, GN>	*s.* C 43		
	simplification <LO>	*s.* R 1492		
S 993	**simplification in interpunction,** omitting parentheses <AL, LO>	Klammereinsparung *f*, Klammerersparung *f*	suppression *f* des parenthèses, simplification *f* dans l'usage des parenthèses	экономия скобок, опускание скобок
	simplification of an expression <GN>	*s.* R 427		
	simplified fraction <AL, NT>	*s.* F 572		
	simply convergent sequence <SS>	*s.* P 806		
	simply convergent series <SS>	*s.* P 808		
S 994	**simplifying assumption** <GN>	vereinfachende Annahme *f*	hypothèse *f* simplificatrice	упрощающее предположение
S 995	**simply additive functional** <FA>	einfachadditives Funktional *n*	fonctionnelle *f* simplement additive	просто аддитивный функционал
S 996	**simply connected group** <AL>	einfach[ ]zusammenhängende Gruppe *f*	groupe *m* simplement connexe	односвязная группа
S 997	**simply connected space,** 1-connected space <TO>	einfach[ ]zusammenhängender Raum *m*	espace *m* simplement connexe	односвязное пространство, 1-связное пространство
S 998	**simply connected spatial domain** <TO>	räumliches einfach-zusammenhängendes Gebiet *n*	domaine *m* simplement connexe de l'espace	пространственно-односвязная область
	simply consistent system <LO>	*s.* S 2509		
S 999	**simply convergent filter** <TO>	einfach konvergenter Filter *m*	filtre *m* simplement convergent	просто сходящийся фильтр
	simply infinite sequence <SS>	*s.* S 922		
S 1000	**simply inflected hyperbola** <AG>	einfach inflektierte Hyperbel *f* <Salmon>	hyperbole *f* simplement infléchie	
S 1001	**simply ordered group,** ordered group, totally ordered group, linearly ordered group <GR>	linear geordnete Gruppe *f*, angeordnete (einfach geordnete, geordnete) Gruppe	groupe *m* réticulé en chaîne, groupe totalement ordonné	линейно (просто, совершенно) упорядоченная группа
S 1002	**simply ordered loop,** ordered loop <AL>	angeordnete Loop *f*	loop *m* totalement ordonné	линейно упорядоченная лупа
	simply ordered set <SE>	*s.* L 822		
S 1003	**simply periodic function,** singly periodic function <FT>	einfach[-]periodische Funktion *f*	fonction *f* simplement périodique	просто периодическая функция, однопериодическая функция
S 1004	**simply transitive group** <GR>	einfachtransitive Gruppe *f*	groupe *m* simplement transitif	просто транзитивная группа
S 1005	**simply uniform convergence** <AN>	einfach[-] gleichmäßige Konvergenz *f*	convergence *f* simplement uniforme	просто равномерная сходимость, простая равномерная сходимость
S 1006	**simply uniformly convergent sequence** <of functions> <AN>	einfach-gleichmäßig konvergente Funktionenfolge *f*	suite *f* <de fonctions> simplement uniformément convergente	просто равномерно сходящаяся последовательность <функций>
	Simpson['s] distribution <ST> ⌐<DI, NU>	*s.* T 913		
	Simpson['s] formula	*s.* S 1008		
S 1007	**Simpson['s] method** <DE, NU>	Simpsonsches Verfahren *n*	méthode *f* de Simpson	метод Симпсона
S 1008	**Simpson['s] rule,** Simpson['s] formula, parabolic rule, parabolic formula, parabolic method; Kepler['s] rule, prismoidal formula <for areas> <for $n = 1$> <for integrals> <DI, NU>	Simpsonsche Regel (Formel) *f*, Parabelformel *f*, Parabelregel *f*, Parabelmethode *f*, Simpson-Regel *f*; Keplersche Faßregel *f*, Faßregel, Faßrechnung *f* <für $n = 1$>	formule (règle, méthode) *f* de Simpson, formule (règle, méthode) des paraboles, méthode de Cotes; formule (règle) du tonneau <pour $n = 1$>	формула парабол (Симпсона), правило парабол (Симпсона), метод парабол; формула Кеплера <для $n = 1$>
S 1009	**Simpson['s] solid** <EG>	Simpsonscher Körper *m*	solide (polyèdre) *m* de Simpson	тело Симпсона
	simultaneous approximation <NT>	*s.* S 1014		
S 1010	**simultaneous character** <of quadratic forms> <NT>	Simultancharakter *m*	caractère *m* simultané	одновременный характер

S 1011	**simultaneous confidence intervals** <ST>	simultane Konfidenzintervalle *npl*	intervalles *mpl* de confiance simultanés	совместные доверительные интервалы
	simultaneous congruences <AL>	*s.* S 2514		
S 1012	**simultaneous diagonalization** <of quadratic forms> <AL>	simultane Hauptachsentransformation *f*	réduction *f* simultanée aux axes principaux	одновременное приведение к главным осям
S 1013	**simultaneous differential equations,** simultaneous ordinary differential equations, system (set) of [ordinary] differential equations <DE>	System *n* von gewöhnlichen Differentialgleichungen, [gewöhnliches] Differentialgleichungssystem *n*, gekoppelte (simultane) Differentialgleichungen *fpl*	système *m* d'équations différentielles [ordinaires]	система [обыкновенных] дифференциальных уравнений
S 1014	**simultaneous Diophantine approximation,** simultaneous approximation <NT>	simultane [diophantische] Approximation *f*, gleichzeitige diophantische Approximation	approximation *f* [diophantienne] simultanée	одновременное [диофантово] приближение
	simultaneous equations <AL, AN>	*s.* S 2517		
S 1015	**simultaneous estimation** <ST>	simultane Schätzung *f*	estimation *f* simultanée	совместная оценка
S 1016	**simultaneous game** <TG>	Simultanspiel *n*	jeu *m* simultané	одновременная игра
	simultaneous inequalities <AN, NT>	*s.* S 2521		
S 1017	**simultaneous invariant** <IV>	simultane (gleichzeitige) Invariante *f*, Simultaninvariante *f*	invariant *m* simultané	одновременный инвариант
	simultaneous linear equations <AL>	*s.* S 2524		
S 1018	**simultaneously satisfiable** <LO>	simultan erfüllbar	simultanément satisfiable	одновременно выполнимый
	simultaneous ordinary differential equations <DE>	*s.* S 1013		
S 1019	**simultaneous recursion** <FO, GN>	simultane Rekursion *f*	induction (récurrence) *f* simultanée	одновременная рекурсия
	simultaneous regression equations <ER, ST>	*s.* N 564		
S 1020	**simultaneous solvability** <GN>	simultane Lösbarkeit *f*	solubilité *f* simultanée	одновременная разрешимость
S 1021	**simultaneous substitution** <LO>	simultane Einsetzung *f*	substitution *f* simultanée	одновременная замена, сложная подстановка
	sin <DI>	*s.* S 1022		
	sin^{-1} <FU>	*s.* I 948		
	sin am <FU>	*s.* A 609		
	sin-cos series <SS>	*s.* T 947		
S 1022	**sine,** sine function, sin <DI>	Sinus *m*, Sinusfunktion *f*, sin	sinus *m*, fonction *f* sinus, sin	синус, функция синус, sin
S 1023	**sine chart,** sine graph, sine paper <IN, NU>	Sinuspapier *n*, Sinusnetz *n*	diagramme (papier) *m* à échelle fonctionnelle sinusoïdale	синусная сетка (бумага)
	sine-cosine series <SS>	*s.* T 947		
S 1024	**sine curve,** sine line, sinusoid <DI>	Sinuskurve *f*, Sinuslinie *f*, Sinusoide *f*	sinusoïde *f*, courbe (ligne) *f* sinus	синусоида, график синуса
S 1025	**sine factorial,** sf <FU>	Sinus-Faktorial *n*, sf	sinus-factorielle *m*, sf	синус-факториал, sf
	sine function <DI>	*s.* S 1022		
	sine graph <IN, NU>	*s.* S 1023		
S 1026	**sine integral, sine-integral function,** integral sine; si; Si <FU>	Integralsinus *m*, Sinus *m* integralis, Sinusintegralfunktion *f*; si; Si	sinus *m* intégral; si; Si	интегральный синус; si; Si
	sine law <EG>	*s.* L 208		
	sine line <DI>	*s.* S 1024		
	sine paper <IN, NU>	*s.* S 1023		
	sine rule <EG>	*s.* L 208		
S 1027	**sine series** <AN, SS>	Sinusreihe *f*	série *f* du sinus	ряд синуса
S 1028	**sine series** <as a special trigonometric series><SS>	Sinusreihe *f*	série *f* en sinus	ряд синусов (по синусам)
S 1029	**sine spiral** <GE>	Sinusspirale *f*	spirale *f* sinusoïde (sinusoïdale)	синусоидальная спираль, синус-спираль, кривая пропорционального изгиба
	single-column matrix <MD>	*s.* C 1164		
	single-curved surface <DG> ⌐<NT>	*s.* D 361		
	single-digit number	*s.* O 93		
S 1030	**single-factor method** <ST>	Einfaktormethode *f*	méthode *f* du facteur commun unique	однофакторный метод
S 1031	**single-index element,** element of one index <GN>	einfachindiziertes Element *n*	élément *m* à un indice	одноиндексный элемент
	single-parameter family of curves <AN, GE>	*s.* O 90		
	single-person game <TG>	*s.* O 92		
	single-primed ideal <AL>	*s.* E 70		
S 1032	**single replication experiment** <ST>	Versuch *m* ohne (in einer) Wiederholung	expérience *f* sans répétitions, expérience à répétition unique, expérience en exécution unique	опыт с одним повторением
	single root <AL, FT>	*s.* S 949		
	single-row matrix <MD>	*s.* R 1432		
	single-step iteration <AL, AX, NU>	*s.* G 98		

No.	English	German	French	Russian
	single-step iteration <AN, NU>	*s.* S 1033		
	single-step iteration for solving linear equations <AL, AX, NU>	*s.* G 98		
S 1033	**single-step method (process),** single-step iteration <AN, NU>	Einzelschrittverfahren *n*, Iteration *f* in Einzelschritten	méthode *f* à pas séparés, méthode à plusieurs pas	метод единичных шагов
	single-tail test <ST>	*s.* O 115		
	singleton <SE>	*s.* O 86		
S 1034	**single-valued analytic function** <on a Riemann surface> <FT>	eindeutige analytische Funktion *f*, eindeutig ausgebreitete analytische Funktion	fonction *f* analytique univoque (univalente)	однозначная аналитическая функция
S 1035	**single-valued correspondence** <of two planes, curves, etc.> <GE>	eindeutige Korrespondenz *f*, monodrome Korrespondenz, eindeutiges Entsprechen *n*	correspondance *f* monodrome, correspondance uniforme, correspondance *f* univoque	однозначное соответствие
	single-valued correspondence <SE>	*s.* S 1037		
S 1036	**single-valued function,** one-valued function <AN>	eindeutige Funktion *f*, einwertige Funktion, monodrome Funktion, einändrige Funktion, monotrope Funktion	fonction *f* univoque, fonction uniforme, fonction monodrome, fonction bien déterminée par une valeur attribuée à la variable, fonction monotrope <Briot>	однозначная функция
	single-valued function <SE>	*s.* S 1037		
S 1037	**single[-] valued mapping,** single-valued transformation, single-valued function, function, mapping, one-valued function, unique correspondence, single-valued correspondence <SE>	eindeutige Abbildung *f*, Funktion *f*, Abbildung *f*, eindeutige Funktion *f*	représentation *f* uniforme, représentation *f* univoque, application *f* univoque, correspondance *f* univoque, fonction *f* univalente	однозначное отображение, однозначная функция
S 1038	**single-valuedness,** univalence <of a transformation> <GN>	Eindeutigkeit *f*	univocité *f*, univalence *f*, uniformité *f*	однозначность; однолистность
S 1039	**single-valuedness** <of a predicate> <LO>	Einstelligkeit *f*	singularité *f*	монадичность
S 1040	**single-valuedness,** functionality <of a relation> <SE>	Eindeutigkeit *f*, Mehreindeutigkeit *f*	univocité *f*	однозначность, функциональность
S 1041	**single-valued operation** <AL>	eindeutige Operation *f*	opération *f* univoque	однозначная операция
	single-valued predicate <LO>	*s.* O 94		
S 1042	**single-valued relation,** mapping relation, many-one relation, many-to-one relation, right-unique relation, functional relation, many-one correspondence, indexed class <SE>	eindeutige Relation *f*, rechts[-]eindeutige Relation, mehr[-]eindeutige Relation, nacheindeutige Relation, nacheindeutige Beziehung *f*, Funktionalrelation *f*	relation *f* univoque (en γ), relation univoque à droite, relation fonctionnelle	однозначное соотношение, однозначное отношение, функциональное [со]отношение, справа однозначное отношение, много-однозначное соответствие
	single-valued transformation <SE>	*s.* S 1037		
	singly periodic function <FT>	*s.* S 1003		
S 1043	**singular affine transformation, singular affinity** <AY>	ausgeartete Affinität *f* (affine Transformation *f*)	application (transformation) *f* affine dégénérée, affinité *f* dégénérée	вырожденное аффинное преобразование (отображение)
	singular application <FA>	*s.* S 1089		
S 1044	**singular automorphism** <AL>	singulärer Automorphismus *m*	automorphisme *m* singulier	сингулярный автоморфизм
S 1045	**singular bivariate normal distribution** <ST>	singuläre zweidimensionale Normalverteilung *f*	distribution *f* normale bidimensionnelle singulière	сингулярное двухмерное нормальное распределение
S 1046	**singular boundary** <AT>	singulärer Rand *m*	bord *m* singulier	сингулярная граница
S 1047	**singular boundary point** <of a convex body> <CS>	singulärer Randpunkt *m*	point *m* frontière singulier	особая точка границы
S 1048	**singular cardinal** <SE>	singuläre Kardinalzahl *f*, Kardinalzahl erster Art	cardinal *m* singulier	сингулярное кардинальное число
S 1049	**singular chain** <*n*-dimensional, with coefficients in *A*> <AT>	singuläre Kette *f* <*n*-dimensionale, mit Koeffizienten in *A*>, // stetiger algebraischer Komplex *m*	chaîne *f* singulière <de dimension *n*, à coefficients dans *A*>	сингулярная цепь <*n*-мерная, со значениями в *A*>
S 1050	**singular chain complex,** singular complex <AT>	singulärer Kettenkomplex (Komplex) *m*	complexe *m* singulier	сингулярный цепной комплекс, сингулярный комплекс
S 1051	**singular chain-derivation** <AT>	Unterteilung *f* singulärer Ketten	subdivision *f* des chaînes singulières	подразделение сингулярных цепей
S 1052	**singular chain group** <AT>	Gruppe *f* der singulären Ketten	groupe *m* des chaînes singulières	группа сингулярных цепей
S 1053	**singular cohomology group** <AT>	singuläre Kohomologiegruppe *f*	groupe *m* de cohomologie singulier	группа сингулярных когомологий
	singular complex <AT>	*s.* S 1050		

No.	English	German	French	Russian
	singular complex <PJ>	*s.* S 1355		
	singular complex of lines (rays) <PJ>	*s.* S 1355		
S 1054	**singular congruence [of lines (rays)]** <DG>	singuläre Strahlenkongruenz (Linienkongruenz, Geradenkongruenz, Kongruenz) *f*, singuläres Strahlensystem *n*	congruence *f* [de droites] singulière	особая (сингулярная) конгруэнция [прямых (лучей)]
S 1055	**singular conic [section],** degenerate conic [section] <AY>	singulärer (zerfallender) Kegelschnitt *m*, zerfallende (ausgeartete, entartete, singuläre) Kurve *f* zweiter (2.) Ordnung, entarteter (ausgearteter) Kegelschnitt	conique *f* singulière (dégénérée, décomposée), section *f* conique singulière (dégénérée, décomposée)	вырожденное коническое сечение, вырожденная кривая второго порядка, сингулярное коническое сечение
S 1056	**singular continued fraction** <NT>	singulärer Kettenbruch *m*, Kettenbruch zweiter Art	fraction *f* continue singulière	сингулярная непрерывная дробь
S 1057	**singular correspondence,** non-valence correspondence <AG>	singuläre Korrespondenz *f*	correspondance *f* singulière	особое соответствие
S 1058	**singular critical lattice** <GU>	singuläres kritisches Gitter *n*, singuläres Gitter	réseau *m* critique singulier	сингулярная критическая решетка
S 1059	**singular curve** <AG>	singuläre (ausgeartete) Kurve *f*	courbe *f* singulière	сингулярная кривая
S 1060	**singular cycle,** "continuous" cycle <AT>	singulärer Zyklus *m*	cycle *m* singulier	сингулярный (непрерывный) цикл
	singular distribution <ST>	*s.* D 155		
S 1061	**singular element** <of a Lie algebra> <AL>	singuläres Element *n*	élément *m* singulier	нерегулярный элемент
S 1062	**singular element** <right or left zero-divisor in a ring> <AL>	singuläres Element *n* <rechter oder linker Nullteiler>	élément *m* singulier	сингулярный (особый) элемент <правый или левый делитель нуля>
S 1063	**singular element** <of a Banach algebra> <FA>	singuläres Element *n*	élément *m* singulier	особый элемент
S 1064	**singular elliptic function** <FT, NT>	singuläre elliptische Funktion *f*	fonction *f* elliptique singulière	сингулярная эллиптическая функция
S 1065	**singular endomorphism** <AL>	ausgearteter (singulärer) Endomorphismus *m*	endomorphisme *m* singulier	вырожденный эндоморфизм
S 1066	**singular extremal** <VA>	singuläre Extremale *f*	extrémale *f* singulière	сингулярная экстремаль
S 1067	**singular extremal lattice,** singular lattice <GU>	singuläres extremes Gitter *n*	réseau *m* extrémal singulier	сингулярная экстремальная решетка
S 1068	**singular focus** <of an algebraic curve> <AG>	außerordentlicher Brennpunkt *m* <Plücker>, singulärer Brennpunkt <Laguerre>	foyer *m* singulier	особый фокус, фокальный центр, асимптотическая точка
S 1069	**singular form,** singular quadratic form <AL, NT>	ausgeartete (singuläre) Form *f*, ausgeartete (singuläre) quadratische Form	forme *f* dégénérée (singulière), forme quadratique dégénérée (singulière)	вырожденная (сингулярная, вырожденная квадратичная) форма
S 1070	**singular function** <RF>; singulary function <LO>	singuläre Funktion *f*	fonction *f* singulière	сингулярная функция
	μ-singular function <ME>	*s.* M 1095		
S 1071	**singular function of bounded variation** <AN>	singuläre Funktion *f* von beschränkter Variation	fonction *f* singulière à variation bornée	сингулярная функция ограниченной вариации
S 1072	**singular graph** <GP>	singulärer Graph *m*	graphe *m* singulier	сингулярный граф
S 1073	**singular homology** <AT>	singuläre Homologie *f*	homologie *f* singulière	сингулярные гомологии
S 1074	**singular homology,** singular perspectivity, parabolic homology (perspectivity) <PJ>	singuläre Perspektivität (Homologie) *f*, parabolische Perspektivität (Homologie)	homologie *f* singulière (parabolique)	особенная (параболическая) гомология
S 1075	**singular homology class** <AT>	singuläre Homologieklasse *f*	classe *f* d'homologie singulière	класс сингулярных гомологий
S 1076	**singular homology functor** <AT>	Funktor *m* der singulären Homologie	foncteur *m* d'homologie singulière	функтор сингулярных гомологий
S 1077	**singular homology sequence** <of a triple *or* pair> <AT>	singuläre Homologiesequenz *f*	suite *f* d'homologie singulière	сингулярная гомологическая последовательность
S 1078	**singular homology theory** <AT>	singuläre Homologietheorie *f*	théorie *f* de l'homologie singulière	теория сингулярных гомологий
S 1079	**singular ideal** <AL>	singuläres Ideal *n*	idéal *m* singulier	сингулярный идеал
S 1080	**singular initial number** <SE>	singuläre (irreguläre) Anfangszahl *f*	nombre *m* initial singulier	сингулярное начальное число
S 1081	**singular integral,** singular solution <DE>	singuläres Integral *n*, singuläre Lösung *f*	intégrale (solution) *f* singulière	особое (сингулярное) решение, особый (сингулярный) интеграл
S 1082	**singular integral** <DI, IE>	singuläres Integral *n*	intégrale *f* singulière	сингулярный интеграл
S 1083	**singular integral curve** <DE>	singuläre Integralkurve *f*	courbe *f* intégrale singulière	особая интегральная кривая
S 1084	**singular integral element** <DE>	singuläres Integralelement *n*	élément *m* intégral singulier	особый интегральный элемент
S 1085	**singular integral equation** <IE>	singuläre Integralgleichung *f*	équation *f* intégrale singulière	особое (сингулярное) интегральное уравнение
	singular integral in the Cauchy sense <AN>	*s.* C 260		
S 1086	**singular invariant** <of complex multiplication> <FT, NT>	singuläre Invariante *f*	invariant *m* singulier	сингулярный инвариант
S 1087	**singularity** <of a vector field> <AT>	Singularität *f*, Nullstelle *f*, 0-Stelle *f*	singularité *f*	особенность

	singularity <DE>	*s.* S 1108		
	singularity <FT>	*s.* S 1111		
	singularity function <DE>	*s.* P 150		
S 1088	**singular kernel** <IE>	singulärer Kern *m*	noyau *m* singulier	особое (сингулярное) ядро
	singular kernel <IE>	*s. a.* E 529		
	singular lattice <GU>	*s.* S 1067		
	singular linear application <FA>	*s.* S 1089		
	singular linear complex <PJ>	*s.* S 1355		
	singular linear complex of lines (rays) <PJ>	*s.* S 1355		
	singular linear map[ping] (transformation) <FA>	*s.* S 1089		
S 1089	**singular linear operator,** singular operator, singular [linear] transformation (application, map, mapping) <FA>	ausgearteter [vollstetiger] linearer Operator *m*, ausgearteter Operator, ausgeartete [lineare] Abbildung (Transformation) *f*	opérateur *m* [linéaire] singulier, transformation (application) *f* [linéaire] singulière	вырожденный [линейный] оператор, вырожденное (особенное, сингулярное) [линейное] преобразование (отображение)
S 1090	**singular linear transformation** <AL, GE>	singuläre lineare Abbildung *f*, singuläre (ausgeartete) lineare Transformation *f*	application *f* linéaire singulière, opérateur *m* linéaire singulier	вырожденное линейное преобразование
S 1091	**singular line element** <DE>	singuläres Linienelement *n*	élément *m* linéaire singulier	особый линейный элемент
S 1092	**singular locus** <of an algebraic variety> <AG>	singulärer Ort *m*	ensemble (lieu) *m* singulier	особое место
	singular map[ping] <FA>	*s.* S 1089		
S 1093	**singular mapping,** degenerate mapping <GE>	singuläre (ausgeartete) Abbildung *f*	application *f* singulière (dégénérée)	сингулярное (вырожденное, особенное) отображение
S 1094	**singular matrix,** non-invertible matrix <MD>	singuläre (ausgeartete) Matrix *f*	matrice *f* singulière (dégénérée)	вырожденная (вырождающаяся, особенная) матрица
S 1095	**singular metric** <DG>	singuläre Metrik *f*	métrique *f* singulière	особая метрика
S 1096	**singular modulus** <of an elliptic function> <FU, NT>	singulärer Modul *m*	module *m* singulier	сингулярный модуль
S 1097	**singular *n*-cochain** <in *K* with values in *A*> <AT>	singuläre *n*-dimensionale Kokette *f*, singuläre *n*-Kokette *f*, *n*-dimensionale singuläre Kokette <in *K* mit Werten in *A*>	cochaîne *f* singulière de degré *n*, *n*-cochaîne *f* singulière <de *K* à valeurs dans *A*>	сингулярная коцепь степени *n* <в *K* со значениями в *A*>
S 1098	**singular *n*-cube** <AT>	singulärer *n*-Würfel *m*, *n*-dimensionaler singulärer Kubus *m*	cube *m* singulier à *n* dimensions	*n*-мерный сингулярный куб
S 1099	**singular *n*-simplex** <AT>	singuläres *n*-Simplex *n*	*n*-simplexe *m* singulier, simplexe *m* singulier de dimension *n*	сингулярный *n*-мерный симплекс, *n*-мерный сингулярный симплекс
S 1100	**singular operator** <FA>	singulärer Operator *m*	opérateur *m* singulier	сингулярный оператор
	singular operator <FA>	*s. a.* S 1089		
S 1101	**singular ordinal** <SE>	singuläre (irreguläre) Ordnungszahl *f*	ordinal *m* singulier	сингулярное ординальное (порядковое) число
	singular part <RF>	*s.* F 770		
S 1102	**singular pencil** <of forms> <AL>	singuläres Formenbüschel *n*	faisceau *m* singulier <de formes>	сингулярный пучок <форм>
	singular perspectivity <PJ>	*s.* S 1074		
S 1103	**singular plane** <AY>	singuläre Ebene *f*	plan *m* singulier	особая (сингулярная) плоскость
S 1104	**singular plane of support** <CS, GE>	singuläre Stützebene *f*	plan *m* d'appui singulier	сингулярная опорная плоскость
S 1105	**singular point,** multiple point <of curve, surface, *or* manifold> <AG, GE>	singulärer (mehrfacher, vielfacher) Punkt *m*; singulärer Flächenpunkt *m*; singulärer Kurvenpunkt *m*	point *m* singulier (multiple)	особая точка
S 1106	**singular point** <of a polyhedron> <GE>	singulärer Punkt *m*	point *m* singulier	особая точка
S 1107	**singular point** <of a differential equation $w' = g(z, w) / h(z, w)$> <DE>	außerwesentlich[e] singuläre Stelle *f* zweiter (2.) Art	point *m* singulier	особая точка
S 1108	**singular point,** singularity <of differential equations in the complex domain> <DE>	singuläre Stelle *f*	singularité *f*	особая точка, особенность
S 1109	**singular point** <of a differential *or* difference equation> <DE, FD>	singulärer Punkt *m*	point *m* singulier	особая точка
S 1110	**singular point,** critical point <of a curve, surface, *or* manifold> <DG>	singulärer Punkt *m*	point *m* singulier	особая точка
S 1111	**singular point,** singularity <of an analytic function> <FT>	singuläre Stelle *f*, singulärer Punkt *m*, Singularität *f*	singularité *f*, point *m* singulier	особенность, особая точка
S 1112	**singular point** <TO>	singulärer Punkt *m*	point *m* singulier	сингулярная точка
S 1113	**singular point** <of an elementary curve> <TO>	Punkt *m* der Ordnung + 2	point *m* d'ordre + 2	особая точка

	singular point <DE>	*s.* 1. C 2678; 2. S 1675		
S 1114	**singular point of multiplicity (order) *k*** <AG>	*k*-facher Punkt *m*	point *m* multiple d'ordre *k*, point *k*-uple	*k*-кратная точка
	singular process <SP>	*s.* S 1121		
S 1115	**singular proposition,** singular statement, singular sentence <LO>	singuläre (einzelne) Aussage *f*	proposition *f* singulière (particulière)	единичное предложение (суждение, высказывание)
	singular quadratic form <AL, NT>	*s.* S 1069		
S 1116	**singular quadric** <GE>	singuläre Quadrik *f*	quadrique *f* singulière	особая квадрика (гиперповерхность второго порядка)
	singular sentence <LO>	*s.* S 1115		
S 1117	**singular series** <AB>	singuläre Reihe *f*	série *f* singulière	особый (сингулярный) ряд
S 1118	**singular set function** <ME>	singuläre Mengenfunktion *f*	fonction *f* d'ensemble singulière	сингулярная функция множеств
S 1119	**singular skeleton** <AT>	singuläres Skelett (Gerüst) *n*	squelette *m* singulier	сингулярный остов
	singular solution <DE>	*s.* S 1081		
S 1120	**singular space** <AG>	singulärer Raum *m*	espace *m* singulier	особое пространство
	singular statement <LO>	*s.* S 1115		
S 1121	**singular stationary process,** singular process, deterministic process <SP>	singulärer stationärer Prozeß *m*, singulärer (deterministischer stationärer, deterministischer) Prozeß	processus *m* stationnaire singulier, processus singulier (déterministe)	сингулярный стационарный процесс, сингулярный (детерминированный) процесс
S 1122	**singular submanifold** <AG>	singuläre Untermannigfaltigkeit *f*	sous-variété *f* singulière	особое подмножество
S 1123	**singular submodule** <AL>	singulärer Untermodul *m*	sous-module *m* singulier	сингулярный подмодуль
S 1124	**singular surface** <AG>	singuläre Fläche *f*	surface *f* singulière	особая (сингулярная) поверхность
S 1125	**singular tangent,** multiple tangent <of an algebraic curve> <AG>	singuläre (mehrfache) Tangente *f*	tangente *f* singulière (multiple)	особая касательная
S 1126	**singular tangential plane,** multiple tangential plane <AG>	singuläre (mehrfache) Tangentialebene *f*	plan *m* tangentiel singulier (multiple)	особая касательная плоскость
S 1127	**singular term** <LO>	singulärer Term *m*	terme *m* singulier	единичный терм
S 1128	**singular transformation** <GE>	singuläre Transformation *f*	transformation *f* singulière	вырожденное (особенное, сингулярное) преобразование
	singular transformation <FA>	*s.* S 1089		
S 1129	**singular value** <in complex multiplication> <FT, NT>	singulärer Wert *m*	valeur *f* singulière	сингулярная величина
S 1130	**singular variational problem** <VA>	singuläres Variationsproblem *n*	problème *m* variationnel singulier	сингулярная вариационная задача
S 1131	**singular vector** <with respect to a quadratic form> <AL>	singulärer Vektor *m* <bezüglich einer quadratischen Form>	vecteur *m* singulier <par rapport à une forme quadratique>	особый вектор <относительно квадратичной формы>
	singulary connective <LO>	*s.* S 1132		
	singulary function <AL, AN>	*s.* F 767		
	singulary function <LO>	*s.* S 1070		
	singulary functional abstraction operator <LO>	*s.* A 152		
	singulary functional calculus <LO>	*s.* O 95		
	singulary predicate calculus of first order <LO>	*s.* C 19		
	singulary propositional (sentence) connective <LO>	*s.* S 1132		
S 1132	**singulary truth-functional connective,** singulary propositional connective, singulary sentence connective, singulary connective, functor of one argument, operator <LO>	einstelliger Junktor *m*	connecteur *m* unaire	сингулярная сентенциональная связка, одноместная сентенциональная связка
	sinh <FU>	*s.* H 648		
	sinistrorse curve <GE>	*s.* L 372		
S 1133	**sinistrorse helix,** left-hand[ed] helix, left-twisted helix <GE>	linksgängige (linkswendige) Schraubenlinie *f*	hélice *f* directe (sinistrorsum, à gauche), hélice à torsion gauche (sinistre)	винтовая линия левого вращения, завитая влево винтовая линия, влево завитая винтовая линия, левовинтовая линия, левая винтовая линия
S 1134	**sinistrorse ruled surface,** left-hand[ed] ruled surface <GE>	negativ gewundene Regelfläche *f*, linksgewundene Regelfläche *f*	surface *f* réglée sinistrorsum	линейчатая поверхность левого вращения, завитая влево линейчатая поверхность
	sinistrorse screw <GE>	*s.* L 486		
	sinistrorsum curve <GE>	*s.* L 372		
S 1135	**sink,** root <GP>	Wurzel *f*	racine *f*	корень
S 1136	**sink** <of a transportation network> <GP, PG>	Senke *f*, Ausgang *m*	sortie *f*	сток

S 1137	**sink** <GP, VT>	Senke *f* <GP, VT>; Knotenpunkt *m* ohne Nachfolger <GP>	puits *m*	сток
S 1138	**sink strength** <of a vector field> <VT>	Senkenstärke *f*, Ergiebigkeit *f* der Senke	intensité *f* du puits	интенсивность стока
	S-integral <AN>	*s.* S 1767		
	sinusoid <DI>	*s.* S 1024		
S 1139	**sinusoidal curve,** sinusoidal line <DI>	sinusförmige Kurve *f*, Sinuskurve *f*	ligne (courbe) *f* sinusoïdale	синусоидальная кривая (линия)
S 1140	**sinusoidal function** <AN>	sinusartige Funktion *f*, Sinusfunktion *f*	fonction *f* sinusoïdale	синусоидальная функция
S 1141	**sinusoidal law** <NU>	Sinusgesetz *n*	loi *f* sinusoïdale	синусоидальный закон
	sinusoidal line <DI>	*s.* S 1139		
	sin vers <AN>	*s.* V 147		
	Sir Wm. Hamilton's Icosian Game <GP>	*s.* H 72		
S 1142	**situation,** point <TG>	Situation *f*, *n*-Tupel *n*	situation *f*	ситуация
	situation <TA>	*s.* S 1659		
S 1143	**situs** <= category with topology> <CA>	Situs *m*	site *m*	ситус
S 1144	**six-point circle** <of the triangle> <EG>	Sechspunktekreis *m*	cercle *m* des six points	шеститочечная окружность
S 1145	**six-point[ic] contact** <GE>	sechspunktige Berührung *f*	contact *m* sextuple	шеститочечное касание
	sixth-degree polynomial equation <AL>	*s.* S 728		
S 1146	**six-vector,** 6-vector, antisymmetric tensor of rank two (2) <VT>	Sechservektor *m*, Flächentensor *m*	sexti-vecteur *m*, vecteur *m* sextuple (à six dimensions, sextidimensionnel)	шестимерный вектор, 6-вектор
S 1147	**size** <of an orbit> <AL>	Elementezahl *f*	nombre *m* d'éléments	порядок, длина
S 1148	**size** <of a polynomial> <AL>	Höhe *f*	hauteur *f*	размер
S 1149	**size,** order <of a matrix> <MD>	Typ *m*, Format *n*	type *m*	размер
S 1150	**size** <in discriminatory analysis> <ST>	Ausdehnungsmaß *n*	mesure *f* d'extension	размер
S 1151	**size** <of a test> <ST>	Umfang *m*, Größe *f*, Niveau *n* <eines Tests>, Testumfang *m*, Testgröße *f*, Testniveau *n*	taille *f* <d'un test>	объем критерия
	size <NT>	*s.* H 170		
	size <ST>	*s.* S 28		
	size of the [critical] region <ST>	*s.* S 842		
S 1152	**SJ-group,** group which has a subnormal abelian series <GR>	SJ-Gruppe *f*	SJ-groupe *m*	SJ-группа
S 1153	**skeletal category** <CA>	reduzierte Kategorie *f*	catégorie *f* réduite	скелетная категория
S 1154	**skeleton,** simplex, abstract simplex <of a skeleton complex> <AT>	Gerüst *n*	simplexe *m*	остов, симплекс
S 1155	**skeleton** <of a category> <CA>	Skelett *n*	squelette *m*	скелет
S 1156	**skeleton** <of a nomogram> <NO>	Nomogrammskelett *n*, Skelett *n* <für Nomogramme>	squelette *m* <d'un abaque>	скелет номограммы
	skeleton <AT>	*s.* S 1158		
	skeleton <GP>	*s.* M 244		
S 1157	**skeleton complex,** unrestricted skeleton complex, simplicial complex, abstract simplicial complex, abstract complex <AT>	Eckpunktbereich *m*, simpliziales Schema *n*, abstrakter Komplex *m*	schéma (complexe) *m* simplicial	симплициальная схема, абстрактный комплекс, комплекс (полный комплекс) остовов, симплициальный комплекс, область вершин
S 1158	**skeleton complex,** skeleton <of a complex> <AT>	Gerüst *n*, Skelett *n*	squelette *m*	остов, комплекс остовов
S 1159	**skeleton of vertices** <AT>	Eckpunktgerüst *n*	squelette *m* des sommets	вершинный остов
S 1160	**skew axonometry,** general axonometry <DS>	schräge Axonometrie *f*	axonométrie *f* générale (oblique)	косоугольная (косая) аксонометрия
	skew curve <DG>	*s.* S 1306		
S 1161	**skew derivation** <of an algebra> <AL>	schiefe Derivation *f*	dérivation *f* gauche	косое дифференцирование
S 1162	**skew determinant** <MD>	schiefe Determinante *f*	déterminant *m* gauche	косой определитель
S 1163	**skew distribution,** asymmetric[al] distribution <ST>	schiefe (asymmetrische) Verteilung *f*	distribution *f* asymétrique (dissymétrique)	асимметричное (скошенное) распределение
	skew field <AL>	*s.* D 813		
S 1164	**skew helicoid** <GE>	schiefes Helikoid *n*, schiefe (scharfgängige) Schraubenfläche *f*, Korkzieherfläche *f*	hélicoïde *m* gauche	косой геликоид
S 1165	**skew-Hermitian bilinear form** <AL>	schiefhermitesche Bilinearform *f*	forme *f* bilinéaire antihermitienne	антиэрмитова билинейная форма
S 1166	**skew-Hermitian kernel,** antihermitian kernel, anti-Hermitian kernel <IE>	schiefhermitescher (antihermitescher) Kern *m*	noyau *m* antihermitien (anti-hermitien)	косоэрмитово (антиэрмитово) ядро
S 1167	**skew[-] Hermitian matrix, skew[-] hermitian matrix** <MD>	schiefhermitesche Matrix *f*	matrice *f* antihermitienne (antihermitique, antiautoadjointe)	косоэрмитова (антиэрмитова) матрица
S 1168	**skew-Hermitian part,** antihermitian part <AL, IE>	schiefhermitescher (antihermitescher) Anteil *m*, antihermitescher Teil *m*	partie *f* antihermitienne (anti-hermitienne)	косоэрмитова (антиэрмитова) часть

No.	English	German	French	Russian
S 1169	**skew-hermiticity** <AL, AN>	Schiefhermitezität *f*	antihermiticité *f*	антиэрмитовость
S 1170	**skew invariant** <AL>	schiefe Invariante *f*	invariant *m* gauche	косой инвариант
S 1171	**skew lines** <GE>	windschiefe (sich kreuzende) Geraden *fpl*	droites *fpl* gauches	скрещивающиеся прямые, некомпланарные прямые, скрещивающиеся линии
	skew matrix <MD>	*s.* S 1184		
S 1172	**skewness** <of a distribution> <ST>	Schiefe *f*, Asymmetrie *f*, Koeffizient *m* der Asymmetrie, Asymmetriekoeffizient *m*	dissymétrie *f*, asymétrie	асимметрия, показатель асимметрии
	skewness <ST>	*s.* M 341		
S 1173	**skew perspective affinity,** general perspective affinity <DS>	schiefe (allgemeine) perspektive Affinität *f*	affinité *f* perspective générale	общее (косое) перспективно-аффинное преобразование
S 1174	**skew polar** <AY>	windschiefe Polare *f*, Raumpolare *f*	polaire *f* gauche	косая поляра
S 1175	**skew polygon,** spatial polygon <EG>	windschiefes Vieleck *n*, Vieleck im Raum	polygone *m* gauche (spatial)	пространственный многоугольник
S 1176	**skew position** <EG>	windschiefe Lage *f*	position *f* gauche	косое (скрещенное) расположение
S 1177	**skew product** <$AB = -BA$> <AL>	schiefes Produkt *n*	produit *m* gauche	косое произведение
S 1178	**skew product,** Rédeian skew product <of groups> <GR>	schiefes Produkt *n*, Rédeisches schiefes Produkt	produit *m* gauche	косое произведение
	skew product <VT>	*s.* V 121		
S 1179	**skew projection,** oblique projection <as a parallel projection> <DS>	schiefe Parallelprojektion (Projektion) *f*, Schrägbild *n*	projection *f* oblique	косоугольная (косая) проекция
S 1180	**skew projection,** oblique projection <Steiner> <DS>	windschiefe Perspektivität *f*, schiefe (gebrochene) Projektion *f*	projection *f* oblique (gauche)	косая (косоугольная, скошенная, ломаная) проекция
S 1181	**skew projection** <in a linear space> <FA>	Schrägprojektion *f*	projection *f* oblique	косая проекция
S 1182	**skew quadrilateral** <GE>	windschiefes Vierseit *n*	quadrilatère *m* gauche	пространственный четырехсторонник
S 1183	**skew representation** <AL>	schiefe Darstellung *f*	représentation *f* gauche	косое представление
	skew ruled surface <GE>	*s.* N 371		
	skew surface <GE>	*s.* N 371		
	skew-symmetrical kernel <IE>	*s.* A 548		
S 1184	**skew[-]symmetrical matrix,** skew[-]symmetric matrix, antisymmetric[al] matrix, skew (alternating) matrix <MD>	schiefsymmetrische (schiefe) Matrix *f*	matrice *f* anti[-]symétrique (symétrique gauche)	кососимметрическая (антисимметрическая) матрица
	skew-symmetrical operator <FA>	*s.* A 777		
	skew-symmetrical tensor <VT>	*s.* A 564		
	skew-symmetrical tensor density <VT>	*s.* A 565		
	skew-symmetric bilinear mapping <AL>	*s.* A 772		
S 1185	**skew-symmetric determinant** <MD>	schiefsymmetrische (halbsymmetrische, überschlagene) Determinante *f*, Determinante einer schiefsymmetrischen Matrix	déterminant *m* antisymétrique (symétrique gauche, gauche-symétrique, semisymétrique)	кососимметрический определитель
	skew-symmetric form <AL>	*s.* A 546		
S 1186	**skew-symmetric inner product** <AL>	schiefsymmetrisches inneres Produkt *n*, schiefsymmetrisches Skalarprodukt *n*	produit *m* scalaire (intérieur) anti[-]symétrique	кососимметрическое скалярное (внутреннее) произведение
	skew[-]symmetric matrix <MD>	*s.* S 1184		
	skew-symmetric operator <FA>	*s.* A 777		
	skew-symmetric second-order tensor <VT>	*s.* A 566		
	skew-symmetric tensor density <VT>	*s.* A 565		
	skew symmetry <AL, AN>	*s.* A 783		
S 1187	**Skitovich['s] theorem** <ST>	Satz *m* von Skitowitsch, Skitowitschscher Satz	théorème *m* de Skitovitch	теорема Скитовича
	Skolem['s] equivalent (form) <LO>	*s.* S 1190		
S 1188	**Skolem['s] function** <LO>	Entscheidungsfunktion *f*, Skolemsche Funktion *f*	fonction *f* de Skolem (décision)	разрешающая функция, функция Сколема
S 1189	**Skolem['s] lattice** <LA>	Skolemscher Verband *m*	treillis *m* de Skolem	структура Сколема (Скулема)
	Skolem-Löwenheim paradox <LO>	*s.* S 1191		
	Skolem-Löwenheim theorem <LO>	*s.* L 1123		
S 1190	**Skolem['s] normal form,** Skolem['s] equivalent, Skolem['s] form <of a sentence> <LO>	Skolemsche Normalform (Normalformel) *f*	forme *f* normale de Skolem	нормальный вид Сколема, нормальная форма (формула) Сколема, сколемовская (скулемовская) [нормальная] форма
	Skolem['s] normal form for satisfiability <LO>	*s.* S 56		

S 1191	**Skolem['s] paradox,** paradox of Skolem-Löwenheim, Skolem-Löwenheim paradox, Löwenheim-Skolem paradox <LO>	Skolemsche Paradoxie *f*, Löwenheim-Skolemsches Paradoxon *n*	paradoxe *m* de Skolem, paradoxe de Löwenheim-Skolem	парадокс Сколема (Скулема)
S 1192	**Skolem['s] theorem** <LO>	Satz *m* von Skolem, Skolemscher Satz	théorème *m* de Skolem	теорема Сколема (Скулема)
S 1193	**sky-scraper sheaf** <AL, TO>	Wolkenkratzergarbe *f*	« sky-scraper sheaf » *m*	пучок небоскребов, небоскребный пучок
S 1194	**slack variable** <PG>	Schlupfvariable *f*, Zusatzvariable *f*, fiktive Variable *f*	variable *f* d'écart, variable additionnelle	слабая (нежесткая, дополнительная, добавочная, скользящая) переменная
S 1195	**slack variables [vector]** <PG>	Schlupfvariablenvektor *m*	vecteur *m* des variables d'écart	вектор слабых переменных
	slant height <EG>	*s.* A 808		
S 1196	**Slater['s] condition** <PG>	Slater-Bedingung *f*, Slatersche Regularitätsvoraussetzung *f*	condition *f* de Slater	условие Слэтера (Слейтера)
S 1197	**slender group** <GR>	schlanke Gruppe *f*		узкая группа
S 1198	**slide** <of a slide rule> <AN, IN>	Zunge *f* <des Rechenschiebers>	coulisseau *m*, réglette *f* [coulissante], coulisse *f* <de la règle à calcul>	движок <счетной линейки>
S 1199	**slide rule,** logarithmic slide rule <IN, NU>	Rechenschieber *m*, Rechenstab *m*, Logarithmenschieber *m*	règle *f* à calcul, règle logarithmique, baguette *f* logarithmique; règle de bureau d'études <à une longueur de 50 cm>; // arithmomètre *m*	логарифмическая линейка, счетная линейка
S 1200	**slide-rule graph (nomogram, nomograph),** nomogram with moving transparents, nomograph with moving transparents <NO>	Flächenschieber *m*, Schiebeblattnomogramm *n*, Gleitflächentafel *f*, Nomogramm *n* mit beweglichen Transparenten	abaque (nomogramme) *m* à transparents mobiles	транспарантная номограмма, номограмма с подвижными транспарантами, номограмма типа счетной линейки
	slice through *x* of *R* <SE>	*s.* F 158		
	slice through *X* of *R* <SE>	*s.* X 2		
	sliding average <ST>	*s.* M 930		
S 1201	**sliding vector** <GE, VT>	linienflüchtiger (gleitender) Vektor *m*, Stab *m*	vecteur *m* glissant, vecteur localisé (localisant) sur une droite	скользящий вектор
S 1202	**slippage test** <ST>	Verschiebungstest *m* <bei festgelegter Reihenfolge>; Slippagetest *m*	test *m* d'homogénéité des moyennes des échantillons successifs	критерий смещения
S 1203	**slit[-] region** <FT>	Schlitzgebiet *n*	domaine *m* muni de fentes	область с разрезами (надрезами)
S 1204	**slope** <tangent of the angle of slope> <DS>	Böschungsverhältnis *n*, Böschung *f*	talus *m*	тангенс угла наклона, коэффициент откоса
	slope <AY>	*s.* A 670		
	slope <DS>	*s.* S 2372		
	slope angle <DS>	*s.* A 664		
	slope curve <VA>	*s.* L 872		
S 1205	**slope function** <of a field of extremals> <VA>	Gefällfunktion *f*, Feldgröße *f*	fonction *f* de pente	функция наклона (спуска)
S 1206	**slope-intercept form,** Cartesian normal form <of the equation of a straight line> <AY>	Richtungsgleichung *f* <einer Geraden>	équation *f* d'une droite en forme $y = mx + b$	уравнение <прямой> в виде $y = mx + b$, уравнение <прямой> с угловым коэффициентом
S 1207	**slope line,** line of constant slope, curve of constant slope <a space curve on an arbitrary surface> <GE>	Loxodrome *f*, Böschungslinie *f*, Kurve *f* konstanter Neigung, allgemeine Schraubenlinie *f*	ligne *f* de pente	линия откоса, кривая постоянного склона, линия ската
	slope of cutting <DS>	*s.* E 195		
	slope of embankment <DS>	*s.* E 196		
	slope scale <DS>	*s.* G 366		
S 1208	**slow convergence** <AN, NU>	langsame (schlechte) Konvergenz *f*	convergence *f* lente	медленная сходимость
S 1209	**slowly increasing sequence** <SS>	langsam wachsende Folge *f*	suite *f* lentement croissante	медленно возрастающая последовательность
S 1210	**slowly oscillating sequence** <SS>	langsam oszillierende Folge *f*	suite *f* lentement oscillante	медленно колеблющаяся последовательность
S 1211	**slowly varying variable** <AN>	sich langsam ändernde Variable *f*	variable *f* à variation lente	медленно меняющаяся переменная
	Sluse['s] conchoid <GE>	*s.* D 338		
S 1212	**Slutski['s] theorem, Slutsky['s] theorem** <ST>	Satz *m* von Slutski (Slutsky), Slutskischer (Slutskyscher) Satz	théorème *m* de Slutsky	теорема Слуцкого
S 1213	**small / in the,** im Kleinen, locally, im kleinen <adv.> <GN>	im Kleinen, lokal, // im kleinen	localement	в малом, локально
S 1214	**small category** <CA>	kleine Kategorie *f*, Diagrammschema *n*	petite catégorie *f*	малая категория
S 1215	**small circle** <of a sphere> <EG>	Kleinkreis *m*, Nebenkreis *m* der Kugelfläche	petit cercle *m*, cercle secondaire	малый круг, окружность малого круга
S 1216	**small diagram** <CA>	kleines Diagramm *n*	petit diagramme *m*	малая диаграмма
S 1217	**small diagram schema** <CA>	kleines Diagrammschema *n*	petit schéma *m* de diagrammes	малая диаграммная схема
	smaller <AN, SE>	*s.* L 585		
	smaller element <SE>	*s.* E 2		
	smallest common multiple <AL, AR, NT>	*s.* L 241		

No.	English	German	French	Russian
S 1218	**smallest convex polygon containing all the points of support** <GE>	Stützpolygon *n*	base *f* (polygone *m*) de sustentation	опорное основание, опорный многоугольник
S 1219	**smallest element (member),** zero element, least element, first element, first member, universally minimal element <of a partially ordered set> <SE>	kleinstes Element *n*, Nullelement *n*, erstes Element, Anfangselement *n*	élément *m* minimum, minorant *m* universel, élément nul, plus petit élément, premier élément	наименьший элемент, минимум, абсолютно минимальный элемент
S 1220	**smallest subgroup containing the given subgroups** <GR>	von Untergruppen erzeugte Untergruppe *f*	réunion *f* complète de sous-groupes	подгруппа, порожденная данными подгруппами
S 1221	**smallest topology,** coarsest topology <TO>	gröbste Topologie *f*	topologie *f* la plus faible	слабейшая (самая грубая) топология
	smallest value <DI>	*s.* A 117		
S 1222	**small group** <CA, GR>	kleine Gruppe *f*	petit groupe *m*	малая группа
	small inductive dimension <TO>	*s.* W 69		
S 1223	**small left module** <AL>	kleiner Linksmodul *m*	petit module *m* à gauche	малый левый модуль
S 1224	**small right module** <AL>	kleiner Rechtsmodul *m*	petit module *m* à droite	малый правый модуль
S 1225	**small ring** <AL>	kleiner Ring *m*	petit anneau *m*	малое кольцо
S 1226	**small sample** <ST>	kleine Stichprobe *f*	petit échantillon *m*	малая выборка
S 1227	**small set** <SE>	kleine Menge *f*	petit ensemble *m*	малое множество
	small side <EG>	*s.* O 540		
S 1228	**small topological space** <TO>	kleiner topologischer Raum *m*	petit espace *m* topologique	малое топологическое пространство
S 1229	**smash [product],** contracted product, reduced product <of based spaces> <TO>	„Smash"-Produkt *n*, ∧-Produkt *n*	produit *m* réduit, « smash » *m*	стянутое произведение, ∧-произведение
	S-method <ST>	*s.* S 113		
S 1230	**Smirnov['s] test** <ST>	Smirnov-Test *m*, Smirnovscher Test *m*	test *m* de Smirnov	критерий Смирнова
S 1231	**Smirnov['s] theorem** <ST>	Satz *m* von N. W. Smirnow, Smirnowscher Satz	théorème *m* de Smirnov	теорема [Н. В.] Смирнова
S 1232	**Smith['s] continued fraction** <NT>	Smithscher Kettenbruch *m*	fraction *f* continue de [Stephen] Smith	цепная дробь Смита
S 1233	**Smith['s] law of variance** <ST>	Varianzgesetz *n* nach Smith, Smithsches Varianzgesetz	loi *f* de variance de Smith, loi de Smith	дисперсионный закон Смита, закон Смита
S 1234	**smooth curve** <GE, NU>	glatte Kurve *f*	courbe *f* lisse; courbe gentille (dérivable, où la différentielle est différente de zéro)	гладкая кривая
S 1235	**smoothing** <*e.g.*: of curves, functions, observations> <AN, ST>	Glättung *f*, Glätten *n*	lissage *m*	сглаживание
S 1236	**smoothing function** <NU>	Glättungsfunktion *f*, glättende Funktion *f*	fonction *f* de lissage	функция сглаживания
S 1237	**smooth morphism** <of an analytical space> <AG>	glatter Morphismus *m*	morphisme *m* lisse	гладкий морфизм
	smooth square <CA, HA>	*s.* E 659		
	smooth test <ST>	*s.* T 210		
	sn <FU>	*s.* A 609		
	snake lemma <CA, HA>	*s.* K 45		
	snakelike continuum <TO>	*s.* C 464		
	snap regula <GN, NU>	*s.* R 1514		
S 1238	**SN-group,** group with an abelian series <GR>	SN-Gruppe *f*	SN-groupe *m*	SN-группа
S 1239	**SN*-group** <GR>	SN*-Gruppe *f*	SN*-groupe *m*	SN*-группа
S 1240	**$\overline{SN}$-group** <GR>	$\overline{SN}$-Gruppe *f*	$\overline{SN}$-groupe *m*	$\overline{SN}$-группа
S 1241	**S-number** <NT>	*S*-Zahl *f*, Mahlersche *S*-Zahl	*S*-nombre *m*	*S*-число
S 1242	**Sobolev['s] embedding theorem** <FA>	Sobolevscher Einbettungssatz *m*	théorème *m* de l'immersion de Sobolev	теорема вложения Соболева
S 1243	**Sobolev['s] formula** <DE>	Formel *f* von Sobolev, Sobolevsche Formel	formule *f* de Sobolev	формула Соболева
S 1244	**Sobolev['s] space** <FA>	Sobolev-Raum *m*, Sobolevscher Raum *m*	espace *m* de Sobolev	пространство Соболева
S 1245	**socle** <of a group *or* module> <AL>	Sockel *m*, Remakscher Sockel <einer Gruppe *oder* eines Moduls>; unterste Schicht *f* <einer primären Gruppe>	socle *m* <d'un groupe *ou* module>	цоколь <группы *или* модуля>; нижний слой <примарной группы>
S 1246	**socle** <of a ring, an object, *or* a number field> <AL, CA, NT>	Sockel *m*	socle *m*	цоколь
S 1247	**soft sheaf** <AL, TO>	weiche Garbe *f*	faisceau *m* mou	мягкий пучок
S 1248	**sojourn time** <ST>	Verweilzeit *f*, Aufenthaltsdauer *f*	temps *m* de séjour	время пребывания
	solenoid <GR>	*s.* S 1249		
	solenoidal field <VT>	*s.* Z 27		
S 1249	**solenoidal group,** solenoid <GR>	solenoidale Gruppe *f*, Solenoidgruppe *f*, Solenoid *n*	solénoïde *m*	соленоидальная группа, соленоид
	solenoidal vector <VT>	*s.* Z 27		
S 1250	**solid,** body, geometric body <EG>	Körper *m*, geometrischer Körper	solide *m*, corps *m*, corps *m* géométrique	тело, геометрическое тело
S 1251	**solid angle** <EG>	Raumwinkel *m*, // räumlicher Winkel *m*	angle *m* solide	телесный угол
	solid geometry <EG>	*s.* S 1755		
	solid *n*-sphere <GE>	*s.* C 900		
	solid *n*-sphere <TO>	*s.* C 886		

S 1252	**solid of equal volume,** [spatial] figure of equal volume <in the three-dimensional space> <EG>	Körper *m* (räumliche Figur *f*, Figur) gleichen Rauminhalts, volumengleicher (inhaltsgleicher) Körper, volumengleiche (inhaltsgleiche) [räumliche] Figur	figure *f* [spatiale] équivalente, solide *m* équivalent	равновеликая [пространственная] фигура; тело, имеющее равный объем
	solid of revolution (rotation) <EG>	*s.* B 529		
S 1253	**solid sine,** S_i <EG>	Eckensinus *m*, Sinus *m* der Ecke <v. Staudt>, S_i	sinus *m* solide (du trièdre *Oxyz*) <v. Staudt>	синус телесного угла
S 1254	**solid space** <TO>	solider Raum *m*	espace *m* solide	
	solid sphere <DI, GE, TO>	*s.* B 38		
	solid sphere <EG>	*s.* S 1431		
S 1255	**solid spherical function (harmonic),** spatial [spherical] harmonic, spherical harmonic, spatial spherical function <of degree *n*> <FU>	räumliche Kugelfunktion *f* <*n*-ter Ordnung, *n*-ten Grades>	fonction *f* [harmonique] sphérique spatiale, harmonique *f* sphérique [spatiale]	объемная (пространственная) сферическая функция, шаровая функция <степени *n*>
	solidus <GN>	*s.* F 571		
S 1256	**solitaire** <TG>	Solitärspiel *n*, Solitaire *n*	solitaire *m*	игра с одним участником, «солитер»
	solubility <GN>	*s.* S 1275		
S 1257	**solubility by radicals** <AL>	Auflösbarkeit *f* durch Radikale	résolubilité *f* par radicaux	разрешимость в радикалах
S 1258	**solubility in integers** <NT>	Lösbarkeit *f* in ganzen Zahlen	résolubilité *f* en nombres entiers	разрешимость в целых числах
	soluble equation <AL>	*s.* E 352		
	soluble group <GR>	*s.* S 1278		
S 1259	**soluble minimax group,** polyminimax group <AL>	Polyminimaxgruppe *f*, auflösbare Minimaxgruppe *f*	groupe *m* poly-minimax	полиминимаксная группа
S 1260	**soluble polynomial** <in Galois' theory> <AL>	auflösbares (metazyklisches) Polynom *n*	polynôme *m* résoluble	разрешимый полином (многочлен)
S 1261	**solution,** root <of an equation> <result> <AL>	Lösung *f*, Wurzel *f*	solution *f*, racine *f*	решение, корень
S 1262	**solution,** solving, integration <process> <DE>	Lösung *f*, Integration *f*	solution *f*, intégration *f*	решение, интегрирование
S 1263	**solution,** strict solution <Bourbaki>, integral <result> <DE>	Lösung *f*, Integral *n*	solution *f*, intégrale *f*, solution stricte <Bourbaki>	решение, интеграл
S 1264	**solution** <of a problem> <result> <GN>	Lösung *f*	résolution *f*	решение
S 1265	**solution,** program[me] <result> <PG>	Lösung *f*, Programm *n*	solution *f*, programme *m*	план, решение, программа
S 1266	**solution** <of a game> <TG>	Lösung *f*	solution *f*	решение
	solution by differentiation <DE>	*s.* I 676		
S 1267	**solution by inspection** <of equations> <AL>	Lösen *n* (Lösung *f*, Auflösen *n*, Auflösung *f*) durch Probieren, Lösen (Lösung) durch Erraten und Einsetzen	solution *f* par tatônnement	решение подбором
S 1268	**solution by radicals** <AL>	Lösung *f* (Lösen *n*, Auflösung *f*, Auflösen *n*) durch Radikale	résolution *f* par (en) radicaux, solution *f* par (en) radicaux	решение в радикалах
	solution curve <DE>	*s.* I 618		
S 1269	**solution formula** <for equations> <AL>	Auflösungsformel *f*	formule *f* [de résolution]	формула решения
S 1270	**solution matrix,** matrix of solutions <FD>	Lösungsmatrix *f*	matrice *f* de solutions	матрица решений
	solution of a primal problem <PG>	*s.* P 1260		
S 1271	**solution space,** subspace of solutions <of linear equations> <AL>	Lösungsraum *m*	espace *m* des solutions	пространство решений
	solution surface <DE>	*s.* I 663		
S 1272	**solution tree** <PG>	Lösungsbaum *m*	arbre *m* de solution	дерево решений
S 1273	**solution vector** <AL, DE, PG>	Lösungsvektor *m*	vecteur *m* solution	вектор-решение <AL, DE, PG>; вектор-план <PG>
S 1274	**solvability** <of a group> <GR>	Auflösbarkeit *f*	résolubilité *f*	разрешимость
S 1275	**solvability,** solubility <of an equation> <GN>	Lösbarkeit *f*, Auflösbarkeit *f*	résolubilité *f*, solubilité *f*	разрешимость
S 1276	**solvability** <of a problem> <GN>	Lösbarkeit *f*	résolubilité *f*	разрешимость
	solvable equation <AL>	*s.* M 425		
S 1277	**solvable extension [field]** <in Galois' theory> <AL>	auflösbarer Erweiterungskörper *m*, metazyklischer Erweiterungskörper, metazyklische Erweiterung *f*	extension *f* résoluble	разрешимое расширение
S 1278	**solvable group,** soluble group <GR>	auflösbare Gruppe *f*, metazyklische Gruppe <Weber>, stark auflösbare Gruppe <Specht>	groupe *m* résoluble (métabélien)	разрешимая группа
S 1279	**solvable ideal** <of a Lie algebra> <AL>	auflösbares Ideal *n*	idéal *m* résoluble	разрешимый идеал
S 1280	**solvable Lie group,** integrable Lie group <GR>	auflösbare Liesche Gruppe *f*, integrierbare Liesche Gruppe	groupe *m* de Lie résoluble	разрешимая группа Ли
S 1281	**solvable [optimization] problem** <of programming> <PG>	lösbares Optimierungsproblem *n*	problème *m* d'optimisation résoluble, problème résoluble <de programmation>	разрешимая задача оптимизации, разрешимая задача <программирования>

S 1282	**solving** <e.g. an equation *or* a problem> <process> <GN>	Lösen *n*, Lösung *f*	solution *f*	решение, нахождение решения
S 1283	**solving,** resolving <an equation for . . . *or* with respect to . . .> <process> <GN>	Auflösung *f*, Auflösen *n* <einer Gleichung nach . . .>	résolution <d'une équation en . . .>	разрешение <уравнения относительно . . . *или* по. . .>
	solving <DE>	*s.* S 1262		
S 1284	**solvmanifold** <AL>	homogener Raum *m* einer zusammenhängenden auflösbaren Lieschen Gruppe	espace *m* homogène de Lie pour un groupe résoluble connexe	солвмногообразие
S 1285	**Sommerfeld['s] integral [equation]** <of the Bessel functions> <FU>	Sommerfeldsche Integraldarstellung *f* <der Zylinderfunktionen>	intégrale *f* de Sommerfeld	интеграл Зоммерфельда
S 1286	**Sonine['s] polynomial** <FU>	Soninesches Polynom *n*, Polynom von Sonine	polynôme *m* de Sonine	полином Сонина
S 1287	**Sono['s] ring** <AL>	Sonoscher Ring *m*	anneau *m* de Sono	кольцо Соно
S 1288	**Soreau['s] equation** <NO>	Soreausche Gleichung *f*	équation *f* de Soreau	уравнение Соро
S 1289	**Sorites,** chain-rule inference, chain inference <LO>	Sorites *m*, Kettenschluß *m*	sorite *m*	сорит, цепное заключение
	soroban <IN>	*s.* C 10		
S 1290	**soundness,** semantic consistency <LO>	semantische Widerspruchsfreiheit *f*	consistance *f* sémantique	семантическая непротиворечивость
S 1291	**sound system,** semantically consistent system <LO>	semantisch (inhaltlich) widerspruchsfreies System *n*, interpretierbares System	système *m* sémantiquement consistant	содержательно непротиворечивая система, интерпретируемая система
S 1292	**source** <of a transportation network> <GP, PG>	Eingang *m*, Quelle *f*	entrée *f*	источник
S 1293	**source** <GP, VT>	Quelle *f* <GP, VT>; Knotenpunkt *m* ohne Vorgänger <GP>	source *f*	источник
S 1294	**source,** leading term <of a covariant> <IV>	Leitglied *n*	terme *m* principal, source *f*	старший член
	source <CA>	*s.* D 851		
	source-free field <VT>	*s.* Z 27		
	source function <DE, PO>	*s.* G 416		
S 1295	**source of variation** <ST>	Variationsursache *f*, Streuungsursache *f*	source *f* de variation	источник (причина) вариации
S 1296	**source strength** <of a vector field> <VT>	Quellstärke *f*, Quellenstärke *f*, Ergiebigkeit *f* der Quelle	intensité *f* de la source	интенсивность источника
S 1297	**Souslin['s] condition,** Suslin['s] condition <for an ordered set> <SE>	Suslinsche Bedingung *f*	condition *f* de Souslin	условие Суслина
S 1298	**Souslin['s] conjecture (hypothesis)** <ME, TO>	Suslinsche Vermutung *f*	hypothèse *f* de Souslin	гипотеза Суслина
S 1299	**Souslin['s] number** <TO>	Suslinsche Zahl *f*	nombre *m* de Souslin	число Суслина
	Souslin['s] problem <SE>	*s.* P 1574		
	Souslin set <TO>	*s.* A 645		
S 1300	**Souslin['s] space** <TO>	Suslinscher Raum *m*, Suslin-Raum *m*	espace *m* [topologique] souslinien, espace de Souslin	суслинское [топологическое] пространство
	Souslin subset <TO>	*s.* A 645		
S 1301	**Souslin['s] theorem** <TO>	Satz *m* von Suslin, Suslinscher Satz	théorème *m* de Souslin	теорема Суслина
S 1302	**Southwell['s] formula** <DE>	Aufspaltungsformel *f* von Southwell, Southwellsche Formel *f*	formule *f* de Southwell	формула Саусвелла
	sp <EG>	*s.* Q 45		
	sp <MD>	*s.* T 714		
S 1303	**space** <AN, GE>	Raum *m*	espace *m*	пространство
S 1304	**space,** body, polyhedron <of a complex> <AT>	Körper *m*, Raum *m*, Polyeder *n* <eines Komplexes>	polyèdre *m* <attaché à un complexe>	тело, пространство, полиэдр <составленный комплексом>
	space <SE>	*s.* U 364		
	space <TO>	*s.* T 544		
	σ-space <TO>	*s.* S 832		
	1-space <AN, GE>	*s.* O 81		
	3-space <GE>	*s.* T 448		
	space complete in the strong topology <FA>	*s.* S 1967		
S 1305	**space connected between *A* and *B*** <TO>	zwischen *A* und *B* zusammenhängender Raum *m*	espace *m* connexe entre *A* et *B*	связное между *A* и *B* пространство
	space connected im kleinen at the point *P* <TO>	*s.* S 1317		
	space contractible into itself <TO>	*s.* C 2265		
S 1306	**space curve,** spatial curve, curve of double curvature, non-plane curve, twisted curve, skew curve <of degree *n*, of the *n*-th order> <in the three-dimensional Euclidean *or* projective space> <DG>	Raumkurve *f*, Kurve *f* doppelter Krümmung, doppelt[-]gekrümmte Kurve, nichtebene Kurve, räumliche Kurve <*n*-ter Ordnung>	courbe *f* spatiale, courbe dans l'espace, courbe à double courbure, courbe gauche, courbe torsadée, courbe non plane <du *n*-e ordre>	пространственная кривая, кривая в пространстве, кривая двоякой кривизны, неплоская кривая <*n*-ой степени>

No.	English	German	French	Russian
S 1307	**space curve of constant curvature** <DG>	Raumkurve *f* konstanter Krümmung, Kurve *f* konstanter Krümmung, windschiefer Kreis *m*, Mongesche Kurve	courbe *f* gauche à courbure constante, courbe à courbure constante, cercle *m* gauche	пространственная кривая постоянной кривизны
S 1308	**space curve of degree four, space curve of fourth order,** quartic space curve, quartic curve in space <AG>	Raumkurve *f* vierter (4.) Ordnung, räumliche Kurve vierter (4.) Ordnung	quartique *f* gauche, quartique, courbe *f* gauche du quatrième (4e) ordre	пространственная кривая четвертой (4-ой) степени
S 1309	**space curve of order three, space curve of third order,** twisted cubic, cubic conic, cubic conic section, C_3 <AG>	kubische Raumkurve *f*, Raumkubik *f*, Raumkurve dritter (3.) Ordnung, räumliche Kurve dritter (3.) Ordnung, kubischer Kegelschnitt *m*, Raumkegelschnitt *m*, C_3	cubique *f* gauche, courbe *f* gauche du troisième ordre, courbe à double courbure du troisième ordre, conique *f* gauche, conique *f* cubique, C_3	пространственная кривая третьего порядка, C_3
	space deformable into a point <TO>	*s.* C 2265		
S 1310	**space element,** element of space <DI>	Raumelement *n*	élément *m* d'espace	элемент пространства
S 1311	**space everywhere of the first category** <TO>	Raum *m*, der überall von erster Kategorie ist	espace *m* toujours de première (I[e]) catégorie	пространство заведомо первой категории
	space form <GE>	*s.* C 822		
	space having a countable basis <TO>	*s.* C 1512		
S 1312	**space homologically locally connected** <in dimension *n*>, homologically locally connected space <in dimension *n*> <AT>	homologisch lokal zusammenhängender Raum *m* <in der Dimension *n*>	espace *m* homologiquement localement connexe <en dimension *n*>	гомологически локально связное <в размерности *n*> пространство
	space integral <DI>	*s.* V 213		
S 1313	**space l^2,** space l_2, Hilbert['s] co-ordinate (sequence) space[l^2], Hilbert['s] space of sequences <FA>	Hilbertscher Folgenraum *m*, Hilbertscher Zahlenraum, Folgenraum l^2, Raum *m* l^2, l^2	espace *m* de Hilbert des coordonnées (suites), espace l^2, l^2	пространство l_2, гильбертово пространство последовательностей, l_2
S 1314	**space L^2,** space L_2, Hilbert['s] function space [L^2], Hilbert['s] space of functions <FA>	Hilbertscher Funktionenraum *m* [$L^2[a,b]$], Funktionenraum $L^2[a,b]$ ($L^2(\mu)$), Raum *m* L^2, L^2, $L^2[a,b]$, $L^2(\mu)$	espace *m* de Hilbert fonctionnel, espace fonctionnel L^2, espace L^2, espace fonctionnel complexe L^2, L^2	пространство L_2, функциональное пространство L_2 (Гильберта), L_2
S 1315	**space-like manifold** <DE>	raumartige Mannigfaltigkeit *f*	variété *f* du genre espace	пространственно-подобное многообразие
S 1316	**space-like oriented surface** <DE>	raumartig orientierte Fläche *f*	surface *f* orientée du genre espace	пространственно-подобно ориентированная поверхность
S 1317	**space locally connected at a point *P*,** space connected im kleinen at the point *P* <TO>	in einem Punkt *P* lokal (im Kleinen) zusammenhängender Raum *m*	espace *m* localement connexe en un point *P*	связное в точке *P* пространство
S 1318	**space l_p,** Hölder-Riesz space, Minkowsky space, l_p <FA>	Raum *m* l_p, Hölder-Rieszscher Raum, l_p	espace *m* l_p, espace de Hölder-Riesz	пространство l_p, l_p, пространство Гельдера-Риса
	space L^p (L_p) <FA>	*s.* L 272		
S 1319	**space of coefficients** <of a quadratic form> <NT>	Koeffizientenraum *m*	espace *m* des coefficients	пространство коэффициентов
S 1320	**space of connectivity *k*** <TO>	*k*-fach zusammenhängender Raum *m*	espace *m* *k*-connexe	*k*-связное пространство
	space of countable weight <TO>	*s.* C 1512		
S 1321	**space of infinite connectivity** <TO>	unendlich[fach]zusammenhängender Raum *m*	espace *m* de connexion infinie	бесконечносвязное пространство
	space of infinite [number of] dimensions <AN, GE, TO>	*s.* I 444		
S 1322	**space of left cosets,** left coset space <AL, TO>	Raum *m* der Linksnebenklassen	espace *m* des classes à gauche	пространство левых смежных классов
	space of loops <TO>	*s.* L 1108		
S 1323	**space of matrices** <AL, FA>	Matrizenraum *m*	espace *m* de matrices	пространство матриц
S 1324	**space of prime parts** <TO>	Kontinuum *n* der Primteile	espace *m* des constituants premiers	пространство простых составляющих
S 1325	**space of quaternions,** quaternion space <GE>	Quaternionenraum *m*	espace *m* de quaternions	кватернионное пространство, пространство кватернионов
S 1326	**space of reals** <TO>	Raum *m* der reellen Zahlen	espace *m* des nombres réels	пространство действительных чисел
	space of representation <AL, RE>	*s.* R 841		
S 1327	**space of right cosets,** right coset space <AL, TO>	Raum *m* der Rechtsnebenklassen	espace *m* des classes à droite	пространство правых смежных классов
	space of right cosets <AL>	*s.* F 56		
S 1328	**space of states,** phase space <SP>	Zustandsraum *m*, Phasenraum *m*	espace *m* des états (phases)	пространство состояний, фазовое пространство
S 1329	**space of the generalized almost periodic functions in the sense**	B^p-fastperiodischer Raum *m*	espace *m* des fonctions presque-périodiques généralisées de	пространство обобщенных почти периодических функций в смысле

No.	English	German	French	Russian
and still: S 1329	**of A.S. Besicovich,** B_p almost-periodic space <AP>		[A.] Besicovitch	А. Безиковича
S 1330	**space of the generalized almost periodic functions in the sense of H. Weyl,** W_p almost-periodic space <AP>	W^p-fastperiodischer Raum *m*	espace *m* des fonctions presque-périodiques généralisées de [H.] Weyl	пространство обобщенных почти периодических функций в смысле Г. Вейля
S 1331	**space of the generalized almost periodic functions in the sense of V. V. Stepanov,** S_p almost-periodic space <AP>	S^p-fastperiodischer Raum *m*	espace *m* des fonctions presque-périodiques généralisées de [W.] Stepanoff	пространство обобщенных почти периодических функций в смысле В. В. Степанова
	space of the same homotopy type <TO>	*s.* H 512		
S 1332	**space point,** point in space <GE>	Raumpunkt *m*	point *m* de (dans) l'espace	точка в пространстве
S 1333	**space point set** <GE, TO>	räumliche Punktmenge *f*	ensemble *m* de points dans l'espace	пространственное точечное множество
S 1334	**space quadratic transformation** <AG>	räumliche quadratische Transformation *f*	transformation *f* quadratique dans l'espace	пространственное квадратичное преобразование
	space satisfying the [second] axiom of countability <TO>	*s.* C 1512		
S 1335	**space singularity** <AG>	Raumsingularität *f*	singularité *f* spatiale	пространственная особенность
S 1336	**space structure,** structure <of a space> <TO>	Raumstruktur *f*, Struktur *f* <eines Raumes>	structure *f* <d'un espace>	структура <пространства>
S 1337	**space which can be made a Banach space** <TO>	Raum *m*, der zu einem Banach-Raum gemacht werden kann	espace *m* banachisable	пространство, которое может быть сделано банаховым
S 1338	**space which is mapped** <TO>	Urbildraum *m*	espace-source *m*	пространство прообразов, пространство-прообраз
	space which is the union of a countable number of compact subsets <TO>	*s.* S 814		
	space with a countable base <TO>	*s.* C 1512		
S 1339	**space with semi-norms,** seminormed space <FA>	Raum *m* mit Seminormen	espace *m* [vectoriel] semi-normé, espace à semi-normes	полунормированное пространство, квазинормированное пространство
	S_p almost-periodic function <AP>	*s.* G 133		
S 1340	**S_p almost-periodic point** <AP>	S^p-fastperiodischer Punkt *m*	point *m* presque-périodique au sens de [W.] Stepanoff	почти периодическая точка в смысле В. В. Степанова
	S_p almost-periodic space <AP>	*s.* S 1331		
S 1341	**span / to,** to generate <a vector space> <AL>	aufspannen, erzeugen, bestimmen	engendrer, sous-tendre, déterminer	натягивать
S 1342	**span / to** <e.g. a figure> <GE>	aufspannen	étendre	натягивать
S 1343	**span** <of arcs of curves> <FA>	Abstand *m*	écart *m* <Fréchet>	расстояние
	spanning tree <GP>	*s.* M 244		
S 1344	**span of a compass (pair of compasses)** <EG, IN>	Zirkelöffnung *f*, Zirkelweite *f*	ouverture *f* de compas	раствор циркуля
	span of *M* <AL, FA>	*s.* S 2187		
S 1345	**sparse matrix** <MD>	dünnbesetzte (schwachbesetzte) Matrix *f*, verdünnte Matrix *f*, Matrix mit nur wenigen Elementen ungleich Null	matrice *f* creuse	разреженная матрица
	spatial configuration <SG>	*s.* C 1869		
S 1346	**spatial co-ordinates** <AY>	Raumkoordinaten *fpl*, räumliche Koordinaten *fpl*	coordonnées *fpl* spatiales	пространственные координаты
	spatial curve <DG>	*s.* S 1306		
	spatial figure of equal volume <EG>	*s.* S 1252		
S 1347	**spatial isomorphism** <of a W^*-algebra, C^*-algebra> <FA>	räumlicher Isomorphismus *m*	isomorphisme *m* spatial	пространственный изоморфизм
S 1348	**spatial point** <of a Riemannian manifold> <DG>	spatialer Punkt *m*	point *m* spatial	пространственная точка
	spatial polygon <EG>	*s.* S 1175		
	spatial spherical function (harmonic) <FU>	*s.* S 1255		
	Spearman['s] coefficient of rank correlation <ST>	*s.* S 1350		
S 1349	**Spearman['s] matrix** <ST>	Spearmansche Matrix *f*	matrice *f* de Spearman	матрица Спирмэна
S 1350	**Spearman['s] rank correlation coefficient,** Spearman['s] coefficient of rank	Spearmans[cher] Rangkorrelationskoeffizient *m*, Rangkorrelationskoeffizient, Koeffizient *m*	coefficient *m* de corrélation des rangs de Spearman, coefficient de Spearman, coefficient de coordi-	коэффициент ранговой корреляции Спирмэна (по Спирмэну), ранговый коэффициент

	correlation, index of cogradualion, rank correlation coefficient, coefficient of rank correlation <ST>	der Rangkorrelation	nation [de Spearman], coefficient de corrélation des rangs	корреляции Спирмэна (по Спирмэну), коэффициент ранговой корреляции, коэффициент корреляции рангов
S 1351	**Spearman['s] rule** <ST>	Spearmansche Faustregel *f*	règle *f* de Spearman	правило Спирмэна
	spec <AL>	*s.* S 1424		
S 1352	**special Abelian function,** Abelian function <FT>	spezielle Abelsche Funktion *f*, Abelsche Funktion	fonction *f* abélienne spéciale, fonction abélienne	специальная абелева функция, абелева функция
	special affine group <GE>	*s.* F 359		
S 1353/4	**special Bézout theorem** <AG, AL>	spezieller Bézoutscher Satz *m*	théorème *m* de Bézout spécial	специальная теорема Безу
	special class <AG>	*s.* S 1357		
S 1355	**special complex [of lines (rays)],** singular complex [of lines (rays)], special (singular) linear complex [of lines (rays)] <PJ>	spezieller (singulärer) [linearer] Strahlenkomplex (Geradenkomplex, Komplex) *m*, Strahlengebüsch *n*	complexe *m* [de droites] spécial (singulier), complexe [de droites] linéaire singulier (spécial)	специальный (сингулярный) комплекс [прямых (лучей)], специальный (сингулярный) линейный комплекс [прямых (лучей)]
S 1356	**special converse law of contraposition** <LO>	spezielles inverses Gesetz *n* der Wendung	loi *f* de contraposition inverse spéciale	особенный обратный закон контрапозиции
S 1357	**special divisor class,** special class <AG>	spezielle Divisorklasse (Klasse) *f*	classe *f* [de diviseurs] spéciale	специальный класс [дивизоров]
S 1358	**special eigenvalue problem** <DE>	spezielles Eigenwertproblem *n*	problème *m* aux valeurs propres spécial	специальная задача на собственные значения
S 1359	**special eigenvalue problem for matrices** <AL, NU>	spezielle Matrizen-Eigenwertaufgabe *f*	problème *m* spécial de valeur propre pour les matrices	специальная матричная задача на собственные значения
S 1360	**special group** <as a linear group> <GR>	spezielle Gruppe *f*	groupe *m* spécial	специальная группа
S 1361	**special homology manifold** <AT>	spezielle Homologiemannigfaltigkeit *f*	variété *f* homologique spéciale	специальное гомологическое многообразие
S 1362	**specialization** <AG, TO>	Spezialisierung *f* <AG, TO>; relationstreue Spezialisierung <AG>	spécialisation *f*	специализация
S 1363	**specialization chain** <for a place> <AL>	Spezialisierungskette *f*	chaîne *f* de spécialisations	цепочка специализаций
S 1364	**specialization class** <AG>	Spezialisierungsklasse *f*	classe *f* de spécialisation	класс специализации
S 1365	**specialization cycle** <AG>	Spezialisierungszyklus *m*	spécialisation *f* d'un cycle	специализация цикла
S 1366	**specialization ideal** <AL>	Spezialisierungsideal *n*	idéal *m* de spécialisation	идеал специализации
S 1367	**specialization multiplicity** <AG>	spezialisierungstheoretische Multiplizität *f*, Spezialisierungsmultiplizität *f*	multiplicité *f* de spécialisation	кратность в смысле теории специализаций
S 1368	**specialization[-] ring,** quotient[-] ring <AG, AL>	Spezialisierungsring *m*	anneau *m* de spécialisation	кольцо специализации
S 1369	**specialization theorem** <AG>	Spezialisierungssatz *m*	théorème *m* de spécialisation	теорема специализации
S 1370	**specialization theory** <AG>	Spezialisierungstheorie *f*	théorie *f* des spécialisations	теория специализаций
S 1371	**special Jordan ring** <AL>	spezieller Jordan-Ring *m*	anneau *m* de Jordan spécial	специальное жорданово кольцо
S 1372	**special Laplace transform[ation]** <IT>	spezielle Laplace-Transformation *f*	transformation *f* de Laplace spéciale	специальное преобразование Лапласа
S 1373	**special law of contraposition** <LO>	spezielles Gesetz *n* der Wendung	loi *f* de contraposition spéciale	особенный закон контрапозиции
S 1374	**special law of reductio ad absurdum** <LO>	Theorem *n* der Selbstwiderlegung, Schluß *m* in contrarium	loi *f* de démonstration par l'absurde, réduction *f* à l'absurde, loi de réduction à l'absurde	
S 1375	**special Lie algebra** <AL>	spezielle Liesche Algebra *f*	algèbre *f* de Lie spéciale	специальная лиева алгебра
	special linear complex [of lines (rays)] <PJ>	*s.* S 1355		
S 1376	**special linear group,** unimodular group, $SL(n)$ <of dimension *n*; over *K*> <GR>	spezielle lineare Gruppe *f*, unimodulare Gruppe <für *n* Variable; über dem Körper *K*>	groupe *m* spécial linéaire, groupe unimodulaire (linéaire unimodulaire) <d'ordre *n*, à *n* variables, de degré *n*, de type *n*; défini sur *K*, sur le corps *K*>	специальная линейная группа, линейная унимодулярная группа, унимодулярная группа <от *n* переменных; над *K*>
S 1377	**special linear homogeneous group,** $SL(n,q)$ <GR>	spezielle lineare homogene Gruppe *f*	groupe *m* linéaire et homogène spécial	специальная линейная однородная группа
	special linear system <AG>	*s.* S 1385		
S 1378	**special orthogonal group,** proper orthogonal group, $SO(n,K)$ <of dimension *n*; over *K*) <AL, GR>	spezielle (eigentliche, engere) orthogonale Gruppe *f* <für *n* Variable; über dem Körper *K*>	groupe *m* orthogonal propre (spécial, unimodulaire), groupe spécial orthogonal <de degré *n*, à *n* variables, de type *n*; défini sur *K*, sur le corps *K*>	специальная ортогональная группа, ортогональная унимодулярная группа, собственная ортогональная группа <от *n* переменных; над *K*>
	special orthogonal group <AY, GR>	*s.* R 1404		
S 1379	**special point[-] group** <AG>	Spezialgruppe *f* <Punktgruppe mit speziellen Eigenschaften>	groupe *m* spécial	специальная точечная группа
S 1380	**special rank** <of a group> <GR>	spezieller Rang *m*	rang *m* spécial	специальный ранг

	English	German	French	Russian
S 1381	**special representation** <of a Jordan algebra> <RE>	spezielle Darstellung *f*	représentation *f* spéciale	специальное представление
S 1382	**special resultant** <Cayley>; reduced resultant <Brill> <AL>	reduzierte Resultante *f* <Cayleysche; Brillsche>	résultant *m* réduit <Cayley, Brill>; résultant spécial <Cayley>	редуцированный результант
	special Riccati equation <DE>	*s.* R 978		
S 1383	**special Ricci manifold (space, variety)** <DG>	spezielle Ricci-Mannigfaltigkeit *f*, spezieller Ricci-Raum *m*	variété *f* de Ricci spéciale, espace *m* de Ricci spécial	специальное многообразие (пространство) Риччи
S 1384	**special rule of detachment** <LO>	spezielle Abtrennungsregel *f*	règle *f* de détachement spéciale	особенное правило отделения
S 1385	**special system,** special linear system <AG>	ausgezeichnete (speziale, speziale lineare) Schar *f*, Spezialschar *f*	système *m* spécial	специальная линейная система
	special unitarian group <GR>	*s.* U 252		
S 1386	**special valuation** <AL>	spezielle Bewertung *f* <Werte sind reelle Zahlen>	valuation *f* spéciale	специальное нормирование
S 1387	**special valuation ring** <AL>	spezieller Bewertungsring *m*	anneau *m* de valuation spéciale	кольцо специального нормирования
	special value <GN>	*s.* S 1393		
S 1388	**special zero** <of a polynomial ideal> <AL>	spezielle Nullstelle *f*	zéro *m* spécial	специальный нуль
	species of algebras <UA> <UA>	*s.* S 872		
S 1389	**species of structure** <AL, CA>	Gattung *f* von Strukturen	espèce *f* de structures	род структуры
S 1390	**specific curvature** <of a surface> <CS>	spezifische Krümmung *f*	courbure *f* spécifique	удельная кривизна <области на выпуклой поверхности>
	specific curvature <DG>	*s.* T 621		
	specific factor <ST>	*s.* U 215		
	specificity <ST>	*s.* U 220		
S 1391	**specific qualitative factor** <ST>	spezifisch qualitativer Faktor *m*	facteur *m* qualitatif spécifique	специфический качественный фактор
	specific regression <ST>	*s.* R 500		
S 1392	**specific sign** <of a theory> <LO>	Einzelzeichen *n*, spezifisches Zeichen *n*	signe *m* spécifique	специальный знак
S 1393	**specific value,** special (particular) value <of a function, etc.> <GN>	besonderer (spezieller) Wert *m*	valeur *f* particulière (spéciale)	особенное значение
S 1394	**spectral category** <CA>	Spektralkategorie *f*	catégorie *f* spectrale	спектральная категория
S 1395	**spectral circle** <FA>	Spektralkreis *m*	cercle *m* spectral	спектральный круг
	spectral decomposition <FA>	*s.* S 1413		
S 1396	**spectral density,** power density <SP>	Spektraldichte *f*	densité *f* spectrale	спектральная плотность
	spectral displacement <DE, MD, NU>	*s.* S 1417		
S 1397	**spectral element** <FA>	Spektralelement *n*	élément *m* spectral	спектральный элемент
S 1398	**spectral family,** spectral function, spectral resolution [of unity], resolution of the identity <FA>	Spektralschar *f*, Spektralfunktion *f*, Zerlegung *f* der Einheit	famille (fonction) *f* spectrale, partition *f* de l'unité, décomposition *f* de l'identité, projecteur *m* spectral	спектральное семейство, спектральная функция, разложение единицы
S 1399	**spectral family,** spectral scale <on a set> <RF>	Spektralschar *f*	famille *f* spectrale	спектральное семейство
S 1400	**spectral family in the broad sense,** generalized spectral family (function), generalized partition of unity <FA>	verallgemeinerte Spektralschar (Spektralfunktion) *f*, verallgemeinerte Zerlegung *f* der Einheit	famille *f* spectrale au sens large, famille (fonction *f*) spectrale généralisée, partition *f* généralisée de l'unité	спектральное семейство в широком смысле, обобщенное спектральное семейство, обобщенная спектральная функция, обобщенное разбиение единицы
S 1401	**spectral function,** power function, integrated power function, power spectrum, integrated power spectrum <SP>	Spektralfunktion *f*, spektrale Verteilungsfunktion *f*	fonction *f* spectrale, fonction de distribution spectrale	спектральная функция
	spectral function <FA>	*s.* S 1398		
S 1402	**spectral functor** <AL, CA>	Spektralfunktor *m*	foncteur *m* spectral	спектральный функтор
S 1403	**spectral integral** <FA, SP>	Spektralintegral *n*, Integral *n* bezüglich eines Spektralmaßes	intégrale *f* spectrale	спектральный интеграл
S 1404	**spectral invariant** <FA>	Spektralinvariante *f*	invariant *m* spectral	спектральный инвариант
S 1405	**spectral mapping theorem [of N. Dunford],** Dunford['s] spectral mapping theorem <FA>	Spektralabbildungssatz *m* von [N.] Dunford, [Dunfordscher] Spektralabbildungssatz	« spectral mapping theorem » *m* de [N.] Dunford, théorème *m* d'application spectrale [de Dunford]	теорема спектрального отображения [Данфорда]
S 1406	**spectral measure** <FA, SP>	Spektralmaß *n*	mesure *f* spectrale	спектральная мера
S 1407	**spectral multiplicity** <FA>	Spektralmultiplizität *f*	multiplicité *f* spectrale	спектральная кратность
S 1408	**spectral norm** <FA>	Spektralnorm *f*	norme *f* spectrale	спектральная норма
	spectral norm <MD>	*s.* S 1412		
S 1409	**spectral point,** point of spectrum <FA>	Spektralpunkt *m*, Punkt *m* des Spektrums	point *m* spectral (du spectre)	спектральная точка, точка спектра
S 1410	**spectral projector,** Riesz['s] projector <FA>	Spektralprojektor *m*, Riesz-Projektor *m*	projecteur *m* spectral (de Riesz)	спектральный проектор, проектор Риса
S 1411	**spectral property** <FA>	Spektraleigenschaft *f*	propriété *f* spectrale	спектральное свойство

No.	English	German	French	Russian
S 1412	**spectral radius,** spectrum radius, spectral norm <of a matrix> <MD>	Spektralradius *m*	rayon *m* spectral	спектральный радиус
S 1413	**spectral representation,** spectral decomposition <of an operator> <FA>	Spektraldarstellung *f*, Spektralzerlegung *f*, Diagonaldarstellung *f*, Spektralentwicklung *f*, spektrale Zerlegung *f*	représentation (décomposition, solution) *f* spectrale	спектральное представление (разложение); спектральный анализ
	spectral resolution [of unity] <FA>	*s.* S 1398		
S 1414	**spectral ring** <of a fibre bundle> <AL, TO>	Spektralring *m*	anneau *m* spectral	спектральное кольцо
	spectral scale <RF>	*s.* S 1399		
S 1415	**spectral sequence** <AL, TO>	Spektralsequenz *f*	suite *f* spectrale	спектральная последовательность
S 1416	**spectral set** <FA>	Spektralmenge *f*	ensemble *m* spectral	спектральное множество
S 1417	**spectral shift,** spectral displacement, shift <DE, MD, NU>	Spektralverschiebung *f*, Shift *m*	déplacement *m* spectral	спектральное смещение
S 1418	**spectral space** <of a ring> <AL>	Ring *m*, versehen mit der Zariski-Topologie	anneau *m* topologisé par la topologie de Zariski	кольцо, снабженное топологией Зарисского
S 1419	**spectral subspace** <FA>	Spektralteilraum *m*	sous-espace *m* spectral	спектральное подпространство
S 1420	**spectral synthesis** <AN>	Spektralsynthese *f*	synthèse *f* spectrale	спектральный синтез
S 1421	**spectral theorem** <FA>	Spektralsatz *m*	théorème *m* spectral	спектральная теорема
S 1422	**spectral theory** <FA, HA>	Spektraltheorie *f*	théorie *f* spectrale	спектральная теория
	spectral topology <AG>	*s.* Z 6		
S 1423	**spectral type** <FA>	Spektraltyp *m*	type *m* spectral	спектральный тип, тип Хеллингера
S 1424	**spectre,** spectrum, spec <of a ring> <AL>	Spektrum *n*, Primspektrum *n*, Spec	spectre *m*, spectre premier, spec	спектр, простой спектр, spec
S 1425	**spectre** <of a graph> <GP>	Spektrum *n*	spectre *m*	спектр
S 1426	**spectrum,** Fourier-Bohr spectrum <of a function> <AN>	Spektrum *n* <einer Funktion>	spectre *m* [de Fourier-Bohr] <d'une fonction>	спектр <функции>
S 1427	**spectrum** <AT, CA, DE, FA, IE, MD>	Spektrum *n*	spectre *m*	спектр
	spectrum <AL>	*s.* S 1424		
S 1428	**spectrum kernel,** kernel <of the spectrum> <of a linear operator> <FA>	Spektralkern *m* <Komplement des Regularitätsgebiets>	noyau *m* de spectre	ядро спектра
S 1429	**spectrum matrix** <FA>	Spektralmatrix *f*	matrice *f* spectrale	спектральная матрица
	spectrum radius <MD>	*s.* S 1412		
	speed of convergence <AX, NU, SS>	*s.* R 158		
S 1430	**Sperner['s] lemma** <AT>	Spernersches Lemma *n*	lemme *m* de Sperner	лемма Шпернера
S 1431	**sphere,** solid sphere <as a solid> <EG>	Kugel *f*	sphère *f*, boule *f*	шар
	sphere <EG>	*s.* S 1493		
S 1432	**sphere bundle** <AT>	Bündel *n* von Sphären, Sphärenbündel *n*	fibré *m* de sphères; espace *m* fibré, fibré en sphères; fibré sphérique	расслоение на сферы
	sphere of complex numbers <FT>	*s.* R 1030		
	sphere of complex numbers with exclusion of *k* points <FT>	*s.* C 1644		
	sphere of complex numbers with exclusion of one point <FT>	*s.* C 1645		
S 1433	**sphere of contact** <of a polyhedron> <EG>	Berührungskugel *f*	sphère *f* de contact (tangence)	сфера касания
	sphere of curvature <DG> ┌<EG>	*s.* O 529		
	sphere of Longchamps	*s.* L 1093		
S 1434	**sphere of similarity,** similarity sphere <GE>	Ähnlichkeitskugel *f*	sphère *f* de similitude	сфера подобия
S 1435	**sphere of the inversion** <GE>	Grundkugel *f* [der Inversion]	sphère *f* d'inversion	сфера инверсии
S 1436	**sphere osculating the edges** <of a tetrahedron> <EG>	Kantenkugel *f*	sphère *f* osculatrice des arêtes <d'un tétraèdre>	сфера, соприкасающаяся с ребрами <четырехгранника>
S 1437	**sphere packing,** packing of spheres <GE>	Kugelpackung *f*, Kugellagerung *f*	empilement *m* de sphères	шаровая упаковка
S 1438	**sphere with handles** <AT>	Henkelkugel *f*, Kugel *f* mit Henkeln	sphère *f* avec anses	сфера с ручками
S 1439	**sphere with $p+1$ cross-caps,** normal closed non-orientable surface of genus *p* <AT>	Kugel *f* mit $p+1$ Kreuzhauben	forme *f* normale d'une surface fermée non orientable de genre *p*	нормальная замкнутая неориентируемая поверхность рода *p*
S 1440	**sphere with *p* handles,** normal closed orientable surface of genus *p*, orientable manifold of genus *p*, orientable manifold of connectivity $2p+1$ <AT>	Kugel *f* mit *p* Henkeln, Kugel mit *p* angesetzten Henkeln	sphère *f* à *p* anses, sphère sur laquelle on a attaché *p* anses	сфера с *p* ручками, нормальная замкнутая ориентируемая сфера рода *p*
	sphere with two cross-caps <GE>	*s.* K 86		
S 1441	**spherical angle** <EG>	sphärischer Winkel *m*, Kugelwinkel *m*	angle *m* sphérique	сферический угол
S 1442	**spherical annulus** <EG>	Kugelring *m*	anneau *m* sphérique	шаровое кольцо, сферическое кольцо

No.	English	German	French	Russian
S 1443	**spherical asymptote** <AG>	Hauptkreis *m*, sphärische Asymptote *f* <Steiner>	asymptote *f* sphérique, arc *m* cyclique <d'une conique sphérique>	сферическая асимптота
S 1444	**spherical Bessel function,** Bessel function of half-odd order <FU>	sphärische (halbzahlige) Zylinderfunktion *f*, Kugel-Zylinderfunktion *f*, Kugel-Bessel-Funktion *f*, Zylinderfunktion halbzahliger Ordnung, Zylinderfunktion mit halbzahligem Index, Zylinderfunktion vom halben Index	fonction *f* de Bessel sphérique (d'indice demi-entier), fonction cylindrique sphérique	функция Бесселя полуцелого порядка, сферическая бесселева функция, сферическая функция Бесселя
S 1445	**spherical Bessel function [of the first kind]** <FU>	sphärische (halbzahlige) Bessel-Funktion *f*, Kugel-Bessel-Funktion *f*, sphärische (halbzahlige) Zylinderfunktion *f* erster Art	fonction *f* de Bessel sphérique de première espèce, fonction de Bessel sphérique	сферическая бесселева функция первого рода, сферическая функция Бесселя первого рода, сферическая бесселева функция, сферическая функция Бесселя
S 1446	**spherical Bessel function of the second kind,** spherical Neumann function, spherical Weber function <FU>	sphärische (halbzahlige) Neumann-Funktion *f*, Kugel-Neumann-Funktion *f*, sphärische (halbzahlige) Weber-Funktion *f*, Kugel-Weber-Funktion *f*, sphärische (halbzahlige) Bessel-Funktion *f* zweiter Art, sphärische (halbzahlige) Zylinderfunktion *f* zweiter Art	fonction *f* de Neumann sphérique, fonction de Bessel sphérique de deuxième espèce, fonction de Weber sphérique	сферическая функция Неймана (Вебера), сферическая бесселева функция второго рода, сферическая функция Бесселя второго рода
S 1447	**spherical Bessel function of the third kind,** spherical Hankel function <FU>	sphärische (halbzahlige) Hankel-Funktion *f*, Kugel-Hankel-Funktion *f*, sphärische (halbzahlige) Bessel-Funktion *f* dritter Art, sphärische (halbzahlige) Zylinderfunktion *f* dritter Art	fonction *f* de Hankel sphérique, fonction de Bessel sphérique de troisième espèce	сферическая функция Ганкеля (Ханкеля), сферическая бесселева функция третьего рода, сферическая функция Бесселя третьего рода
	spherical bundle of circles <AY>	*s.* P 45		
S 1448	**spherical cap,** cap <EG>	Kugelkappe *f*, Kugelhaube *f*, Kalotte *f*, // Kugelkalotte *f*	calotte *f* sphérique, calotte	сегментная поверхность <шарового сектора первого рода>, поверхность шарового (сферического) сегмента, сферический сегмент, шапка сферы
S 1449	**spherical centre,** pole <of a spherical circle> <AG>	sphärischer Mittelpunkt *m*	centre *m* sphérique	сферический центр, полюс
	spherical circle <AY, PJ>	*s.* A 63		
S 1450	**spherical cohomology class** <AT>	sphärische Kohomologieklasse *f*	classe *f* de cohomologie sphérique, classe sphérique	сферический класс когомологий
	spherical cone <EG>	*s.* S 1484		
	spherical continuity <FT>	*s.* C 650		
	spherical co-ordinates <AY>	*s.* S 1479		
S 1451	**spherical curvature** <of a hypersurface> <DG>	sphärische Krümmung *f*	courbure *f* sphérique	сферическая кривизна
S 1452	**spherical curve** <DG>	sphärische Kurve *f*	courbe *f* sphérique	сферическая кривая
S 1453	**spherical cyclic curve,** cyclic curve <AG>	sphärische zyklische Kurve *f*, sphärische Zyklika *f*, Zyklika *f*, zyklische Kurve <Darboux>	courbe *f* cyclique <Darboux>, conique (cyclique) *f* sphérique, sphéro-cyclide *f*, cyclique	сферическая циклическая кривая, циклическая кривая
S 1454	**spherical derivative** <FT>	Kugelableitung *f*	dérivée *f* sphérique	сферическая производная
	spherical digon <EG>	*s.* L 1188		
	spherical distance <FT>	*s.* C 651		
S 1455	**spherical domain** <FT>	Kugelgebiet *n*	domaine *m* sphérique	шаровая область
S 1456	**spherical epicycloid** <GE>	sphärische Epizykloide *f*	épicycloïde *f* sphérique	сферическая эпициклоида
S 1457	**spherical excess,** spheric excess <EG>	sphärischer Exzeß *m*	excès *m* sphérique	сферический избыток (эксцесс), избыток треугольника, эксцесс
S 1458	**spherical fibre** <AT>	sphärische Faser *f*	fibre *f* sphérique	сферический слой
	spherical field <VT>	*s.* S 1498		
S 1459	**spherical function** <AL>	Kugelfunktion *f*	fonction *f* sphérique	сферическая функция
	spherical geometry <DG>	*s.* G 277		
	spherical geometry <EG>	*s.* S 1501		
S 1460	**spherical group** <GE>	Kugelgruppe *f*	groupe *m* sphérique	сферическая группа
	spherical Hankel function <FU>	*s.* S 1447		
	spherical harmonic <FU>	*s.* S 1255		
	spherical harmonic of the first kind <FU>	*s.* L 531		
	spherical harmonic of the second kind <FU>	*s.* L 532		

No.	English	German	French	Russian
S 1461	**spherical helix** <GE>	sphärische Schraubenlinie (Schneckenlinie, Böschungslinie) *f*	hélice *f* sphérique	сферическая винтовая линия
	spherical helix <EG>	*s.* L 1173		
S 1462	**spherical homology class** <AT>	sphärische Homologieklasse *f*	classe *f* d'homologie sphérique	сферический класс гомологий
S 1463	**spherical image,** spherical representation <of a surface> <DG>	sphärisches Bild *n*, Gaußsches sphärisches Bild	image (représentation) *f* sphérique	сферический образ, сферическое изображение
S 1464	**spherical image map,** spherical transformation, spherical mapping, spherical representation, Gaussian representation <DG>	sphärische Abbildung *f*	application *f* sphérique [de Gauss], représentation (transformation) *f* sphérique	сферическое отображение (преобразование, изображение)
S 1465	**spherical indicatrix** <of a ruled surface *or* space curve> <AY>	sphärische Indikatrix *f*	indicatrice *f* sphérique	сферическая индикатриса
S 1466	**spherical indicatrix of binormal** <to a curve> <DG>	Binormalenbild *n*	indicatrice *f* sphérique des binormales	индикатриса бинормалей
S 1467	**spherical indicatrix of principal normal,** indicatrix of principal normals <DG>	Hauptnormalenbild *n*	indicatrice *f* sphérique de la normale principale, indicatrice des normales principales	индикатриса главных нормалей
S 1468/9	**spherical indicatrix of tangents** <to a curve> <DG>	Tangentenbild *n*	indicatrice *f* sphérique des tangentes	индикатриса касательных
	spherical inversion <GE>	*s.* I 971		
S 1470	**spherical layer,** spherical segment of (with) two bases <EG>	Kugelschicht *f*	fibre *f* sphérique, segment *m* sphérique à deux bases, couronne *f* sphérique	шаровой слой, сферический слой
S 1471	**spherical lemniscate** <GE>	sphärische Lemniskate *f*	lemniscate *f* sphérique	сферическая лемниската
S 1472	**spherical line[ar] element** <FT>	sphärisches Linienelement *n*	élément *m* linéaire sphérique	сферический линейный элемент
	spherical lune <EG>	*s.* L 1188		
	spherically continuous function <FT>	*s.* C 652		
	spherically convergent sequence <FT>	*s.* C 653		
	spherical mapping <DG>	*s.* S 1464		
S 1473	**spherical mean** <AN>	sphärischer Mittelwert *m*	moyenne *f* sphérique	сферическое среднее
S 1474	**spherical metric** <TO>	sphärische Metrik *f*	métrique *f* sphérique	сферическая метрика
	spherical metric <FT>	*s.* C 654		
S 1475	**spherical motion** <GE>	sphärische Bewegung *f*, Bewegung im sphärischen Raum, Bewegung der sphärischen Geometrie	mouvement *m* sphérique	сферическое движение
S 1476	**spherical neighbourhood** <of radius *r*> <TO>	Kugelumgebung *f*, sphärische Umgebung *f*, *r*-Umgebung *f*	voisinage *m* sphérique <de rayon *r*>	сферическая окрестность <радиуса *r*>
	spherical neighbourhood in R^n <TO>	*s.* O 154		
	spherical neighbourhood of radius ε <TO>	*s.* E 313		
	spherical Neumann function <FU>	*s.* S 1446		
S 1477	**spherical parabola** <GE>	sphärische Parabel *f*	parabole *f* sphérique	сферическая парабола
S 1478	**spherical parallelogram** <EG>	sphärisches Parallelogramm *n*	parallélogramme *m* sphérique	сферический параллелограмм
	spherical point <DG>	*s.* U 29		
S 1479	**spherical polar coordinates, spherical polars,** spherical coordinates, polar coordinates [in space] <AY>	Kugelkoordinaten *fpl*, räumliche (sphärische) Polarkoordinaten *fpl*, Polarkoordinaten [im Raum], sphärische Koordinaten *fpl*	coordonnées *fpl* sphériques (polaires, polaires dans l'espace)	сферические [пространственные] координаты, сферические (пространственные) полярные координаты, полярные координаты [в пространстве]
S 1480	**spherical polygon** <EG>	sphärisches Polygon *n*	polygone *m* sphérique	сферический многоугольник
S 1481	**spherical power** <of a point> <GE>	sphärische Potenz *f*	puissance *f* sphérique	сферическая степень
S 1482	**spherical pyramid** <GE>	sphärische Pyramide *f*	pyramide *f* sphérique	сферическая пирамида
S 1483	**spherical radius** <of a spherical circle> <GE>	sphärischer Radius *m*	rayon *m* sphérique	сферический радиус
	spherical region <GE>	*s.* O 128		
	spherical region in R^n <TO>	*s.* O 154		
	spherical representation <DG>	*s.* 1. S 1463; 2. S 1464		
	spherical rotation <GE, TO>	*s.* R 1400		
S 1484	**spherical sector [of the first kind],** spherical cone, sector of sphere <EG>	Kugelausschnitt *m*, Kugelsektor *m*, Ausschnitt (Sektor) *m* der Kugel	secteur *m* sphérique [de première espèce], secteur de sphère	шаровой сектор [первого рода], сферический сектор [первого рода], сектор шара
S 1485	**spherical sector of the second kind** <EG>	Kugelrinde *f*	secteur *m* sphérique de deuxième espèce	шаровой сектор второго рода, сферический сектор второго рода
S 1486	**spherical segment,** segment of the sphere <of one base> <EG>	Kugelabschnitt *m*, Kugelsegment *n*, Abschnitt *m*, Segment *n* <der Kugel>	segment *m* sphérique, segment <de la sphère>	шаровой (сферический) сегмент, сегмент <шара>

	spherical segment of (with) two bases <EG>	*s.* S 1470		
	spherical sheaf of circles <AY>	*s.* P 45		
S 1487	**spherical shell** <EG>	Kugelschale *f*	enveloppe (couche) *f* sphérique	сферическая оболочка
S 1488	**spherical shell of minimal breadth** <of a convex body> <CS>	Minimalkugelschale *f*	couche *f* sphérique d'épaisseur minima	сферический слой наименьшей ширины
S 1489	**spherical sinusoid** <GE>	sphärische Sinusoide *f*	sinusoïde *f* sphérique	сферическая синусоида
S 1490	**spherical space,** antipodal space <GE>	sphärischer Raum *m*	espace *m* sphérique	сферическое пространство
	spherical star of circles <AY>	*s.* P 45		
S 1491	**spherical sum** <of a double Fourier series> <SS>	sphärische Summe *f*	somme *f* sphérique	сферическая сумма
S 1492	**spherical surface,** surface of constant positive curvature <DG>	sphärische Fläche *f*, Fläche konstanter positiver Krümmung	surface *f* sphérique (à courbure positive constante)	поверхность постоянной положительной кривизны
S 1493	**spherical surface,** surface of the sphere, sphere <EG>	Oberfläche *f* der Kugel, Kugeloberfläche *f*, Kugelfläche *f*, Kugel *f*, Sphäre *f*	surface *f* sphérique (de la sphère), sphère *f*	сфера, поверхность шара
	spherical symmetry <EG>	*s.* R 9		
S 1494	**spherical tensor** <VT>	Kugeltensor *m*	tenseur *m* sphérique	шаровой тензор, сферический тензор
	spherical transformation <DG>	*s.* S 1464		
S 1495	**spherical triangle** <EG>	sphärisches Dreieck *n*, Kugeldreieck *n*	triangle *m* sphérique	сферический треугольник
S 1496	**spherical triangular co-ordinates,** Möbius['s] spherical triangular co-ordinates <EG>	sphärische Dreieckskoordinaten *fpl* [von Möbius], Möbiussche sphärische Dreieckskoordinaten	coordonnées *fpl* triangulaires sphériques [de Möbius]	сферические треугольные координаты [Мебиуса]
S 1497	**spherical trigonometry** <EG>	sphärische Trigonometrie *f*	trigonométrie *f* sphérique	сферическая тригонометрия
S 1498	**spherical vector field,** spherical field <VT>	sphärisches Vektorfeld *n*, Kugelfeld *n*, sphärisches Feld *n*	champ *m* vectoriel sphérique, champ sphérique	сферическое векторное поле, сферическое поле
	spherical Weber function <FU>	*s.* S 1446		
S 1499	**spherical wedge** <EG>	Kugelkeil *m*	coin *m* sphérique	шаровой клин
S 1500	**spherical zone,** zone <of a ball> <EG>	Kugelzone *f*, Zone *f* <einer Kugel>	zone *f* sphérique, zone <d'une boule>	шаровой пояс, зона <шара>
	spheric excess <EG>	*s.* S 1457		
S 1501	**spherics,** spherical geometry <EG>	sphärische Geometrie *f*, Sphärik *f*, Geometrie auf der Kugel, Kugelgeometrie *f*	géométrie *f* sphérique, sphérique *f*	сферическая геометрия, геометрия на сфере
S 1502	**sphero-conic** <AG>	sphärischer Kegelschnitt *m*	conique *f* sphérique, cono-sphérique *f*	сферическое коническое сечение
S 1503	**spheroform [surface]** <CS, GE>	Sphäroforme *f*, Körper *m* konstanter Breite im [dreidimensionalen] Raum, gleichdicke Fläche *f*, Fläche konstanter Breite	surface *f* sphéroforme (de largeur constante), sphéroforme *f*	поверхность постоянной ширины, тело постоянной ширины в [трехмерном] пространстве
S 1504	**spheroid** <GE>	Sphäroid *n*	sphéroïde *m*	сфероид
	spheroid <EG>	*s.* E 163		
	spheroid <TO>	*s.* O 129		
S 1505	**spheroidal [differential] equation** <DE>	Sphäroiddifferentialgleichung *f*	équation *f* [différentielle] sphéroïdale	сфероидальное [дифференциальное] уравнение
S 1506	**spheroidal function (harmonic)** <FU>	Sphäroidfunktion *f*	fonction *f* harmonique sphéroïdale	сфероидальная гармоническая функция
S 1507	**spheroidal wave function** <of the first, second, *or* third kind> <FU>	Sphäroidwellenfunktion *f* <der ersten, zweiten *oder* dritten Art>	fonction *f* d'onde sphéroïdale <de la première, deuxième ou troisième espèce>	сфероидальная волновая функция <первого, второго или третьего рода>
	spheroid of revolution <EG>	*s.* E 163		
S 1508	**spherometry** <EG>	Sphärometrie *f*	sphérométrie *f*	сферометрия
S 1509	**sphero-quartic** <GE>	sphärische biquadratische [algebraische] Kurve *f*, sphärische algebraische Kurve, Sphäroquartik *f*	courbe *f* algébrique sphérique, quartique *f* sphérique, sphéroquartique *f*	сферическая кривая четвертой степени
S 1510	**spherosymmetrical curve** <EG>	sphärosymmetrische Kurve *f*	courbe *f* sphérosymétrique	сферосиметрическая кривая
	spiegelungsprinzip <FT>	*s.* S 172		
	spike function <FA>	*s.* D 211		
S 1511	**spin base** <DG>	Spinbasis *f*	base *f* spinorielle	спиновая база
	spin group <AL>	*s.* R 344		
	spin index <AL, DG>	*s.* S 1522		
	spinode <GE>	*s.* C 2814		
S 1512	**spinor** <AL, DG, VT>	Spinor *m*, kontravarianter Spintensor *m*	spineur *m*, spinor *m*	спинор
S 1513	**spinor algebra** <AL, DG, VT>	Spinoralgebra *f*	algèbre *f* des spineurs	спинорная алгебра
S 1514	**spinor analysis** <AL, DG, VT>	Spinoranalysis *f*	analyse *f* spinorielle	спинорный анализ
S 1515	**spinor calculus, spinor-calculus** <AL, DG, VT>	Spinorkalkül *m*	calcul *m* des spineurs	спинорное исчисление
S 1516	**spinor field,** spinorial field <DG, VT>	Spinorfeld *n*	champ *m* spinoriel	спинорное поле

No.	English	German	French	Russian
S 1517	**spinor genus** <of quadratic forms> <AL, NT>	Spinorgeschlecht *n*	genre *m* spinoriel	спинорный род
S 1518	**spinor group** <AL, DG>	Spinorengruppe *f*, Spinorgruppe *f*	groupe *m* spinoriel	спинорная группа, группа спиноров
S 1519	**spinor group** <GR>	engere (spezielle) Cliffordsche Gruppe *f*	groupe *m* de Clifford spécial	специальная группа Клиффорда
S 1520	**spinorial connection** <DG>	spinorielle Übertragung *f*	connexion *f* spinorielle	спинорная связность
	spinorial field <DG, VT>	*s.* S 1516		
S 1521	**spinorial manifold** <AL, DG>	Spinormannigfaltigkeit *f*	variété *f* spinorielle	спинорное многообразие
S 1522	**spinor index,** spin index <AL, DG>	Spinorindex *m*	indice *m* spinoriel	спинорный индекс
S 1523	**spinor norm** <of an element of a Clifford group> <AL>	Spinornorm *f*	norme *f* spinorielle	спинорная норма
S 1524	**spinor of four components,** four-component spinor <AL, GE>	vierkomponentiger Spinor *m*	spineur *m* à quatre composantes	четырехкомпонентный спинор
S 1525	**spinor relation** <AL, VT>	Spinorrelation *f*	relation *f* spinorielle	спинорное соотношение
S 1526	**spinor representation,** spin representation <AL, VT>	Spinordarstellung *f*, Spindarstellung *f*	représentation *f* spinorielle	спинорное представление
S 1527	**spinor space** <AL>	Spinorraum *m*	espace *m* des spineurs	спинорное пространство
	spin representation <AL, VT>	*s.* S 1526		
S 1528	**spin tensor** <DG, VT>	Spintensor *m*	tenseur *m* du spin	тензор спина
S 1529	**spiral** <a plane curve> <GE>	Spirale *f*	spirale *f*	спираль
	spiral [line] <GE>	*s.* H 185		
	spiralling <GE>	*s.* S 181		
	spiral of Archimedes	*s.* A 898		
	spiral of Cornu <GE>	*s.* C 2471		
	spiral of Euler <GE>	*s.* C 2471		
S 1530	**spiral of Hamel,** Hamel['s] spiral <GE>	Spirale *f* von Hamel, Hamelsche Spirale, Hamel-Spirale *f*	spirale *f* de Hamel, spirale logarithmique de Hamel	спираль Гамеля
S 1531	**spiral point,** focal point, focus <DE>	Strudelpunkt *m*	foyer *m*	фокус
S 1532	**spiral surface** <GE>	Spiralfläche *f*	surface *f* spirale	спиральная поверхность
S 1533	**spiric curve (line)** <GE>	spirische Linie (Kurve) *f*	ligne (courbe) *f* spirique	кривая, образуемая пересечением тора с плоскостью
S 1534	**spline** <AX, NU>	Spline *n*	spline *m*	сплайн
S 1535	**spline function** <AX, NU>	Spline-Funktion *f*	fonction *f* spline	сплайн-функция
S 1536	**split completely / to** <said of a prime ideal> <AB>	vollständig zerlegt werden	totalement décomposer	полностью разлагаться
S 1537	**split exact sequence,** splitting exact sequence, inessential sequence <HA>	aufspaltende exakte Folge (Sequenz) *f*	suite *f* exacte scindée (splittante)	расщепляющаяся (расщепленная) точная последовательность
	split extension <GR>	*s.* S 1542		
S 1538	**split manifold** <DG>	Spaltmannigfaltigkeit *f*		расщепляющее многообразие
S 1539	**split simple algebra** <by an extension> <AL>	zerfällte einfache Algebra *f* <durch eine Erweiterung>	algèbre *f* simple neutralisée <par une extension>	нейтрализованная простая алгебра
S 1540/1	**splitting** <of an exact sequence> <HA>	Aufspaltung *f*, Zerfallen *n*	scindage *m*	расщепление
	splitting <NT>	*s.* E 785		
	splitting exact sequence <HA>	*s.* S 1537		
S 1542	**splitting extension,** split extension <of a group> <GR>	zerfallende Erweiterung *f*	extension *f* scindée	расщепляемое расширение
S 1543	**splitting[-] field** <of a class of algebras> <AL>	Zerfällungskörper *m*	extension *f* neutralisante, corps *m* neutralisant	нейтрализующее расширение (поле)
S 1544	**splitting[-] field,** decomposition field, root field <of a polynomial, for a polynomial> <AL>	Zerfällungskörper *m*, Wurzelkörper *m*, kleinster Zerfällungskörper <eines Polynoms>	corps *m* des racines, corps de dislocation (rupture, décomposition) <d'un polynôme>	поле разложения <многочлена>
S 1545	**splitting homomorphism** <AL>	aufspaltender Homomorphismus *m*	homomorphisme *m* scindé	расщепляющийся гомоморфизм
	spread <SE>	*s.* S 637		
	spread <ST>	*s.* 1. I 835; 2. R 129		
S 1546	**spring compasses, spring dividers** <GE, IN>	Federzirkel *m*, Federspitzzirkel *m*	compas *m* à ressort	
	spur <MD>	*s.* T 714		
S 1547	**spurious correlation** <ST>	künstliche (willkürliche) Korrelation *f*	corrélation *f* factice	необъективная (схоластическая) корреляция
S 1548	**squarability,** squareability <ME>	Quadrierbarkeit *f*	quarrabilité *f*	квадрируемость
S 1549	**squarable set** <in the sense of Peano-Jordan> <ME>	meßbare Menge *f* im Sinne von Peano-Jordan, quadrierbare Menge im Sinne von Peano-Jordan, quadrierbare Menge bezüglich des Peano-Jordanschen Inhalts, quadrierbare Menge	ensemble *m* mesurable au sens de Peano et Jordan, ensemble quarrable	квадрируемое множество, имеющее определенную площадь множество

S 1550	**square / to,** to raise to the second power, to exponentiate to the second power <AL>	quadrieren	élever au carré, élever à la puissance deux, carrer, porter au carré, mettre au carré	возводить в квадрат
	square <GE>	*s.* S 1561		
	square <GE, IN>	*s.* T 899		
	squareability <ME>	*s.* S 1548		
	square array <MD>	*s.* S 1558		
S 1551	**square bracket,** bracket <GN>	eckige (scharfe) Klammer *f*	crochet *m*	квадратная (прямоугольная) скобка
S 1552	**square bracket function,** Legendre['s] function, greatest integer function <NT>	Funktion *f* der Bildung der größten ganzen Zahl, Funktion des größten Ganzen	fonction *f* du plus grand entier, fonction à gradins	функция образования наибольшего целого числа
S 1553	**square contingency** <ST>	quadratische Kontingenz *f*	carré *m* de contingence, contingence carrée	квадратичная сопряженность признаков, квадратичная контингенция
S 1554	**square deviation** <of one term $(x - \bar{x})^2$> <ST>	quadratische Abweichung *f*	écart *m* quadratique	квадратичное отклонение
S 1555	**square domain** <AN>	Quadratgebiet *n*	domaine *m* quadratique	квадратическая область
	χ^2-squared statistic <ST>	*s.* C 636		
S 1556	**square-free number** <NT>	quadratfreie Zahl *f*	entier *m* « quadratfrei », entier rationnel non divisible par un carré dans $\mathfrak{Z}$, Quadratfrei *m*, nombre *m* sans diviseurs carrés	число, свободное от квадратов; число без крвадратных сомножителей; число, не делящееся на квадрат; бесквадратное число
	square grid <DE, DG>	*s.* S 1562		
S 1557	**square[-] integrable function,** quadratically integrable function, normalizable function <AN>	quadratisch integrierbare (integrable) Funktion *f*, quadratintegrable (normierbare) Funktion, quadratisch L-integrierbare (L-integrable, summierbare) Funktion	fonction *f* de carré intégrable, fonction normable	функция с интегрируемым квадратом, интегрируемая с квадратом функция, нормируемая функция
	square-integrable kernel <FA, IE>	*s.* H 356		
S 1558	**square matrix,** quadratic matrix, square array, // matrix <MD>	quadratische Matrix *f*	matrice *f* carrée	квадратичная матрица
S 1559	**square matrix (a_{ij}) with $a_{ij} = 0$ for $i + j$ even and $a_{ij} \neq 0$ for $i + j$ odd** <or inversely> <MD>	quadratische Matrix *f* (a_{ij}) mit $a_{ij} = 0$ für $i + j$ gerade und $a_{ij} \neq 0$ für $i + j$ ungerade <oder umgekehrt>	matrice *f* en damier	квадратная матрица $\|\|a_{ij}\|\|$ такая, что $a_{ij} = 0$, если $i + j$ четно, $a_{ij} \neq 0$, если $i + j$ нечетно <или наоборот>
	square matrix of order *n* <MD>	*s.* N 723		
S 1560	**square measure,** measure of area, surface measure, superficial measure <ME>	Flächenmaß *n*	mesure *f* de surface, mesure d'aire	квадратная мера, мера площади
S 1561	**square mesh,** square <of a net> <GE>	Netzquadrat *n*	carré *m* <d'un réseau>	квадратная ячейка сети
S 1562	**square mesh grid, square net,** square grid <DE, DG>	Quadratnetz *n*, quadratisches Netz *n*, Quadratliniennetz *n*	quadrillage *m*, réseau *m* quadratique	квадратная сетка, сетка с квадратными клетками, сетка с квадратными ячейками, квадратичная сетка
	square number <NT>	*s.* P 437		
S 1563	**square of opposition** <LO>	aristotelisches Urteilsquadrat *n*, logisches Quadrat *n*	carré *m* des propositions (oppositions)	логический квадрат
S 1564	**square of the distance** <GE>	Abstandsquadrat *n*	carré *m* de la distance	квадрат расстояния
	square of the standard deviation <ST>	*s.* V 62		
S 1565	**square root,** second root <AL>	Quadratwurzel *f*, zweite Wurzel *f*	racine *f* carrée (quadratique, seconde), // racine carré	квадратный корень, корень второй степени
	square-root method <AL, NU>	*s.* C 646		
S 1566	**square root operator** <FA>	Wurzeloperator *m*, Quadratwurzeloperator *m*	opérateur *m* radical	квадратный корень оператора
S 1567	**square-root transformation** <ST>	Quadratwurzeltransformation *f*, Wurzeltransformation *f*	transformation *f* racine carrée	преобразование [путем извлечения] квадратного корня
	square sum <SS>	*s.* S 2267		
S 1568	**square-summable function,** quadratically summable function <AN>	quadratisch summierbare Funktion *f*	fonction *f* de carré sommable	функция с суммируемым квадратом, суммируемая с квадратом функция; функция, суммируемая с квадратом
	squariance <ST>	*s.* D 364		
	squaring <DI, DG>	*s.* Q 50		
	squaring the circle <EG>	*s.* Q 54		
	sr <EG>	*s.* S 1751		
S 1569	**S-ring** <AL>	Skalarenring *m* <Kasch>	S-anneau *m*	S-кольцо
S 1570	***S*-scheme** <AG>	*S*-Schema *n*	*S*-schéma *m*, schéma *m* au-dessus du schéma *S*	*S*-схема
	S-shaped curve <GN>	*s.* S 835		
S 1571	**S-shaped distribution,** sigmoid distribution <ST>	S-förmige Verteilung *f*	distribution *f* en S, distribution sigmoïde	S-образное (сигмоидальное) распределение
S 1572	**S-space** <TO>	metrischer Raum *m* mit abzählbarer Basis	espace *m* métrisable à caractère dénombrable	метризуемое пространство, обладающее счетной базой
	(S)-space <TO>	*s.* S 158		

No.	English	German	French	Russian
S 1573	**s-system** <of sets> <ME, SE>	*s*-System *n*	famille *f* [simplement] additive <d'ensembles>	*s*-система
S 1574	**stability group** <of a series of subgroups> <GR>	Stabilitätsgruppe *f*	groupe *m* de stabilité	группа устойчивости
S 1575	**stability in Liapunov's sense, stability in the Liapunov sense, stability in the sense of Liapunov** <DE>	Stabilität *f* im Sinne von Ljapunow (Liapounoff)	stabilité *f* au sens de Liapounoff (Liapunov)	устойчивость по Ляпунову, устойчивость в смысле Ляпунова
S 1576	**stability in the sense of Poisson** <DE>	Stabilität *f* im Sinne von Poisson	stabilité *f* au sens de Poisson	устойчивость по Пуассону, устойчивость в смысле Пуассона
S 1577	**stability map,** Strutt['s] map <of a Hill-type differential equation> <DE>	Stabilitätskarte *f*, Struttsche Karte *f*	carte *f* de stabilité (Strutt)	карта стабильности (Стретта, Релея)
S 1578	**stability number,** independence number, vertex independence number <GP>	innere Stabilitätszahl *f*	nombre *m* de stabilité, nombre de stabilité interne, stabilité *f* interne	число внутренней устойчивости, вершинное число независимости
S 1579	**stability region** <AN, PG>	Stabilitätsbereich *m*	domaine *m* de stabilité	область устойчивости
	stability subgroup <AL, TO>	*s.* G 484		
	stability theorem of Liapunov <DE>	*s.* L 641		
S 1580	**stabilization of variances** <ST>	Varianzstabilisierung *f*, Stabilisierung *f* der Varianzen	stabilisation *f* des variances	стабилизация дисперсии
	stabilizer <AL, TO>	*s.* G 484		
S 1581	**stable automorphism group** <GR>	stabile Automorphismengruppe *f*	groupe *m* d'automorphismes stable	стабильная группа автоморфизмов
S 1582	**stable chain** <AT>	stabile Kette *f*	chaîne *f* stable	устойчивая цепь
S 1583	**stable convergence** <AX, NU>	stabile Konvergenz *f*	convergence *f* stable	устойчивая сходимость
	stable element <GE>	*s.* I 865		
S 1584	**stable group pair** <GR>	stabiles Gruppenpaar *n*	paire *f* de groupes stable	стабильная пара групп
S 1585	**stable homotopy group** <AT>	stabile Homotopiegruppe *f*	groupe *m* d'homotopie stable	стабильная гомотопическая группа
S 1586	**stable ideal** <AL>	stabiles Ideal *n*	idéal *m* stable	устойчивый идеал
S 1587	**stable isomorphic** <AL>	stabil isomorph	stablement isomorphe	устойчиво изоморфный
S 1588	**stable manifold,** topologically stable manifold <TO>	stabile Mannigfaltigkeit *f*	variété *f* stable	устойчивое многообразие
S 1589	**stable point** <in deformations> <AT>	stabiler Punkt *m*	point *m* stable	устойчивая точка
S 1590	**stable polyhedron** <TO>	stabiles Polyeder *n*	polyèdre *m* stable	устойчивый полиэдр
S 1591	**stable process** <SP>	stabiler Prozeß *m*	processus *m* stable	устойчивый процесс
	stable random sequence <SP>	*s.* S 1593		
S 1592	**stable relation,** composition-stable relation, <under> <AL>	mit einer Verknüpfung verträgliche Relation *f*	relation *f* compatible avec une loi de composition	стабильное отношение относительно операции
S 1593	**stable sequence of random variables,** stable random sequence <SP>	stabile Zufallsfolge *f* (Folge *f* von Zufallsgrößen)	suite *f* aléatoire stable, suite stable de variables aléatoires	устойчивая последовательность случайных величин, устойчивая случайная последовательность
S 1594	**stable set** <TG>	Lösung *f* im Sinne von Neumann-Morgenstern, N-M-Lösung *f*, von-Neumann-Morgenstern-Lösung *f*, stabile Menge *f*	solution *f* au sens de Neumann-Morgenstern	решение по Нейману-Моргенштерну, Н-М-решение, решение фон Неймана-Моргенштерна, I-устойчивое множество
	stable set [from the inside] <GP>	*s.* I 314		
S 1595	**stable solution** <*e.g.*: in the Liapunov *or* Poisson sense> <DE>	stabile Lösung *f* <*z. B.*: im Sinne von Ljapunow (Liapounoff) *oder* Poisson>	solution *f* stable <*par exemple:* au sens de Liapounoff *ou* Poisson>	устойчивое решение <*например:* по Ляпунову *или* Пуассону>
S 1596	**stable space** <TO>	stabiler (stabiler metrischer) Raum *m*	espace *m* stable	устойчивое пространство
S 1597	**stable state** <of a Markov chain> <SP>	stabiler Zustand *m*	état *m* stable	устойчивое состояние
	stable subgroup <AL, TO>	*s.* G 484		
	stable subgroup <GR>	*s.* A 337		
S 1598	**stable subset** <AL>	stabile Untermenge *f*	partie *f* stable	устойчивое подмножество
S 1599	**stable type of distribution** <ST>	stabiler Verteilungstyp *m*	type *m* de distribution stable	устойчивый тип распределения
	stable under a law of composition <AL>	*s.* C 922		
	stable under an operation <AL>	*s.* C 922		
	stable with respect to a law of composition <AL>	*s.* C 922		
	stack <AT>	*s.* P 1243		
S 1600	**Stäckel['s] space** <DG>	Stäckelscher Raum *m*	espace *m* de Stäckel	пространство Штэкеля
	staircase estimation method <ST>	*s.* U 404		
	staircase function <AN>	*s.* S 1747		
	staircase method <ST>	*s.* U 404		
S 1601	**stake,** bet <TG>	Einsatz *m*, Spieleinsatz *m*	mise *f*, enjeu *m*	ставка
S 1602	**stalk** <of a sheaf> <AT>	Halm *m*	fibre *f*	слой, стебель

S 1603	**standard body,** Eichkörper, closed bounded o-symmetric convex body <GU>	Eichkörper *m*	corps *m* étalon	калибровочное тело, тело-эталон
S 1604	**standard complex** <HA>	Standardkomplex *m*	complexe *m* standard	стандартный комплекс
	standard construction <CA>	*s.* C 1288		
S 1605	**standard cube** <AT>	Standardwürfel *m*	cube *m* type	стандартный куб
S 1606	**standard deviation,** coefficient of standard variation, root-mean-square of the deviation, root-mean-square deviation, root deviation, mean square deviation, fluctuation <σ, *s*> <ST>	Standardabweichung *f*, mittlere quadratische Abweichung *f*, quadratische Abweichung, Streuung *f*, mittlere Schwankung (Abweichung) *f*, mittlerer Fehler *m*, Präzisionsmaß *n* <σ>	écart *m* type, écart-type *m*, écart étalon, écart quadratique moyen, écart moyen quadratique, déviation *f* standard, déviation standard de la moyenne, dispersion *f* quadratique moyenne, dispersion, fluctuation *f* <σ>	стандартное отклонение, среднеквадратичное отклонение, среднее квадратичное отклонение, квадратичное отклонение, среднеквадратичное (квадратичное) уклонение, штандарт, срединное отклонение <σ>
	standard deviation of estimate <ST>	*s.* S 1610		
S 1607	**standard domain** <for a conformal mapping> <FT>	Normalgebiet *n*, Normalbereich *m*	domaine *m* canonique	нормальная область
	standard domain <FT>	*s.* R 1031		
	standard elliptic integral in Legendre's notation <FU>	*s.* E 178		
S 1608	**standard equation,** normal equation <GE>	Normalgleichung *f*	équation *f* normale	нормальное уравнение
	standard equations <ER, ST>	*s.* N 564		
	standard error <ER, ST>	*s.* R 1379		
S 1609	**standard error of difference** <ST>	Standardfehler (Fehler) *m* der Differenz	erreur *f* type de la différence	среднеквадратичная ошибка разности
S 1610	**standard error of estimate,** standard deviation of estimate <ST>	Standardabweichung *f* der Schätzung	écart *m* type de l'estimation	стандартное отклонение оценки
S 1611	**standard error of mean** <ST>	Standardfehler *m* des Mittelwertes (Mittels)	erreur *f* type de la moyenne	среднеквадратичная ошибка среднего
S 1612	**standard error of standard deviation** <ST>	Standardfehler *m* der Standardabweichung	erreur *f* type de l'écart-type	среднеквадратичная ошибка стандартного отклонения
S 1613	**standard error of variance component** <ST>	Standardfehler *m* der Varianzkomponente	erreur *f* type de la composante de la variance	среднеквадратичная ошибка компоненты дисперсии
S 1614	**standard form** <AL>	Standardform *f*	forme *f* standard	стандартная форма
S 1615	**standard form** <of a natural number> <NT>	kanonische Darstellung (Zerlegung) *f*	décomposition *f* canonique	каноническое разложение
	standard form <FT>	*s.* N 575		
S 1616	**standard geometric *n*-simplex (simplex of dimension *n*)** <AT>	*n*-dimensionales euklidisches Standardsimplex *n*, euklidisches Standard-*n*-Simplex *n*	simplexe *m* géométrique type de dimension *n*	стандартный геометрический симплекс размерности *n*
S 1617	**standard group** <GR>	Standardgruppe *f*	groupe *m* standard	стандартная группа
S 1618	**standard identity** <AL>	Standardidentität *f*	identité *f* standard	стандартное тождество
S 1619	**standard inner product** <on R^n> <GE>	Standardskalarprodukt *n*	produit *m* scalaire standard	стандартное скалярное произведение
S 1620	**standard interpretation** <MM>	Standardinterpretation *f*	interprétation *f* standard	стандартная интерпретация
S 1621	**standardized distribution,** centred and normed distribution <ST>	standardisierte Verteilung *f*, zentrierte und normierte Verteilung	distribution *f* réduite, distribution centrée et normée	[центрированное и] нормированное распределение, стандартизованное распределение
S 1622	**standardized frequency function,** centred and normed frequency function <ST>	standardisierte Häufigkeitsfunktion *f*, zentrierte und normierte Häufigkeitsfunktion	fonction *f* de fréquence réduite, fonction de fréquence centrée et normée	[центрированная и] нормированная функция частот, стандартизованная функция частот
S 1623	**standardized normal distribution,** *N*(0,1) distribution, centred and normed normal distribution <ST>	standardisierte Normalverteilung *f*, *N*(0,1)-Verteilung *f*, zentrierte und normierte Normalverteilung	distribution *f* normale réduite, distribution *N*(0,1), distribution normale centrée et normée	[центрированное и] нормированное нормальное распределение, распределение *N*(0,1), стандартизованное нормальное распределение
S 1624	**standardized normal variate,** centred and normed normal variate <ST>	standardisierte (zentrierte und normierte) normale Zufallsvariable (Zufallsgröße) *f*	variable *f* normale réduite, variable normale centrée et normée	[центрированная и] нормированная случайная величина, стандартизованная случайная величина
	standardized random variable <ST>	*s.* S 1626		
	standardized realization <ST>	*s.* S 1625		
	standardized regression coefficient <ST>	*s.* S 1631		
S 1625	**standardized sample value,** standardized realization, centred and normed sample value, centred and normed realization <ST>	standardisierter Stichprobenwert *m*, standardisierte Realisierung *f*, zentrierter und normierter Stichprobenwert, zentrierte und normierte Realisierung	réalisation *f* réduite, valeur *f* réduite de l'échantillon, réalisation centrée et normée, valeur centrée et normée de l'échantillon	[центрированное и] нормированное выборочное значение, [центрированная и] нормированная реализация, стандартизованное выборочное значение, стандартизованная реализация
S 1626	**standardized variable (variate),** standardized random variable, [centred	standardisierte Zufallsgröße (Zufallsvariable, Veränderliche) *f*, [zentrierte	variable *f* aléatoire réduite, variable aléatoire [centrée et] normée	стандартизованная случайная величина, [центрированная и] нор-

	and] normed variate, [centred and] normed [random] variable <ST>	und] normierte Zufallsgröße (Zufallsvariable, Veränderliche)		мированная случайная величина
	standard latin square <CT, ST> ⌐<GR>	*s.* S 1634		
	standard Loewy series	*s.* A 1036		
S 1627	**standard method** <ST>	Standardmethode *f*	méthode *f* à témoin	стандартный метод
S 1628	**standard model** <MM>	Standardmodell *n*	modèle *m* standard	стандартная модель
S 1629	**standard *n*-simplex,** standard simplex of dimension *n* <AT>	Standard-*n*-Simplex *n*	*n*-simplexe *m* type	стандартный (единичный) *n*-мерный симплекс
S 1630	**standard order,** original order <CT>	ursprüngliche Reihenfolge *f*	ordre *m* original	стандартный (первоначальный) порядок
	standard polynomial <AX, NU>	*s.* L 23		
S 1631	**standard regression coefficient,** standardized regression coefficient, centred and normed regression coefficient <ST>	standardisierter Regressionskoeffizient *m*, zentrierter und normierter Regressionskoeffizient	coefficient *m* de régression réduit, coefficient de régression centré et normé	[центрированный и] нормированный коэффициент регрессии, стандартизованный коэффициент регрессии
S 1632	**standard representation** <of a *W**-algebra> <FA>	Standarddarstellung *f*	représentation *f* type	стандартное представление
S 1633	**standard ring** <AL>	Standardring *m*	anneau *m* standard	стандартное кольцо
	standard score <ST>	*s.* Z 85		
	standard simplex of dimension *n* <AT>	*s.* S 1629		
	standard simplicial *n*-complex <AT>	*s.* N 67		
S 1634	**standard square,** standard latin square, reduced latin square, latin square in standard form <CT, ST>	Standardquadrat *n*, lateinisches Standardquadrat, Standard-LQ *n*	carré *m* type (latin type, standard, latin standard)	стандартный квадрат (латинский квадрат)
S 1635	**standard topology** <TO>	Standardtopologie *f*	topologie *f* standard	стандартная топология
S 1636	**stand-by redundancy** <ST>	kalte Reserve *f*	élément *m* redondant hors tension, réserve *f* hors tension	ненагруженный резерв
	standpoint <DS>	*s.* P 1060		
S 1637	**star** <AT, FT, GE, GP, ST, TO> ⌐<GP>	Stern *m*; kombinatorischer Stern <AT>	étoile *f*	звезда
S 1638	**star** <of a directed graph>	Büschel *n*	étoile *f*	звезда
	star <AY>	*s.* B 796		
	star <RE>	*s.* S 1656		
	star algebra <FA>	*s.* A 408/9		
S 1639	**star body** <EG>	Sternkörper *m*	corps *m* étoilé	звездное тело
S 1640	**star boundary** <in conformal mapping> <FT>	Sternschranke *f*	borne *f* de l'étoile	граница звездообразности, звездная граница
S 1641	**star[-] bounded** <TO>	sternberandet	de frontière étoilée	звездно ограниченный
S 1642	**star covering** <of a complex> <AT>	Sternüberdeckung *f*	recouvrement *m* étoilé	звездное накрытие
S 1643	**star-finite covering** <TO>	sternendliche Überdeckung *f*		звездно[ ]конечное покрытие
	star-like domain <GE>	*s.* S 1655		
S 1644	**star[-]like mapping** <FT>	sternige Abbildung *f*	application *f* étoilée	звездное отображение
S 1645	**star[-]like set** <from a point *x*> <CS, GE>	sternkonvexe Menge *f*, Sternmenge *f* <bezüglich eines Punktes *x*>	ensemble *m* étoilé <par rapport à un point *x*>	звездное множество <относительно точки *x*>
S 1646	**star neighbourhood** <AT> ⌐<RE>	Sternumgebung *f*	voisinage *m* étoilé	звездная окрестность
	star of a representation	*s.* S 1656		
S 1647	**star of a simplex** <AT>	Simplexstern *m*	étoile *f* d'un simplexe	звезда симплекса
S 1648	**star of a vertex** <AT>	Eckenstern *m*	étoile *f* du sommet	звезда вершины
	star of circles <AY>	*s.* B 798		
	star of complexes <PJ>	*s.* B 800		
S 1649	**star of convergence** <FT>	Konvergenzstern *m*	étoile *f* de convergence	звезда сходимости
	star of lines <AY, DS>	*s.* B 802		
S 1650	**star of meromorphism** <FT>	Meromorphiestern *m*	étoile *f* de méromorphie	звезда мероморфности
	star of planes <AY>	*s.* B 805		
	star of rays <AY, DS>	*s.* B 802		
	star of spheres <AY>	*s.* B 807		
S 1651	**star pentagon** <EG>	Sternfünfeck *n*, fünfstrahliger Stern *m*	pentagone *m* étoilé	звездчатый пятиугольник
S 1652	**star polygon** <EG>	Sternvieleck *n*, Sternpolygon *n*	polygone *m* étoilé, étoile *f*	звездчатый многоугольник, звездный многоугольник, самопересекающийся многоугольник
S 1653	**star polyhedron,** stellated polyhedron <EG>	Sternvielflach *n*, Sternpolyeder *n*, Sternvielflächner *m*, Sternflächner *m*	polyèdre *m* étoilé	звездчатый (звездный) многогранник
S 1654	**star[-] refinement** <of a covering> <TO>	Sternverfeinerung *f*	raffinement *m* étoilé	звездное измельчение
S 1655	**star region,** star-like domain, star-shaped domain <with respect to a point> <GE>	Sternbereich *m*, Sterngebiet *n*, sternförmiges Gebiet *n* <in bezug auf einen Punkt>	domaine *m* étoilé <par rapport à un point>	звездообразная (звездчатая, звездная) область <относительно точки>
S 1656	**star representation,** star [of a representation], contragredient representation <of a group> <RE>	kontragrediente Darstellung *f*, adjungierte Darstellung *f*, konjugierte Darstellung	représentation *f* contragrédiente, contragrédiente *f* [d'une représentation], représentation *f* conjuguée (coadjointe)	контрагредиентное представление, сопряженное представление

	star-shaped domain <GE>	*s.* S 1655		
S 1657	**star tree** <GP>	Sternenbaum *m*		звездчатое дерево, дерево звезд
S 1658	**state,** phase <SP>	Zustand *m*, Phase *f*	état *m*, phase *f*	состояние, фаза
S 1659	**state,** situation <*e.g.:* of a Turing machine> <TA>	Zustand *m*, innerer Zustand	configuration *f* intérieure, m-configuration *f*	внутреннее состояние
S 1660	**state indicator** <SP>	Zustandsanzeiger *m*	indicateur *m* d'état	состояние наблюдателя
	statement <GN>	*s.* S 706		
	statement <LO>	*s.* P 1865		
	statement form <LO>	*s.* S 497		
	statement function <LO>	*s.* P 1870		
S 1661	**state space** <of a C^*-algebra> <FA>	Zustandsraum *m*	espace *m* des états	пространство состояний
S 1662	**state variable** <PG>	Zustandsvariable *f*	variable *f* d'état	переменная состояния
S 1663	**state vector** <PG>	Zustandsvektor *m*	vecteur *m* d'état	вектор состояния
S 1664	**stathm** <AL>	euklidischer Betrag *m*	stathme *m* euclidien	евклидова статма
S 1665	**static model** <PG>	statisches Modell *n*	modèle *m* statique	статическая модель
S 1666	**static multiplicity concept** <AG>	statischer Multiplizitätsbegriff *m*, struktureller Multiplizitätsbegriff, idealtheoretischer Multiplizitätsbegriff	concept *m* statique de la multiplicité d'intersection	статическое понятие кратности пересечения
S 1667	**static programming** <PG>	statische Optimierung *f*, statische Programm[optim]ierung *f*	programmation *f* statique, optimisation *f* statique	статическое программирование
S 1668	**stationary bichain** <CA, HA>	stationäre Bikette *f*, abbrechende Bikette *f*	bi-chaîne *f* stationnaire	стационарная бицепь
	stationary chain <SP>	*s.* H 441		
S 1669	**stationary connected processes** <SP>	stationär verbundene Prozesse *mpl*	processus *mpl* stationnairement joints	стационарно связанные процессы
S 1670	**stationary curve** <GE>	stationäre Kurve *f*	courbe *f* stationnaire	стационарная кривая
S 1671	**stationary distribution** <SP>	stationäre Verteilung *f*	distribution (répartition) *f* stationnaire	стационарное распределение
S 1672	**stationary flow** <SP>	stationäre Strömung *f*	courant *m* stationnaire	стационарный поток
S 1673	**stationary function** <at a point> <AN, VA>	stationäre Funktion *f*	fonction *f* stationnaire	стационарная функция
	stationary Markov chain <SP>	*s.* H 441		
S 1674	**stationary osculating plane** <of a curve> <DG>	stationäre Schmiegebene *f*, stationäre Ebene *f*, Wendeberührebene *f*	plan *m* osculateur stationnaire, plan *m* stationnaire	стационарная соприкасающаяся плоскость
S 1675	**stationary point,** singular point <of an autonomous system> <DE>	stationärer Punkt *m*, Ruhepunkt *m*, singulärer Punkt, stationäre Stelle *f*	point *m* stationnaire, point singulier	стационарная точка, особая точка
	stationary point <GE>	*s.* C 2805		
S 1676	**stationary point process** <SP>	stationärer Punktprozeß *m*	processus *m* ponctuel stationnaire	стационарный точечный процесс
S 1677	**stationary process,** stationary stochastic process <SP>	stationärer [stochastischer] Prozeß *m*	processus *m* [stochastique] stationnaire	стационарный [случайный] процесс
	stationary process in the broad sense <SP>	*s.* S 1679		
S 1678	**stationary process in the narrow sense,** stationary process in the stronger sense, strictly stationary process <SP>	stationärer Prozeß *m* im engeren Sinne, im engeren Sinne stationärer Prozeß, i. e. S. stationärer Prozeß, streng stationärer Prozeß	processus *m* stationnaire au sens strict (étroit), processus complètement (strictement) stationnaire	стационарный процесс в узком смысле, стационарный в узком смысле процесс, строго стационарный процесс
	stationary process in the sense of Khinchine <SP>	*s.* S 1679		
	stationary process in the stronger sense <SP>	*s.* S 1678		
S 1679	**stationary process in the wider sense,** stationary process in the broad sense, stationary process in the sense of Khinchine, Khintchine['s] process <SP>	stationärer Prozeß *m* im weiteren (Chintschinschen) Sinne, im weiteren Sinne stationärer Prozeß, i. w. S. stationärer Prozeß, Chintschinscher (Khintschinescher) Prozeß, Khintchine-Prozeß *m*	processus *m* stationnaire au sens large (de Khintchine), processus de Khintchine	стационарный процесс в широком смысле, стационарный в широком смысле процесс, ковариационно стационарный процесс, процесс Хинчина
S 1680	**stationary sequence** <of random variables> <SP>	stationäre Folge *f*	suite *f* stationnaire	стационарная последовательность
S 1681	**stationary state** <PG, SP>	stationärer Zustand *m*, S-Zustand *m*	état *m* stationnaire	стационарное состояние
	stationary stochastic process <SP>	*s.* S 1677		
	stationary tangent <DG>	*s.* I 503		
S 1682	**stationary tangent plane** <of a surface> <GE>	stationäre Tangentenebene *f*	plan *m* tangent stationnaire	стационарная касательная плоскость
S 1683	**stationary time series** <SP>	stationäre Zeitreihe *f*	série *f* chronologique stationnaire	стационарный временной ряд
S 1684	**stationary transition probability,** constant transition probability <SP>	stationäre Übergangswahrscheinlichkeit *f*, konstante Übergangswahrscheinlichkeit	probabilité *f* de transition stationnaire, probabilité de transition constante	стационарная вероятность перехода, постоянная вероятность перехода
S 1685	**stationary value** <of a function> <AN>	stationärer Wert *m*	valeur *f* stationnaire	стационарное значение
S 1686	**statistic,** sample statistic, sample function <ST>	Stichprobenfunktion *f*, Statistik *f*, statistische Maßzahl *f*, Kennzahl *f*, Kennziffer *f*, Stichprobenmaßzahl *f*	fonction *f* des observations [de l'échantillon], statistique *f*	статистика, функция результатов наблюдения, выборочная функция, функция выборки
	χ-statistic <ST>	*s.* C 643		

	statistic χ^2 <ST>	*s.* C 635		
	χ^2-statistic <ST>	*s.* 1. C 635; 2. C 636		
S 1687	**statistical analysis** <ST>	statistische Analyse *f*	analyse *f* statistique	статистический анализ
S 1688	**statistical decision function,** decision (control) function <ST>	[statistische] Entscheidungsfunktion *f*, Steuerfunktion *f*	fonction *f* de décision [statistique], fonction de contrôle	[статистическая] решающая функция, функция решения
S 1689	**statistical decision [making] problem,** decision making problem, decision problem <ST>	statistisches Entscheidungsproblem *n*, Entscheidungsproblem	problème *m* des décisions statistiques, problème des décisions	проблема статистического решения, проблема решения
S 1690	**statistical decision procedure,** decision procedure <ST>	statistisches Entscheidungsverfahren *n*, Entscheidungsverfahren	procédé *m* de décision statistique, procédé de décision	процедура [статистического] решения, алгоритм [статистического] решения, разрешающая процедура
S 1691	**statistical decision process,** decision process <PG, SP>	statistischer (stochastischer) Entscheidungsprozeß *m*, Entscheidungsprozeß	processus *m* des décisions [statistiques]	процесс статистического решения, процесс решения
S 1692	**statistical decision rule,** decision rule <ST>	statistische Entscheidungsregel *f*, Entscheidungsregel	règle *f* de décision statistique, règle de décision	правило статистического решения, правило решения
	statistical decision theory <ST>	*s.* D 44		
S 1693	**statistical ergodic theorem,** ergodic theorem in the mean, [von] Neumann['s] ergodic theorem <SP>	statistischer Ergodensatz *m*, Ergodensatz *m* im Mittel, Mittelergodensatz *m*, Ergodensatz *m* von [J.] von Neumann, Neumannscher Ergodensatz *m*	théorème *m* ergodique statistique, théorème *m* ergodique en moyenne, théorème *m* ergodique de [J.] von Neumann	статистическая эргодическая теорема, эргодическая теорема в среднем, эргодическая теорема фон Неймана
	statistical estimate <ST>	*s.* E 544		
	statistical estimation <ST>	*s.* E 546		
	statistical extrapolation <SP>	*s.* E 862		
S 1694	**statistical hypothesis,** hypothesis <ST>	statistische Hypothese *f*, Hypothese	hypothèse *f* statistique, hypothèse	статистическая гипотеза, гипотеза
S 1695	**statistical inference,** inference <ST>	statistische Schlußweise *f*, Schlußweise, Schluß *m*	conclusion *f* statistique, conclusion, inférence *f*	статистический вывод, вывод, заключение
	statistical information <ST>	*s.* I 506		
	statistically significant <ST>	*s.* S 844		
	statistical model <ST>	*s.* S 1799		
S 1696	**statistical quality control** <ST>	statistische Qualitätskontrolle *f*, SQK	contrôle *m* statistique de qualité	статистический контроль качества
S 1697	**statistical regularization** <IE, NU> ┌<ST>	statistische Regularisierung *f*	régularisation *f* statistique	статистическая регуляризация
	statistical significance	*s.* S 841		
	statistical sign test <ST>	*s.* S 859		
	statistical straggling <ST>	*s.* S 101		
	statistical test[ing procedure] <ST>	*s.* T 202		
S 1698	**statistical tolerance region,** tolerance region <ST>	statistischer Toleranzbereich *m*, Toleranzbereich, Toleranzschätzung *f*	région *f* de tolérance statistique, région de tolérance	статистическая толерантная область, толерантная область, допустимая область
	statistic chi-square <ST>	*s.* C 635		
	statistics of attributes <ST>	*s.* E 280		
S 1699	**statistics of extremes (extreme values)** <ST>	Extremwertstatistik *f*	statistique *f* des valeurs extrêmes	статистика экстремальных значений
	Steenrod['s] algebra mod *p* <AT>	*s.* M 741		
S 1700	**Steenrod['s] approximation theorem** <for sections of fibre bundles> <AT>	Steenrodscher Approximationssatz *m*	théorème *m* d'approximation de Steenrod	аппроксимационная теорема Стинрода
S 1701	**Steenrod['s] classification theorem** <AT>	Steenrodscher Klassifikationssatz *m*	théorème *m* de classification de Steenrod	теорема Стинрода о классификации
S 1702	**Steenrod['s] cube** <AT>	Steenrodscher Kubus *m*	cube *m* de Steenrod	куб Стинрода
S 1703	**Steenrod['s] operation** <AT>	Steenrod-Operation *f*	opération *f* de Steenrod	операция Стинрода
S 1704	**Steenrod['s] power** <AT>	Steenrodsche Potenz *f*	puissance *f* de Steenrod	степень Стинрода
S 1705	**Steenrod['s] reduced power,** reduced power <AT>	reduzierte Steenrod-Potenz *f*, reduzierte Steenrodsche Potenz *f*	puissance *f* réduite de Steenrod	приведенная степень [Стинрода]
S 1706	**Steenrod['s] square (squaring operation),** reduced square <AT>	Steenrodsches Quadrat *n*	carré *m* de Steenrod, opération *f* de Steenrod	стинродовский квадрат, квадрат Стинрода, приведенный квадрат
	steepest[-] ascent method <AN, NU, PG>	*s.* 1. M 484; 2. M 485		
	steepest[-] descent method <DI>	*s.* M 486		
	steepest line <DS>	*s.* F 75		
S 1707	**Steffen['s] polynomial** <FU>	Steffensches Polynom *n*	polynôme *m* de Steffen	многочлен Штеффена
S 1708	**Stein['s] algebra** <FT> ┌<GR>	Steinsche Algebra *f*	algèbre *f* de Stein	штейнова алгебра, алгебра Штейна
S 1709	**Steinberg['s] group**	Steinberg-Gruppe *f*	groupe *m* de Steinberg	группа Штейнберга
S 1710	**Steiner['s] axis** <EG>	Steinersche Achse *f*	axe *m* de Steiner	ось Штейнера
S 1711	**Steiner['s] circle** <of complete quadrilateral> <GE>	Steinerscher Kreis *m*	cercle *m* de Steiner	окружность Штейнера

No.	English	German	French	Russian
S 1712	**Steiner['s] closure problem** <SG>	Steinersches Schließungsproblem *n*	problème *m* de fermeture de Steiner	проблема замыкания Штейнера
S 1713	**Steiner['s] construction,** Poncelet-Steiner construction <GE>	Steinersche Konstruktion *f*, Poncelet-Steinersche Konstruktion, Steiners geometrische Konstruktion, Konstruktion mit dem Lineal allein und einem [in der Zeichenebene] gegebenen Kreis mit gegebenem Mittelpunkt	construction *f* de Steiner, construction de Poncelet-Steiner, construction géométrique de Steiner	построение Штейнера, построение Понселе-Штейнера, построение с помощью одной линейки <при условии, если на плоскости начерчена окружность и ее центр>
S 1714	**Steiner['s] ellipse** <EG>	Steinersche Ellipse *f*	ellipse *f* de Steiner, ellipse *f* steinérienne	эллипс Штейнера
S 1715	**Steiner['s] focus** <EG>	Steinerscher Brennpunkt *m*	foyer *m* de Steiner	фокус Штейнера
	Steiner['s] generation <PJ, SG>	*s.* P 1688		
S 1716	**Steiner['s] group** <of double tangents> <AG>	Steinersche Gruppe *f*, Symphlegma *n* <Roch>	groupe *m* steinérien, symphlegme *m*	группа Штейнера
S 1717	**Steinerian** <of a plane algebraic curve> <AG>	Steinersche Kurve *f*, Fundamentalkurve *f*, Kernkurve *f*, kovariante Kurve *f* <einer Grundkurve>	courbe *f* steinérienne	штейнериана
S 1718	**Steinerian correspondence** <of two surfaces> <GE>	Steinersche Korrespondenz *f*	correspondance *f* steinérienne	соответствие Штейнера
S 1719	**Steinerian covariant** <of an algebraic form> <AL>	Steinersche Kovariante *f*	covariant *m* steinérien	ковариант Штейнера
S 1720	**Steinerian curve** <of a bundle of curves> <GE>	Steinersche Kurve *f*, Kernkurve *f*, Steineriana *f*	courbe *f* steinérienne	штейнериана <связки кривых>, штейнерова кривая
S 1721	**Steinerian polygon** <AG>	Steinersches Polygon *n*	polygone *m* de J. Steiner, polygone *m* steinérien	многоугольник Штейнера
S 1722	**Steiner-Minkowski formula** <for the volume of a parallel body> <CS, GE>	Steiner-Minkowskische Formel *f*	formule *f* de Steiner-Minkowski	формула Штейнера-Минковского
S 1723	**Steiner['s] parabola** <AG>	Steinersche Parabel *f*	parabole *f* de J. Steiner	парабола Штейнера
S 1724	**Steiner-Plücker line,** i-line <PJ, SG>	Steiner-Plückersche Gerade *f*, Plückersche Gerade *f*	droite *f* de Steiner-Plücker	прямая Штейнера-Плюккера
S 1725	**Steiner['s] point** <in the hexagrammum mysticum, of a triangle *or* a complete quadrilateral> <PJ, SG>	Steinerscher Punkt *m*	point *m* de Steiner	точка Штейнера
S 1726	**Steiner['s] quadrangle** <of a cubic> <AG>	Steinersches Viereck *n*	quadrangle *m* de Steiner	четырехугольник Штейнера
	Steiner['s] quartic surface <AG>	*s.* S 1729		
S 1727	**Steiner['s] quasigroup** <AL>	Steinersche Quasigruppe *f*	quasi-groupe *m* de Steiner	квазигруппа Штейнера
S 1728	**Steiner['s] surface** <of an algebraic surface> <AG>	Steinersche Fläche *f*	surface *f* de Steiner	поверхность Штейнера
S 1729	**Steiner['s] surface,** Steiner['s] quartic surface <a special quartic> <AG>	Steinersche Römerfläche *f*, Steinersche römische Fläche *f*, Steinersche Fläche *f*, Römerfläche *f*	surface *f* de Steiner, surface *f* steinérienne, surface *f* roumaine	поверхность Штейнера
S 1730	**Steiner['s] symmetrization [principle]** <CS, GE>	Steinersche Symmetrisierung *f*	symétrisation *f* de Steiner	симметризация Штейнера
S 1731	**Steiner['s] theorem** <for a parabola> <AY>	Steinerscher Parabelsatz *m*	théorème *m* de Steiner	теорема Штейнера
	Steiner['s] theorem <ST>	*s.* T 824		
	Steiner['s] three-cusped hypocycloid <GE>	*s.* T 931		
	Steiner['s] triple system <CT>	*s.* T 21		
S 1732	**Steiner-Weber problem** <EG, PG>	Steiner-Weber-Problem *n*	problème *m* de Steiner-Weber	задача Штейнера-Вебера
S 1733	**Steinitz['] exchange theorem,** exchange theorem, exchange law <for dependence relations> <AL>	Steinitzscher Austauschsatz *m*, Austauschsatz *m* von Steinitz, Austauschsatz *m*	théorème *m* de l'échange de Steinitz, théorème *m* de Steinitz, théorème *m* de l'échange, théorème *m* d'échange; propriété *f* d'échange des bases	теорема о замене
S 1734	**Steinitz number** <in field theory> <AL>	Steinitzsche Zahl *f*	nombre *m* de Steinitz	число Штейница
S 1735	**Steinitz['] theorem** <in field theory> <AL>	Satz *m* von Steinitz, Steinitzscher Satz	théorème *m* de Steinitz	теорема Штейница
S 1736	**Stein['s] manifold,** holomorphically complete manifold <FT>	Steinsche Mannigfaltigkeit *f*, holomorph-vollständige Mannigfaltigkeit	variété *f* de Stein, variété *f* steinienne, variété holomorphiquement complète	многообразие Штейна, голоморфно полное многообразие, штейново многообразие
S 1737	**Stein['s] method** <ST>	Steinsche Methode *f*	méthode *f* de Stein	метод Штейна
S 1738	**Stein['s] space,** holomorphically complete complex space <FT>	Steinscher Raum *m*, holomorph-vollständiger Raum *m*, holomorph-vollständiger kom-	espace *m* de Stein, espace *m* holomorphiquement complet, espace *m* 1-complet, espace *m*	пространство Штейна, голоморфно полное [комплексное] пространство, штейново

No.	English	German	French	Russian
		plexer Raum *m*	fortement 1-pseudo-convexe lorsque l'ensemble de dégénérescence est compact	пространство
S 1739	**Steklov-Fejér theorem** <DI, NU>	Satz *m* von Steklow-Fejér (Steklov-Fejér), Steklow-Fejérscher (Steklov-Fejérscher) Satz	théorème *m* de Steklov-Fejér	теорема Стеклова-Фейера
S 1740	**Steklov['s] function** <of a function> <AN>	Steklowsche (Steklovsche) Funktion *f*	fonction *f* de Steklov	функция Стеклова
	stellated polyhedron <EG>	*s.* S 1653		
S 1741	**stelloid** <a special curve> <GE>	Stelloide *f*	stelloïde *f*, stelloïde *m*	стеллоида <*n*-й степени>
S 1742	**step,** steplength <of integration> <DI, NU>	Schrittweite *f*	pas *m* d'intégration	шаг
S 1743	**step** <of a scale> <NO, NU>	Schritt *m*, Spanne *f*	pas *m*	шаг
S 1744	**step** <of a distribution> <ST>	Schrittweite *f* <einer gitterförmigen Verteilung>	pas *m* <d'une distribution>	шаг <распределения>
	step <AR>	*s.* C 1241		
	step <FD, NU>	*s.* I 824		
	step <FU>	*s.* S 1748		
	Stepanov['s] almost periodic function <AP>	*s.* G 133		
S 1745	**step curve of cumulative frequencies** <ST>	Treppenkurve *f* der Summenhäufigkeiten	courbe *f* en escalier des fréquences cumulées	ступенчатая кривая накопленных частот
S 1746	**step function,** jump function <not necessarily unit step> <AN>	Sprungfunktion *f*, Schrittfunktion *f*	fonction *f* saut (de saut, échelon, par échelon)	скачкообразная функция, функция скачков
S 1747	**step function,** staircase function <being constant on a finite, seldom a countable number of measurable sets, especially intervals>; simple function <being constant on finitely many measurable sets>, elementary function <being constant on countably many measurable sets> <AN>	Treppenfunktion *f*, Stufenfunktion *f*, gestufte (stückweise konstante) Funktion *f*; einfache Funktion	fonction *f* en escalier, fonction à palier, fonction en gradins, fonction étagée; fonction simple	ступенчатая (кусочно[-] постоянная) функция; простая функция
S 1748	**step index,** step <of a factorial function> <FU>	Schritt *m*	pas *m*	показатель шага, шаг
	steplength <DI, NU>	*s.* S 1742		
	step of iteration <AN, NU>	*s.* I 1224		
S 1749	**stepping stone method,** method of potentials <PG>	Distributionsmethode *f*, Methode *f* der Potentiale, Potentialmethode *f*, „stepping-stone"-Methode *f*	méthode *f* des potentiels	метод потенциалов
	stepwise approximation <AN, NU>	*s.* S 2231		
S 1750	**stepwise construction of the solutions** <NU>	Methode *f* des Stückelns, Stückelungsmethode *f*	méthode *f* de composition des solutions	метод стыка
S 1751	**steradian,** sr <EG>	Steradiant *m*, sr	stéradian *m*, sr	стерадиан
S 1752	**stereogram** <ST>	Stereogramm *n*	stéréogramme *m*	стереограмма
S 1753	**stereographic projection,** azimuthal orthomorphic projection, zenithal orthomorphic projection <DS>	stereographische Projektion *f*, winkeltreue Azimutalprojektion *f*, Kugelprojektion *f*, stereographische Abbildung *f*	projection *f* stéréographique (de Ptolémée), représentation *f* stéréographique	стереографическая проекция
S 1754	**stereographic projection** <FT>	stereographische Projektion *f*	projection *f* stéréographique	стереографическая проекция
S 1755	**stereometry,** solid geometry <EG>	Stereometrie *f*, Körpermessung *f*	stéréométrie *f*	стереометрия
S 1756	**stereotomy** <EG>	Steinschnitt *m*, Stereotomie *f*	stéréotomie *f*, coupe *f* des pierres	стереотомия
S 1757	**Stevens['] distribution** <ST>	Stevens-Verteilung *f*	distribution *f* de Stevens	распределение Стивенса
S 1758	**Stewart['s] theorem** <for a triangle> <EG>	Stewartscher Satz *m*	théorème *m* de Stewart	теорема Стюарта
S 1759	**Stiefel['s] characteristic class** <of differentiable manifolds> <AT>	Stiefelsche charakteristische Klasse *f*	classe *f* de Stiefel	[характеристический] класс Штифеля
S 1760	**Stiefel['s] decomposition** <AL>	Stiefelsche Zerlegung *f*	décomposition *f* de Stiefel <de type p>	разложение Штифеля
S 1761	**Stiefel['s] manifold (variety)** <GE, TO>	Stiefelsche Mannigfaltigkeit *f*	variété *f* de Stiefel, espace *m* des repères	многообразие Штифеля
S 1762	**Stiefel-Whitney [characteristic] class** <AT>	Stiefel-Whitneysche charakteristische Klasse *f*, Stiefel-Whitneysche Klasse	classe *f* caractéristique de Stiefel-Whitney-Chern, classe de Stiefel-Whitney, classe caractéristique de Stiefel-Whitney	характеристический класс Штифеля-Уитни, класс Штифеля-Уитни
S 1763	**Stiefel-Whitney number** <AT>	Stiefel-Whitneysche Zahl *f*	nombre *m* de Stiefel-Whitney, nombre de Stiefel	число Штифеля-Уитни
S 1764	**Stiefel-Whitney polynomial** <AT>	Stiefel-Whitneysches Polynom *n*	polynôme *m* de Stiefel-Whitney	многочлен Штифеля-Уитни

No.	English	German	French	Russian
S 1765	**Stieltjes['] continued fraction** <NT>	Stieltjesscher Kettenbruch *m*	fraction *f* [continue] de Stieltjes	непрерывная цепь Стилтьеса
S 1766	**Stieltjes['] function** <AN>	Stieltjessche Funktion *f*	fonction *f* de Stieltjes	функция Стилтьеса
S 1767	**Stieltjes['] integral,** S-integral <AN>	Stieltjessches Integral *n*, S-Integral *n*, Stieltjes-Integral *n*	intégrale *f* de Stieltjes	интеграл Стилтьеса
S 1768	**Stieltjes['] integral equation** <IE>	Stieltjessche Integralgleichung *f*	équation *f* intégrale de Stieltjes	интегральное уравнение Стилтьеса
S 1769	**Stieltjes['] line integral** <AN>	Stieltjessches Kurvenintegral *n*	intégrale *f* curviligne de Stieltjes	криволинейный интеграл Стилтьеса
S 1770	**Stieltjes['] planimeter** <GE, IN>	Stieltjes-Planimeter *n*, Stieltjesplanimeter *n*, Produktplanimeter *n*, Stieltjes-Integrator *m*	planimètre *m* de Stieltjes	планиметр Стилтьеса
S 1771	**Stieltjes['] problem of moments** <ST>	Stieltjessches Momentenproblem (Momentproblem) *n*, Momentenproblem von Stieltjes	problème *m* des moments de Stieltjes	проблема моментов Стилтьеса
S 1772	**Stieltjes['] series** <AN>	Stieltjessche Reihe *f*	série *f* de Stieltjes	ряд Стилтьеса
S 1773	**Stieltjes['] transform[ation]** <IT>	Stieltjessche Transformation *f*, Stieltjes-Transformation *f*	transformation *f* de Stieltjes	преобразование Стилтьеса
S 1774	**stigm,** circuit <minimal dependent set of a matroid> <GP>	Stigmus *m* <eines Matroids>	stigme *m*, sous-ensemble *m* dependant de cardinal minimal, ensemble *m* minimal dépendant <d'un matroïde>	минимальное зависимое множество <матроида>
	Stirling['s] approximation <AX, NU>	*s.* S 1776		
S 1775	**Stirling['s] expansion,** Stirling['s] series <FU>	Stirlingsche Reihe (Entwicklung) *f*	développement *m* (série *f*) de Stirling	ряд (разложение) Стирлинга
S 1776	**Stirling['s] formula,** Stirling['s] approximation <of *n*! *or* of the Γ-function> <AX, NU>	Stirlingsche Formel *f*, Stirlingsche Näherungsformel *f*, Stirling-Formel *f*	formule *f* de Stirling	формула (приближение) Стирлинга
	Stirling['s] formula <DI>	*s.* M 11		
	Stirling['s] formula <DI, NU>	*s.* S 1777		
	Stirling['s] formula of integration <DI, NU>	*s.* S 1777		
	Stirling['s] formula of interpolation <AN, NU>	*s.* S 1778		
S 1777	**Stirling['s] integration formula,** Stirling['s] formula [of integration] <DI, NU>	Stirlingsche Integrationsformel *f*	formule *f* d'intégration de Stirling, formule de Stirling	формула [численного интегрирования] Стирлинга
S 1778	**Stirling['s] interpolation formula,** Newton-Stirling interpolation formula, Stirling['s] formula of interpolation <AN, NU>	Stirlingsche Interpolationsformel *f*, Interpolationsformel (Formel *f*) von Stirling	formule *f* d'interpolation de Stirling	интерполяционная формула Стирлинга
	Stirling['s] number <AN>	*s.* F 32		
S 1779	**Stirling['s] polynomial** <FU>	Stirlingsches Polynom *n*	polynôme *m* de Stirling	многочлен Стирлинга
	Stirling['s] series <FU>	*s.* S 1775		
S 1780	**stochastically dependent event,** dependent event <ST>	stochastisch abhängiges Ereignis *n*, abhängiges Ereignis	événement *m* stochastiquement dépendant, événement dépendant	стохастически зависимое событие, зависимое событие
S 1781	**stochastically deterministic behaviour** <PG>	stochastisch deterministisches (determiniertes) Verhalten *n*, stochastisch deterministische (determinierte) Verhaltensweise *f*	comportement *m* stochastiquement déterminé	стохастически детерминированное поведение
S 1782	**stochastically independent event,** independent event <ST>	stochastisch unabhängiges Ereignis *n*, unabhängiges Ereignis	événement *m* stochastiquement indépendant, événement indépendant	стохастически независимое событие, независимое событие
S 1783	**stochastically larger random variable** <ST>	stochastisch größere Zufallsvariable *f*	variable *f* aléatoire stochastiquement plus grande	случайная величина, стохастически больше <чем. . .>; стохастически бóльшая случайная величина
S 1784	**stochastically smaller random variable** <ST>	stochastisch kleinere Zufallsvariable *f*	variable *f* aléatoire stochastiquement plus petite	случайная величина, стохастически меньше <чем. . .>; стохастически меньшая случайная величина
S 1785	**stochastic approximation** <ST>	stochastische Approximation *f*	approximation *f* stochastique	стохастическая аппроксимация
S 1786	**stochastic automaton,** stochastic machine <TA>	stochastischer Automat *m*	automate *m* stochastique	вероятностный автомат
S 1787	**stochastic connection,** stochastic relationship <ST>	stochastischer Zusammenhang *m*, stochastische Beziehung *f*	liaison *f* stochastique, relation *f* stochastique	стохастическая связь, стохастическое соотношение
	stochastic convergence <ST>	*s.* C 2338		
	stochastic decision theory <ST>	*s.* D 44		

No.	English	German	French	Russian
S 1788	**stochastic dependence,** dependence <of random variables ><ST>	stochastische Abhängigkeit *f*, Abhängigkeit	dépendance *f* en probabilité, dépendance stochastique, dépendance	стохастическая зависимость, зависимость
S 1789	**stochastic differential equation** <ST>	stochastische Differentialgleichung *f*	équation *f* différentielle stochastique	стохастическое дифференциальное уравнение
S 1790	**stochastic differentiation** <ST>	stochastische Differentiation *f*	dérivation *f* stochastique	стохастическое дифференцирование
S 1791	**stochastic dynamic programming** <PG>	stochastische dynamische Optimierung (Programm[optim]ierung) *f*	programmation *f* dynamique stochastique	стохастическое динамическое программирование
	stochastic extrapolation <SP>	*s.* E 862		
S 1792	**stochastic game** <TG>	stochastisches Spiel *n*	jeu *m* stochastique	стохастическая игра
S 1793	**stochastic independence,** independence <of random variables> <ST>	stochastische Unabhängigkeit *f*, Unabhängigkeit	indépendance *f* en probabilité, indépendance stochastique, indépendance	стохастическая независимость, независимость
S 1794	**stochastic integral** <ST>	stochastisches Integral *n*	intégrale *f* stochastique (aléatoire)	стохастический интеграл
S 1795	**stochastic integral equation** <ST>	stochastische Integralgleichung *f*	équation *f* intégrale stochastique	стохастическое интегральное уравнение
S 1796	**stochastic integration** <ST>	stochastische Integration *f*	intégration *f* stochastique	стохастическое интегрирование
	stochastic machine <TA>	*s.* S 1786		
S 1797	**stochastic matrix,** probability matrix <MD, ST>	stochastische Matrix *f*	matrice *f* stochastique	стохастическая матрица
S 1798	**stochastic maximum principle** <ST>	stochastisches Maximumprinzip *n* [von Kushner]	principe *m* du maximum stochastique	стохастический принцип максимума
S 1799	**stochastic model,** statistical model, probability model <ST>	stochastisches (statistisches) Modell *n*, Wahrscheinlichkeitsmodell *n*	modèle *m* stochastique (statistique, de probabilité)	вероятностная (статистическая, стохастическая) модель
	stochastic modification <SP>	*s.* E 451		
	stochastic optimization <PG>	*s.* S 1809		
S 1800	**stochastic process,** random process, random function <SP>	stochastischer (zufälliger) Prozeß *m*, zufällige (stochastische) Funktion *f*, Zufallsfunktion *f*, Zufallsprozeß *m*	processus *m* stochastique (aléatoire), fonction *f* aléatoire	случайный (вероятностный, стохастический) процесс, случайная (стохастическая) функция
S 1801	**stochastic process continuous almost certain,** stochastic process continuous with probability one <SP>	fast sicher stetiger stochastischer Prozeß *m*, mit Wahrscheinlichkeit Eins stetiger stochastischer Prozeß	processus *m* stochastique continu presque sûr, processus stochastique continu à probabilité un, processus stochastique presque sûrement continu	почти наверное непрерывный случайный процесс, непрерывный с вероятностью единицы случайный процесс
S 1802	**stochastic process continuous in probability** <SP>	stochastisch stetiger Prozeß *m*, in Wahrscheinlichkeit stetiger stochastischer Prozeß	processus *m* stochastique continu en probabilité	стохастически непрерывный процесс, непрерывный по вероятности случайный процесс
S 1803	**stochastic process continuous in quadratic mean** <SP>	im quadratischen Mittel stetiger stochastischer Prozeß *m*	processus *m* stochastique continu en moyenne quadratique	непрерывный в среднем квадратическом стохастический процесс
	stochastic process continuous with probability one <SP>	*s.* S 1801		
S 1804	**stochastic process differentiable almost certain,** stochastic process differentiable with probability one <SP>	fast sicher differenzierbarer stochastischer Prozeß *m*, mit Wahrscheinlichkeit Eins differenzierbarer stochastischer Prozeß	processus *m* stochastique différentiable (dérivable) presque sûr, processus stochastique différentiable (dérivable) à probabilité un, processus stochastique presque sûrement différentiable (dérivable)	почти наверное дифференцируемый случайный процесс, дифференцируемый с вероятностью единицы случайный процесс
S 1805	**stochastic process differentiable in quadratic mean** <SP>	im quadratischen Mittel differenzierbarer stochastischer Prozeß *m*	processus *m* stochastique différentiable (dérivable) en moyenne quadratique	дифференцируемый в среднем квадратическом стохастический процесс
	stochastic process differentiable with probability one <SP>	*s.* S 1804		
	stochastic process of the second order <SP>	*s.* S 219		
S 1806	**stochastic process with after-effect,** process with after-effect <SP>	stochastischer Prozeß *m* mit Nachwirkung, Prozeß mit Nachwirkung	processus *m* aléatoire avec persistance, processus avec persistance	случайный процесс с последействием, процесс с последействием
S 1807	**stochastic process with continuous time,** process with continuous time <SP>	stochastischer Prozeß *m* mit stetiger Zeit, Prozeß mit stetiger Zeit	processus *m* aléatoire à temps continu, processus à temps continu	случайный процесс с непрерывным временем, процесс с непрерывным временем
	stochastic process with discrete time <SP>	*s.* R 113		
S 1808	**stochastic process with independent increments,** process with independent increments, additive process, differential process <SP>	stochastischer (Markovscher) Prozeß *m* mit unabhängigen Zuwächsen, Prozeß mit unabhängigen Zuwächsen, additiver stochastischer Prozeß, additiver Prozeß,	processus *m* stochastique avec (à) incréments indépendants, processus avec (à) incréments indépendants, processus stochastique additif, processus additif	случайный процесс с независимыми приращениями, процесс с независимыми приращениями, аддитивный процесс, дифференциальный процесс

No.	English	German	French	Russian
		Differentialprozeß *m*, translationsinvarianter Markovscher Prozeß, Markovscher Prozeß mit translationsinvarianter Übergangsfunktion		
S 1809	**stochastic programming,** stochastic optimization <PG>	stochastische Optimierung (Programmoptimierung, Programmierung) *f*, stochastisches Programmieren *n*	programmation (optimisation) *f* stochastique	стохастическое программирование
	stochastic relationship <ST>	*s.* S 1787		
S 1810	**stochastics** <ST>	Stochastik *f*, Wahrscheinlichkeitsrechnung *f* und mathematische Statistik *f*	stochastique *f*	стохастика
S 1811	**stochastic semi-group** <DE, FA, ST>	stochastische Halbgruppe *f*	demi-groupe *m* stochastique	стохастическая полугруппа
	stochastic sequence <SP>	*s.* R 113		
	stochastic variable <ST>	*s.* V 67		
S 1812	**Stöhr['s] $\varphi(x)$-density** <AB>	Stöhrsche $\varphi(x)$-Dichte *f*	$\varphi(x)$-densité *f* de Stöhr	$\varphi(x)$-плотность Штера
	Stokes['s] integral formula <AN, DI>	*s.* G 155		
S 1813	**Stokes['s] phenomenon** <for the Thomé series> <DE>	Stokessches Phänomen *n*	phénomène *m* de Stokes	явление Стокса, стоксово явление
S 1814	**Stokes['s] tensor** <VT>	Stokesscher Tensor *m*	tenseur *m* de Stokes	тензор Стокса
S 1815	**Stokes['s] theorem,** theorem of Stokes, integral theorem of Stokes, Kelvin['s] transformation <DI, VT>	Stokesscher Satz (Integralsatz) *m*, Integralsatz (Satz) von Stokes, Stokessche Formel *f*, [gewöhnliche] Stokessche Integralformel *f*	théorème *m* (formule *f*) de Stokes, formule stokienne	теорема Стокса, формула Стокса
S 1816	**Stolz['s] angle** <FT>	Stolzscher Winkel *m*	angle *m* de Stolz	угол Штольца
	Stonean space <TO>	*s.* S 1821		
S 1817	**Stone-Čech compactification,** Čech-Stone compactification, β-compactification, Čech bicompactification <TO>	Stone-Čechsche Kompaktifizierung, Stone-Čechsche Erweiterung *f*, Stone-Čech-Kompaktifizierung *f*, Čech-Stone-Kompaktifizierung *f*	compactifié *m* de Stone-Čech; compactification *f* de Stone-Čech	компактное замыкание Стоуна-Чеха, компактификация Стоуна-Чеха, стоунчеховское расширение, чех-стоуновское расширение
S 1818	**Stone lattice** <LA>	Stone-Verband *m*	treillis *m* de Stone	структура Стоуна
S 1819	**Stone['s] representation theorem,** Stone['s] theorem, representation theorem <for Boolean algebras> <LA>	Stonescher Darstellungssatz (Isomorphiesatz) *m*, Isomorphiesatz *m* von M. H. Stone, Satz *m* von Stone	théorème *m* de Stone	теорема Стоуна
S 1820	**Stone['s] space** <of a Boolean algebra> <LA>	assoziierter Stone-Raum *m*	espace *m* de Stone <d'une algèbre de Boole>	стоуновское пространство <булевой алгебры>
S 1821	**Stone['s] space,** Stonian space, Stonean space, extremely disconnected space <TO>	Stone-Raum *m*, Stonescher Raum *m*	espace *m* stonien (de Stone)	стоуновское (стоуново) пространство
S 1822	**Stone['s] theorem** <for unitary transformations> <FA>	Stonescher Satz *m*, Satz von Stone	théorème *m* de Stone	теорема Стоуна
	Stone['s] theorem <LA>	*s.* S 1819		
S 1823	**Stone-Weierstrass theorem,** theorem of Stone-Weierstrass <for Banach algebras> <FA>	Satz *m* von Stone-Weierstraß, Stone-Weierstraßscher Satz	théorème *m* de Stone-Weierstrass	теорема Стоуна-Вейерштрасса
	Stonian space <TO>	*s.* S 1821		
	s*-topology <FA>	*s.* S 2004		
S 1824	**stopped process** <SP>	gestoppter Prozeß *m*	processus *m* stoppé	остановленный процесс
S 1825	**stopping** <a random process> <SP>	Stoppen *n*	arrêt *m*	остановка
	stopping rule <SP>	*s.* S 1826		
S 1826	**stop time,** Markov['s] time, stopping rule <SP>	Stoppzeit *f*, nicht vorgreifende Zeit *f*, nicht von der Zukunft abhängende zufällige Zeit, Markovsche Zeit, Stoppregel *f*	temps *m* d'arrêt, temps de Markov, temps markovien, règle *f* d'arrêt	время остановки, марковское время, правило остановки
S 1827	**storage model** <PG>	Speichermodell *n*	modèle *m* de Stock	модель хранения
S 1828	**Störmer['s] method,** Adams-Störmer method <DE, NU>	Störmersches Extrapolationsverfahren (Integrationsverfahren, Verfahren) *n*, Adams-Störmersches Verfahren, Verfahren von Adams-Störmer	méthode *f* de Störmer, méthode d'Adams-Störmer	метод Штермера (Адамса-Штермера)
S 1829	**St. Petersburg game** <TG>	Petersburger Spiel *n*	jeu *m* de Pétersbourg	петербургская игра
S 1830	**St. Petersburg paradox** <ST, TG>	Petersburger (Petersburgisches) Paradoxon *n*	paradoxe *m* de Pétersbourg	петербургский парадокс
S 1831	**St. Petersburg problem** <ST>	Petersburger Aufgabe *n* (Problem *n*)	problème *m* de Pétersbourg	петербургская задача
	straggling <ST>	*s.* S 101		
S 1832	**straight angle,** flat angle <EG>	gestreckter Winkel *m*	angle *m* plat, plat *m*, angle déployé	развернутый (выпрямленный) угол
S 1833	**straight-edge-and-compass construction,** construction with compass	Konstruktion *f* mit Zirkel und Lineal	construction *f* par la règle et le compas, construction *f* au moyen d'une règle et	построение с помощью циркуля и линейки, построение циркулем и

	and ruler, ruler and compass construction, construction by ruler and compass <EG>		d'un compas	линейкой
S 1834	**straightening,** straight-line representation <of a graph> <GP>	geradlinige Darstellung *f*	redressement *m*	прямолинейное представление
S 1835	**straight G-space,** straight space <DG>	gerader G-Raum *m*, gerader geodätischer Raum *m*	G-espace *m* droit	прямое пространство (G-пространство)
S 1836	**straight[-]line,** line <EG>	Gerade *f*	droite *f*, ligne *f* droite	прямая, прямая линия; алгебраическая линия первого порядка <в плоскости>
	straight-line asymptote <AG, RF>	*s.* A 1136		
	straight line relationship <GN>	*s.* L 837		
	straight-line representation <GP>	*s.* S 1834		
	straight[-]line segment <EG>	*s.* L 876		
	straight-sided figure <EG>	*s.* R 291		
	straight space <DG>	*s.* S 1835		
	strangling <VT>	*s.* C 2274		
S 1837	**strategic equivalence** <TG>	strategische Äquivalenz *f*	équivalence *f* stratégique	стратегическая эквивалентность
S 1838	**strategic model** <PG>	strategisches Modell *n*	modèle *m* stratégique	стратегическая модель
S 1839	**strategy,** policy <TG>	Strategie *f*, Spielweise *f*	stratégie *f*	стратегия, линия поведения
	strategy <PG>	*s.* P 910		
S 1840	**strategy polygon** <TG>	Strategienpolygon *n*	polygone *m* des stratégies	многогранник (полигон) стратегий
S 1841	**stratification** <GE, TO>	Stratifikation *f*	stratification *f*	расслоение
S 1842	**stratification** <ST>	Schichtung *f*, Stratifikation *f*	stratification *f*	расслоение, стратификация
	stratification <SE>	*s.* P 276		
S 1843	**stratification after selection** <ST>	nachträgliche Schichtung *f*, Schichtung nach erfolgter Auswahl	stratification *f* après sélection	расслоение [выборки] после отбора
S 1844	**stratified sample** <ST>	geschichtete (stratifizierte) Stichprobe *f*	échantillon *m* stratifié	расслоенная выборка
S 1845	**stratified sampling (selection)** <ST>	geschichtete Stichprobennahme (Stichprobenauswahl, Auswahl, Stichprobenerhebung) *f*	sélection *f* stratifiée, échantillonnage (sondage) *m* stratifié	расслоенный выбор
S 1846	**stratum** <ST>	Schicht *f*	strate *f*	слой
	stratum <SE>	*s.* C 763		
S 1847	**stratum weight** <ST>	Schichtgewicht *n*	poids *m* de la strate	вес слоя
S 1848	**stream[-] line** <Rankine> <as a special curve> <GE>	Neoide *f*, Stromlinie *f*	néoïde *f*	линия тока
	stream[-] line <ME, SP>	*s.* F 421		
S 1849	**strength** <of connectives> <LO>	Bindungsstärke *f*	liaison *f*	сила
	strength <ST>	*s.* P 1132		
S 1850	**strengthening,** sharpening, precising <a condition, formulation, theorem, etc.> <GN>	Verschärfung *f*	renforcement *m*, amélioration *f*, précision *f*	усиление, уточнение, улучшение
S 1851	**stretching,** dilatation <EG>	Streckung *f*	allongement *m*, dilatation *f*	растяжение
S 1852	**strict antitonicity (antitony)** <RF, SE>	eigentliche (strenge) Antitonie *f*, Antitonie im engeren Sinne	antitonie *f* stricte	строгая (собственная) антитонность
S 1853	**strict cone** <of a linear space> <FA>	echter Kegel *m* <Kegel, der keine Gerade durch die Spitze enthält>	cône *m* saillant	выступающий конус
S 1854	**strict convexity** <CS, DI>	strikte (strenge) Konvexität *f*	convexité *f* stricte	строгая выпуклость
S 1855	**strict decreasing** <of a function> <RF>	streng monotones Abnehmen *n*	décroissance *f* stricte	строгое убывание
S 1856	**strict epimorphism** <CA>	strenger Epimorphismus *m*	épimorphisme *m* strict	строгий эпиморфизм
S 1857	**strict equality** <GN>	strenge Gleichheit *f*	égalité *f* stricte	строгое равенство
S 1858	**strict equivalence** <LO>	strikte Äquivalenz *f*	équivalence *f* stricte	строгая эквивалентность
S 1859	**strict extremum,** extremum in the narrow sense <DI, VA>; isolated extremum <DI>	eigentliches (strenges) Extremum *n*, Extremum im engeren Sinne <DI, VA>; isoliertes Extremum <DI>	extrémum *m* strict (au sens étroit)	строгий экстремум, экстремум в узком смысле
S 1860	**strict implication** <LO>	starke Implikation *f*	implication *f* stricte	сильная импликация
S 1861	**strict implication** <Lewis> <LO>	strikte (strenge) Implikation *f*	implication *f* stricte, conditionnel *m* strict	строгая импликация [Льюиса]
	strict inclusion <SE>	*s.* S 1909		
S 1862	**strict incompatibility** <LO>	strikte Inkompatibilität *f*	incompatibilité *f* stricte	сильная несовместность
S 1863	**strict increasing** <of a function> <RF>	streng monotones Wachstum *n*	croissance *f* stricte	строгое возрастание
S 1864	**strict inductive limit** <TO>	strikter induktiver Limes *m*	limite *f* inductive stricte	строгий прямой предел
S 1865	**strict inequality,** strong inequality <GN>	strenge (strikte) Ungleichung *f*	inégalité *f* stricte, inégalité au sens strict	строгое неравенство
	strict integral <DE>	*s.* S 1915		
S 1866	**striction band,** band of striction <GE>	Striktionsband *n*	bande *f* de striction	горловая (стрикционная) лента
S 1867	**striction line,** line of striction <of a family of curves> <DG>	Striktionslinie *f*	ligne *f* de striction	стрикционная линия

S 1868	**striction line,** line of striction, gorge line, gorge <of a ruled surface> <DG>	Kehllinie *f*, Striktionslinie *f*, Ort *m* der Zentralpunkte	ligne *f* de striction, ligne des points centraux, ligne de cannelure	линия сжатия, стрикционная (горловая) линия
	striction ray <DG>	*s.* C 390		
S 1869	**strict isotonicity (isotony)** <RF, SE>	eigentliche (strenge) Isotonie *f*, Isotonie im engeren Sinne	isotonie *f* stricte	строгая (собственная) изотонность
	strictly antitone function <RF>	*s.* S 1876		
S 1870	**strictly antitone mapping** <of ordered sets> <SE>	streng antitone Abbildung *f*	application *f* strictement décroissante	строго антимонотонное отображение
	strictly antitone sequence <SS>	*s.* S 1877		
	strictly antitonic function <RF>	*s.* S 1876		
	strictly antitonic sequence <SS>	*s.* S 1877		
S 1871	**strictly categorical set** <MM>	strikt (streng) kategorische Menge *f*	ensemble *m* strictement catégorique	строго категоричное (категорическое) множество
	strictly coarser topology <TO>	*s.* S 1899		
S 1872	**strictly concave function** <RF>	eigentlich (streng) konkave Funktion *f*, im engeren (eigentlichen) Sinne konkave Funktion	fonction *f* strictement concave	строго вогнутая функция
	strictly contained / to be <SE>	*s.* P 1797		
S 1873	**strictly convex function** <RF>	eigentlich (streng) konvexe Funktion *f*, im engeren (eigentlichen) Sinne konvexe Funktion	fonction *f* strictement convexe	строго выпуклая функция
S 1874	**strictly convex space** <FA>	strikt (streng) konvexer Raum *m*	espace *m* strictement convexe	строго выпуклое пространство
S 1875	**strictly cyclic module** <AL>	streng zyklischer Modul *m*	module *m* strictement monogène	строго циклический модуль, циклический модуль
S 1876	**strictly decreasing function,** strictly non-increasing (antitonic, antitone) function, strictly monotonically (monotonic, monotone) decreasing (non-increasing) function <RF>	eigentlich (streng) [monoton] fallende (abnehmende, nicht zunehmende, nicht wachsende) Funktion *f*, [monoton] fallende (abnehmende, nicht zunehmende, nicht wachsende) Funktion im engeren (strengen) Sinne, eigentlich (streng) antitone Funktion, antitone Funktion im engeren Sinne, echt fallende Funktion	fonction *f* strictement décroissante (non croissante, antitone), fonction strictement monotone (monotoniquement) décroissante (non croissante), fonction monotone (monotoniquement) décroissante (non croissante) au sens étroit, fonction décroissante (non croissante, antitone) au sens étroit	строго (собственно) убывающая (невозрастающая, антитонная, антимонотонная) функция, строго (собственно) монотонно (монотонная) убывающая (невозрастающая) функция
S 1877	**strictly decreasing sequence,** strictly non-increasing sequence, strictly monotonically (monotonic, monotone) decreasing (non-increasing) sequence, strictly antitonic (antitone) sequence <SS>	streng (eigentlich) monoton fallende (abnehmende) Folge *f*, streng (eigentlich) abnehmende (fallende, nicht wachsende, niemals wachsende, niemals zunehmende, nicht zunehmende, antitone) Folge, abnehmende (fallende, nicht wachsende, niemals wachsende, niemals zunehmende, nicht zunehmende, antitone) Folge im engeren (strengen) Sinne	suite *f* strictement décroissante (non croissante, antitone), suite décroissante (non croissante, antitone) au sens étroit	строго (собственно) убывающая (монотонно убывающая, невозрастающая, антитонная) последовательность
S 1878	**strictly deterministic behaviour** <PG>	streng deterministisches Verhalten *n*, streng deterministische Verhaltensweise *f*	comportement *m* strictement déterminé	строго детерминированное поведение
S 1879	**strictly elliptic system** <of [partial] differential equations> <DE>	streng (stark) elliptisches System *n* <von partiellen Differentialgleichungen>	système *m* <d'équations aux dérivées partielles> strictement elliptique	строго эллиптическая система <дифференциальных уравнений в частных производных>
S 1880	**strictly equivalent ideal** <AB>	im schärferen Sinne äquivalentes Ideal *n*	idéal *m* équivalent au sens rigoureux	строго эквивалентный идеал
S 1881	**strictly finer topology** <TO>	echt feinere Topologie *f*	topologie *f* strictement plus fine	строго более тонкая топология
	strictly finite field <AL>	*s.* G 14		
S 1882	**strictly homogeneous co-ordinates** <AG>	streng homogene Koordinaten *fpl*	coordonnées *fpl* strictement homogènes	строго однородные координаты
S 1883	**strictly increasing function,** strictly non-decreasing (isotonic, isotone) function, strictly monotonic increasing function <RF>	eigentlich (streng) wachsende (zunehmende, steigende, nicht abnehmende, isotone) Funktion *f*, streng monoton wachsende Funktion, wachsende (zunehmende, steigende, nicht abnehmende, isotone) Funktion im engeren Sinne, monoton wachsende (zunehmende) Funktion im engeren Sinne	fonction *f* strictement croissante (isotone, non décroissante, monotone[-ment] croissante, monotone[ment] non décroissante)	строго (собственно) возрастающая (неубывающая, изотонная) функция, строго (собственно) монотонно (монотонная) неубывающая (возрастающая) функция

No.	English	German	French	Russian
S 1884	**strictly increasing homeomorphism** <TO>	streng wachsender Homöomorphismus *m*	homéomorphisme *m* strictement croissant	строго возрастающий гомеоморфизм
S 1885	**strictly increasing mapping,** strictly isotonic mapping <SE>	streng monoton wachsende Abbildung *f*, streng isotone Abbildung	application *f* strictement croissante	строго возрастающее отображение
S 1886	**strictly increasing sequence,** strictly monotonically (monotonic, monotone) increasing sequence, strictly isotonic (isotone) sequence <SS>	streng (eigentlich) monoton wachsende (zunehmende) Folge *f*, streng (eigentlich) wachsende (zunehmende, nicht fallende, niemals fallende, niemals abnehmende, nicht abnehmende, isotone) Folge, monoton wachsende (zunehmende) Folge im engeren (strengen) Sinne, wachsende (zunehmende, niemals abnehmende, nicht abnehmende, nicht fallende, niemals fallende, aufsteigende, isotone) Folge im engeren (strengen) Sinne	suite *f* strictement croissante (isotone), suite monotone croissante	строго (собственно) возрастающая (монотонно возрастающая, неубывающая, изотонная) последовательность
	strictly isotone function <RF>	*s.* S 1883		
	strictly isotone sequence <SS>	*s.* S 1886		
	strictly isotonic function <RF>	*s.* S 1883		
	strictly isotonic mapping <SE>	*s.* S 1885		
	strictly isotonic sequence <SS>	*s.* S 1886		
S 1887	**strictly linearly compact module** <AL>	streng linear kompakter Modul *m*	module *m* strictement linéairement compact	строго линейно компактный модуль
S 1888	**strictly local ring** <AL>	streng lokaler Ring *m*	anneau *m* strictement local	строго локальное кольцо
	strictly monotone decreasing function <RF>	*s.* S 1876		
	strictly monotone decreasing sequence <SS>	*s.* S 1877		
	strictly monotone function <RF>	*s.* S 1889		
	strictly monotone increasing sequence <SS>	*s.* S 1886		
	strictly monotone non-increasing function <RF>	*s.* S 1876		
	strictly monotone non-increasing sequence <SS>	*s.* S 1877		
	strictly monotonically decreasing function <RF>	*s.* S 1876		
	strictly monotonically decreasing sequence <SS>	*s.* S 1877		
	strictly monotonically increasing sequence <SS>	*s.* S 1886		
	strictly monotonically non-increasing function <RF>	*s.* S 1876		
	strictly monotonically non-increasing sequence <SS>	*s.* S 1877		
	strictly monotonic decreasing function <RF>	*s.* S 1876		
	strictly monotonic decreasing sequence <SS>	*s.* S 1877		
S 1889	**strictly monotonic function,** strictly monotone function <RF>	eigentlich (streng) monotone Funktion *f*, monotone Funktion im engeren Sinne	fonction *f* strictement monotone	строго (собственно) монотонная функция
	strictly monotonic increasing function <RF>	*s.* S 1883		
	strictly monotonic increasing sequence <SS>	*s.* S 1886		
S 1890	**strictly monotonic mapping** <SE>	streng monotone Abbildung *f*	application *f* strictement monotone	строго монотонное отображение
S 1891	**strictly monotonic sequence** <SS>	streng monotone Folge *f*	suite *f* strictement monotone	строго монотонная последовательность
	strictly monotonic non-increasing function <RF>	*s.* S 1876		
	strictly monotonic non-increasing sequence <SS>	*s.* S 1877		
	strictly negative function <AL, AN>	*s.* N 96		

	strictly non-decreasing function <RF>	*s.* S 1883		
	strictly non-increasing function <RF>	*s.* S 1876		
	strictly non-increasing sequence <SS>	*s.* S 1877		
S 1892	**strictly normed linear space** <AL, FA>	streng normierter linearer Raum *m*	espace *m* linéaire strictement normé	строго нормированное линейное пространство
	strictly ordered set <SE> <SE>	*s.* O 318		
	strictly order-preserving mapping <SE>	*s.* O 356		
	strictly partially ordered class <SE>	*s.* S 1897		
S 1893	**strictly positive element,** positive element <of an ordered ring *or* group> <AL, GR>	streng positives Element *n*, positives Element <≠ 0>	élément *m* positif	строго положительный элемент
	strictly positive function <AL, AN>	*s.* P 1072		
S 1894	**strictly positive Hermitian [bilinear] functional** <FA>	eigentlich positives hermitesches [bilineares] Funktional *n*	fonctionnelle *f* [bilinéaire] hermitienne strictement positive	строго положительный эрмитов [билинейный] функционал
S 1895	**strictly positively definite sequence of numbers** <SS>	streng positiv-definite Zahlenfolge (Folge) *f*	suite *f* de nombres strictement définie positive	строго положительно определенная последовательность чисел
S 1896	**strictly positive measure** <ME>	strikt positives Maß *n*, positives Maß	mesure *f* strictement positive	строго положительная мера
S 1897	**strictly quasi-ordered class,** strictly partially ordered class <SE>	irreflexiv halbgeordnete (quasigeordnete) Klasse *f*	classe *f* partiellement ordonnée au sens strict	нерефлексивно полуупорядоченный класс
	strictly stationary process <SP>	*s.* S 1678		
S 1898	**strictly transitive in the sense of the category** <TO>	strikt transitiv im Sinne der Kategorie	strictement transitif au sens de la catégorie	строго транзитивный в смысле категории
	strictly triangular matrix <MD>	*s.* P 1811		
S 1899	**strictly weaker topology,** strictly coarser topology <TO>	echt schwächere (gröbere) Topologie *f*	topologie *f* strictement moins fine	строго (собственно) мажорируемая топология
S 1900	**strict majorant** <SS>	strikte Majorante *f*	majorant *m* strict	строгая мажоранта
S 1901/2	**strict maximum,** maximum in the narrow sense <DI>	eigentliches Maximum *n*, Maximum im engeren Sinne, strenges Maximum *n*	maximum *m* strict, maximum au sens étroit	строгий максимум, максимум в узком смысле
S 1903/4	**strict minimum,** minimum in the narrow sense <DI>	eigentliches Minimum *n*, Minimum im engeren Sinne, strenges Minimum *n*	minimum *m* strict (au sens étroit)	строгий минимум, минимум в узком смысле
S 1905	**strict monotonicity (monotony)** <RF>	eigentliche (strenge) Monotonie *f*, Monotonie im engeren (strengen) Sinne	monotonie *f* stricte (au sens strict)	строгая (собственная) монотонность
S 1906	**strict morphism** <AL>	strikter Morphismus *m*	morphisme *m* strict	строгий морфизм
S 1907	**strict negation** <LO>	strikte Negation *f*	négation *f* stricte	строгое отрицание
S 1908	**strict negativity** <AL, NT>	echtes Negativsein *n*, echte Negativität *f*	négativité *f* stricte	строгая отрицательность
S 1909	**strict ordering (partial order[ing], quasi-order),** strong ordering, ordering relation in the strict sense, antireflexive ordering relation, strict inclusion <SE>	irreflexive Halbordnung *f*, Halbordnung erster (1.) Art, strikte (antireflexive) Ordnungsrelation *f*, asymmetrische transitive Relation *f*	relation *f* d'ordre strictement antisymétrique, ordre *m* partiel strict, ordre partiel, relation d'ordre anti-reflexive, relation d'ordre strict, relation d'ordre au sens strict, ordre strict, ordre, ordre faible, relation d'ordre faible	нерефлексивное (иррефлексивное) полуупорядочение, частичное упорядочение, антирефлексивное отношение порядка
S 1910	**strict relative extremum** <DI>	eigentliches relatives Extremum *n*, relatives Extremum im engeren Sinne	extrémum *m* relatif strict	строгий относительный экстремум
S 1911	**strict relative maximum** <DI>	eigentliches relatives Maximum *n*, relatives Maximum im engeren Sinne	maximum *m* relatif strict	строгий относительный максимум
S 1912	**strict relative minimum** <DI>	eigentliches relatives Minimum, relatives Minimum im engeren Sinne	minimum *m* relatif strict	строгий относительный минимум
	strict sense / in the <GN>	*s.* N 12		
S 1913	**strict sifting** <TO>	strenge Siebung *f*	criblage *m* strict	строгое просеивание
S 1914	**strict simple ordering,** linear strict ordering <SE>	irreflexive (vollständige, konnexe, einfache) Ordnung *f*, *k*-Ordnung *f*, Anordnung *f*, Ordnung	ordre *m* linéaire (strict, fort, simple, total, complet, total strict)	нерефлексивное (иррефлексивное) полное упорядочение, строгое упорядочение, строгий порядок
S 1915	**strict solution,** strict integral <DE>	Lösung *f* (Integral *n*) im engeren Sinne	solution (intégrale) *f* stricte	решение (интеграл) в узком смысле
	strict solution <DE>	*s.* S 1263		
S 1916	**strict triangle inequality** <FA>	strikte Dreiecksungleichung *f*	inégalité *f* triangulaire stricte	строгое неравенство треугольника
S 1917	**strict upper bound** <SE>	strikte obere Schranke *f*	majorant *m* strict	строгая верхняя граница
	string <AL>	*s.* W 289		
S 1918	**string construction** <of an ellipse> <EG>	Gärtnerkonstruktion *f*, Fadenkonstruktion *f* <der Ellipse>	construction *f* des jardiniers	построение <эллипса> с помощью нити
S 1919	**stringency** <of a test> <ST>	Strenge *f*	rigueur *f*	строгость

S 1920	**strip** <of the first *or* second order> <DE>	Streifen *m*, einparametriger Elementverein *m* <erster *oder* zweiter Ordnung>	bande *f* <de premier *ou* deuxième ordre>	полоска, полоса <первого *или* второго порядка>
	strip <FT>	*s.* S 1923		
	striped matrix <MD>	*s.* B 57		
S 1921	**strip of conditional convergence** <of a Dirichlet series> <SS>	Streifen *m* bedingter Konvergenz	région *f* de convergence relative	полоса условной сходимости
S 1922	**strip of the second order,** second-order strip <DE>	Streifen *m* zweiter (2.) Ordnung, Krümmungsstreifen *m*	bande *f* de deuxième ordre	полос[к]а второго порядка
S 1923	**strip region,** strip <FT>	Streifen *m*, Streifengebiet *n*	bande *f*	полосообразная область, полоса
	stroke[-] function <AL, LO>	*s.* S 763		
	stroke[-] operation <AL, LO>	*s.* S 763		
S 1924	**strong additivity** <NT>	starke Additivität *f*	additivité *f* forte	сильная аддитивность
S 1925	**strong approximation** <in an algebraic group> <GR>	starke Approximation *f*	approximation *f* forte	сильная аппроксимация
S 1926	**strong approximation theorem** <for a valuation> <AL>	starker Approximationssatz *m*	théorème *m* d'approximation fort	сильная аппроксимационная теорема
	strong axiom of continuity <GE>	*s.* A 1282		
	strong axiom of continuity of Cantor <GE>	*s.* C 89		
	strong axiom of continuity of Dedekind <GE>	*s.* D 82		
S 1927	**strong Cauchy sequence** <in a unitary space> <FA, TO>	starke Cauchy-Folge *f*	suite *f* de Cauchy [pour la topologie forte]	последовательность Коши в смысле сильной топологии, сильная последовательность Коши
S 1928	**strong component** <of a graph> <GP>	stark[-] zusammenhängende Komponente *f*	composante *f* f-connexe, composante *f* fortement connexe	сильная компонента
S 1929	**strong conjunction** <LO>	starke Konjunktion *f*	conjonction *f* forte	сильная конъюнкция
S 1930	**strong connectedness** <of a directed graph> <GP>	starker Zusammenhang *m*	connexité *f* forte, f-connexité *f*	сильная связность
S 1931	**strong connectedness** <of a relation> <SE>	Linearität *f*	totalité *f*	линейность
S 1932	**strong connectedness** <of a compactum *or* complex> <TO>	starker Zusammenhang *m*	connectivité *f* forte <d'un compactum>; connexité *f* forte <d'un complexe>	сильная связность
S 1933	**strong continuity** <FA>	starke Stetigkeit *f*	continuité *f* forte	сильная непрерывность
S 1934	**strong convergence,** convergence in [the] mean, convergence in p-th mean, mean convergence of p-th order <in L_p> <FA, RF>	starke Konvergenz *f*, Konvergenz im [p-ten] Mittel <in L^p>	convergence *f* forte, convergence en moyenne [d'ordre p]	сильная сходимость, сходимость в среднем [порядка p], сходимость порядка p
S 1935	**strong convergence,** [ordinary] convergence <in a normed *or* unitary space> <FA, TO>	starke Konvergenz *f*, Konvergenz bezüglich der starken Topologie, [gewöhnliche] Konvergenz	convergence *f* forte, convergence [ordinaire]	сильная сходимость, [обыкновенная] сходимость
S 1936	**strong convergence** <for a sequence of distributions> <ST>	starke Konvergenz *f* [nach den Verteilungsfunktionen]	convergence *f* forte	сильная сходимость
	strong convergence <FA, RF>	*s.* C 2341		
S 1937	**strong correlation** <ST>	enge (starke) Korrelation *f*	corrélation *f* forte	сильная корреляция
S 1938	**strong deformation retract** <TO>	starker Deformationsretrakt *m*	rétracte *m* de déformation fort	сильный деформационный ретракт
S 1939	**strong deformation retraction** <TO>	starke Deformationsretraktion *f*	rétraction *f* par déformation forte	сильная деформационная ретракция
	strong differential <FA>	*s.* F 582		
S 1940	**strong discontinuity** <DE>	starke Unstetigkeit *f*	discontinuité *f* forte	сильный разрыв
S 1941	**strong disjunction** <LO>	starke Disjunktion *f*	disjonction *f* forte	сильная дизъюнкция
S 1942	**strong dual** <FA>	Dual *m* mit der starken Topologie, starker Dual	dual *m* fort, dual [topologique] muni de la topologie forte	сильное сопряженное пространство
S 1943	**strong ellipticity** <DE>	starke (strenge) Elliptizität *f*	ellipticité *f* forte	сильная эллиптичность
S 1944	**strong epimorphism** <CA>	starker Epimorphismus *m*	épimorphisme *m* fort	строгий эпиморфизм
S 1945	**strong equivalence** <LO>	starke Äquivalenz *f*	équivalence *f* forte	сильная эквивалентность
S 1946	**stronger formula** <LO>	stärkerer Ausdruck *m*, stärkere (nicht schwächere) Formel *f*	formule *f* plus forte	более сильная формула, не более слабая формула
S 1947	**stronger method of summation** <LI>	stärkeres Summierungsverfahren *n*	méthode *f* de sommation plus forte, procédé *m* de sommation plus fort	более сильный метод суммируемости
S 1948	**stronger metric** <TO>	stärkere Metrik *f*	métrique *f* plus forte	более сильная метрика
S 1949	**stronger norm** <FA>	stärkere Norm *f*	norme *f* plus fine	более сильная норма
S 1950	**stronger theory** <FO>	stärkere Theorie *f*	théorie *f* plus forte (riche)	более сильная теория
	stronger topology <TO>	*s.* 1. C 962; 2. F 247		
S 1951	**strongest topological structure** <TO>	stärkste topologische Zuordnung *f*	structure *f* topologique la plus forte	сильнейшая топологическая структура; <также:> слабейшая из топологических структур
S 1952	**strong excision property** <AT>	starke Exzisionseigenschaft *f*	propriété *f* d'excision forte	сильное свойство вырезания
S 1953	**strong extremal** <VA>	starke Extremale *f*	extrémale *f* forte	сильная экстремаль

S 1954	**strong extremum** <VA>	starkes (starkes relatives) Extremum *n*	extrémum *m* fort	сильный экстремум
S 1955	**strong game** <TG>	starkes Spiel *n*	jeu *m* fort	сильная игра
S 1956	**strong homomorphism** <UA>	starker Homomorphismus *m*	homomorphisme *m* fort	сильный гомоморфизм
	strong induction <FO>	*s.* C 2591		
S 1957	**strong inductive dimension,** large inductive dimension, Čech['s] dimension, Brouwer-Čech dimension <TO>	große induktive Dimension *f*, Brouwer-Čechsche Dimension	dimension *f* de Brouwer-Čech	большая индуктивная размерность, размерность в смысле Чеха, индуктивная большая размерность
	strong inequality <GN>	*s.* S 1865		
S 1958	**strong instability** <AX, DE, NU>	starke Instabilität *f*	instabilité *f* forte	сильная неустойчивость
S 1959	**strong law of large numbers** <ST>	starkes Gesetz *n* der großen Zahlen	loi *f* forte des grands nombres	усиленный закон больших чисел
S 1960	**strong Lefschetz theorem**<AT>	starker Lefschetzscher Satz *m*	théorème *m* de Lefschetz fort	сильная теорема Лефшеца
S 1961	**strong limit** <FA>	starker Limes *m*	limite *f* forte	сильный предел
S 1962	**strong linear (line) element** <VA>	starkes Linienelement *n*	élément *m* linéaire fort	сильный линейный элемент
S 1963	**strongly axiomatizable theory** <MM>	stark axiomatisierbare Theorie *f*	théorie *f* fortement axiomatisable	сильно аксиоматизируемая теория
S 1964	**strongly bounded sequence** <SS>	stark beschränkte Folge *f*	suite *f* fortement bornée	сильно ограниченная последовательность
S 1965	**strongly branched covering** <of Riemann surfaces> <FT> ⌐<AL>	stark verzweigte Überlagerung *f*	recouvrement *m* fortement ramifié	сильно разветвленное покрытие
S 1966	**strongly branched field**	stark verzweigter Körper *m*	corps *m* fortement ramifié	сильно разветвленное поле
	strongly comparable function <RF>	*s.* C 1317		
S 1967	**strongly complete space,** space complete in the strong topology <FA>	stark vollständiger Raum *m*	espace *m* fortement complet	пространство, полное относительно сильной сходимости
S 1968	**strongly connected compactum,** Cantorian manifold <TO>	Cantorsche Mannigfaltigkeit *f*, stark zusammenhängendes Kompaktum *n*	variété *f* cantorienne, multiplicité *f* cantorienne	сильно связный компакт, канторово многообразие
S 1969	**strongly connected graph** <GP>	stark zusammenhängender Graph *m*, stark zusammenhängender gerichteter Graph, streng zusammenhängender Graph	graphe *m* fortement connexe, graphe f-connexe	сильно связный граф, сильный граф
S 1970	**strongly connected relation** <SE>	lineare Relation *f*	relation *f* totale	линейное отношение
S 1971	**strongly consistent estimator** <ST>	stark konsistente Schätzfunktion (Punktschätzung, Schätzung) *f*	estimateur *m* fortement convergent (consistant)	сильно состоятельная оценка
S 1972	**strongly consistent sequence** <of estimators *or* tests> <ST>	stark konsistente Folge *f*	suite *f* fortement consistante	сильно состоятельная последовательность
S 1973	**strongly continuous map** <TO>	stark[-] stetige Abbildung *f*	application *f* fortement continue	сильно непрерывное отображение, взаимно непрерывная функция, квазикомпактная и непрерывная функция
S 1974	**strongly convergent sequence** <in a Banach space> <FA>	stark konvergente Folge, konvergente Folge	suite *f* fortement convergente	сильно сходящаяся последовательность
	strongly convergent sequence <FA>	*s.* S 574		
S 1975	**strongly elliptic[al] operator** <DE>	streng (stark) elliptischer Operator *m*	opérateur *m* fortement elliptique	сильно эллиптический оператор
S 1976	**strongly inaccessible cardinal,** cardinal number inaccessible in the narrower sense <SE>	unerreichbare Kardinalzahl *f* im engeren Sinne, unerreichbarer Aleph *m* im engeren Sinne, stark (Tarskische, im engeren Sinne) unerreichbare Kardinalzahl, Tarskische Zahl *f*	cardinal *m* fortement inaccessible	сильно недостижимое кардинальное число
S 1977	**strongly inaccessible ordinal** <SE>	Zermelosche Zahl (Grenzzahl) *f*, Grenzzahl von Zermelo, Zermelosche (stark unerreichbare) Ordnungszahl *f*	ordinal *m* fortement inaccessible	сильно недостижимое порядковое число
	strongly invariant set <ME, ST>	*s.* I 881		
S 1978	**strongly mixing [measurable] transformation,** rapidly mixing transformation, mixing [measurable] transformation <ME>	stark mischende [meßbare] Transformation *f*, mischende [meßbare] Transformation im engeren Sinne, mischende [meßbare] Transformation	transformation *f* [mesurable] fortement mélangeante, transformation [mesurable] mélangeante	сильно перемешивающее [измеримое] преобразование, перемешивающее [измеримое] преобразование
S 1979	**strongly *n*-dimensional space** <TO>	stark *n*-dimensionaler Raum *m*	espace *m* fortement *n*-dimensionnel	сильно *n*-мерное пространство
S 1980	**strongly *n*-regular ring** <AL>	stark *n*-regulärer Ring *m*	anneau *m* fortement *n*-régulier	сильно *n*-регулярное кольцо
S 1981	**strongly paracompact space** <TO>	stark parakompakter Raum *m*	espace *m* fortement paracompact	сильно паракомпактное пространство
S 1982	**strongly plurisubharmonic function** <PO>	stark plurisubharmonische Funktion *f*	fonction *f* fortement plurisousharmonique	сильно плюрисубгармоническая функция

No.	English	German	French	Russian
S 1983	**strongly[-] primary ideal** <AL>	starkes Primärideal *n*, stark primäres Ideal *n*, stark primäres Primärideal *n*	idéal *m* fortement primaire, idéal *m* primaire-fort	сильно примарный идеал
S 1984	**strongly primary ring** <AL>	starker primärer Nullteilerring *m*, stark primärer Nullteilerring *m*, stark primärer Ring *m*, starker Ring *m*	anneau *m* fortement primaire	сильно примарное кольцо
S 1985	**strongly pseudoconvex domain** <FT>	stark pseudokonvexes Gebiet *n*	domaine *m* fortement pseudoconvexe	строго псевдовыпуклая область
S 1986	**strongly *q*-pseudoconcave space** <FT>	stark *q*-pseudokonkaver Raum *m*	espace *m* fortement *q*-pseudoconcave	сильно *q*-псевдовогнутое пространство
S 1987	**strongly *q*-pseudoconvex function** <FT>	stark *q*-pseudokonvexe Funktion *f*	fonction *f* fortement *q*-pseudoconvexe	сильно *q*-псевдовыпуклая функция
S 1988	**strongly *q*-pseudoconvex space** <FT>	stark *q*-pseudokonvexer Raum *m*	espace *m* fortement *q*-pseudoconvexe	сильно *q*-псевдовыпуклое пространство
S 1989	**strongly reducible set of generators** <of a group> <GR>	stark reduzibles Erzeugendensystem *n*	système *m* générateur fortement réductible	сильно приводимая система образующих
S 1990	**strongly reversible semigroup** <AL>	stark reversible Halbgruppe *f*	demi-groupe *m* fortement réversible	сильно реверсируемая полугруппа, строго обратимая полугруппа
	strongly stable solution <DE>	*s.* A 1148		
S 1991	**strongly summable series** <LI>	stark summierbare Reihe *f*	série *f* fortement sommable	сильно суммируемый ряд
S 1992	**strongly undecidable theory** <MM>	stark unentscheidbare Theorie *f*	théorie *f* fortement indécidable	строго неразрешимая теория
S 1993	**strong Markov process** <SP>	streng (stark) Markovscher Prozeß *m*	processus *m* strictement markovien, processus markovien strict	строго марковский процесс
S 1994	**strong maximum** <VA>	starkes (starkes relatives) Maximum *n*	maximum *m* fort	сильный максимум
S 1995	**strong minimum** <VA>	starkes (starkes relatives) Minimum *n*	minimum *m* fort	сильный минимум
S 1996	**strong monomorphism** <CA>	starker Monomorphismus *m*	monomorphisme *m* fort	строгий мономорфизм
S 1997	**strong norm** <FA>	starke Norm *f*	norme *f* fine	сильная норма
S 1998	**strong operator topology,** strong topology [for operators] <FA>	starke Operatortopologie *f*	topologie *f* forte pour les opérateurs	сильная операторная топология
	strong ordering <SE>	*s.* S 1909		
	strong order unit <AL, FA>	*s.* S 2006		
S 1999	**strong Ore condition** <for rings> <AL>	starke Ore-Bedingung *f*	condition *f* de Ore forte	сильное условие Оре
S 2000	**strong relation [of comparison]** <RF>	starke Relation *f*, starke Vergleichsrelation *f*	relation *f* forte, relation de comparaison forte	сильное отношение, сильное отношение сравнения
S 2001	**strong solution** <DE>	starke Lösung *f*	solution *f* forte	сильное решение
	strong stability <DE>	*s.* A 1175		
S 2002	**strong summability** <LI>	starke Summierbarkeit *f*	sommabilité *f* forte	сильная суммируемость
S 2003	**strong topology,** metric topology, norm topology <on a normed linear space> <TO>	starke Topologie *f*	topologie *f* forte (fine)	сильная топология
S 2004	**strong *-topology, s*-topology** <FA>	starke *-Topologie *f*	topologie *f* *-forte	сильная *-топология
	strong topology <FA>	*s.* S 1998		
	strong topology for operators <FA>	*s.* S 1998		
	strong triangle inequality <AL, TO>	*s.* U 21		
S 2005	**strong unit** <of an l-group> <AL>	starke Einheit *f* <einer Verbandsgruppe>	unité *f* forte <d'un groupe réticulé>	сильная единица <l-группы>
S 2006	**strong unit,** strong order unit <of a partially ordered linear space> <AL, FA>	Ordnungseinheit *f*, starkes Einselement *n*	unité *f* forte	сильная единица
S 2007	**strophoid,** right strophoid, logocyclic <Booth> <AG>	Strophoide *f*, gerade Strophoide, Logozyklika *f*, logozyklische Kurve *f*, Kukumaeide *f*, Kukumeïde *f*, harmonische Kurve *f*, Cornusches Blatt *n*, Gurkenkernkurve *f*, Logocyklika *f*	strophoïde *f*, strophoïde droite, logocyclique *f*, courbe *f* logocyclique, cucuméide *f*	строфоида, прямая строфоида, логоциклическая кривая
	strophoid <GE>	*s.* O 22		
S 2008	**strophoidal curve** <GE>	strophoidale Kurve *f*	courbe *f* strophoïdale	строфоидальная кривая
	structural automorphism <GR>	*s.* L 161		
	structural group <AT>	*s.* G 444		
S 2009	**structural inference figure** <LO>	Struktur-Schlußfigur *f*	règle *f* structurale	структурное правило
S 2010	**structural invariant,** invariant of structure <of a Lie pseudogroup> <AL>	Strukturinvariante *f*	invariant *m* de structure	структурный инвариант
	structural isomorphism <GR, LA>	*s.* P 1735		
S 2011	**structural morphism** <CA>	Strukturmorphismus *m*	morphisme *m* structural	структурный морфизм
S 2012	**structural stability** <AN>	Strukturstabilität *f*	stabilité *f* structurale	структурная устойчивость
S 2013	**structural type** <of an algebra> <AL>	Strukturtyp *m*	type *m* de structure	структурный тип

S 2014	**structure / to** <AL, TO>	strukturieren, mit einer Struktur versehen	structurer, munir d'une structure	снабжать структурой
S 2015	**structure** <in a set> <AT, SE, TO>	Struktur *f* <AT, SE, TO>; Grundstruktur *f*, Mutterstruktur *f* <Bourbaki> <SE, TO>	structure *f*	структура
	structure <LA>	*s.* L 117		
	structure <TO>	*s.* S 1336		
	Ω-structure <UA>	*s.* O 70		
	structure constant <AL>	*s.* C 2108		
S 2016	**structured complex** <AT>	strukturierter Komplex *m*	complexe *m* structuré, complexe doté d'une structure de Weyl	структурированный комплекс
S 2017	**structure equations** <of a continuous group> <GR>	Strukturgleichungen *fpl*, Liesche Gleichungen *fpl*	équations *fpl* de structure	уравнения структуры
S 2018	**structure formula** <AL>	Strukturformel *f*	formule *f* structurale	структурная формула
S 2019	**structure function** <ST>	Strukturfunktion *f*	fonction *f* de structure	структурная функция
S 2020	**structure group** <of a matrix semigroup> <AL>	Strukturgruppe *f*	groupe *m* structural	структурная группа
	structure group <AT>	*s.* G 444		
S 2021	**structure of compact convergence** <TO>	Struktur *f* der kompakten Konvergenz, Struktur der auf kompakten Mengen gleichmäßigen Konvergenz	structure *f* de convergence compacte	структура компактной сходимости
S 2021 a	**structure of finite length** <LA>	beschränkt längenendlicher Verband *m*, längenendlicher (archimedischer) Verband, Verband von lokal endlicher Länge	treillis *m* archimédien	архимедова структура
S 2022	**structure sheaf** <AT>	Strukturgarbe *f*	faisceau *m* structural	структурный пучок
S 2023	**structure tensor** <of a continuous group> <GR>	Strukturtensor *m*	tenseur *m* de structure	структурный тензор
S 2024	**structure theorem** <AL, GR>	Struktursatz *m*	théorème *m* de structure	структурная теорема
	structure theorem for finitely generated modules <GR>	*s.* F 857		
S 2025	**structure transport** <AL>	Strukturverpflanzung *f*	transport *m* de structure	перенос структуры
S 2026	**structure vector** <of a continuous group> <AL>	Strukturvektor *m*	vecteur *m* de structure	структурный вектор
	Strutt['s] map <DE>	*s.* S 1577		
S 2027	**Struve['s] function** <FU>	Struves[che] Funktion *f*	fonction *f* de Struve	функция Штруве
	Student['s] distribution <ST>	*s.* T 111		
S 2028	**studentization** <ST>	Studentisierung *f*	studentisation *f*, transformation *f* de Student	стьюдентизирование, стьюдентизация
S 2029	**studentized range** <ST>	studentisierte Spannweite *f*; studentisierte Variationsbreite *f*	étendue *f* studentisée [de variation]	стьюдентизированный размах
	Student-Newman-Keuls test <ST>	*s.* N 194		
	Student['s] ratio <ST>	*s.* T 1050		
	Student['s] t-distribution <ST>	*s.* T 111		
	Student['s] test <ST>	*s.* T 1051		
	Study['s] normal coordinates <PJ>	*s.* P 1945		
S 2030	**Study['s] principle [of transfer[ence]]** <GE>	Studys[ches] Übertragungsprinzip *n*, Übertragungsprinzip von Study	principe *m* de transfert (corrélation) de Study	принцип перенесения [Котельникова-]Штуди
S 2031	**Study['s] spherical triangle** <EG>	Studysches sphärisches Dreieck *n*	triangle *m* sphérique de Study	сферический треугольник [в смысле] Штуди
S 2032	**Sturges['] rule** <ST>	Sturgessche Regel *f*	règle *f* de Sturges	правило Стургеса
S 2033	**Sturm['s] comparison theorem** <DE>	Sturms[cher] Vergleichssatz *m*, Vergleichssatz von Sturm	théorème *m* de comparaison de Sturm	теорема сравнения Штурма
S 2034	**Sturm['s] conoid** <DE>	Sturmsches Konoid *n*	conoïde *m* de Sturm	коноид Штурма
S 2035	**Sturm['s] curve** <a special roulette> <GE>	Sturmsche Kurve *f*	courbe *f* de Sturm	кривая Штурма
S 2036	**Sturm['s] [differential] equation** <DE>	Sturmsche Differentialgleichung (Gleichung) *f*	équation *f* (équation différentielle) de Sturm	уравнение (дифференциальное уравнение) Штурма
S 2037	**Sturm['s] function, Sturmian function** <of an algebraic equation> <AL>	Sturmsche Funktion *f*	fonction *f* de Sturm, fonction sturmienne	функция Штурма
S 2038	**Sturm-Liouville boundary condition** <DE>	Sturmsche Randbedingung *f*, Sturm-Liouvillesche Randbedingung	condition *f* aux limites de Sturm-Liouville	граничное (краевое, предельное) условие Штурма-Лиувилля
S 2039	**Sturm-Liouville boundary value problem,** Sturm-Liouville problem <DE>	Sturm[-Liouville]sches Randwertproblem (Problem) *n*, Sturmsche (Sturm-Liouvillesche) Randwertaufgabe *f*, Randwertaufgabe von Sturm	problème *m* aux limites de Sturm-Liouville, problème de Sturm-Liouville	[краевая] задача Штурма-Лиувилля, граничная задача Штурма-Лиувилля
	Sturm-Liouville differential equation <DE>	*s.* S 2041		
S 2040	**Sturm-Liouville eigenvalue problem,** Sturm-Liouville problem <DE>	Sturm[-Liouville]sches Eigenwertproblem *n*, Sturm[-Liouville]sche Eigenwertaufgabe *f*	problème *m* [aux valeurs propres] de Sturm-Liouville	задача [на собственные значения] Штурма-Лиувилля

No.	English	German	French	Russian
S 2041	**Sturm-Liouville equation,** Sturm-Liouville differential equation <DE>	Sturm-Liouvillesche Differentialgleichung (Gleichung) *f*	équation *f* [différentielle] de Sturm-Liouville	[дифференциальное] уравнение Штурма-Лиувилля
S 2042	**Sturm-Liouville expansion,** Sturm-Liouville series <DE>	Sturm-Liouvillesche Entwicklung (Reihe) *f*	développement *m* (série *f*) de Sturm-Liouville	разложение Штурма-Лиувилля, ряд Штурма-Лиувилля
S 2043	**Sturm-Liouville operator** <DE>	Sturm-Liouville-Operator *m*, Sturm-Liouvillescher Operator *m*	opérateur *m* de Sturm-Liouville	оператор Штурма-Лиувилля
	Sturm-Liouville problem <DE>	*s.* 1. S 2039; 2. S 2040		
	Sturm-Liouville series <DE>	*s.* S 2042		
S 2044	**Sturm['s] method** <for algebraic equations> <AL, NU>	Sturmsche Methode *f*	méthode *f* de Sturm	метод Штурма
S 2045	**Sturm['s] oscillation theorem** <DE>	Oszillationssatz *m* von Sturm, Sturm[scher] Oszillationssatz	théorème *m* d'oscillation de Sturm	теорема Штурма <о разделении нулей>, теорема колебаний Штурма
S 2046	**Sturm['s] problem** <for the number of real roots> <AL>	Sturmsches Problem *n*	problème *m* de Sturm	проблема Штурма
	Sturm['s] separation theorem <DE>	*s.* S 566		
S 2047	**Sturm['s] sequence,** sequence of Sturm['s] functions <AL, NU>	Sturmsche Kette (Reihe) *f*	suite *f* de Sturm	последовательность (ряд) Штурма
S 2048	**Sturm['s] theorem** <AL, NU>	Sturmscher Satz *m*, Sturmsche Regel *f*	théorème *m* (règle *f*) de Sturm	теорема (правило) Штурма
S 2049	**Sturm['s] theory** <DE>	Sturmsche Theorie *f*	théorie *f* de Sturm	теория Штурма
	suan-pan <IN>	*s.* C 10		
S 2050	**subadditive function** <AN>	subadditive Funktion *f*	fonction *f* sous-additive	субаддитивная функция
	subadditive function <AN>	*s.* S 2052		
	σ-subadditive function <AN>	*s.* C 2570		
S 2051	**subadditive interval function** <AN>	subadditive (vereinigungsbeschränkte) Intervallfunktion *f*	fonction *f* d'intervalle non décroissante par décomposition	неубывающая при разложении функция, аддитивная снизу функция интервала
S 2052	**subadditive set function,** subadditive function <AN>	unteradditive (vereinigungsbeschränkte) Mengenfunktion (Funktion) *f*	fonction *f* d'ensemble sous-additive, fonction sous-additive	аддитивная снизу функция [множества]
	σ-subadditive set function <AN>	*s.* C 2570		
S 2053	**subadditivity** <of a set function> <AN>	Unteradditivität *f*, Vereinigungsbeschränktheit *f*	sous-additivité *f*	аддитивность снизу
S 2054	**subadditivity** <AN>	Subadditivität *f*	sous-additivité *f*	субаддитивность
	σ-subadditivity <AN>	*s.* C 2562		
S 2055	**subadjoint surface** <to an algebraic surface> <AG>	subadjungierte Fläche *f*	surface *f* sous-adjointe	субсопряженная поверхность
S 2056	**subadjunction** <AG>	Subadjunktion *f*	sous-adjonction *f*	субсопряжение
	sub-aggregate <SE>	*s.* S 2177		
S 2057	**subalgebra** <AL>	Teilalgebra *f*, Subalgebra *f*, Unteralgebra *f*	sous-algèbre *f*	подалгебра
S 2058	**subalgebra** <UA>	Unteralgebra *f*, algebraisches Untersystem *n*	sous-algèbre *f*	подсистема
	subalgebra <AL>	*s.* B 560		
S 2059	**subalternation** <LO>	Subalternation *f*	subalternation *f*, loi *f* d'implication de l'existence par la totalité	подчинение
S 2060	**sub[-]base** <of a filter> <SE, TO>	Erzeugendensystem *n*, Subbasis *f*	système *m* de générateurs	система образующих
S 2061	**sub[-]base** <of a space> <TO>	Subbasis *f*, Erzeugendensystem *n*, System *n* von Erzeugenden <einer Topologie>	sous-base *f* <d'un espace>	подбаза <пространства>, система образующих топологии
S 2062	**sub[-]base at a point *x*, sub[-]base for the neighbourhood system of a point *x*,** local sub[-]base at a point *x*, sub[-]base of the neighbourhoods of a point *x* <TO>	Subbasis *f* für das Umgebungssystem eines Punktes *x*	sous-base *f* <en *x*>	подбаза, локальная подбаза <в точке *x*>
	sub-base of open sets <TO>	*s.* O 157		
	sub[-]base of the neighbourhoods of a point *x* <TO>	*s.* S 2062		
	sub-basis of closed sets <TO>	*s.* C 903		
S 2063	**subbundle** <AT>	Teilbündel *n*, stetiges Teilbündel	sous-fibré *m*	подрасслоение
S 2064	**subcategory** <CA>	Unterkategorie *f*, Teilkategorie *f*	sous-catégorie *f*	подкатегория
	subcell <ST>	*s.* S 2070		
S 2065	**subchain** <AT, SE>	Unterkette *f*, Teilkette *f*	sous-chaîne *f*	подцепь
S 2066	**sub-chain complex,** subcomplex <of chains> <AT, HA>	Teilkettenkomplex *m*, Teilkomplex *m*	sous-complexe *m* [de chaînes]	подкомплекс
S 2067	**subcharacter** <RE>	Teilcharakter *m*	sous-caractère *m*	подхарактер
S 2068	**subcharacter** <ST>	Untermerkmal *n*	sous-caractère *m*	подпризнак
S 2069	**subclass** <of a class> <SE>	Unterklasse *f*, Teilklasse *f*	sous-classe *f*	подкласс

S 2070	**subclass,** subcell <ST>	Unterklasse *f*	sous-classe *f*	подкласс
S 2071	**subclass number** <ST>	Klassenbesetzung *f*	effectif *m* des sous-classes	численность в подклассах
S 2072	**subcoalgebra** <AL>	Unterkoalgebra *f*	sous-cogèbre *f*	подкоалгебра
	subcollection <SE>	*s.* S 2177		
S 2073	**subcomplex** <AT> ⌐<AT>	Subkomplex *m* <in seiner Hülle offene Menge von Simplizes>	sous-complexe *m*	субкомплекс
S 2074	**subcomplex** <of cells>	Teilkomplex *m*	sous-complexe *m*	подкомплекс
S 2075	**subcomplex** <of a simplicial set> <AT>	Teilkomplex *m*, simpliziale Untermenge *f*	sous-ensemble *m* simplicial	симплициальное подмножество
S 2076	**subcomplex** <of a simplicial complex> <TO>	Unterkomplex *m*	sous-complexe *m*	подкомплекс
	subcomplex <AT, HA>	*s.* S 2066		
S 2077	**subcontinuum** <TO>	Teilkontinuum *n*	sous-continu *m*	подконтинуум
S 2078	**subcontrarity** <LO>	Subkonträrsein *n*	subcontrariété *f*	субконтрарность
S 2079	**subcontrary [proposition]** <LO>	subkonträre Aussage *f*	proposition *f* subcontraire	субконтрарное высказывание, подпротивное высказывание
S 2080	**subcovering** <TO>	Teilüberdeckung *f*	sous-recouvrement *m*	подпокрытие
S 2081	**subcritical branching process** <SP>	unterkritischer Verzweigungsprozeß *m*	processus *m* à ramification souscritique	докритический ветвящийся процесс
S 2082	**subdecomposition,** refinement <of a direct *or* free decomposition> <UA>	Verfeinerung *f* <einer direkten *oder* freien Zerlegung>	raffinement *m* <d'une décomposition directe *ou* libre>	подразложение, продолжение <прямого *или* свободного разложения>
	subdeterminant <MD>	*s.* M 641		
S 2083	**subdeterminant of a_{ik},** minor of a_{ik} <MD>	zu a_{ik} gehörige Unterdeterminante *f*, adjungierte Unterdeterminante zu a_{ik}	sous-déterminant *m* relatif à l'élément a_{ik}	адъюнкт элемента a_{ik}
S 2084	**subdiagonal** <MD>	Diagonale *f* unterhalb der Hauptdiagonale	sous-diagonale *f*	поддиагональ
S 2085	**subdiagonal element** <of a matrix> <MD>	Element *n* unterhalb der Diagonale (Hauptdiagonale)	élément (terme) *m* au-dessous de la diagonale [principale]	поддиагональный элемент
	subdiagonal matrix <MD>	*s.* L 1171		
S 2086	**subdirect decomposition (factorization)** <AL, UA>	subdirekte Zerlegung *f*	décomposition *f* sous-directe	подпрямое разложение
S 2087	**subdirectly irreducible group** <GR>	subdirekt unzerlegbare Gruppe *f*	groupe *m* indécomposable en produit sous-direct	подпрямо неразложимая подгруппа
S 2088	**subdirectly irreducible ring** <AL>	subdirekt irreduzibler Ring *m*	anneau *m* indécomposable en produit sous-direct	подпрямо неразложимое кольцо
S 2089	**subdirectly reducible algebra** <UA>	subdirekt zerlegbare [universelle] Algebra *f*	algèbre *f* décomposable en produit sous-direct	подпрямо разложимая алгебра
S 2090	**subdirect product** <GR>	subdirektes Produkt *n*	produit *m* sous-direct	подпрямое произведение
S 2091	**subdirect sum** <e.g. of rings> <AL, CA>	subdirekte Summe *f*	somme *f* sous-directe	подпрямая сумма
S 2092	**subdirect union** <AL>	subdirekte Vereinigung *f*	réunion *f* sous-directe	подпрямое объединение
S 2093	**subdivision,** division, partition <of an interval> <AN>	Unterteilung *f*, Zerlegung *f*	subdivision *f*, sous-division *f*, partition *f*	подразделение, разбиение
S 2094	**subdivision** <of a scale> <NO>	Unterteilung *f*, Verdichtung *f*	subdivision *f*	подразделение, подраздел
	subdivision <AT>	*s.* T 923		
S 2095	**subdivision chain** <AT>	Unterteilungskette *f*	chaîne *f* de la subdivision	цепь подразделения
S 2096	**sub-division ring** <AL>	Unterschiefkörper *m*	sous-corps *m*	подтело
S 2097	**sub[-]domain** <AL>	Teilbereich *m*, Unterbereich *m*	sous-domaine *m*	подобласть
S 2098	**sub[-]domain,** partial domain, subregion <TO>	Untergebiet *n*, Teilgebiet *n*, Unterbereich *m*, Teilbereich *m*	sous-domaine *m*, partie *f* <d'un domaine>	подобласть
S 2099	**subdomain method,** method of subdomains <DE>	Teilgebietsmethode *f*	méthode *f* des sous-domaines	метод подобластей
	subextension <AL>	*s.* I 749		
S 2100	**subfamily** <SE>	Unterfamilie *f*, Teilfamilie *f*	sous-famille *f*, famille *f* extraite, partie *f* <d'une famille>	подсемейство
S 2101	**subfield** <of a field> <AL>	Unterkörper *m*, Teilkörper *m*, // Divisor *m*, Teiler *m* <eines Körpers>	sous-corps *m*, sous-extension *f*, corps *m* inférieur, // diviseur *m* <d'un corps>	подполе
S 2102	**sub-finite** <SE>	subfinit	sous-fini	субфинитный
S 2103	**subformula** <LO>	Teilformel *f*	sous-formule *f*	подформула, часть <формулы>
	subfunctor of the identity <CA>	*s.* P 1234		
S 2104	**subgame** <TG>	Unterspiel *n*, Teilspiel *n*	sous-jeu *m*	подыгра
S 2105	**subgraph,** induced subgraph <spanned by a set of vertices>, // section graph <GP> ⌐<GP>	Untergraph *m* <von einer Eckpunktmenge aufgespannt>	sous-graphe *m* <engendré par un ensemble de sommets>	подграф, суграф
	subgraph complement	*s.* C 1372		
S 2106	**subgroup** <*e.g.:* of finite, normal index> <of a group> <GR>	Untergruppe *f*, Subgruppe *f*, Teiler *m*, Divisor *m* <der Gruppe> <*z. B.:* von endlichem Index>	sous-groupe *m*, diviseur *m* <du groupe> <*par exemple:* d'indice fini>	подгруппа <*например:* конечного индекса>
S 2107	**subgroup** <ST>	Untergruppe *f*	sous-groupe *m*	подгруппа
S 2108	**Π-subgroup** <GR>	Π-Untergruppe *f*	Π-sous-groupe *m*	Π-подгруппа
S 2109	**subgroup of boundaries,** group of boundaries <AT, HA>	Gruppe *f* der Ränder, Rändergruppe *f*	groupe *m* des bords	подгруппа границ

No.	English	German	French	Russian
S 2110	**subgroupoid** <AL>	Untergruppoid *n*, Teilgruppoid *n*, Teiloperativ *n*	sous-groupoïde *m*	подгруппоид
S 2111	**subgroup scheme** <AG>	Untergruppenschema *n*	schéma *m* de sous-groupes	схема подгрупп
S 2112	**subhalfgroupoid** <AL>	Teilhalbgruppoid *n*	sous-groupoïde *m* partiel	частичный подгруппоид
S 2113	**subharmonic function** <PO>	subharmonische Funktion *f*	fonction *f* sous-harmonique (subharmonique)	субгармоническая функция
S 2114	**sub-hypergraph** <GP>	Unterhypergraph *m*	sous-hypergraphe *m*	подгиперграф
S 2115	**sub[-]ideal** <AL>	Unterideal *n*, Teilideal *n*	sous-idéal *m*, multiple *m*	подыдеал, подидеал
S 2116	**subidempotent radical** <AL>	subidempotentes Radikal *n*	radical *m* sous-idempotent	подыдемпотентный радикал
S 2117	**subinductive class** <CA>	subinduktive Klasse *f*	classe *f* sous-inductive	подындуктивный класс
S 2118	**subinterval** <AN, SE>	Teilintervall *n*	intervalle *m* partiel, sous-intervalle *m* <général>; sous-segment *m*, segment *m* partiel <fermé>	субинтервал, подынтервал, подинтервал, частичный интервал
S 2119	**subinvariant** <AL>	Subinvariante *f*, Unterinvariante *f*	sous-invariant *m*	подинвариант, подынвариант
S 2120	**subinvariant series,** subnormal series <of groups> <GR>	subinvariante Reihe *f*	série *f* sous-invariante	субинвариантный ряд
S 2121	**subject** <LO>	Subjekt *n*	sujet *m*	субъект
S 2122	**subjective probability,** personal probability <ST>	subjektive (personalistische) Wahrscheinlichkeit *f*	probabilité *f* subjective (personnelle)	субъективная вероятность
	subject-predicate proposition <LO>	*s.* C 200		
S 2123	**sublattice** <GU>	Untergitter *n*, Teilgitter *n*	sous-réseau *m*	частичная решетка
S 2124	**sublattice,** substructure <LA>	Teilverband *m*, Unterverband *m*	sous-treillis *m*, sous-structure *f*, sous-lattice *m*	подструктура, подрешетка, субрешетка
S 2125	**sublinear functional** <on a linear space> <FA>	sublineares Funktional *n*	fonctionnelle *f* sous-linéaire (sublinéaire)	сублинейный (подлинейный) функционал
S 2126	**subloop** <AL>	Subloop *f*, Teilloop *f*	sous-loop *m*	подлупа
	submanifold <GE, TO>	*s.* S 2223		
S 2127	**submarkovian measure** <ME>	submarkovsches (sub-Markovsches) Maß *n*	mesure *f* sous-markovienne	субмарковская мера
S 2128	**submarkovian operator** <FA>	submarkovscher (sub-Markovscher) Operator *m*	opérateur *m* [linéaire] sous-markovien	субмарковский оператор
S 2129	**submartingale,** growing semi-martingale <ST>	Submartingal *n*, wachsendes Halbmartingal *n*	sous-martingale *f*, sousmartingale *f*, semi-martingale *f* croissante	субмартингал, возрастающий полумартингал
S 2130	**submatrix,** partial matrix, minor array <of a matrix> <MD>	Untermatrix *f*, Teilmatrix *f*, Abschnitt *m*	sous-matrice *f*, matrice *f* partielle (extraite)	подматрица, частичная матрица, субматрица; блок <блочной матрицы>
S 2131	**submaximal space** <TO>	submaximaler Raum *m*	espace *m* submaximal	субмаксимальное пространство
S 2132	**submersion** <DG>	Submersion *f*	submersion *f*	субмерсия
S 2133	**submersive morphism** <of schemes> <AG>	submersiver Morphismus *m*	morphisme *m* submersif	субмерсивный морфизм
S 2134	**submetric topological space** <TO>	submetrischer topologischer Raum *m*	espace *m* topologique sous-métrique (submétrique)	субметрическое топологическое пространство
S 2135	**submetrizable topological space** <TO>	submetrisierbarer topologischer Raum *m*	espace *m* topologique submétrisable	субметризуемое топологическое пространство
S 2136	**submodel** <LO, UA>	Teilmodell *n*, Untermodell *n*	sous-modèle *m*	подмодель, субмодель
S 2137	**submodule** <AL>	Untermodul *m*, Teilmodul *m*	sous-module *m*	подмодуль
S 2138	**submonoid** <AL>	Untermonoid *n*, Submonoid *n*	sous-monoïde *m*	подмоноид
	submonoid <AL>	*s.* S 2171		
S 2139	**submultiple** <AR>	Teil *m*, Bruchteil *m*, Submultiplum *n*	sous-multiple *m*	доля, дробная часть, дробь
S 2140	**subnet** <DG>	Teilnetz *n*	sous-réseau *m*	подсеть
S 2141	**subnet** <SE, TO>	Moore-Smithsche Teilfolge *f*, Teilfamilie *f* <einer gerichteten Familie>	sous-famille *f* [filtrante]	подсеть
S 2142	**subnormal** <AY>	Subnormale *f*	sous-normale *f*	поднормаль, субнормаль
S 2143	**subnormal element** <of a group> <GR>	subnormales (erreichbares) Element *n*	élément *m* sous-normal	достижимый элемент
	subnormal series <GR>	*s.* S 2120		
S 2144	**subobject** <CA>	Teilobjekt *n*, Unterobjekt *n*	sous-objet *m*, sous-truc *m*	подобъект
S 2145	**subordinate category** <CA>	untergeordnete Kategorie *f*	catégorie *f* subordonnée	подчиненная категория
S 2146	**subordinate construction** <AT>	untergeordnete Konstruktion *f*	construction *f* subordonnée	подчиненная конструкция
S 2147	**subordinate filtration** <to a graduation> <AL>	zugehörige Filtration *f* <zu einer Graduierung>	filtration *f* inférieure <à une graduation>	подчиненная <градуировке> фильтрация
S 2148	**subordinate partition of a section** <to a covering> <AL, TO>	untergeordnete Zerlegung *f* eines Schnitts	partition *f* d'une section subordonnée <à un recouvrement ouvert>	разложение сечения, подчиненное покрытию
S 2149	**subordinate partition of unity** <to an open covering> <TO>	untergeordnete Zerlegung der Eins <einer offenen Überdeckung>	partition *f* de l'unité subordonnée <à un recouvrement ouvert>	разбиение единицы, подчиненное локально конечному открытому покрытию
S 2150	**subpair** <of a group *or* topological pair> <GR, TO>	Unterpaar *n*	sous-paire *f* <GR>; sous-couple *m* <TO>	подпара
S 2151	**subparabolic function** <DE>	subparabolische Funktion *f*	fonction *f* sous-parabolique	субпараболическая функция

	subpath <AT>	*s.* E 24		
S 2152	**subplane** <of a projective plane> <PJ>	Unterebene *f*	sous-plan *m*	подплоскость
S 2153	**subpolyhedron** <of a complex> <AT>	Teilpolyeder *n*	sous-polyèdre *m*	подполиэдр
	subpopulation of *k* elements without regard to order <CT>	*s.* K 29		
S 2154	**subpresheaf** <AL, TO>	Untergarbendatum *n*	sous-préfaisceau *m*	подпредпучок
S 2155	**subproduct** <of groups> <GR>	Unterprodukt *n*	sous-produit *m*	подпроизведение
S 2156	**subproduct** <of a cartesian product> <SE>	Partialprodukt *n*	sous-produit *m*	подпроизведение
	subprojective connection <DG>	*s.* S 2158		
S 2157	**subprojective manifold** <DG>	subprojektive Mannigfaltigkeit *f*, subprojektiver Raum *m*, Mannigfaltigkeit mit subprojektiver Übertragung	espace *m* sous-projectif	субпроективное пространство
S 2158	**subprojective transfer,** subprojective connection <DG>	subprojektive Übertragung *f*, subprojektiver Zusammenhang *m*	transfert *m* sous-projectif, connexion *f* sous-projective	субпроективное перенесение, субпроективная связность
S 2159	**subquasigroup** <AL>	Unterquasigruppe *f*	sous-quasi-groupe *m*	подквазигруппа
S 2160	**subquotient** <of a module> <AL>	Unterfaktormodul *m*	sous-module *m* quotient	фактор-подмодуль
S 2161	**subreflexive** <SE>	subreflexiv	sous-réflexif	субрефлексивный
	subregion <TO>	*s.* S 2098		
S 2162	**subrepresentation** <RE>	Teildarstellung *f*	sous-représentation *f*	подпредставление
S 2163	**sub*-representation** <of a C^*-algebra> <AL, FA>	Teil-*Darstellung *f*	sous-*-représentation *f*	*подпредставление
S 2164	**subresultant** <AL>	Teilresultante *f*	résultant *m* partiel	подрезультант
S 2165	**subring** <AL>	Unterring *m*, Teilring *m*	sous-anneau *m*	подкольцо
S 2166	**subsample** <ST>	Teilstichprobe *f*, Unterprobe *f*	sous-échantillon *m*	подвыборка, выборка из выборки
S 2167	**subsampling** <ST>	Teilstichprobenverfahren *n*	sous-échantillonnage *m*, méthode *f* des sous-échantillons	метод подвыборок
S 2168	**subsampling unit** <ST>	Teilstichprobeneinheit *f*, Teileinheit *f* der Stichprobe	sous-unité *f* d'échantillonnage	подэлемент выборки, элемент подвыборки
S 2169	**subscheme** <AG>	Unterschema *n*	sous-schéma *m*	подсхема
	subscript <GN>	*s.* L 1146		
S 2170	**subscripted variable** <GN>	Variable *f* mit unterem Index	variable *f* à indice inférieur	переменная с нижним индексом
S 2171	**sub[-]semigroup,** submonoid <AL>	Unterhalbgruppe *f*, Teilhalbgruppe *f*	sous-demi-groupe *m*, sous-monoïde *m*	подполугруппа, подмоноид
S 2172	**sub-semilattice** <AL>	Teilhalbverband *m*	sous-demi-treillis *m*	подполуструктура
S 2173	**subsemiring, sub-semiring** <AL>	Unterhalbring *m*, Teilhalbring *m*, Untersemiring *m*	sous-demi-anneau *m*	подпочти-кольцо, подполукольцо
S 2174	**subsequence** <AL>	Teilsequenz *f*	sous-suite *f*	подпоследовательность
S 2175	**subsequence,** partial sequence <SS, TO>	Teilfolge *f*	sous-suite *f*, suite *f* partielle, suite extraite, partie *f* <d'une suite>	подпоследовательность, частичная последовательность
S 2176	**subseries** <of an infinite series> <SS>	Teilreihe *f*	série *f* partielle (extraite)	подряд
S 2177	**subset,** subcollection, part, sub-aggregate <SE>	Untermenge *f*, Teilmenge *f*, Teil *m*, Menge *f* <in einer Obermenge>	sous-ensemble *m*, partie *f*, ensemble *m* contenu, sous-agrégat *m*	подмножество, часть, подсовокупность, подсистема, подагрегат
S 2178	**subset** <of a partial algebra> <UA>	Komplex *m*, Teilmenge *f*, Untermenge *f* <einer partiellen algebraischen Struktur>	partie *f* <d'une algèbre partielle>	подмножество <частичной алгебраической системы>
	subset axiom <LO, SE>	*s.* A 1293		
S 2179	**subset bounded from below,** bounded from below subset <SE>	nach unten beschränkte Untermenge *f*	partie *f* minorée	минорированное подмножество
	subset closed above <SE>	*s.* R 789		
	subset closed below <SE>	*s.* I 536		
S 2180	**subset closed under the inverse mapping** <GR>	gegenüber Inversenbildung abgeschlossene Untermenge *f*	partie *f* symétrique <d'un groupe>	подмножество, замкнутое относительно перехода к обратному элементу
	subset cofinal from the right <SE>	*s.* C 1053		
	subset contained properly <SE>	*s.* P 1835		
S 2181	**subset generated by a set of subgroups** <GR>	von einer Menge von Untergruppen erzeugte Untergruppe *f*	réunion *f* complète <des sous-groupes>, borne *f* supérieure d'une famille de sous-groupes <dans la famille des sous-groupes d'un groupe>	подгруппа, порожденная множеством подгрупп
	subset having the property of Baire <RF, TO>	*s.* B 23		
S 2182	**subset of a lattice which is a lattice with respect to the inclusion relation** <LA>	Teilbund *m*	partie *f* d'un treillis qui est un treillis par rapport à l'inclusion	подмножество структуры, являющееся структурой относительно включения

No.	English	German	French	Russian
	subset of first category <TO>	*s.* M 294		
	subset of the first category <TO>	*s.* M 294		
	subset relation <SE>	*s.* I 246		
	subset stable under an operation <AL>	*s.* C 906		
S 2183	**subset whose complement is disconnected** <of a space> <TO>	Schnitt *m*, Komplementärmenge *f* einer unzusammenhängenden Menge	coupure *f*	разрез
	subset whose diameter is less than V <TO>	*s.* V 226		
S 2184	**subsheaf** <AL, TO>	Untergarbe *f*	sous-faisceau *m*	подпучок
S 2185	**subsidiary deduction** <LO>	Hilfsschluß *m*	déduction *f* auxiliaire	вспомогательный вывод
	subsidiary variable <GN>	*s.* A 1252		
S 2186	**subspace** <GE, TO>	Unterraum *m*, Teilraum *m* <GE, TO>; Relativraum *m* <TO>	sous-espace *m*	подпространство <GE, TO>; часть пространства, относительное пространство <TO>
	subspace <AL>	*s.* V 128		
	subspace <AL, TO>	*s.* L 843		
S 2187	**subspace generated by *M***, subspace spanned by *M*, span of *M*, linear closure of *M* <*M* is subset of a linear space> <AL, FA>	<von *M*> aufgespannter (erzeugter, bestimmter) Unterraum *m*, lineare Hülle *f* <von *M*>, Verbindungsraum *m* <der Vektoren von *M*>	sous-espace *m* sous-tendu (déterminé, engendré) par *M*, clotûre *f* linéaire <de *M*>	подпространство, натянутое (порожденное) на *M*; объединяющее пространство <векторов подмножества *M*>, линейная оболочка <векторов подмножества *M*>
	subspace of solutions <AL>	*s.* S 1271		
	subspace spanned by *M* <AL, FA>	*s.* S 2187		
	subspace topology <TO>	*s.* R 774		
S 2188	**subsphere** <TO>	Untersphäre *f*	sous-sphère *f*	подсфера
S 2189	**substituend** <LO>	Substituend *m*, einzusetzender Ausdruck *m*	expression *f* à substituer	субституэнд, подставляемое выражение, подставляемое
S 2190	**substitute *F*-ratio** <ST>	Spannweite-*F*-Wert *m*	variable *f F* substituée, critère *m F* substitué	замещенная *F*-статистика, замещенное *F*-значение
S 2191	**substitute *F*-test**, *F'*-test <ST>	Spannweite-*F*-Test *m*, *F'*-Test *m*	test *m* de *F* substitué, test de *F'*	*F*-критерий с заменой оценок дисперсий на ранговые, *F'*-критерий
S 2192	**substitute *t*-ratio** <ST>	Spannweite-*t*-Wert *m*	variable *f t* substituée, critère *m t* substitué	замещенная *t*-статистика, замещенное *t*-значение
S 2193	**substitute *t*-test**, *G*-test <ST>	Spannweite-*t*-Test *m*, *G*-Test *m*	test *m* de *t* substitué, test *G*	*t*-критерий с заменой оценок дисперсий на ранговые, *G*-критерий
S 2194	**substitutible term** <LO>	substituierbarer Term *m*	terme *m* substituable	терм, допустимый для подстановки
S 2195	**substitution** <AL>	Einsetzen *n*, Einsetzung *f*, Substitution *f*	substitution *f*	подстановка
S 2196	**substitution**; replacement <GN>	Substitution *f*, Substituieren *n*; Einsetzung *f*, Einsetzen *n*, Ersetzung *f*, Ersetzen *n*	substitution *f*	подстановка; замена, замещение
S 2197	**substitution** <LO>	Einsetzen *n*, Einsetzung *f*, Substitution *f*; A-Einsetzung *f* <im Aussagenkalkül>	substitution *f*	замена
S 2198	**substitution equation** <AL>	Substitutionsgleichung *f*	équation *f* de substitution	уравнение подстановки
S 2199	**substitution formula**, substitution rule, rule of substitution <DI>	Substitutionsformel *f*, Substitutionsregel *f*	formule *f* du changement de variables, règle *f* de substitution	формула (правило) подстановки
S 2200	**substitution group** <as a subgroup of GL_n (*K*)> <GR>	Substitutionsgruppe *f*	groupe *m* des substitutions	группа подстановок
	substitution group <GR>	*s.* P 487 a		
S 2201	**substitution mapping** <AL>	Substitutionsabbildung *f*	application *f* de substitution	отображение с помощью подстановки
S 2202	**substitution method** <for solving systems of linear equations> <AL>	Einsetzungsmethode *f*, Einsetzungsverfahren *n*, Substitutionsmethode *f*, Substitutionsverfahren *n*	méthode *f* de substitution	метод подстановки
	substitution of the variable <DI>	*s.* C 503		
	substitution property <IT>	*s.* F 652		
S 2203	**substitution rate** <ST>	Substitutionsrate *f*	taux *m* de substitution	норма замены (подстановки)
S 2204	**substitution rule**, rule of substitution <LO>	Einsetzungsregel *f*	règle *f* de substitution	правило подстановки
	substitution rule <DI>	*s.* S 2199		
	substitution tensor <VT>	*s.* U 298		
S 2205	**substitutivity**, replaceability <LO>	Ersetzbarkeit *f*	substituabilité *f*	заменимость
S 2206	**substochastic matrix** <AL>	substochastische (zeilensubstochastische) Matrix *f*	matrice *f* sous-stochastique	субстохастическая матрица [по строкам]
S 2207	**substratum** <ST>	Unterschicht *f*	sous-strate *f*	подслой
S 2208	**substructure** <AL, PJ>	Teilstruktur *f*, Unterstruktur *f*	sous-structure *f*	подструктура, подстроение
S 2209	**substructure** <FO>	Unterstruktur *f*	sous-structure *f*	подструктура

	substructure <LA>	*s.* S 2124		
S 2210	**subsystem** <AG, GN>	Teilsystem *n* <AG, GN>; Teilschar *f* <AG>	sous-système *m*	подсистема <AG, GN>; частичная система <GN>
S 2211	**subtangent** <AY>	Subtangente *f*	sous-tangente *f*	подкасательная
S 2212	**subtheory** <MM>	Untertheorie *f*	sous-théorie *f*	подтеория
	subtotal <SS>	*s.* P 266		
S 2213	**subtraction** <*also:* of sets> <AL, AR, SE>	Subtraktion *f* <*auch:* von Mengen>; Abziehen *n*	soustraction *f*	вычитание
S 2214	**subtraction curve** <NU>	Subtraktionskurve *f*, subtraktionslogarithmische Kurve *f*	courbe *f* de soustraction	кривая вычитания
S 2215	**subtraction logarithm** <AN, NU>	Subtraktionslogarithmus *m* <Leonelli>	logarithme *m* de soustraction	
S 2216	**subtraction sign,** sign of subtraction, minus sign, minus symbol, — <*to be read:* minus> <AR>	Subtraktionszeichen *n*, Minuszeichen *n*, — <*gelesen:* minus, weniger>	signe *m* de soustraction, — <*se lit:* moins>	знак вычитания, знак минус, — <*читается:* минус, без>
S 2217	**subtractive set function** <FA>	subtraktive Mengenfunktion *f*	fonction *f* d'ensemble soustractive	субтрактивная функция множеств
S 2218	**subtrahend** <AR>	Subtrahend *m*, Subtrahendus *m*	nombre *m* à soustraire	вычитаемое
S 2219	**subtrahend** <as an ordinal number> <SE>	Subtrahendus *m*	ordinal *m* à soustraire	вычитаемое
S 2220	**subtree** <GP>	Teilbaum *m*	arbre *m* partiel, ensemblin *m*	поддерево
	subtree <GP>	*s. a.* A 881		
S 2221	**subuniverse** <of a structure> <SE, UA>	Unteruniversum *n*	sous-univers *m*	подуниверсум
S 2222	**subvariety** <over *k*> <AG>	Untervarietät *f* <über *k*>	sous-variété *f* <sur *k*>; sous *k*-variété *f*	подмногообразие <над *k*>
S 2223	**subvariety,** submanifold <GE, TO>	Untermannigfaltigkeit *f*, Teilmannigfaltigkeit *f*	sous-variété *f*	подмногообразие
S 2224	**subvector space spanned by a system of vectors** <AL>	Untervektorraum *m*, der von einem System von Vektoren aufgespannt wird	réunion *f* complète d'un système de vecteurs	векторное подпространство, порожденное системой векторов
S 2225	**subword** <AL>	Unterwort *n*	sous-mot *m*	подслово
S 2226	**succedent,** consequent <LO>	Sukzedens *n*, Succedens *n*	conséquent *m*	сукцедент, последующий член
S 2227	**succeed / to,** to be greater <than> <in an order relation> <NT, SE>	nachfolgen, größer sein <als>	être plus grand [strictement] <que>, être supérieur <à>	быть больше <чем>
S 2228	**successive adjunction** <AL>	sukzessive Adjunktion *f*	adjonction *f* successive	последовательное присоединение
S 2229	**successive application** <AL, SE, TO>	Hintereinanderausführung *f*, Nacheinanderausführung *f*, Hintereinanderanwendung *f*	application *f* successive	последовательное применение (выполнение)
S 2230	**successive approximation,** stepwise approximation, iteration <AN, NU>	sukzessive Approximation *f*, schrittweise Näherung *f*, Iteration *f*	approximation *f* successive, itération *f*	последовательное приближение, итерация
S 2231	**successive diagonalization** <MD>	schrittweise Diagonalisierung *f*	diagonalisation *f* successive	последовательная диагонализация
S 2232	**successive differences** <of a series> <SS>	aufeinanderfolgende Differenzen *fpl*	différences *fpl* successives	последовательные разности
S 2233	**successive elimination** <AL>	sukzessive (schrittweise) Elimination *f*	élimination *f* successive	последовательное исключение
S 2234	**successive integers** <NT>	aufeinanderfolgende ganze Zahlen *fpl*	nombres *mpl* entiers consécutifs	последовательные целые числа
S 2235	**successive minima** <GU>	sukzessive Minima *npl*	minima *mpl* successifs	последовательные минимумы
S 2236	**successive roots (solutions)** <of an equation> <AL>	aufeinanderfolgende Wurzeln *fpl*	racines *fpl* consécutives	последовательные корни
S 2237	**successor,** consequent <NT, SE>	Nachfolger *m*	successeur *m*, suivant *m*	следующее, последователь, последующий элемент
S 2238	**successor axiom** <AN, NT>	Nachfolgeraxiom *n*	axiome *m* du suivant	аксиома следования
S 2239	**successor function** <SE>	Nachfolgerfunktion *f*	fonction *f* successeur (de successeur)	функция следования
	successor ordinal <SE>	*s.* N 410		
	successor relation <NT, SE>	*s.* R 683		
S 2240	**success probability** <ST>	Erfolgswahrscheinlichkeit *f*	probabilité *f* de succès	вероятность удачи
S 2241	**sufficiency** <GN, LO>	Hinlänglichkeit *f*	suffisance *f*	достаточность
S 2242	**sufficiency** <ST>	Suffizienz *f*	exhaustivité *f*	достаточность
S 2243	**sufficient condition** <GN, LO>	hinreichende Bedingung *f*	condition *f* suffisante	достаточное условие, достаточный признак
	sufficient condition <VA>	*s.* C 817		
	sufficient condition of Jacobi <VA>	*s.* J 31		
S 2244	**sufficient co-ordinate** <ST>	hinreichende Koordinate *f*	coordonnée *f* exhaustive	достаточная координата
S 2245	**sufficient criterion of convergence** <SS, TO>	hinreichendes Konvergenzkriterium *n*	règle *f* de convergence	достаточный признак сходимости
S 2246	**sufficient estimating function, sufficient estimator,** sufficient point estimation <ST>	erschöpfende (hinreichende, suffiziente) Schätzung (Punktschätzung, Schätzfunktion) *f*	estimateur *m* exhaustif, fonction *f* d'estimation exhaustive, estimation *f* ponctuelle exhaustive	достаточная оценка, достаточная точечная оценка
	sufficiently general point of *V* / for a <AG>	*s.* G 168		

S 2247	**sufficiently rapid convergence** <SS>	hinreichend (hinlänglich) schnelle Konvergenz *f*	convergence *f* suffisamment rapide	достаточно быстрая сходимость
S 2248	**sufficiently rich space** <TO>	genügend reicher Raum *m*	espace *m* suffisamment riche	достаточно богатое пространство
	sufficient point estimation <ST>	*s.* S 2246		
S 2249	**sufficient statistic** <ST>	erschöpfende Maßzahl (Stichprobenfunktion) *f*, hinreichende Maßzahl (Stichprobenfunktion), suffiziente Maßzahl (Stichprobenfunktion)	statistique *f* exhaustive, fonction *f* exhaustive des observations	достаточная статистика
S 2250	**suffix** <LO>	Suffix *n*	suffixe *m*	суффикс
S 2251	**Sullivan['s] normal,** normal of Sullivan <ß- (beta-) *or* γ- (gamma-)> <DG>	Normale *f* von Sullivan, Sullivansche Normale <ß- (Beta-) *oder* γ- (Gamma-)>	normale *f* de Sullivan <ß *ou* γ>	нормаль Салливена <ß- (бета-) *или* γ- (гамма-)>
S 2252	**sum** <*e.g.*: modulo 2> <AL>	Summe *f* <*z. B.*: modulo 2>	somme *f* <*par exemple:* modulo 2>	сумма <*например:* по модулю 2>
S 2253	**sum** <of vector subspaces> <AL>	Vektorsumme *f*, Summe *f* <von Teilräumen>	somme *f* <de sous-espaces vectoriels>	сумма <векторных подпространств>
S 2254	**sum** <as the result of addition> <AR>	Summe *f*, Betrag *m*, Ergebnis *n*	somme *f*, agrégat *m*	сумма
S 2255	**sum** <of cardinal numbers, cardinals>, cardinal sum <SE>	Summe *f* von Kardinalzahlen	somme *f* cardinale	кардинальная сумма
S 2256	**sum** <of filters> <SE>	Filtersumme *f*	filtre *m* somme, somme *f* <de filtres>	фильтр-сумма, сумма <фильтров>
S 2257	**sum,** sum by rectangles, double sum <of a double series> <SS>	Summe *f*, Summe nach Rechtecken	somme *f*, somme par rectangles, somme double	сумма, сумма по четырехугольникам
	sum <AL>	*s.* 1. H 310; 2. L 242a		
	sum <AR>	*s.* A 963		
	sum <CA>	*s.* C 2449		
	sum <LA>	*s.* J 59		
	sum <SE>	*s.* U 202		
	sum axiom <SE>	*s.* A 1295		
S 2258	**sum book,** arithmetic book <AR, GN>	Rechenheft *n*	cahier *m* d'arithmétique	тетрадь по арифметике
	sum by Abel's method <LI>	*s.* A 1126		
	sum by Borel's method <LD>	*s.* B 605		
	sum by Borel's method of *r*-th order <LI>	*s.* B 783		
S 2259	**sum by Cesàro's method,** *C*-sum <LI>	*C*-Summe *f*, Summe *f* nach dem *C*-Verfahren	somme *f* par la méthode de Cesàro, *C*-somme *f*	[обобщенная] сумма по [методу] Чезаро
S 2260	**sum by Cesàro's method of *k*-th order,** (*C*,*k*) sum, C_k-sum <LI>	C_k-Summe *f*, (*C*,*k*)-Summe *f*, Summe *f* nach dem C_k-Verfahren	somme *f* par la méthode de Cesàro d'ordre *k*, C_k-somme *f*, (*C*,*k*)-somme *f*	[обобщенная] сумма по [методу] Чезаро *k*-го порядка
S 2261	**sum by columns,** column sum <of a matrix *or* double series> <MD, SS>	Spaltensumme *f*, Kolonnensumme *f*	somme *f* par colonnes; somme de colonne	сумма по столбцам; сумма по столбцу
S 2262	**sum by diagonals,** Cauchy sum, diagonal sum <of a double series> <SS>	Diagonalsumme *f*, Summe *f* nach Schräglinien (Diagonalen)	somme *f* par diagonales, somme de Cauchy, somme diagonale	сумма по диагоналям, сумма Коши, диагональная сумма
	sum by Euler's method <LI>	*s.* E 551		
	sum by Euler's method of *p*-th order <LI>	*s.* E 319		
	sum by Hausdorff's method <LI>	*s.* H 592		
S 2263	**sum by Hölder's method,** *H*-sum <LI>	*H*-Summe *f*, Summe *f* nach dem *H*-Verfahren	somme *f* par la méthode de Hölder, *H*-somme *f*	[обобщенная] сумма по методу Гельдера, [обобщенная] сумма по Гельдеру, *H*-сумма
S 2264	**sum by Hölder's method of *p*-th order,** (*H*,*p*) sum, H_p-sum <LI>	H_p-Summe *f*, (*H*,*p*)-Summe *f*, Summe *f* nach dem H_p-Verfahren	somme *f* par la méthode de Hölder d'ordre *p*, H_p-somme *f*	[обобщенная] сумма по методу Гельдера *p*-го порядка, (*H*,*p*)-сумма, H_p-сумма
S 2265	**sum by hyperbolas,** Dirichlet['s] sum <of a double series> <SS>	Summe *f* nach Hyperbeln, Dirichletsche Summe	somme *f* par hyperboles, somme de Dirichlet	сумма по гиперболам, сумма Дирихле
	sum by Nörlund's method <LI>	*s.* N 719		
	sum by rectangles <SS>	*s.* S 2257		
	sum by Riesz's method <LI>	*s.* R 1051/2		
S 2266	**sum by rows,** row sum <of a double series *or* matrix> <MD, SS>	Zeilensumme *f*	somme *f* par lignes; somme de ligne	сумма по строкам; сумма по строке
S 2267	**sum by squares,** square sum <of a double series> <SS>	Summe *f* nach Quadraten, Quadratsumme *f*	somme *f* par carrées	сумма по квадратам
	sum by the method of arithmetic means <LI>	*s.* C 2717		
S 2268	**sum chain complex** <HA>	Summe *f* von Kettenkomplexen	somme *f* de complexes de chaînes	сумма цепных комплексов
S 2269	**sum cycle** <AT>	Summenzyklus *m*	« Summenzyklus » *m*	цикл-сумма
S 2270	**sum graph** <GP>	identische Summe *f* von Graphen	somme *f* de graphes	объединение <пересекающихся> графов

No.	English	German	French	Russian
	sum ideal <AL>	*s.* I 6		
S 2271	**sum index** <sum subscript *or* sum superscript> <GN>	Summationsindex *m* <unterer *oder* oberer>	indice *m* de sommation <inférieur *ou* supérieur>	индекс суммирования, указатель суммирования <нижний *или* верхний>
S 2272	**summability** <of a function *or* integral *or* series> <AN, SS>	Summierbarkeit *f*	sommabilité *f*	суммируемость
	summability by Abel's method <LI>	*s.* A 1127		
S 2273	**summability factor** <of a divergent series> <LI>	Summierbarkeitsfaktor *m*, Summabilitätsfaktor *m*	facteur *m* de sommabilité	коэффициент суммируемости
S 2274	**summability factors** <of a divergent series> <LI>	Summabilitätsfaktorenfolge *f*, Summierbarkeitsfaktorenfolge *f*	suite *f* de facteurs de sommabilité	последовательность коэффициентов суммируемости
S 2275	**summability theory of divergent series** <LI>	Summierbarkeitstheorie *f* divergenter Reihen	théorie *f* de la sommabilité des séries divergentes	теория суммируемости расходящихся рядов
S 2276	**summable family** <*also* of morphisms *or* vectors> <AL, CA, FA>	summierbare Familie *f*	famille *f* sommable	суммируемое семейство
S 2277	**summable function** <AN>	summierbare Funktion *f*	fonction *f* sommable	суммируемая функция
	μ-summable function <AN>	*s.* M 1096		
S 2278	**summable series in the Lebesgue sense,** L-summable series <DI>	Lebesgue-summierbare Reihe *f*, L-summierbare Reihe	série *f* sommable au sens de Lebesgue, série sommable (L)	суммируемый в смысле Лебега ряд, суммируемый по Лебегу ряд
S 2279	**summand,** term, addend <of a sum> <AL, AR>	Summand *m*, Summenglied *n*, Glied *n*, Addend *m*	terme *m* à ajouter, terme additionnel, terme; nombre *m* à ajouter, nombre additionnel	слагаемое
	summand <LO>	*s.* M 381		
S 2280	**sum mapping** <of a system of mappings> <TO>	Summenabbildung *f*	application *f* somme	отображение-сумма
	summation <FD>	*s.* S 2286		
S 2281	**summation by bracketing** <AN>	Summation *f* durch Beklammerung	sommation *f* par paquets	суммирование пачками
S 2282	**summation check** <AL, NU>	Summenprobe *f*	total *m* de contrôle	проверка суммированием (сложением), контроль суммированием, контрольная сумма
S 2283	**summation convention [of Einstein],** Einstein['s] summation convention, Einstein['s] convention, dummy suffix notation, dummy suffix summation convention, Einstein['s] sum-notation <VT>	Einsteinsche Summationsbezeichnung (Summationskonvention, Summenkonvention) *f*, Einsteinsche Konvention *f* [für die Summation], Einsteinsche Summation *f*, Einsteinsche Summierungsvorschrift (Summationsvorschrift, Summationsübereinkunft, Summationsvereinbarung, Festlegung) *f*, Einstein-Summation *f*, Einstein-summation *f*, Einstein-Konvention *f* [für die Summation], Summationskonvention [von Einstein], Summierungsvorschrift *f* [von Einstein], Summationsvorschrift *f* [von Einstein], Summationsübereinkunft [von Einstein], Summationsvereinbarung, Summenkonvention [von Einstein]	convention *f* de sommation [sur les indices muets], convention d'Einstein, convention d'Einstein pour la sommation des indices	правило Эйнштейна (суммирования), общее правило написания сумм, обозначение суммирования Эйнштейна
	summation dummy <VT>	*s.* D 1049		
S 2284	**summation formula** <NT>	Summationsformel *f*, Summenformel *f*	formule *f* de sommation, formule sommatoire	формула суммирования, сумматорная формула
	summation index <VT>	*s.* D 1049		
S 2285	**summation limit** <GN>	Summationsgrenze *f*	limite *f* de sommation	предел суммирования
S 2286	**summation method,** summation <for solving difference equations> <FD>	Summationsmethode *f*	méthode *f* de sommation	метод суммирования
S 2287	**summation method,** method of summation <of divergent series> <LI>	Summationsverfahren *n*, Summationsmethode *f*, Summierungsverfahren *n*	méthode *f* (procédé *m*) de sommation	метод суммирования
S 2288	**summation polygon** <LI>	Summationspolygon *n*	polygone *m* de sommation	многогранник (полигон) суммирования
S 2289	**summation sign,** Σ <GN>	Summenzeichen *n*, Σ	signe *m* de la sommation, signe somme (d'une somme), signe sommatoire, Σ	знак (символ) суммирования, Σ
	sum of irrational radicals <AL, NT>	*s.* S 2353		
S 2290	**sum of order types** <SE>	Summe *f* von Ordnungstypen	somme *f* de types ordinaux	сумма порядковых типов
S 2291	**sum of powers** <*n*-th> <AL, NT>	Potenzsumme *f*, Newtonsche Summe *f* <*n*-te>	somme *f* des (de) puissances, somme (polynôme *m*) de Newton <de degré *n*>	степенная сумма <*n*-я>

S 2292	**sum of products** <of deviations from the mean> <ST>	Summe *f* der Abweichungsprodukte (Produkte), Produktsumme *f*	somme *f* des produits <des écarts>	сумма произведений <отклонений от среднего значения>
S 2293	**sum of sequences** <AB>	Schnirelmannsche Summe *f*, Summenmenge *f*, Summe *f* <von Mengen nichtnegativer ganzer Zahlen>	somme *f* selon Schnirelmann <des suites>, ensemble *m* somme	сумма множеств
S 2294	**sum of squares** <AL>	Quadratsumme *f*	somme *f* des carrés	сумма квадратов
	sum of squares <ST>	*s.* D 364		
S 2295	**sum of the digits,** total of the digits, transverse sum, transverse total <of a number, *especially:* in the decimal system> <AR, NT>	Quersumme *f*; <*speziell:*> dekadische Quersumme	somme *f* des chiffres [significatifs], somme transversale <*en particulier:* en système décimal>	сумма цифр [числа], сумма одноциферных граней, поперечная сумма <*в частности:* в десятичной системе>
S 2296	**sum of types of partially ordered sets** <SE>	Summe *f* von Halbordnungstypen	somme *f* de types d'ordre	сумма типов полуупорядоченных множеств
S 2297	**sum over the absolute values of the elements of a column** <of a matrix> <MD>	Spaltenbetragssumme *f*	somme *f* des valeurs absolues des éléments d'une colonne	сумма абсолютных величин элементов столбца
S 2298	**sum over the absolute values of the elements of a row** <of a matrix> <MD>	Zeilenbetragssumme *f*	somme *f* des valeurs absolues des éléments d'une ligne	сумма абсолютных величин элементов строки
	sum over the classes <AL, ST>	*s.* C 805		
S 2299	**sum relation** <of two relations> <SE>	Summenrelation *f*	relation *f* somme	сумма отношений
S 2300	**sum sequence** <FD>	Summenfolge *f*	suite *f* sommatoire	сумматорная последовательность
S 2301	**sum series** <AR>	Summenreihe *f*	série *f* de sommes	ряд сумм
	sum-set <SE>	*s.* U 202		
	sum-set axiom <SE>	*s.* A 1295		
S 2302	**SUMT,** SUMT method, sequential unconstrained minimization technique <PG>	SUMT-Methode *f*, [Methode *f*] SUMT <nach Fiacco-McCormick>	méthode *f* SUMT, SUMT	метод SUMT, SUMT
S 2303	**sum term** <AR>	Summenglied *n*	terme *m* sommatoire	сумматорный член
S 2304	**sum theorem** <TO>	Summensatz *m*, dimensionstheoretischer Summensatz	théorème *m* de la somme	теорема сложения
	SUMT method <PG>	*s.* S 2302		
S 2305	**sum topology** <TO>	Summentopologie *f*, Summe *f* <von Topologien>	topologie *f* somme	сумма топологий (семейства топологий)
	sum total <AR>	*s.* T 615		
S 2306	**sum vector** <VT>	Summenvektor *m*	vecteur *m* somme	суммарный вектор
	sup <DI, SE>	*s.* L 252		
S 2307	**superabundance** <AG>	„superabundance" *f*	superabondance *f*	избыточность
S 2308	**superabundant system** <AG>	superabundantes System *n*	système *m* superabondant	избыточная система
	superadditive function <AN>	*s.* S 2310		
S 2309	**superadditive functional** <FA>	superadditives Funktional *n*	fonctionnelle *f* suradditive	супераддитивный функционал
S 2310	**superadditive set function,** superadditive function <AN>	oberadditive Funktion (Mengenfunktion) *f*	fonction *f* [d'ensemble] sur[-]additive	аддитивная сверху функция [множества]
S 2311	**superadditivity** <*e.g.:* of a set function> <AN, TG>	Superadditivität *f*	superadditivité *f*	супераддитивность
S 2312	**superadditivity** <of a function> <AN>	Oberadditivität *f*	suradditivité *f*	аддитивность сверху
S 2313	**supercharacter** <ST>	Komplexmerkmal *n*	caractère *m* complexe	комплексный показатель (признак)
S 2314	**super-class** <SE>	Überklasse *f*	super-classe *f*	сверхкласс
S 2315	**supercompact space** <TO>	superkompakter Raum *m*	espace *m* supercompact	суперкомпактное (сверхкомпактное) пространство, суперкомпакт
S 2316	**supercritical branching process** <SP>	überkritischer Verzweigungsprozeß *m*	processus *m* à ramification surcritique	сверхкритический ветвящийся процесс
	supercurve <GE>	*s.* H 702		
S 2317	**superdeterminant** <AL, MD>	Superdeterminante *f*	superdéterminant *m*	надопределитель
S 2318	**superdiagonal** <MD>	Diagonale *f* oberhalb der Hauptdiagonale, Oberdiagonale *f*	surdiagonale *f*	наддиагональ
S 2319	**superdiagonal element** <of a matrix> <MD>	Element *n* oberhalb der Diagonale (Hauptdiagonale)	élément (terme) *m* au-dessus de la diagonale [principale]	наддиагональный элемент
	superdiagonal matrix <MD>	*s.* U 442		
S 2320	**superefficiency** <ST>	Supereffizienz *f*, Superwirksamkeit *f*, Überwirksamkeit *f*	superefficacité *f*, surefficacité *f*, surefficience *f*	сверхэффективность
S 2321	**superefficient estimating function, superefficient estimator** <ST>	supereffiziente Schätzfunktion (Punktschätzung, Schätzung) *f*, überwirksame Schätzfunktion	estimateur *m* superefficace (surefficient), fonction *f* estimatrice superefficace	сверхэффективная оценка
S 2322	**superficial [element]** <of order *s*> <AL>	Oberflächenelement *n* <der Ordnung *s*>	élément *m* superficiel <d'ordre *s*>	поверхностный элемент <порядка *s*>
S 2323	**superficial irregularity,** bidimensional irregularity <AG>	zweidimensionale Irregularität *f*, Flächenirregularität *f*	irrégularité *f* superficielle	двумерная (поверхностная) иррегулярность
	superficial measure <ME>	*s.* S 1560		

No.	English	German	French	Russian
	superfluous number <NT>	*s.* A 161		
S 2324	**superfluous parameters** <AN, GE>	überzählige Parameter *mpl*	paramètres *mpl* surabondants	избыточные параметры
S 2324a	**supergraph** <GP>	Obergraph *m*	sur-graphe *m*	надграф
S 2324b	**supergroup** <GR, ST>	Obergruppe *f* <GR, ST>; Übergruppe *f* <GR>	surgroupe *m*	надгруппа
S 2324c	**superhamiltonian graph** <GP>	hyperhamiltonscher Graph *m*	graphe *m* hyperhamiltonien	гипергамильтонов граф
S 2324d	**superharmonic function** <PO>	superharmonische Funktion *f*	fonction *f* surharmonique	супергармоническая функция
	superimposition <AY, EG>	*s.* C 1112		
	superior approximate limit <AN>	*s.* U 406		
S 2324e	**superior double limit** <of a double series> <SS>	oberer Doppellimes *m*	double limite *f* supérieure	верхний двойной предел
	superior figure <GN>	*s.* S 2330		
	superior function <AN>	*s.* O 426		
	superior limit <DI, SS>	*s.* U 427		
	superior limit <RF>	*s.* M 251		
	superior space <FA>	*s.* O 427		
S 2324f	**superlinear branch** <of an algebraic curve> <AG>	superlinearer Zweig *m*	branche *f* superlinéaire	суперлинейная ветвь
S 2324g	**supermagic square** <CT, ST>	supermagisches Quadrat *n*	carré *m* supermagique	супермагический квадрат
S 2324h	**supermartingale,** decreasing semi-martingale <ST>	Supermartingal *n*, fallendes Halbmartingal *n*	supermartingale *f*, surmartingale *f*, semi-martingale *f* décroissante	супермартингал, невозрастающий полумартингал
S 2324i	**superosculating conic [section]** <AY>	hyperoskulierender Kegelschnitt *m*	conique *f* (section *f* conique) surosculatrice	сверхсоприкасающееся коническое сечение
S 2324j	**superosculation** <AY>	Hyperoskulation *f*	surosculation *f*	сверхсоприкосновение
S 2325	**superparabolic function** <DE>	superparabolische Funktion *f*	fonction *f* superparabolique	суперпараболическая функция
	superposable <EG>	*s.* C 1935		
S 2326	**superposed graph** <GP>	zusammengesetzter Graph *m*	graphe *m* composé	составленный (составной) граф
S 2327	**superposition** <of functions> <AN>	Superposition *f* <von Funktionen>	superposition *f* <des fonctions>	суперпозиция, наложение <функций>
S 2328	**superposition** <of graphs> <GP>	Überlagerung *f*, Superposition *f*	couverture *f*	покрытие
	superposition <AY, EG>	*s.* C 1112		
	superposition of distributions <ST>	*s.* C 1729		
S 2329	**superposition principle,** principle of superposition <DE>	Superpositionsprinzip *n*	principe *m* de superposition (la superposition)	принцип наложения (суперпозиции)
	superrelaxation <NU>	*s.* O 584		
S 2330	**superscript,** upper index; superior figure, raised figure <GN>	oberer (hochgestellter) Index *m*; hochgestellte Zahl *f*	indice *m* supérieur, indice en haut	верхний индекс, верхний значок
S 2331	**superscripted variable** <GN>	Variable *f* mit oberem Index	variable *f* à indice supérieur	переменная с верхним индексом
	superset <SE>	*s.* I 241		
S 2332	**supersingular curve** <AG>	supersinguläre Kurve *f*	courbe *f* supersingulière	суперсингулярная кривая
S 2333	**supersolubility** <of a group> <GR>	Überauflösbarkeit *f*	hyper-résolubilité *f*	сверхразрешимость
	supersoluble group <GR>	*s.* S 2334		
S 2334	**supersolvable group,** supersoluble group <GR>	überauflösbare Gruppe *f*	groupe *m* hyper-résoluble	сверхразрешимая группа
	sup metric <FA>	*s.* S 2350		
	sup norm <FA>	*s.* S 2351		
S 2335	**supplement** <of a subcomplex> <AT>	Komplement *n*	complément *m*	дополнение
	supplement <EG>	*s.* S 2337		
	supplement <TO>	*s.* A 271		
	supplemental angle <EG>	*s.* S 2337		
S 2336	**supplemental chord** <of a conic> <AY>	Supplementärsehne *f*, Ergänzungssehne *f*	corde *f* supplémentaire	хорда, проведенная из точки конического сечения в конец диаметра
	supplemental information <ST>	*s.* A 648		
S 2337	**supplementary angle,** supplemental angle, supplement <EG>	Supplementwinkel *m*	angle *m* supplémentaire	дополнительный угол
	supplementary information <ST>	*s.* A 648		
S 2338	**supplementary multivector** <of a multivector> <VT>	Ergänzung *f*, adjungierter Tensor *m*, Ergänzungsmultivektor *m*, // Ergänzungseinheit *f*	multivecteur *m* supplémentaire, // unité *f* complémentaire <Grassmann>	дополнительный мультивектор
S 2339	**supplementary parallelogram** <EG>	Ergänzungsparallelogramm *n*	parallélogramme *m* complémentaire	дополнительный параллелограмм
S 2340	**supplementary pyramid** <EG>	Ergänzungspyramide *f*	pyramide *f* complémentaire	дополнительная пирамида
S 2341	**supplementary tetrahedron** <EG>	supplementäres Tetraeder *n*	tétraèdre *m* supplémentaire	дополнительный тетраэдр
	supplements <NT>	*s.* C 1377		
S 2342	**support** <of a cycle *or* section>; carrier <of a module> <AG, AL, AT>	Träger *m*	support *m*	носитель
S 2343	**support** <of an element of a W^*-algebra> <FA>	Träger *m*	support *m*	носитель
	support <AN>	*s.* C 142		

	support <FA, RF, TO>	*s.* C 145		
	support <UA>	*s.* B 108		
	support curve <CS, GE>	*s.* C 2787		
S 2344	**support function,** supporting function, function of support, tac-function <CS>	Stützfunktion *f*	fonction *f* d'appui	опорная функция
	supporting curve <CS, GE>	*s.* C 2787		
	supporting function <CS>	*s.* S 2344		
S 2345	**supporting half-space,** half-space of support <CS, GE>	Stützhalbraum *m*	demi-espace *m* d'appui	опорное полупространство
	supporting hyperplane <CS, GE>	*s.* H 711		
S 2346	**supporting line,** line of support, tac-line <CS, GE>	Stützgerade *f*	droite *f* d'appui	опорная прямая
	supporting plane <CS, GE>	*s.* P 653		
	supporting point <DG>	*s.* P 776		
S 2347	**supporting property** <CS, GE>	Stützeigenschaft *f*	propriété *f* d'appui	опорное свойство
	supporting segment <DG>	*s.* S 246		
S 2348	**supporting set,** set of support <CS, GE>	Stützmenge *f*	ensemble *m* d'appui	опорное множество
S 2349	**supporting triangle,** triangle of support <DS>	Stützdreieck *n*	triangle *m* d'appui	опорный треугольник
	support[ ]plane <CS, GE>	*s.* P 653		
	supremum <CA>	*s.* C 1130		
	supremum <DI, SE>	*s.* L 252		
S 2350	**supremum metric,** sup metric, uniform metric <FA>	Supremummetrik *f*, uniforme Metrik *f*	sup-métrique *f*, métrique *f* uniforme	sup-метрика, равномерная метрика
S 2351	**supremum norm,** sup norm, uniform norm <FA>	Supremumnorm *f*	sup-norme *f*, norme *f* uniforme	sup-норма, равномерная норма
S 2352	**surd,** radical <AL>	numerus *m* surdus, Wurzelausdruck *m*	nombre *m* sourd	иррациональность, иррациональное выражение
S 2353	**surd,** sum of irrational radicals <AL, NT>	Summe *f* irrationaler Wurzelausdrücke	somme *f* de nombres sourds	сумма иррациональных выражений
	surd <AL>	*s.* I 1013		
	surd <NT>	*s.* I 1019		
S 2354	**surface** <of *n*-th order, of *n*-th degree> <AG>	Fläche *f* <*n*-ter Ordnung, *n*-ten Grades>	surface *f* <du *n*-e ordre, d'ordre *n*, de degré *n*, du *n*-e degré>	поверхность <порядка *n*, степени *n*>
S 2355	**surface,** 2-manifold, two-manifold, two-dimensional manifold <of class *r*> <GE>	Fläche *f*, zweidimensionale Mannigfaltigkeit *f* <der Klasse *r*>	surface *f*, variété *f* bidimensionnelle <de classe *r*>	поверхность, двумерное многообразие <класса *r*>
S 2356/7	**surface** <of a polyhedron> <EG>	Oberfläche *f*	surface *f*	поверхность
	surface area <EG>	*s.* A 920		
S 2358	**surface convex toward one side** <GE>	von einer Seite konvexe Fläche *f*	surface *f* convexe vers un côté	выпуклая к одной стороне поверхность
	surface curl <VT>	*s.* C 2759		
	surface derivative <FT>	*s.* A 926		
	surface divergence <VT>	*s.* D 785		
S 2359	**surface element** <of *r*-th order> <DE>	Flächenelement *n* <der Ordnung *r*>	élément *m* de surface, élément superficiel <d'ordre *r*>	элемент поверхности <порядка *r*>
S 2360	**surface element** <GE>	Flächenelement *n*	surface *f* élémentaire	элементарная площадка
	surface element <DG, DI>	*s.* E 131		
S 2361	**surface free from singularities,** algebraic surface without singularities <AG>	singularitätenfreie Fläche *f*	surface *f* sans singularité, surface non singulière	поверхность без особенностей
	surface gradient <VT>	*s.* G 363		
S 2362	**surface harmonic,** surface spherical harmonic <FU>	Kugelflächenfunktion *f*, Kugelfunktion *f*	harmonique *f* sphérique superficielle (générale), fonction *f* [harmonique] sphérique superficielle (générale)	поверхностная сферическая функция, [общая] сферическая функция
S 2363	**surface integral** <DI>	Oberflächenintegral *n*, Flächenintegral *n*	intégrale *f* superficielle	интеграл по поверхности, поверхностный интеграл
S 2364	**surface in the Minkowski sense** <CS, GE>	Minkowskische Oberfläche *f*	surface *f* au sens de Minkowski	поверхность в смысле Минковского
	surface measure <ME>	*s.* S 1560		
	surface metric <GE, TO>	*s.* A 927		
	surface normal <DG>	*s.* N 663		
S 2365	**surface of centres** <of another surface> <GE>	Mittelpunktsfläche *f*, Zentrafläche *f*, Fläche *f* der Zentra	surface *f* des centres	поверхность центров
	surface of centres <DG>	*s.* E 645		
S 2366	**surface of coincidence,** coincidence surface <DG>	Koinzidenzfläche *f*	surface *f* de coincidence	прилегающая поверхность

No.	English	German	French	Russian
	surface of constant negative curvature <DG>	*s.* P 1993		
	surface of constant positive curvature <DG>	*s.* S 1492		
S 2367	**surface of contact** <GE>	Berührungsfläche *f*	surface *f* de contact	поверхность прикосновения (касания)
	surface of discontinuity <DE>	*s.* D 646		
	surface of fifth order <AG>	*s.* Q 304		
	surface of fourth order <AG>	*s.* Q 91		
S 2368	**surface of genus zero (0)** <AG, AT>	Fläche *f* vom Geschlecht Null (0)	surface *f* du genre nul (0)	поверхность рода нуль (0)
S 2369	**surface of intersection,** section, cut <EG>	Schnittfläche *f*	surface *f* d'intersection	поверхность пересечения
	surface of Liouville <DG>	*s.* L 888		
	surface of one side <DG, GE>	*s.* O 114		
S 2370	**surface of revolution (rotation),** rotationally symmetric surface, rotation-symmetric surface <EG>	Drehfläche *f*, Rotationsfläche *f*, Umdrehungsfläche *f*, rotationssymmetrische Fläche *f*	surface *f* de révolution, surface à symétrie de révolution	поверхность вращения (вращательной симметрии), вращательно-симметричная поверхность
	surface of second order <AG>	*s.* Q 55		
S 2371	**surface of singularities** <of a quadratic complex> <GE>	Singularitätenfläche *f*	surface *f* des singularités	поверхность особенностей
S 2372	**surface of slope,** slope <DS>	Böschungsfläche *f*, Böschung *f*	surface *f* de pente, pente *f*	поверхность откоса, откос
S 2373	**surface of the second class,** quadric-envelope <AG>	Fläche *f* zweiter Klasse, Klassenquadrik *f*	surface *f* de seconde classe, surface de la deuxième (2e) classe	поверхность второго класса
	surface of the sphere <EG>	*s.* S 1493		
	surface of third order <AG>	*s.* C 2725		
S 2374	**surface patch** <GE, TO>	Flächenstück *n*	aire *f*	кусок поверхности
S 2375	**surface representing a real-valued function of two variables** <RF>	Funktionsgebirge *n*	surface *f* représentant une fonction réelle de deux variables	поверхность, представляющая действительную функцию двух переменных
	surface spherical harmonic <FU>	*s.* S 2362		
S 2376	**surface tangent,** tangent <to a surface, of a surface> <DG>	Flächentangente *f*, Tangente *f* <der Fläche, an eine Fläche>	tangente *f* <à une surface>	касательная <[к] поверхности>
S 2377	**surface with boundary** <GE>	berandete Fläche *f*	surface *f* à bord	поверхность с краем
	surface zonal harmonic of the second kind <FU>	*s.* L 532		
S 2378	**surjection,** mapping onto . . ., surjective function, function onto . . ., onto function, mapping upon . . ., onto mapping, map onto . . . <SE>	surjektive Abbildung *f*, Abbildung auf . . ., Surjektion *f*, epimorphe Abbildung	application *f* surjective, surjection *f*, application sur . . .	сюръективное отображение, сюръекция, отображение на . . ., эпиморфное отображение, суперъективное (надъективное, накрывающее) отображение, накрытие
	surjection <AL>	*s.* O 127		
	surjective endomorphism <AL>	*s.* E 295		
S 2379	**surjective function** <AN>	surjektive Funktion *f*	fonction *f* surjective	сюръективная функция
	surjective function <SE>	*s.* S 2378		
S 2380	**surjective function whose domain and values are the same as the given function, but whose codomain has been shrunk to equal the range of the given function** <SE>	reduzierte Abbildung *f* <Nachbereich wird eingeschränkt>	application *f* réduite <d'une application>	приведенное отображение
	surjective homomorphism <AL>	*s.* O 127		
S 2381	**surjective relation** <SE>	surjektive Relation *f*	relation *f* surjective (totale à droite)	сюръективное отношение
S 2382	**surjectivity** <of a map> <SE>	Surjektivität *f*, Epimorphie *f*	surjectivité *f*	сюръективность, эпиморфность
S 2383	**survey** <collection of existing statistical data following a prepared plan> <ST>	Erhebung *f*	enquête *f*	обследование, обозрение, осмотр
S 2384	**survival density** <ST>	Überlebensdichte *f*	densité *f* de survie	плотность дожития
	survival function <ST>	*s.* R 782		
S 2385	**survival probability** <ST>	Überlebenswahrscheinlichkeit *f*	probabilité *f* de survie	вероятность долговечности, выживаемость
S 2386	**survivership function** <ST>	Überlebensfunktion *f*	fonction *f* de survie	функция дожития
	Suslin['s] condition <SE>	*s.* S 1297		

S 2387	**suspension,** Freudenthal['s] suspension <TO>	Einhängung *f*, Freudenthalsche Einhängung, Suspension *f*	suspension *f*, suspension de Freudenthal	надстройка, надстройка Фрейденталя
	suspension <TO>	*s.* R 378		
S 2388	**suspension category** <AT, CA>	stabile Kategorie *f*	catégorie *f* stable	стабильная категория
S 2389	**suspension functor** <TO>	Einhängungsfunktor *m*	foncteur *m* suspension	функтор надстройки
S 2390	**suspension homomorphism [of Freudenthal]** <AT>	Einhängungshomomorphismus *m*	suspension *f*	надстройка, надстроечный гомоморфизм, гомоморфизм надстройки
S 2391	**suspension isomorphism** <AT>	Einhängungsisomorphismus *m*	isomorphisme *m* de suspension	изоморфизм надстройки
S 2392	**suspension map** <TO>	Einhängungsabbildung *f*	application *f* de suspension	отображение надстройки
S 2393	**suspension theorem** <AT>	Einhängungssatz *m*	théorème *m* de suspension	теорема о надстройке
S 2394	**Suzuki['s] group** <GR>	Suzuki-Gruppe *f*	groupe *m* de Suzuki	группа Судзуки
	sweep <PO>	*s.* B 37		
	sweeping [out] <PO>	*s.* B 37		
	sweeping-out method <DE>	*s.* M 446		
	sweep out <PO>	*s.* B 37		
	sweep out method <DE>	*s.* M 446		
S 2395	**syllogism** <LO>	Syllogismus *m*	syllogisme *m*	силлогизм
	syllogism <LO>	*s.* F 220		
	syllogismus cornutus <LO>	*s.* D 496		
S 2396	**syllogistic** <LO>	syllogistisch	syllogistique	силлогистический
S 2397	**syllogistics** <LO>	Syllogistik *f*	syllogistique *f*	силлогистика
S 2398	**Sylow['s] base** <of a group> <GR>	Sylow-Basis *f*	base *f* de Sylow	силовская база
S 2399	**Sylow['s] group** <GR>	Sylow-Gruppe *f*, Sylowgruppe *f*, Sylow-Untergruppe *f*, Sylowsche Gruppe *f*, Sylowsche Untergruppe *f*	sous-groupe *m* de Sylow, groupe *m* de Sylow	силовская группа (подгруппа), подгруппа Силова
S 2400	**Sylow *p*-subgroup** <GR>	Sylow-Gruppe (Sylowgruppe) *f* zur Primzahl *p*, *p*-Sylowgruppe *f*	*p*-sous-groupe *m* de Sylow	силовская *p*-подгруппа, *p*-подгруппа Силова
S 2401	**Sylow Π-subgroup** <GR>	Sylowsche Π-Untergruppe *f*, Π-Sylow-Gruppe *f*	Π-sous-groupe *m* de Sylow	силовская Π-подгруппа
S 2402	**Sylow['s] theorem** <GR>	Satz *m* von Sylow, Sylows Satz	théorème *m* de Sylow	теорема Силова
S 2403	**Sylvester['s] criterion** <AL>	Determinantenkriterium *n* für die positive Definitheit einer quadratischen Form, Sylvestersches Kriterium *n*	critère *m* de Sylvester	критерий Сильвестра, детерминантный критерий положительной определенности
S 2404	**Sylvester['s] determinant** <AL>	Sylvestersche Determinante *f*	déterminant *m* de Sylvester	определитель Сильвестра
S 2405	**Sylvester['s] dialytic method,** dialytic method <AL>	Sylvestersche dialytische Methode *f*, dialytische Methode	méthode *f* dialytique de Sylvester, méthode dialytique, méthode de Sylvester	диалитический метод [Сильвестра]
S 2406	**Sylvester['s] form** <of a cubic surface> <GE>	Pentaederdarstellung *f*	représentation *f* pentaédrique	представление Сильвестра
S 2407	**Sylvester['s] formula** <for expansion in a matrix polynomial> <FT>	Sylvestersche Formel *f*	formule *f* de Sylvester	формула Сильвестра
	Sylvester['s] law [of inertia] <AL>	*s.* L 191		
	Sylvester['s] law of nullity <MD>	*s.* L 202		
S 2408	**Sylvester['s] operator** <IV>	Sylvesterscher Operator *m*	opérateur *m* de Sylvester	оператор Сильвестра
S 2409	**Sylvester['s] resultant** <AL>	Sylvesters Resultante *f*	résultant *m* de Sylvester	результант Сильвестра
S 2410	**Sylvester['s] theorem** <for elimination> <AL>	Satz *m* von Sylvester, Sylvesters Satz <über Elimination>	théorème *m* de Sylvester <sur l'élimination>	теорема Сильвестра <об исключении>
S 2411	**Sylvester['s] theorem** <for determinants *or* matrices> <MD>	Sylvesterscher Satz *m*	théorème *m* de Sylvester	теорема Сильвестра
S 2412	**symbol,** sign <GN, LO>	Symbol *n*, Zeichen *n*	symbole *m*, signe *m*	символ, знак
	ε-symbol <DG, VT>	*s.* A 577		
	ε-symbol <LO>	*s.* H 360		
	∃-symbol <LO>	*s.* 1. E 698; 2. E 699		
	¬-symbol <LO>	*s.* N 85		
	&-symbol <LO>	*s.* S 2437		
	∀-symbol <LO>	*s.* U 356		
	symbol for equality <GN>	*s.* S 850		
	symbol for set-membership <SE>	*s.* S 856		
	symbol for the denial of equality <GN>	*s.* I 420		
S 2413	**symbolic adjunction** <AL>	symbolische Adjunktion *f*	adjonction *f* formelle (symbolique)	формальное присоединение
	symbolical logic <LO>	*s.* M 166		
S 2414	**symbolically expressed invariant** <IV>	symbolisch dargestellte Invariante *f*	invariant *m* représenté symboliquement	символически представленный инвариант
	symbolical method <DE>	*s.* S 2416		
S 2415	**symbolic calculus** <IV>	symbolischer Kalkül *m*	calcul *m* symbolique	символическое исчисление
	symbolic logic <LO>	*s.* M 166		

	English	German	French	Russian
S 2416	**symbolic method,** operator (symbolical) method <DE>	Operatorenmethode *f*	méthode *f* symbolique	символический метод, операторный метод, операционный метод
	symbolic method of Aronhold <IV>	*s.* A 978		
S 2417	**symbolic model** <PG>	Zeichenmodell *n*, Symbolmodell *n*	modèle *m* symbolique	символическая модель
S 2418	**symbolic notation,** operational notation, writing in operator form <DE>	Operator[en]schreibweise *f*	notation *f* symbolique (opératoire)	символическая запись, операторная запись
S 2419	**symbolic notation** <IV>	symbolische Bezeichnung (Schreibweise) *f*	notation (écriture) *f* symbolique	символическое обозначение, символическая запись
S 2420	**symbolic of Aronhold,** Aronhold['s] symbolic <IV>	Aronholdsche Symbolik *f*	symbolisme *m* d'Aronhold	символика Аронгольда
S 2421	**symbolic of Cayley,** Cayley['s] symbolic <IV>	Cayleysche Symbolik *f*	symbolisme *m* de Cayley	символика Кэли
S 2422	**symbolism** <IV>	Symbolik *f*	symbolisme *m*, symbolique *f*	символика
S 2423/33	**symbolism,** symbology <GN>	Symbolik *f*, Symbolisation *f*	symbolique *f*, symbolisme *m*, symbolisation *f*	символика, символизм
S 2434	**symbolization** <GN, LO>	Symbolisierung *f*	symbolisation *f*	символизация, изображение с помощью символов
S 2435	**symbol of a binary composition** <AL>	binäres Verknüpfungszeichen *n*	signe *m* substantifique de poids 2, signe substantifique de degré 2	знак бинарной композиции
	symbol of alternative negation <LO>	*s.* S 762		
S 2436	**symbol of a unary operation** <AL, LO>	einstelliges Verknüpfungszeichen *n*	signe *m* substantifique de poids 1	знак одноместной операции
S 2437	**symbol of conjunction,** symbol of logical product, conjunction symbol (sign), &-symbol, ∧, & <*to be read:* and> <LO>	Zeichen *n* der Konjunktion, Konjunktionszeichen *n*, Und-Zeichen *n*, Konjunktor *m*, ∧, & <*lies:* und>	symbole *m* de la conjonction, signe *m* de conjonction, ∧, & <*se lit:* et>	знак конъюнкции (логического умножения), ∧, & <*читается:* и>
	symbol of disjunction <LO>	*s.* D 708		
S 2438	**symbol of equivalence,** equivalence symbol (sign), biconditional, ≡, ∼, ⇔, ⟷ <*to be read:* equivalent to> <LO>	Äquivalenzzeichen *n*, Zeichen *n* der Äquivalenz, Zeichen der Gleichwertigkeit, Bijugat *n*, ≡, ∼, ⇔, ⟷ <*lies:* äquivalent>	symbole *m* du biconditionnel, signe *m* d'équivalence, ≡, ∼, ⇔, ⟷ <*se lit:* équivalent à>	знак равносильности (эквивалентности), знак логической эквивалентности, ≡, ∼, ⇔, ⟷ <*читается:* эквивалентным>
	symbol of implication <LO>	*s.* S 852		
S 2439	**symbol of joint negation,** non-disjunction, joint denial, rejection, neq <neither ... nor> <LO>	Nicodsche Wahrheitsfunktion (Funktion) *f*, einschließende Negation *f*, non-disjunctio *f*, Antialternative *f* neq <weder ... noch>	négation *f* connexe, rejet *m*, fonction *f* de Peirce, fonction NJ, neq <ou ... ou>	антидизъюнкция, отрицание дизъюнкции, стрелка Пирса, отрицательная дизъюнкция, функция Вебба, neq <ни ... ни>
	symbol of logical product <LO>	*s.* S 2437		
	symbol of logical sum <LO>	*s.* D 708		
	symbol of negation <LO>	*s.* N 85		
	symbology <GN>	*s.* S 2423/33		
S 2440	**symmedian** <EG>	Symmediane *f*	symédiane *f*	симедиана
	symmetric about a line <EG>	*s.* A 1322		
	symmetric about an axis <EG>	*s.* A 1322		
	symmetric about O <CS, EG>	*s.* O 539		
	symmetrical difference <SE>	*s.* S 2450		
	symmetrical function <GN>	*s.* S 2452		
S 2441	**symmetrical group,** full symmetric group, full group of permutations <GR>	symmetrische Gruppe *f*, symmetrische (volle) Permutationsgruppe *f*	groupe *m* symétrique (de tous les permutations, des permutations)	симметрическая группа
	symmetrical group S_n <GR>	*s.* S 2455		
S 2442	**symmetrical kernel [function]** <IE>	symmetrischer (reellsymmetrischer) Kern *m*, symmetrische Kernfunktion *f*	noyau *m* symétrique	симметричное ядро
S 2443	**symmetrical matrix,** symmetric matrix <MD>	symmetrische Matrix *f*	matrice *f* symétrique	симметрическая матрица
	symmetrical operator <FA>	*s.* 1. H 251; 2. S 2460		
	symmetrical orthogonalization process <MD, NU>	*s.* L 1121/2		
	symmetrical relation <SE>	*s.* S 2463		
S 2444	**symmetrical tensor,** symmetric tensor <VT>	symmetrischer Tensor (Affinor) *m*, // Tensor	tenseur *m* symétrique [droit]	симметричный тензор

No.	English	Deutsch	Français	Русский
S 2445	**symmetrical test** <ST>	symmetrischer Test *m*	test *m* symétrique	симметричный критерий
S 2446	**symmetric bilinear form** <AL, FA>	symmetrische Bilinearform *f*	forme *f* bilinéaire symétrique, forme bilinéaire auto-adjointe	симметрическая билинейная форма
S 2447	**symmetric bilinear functional,** symmetric functional <in a linear space> <FA>	symmetrisches bilineares Funktional *n*, symmetrisches Funktional	fonctionnelle *f* bilinéaire symétrique, fonctionnelle symétrique	симметрический билинейный функционал, симметрический функционал
	symmetric bilinear functional <FA>	*s.* H 231		
	symmetric binary relation <SE>	*s.* S 2463		
S 2448	**symmetric continuous group** <GR>	symmetrische kontinuierliche Gruppe *f*	groupe *m* continu symétrique	симметрическая непрерывная группа
S 2449	**symmetric determinant** <MD>	Determinante *f* einer symmetrischen Matrix, symmetrische Determinante	déterminant *m* symétrique, déterminant unisymétrique, déterminant axisymétrique	симметричный определитель
S 2450	**symmetric difference,** symmetrical difference, △ <*to be read:* delta> <SE>	symmetrische Differenz *f*, Überschuß *m*, Boolesche Summe *f*, Diskrepanz *f*, △ <*lies:* delta>	différence *f* symétrique, somme *f* binaire (booléenne, disjonctive), réunion *f* exclusive, △ <*se lit:* delta>	симметрическая разность, дизъюнктивная сумма, △ <*читается:* дельта>
S 2451	**symmetric distance function** <CS, GU>	wechselseitige Strahldistanz *f*	jauge *f* symétrique	симметрическая дистанционная функция
	symmetric entourage <TO>	*s.* S 2459		
	symmetric form <AY>	*s.* T 1103		
S 2452	**symmetric function,** symmetrical function <GN>	symmetrische Funktion *f*	fonction *f* symétrique	симметрическая функция
	symmetric functional <FA>	*s.* 1. H 231; 2. S 2447		
S 2453	**symmetric graph** <GP>	symmetrischer Graph *m*	graphe *m* symétrique	симметрический граф
	symmetric graph <GP>	*s.* N 437		
S 2454	**symmetric group of a countable set** <AL>	abzählbare symmetrische Gruppe *f*	groupe *m* symétrique d'un ensemble dénombrable	счетная симметрическая группа
	symmetric group on *n* letters (symbols) <GR>	*s.* S 2455		
S 2455	**symmetric group S_n,** symmetrical group S_n, group of permutations of n objects, symmetric group on n letters, symmetric group on n symbols <GR>	symmetrische Gruppe *f* S_n (n-ten Grades), symmetrische Permutationsgruppe *f* in n Symbolen	groupe *m* symétrique S_n (de n lettres), groupe symétrique sur n objets (lettres)	симметрическая группа S_n (от n символов), симметрическая группа на n символах, симметрическая группа степени n, симметрическая группа n-ой степени
S 2456	**symmetric lattice S_n of order n** <GE, LA>	symmetrischer Verband *m* S_n der Ordnung n	treillis *m* symétrique S_n d'ordre n	симметрическая структура S_n порядка n
S 2457	**symmetric Lie group** <GR>	symmetrische [Liesche] Gruppe *f*	groupe *m* de Lie symétrique	симметрическая группа Ли
	symmetric matrix <MD>	*s.* S 2443		
S 2458	**symmetric neighbourhood** <of the neutral element of a group> <GR>	symmetrische Umgebung *f*	voisinage *m* symétrique	симметричная окрестность
S 2459	**symmetric neighbourhood,** symmetric entourage <in a uniform space> <TO>	symmetrische Umgebung *f*	entourage *m* symétrique	симметричное окружение
S 2460	**symmetric operator,** symmetrical operator <FA>	symmetrischer Operator *m*	opérateur *m* (transformation *f*) symétrique	симметричный (симметрический) оператор
S 2461	**symmetric part** <of a tensor> <VT>	symmetrisierter Tensor *m*	symétrisé *m* <d'un tenseur>	симметрированный тензор
S 2462	**symmetric polynomial** <AL>	symmetrisches Polynom *n*, symmetrische ganze rationale Funktion *f*, symmetrische Funktion	polynôme *m* symétrique	симметрический многочлен, симметричный полином
S 2463	**symmetric relation,** symmetrical relation, symmetric binary relation <SE>	symmetrische Relation *f*	relation *f* symétrique (commutative)	симметричное отношение (соотношение), симметрическое соотношение
S 2464	**symmetric semigroup,** full transformation semigroup <on a set> <AL>	symmetrische Halbgruppe *f*, Halbgruppe aller Transformationen <einer Menge>	demi-groupe *m* symétrique <d'un ensemble>	симметрическая полугруппа, полугруппа всех преобразований, полная полугруппа преобразований, симметрический группоид <множества>
	symmetric tensor <VT>	*s.* S 2444		
	symmetric with respect to a line <EG>	*s.* A 1322		
	symmetric with respect to an axis <EG>	*s.* A 1322		
	symmetric with respect to the origin <CS, EG>	*s.* O 539		
S 2465	**symmetrizable integral equation** <IE>	symmetrisierbare Integralgleichung *f*	équation *f* intégrale symétrisable	симметризируемое интегральное уравнение
S 2466	**symmetrizable kernel** <IE>	symmetrisierbarer Kern *m*	noyau *m* symétrisable	симметризируемое ядро; ядро, допускающее симметризацию
	symmetrization <VT>	*s.* M 705		
S 2467	**symmetrization operator** <AL>	Symmetrisierungsoperator *m*	opérateur *m* de symétrisation	оператор симметрирования
S 2468	**symmetrization with respect to a plane** <CS, GE>	Symmetrisierung *f* bezüglich einer Ebene	symétrisation *f* par rapport à un plan	симметрирование (симметризация) относительно плоскости

No.	English	German	French	Russian
S 2469	**symmetrized representation** <AL>	symmetrisierte Darstellung *f*	représentation *f* symétrisée	симметризированная степень представления
S 2470	**symmetroid,** Cayley['s] symmetroid <a special quartic> <AG>	Symmetroid *n*	symétroïde *f*	симметроид
	symmetry <GR>	*s.* G 154		
S 2471	**symmetry / by,** by reasons of symmetry, for sake of symmetry, for symmetry sake <GN>	aus Symmetriegründen	par raison de symétrie, à cause de la symétrie	по соображениям симметрии, по условиям симметрии, в силу симметрии
	symmetry[-] centre <EG, ST>	*s.* C 430		
	symmetry function <EG>	*s.* S 2472		
	symmetry group <GE>	*s.* P 747		
	symmetry number <GP>	*s.* O 351		
S 2472	**symmetry[-] operation,** symmetry transformation, symmetry function <of a figure, e.g. in R_3> <EG>	Symmetrieoperation *f*, Deckoperation *f*, Decktransformation *f*	opération *f* isométrique (de symétrie)	операция симметрии, симметрическое преобразование
S 2473	**symmetry operator** <of a tensor algebra> <AL>	Symmetrieoperator *m*	opérateur *m* de symétrie	оператор симметрии
	symmetry principle <FT>	*s.* S 172		
S 2474	**symmetry property** <GN>	Symmetrieeigenschaft *f*	propriété *f* de symétrie	свойство симметрии
	symmetry sake / for <GN>	*s.* S 2471		
	symmetry transformation <EG>	*s.* S 2472		
	symmetry with respect to a line <EG>	*s.* A 1267		
	symmetry with respect to an axis <EG>	*s.* A 1267		
S 2475	**symplectically irreducible representation** <RE>	symplektisch irreduzible Darstellung *f*	représentation *f* symplectiquement irréductible	симплектически неприводимое представление
	symplectic automorphism <AL>	*s.* S 2483		
S 2476	**symplectic basis** <AL>	symplektische Basis *f*	base *f* symplectique	симплектический базис
S 2477	**symplectic bilinear form,** alternating bilinear form <AL>	alternierende (symplektische) Bilinearform *f*	forme *f* bilinéaire alternée	знакопеременная билинейная форма
S 2478	**symplectic geometry** <PJ>	symplektische Geometrie *f*	géométrie *f* symplectique	симплектическая геометрия
S 2479	**symplectic group,** complex group, Abelian linear group; linear symplectic group <GR>	symplektische Gruppe *f*, Komplexgruppe *f*, Abelsche lineare Gruppe; lineare symplektische Gruppe	groupe *m* symplectique (unitaire symplectique), groupe complexe	симплектическая (унитарная симплектическая) группа
S 2480	**symplectic group with respect to the form Q** <AL>	symplektische Gruppe *f* in bezug auf die Form Q	groupe *m* symplectique associé à la forme Q	симплектическая группа формы Q
S 2481	**symplectic inner product,** alternating inner product <AL>	alternierendes Skalarprodukt *n*, symplektisches inneres Produkt *n*	produit *m* scalaire alterné	знакопеременное скалярное произведение
S 2482	**symplectic invariant** <IV>	symplektische Invariante *f*, Komplexinvariante *f*	invariant *m* symplectique	симплектический инвариант
S 2483	**symplectic mapping,** symplectic transformation, symplectic automorphism <AL>	symplektische Transformation (Abbildung) *f*, symplektischer Automorphismus *m*	automorphisme *m* (transformation *f*) symplectique	симплектическое преобразование (отображение), симплектический автоморфизм
S 2484	**symplectic semi-similarity [transformation]** <AL>	halbähnlich symplektische Transformation *f*	semi-similitude *f* symplectique	симплектическое преобразование полуподобия
S 2485	**symplectic space** <GE>	symplektischer Raum *m*	espace *m* symplectique	симплектическое пространство
	symplectic transformation <AL>	*s.* S 2483		
S 2486	**symplectic transvection** <AL>	symplektische Transvektion *f*	transvection *f* symplectique	симплектический сдвиг
S 2487	**symptotic line** <connecting two points of intersection of two conics> <AY>	symptotische Gerade *f*	axe *m* de symptose, droite *f* symptotique	симптотическая прямая
	syncategorematic symbol <LO>	*s.* I 202		
	syncategorematic word <LO>	*s.* L 1061		
	synclinal line <DS>	*s.* T 31		
	syncline <DS>	*s.* T 31		
S 2488	**synectic anticorrelation** <PJ>	synektische Antikorrelation *f*	anticorrélation *f* synectique	синэктическое антикоррелятивное преобразование, синэктическая антикорреляция
S 2489	**synectic correlation** <PJ>	synektische Korrelation *f*	corrélation *f* synectique	синэктическое коррелятивное преобразование, синэктическая корреляция
S 2490	**synectic function** <Study> <PJ>	synektische Funktion *f*	fonction *f* synectique	синэктическая функция
	synectic plane <PJ>	*s.* A 626		
	synentropy <ST>	*s.* M 1099		
S 2491	**synnormal** <GE>	Synnormale *f*	synormale *f*, synnormale *f*	синормаль
S 2492	**syntactically complete set of formulas** <MM>	syntaktisch (formal) vollständige Menge *f* von Ausdrücken	ensemble *m* de formules complet au sens étroit	полная в узком смысле совокупность формул

No.	English	German	French	Russian
S 2493	**syntactically complete system** <LO>	syntaktisch (formal) vollständiges System *n*, im engeren Sinne vollständiger Kalkül *m*	système *m* complet au sens étroit (fort), système complet au sens syntaxique, système syntaxiquement complet, système saturé	полная в узком смысле логическая система, полное в узком смысле логическое исчисление
S 2494	**syntactically equivalent formula** <LO>	syntaktisch äquivalenter Ausdruck *m*	formule *f* syntaxiquement équivalente	синтаксически эквивалентная формула
S 2495	**syntactical theorem** <MM>	syntaktischer Satz *m*	théorème *m* syntaxique	синтаксическая теорема
S 2496	**syntactic completeness** <LO>	syntaktische (formale) Vollständigkeit *f*, Vollständigkeit im engeren Sinne	complétude *f* au sens étroit (fort), saturation *f* (complétude) syntaxique, saturation	полнота в узком смысле
S 2497	**syntactic consistency** <MM>	formale (syntaktische) Widerspruchsfreiheit *f*	consistance *f* absolue	формальная непротиворечивость
S 2498	**syntactic definition** <LO>	syntaktische Definition *f*	définition *f* syntaxique	синтаксическое (синтактическое) определение
S 2499	**syntactics** <LO>	Syntaktik *f*	syntactique *f*	синтактика, логический синтаксис
S 2500	**syntactic variable** <LO>	syntaktische Variable *f*, Mitteilungszeichen *n*	variable *f* syntaxique	синтаксическая переменная
S 2501	**syntax** <MM>	Syntax *f*	syntaxe *f*, métathéorie *f* syntaxique	синтаксис
S 2502	**synthetic geometry,** pure geometry <SG>	synthetische Geometrie *f*	géométrie *f* synthétique	синтетическая геометрия
S 2503	**synthetic method of proof** <FO, SG>	synthetischer Beweis *m*	démonstration *f* synthétique	синтетическое доказательство
S 2504	**syntractrix** <a special transcendental curve> <GE>	Syntraktrix *f* <Sylvester>	syntractrice *f*	синтрактриса
S 2505	**system** <over *A*> <SE>	System *n* von Untermengen, Untermenge *f* der Potenzmenge <von *A*>	système *m* de parties <d'un ensemble *A*>	система подмножеств <множества *A*>
	δ-system <SE, TO>	*s.* D 214		
	ε-system <DG, VT>	*s.* A 577		
	σ-system <SE>	*s.* S 833		
	systematic error <ST>	*s.* B 269		
S 2506	**systematic fraction** <NT>	systematischer Bruch *m* <zur Basis *p*>	fraction *f* systématique <à base *p*>	систематическая дробь <в *p*-адической системе счисления>
S 2507	**systematic sample** <ST>	systematische Stichprobe (Probe) *f*	échantillon *m* systématique	систематическая выборка
S 2508	**systematic sampling,** patterned sampling <ST>	systematisches Stichprobenverfahren (Stichprobenerhebungsschema) *n*	échantillonnage (sondage) *m* systématique	систематический выбор
S 2509	**system consistent as to consequences,** negation consistent system, [simply] consistent system, satisfiable system <LO>	widerspruchsfreies (klassisch widerspruchsfreies) System *n*	système *m* non contradictoire, système consistant par rapport à la négation, système cohérent	внутренне непротиворечивая система, совместная система, [просто] непротиворечивая система
	system consistent in Post's sense <LO>	*s.* L 1083		
S 2510	**system determinant** <AL>	Systemdeterminante *f*, Gleichungsdeterminante *f*	déterminant *m* du système	определитель системы, определитель системы уравнений, детерминант системы [уравнений]
	system in row echelon form <AL, NU>	*s.* S 2545		
S 2511	**system matrix,** matrix of the coefficients <of linear equations> <AL>	Gleichungsmatrix *f*, Systemmatrix *f*, Matrix *f* der Koeffizienten <eines Gleichungssystems>	matrice *f* du système, matrice des coefficients [du système]	матрица системы [уравнений, основная матрица [системы]
S 2512	**system of Appell polynomials** <FU>	Appellsche Polynomfolge *f*, System *n* Appellscher Polynome	système *m* de polynômes d'Appell	система многочленов Аппеля
	system of axioms <MM>	*s.* A 1275		
	system of axioms invariant under dualization <FO>	*s.* S 285		
	system of canonical co-ordinates <GR>	*s.* C 58		
S 2513	**system of coefficients over *K*** <AT>	Koeffizientensystem *n* über *K*	système *m* de coefficients sur *K*	система коэффициентов над *K*
S 2514	**system of congruences,** simultaneous congruences <AL>	Kongruenzensystem *n*, simultane Kongruenzen *fpl*, System *n* von Kongruenzen	système *m* des congruences	система сравнений
	system of co-ordinates <AN, AY>	*s.* C 2433		
	system of curves <AY>	*s.* F 81		
	system of differential equations <DE>	*s.* S 1013		
	system of dimension *n* <AG>	*s.* N 709		
S 2515	**system of diophantine equations** <NT>	diophantisches Gleichungssystem *n*, System *n* diophantischer Gleichungen	système *m* diophantien	диофантова система, система диофантовых уравнений
S 2516	**system of diophantine equations of higher degree** <NT>	höheres diophantisches Gleichungssystem *n*	système *m* diophantien de degré supérieur <>1>	диофантова система высшей степени
	system of double composition <AL>	*s.* A 463		
	system of elements <SE>	*s.* F 82		

S 2517	**system of equations,** simultaneous equations, set of equations <AL, AN>	Gleichungssystem *n*, simultane Gleichungen *fpl*, gleichzeitiges (simultanes) System *n* <von Gleichungen>	système *m* d'équations, système simultané	система уравнений
S 2518	**system of equations of maximal rank** <AL>	Gleichungssystem *n* von maximalem Rang	système *m* total d'équations	система уравнений максимального ранга
	system of forward equations <SP>	*s.* K 122		
S 2519	**system of generators,** generating set, generating system <of a group> <AL, GR>	Erzeugendensystem *n*	système *m* générateur, système (ensemble *m*) de générateurs, partie *f* génératrice	система образующих, образующие элементы, порождающее множество
S 2520	**system of imprimitivity,** set of imprimitivity, imprimitive subset, block, imprimitive system <of a permutation group> <GR>	Imprimitivitätssystem *n*, Imprimitivitätsbereich *m*, Imprimitivitätsgebiet *n*, System *n* der Imprimitivität, Block *m*	système *m* d'imprimitivité, domaine *m* d'imprimitivité, classe *f* d'imprimitivité, système de non-primitivité	система (область, класс) импримитивности
S 2520a	**system of imprimitivity,** imprimitive variety <of a continuous group> <GR>	Imprimitivitätssystem *n*, Imprimitivitätsmannigfaltigkeit *f*	système *m* (variété *f*) d'imprimitivité	система импримитивности
S 2520b	**system of imprimitivity** <elements are the imprimitive subsets> <GR>	System *n* der Imprimitivitätsgebiete	système *m* des domaines d'imprimitivité	система импримитивности
S 2521	**system of inequalities,** simultaneous inequalities <AN, NT>	Ungleichungssystem *n*, simultane Ungleichungen *fpl*	système *m* d'inéquations, inéquations *fpl* simultanées	система неравенств
S 2522	**system of intransitivity** <GR>	Intransitivitätsbereich *m*	classe *f* d'intransitivité	область интранзитивности, класс интранзитивности
S 2523	**system of least residues** <NT>	kleinstes Restsystem *n*, kleinstes nicht-negatives Restsystem, kleinstes positives Restsystem	système *m* de restes minimés	система наименьших неотрицательных вычетов
S 2524	**system of linear equations,** [set of] simultaneous linear equations <in *n* unknowns> <AL>	lineares Gleichungssystem *n*, System *n* von linearen Gleichungen <in *n* Unbekannten>	système *m* d'équations linéaires [algébriques] <à *n* inconnues>	система линейных уравнений (алгебраических уравнений), система уравнений первой степени <с *n* неизвестными>
S 2525	**system of linear equations possessing a unique solution** <AL>	eindeutig lösbares lineares Gleichungssystem *n*	système *m* d'équations linéaires à solution unique	определенная совместная система [линейных уравнений]
S 2526	**system of linear equations possessing several different solutions** <AL>	mehrdeutig lösbares lineares Gleichungssystem *n*	système *m* d'équations linéaires à plusieurs solutions	неопределенная совместная система линейных уравнений
S 2527	**system of linear functions,** set of linear functions, linear system of functions <AN>	System *n* linearer Funktionen, lineares Funktionensystem *n*	système *m* de fonctions linéaires, système linéaire de fonctions	система линейных функций, линейная система функций
	system of lines <AY, DG>	*s.* C 1923		
	system of local coefficients <AT>	*s.* B 799		
S 2528	**system of logarithms,** logarithmic system <AR>	Logarithmensystem *n*	système *m* de logarithmes, système logarithmique	система логарифмов
	system of logic with functions <LO>	*s.* F 734		
	system of logic with identity <LO>	*s.* F 348		
	system of logic with identity and functions <LO>	*s.* F 735		
S 2529	**system of multiplicative representatives** <AL>	multiplikationstreues Restsystem *n*, multiplikationstreues Vertretersystem *n*	système *m* de représentants multiplicativement fermé	мультипликативная система представителей
S 2530	**system of mutually disjoint sets** <SE>	System *n* paarweise disjunkter Mengen	système *m* d'ensembles mutuellement disjoints	расчлененная система множеств
S 2531	**system of natural deduction,** natural deduction system <LO>	System *n* des natürlichen Schließens	système *m* de la déduction naturelle	система натурального вывода
	system of neighbourhoods <TO>	*s.* N 137		
	system of numbers <NT>	*s.* N 842		
	system of ordinary differential equations <DE>	*s.* S 1013		
S 2532	**system of partial differential equations,** set of partial differential equations <DE>	System *n* von partiellen Differentialgleichungen, partielles Differentialgleichungssystem *n*	système *m* d'équations [différentielles] aux dérivées partielles	система дифференциальных уравнений в частных производных
S 2533	**system of periods,** period system, period <of an Abelian *or* theta function> <FU>	Periodensystem *n*, Periode *f*	système *m* des périodes, période *f*	система периодов, период
S 2534	**system of polar co-ordinates** <AY>	Polarkoordinatensystem *n*	système *m* de coordonnées polaires	полярная система координат, система полярных координат
	system of projective co-ordinates <AG, AY, PJ>	*s.* P 1676		
S 2535	**system of punctuation;** rules of punctuation <LO>	Klammersetzungsregeln *fpl*, Klammerregeln *fpl*	règles *fpl* de parenthèses, convention *f* des parenthèses	правила скобок

No.	English	German	French	Russian
	system of rays <AY, DG>	*s.* C 1923		
S 2536	**system of representatives** <AL>	Repräsentantensystem *n*, Vertretersystem *n*	système *m* de représentants	система представителей
S 2537	**system of residue classes** <of a polynomial ideal> <AL>	Restsystem *n*, System *n* der Restklassen <eines Polynomideals>	système *m* des classes suivant un idéal de polynômes	система классов вычетов <по многочленному идеалу>
	system of roots <AL>	*s.* R 1385		
	system of sets <SE>	*s.* 1. F 86; 2. S 676; 3. S 961		
	system of sets having the finite intersection property <SE>	*s.* C 412		
S 2538	**system of Shapley axioms** <TG>	Shapleysches Axiomensystem *n*	système *m* des axiomes de Shapley	аксиоматика Шепли
	system of surfaces <AY> <AY>	*s.* F 90		
	system of tetracyclic co-ordinates <DG>	*s.* T 226		
S 2539	**system of the second order,** double system [of quantities] <GN>	zweifach indiziertes Größensystem *n*	système *m* [de grandeurs] à deux indices	система с двумя индексами
	system of transitivity <GR>	*s.* D 874		
S 2540	**system of variational equations** <DE, VA>	Variationssystem *n*, System *n* der Variationsgleichungen	système *m* des équations variationnelles	система вариационных уравнений
S 2541	**system of vectors,** vector system <GE>	Vektorsystem *n*, Vektorensystem *n*, Stabsumme *f*, Stäbesumme *f*, Stabwert *m*, Liniensumme *f*, Streckensystem *n*, heteraptische Summe *f*	système *m* de vecteurs glissants, système de vecteurs, torseur *m*	векторная система, система (сумма) скользящих векторов
S 2542	**system of Walsh,** Walsh['s] system <RF>	System *n* von Walsh, Walshsches System	système *m* de Walsh	система Уолша
	system to be controlled <PG>	*s.* C 2311		
	system with a matrix in row echelon form <AL, NU>	*s.* S 2545		
S 2543	**system with complete connections** <SP>	System *n* mit vollständigen Bindungen	système *m* à liaisons complètes	система с полными связями
S 2544	**system with exterior multiplication** <NT>	alternierendes Zahlensystem *n* <Hankel> <System mit äußerer Multiplikation>	système *m* à multiplication extérieure, nombres *mpl* alternés <Houël>	система с внешним умножением
S 2545	**system** <of linear equations> **with triangular matrix,** system [with a matrix] in row echelon form <AL, NU>	gestaffeltes System (Gleichungssystem) *n*	système *m* <d'équations linéaires> échelonné	эшелонированная система <линейных уравнений>
S 2546	**syzygant** <IV>	Syzygante *f*	syzygant *m*	сизигант
S 2547	**syzygetic covariant** <AL>	syzygetische Kovariante *f* <Cayley>	covariant *m* syzygétique	сизигетический ковариант
S 2548	**syzygetic cubic** <GE>	syzygetische Kurve *f*	courbe (cubique) *f* syzygétique	сизигетическая кривая K_3
S 2549	**syzygetic group** <for the theta functions> <FT, FU>	syzygetische Gruppe *f*	groupe *m* syzygétique	сизигетическая группа
S 2550	**syzygetic pencil** <AG>	syzygetisches Büschel *n*	faisceau *m* syzygétique	сизигетический пучок, пучок сизигетических кривых
S 2551	**syzygetic relation** <of algebraic forms> <AL>	syzygetische Beziehung *f*	relation *f* syzygétique	сизигетическое соотношение
S 2552	**syzygetic tetrahedron,** Göpel['s] tetrahedron <AG, FT, FU>	syzygetisches (Göpelsches) Tetraeder *n*	tétraèdre *m* syzygétique (de Göpel)	сизигетический тетраэдр
S 2553	**syzygy** <*e.g.:* of the first . . ., *n*-th kind> <AL, IV>	Syzygie *f* <*z. B.:* erster (1.), . . ., *n*-ter Art>	syzygie *f* <*par exemple:* de la première, . . ., *n*-e espèce>	сизигия, соотношение <*например:* первого, . . ., *n*-го рода>
	syzygy chain <AL, IV>	*s.* C 490		
	syzygy module <AL>	*s.* M 781		
S 2554	**syzygy of Cayley,** Cayley['s] syzygy <IV>	Cayleysche Syzygie *f*	syzygie *f* de Cayley	сизигия Кэли
S 2555	**Szegő['s] kernel** <FT>	Szegő-Kern *m*	noyau *m* de Szegő	ядро Сеге
S 2556	**Szegő['s] orthogonal polynomials** <FU>	Orthogonalpolynome *npl* von Szegő, Szegősche Orthogonalpolynome	polynômes *mpl* orthogonaux de Szegő	ортогональные многочлены (полиномы) Сеге
S 2557	**Szegő['s] theorem** <for convergence> <AX>	Szegőscher Konvergenzsatz *m*	théorème *m* (règle *f*, critère *m*) de Szegő	теорема [сходимости] Сеге
S 2558	**Szegő['s] theorem** <for power series> <FT>	Satz *m* von Szegő	théorème *m* de Szegő	теорема Сеге
S 2559	**Szép['s] group extension** <GR>	Szépsche Erweiterung *f* <von Gruppen>	extension *f* <de groupes> de Szép	сэпово расширение групп
	Szidon theorem <SS>	*s.* S 793		
	Szidon's theorem <SS>	*s.* S 793		

T

No.	English	German	French	Russian
	2 · 2 table, 2 × 2 table <ST>	*s.* F 513		
	tableau <AL>	*s.* Y 11		
T 1	**table cell,** cell <of a table> <GN, ST>	Tabellenfeld *n*, Feld *n*	case *f* <d'un tableau>	ячейка, клетка, поле <таблицы>

No.	English	German	French	Russian
T 2	**table difference,** tabular difference, proportional part <NU>	Tafeldifferenz *f*	différence *f* tabulaire	табличная разность (разница)
T 3	**table head[ing],** box[-] head, box heading, boxed head, head <of a table>, caption <in a table> <GN>	Tabellenkopf *m*, Kopf *m* <einer Tabelle>	en-tête *m*, tête *f* <de tableau, table>	заголовок, верхняя часть, головка <таблицы>
T 4	**table of cosines,** table of natural cosines <IN, NU>	Kosinustafel *f*	table *f* des cosinus	таблица косинусов
	table of inverse numbers <AR, NU>	*s.* T 7		
	table of logarithms <AR, IN, NU>	*s.* L 1057		
	table of natural cosines <IN, NU>	*s.* T 4		
	table of natural sines <IN, NU>	*s.* T 8		
T 5	**table of primes** <NT>	Primzahltabelle *f*	table *f* de nombres premiers	таблица простых чисел
T 6	**table of random [sampling] numbers** <ST>	Zufallszahlentafel *f*	tableau *m* de nombres aléatoires	таблица случайных чисел
T 7	**table of reciprocals,** table of inverse numbers <AR, NU>	Kehrwerttafel *f*, Tabelle *f* der Kehrwerte	table *f* des inverses	таблица обратных величин, таблица обратных чисел
T 8	**table of sines,** table of natural sines <IN, NU>	Sinustafel *f*	table *f* des sinus	таблица синусов
T 9	**table of square roots** <IN, NU>	Quadratwurzeltafel *f*	table *f* des racines carrées	таблица квадратных корней
T 10	**table of squares** <AR, NU>	Quadrattafel *f*	table *f* des carrés	таблица квадратов
T 11	**table of values** <of a function> <AN, LO>	Wertetafel *f*, Wertetabelle *f*	table *f* des valeurs	таблица значений, таблица функции
T 12	**table with double entry,** double-entry table <GN>	Tabelle *f* mit doppeltem Eingang	table *f* à double entrée, tableau *m* à double entrée	таблица с двумя входами
T 13	**table with simple entry** <GN>	Tabelle *f* mit einfachem Eingang	tableau *m* à simple entrée	таблица с одним входом
T 14	**tabular,** in tabular form <GN>	tabellarisch, in Tabellenform	tabellaire; en forme de tableau, tabulaire	табличный, представленный в виде таблицы
	tabular difference <NU>	*s.* T 2		
	tabular form / in <GN>	*s.* T 14		
T 15	**tabular method** <of representing a function> <NU>	Tabellenmethode *f*	méthode *f* tabulaire	табличный способ
T 16	**tabular value** <NU>	Tafelwert *m*, Tabellenwert *m*	valeur *f* tabulaire	табличное значение
	tabulated significance point <ST>	*s.* P 401		
	tabulating <GN>	*s.* T 17		
T 17	**tabulation,** tabulating <GN>	Tabellierung *f*, Tabellarisierung *f*, Vertafelung *f*	tabulation *f*	представление (составление, расположение) в виде таблицы, табулирование
	tac-function <CS>	*s.* S 2344		
	tac-hyperplane <CS, GE>	*s.* H 711		
	tac-line <CS, GE>	*s.* S 2346		
T 18	**tacnode** <GE>	Berührungsknoten *m*	nœud *m* de contact	узел касания
T 19	**tacnode,** double cusp, osculation point, point of osculation, close-point <of a curve> <GE>	Selbstberührungspunkt *m*, Knotenpunkt *m* zweiter Art, Berührungspunkt *m*	tacnode *m*, point *m* autotangentiel (d'autotangence, de rebroussement, de contact de la courbe avec elle-même)	точка самоприкосновения (самокасания), такнодальная точка
	tac-plane <CS, GE>	*s.* P 653		
T 20	**tac-strip** <of a convex set> <CS>	Stützstreifen *m*	bande *f* d'appui	опорная полоса
T 21	**tactical system,** Steiner['s] triple system <CT>	Steiner-System *n*, Steinersches System (Tripelsystem) *n*, Tripelsystem	système *m* de Steiner, système triple	система троек Штейнера, система троек, штейнерова система троек
T 22	**tail** <of a distribution> <ST>	Verteilungsende *n*, Ende *n*, Schwanz *m*	queue *f*	хвост
T 23	**tail area** <of a distribution> <ST>	Fläche *f* am Ende, Rand *m* <einer Verteilung>	queue *f* <d'une distribution>	хвост, шлейф <распределения>
T 24	**Takagi['s] group** <of a field extension> <AL>	Takagische Gruppe *f*	groupe *m* de Takagi	группа Такаги
	take / to <GN>	*s.* A 1199		
T 25	**taken absolutely,** in absolute value, in modulus <AL, AN>	dem Betrage nach	en module, en valeur absolue	по модулю, по абсолютной величине
T 26	**taken positively** <AR>	mit positivem Vorzeichen genommen	pris positivement	взятый со знаком плюс
T 27	**take the logarithm / to** <AR>	logarithmieren	prendre le logarithme	логарифмировать
T 28	**taking of the logarithm** <AR>	Logarithmieren *n*	recherche *f* du logarithme <de *a*, dans la base *b*>	логарифмирование
	taking of the mean <GN>	*s.* A 1260		
T 29	**taking of the root,** finding of the root, computing of the root, estimating of the root, extraction of the root, evolution <AL, AR>	Wurzelziehen *n*, Radizieren *n*, Wurzelausziehung *f*, Radizierung *f*, Ausziehen (Ziehen) *n* der Wurzel	extraction *f* de racine	извлечение корня
T 30	**tally sheet** <ST>	Strichliste *f*	liste *f* de pointage	итоговая карта
T 31	**talweg,** thalweg, syncline, synclinal line <DS>	Talweg *m*, Muldenlinie *f*	ligne *f* de thalweg (talweg), t[h]alweg *m*, ligne de synclinal	тальвег, ось долины, синклинальная линия
	t am <FU>	*s.* A 610		
T 32	**Tamagawa['s] measure** <AB>	Tamagawa-Maß *n*	mesure *f* de Tamagawa	мера Тамагава

T 33	**Tamagawa['s] number** <AB>	Tamagawa-Zahl *f*	nombre *m* de Tamagawa	число Тамагава
	tame <TO>	*s.* T 36		
T 34	**tame curve** <DI, TO>	einfache (zahme) Kurve *f*	courbe *f* simple	простая кривая
	tame distribution <AN>	*s.* T 122		
T 35	**tame imbedding,** nice imbedding <TO>	zahme (regelmäßige) Einbettung *f*	plongement *m* trivial, immersion *f* régulière (paisible)	ручное (правильное) вложение
T 36	**tamely imbedded,** tame, nicely imbedded <TO>	zahm (regelmäßig) eingebettet	régulièrement (paisiblement) immersé	правильно (хорошо) вложенный
T 37	**tamely ramified extension** <AL>	zahm verzweigte Erweiterung *f*	extension *f* modérément ramifiée	слабо разветвленное расширение
T 38	**tame set** <TO>	zahme Menge *f*	ensemble *m* paisible	правильное множество
	tan <DI>	*s.* T 39		
	tan^{-1} <FU>	*s.* I 953		
	tan am <FU>	*s.* A 610		
	tangency <GE>	*s.* C 2142		
T 39	**tangent,** tangent function, tan, // tg <DI>	Tangens *m*, Tangensfunktion *f*, tan, // tg	tangente *f*, fonction *f* tangente, tan, // tg	тангенс, функция тангенс, tan, // tg
T 40	**tangent,** tangent line <GE>	Tangente *f*, Berührende *f*	tangente *f*, // touchante *f*	касательная
	tangent <DG>	*s.* 1. S 2376; 2. T 63		
	tangent <GE>	*s.* 1. C 1579; 2. L 573		
T 41	**tangent at the vertex,** tangent to the vertex <AY>	Scheiteltangente *f*	tangente *f* au sommet	касательная в (к) вершине
T 42	**tangent bundle** <AT, DG>	Tangentialbündel *n*	fibré *m* tangent	касательное расслоение, касательный пучок
T 43	**tangent cone** <AL>	Tangentialkegel *m*	cône *m* des tangentes, cône tangentiel (tangent)	касательный конус
T 44	**tangent cone** <of a surface> <AY>	Tangentenkegel *m*, Tangentialkegel *m*, Berührungskegel *m*	cône *m* tangentiel (des tangentes)	касательный конус
T 45	**tangent curve,** tangent line, tangentoid <DI>	Tangenskurve *f*, Tangenslinie *f*, Tangensoide *f*	tangentoïde *f*, courbe *f* tangente, ligne *f* tangente	тангенсоида, график тангенса
T 46	**tangent developable,** developable tangent surface <DG>	abwickelbare Tangentenfläche *f*	développable *f* tangentielle, surface *f* tangentielle développable	развертывающаяся касательная поверхность
	tangent formula <DI, NU>	*s.* M 12		
	tangent function <DI>	*s.* T 39		
	tangential <AG>	*s.* C 1999		
T 47	**tangential approximation** <AX>	Näherung (Approximation) *f* durch Tangenten	approximation *f* tangentielle	аппроксимация (приближение) касательными
T 48	**tangential body** <CS, GE>	Tangentialkörper *m*	corps *m* tangentiel	касательное тело
	1-tangential body <GE>	*s.* C 105		
T 49	**tangential complex** <GE>	tangentialer Komplex *m*	complexe *m* tangent	касательный комплекс
T 50	**tangential composition law** <AL, GE>	tangentiales Kompositionsgesetz *n*	loi *f* de composition tangente	касательный закон композиции
	tangential co-ordinates <AY>	*s.* L 856		
	tangential co-ordinates of the hyperplane <PJ>	*s.* H 709		
	tangential co-ordinates of the line <AY>	*s.* L 856		
	tangential co-ordinates of the plane <AY>	*s.* P 643		
	tangential curvature <DG>	*s.* G 234		
T 51	**tangential curve** <of a curve> <DG>	Tangentialkurve *f*	courbe *f* tangentielle	касательная кривая, тангенциальная кривая <по отношению к кривой>
	tangential developable <GE>	*s.* T 71		
T 52	**tangential element** <in a point of a differentiable curve <DG>	Tangentialelement *n*	élément *m* tangentiel	тангенциальный элемент
T 53	**tangential equation,** envelope equation <of a curve> <AG>	Tangentengleichung *f*, Klassengleichung *f*, Gleichung *f* in Linienkoordinaten, Tangentialgleichung *f*	équation *f* tangentielle	тангенциальное уравнение
T 54	**tangential invariant** <of two algebraic curves> <AG>	Taktinvariante *f*, Tangentialinvariante *f*	tactinvariant *m*, invariant *m* tangentiel	
	tangential line integral <VT>	*s.* C 734		
T 55	**tangential map** <of a Lie group> <AL, GE>	Tangentialabbildung *f*	application *f* tangente	касательное отображение
T 56	**tangential multiplicity** <AG>	Tangentenmultiplizität *f*	multiplicité *f* tangentielle	касательная кратность
T 57	**tangential net** <of algebraic curves> <AG>	Tangentialnetz *n*	réseau *m* tangentiel	касательная сетка
	tangential net <GE>	*s.* 1. W 133; 2. W 135		
T 58	**tangential osculating space** <DG>	Tangentialschmiegraum *m*, TSR	espace *m* osculateur tangentiel	касательное соприкасающееся пространство
T 59	**tangential pencil,** range <of algebraic curves *or* surfaces> <AG>	Schar *f*, Berührungsbüschel *n*, Tangentialbüschel *n*	faisceau *m* tangentiel, gerbe *f*, faisceau de contact	пучок <кривых *или* поверхностей *n*-го класса>
	tangential pencil <AY>	*s.* R 119		
	tangential plane <DG>	*s.* T 68		
T 60	**tangential point** <of a cubic> <AG>	Tangentialpunkt *m*	point *m* tangentiel	тангенциальная точка
T 61	**tangential point of the second kind** <of a cubic> <AG>	Tangentialpunkt *m* zweiter Art	point *m* intersécant	тангенциальная точка второго рода, междусекущая точка

T 62	**tangential variety** <GE>	Tangentenmannigfaltigkeit *f*, Tangentialmannigfaltigkeit *f*	variété *f* tangente	касательное многообразие
	tangential vector <DG>	*s.* T 72		
	tangent law <EG>	*s.* L 210		
T 63	**tangent line,** tangent <to (of) a curve> <DG>	Tangente *f* <einer Kurve, an eine Kurve>, Kurventangente *f*	tangente *f* <à une courbe>	касательная <[к] кривой>
	tangent line <DI>	*s.* T 45		
	tangent line <GE>	*s.* T 40		
	tangent method <DI, NU>	*s.* M 12		
	tangentoid <DI>	*s.* T 45		
T 64	**tangentoidal curve (line)** <DI>	tangensförmige Kurve *f*, Tangenskurve *f*	ligne (courbe) *f* tangentoïdale	тангенсоидальная кривая (линия)
T 65	**tangent osculating circle** <DG>	Tangentialschmiegkreis *m*, gebundener Schmiegkreis *m*	cercle *m* osculateur tangentiel	касательная соприкасающаяся окружность
T 66	**tangent osculating half-space** <DG>	Tangentialschmieghalbraum *m*, TSHR	demi-espace *m* osculateur tangentiel	касательное соприкасающееся полупространство
T 67	**tangent parallelogram** <of an ellipse> <DS>	Tangentenparallelogramm *n*	parallélogramme *m* de tangentes	параллелограмм касательных
T 68	**tangent plane,** tangential plane <of a surface> <DG>	Tangentialebene *f*, Tangentenebene *f*, Berührungsebene *f*	plan *m* tangent	касательная плоскость
T 69	**tangent plane method** <DS>	Tangentialebenenverfahren *n*	méthode *f* des plans tangents	метод касательных плоскостей
	tangent rule <DI, NU>	*s.* M 12		
	tangent space <DG>	*s.* T 75		
T 70	**tangent subbundle** <AT>	Teiltangentialbündel *n*	sous-fibré *m* tangent	касательное подрасслоение
T 71	**tangent surface,** tangential developable <of a space curve> <GE>	Tangentenfläche *f*	surface *f* tangentielle	касательная поверхность
	tangent to the vertex <AY>	*s.* T 41		
	tangent-trapezoidal formula <DI, NU>	*s.* M 12		
	tangent-trapezoidal method <DI, NU>	*s.* M 12		
	tangent-trapezoidal rule <DI, NU>	*s.* M 12		
	tangent-trapezoid formula <DI, NU>	*s.* M 12		
	tangent-trapezoid method <DI, NU>	*s.* M 12		
	tangent-trapezoid rule <DI, NU>	*s.* M 12		
	tangent unit vector <DG>	*s.* U 297		
T 72	**tangent vector,** tangential vector <DG>	Tangentenvektor *m*, Tangentialvektor *m*	vecteur *m* tangent	касательный вектор
T 73	**tangent vector** <to a variety> <DG>	Tangentialvektor *m*, Vektor *m* in einem Punkt	vecteur *m* tangent	касательный (тангенциальный) вектор, вектор в точке
	tangent vector <DG>	*s.* U 297		
T 74	**tangent vector field** <of a manifold> <DG, TO>	Tangentenvektorfeld *n*, Tangentialvektorfeld *n*	champ *m* de vecteurs tangents	касательное векторное поле
T 75	**tangent vector space,** tangent space <DG>	Tangentialraum *m*, tangierender Vektorraum *m*	espace *m* tangent	касательное пространство
T 76	**Tang['s] tables** <ST>	Tangsche Tabellen *fpl*	tables *fpl* (tableaux *mpl*) de Tang	таблицы Танга
	tanh <FU>	*s.* H 654		
T 77	**Tannaka-Artin problem** <AB>	Tannaka-Artinsches Problem *n*	problème *m* de Tannaka-Artin	проблема Таннака-Артина
	tape <AL>	*s.* W 289		
	target <CA>	*s.* R 120		
	target <SE, TO>	*s.* R 123		
T 78	**target space** <TO>	Zielraum *m* <Raum, in den abgebildet wird>	espace-but *m*	пространство, в которое отображается; пространство пробытия
T 79	**target theory** <ST>	Treffertheorie *f*, Treffbereichstheorie *f*, Trefferbereichstheorie *f*	théorie *f* de la cible	теория мишени
	Tarry-Escott problem <AB>	*s.* T 381		
	Tarry-Escott problem <NT>	*s.* T 80		
T 80	**Tarry['s] problem,** Prouhet['s] problem, Tarry-Escott problem <NT>	Prouhet-Problem *n*, Tarry-Problem *n*, Tarry-Escott-Problem *n*, Tarry-Escottsches Problem *n*	problème *m* de Prouhet (Tarry-Escott)	
T 81	**Tarski['s] axiom for inaccessible sets,** axiom for inaccessible sets, axiom of inaccessibility, axiom of inaccessible cardinals <SE>	Unerreichbarkeitsaxiom *n*, Axiom *n* der unerreichbaren Mengen, Tarskisches Axiom der unerreichbaren Mengen	axiome *m* des alephs inaccessibles; hypothèse *f* des alephs inaccessibles	аксиома о недостижимых кардиналах, аксиома недостижимости
T 82	**Tarski['s] finiteness,** finiteness in the sense of double-well-ordered <SE>	Endlichkeit *f* im Sinne von Tarski, T-Endlichkeit *f*	finitude *f* au sens de Tarski	конечность в смысле Тарского

No.	English	German	French	Russian
T 83	**Tarski finite set,** finite set in the sense of Tarski <SE>	T-endliche Menge *f*, im Tarskischen Sinne endliche Menge	ensemble *m* fini au sens de Tarski	конечное множество в смысле Тарского
T 84	**Tarski['s] lemma** <MM>	Lemma *n* von Tarski, Tarskis Lemma	lemme *m* de Tarski	лемма Тарского
T 85	**Tarski['s] principle** <AL, FO>	Tarskisches Prinzip *n* [der Isonomie]	principe *m* de Tarski	принцип Тарского
T 86	**Tartaglia['s] formula** <for the volume of a tetrahedron> <EG>	Tartagliasche Tetraederformel *f*	formule *f* de Tartaglia	формула Тарталья
T 87	**Tate['s] group** <AB, AG>	Tate-Gruppe *f*	groupe *m* de Tate-Šafarevič	группа Тейта (Тейта-Шафаревича)
T 88	**Tate['s] space** <of an Abelian manifold> <AG> <AG>	Tatescher Raum *m*	espace *m* de Tate	пространство Тейта
T 89	**Tauberian asymptotic method** <AN>	Taubersche Asymptotik *f*, Asymptotik von Tauberschem Charakter	méthode *f* asymptotique de type Tauber	асимптотика тауберова типа
T 90	**Tauberian condition** <LI>	Taubersche Bedingung *f*, Konvergenzbedingung *f*	condition *f* taubérienne	тауберово условие
T 91	**Tauberian theorem** <AB, LI>	Satz *m* vom Tauberschen Typus, Tauberscher Satz	théorème *m* de type taubérien, théorème taubérien	теорема тауберова типа, теорема типа Таубера, тауберова теорема
T 92	**Tauberian theorem of Ikehara** <for a Dirichlet series> <SS>	Ikeharascher Tauber-Satz *m*	théorème *m* taubérien de Ikehara	
	Tauber['s] theorem <FT>	*s.* T 347		
T 93	**Tauber['s] theorems** <for the Laplace transform> <IT>	Taubersche Sätze *mpl*	théorèmes *mpl* de Tauber	тауберовы теоремы
T 94	**tautly imbedded pair,** taut pair <in X> <AT>	starr eingebettetes Paar *n*		жестко вложенная пара <в пространстве X>
T 95	**tautological implication,** implicational form, sentential inference <LO>	implikative Wahrform *f*, implikative Form *f*	implication *f* tautologique	тавтологическая импликация
T 96	**tautologically complete set of formulas** <LO>	tautologisch vollständige Menge *f* von Ausdrücken		тавтологически полное множество формул
T 97	**tautology** <LO>	Tautologie *f*	tautologie *f*	тавтология
T 98	**tautology,** truth, identically true formula, valid expression, valid formula, universally valid formula, true formula <of propositional calculus> <LO>	aussagenlogische Identität *f*, allgemeingültiger (aussagenlogisch allgemeingültiger) Ausdruck *m*, identisch wahre Aussagenform *f*, Wahrform *f*, allgemeingültige (wahre) Formel *f*, allgemeingültiger A-Ausdruck *m*, identischer [A-]Ausdruck, A-Identität *f*, A-identischer Ausdruck, allgemeingültige (immer gültige) Aussageform *f*	tautologie *f*, expression *f* valide (valable), proposition *f* universellement (logiquement) vraie, fonction *f* propositionnelle identique vraie, proposition toujours vraie, formule *f* vraie (logiquement vraie, valide, tautologique), loi *f* logique	всегда-истинная (истинная, тождественно истинная, классически общезначимая, общезначимая, тождественная) формула, тавтология, логическая тавтология, тождественно-истинное (всегда истинное) высказывание, тождественно истинная функция высказывания, тождественно истинная пропозициональная функция, тождество, логически истинное предложение, всегда истинная форма высказывания, универсально верное суждение
	taut pair <AT>	*s.* T 94		
T 99	**Taylor['s] circle** <of a triangle> <EG>	Taylorscher (Taylors) Kreis *m*	cercle *m* de Taylor	окружность Тейлора
T 100	**Taylor['s] coefficient** <DI>	Taylor-Koeffizient *m*, Taylorkoeffizient *m*, Taylorscher Koeffizient *m*	coefficient *m* taylorien (de Taylor)	коэффициент Тейлора, тейлоров коэффициент, тейлоровский коэффициент
	Taylor['s] expansion <DI>	*s.* T 106		
T 101	**Taylor['s] expansion with remainder** <DI>	Taylorsche Entwicklung *f* mit Restglied, Taylorsche Formel *f* mit Restglied	développement *m* de Taylor avec reste, développement limité <d'une fonction>	тейлоровское разложение с остаточным членом, формула Тейлора с остаточным членом
T 102	**Taylor['s] formula,** Taylor['s] theorem, general (generalized, extended, n-th) mean value theorem <DI>	Taylorsche Formel *f*, Taylorscher Satz *m*, Taylor-Formel *f*	formule *f* de Taylor	формула Тейлора
	Taylor['s] formula <DI, NU>	*s.* T 105		
T 103	**Taylor['s] interpolation formula** <AX, FD, NU>	Taylorsche Interpolationsformel *f*, Interpolationsformel von Taylor	formule *f* d'interpolation de Taylor	интерполяционная формула Тейлора
T 104	**Taylor['s] polynomial** <DI>	Taylorsches Polynom *n*	polynôme *m* de Taylor	многочлен Тейлора
T 105	**Taylor['s] quadrature formula,** Taylor['s] formula <for numerical quadrature> <DI, NU>	Taylorsche Quadraturformel *f*	formule *f* d'intégration de Taylor, formule de Taylor	формула <численного интегрирования> Тейлора
T 106	**Taylor['s] series;** Taylor['s] expansion <DI>	Taylor-Reihe *f*, Taylorsche Reihe *f*; Taylor-Entwicklung *f*, Taylorsche Entwicklung *f*	série *f* de Taylor, série taylorienne; développement *m* de Taylor, développement taylorien	ряд Тейлора, тейлоров ряд, тейлоровский ряд; разложение Тейлора, тейлорово разложение, тейлоровское разложение, разложение в ряд Тейлора

No.	English	German	French	Russian
	Taylor['s] series with gaps <FT, SS>	*s.* G 46		
	Taylor['s] theorem <DI>	*s.* T 102		
T 107	**T-characteristic** <AT>	T-Charakteristik *f*	T-caractéristique *f*	T-характеристика
	Tchebycheff['s] net <DG>	*s.* C 601		
	Tchebycheff['s] polynomial <FU>	*s.* C 613		
T 108	***T*-critical graph** <GP>	T-kritischer Graph *m*	graphe *m* T-critique	T-критический граф
T 109	***t*-different** <AL>	t-Differente *f*	t-différente *f*	t-дифферента
T 110	***t*-discriminant** <AL>	t-Diskriminante *f*	t-discriminant *m*	t-дискриминант
T 111	***t*-distribution,** Student['s] distribution, Student['s] t-distribution <ST>	t-Verteilung *f*, Student-Verteilung *f*, Studentsche Verteilung (t-Verteilung) *f*	distribution *f* de t (Student), distribution [de] t de Student, distribution t, loi *f* de Student	t-распределение, распределение Стьюдента (t Стьюдента)
T 112	**technical error** <ER>	technischer Fehler *m*	erreur *f* technique	техническая ошибка
T 113	**technical term,** primitive term <GN>	technischer Ausdruck *m*, Kunstausdruck *m*	terme *m* technique	специальное выражение
	ε-technique <AN>	*s.* E 316		
T 114	**Teichmüller['s] cocycle** <AB>	Teichmüllerscher Kozyklus *m*	cocycle *m* de Teichmüller	коцикл Тейхмюллера
T 115	**Teichmüller['s] modular group** <AL, FT>	Teichmüllersche Modulgruppe *f*	groupe *m* modulaire de Teichmüller	модулярная группа Тейхмюллера
T 116	**Teichmüller['s] space** <AG>	Teichmüllerscher Raum *m*	espace *m* de Teichmüller	пространство Тейхмюллера
T 117	**Teichmüller['s] surface of genus *g*** <FT, TO>	Teichmüllersche Fläche *f* vom Geschlecht g	surface *f* de Teichmüller de genre g	поверхность Тейхмюллера рода g
T 118	**Teichmüller-Tukey lemma,** Tukey['s] lemma, Tukey['s] statement <SE>	Lemma *n* von Teichmüller-Tukey, Teichmüller-Tukeyscher Maximalmengensatz *m*	lemme *m* de Teichmüller-Tukey	лемма Тейхмюллера-Тьюки, лемма Тайхмюллера-Тьюки
T 119	**telegraph (telegrapher's, telegraphic, telegraphy) equation,** equation of telegraphy <DE>	Telegraphengleichung *f*	équation *f* des télégraphistes	телеграфное уравнение
T 120	**teleparallelism,** absolute parallelism <DG>	Fernparallelismus *m*, absoluter Parallelismus *m*	téléparallélisme *m*, parallélisme *m* à distance, parallélisme absolu	абсолютный параллелизм
T 121	**telescopic series** <SS>	Reihe *f* $\sum_{n=0}^{\infty} \frac{1}{(k+n)(k+n+1)}$	série *f*	ряд вида
T 122	**tempered distribution,** tame distribution <AN>	gemäßigte Distribution *f*	distribution *f* tempérée	обобщенная функция медленного роста, линейный функционал над пространством быстро убывающих на бесконечности функций
T 123	**Temple['s] bound** <DE, NU>	Templesche Schranke *f*	borne *f* de Temple	грань Темпля
T 124	**Temple['s] lower bound** <DE>	untere Schranke *f* nach Temple, untere Templesche Schranke, Templesche untere Schranke, erweiterte untere Templesche Schranke	borne *f* inférieure de Temple	нижняя грань Темпля
T 125	**Temple['s] quotient** <DE, NU>	Templescher Quotient *m*	quotient *m* de Temple	отношение Темпля
T 126	**Temple['s] theorem** <DE, NU>	Einschließungssatz *m* von Temple, Templescher Einschließungssatz	théorème *m* de Temple	теорема Темпля
	ten <NT>	*s.* U 287		
	tend <AN, SS>	*s.* C 2318		
T 127	**tendency,** evolution <ST>	Tendenz *f*, Evolution *f*, langfristige Entwicklung *f*	tendance *f*, évolution *f*	тенденция, эволюция, долгосрочное развитие
T 128	**tending to zero** <AN>	nach Null gehend (strebend)	tendant vers le zéro, tendant vers zéro	стремящийся к нулю
	tend to infinity / to <DI>	*s.* A 818		
	tend to zero of the same order / to <AN, SS>	*s.* A 820		
T 129	**tens digit,** ten's place, tens place <NT>	Zehnerstelle *f*	place *f* des dizaines	разряд десятков
T 130	**tension,** potential difference <GP>	Spannung *f*	tension *f*, différence *f* de potentiel	напряжение
T 131	**tensor** <of a quaternion> <AL>	Betrag *m*, Tensor *m*, Länge *f*, Zahlenwert *m*, Wurzel *f* aus der Norm	tenseur *m*	норма
T 132	**tensor** <over an R-module> <AL>	Tensor *m*	tenseur *m*	тензор
T 133	**tensor,** // affinor <over a vector space> <VT>	Tensor *m*, // Affinor *m*	tenseur *m*, // affineur *m*, affinor *m*	тензор, // аффинор
	ε-tensor <DG, VT>	*s.* A 563		
T 134	**tensor algebra** <AL>	Tensoralgebra *f*, tensorielle Algebra *f*	algèbre *f* tensorielle	тензорная алгебра
	tensor algebra <VT>	*s.* A 476		
T 135	**tensor analysis** <VT>	Tensoranalysis *f*	analyse *f* tensorielle	тензорный анализ
T 136	**tensor bundle** <of type h> <AT>	Tensorbündel *n* <vom Typ h>	fibré *m* tensoriel <de type h>	тензорное расслоение <типа h>
	tensor calculus <DG, VT>	*s.* R 979		
	tensor compounded from two given tensors <VT>	*s.* I 561		

No.	English	German	French	Russian
T 137	**tensor contravariant of degree q and covariant of degree p, tensor contravariant of order q and covariant of order p,** tensor of type (p,q) <AL, VT>	p-stufig kovarianter und q-stufig kontravarianter Tensor *m*	tenseur *m* p fois covariant et q fois contravariant, tenseur d'espèce $\binom{p}{q}$	тензор, q раз контравариантный и p раз ковариантный
T 138	**tensor criterion,** criterion for tensors <VT>	Tensorkriterium *n*, Kriterium *n* für die Tensoreigenschaft	critère *m* de tensorialité	критерий тензорности
T 139	**tensor density** <VT>	Tensordichte *f*	densité *f* tensorielle	тензорная плотность
T 140	**tensor density [of unit weight],** relative tensor of unit weight, relative tensor of weight unity <VT>	Tensordichte *f* vom Gewicht Eins, Tensordichte	densité *f* tensorielle de poids 1, densité tensorielle	тензорная плотность веса 1, тензорная плотность
T 141	**tensor differential equation,** affinor differential equation <DE, DG, VT>	Tensordifferentialgleichung *f*, Affinordifferentialgleichung *f*	équation *f* différentielle tensorielle	тензорное дифференциальное уравнение
T 142	**tensor field,** tensorial field <VT>	Tensorfeld *n*	champ *m* de tenseurs (tenseur), champ tenseur	тензорное поле
	tensor flux <VT>	*s.* F 425		
T 143	**tensor form of the first kind** <FT, VT>	Tensorform *f* erster Gattung <Kähler>	forme *f* tensorielle de première espèce	тензорная форма первого рода
T 144	**tensorial derivative** <of a vector field> <VT>	tensorielle Ableitung *f*	dérivée *f* tensorielle	тензорная производная
	tensorial field <VT>	*s.* T 142		
	tensorial flux <VT>	*s.* F 425		
T 145	**tensoriality** <VT>	Tensoreigenschaft *f*	tensorialité *f*	тензорность
T 146	**tensorial mapping** <of a tensor space> <AL>	tensorielle Abbildung *f*	application *f* tensorielle	тензорное отображение
T 147	**tensorial multiplication** <CA>	tensorielle Multiplikation *f*	multiplication *f* tensorielle	тензорное умножение
T 148	**tensorial power** <AL>	tensorielle Potenz *f*, Tensorpotenz *f*	puissance *f* tensorielle	тензорная степень
T 149	**tensorial sum** <of representations> <AL>	tensorielle Summe *f*	somme *f* tensorielle <p-e>	тензорная сумма
	tensor identity of Levi-Cività <DG, VT>	*s.* A 563		
T 150	**tensoring** <AL>	Tensorierung *f*, Bildung *f* des Tensorprodukts	tensorisation *f*	тензорное умножение
T 151	**tensor invariant** <VT>	Tensorinvariante *f*, tensorielle Invariante *f*	invariant *m* de tenseur	тензорный инвариант
T 152	**tensor multiplication,** outer multiplication <of tensors> <VT>	tensorielle Multiplikation *f*, Tensormultiplikation *f*	multiplication *f* générale (tensorielle), multiplication	общее (тензорное) умножение
T 153	**tensor notation** <AL, VT>	Tensorschreibweise *f*	notation *f* tensorielle	тензорная запись, запись в тензорной форме
T 154	**tensor of order four,** fourth-order tensor <VT>	vierstufiger Tensor *m*, Tensor vierter Stufe	tenseur *m* de quatrième ordre	четырехвалентный тензор
	tensor of order n <VT>	*s.* T 155		
	tensor of order two <VT>	*s.* D 949		
	tensor of rank 1 <VT>	*s.* V 92		
T 155	**tensor of rank n,** tensor of order n, tensor of valence n <VT>	Tensor *m* n-ter Stufe, n-stufiger Tensor	tenseur *m* d'ordre n	тензор n-го ранга, тензор n-ой валентности
	tensor of torsion <DG>	*s.* T 609		
	tensor of type (p,q) <AL, VT>	*s.* T 137		
	tensor of valence n <VT>	*s.* T 155		
	tensor of zero order <VT>	*s.* S 73		
T 156	**tensor product,** direct product <of vector spaces, modules> <AL>	Tensorprodukt *n*, tensorielles (direktes) Produkt *n*	produit *m* tensoriel	тензорное произведение
T 157	**tensor product** <of linear mappings, rings, *or* vector bundles> <AL, AT>	Tensorprodukt *n*	produit *m* tensoriel	тензорное произведение
	tensor product <AN>	*s.* D 594		
	tensor product <FA>	*s.* D 595		
	tensor product <MD>	*s.* K 163		
	tensor product <VT>	*s.* 1. D 1069; 2. P 1596		
T 158	**tensor-product functor** <AL, CA>	Funktor *m* des Tensorprodukts	foncteur *m* produit tensoriel	функтор тензорного произведения
T 159	**tensor representation** <AL>	Tensordarstellung *f* <m-ter Stufe>	représentation *f* tensorielle	тензорное представление
T 160	**tensor space** <of order n> <AL>	Tensorraum *m* <n-ter Stufe>	espace *m* tensoriel <d'ordre n>	тензорное пространство <n-ой валентности>
T 161	**tensor subspace** <AL>	Untertensorraum *m*	sous-espace *m* tensoriel	тензорное подпространство
	ten's (tens) place <NT>	*s.* T 129		
T 162	**term,** member <of an equation> <AL>	Glied *n*	terme *m*, membre *m*	член
T 163	**term** <of an expression, a product> <AL, AN>	Glied *n*, Term *m*	terme *m*	член
T 164	**term** <of a proportion> <AR>	Glied *n*	terme *m*	член

No.	English	German	French	Russian
T 165	**term** <LO>	Term *m*	terme *m*, mot *m*	терм
T 166	**term** <of a relation> <SE>	Glied *n*, Element *n*	membre *m*	член
	term <AL, AR>	*s.* S 2279		
	term <LO>	*s.* I 386		
	term <NT>	*s.* P 253		
	ε-term <LO>	*s.* E 317		
	term-by-term addition <AL, AR>	*s.* T 180		
	term-by-term differentiation <DI>	*s.* D 472		
	term-by-term integration <DI>	*s.* I 682		
	α-termed sequence <SE>	*s.* A 537		
	term function <UA>	*s.* P 975		
	terminal cone <CA>	*s.* L 726		
T 167	**terminal decision,** final decision <ST>	abschließende Entscheidung *f*	décision *f* finale	окончательное решение
T 168	**terminal edge,** edge starting from a pendant vertex <GP>	Endkante *f*, hängende Kante *f*	arête *f* terminale	концевое ребро
	terminal end-point <GP>	*s.* T 172		
T 169	**terminal group** <of a spectral sequence> <HA>	Endgruppe *f*	groupe *m* terminal	предельная группа
	terminal object <CA>	*s.* N 784		
T 170	**terminal point,** tip, terminus, end-point <of a vector> <VT>	Endpunkt *m*, Spitze *f*	extrémité *f*	конец, концевая точка
	terminal point <AN>	*s.* E 217		
	terminal point <TO>	*s.* E 219		
T 171	**terminal position** <GE>	Endlage *f*, Endstellung *f*	position *f* finale	конечное положение
T 172	**terminal vertex,** terminal end-point <of a directed edge> <GP>	Zielpunkt *m*, Schlußpunkt *m*, Endpunkt *m*, rechter Eckpunkt *m*, Endknoten *m*	extrémité *f* terminale	конец, конечная вершина
T 173	**terminal vertex** <TG>	Endposition *f*	position *f* finale	окончательная позиция
T 174	**terminate / to,** to be finite <*e.g.:* said of a chain of commutators> <GR>	abbrechen, stationär werden	être stationnaire	стабилизоваться, обрываться
T 175	**terminating chain** <of subsets> <SE>	abbrechende Kette *f* (Folge *f*)	suite *f* stationnaire	стационарная (обрывающаяся) последовательность
T 176	**terminating continued fraction,** finite continued fraction <NT>	abbrechender (endlicher) Kettenbruch *m*	fraction *f* continue finie	конечная непрерывная цепь, конечная цепная дробь
T 177	**terminating decimal [fraction]** <AR, NT>	endlicher (abbrechender) Dezimalbruch *m*	fraction *f* décimale limitée, fraction décimale finie, décimale *f* limitée	конечная десятичная дробь, оканчивающаяся десятичная дробь
T 178	**termination** <at the *n*-th term> <*e.g.:* of a chain of syzygies> <AL>	Abbrechen *n*, Abbruch *m* <mit dem *n*-ten Glied>	stationnarité *f* <d'après le *n*-e terme>	обрыв <с *n*-им членом>
	terminus <AN>	*s.* E 217		
	terminus <VT>	*s.* T 170		
T 179	**term of higher degree (order),** higher[-] degree term, higher order term <AN>	Glied *n* höherer Ordnung	terme *m* de degré supérieur	член высшего порядка, член выше первого порядка малости
	term of the Farey sequence <NT>	*s.* F 573		
	term variable <LO>	*s.* O 11		
T 180	**termwise addition,** addition term by term, term-by-term addition <AL, AR>	gliedweise Addition *f*	addition *f* membre à membre	почленное сложение, сложение по членам
	termwise differentiation <DI> ⌐<DI>	*s.* D 472		
	termwise integration	*s.* I 682		
T 181	**term with the same index** <in a sequence> <SS>	Glied *n* mit dem gleichen Index	terme *m* de même rang	член с одинаковым индексом
T 182	**ternariant** <IV>	Ternariante *f* <Forsyth>	ternariant *m*	тернариант
	ternary <CT>	*s.* 1. T 445; 2. T 891		
	ternary composition <UA>	*s.* T 190		
T 183	**ternary connective** <LO>	dreistelliger Junktor *m*, ternäres Verknüpfungszeichen *n*	connecteur *m* ternaire, signe *m* substantifique de poids (degré) 3	триадическая (тернарная) связка
T 184	**ternary continued fraction** <NT>	ternärer Kettenbruch *m*	fraction *f* continue ternaire	тернарная цепная дробь
T 185	**ternary domain** <PJ>	ternäres Gebiet *n*, Gebiet dritter Stufe	domaine *m* ternaire	тернарная область
	ternary expansion <NT>	*s.* T 894		
T 185a	**ternary field,** planar ternary ring <AL>	Ternärkörper *m*	corps *m* ternaire	тернарное тело
T 186	**ternary form,** ternary (3-ary) quantic <AL>	ternäre (3-äre) Form *f*, Ternärform *f*, Form von drei Variablen, ternäre algebraische Form *f*	forme *f* ternaire (3-aire), forme de trois variables, forme algébrique ternaire	тернарная (3-арная) форма, тройничная форма, форма от трех переменных
T 187	**ternary monomial group** <AL>	monomiale ternäre Gruppe *f*	groupe *m* monomial ternaire	тернарная мономиальная группа
T 188	**ternary [number] notation,** ternary representation <of numbers> <NT>	ternäre Zahlendarstellung *f*, ternäre Schreibweise *f*, triadische Darstellung *f*	notation *f* <de nombres> ternaire	троичное представление, представление <чисел> в троичной системе

No.	English	German	French	Russian
T 189	**ternary number system** <NT>	Ternärsystem *n*, triadisches System *n*	système *m* ternaire (triadique)	троичная система [счисления]
T 190	**ternary operation,** three-place operation, ternary composition <UA>	ternäre algebraische Operation (Verknüpfung) *f*, ternäre (dreistellige) Operation	opération *f* ternaire, opération à trois (3) termes	тернарная алгебраическая операция, тернарная операция
T 191	**ternary projective group** <GR>	ternäre projektive Gruppe *f*	groupe *m* projectif ternaire	тернарная проективная группа
	ternary quantic <AL>	*s.* T 186		
T 192	**ternary relation,** three-place relation, triadic relation <SE, UA>	dreistellige (ternäre) Relation *f*	relation *f* ternaire, relation à trois (3) termes	трехместное отношение, трехчленное отношение, тернарное отношение
	ternary representation <NT>	*s.* T 188		
T 193	**ternary ring** <AL>	Ternärring *m*, ternärer Ring *m*	anneau *m* ternaire	тернарное кольцо
	ternion <CT>	*s.* T 445		
T 194	**tertiary element** <in a ring> <AL>	tertiäres Element *n*	élément *m* tertiaire	терциарный элемент
T 195	**tertiary ideal** <AL>	Tertiärideal *n*	idéal *m* tertiaire	терциарный идеал
T 196	**tertiary module** <AL>	Tertiärmodul *m*	sous-module *m* tertiaire	терциарный подмодуль
T 197	**tertiary radical** <AL>	tertiäres Radikal *n*	radical *m* tertiaire	терциарный радикал
T 198	**tertiary representation** <AL>	Tertiärzerlegung *f*	décomposition *f* tertiaire	терциарное разложение
T 199	**tertiary right ideal** <AL>	tertiäres Rechtsideal *n*	idéal *m* tertiaire à droite	терциарный правый идеал
	tertium exclusum <LO>	*s.* L 184		
	tertium non datur <LO>	*s.* L 184		
T 200	**tessellation,** tiling <EG>	Überdeckung *f* der Ebene, Parkettierung *f* <mit regulären Vielecken>	pavage *m*	замощение плоскости <правильными многоугольниками>, разбиение плоскости <на правильные многоугольники>
T 201	**tesseral Legendre function [of the first kind], tesseral [spherical] harmonic** <FU>	tesserale Kugelfunktion *f* [erster Art], tesserale Legendresche Funktion *f* [erster Art]	fonction *f* de Legendre tessérale [de la première espèce], fonction harmonique tessérale, fonction sphérique tessérale [de la première espèce], fonction tessérale	тессеральная сферическая функция [Лежандра] первого рода, тессеральная сферическая функция [Лежандра]
T 202	**test,** statistical test, test[ing] of a statistical hypothesis, statistical testing procedure <ST>	Test *m*, statistischer Test, Test einer statistischen Hypothese, Prüfung *f* einer statistischen Hypothese, Prüfung, statistische Prüfung [einer Hypothese], Prüfverfahren *n*, statistisches Prüfverfahren	test *m*, test statistique (d'hypothèse), test d'une hypothèse statistique	критерий, статистический критерий, проверка, проверка гипотезы (статистической гипотезы), статистическая проверка [гипотезы]
T 203	**59 test** <NT>	59er-Probe *f*	preuve *f* par 59	проверка с помощью числа 59
	χ^2-test <ST>	*s.* C 637		
	χ^2-test of goodness of fit <ST>	*s.* C 638		
	χ^2-test of homogeneity <ST>	*s.* C 639		
	χ^2-test of independence <ST>	*s.* C 640		
	χ^2-test of variances <ST>	*s.* C 641		
	ω^2-test <ST>	*s.* C 2649		
	test criterion <ST>	*s.* T 223		
T 204	**test for additivity,** test of additivity <ST>	Additivitätstest *m*, Test *m* auf Additivität	test *m* d'additivité	критерий аддитивности
	test for convergence <SS>	*s.* C 2670		
T 205	**test for uniform convergence** <SS>	Kriterium *n* der gleichmäßigen Konvergenz	critère *m* de la convergence uniforme	признак равномерной сходимости
T 206	**test function** <AN>	Testfunktion *f*	fonction *f* test	тест-функция
T 207	**test function,** critical function <of a generalized test> <ST>	Testfunktion *f*, kritische Funktion *f*	fonction *f* critique	функция критерия, критическая функция
	testing of a statistical hypothesis <ST>	*s.* T 202		
	test of additivity <ST>	*s.* T 204		
	test of a statistical hypothesis <ST>	*s.* T 202		
	test of convergence <SS>	*s.* C 2670		
T 208	**test of dispersion** <ST>	Streuungstest *m*	test *m* de dispersion	критерий рассеивания
T 209	**test of divergence** <SS>	Divergenzkriterium *n*	critère *m* de divergence	критерий (признак) расходимости
T 210	**test of goodness of fit,** smooth test <ST>	Anpassungstest *m*	test *m* de validité de l'ajustement (l'enregistrement), test de bon ajustement, test d'accord	критерий согласия (приспособления)
T 211	**test of homogeneity** <ST>	Homogenitätstest *m*, Heterogenitätstest *m*	test *m* d'homogénéité	критерий однородности
T 212	**test of independence** <ST>	Unabhängigkeitstest *m*, Prüfung *f* auf Unabhängigkeit	test *m* d'indépendance	критерий независимости
T 213	**test of linearity,** Fisher['s] test of linearity <ST>	Linearitätstest *m*, Linearitätstest von Fisher	test *m* de linéarité, test de linéarité de Fisher	проверка (критерий) линейности, проверка (критерий) линейности Фишера
T 214	**test of location,** test of position <ST>	Lagetest *m*	test *m* de position	проверка местоположения, проверка положения, определение местоположения

No.	English	German	French	Russian
T 215	**test of normality** <ST>	Normalitätstest *m*	test *m* de normalité	критерий нормальности
T 216	**test of parallelism** <ST>	Parallelitätstest *m*	test *m* de parallélisme	критерий (проверка) параллельности
	test of position <ST>	*s.* T 214		
T 217	**test of randomness** <ST>	Zufälligkeitstest *m*	test *m* d'échantillonnage au hasard, test du caractère aléatoire	критерий случайности
	test of significance <ST>	*s.* S 843		
T 218	**test of symmetry [by Hemelrijk]** <ST>	Symmetrietest *m* [von Hemelrijk]	test *m* de symétrie [de Hemelrijk]	критерий симметрии (Гемельрика), проверка симметричности распределения
T 219	**test of trend** <ST>	Trendtest *m*	test *m* de la tendance	проверка (критерий для проверки) тренда
T 220	**test of validity** <ST>	Gültigkeitstest *m*	test *m* de validité	проверка справедливости предпосылок
T 221	**test point** <PG>	Testpunkt *m*, Teststelle *f*	point *m* d'essai	контрольная точка
T 222	**test sequence,** sequence of tests <ST>	Testfolge *f*	suite *f* de tests	последовательность критериев
T 223	**test statistic (variable),** test criterion <ST>	Testgröße *f*, Prüfzahl *f*, Testkriterium *n*	variable *f* à tester, fonction *f* des observations à tester, critère *m* utilisé dans un test	статистика, лежащая в основе критерия
	tetrachoric correlation <ST>	*s.* T 224		
T 224	**tetrachoric correlation coefficient,** tetrachoric correlation <ST>	tetrachorischer Korrelationskoeffizient *m*, tetrachorische Korrelation *f*	coefficient *m* de corrélation tétrachorique, corrélation *f* tétrachorique	коэффициент тетрахорической (четырехклеточной) корреляции, тетрахорическая (четырехклеточная) корреляция
T 225	**tetrachoric function** <ST>	tetrachorische Funktion *f*	fonction *f* tétrachorique	тетрахорическая (четырехклеточная) функция
	tetracuspid <GE>	*s.* A 1125		
T 226	**tetracyclic co-ordinates;** system of tetracyclic co-ordinates <DG>	tetrazyklische Koordinaten *fpl*; tetrazyklisches Koordinatensystem *n*	coordonnées *fpl* tétracycliques; système *m* de coordonnées tétracycliques	тетрациклические координаты; система тетрациклических координат
T 227	**tetrad** <CT, ST>	Tetrade *f*, Vierzahl *f*	tétrade *f*	тетрада, четверка
	tetradic relation <LO>	*s.* F 545		
T 228	**tetrad of Maclaurin,** Maclaurin['s] tetrad <of a cubic> <AG>	Maclaurinsche Tetrade *f*, Tetrade von Maclaurin	tétrade *f* de Maclaurin	тетрэд Маклорена
	tetrad symmetry <EG>	*s.* Q 92		
T 229	**tetragonal number** <a figurate number> <NT>	Tetragonalzahl *f*, Viereckszahl *f*	nombre *m* tétragone (tétragonal)	четырехугольное число
	tetragonal symmetry <EG>	*s.* Q 92		
T 230	**tetragonometry** <EG>	Tetragonometrie *f*, Vierecksmessung *f*	tétragonométrie *f*	тетрагонометрия
	tetrahedral <DG>	*s.* F 514		
T 231	**tetrahedral angle** <EG>	Vierkant *n*, vierseitige Ecke *f*	angle *m* tétraédrique (tétraèdre)	четырехгранный угол
T 232	**tetrahedral complex,** Reye['s] complex <PJ>	tetraedraler (Reyescher) Komplex *m*	complexe *m* tétraédral (de Reye)	тетраэдральный комплекс
T 233	**tetrahedral co-ordinates** <AY>	Tetraederkoordinaten *fpl*, tetraedrische Koordinaten *fpl*	coordonnées *fpl* tétraédriques	тетраэдрические координаты
T 234	**tetrahedral co-ordinates of a plane** <AY>	tetraedrische Ebenenkoordinaten *fpl*	coordonnées *fpl* tétraédriques d'un plan	тетраэдрические координаты плоскости
T 235	**tetrahedral form** <AL>	Tetraederform *f*	forme *f* tétraédrique (du tétraèdre)	тетраэдрическая форма
T 236	**tetrahedral group** <GR>	Tetraedergruppe *f*	groupe *m* tétraédral (du tétraèdre), groupe tétraédrique	группа тетраэдра, тетраэдральная группа
T 237	**tetrahedral number** <a figurate number> <NT>	Pyramidalzahl *f*, Tetraedralzahl *f*, Pyramidenzahl *f*	nombre *m* pyramidal (figuré du troisième ordre), nombre figuré d'ordre 3, nombre tétraédral	тетраэдральное число, тетраэдрическое число
	tetrahedral pyramid <EG>	*s.* T 240		
T 238	**tetrahedral surface** <G. Tzitzeica> <AG>	tetraedrale Fläche *f*, Tetraedralfläche *f*	surface *f* tétraédrale	тетраэдрическая поверхность
T 239	**tetrahedroid,** Cayley['s] tetrahedroid <AG>	Cayleys[ches] Tetraedroid *n*, Tetraedroid, Tetraedroid von Cayley	tétraédroïde *m*	тетраэдроид
T 240	**tetrahedron,** triangular (tetrahedral) pyramid <EG>	Vierflach *n*, Tetraeder *n*, Vierflächner *m*, Dreieckpyramide *f*, dreiseitige Pyramide *f*	tétraèdre *m*, pyramide *f* triangulaire (tétraédrique)	тетраэдр, четырехгранник, треугольная (четырехгранная) пирамида
	tetrahedron <EG>	*s.* R 636		
T 241	**tetrahedron equation** <AL>	Tetraedergleichung *f*	équation *f* du tétraèdre, équation tétraédrique	уравнение тетраэдра
T 242	**tetrahedron of reference,** co-ordinate tetrahedron <for tetrahedral co-ordinates> <AY>	Fundamentaltetraeder *n*, Koordinatentetraeder *n*, Bezugstetraeder *n*, Beziehungstetraeder *n*, Grundtetraeder *n*, Grundvierflach *n*	tétraèdre *m* de référence, tétraèdre de coordonnées, tétraèdre fondamental	основной тетраэдр, координатный тетраэдр
T 243	**tetriamond** <EG>	Tetriamant *m*	tétriamant *m*	тетриамант
T 244	**tetromino** <EG>	Tetromino *n*	tétromino *m*	тетромино
T 245	**T_2-extension** <of a topological space> <TO>	Hausdorffsche Erweiterung *f*, T_2-Erweiterung *f*	T_2-extension *f*	хаусдорфово расширение
	tg <DI>	*s.* T 39		
	tg am <FU>	*s.* A 610		
	T-genus <AT>	*s.* T 487		
	tgh <FU>	*s.* H 654		
	T-graph <GP>	*s.* T 705		

No.	English	Deutsch	Français	Русский
T 246	**t-group** <GR>	t-Gruppe *f*	t-groupe *m*	t-группа
T 247	**T-group** <GR>	T-Gruppe *f*	groupe *m* T	T-группа
	th <FU>	*s.* H 654		
T 248	**Thales['s] circle** <EG>	Thales-Kreis *m*	cercle *m* de Thales (Thalès)	окружность Фалеса
T 249	**Thales['s] theorem,** theorem of Thales <EG>	Satz *m* des (von) Thales	théorème *m* de Thales (Thalès)	теорема Фалеса
	thalweg <DS>	*s.* T 31		
T 250	**theaetetical field** <AL>	euklidischer Körper *m*	corps *m* ordonné euclidien	евклидово упорядоченное поле
T 251	**the four basic arithmetical operations, the four basic operations of arithmetics, the four fundamental operations of arithmetic [and algebra], the four primary computations** <AR>	die vier Grundrechnungsarten *fpl* [der Arithmetik], die vier Spezies (Grundrechenoperationen, arithmetischen Operationen, Rechenstufen) *fpl*	les quatre opérations *fpl* [en arithmétique], les quatre règles *fpl* [fondamentales], les quatre opérations arithmétiques	четыре основных действия арифметики, четыре арифметических действия, счет, четыре основных арифметических действия
T 252	**then and only then** <GN>	dann und nur dann, genau dann	alors et seulement alors	тогда и только тогда, в том и только в том случае, те и только те, ттогда
T 253	**theorem,** proposition <GN>	Satz *m*, Theorem *n*, Aussage *f*	théorème *m*, proposition *f*	теорема, предложение
	Theorema egregium <DG>	*s.* G 68		
T 254	**theorem of Abel-Ruffini,** Abel-Ruffini theorem <AL>	Abelscher Unmöglichkeitssatz *m*, Abelscher Satz *m* <über die Nichtlösbarkeit der allgemeinen Gleichung *n*-ten Grades durch Radikale>	théorème *m* de Ruffini-Abel	теорема Руффини-Абеля, теорема Абеля об алгебраических уравнениях
T 255	**theorem of Ahlfors,** Ahlfors['s] [distortion] theorem <FT>	Verzerrungssatz (Randverzerrungssatz) *m* von Ahlfors, Ahlforsscher Verzerrungssatz	théorème *m* d'Ahlfors	теорема Алфорса
T 256	**theorem of Albert,** Albert['s] theorem <AL>	Satz *m* von Albert, Albertscher Satz	théorème *m* d'Albert	теорема Альберта
T 257	**theorem of Alexandroff,** Alexandroff['s] theorem <TO>	Satz *m* von Alexandroff (Aleksandrov), Alexandroffscher Satz	théorème *m* d'Alexandroff	теорема Александрова
T 258	**theorem of alternative,** alternative theorem <for linear equations *or* a linear operator *or* in geometry of numbers> <AL, FA, GU>	Alternativsatz *m*	théorème *m* de l'alternative	теорема об альтернативе
	theorem of A. N. Tihonov <TO>	*s.* T 356		
T 259	**theorem of Appell-Humbert,** Appell-Humbert theorem <AG>	Satz *m* von Appell-Humbert, Appell-Humbertscher Satz	théorème *m* d'Appell-Humbert	теорема Аппеля-Гумберта
T 260	**theorem of arithmetic progression,** Dirichlet['s] theorem on primes <NT>	Dirichletscher Satz *m* von den arithmetischen Progressionen, Dirichletscher Primzahlsatz *m*, Dirichletscher Satz *m* von den Primzahlen in einer arithmetischen Progression	théorème *m* de Dirichlet, théorème de la progression arithmétique	теорема Дирихле [о бесконечности простых чисел в арифметических прогрессиях], теорема Дирихле о бесконечности простых чисел в арифметической прогрессии, теорема Дирихле о прогрессиях
	theorem of Arzelà-Ascoli <FA>	*s.* A 1027		
	theorem of Baire on category <TO>	*s.* B 14		
	theorem of Beppo Levi <FA>	*s.* B 495		
	theorem of Bernstein-Schröder <SE>	*s.* E 425		
	theorem of B. Levi <FA>	*s.* B 495		
T 261	**theorem of Blichfeldt,** Blichfeldt['s] theorem <CS>	Satz *m* von Blichfeldt, Blichfeldtscher Satz	théorème *m* de Blichfeldt	теорема Блихфельдта
T 262	**theorem of Bohr-Landau,** Bohr-Landau theorem <NU>	Satz *m* von Bohr-Landau, Bohr-Landauscher Satz	théorème *m* de Bohr-Landau	теорема Бора-Ландау
	theorem of Bolzano-Cauchy <RF>	*s.* L 1017		
T 263	**theorem of Borel,** Borel['s] theorem <in Diophantine approximation> <NT>	Satz *m* von Borel, Borelscher Satz	théorème *m* de Borel	теорема Бореля
T 264	**theorem of Brunn-Minkowski,** Brunn-Minkowski theorem <CS>	Brunn-Minkowskischer Satz *m*	théorème *m* de Brunn-Minkowski	теорема Брунна-Минковского
	theorem of Cantor <SE>	*s.* C 101		
	theorem of Cantor <TO>	*s.* C 98		
T 265	**theorem of Cantor-Bendixson,** Cantor-Bendixson theorem <TO>	Satz *m* von Cantor-Bendixson, Cantor-Bendixsonscher Satz	théorème *m* de Cantor-Bendixson	теорема Кантора-Бендиксона
T 266	**theorem of Cantor-Lebesgue,** Cantor-Lebesgue theorem <AN>	Satz *m* von Cantor-Lebesgue, Cantor-Lebesguescher Satz	théorème *m* de Cantor-Lebesgue	теорема Кантора-Лебега
T 267	**theorem of Cauchy,** Cauchy['s] theorem <GR>	Satz *m* von Cauchy, Cauchyscher Satz	théorème *m* de Cauchy	теорема Коши

	theorem of Cauchy <SS>	*s.* C 234		
	theorem of Cauchy-Kowalewskaya <DE>	*s.* C 251		
	theorem of Cauchy-Kowalewski <DE>	*s.* C 251		
T 268	**theorem of Chebyshev,** Chebyshev['s] theorem <for polynomials of best approximation> <AX, NU>	Theorem *n* von Tschebyscheff, Tschebyscheffsches Theorem	théorème *m* de Tchebyshev	теорема Чебышева
T 269	**theorem of Chevalley** <for algebraic groups> <GR>	Struktursatz *m* von Chevalley, Chevalleyscher Struktursatz	théorème *m* de Chevalley	теорема Шевалле
	theorem of choice [for sequences of functions] <FA, SS>	*s.* A 1027		
T 270/1	**theorem of Cohen** <for local rings> <AL>	Struktursatz *m* von Cohen, Cohenscher Struktursatz	théorème *m* de Cohen	структурная теорема Коэна
	theorem of coresiduation <AG>	*s.* R 901		
	theorem of Denjoy-Carleman-Ahlfors <FT>	*s.* D 226		
T 272	**theorem of dependence,** dependence theorem <DE>	Abhängigkeitssatz *m*	théorème *m* de dépendance	теорема зависимости
T 273	**theorem of de Rham** <DG>	Satz *m* von de Rham, de Rhamscher Satz	théorème *m* de de Rham	теорема де Рама
	theorem of Desargues <PJ>	*s.* D 303		
	theorem of Euclid <EG>	*s.* E 573		
T 274	**theorem of Euler,** Euler['s] theorem <on Euler paths> <GP>	Satz *m* von Euler, Eulerscher Satz	théorème *m* d'Euler	теорема Эйлера
	theorem of Euler <AN>	*s.* E 623		
	theorem of Euler <EG>	*s.* E 622		
T 275	**theorem of F. and M. Riesz** <FT>	Satz *m* von F. und M. Riesz	théorème *m* de F. et M. Riesz	теорема Ф. и М. Риса
T 276	**theorem of Farey,** Farey['s] theorem <NT>	Fareyscher Satz *m*	théorème *m* de Farey	теорема Фарея
T 277	**theorem of Favard** <AN>	Satz *m* von Favard, Favardscher Satz	théorème *m* de Favard	теорема Фавара
T 278	**theorem of Ford and Fulkerson,** maximum flow theorem <GP, PG>	Ford-Fulkersonscher Satz *m*, Maximalfluß-Minimalschnitt-Theorem *n*	théorème *m* de Ford et Fulkerson, théorème du flot maximum, théorème du « min-cut max-flow »	теорема Форда-Фалкерсона, теорема о максимальном потоке и минимальном разрезе
	theorem of Fourier-Budan <AL>	*s.* B 790		
T 279	**theorem of Frégier,** Frégier['s] theorem <AY>	Theorem *n* von Frégier, Frégiersches Theorem	théorème *m* de Frégier	теорема Фрежье
T 280	**theorem of Frink,** Frink['s] theorem <GP>	Satz *m* von Frink, Frinkscher Satz	théorème *m* de Frink	теорема Фринка
T 281	**theorem of Frobenius,** Frobenius['] theorem <for algebras, groups, in solving linear equations> <AL, GR>	Satz *m* von Frobenius, Frobeniusscher Satz	théorème *m* de Frobenius	теорема Фробениуса
	theorem of Gelfand-Neumark <FA>	*s.* G 113		
T 282	**theorem of Gelfond,** Gelfond['s] theorem <NT>	Gelfondscher Satz *m*	théorème *m* de Gelfond	теорема Гельфонда
T 283	**theorem of Gordan,** Gordan['s] theorem <on binary forms and form systems> <AL>	Gordans[cher] Satz *m*	théorème *m* de Gordan	теорема Гордана
T 284	**theorem of Grötzsch,** Grötzsch['s] [distortion] theorem <FT>	Verzerrungssatz *m* von Grötzsch, Grötzschscher Verzerrungssatz	théorème *m* de Grötzsch	теорема Гретша
T 285	**theorem of Grün,** Grün['s] theorem <GR>	Satz *m* von Grün, Grünscher Satz	théorème *m* de Grün	теорема Грюна
T 286	**theorem of Hamel,** Hamel['s] theorem <FA>	Satz *m* von Hamel, Hamelscher Satz	théorème *m* de Hamel	теорема Гамеля
T 287	**theorem of Hardy,** Hardy['s] theorem <DE, NT>	Satz *m* von Hardy, Hardyscher Satz	théorème *m* de Hardy	теорема Харди
	theorem of Hartogs <FT, SE>	*s.* H 121		
T 288	**theorem of Hasse-Arf,** Hasse-Arf theorem <AL>	Satz *m* von Hasse-Arf, Hasse-Arfscher Satz	théorème *m* de Hasse-Arf	теорема Хассе-Арфа
T 289	**theorem of Heine,** Heine['s] theorem <AN, TO>	Satz *m* von Heine, Heinescher Satz, Satz von der gleichmäßigen Stetigkeit <einer auf einem abgeschlossenen Intervall stetigen Funktion>	théorème *m* de Heine	теорема Гейне (Кантора), теорема Гейне-Кантора
	theorem of Heine-Borel-Lebesgue <TO>	*s.* B 588		
	theorem of Hellinger and Toeplitz <FA>	*s.* H 187		
T 290	**theorem of Herbrand,** Herbrand['s] theorem <LO>	Herbrandscher Satz *m*	théorème *m* d'Herbrand	теорема Эрбрана
T 291	**theorem of Herglotz,** Herglotz['s] theorem <GE>	Satz *m* von Herglotz, Herglotzscher Satz	théorème *m* de Herglotz	теорема Херглоца (Герглотца)

T 292	**theorem of Hessenberg,** Hessenberg['s] theorem <GE>	Satz *m* von Hessenberg, Hessenbergscher Satz	théorème *m* de Hessenberg	теорема Гессенберга
T 293	**theorem of Hilbert,** Hilbert['s] theorem <on surfaces of constant negative curvature> <DG>	Satz *m* von Hilbert, Hilbertscher Satz	théorème *m* de Hilbert	теорема Гильберта <о поверхностях отрицательной кривизны>
T 294	**theorem of Hilbert-Waring** <NT>	Hilbert-Waringscher Satz *m*, Hilbertsche Antwort *f* auf das Waringsche Problem	théorème *m* de Waring-Hilbert	теорема Гильберта-Варинга
T 295	**theorem of Hölder,** Hölder['s] theorem <on ordered rings <AL>	Satz *m* von Hölder, Hölderscher Satz	théorème *m* de Hölder	теорема Гельдера
T 296	**theorem of Hurewicz,** Hölder['s] theorem <TO>	Satz *m* von Hurewicz, Hurewiczscher Satz	théorème *m* de Hurewicz	теорема Гуревича
	theorem of Hurewicz <AT>	*s.* H 600		
T 297	**theorem of Hurewicz-Tumarkin,** Hurewicz-Tumarkin theorem <TO>	Satz *m* von Hurewicz-Tumarkin, Hurewicz-Tumarkinscher Satz	théorème *m* de Hurewicz-Tumarkin	теорема Гуревича-Тумаркина
	theorem of Hurwitz <FT>	*s.* H 607		
T 298	**theorem of implicit functions,** theorem on implicit functions, implicit-function theorem <for systems of differentiable functions> <AN>	Auflösungssatz *m*, Umkehrsatz *m* <für Systeme differenzierbarer Funktionen>, Satz *m* über implizite Funktionen	théorème *m* de la fonction implicite, théorème d'existence des fonctions implicites	теорема существования неявных функций
	theorem of intermediate values <RF>	*s.* L 1017		
	theorem of J. König <SE>	*s.* K 136		
	theorem of Jordan <TO>	*s.* J 103		
	theorem of Jordan-Hölder-Schreier-Zassenhaus <AL>	*s.* J 90		
T 299	**theorem of Jordan-Schoenflies** <TO>	Satz *m* von Jordan-Schoenflies, Jordan-Schoenfliesscher Satz	théorème *m* de Jordan-Schoenflies	теорема Жордана-Шенфлиса
T 300	**theorem of Kan** <CA>	Satz *m* von Kan, Kanscher Satz	théorème *m* de Kan d'extension de foncteur	теорема Кана
T 301	**theorem of Kaplansky,** Kaplansky['s] theorem <AL>	Satz *m* von Kaplansky, Kaplanskyscher Satz	théorème *m* de Kaplansky	теорема Капланского
	theorem of Killing <GR>	*s.* K 73		
	theorem of Koebe <FT>	*s.* K 115		
T 302	**theorem of Korovkin type,** Korovkin-type theorem <for a vector lattice> <LA>	Korovkin-Satz *m*, Satz *m* vom Korovkin-Typ	théorème *m* de type Korovkin	теорема типа Коровкина
T 303	**theorem of Kronecker** <on power series> <SS>	Satz *m* von Kronecker, Kroneckerscher Satz	théorème *m* de Kronecker	теорема Кронекера
T 304	**theorem of Kronecker-Weber,** Kronecker-Weber theorem <AB>	Kronecker-Weberscher Satz *m*	théorème *m* de Kronecker-Weber	теорема Кронекера-Вебера
T 305	**theorem of Krull-Akizuki,** Krull-Akizuki theorem <AL>	Satz *m* von Krull-Akizuki, Krull-Akizukischer Satz	théorème *m* de Krull-Akizuki	теорема Крулля-Акидзуки
T 306	**theorem of Krull-Seidenberg** <AL>	Satz *m* von Krull-Seidenberg, Krull-Seidenbergscher Satz	théorème *m* de Krull-Seidenberg	теорема Крулля-Сейденберга
T 307	**theorem of Kummer,** Kummer['s] theorem <AB>	Satz *m* von Kummer, Kummerscher Satz	théorème *m* de Kummer	теорема Куммера
T 308	**theorem of Künneth,** Künneth['s] theorem <AT>	Satz *m* von Künneth, Künnethscher Satz	théorème *m* de Künneth	теорема Кюннета
	theorem of Legendre <EG>	*s.* L 540		
	theorem of Lehmus <EG>	*s.* L 545		
T 309	**theorem of Leray-Hirsch,** Leray-Hirsch theorem <AT>	Satz *m* von Leray-Hirsch, Leray-Hirschscher Satz	théorème *m* de Leray-Hirsch	теорема Лерэ-Хирша (Лере-Хирша)
T 310	**theorem of Lerch,** Lerch['s] theorem <NT>	Lerchsche Formel *f*	formule *f* de Lerch	формула Лерха
T 311	**theorem of Levi,** Levi['s] theorem <for a Lie algebra> <AL>	Levi-Malcevsches Theorem *n*	théorème *m* de Levi-Malcev	теорема Леви-Мальцева
T 312	**theorem of Lindelöf,** Lindelöf['s] theorem <DE>	Satz *m* von Lindelöf, Lindelöfscher Satz	théorème *m* de Lindelöf	теорема Линделефа
T 313	**theorem of Lindelöf,** Lindelöf['s] theorem <TO>	Lindelöfscher Überdeckungssatz *m*, Satz *m* von Lindelöf, Lindelöfscher Satz; Überdekkungssatz von Lindelöf-Young	théorème *m* de [M.] Lindelöf	теорема Линделефа
T 314	**theorem of Lindelöf,** Lindelöf['s] theorem <on isoperimetry> <VA>	Theorem *n* von Lindelöf, Lindelöfsches Theorem	théorème *m* de Lindelöf	теорема Линделефа
T 315	**theorem of Lindenbaum,** Lindenbaum['s] theorem <LO>	Satz *m* von Lindenbaum, Lindenbaumscher Satz	théorème *m* de Lindenbaum	теорема Линденбаума

	theorem of Lindenbaum <LO>	*s.* L 770		
T 316	**theorem of Linnik,** Linnik['s] theorem <NT>	Satz *m* von Linnik, Linnikscher Satz	théorème *m* de Linnik	теорема Линника
T 317	**theorem of Liouville,** Liouville['s] theorem <for Diophantine approximations> <NT>	Satz *m* von Liouville, Liouvillescher Satz	théorème *m* de Liouville	теорема Лиувилля
	theorem of Löwenheim-Skolem[-Gödel] <LO>	*s.* L 1123		
	theorem of Lusin <ME>	*s.* L 1196		
T 318	**theorem of Magnus,** Magnus['s] theorem <GR>	Satz *m* von Magnus, Magnusscher Satz	théorème *m* de Magnus	теорема Магнуса
T 319	**theorem of Mazur-Gelfand,** Mazur-Gelfand theorem <AL, FA>	Satz *m* von Gelfand-Mazur, Gelfand-Mazurscher Satz	théorème *m* de Gelfand-Mazur (Guelfand-Mazur)	теорема Гельфанда-Мазура
T 320	**theorem of Menger-Nöbeling,** Menger-Nöbeling theorem <TO>	Menger-Nöbelingscher Einbettungssatz *m*, Einbettungssatz von Menger-Nöbeling	théorème *m* [de plongement] de Menger-Nöbeling	теорема [вложения] Менгера и Небелинга
	theorem of Meusnier <DG>	*s.* M 518		
T 321	**theorem of Meyer,** Meyer['s] theorem <on quadratic forms> <NT>	Satz *m* von [A.] Meyer, Meyerscher Satz	théorème *m* de Meyer	теорема Мейера
	theorem of Minkowski <CS, GE>	*s.* M 632		
T 322	**theorem of Minkowski-Hajós,** Minkowski-Hajós theorem <GU>	Minkowski-Hajósscher Satz *m*	théorème *m* de Minkowski-Hajós	теорема Минковского-Хайоша
T 323	**theorem of Montel,** Montel['s] theorem <FT>	Satz *m* von Montel, Montelscher Satz	théorème *m* de Montel	теорема Монтеля
T 324	**theorem of Nielsen-Schreier** <GR>	Satz *m* von Schreier-Nielsen (Nielsen-Schreier), Schreier-Nielsenscher Satz	théorème *m* de Nielsen-Schreier	теорема Нильсена-Шрейера
	theorem of Pappus <DI, EG>	*s.* P 38		
	theorem of Pappus <PJ>	*s.* P 39		
T 325/6	**theorem of Picard,** Picard['s] theorem <AG>	Satz *m* von Picard, Picardscher Satz	théorème *m* de Picard	теорема Пикара
	theorem of Picone <DE>	*s.* I 67		
T 327	**theorem of Poincaré** <AT, HA>	Poincaréscher Satz *m*	théorème *m* de Poincaré	теорема Пуанкаре
T 328	**theorem of Poincaré,** Poincaré['s] theorem, Poincaré['s] lemma <on differential forms> <DG>	Satz *m* (Lemma *n*) von Poincaré, Poincaréscher Satz <über äußere Differentialformen>	théorème *m* de Poincaré	теорема Пуанкаре
T 329	**theorem of Poincaré** <for a difference equation> <FD>	Satz *m* von Poincaré, Poincaréscher Satz	théorème *m* de Poincaré	теорема Пуанкаре
T 330	**theorem of Poincaré** <GR>	Satz *m* von Poincaré, Poincaréscher Satz	théorème *m* de Poincaré	теорема Пуанкаре
T 331	**theorem of Poincaré-Birkhoff** <TO>	Fixpunktsatz *m* von Poincaré-Birkhoff, Poincaré-Birkhoffscher Fixpunktsatz	théorème *m* de points fixes de Poincaré-Birkhoff	теорема неподвижных точек Пуанкаре-Биркгофа
T 332	**theorem of Poincaré-Bohl** <AT>	Satz *m* von Poincaré-Bohl, Poincaré-Bohlscher Satz	théorème *m* de Poincaré-Bohl	теорема Пуанкаре-Боля
T 333	**theorem of Poincaré-Brouwer** <AT>	Satz *m* von Poincaré-Brouwer, Poincaré-Brouwerscher Satz	théorème *m* de Poincaré-Brouwer	теорема Пуанкаре-Брауэра (о еже)
T 334	**theorem of Poincaré-Liapunov** <DE>	Satz *m* von Poincaré-Ljapunow, Poincaré-Ljapunowscher Satz	théorème *m* de Poincaré-Liapounoff	теорема Пуанкаре-Ляпунова
T 335	**theorem of Poincaré-Volterra,** Poincaré-Volterra theorem <TO>	Satz *m* von Poincaré und Volterra, Poincaré-Volterrascher Satz	théorème *m* de Poincaré-Volterra	теорема Пуанкаре-Вольтерра
	theorem of Poisson-Jacobi <DE>	*s.* P 825		
T 336	**theorem of principal axes,** principal axes (axis) theorem <AL, AY>	Hauptachsentheorem *n*, Hauptachsensatz *m*	théorème *m* des axes principaux	теорема главных осей
	theorem of Pringsheim <FT, SS>	*s.* P 1522		
	theorem of Pythagoras <EG>	*s.* P 2083		
	theorem of residuation <AG>	*s.* R 901		
	theorem of residues <FT>	*s.* C 266		
	theorem of residues <FU>	*s.* R 902		
	theorem of Riemann <FT>	*s.* R 1044		
	theorem of Riemann-Roch <AG, FT>	*s.* R 1028		

T 337	**theorem of Riesz** <for the Radon measure> <ME>	Satz *m* von F. Riesz, Rieszscher Satz	théorème *m* de Riesz	теорема Риса
T 338	**theorem of Riesz** <TO>	Satz *m* von Riesz, Riesz-scher Satz	théorème *m* de Riesz	теорема Риса; условие Риса
T 339	**theorem of Scherk** <for the Bernoulli numbers> <FD, FU, NT>	Scherks Satz *m*	théorème *m* de Scherk	теорема Шерка
T 340	**theorem of Schoenflies** <TO>	Satz *m* von Schoenflies, Schoenfliesscher Satz	théorème *m* de Schoenflies	теорема Шенфлиса
T 341	**theorem of Schur** <for a Riemannian manifold> <DG>	Satz *m* von Schur, Schurscher Satz	théorème *m* de Schur	теорема Шура
T 342	**theorem of Schur** <GR>	Satz *m* von Schur	théorème *m* de Schur	теорема Шура
T 343	**theorem of Skolem-Noether** <AL>	Satz *m* von Skolem-Noether, Skolem-Noetherscher Satz	théorème *m* de Skolem-Noether	теорема Сколема-Нетера
T 344	**theorem of Sperner** <AT>	Satz *m* von Sperner, Spernerscher Satz	théorème *m* de Sperner	теорема Шпернера
T 345	**theorem of Stickelberger** <AL>	Satz *m* von Stickelberger, Stickelbergerscher Satz	théorème *m* de Stickel-berger	теорема Штикельбергера
	theorem of Stokes <DI, VT>	*s.* S 1815		
	theorem of Stone-Weierstrass <FA>	*s.* S 1823		
T 346	**theorem of Tarski** <MM>	Satz *m* von Tarski, Tarskischer Satz	théorème *m* de Tarski	теорема Тарского
T 347	**theorem of Tauber,** Tauber['s] theorem <FT>	Satz *m* von Tauber, Tauberscher Satz	théorème *m* de Tauber	теорема Таубера
	theorem of Thales <EG>	*s.* T 249		
T 347a	**theorem of the complete quadrangle** <PJ>	Satz *m* vom vollständigen Viereck	théorème *m* du quadrangle complet	теорема о полном четы-рехугольнике (четырех-вершиннике)
T 348	**theorem of the cube** <AG>	Satz *m* vom Würfel	théorème *m* du cube	теорема о кубе
T 349	**theorem of the invariance of the region** <under holomorphic mappings> <FT>	Satz *m* von der Gebiets-treue <holomorpher Funktionen>	théorème *m* de l'invariance de domaine	принцип сохранения области
T 350	**theorem of the least upper bound** <AN>	Satz *m* von der oberen (unteren und oberen, oberen und unteren) Grenze	théorème *m* de Weierstrass	принцип Вейерштрасса
	theorem of the mean for harmonic functions <PO>	*s.* G 77		
	theorem of the open mapping of Banach <FA, TO>	*s.* O 143		
T 351	**theorem of the prime base** <AL>	Satz *m* von der Primbasis	théorème *m* de la base première	теорема простого базиса
T 352	**theorem of the primitive element** <AL>	Satz *m* vom primitiven Element	théorème *m* de l'élement primitif, théorème des éléments primitifs	теорема о примитивном элементе
T 353	**theorem of the square** <AG>	Satz *m* vom Quadrat	théorème *m* du carré	теорема о квадрате
T 354	**theorem of Thue-Siegel-Roth,** Thue-Siegel theorem <NT>	Thue-Siegel-Rothscher Approximationssatz *m* für algebraische Zahlen, Rothscher Approximationssatz für algebraische Zahlen, Siegelscher Approximationssatz für algebraische Zahlen, Thue-Siegel-Rothscher Satz *m*, Rothscher Satz, Siegel-Thuescher Satz, Thue-Siegelscher Satz über die Approximation algebraischer Zahlen	théorème *m* de Thue-Siegel, théorème de Thue-Siegel-Roth, théorème de Roth	теорема Туэ-Зигеля-Рота
T 355	**theorem of Toeplitz** <for normal matrices> <MD>	Satz *m* von Toeplitz, Toeplitzscher Satz	théorème *m* de Toeplitz	теорема Теплица
T 356	**theorem of Tychonoff,** Tychonoff['s] product theorem, theorem of A. N. Tihonov <TO>	Satz *m* von Tychonoff (Tychonov), Tychonoff-scher (Tichonovscher, Tychonowscher) Satz	théorème *m* de Tychonoff (Tychonov)	теорема А. Н. Тихонова, теорема Тихонова (Тихонова о произ-ведении)
	theorem of unique prime factorization <AL>	*s.* L 216		
T 357	**theorem of unique prime ideal factorization** <AL>	ZPI-Satz *m*, Satz *m* von der eindeutigen Primidealzerlegung, Zerlegungssatz *m* in Primideale, Z.P.I.	théorème *m* de la factorisation unique en idéaux premiers	теорема о единствен-ности разложения на простые идеалы
	theorem of unique prime number factorization <NT>	*s.* E 570		
	theorem of Vitali <FT, SS>	*s.* V 197		
T 358	**theorem of Vitali-Carathéodory** <ME>	Vitali-Carathéodoryscher Satz *m*	théorème *m* de Vitali-Carathéodory	теорема Витали-Кара-теодори
T 359	**theorem of von Dyck** <GR>	Satz *m* von v. Dyck, Satz von Dyck, [von] Dyckscher Satz	théorème *m* de von Dyck	теорема Дика

No.	English	German	French	Russian
T 360	**theorem of Weierstrass** <on the term-by-term differentiation of sequences of holomorphic functions>, Weierstrass['s] theorem <for series>, Weierstrass['s] uniform convergence theorem; Weierstrass['s] double series theorem <FT, SS>	Weierstraßscher Summensatz *m*, Satz *m* von Weierstraß <über gleichmäßig konvergente Reihen holomorpher Funktionen>; Weierstraßscher Doppelreihensatz *m*	théorème *m* de Weierstrass <pour la convergence uniforme>	теорема [сходимости] Вейерштрасса
	theorem of Weierstrass <DI, TO>	*s.* W 175		
	theorem on congruence <EG>	*s.* C 1932		
T 361	**theorem on constants** <LO>	Konstantensatz *m*	théorème *m* sur des constantes	теорема о константах
	theorem on diagonalization <SE>	*s.* D 390		
	theorem on distortion <FT>	*s.* D 752		
T 362	**theorem on embedding (imbedding)** <of a finite unrestricted skeleton complex> <AT>	Realisierungssatz *m*, Einbettungssatz *m*	théorème *m* de plongement	теорема о включении
	theorem on implicit functions <AN>	*s.* T 298		
T 363	**theorem on normal form** <Kleene> <FO>	Kleenescher Rekursionssatz *m*	théorème *m* de recursion de Kleene	
T 363 a	**theorem on pentagonal numbers** <AB>	Pentagonalzahlensatz *m*	théorème *m* sur les nombres pentagonaux	теорема о пентагональных числах
T 364	**theorem on representability** <MM>	Darstellbarkeitssatz *m*	théorème *m* sur la représentabilité	теорема о представимости
	theorem on the chords <EG>	*s.* C 657		
T 365	**theorem on the invariance of dimensionality** <AT>	[Brouwerscher] Satz *m* von der Invarianz der Dimensionszahl <des Euklidischen Raumes>	théorème *m* sur l'invariance de dimension	теорема об инвариантности числа измерений
T 366	**theorem on the invariance of orientability** <AT>	Satz *m* von der Invarianz der Orientierbarkeit	théorème *m* sur l'invariance de l'orientabilité	теорема инвариантности ориентируемости
T 367	**theorem on the invariance of the homology groups** <AT>	Satz *m* von der Invarianz der Homologiegruppen	théorème *m* sur l'invariance des groupes d'homologie	теорема об инвариантности групп гомологий
	theorem on the transitivity of implication <FO, LO>	*s.* L 213		
	theorem on units <AB>	*s.* U 299		
	theorem on zeros <AL>	*s.* N 800		
T 368	**theorem saying that a system of linear equation is consistent, if and only if the rank of the matrix of coefficients is equal to the rank of the augmented matrix** <AL>	Rangkriterium *n* für die Lösbarkeit eines linearen Gleichungssystems	théorème *m* de Fontené-Rouché, théorème *m* de Kronecker	теорема Кронекера-Капелли
T 369	**theorems for limits** <of sum, difference, product, and quotient of sequences> <SS>	Limessätze *mpl*	théorèmes *mpl* pour les limites	теоремы для пределов
T 370	**theorems for term-by-term integration**, limit theorems <relative to Lebesgue-Stieltjes integrals; common name of Fatou's lemma, B. Levi's theorem, and Lebesgue's theorem> <AN>	Sätze *mpl* über gliedweise Integration, Grenzwertsätze *mpl*	théorèmes *mpl* relatifs à l'intégration terme à terme, théorèmes limites	теоремы о почленном интегрировании, предельные теоремы
T 371	**theorems of Mertens**, Merten['s] theorems <AB>	Mertenssche Sätze *mpl*	théorèmes *mpl* de Mertens	теоремы Мертенса
T 372	**theorem that any [linearly] independent set can be enlarged (extended) to a basis** <AL>	Basisergänzungssatz *m*	théorème *m* de la base incomplète	теорема, что всякая [линейно] независимая система векторов есть часть некоторой базы
	theory categorical in power m <MM>	*s.* M 286		
	theory of adjustment <ER, NU>	*s.* C 26		
	theory of aggregates <SE>	*s.* S 703		
	theory of algorithms <FO>	*s.* R 322		
	theory of algorithms <FO, NU>	*s.* A 488		
T 373	**theory of automata**, automata theory <TA>	Automatentheorie *f*	théorie *f* des automates	теория автоматов
T 374	**theory of cardinals** <SE>	kardinale Theorie *f*, Theorie der Kardinalzahlen	théorie *f* des nombres cardinaux	теория кардинальных чисел

	theory of chance[s] <ST>	*s.* P 1547		
T 375	**theory of characteristics** <AG>	Charakteristikentheorie *f*	théorie *f* des caractéristiques	теория характеристик
	theory of choice <ST>	*s.* D 44		
T 376	**theory of classes** <SE>	Klassentheorie *f*	théorie *f* des classes	теория классов
	theory of coding <ST>	*s.* I 512		
	theory of combinations <CT>	*s.* C 1187		
T 377	**theory of continued fractions** <NT>	Kettenbruchlehre *f*	théorie *f* des fractions continues	теория цепных дробей
T 378	**theory of correspondences** <AG>	Korrespondenztheorie *f*	théorie *f* des correspondances	теория соответствий
	theory of deduction <LO>	*s.* P 1868		
T 379	**theory of descent** <AG>	Abstiegstheorie *f*	théorie *f* de la descente	теория спуска
T 380	**theory of elementary divisors** <AL>	Elementarteilertheorie *f*	théorie *f* des diviseurs élémentaires	теория элементарных делителей [матриц]
T 381	**theory of equal sums of like powers,** Tarry-Escott problem <AB>	Tarry-Escott-Problemkreis *m*, Theorie *f* der multigraden Gleichungen	théorie *f* des multigrades	теория многостепенных уравнений
T 382	**theory of errors;** calculus of errors <ER>	Fehlertheorie *f*; Fehlerrechnung *f*	théorie *f* des erreurs (incertitudes); calcul *m* des erreurs	теория ошибок; исчисление ошибок (погрешностей)
T 383	**theory of estimation,** estimation theory <ST>	Schätztheorie *f*, Schätzungstheorie *f*	théorie *f* de l'estimation	теория статистического оценивания, теория оценок
T 384	**theory of Fuchs,** Fuchs['s] theory <DE>	Fuchssche Theorie *f*	théorie *f* de Fuchs	теория Фукса
	theory of functions <FT>	*s.* F 782		
T 384a	**theory of geometrical construction** <EG>	Theorie *f* der geometrischen Konstruktionen	théorie *f* des constructions géométriques	теория геометрических построений, конструктивная геометрия
T 385	**theory of higher-order ramification** <NT>	höhere Verzweigungstheorie *f*	théorie *f* de la ramification supérieure	теория разветвления высшего порядка
T 386	**theory of hyperbolic functions,** hyperbolic trigonometry <FU, GE>	Theorie *f* der hyperbolischen Funktionen	trigonométrie *f* hyperbolique, théorie *f* des fonctions hyperboliques	теория гиперболических функций
	theory of intersections <AG>	*s.* I 819		
	theory of invariants <IV>	*s.* I 888		
T 387	**theory of judg[e]ment** <LO>	Urteilslehre *f*	théorie *f* des jugements	учение о суждении
	theory of lattices <LA>	*s.* L 153		
T 388	**theory of links** <AT>	Verschlingungstheorie *f*	théorie *f* d'entrelacements	теория зацеплений
	theory of logical types <LO>	*s.* T 404		
	theory of modules <AL>	*s.* M 783		
T 389	**theory of multiplicity** <AG>	Multiplizitätstheorie *f*, Vielfachheitstheorie *f*	théorie *f* de la multiplicité	теория кратностей
	theory of numbers <NT>	*s.* N 849		
T 390	**theory of ordinals** <SE>	ordinale Theorie *f*, Theorie der Ordnungszahlen	théorie *f* des [nombres] ordinaux	теория порядковых чисел
	theory of *p*-adic numbers <NT>	*s.* P 13		
	theory of perturbations <DE, FA>	*s.* P 528		
T 391	**theory of polarity (poles and polars)** <AY>	Theorie *f* von Pol und Polare, Theorie der Polarverwandtschaft	théorie *f* de la polarité, théorie des pôles et des polaires	теория полюса и поляры
	theory of probabilities <ST>	*s.* P 1547		
T 392	**theory of proportions** <AR>	Verhältnisrechnung *f*, Verhältnislehre *f*, Proportionslehre *f*	calcul *m* de proportion	теория отношений
	theory of propositions <LO>	*s.* P 1868		
T 393	**theory of quantities** <AL>	Größenlehre *f*	théorie *f* des grandeurs	теория величин
	theory of queues <ST>	*s.* Q 292		
T 394	**theory of relations** <LO, SE>	Relationentheorie *f*, Relativkalkül *m* <Schröder>	théorie *f* des relations	теория отношений
T 395	**theory of reliability** <ST>	Zuverlässigkeitstheorie *f*	théorie *f* de la fiabilité	теория надежности
T 396	**theory of representations,** representation theory <RE>	Darstellungstheorie *f*	théorie *f* de la représentation linéaire, théorie des représentations; théorie des représentations des groupes	теория представлений
T 397	**theory of runs,** iteration theory <ST>	Iterationstheorie *f*	théorie *f* des suites (itérations)	теория итераций
T 398	**theory of screws** <VT>	Schraubenrechnung *f*	calcul *m* (théorie *f*) des vis	винтовое исчисление
T 399	**theory of search** <PG>	Suchtheorie *f*	théorie *f* de recherche	теория поиска (отыскания)
	theory of sets <SE>	*s.* S 703		
T 400	**theory of sheaves,** sheaf theory <AL, AT>	Garbentheorie *f*	théorie *f* des faisceaux	теория пучков
T 401	**theory of solving** <an equation> <GN>	Auflösungstheorie *f*	théorie *f* de résolution	теория решения
	theory of statistical decision[s] <ST>	*s.* D 44		
T 402	**theory of testing** <ST>	Testtheorie *f*, statistische Testtheorie	théorie *f* des tests [statistiques]	теория проверки [статистических] гипотез

T 403	**theory of transversals** <AG>	Transversalentheorie *f*	théorie *f* des transversales	теория трансверсалей
	theory of truth-functions <LO>	*s.* P 1868		
T 404	**theory of types,** theory of logical types, type theory <LO>	Typentheorie *f*, Typenlehre *f*, Stufentheorie *f*	théorie *f* des types	теория типов
	theory of uniformization <FT>	*s.* U 140		
	theory of valuation <AL>	*s.* V 246		
	theory of Zermelo[-Fraenkel] <SE>	*s.* S 704		
T 405	**theory without use of determinants** <AL>	determinantenfreie Theorie *f*	théorie *f* n'utilisant pas des déterminants	теория, не использующая определителей
	thesis <LO>	*s.* P 1881		
T 406	**theta characteristic,** period characteristic <FT, FU>	Thetacharakteristik *f*, Periodencharakteristik *f*	caractéristique *f* thêta	тэта-характеристика
T 407	**theta[-] constant** <AL, FU>	Thetakonstante *f*	thêta-constante *f*	тэта-константа
T 408	**theta formula** <AB>	Thetaformel *f*	thêta-formule *f*	тэта-формула
T 409	**theta function,** ϑ-function <of *n*-th order> <FU>	Thetafunktion *f*, Theta-Funktion *f*, ϑ-Funktion *f* <*n*-ter Ordnung>	fonction *f* thêta, fonction ϑ <d'ordre n>	тэта-функция, тета-функция, функция тэта, ϑ-функция <*n*-ая, порядка *n*>
	theta function *n* <FU>	*s.* J 36		
T 410	**theta relations** <FT>	Thetarelationen *fpl*	relations *fpl* thêta	тэта-соотношения Римана
T 411	**theta series,** ϑ series <FT>	Thetareihe *f*, Theta-Reihe *f*, ϑ-Reihe *f*	série *f* thêta, série ϑ	тэта-ряд, ϑ-ряд
T 412	**Thibaut['s] proof** <for the sum of angles in a triangle> <EG>	Thibautscher Beweis (Scheinbeweis) *m*	démonstration *f* de Thibaut	доказательство Тибо
T 413	**thickness** <of a convex solid *or* a graph> <GE, GP>	Dicke *f*	épaisseur *f*	толщина
T 414	**thick subcategory,** Serre['s] subcategory <CA>	dicke (Serresche) Unterkategorie *f*	sous-catégorie *f* épaisse	плотная подкатегория в смысле Гротендика
T 415	**thinning,** weakening <LO>	Verdünnung *f*	atténuation *f*, addition *f*	ослабление, уточнение
T 416	**thinning in the antecedent** <LO>	Verdünnung *f* im Antezedens	atténuation *f* dans l'antécédent	ослабление в антецеденте, разрешение усилить посылки
T 417	**thinning in the succedent** <LO>	Verdünnung *f* im Sukzedens	atténuation *f* dans le conséquent	ослабление в сукцеденте
T 418	**thinning rule,** rule of weakening <LO>	Verdünnungsregel *f*	règle *f* d'atténuation, règle d'addition	правило ослабления
T 419	**thin set** <PO>	dünne Menge *f*	ensemble *m* effilé	разреженное множество
	thin set <TO>	*s.* 1. M 293; 2. S 103		
T 420	**third boundary condition** <for a partial differential equation>; boundary condition of the third kind <also for an ordinary differential equation of the second order> <DE, PO>	dritte (3.) Randbedingung *f*; Randbedingung dritter (3.) Art	troisième condition *f* aux limites; condition aux limites de troisième espèce	третье краевое условие; краевое (граничное) условие третьего рода
T 421	**third boundary [value] problem,** mixed boundary [value] problem, third (mixed) problem <for a partial differential equation>; boundary [value] problem of the third kind <also for an ordinary differential equation of the second order> <DE, PO>	drittes Randwertproblem *n*, gemischtes Randwertproblem, drittes fundamentales Randwertproblem, dritte Randwertaufgabe *f*, gemischte Randwertaufgabe, Randwertproblem dritter Art, Randwertaufgabe dritter Art	troisième problème *m* aux limites, troisième problème, problème aux limites mixte, problème mixte, problème de Fourier; problème aux limites de troisième espèce	третья краевая задача, смешанная (третья основная) краевая задача; краевая задача третьего рода
	third boundary value problem <PO>	*s.* R 1357		
T 422	**third cartesian power** <of a set> <SE>	dritte kartesische (cartesische) Potenz *f*	cube *m* direct	третья декартова степень
	third-degree polynomial equation <AL>	*s.* C 2739		
T 423	**third fundamental form** <in Euclidean surface theory> <DG>	dritte Grundform (Fundamentalform) *f*	troisième forme *f* fondamentale	третья основная [квадратичная] форма, третья дифференциальная форма
T 424	**third isomorphism theorem,** double quotient theorem <for groups> <GR>	zweiter Isomorphiesatz *m*	premier théorème *m* d'isomorphisme, principe *m* d'isomorphisme de Hasse	теорема о соответствии между подгруппами при гомоморфном отображении
	third isomorphism theorem <GR>	*s.* Z 8		
T 425	**third-order language** <FO>	Sprache *f* der dritten Stufe, Meta-Metasprache *f*	langage *m* tertiaire, métamétalangage *m*	язык третьей ступени
	third plane [of projection] <DS>	*s.* S 792		
T 426	**third principal line,** third trace parallel, profile line <DS>	dritte Hauptlinie (Tafellinie, Streichlinie) *f*, Hauptlinie (Tafellinie, Streichlinie) dritter Ordnung	troisième ligne *f* principale	третья главная (основная) линия, профильная линия
T 427	**third principal plane** <in two-plane projection> <DS>	dritte Hauptebene *f*, Hauptebene dritter Ordnung	troisième plan *m* principal	третья главная плоскость

No.	English	German	French	Russian
	third problem <DE, PO>	*s.* T 421		
	third projection <DS>	*s.* S 789		
T 428	**third proportional** <AR>	dritte harmonische (stetige) Proportionale *f*	troisième proportionnelle *f* harmonique	гармонический третий член пропорции
	third quartile <ST>	*s.* U 431		
T 429	**third trace,** third trace point <of a line> <DS>	dritter Spurpunkt *m*, dritte Spur *f*	troisième trace *f* (point *m* trace)	третий (профильный) след <прямой>, след в профильной плоскости <проекций>
T 430	**third trace,** side trace, third (side) trace line <of a plane> <DS>	dritte Spurlinie (Spur) *f*, Seitenspur[linie] *f*	trace *f* de profil, troisième trace	профильный след <плоскости>, след в профильной плоскости <проекций>
	third trace line <DS>	*s.* T 430		
	third trace parallel <DS>	*s.* T 426		
	third trace point <DS>	*s.* T 429		
	Thomas['s] distribution <ST>	*s.* D 937		
	Thomas-Fermi [differential] equation <DE>	*s.* F 138		
T 431	**Thom['s] class** <of fibre bundles> <AT>	Thomsche Klasse *f*	classe *f* de Thom	класс Тома
T 432	**Thom['s] complex, Thom-complex** <AT>	Thomscher Komplex *m*	complexe *m* de Thom	комплекс Тома
	Thomé['s] normal integral <DE>	*s.* N 592		
	Thomé['s] normal series <DE>	*s.* N 646		
	Thom-Gysin homomorphism <AT>	*s.* G 546		
T 433	**Thom-Gysin sequence,** Gysin['s] sequence <of a sphere bundle> <AT>	Thom-Gysin-Sequenz *f*, Gysinsche exakte Sequenz *f*	suite *f* exacte de Gysin (Guisyn)	последовательность Тома-Гизина, точная последовательность Гизина
T 434	**Thom['s] isomorphism theorem** <of sphere bundles> <AT>	Thomscher Isomorphiesatz *m*	théorème *m* d'isomorphisme de Thom	теорема Тома об изоморфизме
T 435	**Thomsen['s] closure condition** <for a web> <GE, TO>	Thomsensche Schließungsbedingung *f*	condition *f* de fermeture de Thomsen	условие замыкания Томсена, условие Томсена
T 436	**Thomsen['s] graph** <GP>	Thomsenscher Graph *m*	graphe *m* de Thomsen	граф Томсена
T 437	**Thomsen['s] triangle** <AL, GE>	Thomsensches Dreieck *n*, Thomsens Dreieck	triangle *m* de Thomsen	треугольник Томсена
T 438	**Thomson['s] conic** <AY>	Thomsonscher Kegelschnitt *m*	conique *f* de Thomson	коническое сечение Томсона
	Thomson['s] transformation <PO>	*s.* K 39		
T 439	**Thom['s] theorem** <TO>	Satz *m* von Thom, Thomscher Satz	théorème *m* de Thom	теорема Тома
T 440	**thought experiment,** imaginary experiment, mental experiment, gedanken experiment <ST>	Gedankenversuch *m*, Gedankenexperiment *n*	expérience *f* imaginaire	абстрактный эксперимент
T 441	**thread** <GR>	Faden *m*	filet *m*	нить
T 442	**three-arc,** 3-arc <TO>	Dreibein *n*, topologisches Dreibein	triode *f*	триод
	three-by-three lemma <CA, HA>	*s.* N 260		
T 443	**three-centred curve,** false ellipse <GE>	Korbbogen *m*, Korblinie *f*, Korbbogenlinie *f*	courbe *f* en anse de panier, anse *f* de panier	коробовая кривая
	three-circle[s] theorem <FT>	*s.* H 18		
T 444	**three-colour theorem** <GP>	Dreifarbentheorem *n*, Dreifarbensatz *m*	théorème *m* des trois couleurs	теорема о трех красках
T 445	**three-combination,** 3-combination, ternary, ternion <CT>	Kombination (Komplexion) *f* zur (der) dritten (3.) Klasse, Kombination zu je 3, Terne *f*, Ternion *f*	terne *m*, groupe *m* de trois, ternion *m*	сочетание по 3, тройка
T 446	**three-cycle,** 3-cycle, cycle of length 3 <as a permutation> <AL, CT>	Dreierzyklus *m*, dreigliedriger Zyklus *m*, Zyklus *m* der Länge 3	cycle *m* ternaire	тройной цикл
T 447	**three-decision test** <ST>	Dreientscheidungstest *m*	test *m* à trois décisions	критерий с тремя решениями
	three-digit group <NT>	*s.* T 892		
	three-digit number <NT>	*s.* T 455		
T 448	**three-dimensional space,** three-space, tridimensional space, 3-space <GE>	dreidimensionaler Raum *m*	espace *m* tridimensionnel	трехмерное пространство
T 449	**three-dimensional torus** <topological product of three 1-spheres> <TO>	dreidimensionaler Torus *m*, dreidimensionale Torusmannigfaltigkeit *f*	tore *m* à trois dimensions	трехмерный тор
T 450	**three-eighths rule,** Newton['s] three-eighths rule, 3/8 rule <DI, NU>	Newtons Lieblingsformel *f*, Drei-Achtel-Regel *f*, Newtonsche Formel *f*, 3/8-Regel *f*	seconde formule *f* de Simpson, formule négligeant $\triangle^4$, formule de Simpson	[ньютонова] формула трех восьмых, [ньютоново] правило трех восьмых
T 451	**three-excess[-] code,** excess-three-code, 3XS-code <NT>	Dreier-Exzeß-Zahlensystem *n*, Dreierexzeßcode *m*, Stibitz-Code *m*, Stibitzcode *m*, Drei-Exzeß-Code *m*, Plus-Drei-Code *m*	code-excès-trois *m*, code *m* par.excès de trois, code *m* plus trois	код с избытком три, код «три в избытке»
T 452	**three-factor experiment** <ST>	dreifaktorieller Versuch *m*, Dreifaktorversuch *m*	expérience *f* trifactorielle	трехфакторный эксперимент
T 453	**three-figure number,** three-digit number, three-place number <NT>	dreistellige Zahl *f*	nombre *m* de trois chiffres	трехразрядное число, трехзначное число

T 454	**three-fold classification** <ST>	dreifache Klassifikation *f*	classification *f* à trois entrées	классификация по трем признакам
	threefold transitive group <GR>	*s.* T 976		
T 455	**threefold transitivity** <of a group> <GR>	dreifache Transitivität *f*	transitivité *f* triple	троекратная транзитивность
	three houses problem <GP>	*s.* P 1578		
	three-index symbol <DG>	*s.* C 667		
	three-leafed figure <GE>	*s.* T 936		
T 456	**three-leafed rose** <GE>	reguläres (regelmäßiges) Dreiblatt *n*, Dreiblatt, Kleeblatt *n*	rose *f* à trois branches (feuilles)	трехлепестковая роза, равносторонний трилистник
T 456a	**three-net,** 3-net <as a partial plane> <AL, PJ>	3-Gewebe *n*	3-tissu *m*	3-сеть, три-сеть
T 457	**three-parameter linear system,** 3-parameter linear system <AG, AY>	Gebüsch *n*, lineares System *n* dritter (3.) Stufe, lineares System von ∞^2 Kurven und Flächen des projektiven P_3	réseau *m*, système *m* linéaire à trois paramètres, système linéaire [ponctuel] de troisième espèce, système linéaire ponctuel de rang 3	линейная система ∞^2 кривых и поверхностей трехмерного проективного пространства, линейная система размерности 3
T 458	**three-parameter linear system of quadrics** <AG, AY>	Gebüsch *n* von Flächen zweiter (2.) Ordnung, lineares System *n* dritter (3.) Stufe von Flächen zweiter (2.) Ordnung, F_2-Gebüsch *n*	système *m* linéaire de quadriques à trois paramètres	линейная система ∞^2 поверхностей второго порядка
	three-place number <NT>	*s.* T 455		
	three-place operation <UA>	*s.* T 190		
	three-place predicate <LO>	*s.* P 1190		
	three-place relation <SE, UA>	*s.* T 192		
T 459	**three-plan method** <DS>	Dreitafelverfahren *n*	méthode *f* de projection sur trois plans	метод проектирования на три плоскости
T 460	**three-plan projection** <DS>	Dreitafelprojektion *f*	projection *f* sur trois plans	проектирование на три плоскости
T 461	**three-point condition** <DE>	Dreipunktebedingung *f*	condition *f* des trois points	условие трех точек
T 462	**three-point problem** <GE>	Dreipunkteproblem *n*	problème *m* des trois points	задача о трех точках
T 463	**three primes theorem** <due to Vinogradov> <NT>	Dreiprimzahlensatz *m* <von Vinogradov>	théorème *m* des trois nombres premiers	теорема трех простых чисел
T 464	**three-series theorem [of Khintchine and Kolmogorov],** Kolmogorov['s] three-series theorem <ST>	Dreireihensatz *m* der Wahrscheinlichkeitsrechnung [nach Chintschin (Chinčin, // Khintchine) und Kolmogorow (Kolmogorov, // Kolmogoroff)], Kolmogorovscher Dreireihensatz, Dreireihensatz [von Chinčin (Chintschin) und Kolmogorov (Kolmogorow)]	théorème *m* de trois séries [de Kolmogorov]	теорема трех рядов [Колмогорова]
T 465	**three-sigma rule,** 3σ-rule <ST>	Dreisigmaregel *f*, Drei-Sigma-Regel *f*, 3σ-Regel *f*	règle *f* des trois sigmas	правило трех сигм
	three-space <GE>	*s.* T 448		
	three-termed equation <AL>	*s.* T 962		
	three-term relation <LO>	*s.* P 1190		
T 466	**three-valued logic[al calculus]** <LO>	dreiwertige Logik *f*	logique *f* trivalente, logique trivalente de Łukasiewicz, calcul *m* trivalent, calcul trivalent de Łukasiewicz	трехзначная логика
T 467	**threshold character** <ST>	Schwellenmerkmal *n*	caractère *m* seuil	пороговый признак
	threshold function <LO, TA>	*s.* M 40		
T 468	**threshold logic** <LO, TA>	Schwellenwertlogik *f*	logique *f* à seuil	пороговая логика
T 469	**throw,** cast <of a die> <ST>	Wurf *m*	coup *m*	однократное бросание, бросание
T 470	**Thue['s] problem** <AL>	Thuesches Problem *n*	problème *m* de Thue	проблема Туэ
	Thue-Siegel theorem <NT>	*s.* T 354		
T 471	**Thue['s] theorem** <for Diophantine equations> <NT>	Thuescher Satz *m*, Satz von Thue	théorème *m* de Thue	теорема Туэ
	Tichonov['s] space <TO>	*s.* C 1510		
T 472	**tie** <ST>	Bindung *f*, Ranggleichheit *f*	lien *m*, égalité *f* du rang	связь, равенство ранга
T 473	**tied latin square** <CT, ST>	gebundenes lateinisches Quadrat *n*	carré *m* latin lié	связанный латинский квадрат
T 474	**Tietze['s] extension theorem,** Tietze['s] theorem, Urysohn-Tietze extension theorem <TO>	Tietzescher Erweiterungssatz *m*, Erweiterungssatz, Theorem *n* von Tietze (Tietze-Urysohn)	théorème *m* de Tietze, théorème fondamental de Tietze	теорема продолжения Титце, фундаментальная теорема Титце
T 475	**Tietze['s] operation,** Tietze['s] transformation <of the first *or* second kind> <GR>	Tietzesche Operation (Transformation) *f* <erster *oder* zweiter Art>	transformation *f* de Tietze <de première *ou* seconde espèce, de type I, II *ou* II'>	преобразование Титце, ти[т]цевское преобразование <первого *или* второго рода>

No.	English	German	French	Russian
	Tietze['s] theorem <TO>	*s.* T 474		
	Tietze['s] transformation <GR>	*s.* T 475		
T 476	**tilde,** wave, ~ <*to be read:* wave> <as a mathematical symbol> <GN>	Tilde *f*, ~ <*gelesen:* Schlange>	tilde *m*, ~ <*se lit:* tildé>	тильда, ~ <*читается:* с тильдой>
	tiling <EG>	*s.* T 200		
T 477	**time-like line[ar] element** <DE>	zeitartiges Linienelement *n*	élément *m* linéaire du genre temps	временноподобный (временеподобный) линейный элемент
T 478	**time series** <SP>	Zeitreihe *f*	série *f* chronologique (temporelle), chronique *f*, « time series » *m*	временной ряд
	time series analysis <SP>	*s.* A 616		
T 479	**time-shift theorem,** [second] shifting theorem, lag theorem, translation property <of Laplace transform> <IT>	Verschiebungssatz *m*, Heavisidescher Verschiebungssatz	théorème *m* de retard, « shifting theorem » *m*	теорема запаздывания (смещения), принцип смещения Хевисайда
T 480	**time trend** <ST>	Zeittrend *m*	tendance *f* due au temps	временной тренд
T 481	***T*-invariant measure** <ST>	*T*-invariantes Maß *n*	mesure *f* invariante par rapport à *T*	*T*-инвариантная мера
	tip <AL, CA, GN>	*s.* A 997		
	tip <VT>	*s.* T 170		
T 482	**Tissot['s] [differential] equation** <DE>	Tissotsche Differentialgleichung *f*	équation *f* [différentielle] de Tissot	[дифференциальное] уравнение Тиссо
T 483	**Tissot indicatrix,** indicatrix, distortion ellipse <DG>	Tissotsche Indikatrix *f*, Verzerrungsellipse *f*, Indikatrix	indicatrice *f* de Tissot, indicatrice, ellipse *f* des distorsions	индикатриса Тиссо, эллипс искажений
T 484	**Titchmarsh['s] theorem** <FT>	Satz *m* von Titchmarsh, Titchmarshscher Satz	théorème *m* de Titchmarsh	теорема Титчмарша
	Tits['] system <AL>	*s.* B 514		
	***T*-method** <ST>	*s.* T 1059		
T 485	***T*-number** <NT>	*T*-Zahl *f*	*T*-nombre *m*	*T*-число, *T*-число Малера
T 486	**Todd['s] class,** Eger-Todd class, canonical class of Eger-Todd <of a variety> <AT>	Toddsche Klasse *f*, Eger-Toddsche Klasse, kanonische Klasse *f* von Eger-Todd	classe *f* de Todd, classe canonique d'Eger-Todd	класс Эгера-Тодда, класс Тодда, канонический класс Эгера-Тодда
T 487	**Todd['s] genus,** T-genus <AT>	Toddsches Geschlecht *n*, T-Geschlecht *n*	genre *m* de Todd	род Тодда, Т-род
T 488	**Todd['s] polynomial** <AT>	Toddsches Polynom *n*	polynôme *m* de Todd	многочлен Тодда
T 489	**Toeplitz['s] limit theorem,** Toeplitz['s] theorem <LI>	Toeplitzscher Grenzwertsatz (Permanenzsatz) *m*, Toeplitzscher Satz *m*	théorème *m* limite de Toeplitz, théorème de Toeplitz	предельная теорема Теплица, теорема Теплица
T 490	**Toeplitz['s] matrix** <LI>	Toeplitzsche Matrix *f*	matrice *f* de Toeplitz	матрица Теплица
T 491	**Toeplitz['s] theorem** <for reciprocals> <FA>	Toeplitzsches Reziprokentheorem *n*	théorème *m* de Toeplitz <pour les opérateurs inverses>	теорема Теплица <для обратных операторов>
	Toeplitz['s] theorem <LI>	*s.* T 489		
T 492	**tolerance,** reflexive and symmetric binary relation <SE>	reflexive und symmetrische binäre Relation *f*	relation *f* binaire réflexive et symétrique	рефлексивное и симметрическое бинарное отношение
	tolerance <ST>	*s.* T 496		
T 493	**tolerance distribution** <ST>	Toleranzverteilung *f*	distribution *f* de tolérance	толерантное (допустимое) распределение
T 494	**tolerance estimation** <ST>	Toleranzschätzung *f*	estimation *f* de tolérance	толерантное оценивание, оценивание толерантной области
T 495	**tolerance factor** <ST>	Toleranzfaktor *m*	tolérance *f* relative, coefficient *m* de tolérance	коэффициент допустимости
T 496	**tolerance level,** tolerance threshold, tolerance <ST>	Toleranzschwelle *f*, Toleranz *f*	seuil (niveau) *m* de tolérance, tolérance	толерантный уровень, допустимый уровень, допуск, допустимое отклонение, толерантность
T 497	**tolerance limit** <ST>	Toleranzgrenze *f*, Duldungsgrenze *f*, Toleranzschwelle *f*, Toleranz *f*	limite *f* de tolérance	толерантный предел, допустимый предел
	tolerance region <ST>	*s.* S 1698		
	tolerance threshold <ST>	*s.* T 496		
T 498	**Tonelli['s] method** <VA>	Tonellische Methode *f*	méthode *f* de Tonelli	метод Тонелли
T 499	**top digit,** highest number, maximum number, highest figure, maximum figure <of a number> <NT>	höchste Stelle *f*, Höchstziffer *f*	chiffre *m* à l'ordre le plus haut	[самый] старший разряд
T 500	**topographical surface** <DS>	Geländefläche *f*, topographische Fläche *f*	surface *f* topographique	топографическая поверхность
T 501	**topographic projection,** projection with elevations (heights), coted projection <DS>	kotierte (bezifferte) Projektion *f*, topographisches Verfahren *n*	projection *f* cotée (topographique); géométrie *f* cotée	топографическая проекция, проекция с числовыми отметками
T 502	**topological Boolean algebra,** closure algebra <AL>	topologische Boolesche Algebra *f*	algèbre *f* de Boole topologique	топологическая булева алгебра
T 503	**topological cell** <TO>	topologische (krumme) Zelle *f*, Element *n* <r-dimensional>	cellule *f* topologique	кривая клетка
T 504	**topological circle** <TO>	topologische Kreisscheibe *f*	cercle *m* topologique	топологический круг

T 505	**topological circumference** <TO>	topologischer Kreis *m*, Kreis	circonférence *f* topologique	топологическая окружность
T 506	**topological closure [operation]** <TO>	topologische Hüllenoperation *f*	opération *f* de fermeture topologique	топологическая операция замыкания
T 507	**topological complement, topological complementary [sub]space,** complementary [sub]space, complement, topologically complementary vector subspace	topologisches Komplement *n*, topologischer Komplementärraum *m*, topologisch komplementärer Raum *m*, Komplementärraum, komplementärer Raum (Unterraum *m*), Komplement *n*	supplémentaire *m* topologique, [sous-]espace *m* supplémentaire topologique, sous-espace vectoriel topologiquement supplémentaire, espace *m* (sous-espace) supplémentaire, supplémentaire	топологическое дополнение (дополнительное пространство), дополнительное подпространство (пространство)
T 508	**topological completeness** <AL, TO>	topologische Vollständigkeit *f*	complétude *f* topologique	топологическая полнота
T 509	**topological complex,** topological simplicial complex <AT>	krummer (topologischer) Komplex *m*	complexe *m* topologique	кривой комплекс, криволинейный комплекс, топологический комплекс
T 510	**topological convergence,** convergence in the topology <TO>	topologische Konvergenz *f*, Konvergenz im Sinne der Topologie	convergence *f* topologique, convergence pour la topologie	топологическая сходимость, сходимость в топологии
T 511	**topological cycle** <AT>	krummer (topologischer) Zyklus *m*	cycle *m* topologique	кривой цикл
	topological dimension <TO>	*s.* D 512		
T 512	**topological direct sum** <AL, TO>	topologische direkte Summe *f*	somme *f* directe topologique	топологическая прямая сумма
T 513	**topological divisor of zero** <in a Banach algebra> <FA>	Nullteiler *m* im verallgemeinerten Sinn	diviseur *m* de zéro topologique	топологический делитель нуля
T 514	**topological dynamics** <SP, TO>	topologische Dynamik *f*	dynamique *f* topologique	топологическая динамика
T 515	**topological embedding,** embedding <of a topological space> <TO>	topologische Einbettung *f*, Einbettung	plongement *m* topologique, plongement	топологическое вложение, вложение
T 516	**topological field** <AL>	topologischer Körper *m*	corps *m* topologique	топологическое поле (тело)
T 517	**topological graph,** topologic graph, graph, linear graph, linear complex, 1-complex, one-dimensional complex <AT, GP>	topologischer Graph *m*, Graph, Streckenkomplex *m*, Linienkomplex *m*, Kantenkomplex *m*, Bogenkomplex *m*, Linearkomplexion *f*, Liniensystem *n*, Netz *n*	graphe (réseau) *m* topologique, graphe, réseau	топологический граф, граф, одномерный комплекс, линейный комплекс
T 518	**topological group,** continuous group <GR>	topologische Gruppe *f*	groupe *m* topologique (continu)	топологическая (непрерывная) группа
T 519	**topological homeomorphism,** topological mapping, homeomorphic mapping, bi[-]continuous mapping, topological transformation, homeomorphism, one-to-one bicontinuous transformation, topological isomorphism <TO>	Homöomorphismus *m*, homöomorphe (topologische, beiderseits stetige) Abbildung *f*, topologischer Isomorphismus *m*, Isomorphismus, doppeltstetige (umkehrbarstetige) Abbildung, Homöomorphie *f*	homéomorphisme *m*, application *f* homéomorphe (topologique), représentation *f* (isomorphisme *m*, équivalence *f*) topologique, application bicontinue, homéomorphie *f*	гомеоморфизм, гомеоморфное (топологическое) отображение, топологическое преобразование, топологический изоморфизм, взаимно однозначное и взаимно непрерывное отображение, взаимно непрерывное отображение
	topological identification <TO>	*s.* P 598		
T 520	**topological index** <of an elliptic differential operator> <AN, AT>	topologischer Index *m*	indice *m* topologique	топологический индекс
	topological inductive limit <TO>	*s.* I 408		
T 521	**topological invariant,** Analysis Situs invariant <TO>	topologische Invariante *f*	invariant *m* topologique	топологический инвариант, топологическая инварианта
	topological isomorphism <TO>	*s.* T 519		
T 522	**topological kernel** <of a graph> <GP>	topologischer Kern *m*	noyau *m* topologique	топологическое ядро
T 523	**topological limit** <TO>	topologischer Limes *m*, Limes im Sinne der Topologie	limite *f* topologique	топологический предел
T 524	**topological linear space,** topological vector space <FA>	linearer topologischer Raum *m*, topologischer linearer Raum, topologischer Vektorraum *m*	espace *m* vectoriel topologique	линейное топологическое пространство, топологическое векторное пространство
	topologically complementary vector subspace <FA, TO>	*s.* T 507		
T 525	**topologically complete set** <TO>	Youngsche Menge *f*, topologisch vollständige Menge	ensemble *m* topologiquement complet	топологически полное множество <метризуемое топологическое пространство *E*, допускающее расстояние, согласующееся с его топологией, при котором *E* есть полное метрическое пространство>
T 526	**topologically complete [topological] space** <TO>	topologisch vollständiger Raum *m*, topologisch vollständiger topologischer Raum	espace *m* topologiquement complet, espace complet au sens topologique	топологически полное пространство

No.	English	German	French	Russian
T 527	**topologically contained space** <TO>	topologisch enthaltener Raum *m*	espace *m* topologiquement contenu	пространство, топологически содержащееся в данном пространстве; пространство, гомеоморфное подпространству данного пространства
T 528	**topologically convergent sequence of sets** <SE, TO>	abgeschlossen (topologisch) konvergente Mengenfolge *f*	suite *f* d'ensembles topologiquement convergente	топологически сходящаяся последовательность множеств
T 529	**topologically equivalent space,** homeomorphic space, topologically isomorphic space <TO>	topologisch äquivalenter Raum *m*, homöomorpher [topologischer] Raum, isomorpher [topologischer] Raum, Raum vom gleichen topologischen Typ[us], [topologischer] Raum mit der gleichen topologischen Struktur	espace *m* topologique homéomorphe, espace homéomorphe, espace topologiquement équivalent, espace de même type topologique	гомеоморфное [топологическое] пространство, топологически эквивалентное пространство, пространство одинакового топологического типа, пространство одного и того же топологического типа
	topologically identical graph <GP>	*s.* H 421		
	topologically isomorphic space <TO>	*s.* T 529		
T 530	**topologically nilpotent element** <of a topological ring> <AL>	topologisch nilpotentes Element *n*	élément *m* topologiquement nilpotent	топологически нильпотентный элемент
T 531	**topologically ringed space** <AL>	topologisch geringter Raum *m*	espace *m* topologiquement annelé	топологически кольцованное пространство
T 532	**topologically solvable group** <GR>	topologisch auflösbare Gruppe *f*	groupe *m* topologiquement résoluble	топологически разрешимая группа
	topologically stable manifold <TO>	*s.* S 1588		
T 533	**topological manifold** <TO>	topologische Mannigfaltigkeit *f*	variété *f* topologique	топологическое многообразие
	topological mapping <TO>	*s.* T 519		
T 534	**topological mapping of a space onto itself** <TO>	topologische Abbildung *f* eines Raumes auf sich	automorphie *f*, automorphie topologique	автоморфизм, гомеоморфизм пространства на себя, топологический автоморфизм
T 535	**topological mapping of degree +1** <AT>	die Orientierung erhaltende topologische Abbildung *f*; topologische Abbildung vom Grad +1; topologische Abbildung, die die Orientierung erhält	homéomorphie *f* positive, transformation *f* homéomorphe positive	топологическое отображение, степень которого +1
T 536	**topological mapping of degree —1** <AT>	topologische Abbildung *f* vom Grad —1; topologische Abbildung, die die Orientierung umkehrt	homéomorphie *f* négative, transformation *f* homéomorphe négative	топологическое отображение, степень которого —1
	topological *n*-cell <AT>	*s.* N 44		
T 537	**topological *n*-sphere,** *n*-sphere <TO>	*n*-dimensionale topologische Sphäre *f*, topologische *n*-Sphäre *f*	*n*-sphère *f* topologique	топологическое пространство, гомеоморфное S_n
	topological one-sphere <TO>	*s.* S 894		
T 538	**topological pair** <TO>	topologisches Paar *n*	couple *m* topologique	пара топологических пространств
	topological phase space <SP>	*s.* T 546		
	topological polyhedron <AT>	*s.* C 2777		
T 539	**topological product,** Cartesian product <of topological spaces> <TO>	topologisches Produkt *n*, Produkt *n*, direktes Produkt	produit *m* cartésien; espace *m* produit	топологическое произведение, произведение
	topological quotient <TO>	*s.* Q 347		
T 540	**topological rank** <of a topological space> <TO>	topologischer Rang *m*, Dimensionstypus *m*	rang *m* topologique, type *m* de dimensions, Homoïe *f*	топологический ранг, тип размерностей
T 541	**topological residue-class ring** <AL>	topologischer Restklassenring *m*	anneau *m* topologique quotient	топологическое фактор-кольцо
T 542	**topological simplex** <AT>	topologisches (krummliniges, krummes) Simplex *n*	simplexe *m* topologique	топологический (кривой) симплекс
	topological simplicial complex <AT>	*s.* T 509		
T 543	**topological skew field** <AL>	topologischer Schiefkörper *m*	corps *m* topologique	топологическое тело
T 544	**topological space,** T-space, space <TO>	topologischer Raum *m*, Raum	espace *m* topologique, espace	топологическое пространство, пространство
	topological space having a countable basis <TO>	*s.* C 1512		
T 545	**topological space in which any two elements are separated** <TO>	total zusammenhangsloser topologischer Raum *m*	espace *m* nulle part connexe	нигде не связное пространство
T 546	**topological space of states,** topological phase space <SP>	topologischer Zustandsraum (Phasenraum) *m*	espace *m* des états (phases) topologique	топологическое пространство состояний, топологическое фазовое пространство

	English	German	French	Russian
	topological space satisfying the first axiom of countability <TO>	*s.* F 336		
T 547	**topological space with [selected] base point,** pointed topological space, based space <TO>	topologischer Raum *m* mit ausgezeichnetem Grundpunkt, punktierter topologischer Raum	espace *m* [topologique] pointé	топологическое пространство с отмеченной точкой, пунктированное топологическое пространство, пространство с отмеченной базисной точкой
T 548	**topological sphere** <TO>	topologische Sphäre *f*	sphère *f* topologique	топологическая сфера
T 549	**topological structure,** topology <TO>	topologische Struktur *f*, Topologie *f*	structure *f* topologique, topologie *f*	топологическая структура, топология
T 550	**topological sum** <TO>	Summenraum *m*, Summe *f* <topologischer Räume>	espace-somme *m*, espace *m* somme, espace topologique somme, somme *f* <d'espaces topologiques>	сумма топологических пространств, топологическая сумма <семейства пространств>
T 551	**topological sum** <of topological spaces> <TO>	topologische Summe *f*	somme *f* topologique	топологическая (несвязная) сумма
T 552	**topological tensor product** <of Hilbert spaces> <FA>	direktes Produkt *n*, topologisches Tensorprodukt *n*	produit *m* tensoriel topologique	топологическое тензорное произведение
	topological transformation <TO>	*s.* T 519		
	topological tree <GP>	*s.* T 885		
T 553	**topological triangulation** <AT>	krumme Simplizialzerlegung (Triangulation) *f*	triangulation *f* topologique	кривая триангуляция
T 554	**topological type** <TO>	Homöomorphietyp *m*, Raumtyp *m*	type *m* topologique	топологический тип
	topological vector space <FA>	*s.* T 524		
	topologic graph <AT, GP>	*s.* T 517		
T 555	**topologico-algebraical** <AL, TO>	topologisch-algebraisch	topologico-algébrique	тополого-алгебраический
T 556	**topologico-differential invariant** <of a transformation> <DG, TO>	topologische Differentialinvariante *f*	invariant *m* différentiel topologique	тополого-дифференциальный инвариант
T 557	**topologist** <TO>	Topologe *m*	topologiste *m*	тополог
T 558	**topologization** <TO>	Topologisierung *f*	topologisation *f*	топологизация
T 559	**topologize / to** <TO>	topologisieren	topologiser, munir d'une topologie	определять топологию <на>, наделить топологией, топологизировать
T 560	**topologizing system** <of ideals> <AL>	topologisierende Menge *f*	ensemble *m* topologisant	топологизующая система
T 561	**topology,** analysis situs <AT>	Topologie *f*, Analysis *f* situs (der Lage), // Lagerechnung *f*, Situationskalkül *m* <Scheffer>, Geometrie *f* der Lage	topologie *f*, analysis *f* situs, géométrie *f* de situation, // calcul *m* de situation	топология, анализ ситус, геометрия положения
T 562	**topology** <as the theory of the structure of topological spaces> <TO>	Topologie *f*	topologie *f*	топология
	topology <TO>	*s.* T 549		
	σ-topology <FA>	*s.* W 128		
T 563	**topology generated by a family of closed sets** <TO>	Abgeschlossenheitstopologie *f*	topologie *f* induite par une famille d'ensembles fermés	топология, порожденная семейством замкнутых множеств
T 564	**topology induced by a metric,** metric topology, natural topology <of a metric space> <TO>	metrische (von einer Metrik erzeugte, durch einer Metrik induzierte, unterliegende, natürliche) Topologie *f*	topologie *f* induite par une métrique, topologie métrique	метрическая топология; топология, индуцированная метрикой; топология, определяемая данной метрикой; естественная топология
T 565	**topology of bounded convergence** <FA, TO>	beschränkt-offene Topologie *f*, Topologie der beschränkten Konvergenz	topologie *f* de la convergence bornée	топология ограниченной сходимости
T 566	**topology of compact convergence,** compact open topology, compact-open topology, C-O topology, k-topology <TO>	Topologie *f* der kompakten Konvergenz, kompakt-offene Topologie, kompakte Topologie	topologie *f* de convergence compacte, topologie de la convergence compacte, topologie compacte-ouverte	компактно-открытая топология, топология компактной сходимости, открыто-компактная топология, естественная топология, компактная топология, бикомпактно открытая топология
T 567	**topology of coordinatewise (pointwise, simple) convergence,** pointwise topology, simple convergence topology <FA, TO>	Topologie *f* der punktweisen (gewöhnlichen, einfachen) Konvergenz	topologie *f* de la convergence simple	топология простой (поточечной) сходимости
	topology of the uniformity <TO>	*s.* U 185		
T 568	**topology of uniform convergence,** u.c. topology <TO>	Topologie *f* der gleichmäßigen Konvergenz	topologie *f* de la convergence uniforme	топология равномерной сходимости
T 569	**topology of uniform convergence on compact sets** <TO>	Topologie *f* der gleichmäßigen Konvergenz auf kompakten Mengen,	topologie *f* de la convergence uniforme sur les ensembles com-	топология равномерной сходимости на компактных множествах

		Topologie der kompakten Konvergenz, Topologie der auf kompakten Mengen gleichmäßigen Konvergenz	pactes	
T 570	**topology on a group** <GR>	Gruppentopologie *f*, Topologie *f* auf einer Gruppe	topologie *f* de groupe	групповая топология
T 571	**topos** <CA>	Topos *m*	topos *m*	топос
	Tor <HA>	*s.* T 605		
T 572	**tore** <AL>	Torus *m*	tore *m*	тор
	tore <EG>	*s.* 1. T 612; 2. T 613		
T 573	**toroid** <as a curve> <GE>	Toroide *f*, Parallelkurve *f* einer Ellipse	toroïde *f*	тороида
T 574	**toroid** <as a surface> <GE>	Toroid *n*	toroïde *m*	тороид
T 575	**toroid,** torus group, toroid group <a real compact connected abelian Lie group> <GR>	Toroid *n*, Torusgruppe *f*	toroïde *m*, groupe *m* toroïdal	тороид, тороидальная (торовидная) группа
T 576	**toroidal co-ordinates** <AN>	Ringkoordinaten *fpl*, Toruskoordinaten *fpl*, Thomsonsche Koordinaten *fpl*, Koordinaten von Thomson, annulare (toroidale) Koordinaten	coordonnées *fpl* toriques (toroïdales)	тороидальные координаты
T 577	**toroidal function,** torus function, ring[-] function <FU>	Ringfunktion *f*, toroidale Funktion *f*, Torusfunktion *f*	fonction *f* toroïdale (torique, annulaire)	тороидальная (кольцевая) функция
T 578	**toroidal group,** torus group, one-dimensional torus group <a topological group> <GR>	Torusgruppe *f*, Toroid *n*, eindimensionale Torusgruppe	groupe *m* toroïdal	тороидальная группа, аддитивная группа вещественных чисел по модулю 1
T 579	**toroidal manifold** <TO>	Torusmannigfaltigkeit *f*	variété *f* toroïdale	торовидное многообразие
T 580	**toroidal neighbourhood** <TO>	Volltorusumgebung *f*	voisinage *m* toroïdal	торовидная окрестность
	toroid group <GR>	*s.* T 575		
T 581	**Toronto['s] function** <$T(m,n,z)$> <FU>	Toronto-Funktion *f*	fonction *f* de Toronto	функция Торонто
T 582	**Torricelli['s] point** <of a triangle> <EG>	Torricellischer Punkt *m*	point *m* de Torricelli	точка Торричелли
T 583	**torsal direction** <DG>	Torsalrichtung *f*	direction *f* torsale	торсальное направление
T 584	**torsal line** <of a ruled surface> <DG>	Torsallinie *f*, torsale Linie *f*	ligne *f* torsale	торсальная линия
T 585	**torsal plane** <of a ruled surface> <DG>	Torsalebene *f*	plan *m* torsal	торсальная плоскость
	torse <DG>	*s.* D 361		
T 586	**torsion,** second curvature <of a space curve> <DG>	Windung *f*, Torsion *f*, Schmiegung *f*, zweite Krümmung *f*	torsion *f*, deuxième courbure *f*	кручение, вторая кривизна
T 587	**torsion** <of a metric space> <TO>	Torsion *f*	torsion *f*	кручение
	σ-torsion <AL>	*s.* S 834		
T 588	**torsion basis** <AT>	Torsionsbasis *f*	base *f* de torsion	базис кручения
T 589	**torsion coefficient,** coefficient of torsion <*q*-th, of dimensionality *q*> <AT>	Torsionszahl *f*, Torsionskoeffizient *m* <*q*-dimensional>	coefficient *m* de torsion <de dimension *q*>	коэффициент кручения <*q*-й>, число кручения <*q*-ое>
T 590	**torsion coefficient** <of an abelian group> <GR>	Torsionskoeffizient *m*	coefficient *m* de torsion	коэффициент кручения
T 591	**torsion divisor** <AG>	Torsionsdivisor *m*	diviseur *m* de torsion	дивизор кручения
	torsion element <GR>	*s.* E 134		
T 592	**torsion form** <DG>	Torsionsform *f*	forme *f* de torsion	форма кручения
T 593	**torsion[-] free connection** <DG>	torsionsfreie Übertragung *f*, torsionsfreier Zusammenhang *m*	connexion *f* sans torsion	связность без кручения
	torsion free group, torsion[-]free group <GR>	*s.* G 524		
T 594	**Π-torsion-free group** <GR>	Π-torsionsfreie Gruppe *f*	groupe *m* sans Π-torsion	группа без Π-кручения
T 595	**torsion-free group of finite type** <GR>	rationale (torsionsfreie) Gruppe *f* endlichen Typs	groupe *m* de type fini sans torsion	рациональная группа конечного типа
T 596	**torsion[-] free module,** module without torsion <AL>	torsionsfreier Modul *m*	module *m* sans torsion, module normal	модуль без кручения; модуль, не имеющий кручения
T 597	**torsion[-] free module,** semi-simple module <a module with zero radical in torsion theory> <AL>	torsionsfreier Modul *m*	module *m* sans torsion, module semi-simple	модуль без кручения, полупростой модуль
T 598	**torsion[-] free ring** <AL>	torsionsfreie Algebra *f*	anneau *m* sans torsion	кольцо без кручения
T 599	**torsion group,** group of torsion <of a homology group> <AT>	Torsionsgruppe *f*	groupe *m* de torsion	группа с кручением, группа кручения
	torsion group <GR>	*s.* P 452		
T 600	**torsion ideal** <AL>	Torsionsideal *n*	idéal *m* de torsion	идеал кручения
T 601	**torsion module** <in torsion theory> <AL>	Torsionsmodul *m*	module *m* de torsion	модуль кручения
	torsion module <AL>	*s.* P 456		
T 602	**torsion object** <CA>	Torsionsobjekt *n*	objet *m* de torsion	периодический объект
T 603	**torsion prime** <NT>	Torsionsprimzahl *f*	nombre *m* premier de torsion	простое число кручения
T 604	**torsion product** <of groups> <GR>	Torsionsprodukt *n*	produit *m* périodique	периодическое произведение

No.	English	German	French	Russian
T 605	**torsion product,** Tor <*e.g.:* Tor_q, *q*-th> <of modules> <HA>	Torsionsprodukt *n*, Tor <*z. B.:* Tor_q>	produit *m* de torsion, produit dual, Tor <*par exemple:* Tor_q>	периодическое произведение, произведение кручения Картана-Эйленберга <*например:* *q*-ое>
T 606	**torsion radical** <in torsion theory> <AL>	Torsionsradikal *n*	radical *m* de torsion	радикал кручения
	torsion radical <CA>	*s.* H 215		
	torsion radius <DG>	*s.* R 40		
T 607	**torsion ring** <AL>	Torsionsring *m*	anneau *m* à torsion	кольцо с кручением
	torsion semigroup <AL>	*s.* P 457		
T 608	**torsion subgroup,** maximal periodic subgroup <of a group> <GR>	Torsionsuntergruppe *f*, maximale periodische Untergruppe *f*, periodischer Teil *m*, maximale Torsionsuntergruppe, maximalperiodische Untergruppe	sous-groupe *m* périodique maximal, sous-groupe de torsion	подгруппа кручения, периодическая часть, максимальная (максимально) периодическая подгруппа, подгруппа кручений
T 609	**torsion tensor,** tensor of torsion <DG>	Torsionstensor *m*, Windungstensor *m*, Schmiegungstensor *m*	tenseur *m* de torsion	тензор кручения (скручивания)
T 610	**torsion theory** <AL>	Torsionstheorie *f*	théorie *f* de torsion	теория кручения
T 611	**torsion vector,** vector of torsion <DG>	Torsionsvektor *m*, Windungsvektor *m*, Schmiegungsvektor *m*, zweiter Krümmungsvektor *m*	vecteur *m* de torsion (la deuxième courbure)	вектор кручения (второй кривизны)
	torsor <GE>	*s.* I 204		
T 612	**torus,** tore <as a solid> <EG>	Torus *m*, Ringkörper *m*, Ring *m*	tore *m*, tore circulaire (de révolution)	тор, баранка, бублик, спасательный круг
T 613	**torus,** tore, anchor ring, ring surface <as a surface> <EG>	Torus *m*, Ringfläche *f*, Kreiswulst *f*, Ringwulst *f*, Wulstfläche *f*, Wulst *f*, Ring *m*	tore *m*, tore circulaire (de révolution), surface *f* annulaire	тор, поверхность тора; поверхность, ограничивающая тор; кольцевая поверхность, торус
	torus function <FU>	*s.* T 577		
	torus group <GR>	*s.* 1. T 575; 2. T 578		
T 614	**torusknot,** torus knot <AT>	Torusknoten *m*, Schlauchknoten *m* erster Stufe	nœud *m* torique	торический узел
	toss <ST>	*s.* C 1124		
	tossing of coin <ST>	*s.* C 1124		
T 615	**total,** grand total, sum total <AR>	Endsumme *f*	total *m*	окончательная сумма, итоговая сумма
	total <AR>	*s.* T 697		
	total additivity <AN, SE>	*s.* C 2556		
	total boundedness <FA, TO>	*s.* P 1175		
T 616	**total character** <of quadratic forms> <NT>	Totalcharakter *m*	caractère *m* total <d'une classe>	полный характер
T 617	**total Chern character** <AT>	totaler Chernscher Charakter *m*	caractère *m* de Chern total	полный характер Чженя
T 618	**total Chern class** <AT>	totale Chernsche Klasse *f*	classe *f* de Chern totale	полный класс Чженя
T 619	**total correlation** <contrary to partial correlation> <ST>	totale Korrelation *f*	corrélation *f* totale	полная корреляция
	total correlation <ST>	*s.* O 565		
	total correlation coefficient <ST>	*s.* S 901		
T 620	**total curvature** <of a closed surface> <DG>	Gesamtkrümmung *f*, Totalkrümmung *f*, Curvatura *f* integra	courbure *f* totale	полная кривизна
T 621	**total curvature,** total normal curvature, Gaussian curvature, Gauss['s] curvature, specific curvature <of a surface> <DG>	Gaußsche Krümmung *f*, [Gaußsches] Krümmungsmaß *n*, Totalkrümmung *f*, totale Krümmung, // Gaußische Krümmung <Bianchi>	courbure *f* de Gauss, courbure gaussienne	полная (гауссова) кривизна
T 622	**total defect** <of a meromorphic function> <FT>	totaler Defekt *m*	défaut *m* total	полный дефект
T 623	**total degree** <in filtration *or* graduation, *or* of a polynomial> <AL, AT>	Gesamtgrad *m*	degré *m* total, degré	полная степень
T 624	**total differential,** exact differential, perfect differential, complete differential, differential <of a differential form> <DI>	vollständiges (exaktes, totales) Differential *n*, Differential	différentielle *f*, différentielle exacte (totale, totale exacte)	полный (точный) дифференциал
	total differential <FA>	*s.* F 582		
	total differential equation <DE>	*s.* 1. E 652; 2. P 545		
	total differential system <DE>	*s.* P 548		
T 625	**total discontinuity** <RF>	totale Diskontinuität *f*	discontinuité *f* totale	полная разрывность
	total dispersion <ST>	*s.* T 700		
T 626	**total endomorphism** <of a group> <GR>	totaler Endomorphismus *m*	endomorphisme *m* total	полный эндоморфизм
	total equation <DE>	*s.* E 652		
T 627	**total error** <ER, NU>	Gesamtfehler *m*, vollständiger Fehler *m*	erreur *f* totale	полная погрешность
T 628	**total family of seminorms** <FA>	totale Familie *f* von Halbnormen	famille *f* totale de seminormes	тотальное семейство полунорм
	total fluctuation <AN>	*s.* T 701		
T 629	**total functional** <MM>	überall definiertes Funktional *n*	fonctionnelle *f* partout définie	всюду определенный функционал

T 630	**total graduation** <AL>	totale Graduierung *f*	graduation *f* totale	полная градуировка
T 631	**total graph** <GP>	totaler Graph *m*	graphe *m* total	тотальный граф
T 632	**total homology group** <of a complex> <HA>	totale Homologiegruppe *f*	groupe *m* d'homologie total	полная группа гомологий
T 633	**total increment** <AN>	totaler (vollständiger) Zuwachs *m*	incrément *m* total	полное приращение
T 634	**total inspection** <ST>	vollständige Prüfung *f*	inspection *f* totale (à 100%)	сплошная проверка, полное обследование
T 635	**total instability** <DE>	totale Instabilität *f*	instabilité *f* totale	полная неустойчивость
T 636	**totalizable,** D-integrable, integrable in the sense of Denjoy-Khinchine <RF>	totalisierbar, D-integrierbar, integrierbar im Sinne von Denjoy-Chintschin	totalisable, intégrable au sens de Denjoy-Khintchine	тотализуемый, интегрируемый в смысле Данжуа-Хинчина
T 637	**totalization** <AN>	Totalisation *f*	totalisation *f*	тотализация
	totalization <AR>	*s.* T 638		
T 638	**totalling,** totalization, adding together, adding up <AR>	Aufsummieren *n*, Summierung *f*	totalisation *f*	складывание, нахождение суммы, суммирование, накопление
	totally additive content <ME>	*s.* A 81		
	totally additive [set] function <AN>	*s.* C 2566		
T 639	**totally bounded set** <of a metric space> <TO>	totalbeschränkte Menge *f*	ensemble *m* totalement borné	вполне ограниченное множество
	totally bounded set <FA, TO>	*s.* P 1176		
	totally bounded space <FA, TO>	*s.* P 1177		
T 640	**totally complex field** <NT>	totalimaginärer Körper *m*	corps *m* totalement imaginaire	вполне мнимое поле
T 641	**totally complex quadratic field** <AB>	imaginärquadratischer Körper *m*, imaginärer quadratischer Zahlkörper *m*	corps *m* quadratique imaginaire, corps imaginaire quadratique	мнимоквадратичное поле, квадратично-мнимое поле, мнимое квадратичное поле
T 642	**totally contained linear system** <AG>	vollständig enthaltenes lineares System *n*	système *m* linéaire complètement contenu	вполне включенная линейная система
T 643	**totally definite quadratic form** <AB>	total definite quadratische Form *f*	forme *f* quadratique totalement définie	вполне определенная квадратичная форма
T 644	**totally differentiable function,** function differentiable in the sense of Stolz, differentiable function <DI>	total (im Stolzschen Sinne) differenzierbare Funktion *f*, differenzierbare Funktion [im Stolzschen Sinne]	fonction *f* totalement dérivable (différentiable), fonction dérivable [au sens de Stolz], fonction différentiable [au sens de Stolz]	вполне дифференцируемая функция, дифференцируемая [в смысле Штольца] функция
T 645	**totally disconnected graph** <GP>	vollständig unzusammenhängender Graph *m*	graphe *m* totalement discontinu	вполне несвязный граф
T 646	**totally disconnected group** <GR>	total unzusammenhängende Gruppe *f*, nulldimensionale Gruppe	groupe *m* totalement discontinu	вполне несвязная группа
T 647	**totally disconnected groupoid** <CA>	total unzusammenhängendes Gruppoid *n*	groupoïde *m* totalement discontinu	вполне несвязный группоид
T 648	**totally disconnected set,** pointlike set <TO>	total unzusammenhängende Menge *f*, punkthafte (zusammenhangslose) Menge	ensemble totalement discontinu, ensemble dispersé (entièrement séparé, totalement inconnexe)	вполне несвязное (разрывное) множество, рассеянное множество
	totally disconnected set <TO>	*s. a.* S 650		
T 649	**totally disconnected [topological] space** <TO>	total unzusammenhängender [topologischer] Raum *m*, zusammenhangsloser [topologischer] Raum, punkthafter [topologischer] Raum, vollständig unzusammenhängender Raum	espace *m* [topologique] totalement discontinu, espace dispersé (complètement discontinu)	вполне (наследственно) несвязное пространство, дисперсное пространство
T 650	**totally disconnected topology** <TO>	total unzusammenhängende Topologie *f*	topologie *f* totalement discontinue	вполне несвязная топология
T 651	**totally flat module** <AL>	total flacher Modul *m*	module *m* totalement plat	вполне плоский модуль
	totally geodesic manifold <DG>	*s.* G 242		
T 652	**totally imperfect set** <TO>	total[ ]imperfekte Menge (Punktmenge) *f*	ensemble *m* totalement imparfait	вполне несовершенное множество; множество, не содержащее ни одного непустого совершенного подмножества
T 653	**totally imperfect space** <TO>	totalimperfekter Raum *m*	espace *m* totalement imparfait	вполне несовершенное пространство
	totally integrable system <DE>	*s.* C 1478		
T 654	**totally irreducible linear system** <AG>	total irreduzibles lineares System *n*	système *m* linéaire totalement irréductible	вполне неприводимая линейная система
	totally monotone (monotonic) sequence <FD, SS>	*s.* C 1492		
T 655	**totally negatively definite quadratic form** <AB>	total negativ definite quadratische Form *f*	forme *f* quadratique totalement définie négative	вполне отрицательно определенная квадратичная форма
T 656	**totally non-homologous to zero** <AT>	total nicht nullhomolog	totalement non homologue à zéro	вполне негомологичный нулю
T 657	**totally nonnegative matrix** <MD>	vollständig nichtnegative Matrix *f*	matrice *f* totalement non négative	вполне неотрицательная матрица
	totally ordered group <GR>	*s.* S 1001		

No.	English	German	French	Russian
	totally ordered set <SE>	*s.* L 822		
T 658	**totally orthogonal manifold,** orthogonal manifold <to> <GE>	totalsenkrechte (orthogonale) Mannigfaltigkeit *f* <zu>	variété *f* [totalement] orthogonale <à>	[вполне] ортогональное многообразие <к>
T 659	**totally orthogonal plane** <GE>	totalsenkrechte (total orthogonale) Ebene *f*	plan *m* totalement orthogonal	вполне ортогональная плоскость
T 660	**totally orthogonal space** <AL, GE>	totalsenkrechter (orthogonaler, konjugierter) Raum *m*	sous-espace *m* conjugué <d'un sous-espace>	вполне ортогональное пространство
T 661	**totally positively definite quadratic form** <AB>	total positiv definite quadratische Form *f*	forme *f* quadratique totalement définie positive	вполне положительно определенная квадратичная форма
T 662	**totally positive matrix** <MD>	vollständig positive Matrix *f*	matrice *f* totalement positive	вполне положительная матрица
T 663	**totally positive number** <AB>	total positive Zahl *f*	nombre *m* totalement positif	вполне положительное число
T 664	**totally projective group** <GR>	total projektive Gruppe *f*	groupe *m* totalement projectif	тотально проективная группа
T 665	**totally quasi-ordered set** <SE>	total vorgeordnete Menge *f*	ensemble *m* totalement préordonné	совершенно предупорядоченное множество
	totally ramified prime [number] <NT>	*s.* C 1499		
T 666	**totally real [number] field** <AB>	totalreeller Zahlkörper (Körper) *m*	corps *m* de nombres totalement réel, corps totalement réel	вполне вещественное [числовое] поле
T 667	**totally recursively enumerable subclass** <MM>	total rekursiv aufzählbare Teilklasse *f*	sous-classe *f* totalement récursivement énumérable	тотально рекурсивно перечислимый подкласс
T 668	**totally recursive subclass** <MM>	total rekursive Teilklasse *f*	sous-classe *f* totalement récursive	тотально рекурсивный подкласс
T 669	**totally reflexive relation** <SE>	total reflexive Relation (Beziehung) *f*	relation *f* totalement réflexive	вполне рефлексивное отношение
T 670	**totally regular matrix method** <LI>	totalreguläres (totalpermanentes) Matrizenverfahren *n*	méthode *f* matricielle totalement régulière	полностью (вполне) регулярный матричный метод
	totally semi-additive [set] function <AN>	*s.* C 2569		
T 671	**totally singular subspace** <of a linear space with respect to a quadratic form> <AL, GE>	totalsingulärer Teilraum (Raum) *m*	sous-espace *m* totalement singulier	вполне особое подпространство
T 672	**totally stable solution** <DE>	total stabile Lösung *f*	solution *f* totalement stable	вполне устойчивое решение
T 673	**totally symmetric loop** <AL>	totalsymmetrische Loop *f*	loop *m* totalement symétrique	тотально симметрическая лупа
T 674	**totally symmetric quasigroup,** TS-quasigroup <AL>	totalsymmetrische Quasigruppe *f*	quasi-groupe *m* totalement symétrique	тотально симметрическая квазигруппа, TS-квазигруппа
T 675	**totally unstable solution** <DE>	total instabile Lösung *f*	solution *f* totalement instable	вполне неустойчивое решение
T 676	**total mapping,** completely defined mapping <contrary to partial mapping> <AL, SE>	überall definierte Abbildung *f*	application *f* partout définie	всюду определенное отображение
	total matric (matrix) algebra <AL>	*s.* T 677		
T 677	**total matrix ring,** full matrix ring, complete matrix ring, full matrix algebra, total matrix (matric) algebra <of degree *n*> <AL>	voller Matrixring (Matrizenring) *m*, volle Matrizenalgebra *f*, einfaches System *n*, voller Matricesring *m*, volle Matricesalgebra *f* <vom Range *n*, *n*-ten Grades>	algèbre *f* matricielle totale <de degré *n*>	полное кольцо матриц, полная матричная алгебра <степени *n*>
	total mean square <ST>	*s.* T 700		
	total monotonicity (monotony) <SS>	*s.* C 1491		
	total normal curvature <DG>	*s.* T 621		
T 678/9	**total norm residue** <AB>	totaler Normenrest *m*	résidu *m* normique total	общий норм-вычет
	total of the digits <AR, NT>	*s.* S 2295		
	total operation <AL, SE>	*s.* O 171		
	total ordering <SE>	*s.* L 830		
T 680	**total Pontryagin class** <AT>	totale Pontrjaginsche Klasse *f*	classe *f* de Pontrjagin totale	полный класс Понтрягина
T 681	**total predicate** <FO>	überall definiertes Prädikat *n*	prédicat *m* partout défini	всюду определенный предикат
T 682	**total probability** <ST>	totale (vollständige) Wahrscheinlichkeit *f*	probabilité *f* totale	полная вероятность
T 683	**total probability formula (theorem),** formula of total probability <ST>	Formel *f* der totalen (vollständigen) Wahrscheinlichkeit, Satz *m* über die totale (vollständige) Wahrscheinlichkeit, Satz von der totalen (vollständigen) Wahrscheinlichkeit	formule *f* (théorème *m*) de la probabilité totale	формула (теорема) полной вероятности
T 684	**total projective group** <GR>	volle projektive Gruppe *f*	groupe *m* projectif complet	полная проективная группа
	total quotient ring <AL>	*s.* C 1561		
T 685	**total regression** <ST>	totale Regression *f*	régression *f* totale	полная регрессия
	total regression coefficient <ST>	*s.* S 945		

No.	English	German	French	Russian
T 686	**total relation** <SE>	überall definierte Relation *f*; Relation, deren Vorbereich die ganze Menge ist	relation *f* totale à gauche	всюду (полностью) определенное отношение
T 687	**total relation,** universal relation, all relation, complete relation <SE>	Allrelation *f*, Totalrelation *f*, totale Relation *f*, Universalrelation *f*	relation *f* universelle; équivalence *f* universelle	всеобщее (универсальное, единичное, полное) отношение; аморфная эквивалентность
T 688	**total rotation** <of a curve> <PO>	totale Drehung *f*	rotation *f* totale	полное вращение
	total semi-additivity <AN>	*s.* C 2560		
T 689	**total sequence** <FA>	totale Folge *f*	suite *f* totale (complète, fermée)	тотальная последовательность
T 690	**total set** <of continuous linear forms> <FA>	totale Menge *f*	ensemble *m* total (fondamental)	тотальное множество
T 691	**total set** <of numbers> <SE>	totale Mannigfaltigkeit *f*, Gesamtmenge *f*	ensemble *m* total	полное множество
	total set <TO>	*s.* F 846		
T 692	**total space** <of a bundle>, bundle space, bundle <AT>	Bündelraum *m*, Gesamtraum *m*, Totalraum *m*	espace *m* total	пространство расслоения
T 693	**total stability** <DE>	totale Stabilität *f*	stabilité *f* totale	полная устойчивость
T 694	**total-step iteration (method, process)** <AN, NU>	Gesamtschrittverfahren *n*, Iteration *f* in Gesamtschritten	méthode *f* des pas totaux, itération *f* par pas totaux, méthode à pas multiple	метод общих (полных) шагов
T 695	**total Stiefel-Whitney class** <AT>	totale Stiefel-Whitneysche Klasse *f*	classe *f* de Stiefel-Whitney totale	полный класс Штифеля-Уитни
T 696	**total subset** <FO>	überall definierte Untermenge *f*	partie *f* totale	всюду определенное подмножество
T 697	**total sum,** total <AR>	Gesamtsumme *f*, Gesamtbetrag *m*	somme *f* totale (globale), total *m*	общая сумма, целое, итог
T 698	**total sum of squares** <ST>	Gesamtsumme *f* der Abweichungsquadrate	somme *f* totale des carrés des écarts	общая сумма квадратов
T 699	**total Todd class** <of a variety> <AT>	totale Toddsche Klasse *f*	classe *f* de Todd totale	полный класс Тодда
T 700	**total variance,** total dispersion, total mean square <ST>	Gesamtvarianz *f*	variance *f* totale	общая дисперсия
T 701	**total variation,** total fluctuation, absolute variation <of a continuous transformation in E^n> <AN>	totale (absolute) Variation *f*	variation *f* totale (absolue)	полная (абсолютная) вариация, полное (абсолютное) изменение
T 702	**total variation** <of a function *or* interval function> <RF>	Totalvariation *f*, totale (vollständige) Variation *f*	variation *f* totale	полная вариация, полное изменение, вариация, изменение
T 703	**total Whitney class** <AT>	totale Whitneysche Klasse *f*	classe *f* de Whitney totale	полный класс Уитни
	totient <NT>	*s.* E 588		
T 704	**totitive** <of an integer> <NT>	kleinere natürliche Zahl *f*, die zu der gegebenen Zahl prim ist	entier *m* [naturel] au plus égal au nombre donné et premier à lui	число, меньшее данного и взаимно простое с ним
T 705	**tournament,** T-graph, round-robin tournament <GP>	Turnier *n*	tournoi *m*	турнир
	tower <SE>	*s.* M 874		
T 706	**tower formula** <for the different> <AL>	Schachtelungsformel *f* für die Differente, Schachtelungssatz *m*	formule *f* de transitivité des différentes	формула башен для дифферента
T 707	**tower formula** <for the discriminant> <AL>	Schachtelungsformel *f* für die Diskriminante	formule *f* de transitivité des discriminants	формула башен для дискриминанта
	tower of class fields <AB>	*s.* C 770		
T 708	**tower of subfields** <AL>	Unterkörperturm *m*	tour *f* de sous-corps	башня подполей
	tower of subgroups <AL>	*s.* D 320		
	to within ... <GN>	*s.* U 445		
	tr <MD>	*s.* T 714		
T 709	**trace** <of a repartition, of an adele> <AL>	Spur *f* <einer Repartition, eines Adels>, Trace *f* <einer Repartition>	trace *f* <d'un adèle, d'une répartition>	след <аделя>
T 710	**trace** <of a divisor, endomorphism, ideal, *or* element> <AL, GR>	Spur *f*	trace *f*	след
T 711	**trace,** trace point, piercing point <of a line in the projection plane> <DS>	Spurpunkt *m*, Spur *f*, Durchstoßpunkt *m*	trace *f*, point *m* trace (de trace)	след <прямой>, точка-след, основание <следа прямой> в картинной плоскости, точечный след
T 712	**trace,** trace line <of the object plane in the projection plane> <DS>	Spurlinie *f*, Spurgerade *f*, Spur *f*	trace *f*, ligne (droite) *f* trace	след <плоскости>, линия-след, основание картинной плоскости
T 713	**trace,** trace curve <of a surface> <DS>	Spurkurve *f*	trace *f*, courbe *f* trace	след <поверхности>, кривая-след
T 714	**trace,** diagonal sum, spur, main diagonal sum, tr, sp <of a matrix> <MD>	Spur *f*, Diagonalsumme *f*, Charakter *m*, Sp	trace *f*, tr	след, шпур, сумма диагональных элементов, Sp
	trace curve <DS>	*s.* T 713		
T 715	**trace form** <AL>	spurige Form *f*, Spurenform *f*	forme *f* tracique	следовая форма
T 716	**trace function** <AL>	Spurfunktion *f*	fonction *f* trace	функция следа
	trace line <DS>	*s.* T 712		

No.	English	German	French	Russian
T 717	**trace operator** <AL>	Spuroperator *m*	opérateur *m* trace	оператор следа
	trace parallel <DS>	*s.* P 1441		
	trace point <DS>	*s.* T 711		
T 718	**tracing point,** tracking point, moving point, scriber <of a planimeter> <GE, IN>	Fahrstift *m*	traçoir *m*	обводной штифт
	track <GR>	*s.* M 33		
T 719	**track group** <AT>	Trackgruppe *f*	« track group » *m*	колейная группа
	track groupoid <TO>	*s.* F 827		
	tracking point <GE, IN>	*s.* T 718		
	tractor <VT>	*s.* D 295		
T 720	**tractory** <of a curve> <GE>	Traktorie *f*, Gleichtangentenkurve *f*, Zuglinie *f*, Schleppkurve *f*	tractoire *f*, courbe *f* aux tangentes égales	трактория
T 721	**tractrix** <GE>	Traktrix *f*, Traktorie *f* von Huygens, Schleppkurve *f*	tractrice *f*, tractoire *f*, tractoria *f* de Huygens et Leibniz	трактриса
	trail <GP>	*s.* E 29		
T 722	**trajectory,** orbit, path <of an infinitesimal transformation> <DE>	Bahnkurve *f*	trajectoire *f*	траектория
T 723	**trajectory** <of a family of curves> <DG>	Trajektorie *f*	trajectoire *f*	траектория
	trajectory <SP>	*s.* R 219		
	trajectory space <TO>	*s.* Q 348		
	trammel <IN>	*s.* E 159		
T 724	**transbinariant** <of algebraic forms> <AL>	Transbinariante *f*, Binariante *f* zweiter (2.) Art	transbinariant *m*	трансбинариант
	transcendality <AL>	*s.* T 725		
T 725	**transcendence,** transcendency, transcendality <AL>	Transzendenz *f*	transcendance *f*	трансцендентность
T 726	**transcendence basis,** transcendental basis, algebraically independent generating set <of a field extension> <AL>	Transzendenzbasis *f*	base *f* de transcendance, base pure	базис трансцендентности, трансцендентный базис
T 727	**transcendence degree** <of a field extension> <AL>	Transzendenzgrad *m*, Dimension *f*	degré *m* de transcendance, dimension *f* algébrique	степень трансцендентности, размерность
T 728	**transcendence set over *k*,** set of algebraically independent elements over *k*, algebraically independent elements over *k* <AL>	Menge *f* über *k* algebraisch unabhängiger Elemente, über *k* algebraisch unabhängige Menge, algebraisch-unabhängige Elemente *npl* über *k*, irreduzibles System *n* über *k*	éléments *mpl* algébriquement indépendants sur *k*, famille *f* d'éléments algébriquement libre sur *k*	алгебраически независимые элементы над *k*, алгебраически независимая система элементов над *k*; семейство элементов, алгебраически свободное над *k*
	transcendency <AL>	*s.* T 725		
T 729	**transcendent[al],** trancendental element <AL>	transzendentes Element *n*	élément *m* transcendant	трансцендентный элемент
	transcendental <NT>	*s.* T 731		
	transcendental basis <AL>	*s.* T 726		
	transcendental element ⌐<AL>	*s.* T 729		
T 730	**transcendental equation** <AL, AN>	transzendente Gleichung *f*	équation *f* transcendante	трансцендентное уравнение
T 731	**transcendental number,** transcendental <NT>	transzendente (nicht-algebraische) Zahl *f*	nombre *m* transcendant, transcendant *m*	трансцендентное (неалгебраическое) число
T 732	**transcendental singularity** <of a function> <DE>	transzendente Singularität *f* <Painlevé>	singularité *f* transcendante	трансцендентная особенность
T 733	**transcendental surface** <AY>	transzendente Fläche *f*	surface *f* transcendante	трансцендентная поверхность
T 734	**transfer,** verlagerung <in class field theory> <AB>	Verlagerung *f*	transfert *m*	перенос
T 735	**transfer** <of a topology *or* structure> <TO>	Übertragung *f*, Verpflanzung *f*	transport *m*	перенос, перенесение
	transfer / to <GN>	*s.* T 846		
	transfer <AB>	*s.* G 516		
	transfer <DG>	*s.* C 2055		
	transfer <GN>	*s.* T 857		
T 736/7	**transferable utility** <TG>	transferierbarer Nutzen *m*	utilité *f* transférable	трансферабельная полезность
	transference theorem <AB>	*s.* T 841		
T 738	**transference theorem** <AL, LO>	Übertragungssatz *m*	théorème *m* de transfert	теорема перенесения
	transference theorem <GU>	*s.* T 741		
T 739	**transfer ideal** <AL>	Verlagerungsideal *n*	idéal *m* de transfert	идеал переноса
T 740	**transfer principle,** principle of transfer <PJ>	Übertragungsprinzip *n*, korrelatives Prinzip *n*	principe *m* de transfert (corrélation, translation, transformation), Uebertragungsprincip *m*	принцип перенесения (соответствия)
T 741	**transfer principle,** transference theorem <GU>	Übertragungssatz *m*, Übertragungsprinzip *n*	théorème *m* de transfert	теорема переноса
	transfinite cardinal <SE>	*s.* I 440		
	transfinite cardinal number <SE>	*s.* 1. I 440; 2. T 747		

No.	English	German	French	Russian
T 742	**transfinite diameter** <AL, FT>	transfiniter Durchmesser *m*	diamètre *m* transfini	трансфинитный диаметр
T 743	**transfinite function** <SE>	transfinite Funktion *f*	fonction *f* transfinie	трансфинитная функция
T 744	**transfinite induction,** recurrence, recursion, transfinite recurrence, transfinite recursion; method of transfinite induction <GN, MM>	transfinite Induktion *f*, Rekursion *f*, transfinite Rekursion; Methode *f* der transfiniten Induktion	induction *f* transfinie, récurrence *f*, récursion *f*, récurrence (récursion) transfinie; méthode *f* de l'induction transfinie	трансфинитная индукция, рекурсия, трансфинитная рекурсия; метод трансфинитной индукции
T 745	**transfinite number** <SE>	transfinite (überendliche) Zahl *f*, // eigentlich-unendliche Zahl	nombre *m* transfini, // nombre suprafini	трансфинитное число
	transfinite number <SE>	*s.* T 746		
	transfinite order[-] type <SE>	*s.* T 751		
T 746	**transfinite ordinal,** transfinite number, infinite ordinal, infinite ordinal number <SE>	transfinite (unendliche) Ordnungszahl *f*	ordinal *m* transfini (infini)	трансфинитное [ординальное] число, бесконечное порядковое (ординальное) число
T 747	**transfinite power,** transfinite cardinal number, reflexive cardinal <SE>	transfinite (reflexive) Mächtigkeit *f*	puissance *f* transfinie, nombre *m* cardinal transfini	трансфинитная мощность, трансфинитное кардинальное число
	transfinite recurrence <GN, MM>	*s.* T 744		
T 748	**transfinite recursion** <MM>	transfinite Rekursion *f*	récursion *f* transfinie	трансфинитная рекурсия
	transfinite recursion <GN, MM>	*s.* T 744		
T 749	**transfinite recursion theorem,** principle of definition by transfinite induction <FO>	Rechtfertigungssatz *m* für die Definition durch transfinite Induktion	théorème *m* de légitimation de la définition par récurrence transfinie	теорема узаконения определения трансфинитной индукцией
T 750	**transfinite relation[-] type** <SE>	transfiniter Relationstyp *m*	type *m* relationnel transfini	трансфинитный реляционный тип
	transfinite sequence of type alpha (α) <SE>	*s.* A 537		
T 751	**transfinite type,** transfinite order[-] type <SE>	transfiniter Ordnungstypus *m*	type *m* transfini	трансфинитный тип
T 752	**transform** <of a manifold> <AG>	Transformierte *f* <einer Mannigfaltigkeit>	transformée *f* <d'une variété>	преобразованное многообразие
T 753	**transform** <of a curve> <GE>	Transformierte *f* <einer Kurve>	conséquente *f* <d'une courbe>	преобразованная кривая
T 754	**transform** <of an element by x> <GR>	transformiertes Element *n* <mit x>	élément *m* transformé (transformé canonique, conjugué), transformé *m* <par x>	трансформированный (сопряженный) элемент <элементом x>
T 755	**transform** <of a series> <LI>	Transformierte *f* <einer Reihe>	transformée *f* <d'une série>	преобразованный ряд
T 756	**transform** <of a matrix by a matrix $\mathfrak{S}$> <MD>	transformierte Matrix *f*, Transformierte *f* <einer Matrix mit einer Matrix $\mathfrak{S}$>	transformée *f*, transformée canonique (homologue), conjuguée *f* canonique <d'une matrice par une matrice $\mathfrak{S}$>	преобразованная матрица <при помощи матрицы $\mathfrak{S}$>
	transform <AN>	*s.* I 77		
T 757	**transformability** <AL>	Transformierbarkeit *f*	transformabilité *f*	преобразуемость
T 758	**transformable group** <GR>	transformierbare Gruppe *f*	groupe *m* transformable	преобразуемая группа
T 759	**transformable system** <for a group of linear transformations> <AL>	transformables System *n*, Eigensystem *n*	système *m* transformable	трансформируемая система
T 760	**transformation** <of an equation> <AL>	Transformation *f* <einer Gleichung>	transformation *f* <d'une équation>	преобразование <уравнения>
T 761	**transformation,** rewriting, conversion <e.g. of an equation> <GN>	Umformung *f*, Umschreibung *f*, Transformation *f*	transformation *f*, conversion *f*	преобразование, превращение, переписание
T 762	**transformation** <of propositions> <LO>	Umformung *f*	transformation *f*	преобразование
	transformation <AN, FA>	*s.* M 96		
	transformation <AN, SE, TO>	*s.* M 102		
	transformation <GE>	*s.* M 97		
	transformation <GR>	*s.* C 2014		
	ε-transformation <TO>	*s.* E 312		
T 763	**transformation by homothetic sections** <CS, GE>	Transformation *f* durch homothetische Schnitte	transformation *f* par sections homothétiques	преобразование гомотетичными сечениями
T 764	**transformation by parallel normals,** mapping by parallel normals <GE>	Abbildung (Transformation) *f* durch parallele Normalen	transformation (application) *f* par normales parallèles	преобразование (отображение) посредством параллельных нормалей
	transformation carrying circles into circles <GE>	*s.* C 729		
T 765	**transformation equation** <GN>	Transformationsgleichung *f*	équation *f* de transformation	уравнение преобразования
T 766	**transformation factor** <AL>	Transformationsfaktor *m*	facteur *m* de transformation	коэффициент преобразования
T 767	**transformation formulas of the co-ordinates** <AL, AY>	Transformationsformeln *fpl* für die Koordinaten	formules *fpl* de changement de coordonnées	формулы преобразования координат
T 768	**transformation function** <PG>	Transformationsfunktion *f*	fonction *f* de transformation	функция преобразования

T 769	**transformation group,** group of transformations <AL, AY>	Transformationsgruppe *f*, Gruppe *f* von Transformationen	groupe *m* de transformations (substitutions)	группа преобразований (трансформаций)
	transformation into a continued fraction <SS>	*s.* T 770		
T 770	**transformation** <of a series> **into an equivalent continued fraction,** transformation into a continued fraction <SS>	Umwandlung *f* in einen [äquivalenten] Kettenbruch	conversion *f* en fraction continue	преобразование в [равноценную] цепную дробь
T 771	**transformation** <of a form> **into itself** <AL>	Transformation *f* in sich [selbst]	transformation *f* en elle-même	преобразование в себя
	transformation into itself <NT>	*s.* A 1227		
T 772	**transformation law** <of a geometric object *or* quantity> <GE>	Transformationsweise *f*, Transformationsgesetz *n* <eines geometrischen Objekts>	loi *f* de transformation <d'un objet géométrique>	закон (способ) преобразования <геометрического объекта>
	transformation matrix <AL>	*s.* M 203		
	transformation of a common fraction to a decimal fraction <NT>	*s.* T 774		
T 773	**transformation of a rational fraction into a continued fraction** <NT>	Transformation *f* eines rationalen Bruches in einen Kettenbruch	transformation *f* d'une fraction commensurable en fraction continue	преобразование рациональной дроби в цепную дробь
T 774	**transformation of a vulgar fraction to a decimal fraction,** reduction of a vulgar fraction to a decimal fraction, transformation (reduction) of a common fraction to a decimal fraction, change of a common fraction into a decimal fraction <NT>	Umwandlung (Verwandlung) *f* eines gewöhnlichen Bruches in einen Dezimalbruch	conversion *f* d'une fraction ordinaire en une fraction décimale, conversion d'une fraction ordinaire en un nombre décimal	превращение (обращение) обыкновенной дроби в десятичную
T 775	**transformation of bounded variation** <in E^n> <AN>	Transformation *f* von beschränkter Schwankung	transformation *f* de variation bornée	преобразование ограниченного колебания
	transformation of Clebsch <IV>	*s.* C 818		
T 776	**transformation of Combescure,** Combescure['s] transform[ation] <of two space curves> <DG>	Paralleltransformation *f*, Combescuresche Transformation *f*	transformation *f* de Combescure	параллельное преобразование
T 777	**transformation of co-ordinates,** co-ordinate transformation; change of co-ordinates <AN, AY>	Koordinatentransformation *f*, Transformation *f* des Koordinatensystems; Koordinatenwanderung *f*, Koordinatenwechsel *m*, Änderung *f* (Wechsel *m*) des Koordinatensystems, Übergang *m* zu einem anderen Koordinatensystem	transformation *f* de[s] coordonnées; changement *m* de[s] coordonnées	преобразование координат (системы координат)
T 778	**transformation of higher order** <AL>	höhere Transformation *f*	transformation *f* supérieure	преобразование высшего степени
	transformation of Hilbert-Schmidt class (type) <FA>	*s.* H 357		
T 779	**transformation of Jacobi** <of quadratic forms> <AL>	Jacobische Transformation *f*	transformation *f* jacobienne (de Jacobi)	преобразование Якоби
T 780	**transformation of parameter,** parameter transformation, parameter change <AN, DG>	Parametertransformation *f*, Parameteränderung *f*	transformation *f* (changement *m*) du paramètre	преобразование (изменение) параметра
	transformation of similarity (similitude) <AY>	*s.* S 884		
T 781	**transformation of similitude,** similarity transformation, similitude <DS>	Ähnlichkeitstransformation *f*, Ähnlichkeitsabbildung *f*, Ähnlichkeit *f*	transformation *f* par similitude, similitude *f*	преобразование подобия, подобное преобразование, подобие
	transformation of the variable <DI>	*s.* C 503		
	transformation rule <LO>	*s.* R 1478		
T 782	**transformation rules** <AL, LO>	Umformungsregeln *fpl*, Transformationsregeln *fpl*	règles *fpl* de transformation	правила преобразования
	transformation satisfying a global Lipschitz condition <AN, TO>	*s.* M 109		
	transformation satisfying a Lipschitz condition <AN, TO>	*s.* 1. M 109; 2. M 110		
	transformation satisfying a local Lipschitz condition <AN, TO>	*s.* L 983		
	transformation satisfying a punctual Lipschitz condition <AN, TO>	*s.* M 111		

	transformation taking circles into circles <GE>	*s.* C 729		
T 783	**transformation theory** <AL, GE>	Transformationstheorie *f*	théorie *f* de transformation	теория преобразований
T 784	**transformation to principal axes,** principal axes (axis) transformation, principal-axis transformation, reduction to normal form <especially of a conic *or* quadric> <AL, AY>; diagonalization <of a quadratic form> <AL>	Hauptachsentransformation *f*, Transformation *f* auf [die] Hauptachsen	transformation *f* aux (des) axes principaux, réduction *f* à la forme normale, réduction [aux axes principaux]	приведение к главным осям, приведение к каноническому виду
T 785	**transformed complex** <of a group> <GR>	transformierter Komplex *m* <mit *t*>	partie *f* transformée	преобразованный комплекс
T 786	**transformed contragrediently / to be** <AL>	sich kontragredient transformieren	se transformer de façon contravariante	преобразоваться контрагредиентно
T 787	**transformed domain** <TO>	Bildgebiet *n*	domaine *m* transformé	отображенная область; область, получающаяся в результате отображения
	transforming function <AN>	*s.* M 100		
T 788	**transforming matrix** <AL>	transformierende Matrix *f*	matrice *f* transformante	преобразующая матрица
	transform of *p* <AL>	*s.* C 1947		
	transform to canonical form / to <AL, AY, DE, VA>	*s.* R 384		
T 789	**transgression, transgression homomorphism** <AT, HA>	Transgression *f*	transgression *f*	трансгрессия
T 790	**transgressive element** <AT>	transgressives Element *n*	élément *m* transgressif	трансгрессивный элемент
T 791	**transient state** <SP>	transienter (vorübergehender, durchgehender) Zustand *m*, T-Zustand *m*	état *m* transitoire	невозвратное (переходное) состояние
T 792	**transinformation** <ST>	Transinformation *f*, Wirkinformation *f*, richtig übermittelte Information *f*	transinformation *f*	правильно переданная информация, переданная информация
T 793	**transition $a \to a'$** <IV>	Übergang *m* $a \to a'$	transition *f* $a \to a'$	переход $a \to a'$
T 794	**transition function** <for a fibre bundle> <AT>	Übergangsfunktion *f*	fonction *f* structurale	структурная функция
T 795	**transition function,** next state function <TA>	Überführungsfunktion *f*	fonction *f* de transition	функция перехода
	transition function <SP>	*s.* T 799		
T 796	**transition graph** <of an automaton> <TA>	Übergangsgraph *m*	graphe *m* de transition	граф перехода
T 797	**transition matrix,** Boolean matrix <of a graph> <GP>	Übergangsmatrix *f*, Boolesche Matrix *f*	matrice *f* booléienne (booléenne)	матрица переходов, булева матрица
T 798	**transition matrix** <of a Markov chain> <SP>	Übergangsmatrix *f*, Matrix *f* der Übergangswahrscheinlichkeiten	matrice *f* de transition	матрица перехода
	transition matrix <AL>	*s.* M 203		
T 799	**transition probability,** transition function <SP>	Übergangswahrscheinlichkeit *f*, Übergangsfunktion *f*	probabilité *f* de transition (passage), fonction *f* de transition	вероятность (функция) перехода, переходная вероятность (функция)
T 800	**transition to the inverse relation** <SE>	Übergang *m* zur konversen Relation	symétrisation *f* d'une relation	переход к обратному отношению
T 801	**transitive class,** complete class <SE>	transitive Klasse *f*	classe *f* transitive	транзитивный (полный) класс
T 802	**transitive closure,** closure <of a relation> <SE>	Transitivitätshülle *f*, transitive Erweiterung *f*	fermeture *f* transitive	транзитивное замыкание
T 803	**transitive graph** <GP>	transitiver (abgeschlossener) Graph *m*	graphe *m* transitif	транзитивный граф
T 804	**transitive group of motions** <of a metric space> <TO>	transitive Bewegungsgruppe *f*	groupe *m* des déplacements transitif	транзитивная группа движений
T 805	**transitive law** <AL>	transitives Gesetz *n*	loi *f* transitive	транзитивный закон
T 806	**transitive monomial group** <GR>	transitive monomiale Gruppe *f*	groupe *m* monomial transitif	транзитивная мономиальная группа
	transitiveness <AL, LO, SE>	*s.* T 810		
T 807	**transitive permutation group** <GR>	transitive Permutationsgruppe *f*	groupe *m* transitif de substitutions, groupe de permutations transitif	транзитивная группа подстановок
T 808	**transitive relation,** quasi-order <SE>	transitive Relation *f*	relation *f* transitive	транзитивное отношение
T 809	**transitive set,** complete set <SE>	transitive Menge *f*	ensemble *m* transitif	транзитивное (полное) множество
T 810	**transitivity,** transitiveness <AL, LO, SE>	Transitivität *f*	transitivité *f*	транзитивность
T 811	**transitivity formula** <for the norm>, transitivity property <of the norm> <AL>	Normschachtelungsformel *f*, Schachtelungsformel *f* für die Norm	formule *f* de transitivité des normes	формула транзитивности нормы, транзитивность нормы
T 812	**transitivity formula** <for the trace>, transitivity property <of the trace>, transitivity of the trace <AL>	Spurschachtelungsformel *f*, Schachtelungsformel (Transitivitätsformel) *f* für die Spur	formule *f* de transitivité des traces	формула транзитивности следа, транзитивность следа
T 813	**transitivity formula** <RE>	Transitivitätsformel *f*	formule *f* de transitivité	формула транзитивности

No.	English	German	French	Russian
T 814	**transitivity laws** <LO>	Transitivgesetze *npl*	lois *fpl* de transitivité	законы транзитивности
T 815	**transitivity lemma** <FO>	Transitivitätslemma *n*	lemme *m* de transitivité	лемма о транзитивности
T 816	**transitivity of equipollence** <of sets> <SE>	Transitivität *f* der Äquivalenz	principe *m* de transitivité	транзитивность равномощности
	transitivity of the trace <AL>	*s.* T 812		
	transitivity property <AL>	*s.* 1. T 811; 2. T 812		
	transitivity set <GR>	*s.* 1. D 874; 2. O 248		
T 817	**translation** <of a groupoid *or* ring> <AL>	Translation *f*, äußere Homothetie *f*	homothétie *f* externe	сдвиг
T 818	**translation** <of a function *or* distribution> <AL, AN>	Translation *f*	translation *f*	сдвиг, перенос
T 819	**translation,** parallel displacement, parallel shift <AY>	Translation *f*, Parallelverschiebung *f*, Verschiebung *f*	translation *f*, déplacement *m* parallèle	параллельный перенос, перенос, параллельный сдвиг, трансляция, параллельное перемещение (смещение)
T 820	**translation** <in elliptic *or* hyperbolic geometry> <GE>	Schiebung *f*	translation *f*	перенос
T 821	**translation** <UA>	Translation *f*	translation *f*	трансляция, сдвиг
	translational group <GE>	*s.* T 826		
T 822	**translation curve** <AY>	Schiebkurve *f*, Erzeugende *f* <der Schiebfläche>	courbe *f* de translation	кривая переноса
T 823	**translation density** <IG>	Translationsdichte *f*	densité *f* de translations	плотность сдвигов
T 824	**translation formula,** Steiner['s] theorem <for variance> <ST>	Verschiebungssatz *m* <für die Varianz>, Verschiebungssatz von Steiner, Steinerscher Verschiebungssatz (Satz *m*), Satz von Steiner	théorème *m* (formule *f*) de translation <pour la variance>, théorème de Steiner	формула смещения <для дисперсии>, формула смещения Штейнера, теорема Штейнера
T 825	**translation function** <AP>	Verschiebungsfunktion *f*	fonction *f* de translation	функция сдвига
T 826	**translation group,** translational group, group of translations <GE>	Translationsgruppe *f*, Gruppe *f* der Schiebungen (Translationen)	groupe *m* des (de) translations	группа переносов (трансляций), трансляционная группа
T 827	**translation invariance,** invariance of translation <AL, GE>	Translationsinvarianz *f*	invariance *f* par (de) translation	трансляционная инвариантность
T 828	**translation[-] invariant** <AL, GE>	schiebungsinvariant <GE>; translationsinvariant <AL, GE>	invariant par (à) translation	инвариантный относительно переносов
T 829	**translation invariant** <AL, GE>	Schiebungsinvariante *f* <GE>; Translationsinvariante *f* <AL, GE>	invariant *m* de translation	инвариант переноса, трансляционный инвариант
T 830	**translation[-] invariant functional** <CS, GE>	translationsinvariantes (bewegungsinvariantes) Funktional *n*	fonctionnelle *f* invariante par (à) translation	функционал, инвариантный относительно переносов
T 831	**translation[-] invariant metric** <FA, TO>	translationsinvariante Metrik *f*	métrique *f* invariante par (à) translation	инвариантная относительно переносов метрика
T 832	**translation lattice** <GU>	Vektorgitter *n*	réseau *m* à la Bravais	трансляционная решетка
T 833	**translation number** <of an almost periodic function> <AP>	Fastperiode *f*, Verschiebungszahl *f*	presque-période *f*	почти-период
T 834	**translation of origin** <AY>	Verschiebung *f* des Nullpunkts, Nullpunktverschiebung *f*, Übergang *m* zu einem neuen Koordinatenursprung	changement *m* de l'origine	перенос начала [координат]
T 835	**translation of the first kind** <GE>	Schiebung *f* erster (1.) Art, Linksschiebung *f*	translation *f* de première espèce	перенос первого рода
T 836	**translation of the second kind** <GE>	Schiebung *f* zweiter (2.) Art, Rechtsschiebung *f*	translation *f* de deuxième espèce	перенос второго рода
T 837	**translation operator** <in a polynomial algebra> <AL>	Verschiebungsoperator *m*, Translationsoperator *m*	opérateur *m* de translation	оператор сдвига
T 838	**translation parameter** <ST>	Verschiebungsparameter *m*	paramètre *m* de translation	параметр сдвига
	translation plane <AL, GE>	*s.* V 89		
	translation property <IT>	*s.* T 479		
T 839	**translation surface** <AY>	Translationsfläche *f*, Schiebungsfläche *f*, Schiebfläche *f*	surface *f* de translation	поверхность переноса (трансляции)
T 840	**translation symmetry** <GE>	Translationssymmetrie *f*	symétrie *f* de translation	симметрия переноса, трансляционная симметрия
T 841	**translation theorem,** transference theorem <in class field theory> <AB>	Verschiebungssatz *m*, Verlagerungssatz *m*	théorème *m* de transfert	теорема перенесения, теорема переноса
T 842	**transportation algorithm** <PG>	Transportalgorithmus *m*	algorithme *m* de transport	транспортный алгоритм, алгоритм транспортной задачи
T 843	**transportation matrix** <PG>	Transportmatrix *f*	matrice *f* de transport	транспортная матрица
T 844	**transportation network** <GP>	Transportnetz *n*, Netzwerk *n* mit Kapazitätsangaben	réseau *m* de transport	транспортная сеть, сеть с ограниченной пропускной способностью
T 845	**transportation problem,** transport problem <GP, PG>	Transportproblem *n*	problème *m* de transport	задача о перевозках, транспортная задача
	transport problem <GP, PG>	*s.* T 845		

No.	English	Deutsch	Français	Русский
T 846	**transpose / to,** to transfer, to shift <terms from one side of an equation to the other> <GN>	auf die andere Seite bringen, hinüberschaffen, transponieren <Glieder einer Gleichung>	transposer, faire passer <un terme d'un membre dans un autre>	переносить <члены из одной части равенства в другую>
T 847	**transpose** <of a linear mapping>, transposed map, transposed mapping <AL>	transponierte Abbildung *f*, Transponierte *f* <einer linearen Abbildung>	transposée *f*, application *f* transposée <d'un homomorphisme, d'une application linéaire>	транспонированное (сопряженное) отображение, сопряженное слева отображение, сопряженное преобразование <линейного отображения>
T 848	**transpose,** transpose[d] matrix, conjugate matrix <MD>	transponierte (gestürzte) Matrix *f*, Transponierte *f*, gekippte (gespiegelte) Matrix	transposée *f*, matrice *f* transposée, conjuguée *f*, transverse *f* <Cayley>	транспонированная (переставленная) матрица; матрица, симметричная к . . .
	transpose <MD>	*s.* T 851		
T 849	**transposed endomorphism** <AL>	transponierter Endomorphismus *m*	endomorphisme *m* adjoint	сопряженный (транспонированный) эндоморфизм
T 850	**transposed homomorphism** <of a simplicial map> <AT>	transponierte simpliziale Abbildung *f*	transposé *m* <d'une application simpliciale>	транспонированный гомоморфизм
	transposed intervals <LA>	*s.* T 855		
T 851	**transposed inverse matrix,** transpose <of the inverse matrix> <MD>	kontragrediente (transponierte inverse) Matrix *f*	matrice *f* contragrédiente, contragrédiente *f* <d'une matrice>	контрагредиентная (обратно транспонированная) матрица
T 852	**transposed kernel** <IE>	transponierter Kern *m*	noyau *m* transposé	транспонированное (переставленное) ядро
	transposed map[ping] <AL>	*s.* T 847		
	transposed matrix <MD> <MD>	*s.* T 848		
	transposed quasigroup <AL>	*s.* P 155		
T 853	**transposed substitution** <of quadratic forms> <AL, NT>	transponierte (versetzte) Substitution *f*	substitution *f* transposée	транспонированная подстановка
T 854	**transposed tensor** <VT>	transponierter Tensor *m*	tenseur *m* adjoint	транспонированный тензор
	transpose matrix <MD>	*s.* T 848		
T 855	**transposes,** transposed intervals, perspective intervals <of a lattice> <LA>	transponierte (perspektive) Intervalle *npl*	intervalles *mpl* perspectifs	перспективные интервалы
T 856	**transposition** <as a permutation> <AL, CT>	Transposition *f*	transposition *f*	транспозиция
T 857	**transposition,** transfer, shift <of the terms of an equation> <GN>	Auf-die-andere-Seite-Bringen *n*, Hinüberschaffen *n*, Transposition *f*	transposition *f*	перенесение в другую часть уравнения
T 858	**transposition,** contraposition <LO>	Kontraposition *f*, Transposition *f*	contraposition *f*	контрапозиция
T 859	**transposition,** interchanging of the rows and columns <of a matrix> <MD>	Transponieren *n*, Stürzen *n*, Vertauschung *f* der Zeilen und Spalten, Transposition *f* <einer Matrix>	transposition *f* <d'une matrice>	транспонирование <строк и столбцов>, перестановление, перестановка <матрицы>
T 860	**transposition rule** <for the terms of an equation> <AL, AR>	Transpositionsregel *f* <für die Glieder einer Gleichung>	règle *f* de transposition <pour les termes d'une équation>	правило перенесения <членов> в другую часть уравнения
T 861	**transvectant** <*n*-th, of index *n*> <result> <IV>	Transvektante *f*, Überschiebung *f* <*n*-te>	transvectant *m* <*n*-e>	трансвектант <*n*-й>
	transvectant of index k <IV>	*s.* K 194		
T 862	**transvection,** shear transformation, shear <AL>	Transvektion *f*	transvection *f*, cisaillement *m*	трансвекция, преобразование поворота
	transvection <VT>	*s.* I 557		
T 863	**transversal,** secant, secant line, intersecting line <of an algebraic space curve *or* variety> <AG>	Transversale *f*, geradlinige Transversale, Treffgerade *f*, Sekante *f*	transversale *f*, sécante *f*, droite *f* sécante	пересекающая линия, трансверсаль
T 864	**transversal** <also of a triangle> <EG, UA>	Transversale *f*	transversale *f*	трансверсаль
T 865	**transversal curve** <GE>	Transversalkurve *f*	courbe *f* transversale	трансверсальная кривая
T 866	**transversal field** <AG, TO>	transversales Feld *n*	champ *m* transversal	трансверсальное поле
T 867	**transversal intersecting a vertex,** transversal through a vertex <EG>	Eckenlinie *f*, Eckentransversale *f* <Tetraeder, Dreieck>	transversale *f* à travers un sommet	трансверсаль через вершину
T 868	**transversality** <AN, GE, TO>	Transversalität *f*	transversalité *f*	трансверсальность, поперечность
T 869	**transversality condition,** condition of transversality <VA>	Transversalitätsbedingung *f*	condition *f* de transversalité	условие трансверсальности (поперечности)
T 870	**transversality theorem** <VA>	Transversalitätssatz *m*	théorème *m* de transversalité	теорема трансверсальности
T 871	**transversal lines** <PJ>	transversale Geraden *fpl* <ihr Schnitt ist Punkt>	droites *fpl* transversales	трансверсальные прямые
T 872	**transversal manifold** <AG>	transversale Mannigfaltigkeit *f*	variété *f* transversale	трансверсальное многообразие
T 873	**transversal plane** <AG>	Transversalebene *f*	plan *m* transversal	трансверсальная плоскость
T 874	**transversal set** <of the edges of a hypergraph> <GP>	transversale Menge *f*	ensemble *m* transversal	трансверсальное множество
	transversal through a vertex <EG>	*s.* T 867		

T 875	**transverse axis** <of a hyperbola> <AY>	Hauptachse *f*, reelle Achse *f*, Brennpunktachse *f*, transversale Achse; Länge *f* der Hauptachse	axe *m* focal (transverse, principal)	действительная (главная) ось
T 876	**transverse diameter** <of a hyperbola> <AY>	Hauptdurchmesser *m*	diamètre *m* focal (transverse, principal)	главный диаметр
	transverse sum <AR, NT>	*s.* S 2295		
T 877	**transverse sum checking,** transverse total checking <AR, NU>	Quersummenprüfung *f*	essai *m* par somme transversale	проверка при помощи поперечной суммы
T 878	**transverse surface** <VA>	Transversalfläche *f*	surface *f* transversale	трансверсальная (поперечная) поверхность
	transverse total <AR, NT>	*s.* S 2295		
	transverse total checking <AR, NU>	*s.* T 877		
T 879	**trapezium** <*pl*: trapezia>, trapezoid <US> <having two parallel sides> <EG>	Trapez *n*, // Paralleltrapez *n* <Euklid>	trapèze *m*	трапеция
	trapezium <EG>	*s.* T 880		
	trapezium rule <DI, NU>	*s.* T 881		
T 880	**trapezoid,** trapezium <US> <having no parallel sides> <EG>	Trapezoid *n*	trapézoïde *m*	трапецоид; четырехугольник, никакие две стороны которого не параллельны
	trapezoid <EG>	*s.* T 879		
T 881	**trapezoid[al] formula (method, rule),** trapezium rule <DI, NU>	Trapezregel *f*, Trapezformel *f*, Trapezmethode *f*, Sehnentrapezregel *f*, Sehnentrapezformel *f*, Sehnentrapezmethode *f*	formule *f* des trapèzes, formule trapézoïdale, règle (méthode) *f* des trapèzes	формула (правило, метод) трапеций
T 882	**travelling[-] salesman problem,** shortest-route problem <CT, GP, PG>	Rundfahrtproblem *n*, Handlungsreisendenproblem *n*, Rundreiseproblem *n*, „travelling-salesman"-Problem *n*, Problem *n* des Handlungsreisenden	problème *m* du commis voyageur, problème du voyageur de commerce	задача коммивояжера (о бродячем торговце, о коммивояжере)
	traversal <GN>	*s.* T 883		
	traverse <GN>	*s.* T 883		
T 883	**traversing,** traversal, traverse <of a curve> <GN>	Durchlaufung *f*; Umlauf *m* <einer geschlossenen Kurve>	parcours *m*	обход
T 884	**tree** <of a groupoid> <AL, CA>	Baum *m*	arbre *m*, base *f*, ensemblin *m* maximal	дерево
T 885	**tree,** ramification <Sylvester>, topological tree <GP>	Baum *m*, baumartiger Graph *m*, baumförmiger Typus *m*	arbre *m*, ramification *f*, assemblage *m* [de lignes] à continuité simple, base *f*, ensemblin *m* maximal, arborescence *f*	дерево
	tree <GP>	*s.* 1. A 881; 2. M 244		
	tree <TG>	*s.* G 38		
	tree-like continuum <TO>	*s.* D 225		
T 886	**tree with sink *e*,** root-tree (rooted tree) with root *e*, directed tree with reference node *e* <of a digraph> <GP>	Wurzelbaum *m* mit Wurzel *e*, in *e* verwurzelter Wurzelbaum	arborescence *f* à la racine *e*, arbre *m* à racine *e*	дерево с корнем *e*; дерево, которое растет из корня *e*
T 887	**trefoil knot** <TO>	Kleeblattschlinge *f*	nœud *m* de trèfle	петля трилистника, трилистниковая петля
T 888	**Trémaux['s] algorithm** <GP>	Trémaux-Algorithmus *m*	algorithme *m* de Trémaux	алгоритм Тремо
T 889	**trend** <ST>	Trend *m*	tendance *f*	тренд
T 890	**trend estimation (fitting)** <ST>	Trendbestimmung *f*, Trendschätzung *f*	estimation *f* (ajustement *m*) de la tendance	оценка (вычерчивание) тренда
T 891	**triad,** ternary, triplet <of elements> <CT>	Triade *f*, Terne *f*, Tertie *f*, Dreiergruppe *f*, Dreizahl *f*, je drei Elemente *npl*, Reihenfolge *f* von je dreien	triade *f*, terne *m*, groupe *m* de trois, triplet *m*, tierce *f*	триада, тройка, тернар
T 892	**triad,** three-digit group <NT>	Triade *f*, Gruppe *f* von drei Ziffern	triade *f*, groupe *m* de trois chiffres	триада, группа из трех цифр
T 893	**triad** <dyadic product of three vectors> <VT>	Triade *f*	triade *f*	триада
	triad <CA>	*s.* M 815		
T 894	**triadic expansion,** ternary expansion <of a number> <NT>	triadische Entwicklung *f*	développement *m* triadique	троичное разложение
T 895	**triadic fraction** <NT>	triadischer Bruch *m*	fraction *f* triadique	троичная дробь
	triadic predicate <LO>	*s.* P 1190		
	triadic relation <SE, UA>	*s.* T 192		
T 896	**trial,** attempt <ST>	zufälliger Versuch *m*, Versuch	essai *m*	попытка
	trial solution in form of a product <DE, NU>	*s.* E 755		
T 897	**triamond** <EG>	Triamant *m*	triamant *m*	триамант
T 898	**triangle** <consisting of three sides> <EG>	Dreieck *n*	triangle *m*	треугольник, одномерный треугольник, контурный треугольник, каркасный треугольник
T 899	**triangle,** set square, square <GE, IN>	Winkel *m*, Zeichendreieck *n*, Winkelmaß *n*, Reißdreieck *n*	équerre *f*	треугольная линейка, чертежный треугольник, угольник

T 900	**triangle,** cycle of length 3 <GP>	Dreikreis *m*, zyklisch gerichtetes 3-Turnier (Drei-Turnier) *n*, 3-Clique *f*, Drei-Clique *f*	triangle *m*, circuit *m* de 3 arcs	треугольник, циклическая тройка
	triangle <EG>	*s.* T 919		
	triangle <GE>	*s.* T 916		
T 901	**triangle axiom (condition),** triangular (triangle) inequality <FA, TO>	Dreiecksungleichung *f*, Dreiecksaxiom *n*, Abstandsungleichung *f*, Dreiecksrelation *f*	axiome *m* de triangle (l'inégalité triangulaire), inégalité *f* du triangle, inégalité triangulaire [de Minkowski]	аксиома треугольника, неравенство треугольника
	triangle formed by the mid-points <EG>	*s.* C 1394		
	triangle inequality <FA, TO>	*s.* T 901		
T 902	**triangle of inflection points** <of a cubic> <AG>	Wendepunktsdreieck *n*	triangle *m* de points d'inflexion	тройка перегиба
T 903	**triangle of reference,** co-ordinate triangle <for triangular co-ordinates> <AY>	Fundamentaldreieck *n*, Koordinatendreieck *n*, Bezugsdreieck *n*, Beziehungsdreieck *n*, Grunddreieck *n*	triangle *m* de référence, triangle de coordonnées, triangle fondamental	основной треугольник, координатный треугольник
	triangle of support <DS>	*s.* S 2349		
T 904	**triangle of traces** <DS>	Spurdreieck *n*	triangle *m* des traces	треугольник следов
T 905	**triangulability** <AT>	Triangulierbarkeit *f*	propriété *f* d'être triangulable	триангулируемость
T 906	**triangulable linear transformation** <of a vector space> <AL>	trigonalisierbarer Endomorphismus *m*; lineare Transformation *f*, deren Matrix zu einer Dreiecksmatrix ähnlich ist	endomorphisme *m* d'un espace vectoriel trigonalisable, endomorphisme trigonalisable	эндоморфизм, приводимый к треугольному виду
T 907	**triangulable matrix,** matrix reducible to a triangular matrix <MD>	trigonalisierbare Matrix *f*, zu einer Dreiecksmatrix ähnliche Matrix	matrice *f* trigonalisable	матрица, приводимая к треугольному виду; матрица, подобная треугольной
T 908	**triangulable set** <AT>	triangulierbare Menge *f*	ensemble *m* triangulable	триангулируемое множество, криволинейный полиэдр
T 909	**triangulable space** <AT>	triangulierbarer Raum *m*	espace *m* triangulable	триангулируемое пространство
T 910	**triangular chart,** triangular graph (map) <NO>	Dreieckstafel *f*	abaque *m* triangulaire	треугольная номограмма
T 911	**triangular co-ordinates,** trilinear co-ordinates <AY>	Dreieckskoordinaten *fpl*	coordonnées *fpl* de triangle, coordonnées du triangle, coordonnées triangulaires, coordonnées trilinéaires	треугольные координаты, трилинейные координаты
T 912	**triangular decomposition** <EG>	Dreiecksteilung *f*, Zerlegung *f* in Dreiecke	décomposition *f* triangulaire	разбиение на треугольники
T 913	**triangular distribution,** Simpson['s] distribution <ST>	Dreieckverteilung *f*, Simpson-Verteilung *f*, Dreiecksverteilung *f*, dreieckige Verteilung *f*	distribution *f* triangulaire (de Simpson)	треугольное распределение, распределение Симпсона
T 914	**triangular form** <MD>	Dreiecksgestalt *f*, Dreiecksform *f*	forme *f* triangulaire	треугольный вид
	triangular graph <NO>	*s.* T 910		
	triangular group <AL>	*s.* L 1170		
	triangular inequality <FA, TO>	*s.* T 901		
	triangularization <MD>	*s.* R 438		
	triangular map <NO>	*s.* T 910		
T 915	**triangular matrix** <MD>	Dreiecksmatrix *f*, Halbmatrix *f*, Halbdiagonalmatrix *f*	matrice *f* triangulaire, matrice trigonale, triangulaire *f*	треугольная матрица, квазидиагональная матрица; матрица, имеющая треугольную форму
	triangular matrix with ones in the diagonal <MD>	*s.* U 300		
T 916	**triangular mesh,** triangle <of a net> <GE>	Netzdreieck *n*	triangle *m* <d'un réseau>	треугольная ячейка сети
	triangular net <FD, NU>	*s.* M 414		
T 917	**triangular number** <a figurate number> <NT>	Dreieckszahl *f*, Trigonalzahl *f*, Triangularzahl *f*	nombre *m* triangulaire (figuré du second ordre, figuré d'ordre 2, trigonal), trigone *m*	треугольное число, число второго порядка Паскаля
	triangular pattern <FD, NU>	*s.* M 414		
T 918	**triangular prism** <EG>	dreiseitiges Prisma *n*, Dreikantprisma *n*	prisme *m* triangulaire	треугольная призма
	⌐<EG> **triangular pyramid**	*s.* T 240		
T 919	**triangular surface,** triangle <EG>	Dreieckfläche *f*, Dreieck *n*	surface *f* triangulaire, triangle *m*	двумерный треугольник, сплошной треугольник, пластиночный треугольник, треугольная пластинка, треугольник
T 920	**triangular-symmetric curve** <GE>	triangulär-symmetrische Kurve *f*	courbe *f* symétrique triangulaire	треугольно-симметричная кривая
T 921	**triangular system of equations** <AL>	dreieckiges Gleichungssystem *n*, Gleichungssystem mit einer Dreiecksmatrix als Koeffizientenmatrix	système *m* d'équations triangulaire	триангулярная система уравнений

T 922	**triangulated manifold** <AT>	triangulierte Mannigfaltigkeit *f*	variété *f* triangulée	триангулированное многообразие
T 923	**triangulation,** subdivision <of a polyhedron> <process> <AT>	Triangulation *f*	triangulation *f*	триангуляция
	triangulation <AT>	*s.* S 981		
T 924	**tri[-]axial ellipsoid,** asymmetric[al] ellipsoid <AY, EG>	dreiachsiges Ellipsoid *n*	ellipsoïde *m* à trois axes inégaux, ellipsoïde à trois axes, ellipsoïde asymétrique	трехосный эллипсоид
	tribe <AL>	*s.* B 548		
T 925	**trichotomy** <SE>	Trichotomie *f*	trichotomie *f*	трихотомия, деление на три части
T 926	**trichotomy law,** comparability theorem, law of trichotomy, law of probability <SE>	Gesetz *n* der Trichotomie, Vergleichbarkeitssatz *m* für Mengen	loi *f* de la trichotomie	закон трихотомии
T 927	**tricircular curve** <GE>	trizirkulare Kurve *f*	courbe *f* tri[-]circulaire	трициркулярная кривая
T 928	**trick card** <CT, NT>	Zauberkarte *f*	carte *f* magique	волшебная карта
	Tricomi['s] boundary value problem <DE>	*s.* T 930		
T 929	**Tricomi['s] [differential] equation** <DE>	Tricomische Differentialgleichung (Gleichung) *f*, Tricomi-Gleichung *f*	équation *f* de Tricomi, équation différentielle de Tricomi	уравнение Трикоми, дифференциальное уравнение Трикоми
T 930	**Tricomi['s] problem,** Tricomi['s] boundary value problem <DE>	Tricomisches Problem (Randwertproblem) *n*	problème *m* de (du type) Tricomi	задача Трикоми
T 931	**tricuspid [curve],** Steiner['s] three-cusped hypocycloid, // deltoid <GE>	dreispitzige Hypozykloide *f*, Hypozykloide mit drei Rückkehrpunkten, Steinersche Kurve *f* (Hypozykloide), dreispitzige Steinersche Hypozykloide, Dreispitz *m*, trianguläre Hypozykloide, Dreieckshypozykloide *f*; dreispitzige (trikuspidale) Kurve <4. Ordnung>	hypocycloïde *f* de Cremona, hypocycloïde steinérienne (à trois rebroussements, triangulaire); courbe (quartique) *f* tricuspidale	гипоциклоида Штейнера
T 932	**tridegree** <AL>	Trigrad *m*	tridegré *m*	тройная степень
T 933	**trident [of Newton],** parabola of Descartes, Descartes['s] parabola, Cartesian parabola <AG>	Cartesische (kartesische, Descartessche) Parabel *f*, Newtons Dreizackkurve *f*, Dreizackkurve, Dreizack *m*, Newtons Tridens *m*, Tridens, parabolische Konchoide *f*	parabole *f* cartésienne (de Descartes), trident *m* newtonien, trident, conchoïde *f* parabolique	трезубец Ньютона, трезубец [Декарта], параболическая конхоида, парабола Декарта, декартова парабола
T 934	**tridiagonal matrix,** triple-diagonal matrix, Jacobi['s] matrix, J-matrix <MD>	Jacobische Matrix *f*, Tridiagonalmatrix *f*	matrice *f* continuante (jacobienne)	матрица Якоби, якобиева матрица, тридиагональная матрица
	tridimensional space <GE>	*s.* T 448		
T 935	**tridual module** <AL>	tridualer Modul *m*	tridual *m* <d'un module>	тридуальный модуль
T 936	**trifolium,** three-leafed figure <GE>	Dreiblatt *n*, Dreiblattkurve *f*, Kleeblattkurve *f*, Trifolium *n*	trifolium *m*, trèfle *m*	кривая трилистника, трилистник, трефль
T 937	**trifunctor** <CA>	Trifunktor *m*, dreistelliger Funktor *m*	trifoncteur *m*	трехместный функтор
T 938	**trigamma[-] function** <FU>	Trigammafunktion *f*	fonction *f* trigamma	тригамма-функция
T 939	**trigonal residue** <NT>	trigonaler Rest *m* <Stern>, Rest der Trigonalzahlen	résidu *m* des nombres triangulaires, résidu trigonal	тригональный вычет
T 940	**trigonoid** <GE>	Trigonoid *n*	trigonoïde *m*	тригоноид
T 941	**trigonometric[al] approximation polynom** <of *k*-th order> <AX, NU>	trigonometrisches Approximationspolynom *n* <*k*-ter Ordnung>	polynôme *m* d'approximation trigonométrique <d'ordre *k*>	тригонометрический аппроксимирующий многочлен (полином) <*k*-го порядка>
T 942	**trigonometric convexity** <CS>	trigonometrische Konvexität *f*	convexité *f* trigonométrique	тригонометрическая выпуклость
T 943	**trigonometric equation** <AN, EG>	trigonometrische Gleichung *f*	équation *f* trigonométrique	тригонометрическое уравнение
	trigonometric form <AN, FT>	*s.* P 862		
	trigonometric Fourier series <AN, SS>	*s.* F 534		
T 944	**trigonometric function,** circular function <AN>	trigonometrische Funktion *f*, Kreisfunktion *f*, Winkelfunktion *f*	fonction *f* trigonométrique (circulaire), // ligne *f* trigonométrique	тригонометрическая (круговая) функция
T 945	**trigonometric moment problem,** problem of trigonometric moments, trigonometric problem of moments <AN, ST>	Problem *n* der trigonometrischen Momente, trigonometrisches Momentenproblem *n*	problème *m* des moments trigonométrique[s]	проблема тригонометрических моментов, тригонометрическая проблема моментов
T 946	**trigonometric polynomial,** [finite] trigonometric sum <AN>	trigonometrisches Polynom *n*, [endliche] trigonometrische Summe *f*, Exponentialpolynom *n*	polynôme *m* trigonométrique, somme *f* trigonométrique [finie]	тригонометрический многочлен (полином), [конечная] тригонометрическая сумма
	trigonometric problem of moments <AN, ST>	*s.* T 945		
	trigonometric representation <AN, FT>	*s.* P 862		

T 947	**trigonometric series,** sine-cosine series, sin-cos series <SS>	trigonometrische Reihe *f*, Sinus-Kosinus-Reihe *f*, sin-cos-Reihe *f*	série *f* trigonométrique (en sinus et cosinus)	тригонометрический ряд
T 948	**trigonometric solution** <of a cubic equation> <AL>	trigonometrische Lösung (Auflösung) *f*, goniometrische Lösung	solution *f* trigonométrique (goniométrique)	тригонометрическое решение
	trigonometric sum <AN>	*s.* T 946		
	trigonometry in the plane <EG>	*s.* P 658		
T 949	**trigraded ring** <AL>	trigraduierter Ring *m*	anneau *m* trigradué	триградуированное кольцо
T 950	**trihedral**<GE>	Dreibein *n*	trièdre *m*	триэдр
T 951	**trihedral angle** <EG>	Triederwinkel *m*, dreiseitige körperliche Ecke *f*, Dreikant *n*	angle *m* trièdre	трехгранный угол
T 952	**trilateral** <GE>	Dreiseit *n*	trilatère *m*	трехсторонник; трехвершинник
T 953	**trilateral cubic (curve)** <AG>	trilaterale (dreiseitige) Kurve *f*	courbe (cubique) *f* trilatérale	трехсторонняя кривая
T 954	**trilateral of inflection points** <of a cubical curve> <AG>	Wendedreiseit *n*, Wendepunktsdreiseit *n*, syzygetisches Dreiseit *n*	trilatère *m* des points d'inflexion	трехсторонник перегиба, трехсторонник точек перегиба, сизигетический трехсторонник
	trilinear co-ordinates <AY>	*s.* T 911		
T 955	**trilinear form** <AL>	Trilinearform *f*, trilineare (dreifach lineare) Form *f*	forme *f* trilinéaire	трилинейная форма
T 956	**trilinearity** <AL, GE>	Trilinearität *f*	trilinéarité *f*	трилинейность <AL>; трилинеаритет <GE>
T 957	**trilinear mapping** <AL>	trilineare Abbildung *f*	application *f* trilinéaire	трилинейное отображение
	trilinear polar <AY>	*s.* H 105		
	trilinear pole <AY>	*s.* H 109		
T 958	**trimetric image** <DS>	trimetrisches Bild *n*	image *f* trimétrique	триметрическое изображение
	trimetric projection <DS>	*s.* T 959		
T 959	**trimetry,** trimetric (anisometric) projection <DS>	Trimetrie *f*, trimetrische Axonometrie (Projektion) *f*, anisometrische Projektion	trimétrie *f*, projection *f* trimétrique (anisométrique)	триметрия, кабинетная (триметрическая) проекция, неизометрическая [аксонометрическая] проекция
T 960	**trinodal curve** <GE>	trinodale (dreiknotige) Kurve *f*, Kurve mit drei Knoten	courbe *f* trinodale	тринодальная кривая
T 961	**trinomial** <AL>	Trinom *n*	trinôme *m*	трехчлен
T 962	**trinomial equation,** three-termed equation <AL>	trinomische (dreigliedrige) Gleichung *f*	équation *f* trinôme (à trois termes)	трехчленное уравнение
T 963	**tripartite curve** <AY>	dreiteilige Kurve *f*	courbe *f* tripartite, courbe ayant (possédant) trois branches distinctes	трехдольная кривая
T 964	**triplanar point** <for a surface> <GE>	triplanarer Punkt *m*; // Dreiebenenpunkt *m*	point *m* triplanaire	трипланарная точка
	triple <CA>	*s.* M 815		
	tripleable functor <CA>	*s.* M 817		
T 965	**triple curve** <GE>	Dreifachkurve *f*, dreifache Kurve *f*	courbe *f* triple	тройная кривая
	triple-diagonal matrix <MD>	*s.* T 934		
T 966	**triple line** <GE>	Dreifachgerade *f*, dreifache Gerade *f*	droite *f* triple	тройная прямая
T 967	**triple of points,** triplet of points <GE>	Punktetripel *n*, Punkttripel *n*	triplet (triple, terne) *m* de points	тройка точек
T 968	**triple point** <GE>	Dreifachpunkt *m*, dreifacher Punkt *m*	point *m* triple	тройная точка
T 969	**triple primed quantity** <GN>	dreigestrichene (dreifach gestrichene) Größe *f*	quantité *f* tierce primée	величина с тремя штрихами
	triple product <VT>	*s.* P 101		
T 970	**triple root** <of an equation> <AL>	dreifache Wurzel (Nullstelle) *f*	racine *f* triple (de multiplicité 3)	корень третьей кратности
	triple scalar product <VT>	*s.* P 101		
T 971	**triple sequence** <SS>	Tripelfolge *f*, Dreifachfolge *f*, dreifach unendliche Folge *f*	suite *f* triple	тройная последовательность
T 972	**triple series** <SS>	Dreifachreihe *f*, dreifach unendliche Reihe *f*, Tripelreihe *f*	série *f* triple	тройной ряд
	triplet <CT>	*s.* T 891		
	triplet <SE>	*s.* U 373		
T 973	**triple tangent** <GE>	Dreifachtangente *f*, dreifache Tangente *f*	tangente *f* triple	тройная касательная
	triplet of points <GE>	*s.* T 967		
	triplet of primes <NT>	*s.* P 1343		
T 974	**triply orthogonal system** <of surfaces> <DG>	dreifach orthogonales Flächensystem (System) *n*	système *m* triplement orthogonal <de surfaces>	триортогональная система поверхностей
T 975	**triply tangent,** tritangent <GE>	dreifach berührend	tritangent, triplement tangent	трижды касательный, касательный в три раза
T 976	**triply-transitive group,** threefold transitive group <GR>	dreifach transitive Gruppe *f*	groupe *m* trois fois transitif	трехточечно транзитивная группа
T 977	**triquaternion** <AL>	Triquaternion *f*	triquaternion *m*	трикватернион
T 978	**trisecant** <of a rational quartic> <GE>	Trisekante *f*	trisécante *f*	трисекущая

No.	English	German	French	Russian
T 979	**trisection of [the] angle** <EG>	Winkeldreiteilung *f*, Dreiteilung *f* des Winkels, Trisektion *f* des Winkels	trisection *f* de l'angle	трисекция угла
T 980	**trisectrix** <GE>	Trisektrix *f*, Trisektionskurve *f*, winkeldreiteilende Kurve *f*	trisectrice *f*, courbe *f* trisectrice	трисектриса
	trisectrix of Catalan <AG>	*s.* C 196		
T 981/2	**trisectrix of Delanges** <GE>	Trisektrix *f* von Delanges, Delangessche Trisektrix	trisectrice *f* de Delanges	трисектриса Деланжа
T 983	**trisectrix of Longchamps,** Longchamps['s] trisectrix <GE>	Trisektrix *f* von Longchamps, Longchampssche Trisektrix	trisectrice *f* de Longchamps	трисектриса Лоншама
T 984	**trisectrix of Maclaurin,** Maclaurin['s] trisectrix <GE>	Trisektrix *f* von Maclaurin, Maclaurinsche Trisektrix	trisectrice *f* de Maclaurin	трисектриса Маклорена
	tritangent <GE>	*s.* T 975		
	trivalent graph <GP>	*s.* C 2729		
T 985	**trivalent map,** regular map of degree 3 <GP>	dreiwertige (kubische, normale) Karte *f*, reguläre Karte vom Grad 3	carte *f* de degré 3	тривалентная карта, однородная карта степени три
T 986/7	**trivector,** 3-vector <AL> VT>	Trivektor *m*, 3-Vektor *m*, schiefsymmetrischer Tensor *m* dritter Stufe	trivecteur *m*, 3-vecteur *m*	тривектор, 3-вектор
	trivial absolute value <AL>	*s.* T 1003		
	trivial character <AL>	*s.* U 266		
T 988	**trivial circuit** <GP>	trivialer Kreis *m*	circuit *m* trivial	тривиальный контур
T 989	**trivial cohomology functor** <CA>	trivialer Kohomologiefunktor *m*	foncteur *m* cohomologique banal	тривиальный когомологический функтор
	trivial cycle <AT>	*s.* C 2840		
T 990	**trivial derivation** <AL>	triviale Derivation *f*	dérivation *f* nulle	тривиальное дифференцирование
T 991	**trivial extension** <of *G* by *E*> <of modules *or* groups> <AL, GR>	triviale Erweiterung *f* <von *G* durch *E*>	extension *f* triviale <de *G* par *E*>	тривиальное расширение <*G* при помощи *E*>
T 992	**trivial extension** <of a sheaf> <AL, TO>	triviale Erweiterung *f* <einer Garbe>	extension *f* triviale <d'un faisceau>	тривиальное распространение <пучка>
T 993	**trivial fibre bundle,** simple bundle, bundle equivalent to the product bundle <AT>	triviales Faserbündel *n* <äquivalent zu Produktbündel>	espace *m* fibré trivial	тривиальное расслоение, тривиальное расслоенное пространство
T 994	**trivial graph** <GP>	Punktgraph *m*	graphe *m* trivial	тривиальный граф
	trivial group <GR>	*s.* O 85		
T 995	**trivial homogeneous ideal,** improper ideal <AG, AL>	triviales H-Ideal *n*	idéal *m* homogène impropre	тривиальный однородный идеал
T 996	**triviality** <GN>	Trivialität *f*	trivialité *f*	тривиальность
T 997	**trivialization** <of sheafs *or* bundles> <AT>	Trivialisierung *f*	trivialisation *f*	тривиализация
T 998	**trivial knot** <AT>	Kreisknoten *m*, trivialer Knoten *m*; unverknotetes Polygon *n*	nœud *m* trivial	тривиальный узел
	trivial map <SE>	*s.* C 2107		
T 999	**trivial metric** <TO>	triviale Metrik *f*	métrique *f* triviale	тривиальная метрика
	trivial representation <RE>	*s.* I 47		
	trivial ring <AL>	*s.* Z 56		
T 1000/1	**trivial solution,** zero solution <of a set of homogeneous linear equations> <AL>	triviale (uneigentliche) Lösung *f*, Nullösung *f*	solution *f* triviale (nulle, banale, zéro)	нулевое (тривиальное) решение
	trivial subgroup <GR>	*s.* U 304		
T 1002	**trivial subset** <SE>	triviale Untermenge *f*	partie *f* triviale, sous-ensemble *m* impropre	тривиальное (несобственное) подмножество
	trivial topology <TO>	*s.* I 382		
T 1003	**trivial valuation;** trivial absolute value <AL>	identische (triviale, uneigentliche) Bewertung *f*	valuation *f* impropre; valeur *f* absolue impropre	несобственное (тривиальное) нормирование, тривиальная (тождественная) нормировка, несобственная норма; несобственное абсолютное значение
T 1004	**trivial variety** <UA>	triviale Mannigfaltigkeit (primitive Klasse) *f*	variété *f* triviale	тривиальное многообразие
T 1005	**trivial zero** <of a form *or e.g.* of the zeta-function> <AL, AN, NT>	triviale Nullstelle *f*	zéro *m* trivial	тривиальный нуль
T 1006	**trivial zero-divisor** <AL>	trivialer Nullteiler *m*	diviseur *m* de zéro nul	тривиальный делитель нуля
T 1007	**trochoid** <common name of curtate and prolate cycloid> <GE>	Trochoide *f*, gemeine Trochoide	trochoïde *f*	трохоида
	trochoid <GE>	*s.* T 1008		
T 1008	**trochoidal curve,** trochoid <base curve: circle, moving curve: circle> <GE>	Trochoide *f*, Trochoidale *f*	trochoïde *f*, courbe *f* trochoïdale	трохоида
T 1009	**Trofimov['s] number** <of a group> <GR>	Trofimov-Zahl *f*	nombre *m* de Trofimov	число Трофимова
T 1010	**tromino** <EG>	Tromino *n*	tromino *m*	тромино
	true anti-representation <RE>	*s.* F 66		

T 1011	**true contour** <DS>	wahrer Umriß *m*	contour *m* vrai	истинный контур, истинное очертание
T 1012	**true error** <ER>	wahrer Fehler *m*	erreur *f* vraie	истинная погрешность (ошибка)
T 1013	**true formula** <LO>	wahrer Ausdruck *m*, wahre Formel *f*	formule *f* vraie	истинная формула
	true formula <LO>	*s.* T 98		
T 1014	**true implication** <LO>	wahre Implikation *f*	implication *f* vraie	истинная импликация
	true max <AN>	*s.* V 222		
	true maximum <AN>	*s.* V 222		
	true mean <ST>	*s.* P 1043		
T 1015	**true measure** <DS>	wahre Größe *f*	mesure *f* vraie	истинная величина
	true min <AN>	*s.* V 223		
	true minimum <AN>	*s.* V 223		
T 1016	**true obstruction** <AT>	wahres Hindernis *n*	obstacle *m* vrai	истинное препятствие
T 1017	**true prolongation** <of an operator> <FA>	echte Fortsetzung (Erweiterung) *f*	vrai prolongement *m*	истинное продолжение
T 1018	**true proposition** <LO>	wahre Aussage *f*	proposition *f* vraie	истинное высказывание (предложение)
T 1019	**true relation** <AL, LO>	wahre Relation *f*	relation *f* vraie	истинное соотношение
	true representation <RE>	*s.* F 73		
T 1020	**true shape** <DS>	wahre Gestalt *f*	vraie forme *f*	истинная форма
T 1021	**true sign** <of a number> <AR>	wahres Vorzeichen *n*	signe *m* vrai	истинный знак
T 1022	**true value** <value which eliminates a removable discontinuity> <DI>	wahrer Wert *m* <eines unbestimmten Ausdrucks>	vraie valeur *f*, valeur de continuité, valeur vraie <d'une expression indéterminée>	истинное значение <неопределенного выражения>
T 1023	**true value** <ER, ST>	wahrer (echter) Wert *m*	valeur *f* vraie	истинное значение, истинная величина
T 1024	**truncated cone,** obliquely truncated cone <EG>	[schräg] abgeschnittener Kegel *m*	cône *m* [obliquement] tronqué	наклонно усеченный конус
	truncated cone <EG>	*s. a.* F 681		
T 1025	**truncated cylinder,** obliquely truncated cylinder <EG>	schräg abgeschnittener Zylinder (senkrechter Kreiszylinder) *m*	cylindre *m* [obliquement] tronqué	наклонно усеченный цилиндр (прямой круговой цилиндр)
T 1026	**truncated distribution** <ST>	gestutzte Verteilung *f*	distribution *f* tronquée	усеченное распределение
T 1027	**truncated polynomial algebra** <over R, generated by x of degree n and height h> <AL>	trunkierte Polynomalgebra *f*	algèbre *f* de polynômes tronquée	срезанная алгебра полиномов <над R, порожденная элементом x степени n и веса h>
T 1028	**truncated polynomial ring** <AL>	trunkierter Polynomring *m*	anneau *m* de polynômes tronqué	срезанное кольцо многочленов
	truncated pyramid <EG>	*s.* F 683		
	truncated right [circular] cone <EG>	*s.* F 681		
T 1029	**truncated sample** <ST>	gestutzte Stichprobe *f*	échantillon *m* tronqué	усеченный выбор
T 1030	**truncated sequence** <AT, CA, HA>	verkürzte Sequenz *f*	suite *f* tronquée	укороченная последовательность
T 1031	**truncated tetrahedral number** <NT>	abgestumpfte (abgekürzte) Pyramidalzahl *f*	nombre *m* pyramidal tronqué	усеченное тетраэдральное число
T 1032	**truncation** <of a decimal fraction> <AR, NT>	Abbrechen *n*, Abbruch *m*	troncation *f*	обрыв
T 1033	**truncation,** break-off, breaking-off <of an expansion *or* series> <SS>	Abbrechen *n*, Abbruch *m*	coupure *f*, interruption *f*, troncation *f*	обрыв, отбрасывание членов [ряда]
T 1034	**truncation** <ST>	Stutzung *f*	troncature *f*, troncation *f*	усечение
T 1035	**truncation error,** error of truncation <NU>	Abbrechfehler *m*, Abbruchfehler *m*	erreur *f* de troncature, erreur de tronquage, erreur de chute	погрешность от обрыва, ошибка отбрасывания
	truncation error <ST>	*s.* E 482		
T 1036	**truncation point** <ST>	Stutzungspunkt *m*	point *m* de troncature	точка усечения
T 1037	**truth,** veracity <property> <LO>	Wahrheit *f*, Wahrsein *n*	veracité *f*	истинность
T 1038	**truth** <of a proposition> <LO>	Wahrheit *f*	vérité *f*	истинность
	truth <GN>	*s.* V 17		
	truth <LO>	*s.* T 98		
T 1039	**truth criterion** <LO>	Wahrheitskriterium *n*	critère *m* de vérité	критерий истинности
T 1040	**truth function,** function of formal logic <LO>	Wahrheitsfunktion *f*	fonction *f* de vérité (logique formale)	функция истинности, истинностная функция
	truth-functional biconditional <LO>	*s.* M 160		
	truth-functional conditional <LO>	*s.* M 161		
	truth-functional connective [of propositional calculus] <LO>	*s.* S 498		
	truth-functional sentential connective <LO>	*s.* S 498		
T 1041	**truth functor** <LO>	Wahrheitsfunktor *m*	foncteur *m* de vérité	функтор истинности
	truth matrix <LO>	*s.* T 1044		
T 1042	**truth set** <LO>	Wahrheitsmenge *f*	ensemble *m* de vérité	множество истинности
T 1043	**truth symbol** <LO>	Wahr-Zeichen *n*	signe *m* du vrai	знак истинности
T 1044	**truth table,** truth matrix <LO>	Wahrheitstafel *f*, Wahrheitswert[e]tabelle *f*, Wahrheitsmatrix *f*, Bewertungstafel *f*, logische Bewertungstafel (Matrix *f*), Matrix der Wahrheitswerte, Matrix	table *f* (tableau *m*, matrice *f*) de vérité, tableau des valeurs logiques, matrice logique	таблица истинности, истинностная таблица (матрица), матрица истинности, логическая матрица

No.	English	German	French	Russian
	truth-table decision procedure <LO>	*s.* Z 49		
	truth table method <LO>	*s.* Z 49		
T 1045	**truth valuation** <LO>	Wahrheitsbelegung *f*	valuation *f* par des valeurs de vérités	истинностная оценка
T 1046	**truth[-] value,** modality of truth, degree of truth <LO>	Wahrheitswert *m*, Wahrheitsmodul *m*	valeur *f* logique (de vérité, juste)	значение истинности, истинностное (логическое) значение, модальность (степень) истинности
T 1047	**Tschirnhausen['s] transformation** *f* <AL>	Tschirnhausen-Transformation *f*, Tschirnhausensche Transformation *f*, // Tschirnhaus-Transformation *f*	transformation *f* de Tschirnhausen	преобразование Чирнгауза
T 1048	**T_0-separation axiom** <TO>	Kolmogorovsches (nulltes) Trennungsaxiom *n*	axiome *m* de Kolmogoroff, axiome T_0	аксиома Колмогорова, аксиома (T_0)
	T_1-separation axiom <TO>	*s.* F 578		
	T_2-separation axiom <TO>	*s.* H 147		
	T_3-separation axiom <TO>	*s.* R 571		
	T_4-separation axiom <TO>	*s.* N 595		
	T_5-separation axiom <TO>	*s.* C 1537		
	$T_{3\cdot 5}$-separation axiom <TO>	*s.* C 1554		
T 1049	**T-space** <TO>	T-Raum *m*	espace *m* T (topologique satisfaisant à un axiome de séparation)	T-пространство
	T-space <TO>	*s.* T 544		
	T_0-space <TO>	*s.* F 120		
	T_1-space <TO>	*s.* F 587		
	T_2-space <TO>	*s.* S 536		
	T_{2a}-space <TO>	*s.* U 456		
	T_3-space <TO>	*s.* R 637		
	T_4-space <TO>	*s.* N 654		
	T_5-space <TO>	*s.* H 210		
	$T3\frac{1}{2}$-space <TO>	*s.* C 1510		
	TS-quasigroup <AL>	*s.* T 674		
T 1050	**t-statistic,** *t*-value, Student['s] ratio <ST>	*t*-Prüfzahl *f*, *t*-Wert *m*, Students *t*-Wert, *t*-Stichprobenfunktion *f*, Studentsche [*t*-]Stichprobenfunktion *f*	critère *m* (variable *f*, valeur *f* de) *t*, rapport *m* de Student	*t*-статистика, *t*-значение, отношение Стьюдента
	***T*-statistic** <ST>	*s.* H 582		
	T^2-statistic <ST>	*s.* H 582		
T 1051	**t-test,** Student['s] test <ST>	*t*-Test *m*, Student-Test *m*	test *m t* (de Student, *t* de Student)	*t*-критерий, критерий *t* (Стьюдента, *t* Стьюдента)
	***T*-test** <ST>	*s.* H 583		
	T_0 topological space <TO>	*s.* F 120		
	T_1 topological space <TO>	*s.* F 587		
	T_2 topological space <TO>	*s.* S 536		
	T_{2a} topological space <TO>	*s.* U 456		
	T_3 topological space <TO>	*s.* R 637		
	T_4 topological space <TO>	*s.* N 654		
	T_5 topological space <TO>	*s.* H 210		
T 1052	**T_0-topology** <TO>	T_0-Topologie *f*	T_0-topologie *f*	T_0-топология
T 1053	**tube [domain]** <FT>	Tubenkörper *m*, Zylinderbereich *m*	domaine *m* tubulaire	трубчатая (трубообразная, цилиндрическая) область
	tube of a vector field <AN, DG>	*s.* V 129		
T 1054	**tubular knot,** Schlauchknot <TO>	Schlauchknoten *m* <*s*-ter Stufe>	nœud *m* tubulaire	трубчатый узел
T 1055	**tubular neighbourhood** <TO>	Tubenumgebung *f*	voisinage *m* tubulaire	трубчатая окрестность
T 1056	**tubular surface** <DG, TO>	Röhrenfläche *f*, Schlauchfläche *f*, Kanalfläche *f*	surface *f* tubulaire, tube *m*, tuyau *m*, surface canal	трубчатая поверхность
T 1057	**Tucker['s] circle** <of a triangle> <EG>	Tuckers[cher] Kreis *m*	cercle *m* de Tucker	окружность Таккера
T 1058	**Tucker['s] triangle** <of a triangle> <EG>	Tuckersches Dreieck *n*	triangle *m* de Tucker	треугольник Таккера
	Tukey['s] HSD (hsd) test <ST>	*s.* T 1059		
	Tukey['s] lemma <SE>	*s.* T 118		
	Tukey['s] statement <SE>	*s.* T 118		
T 1059	**Tukey['s] test,** Tukey['s] HSD (hsd) test, HSD (hsd) test [of Tukey], *T*-method <ST>	Tukey-Test *m*, HSD-Test *m* [von Tukey], *T*-Methode *f*	test *m* de Tukey, test hsd [de Tukey], méthode *f T*	критерий Тьюки, метод *T*, *T*-метод
T 1060	**Tukey test for additivity** <ST>	Additivitätstest *m* von Tukey, Tukeyscher Additivitätstest	test *m* d'additivité de Tukey	критерий аддитивности Тьюки

	tunneled space <FA, TO>	*s.* B 67		
T 1061	**tuple,** ordered sample, regular multiplet of elements, ordered sequence <SE>	Tupel *n* , endliche Zeichenreihe *f*, geordneter Komplex *m*, Cortege *n*	multiplet *m*, séquence *f*, système *m* ordonné, suite *f*, échantillon *m*, cortège *m*	набор, кортеж, серия, упорядоченный комплекс
T 1062	**Turán['s] determinant** <FU> ┌<FU>	Turánsche Determinante *f*	déterminant *m* de Turán	определитель Турана
T 1063	**Turán['s] inequality**	Turánsche Ungleichung *f*	inégalité *f* de Turán	неравенство Турана
T 1064	**Turing['s] algorithm** <FO>	Turingscher Algorithmus *m*	algorithme *m* de Turing	алгоритм Тьюринга
T 1065	**Turing computability** <FO>	Turing-Berechenbarkeit *f*	calculabilité *f* au sens de Turing	вычислимость по Тьюрингу
T 1066	**Turing-computable function** <FO>	Turing-berechenbare Funktion *f*	fonction *f* calculable au sens de Turing, fonction Turing-calculable (Turing calculable)	функция, вычислимая по Тьюрингу
T 1067	**Turing degree** <SE>	Turing-Grad *m*	Turing-degré *m*	степень Тьюринга
T 1068	**Turing['s] machine** <FO, TA>	Turing-Maschine *f*	machine *f* de Turing	машина Тьюринга
T 1069	**Turing reducibility** <FO>	Turing-Reduzibilität *f*	réductibilité *f* au sens de Turing	приводимость по Тьюрингу
T 1070	**Turing reducible set** <FO>	Turing-reduzible Menge *f*	ensemble *m* réductible au sens de Turing	множество, приводимое по Тьюрингу
T 1071	**turn** <of a screw> <EG>	Windung *f* <einer Schraube>	spire *f* <d'une hélice>	виток <винта>
	turning function <TO>	*s.* A 660		
	turning point <AN>	*s.* B 186		
	t-value <ST>	*s.* T 1050		
T 1072	**twelve-point sphere** <of an orthotetrahedron> <EG>	Zwölfpunktekugel *f*	sphère *f* des douze points	сфера двенадцати точек
T 1073	**twice differentiable function** <DI>	zweimal differenzierbare Funktion *f*	fonction *f* deux fois dérivable (différentiable)	двукратно дифференцируемая функция
T 1074	**twin-point** <of a triangle> <EG>	Zwillingspunkt *m*	point *m* jumeau	
	twin primes <NT>	*s.* P 1325		
	twins <NT>	*s.* P 1325		
	twisted cubic <AG>	*s.* S 1309		
	twisted curve <DG>	*s.* S 1306		
	twisted product <AT>	*s.* F 150		
	twisted surface <GE>	*s.* N 371		
T 1075	**twisted torus** <TO>	verdrehter Torus *m*	tore *m* tordé	закрученный тор
	two-by-two contingency table <ST>	*s.* F 513		
	two-by-two disjoint events <ST>	*s.* T 1076		
	two-by-two independent events <ST>	*s.* M 1103		
T 1076	**two-by-two mutually exclusive events,** two-by-two disjoint events, pairwise incompatible events <ST>	paarweise (einander paarweise) ausschließende Ereignisse *npl*	événements *mpl* s'excluant mutuellement deux à deux, événements disjoints deux à deux	попарно непересекающиеся (несовместимые, взаимно исключающие) события
	two-by-two mutually independent events <ST>	*s.* M 1103		
	two-by-two Pauli matrix <AL>	*s.* P 315		
T 1077	**two-combination,** 2-combination, binion, binary <CT>	Kombination (Komplexion) *f* der (zur) zweiten (2.) Klasse, Kombination *f* zu je 2, Ambe *f*, Binion *f*	ambe *m*, binion *m*, groupe *m* de deux	сочетание по 2
T 1078	**two-constant theorem** <FT>	Zweikonstantensatz *m*	théorème *m* des deux constantes	теорема двух постоянных
T 1079	**two-decision problem** <ST>	Zweientscheidungsproblem *n*, Alternativentscheidungsproblem *n*	problème *m* des décisions alternatives	задача с двумя решениями
T 1080	**two-digit integer,** two-figure integer <NT>	zweistellige (zweiziffrige) ganze Zahl *f*	entier *m* à deux unités (chiffres)	двухразрядное (двузначное, двухцифровое) целое число
	two-dimensional category <CA>	*s.* C 206		
	two-dimensional density function <ST>	*s.* B 479		
	two-dimensional distribution <ST>	*s.* B 480		
	two-dimensional distribution function <ST>	*s.* B 481		
	two-dimensional Fourier transform[ation] <IT>	*s.* D 917		
	two-dimensional frequency function <ST>	*s.* B 482		
	two-dimensional G-space <DG>	*s.* G 537		
	two-dimensionality <AL, GE>	*s.* B 306		
	two-dimensional Laplace transform[-ation] <IT>	*s.* D 920		
	two-dimensional manifold <GE>	*s.* S 2355		
	two-dimensional normal distribution <ST>	*s.* B 483		
	two-dimensional polar co-ordinates <AY>	*s.* P 849		

No.	English	German	French	Russian
	two-dimensional population <ST>	*s.* B 484		
	two-dimensional probability function <ST>	*s.* B 485		
T 1081	**two-dimensional quadric,** algebraic surface of the second order, second-order algebraic surface <AG>	zweidimensionale Quadrik *f*, algebraische Fläche *f* zweiter Ordnung	quadrique *f* bidimensionnelle, surface *f* algébrique de deuxième ordre	двумерная квадрика, алгебраическая поверхность второго порядка
T 1082	**two-dimensional Riemannian manifold** <DG>	zweidimensionale Riemannsche Mannigfaltigkeit *f*, Riemannsche Fläche *f*	variété *f* de Riemann à deux dimensions	двумерное риманово многообразие
T 1083	**two-dimensional topological manifold** <AT>	topologische Fläche *f*, zweidimensionale topologische Mannigfaltigkeit *f*	variété *f* topologique à deux dimensions	двумерное топологическое многообразие
	two-dimensional universe <ST>	*s.* B 484		
T 1084	**two-dimensional vector space,** vector space of dimension two <AL>	zweidimensionaler Vektorraum *m*	espace *m* vectoriel à deux dimensions, plan *m* homogène	двумерное векторное пространство
T 1085	**two-element set,** pair set <SE>	zweielementige Menge *f*	ensemble *m* à deux éléments	двуэлементное множество
T 1086	**two-factor experiment** <ST>	zweifaktorieller Versuch *m*	expérience *f* bifactorielle	двухфакторный эксперимент
T 1087	**two-factor model,** 2 factorial model <ST>	Zweifaktormodell *n*	modèle *m* des deux facteurs	двухфакторная модель, модель двух факторов
T 1088	**two-figure decimal,** two-place decimal <NT>	zweistellige Dezimalzahl *f*	nombre *m* décimal à deux chiffres	двузначное (двухразрядное) десятичное число
	two-figure integer <NT>	*s.* T 1080		
	two-fold classification <ST>	*s.* T 1135		
	two-fold grouping <ST>	*s.* D 918		
	two-fold root <AL>	*s.* D 940		
T 1089	**two-fold transitive group,** doubly-transitive group, pairwise transitive group <GR>	doppelt (zweifach) transitive Gruppe *f*	groupe *m* deux fois transitif, groupe doublement transitif	двоекратная (двуточечно транзитивная) группа
	two-ideal <AL>	*s.* T 1116		
T 1090	**two lines** <as a conic> <AY>	Geradenpaar *n*	couple *m* (paire *f*) de droites	пара прямых
	two-manifold <GE>	*s.* S 2355		
T 1091	**two-parameter family** <AN, GE>	zweiparametrige Schar *f*	famille *f* biparamétrique	двупараметрическое семейство
T 1092	**two-parameter group** <GR>	zweigliedrige (zweiparametrige) Gruppe *f*	groupe *m* à deux paramètres	двупараметрическая группа
	two-parameter linear system <AG>	*s.* N 159		
	two-parametric gradient <DG, VT>	*s.* D 468		
T 1093	**two-person game** <TG>	Zweipersonenspiel *n*	jeu *m* à deux personnes, duel *m*	игра двух игроков (лиц), игра с двумя участниками, парная игра, дуэль, поединок
	two-person zero-sum game <TG>	*s.* Z 65		
T 1094	**two-phase sampling** <ST>	zweiphasiges Stichprobenverfahren *n*	sondage (échantillonnage) *m* à deux phases	двухфазный выбор, метод двухфазной выборки
	two-place decimal <NT>	*s.* T 1088		
T 1095	**two-place number** <NT>	zweistellige Zahl *f*	nombre *m* à deux chiffres	двузначное число
T 1096	**two-place predicate,** predicate of two arguments, binary predicate <LO>	zweistelliges Prädikat (Attribut) *n*, zweistellige (binäre) Relation *f*	prédicat *m* diadique (dyadique, à deux arguments, à deux variables, portant sur deux objets)	двуместный (бинарный) предикат
T 1097	**two-place predicate parameter (variable),** binary predicate parameter <LO>	zweistellige Prädikatenvariable *f*	variable *f* de prédicat à deux variables	переменный предикат от двух переменных
T 1098	**two-place relation,** dyadic relation <LO>	zweistellige Relation *f*, binäre logische Funktion *f*, binäre Relation	relation *f* binaire	диадическое (двучленное, двуместное, бинарное) отношение
	two-place relation <SE, UA>	*s.* B 377		
T 1099	**two-plane method,** two-plane projection <DS>	Zweitafelverfahren *n*	projection *f* sur deux plans, méthode *f* de Monge (projection sur deux plans)	метод Монжа (проектирования на две плоскости)
T 1100	**two-plane projection** <DS>	Zweitafelprojektion *f*	projection *f* sur deux plans	проекция на две плоскости; проектирование на две плоскости
	two-plane projection <DS>	*s.* T 1099		
T 1101	**two-point discrete space,** doublet <as a topological space> <TO>	einfaches Punktepaar *n*	espace *m* topologique consistant de deux points isolés	простое двоеточие, двоеточие
T 1102	**two-point distribution** <ST>	Zweipunktverteilung *f*	distribution *f* à deux points	двухточечное распределение
	two-point equation <AY>	*s.* T 1103		
T 1103	**two-point form,** symmetric form <of the equation of a straight line>, two-point equation <of a line> <AY>	Zweipunktegleichung *f* <der Geraden>	équation *f* de la droite passant par deux points donnés	уравнение прямой, проходящей через две <данные> точки
T 1104	**two-point property** <in a metric space> <TO>	Zweitripeleigenschaft *f*	propriété *f* des deux points	свойство двух точек (троек)
	two points <GE>	*s.* P 781		
T 1105	**two-row[ed] matrix** <MD>	zweireihige (zweireihige quadratische) Matrix *f*	matrice *f* à deux colonnes, matrice carrée d'ordre 2	двухрядная (двурядная) матрица

T 1106	**two-sample method** <ST>	Zweistichprobenverfahren *n*	méthode *f* des deux échantillons	метод двойной выборки
T 1107	**two-sample problem** <ST>	Zweistichprobenproblem *n*	problème *m* des deux échantillons	проблема двух выборок, проблема двойной выборки
T 1108	**two-sample test** <ST>	Zweistichprobentest *m*	test *m* des deux échantillons	критерий, основанный на двойной выборке
T 1109	**two-sample t-test** <ST>	doppelter *t*-Test *m*	double test *m t* [de Student]	критерий *t* (Стьюдента) для двух выборок
	two-sheeted function <FT>	*s.* D 950		
	two-sheet hyperboloid <AY>	*s.* H 661		
T 1110	**two-sided condition** <AL>	zweiseitige Bedingung *f*	condition *f* bilatère	двустороннее условие
	two-sided continuity <DI>	*s.* C 2193		
	two-sided cut <AT>	*s.* C 911		
T 1111	**two-sided decomposition** <AL>	zweiseitige Zerlegung *f*	décomposition *f* bilatère	двустороннее разложение
T 1112	**two-sided Dini['s] derivative,** bilateral Dini['s] derivative <RF>	zweiseitige extreme Derivierte *f*, zweiseitige Derivierte (Ableitungszahl *f*)	nombre *m* dérivé bilatéral (à deux côtés)	двустороннее производное число
T 1113	**two-sided divisor** <of a ring element> <AL>	zweiseitiger Teiler *m*	diviseur *m* bilatère	полный делитель
T 1114	**two-sided divisor of zero** <AL>	zweiseitiger Nullteiler *m*	diviseur *m* de zéro bilatère	двусторонний делитель нуля
T 1115	**two-sided estimation** <AN, AX>	zweiseitige Abschätzung *f*	encadrement *m*	двусторонняя оценка
T 1116	**two-sided ideal,** two-ideal, ideal <AL>	zweiseitiges Ideal *n*, Ideal	idéal *m* bilatère, idéal	двусторонний идеал, идеал
	two-sided identity element <AL>	*s.* 1. I 62; 2. N 183		
T 1117	**two-sided inequality** <AN>	zweiseitige Ungleichung *f*	double inégalité *f*, inégalité double	двойное неравенство
T 1118	**two-sided inverse,** 2-sided inverse <AL>	zweiseitiges Inverses *n*	inverse *m* bilatère	двусторонний обратный элемент
T 1119	**two-sided inverse,** 2-sided inverse <of an infinite matrix> <MD>	zweiseitige Inverse *f*, Inverse, Reziproke *f* <einer unendlichen Matrix>	inverse *m* bilatère <d'une matrice infinie>	двусторонняя обратная матрица
	two-sided Laplace transform[ation] <IT>	*s.* B 335		
T 1120	**two-sided module** <AL>	zweiseitiger Modul *m*	module *m* bilatère	двусторонний модуль
T 1121	**two-sided neighbourhood** <of a real point> <AN, TO>	zweiseitige Umgebung *f*	voisinage *m* bilatère	двусторонняя окрестность
T 1122	**two-sided order** <of a ring> <AL>	zweiseitige Ordnung *f*	ordre *m* bilatère	двусторонний порядок
	two-sided ring <AL>	*s.* I 878		
T 1123	**two-sided surface** <TO>	zweiseitige Fläche *f*	surface *f* à deux côtés, surface bilatère	двусторонняя поверхность
T 1124	**two-sided test,** double-tailed test <ST>	zweiseitiger Test *m*	test *m* bilatéral (à deux queues)	двусторонний критерий
T 1125	**two-sided topological divisor of zero** <in a Banach algebra> <FA>	zweiseitiger Nullteiler *m* im verallgemeinerten Sinn	diviseur *m* de zéro topologique bilatère	двусторонний топологический делитель нуля
T 1126	**two-sided uniformity** <of a topological group> <AL>	[zweiseitige] uniforme Struktur *f* <einer topologischen Gruppe>	structure *f* uniforme bilatère <sur un groupe topologique>	двусторонняя равномерная структура <в топологической группе>
T 1127	**two squares theorem** <NT>	Zwei-Quadrate-Satz *m*	théorème *m* de deux carrés	теорема о двух квадратах
T 1128	**two-stage sampling** <ST>	zweistufiges Stichprobenverfahren (Stichprobenerhebungsschema) *n*	sondage (échantillonnage) *m* à deux degrés	двухступенчатый выбор, метод двухступенчатой выборки
	two-term[ed] expression <AL>	*s.* B 386/7		
T 1129	**two-valued homomorphism** <of a Boolean algebra> <AL>	zweiwertiger Homomorphismus *m*	homomorphisme *m* bivalué	двухзначный гомоморфизм
T 1130	**two-valued logic** <LO>	zweiwertige Logik *f*	logique *f* à deux valeurs, logique bivalente, calcul *m* bivalent, logique linéaire	двухзначная логика
T 1131	**two-valued measure** <on a Boolean algebra> <AL>	zweiwertiges Maß *n*	mesure *f* bivalente	двухзначная мера
	two-valuedness <AL>	*s.* D 951		
T 1132	**two-valued propositional logic** <LO>	zweiwertige (alternäre) Aussagenlogik *f*	logique *f* des propositions bivalentes	двухзначная пропозициональная логика
	two-valued sentential calculus <LO>	*s.* C 778		
T 1133	**two-valued spin representation** <AL>	zweideutige Spindarstellung *f*	représentation *f* spinorielle bivalente	двузначное спинорное представление
	two variable functor <CA>	*s.* B 313		
T 1134	**two-variable matrix** <MD>	Zweivariablenmatrix *f*	matrice *f* à deux variables	матрица для двух переменных
T 1135	**two-way array (classification),** two-fold classification <ST>	zweifache Klassifikation *f*, Zweiwegklassifikation *f*	classification *f* à double entrée	классификация по двум признакам, двусторонняя (двукратная) классификация
T 1136	**two-way [cross] classification** <ST>	Zweiwegklassifikation *f*, Kreuzklassifikation *f* <von zwei Faktoren>	classification *f* croisée à double entrée, classification à double entrée	обратная классификация по двум признакам, классификация по двум признакам

No.	English	German	French	Russian
T 1137	**two-way table** <in two-way classification> <ST>	Zweiwegetafel *f*	tableau *m* (table *f*) à double entrée	таблица с двумя входами
	Tychonoff['s] product theorem <TO>	*s.* T 356		
	Tychonoff['s] space <TO>	*s.* C 1510		
	Tychonoff['s] topology <TO>	*s.* P 1637		
	T_y-genus <AG>	*s.* G 156		
T 1138	**type** <of growth of a meromorphic function> <FT>	Wachstumstypus *m*, Typus *m*, Indikator *m*	indicatrice *f* de croissance	индикатриса роста
T 1139	**type** <of an abelian group> <GR>	Typus *m*, Typ *m* <einer abelschen Gruppe>	type *m* <d'un groupe abélien>	тип <абелевой группы>
T 1140	**type** <of groups of rank 1> <GR>	Typ *m*, Untertyp *m*, Geschlecht *n*	type *m*	тип, надтип, род
T 1141	**type,** similarity type, multiplicity type <of an algebra> <UA>	Typ *m*, Typus *m*, Signatur *f*	type *m*, signature *f*	тип, сигнатура
	type <LO, UA>	*s.* A 973		
	type <SE>	*s.* O 381		
	type A distribution <ST>	*s.* N 214		
	type I algebra <FA>	*s.* W 5		
	type I_n algebra <FA>	*s.* W 6		
	type II algebra <FA>	*s.* W 7		
	type III algebra <FA>	*s.* W 10		
	type B distribution <ST>	*s.* N 215		
	type C distribution <ST>	*s.* N 216		
T 1142	**type class** <LO, SE>	Typenklasse *f*	classe *f* de types	класс типов
T 1143	**type-conserving isomorphism** <GR>	typerhaltender Isomorphismus *m*	isomorphisme *m* indiciel	сохраняющий типы изоморфизм
	type I error <ST>	*s.* E 477		
	type II error <ST>	*s.* E 479		
	type III error <ST>	*s.* E 481		
	type I error rate <ST>	*s.* L 599		
	type I error rate determined by comparison <ST>	*s.* E 484		
	type I error rate determined by experiment <ST>	*s.* E 485		
T 1144	**type[-] number** <Russell> <LO>	Typenzahl *f*	nombre *m* typique	типовое число
T 1145	**type number** <of a lens space> <TO>	Typenzahl *f*	nombre *m* type	типовое число
T 1146	**type number** <of a function> <VA>	Typenzahl *f*	nombre *m* typique	типовое число
T 1147	**type of a partially ordered set** <SE>	Halbordnungstypus *m*	type *m* d'ordre	тип полуупорядоченного множества
T 1148	**type of decomposition** <of a prime ideal> <AB>	Zerlegungstypus *m*	type *m* de décomposition	тип разложения
T 1149	**type of distribution,** distribution type <ST>	Verteilungstyp *m*	type *m* de distributions	тип распределений
T 1150	**type of infinity** <of the limits> <SS>	Unendlichkeitstypus *m*	type *m* d'infinité	тип бесконечности
	type ordered inversely <SE>	*s.* C 2374		
T 1151	**type problem** <FT>	Typenproblem *n*	problème *m* des types	проблема типов
	type I risk <ST>	*s.* R 1342		
	type II risk <ST>	*s.* R 1343		
	type III risk <ST>	*s.* R 1344		
	I type risk <ST>	*s.* R 1342		
	II type risk <ST>	*s.* R 1343		
	III type risk <ST>	*s.* R 1344		
T 1152	**type symbol** <LO>	Typensymbol *n*	symbole *m* de types	типовой символ
	type theory <LO>	*s.* T 404		
	type I von Neumann algebra <FA>	*s.* W 5		
	type I_n von Neumann algebra <FA>	*s.* W 6		
	type II von Neumann algebra <FA>	*s.* W 7		
	type I W*-algebra <FA>	*s.* W 5		
	type I_n W*-algebra <FA>	*s.* W 6		
	type II W*-algebra <FA>	*s.* W 7		
	typical element <AL, SE>	*s.* A 879		
T 1153	**typical fibre,** fibre <AT>	typische Faser *f*	fibre *f* type	типовой (типический, стандартный) слой, слой
T 1154	**typically real function** <FT>	typisch-reelle Funktion *f*	fonction *f* du type réel	типично-вещественная функция
T 1155	**typical mean** <LI>	typisches Mittel *n*, typischer Mittelwert *m*	moyenne *f* typique	типическое среднее
T 1156	**typical representation** <of a form> <AL>	typische Darstellung *f*, Typik *f*	représentation *f* typique	типическое представление
T 1157	**typical transformation** <AL>	typische Transformation *f*	transformation *f* typique	типичное преобразование

U

No.	English	German	French	Russian
	u-algebra <AL>	*s.* R 932		
	U.B.C.R. estimator <ST>	*s.* U 148		
	Überschiebung <VT>	*s.* I 557		
	u.c. topology <TO>	*s.* T 568		
	u.c. uniformity <TO>	*s.* U 183		
	u-element <AL>	*s.* U 209		
	UFD <AL>	*s.* U 216		
	Ulam-von Neumann ergodic theorem <SP>	*s.* R 97		
	U-language <FO>	*s.* M 432		
U 1	**Ulm['s] factor** <of a group> <GR>	Ulmscher Faktor *m*	facteur *m* d'Ulm	ульмовский фактор
U 2	**Ulm['s] function** <of a group> <GR>	Ulmsche Funktion *f*	fonction *f* d'Ulm	ульмовская функция, функция Ульма
U 3	**Ulm-Kaplansky invariant** <of a group> <GR>	Ulmsche Invariante *f*	invariant *m* d'Ulm	ульмовский инвариант
U 4	**Ulm length,** Ulm type <of an abelian group> <GR>	Typ *m*, Typus *m* <einer reduzierten abelschen Gruppe>	type *m* <d'un groupe abélien réduit>	тип <редуцированной абелевой группы>
U 5	**Ulm['s] sequence** <GR>	Folge *f* der Ulmschen Faktoren, Ulmsche Folge	suite *f* d'Ulm	последовательность ульмовских факторов
U 6	**Ulm['s] subgroup** <GR>	Ulmsche Untergruppe *f*	sous-groupe *m* d'Ulm	ульмовская подгруппа
U 7	**Ulm['s] theorem** <GR>	Satz *m* von Ulm, Ulmscher Satz	théorème *m* d'Ulm-Zippin	теорема Ульма-Циппина (Ульма)
	Ulm type <GR>	*s.* U 4		
U 8	**ultimate reduction,** reduction <of a representation>; decomposition <RE>	Ausreduktion *f*, Ausreduzieren *n*; Zerlegung *f*	décomposition *f*	полное приведение, определение неприводимых составляющих; разложение
U 9	**ultra[-]barrelled space** <FA>	ultratonnelierter Raum *m*	espace *m* ultratonnelé	ультрабочечное пространство
U 10	**ultrabornological space** <FA, TO>	ultrabornologischer Raum *m*	espace *m* ultrabornologique	ультраборнологическое пространство
U 11	**ultra-characteristic [normal] subgroup** <GR>	ultracharakteristischer Normalteiler *m*, ultracharakteristische Untergruppe *f*	sous-groupe *m* ultracaractéristique	ультрахарактеристическая подгруппа
	ultraclosed <UA>	*s.* C 921		
U 12	**ultra[-]filter** <SE>	Ultrafilter *m*	ultrafiltre *m*, ultra-filtre *m*	ультрафильтр, сверхфильтр, максимальный фильтр
	ultrafilter <LA>	*s.* P 1291		
U 13	**ultra-filter base** <SE>	Ultrafilterbasis *f*	base *f* d'ultrafiltre	базис ультрафильтра
U 14	**ultrafilter space** <associated with a set> <SE, TO>	Ultrafilterraum *m*	espace *m* des ultrafiltres	пространство ультрафильтров
U 15	**ultragroup** <AL>	Ultragruppe *f*	ultra-groupe *m*	ультрагруппа
U 16	**ultrahyperbolic [differential] equation, ultrahyperbolic partial differential equation** <DE>	ultrahyperbolische Differentialgleichung (Gleichung, partielle Differentialgleichung) *f*, Differentialgleichung vom ultrahyperbolischen Typ[us]	équation *f* ultra[-]hyperbolique (aux dérivées partielles ultra[-]hyperbolique)	ультрагиперболическое уравнение, ультрагиперболическое дифференциальное уравнение [в частных производных]
U 17	**ultra-ideal** <AL>	Ultraideal *n*	ultra-idéal *m*	ультраидеал
U 18	**ultra-intuitionism** <FO>	Ultraintuitionismus *m*	ultra-intuitionisme *m*	ультраинтуиционизм
U 19	**ultrametric** <AL, TO>	Ultrametrik *f*, nichtarchimedische Metrik *f*	ultramétrique	ультраметрика
U 20	**ultrametric space** <TO>	ultrametrischer Raum *m*	espace *m* ultramétrique (topologique ultramétrique)	ультраметрическое пространство
U 21	**ultrametric triangle inequality,** strong triangle inequality <AL, TO>	ultrametrische Ungleichung (Dreiecksungleichung) *f*	inégalité *f* ultramétrique	ультраметрическое неравенство
	ultrametric valuation <AL>	*s.* N 314		
	ultra power <UA>	*s.* P 1331		
U 22	**ultra[-] product,** prime product <UA>	Ultraprodukt *n*, Primprodukt *n*	ultra-produit *m*	ультрапроизведение
U 23	**ultraregular space** <TO>	ultraregulärer Raum *m*	espace *m* ultrarégulier	ультрарегулярное пространство
U 24	**ultraregular topology** <TO>	ultrareguläre Topologie *f*	topologie *f* ultrarégulière	ультрарегулярная топология
U 25	**ultrascheme** <AG>	Ultraschema *n*	ultraschéma *m*	ультрасхема
	ultraspherical function <FU>	*s.* G 105		
	ultraspherical polynomial <FU>	*s.* G 107		
U 26	**ultrastrong dual** <FA, TO>	ultrastarker Dual *m*	dual *m* ultrafort	ультрасильное сопряженное пространство
U 27	**ultrastrong topology** <FA, TO>	ultrastarke Topologie *f*	topologie *f* ultra-forte	ультрасильная топология
	umbilic <DG>	*s.* U 29		
U 28	**umbilical [line]** <DG>	Nabelpunktlinie *f*, Umbilikale *f*, Ombilikale *f*	ombilicale *f*	омбилическая линия
U 29	**umbilical point,** umbilic, circular point, spherical point <on a surface> <DG>	Nabelpunkt *m*, Kreispunkt *m*, Nabel *m*, Umbilikalpunkt *m*, Umbilicus *m*	ombilic *m*, point *m* ombilique (ombilical, circulaire), point-cercle *m*, point sphérique	круговая точка [на поверхности], точка округления, омбилическая (округленная, шаровая) точка, омбилик
	umbral index (suffix) <VT>	*s.* D 1049		

	English	German	French	Russian
	U.M.P. test <ST>	*s.* U 172		
	unabridged division <AL, AR>	*s.* L 1095		
U 30	**unadjusted [sample] moment,** raw moment, raw sample moment <ST>	unbereinigtes Moment (Stichprobenmoment) *n*	moment *m* non corrigé (corrigé de l'échantillon)	момент без поправок на группировку
	unaffected equation <AL>	*s.* E 354		
U 31	**unaligned systematic sampling** <ST>	ungezieltes systematisches Stichprobenverfahren *n*	échantillonnage (sondage) *m* systématique non aligné	невыровненный систематический выбор
U 32	**unambiguous definition** <GN>	eindeutige Definition *f*	définition *f* univoque	однозначное определение
U 33	**unary algebra,** unoid <UA>	unäre (unäre universelle) Algebra *f*	algèbre *f* unaire	унарная алгебра, уноид
U 34	**unary composition law** <AL>	unäres Verknüpfungsgesetz *n*	loi *f* unaire	унарный закон
U 35	**unary extension** <of a structure> <UA>	unäre Erweiterung *f*	extension *f* unaire	унарное расширение
U 36	**unary operation,** one-place operation, operation of rank 1 <AL>	einstellige (unäre, unäre algebraische) Operation *f*, unäre algebraische Verknüpfung *f*	opération *f* monaire (à un terme, unaire), application *f* dans lui-même	одинарная (1-арная, унарная, унарная алгебраическая) операция
	unary predicate <LO>	*s.* O 94		
	unary predicate parameter <LO>	*s.* O 96		
U 37	**unary relation,** one-place relation <AL, LO>	einstellige (unäre) Relation *f*	relation *f* unaire (monaire)	унарное отношение
U 38	**unattainability** <GP>	Unerreichbarkeit *f*	inaccessibilité *f*	недостижимость
U 39	**unattainable vertex** <of a graph> <GP>	unerreichbarer Knotenpunkt *m*	sommet *m* inaccessible	недостижимая вершина
U 40	**unbased map** <TO>	Abbildung *f* <als Abbildung von Räumen ohne Basispunkt aufgefaßt>	application *f* non pointée	отображение без учета отмеченной точки
U 41	**unbiased confidence estimation** <ST>	unverfälschte (unverzerrte, erwartungstreue, biasfreie) Konfidenzschätzung *f*	estimation *f* de confiance non biaisée	несмещенная доверительная оценка
U 42	**unbiased estimating equation** <ST>	erwartungstreue (unverzerrte, unverfälschte, nichtverzerrende, biasfreie) Schätzgleichung *f*	équation *f* d'estimation sans biais	несмещенное уравнение оценки
U 43	**unbiased estimating function, unbiased estimator** <ST>	erwartungstreue (unverzerrte, unverfälschte, biasfreie, nichtverzerrende, treffgenaue, genaue) Schätzfunktion (Punktschätzung, Schätzung) *f*, Schätzfunktion (Punktschätzung, Schätzung) ohne systematischen Fehler	estimateur *m* non biaisé, estimateur sans biais (erreur systématique), fonction *f* estimatrice sans biais, fonction estimatrice non biaisée. estimateur correct	несмещенная оценка
U 44	**unbiasedness** <ST>	Unverzerrtheit *f*, Erwartungstreue *f*, Biasfreiheit *f*	propriété *f* d'être sans biais, propriété d'être non biaisé	несмещенность
U 45	**unbiased sample** <ST>	unverzerrte (unverfälschte, biasfreie) Stichprobe, *f* Stichprobe ohne systematischen Fehler	échantillon *m* sans biais, échantillon non biaisé	беспристрастная выборка
U 46	**unbiased sampling** <ST>	Stichprobennahme *f* ohne Verzerrungen, nichtverzerrende Stichprobennahme	échantillonnage (sondage) *m* sans biais	беспристрастный выбор
U 47	**unbiased test** <ST>	unverzerrter (unverfälschter, überall wirksamer) Test *m*	test *m* non biaisé, test sans erreurs systématiques	несмещенный критерий
U 48	**unbounded function** <DI>	unbeschränkte Funktion *f*	fonction *f* non bornée	неограниченная функция
U 49	**unbounded interval** <DI>	unbeschränktes Intervall *n*	intervalle *m* illimité	безграничный интервал
	unbounded interval closed at the left <AN>	*s.* I 828		
	unbounded interval closed at the right <AN>	*s.* I 829		
	unbounded linearly ordered set <SE>	*s.* O 146		
U 50	**unboundedly continual function element** <FT>	unbeschränkt [analytisch] fortsetzbares Funktionselement *n*	élément *m* de fonction indéfiniment prolongeable	неограниченно [аналитически] продолжаемый элемент функции
U 51	**unboundedness** <GN>	Unbeschränktheit *f*	propriété *f* de n'être pas borné	неограниченность
	unbounded number sequence <SS>	*s.* U 54		
U 52	**unbounded operator** <FA>	unbeschränkter (nichtbeschränkter) Operator *m*	opérateur *m* non borné	неограниченный оператор
U 53	**unbounded quantifier** <LO>	unbeschränkter Quantor *m*	quantificateur *m* illimité	неограниченный квантор
U 54	**unbounded sequence,** unbounded number sequence <SS>	unbeschränkte Zahlenfolge (Folge) *f*	suite *f* [de nombres] non bornée	неограниченная последовательность (числовая последовательность)
U 55	**unbounded set** <AN, TO>	unbeschränkte Menge *f*	ensemble *m* illimité (non borné)	неограниченное множество

U 56	**unbounded variation,** unlimited variation <of a function> <AN>	unbeschränkte Variation *f*, unbeschränkte (unendliche) Schwankung *f*	variation *f* illimitée	неограниченная вариация, неограниченное (бесконечное) колебание
U 57	**uncertainty** <ST>	Ungewißheit *f*, Unbestimmtheit *f*, Unsicherheit *f*	incertitude *f*	неопределенность
U 58	**uncertainty** <TG>	Unbestimmtheit *f*	indétermination *f*	неопределенность
U 59	**unconditional convergence,** commutative convergence <SS>	unbedingte (kommutative) Konvergenz *f*	convergence *f* commutative, // convergence illimitée	безусловная (коммутативная) сходимость
U 60	**unconditional differential form** <DG>	bedingungslose Differentialform *f*	forme *f* différentielle inconditionnelle	безусловная дифференциальная форма
	unconditional inequality <AN>	*s.* A 77		
U 61	**unconditionally convergent continued fraction,** absolutely convergent continued fraction <NT>	unbedingt konvergenter Kettenbruch *m* <Konvergenzverhalten wird durch Weglassen endlich vieler Anfangsglieder nicht geändert>	fraction *f* continue infinie parfaitement convergente	безусловно сходящаяся цепная дробь
U 62	**unconditionally convergent series,** commutatively convergent series <SS>	unbedingt (kommutativ) konvergente Reihe *f*	série *f* commutativement convergente	безусловно (коммутативно) сходящийся ряд
U 63	**unconditionally divergent continued fraction** <NT>	unbedingt divergenter Kettenbruch *m*	fraction *f* continue infinie parfaitement divergente	безусловно расходящаяся цепная дробь
	unconditionally divergent series <SS>	*s.* P 1805		
U 64	**unconnected graph** <GP>	nichtzusammenhängender Graph *m*	graphe *m* non connexe	несвязный граф
U 65	**unconnected set** <of a graph> <GP>	nichtzusammenhängende Menge *f*	ensemble *m* non connexe	разделяющее множество
	unconnected space <TO>	*s.* D 638		
U 66	**uncorrelated random variables, uncorrelated variates** <ST>	unkorrelierte (nicht korrelierte, nicht-korrelierte) Zufallsgrößen (Zufallsvariable) *fpl*	variables *fpl* aléatoires non corrélées	некоррелированные случайные величины
	uncountability <SE>	*s.* N 365		
U 67	**uncountable cardinal [number]** <SE>	überabzählbare (nichtabzählbare) Kardinalzahl *f*	cardinal *m* (nombre *m* cardinal) non dénombrable	несчетное кардинальное число
U 68	**uncountable ordinal [number]** <SE>	überabzählbare (nichtabzählbare) Ordnungszahl *f*	ordinal *m* (nombre *m* ordinal) non dénombrable	несчетное порядковое число
	uncountable set <SE>	*s.* N 366		
U 69	**undecidability** <FO>	Unentscheidbarkeit *f*	indécidabilité *f*, nondécidabilité *f*	неразрешимость
U 70	**undecidability theorem** <FO>	Unentscheidbarkeitssatz *m*	théorème *m* de nondécidabilité	теорема неразрешимости
U 71	**undecidable theory** <MM>	unentscheidbare Theorie *f*	théorie *f* indécidable (non décidable)	неразрешимая теория
U 72	**undercrossing** <TO>	Unterkreuzungsstelle *f*		проходящая точка
U 73	**underdegree,** order <of a power series> <SS>	Anfangsgrad *m*, Untergrad *m*	ordre *m* total, ordre, valuation *f*	порядок
U 74	**underdeterminate system** <AL, AN>	unterbestimmtes System (Gleichungssystem) *n*	système *m* sous[-]déterminé	недоопределенная система (система уравнений), недоопределимая система
U 75	**underdeterminate system of partial differential equations, underdetermined [system of partial differential] equations** <DE>	unterbestimmtes System *n* von partiellen Differentialgleichungen, unterbestimmtes System	système *m* sous[-]déterminé d'équations [différentielles] aux dérivées partielles, système sous[-]déterminé [aux dérivées partielles]	недоопределенная система дифференциальных уравнений в частных производных
U 76	**underlying algebraic structure** <AL>	unterliegende algebraische Struktur *f*	structure *f* algébrique sous-jacente	соответствующая алгебраическая структура
U 77	**underlying diagram scheme** <of a small category> <CA>	unterliegendes Diagrammschema *n*	schéma *m* de diagrammes sous-jacent	подлежащая схема [диаграммы]
	underlying functor <CA>	*s.* F 460		
U 78	**underlying graph** <CA, GP>	unterliegender Graph *m*	graphe *m* sous-jacent <à>	нижележащий граф
U 79	**underlying group** <*e.g.:* of a ring> <AL>	unterliegende Gruppe *f*	groupe *m* sous-jacent	соответствующая группа
U 80	**underlying set** <of a manifold> <TO>	Trägermenge *f*	ensemble *m* sous-jacent	носитель
U 81	**underlying set** <of a metric space> <TO>	unterliegende Menge *f* <eines metrischen Raums>	ensemble *m* sous-jacent <à un espace métrique>	множество точек <метрического пространства>, рассматриваемое безотносительно к метрике
U 82	**underlying set** <of a topological space> <TO>	unterliegende Menge *f*, Trägermenge *f*	ensemble *m* sous-jacent	носитель
	underlying set <AL>	*s.* C 141		
U 83	**underlying-set functor** <CA>	Funktor *m* unterliegende Menge	foncteur *m* ensemble sous-jacent	функтор носитель
U 84	**underlying topological space** <*e.g.:* of a uniform space> <TO>	unterliegender topologischer Raum *m* <*z. B.:* eines uniformen Raums>	espace *m* topologique sous-jacent <*par exemple:* à un espace uniforme>	топологическое пространство-носитель <*например:* равномерного пространства>
U 85	**underlying topology** <of a topological group> <AL, TO>	unterliegende Topologie *f*	topologie *f* sous-jacente	нижележащая топология

No.	English	German	French	Russian
U 86	**underlying variety** <of an analytic group> <TO>	unterliegende Mannigfaltigkeit *f*	variété *f* sous-jacente	многообразие-носитель
U 87	**undetermined coefficient** <AL, AN>	unbestimmter Koeffizient *m*	coefficient *m* indéterminé	неопределенный коэффициент
	undetermined multiplier <DI>	*s.* L 26		
	undeterminedness <GN>	*s.* I 322		
U 88	**undetermined number** <AN>	unbestimmte Zahl *f*	nombre *m* indéterminé	неопределенное число
U 89	**undirected edge** <GP>	ungerichtete Kante *f*	arête *f* non dirigée	ненаправленное ребро
	undirected graph <GP>	*s.* N 437		
U 90	**undirected loop** <of a graph> <GP>	ungerichtete Schlinge *f*	lacet *m* non dirigé	ненаправленная петля
	undirected path <GP>	*s.* S 428		
U 91	**undisturbed differential equation** <DE>	ungestörte Differentialgleichung *f*	équation *f* différentielle non perturbée	невозмущенное дифференциальное уравнение
U 92	**undor** <VT>	Undor *m*	ondeur *m*	ундор
U 93	**unduloid** <a surface of revolution of constant mean curvature> <DG>	Unduloid *n*	unduloïde *m*	ундулоид
	unending decimal <NT>	*s.* I 441		
U 94	**unequal** <to>, not equal <to>, ≠ <GN>	ungleich, ≠	différent <de>, inégal <à>, ≠	неравный, ≠
U 95	**unequal subclass numbers** <ST>	ungleiche Klassenbesetzung *f*	effectifs *mpl* inégaux des sous-classes	неодинаковая численность в подклассах
U 96	**unessential expansion** <of a theory> <MM>	unwesentliche Erweiterung *f*	extension *f* conservative, théorie *f* inessentielle	несущественное обогащение
U 97	**unessentially singular quaternion function** <FT>	unwesentlich singuläre Quaternionenfunktion *f*	fonction *f* quaternionienne inessentiellement singulière	несущественно особая кватернионная функция
	uneven number <AR, NT>	*s.* O 58		
	uneven value <AR>	*s.* O 62		
U 98	**unfair game** <TG>	unfaires (ungerechtes) Spiel *n*	jeu *m* non équitable	несправедливая игра
U 99	**unfaithful representation** <RE>	untreue Darstellung *f*	représentation *f* infidèle	неточное представление
U 100	**Unger['s] iteration [method]** <MD, NU>	Ungersche Iteration *f*	méthode *f* de l'itération d'Unger, itération *f* d'Unger	итерация (итерационный метод) Унгера
U 101	**ungula of the cone,** ungula of the right [circular] cone, conical ungula <EG>	Kegelhuf *m*, senkrechter Kegelhuf, Kegelabschnitt *m*	onglet *m* de cône, onglet de cône [circulaire] droit, onglet conique	отрезок (отсек) конуса, отрезок (отсек) прямого [кругового] конуса
U 102	**ungula of the cylinder,** ungula of the right [circular] cylinder, cylindrical ungula <EG>	Zylinderhuf *m*, senkrechter Zylinderhuf, Zylinderabschnitt *m*	onglet *m* de cylindre, onglet de cylindre [circulaire] droit, onglet cylindrique	отрезок (отсек) цилиндра, отрезок (отсек) прямого [кругового] цилиндра, цилиндрический отрезок
U 103	**ungula of the prism,** ungula of the right prism, prismatic ungula <EG>	Prismenhuf *m*, senkrechter (gerader) Prismenhuf, Prismenabschnitt *m*	onglet *m* de prisme (prisme droit), onglet prismatique	отрезок (отсек) призмы, отрезок (отсек) прямой призмы
U 104	**ungula of the pyramid,** ungula of the right pyramid, pyramidal ungula <EG>	Pyramidenhuf *m*, senkrechter (gerader) Pyramidenhuf, Pyramidenabschnitt *m*	onglet *m* de pyramide (pyramide droite), onglet pyramidal	отрезок (отсек) пирамиды, отрезок (отсек) прямой пирамиды
	ungula of the right circular cone <EG>	*s.* U 101		
	ungula of the right circular cylinder <EG>	*s.* U 102		
	ungula of the right cone <EG>	*s.* U 101		
	ungula of the right cylinder <EG>	*s.* U 102		
	ungula of the right prism <EG>	*s.* U 103		
	ungula of the right pyramid <EG>	*s.* U 104		
U 105	**uniaxial spherical function** <FU>	einachsige Kugelfunktion *f*	fonction *f* sphérique uniaxe	одноосная сферическая функция
U 106	**unicity,** uniqueness <of a solution> <GN>	Eindeutigkeit *f*, Unität *f*	unicité *f*	единственность
U 107	**unicoherence** <TO>	Unikohärenz *f*	unicohérence *f*	уникогерентность
U 108	**unicoherent continuum** <TO>	unikohärentes Kontinuum *n*	continu *m* unicohérent	уникогерентный континуум
U 109	**unicoherent space** <TO>	unikohärenter Raum *m*	espace *m* unicohérent	уникогерентное [топологическое] пространство
U 110	**uniconvergence space** <AN>	Raum *m* gleichmäßiger Konvergenz	espace *m* d'uniconvergence	пространство равномерной сходимости
U 111	**unicursal curve,** rational curve <AG>	unikursale Kurve *f*, Unikursalkurve *f*, rationale Kurve (Mannigfaltigkeit *f* der Dimension 1), einläufige rationale Kurve	courbe *f* unicursale (rationnelle), // courbe barycentrique	уникурсальная (рациональная) кривая
	unicursal curve <NO>	*s.* U 114		
U 112	**unicursal graph,** closed graph, Eulerian graph, eulerian graph <GP>	unikursaler (geschlossener Eulerscher, Eulerscher) Graph *m*	graphe *m* eulérien	уникурсальный (эйлеров) граф
U 113	**unicursal involution,** rational involution <GE>	unikursale (einläufige) Involution *f*	involution *f* unicursale	уникурсальная инволюция
U 114	**unicursal line,** unicursal curve <NO>	unikursale Kurve *f*	ligne (courbe) *f* unicursale	уникурсальная линия (кривая)
	unicursal space curve <AG>	*s.* R 187		

U 115	**unicursal surface** <AG>	unikursale (einläufige) Fläche *f* <Cayley>	surface *f* unicursale	уникурсальная поверхность
U 116	**unicyclic graph** <GP>	unizyklischer Graph *m*	graphe *m* connexe ne contenant qu'un cycle	одноциклический граф
U 117	**unidecimal [number] system** <NT>	Undezimalsystem *n*	système *m* hendécagonal (à base onze (11), à onze chiffres)	одиннадцатеричная система
	uniformalization <FT>	*s.* U 136		
U 118	**uniform approximation** <AX>	gleichmäßige Approximation *f*	approximation *f* uniforme	равномерная аппроксимация, равномерное приближение
U 119	**uniform bound** <of a sequence of functions> <SS>	gleichmäßige Schranke *f*	borne *f* uniforme	равномерная грань
U 120	**uniform-boundedness principle,** principle of uniform boundedness <FA>	Prinzip *n* der gleichmäßigen Beschränktheit	principe *m* de la borne uniforme	принцип равномерной ограниченности
	uniform-boundedness principle <AN>	*s.* B 50		
U 121	**uniform characteristic** <NO>	gleichförmige Charakteristik *f*	caractéristique *f* uniforme	равномерная характеристика
	uniform chart <NO, NU>	*s.* U 178		
U 122	**uniform chordal convergence,** chordal uniform convergence <FT, SS>	gleichmäßig chordale Konvergenz *f*, chordale gleichmäßige Konvergenz, gleichmäßige chordale Konvergenz	convergence *f* cordale uniforme, convergence uniforme (uniformément) cordale	хордально равномерная сходимость, равномерная хордальная сходимость
U 123	**uniform completeness** <TO>	uniforme Vollständigkeit *f*	complétude *f* uniforme	равномерная полнота
U 124	**uniform convergence** <SS, TO>	gleichmäßige Konvergenz *f*	convergence *f* uniforme	равномерная сходимость
	uniform convergence <FA>	*s.* C 2337		
U 125	**uniform cover** <TO>	uniforme Überdeckung *f*	recouvrement *m* uniforme	равномерное покрытие
U 126	**uniform distribution** <*e.g.:* modulo 1> <NT>	Gleichverteilung *f* <*z. B.:* modulo 1>	équirépartition *f* <*par exemple:* modulo 1>	равномерное распределение <*например:* mod. 1>
U 127	**uniform distribution,** equidistribution, equipartition <ST>	gleichmäßige Verteilung *f*, Gleichverteilung *f*	distribution (répartition, loi) *f* uniforme, équipartition *f*	равномерное распределение
	uniform distribution <ST>	*s.* C 2245		
U 128	**uniform equicontinuity** <AN>	gleichmäßige gleichgradige Stetigkeit *f*	équicontinuité *f* uniforme	равномерная равностепенная непрерывность
U 129	**uniform group structure** <GR>	uniforme Gruppenstruktur *f*	structure *f* uniforme de groupe	равномерная структура групп
U 130	**uniform hypergraph** <of rank *r*> <GP>	gleichförmiger Hypergraph *m*	hypergraphe *m* uniforme <de rang *r*>	одномерный гиперграф
U 131	**uniform invariant** <TO>	uniforme Invariante *f*	invariant *m* uniforme	равномерный инвариант
	uniformisation <FT>	*s.* U 136		
U 132	**uniform isomorphism** <of spaces> <TO>	uniformer Isomorphismus *m*	isomorphisme *m* uniforme	равномерный изоморфизм
	uniformity <TO>	*s.* U 181		
	uniformity generated by a pseudo-metric <TO>	*s.* P 1958		
	uniformity of compact convergence <TO>	*s.* U 182		
U 133	**uniformity of pointwise (simple) convergence,** s.c. uniformity <TO>	uniforme Struktur *f* der punktweisen Konvergenz	structure *f* uniforme de la convergence simple	равномерная структура простой сходимости
	uniformity of uniform convergence <TO>	*s.* U 183		
U 134	**uniformizable point** <of a complex variety> <FT>	uniformisierbarer Punkt *m*	point *m* uniformisable	униформизируемая точка
U 135	**uniformizable space,** uniformizable topological space> <TO>	uniformisierbarer (uniformisierbarer topologischer) Raum *m*	espace *m* uniformisable (topologique uniformisable)	равномеризуемое топологическое пространство
	uniformizable space <TO>	*s.* C 1510		
	uniformizable topological space <TO>	*s.* U 135		
U 136	**uniformization,** uniformisation, uniformalization <FT>	Uniformisierung *f*	uniformisation *f*	униформизация
	uniformization in the large <FT>	*s.* G 310		
U 137	**uniformization principle [of Koebe],** uniformization theorem [of Koebe], general uniformization theorem [of Koebe] <FT>	Uniformisierungsprinzip *n* von Koebe, allgemeines (Koebesches) Uniformisierungsprinzip, allgemeiner Uniformisierungssatz *m*	théorème (principe) *m* d'uniformisation général <de Koebe>, théorème (principe) général d'uniformisation	общая теорема униформизации
U 138	**uniformization problem** <FT>	Uniformisierungsproblem *n*, Problem *n* der Uniformisierung	problème *m* de l'uniformisation	задача униформизации
U 139	**uniformization theorem** <FO, FT>	Uniformisierungssatz *m*	théorème *m* d'uniformisation	теорема униформизации
	uniformization theorem [of Koebe] <FT>	*s.* U 137		
U 140	**uniformization theory,** theory of uniformization <FT>	Uniformisierungstheorie *f*	théorie *f* d'uniformisation	теория униформизации
	uniformizing <FT>	*s.* U 142/3		

U 141	**uniformizing covering surface** <FT>	uniformisierende Überlagerungsfläche *f*	surface *f* de recouvrement uniformisante	униформизирующая накрывающая поверхность, униформизирующая поверхность наложения
	uniformizing element <AL>	*s.* L 1007		
U 142/3	**uniformizing function,** uniformizing <FT>	Uniformisierende *f*	fonction *f* uniformisante, uniformisante *f*	униформизирующая функция, униформизирующая
	uniformizing parameter <AL>	*s.* L 1007		
	uniformizing parameter <FT>	*s.* U 145		
U 144	**uniformizing transcendental [function]** <FT>	Uniformisierungstranszendente *f*, uniformisierende Transzendente *f*	fonction *f* transcendante uniformisante, transcendante *f* uniformisante	униформизирующая трансцендентная [функция]
U 145	**uniformizing variable,** uniformizing parameter <FT>	uniformisierende Variable *f*, uniformisierender Parameter *m*	variable *f* uniformisante, paramètre *m* uniformisant	униформизирующий параметр
U 146	**uniform limit,** limit in the sense of uniform convergence <AN>	Grenzwert (Limes) *m* im Sinne der gleichmäßigen Konvergenz, gleichmäßiger Grenzwert (Limes)	limite *f* uniforme	равномерный предел, предел в смысле равномерной сходимости
U 147	**uniform Lipschitz condition** <DE>	gleichmäßige Lipschitz-Bedingung *f*	condition *f* de Lipschitz uniforme	равномерное условие Липшица
U 148	**uniformly best constant risk estimator,** U.B.C.R. estimator <ST>	Schätzfunktion (Punktschätzung, Schätzung) *f* mit gleichmäßig bestem Risiko	estimateur *m* (fonction *f* estimatrice) à risque constant uniformément le meilleur	оценка с равномерно наилучшим риском
U 149	**uniformly bounded above** <AN>	gleichmäßig nach oben beschränkt	uniformément majoré	равномерно ограниченный сверху
U 150	**uniformly bounded below** <AN>	gleichmäßig nach unten beschränkt	uniformément minoré	равномерно ограниченный снизу
U 151	**uniformly bounded sequence of functions** <SS>	gleichmäßig beschränkte Funktionenfolge *f*	suite *f* de fonctions uniformément bornée, suite de fonctions équibornée, // suite de fonctions oscillant uniformément <London>	равномерно ограниченная последовательность функций
U 152	**uniformly bounded series** <SS>	gleichmäßig beschränkte Reihe *f*	série *f* uniformément bornée	равномерно сходящийся ряд
U 153	**uniformly bounded set** <SE>	gleichmäßig beschränkte Menge *f*	ensemble *m* équiborné	равномерно ограниченное множество
U 154	**uniformly chordal convergent sequence,** <of functions> <FT>	gleichmäßig chordal konvergente Folge *f*, chordal gleichmäßig konvergente Folge, gleichmäßig) kugelkonvergente Folge	suite *f* de (à) convergence sphérique (cordale) uniforme	хордально (сферически) равномерно сходящаяся последовательность
	uniformly connected im kleinen point set <TO>	*s.* P 787		
	uniformly continuous function <AN, TO>	*s.* U 156		
U 155	**uniformly μ-continuous function set,** uniformly μ-continuous set of functions <AN>	gleichgradig (gleichmäßig) μ-stetige Menge *f* von Funktionen, gleichgradig (gleichmäßig) absolutstetige (totalstetige) Menge *f* von Funktionen *f* [bezüglich μ]	famille *f* de fonctions uniformément μ-continue	равномерно μ-непрерывное множество функций
U 156	**uniformly continuous map,** uniformly continuous function <AN, TO>	gleichmäßig stetige Abbildung (Funktion) *f*	application (fonction) *f* uniformément continue	равномерно непрерывное отображение, равномерно непрерывная функция
	uniformly μ-continuous set of functions <AN>	*s.* U 155		
U 157	**uniformly convergent sequence of functions** <AN>	gleichmäßig konvergente Funktionenfolge *f*	suite *f* de fonctions uniformément convergente	равномерно сходящаяся последовательность функций
U 158	**uniformly convex space** <FA, TO>	uniform (gleichmäßig) konvexer Raum *m*	espace *m* uniformément convexe	однообразно[-] выпуклое пространство, однородно[-] выпуклое пространство, равномерно выпуклое пространство
U 159	**uniformly countably additive family (set) of set functions** <AN>	gleichmäßig (gleichgradig) [abzählbar] additive Familie (Menge) *f* von Mengenfunktionen	famille *f* uniformément dénombrablement additive de fonctions d'ensemble	равномерно счетно-аддитивное семейство (множество) функций множеств
U 160	**uniformly differentiable function** <RF>	gleichmäßig differenzierbare Funktion *f*	fonction *f* uniformément dérivable	равномерно дифференцируемая функция
U 161	**uniformly distributed random variable,** equidistributed (equipartitioned, equally distributed) random variable <ST>	gleichverteilte Zufallsvariable *f*	variable *f* aléatoire équidistribuée (équirépartie, uniformément distribuée, uniformément répartie au hasard)	равномерно распределенная случайная переменная
U 162	**uniformly elliptic[al] operator** <DE>	gleichmäßig elliptischer Operator *m*	opérateur *m* uniformément elliptique	равномерно эллиптический оператор
U 163	**uniformly equicontinuous family of functions** <AN>	gleichmäßig gleichgradig stetige Familie *f* von Funktionen, gleichmäßig gleichgradig stetiges Funktionensystem *n*	famille *f* de fonctions uniformément équicontinue	равномерно равностепенно непрерывное семейство (множество) функций, равномерно равностепенно непрерывная система функций
U 164	**uniformly equivalent metric** <TO>	uniform äquivalente Metrik *f* <identische Abbildung ist gleichmäßig stetig>	distance *f* uniformément équivalente	равномерно эквивалентная метрика

U 165	**uniformly equivalent space,** uniformly isomorphic space <TO>	uniform isomorpher uniformer Raum *m*	espace *m* uniforme uniformément équivalent	равномерно эквивалентное равномерное пространство
U 166	**uniformly hyperfinite C*-algebra** <FA>	gleichmäßig hyperendliche *C**-Algebra *f*	*C**-algèbre *f* uniformément hyperfinie	равномерно гиперконечная *C**-алгебра
U 167	**uniformly integrable family (set) of functions** <AN>	gleichmäßig integrierbare Familie (Menge) *f* von Funktionen	famille *f* (ensemble *m*) de fonctions uniformément intégrable	равномерно интегрируемое семейство (множество) функций
	uniformly isomorphic space <TO>	*s.* U 165		
U 168	**uniformly locally compact space** <TO>	gleichmäßig lokal kompakter Raum *m*	espace *m* uniformément localement compact	равномерно локально компактное пространство
U 169	**uniformly more powerful test** <ST>	gleichmäßig besserer Test *m*	test *m* uniformément meilleur	равномерно более мощный критерий
U 170	**uniformly most powerful confidence estimation** <ST>	gleichmäßig beste Konfidenzschätzung *f*, trennscharfe Konfidenzschätzung	estimation *f* de confiance uniformément la meilleure	однородно наилучшая доверительная оценка
U 171	**uniformly most powerful critical region,** uniformly the most powerful critical region <ST>	gleichmäßig schärfster kritischer Bereich *m*	région *f* critique uniformément la plus puissante	равномерно наиболее мощная критическая область
U 172	**uniformly most powerful test,** uniformly the most powerful test, U.M.P. test <ST>	gleichmäßig bester (der mächtigste, trennschärfster) Test *m*, trennscharfer Test, UMP-Test *m*, U.M.P.-Test *m*	test *m* uniformément le plus puissant, test « uniformly most powerful », test uniformément le meilleur	равномерно наиболее мощный критерий
U 173	**uniformly open map** <TO>	gleichmäßig offene Abbildung *f*	application *f* uniformément ouverte	равномерно открытое отображение
U 174	**uniformly strongly elliptic[al] operator** <DE>	gleichmäßig stark elliptischer Operator *m*	opérateur *m* uniformément fortement elliptique	равномерно сильно эллиптический оператор
U 175	**uniformly summable family of functions** <TO>	gleichmäßig summierbare Familie *f* von Funktionen	famille *f* de fonctions uniformément sommable	равномерно суммируемое семейство функций
	uniformly the most powerful critical region <ST>	*s.* U 171		
	uniformly the most powerful test <ST>	*s.* U 172		
	uniform metric <FA>	*s.* S 2350		
	uniform norm <FA>	*s.* S 2351		
	uniform operator topology <FA>	*s.* N 691		
U 176/7	**uniform product** <of groups> <GR>	gleichmäßiges Produkt *n*	produit *m* uniforme	равномерное произведение
	uniform random noise <ST>	*s.* W 238		
	uniform sample fraction <ST>	*s.* P 1854		
U 178	**uniform scale,** uniform chart, linear scale, linear chart <NO, NU>	gleichförmige (reguläre, lineare) Skala *f*, gleichförmige Zahlenreihe *f*	échelle *f* uniforme (linéaire)	равномерная (линейная) шкала
	uniform scale <AN, SE>	*s.* N 872		
U 179	**uniform space** <TO>	uniformer (gleichmäßiger) Raum *m*	espace *m* uniforme	равномерное пространство
U 180	**uniform stability** <DE>	gleichmäßige Stabilität *f*	stabilité *f* uniforme	равномерная устойчивость
U 181	**uniform structure,** uniformity <TO>	uniforme (gleichmäßige) Struktur *f*, Uniformität *f*	structure *f* uniforme	равномерная структура
U 182	**uniform structure of compact convergence,** uniformity of compact convergence, c.c. uniformity <TO>	uniforme Struktur *f* der kompakten Konvergenz	structure *f* uniforme de la convergence compacte	равномерная структура компактной сходимости
U 183	**uniform structure of uniform convergence,** uniformity of uniform convergence, u.c. uniformity <TO>	uniforme Struktur *f* der gleichmäßigen Konvergenz	structure *f* uniforme de la convergence uniforme	равномерная структура равномерной сходимости
U 184	**uniform topology** <FA>	Topologie *f* der gleichmäßigen Konvergenz	topologie *f* de la convergence bornée sur L(E,E')	равномерная топология
U 185	**uniform topology,** topology of the uniformity <TO>	uniforme Topologie *f*	topologie *f* uniforme	равномерная топология
	uniform topology <FA>	*s.* N 691		
	unilateral derivative <AN>	*s.* O 104		
	unilateral differentiability <AN>	*s.* O 105		
U 186	**unilateral Dirichlet problem,** obstacle problem <DE>	einseitiges Dirichletsches Problem *n*, Hindernisproblem *n*	problème *m* de Dirichlet unilatéral	односторонняя задача Дирихле
U 187	**unilateral equation** <AL>	einseitige (unilaterale) Gleichung *f*	équation *f* unilatérale <Sylvester>	одностороннее уравнение
U 188	**unilateral Laplace transform[ation],** one-sided Laplace transform[ation] <IT>	einseitige (unilaterale) Laplace-Transformation *f*	transformation *f* unilatérale de Laplace	одностороннее преобразование Лапласа
	unilateral limit <AN>	*s.* O 110		
	unilaterally continuous <AN>	*s.* C 2230		
	unilateral surface <DG, GE>	*s.* O 114		

No.	English	German	French	Russian
U 189	**unimodal distribution [function]** <ST>	unimodale (eingipflige) Verteilung[sfunktion] *f*	distribution *f* (fonction *f* de distribution) unimodale	одновершинное (унимодальное) распределение, одновершинная (унимодальная) функция распределения
U 190	⌐<MD> **unimodular determinant**	unimodulare Determinante *f*	déterminant *m* unimodulaire	унимодулярный определитель
	unimodular group <GR>	*s.* S 1376		
U 191	**unimodular hypergraph** <GP>	unimodularer Hypergraph *m*	hypergraphe *m* unimodulaire	унимодулярный гиперграф
U 192	**unimodularly bounded function** <FT>	unimodular beschränkte Funktion *f*	fonction *f* unimodulairement bornée	унимодулярно ограниченная функция
U 193	**unimodular map[ping],** unimodular transformation <FT>	unimodulare lineare Transformation *f*, unimodulare Abbildung *f* (Transformation)	transformation (application) *f* unimodulaire	унимодулярное отображение (преобразование)
U 194	**unimodular matrix,** unit matrix <MD>	unimodulare Matrix *f*	matrice *f* unimodulaire	унимодулярная матрица
U 195	**unimodular substitution** <AL, NT>	unimodulare Substitution *f*, Einheitssubstitution *f*	substitution *f* unimodulaire (unité)	унимодулярная подстановка
	unimodular transformation <FT>	*s.* U 193		
U 196	**unimodulus matrix** <MD>	Matrix *f* mit der Determinante Eins <Elemente nicht notwendig ganzzahlig>	matrice *f* à déterminant unité	матрица с единичным определителем
U 197	**uninodal curve** <AG>	uninodale Kurve *f*, Einknotenkurve *f*	courbe *f* uninodale	унинодальная кривая
U 198	**union** <of a compatible collection of halfgroupoids> <AL>	Vereinigung *f*	réunion *f*	объединение
U 199	**union** <of fields> <AL>	Vereinigungskörper *m*	corps *m* réunion	поле-объединение, объединение полей
U 200	**union** <of monomorphisms> <CA>	Vereinigung *f*	réunion *f*	объединение
U 201	**union,** join <of classes> <SE>	Vereinigungsklasse *f*	classe *f* réunion	класс-объединение, объединение классов
U 202	**union,** join, sum-set, sum, logical sum, [point] set union, set-theoretic[al] union, element-sum <of sets> <SE>	Vereinigung *f*, Vereinigungsmenge *f*, Summe *f*, logische Summe, Summenmenge *f*, // Gesamtmenge *f*	réunion *f*, union *f*, ensemble-somme *m*, ensemble *m* somme, réunion d'ensembles, somme *f* logique	объединение, сумма, соединение, теоретико-множественная сумма, полное множество
U 203	**union** <of domains> <TO>	Vereinigungsgebiet *n*	domaine *m* réunion	объединяющая область
	union <CA>	*s.* 1. F 155; 2. P 2076		
	union <SE>	*s.* S 696		
	union axiom <SE>	*s.* 1. A 1295; 2. A 1297		
	union of groups <AL>	*s.* C 1509		
U 204	**union of spheres,** wedge product of spheres <TO>	Bouquet *n* von Sphären	bouquet *m* de sphères	букет сфер
U 205	**union space** <TO>	Vereinigungsraum *m*	espace *m* réunion	объединение пространств
U 206	**unipartite conic** <AY>	einteilige Kurve *f* zweiter Ordnung, einteiliger Kegelschnitt *m*	conique (section conique) *f* unipartite	однодольная кривая второго порядка, однодольное коническое сечение
U 207	**unipartite curve** <AY>	einteilige Kurve *f*	courbe *f* unipartite, courbe ayant (possédant) une seule branche	однодольная кривая
U 208	**uniplanar point,** unode <of a surface> <AG>	uniplanarer Doppelpunkt (Knotenpunkt, Knoten, Punkt) *m*, Uniknoten *m*	point *m* double uniplanaire	унипланарная двойная точка
U 209	**unipotent element,** u-element <AL>	unipotentes Element *n*	élément *m* unipotent	унипотентный элемент
U 210	**unipotent group** <GR>	unipotente Gruppe *f*	groupe *m* unipotent	унипотентная группа
U 211	**unipotent matrix** <MD>	unipotente Matrix *f*	matrice *f* unipotente	унипотентная матрица
U 212	**unique,** well-determined <GN> ⌐<SE>	eindeutig bestimmt, wohlbestimmt	bien déterminé	однозначно (вполне) определенный
	unique correspondence	*s.* S 1037		
U 213	**unique existence** <DE, GN>	Existenz *f* und Eindeutigkeit *f*	existence *f* et unicité *f*	существование и единственность
U 214	**unique existence theorem of Picard-Lindelöf,** Picard-Lindelöf unique existence theorem *m*, fundamental existence and uniqueness theorem for differential equations <DE>	Existenz- und Eindeutigkeitssatz *m* von Picard-Lindelöf, Picard-Lindelöfscher Existenz- und Eindeutigkeitssatz	théorème *m* d'existence et d'unicité de Picard-Lindelöf	теорема существования и единственности Пикара-Линделефа
U 215	**unique factor** <in the wider sense>; specific factor <in the narrower sense> <ST>	spezifischer Faktor *m* <im weiteren *oder* engeren Sinne>	facteur *m* unique <au sens large>; facteur spécifique <au sens étroit>	специфический фактор <в широком *или* узком смысле>
U 216	**unique factorization domain,** unique factorization ring, factorial ring, UFD <AL>	ZPE-Ring *m*, Z. P. E.-Ring *m*, Ring *m* mit Z. P. E., Ring mit eindeutiger Primfaktorzerlegung	anneau *m* factoriel (à factorisation unique, de factorisation unique, gaussien, de Gauss)	факториальное кольцо, кольцо с разложением, область [целостности] с однозначным разложением на множители, гауссово кольцо
U 217	**unique factorization property** <of a ring> <AL>	ZPE-Eigenschaft *f*	factorialité *f*	факториальность
	unique factorization ring <AL>	*s.* U 216		
	unique factorization theorem [for integers] <NT>	*s.* E 570		

U 218	**uniquely differentiable function** <DI>	eindeutig differenzierbare Funktion *f*	fonction *f* uniquement dérivable	однозначно дифференцируемая функция
U 219	**uniquely divisible module** <AL>	eindeutig teilbarer Modul *m m*	module *m* uniquement divisible	однозначно делимый модуль
U 220	**uniqueness,** specificity <ST>	Spezifität *f*	spécificité *f*	специфичность
	uniqueness <GN>	*s.* U 106		
U 221	**uniqueness axiom** <GR>	Eindeutigkeitsaxiom *n*	axiome *m* d'unicité	аксиома единственности
U 222	**uniqueness[-] base** <of a group> <GR>	Eindeutigkeitsbasis *f*	base *f* d'unicité	база единственности
U 223	**uniqueness condition** <LO>	Eindeutigkeitsbedingung *f*	condition *f* d'unicité	условие единственности
U 224	**uniqueness theorem** <in class field theory> <AB>	Eindeutigkeitssatz *m*	loi *f* d'unicité	теорема единственности
U 225	**uniqueness theorem** <AN>	Eindeutigkeitssatz *m*, Unitätssatz *m*, Eindeutigkeitstheorem *n*	théorème *m* d'unicité	теорема единственности (одинаковости)
U 226	**uniqueness theorem of Nagumo,** Nagumo['s] uniqueness theorem <DE>	Eindeutigkeitssatz *m* von Nagumo, Nagumoscher Eindeutigkeitssatz	théorème *m* d'unicité de Nagumo	теорема единственности Нагумо
U 227	**uniqueness theorems of Privalov** <for a holomorphic *or* meromorphic function> <FT>	Unitätssätze *mpl* von Priwalow (Privalov), Priwalowsche (Privalovsche) Unitätssätze	théorèmes *mpl* d'unicité de Privalov	теоремы единственности Привалова
U 227a	**unique solution** <GN>	eindeutige (eindeutig bestimmte, einzige) Lösung *f*	solution *f* unique	единственное решение
U 228	**unirationality** <AG>	Unirationalität *f*	unirationalité *f*	унирациональность
U 229	**unirational variety** <AG>	unirationale Mannigfaltigkeit *f*	variété *f* unirationnelle	унирациональное многообразие
U 230	**uniserial algebra** <AL>	einreihige Algebra *f*	algèbre *f* unisérielle	однорядная алгебра
U 231	**uniserial ring** <AL>	einreihiger Ring *m*	anneau *m* unisériel	однорядное кольцо
U 232	**unit** <a right and left invertible element> <of a semigroup> <AL>	Einheit *f*	élément *m* inversible	обратимый элемент
U 233	**1-unit,** one-unit <NT>	Einseinheit *f*	Einseinheit *f*	единица ≡ 1 mod p
	unit <AL>	*s.* 1. B 80; 2. E 858; 3. I 59; 4. I 58; 5. U 303		
	unit <CA>	*s.* 1. I 44; 2. I 1127		
	unit <LA>	*s.* 1. U 274; 2. W 131		
	unit <NT>	*s.* U 286		
	unit <SE>	*s.* G 409		
	unital left module <AL>	*s.* U 250		
	unital right module <AL>	*s.* U 254		
	unital R-module <AL>	*s.* U 255		
	unitarian matrix <MD>	*s.* U 251		
	unitarian transformation <AL>	*s.* U 263		
U 234	**unitarily equivalent operator** <in a Hilbert space> <FA>	unitär äquivalenter Operator *m*, unitär äquivalente Transformation *f*	opérateur *m* unitairement équivalent, transformation *f* unitairement équivalente	унитарно эквивалентный оператор
U 235	**unitarily equivalent representation** <AL>	unitär äquivalente Darstellung *f*	représentation *f* unitairement équivalente	унитарно эквивалентное представление
U 236	**unitarity** <GN>	Unitarität *f*	unitarité *f*	унитарность
U 237	**unitary algebra** <AL>	unitäre Algebra *f*	algèbre *f* unitaire	унитарная алгебра
U 238	**unitary bundle** <AT>	unitäres Faserbündel *n*	fibré *m* unitaire	унитарное расслоение
U 239	**unitary character** <of a group> <RE>	unitärer Charakter *m*	caractère *m* unitaire	унитарный характер
U 240	**unitary connection,** unitary transfer <DG>	unitäre Übertragung *f*, unitärer Zusammenhang *m*	connexion *f* (transfert *m*) unitaire	унитарная связность, унитарное перенесение
U 241/2	**unitary eigenvector** <MD>	unitärer Eigenvektor *m*	vecteur *m* propre unitaire	унитарный собственный вектор
	unitary equivalence <MD>	*s.* U 258		
U 243	**unitary geometry** <GE>	unitäre Geometrie *f*	géométrie *f* unitaire	унитарная геометрия
U 244	**unitary group** <of dimension *n*; over *K*> <GR>	unitäre (hyperorthogonale) Gruppe *f*, Gruppe der unitären Transformationen <für *n* Variable; über dem Körper *K*>	groupe *m* unitaire <de type *n*, à *n* variables, d'ordre *n*, de degré *n*; défini sur *K*, sur le corps *K*>	унитарная группа <от *n* переменных; над *K*>
U 245	**unitary group over the quaternions** <GR>	unitäre Gruppe *f* über den Quaternionen	groupe *m* unitaire quaternionique	кватернионная унитарная группа
U 246	**unitary group with respect to the form Q** <GR>	unitäre Gruppe *f* in bezug auf die Form Q	groupe *m* unitaire associé à Q	унитарная группа формы Q
U 247	**unitary homomorphism** <of an algebra> <AL>	unitärer Homomorphismus *m*	homomorphisme *m* unitaire	унитарный гомоморфизм
U 248	**unitary integral equation** <IE>	unitäre Integralgleichung *f*	équation *f* intégrale unitaire	унитарное интегральное уравнение
U 249	**unitary invariant** <AL, GE>	unitäre Invariante *f*, Invariante bei unitären Transformationen, Unitärinvariante *f*	invariant *m* unitaire	унитарный инвариант
	unitary kernel on the left <IE>	*s.* L 518		
	unitary kernel on the right <IE>	*s.* R 1289		
U 250	**unitary left module,** unital left module <AL>	unitärer Linksmodul *m*	module *m* à gauche unitaire	унитарный левый модуль
U 251	**unitary matrix,** unitarian matrix <MD>	unitäre Matrix *f*	matrice *f* unitaire	унитарная матрица

U 252	**unitary modular group,** special unitarian group, unitary unimodular group, $SU(n)$ <GR>	spezielle (unimodulare) unitäre Gruppe *f*	groupe *m* unitaire spécial (unimodulaire), groupe spécial unitaire, groupe des matrices unitaires unimodulaires	специальная (унимодулярная) унитарная группа
U 253	**unitary operator,** orthogonal operator <FA>	unitärer (orthogonaler) Operator *m*, unitäre Transformation *f*	opérateur *m* unitaire (orthogonal), transformation *f* unitaire	унитарный (ортогональный) оператор
U 254	**unitary right module,** unital right module <AL>	unitärer Rechtsmodul *m*	module *m* à droite [unitaire]	унитарный правый модуль
U 255	**unitary *R*-module,** unital *R*-module <AL>	unitärer *R*-Modul *m*	*R*-module *m* unitaire	унитарный (унитальный) *R*-модуль
U 256	**unitary sampling** <ST>	einstufiges Stichprobenverfahren *n*, unmittelbare Stichprobennahme *f*	échantillonnage *m* unique	однократный выбор
U 257	**unitary semi-similarity [transformation]** <AL>	halbähnlich unitäre Transformation *f*, halbähnlich unitäre Kollineation *f*	semi-similitude *f* unitaire	унитарное преобразование полуподобия
U 258	**unitary similarity,** unitary equivalence, conjunctivity by a unitary transformation <of quadratic matrices> <MD>	Unitärkongruenz *f*, Unitäräquivalenz *f*, Unitärähnlichkeit *f*, unitäre Ähnlichkeit (Äquivalenz) *f*	similitude *f* unitaire, équivalence *f* unitaire	унитарное подобие, унитарная эквивалентность
U 259	**unitary similar matrix,** conjunctive matrix by a unitary transformation <MD>	unitär[-]ähnliche (unitär[-]kongruente, unitär-äquivalente) Matrix *f*	matrice *f* semblable par une transformation unitaire, matrice unitairement semblable	унитарно подобная матрица
U 260	**unitary space,** prehilbert space, pre-Hilbert space, Hermitian vector space, hermitian [inner product] space <FA>	unitärer (prä[-]hilbertscher, prä-Hilbertscher) Raum *m*, Prähilbertraum *m*, Innenproduktraum *m*	espace *m* unitaire (préhilbertien, hermitien)	унитарное (предгильбертово, эрмитово) пространство
U 261	**unitary subalgebra** <AL>	Unteralgebra *f* mit Einselement, unitäre Unteralgebra (Teilalgebra *f*)	sous-algèbre *f* unitaire	унитарная подалгебра
U 262	**unitary subring** <having the same unit element as the whole ring> <AL>	unitärer Unterring *m*	sous-anneau *m* unitaire	унитарное подкольцо
	unitary transfer <DG>	*s.* U 239		
U 263	**unitary transformation,** unitarian transformation <AL>	unitäre Transformation *f*	transformation *f* (application *f*, automorphisme *m*) unitaire	унитарное преобразование, унитарный автоморфизм
U 264	**unitary transformation** <of a matrix> <MD>	unitäre Ähnlichkeitstransformation *f*	transformation *f* par une matrice unitaire	преобразование при помощи унитарной матрицы
	unitary unimodular group <GR>	*s.* U 252		
U 265	**unit ball,** unit sphere <GE, TO>	Einheitskugel *f*, Einheitsvollkugel *f*	boule *f* unité, boule-unité *f*, sphère *f* unitaire	единичный шар, шар радиуса единицы
	unit binormal [vector] <DG>	*s.* B 407		
U 266	**unit character,** trivial character <AL>	Einheitscharakter *m*, trivialer Charakter *m*	caractère *m* unité, caractère-unité *m*, caractère trivial	единичный (тривиальный) характер
U 267	**unit circle** <as a line> <GN>	Einheitskreis *m*	cercle *m* unité, cercle-unité *m*	единичная окружность, окружность радиуса единицы, граница единичного круга
U 268	**unit circle,** unit disk <as a surface> <GN>	Einheitskreis *m*	disque *m* unité	единичный круг
U 269	**unit circle centred at the origin** <in trigonometry> <EG>	Einheitskreis *m*	cercle *m* trigonométrique	окружность с радиусом 1
U 270	**unit class** <AL>	Einsklasse *f*, Restklasse *f* des Einselements	classe-unité *f*, classe *f* unité	класс единичного элемента
	unit disk <GN>	*s.* U 268		
U 271	**unit divisor** <AG, FT>	Einheitsdivisor *m*, Eins-Divisor *m*	diviseur *m* unité	единичный дивизор, единица группы дивизоров
U 272	**unit doublet** <FA>	Einheits-Wechselstoß *m*	doublet *m* unité	импульсная функция второго порядка
U 273	**unit dyad,** identity dyad, dyadic product of two unit base vectors <VT>	Einheitsdyade *f*, Identitätsdyade *f*	dyade *f* unité	единичная диада
U 274	**unit element,** unit <of a lattice> <LA>	Einselement *n*, verbandstheoretisches Einselement	élément *m* maximum (universel)	единица, единичный элемент, наибольший элемент структуры
	unit element <AL>	*s.* 1. I 58; 2. I 59; 3. I 62; 4. N 183		
	unit[-] element <GR>	*s.* I 63		
U 275	**unit filter** <of a Boolean algebra> <AL, SE>	Einheitsfilter *m*	filtre *m* trivial, filtre unité	единичный фильтр
	unit first normal [vector] <DG>	*s.* P 1455		
U 276	**unit fraction** <AR>	Stammbruch *m*, primitiver Bruch *m* <Bruch der Form $1/n$>	quantième *m*, partie *f* aliquote, fraction *f* primitive	аликвотная (единичная) дробь, доля единицы, основная (египетская) дробь, дробь с числителем единицы, аликвотная часть, // египтическая дробь
U 277	**unit function** <FT>	Einheitsfunktion *f*	fonction *f* unité, fonction-unité *f*	единичная функция
	unit function [of Heaviside] <AN>	*s.* H 158		

No.	English	Deutsch	Français	Русский
U 278	**unit group,** group of units <of a ring> <AL>	Einheitengruppe *f*	groupe *m* multiplicatif, groupe des unités	единичная группа, группа единиц, группа обратимых элементов, мультипликативная группа
	unit group <AL>	*s.* G 482		
U 279	**unit ideal** <AL>	Einsideal *n*, Einheitsideal *n*	idéal-unité *m*, idéal *m* unité	единичный идеал; идеал, содержащий единицу
U 280	**unit idele** <AB>	Ideleinheit *f*, Idel-Einheit *f*	idèle-unité *m*	единичный идель
	unit impulse function [of order one] <FA>	*s.* D 211		
U 281	**unit impulse response, unit-impulse response,** unit-pulse (unit pulse) response <AN>	Einheitsübergangsfunktion *f*, Einheitsimpulsantwort[funktion] *f*	réponse *f* impulsionnelle unité	единичная переходная функция
	unit in hundred's place <NT>	*s.* U 289		
	unit in ten's place <NT>	*s.* U 287		
U 282	**unit interval** <AN>	Einheitsintervall *n*	segment *m* unité, segment-unité *m*, intervalle *m* unité, intervalle-unité *m*	единичный интервал, единичный сегмент, единичный отрезок
	unit in unit's place <NT>	*s.* U 286		
U 283	**unit line** <AY>	Einheitsgerade *f*	droite *f* unité, droite-unité *f*	единичная прямая
U 284	**unit lower triangular matrix,** lower triangular matrix with ones in the diagonal, lower unitriangular matrix <MD>	untere Halbmatrix *f* mit lauter Einsen in der Hauptdiagonale, untere Dreiecksmatrix *f* mit Einsen in der Hauptdiagonale	matrice *f* triangulaire inférieure uniprincipale (unitaire)	нижняя унитреугольная матрица
	unit matrix <MD>	*s.* 1. I 66; 2. U 194		
	unit morphism <CA>	*s.* I 44		
	unit normal [vector] <DG>	*s.* N 669		
U 285	**unit *n*-sphere bundle** <AT>	Bündel *n* von *n*-Einheitssphären	fibré *m* de *n*-sphères-unité	расслоение на единичные *n*-мерные сферы
	unit of adjunction <CA>	*s.* U 288		
U 286	**unit of first order,** unit in unit's place, unit, digit in the units place <NT>	Einer *m*, Einerziffer *f*, Fingerzahl *f*	unité *f* simple, unité du premier ordre, unité, digit *m*	единица, цифра первого разряда
	unit of imaginaries <FT>	*s.* I 104		
U 287	**unit of second order,** unit in ten's place, ten <NT>	Zehner *m*	dizaine *f*, unité *f* du second ordre	десяток, цифра второго разряда
U 288	**unit of the adjunction,** front adjunction, unit of adjunction, adjunction morphism <CA>	Einheit *f* der Adjunktion	unité *f* d'adjonction	единица сопряжения
U 289	**unit of third order,** unit in hundred's place, hundred <NT>	Hunderter *m*	centaine *f*, unité *f* du troisième ordre	цифра третьего порядка, сотня
	unit operator <AL>	*s.* I 68		
U 290	**unit point** <PJ>	Einheitspunkt *m*	point *m* unité, point-unité *m*	единичная точка
	unit principal normal [vector] <DG>	*s.* P 1455		
	unit pulse response, unit-pulse response <AN>	*s.* U 281		
U 291	**unit quantifier** <LO>	Einsquantifikator *m*	quantificateur *m* d'unicité	ограниченный квантор существования, квантор единственности ∃! <*читается:* существует единственный *x*>
	unit quaternion <AL>	*s.* N 617		
	unit representation <RE>	*s.* I 47		
U 292	**unitriangular group,** lower unitriangular group, group of lower-triangular matrices with ones in the diagonal <GR>	Gruppe *f* der unteren Halbmatrizen (Dreiecksmatrizen) mit Einsen in der Diagonale, Gruppe der unteren Dreiecksmatrizen mit Diagonaleinsen	groupe *m* trigonal strict inférieur	группа нижних унипотентных треугольных матриц
	unitriangular matrix <MD>	*s.* U 300		
	unit second normal [vector] <DG>	*s.* B 407		
	unit[-] set <SE>	*s.* O 86		
U 293	**unit simplex** <AT>	Einheitssimplex *n*	simplexe *m* unité, simplexe-unité *m*	единичный симплекс
U 294	**unit sphere** <surface of unit ball> <GN>	Einheitssphäre *f*, Einheitskugel *f*	sphère *f* unité, sphère-unité *f*	единичная сфера
	unit sphere <GE, TO>	*s.* U 265		
U 295	**unit's place, units place,** ones digit <NT>	Einerstelle *f*	unité *f*	разряд единиц
U 296	**unit square** <GE>	Einheitsquadrat *n*	carré *m* unité, carré-unité *m*	единичный квадрат
	unit step [function] <AN>	*s.* H 158		
U 297	**unit tangent [vector],** tangent unit vector, tangent vector <DG>	Tangenteneinheitsvektor *m*, Tangentenvektor *m*	vecteur *m* unitaire tangent (de la tangente), tangente-unité *f*, vecteur tangent	единичный вектор касательной, орт касательной, касательный единичный вектор, единичный касательный (тангенциальный) вектор, касательный орт (вектор)

U 298	**unit tensor,** unit two (2) tensor, identity tensor, substitution tensor, Kronecker['s] tensor, idemfactor <VT>	Einheitstensor *m*, Einheitstensor zweiter Stufe, Einheitsaffinor *m*, Kroneckerscher Tensor *m*, Idemfaktor *m*	tenseur *m* unité [de valence 2]	единичный тензор [валентности 2], тензорная единица, идемфактор, единичный аффинор
U 299	**unit theorem,** theorem on units <AB>	Einheitensatz *m*	théorème *m* des unités, théorème sur les unités	теорема о единицах
	unit transformation <AN>	*s.* I 48		
U 300	**unit triangular matrix,** unitriangular matrix, properly triangular matrix, triangular matrix with ones in the diagonal <MD>	Dreiecksmatrix *f* mit lauter Einsen in der Diagonale (Hauptdiagonale)	matrice *f* triangulaire uniprincipale, matrice triangulaire unitaire, matrice uniprincipale, matrice unitaire	унитреугольная матрица, унипотентная треугольная матрица
	unit two (2) tensor <VT>	*s.* U 298		
U 301	**unit upper triangular matrix,** upper unitriangular matrix <MD>	obere Halbmatrix *f* mit lauter Einsen in der Hauptdiagonale, obere Dreiecksmatrix *f* mit Einsen in der Hauptdiagonale	matrice *f* triangulaire supérieure uniprincipale (unitaire)	верхняя унитреугольная матрица
U 302	**unit vector,** normalized vector, direction vector, versor <in the direction of ***a***> <VT>	Einheitsvektor *m*, Einsvektor *m*, normierter Vektor *m*, Richtungsvektor *m*, Maßvektor *m* <in der Richtung von ***a***>	vecteur *m* unité (unitaire), vecteur-unité *m*, vecteur normé (directeur) <ayant la même direction et le même sens que ***a***>	единичный (нормированный, направляющий) вектор; орт <особенно евклидова пространства> <в направлении вектора ***a***>
	unit vector <TO>	*s.* N 616		
	unit vector field <TO>	*s.* D 564		
	unit vector of binormal <DG>	*s.* B 407		
	unit vector of first (principal) normal <DG>	*s.* P 1455		
	unit vector of second normal <DG>	*s.* B 407		
	unity <AL<	*s.* I 62		
U 303	**unity element,** unit <of a ring> <AL>	Einheit *f*, invertierbares Element *n*, Ringeinheit *f*, Teiler *m* des Einselementes	élément *m* inversible (unitaire), unité *f*	единичный элемент, делитель единицы, единица кольца
	unity element <AL>	*s.* I 62		
U 304	**unity group,** identity subgroup, trivial subgroup; zero subgroup <GR>	Einsuntergruppe *f*, Einheitsuntergruppe *f*, triviale Untergruppe *f*; Nulluntergruppe *f*	sous-groupe *m* unitaire	единичная (тривиальная) подгруппа; нулевая подгруппа
	unity group <GR>	*s.* O 85		
U 305	**unity operator** <in an operator domain> <AL>	Einheitsoperator *m*, Einsoperator *m*, Identität *f*	opérateur *m* identique, opérateur-unité *m*, opérateur unité	тождественный оператор, единичный оператор
	unity quantity <AL>	*s.* 1. I 58; 2. P 1435		
	univalence <GN>	*s.* S 1038		
U 306	**univalence indicatrix** <FD, FT, NU>	Eindeutigkeitsindikatrix *f*	indicatrice *f* d'univalence	индикатриса однозначности
	univalent function <FT>	*s.* S 915		
	univalent function (mapping) <SE>	*s.* I 548		
	univalent predicate <LO>	*s.* O 94		
U 307	**univalent representation** <RE>	eindeutige Darstellung *f*	représentation *f* univaluée	однозначное представление
U 308	**univariable series** <SS>	Reihe *f* in einer Variablen (Veränderlichen)	série *f* d'une seule variable	ряд одной переменной
U 309	**univariate distribution,** one-dimensional distribution <ST>	eindimensionale (univariate) Verteilung *f*	distribution *f* à une variable, distribution unidimensionnelle	одномерное распределение
U 310	**universal affirmative proposition,** general affirmative proposition; A-proposition <LO>	allgemein[es] bejahendes Urteil *n*, affirmative Allaussage *f*	proposition *f* universelle affirmative	общеутвердительное суждение, общее утвердительное суждение
U 311	**universal algebra,** algebraic system, abstract algebra, algebra <UA>	universelle Algebra *f*, algebraische Struktur *f*, algebraisches System *n*, abstrakte Algebra, Algebra, Bereich *m*, algebraischer Bereich, Menge *f* mit algebraischer Struktur, vollständige (volle) Algebra <v. Neumann>	système *m* algébrique, algèbre *f*, domaine *m*	алгебра, алгебраическая система, универсальная (абстрактная) алгебра; множество, наделенное алгебраической структурой
U 312	**universal algebra of equal type,** algebra of the same type, algebra belonging to the same similarity class, similar structure <UA>	gleichartige universelle Algebra *f*, gleichartige (homologe) algebraische Struktur *f*, [universelle] Algebra gleichen Typs	algèbre *f* de même type, structure *f* [algébrique] homologue	однотипная универсальная алгебра, однотипная алгебра
U 313	**universal arrow** <as a common name of liberty and coliberty morphisms> <CA>	universeller Pfeil *m*	flèche *f* universelle	универсальная стрелка
	universal arrow <CA>	*s.* L 644		
	universal arrow from <CA>	*s.* C 1129		
	universal arrow to <CA>	*s.* L 644		

No.	English	German	French	Russian
	universal associative algebra (envelope) <AL>	*s.* U 334		
U 314	**universal bundle,** universal principal bundle <AT>	universelles Bündel (Prinzipalfaserbündel) *n*	fibré *m* principal universel	универсальное расслоение
U 315	**universal bundle for the dimension *n*,** *n*-universal bundle, *n*-universal principal bundle <AT>	universelles Bündel (Prinzipalfaserbündel) *n* für die Dimension *n*, *n*-universelles Prinzipalfaserbündel	fibré *m* principal universel pour la dimension *n*	*n*-универсальное главное расслоение, *n*-универсальное расслоение
U 316	**universal class** <SE>	Allklasse *f*, Elementebereich *m*	classe *f* universelle	универсальный класс, полный класс
U 317	**universal class** <UA>	universelle Klasse *f*	classe *f* universelle	универсальный класс, класс открытых предложений
	universal class in the wider sense <UA>	*s.* U 318		
U 318	**universal class of structures** <Grätzer>, universal class in the wider sense <Tarski> <UA>	universelle Klasse *f* von Strukturen	classe *f* universelle de structures	универсальный класс структур
U 319	**universal closure** <LO>	Generalisierte *f*	universalisée *f*	формула, связанная квантором общности
U 320	**universal closure,** universal generalization <of a formula> <LO>	universelle Abschließung *f* <Bindung aller freien Variablen durch Generalisatoren>	clôture *f* universelle	замыкание квантором всеобщности
U 321	**universal coefficient formula** <AT, HA>	universelle Koeffizientenformel *f*	formule *f* des coefficients universels	формула универсальных коэффициентов
U 322	**universal coefficient theorem** <AT, HA>	universeller Koeffizientensatz *m*, universelles Koeffiziententheorem *n*	théorème *m* des coefficients universels	теорема об универсальных коэффициентах, теорема универсальных коэффициентов
	universal cone <CA>	*s.* L 726		
U 323	**universal congruence,** all relation <UA>	totale Kongruenzrelation *f*	congruence *f* universelle	универсальная конгруэнция
	universal cover <TO>	*s.* U 327		
U 324	**universal covering** <AT, TO>	universelle Überlagerung *f*	revêtement *m* universel	универсальное наложение (накрытие)
U 325	**universal covering group** <AL, FT>	universelle Überlagerungsgruppe *f*	groupe *m* de recouvrement universel, revêtement *m* universel	универсальная накрывающая группа, универсальная группа наложения, универсальная накрывающая связная группа
U 326	**universal covering manifold,** largest covering manifold <TO>	universelle Überlagerungsmannigfaltigkeit *f*	recouvrement (revêtement) *m* universel, variété *f* universelle de recouvrement	универсальное многообразие наложения, универсальное накрывающее многообразие
U 327	**universal covering space,** universal cover <TO>	universeller Überlagerungsraum *m*	revêtement *m* universel	универсальное накрывающее пространство, универсальное покрытие <пространства>
U 328	**universal covering surface** <FT, TO>	universelle Überlagerungsfläche *f*, Hauptüberlagerungsfläche *f*; hauptuniformisierende Überlagerungsfläche	surface *f* de recouvrement universelle, surface universelle de recouvrement	универсальная накрывающая поверхность, универсальная поверхность наложения
U 329	**universal curve** <of genus 0> <AG>	universale Kurve *f*	courbe *f* universelle	универсальная кривая
U 330	**universal diagram** <CA, TO>	universelles Diagramm *n*	diagramme *m* universel	универсальная диаграмма
U 331	**universal differential algebra** <AL, AT>	universelle Algebra *f* mit Differentiation	algèbre *f* différentielle universelle	универсальная дифференциальная алгебра
U 332	**universal domain,** universal field <AG, AL>	universaler (universeller) Bereich *m*, universaler Körper *m*, Universalkörper *m*	domaine (corps) *m* universel	универсальная область, универсальное поле
U 333	**universal dynamic game** <TG>	allgemeines dynamisches Spiel *n*	jeu *m* dynamique universel	общая динамическая игра
	universal element <SE>	*s.* G 409		
U 334	**universal enveloping algebra,** associative envelope, universal associative envelope, universal associative algebra <for a Lie algebra> <AL>	universelle Hüllalgebra (Enveloppe, Algebra) *f*	algèbre *f* enveloppante universelle, algèbre universelle	универсальная обертывающая алгебра (алгебра Ли), ассоциативная оболочка
U 335	**universal-existential sentence, $\forall\exists$** sentence <LO>	$\forall\exists$-Aussage *f*	proposition *f* existentielle universalisée	$\forall\exists$-высказывание
	universal field <AG, AL>	*s.* U 332		
U 336	**universal field extension** <AL>	universelle Körpererweiterung *f*	extension *f* universelle	универсальное расширение поля
U 337	**universal form** <IV>	universale Form *f*	forme *f* universelle	универсальная форма
U 338	**universal formula,** $\forall$-formula <LO>	universelle Formel *f*	$\forall$-formule *f*	универсальная формула $\forall$-формула
U 339	**universal function** <in the broader *or* in the narrower sense> <FO, LO>	Universalfunktion *f* <im weiteren *oder* engeren Sinne>	fonction *f* universelle	универсальная функция
U 340	**universal function** <with respect to a family of sets> <TO>	universelle Funktion *f* <bezüglich einer Mengenfamilie>	fonction *f* universelle <relative à une famille d'ensembles>	универсальная функция <относительно семейства множеств>
	universal generalization <LO>	*s.* 1. R 1475; 2. U 320		

	universal generalization under limitation <LO>	*s.* R 1480		
U 341	**universal Hall group** <GR>	universale abzählbare lokal endliche Gruppe *f*, universelle Gruppe von Hall	groupe *m* universel de Hall	универсальная счетная локально конечная группа, универсальная группа Холла
	universal Horn sequence <LO, UA>	*s.* Q 174		
U 342	**universally closed morphism** <of a scheme> <AG>	universell abgeschlossener Morphismus *m*	morphisme *m* universellement fermé	универсально замкнутый морфизм
U 343	**universally Japanese ring** <AL>	universell japanischer Ring *m*	anneau *m* universellement japonais	универсально японское кольцо
	universally maximal ideal <AL>	*s.* G 410		
U 344	**universally maximal left ideal,** greatest left ideal <of a semigroup> <AL>	universal maximales Linksideal *n*, größtes Linksideal	idéal *m* à gauche maximum	универсально максимальный левый идеал, наибольший левый идеал
U 345	**universally maximal twosided ideal** <of a semigroup> <AL>	universal maximales zweiseitiges Ideal *n*, größtes zweiseitiges Ideal	idéal *m* bilatère maximum	универсально максимальный двусторонний идеал, наибольший двусторонний идеал
	universally minimal element <SE>	*s.* S 1219		
U 346	**universally minimal right ideal,** least right ideal <of a semigroup> <AL>	universal minimales Rechtsideal *n*, kleinstes Rechtsideal	idéal *m* à droite minimum	универсально минимальный правый идеал, наименьший правый идеал
U 347	**universally prorepresentable functor** <CA>	universell prodarstellbarer Funktor *m*	foncteur *m* universellement pro-représentable	универсально пропредставимый функтор
	universally quantified formula <LO>	*s.* G 173		
U 348	**universally submersive morphism** <of a scheme> <AG>	universell submersiver Morphismus *m*	morphisme *m* universellement submersif	универсально субмерсивный морфизм
U 349	**universally valid formula,** identically (generally, logically) valid formula, valid formula, always (identically, logically) true sentence, valid expression, logical identity <of predicate calculus>, valid predicate formula <LO>	allgemeingültige (identische, immer wahre, wahre) Formel *f*, allgemeingültiger (identisch wahrer, immer wahrer, immer richtiger, P-identischer) Ausdruck *m*, allgemeingültiger (identischer) P-Ausdruck *m*	formule *f* identiquement (toujours, logiquement) vraie, formule vraie	тождественно[-] истинная формула, логически истинная (общезначимая) формула, общезначимая (всеобщая, истинная) формула, всегда[-] истинная формула, тождественная (универсально верная) формула
	universally valid formula <LO>	*s.* T 98		
U 350	**universal map** <AL, CA>	universelle Abbildung *f*	application *f* universelle	универсальное отображение
U 351	**universal map[ping] (morphism)** <CA>	universeller Morphismus *m*	morphisme *m* universel	универсальный морфизм
U 352	**universal negative proposition** <LO>	allgemein verneinendes Urteil *n*, negative Allaussage *f*	proposition *f* universelle négative	общеотрицательное (общее отрицательное) суждение
U 353	**universal pair** <CA>	universelles Paar *n*	couple *m* universel	универсальная пара
	universal principal bundle <AT>	*s.* U 314		
U 354	**universal projective cone** <CA>	universeller Pinsel *m*	cône *m* projectif universel	универсальный конус
U 355	**universal property** <CA>	universelle Eigenschaft *f*, Universaleigenschaft *f*	propriété *f* universelle	универсальное свойство, свойство универсальности
	universal proposition <LO>	*s.* G 173		
	universal quantification elimination <LO>	*s.* R 1456		
	universal quantification introduction <LO>	*s.* R 1475		
U 356	**universal quantifier,** universal symbol, generality quantifier, all symbol, ∀-symbol, ∀, ∧ <*to be read:* for all, for every) <LO>	Generalisator *m*, Alloperator *m*, Allzeichen *n*, Allgemeinheitszeichen *n*, Allheitsquantifikator *m*, Allquantor *m*, Allquantifikator *m*, ∀, ∧ <*gelesen:* für alle>	quantificateur *m* universel (général, grand, de totalité), quanteur *m* universel, quantificateur d'universalité, symbole *m* quel que soit, ∀, ∧ <*se lit:* pour tout>; généralisateur *m* universel	квантор общности (всеобщности), универсальный квантор, знак общности, ∀, ∧ <*читается:* для всех>; знак квантора общности
	universal relation <SE>	*s.* T 687		
	universal sentence <LO>	*s.* G 173		
U 357	**universal set,** univers de discours <SE>	Allmenge *f*, universale Menge *f*	ensemble *m* universel, référentiel *m*, ensemble référentiel, catégorie *f* de base, univers *m* du discours	полное (универсальное, основное) множество
U 358	**universal set** <for a system of sets> <SE>	Universalmenge *f*, universale Menge *f*	ensemble *m* universel	универсальное множество
U 359	**universel set** <*n*-dimensional> <TO>	Universalmenge *f* <*n*-dimensionale>	ensemble *m* universel <à *n* dimensions>	универсальное множество <*n*-мерное>
	universal set <SE>	*s.* U 364		
U 360	**universal space** <TO>	Universalraum *m*	espace *m* universel	универсальное пространство
	universal specification <LO>	*s.* 1. L 209; 2. R 1456		
	universal square <CA>	*s.* 1. P 2076; 2. P 2077		
U 361	**universal subgroup** <GR>	universale Untergruppe *f*	sous-groupe *m* universel	универсальная подгруппа
	universal symbol <LO>	*s.* U 356		
U 362	**universal** $\mathfrak{U}(q)$**-bundle** <AT>	universelles $\mathfrak{U}(q)$-Bündel *n*	$\mathfrak{U}(q)$-fibré *m* universel	универсальное $\mathfrak{U}(q)$-расслоение

No.	English	German	French	Russian
	universal validity <LO>	*s.* G 186		
U 363	**universal variety** <AG>	universelle Mannigfaltigkeit (Varietät) *f*	variété *f* universelle	универсальное многообразие
	univers de discours <SE>	*s.* U 357		
U 364	**universe,** space, universal set <*e.g.:* first-order> <SE>	Universum *n*, universale Menge *f* <*z. B.:* erster Stufe>	ensemble *m* universel, univers *m*, catégorie *f* de base <*par exemple:* du premier ordre>	универсальное множество, мир, универсум, генеральная совокупность <*например:* первой ступени>
	universe <ST>	*s.* P 164		
U 365	**unknottedness** <TO>	Unverknotetheit *f*	propriété *f* d'être non noué	незаузленность
U 366	**unknown,** unknown quantity <AL, AN>	Unbekannte *f*, unbekannte Größe *f*	inconnue *f*, grandeur *f* inconnue (cherchée)	неизвестная, неизвестное, искомое, неизвестная (искомая) величина
	unknown <LO>	*s.* F 637		
	unknown quantity <AL, AN>	*s.* U 366		
U 367	**unlabelled graph** <GP>	nicht[-]markierter Graph *m*, freier Graph	graphe *m* non marqué <classe d'isomorphie de graphes simples>	непомеченный (свободный) граф
U 368	**unlike fraction** <AL, NT>	ungleichnamiger Bruch *m*, Bruch mit ungleichem Nenner	fraction *f* non semblable, fraction de différent dénominateur	разноименная дробь, дробь с неравным знаменателем
U 369	**unlimited abstraction principle** <SE>	uneingeschränktes Abstraktionsprinzip *n*	principe *m* d'abstraction illimité	интуитивный принцип абстракции, принцип свертывания
U 370	**unlimited covering manifold** <TO>	unbegrenzte Überlagerungsmannigfaltigkeit *f*	variété *f* de recouvrement illimitée	безграничное накрывающее многообразие
	unlimited variation <AN>	*s.* U 56		
	unmixed ideal <AL>	*s.* E 378		
	unmixed submodule <AL>	*s.* E 383		
	unnamed number <AR, NU>	*s.* A 154		
	unode <AG>	*s.* U 208		
	unoid <UA>	*s.* U 33		
U 371	**unordered pair [set],** plain pair, non-ordered pair, pair set <SE>	ungeordnetes Paar *n*, Paar, Paarmenge *f*	paire *f*, couple *m* non ordonné, couple mathématique, ensemble *m* binaire (à deux éléments)	неупорядоченная пара, пара
U 372	**unordered quadruple,** plain quadruple <SE>	ungeordnetes Quadrupel *n*, Viermenge *f*	quadruple *m*, quaterne *m*, ensemble *m* quaternaire	неупорядоченная четверка
	unordered set <SE>	*s.* P 627		
U 373	**unordered triplet,** triplet <SE>	ungeordnetes Tripel *n*, Dreiermenge *f*	triple *m*, ensemble *m* ternaire, triplet *m*, 3-tuple *m* [non ordonné]	тройка, неупорядоченная тройка, тройное (утроенное) количество
U 374	**unpointed cone,** blunted cone <CS, FA, PG>	[konvexer] Kegel *m* ohne Spitze, stumpfer [konvexer] Kegel, abgestumpfter Kegel	cône *m* épointé, cône convexe épointé	тупой [выпуклый] конус, затупленный [выпуклый] конус, [выпуклый] конус без вершины
U 375	**unprimed quantity** <GN>	ungestrichene Größe *f*	grandeur *f* non primée	нештрихованная величина, величина без штриха (черты, прима)
U 376	**unprovability** <FO>	Unbeweisbarkeit *f*	non-démontrabilité *f*, indémontrabilité *f*	недоказуемость
U 377	**unprovable proposition** <FO>	unbeweisbare Aussage *f*	proposition *f* indémontrable	недоказуемое высказывание (предложение)
U 378	**unramified algebraic function element** <FT>	unverzweigtes algebraisches Funktionselement *n*, algebraisches Funktionselement von rationalem Charakter	élément *m* de fonction algébrique non ramifié	неразветвленный алгебраический элемент функции
U 379	**unramified covering surface,** relatively unramified covering surface <FT, TO>	relativ unverzweigte Überlagerungsfläche *f*, unverzweigte Überlagerungsfläche	surface *f* de recouvrement non ramifiée	неразветвленная поверхность наложения
	unramified [field] extension <AL>	*s.* N 456		
U 380	**unramified function** <FT> <FT>	unverzweigte Funktion *f*	fonction *f* non ramifiée	неразветвленная функция
U 381	**unramified local domain** <AL>	unverzweigter lokaler Integritätsbereich *m*	anneau *m* local intègre unibranche	униразветвленное целостное локальное кольцо
U 382	**unramified local ring** <AL>	unverzweigter lokaler Ring *m*	anneau *m* local unibranche	униразветвленное локальное кольцо
U 383	**unramified manifold** <TO>	unverzweigte Mannigfaltigkeit *f*	variété *f* non ramifiée	неразветвленное многообразие
U 384	**unramifiedness** <AB>	Unverzweigtheit *f*	propriété *f* d'être non ramifié	неразветвленность
U 385	**unramified prime ideal** <AL>	unverzweigtes Primideal *n*	idéal *m* premier non ramifié	неразветвленный простой идеал
U 386	**unramified ring** <AL>	unverzweigter Ring *m*	anneau *m* non ramifié	неразветвленное кольцо
U 387	**unramified subfield** <AB>	unverzweigter Teilkörper *m* <über *k*>	sous-corps *m* non ramifié	неразветвленное подполе
	unrelated set <GP>	*s.* I 314		
	unrestricted direct product <GR>	*s.* C 1425		
U 388	**unrestricted free product** <GR>	uneingeschränktes freies Produkt *n*	produit *m* libre général	полное свободное произведение
U 389/90	**unrestricted nilpotent product** <GR>	uneingeschränktes nilpotentes Produkt *n*	produit *m* nilpotent complet	полное нильпотентное произведение
	unrestricted random sample <ST>	*s.* S 951		
	unrestricted random sampling <ST>	*s.* S 942		

No.	English	German	French	Russian
U 391	**unrestricted sampling** <ST>	unbeschränkte Auswahl (Stichprobenauswahl, Stichprobenerhebung) *f*	sélection *f* (échantillonnage *m*, sondage *m*) sans restriction	выбор без каких-либо ограничений
U 392	**unrestricted simplicial complex** <AT>	vollständiger simplizialer Komplex *m*	complexe *m* simplicial complet	полный симплициальный комплекс
	unrestricted skeleton complex <AT>	*s.* S 1157		
U 393	**unrestricted symmetric group** <GR>	uneingeschränkte symmetrische Gruppe *f*	groupe *m* symétrique non limité	неограниченная симметрическая группа
U 394	**unsaturated transportation problem** <PG>	nichtabgesättigtes Transportproblem *n*	problème *m* de transport non saturé	ненасыщенная транспортная задача
U 395	**unsaturated vertex** <GP>	ungesättigter Knotenpunkt *m*	sommet *m* insaturé	ненасыщенная вершина
	unsigned number <AR>	*s.* S 847		
U 396	**unsolvable equation,** insoluble (irresoluble, inconsistent) equation, equation incapable of solution <AL>	unlösbare (unauflösbare, nicht auflösbare) Gleichung *f*	équation *f* non résoluble, équation irrésoluble, contradictoire, impossible)	неразрешимое (не поддающееся решению, противоречивое) уравнение
U 397	**unstable algorithm** <NU>	instabiler Algorithmus *m*	algorithme *m* non stable	нестабильный алгоритм
U 398	**unstable solution** <DE>	instabile Lösung *f*, labile Lösung, instabiles (labiles) Integral *n*	solution *f* instable	неустойчивое решение
U 399	**unstable state** <of a Markov chain> <SP>	instabiler Zustand *m*	état *m* instable	неустойчивое состояние
U 400	***U*-number** <in Mahler's classification> <NT>	*U*-Zahl *f*	*U*-nombre *m*	*U*-число [Малера]
U 401	**unweighted mean** <ST>	ungewogenes Mittel *n*	moyenne *f* non pondérée	невзвешенное среднее
U 402	**unwinding** <of a curve> <AY>	Abwicklung *f*	développement *m*	развертка
U 403	***u*-omnibus test** <ST>	*u*-Omnibustest *m*	test *m u* omnibus	*u*-критерий объединения
U 404	**up-and-down method,** staircase estimation method, staircase method <ST>	Pendelmethode *f*, Treppenstufenmethode *f*, Auf-und-Ab-Methode *f*	méthode *f* de haut en bas, méthode « staircase »	метод «вверх и вниз», ступенчатый метод
U 405	**upcross, up-cross** <SP>	Niveauschnitt *m* nach oben	intersection de niveau vers le haut	пересечение уровня вверх <точка временного ряда, в которой знак отклонения от средней меняется с минуса на плюс>
	4-uple <CT, SE>	*s.* Q 65		
	5-uple <SE>	*s.* Q 306		
U 406	**upper approximate limit,** superior approximate limit, lim sup ap <AN>	oberer approximativer Limes (Hauptlimes) *m*, oberer approximativer extremer Limes, obere approximative Unbestimmtheitsgrenze (Häufungsgrenze) *f*, lim sup ap	limite *f* approximative supérieure, limite supérieure approximative. lim sup ap	верхний аппроксимативный предел, lim sup ap
U 407	**upper asymptotic density** <of a set of numbers> <AB>	obere asymptotische Dichte *f*, obere Dichte im Großen	densité *f* asymptotique supérieure	верхняя асимптотическая плотность
	upper base <EG>	*s.* U 440		
U 408	**upper bound** <of a sequence *or* function> <DI, SS>	obere Schranke *f*, rechte Schranke	borne *f* supérieure, limite *f* supérieure, majorant *m*	верхняя грань, верхняя граница
U 409	**upper bound** <of a symmetric operator> <FA>	obere Grenze *f*, obere Schranke *f*	borne *f* supérieure	верхняя грань
U 410	**upper bound** <of an infinite matrix> <MD>	obere Grenze *f*, Norm *f*	borne *f* supérieure	верхняя грань
U 411	**upper bound,** majorant, right bound <of a partially ordered set> <SE>	obere Schranke *f*, Majorante *f*	élément *m* majorant, majorant *m*, borne *f* supérieure, limite *f* supérieure, majorante *f*	верхняя грань, верхняя граница, мажоранта
	upper boundary <DI, SE>	*s.* L 252		
	upper cell limit <ST>	*s.* U 415		
U 412	**upper central chain** <GR>	obere Zentralkette *f*	chaîne *f* centrale ascendante	верхняя центральная цепь
U 413	**upper central series** <GR>	aufsteigende Zentralfolge *f*, oberste (obere) Zentralfolge, aufsteigende Zentrenfolge *f*, aufsteigende Zentralreihe (Zentrenreihe) *f*, aufsteigend wohlgeordnetes zentrales System *n*	suite (série) *f* centrale ascendante, suite spéciale, série centrale supérieure	возрастающий (восходящий) центральный ряд, вполне упорядоченная по возрастанию центральная система
U 414	**upper class** <of a Dedekind cut> <AN, SE>	Oberklasse *f*, zweite (obere) Klasse *f*	classe *f* supérieure	верхний (правый, второй) класс
U 415	**upper class limit,** upper cell limit <ST>	obere Klassengrenze *f*	limite *f* supérieure de classe	верхний предел класса, верхняя граница класса
	upper complete square <CA>	*s.* P 2029		
	upper continuous <RF>	*s.* U 433		
U 416	**upper control limit** <ST>	obere Kontrollgrenze *f*	limite *f* supérieure de contrôle	верхняя контрольная граница, верхний контрольный предел
U 417	**upper Darboux integral,** upper Riemann integral, upper integral <DI>	oberes Darbouxsches Integral *n*, oberes Riemannsches Integral, oberes Integral, [Riemannsches] Oberintegral *n*	intégrale *f* par excès [de Darboux], intégrale supérieure de Darboux, intégrale supérieure	верхний интеграл Дарбу, верхний интеграл Римана, верхний интеграл
U 418	**upper Darboux sum,** upper sum <DI>	Darbouxsche Obersumme *f*, Obersumme	somme *f* supérieure, somme supérieure de Darboux	верхняя сумма Дарбу, верхняя сумма, верхняя интегральная сумма
U 419	**upper deviation,** upward deviation <AX>	Abweichung *f* nach oben	écart *m* en (vers le) haut	отклонение вверх, отклонение в сторону увеличения

No.	English	German	French	Russian
U 420	**upper Dini['s] derivative** <RF>	obere Derivierte (Hauptderivierte, Ableitungszahl) *f*	nombre *m* dérivé supérieur	верхнее производное число
	upper Dini['s] derivative on the left <RF>	*s.* L 388		
	upper Dini['s] derivative on the right <RF>	*s.* R 1171		
U 421	**upper Dini['s] partial derivative** <RF>	obere partielle Derivierte *f*	nombre *m* dérivé partiel supérieur, dérivée *f* partielle supérieure de Dini	верхнее частичное производное число, верхняя частная производная Дини
U 422	**upper Dirichlet density** <AB>	obere Dirichlet-Dichte *f*	densité *f* de Dirichlet supérieure	верхняя плотность Дирихле
U 423	**upper envelope** <of a family of functions> <AN>	obere Enveloppe (Grenze, Hüllfunktion) *f*	enveloppe *f* supérieure	верхняя огибающая
	upper estimate <AN, AX, ER>	*s.* M 49		
U 424	**upper-finite group,** colocally finite group <GR>	kolokal (colokal) endliche Gruppe *f*	groupe *m* colocalement fini	колокально конечная группа
	upper half-plane <GE>	*s.* P 708		
	upper half plane of degree *n* <FT>	*s.* G 157		
	upper hemitropism <GR>	*s.* J 62		
	upper homology <AT>	*s.* C 1085		
U 425	**upper ideal,** upper set, ideal <of a quasi-ordered set *or* a set-ring> <SE>	Mengenideal *n*, Ideal *n*	idéal *m*	идеал
	upper index <GN>	*s.* S 2330		
	upper integral <DI>	*s.* U 417		
U 426	**upper left corner** <MD, PG>; north-west corner <PG> <of a matrix>	linke obere Ecke *f*; Nordwestecke *f*	coin *m* supérieur gauche; coin nord-ouest	левая верхняя вершина; северно-западный угол
	upper left-handed limit <DI>	*s.* L 375		
U 427	**upper limit,** superior limit, limit superior, maximum limit, greatest of the limits, lim sup, $\overline{\lim}$ <of a number sequence *or* a set of real numbers> <DI, SS>	oberer Limes *m*, oberer Hauptlimes *m*, oberer extremer Limes, obere Häufungsgrenze (Unbestimmtheitsgrenze) *f*, Limes *m* superior, lim sup, $\overline{\lim}$, // obere Grenze *f* <Pasch>	limite *f* supérieure, limite supérieure d'indétermination, la plus grande (haute) *f* des limites, la plus grande (haute) limite, limite maximum, lim sup, $\overline{\lim}$	верхний предел, наибольший предел, верхняя граница неопределенности, lim sup, $\overline{\lim}$
U 428	**upper limit,** upper topological limit, $\overline{\mathrm{lt}}$ <of a sequence of sets> <TO>	oberer topologischer (abgeschlossener) Limes *m*, $\overline{\mathrm{lt}}$, $\overline{\mathrm{F\text{-}lim}}$	limite *f* supérieure topologique, limite supérieure, limite topologique supérieure	верхний топологический предел, верхний предел
	upper limit <RF>	*s.* M 251		
	upper limit on one side <DI>	*s.* U 429		
	upper limit on the left <DI>	*s.* L 375		
	upper limit on the right <DI>	*s.* R 1172		
	upper Loewy series <GR>	*s.* A 1036		
	upper measure <ME>	*s.* O 548		
	upper nilradical <AL>	*s.* F 373		
U 429	**upper one-sided limit,** upper limit on one side <DI>	oberer einseitiger Limes (Hauptlimes, Grenzwert) *m*	limite *f* supérieure à un seul côté, limite supérieure unilatérale	верхний односторонний предел
U 430	**upper pure value,** upper value <of a game> <TG>	oberer reiner Wert *m*, oberer Wert	valeur *f* supérieure pure, valeur supérieure	верхнее чистое значение, верхнее значение
U 431	**upper quartile,** third quartile <ST>	oberes Quartil *n*, drittes (3.) Quartil, 75%iges Quartil	quartile *m* supérieur, troisième quartile	третий квартиль, верхний квартиль
	upper radical <AL>	*s.* F 373		
	upper Riemann integral <DI>	*s.* U 417		
	upper right-hand limit <DI>	*s.* R 1172		
U 432	**upper semi[-]continuity** <AN, TO>	Halbstetigkeit *f* nach oben, obere Halbstetigkeit	semi-continuité *f* supérieure[ment]	полунепрерывность сверху
U 433	**upper semi[-]continuous,** upper continuous <RF>	oberhalb stetig, oberhalbstetig, nach oben stetig, nach oben halbstetig, aufwärts stetig, aufwärts halbstetig	semi-continu supérieurement, continu supérieurement	полунепрерывный сверху, непрерывный сверху
U 434	**upper semi-continuous collection (decomposition)** <of a space> <TO>	nach oben halbstetige Zerlegung *f*, stetige Zerlegung *f* <zu abgeschlossener Äquivalenzrelation gehörig>	décomposition *f* semi-continue supérieurement	полунепрерывное сверху разбиение, непрерывное разложение
U 435	**upper semi-continuous equivalence** <TO>	oberhalbstetige Äquivalenzrelation *f*, nach oben halbstetige Äquivalenzrelation	relation *f* d'équivalence semi-continue supérieurement	полунепрерывное сверху отношение эквивалентности
U 436	**upper semi[-]lattice,** join[-] semilattice <AL>	$\cup$-Halbverband *m*, Vereinigungshalbverband *m*	demi-treillis *m* relatif à l'union, $\cup$-demi-treillis *m*, ensemble *m* semi-réticulé supérieurement, demi-treillis supérieur, sup-demi-treillis *m*, sup demi-treillis *m*, $\vee$-demi-treillis *m*	верхняя полурешетка (полуструктура)
	upper semi-modular lattice <LA>	*s.* B 447		

U 437/8	**upper semi-modular lattice of subgroups,** semi-modular lattice of subgroups <AL>	von oben semimodularer Untergruppenverband *m*, semimodularer Untergruppenverband	treillis *m* semi-modulaire [supérieurement] de sous-groupes	полумодулярная сверху структура подгрупп
	upper set <SE>	*s.* U 425		
U 439	**upper subsemilattice** <AL>	Teil-∪-Halbverband *m*	sous-sup-demi-treillis *m*	верхняя подполуструктура
	upper sum <DI>	*s.* U 418		
U 440	**upper surface,** covering surface, upper base, covering base, cover <of a frustum *or* another solid> <EG> ⌐<TO>	Deckfläche *f*; Deckkreis *m* <Kegelstumpf>	base *f* supérieure, surface *f* à haut	верхнее основание
	upper topological limit	*s.* U 428		
U 441	**upper triangular group,** full upper triangular group <AL>	Gruppe *f* der oberen Dreiecksmatrizen (Halbmatrizen)	groupe *m* trigonal large supérieur, groupe des matrices triangulaires supérieures	группа верхних треугольных матриц
U 442	**upper triangular matrix,** superdiagonal matrix <MD>	obere Halbmatrix (Dreiecksmatrix) *f*	matrice *f* triangulaire (trigonale) supérieure, triangulaire *f* supérieure	верхняя треугольная матрица
U 443	**upper type** <of a sequence of complex numbers> <SS>	oberer Typus *m*	type *m* supérieur	верхний тип
U 444	**upper unitriangular group,** group of upper-triangular matrices with ones in the diagonal <AL>	Gruppe *f* der oberen Halbmatrizen (Dreiecksmatrizen) mit Einsen in der Diagonale, Gruppe der oberen Dreiecksmatrizen mit Diagonaleinsen	groupe *m* trigonal strict supérieur	группа верхних унипотентных треугольных матриц
	upper unitriangular matrix <MD>	*s.* U 301		
	upper valency <GP>	*s.* D 175		
	upper value <TG>	*s.* U 430		
	upper variation <AN>	*s.* P 1101		
U 445	**up to . . . ,** to within . . . , apart from . . . ; accurate to . . . , correct to . . . <GN>	bis auf . . . ; bis auf . . . genau, genau bis auf . . .	à . . . près	с точностью до . . .
U 446	**upward bias** <ST>	Verzerrung *f* nach oben, [systematische] Abweichung *f* nach oben	biais *m* en (vers le) haut	смещение вверх (в сторону увеличения)
	upward deviation <AX>	*s.* U 419		
U 447	**upward induction,** ascending induction <on> <FO>	aufsteigende Induktion *f* <nach>	récurrence *f* ascendante	индукция по возрастающим значениям
U 448	**urelement,** individual <SE>	Urelement *n*, Individuum *n*	individu *m*, non-ensemble *m*, élément *m* primitif, Urelement *m*	праэлемент, примитивный элемент
U 449	***u*-resultant** <AL>	*u*-Resultante *f*	*u*-résultante *f*	*u*-результант
	U-ring <AL>	*s.* M 1		
U 450	**urn model,** bowl model <ST>	Urnenmodell *n*, Urnenschema *n*	modèle *m* d'urnes, modèle des urnes, schéma *m* d'urnes	урновая схема (модель), схема урн
U 451	**Urysohn['s] axiom** <of functional separability> <TO>	Urysohnsches Axiom *n*	axiome *m* d'Urysohn	аксиома Урысона
U 452	**Urysohn['s] characteristic function** <of a pair (*A*, *B*) of closed sets> <TO>	Urysohnsche charakteristische Funktion *f*	fonction *f* caractéristique d'Urysohn	непрерывная числовая функция со значениями в [0, 1], определенная на всем пространстве, равная 0 на *A* и 1 на *B*
U 453	**Urysohn-closed space** <TO>	Urysohn-abgeschlossener Raum *m*	espace *m* U-fermé	U-замкнутое пространство, замкнутое по Урысону пространство
U 454	**Urysohn['s] lemma** <TO>	Urysohnsches Lemma *n*, Lemma von Urysohn	théorème *m* d'Urysohn	теорема Урысона
	Urysohn-Menger dimension <TO>	*s.* W 69		
U 455	**Urysohn['s] separation axiom** <TO>	Urysohnsches (verschärftes Hausdorffsches) Trennungsaxiom *n*, Trennungsaxiom von Urysohn	axiome *m* d'Urysohn	аксиома отделимости Урысона, аксиома Урысона, U-аксиома отделимости
U 456	**Urysohn['s] space,** T_{2a}-space, T_{2a} topological space <TO>	Urysohn-Raum *m*, T_{2a}-Raum *m*	espace *m* topologique complètement séparé, espace T_{2a}	урысоновское (вполне отделимое) пространство, T_{2a}-пространство
U 457	**Urysohn['s] theorem** <TO> ⌐<TO>	Urysohnscher Einbettungssatz *m*, Einbettungssatz von Urysohn	théorème *m* d'Urysohn	теорема Урысона
	Urysohn['s] theorem	*s.* M 516		
	Urysohn-Tietze extension theorem <TO>	*s.* T 474		
U 458	**Urysohn['s] topology** <TO>	T_{2a}-Topologie *f*	topologie *f* complètement séparée	вполне отделимая топология
U 459	**U-shaped distribution** <ST>	U-förmige Verteilung *f*, U-Verteilung *f*	distribution *f* en U	U-образное распределение
U 460	***u*-statistic,** *u*-value <ST>	*u*-Stichprobenfunktion *f*, *u*-Prüfzahl *f*, *u*-Wert *m*, Prüfzahl *f* des *u*-Tests	valeur *f* d'*u*, fonction *f* des observations d'*u*	*u*-статистика, *u*-значение, статистика *u*-критерия
U 461	***U*-statistic,** Mann-Whitney statistic <ST>	*U*-Prüfzahl *f*, *U*-Stichprobenfunktion *f*, Mann-Whitneysche Stichprobenfunktion *f*	fonction *f* des observations d'*U*, fonction des observations de Mann-Whitney	*U*-статистика, статистика *U*-критерия

No.	English	German	French	Russian
U 462	**usual absolute value** <AL>	gewöhnlicher Absolutbetrag *m*	valeur *f* absolue ordinaire	обычная абсолютная величина
U 463	**usual metric** <AN>	gewöhnliche (übliche) Metrik *f*	métrique *f* usuelle	обыкновенная метрика
U 464	**usual topology** <TO>	gewöhnliche Topologie *f*	topologie *f* usuelle	обыкновенная топология
U 465	***u*-test** <ST>	*u*-Test *m*	test *m u*	*u*-критерий
	***U*-test** <ST>	*s.* W 257		
U 466	**utility** <ST, TG>	Nutzen *m*	utilité *f*	полезность, выгодность, выгода
U 467	**utility function** <ST, TG>	Nutzenfunktion *f*	fonction *f* d'utilité	функция полезности
U 468	**utility theory** <ST>	Utilitytheorie *f*	théorie *f* de l'utilité	теория выгоды (выгодности)
	***u*-value** <ST>	*s.* U 460		
U 469	**Uzawa['s] method** <PG>	Uzawa-Methode *f*	méthode *f* d'Uzawa	метод Узавы

V

No.	English	German	French	Russian
	vacant place <AL, AN, SE, TO>	*s.* L 279		
V 1	**vacuous assertion** <GN, LO>	gegenstandslose Behauptung *f*	assertion *f* vide	беспредметное утверждение
	vacuous set <SE>	*s.* V 204		
V 2	**vacuous subset** <SE>	leere Untermenge (Teilmenge) *f*	partie *f* vide	пустое подмножество
V 3	**VA-group** <GR>	VA-Gruppe *f*	VA-groupe *m*	VA-группа
V 4	**vague compactness** <FA>	vage Kompaktheit *f*	compacité *f* vague	грубая компактность
V 5	**vague convergence** <FA>	vage Konvergenz *f*	convergence *f* vague	широкая (грубая) сходимость
V 6	**vague limit** <FA>	vager Limes *m*	limite *f* vague	широкий предел
V 7	**vaguely bounded operator** <FA>	vage beschränkter Operator *m*	opérateur *m* vaguement borné	широко ограниченный оператор
V 8	**vaguely compact set** <FA>	vage kompakte Menge *f*	ensemble *m* vaguement compact	широко компактное множество
V 9	**vaguely continuous measure** <FA>	vage stetiges Maß *n*	mesure *f* vaguement continue	широко непрерывная мера
V 10	**vaguely convergent sequence** <FA>	vage konvergente Folge *f*	suite *f* convergente vaguement	широко сходящаяся последовательность
V 11	**vague topology,** weak* topology <in a space of measures> <FA>	vage Topologie *f*	topologie *f* vague	широкая топология
V 12	**valence,** value <of a correspondence> <AG>	Wertigkeit *f*, Valenz *f* <Brill>	valence *f*	валентность
V 13	**valence** <of forms> <AL, FT, NT>	Valenz *f*	valence *f*	валентность
	valence <AL, VT>	*s.* R 133		
V 14	**valence correspondence** <AG>	Wertigkeitskorrespondenz *f* <Brill>	correspondance *f* à valence	валентностное соответствие
	valency <GP>	*s.* D 176		
	valid digit <NU>	*s.* 1. S 846; 2. V 15		
	valid expression <LO>	*s.* 1. T 98; 2. U 349		
V 15	**valid figure,** valid digit <NU>	gültige Ziffer *f*	chiffre *m* exact	верная цифра
V 16	**valid formula** <LO>	gültige Formel *f* <über einem festen Individuenbereich>	formule *f* valide	тождественная формула <для данной области>, верная формула
	valid formula <LO>	*s.* 1. T 98; 2. U 349		
V 17	**validity,** truth <of an expansion, a formula> <GN>	Gültigkeit *f*	validité *f*	справедливость
V 18	**validity** <of a definition> <LO> ⌐<LO>	Korrektheit *f*	validité *f*	корректность
	valid predicate formula	*s.* U 349		
V 19	**valid statement** <LO>	wahres Urteil *n*	jugement *m* vrai	верное (истинное) суждение
V 20	**Valiron['s] defect** <of a meromorphic function> <FT>	Valironscher Defekt *m*	défaut *m* au sens de Valiron	дефект Валирона
V 21	**valuation** <AL, LA>	Bewertung *f*	valuation *f*	нормировка, оценка, норма, метрика; метризация, нормирование
V 22	**valuation** <LO>	Belegung *f*	valuation *f*	обложение
	valuation <AL>	*s.* N 314		
V 23	**valuation of rank 1,** real valuation <AL>	reelle Bewertung *f*	valuation *f* réelle, valuation de rang 1	нормирование ранга 1
V 24	**valuation ring of rank *n*** <AL>	*n*-rangiger Bewertungsring *m*	anneau *m* de valuation de rang *n*	кольцо нормирования ранга *n*
V 24a	**valuation ring,** V-ring <AL>	Bewertungsring *m*	anneau *m* de [la] valuation	кольцо нормирования (оценок, оценки), метризационное кольцо
V 24b	**valuation theory,** theory of valuation <AL>	Bewertungstheorie *f*	théorie *f* des valuations	теория нормирований, теория норм
V 25	**valuation topology** <AL>	Bewertungstopologie *f*	topologie *f* valuative (définie par la valuation)	топология нормирования
	valuation vector, valuation-vector <AB, AL>	*s.* A 264		
V 26	**value,** point <belonging to a spectrum> <FA>	Punkt *m* <eines Spektrums>, Wert *m* <aus einem Spektrum>, Spektralwert *m*	valeur *f* spectrale	спектральное значение
V 27	**value** <*e.g.:* of a function at [a point] *x*> <GN>	Wert *m* <*z.B.:* einer Funktion in (an einer Stelle) *x*>	valeur *f* <*par exemple:* d'une fonction en (dans un point) *x*>	значение [величины], величина <*например:* функции в [точке] *x*>

V 28	**value** <of a mapping> <SE>	Bildelement *n*	élément *m* d'arrivée	образ элемента
V 29	**value** <of a discrete random variable> <ST>	Sprungstelle *f*	valeur *f* <d'une variable aléatoire discrète>	значение <дискретной случайной величины>
	value <AG>	*s.* V 12		
	value <TG>	*s.* P 2070		
	value <VT>	*s.* M 24		
V 30	**value distribution,** distribution of values <FT>	Wertverteilung *f*, Werteverteilung *f*	répartition *f* des valeurs, distribution *f* des valeurs	распределение значений
V 31	**value distribution theory** <FT>	Wert[e]verteilungslehre *f*, Theorie *f* der Wertverteilung, Werteverteilungstheorie *f*	théorie *f* de la répartition des valeurs	теория распределения значений
V 32	**value field** <AL>	Wertkörper *m*	corps *m* des valeurs	поле значений
V 33	**value group** <of a valuation> <AL>	Wertgruppe *f*, Wertegruppe *f*	groupe *m* des ordres (valeurs), groupe *m* de valeurs	группа порядков, группа значений
V 34	**value group of rank 1** <in valuation theory> <AL>	einrangige Wertgruppe *f*, Wertgruppe *f* vom Rang 1, archimedische Wertgruppe *f*	groupe *m* de valeurs archimédien	группа дискретного нормирования вполне упорядоченного ранга
V 35	**value group of rank *n*** <AL>	*n*-rangige Wertgruppe *f*	groupe *m* de valeurs de rang *n*	группа нормирования ранга *n*
V 36	**value of order *k*** <of a map> <TO>	*k*-mal angenommener Wert *m*, Wert *m* der Ordnung *k*	valeur *f* d'ordre *k*	значение порядка *k*
	value of x at the place 𝔓 <AL>	*s.* P 2082		
V 37	**value set** <of a valuation> <AL>	Wertmenge *f*, Wertemenge *f*	ensemble *m* de valuations	множество значений; множество показателей
V 38	**value with sense,** directed (signed) value <GN>	Wert *m* mit Vorzeichen, algebraischer Wert *m*	valeur *f* algébrique	значение со знаком
V 39	**Van den Berg['s] elimination method, Van den Berg['s] method [of elimination]** <NU>	van den Bergsches Eliminationsverfahren *n*	méthode *f* d'élimination de Van den Berg	метод исключения Ван ден Берга
V 40	**Vandermonde['s] determinant,** alternant <MD>	Vandermondesche (Cauchysche) Determinante *f*, Alternante *f*, alternierende Funktion *f*, Vandermondes Determinante	déterminant *m* de Vandermonde, Vandermonde *m*, alternant *m* de Vandermonde, déterminant de Cauchy	определитель (детерминант) Вандермонда, альтернант
V 41	**Vandermonde['s] formula** <for Vandermonde's determinant> <MD>	Vandermondesche Formel *f*	formule *f* de Vandermonde	формула Вандермонда
V 42	**Vandermonde['s] matrix** <AL>	Vandermondesche Matrix *f*	matrice *f* de Vandermonde	матрица Вандермонда
	Van der Waerden['s] [X-]test <ST>	*s.* X 3		
V 43	**vanish / to** <GN>	verschwinden, Null werden	devenir nul, s'annuler	обращаться в нуль, исчезать
V 44	**vanish identically / to** <GN>	identisch verschwinden (Null werden (sein))	s'annuler identiquement	тождественно обращаться в нуль
V 45	**vanishing** <GN>	Verschwinden *n*, Nullwerden *n*	annulation *f*, propriété *f* de devenir nul	обращение в нуль, исчезновение
V 46	**vanishing cycle** <AG>	Verschwindungszyklus *m*	cycle *m* évanescent	исчезающий цикл
V 47	**vanishing function** <AN>	verschwindende Funktion *f*	fonction *f* s'annulante	функция, обращающаяся в нуль; функция, принимающая нулевое значение
V 48	**vanishing line** <DS>	Fluchtlinie *f*, Fluchtgerade *f*	ligne *f* de fuite	линия схода
	vanishing line <DS>	*s.* N 186		
V 49	**vanishing plane** <DS>	Fluchtebene *f*	plan *m* de fuite	плоскость схода
	vanishing plane <DS>	*s.* N 187		
V 50	**vanishing point** <DS>	Fluchtpunkt *m*	point *m* de fuite	точка схода
	vanishing point <DS>	*s.* N 188		
V 51	**vanishing polynomial** <AL>	verschwindendes Polynom *n*; Polynom, das die Nullfunktion definiert	polynôme *m* définissant une fonction polynomiale qui est identiquement zéro	многочлен, для которого соответствующая полиномиальная функция является нуль-функцией
V 52	**vanishing theorem** <AG, DE, HA>	Verschwindungssatz *m*	théorème *m* d'annulation, « vanishing theorem » *m*	теорема об обращении в нуль
V 53	**Van Kampen['s] theorem** <for simplicial complexes> <AT>	Satz *m* von van Kampen für simpliziale Komplexe, van Kampenscher Satz	théorème *m* de van Kampen	теорема Ван Кампена для симплициальных комплексов
	var <ST>	*s.* V 62		
V 54	**variability** <ST>	Variabilität *f*, Verstreutheit *f*	variabilité *f*	изменчивость
	variability <ST>	*s.* S 101		
V 55	**variable,** figurative symbol <LO, SE>	Variable *f*	variable *f*, symbole *m* figuratif	переменная
V 56	**variable boundary** <of the domain of integration> <AN>	variable Grenze *f*	limite *f* variable	переменная граница
V 57	**variable bound by the universal quantifier** <LO>	Allvariable *f*	variable *f* liée par le généralisateur	переменная, связанная знаком общности

	variable co-ordinate <AY>	*s.* R 1530		
V 58	**variable-free expression** <LO>	Ausdruck *m* ohne Variable	formule *f* sans variable	выражение, свободное от переменных
	variable index <GN>	*s.* R 1531		
V 59	**variable intersection** <AG>	beweglicher Schnitt *m*	intersection *f* mobile	подвижное сечение
V 60	**variable multiple point** <AG>	beweglicher mehrfacher Punkt *m*	point *m* multiple mobile	подвижная кратная точка
	variable representing predicates <LO>	*s.* P 1192		
	variables inspection <ST>	*s.* I 591		
	variable transformation <DI>	*s.* C 503		
V 61	**variance** <of a functor> <+ 1 for covariant, — 1 for contravariant> <CA>	Varianz *f*	variance *f*	вариантность
V 62	**variance,** dispersion, square of the standard deviation, mean square deviation, var <σ^2> <ST>	Varianz *f*, Streuung *f*, Dispersion *f*, mittlere quadratische Abweichung *f*, Streuungsquadrat *n*, var <σ^2>	variance *f*, dispersion *f*, moment *m* de dispersion, fluctuation *f*, écart *m* quadratique moyen, var <σ^2>	дисперсия, дисперсия распределения вероятностей, рассеяние, квадрат стандартного отклонения, среднеквадратичное отклонение, var <σ^2>
V 63	**variance analysis,** analysis of variance, ANOVA <ST>	Varianzanalyse *f*, Dispersionsanalyse *f*, F-Verfahren *n*, VA, ANOVA; Streuungszerlegung *f*	analyse *f* de variance (dispersion), analyse dispersionnelle	дисперсионный анализ
	variance between classes (treatments) <ST>	*s.* I 704		
	variance component <ST>	*s.* C 1667		
V 64	**variance ratio,** *F*-ratio, *F*-statistic <ST>	Varianzquotient *m*, Snedecorsche Stichprobenfunktion *f*, [Snedecorsche] *F*-Stichprobenfunktion *f*, *F*-Statistik *f*, *F*-Maßzahl *f*, *F*-Prüfzahl *f*	rapport *m* des variances, variable *f F*, statistique *f F*, critère *m F*	дисперсионное отношение, отношение *F*, статистика *F*
	variance ratio distribution <ST>	*s.* F 109		
V 65	**variance ratio test** <ST>	Varianzquotiententest *m*	test *m* [F] du rapport des variances	критерий дисперсионного отношения
	variance within classes (groups, treatments) <ST>	*s.* W 273		
V 66	**variant** <AL>	Variante *f*	variant *m*, variante *f*	вариант
V 67	**variate,** random (chance, aleatory, stochastic) variable <ST>	zufällige Variable (Veränderliche) *f*, zufälliges Element *n*, stochastische Variable (Veränderliche), Stochastik *f*, aleatorische Variable, Zufallsvariable *f*, Zufallsveränderliche *f*, Variate *f*; Zufallsgröße *f*, zufällige (aleatorische) Größe *f*	variable *f* aléatoire (stochastique, éventuelle), variate *f*, aléatoire *f*, aléa *m* numérique	случайная величина (переменная, переменная величина), стохастическая величина (переменная)
V 68	**variate-difference method** <ST>	Student-Andersonsche Differenzmethode *f*, Differenzmethode nach Student-Anderson, Variate-Differenz-Methode *f*	méthode *f* de différences de Tintner, méthode des différences de Student-Anderson, méthode « variate difference »	разностно-дисперсионный метод [Андерсона-Стьюдента]
V 69	**variation,** infinitesimal variation, δf <of a function *f*> <AN>	Variation *f*, Schwankung *f*	variation *f*, variation infinitesimale	вариация, варьирование, изменение
	λ-variation <RF>	*s.* L 51		
	variational calculus <VA>	*s.* C 32		
V 70	**variational derivative,** variation (Lagrangian, functional) derivative <VA>	Variationsableitung *f*, Lagrangesche (Euler-Lagrangesche, funktionale) Ableitung *f*	dérivée *f* variationnelle (fonctionnelle)	вариационная (функциональная) производная
V 71	**variational equation** <VA>	Variationsgleichung *f*	équation *f* aux variations, équation variationnelle	уравнение в вариациях, вариационное уравнение
V 72	**variational equations,** accessory differential equations <DE, VA>	akzessorische Differentialgleichungen *fpl* <von Escherich>, Variationsgleichungen *fpl* <Poincaré>	équations *fpl* variationnelles (différentielles accessoires)	вариационные (присоединенные дифференциальные) уравнения
V 73	**variational equations of side and final conditions** <VA>	Variationsgleichungen *fpl* der Neben- und Endbedingungen	équations *fpl* aux variations des conditions secondaires et finales	уравнения в вариациях дополнительных и концевых условий
V 74	**variational inequality** <VA>	Variationsungleichung *f*	inéquation *f* variationnelle	вариационное неравенство
V 75	**variational principle** <VA>	Variationsprinzip *n*	principe *m* variationnel	вариационный принцип
V 76	**variational problem** <VA>	Variationsproblem *n*, Variationsaufgabe *f*	problème *m* variationnel	вариационная задача
	variational solution <DE>	*s.* W 125		

	English	German	French	Russian
V 77	**variational symbol,** δ, // δ <VA>	Variationszeichen *n*, δ, // δ	symbole *m* de variation, δ, // δ	знак вариации, δ, // δ
	variation coefficient <ST>	*s.* C 1035		
	variation derivative <VA>	*s.* V 70		
V 78	**variation in sign,** variation of sign <in a sequence> <AL>	Zeichenwechsel *m*, Alternanz *f*	variation *f* [de signe], alternance *f* [de signes], changement *m* de signe	перемена (чередование) знаков
	variation in sign <GN>	*s.* C 498		
V 79	**variation in the sense of Vitali,** Vitali variation, V-variation <of a function> <AN>	Vitali-Variation *f*, Variation *f* im Sinne von Vitali	variation *f* au sens de Vitali	колебание в смысле Витали
V 80	**variation of constants (parameters),** method of variation of the constants (parameters) <DE>	Variation *f* der Konstanten, Methode *f* der Variation der Konstanten (Parameter), Variation der Parameter	variation *f* des constantes [arbitraires], méthode *f* de variation des constantes (paramètres), variation des paramètres [arbitraires]	вариация произвольных постоянных (параметров), вариация постоянных (параметров), метод вариации [произвольных] постоянных (параметров)
	variation of sign <AL>	*s.* V 78		
	variation of sign <GN>	*s.* C 498		
V 81	**variation statistics** <ST>	Variationsstatistik *f*, Variationsanalyse *f*	statistique *f* des variations, statistique de variation	вариационная статистика, статистика вариаций
V 82	**varied density** <AB>	variierte Dichte (Schnirelmann-Dichte) *f*	densité *f* variée	варьированная плотность
	variety <AG>	*s.* 1. A 104; 2. A 458; 3. I 1025		
	variety <AG, DG, TO>	*s.* M 61		
	variety <UA>	*s.* E 337		
V 83	**variety free from singularities,** manifold free from singularities <AG>	singularitätenfreie Mannigfaltigkeit *f*	variété *f* non singulière, variété sans singularités	неособое многообразие
	variety of Albanese <AG>	*s.* A 394		
	variety of elements <DE, GE>	*s.* C 1634		
V 84	**variety of groups,** equational class of groups <UA>	Varietät (primitive Klasse) *f* von Gruppen, Gruppenmannigfaltigkeit *f*	variété *f* de groupes	многообразие (примитивный класс) групп
V 85	**variety of moduli,** modular variety <AG, FT>	Modulmannigfaltigkeit *f*	variété *f* modulaire	модулярное многообразие
	variety of Picard <AG>	*s.* P 576		
	variety of Segre <AG>	*s.* S 254		
	variety over *k* <AG>	*s.* K 185		
	variety relatively normal with respect to *k* <AG>	*s.* L 982		
	variety relatively simple with reference to *k* <AG>	*s.* K 186		
V 86	**Varignon['s] theorem** <GE>	Varignonscher Satz *m*, Satz (Theorem *n*) von Varignon	théorème *m* de Varignon	теорема Вариньона
V 87	**vary / to** <GN>	alle Werte durchlaufen, variieren	parcourir toutes les valeurs	пробегать (принимать последовательно) все значения
V 88	**vary continuously / to** <AN, TO>	sich stetig ändern	varier continûment	непрерывно меняться
	v-critical graph <GP>	*s.* V 160		
	V-cycle of dimension *r* <AG>	*s.* R 207		
	Veblen-Wedderburn number system <AL>	*s.* Q 154		
V 89	**Veblen-Wedderburn plane,** translation plane <AL, GE>	Translationsebene *f*, Veblen-Wedderburn-Ebene *f*	géométrie *f* plane affine de translation, plan *m* de translation	веблен-веддербернова плоскость, плоскость переноса (трансляций)
	vectogram <NU>	*s.* V 105		
V 90	**vector** <of a quaternion> <AL>	Vektor *m*, Vektorteil *m*, Vektorglied *n*, vektorieller Bestandteil *m*	partie *f* vectorielle, terme *m* vectoriel, vecteur *m*	векторная (мнимая) часть
V 91	**vector,** sequence <as an element of a sequence space> <FA>	Vektor *m*, Stelle *f*, Folge *f*	vecteur *m*, suite *f*	вектор, последовательность
V 92	**vector,** tensor of rank 1, first-order [Cartesian] tensor <VT>	Vektor *m*, einstufiger Tensor *m*, Tensor erster Stufe	vecteur *m*, tenseur *m* d'ordre 1	вектор, тензор валентности (ранга) 1
	vector <AL, FA>	*s.* P 721		
	3-vector <AL, VT>	*s.* T 986		
	4-vector <DG, VT>	*s.* F 552		
	6-vector <VT>	*s.* S 1146		
V 93	**vector addition,** vector composition, geometric addition <VT>	Vektoraddition *f*, geometrische Addition *f*	addition *f* de vecteurs, addition vectorielle (géométrique)	векторное (геометрическое) сложение, сложение векторов
	vector addition coefficient <AL>	*s.* C 811		
V 94	**vector algebra** <VT>	Vektoralgebra *f*	algèbre *f* vectorielle	векторная алгебра
V 95	**vector algebra of Gibbs,** Gibbs['] vector algebra <AL, GE>	Gibbssche Vektoralgebra *f*, Vektoralgebra von Gibbs	algèbre *f* vectorielle de Gibbs	алгебра векторов Гиббса
V 96	**vector analysis** <VT>	Vektoranalysis *f*	analyse *f* vectorielle	векторный анализ

No.	English	German	French	Russian
V 97	**vector basis,** linear basis, basis, co-ordinate system, minimal spanning set <of a vector space> <AL>	Basis *f*, Vektorbasis *f*, Bezugssystem *n*	base *f*, base d'une multiplicité	базис, алгебраический базис
V 98	**vector bundle,** bundle [of linear spaces] <AT>	Vektorraumbündel *n*	espace *m* fibré à fibre vectorielle, fibré *m* vectoriel	расслоенное пространство, слоями которого являются векторные пространства; векторное расслоение
	vector bundle of contravariant tangent vectors <AT>	*s.* C 2303		
	vector bundle of covariant tangent vectors <AT>	*s.* C 2611		
V 99	**vector calculus** <VT>	Vektorrechnung *f*	calcul *m* vectoriel	векторное исчисление
	vector composition <VT>	*s.* V 93		
V 100	**vector correlation coefficient** <ST>	Vektorkorrelationskoeffizient *m*	coefficient *m* de corrélation vectoriel	векторный коэффициент корреляции
V 101	**vector couple,** couple of vectors <GE, VT>	Vektorpaar *n*	couple *m* [de vecteurs]	пара векторов
V 102	**vector decomposition,** vector resolution, resolution, resolving, decomposition <of a vector into its components> <VT>	Komponentenzerlegung *f*, Zerlegung *f* <eines Vektors in seine Komponenten>, Komponentendarstellung *f* <eines Vektors>	décomposition *f*, partition *f* <d'un vecteur en composantes>	разбиение, разбивка, разложение <вектора в составляющих>
V 103	**vector density** <VT>	Vektordichte *f*, vektorielle Dichte *f*	densité *f* vectorielle	векторная плотность
V 104	**vector derivative** <VT>	vektorielle Ableitung *f*	dérivée *f* vectorielle	векторная производная
V 105	**vector diagram,** vectogram <NU>	Vektordiagramm *n*, Zeigerdiagramm *n*	diagramme *m* vectoriel, diagramme-vecteur *m*, diagramme de Fresnel	векторная диаграмма
	vectored quantity <GE>	*s.* D 550		
	vector equal in length and opposite in direction <VT>	*s.* O 230		
V 106	**vector equation** <GN>	Vektorgleichung *f*	équation *f* vectorielle	векторное уравнение (равенство)
V 107	**vector field** <VT>	Vektorfeld *n*, Tensorfeld *n* erster Stufe	champ *m* vectoriel (de vecteurs, de vecteur)	векторное поле
	vector field derivable from a scalar potential <VT>	*s.* I 1070		
	vector flux <VT>	*s.* F 424		
V 108	**vector function** <AL, AN>	Vektorfunktion *f*	fonction *f* vectorielle	вектор-функция, векторная функция <скалярного аргумента>
	vectorial angle <AY>	*s.* A 604		
V 109	**vectorial co-ordinates** <of a sliding vector> <GE>	Stabkoordinaten *fpl*, Koordinaten *fpl* <eines Stabes>	coordonnées *fpl* vectorielles <d'un vecteur glissant>	векторные координаты <скользящего вектора>
	vectorial flux <VT>	*s.* F 424		
V 110	**vectorial Gaussian process** <SP>	vektorieller Gaußscher Prozeß *m*	processus *m* vectoriel gaussien	гауссовский векторный случайный процесс
V 111	**vectorial part** <of a dual number> <AL>	Dualteil *m*	coefficient *m* vectoriel	векторная часть
	vectorial sum <VT>	*s.* G 270		
	vector in the affine space <VT>	*s.* G 252		
V 112	**vector iteration** <MD, NU>	Vektoriteration *f*	itération *f* vectorielle	векторная итерация
V 113	**vector lattice,** K-lineal <FA>	Vektorverband *m*, K-Lineal *n*	lattice *m* vectoriel	векторная структура, K-линеал
	vector line <DG, VT>	*s.* L 873		
V 114	**vector maximum problem** <PG>	Vektormaximumproblem *n*	problème *m* du vecteur maximum	проблема (задача) максимального вектора
V 115	**vector measure** <ME>	vektorielles Maß *n*	mesure *f* vectorielle	векторная мера
V 116	**vector module** <AL>	Vektormodul *m*	module *m* de vecteurs	векторный модуль
V 117	**vector norm** <of a matrix ><MD>	Vektornorm *f*	norme *f* vectorielle	векторная норма
	vector of binormal <DG>	*s.* B 407		
	vector of first normal <DG>	*s.* P 1455		
	vector of principal normal <DG>	*s.* P 1455		
	vector of second normal <DG>	*s.* B 407		
V 118	**vector of the same direction** <VT>	richtungsgleicher Vektor *m*	vecteur *m* ayant la même direction	вектор одинакового направления
	vector of torsion <DG>	*s.* T 611		
V 119	**vector operator** <AL, FA>	vektorieller Operator *m* <AL, FA>; Vektoroperator *m* <FA>	opérateur *m* vectoriel	векторный оператор
V 120	**vector polygon,** polygon of vectors <GE>	Vektorpolygon *n*	polygone *m* des vecteurs, polygone de Varignon	многоугольник (полигон) векторов
V 121	**vector product,** outer product, cross product, skew product, alternating product, × <*to be read:* cross>, ∨ <of vectors> <VT>	vektorielles (äußeres) Produkt *n*, Vektorprodukt *n*, Kreuzprodukt *n*, alternierendes Produkt, × <*lies:* Kreuz>, ∧	produit *m* vectoriel (extérieur, gauche, alterné), produit angulaire <Cauchy>, produit géométrique <St. Venant>, × <*se lit:* croix>, ∧	векторное (внешнее) произведение, ×, ∧
V 122	**vector representation** <contrary to spin representation> <AL>	Vektordarstellung *f*	représentation *f* vectorielle	векторное представление

No.	English	German	French	Russian
	vector resolution <VT>	*s.* V 102		
V 123	**vector resolution into a solenoidal and irrotational vector,** resolution <of a vector> into a solenoidal and irrotational vector <VT>	Zerlegung *f* <eines Vektorfelds> in ein quellenfreies und ein wirbelfreies Feld	décomposition *f* <d'un champ vectoriel> en somme d'un champ solénoïdal et d'un champ irrotationnel	представление <векторного поля> в виде суммы безвихревого поля и соленоидального поля
V 124	**vector series** <SS>	Vektorreihe *f*	série *f* vectorielle	векторный ряд
V 125	**vector space,** vector-space, vectorspace, linear vector space, linear space <over *K*> <AL>	Vektorraum *m*, linearer Raum *m* (Vektorraum), lineares System *n*, Linearsystem *n*, Vektormannigfaltigkeit *f*, Vektorgebilde *n* <über *K*>	espace *m* vectoriel (linéaire), vectoriel *m* <sur *K*>	векторное (линейное, линейное векторное) пространство <над *K*>
V 126/7	**vector space direct sum,** module direct sum <AL>	modultheoretische direkte Summe *f*	composé *m* direct de modules	прямая сумма модулей
	vector space isomorphism <AL>	*s.* L 806		
	vector space of dimension two <AL>	*s.* T 1084		
V 128	**vector subspace,** subspace, linear manifold <of a vector space> <AL>	linearer Unterraum (Teilraum) *m*, Untervektorraum *m*	sous-espace *m* [vectoriel], variété *f* (ensemble *m*) linéaire	линейное (векторное) подпространство, подпространство
	vector sum <VT>	*s.* G 270		
	vector system <GE>	*s.* S 2541		
V 129	**vector tube,** tube of a vector field <AN, DG>	Vektorröhre *f*, Vektorfeldröhre *f*, Feldröhre *f*, Feldlinienröhre *f*	tube *m* de champ [vectoriel]	векторная трубка, трубка линий поля, трубка поля (в векторном поле)
V 130	**vector-valued function** <AN>	vektorwertige Funktion *f*	fonction *f* à valeurs vectorielles	векторнозначная функция
	vector variate <ST>	*s.* R 115		
V 131	**Veitch['s] diagram** <LO>	Veitch-Diagramm *n*	diagramme *m* de Veitch	диаграмма Вейча
V 132	**Vekua['s] boundary problem** <IE>	Vekuasches Randwertproblem (Problem) *n*	problème *m* aux limites de Vekua	краевая задача Векуа
V 133	**Vekua['s] [differential] equation** <DE>	Vekuasche Differentialgleichung *f*	équation *f* [différentielle] de Vekua	[дифференциальное] уравнение Векуа
	vel <LO>	*s.* D 705		
	vel function <LO>	*s.* D 705		
V 134	**V-elliptic form** <DE>	V-elliptische Form *f*	forme *f* V-elliptique	V-эллиптическая форма
V 135	**V-ellipticity** <DE>	V-Elliptizität *f*	V-ellipticité *f*	V-эллиптичность
V 136	**Venn['s] circle** <LO, SE>	Eulerscher Kreis *m*	cercle *m* d'Euler	эйлеров круг, круг Эйлера
	Venn['s] diagram <LO>	*s.* E 626		
	veracity <LO>	*s.* T 1037		
V 137	**verbal product** <of groups> <GR>	Wortprodukt *n*, verbales Produkt *n*	produit *m* verbal	вербальное произведение
V 138	**verbal subgroup,** word subgroup <GR>	Wortuntergruppe *f*, verbale Untergruppe *f*	sous-groupe *m* verbal	вербальная подгруппа
V 139	**Verhulst-Brody['s] growth function,** Brody['s] growth function <ST, SP>	Wachstumsfunktion *f* nach Verhulst-Brody (Brody), Verhulst-Brodysche (Brodysche) Wachstumsfunktion	fonction *f* de croissance de Verhulst-Brody (Brody)	функция роста Верхульста-Броди (по Верхульсту-Броди, Броди, по Броди)
	Verhulst['s] formula	*s.* V 140		
	Verhulst['s] growth function <ST>	*s.* L 1080		
V 140	**Verhulst['s] law,** Verhulst['s] formula <SP>	Wachstumsgesetz *n* von Verhulst, Verhulsts Gesetz *n* (Formel *f*), Verhulstsches Gesetz, Verhulstsche Formel, Verhulst-Formel *f*	loi (formule) *f* de Verhulst	закон (формула, закон роста) Верхульста
V 141	**verifiable formula** <GN>	verifizierbare Formel *f*	formule *f* vérifiable	проверяемая (верифицируемая, поддающаяся проверке) формула
V 142	**verification** <e.g.: a formula> <GN>	Verifizierung *f*, Bestätigung *f*, Verifikation *f*	vérification *f*	проверка, верификация
	verify / to <FO, LO>	*s.* P 1882		
	verlagerung <AB>	*s.* 1. G 516; 2. T 734		
V 143	**Veronese['s] cone** <AG>	Veronesescher Kegel *m*	cône *m* de Veronese	конус Веронезе
V 144	**Veronese['s] surface** <AG>	Veronesesche Fläche *f*	surface *f* de Veronese	поверхность Веронезе
V 145	**Veronese['s] variety** <AG>	Veronesesche Mannigfaltigkeit (Varietät) *f*	variété *f* de Veronese (Véronèse)	многообразие Веронезе
	vers <AN>	*s.* V 147		
V 146	**versed cosine,** coversine, coversed sine, cos vers, cover <= 1 — sin> <DI>	Kosinusversus *m*, Cosinus *m* versus, cos vers	cosinus *m* versus, cos vers	косинус-верзус, обращенный косинус, cos vers
V 147	**versed-sine,** versine, sin vers, vers <= 1 — cos> <AN>	Sinus *m* versus, Sinusversus *m*, sin vers	sinus *m* versus, sin vers	синус-верзус, обращенный синус, sin vers
	versiera <GE>	*s.* W 272		
	versine <AN>	*s.* V 147		
	versor <AL>	*s.* N 612		
	versor <VT>	*s.* U 302		
V 148	**vertex** <of a simplex *or* abstract simplex>; abstract vertex <of an abstract simplex> <AT>	Eckpunkt *m*, Ecke *f*	sommet *m*	вершина
V 149	**vertex** <in a simplicial set> <AT>	Ecke *f*, Eckpunkt *m*	sommet *m*	симплициальная точка, стандартный нульмерный симплекс
V 150	**vertex** <of a conic, curve, *or* angle> <AY, DG, EG>	Scheitel *m*	sommet *m*	вершина

V 151	**vertex** <in a diagram scheme> <CA>	Ecke *f*	sommet *m*	вершина
V 152	**vertex** <CS>	Eckpunkt *m*	pointe *f*	особая точка типа вершины
V 153	**vertex,** apex <of a cone> <EG>	Spitze *f*, Scheitel *m*, Scheitelpunkt *m*	sommet *m*	вершина
V 154	**vertex** <of an isosceles triangle> <EG>	Spitze *f*	sommet *m*	вершина
V 155	**vertex,** apex <of a pyramid> <EG>	Spitze *f*	sommet *m*	вершина
V 156	**vertex,** node, knot, point; junction <in a network> <GP>	Knotenpunkt *m*, Punkt *m*, Ecke *f*	sommet *m*, nœud *m* carrefour, point *m*, point de concours	вершина, точка
V 157	**vertex** <TG>	Position *f*	position *f*	позиция
	vertex <EG>	*s.* C 2465		
	vertex <PJ>	*s.* 1. C 402; 2. C 403; 3. C 423		
V 158	**vertex angle,** apex angle, apical angle <of isosceles triangle> <EG>	Winkel *m* an der Spitze, Scheitelwinkel *m*	angle *m* au sommet	угол при вершине
	vertex angle <EG>	*s.* A 796		
	vertex colouration <GP>	*s.* C 1158		
V 159	**vertex connectivity, vertex-connectivity number,** connection number, connectivity <of a graph> <GP>	Knotenzusammenhangszahl *f*, Zusammenhangszahl *f*	nombre *m* de connectivité, connectivité *f*	связность, вершинная связность
V 160	**vertex critical graph,** γ-critical graph, v-critical graph <with respect to a chromatic number> <GP>	punktkritischer Graph *m* <in bezug auf die chromatische Zahl>	point *m* γ-critique	критический <по раскраске> граф
	vertex degree <GP>	*s.* D 176		
	vertex direct sum <GP>	*s.* D 607		
V 161	**vertex disjoint subgraphs,** disjoint subgraphs <GP>	elementefremde Teilgraphen *mpl*, [element-] fremde Teilgraphen	sous-graphes *mpl* sans sommets communs	подграфы без общих вершин
V 162	**vertex equation,** canonical equation <referred to the vertex as origin> <of a conic> <AY>	Scheitelgleichung *f*	équation *f* d'une conique en fonction de l'excentricité numérique et du paramètre	каноническое уравнение конического сечения, отнесенное к его вершине
	vertex incidence matrix <GP>	*s.* I 228		
	vertex independence number <GP>	*s.* S 1578		
V 163	**vertex map,** vertex transformation <of a complex> <AT>	Eckpunktabbildung *f*	application *f* des sommets	отображение множества вершин
	vertex matrix <GP>	*s.* 1. A 274; 2. I 228		
	vertex of a cocartesian square <CA>	*s.* F 155		
V 164	**vertex of degree 3** <GP>	dreiwertiger Knoten *m*, Knotenpunkt *m* vom Grade 3	sommet *m* de valence 3	вершина степени 3
V 165	**vertex separation theorem,** Menger['s] theorem, Menger['s] graph theorem <GP>	Satz *m* von Menger, Mengerscher Satz (Graphensatz *m*), Theorem *n* von Menger-Dirac	théorème *m* de Menger	теорема Менгера-Дирака
V 166	**vertex set** <of a complex> <AT>	Eckpunktmenge *f*	ensemble *m* des sommets	множество вершин
V 167	**vertex set** <GP>	Menge *f* der Knotenpunkte, Knotenpunktmenge *f*, Eckenmenge *f*	ensemble *m* des sommets	множество вершин
V 168	**vertex that is not saturated** <by a matching *M*> <GP>	freier Knoten *m* <relativ zu einer Kantenmenge *M*>	sommet *m* non saturé <par un couplage *M*>	непокрытая вершина <относительно *M*>
	vertex transformation <AT>	*s.* V 163		
	vertical <DS>	*s.* F 679		
V 169	**vertical angles, vertically opposite angles** <EG>	Scheitelwinkel *mpl*	angles *mpl* opposés par le sommet	вертикальные углы
V 170	**vertical plane [of projection],** vertical projection plane, second plane [of projection] <DS>	Vertikalebene *f*, Aufrißebene *f*, zweite Projektionsebene (Tafel) *f*, Aufrißtafel *f*	plan *m* vertical [de projection], second (deuxième) plan [de projection]	плоскость вертикальной проекции
	vertical projection <DS>	*s.* E 143		
	vertical projection plane <DS>	*s.* V 170		
	vertical row <GN, MD, SS>	*s.* C 1160		
	vertical row index <MD>	*s.* C 1163		
	vertical trace [line] <DS>	*s.* S 225		
V 171	**very feeble solution** <DE>	sehr schwache Lösung *f*	solution *f* très faible	очень слабое решение
V 172	**V-group** <GR>	V-Gruppe *f*	V-groupe *m*	V-группа, вполне доупорядочиваемая группа
V 173	**V*-group** <GR>	V*-Gruppe *f*	V*-groupe *m*	V*-группа
V 174	**Vianello['s] method** <DE, NU>	Vianellosches Verfahren *n*, Vianello-Verfahren *n*	méthode *f* de Vianello	метод Вианелло
V 175	**vicenary [number] system** <NT>	Vigesimalsystem *n*, Zahlensystem *n* zur Basis 20	système *m* vicésimal, système [de numération] à base 20	двадцатеричная система счисления

V 176	**vicious circle,** circularity <LO>	circulus *m* vitiosus, Zirkelschluß *m*	cercle *m* vicieux, pétition *f* de principe	порочный круг, круг в доказательстве, ложный (заколдованный) круг, circulus vitiosus (in probando, in demonstrando)
V 177	**vicious-circle principle,** Russell['s] vicious-circle principle <LO>	Prinzip *n* des Zirkelschlusses	principe *m* du cercle vicieux	принцип порочного круга
	vid <AL>	*s.* E 858		
V 178	**v-ideal** <AL>	v-Ideal *n*	V-idéal *m*	v-идеал
V 179	**Vieille['s] problem** <VA>	Problem *n* von Vieille, Vieillesches Problem	problème *m* de Vieille	задача Вьей
	vierer group <GR>	*s.* K 90		
	Vierergruppe <GR>	*s.* K 90		
V 180	**Vieta['s] formulae (root theorem),** relation between the roots and coefficients of an algebraic equation <AL>	Viëtàscher (Vietàscher) Wurzelsatz *m*, Vietàscher (Viètescher) Lehrsatz *m*	formules *fpl* de Viète	формулы Виета (Вьéта), обобщенная теорема Виета
V 181	**Vieta['s] theorem** <GE>	Viëtascher Satz *m*, Hauptsatz *m* der Theorie der Inversionen	théorème *m* de Viète	теорема Виета (Вьéта)
V 182	**Vietoris-Begle mapping theorem** <AT>	Vietoris-Beglescher Abbildungssatz *m*	théorème *m* de Vietoris-Begle	теорема Виеториса-Бегля <об отображении>
V 183	**Vietoris['s] complex** <AT>	Vietoris-Komplex *m*	complexe *m* de Vietoris	виеторисиан
V 184	**Vietoris['s] cycle** <AT>	Vietorisscher Zyklus *m*	cycle *m* de Vietoris	цикл Виеториса
V 185	**Vietoris['s] topology,** exponential topology <TO>	Vietoris-Topologie *f*	topologie *f* de Vietoris	экспоненциальная топология, топология Виеториса (Вьеториса)
V 186	**Viggo-Brun['s] method,** Brun['s] method, Brun['s] sieve method <AB>	Viggo Brunsche Siebmethode (Methode) *f*, Brunsche Methode	méthode *f* de V. Brun	метод [решета] Бруна, метод В. Бруна, решето Вигго Бруна, «двойное треугольное решето», решето Бруна
	vincinity <SE>	*s.* R 471		
V 187	**vinculum,** bar, overlining <as a sign of aggregation> <GN>	Überstreichung *f* <als Klammerzeichen>	surlignéation *f*	[объединительная] черта <над выражением>
	vinculum <GN>	*s.* O 567		
V 188	**Vinogradov['s] constant** <NT>	Vinogradovsche (Winogradowsche) Konstante *f*	constante *f* de Vinogradov	константа Виноградова
V 189	**Vinogradov['s] mean-value theorem** <NT>	Mittelwertsatz *m* von Vinogradov, Vinogradovscher (Winogradowscher) Mittelwertsatz	théorème *m* de la moyenne de Vinogradov	теорема Виноградова о среднем
V 190	**Vinogradov['s] method** <AB>	Vinogradovsche (Winogradowsche) Methode *f*	méthode *f* de Vinogradov	метод Виноградова
V 191	**virtual genus** <AG>	virtuelles Geschlecht *n*	genre *m* virtuel	виртуальный род
	virtual infinity <FO, SE>	*s.* P 1124		
V 192	**virtual linear genus,** Castelnuovo-Enriques invariant <AG>	virtuelles lineares Geschlecht *n*	genre *m* linéaire virtuel	виртуальный линейный род
V 193	**virtual multiplicity,** assigned multiplicity <AG>	virtuelle Multiplizität *f*	multiplicité *f* virtuelle	виртуальная кратность
V 194	**virtual point group, virtual point-group** <AG>	virtuelle Punktgruppe *f*	groupe *m* ponctuel virtuel	виртуальная точечная группа
V 195	**virtual variety** <AG>	virtuelle Mannigfaltigkeit *f*	variété *f* virtuelle	виртуальное многообразие
	virtual variety <AG>	*s.* D 828		
V 196	**visible point** <GU>	sichtbarer Punkt *m*	point *m* visible	видимая точка
V 197	**Vitali['s] theorem,** theorem of Vitali <FT, SS>	Vitalischer Satz *m*, Satz von Vitali; Vitalischer Doppelreihensatz *m*	théorème *m* de Vitali	теорема Витали
	Vitali variation <AN>	*s.* V 79		
V 198	**Vivanti['s] theorem** <FT, SS>	Vivantischer (Vivanti-Landauscher) Satz *m*	théorème *m* de Vivanti	теорема Виванти
V 199	**Viviani['s] curve,** Viviani['s] windows <GE>	Vivianische Kurve *f*, Fenster *n* des Viviani, Vivianisches Fenster	fenêtre (courbe) *f* de Viviani	кривая Вивиани; кусок полусферы $z = \sqrt{a^2 - x^2 - y^2}$, высекаемый цилиндром $x^2 + y^2 - ax \leqq 0$
V 200	**Viviani['s] problem** <EG>	Florentiner Problem *n* (Aufgabe *f*), Vivianisches (Vivianis) Problem, Vivianische Aufgabe	problème *m* florentin (de Viviani)	флорентинская задача (проблема)
	Viviani['s] windows <GE>	*s.* V 199		
	v. max <AN>	*s.* V 222		
	v. min <AN>	*s.* V 223		
V 201	**VN-group** <GR>	VN-Gruppe *f*	VN-groupe *m*	VN-группа
V 202	**Vogel['s] [approximation] method** <for solving the transportation problem> <GP, PG>	Vogelsche Approximationsmethode (Näherungsmethode) *f*	méthode *f* [d'approximation] de Vogel	[приближенный] метод Фогеля
V 203	**Vogler['s] theorem** <NO>	Voglerscher Satz *m*	théorème *m* de Vogler	теорема Фоглера
	void class <LO, SE>	*s.* N 765		
V 204	**void set,** empty set, vacuous set, // null[-]set <SE>	leere Menge *f*, // Nullmenge *f*	ensemble *m* vide	пустое (нулевое) множество, нуль-множество
	Volterra['s] equation <IE>	*s.* V 206		

No.	English	German	French	Russian
V 205	**Volterra['s] equations** <for biocenoses> <DE>	Volterrasche Gleichungen *fpl*	équations *fpl* de Volterra	уравнения Вольтерра
V 206	**Volterra['s] integral equation,** Volterra['s] equation, Volterra-type [integral] equation, integral equation of [the] Volterra type; <*especially:*> [linear] integral equation with variable upper limit of integration <of the first *or* second kind> <IE>	Volterrasche Integralgleichung *f*, Integralgleichung vom Volterraschen Typ, Integralgleichung vom Volterra-Typ, <insbesondere:> [lineare] Integralgleichung mit variabler oberer Integrationsgrenze <erster *oder* zweiter Art>	équation *f* intégrale de Volterra, équation de Volterra, équation de (du) type Volterra, équation intégrale <en particulier:> [linéaire] à limite supérieure variable d'intégration <de première *ou* seconde (deuxième) espèce>	интегральное уравнение Вольтерра, уравнение Вольтерра, интегральное уравнение типа Вольтерра, <в частности:> [линейное] интегральное уравнение с переменным верхним пределом <первого *или* второго рода>
	Volterra['s] integral transformation <IT>	*s.* V 210		
V 207	**Volterra['s] kernel** <IE>	Volterrascher Kern *m*	noyau *m* de Volterra	ядро Вольтерра
V 208	**Volterra['s] operator** <FA>	Volterrascher Operator *m*	opérateur *m* de Volterra	оператор Вольтерра
V 209	**Volterra['s] singular equation** <IE>	singuläre Volterrasche Integralgleichung *f*	équation *f* intégrale de Volterra singulière	особое интегральное уравнение Вольтерра
V 210	**Volterra['s] transformation,** Volterra['s] integral transformation <IT>	Volterrasche Integraltransformation *f*, Volterra-Transformation *f*	transformation *f* [intégrale] de Volterra	[интегральное] преобразование Вольтерра
	Volterra-type [integral] equation <IE>	*s.* V 206		
V 211	**volume** <EG>	Volumen *n*, Rauminhalt *m*, Kubikinhalt *m*, Inhalt *m*	volume *m*	объем
V 212	**volume** <ME>	Volumen *n* [im Peano-Jordanschen Sinne]	volume *m*	объем
V 213	**volume integral,** space integral <DI>	Raumintegral *n*, Volumintegral *n*, Volumenintegral *n*	intégrale *f* étendue à un volume, intégrale de volume	интеграл по объему
	volume of information <ST>	*s.* I 506		
V 214	**volume of the sphere** <EG>	Volumen *n* der Kugel, Kugelvolumen *n*	volume *m* de la sphère	объем шара
V 215	**[von] Bertalanffy['s] formula (law)** <ST>	Wachstumsgesetz *n* (Gesetz *n*, Formel *f*) von Bertalanffys, [von] Bertalanffysche Formel	loi (formule) *f* de [von] Bertalanffy	закон роста фон Берталанфи, закон (формула) фон Берталанфи
V 216	**von Mangoldt['s] function** <NT>	Mangoldtsche Funktion *f*	fonction *f* de Mangoldt	функция Мангольдта
	von Neumann ...	*s. a.* Neumann ...		
	von Neumann['s] algebra <FA>	*s.* W 4		
	von Neumann algebra of type I <FA>	*s.* W 5		
	von Neumann algebra of type I_n <FA>	*s.* W 6		
	von Neumann algebra of type II <FA>	*s.* W 7		
	von Neumann algebra of type II_1 <FA>	*s.* W 8		
	von Neumann algebra of type II_∞ <FA>	*s.* W 9		
	von Neumann algebra of type III <FA>	*s.* W 10		
	von Neumann['s] ergodic theorem <SP>	*s.* S 1693		
	von Neumann['s] regular ideal <AL>	*s.* R 565		
	von Neumann['s] regularity <AL>	*s.* R 569		
	von Neumann['s] regular ring <AL>	*s.* R 624		
	von Neumann['s] ring <AL>	*s.* R 624		
V 217	**von Staudt-Clausen theorem** <for the Bernoulli numbers> <FD, FU, NT>	von (v.) Staudtscher Satz *m*, Staudt-Clausenscher Satz *m*, Satz *m* von von (v.) Staudt	théorème *m* de Clausen-von Staudt	теорема Клаузена-фон Штаудта, теорема [фон] Штаудта
V 218	**von Staudt['s] conic** <GE>	von (v.) Staudtscher Kegelschnitt *m*	conique *f* de [von] Staudt	коническое сечение [фон] Штаудта
V 219	**v-operation** <in ideals> <AL>	v-Operation *f*	v-opération *f*	v-операция
V 220	**Voronoï['s] polyhedron** <of a regular hexagonal lattice>, **Voronoï['s] polytope,** parallelohedron of Voronoï <GE>	Voronojsches Polyeder *n*, Woronoisches Polyeder	polyèdre *m* de Voronoï	полиэдр Вороного
	vortex point <DE>	*s.* C 395		
V 221	**Voss['s] surface** <DG>	Voßsche Fläche *f*	surface *f* de Voss	поверхность Фоса
	vrai max <AN>	*s.* V 222		
V 222	**vrai maximum,** true maximum, v. max, vrai max, true max <AN>	„vrai maximum" *n*, „wahres" Maximum *n*, vrai max	vrai maximum *m*, vrai max	истинный максимум, наибольшее значение с точностью до множества меры нуль, существенная верхняя грань, v. max, vrai max
	vrai min <AN>	*s.* V 223		
V 223	**vrai minimum,** true minimum, v. min, vrai min, true min <AN>	„vrai minimum" *n*, „wahres" Minimum *n*, vrai min	vrai minimum *m*, vrai min	истинный минимум, наименьшее значение с точностью до множества меры нуль, существенная нижняя грань, v. min, vrai min

V 224	**V-ring** <AL>	V-Ring *m*	V-anneau *m*	V-кольцо
V 225	**V′-ring** <AL>	V′-Ring *m*	V′-anneau *m*	V′-кольцо
V 226	**V-small subset,** subset whose diameter is less than *V* <subset *A* such that $A \times A \subset V$> <TO>	*V*-kleine (von der Ordnung *V* kleine) Untermenge *f*	partie *f* petite d'ordre *V*	*V*-малое подмножество
V 227	**V-sum** <of a series> <LI>	*V*-Summe *f*	*V*-somme *f*	*V*-сумма
V 228	**V-summable series** <LI>	*V*-summierbare Reihe *f*	série *f* *V*-sommable	*V*-суммируемый ряд
	vulgar fraction <AR>	*s.* C 1234		
	vulgar logarithm <AR, NU>	*s.* B 754		
	V-variation <AN>	*s.* V 79		

W

	waiting line <ST>	*s.* Q 289		
	waiting line theory <ST>	*s.* Q 292		
W 1	**waiting system** <ST>	Wartesystem *n*	système *m* avec attente	система с ожиданием
W 2	**waiting time** <ST>	Wartezeit *f*	temps *m* d'attente	время ожидания
W 3	**Wald-Wolfowitz test** <ST>	Wald-Wolfowitz-Test *m*, Iterationstest (Test) *m* von Wald und Wolfowitz	test *m* de Wald-Wolfowitz	критерий Вальда-Вольфовица
W 4	**W^*-algebra** <in the abstract case>; von Neumann['s] algebra, algebra of operators <in a concrete case> <FA>	W^*-Algebra *f* <abstrakt>; von Neumannsche Algebra *f*, Neumann-Algebra *f*, Operatoralgebra *f* <konkret>	algèbre *f* W^* <dans le cas abstrait>; algèbre *f* de von Neumann <dans le cas concret>	алгебра W^* <абстрактно>; алгебра фон Неймана <конкретно>
W 5	**W^*-algebra of type I,** discrete W^*-algebra, type I W^*-algebra; [von Neumann] algebra of type I, discrete [von Neumann] algebra, type I [von Neumann] algebra <FA>	W^*-Algebra *f* vom Typ I, diskrete W^*-Algebra; [von Neumannsche] Algebra *f* vom Typ I, diskrete [von Neumannsche] Algebra *f*	algèbre *f* W^* de type I, algèbre *f* W^* discrète; algèbre *f* [de von Neumann] de type I, algèbre *f* [de von Neumann] discrète	алгебра W^* типа I; алгебра [фон Неймана] типа I
W 6	**W^*-algebra of type I_n** *n*-homogeneous W^*-algebra, type I_n W^*-algebra; von Neumann algebra of type I_n, type I_n [von Neumann] algebra <FA>	W^*-Algebra *f* vom Typ I_n; [von Neumannsche] Algebra *f* vom Typ I_n	algèbre *f* W^* de type I_n; algèbre *f* [de von Neumann] de type I_n	алгебра W^* типа I_n; алгебра [фон Неймана] типа I_n
W 7	**W^*-algebra of type II,** type II W^*-algebra; von Neumann algebra of type II, type II [von Neumann] algebra <FA>	W^*-Algebra *f* vom Typ II; [von Neumannsche] Algebra *f* vom Typ II	algèbre *f* W^* de type II; algèbre *f* [de von Neumann] de type II	алгебра W^* типа II; алгебра [фон Неймана] типа II
W 8	**W^*-algebra of type II_1,** finite type II W^*-algebra; von Neumann algebra of type II_1, finite type II algebra	W^*-Algebra *f* vom Typ II_1; [von Neumannsche] Algebra *f* vom Typ II_1	algèbre *f* W^* de type II_1; algèbre *f* [de von Neumann] de type II_1; algèbre [de von Neumann] de type II fini	алгебра W^* типа II_1; алгебра [фон Неймана] типа II_1, конечная алгебра [фон Неймана типа II
W 9	**W^*-algebra of type II_∞,** properly infinite type II algebra; von Neumann algebra of type II_∞ <FA>	W^*-Algebra *f* vom Typ II_∞; [von Neumannsche] Algebra *f* vom Typ II_∞	algèbre *f* W^* de type II∞; algèbre *f* [de von Neumann] de type II_∞, algèbre *f* [de von Neumann] de type II proprement infinie	алгебра W* типа II_∞; алгебра [фон Неймана] типа II_∞, собственно бесконечная алгебра [фон Неймана] типа II
W 10	**W^*-algebra of type III;** von Neumann algebra of type III, type III algebra <FA>	W^*-Algebra *f* vom Typ III; [von Neumannsche] Algebra *f* vom Typ III, vollunendliche [von Neumannsche] Algebra *f*	algèbre *f* W^* de type III; algèbre *f* de von Neumann de type III	алгебра W^* типа III; алгебра [фон Неймана] типа III
	walk <GP>	*s.* E 27		
	walk <SP>	*s.* R 116		
W 11	**Wallace['s] line,** pedal line <GE>	Wallacesche Gerade *f*, Wallace-Gerade *f*, // Simsonsche Gerade *f*, Simson-Gerade *f*	droite *f* de [W.] Wallace, droite *f* de Simson	прямая Симсона
	Wallis['] conic wedge <AG>	*s.* C 710		
W 12	**Wallis['] continued fraction** <NT>	Wallisscher (Wallis') Kettenbruch *m*	fraction *f* continue de Wallis	цепная дробь Валлиса
W 13	**Wallis['] formula** <for $\sqrt{\pi}$> <AN>	Wallissche Formel *f*	formule *f* de Wallis	формула Валлиса
W 14	**Wallis['] product [formula]** <for π, π/2 or 4/π> <AN>	Wallissches Produkt *n*, Wallissche Produktdarstellung (Formel) *f*	formule *f* de Wallis	формула Валлиса
W 15	**Wallis['] theorem** <for the product of two continued fractions> <NT>	Wallisscher (Wallis') Satz *m*	théorème *m* de Wallis	теорема Валлиса
W 16	**Wallman['s] compactification,** Wallman-type compactification <TO>	Wallmansche Erweiterung *f*, Wallmansche Kompaktifizierung *f*	compactifié *m* de Wallman <résultat>; compactification *f* de Wallman <procédé>	волмэновская бикомпактификация, [бикомпактное] расширение волмэновского типа, расширение W-типа
W 17	**Wallman['s] topology** <TO>	Wallmansche Topologie *f*	topologie *f* de Wallman	волмэновская топология
	Wallman-type compactification <TO>	*s.* W 16		
	Walsh['s] system <RF>	*s.* S 2542		
W 18	**Walsh['s] test** <ST>	Walsh-Test *m*	test *m* de Walsh	критерий Уолша
W 19	**wandering set** <SP>	wandernde Menge *f*	ensemble *m* migrant	блуждающее множество

W 20	**Wang['s] cohomology sequence** <AT>	Wangsche Kohomologiesequenz *f*	suite *f* de cohomologie de Wang	когомологическая последовательность Вана
W 21	**Wang['s] homology sequence** <AT>	Wangsche Homologiesequenz *f*	suite *f* d'homologie de Wang	гомологическая последовательность Вана
W 22	**Wang['s] sequence** <of a fibration> <AT> ⌈<PG>	Wang-Sequenz *f*	suite *f* exacte de Wang	точная последовательность Вана, последовательность Вана
	warehouse problem	*s.* W 23		
W 23	**warehousing problem,** warehouse problem <PG>	Lagerhaltungsproblem *n*, Warenhausproblem *n*	problème *m* de stockage	задача о хранении на складе
W 24	**Waring['s] conjecture,** Waring['s] theorem <NT>	Waringsche Vermutung *f*	hypothèse *f* de Waring	гипотеза Варинга
W 25	**Waring['s] formula** <AL, AN>	Waringsche Formel *f*, Warings Formel *f*	formule *f* de Waring	формула Варинга
W 26	**Waring['s] problem** <NT>	Waringsches Problem *n*, Waring-Problem *n*	problème *m* de Waring	проблема Варинга
W 27	**Waring['s] theorem** <for polynomials> <AL>	Waringscher Satz *m*	théorème *m* de Waring	теорема Варинга
	Waring['s] theorem <NT>	*s.* W 24		
	warning limit <ST>	*s.* A 1201		
	warped surface <GE>	*s.* N 371		
W 28	**Watson['s] general transform[ation], Watson['s] transform[ation]** <FA>	Watson-Transformation *f*, Watsonsche [allgemeine] Transformation *f*, [allgemeine] Transformation von Watson	transformation *f* de Watson, transformation générale de Watson	преобразование Уатсона (Ватсона), общее преобразование Уатсона (Ватсона)
W 29	**Watt['s] curve** <GE>	Wattsche Kurve *f*, Kurve *f* weiter Biegung <C_6>	courbe *f* de Watt, courbe *f* à longue inflexion	кривая Уатта
W 30	**wave** <AB>	„wave" *f*	« wave » *f* <Sylvester>	«wave»
	wave <GN>	*s.* T 476		
W 31	**wave parabola** <in interpolation> <AX, NU>	Wellenparabel *f*	parabole *f* d'onde	волновая парабола
W 32	**W-congruence [of lines (rays)],** Weingarten['s] congruence [of lines (rays)] <DG>	W-Strahlenkongruenz *f*, W-Linienkongruenz *f*, W-Geradenkongruenz *f*, W-Kongruenz *f*, W-Strahlensystem *n*, W-Strahlsystem, Weingartensche Strahlenkongruenz (Linienkongruenz, Geradenkongruenz, Kongruenz) *f*, Weingartensches Strahl[en]system *n*	congruence *f* [de droites] W, congruence [de droites] de Weingarten	W-конгруэнция [прямых (лучей)], конгруэнция [прямых (лучей)] Вайнгартена
W 33	**W-curve,** *W* curve; binomial curve <PJ>	*W*-Kurve *f*; binomische Kurve *f*	*W*-courbe *f*, courbe (*W*); courbe binomiale	*W*-кривая, дубльве-кривая; биномиальная кривая
W 34	**weak approximation theorem,** independence theorem <for valuations> <AL>	schwacher Approximationssatz (Annäherungssatz) *m*, Unabhängigkeitssatz *m*	théorème *m* d'approximation faible	слабая аппроксимационная теорема
W 35	**weak basis** <FA>	schwache Basis *f*	base *f* faible	слабый базис, базис в смысле слабой топологии
	weak Bézout domain <AL>	*s.* G 102		
W 36	**weak Cauchy sequence** <FA, TO>	schwache Cauchy-Folge *f*	suite *f* de Cauchy [pour la topologie] faible	последовательность Коши в смысле слабой топологии, слабая последовательность Коши
W 37	**weak closure** <FA>	schwacher Abschluß *m*	adhérence *f* faible	слабое замыкание
W 38	**weak completeness** <LO>	schwache Vollständigkeit *f*	complétude *f* faible	слабая полнота
W 39	**weak conjunction** <in trivalent logic> <LO>	schwache Konjunktion *f*	conjonction *f* faible	слабая конъюнкция
W 40	**weak continuity** <FA, TO>	schwache Stetigkeit *f*	continuité *f* faible	слабая непрерывность
W 41	**weak convergence** <in a normed *or* unitary space> <FA, TO>	schwache Konvergenz *f*, Konvergenz bezüglich der schwachen Topologie	convergence *f* faible, faible convergence	слабая сходимость
W 42	**weak convergence** <in a sequence space> <FA>	relative (schwache) Konvergenz *f*	convergence *f* faible	слабая сходимость
	weak convergence <ST>	*s.* C 2338		
W 43	**weak coproduct** <CA>	schwaches Koprodukt *n*	coproduit *m* faible	слабое копроизведение
W 44	**weak correlation** <ST>	schwache Korrelation *f*	corrélation *f* faible	слабая корреляция
W 45	**weak countable distributivity** <AL>	schwache abzählbare Distributivität *f*	distributivité *f* faiblement dénombrable	слабая счетная дистрибутивность
W 46	**weak descending chain condition** <GR>	abgeschwächter Vielfachenkettensatz *m*, abgeschwächter U-Satz *m*	condition *f* de chaîne descendante affaiblie	слабое условие минимальности
	weak differential <FA>	*s.* G 53		
W 47	**weak direct product,** direct product <of groups> <GR>	eingeschränktes direktes Produkt *n*, diskretes direktes Produkt, externes eingeschränktes direktes Produkt	produit *m* direct [restreint], produit restreint	неполное прямое произведение, дискретное прямое произведение, слабое произведение
W 48	**weak direct product** <of algebras> <UA>	schwaches (diskretes, eingeschränktes) direktes Produkt *n*	produit *m* restreint	дискретное прямое произведение
W 49	**weak direct sum,** discrete direct sum, direct sum <AL>	eingeschränkte direkte Summe *f*, diskrete direkte Summe	somme *f* directe discrète	дискретная прямая сумма, слабая прямая сумма
W 50	**weak discontinuity** <DE>	schwache Unstetigkeit *f*	discontinuité *f* faible	слабый разрыв
W 51	**weak disjunction** <in trivalent logic> <LO>	schwache Disjunktion *f*	disjonction *f* faible	слабая дизъюнкция
W 52	**weak distributivity** <LA>	schwache Distributivität *f*, n-Distributivität *f*	loi *f* de distributivité affaiblie	слабая дистрибутивность

W 53	**weakening** <of a condition> <GN>	Abschwächung *f*	affaiblissement *m*	ослабление
	weakening <LO>	*s.* T 415		
W 54	**weak epimorphism** <CA>	schwacher Epimorphismus *m*	épimorphisme *m* faible	слабый эпиморфизм
W 55	**weaker formula** <LO>	schwächerer Ausdruck *m*	formule *f* plus faible	более слабая формула
W 56	**weaker metric** <TO>	schwächere Metrik *f*	métrique *f* plus faible	более слабая метрика
W 57	**weaker norm** <FA>	schwächere Norm *f*	norme *f* plus faible	более слабая норма
W 58	**weaker theory** <FO>	schwächere Theorie *f*	théorie *f* moins forte (riche)	более слабая теория
	weaker topology <TO>	*s.* 1. C 962; 2. F 247		
W 59	**weak extension** <of a space> <TO>	schwache Erweiterung *f*	extension *f* faible	слабое расширение
W 60	**weak extremal** <VA>	schwache Extremale *f*	extrémale *f* faible	слабая экстремаль
W 61	**weak extremum** <VA>	schwaches (schwaches relatives) Extremum *n*	extrémum *m* faible	слабый экстремум
W 62	**weak fibration,** Serre['s] fibre space, Serre['s] fibre map, fibration in the sense of Serre <AT>	Faserraum *m* im Sinne von Serre, Serresche (schwache) Faserung *f*	espace *m* fibré au sens de Serre, espace fibré	слабое расслоение, расслоение в смысле Серра, расслоенное пространство
W 63	**weak Galois subring** <AL>	schwach galoisscher Unterring *m*	sous-anneau *m* faiblement galoisien	слабое подкольцо Галуа
W 64	**weak global dimension** <AL>	schwache globale Dimension *f*	dimension *f* globale faible	слабая глобальная размерность
W 65	**weak Hauptvermutung** <of combinatorial topology> <TO>	abgeschwächte Hauptvermutung *f*	forme *f* affaiblie de la Hauptvermutung	ослабленная основная гипотеза
W 66	**weak homotopy equivalence,** ∞-equivalence <TO>	schwache Homotopieäquivalenz *f*	homotopie-équivalence *f* faible	слабая гомотопическая эквивалентность, ∞-эквивалентность
W 67	**weak implication** <in trivalent logic> <LO>	schwache Implikation *f*	implication *f* faible	слабая импликация
W 68	**weak independence** <UA>	schwache Unabhängigkeit *f*, S-Unabhängigkeit *f*	indépendance *f* faible	слабая независимость
W 69	**weak inductive dimension,** small inductive dimension, Urysohn-Menger dimension, Menger-Urysohn dimension <TO>	kleine induktive Dimension *f*, Menger-Urysohnsche Dimension	dimension *f* d'Urysohn-Menger	малая индуктивная размерность
W 70	**weak inequality** <GN>	Ungleichung *f*, Gleichheit zugelassen	inégalité *f* au sens large, inégalité prise au sens large, inégalité large	неравенство в широком смысле
W 71	**weak instability** <NU>	schwache Instabilität *f*	instabilité *f* faible	слабая неустойчивость
W 72	**weak isomorphism** <UA>	schwacher Isomorphismus *m*	isomorphisme *m* faible	слабый изоморфизм
W 73	**weak law of large numbers** <ST>	schwaches Gesetz *n* der großen Zahlen	loi *f* faible des grands nombres	ослабленный закон больших чисел
W 74	**weak Lefschetz theorem** <AT>	schwacher Lefschetzscher Satz *m*	théorème *m* de Lefschetz faible	слабая теорема Лефшеца
W 75	**weak limit** <FA>	schwacher Grenzwert (Limes) *m*	limite *f* faible	слабый предел
W 76	**weak linear ordering,** weak simple ordering, weak total ordering <SE>	reflexive (lineare, einfache) Ordnung *f*, *k*-Ordnung *f*, Anordnung *f*, strenge (strikte) Ordnung	relation *f* d'ordre complet, ordre *m* complet (simple), chaîne *f*, ordre total, ordre total large, comparaison *f* totale	рефлексивное полное упорядочение, полное упорядочение, упорядочение, линейный порядок
W 77	**weak local holomorphy** <FA>	schwache lokale Holomorphie *f*	holomorphie *f* locale faible	слабая локальная голоморфность
W 78	**weakly σ-additive Boolean algebra,** weakly sigma-additive Boolean algebra <FA>	schwach σ-additive (sigma-additive) Boolesche Algebra *f*	algèbre *f* de Boole faiblement σ-additive (sigma-additive)	слабо σ-аддитивная (сигма-аддитивная) булева алгебра
W 79	**weakly almost complex manifold** <GE>	schwach fast-komplexe Mannigfaltigkeit *f*	variété *f* faiblement presque complexe	слабо почти комплексное многообразие
W 80	**weakly associated prime ideal** <AL>	schwach assoziiertes (zugehöriges) Primideal *n*	idéal *m* premier faiblement associé	слабо ассоциированный простой идеал
	weakly bounded function <AN>	*s.* Q 108		
W 81	**weakly bounded set** <FA>	schwach beschränkte Menge *f*	ensemble *m* faiblement borné	слабо ограниченное множество
W 82	**weakly closed algebra** <FA>	schwach abgeschlossene Algebra *f*	algèbre *f* fermée pour la topologie faible, algèbre faiblement fermée	слабо замкнутая алгебра
W 83	**weakly closed space** <FA>	schwach abgeschlossener Raum *m*	espace *m* faiblement fermé	слабо замкнутое пространство
W 84	**weakly compact set** <FA, TO>	schwach kompakte Menge *f*	ensemble *m* faiblement compact	слабо компактное множество
W 85	**weakly comparable functions** <RF>	schwach vergleichbare Funktionen *fpl*	fonctions *fpl* faiblement comparables	слабо сравнимые функции
W 86	**weakly complete space** <FA, TO>	schwach vollständiger (folgenvollständiger) Raum *m*	espace *m* faiblement complet	слабо полное пространство
	weakly consistent estimate (estimator) <ST>	*s.* C 2093		
	weakly consistent sequence <ST>	*s.* C 2097		
W 87	**weakly continuous cohomology theory** <AT>	schwach stetige Kohomologietheorie *f*	théorie *f* de cohomologie faiblement continue	слабо непрерывная теория когомологий
W 88	**weakly convergent sequence** <FA, TO>	schwach konvergente Folge *f*	suite *f* faiblement convergente	слабо сходящаяся последовательность
W 89	**weakly dense set** <FA>	schwach dichte Menge *f*	ensemble *m* faiblement dense	слабо плотное множество

W 90	**weakly derived set** <FA>	schwache Ableitung *f* <einer Menge>	dérivée *f* faible <d'un ensemble dans le dual d'un espace de Banach>	слабо производное множество
W 91	**weakly differentiable function** <FA>	schwach differenzierbare Funktion *f*	fonction *f* faiblement dérivable	слабо дифференцируемая функция
	weakly differentiable mapping <FA>	*s.* G 52		
W 92	**weakly distributive Boolean algebra** <AL>	schwach distributive Boolesche Algebra *f*	algèbre *f* de Boole faiblement distributive	слабо дистрибутивная булева алгебра
W 93	**weakly equivalent theory** <MM>	schwach äquivalente Theorie *f*	théorie *f* faiblement équivalente	слабо эквивалентная теория
W 94	**weakly exact category** <CA> ⌐<ME>	schwach exakte Kategorie *f*	catégorie *f* faiblement exacte	слаботочная категория
	weakly finite measure	*s.* S 824		
	weakly inaccessible cardinal <SE>	*s.* C 125		
W 95	**weakly inaccessible ordinal** <SE>	Hausdorffsche Zahl (unerreichbare Ordnungszahl *f*, Ordnungszahl), exorbitante (schwach unerreichbare) Ordnungszahl	ordinal *m* faiblement inaccessible	слабо недостижимое порядковое число
W 96	**weakly independent set** <of an algebra> <UA>	schwach unabhängige Menge *f*	ensemble *m* faiblement indépendant	слабо независимое множество
W 97	**weakly injective module** <AL>	schwach injektiver Modul *m*	module *m* faiblement injectif	слабо инъективный модуль
W 98	**weakly isomorphic algebra** <UA>	schwachisomorphe Algebra *f*	algèbre *f* faiblement isomorphe	слабо изоморфная алгебра
W 99	**weakly mixing [measurable] transformation** <ME>	schwach mischende [meßbare] Transformation *f*, mischende [meßbare] Transformation im weiteren Sinne	transformation *f* [mesurable] faiblement mélangeante	слабо перемешивающее [измеримое] преобразование
W 100	**weakly *n*-dimensional space** <TO>	schwach *n*-dimensionaler Raum *m*	espace *m* faiblement *n*-dimensionnel	слабо *n*-мерное пространство
W 101	**weakly nilpotent group** <each 2-generator subgroup is nilpotent> <GR>	schwach nilpotente Gruppe *f*	groupe *m* faiblement nilpotent	слабо нильпотентная группа
	weakly normal family [of functions] <AN>	*s.* Q 207		
W 102	**weakly normal subgroup** <GR>	schwachnormale Untergruppe *f*	sous-groupe *m* faiblement normal	слабонормальная подгруппа
W 103	**weakly ordered field** <AL>	schwach geordneter Körper *m*	corps *m* faiblement ordonné	слабо упорядоченное поле
W 104	**weakly orthogonal subspace** <AL> ⌐<IE>	schwach orthogonaler Unterraum *m*	sous-espace *m* faiblement orthogonal	слабо ортогональное подпространство
W 105	**weakly polar kernel**	schwach polarer Kern *m*	noyau *m* faiblement polaire	слабо полярное ядро
W 106	**weakly precompact set** <TO>	schwach präkompakte Menge *f*	ensemble *m* faiblement précompact	слабо предкомпактное множество
W 107	**weakly primary ideal** <AL>	schwach primäres Ideal *n*, schwaches (schwach primäres) Primärideal *n*	idéal *m* faiblement primaire	слабо примарный идеал
W 108	**weakly primary ring** <AL>	schwacher (schwach) primärer Nullteilerring *m*, schwach primärer Ring *m*	anneau *m* faiblement primaire	слабо примарное кольцо
	weakly sigma-additive Boolean algebra <FA>	*s.* W 78		
W 109	**weakly singular integral equation** <IE>	schwachsinguläre Integralgleichung *f*	équation *f* intégrale faiblement singulière	слабо особое интегральное уравнение
W 110	**weakly singular kernel,** inessential singular kernel <IE>	schwach (außerwesentlich) singulärer Kern *m*	noyau *m* faiblement singulier, noyau singulier inessentiel	несущественно особое ядро, ядро со слабой особенностью
W 111	**weakly stable solution** <DE>	schwach stabile Lösung *f*	solution *f* faiblement stable	слабо устойчивое решение
W 112	**weakly wandering set** <SP>	schwach wandernde Menge *f*	ensemble *m* faiblement migrant	слабо блуждающее множество
W 113	**weak maximal condition, weak maximality condition** <for groups> <GR>	schwache (abgeschwächte) Maximalbedingung *f*, abgeschwächte aufsteigende Kettenbedingung *f*	condition *f* maximale affaiblie, condition de chaîne ascendante affaiblie, condition affaiblie des chaînes ascendantes	слабое условие максимальности, ослабленное условие обрыва восходящих цепей
W 114	**weak maximum,** improper maximum <of a function> <RF>	Maximum *n*, nichtisoliertes Maximum	maximum *m* impropre (faible)	нестрогий максимум
W 115	**weak maximum** <VA>	schwaches (schwaches relatives) Maximum *n*	maximum *m* faible	слабый максимум
W 116	**weak minimal condition, weak minimality condition** <for groups> <GR>	schwache (abgeschwächte) Minimalbedingung *f*	condition *f* minimale affaiblie	слабое условие минимальности <для подгрупп>
W 117	**weak minimum,** improper minimum <of a function> <RF>	Minimum *n*, nichtisoliertes Minimum	minimum *m* impropre (faible)	нестрогий минимум
W 118	**weak minimum** <VA>	schwaches (schwaches relatives) Minimum *n*	minimum *m* faible	слабый минимум
	weak multiplication <AL>	*s.* Q 202		
W 119	**weak neighbourhood** <TO>	schwache Umgebung *f*	voisinage *m* faible	слабая окрестность
	weak ordering <SE>	*s.* Q 214		
W 120	**weak product** <CA>	schwaches Produkt *n*	produit *m* faible	слабое произведение
W 121	**weak pullback** <CA>	schwaches Pullback *n*, schwach kartesisches Quadrat *n*	produit *m* fibré faible	слабый декартов квадрат

W 122	**weak pushout** <CA>	schwaches Pushout *n*, schwach kokartesisches Quadrat *n*	somme *f* fibrée faible	слабый универсальный квадрат
W 123	**weak relation [of comparison]** <RF>	schwache Relation (Vergleichsrelation) *f*	relation *f* faible (de comparaison faible)	слабое отношение [сравнения]
W 124	**weak retract** <TO>	schwacher Retrakt *m*	rétracte *m* faible	слабый ретракт
	weak semi-complex <AT> ┌<SE>	*s.* Q 121		
	weak simple ordering	*s.* W 76		
W 125	**weak solution,** variational solution, distribution solution <of a Dirichlet problem> <DE>	schwache (verallgemeinerte) Lösung *f*	solution *f* faible (variationnelle)	слабое (вариационное) решение
W 126	**weak spherical four-point property** <TO>	schwache sphärische Vierpunkteigenschaft *f*	propriété *f* sphérique faible de quatre points	слабое сферическое свойство четырех точек
W 127	**weak tautology** <in trivalent logic> <LO>	schwache Tautologie *f*	tautologie *f* faible	слабая тавтология
W 128	**weak topology,** σ-topology, sigma-topology <FA>	schwache (minimale) Topologie *f*, σ-Topologie *f*, Sigma-Topologie *f*	topologie *f* faible (affaiblie)	слабая (ослабленная) топология
	weak topology <AT>	*s.* C 1075		
W 129	**weak* topology,** w*-topology <FA, TO>	schwache *-Topologie *f*, w*-Topologie *f*	topologie *f* *faible	слабая* топология
	weak* topology <FA>	*s.* V 11		
	weak total ordering <SE>	*s.* W 76		
W 130	**weak tripleability theorem** <CA>	schwache Version *f* des Satzes von Beck	théorème *m* de Beck affaibli	ослабленная теорема Бека
W 131	**weak unit,** unit <in a linear ordered space> <LA>	schwache Einheit *f*, schwaches Einselement *n*	unité *f* faible	слабая единица, единица
W 132	**web,** linear system of dimension 2 <of algebraic curves> <AG>	Gewebe *n*, lineares System *n* von ∞^2 [algebraischen] Kurven	système *m* linéaire de la dimension 2 <de courbes algébriques>	линейная система размерности 2 <алгебраических кривых>
W 133	**web,** tangential net <of conics> <GE> ┌<GE>	Kegelschnittgewebe *n*, Scharschar *f*, lineares System *n* von ∞^2 Kurven zweiter (2.) Klasse	réseau *m* tangentiel, tissu *m* <de coniques>	линейная система от ∞^2 кривых второго класса
W 134	**web** <of curves *or* surfaces>	Gewebe *n*	tissu *m*	сеть
W 135	**web,** tangential net <of quadrics> <GE>	Scharschar *f*, lineares System von ∞^2 Flächen zweiter (2.) Klasse	système *m* tangentiel de quadriques	линейная система поверхностей второго класса размерности 2
	Weber['s] Bessel function of the second kind <FU>	*s.* B 233		
W 136	**Weber['s] [differential] equation** <DE>	Webersche Differentialgleichung *f*, Webersche Gleichung *f*	équation *f* de Weber, équation différentielle de Weber	уравнение Вебера, дифференциальное уравнение Вебера
W 137	**Weber['s] function** <solution of an inhomogeneous Bessel-type differential equation> <FU>	Weber-Funktion *f*, Webersche Funktion *f*	fonction *f* de Weber	функция Вебера
	Weber['s] function <FU>	*s.* B 233		
W 138	**Weber['s] series** <AB>	Webersche Reihe *f*	série *f* de Weber	ряд Вебера
W 139	**web of curves** <GE>	Kurvengewebe *n*	tissu *m* de courbes	сеть кривых
W 140	**web of surfaces** <GE>	Flächengewebe *n*	tissu *m* de surfaces	сеть поверхностей
W 141	**Wedderburn['s] first theorem** <AL>	erster Satz *m* von Wedderburn, erster Wedderburnscher Satz	premier théorème *m* de Wedderburn	первая теорема Веддерберна
W 142	**Wedderburn['s] representation** <of an algebra> <AL>	Wedderburnsche Darstellung *f*	représentation *f* de Wedderburn	представление Веддерберна
W 143	**Wedderburn['s] second theorem** <AL>	zweiter Wedderburnscher Satz *m*	second théorème *m* de Wedderburn	вторая теорема Веддерберна
W 144	**Wedderburn['s] structure theorem** <for algebras> <AL>	Wedderburnscher Struktursatz *m*	théorème *m* de structure de Wedderburn	структурная теорема Веддерберна
W 145	**Wedderburn['s] theorem** <AL>	Satz *m* von Wedderburn, Wedderburnscher Satz *m*	théorème *m* de Wedderburn	теорема Веддерберна
W 146	**Weddle['s] formula (rule)** <for numerical quadrature> <DI, NU>	Weddlesche Regel *f*, Weddlesche Formel *f*	règle (formule) *f* de Weddle	формула (правило) Уэддля
W 147	**Weddle['s] surface** <AG>	Weddlesche Fläche *f*, Kegelspitzenfläche *f*, Weddles Fläche *f*	surface *f* de Weddle	поверхность Уэддля
W 148	**wedge** <EG>	Keil *m*	coin *m*	клин
W 149	**wedge [product],** one-point union <of pointed spaces> <TO>	Bouquet *n*, direkte Summe *f*	bouquet *m*, wedge *m*	букет
	wedge product <AL>	*s.* O 550		
	wedge product of spheres <TO>	*s.* U 204		
W 150	**Weibull['s] distribution** <ST>	Weibull-Verteilung *f*	distribution *f* de Weibull	распределение Вейбулла [и Рэлея]
W 151	**Weierstrass['s] Al series,** Al series, $Al_i(u)$ <FU>	Al-Reihe *f* von Weierstraß, Weierstraßsche Al-Reihe *f*, $Al_i(u)$	série *f* $Al_i(u)$ de Weierstrass, $Al_i(u)$	ряд $Al_i(u)$ Вейерштрасса
W 152	**Weierstrass['s] approximation theorem** <AX>	Weierstraßscher Approximationssatz *m*, Approximationssatz *m* (Satz *m*, Theorem *n*) von Weierstraß, Weierstraßscher Satz, Weierstraßsches Theorem	théorème *m* d'approximation de Weierstrass, théorème de Weierstrass	теорема Вейерштрасса <по приближении функции полиномами>, теорема аппроксимации Вейерштрасса, аппроксимационная теорема Вейерштрасса

No.	English	German	French	Russian
	Weierstrass['s] comparison test <FT, SS>	*s.* W 168		
W 153	**Weierstrass['s] condition** <VA>	Weierstraßsche Bedingung *f*	condition *f* de Weierstrass	условие Вейерштрасса
	Weierstrass['s] double series theorem <FT, SS>	*s.* T 360		
W 154	**Weierstrass['s] ∈-function,** Weierstrass['s] function ∈, ∈-function of Weierstrass, excess function <VA>	Weierstraßsche ∈-Funktion *f*, ∈-Funktion von Weierstraß, Exzeßfunktion *f*	fonction *f* ∈ [de Weierstrass], fonction de Weierstrass ∈, fonction d'excès	функция ∈ Вейерштрасса, функция Вейерштрасса ∈
W 155	**Weierstrass['s] elliptic functions** <$p(z)$ or $p'(z)$> <FU>	Weierstraßsche elliptische Funktionen *fpl*	fonctions *fpl* elliptiques de Weierstrass	эллиптические функции Вейерштрасса
	Weierstrass-Erdmann corner (vertex) condition <VA>	*s.* E 456		
W 156	**Weierstrass['s] factorization,** factorization <of an entire function> <FT>	Weierstraßsche Produktdarstellung *f*, Produktdarstellung *f*	représentation *f* en forme de produit, produit *m* infini de Weierstrass	представление в виде бесконечного произведения Вейерштрасса, бесконечное произведение Вейерштрасса
W 157	**Weierstrass['s] factorization theorem** <for an entire function> <FT>	Weierstraßscher Produktsatz *m*	théorème *m* de Weierstrass	теорема Вейерштрасса <о представлении целой функции в виде бесконечного произведения>
W 158	**Weierstrass['s] formula** <a generalization of Weierstrass's preparation theorem> <FT>	Weierstraßsche Formel *f*	formule *f* de Weierstrass	формула Вейерштрасса
W 159	**Weierstrass['s] formula,** Weierstrass['s] representation <of the Γ-function> <FU>	Weierstraßsche Produktdarstellung *f*	formule *f* de Weierstrass	формула Вейерштрасса, представление Вейерштрасса
	Weierstrass['s] function <FU>	*s.* W 162		
	Weierstrass['s] ζ-function <FU>	*s.* W 177		
	Weierstrass['s] function ∈ <VA>	*s.* W 159		
W 160	**Weierstrass['s] gap theorem,** gap theorem of Weierstrass <for orders of algebraic functions> <FT>	Weierstraßscher Lückensatz *m*, Lückensatz *m* von Weierstraß, Lückensatz	théorème *m* des lacunes de Weierstrass	вейерштрассова теорема о пробелах
	Weierstrassian <FU>	*s.* W 162		
W 161	**Weierstrassian curve** <DI>	Weierstraßsche Kurve *f*, Weierstraßsches Beispiel *n*	courbe *f* de Weierstrass	кривая Вейерштрасса
W 162	**Weierstrassian elliptic function,** Weierstrass['s] *p*-function, Weierstrass['s] function, Weierstrassian <FU>	*p*-Funktion *f* von Weierstraß, Weierstraßsche [*p*-]Funktion *f*, Weierstraßsche elliptische Funktion *f*	fonction *f* elliptique de Weierstrass, fonction *p* [de Weierstrass], *p* (*z*) de Weierstrass	эллиптическая функция Вейерштрасса, *p*-функция [Вейерштрасса], эллиптическая функция *p* (*z*)
	Weierstrassian σ-function <FT>	*s.* W 165		
W 163	**Weierstrassian inequalities** <AN>	Weierstraßsche Ungleichungen *fpl*	inégalités *fpl* de Weierstrass	неравенства Вейерштрасса
	Weierstrassian infinite product <FT>	*s.* W 164		
W 164	**Weierstrassian product,** Weierstrassian infinite product <FT>	Weierstraßsches Produkt *n*, Weierstraßsches unendliches Produkt	produit *m* canonique de facteurs premiers	[бесконечное] произведение Вейерштрасса, каноническое произведение [Вейерштрасса]
W 165	**Weierstrassian sigma[-] function,** Weierstrassian σ-function, sigma[-] function (σ-function) [of Weierstrass] <FT>	Weierstraßsche Sigma-Funktion (σ-Funktion) *f*, Sigma-Funktion (σ-Funktion) von Weierstraß	fonction *f* sigma (σ) [de Weierstrass]	сигма-функция (σ-функция) [Вейерштрасса]
W 166	**Weierstrassian space** <TO>	Weierstraßscher Raum *m*, Weierstraß-Raum *m*	espace *m* weierstrassien	вейерштрассово пространство
W 167	**Weierstrass['s] integral** <VA>	Weierstraßsches Integral *n*, Weierstraß-Integral *n*	intégrale *f* de Weierstrass	интеграл Вейерштрасса
W 168	**Weierstrass['s] M-test,** M-test, Weierstrass['s] comparison test, Weierstrass['s] test <for uniform convergence> <FT, SS>	Weierstraßsches Vergleichskriterium *n*, Weierstraßsches Kriterium (Majorantenkriterium) *n* <für gleichmäßige Konvergenz>, Majorantenkriterium	règle *f* de Weierstrass, critère *m* de comparaison de Weierstrass, critère de convergence uniforme de Weierstrass	признак Вейерштрасса, признак [равномерной] сходимости Вейерштрасса
W 169	**Weierstrass['s] necessary condition** <VA>	Weierstraßsche notwendige Bedingung *f*	condition *f* nécessaire de Weierstrass	необходимое условие Вейерштрасса
	Weierstrass['s] normal form <FT>	*s.* N 584		
	Weierstrass['s] *p*-function <FU>	*s.* W 162		
W 170	**Weierstrass['s] point** <FT>	Weierstraß-Punkt *m*	point *m* de Weierstrass	точка Вейерштрасса
W 171	**Weierstrass['] preparation theorem** <FT>	Weierstraßscher Vorbereitungssatz *m*	théorème *m* de préparation [de Weierstrass], « Vorbereitungssatz » *m* de Weierstrass	подготовительная теорема [Вейерштрасса]

W 172	**Weierstrass['s] prime function** <AL>	Primfunktion *f*, Weierstraßsche Primfunktion *f*, transzendente Primfunktion *f*	fonction *f* transcendante première, facteur *m* primaire	простая функция Вейерштрасса
	Weierstrass['s] quotient test <SS>	*s.* W 173		
W 173	**Weierstrass['s] ratio test,** Weierstrass['s] quotient test <for absolute convergence> <SS>	Weierstraßsches Quotientenkriterium *n*	critère *m* de quotient de Weierstrass, critère *m* [de convergence absolue] de Weierstrass	признак (критерий) абсолютной сходимости Вейерштрасса, признак Вейерштрасса
W 174	**Weierstrass['s] sufficient condition** <VA>	Weierstraßsche hinreichende Bedingung *f*	condition *f* suffisante de Weierstrass	достаточное условие Вейерштрасса
	Weierstrass['s] test <FT, SS>	*s.* W 168		
W 175	**Weierstrass['s] theorem** <on continuous functions>, theorem of Weierstrass <DI, TO>	Weierstraßscher Satz *m*, Satz *m* von Weierstraß <über Extremwerte>	théorème *m* de Weierstrass	теорема Вейерштрасса <первая *и* вторая>
W 176	**Weierstrass['s] theorem,** Harnack['s] first theorem on convergence <for uniform convergence of a sequence of harmonic functions> <PO>	Weierstraßscher Konvergenzsatz (Satz) *m*, erster Harnackscher Satz *m*, Satz von Weierstraß	théorème *m* de Weierstrass	теорема Вейерштрасса, первая теорема Гарнака
	Weierstrass['] theorem <FT>	*s.* C 186		
	Weierstrass['s] theorem <FT, SS>	*s.* T 360		
	Weierstrass['s] uniform convergence theorem <FT, SS>	*s.* T 360		
W 177	**Weierstrass['s] zeta function,** Weierstrass['s] ζ-function, zeta function [of Weierstrass], ζ-function [of Weierstrass] <FU>	Weierstraßsche Zeta-Funktion (ζ-Funktion) *f*, Zetafunktion (ζ-Funktion) [von Weierstraß]	fonction *f* zêta (ζ) de Weierstrass, fonction zêta (ζ)	дзета-функция (ζ-функция) Вейерштрасса, дзета-функция, ζ-функция
W 178	**weight** <of a polynomial> <AL>	Gewicht *n*	poids *m*, pesanteur *m* <Cayley>	вес
W 179	**weight** <of a vertex of a tree> <GP>	Höhe *f*	poids *m*	вес
W 180	**weight** <of quadratic forms> <NT>	Maß *n*, Dichtigkeit *f*	mesure *f*, densité *f*	мера
W 181	**weight,** weighting factor, weight factor, weighting coefficient <ST>	Gewicht *n*, Gewichtsfaktor *m*, Wägungsfaktor *m*	poids *m*, facteur (coefficient) *m* de pondération	вес, весовой коэффициент
	weight <AX>	*s.* W 188		
	weight <LO, UA>	*s.* A 973		
	weight <ST>	*s.* W 189		
W 182	**weight diagram** <of Lie groups> <GR>	Gewichtsdiagramm *n*	diagramme *m* des poids	диаграмма весов
	weighted arithmetic average <ER, GN, ST>	*s.* W 186		
W 183	**weighted arithmetic mean [value]** <of a real-valued function> <RF>	gewogener arithmetischer Mittelwert *m*	moyenne *f* arithmétique pondérée	взвешенное арифметическое среднее [значение]
	weighted arithmetic mean [value] <ER, GN, ST>	*s.* W 186		
	weighted average <ER, GN, ST>	*s.* 1. W 185; 2. W 186		
W 184	**weighted majority game** <TG>	gewichtetes Majoritätsspiel *n*	jeu *m* pondéré	взвешенная мажоритарная игра
W 185	**weighted mean [value],** weighted average <in the general sense> <ER, GN, ST>	gewogenes Mittel *n*, gewogener Mittelwert *m*, Gewichtsmittel *n*, gewichtetes Mittel, gewichteter Mittelwert	moyenne *f* pondérée, valeur *f* moyenne pondérée, moyenne par poids, valeur moyenne par poids	среднее взвешенное, средневзвешенное, взвешенное среднее [значение]
W 186	**weighted mean [value],** weighted average, weighted arithmetic mean [value], weighted arithmetic average <in the special sense> <ER, GN, ST>	gewogenes (gewichtetes) Mittel *n*, Gewichtsmittel *n*, gewogener (gewichteter) Mittelwert *m*, allgemeines (gewogenes) arithmetisches Mittel, allgemeiner (gewogener) arithmetischer Mittelwert	moyenne *f* pondérée (corrigée, par poids, composée, arithmétique pondérée)	среднее взвешенное, средневзвешенное, взвешенное среднее, взвешенное арифметическое среднее [значение]
	weighted orthogonalization process <MD, NU>	*s.* L 1121/2		
W 187	**weighted sampling** <ST>	gewogene Stichprobennahme *f*, gewogenes Stichprobenverfahren *n*	échantillonnage (sondage) *m* pondéré	взвешенная выборка
	weight factor <ST>	*s.* W 181		
W 188	**weight function,** weight, covering <associated with an inner product> <AX>	Gewichtsfunktion *f*, Gewicht *n*, Belegungsfunktion *f*, Belegung *f*	fonction *f* de poids, poids *m*	весовая функция, вес, функция обложения, обложение
W 189	**weight function,** weighting function, weight <ST>	Gewichtsfunktion *f*, Gewicht *n*	fonction *f* de poids (pondération), poids *m*	весовая функция, вес

W 190	**weighting** <GN, ST>	Wägen *n*, Wichten *n*	pondération *f*	взвешивание
	weighting coefficient <ST>	*s.* W 181		
	weighting factor <ST>	*s.* W 181		
	weighting function <ST>	*s.* W 189		
W 191	**weight lowering operator** <of a Lie group> <GR>	gewichtserniedrigender Operator *m*	opérateur *m* abaissant le poids	оператор, понижающий вес
W 192	**Weil['s] algebra** <of a Lie algebra> <AL>	Weilsche Algebra *f*	algèbre *f* de Weil	алгебра Вейля
W 193	**Weil['s] cohomology** <AG>	Weilsche Kohomologie *f*	cohomologie *f* de Weil	когомологии Вейля
W 194	**Weil['s] conjecture** <AG, AL>	Weilsche Vermutung *f*	hypothèse *f* de Weil	гипотеза Вейля <о ζ-функции алгебраических многообразий>
W 195	**Weil group** <AB>	Weil-Gruppe *f*, Weilgruppe *f*	groupe *m* de Weil	группа Вейля
W 196	**Weil['s] *L*-series** <AB>	Weilsche *L*-Reihe *f*	série *f L* de Weil	*L*-ряд Вейля
W 197	**Weil['s] reciprocity formula (theorem)** <AB>	Weilscher Reziprozitätssatz *m*	théorème *m* de réciprocité de Weil	теорема взаимности Вейля
	Weingarten['s] characteristic function <DG>	*s.* W 198		
	Weingarten['s] congruence <DG>	*s.* W 32		
	Weingarten['s] congruence of lines (rays) <DG>	*s.* W 32		
W 198	**Weingarten['s] displacement function,** Weingarten['s] characteristic function, characteristic function <of an infinitesimal deformation> <DG>	[Weingartensche] Verschiebungsfunktion *f*, [Weingartensche] charakteristische φ-Funktion *f*, [Weingartensche] charakteristische Funktion, Weingartensche φ-Funktion *f*	fonction *f* de déplacement [de Weingarten], fonction caractéristique [de Weingarten]	функция сдвига [Вейнгартена], характеристическая функция [Вейнгартена]
W 199	**Weingarten['s] equations (formulas)** <DG>	Weingartensche Ableitungsgleichungen *fpl*, Weingartensche Formeln (Gleichungen) *fpl*, Formeln (Gleichungen) von Weingarten	équations (formules) *fpl* de Weingarten	уравнения Вейнгартена, формулы Вейнгартена
W 200	**Weingarten['s] surface,** W-surface <DG>	Weingartensche Fläche *f*, W-Fläche *f*	surface *f* de Weingarten	поверхность Вейнгартена
W 201	**Weingarten['s] theorem** <DG>	Satz *m* von Weingarten, Weingartenscher Satz	théorème *m* de Weingarten	теорема Вейнгартена
W 202	**Weinstein['s] bound** <for eigenvalues> <DE>	Weinsteinsche Schranke *f*	borne *f* de Weinstein	грань Вайнштейна
	Weinstein['s] theorem <DE, FA>	*s.* K 179		
	Welch analysis <ST>	*s.* Q 24		
W 203	**Welch-Smith analysis** <ST>	Welch-Smith-Analyse *f*	analyse *f* de Welch-Smith	анализ Уэлча-Смита
	welk sheaf <AT>	*s.* F 396		
W 204	**well-chained set** <TO>	0-verkettete (nullverkettete) Menge *f*, im Cantorschen Sinne zusammenhängende Menge <für jedes ε ε-verkettet>	ensemble *m* bien enchaîné, ensemble continu	множество, каждые две точки которого при любом ε > 0 соединимы ε-цепью, состоящей из точек множества
W 205	**well-chained space** <TO>	0-verketteter (nullverketteter) Raum *m*	espace *m* bien enchaîné, espace continu	метрическое пространство, каждые две точки которого соединимы ε-цепью при всяком ε > 0
W 206	**well-defined** <GN>	eindeutig definiert, wohldefiniert	parfaitement défini	однозначно определенный
	well-determined <GN>	*s.* U 212		
W 207	**well-distinguishable objects** <SE>	wohlunterscheidbare (wohlunterschiedene) Objekte *npl*	objets *mpl* bien distincts	хорошо различимые объекты
W 208	**well-distributed sequence** <NT>	wohlverteilte Folge *f*	suite *f* bien répartie	хорошо распределенная последовательность
	well-formed formula <LO>	*s.* 1. F 488; 2. M 307		
W 209	**well-order / to,** to make well-ordered, to render well-ordered <SE>	wohlordnen	bien ordonner	вполне упорядочивать
	well-ordered aggregate <SE>	*s.* W 210		
	well-ordered downward <SE>	*s.* A 790		
	well-ordered partially ordered set <SE>	*s.* P 284		
W 210	**well-ordered set,** normally ordered set, well-ordered aggregate, eutactic set <SE>	wohlgeordnete Menge *f*, total (voll) wohlgeordnete Menge	ensemble *m* bien ordonné	вполне упорядоченное множество
W 211	**well-ordering,** well-ordering relation, complete ordering <SE>	Wohlordnung *f*	bon ordre *m*, relation *f* de bon ordre	полная (вполне) упорядоченность, отношение полного порядка, полный порядок, полное (вполне) упорядочивающее отношение

W 212	**well-ordering principle,** well-ordering theorem, Zermelo['s] theorem, well-ordering statement <SE>	Wohlordnungssatz *m*, Wohlordnungssatz von Zermelo, Zermeloscher Wohlordnungssatz, Satz *m* von Zermelo, Wohlordnungssatz für Mengen	théorème *m* de Zermelo, théorème du bon ordre; axiome *m* de Zermelo	теорема Цермело о полной упорядоченности, теорема о полной упорядоченности [Цермело], теорема Цермело, теорема о полном упорядочении, принцип вполне упорядочения; аксиома полной упорядочиваемости
	well-ordering relation <SE>	*s.* W 211		
W 213	**well-ordering set** <SE>	wohlordnende Menge *f*	ensemble *m* bien ordonnant	вполне упорядочивающее множество
	well-ordering statement <SE>	*s.* W 212		
W 214	**well-ordering structure** <UA>	Wohlordnungsstruktur *f*	structure *f* de bon ordre	структура вполне упорядочения
	well-ordering theorem <SE>	*s.* W 212		
	well-partially-ordered set <SE>	*s.* P 284		
W 215	**well poised [Saalschütz] series** <SS>	Saalschützsche Reihe *f* erster Art	série *f* de Saalschütz de la première espèce	хорошо уравновешенный ряд [Заальшютца], ряд Заальшютца первого рода
W 216	**well-posedness** <of a problem> <DE>	Korrektheit *f*		корректная постановка, точность
W 217	**well-posed problem,** properly posed problem <for a partial differential equation> <DE>	sachgemäßes (korrekt gestelltes) Problem *n*	problème *m* bien (correctement) posé	корректно поставленная задача, хорошо установленная задача, корректная (точная) задача
	well[-]powered category <CA>	*s.* L 995		
W 217a	**well quasi order** <SE>	Quasiwohlordnung *f*	prébelordre *m*	полный квазипорядок
W 218	**well-quasi-ordered set** <SE>	quasi-wohlgeordnete Menge *f*	ensemble *m* bien quasi-ordonné, ensemble prébelordonné	вполне квазиупорядоченное множество
W 219	**Weyl['s] algebra** <AL>	Weylsche Algebra *f*	algèbre *f* de Weyl	алгебра Вейля
	Weyl['s] almost periodic function <AP>	*s.* A 531		
W 220	**Weyl-Cartan problem** <DG>	Weyl-Cartansches Raumproblem *n*	problème *m* de Weyl-Cartan	задача Вейля-Картана
W 220a	**Weyl chamber** <GR>	Weylsche Kammer *f*	chambre *f* de Weil	камера Вейля
	Weyl['s] conform[al curvature] tensor <DG>	*s.* W 232		
W 221	**Weyl['s] connection,** Weyl['s] transfer <DG>	Weylsche Übertragung *f*, Weylscher Zusammenhang *m*	connexion *f* (transfert *m*) de Weyl	связность (перенесение) Вейля
	Weyl['s] curvature tensor <DG>	*s.* P 1679		
W 222	**Weyl['s] density** <DG, VT>	Weylsche Dichte *f*	densité *f* de Weyl	плотность Вейля
W 223	**Weyl['s] function** <FA>	Weylsche Funktion *f*	fonction *f* de Weyl	функция Вейля
W 224	**Weyl['s] group** <GR>	Weylsche Gruppe *f*	groupe *m* de Weyl	группа [Г.] Вейля
W 225	**Weyl['s] inequality** <NT>	Weylsche Ungleichung *f*	inégalité *f* de Weyl	неравенство Вейля
W 226	**Weyl['s] invariant** <DG>	Weylsche Invariante *f*, deskriptive Weylsche Invariante	invariant *m* de Weyl	инвариант Вейля
W 227	**Weyl-Neumann theorem** <FA>	Weyl-Neumannscher Satz *m*, Satz von Weyl-Neumann	théorème *m* de Weyl-Neumann	теорема Вейля-Неймана
W 228	**Weyl['s] space** <DG>	Weylscher Raum *m*	espace *m* de Weyl	пространство Вейля
W 229	**Weyl['s] spectrum** <FA>	essentielles Spektrum *n*, Weylsches Spektrum	spectre *m* de Weyl	спектр Вейля
W 230	**Weyl['s] structure** <in a complex> <AL>	Weylsche Struktur *f*	structure *f* de Weyl	структура Вейля
W 231	**Weyl['s] sum** <NT>	Weylsche Summe (Exponentialsumme) *f*	somme *f* de Weyl	экспоненциальная сумма Вейля, сумма [Г.] Вейля
W 232	**Weyl['s] tensor,** Weyl['s] conform tensor, conform tensor, Weyl['s] conformal curvature tensor, conformal curvature tensor <DG>	Weylscher Tensor *m*, Konformkrümmungstensor *m*	tenseur *m* de Weyl	тензор Вейля, тензор Вейля прилегающей кривизны, тензор Вейля конформной кривизны
W 233	**Weyl['s] theorem** <on addition of a completely continuous operator> <FA>	Weylscher Satz *m*, Satz von [H.] Weyl	théorème *m* de [H.] Weyl	теорема Вейля
	Weyl['s] transfer <DG>	*s.* W 221		
	wheel <AN, GE, IN>	*s.* I 674		
	when and only when <GN>	*s.* I 72		
W 234	**Whitehead['s] group** <AL>	Whitehead-Gruppe *f*	groupe *m* de Whitehead	группа Уайтхеда
W 235	**Whitehead['s] product** <AT>	Whitehead-Produkt *n*	produit *m* de Whitehead	произведение Уайтхеда
W 236	**Whitehead product mapping** <AT>	Whitehead-Produktabbildung *f*	application *f* par le produit de Whitehead	отображение при помощи произведения Уайтхеда
W 237	**Whitehead['s] theorem** <AT>	Satz *m* von Whitehead, Whiteheadscher Satz	théorème *m* de J.H.C. Whitehead	теорема [Дж.Г.К.] Уайтхеда
W 238	**white noise,** uniform random noise <ST>	weißes Rauschen *n*	bruit *m* blanc	белый шум
W 239	**Whitney['s] characteristic class,** character-	Whitneysche charakteristische Klasse *f*	classe *f* [caractéristique] de Whitney	класс Уитни

No.	English	German	French	Russian
	istic class in the sense of Whitney, Whitney['s] class <AT>			
	Whitney['s] class <AT<	*s.* W 239		
W 240	**Whitney['s] duality** <AT>	Whitneysche Dualität *f*	dualité *f* de Whitney	двойственность Уитни
W 241	**Whitney['s] duality theorem** <on fibre bundles> <AT>	Whitneyscher Dualitätssatz *m*	théorème *m* de dualité de Whitney	теорема двойственности Уитни
W 242	**Whitney['s] multiplication formula,** duality formula <AT>	Whitneysche Multiplikationsformel *f*, „duality formula" *f*	formule *f* de dualité de Whitney	формула умножения Уитни, формула двойственности
	Whitney['s] product <AT>	*s.* C 106		
W 243	**Whitney['s] sum,** fibre product <of vector bundles> <AT>	Whitneysche Summe *f*, Whitney-Summe *f*	somme *f* de Whitney	сумма Уитни
	Whittaker['s] confluent hypergeometric function <FU>	*s.* W 245		
W 244	**Whittaker['s] [differential] equation** <DE>	Whittakersche Differentialgleichung (Gleichung) *f*, konfluente hypergeometrische Differentialgleichung in reduzierter Form	équation *f* [différentielle] de Whittaker	[дифференциальное] уравнение Уиттекера
W 245	**Whittaker['s] function,** Whittaker['s] confluent hypergeometric function, Coulomb['s] wave function <FU>	Whittakers[che] Funktion *f*, Whittaker-Funktion *f*, konfluente hypergeometrische Funktion von Whittaker, Coulomb-Wellenfunktion *f*	fonction *f* de Whittaker, fonction hypergéométrique confluente de Whittaker, fonction d'onde coulombienne	функция Уиттекера, конфлюентная гипергеометрическая функция Уиттекера, кулоновская [волновая] функция
	whole algebraic number <NT>	*s.* A 442		
	whole multiple <AR, NT>	*s.* M 987		
	whole number <NT>	*s.* 1. A 442; 2. I 596		
	whole rational number <NT>	*s.* I 596		
	width <EG>	*s.* B 745		
W 246	**Wielandt['s] broken iteration** <MD, NU>	Wielandt-Iteration *f*, Wielandt-Verfahren *n*, gebrochene Iteration *f* nach Wielandt	itération *f* de Wielandt	[дробная] итерация Виландта, метод дробной итерации
W 247	**Wielandt['s] operator** <FA>	Wielandt-Operator *m*	opérateur *m* de Wielandt	оператор Виландта
W 248	**Wielandt['s] theorem** <MD, NU>	Wielandtscher Einschließungssatz *m*, Einschließungssatz von Wielandt	théorème *m* de Wielandt	теорема Виландта
W 249	**Wiener['s] algebra** <FA>	Wienersche Algebra *f*	algèbre *f* de Wiener	алгебра Винера
W 250	**Wiener['s] ergodic theorem,** dominant ergodic theorem <SP>	dominierender Ergodensatz *m*, Ergodensatz von Wiener, Wienerscher Ergodensatz	théorème *m* ergodique de Wiener, théorème ergodique dominant	эргодическая теорема Винера, доминантная эргодическая теорема
W 251	**Wiener['s] integral** <ME>	Wienersches Integral (Funktionalintegral) *n*	intégrale *f* de Wiener	интеграл Винера, винеровский интеграл
W 252	**Wiener['s] measure** <ME, ST>	Wienersches Maß *n*	mesure *f* de Wiener, mesure [de] Wiener-Lévy	винеровская мера, мера Винера, W-мера
W 253	**Wiener['s] process,** Brownian process, Brownian movement <SP>	Wienerscher Prozeß *m*, Brownscher Bewegungsprozeß (Prozeß) *m*, Prozeß der Brownschen Standardbewegung (Bewegung), Brownsche Standardbewegung (Bewegung) *f*	processus *m* de Wiener, processus brownien, mouvement *m* de Brown, mouvement brownien, fonction *f* aléatoire du mouvement brownien, fonction aléatoire de Wiener-Lévy	винеровский (броуновский) процесс, броуновское движение, винеровская случайная функция
W 254	**Wiener['s] theorem** <FT, SS>	Wienerscher Satz *m*, Satz von [N.] Wiener	théorème *m* de [N.] Wiener	теорема Винера
W 255	**Wigert['s] theorem** <FT>	Satz *m* von Wigert, Wigertscher Satz	théorème *m* de Wigert	теорема Вигерта
W 256	**Wilcoxon['s] matched pair rank test,** signed rank test <ST>	Wilcoxon-Test *m* für gepaarte Stichproben, Vorzeichenrangtest *m*	test *m* de Wilcoxon pour les observations appariées	ранговый критерий Вилкоксона для попарных сравнений
W 257	**Wilcoxon['s] test,** *U*-test, Mann-Whitney test <ST>	Wilcoxon-Test *m*, Wilcoxonscher Test *m*, *U*-Test *m*, Mann-Whitney-Test *m*, Wilcoxon-Mann-Whitney-Test *m*, Test von Wilcoxon-Mann-Whitney	test *m* de Wilcoxon, test des deux échantillons de Wilcoxon, test *U*, test de Mann-Whitney	критерий Вилкоксона (Уилкоксона), *U*-критерий, критерий *U*, критерий Манна-Уитни
W 258	**Wilczynski['s] normal,** directrix <DG>	Normale *f* von Wilczynski, Wilczynskische Normale, Direktrix *f*	normale *f* de Wilczynski, directrice *f*	нормаль Вильчинского, директриса
W 259	**wild embedding (imbedding)** <TO>	wilde Einbettung *f*	plongement *m* non trivial, plongement sauvage	дикое вложение
W 260	**wildly imbedded set** <TO>	wild eingebettete Menge *f*	ensemble *m* non trivialement plongé	дико вложенное множество
W 261	**wild ramification** <AG>	wilde Verzweigung *f*	ramification *f* sauvage	дикое ветвление
W 262	**Wilk['s] test** <ST>	Wilks-Test *m*	test *m* de Wilks	критерий Вилкса
W 263	**Wilson['s] theorem** <NT>	Wilsonscher (Wilsons) Satz *m*	théorème *m* de Wilson	критерий (теорема) Вильсона

W 264	**winding number,** index, number of turns <of a curve around a point> <FT, TO>	Umlaufzahl *f*, Windungszahl *f*, Index *m* <einer Kurve um einen Punkt>, Verschlingungszahl *f* bezüglich des Nullpunktes	indice *m*, nombre *m* de tours <d'une courbe autour d'un point>	число обходов, индекс, винтовое число, порядок <кривой относительно точки>
W 265	**winning coalition** <TG>	Gewinnkoalition *f*	coalition *f* gagnante	выигрывающая коалиция
W 266	**winning position** <TG>	Gewinnposition *f*	position *f* gagnante	выигрывающая позиция, выигрывающее состояние
W 267	**winsorization** <ST>	Winsorisation *f*, Winsorisierung *f*	winsorisation *f*, méthode *f* de winsorisation	винсоризация, винсорирование
W 268	**winsorized sample** <ST>	winsorisierte Stichprobe *f*	échantillon *m* winsorisé	винсорированная выборка
W 269	**Wirtinger['s] class** <AT>	Wirtinger-Klasse *f*	classe *f* de Wirtinger	класс Виртингера
W 270	**Wirtinger['s] plane sextic curve** <AG>	Wirtingersche ebene Kurve *f* sechster Ordnung	courbe *f* plane sextique de Wirtinger	плоская кривая Виртингера шестого порядка
W 271	**Wishart['s] distribution** <ST>	Wishart-Verteilung *f*, Wishartsche Verteilung *f*	distribution *f* de Wishart	распределение Уишарта
	witch <GE>	*s.* W 272		
W 272	**witch of Agnesi,** witch, versiera, Agnesi['s] versiera <GE>	Versiera *f*, Versiera von Guido Grandi, Versiera der (di) Agnesi, Locke *f* der Agnesi, Agnesische Kurve *f*	versiera (cubique) *f* d'Agnesi, agnésienne *f*, courbe *f* agnésienne (d'Agnesi)	локон Аньези, верзиера, версьера, аньезера
	within / to <GN>	*s.* U 445		
W 273	**within-class (within-group) variance,** intraclass variance, variance within groups (classes, treatments), internal variance <ST>	Innerklassenvarianz *f*, Varianz *f* innerhalb der Klassen (Gruppen), Varianz in den Klassen (Gruppen), Binnenvarianz *f*, innere Varianz	variance *f* à l'intérieur des groupes (classes), variance intra-classe (interne)	дисперсия внутри групп (классов), внутригрупповая (внутриклассовая, внутренняя) дисперсия
W 274	**without loss of generality** <GN>	ohne Beschränkung der Allgemeinheit (Allgemeingültigkeit), o. B. d. A.	sans restreindre la généralité, sans restriction de la généralité, sans perte de généralité	без ограничения общности, не ограничивая (нарушая) общности, без потери общности
W 275	**Witt['s] algebra** <of quadratic inner product spaces> <AL>	Wittsche Algebra *f*	algèbre *f* de Witt	алгебра Витта
W 276	**Witt['s] base** <AL>	Wittsche Basis *f*	base *f* de Witt	база Витта
W 277	**Witt['s] class** <AL>	Wittsche Klasse *f*	classe *f* de Witt	класс Витта
W 278	**Witt['s] component** <of a Witt vector> <AL>	Hauptkomponente *f*	composante *f* principale	компонента Витта
W 279	**Witt['s] decomposition** <AL>	Wittsche Zerlegung *f*	décomposition *f* de Witt	разложение Витта
W 280	**Witt-Grothendieck group** <over *k*> <AL>	Witt-Grothendiecksche Gruppe *f* <über *k*>	groupe *m* de Witt-Grothendieck <sur *k*>	группа Витта-Гротендика <над *k*>
W 281	**Witt['s] group** <AL>	Wittsche Gruppe *f*, Witt-Gruppe *f*	groupe *m* de Witt, groupe des types de formes quadratiques	группа Витта, группа типов квадратичных форм
W 282	**Witt-Jacobson algebra,** Jacobson-Witt algebra <AL>	Witt-Jacobsonsche Algebra *f*	algèbre *f* de Witt-Jacobson	алгебра Витта-Джекобсона
W 283	**Witt['s] ring** <AL>	Witt-Ring *m*, Wittscher Ring *m*	anneau *m* des types de formes quadratiques, anneau de Witt	кольцо Витта, кольцо типов квадратичных форм
W 284	**Witt['s] theorem** <AL>	Satz *m* von Witt, Wittscher Satz	théorème *m* de Witt	теорема Витта
W 285	**Witt['s] vector** <AL>	Wittscher Vektor *m*	vecteur *m* de Witt	вектор Витта
W 286	**Wold['s] decomposition** <ST>	Woldsche Zerlegung *f*	décomposition *f* de Wold	разложение Вольда
	Wolfe['s] algorithm <PG>	*s.* R 362		
W 287	**Wolfe['s] duality theorem,** duality theorem of Wolfe <in convex programming> <PG>	Dualitätssatz *m* von Wolfe, Wolfescher Dualitätssatz	théorème *m* de dualité de Wolfe	теорема двойственности Волфа
	Wolfe['s] method <PG>	*s.* R 362		
W 288	**Wooley['s] formula** <for numerical cubature> <DI, NU>	Wooleysche Formel *f* <für die angenäherte Kubatur>	formule *f* <de cubature numérique> de Wooley	формула <численного интегрирования двойных интегралов> Вули (Вулея)
W 289	**word;** string, tape <AL>	Wort *n*	mot *m*	слово
	word <UA>	*s.* P 975		
	word group <GR>	*s.* F 615		
W 290	**word length,** length <of a word> <AL>	Wortlänge *f*, Länge *f* <eines Wortes>	longueur *f* du mot, longueur <d'un mot>	длина слова, длина <слова>
	word problem <AL>	*s.* I 70		
W 291	**word problems** <one of them being the identity problem> <AL>	Wortprobleme *npl*	problèmes *mpl* de mots	проблемы слов, [фундаментальные] проблемы Дэна
W 292	**word ring** <AL>	freier Ring *m*	anneau *m* libre	свободное кольцо, кольцо слов
	word subgroup <GR>	*s.* V 138		
W 293	**working definition** <GN>	Arbeitsdefinition *f*	définition *f* de travail	рабочее определение
W 294	**working mean,** assumed mean, provisional mean, auxiliary mean <ST>	Arbeitsmittel *n*, angenommenes (vorläufiges, provisorisches) Mittel *n*, provisorischer (angenommener) Mittelwert *m*	moyenne *f* de travail, moyenne supposée (provisoire)	рабочее (произвольно принятое, предположительное) среднее
W 295	**working probit** <ST>	Rechenprobit *m*	probit *m* de travail	рабочий пробит
W 296	**worm's eye perspective (view),** bottom view <DS>	Froschperspektive *f*	perspective *f* à ras de terre	«лягушачья» перспектива

	W_p (W^p) almost-periodic function <AP>	*s.* A 531		
	W_p almost-periodic space <AP>	*s.* S 1330		
W 297	**wreath product,** composition <of groups> <GR>	Kranzprodukt *n*, Gruppenkranz *m*	couronne *f* <de groupes>	сплетение, композиция, веночное произведение, венок <групп>
	wreath product <GR>	*s.* C 1585		
	writing in operator form <DE>	*s.* S 2418		
W 298	**Wronskian,** Wronski['s] determinant <DE>	Wronski-Determinante *f*, Wronskische Determinante *f*, Wronskiana *f*	wronskien *m*, déterminant *m* de Wronski, déterminant wronskien	вронскиан, определитель (детерминант) Вронского
	Wronski['s] determinant <DE>	*s.* W 298		
W 299	**Wronski['s] law of series,** Wronski['s] theorem <SS>	Wronskis[ches] Gesetz *n* der Reihen, Wronskis[cher] Satz *m*, Wronskisches Theorem *n*	loi *f* des séries de Wronski, théorème *m* de Wronski	закон рядов Вронского, теорема Вронского
W 300	**Wronski['s] matrix** <of a function system> <DE>	Wronski-Matrix *f*, Wronskische Matrix *f*	matrice *f* de Wronski, matrice wronskienne	матрица Вронского
W 301	**Wronski['s] method** <AL, NU>	Wronskis[che] Methode *f*	méthode *f* de Wronski	метод Вронского
	Wronski['s] theorem <SS>	*s.* W 299		
W 302	**W^*-subalgebra** <FA>	W^*-Unteralgebra *f*	sous-algèbre *f* W^*	подалгебра W^*
W 303	**W-surface** <F. Klein, S. Lie> <PJ>	W-Fläche *f*	W-surface *f*	W-поверхность
	W-surface <DG>	*s.* W 200		
	w^*-topology <FA, TO>	*s.* W 129		
W 304	**"Wurf"** <PJ>	Wurf *m* <von vier Elementen> <Staudt>	« Wurf » *m*, jet *m*, ensemble *m* de quatre éléments, quaterne *m* <groupe de quatre points de rapport anharmonique donné>	вурф
W 305	**W-valued differential form** <AT, DG>	W-wertige Differentialform *f*	forme *f* différentielle W-valuée	W-значная дифференциальная форма

X

	x-axis <GN>	*s.* A 1307		
X 1	**x-intercept,** intercept on the axis of abscissas, intercept on the x-axis, cut off from the x-axis <AY>	Abschnitt *m* auf der x-Achse	segment *m* sur l'axe x	отрезок на оси x
X 2	**X-section of a correspondence R,** slice through X of R <SE>	Bild *n* einer Menge X bei einer Korrespondenz R	coupe *f* d'une correspondance R suivant X	срез соответствия R относительно X
	x-section of R <SE>	*s.* F 158		
X 3	**X-test,** Van der Waerden['s] X-test, Van der Waerden['s] test <ST>	X-Test *m* [von van der Waerden], Van-der-Waerden-Test *m*, van der Waerdenscher Test *m*	test *m* X [de Van der Waerden], test de Van der Waerden	X-критерий [Ван дер Вардена], критерий X [Ван дер Вардена], критерий Ван дер Вардена
X 4	**xy[-]plane** <AY>	x,y-Ebene *f*, xy-Ebene *f*, (x,y)-Ebene *f*, x-y-Ebene *f*	plan *m* (x,y), plan des xy	плоскость xy, плоскость xOy

Y

	Yates['] adjustment <ST>	*s.* Y 1		
Y 1	**Yates['] correction,** Yates['] adjustment <ST>	Yatessche Korrektur *f*, Yates-Korrektur *f*	correction *f* de Yates	поправка Иейтса
	y-axis <AY>	*s.* A 1315		
	Yegorov['s] theorem <ME>	*s.* E 53		
	Yermakov['s] test <SS>	*s.* E 467		
Y 2	**yield function,** reward function <PG>	Ertragsfunktion *f*	fonction *f* de rendement	функция выхода
Y 3	**Yoneda['s] embedding** <CA>	Yoneda-Einbettung *f*	plongement *m* de Yoneda	вложение Ионеда
Y 4	**Yoneda['s] functor** <CA>	Yoneda-Funktor *m*	foncteur *m* de Yoneda	функтор Ионеда
Y 5	**Yoneda['s] lemma** <CA>	Yoneda-Lemma *n*	lemme *m* de Yoneda	лемма Ионеда
Y 6	**Yoneda['s] map** <CA>	Yoneda-Abbildung *f*	application *f* de Yoneda	отображение Ионеда
Y 7	**Young['s] criterion** <on development in a Fourier series> <AN, SS>	Youngsches Kriterium *n*	critère *m* d'Young	критерий Юнга
	Young['s] diagram <AL>	*s.* 1. Y 11; 2. Y 12		
Y 8	**Young['s] inequality** <RF>	Youngsche Ungleichung *f*	inégalité *f* d'Young	неравенство Юнга
Y 9	**Young['s] integral** <AN>	Youngsches Integral *n*	intégrale *f* d'Young	интеграл Юнга
Y 10	**Young['s] operator** <RE>	Youngscher Operator *m*	opérateur *m* d'Young	оператор Юнга
Y 11	**Young['s] scheme,** Young['s] tableau (diagram), tableau <no numbers inside> <AL>	Youngsches Schema (Tableau) *n*, Young-Schema *n*, Young-Tableau *n*, Tableau *n*, Young-Diagramm *n*	tableau (schéma, diagramme) *m* d'Young	диаграмма (схема) Юнга
Y 12	**Young['s] scheme,** Young['s] diagram <with	Youngsches Schema *n*, Young-Schema *n*,	schéma (diagramme) *m* d'Young	схема Юнга

and still: Y 12	numbers inside> <AL>	Youngscher Rahmen *m*, Rahmen *m*, Young-Diagramm *n*		
Y 13	**Young symmetrizer** <RE>	Youngscher Symmetrisator *m*	symétriseur *m* d'Young	симметризатор Юнга
	Young['s] tableau <AL>	*s.* Y 11		

Z

	Zacharias['s] configuration <SG>	*s.* C 1877		
Z 1	**ZA-group,** hypercentral group <GR>	ZA-Gruppe *f*, hyperzentrale Gruppe *f*	groupe *m* hypercentral	ZA-группа
Z 2	**Zariski-closed** <AL, TO>	abgeschlossen in der Zariski-Topologie	fermé en topologie de Zariski	замкнутый в топологии Зарисского
Z 3	**Zariski-open set, Zariski open set, Zariski open subset** <AL>	offene Menge *f* in der Zariski-Topologie	ouvert *m* de Zariski	открытое по Зарисскому множество
Z 4	**Zariski['s] ring,** ring of Zariski <AL>	Zariski-Ring *m*	anneau *m* de Zariski	кольцо Зарисского
Z 5	**Zariski['s] space** <TO>	Zariskischer Raum *m*	espace *m* de Zariski	пространство Зарисского
Z 6	**Zariski['s] topology,** spectral topology <AG>	Zariski-Topologie *f*, Spektraltopologie *f*	topologie *f* de Zariski, topologie spectrale	топология Зарисского (Зариского), спектральная топология
Z 7	**Zassenhaus['] group** <GR>	Zassenhaus-Gruppe *f*	groupe *m* de Zassenhaus	группа Цассенгауза
Z 8	**Zassenhaus['] lemma,** third isomorphism theorem <GR>	Lemma *n* (Satz *m*) von Zassenhaus, dritter (3.) Isomorphiesatz *m*, Zassenhaussches Lemma	théorème (lemme) *m* de Zassenhaus	лемма Цассенхауза (Цасенхауза), лемма о бабочке, третья теорема об изоморфизмах
	z-axis <GN>	*s.* A 816		
Z 9	**Z-chart,** *Z*-diagram <of a time series> <SP>	*Z*-Karte *f*, *Z*-Diagramm *n*	diagramme *m* en *Z*	*Z*-карта, *Z*-диаграмма
	z co-ordinate <AY>	*s.* A 815		
Z 10	**ZD-group,** hypocentral group <GR>	ZD-Gruppe *f*, hypozentrale Gruppe *f*	groupe *m* hypocentral	ZD-группа, нильпотентная в обобщенном смысле группа
	Z-diagram <SP>	*s.* Z 9		
Z 11	**z-distribution,** Fisher['s] *z*-distribution, arth distribution <ST>	*z*-Verteilung *f*, Fishersche *z*-Verteilung, Areatangensverteilung *f*, arth-Verteilung *f*	distribution *f* de *z* [de Fisher], distribution de l'argument de la tangente hyperbolique	*z*-распределение, *z*-распределение Фишера, ареатангенс-распределение
	zenithal orthomorphic projection <DS>	*s.* S 1753		
Z 12	**Zeno['s] paradox of Achilles and the tortoise** <FO>	Zenonsches Paradoxon *n* <von Achilles und der Schildkröte>	paradoxe *m* de Zénon, paradoxe d'Achill et de la tortue	парадокс [Зенона] «Ахиллес и черепаха» [апория] Ахиллес и черепаха
	Zermelo['s] axiom <SE>	*s.* A 1280		
	Zermelo['s] axiom scheme of separation <LO, SE>	*s.* A 1293		
	Zermelo['s] choice principle <SE>	*s.* A 1280		
	Zermelo-Fraenkel axiom system <SE>	*s.* S 704		
	Zermelo-Fraenkel[-Skolem] set theory <SE>	*s.* S 704		
	Zermelo-Fraenkel system <SE>	*s.* S 704		
	Zermelo['s] separation principle <LO, SE>	*s.* A 1293		
	Zermelo['s] set theory <SE>	*s.* S 704		
	Zermelo['s] theorem <SE>	*s.* W 212		
Z 13	**Zernike['s] orthogonal polynomial,** circle polynomial <FU>	Zernikesches Orthogonalpolynom *n*	polynôme *m* orthogonal de Zernike	ортогональный многочлен (полином) Цернике
Z 14	**zero,** null element, zero element, additive identity element, additive identity <in additive composition> <AL>	Nullelement *n*, Null *f*	zéro *m*, élément-zero *m*, zéro-additif *m*, zéro *m* additif, élément *m* neutre pour l'addition, origine *f*, élément nul (zéro)	нулевой элемент, нуль, нульэлемент
Z 15	**zero,** zero element <of a hypercomplex number system> <AL>	Nullelement *n*	module *m*, nombre *m* indifférent, zéro *m*	нуль, нулевой элемент
Z 16	**zero** <of a polynomial ideal> <AL>	Nullstelle *f*	zéro *m*	нуль
Z 17	**zero,** null element, zero element <of a ring *or* field> <AL>	Nullelement *n*, Null *f*	zéro *m*, élément *m* zéro	нуль, нулевой элемент
Z 18	**zero,** null <of a polynomial *or* function> <AL, AN>	Nullstelle *f*, Wurzel *f*	zéro *m*, racine *f*	нуль
	zero <AL>	*s.* Z 30		
	zero <LA>	*s.* Z 31		
Z 19	**zero algebra** <all products = 0> <AL>	Zeroalgebra *f*	algèbre *f* de zéro	алгебра с нулевым умножением
	zero arrow <CA>	*s.* Z 43		
Z 20	**zero bilinear form** <AL>	verschwindende Bilinearform *f*	forme *f* bilinéaire nulle	нулевая билинейная форма
Z 21	**zero category** <CA>	Nullkategorie *f*	catégorie *f* nulle	нулевая категория
Z 22	**zero chain** <AT>	Nullkette *f*: Nullkomplex *m*	chaîne *f* nulle	нуль-цепь, нуль-комплекс

	zero-circuit <AT>	*s.* D 513		
Z 23	**zero curve** <of a rational function> <AG>	Nullstellenkurve *f*	courbe *f* des zéros	кривая нулей
	zero-dimensional circuit <AT>	*s.* D 513		
Z 24	**zero-dimensionality** <AL, TO>	Nulldimensionalität *f*	propriété *f* d'être à zéro dimensions	нульмерность
	zero-dimensional manifold <AT>	*s.* D 513		
Z 25	**zero-dimensional [topological] space** <TO>	nulldimensionaler (nulldimensionaler topologischer) Raum *m*	espace *m* de dimension 0 (zéro, nulle), espace 0-dimensionnel, espace à zéro dimension, espace [topologique] éparpillé	нульмерное (0-мерное, раздробленное) пространство
	zero direction <AY>	*s.* P 840		
Z 26	**zero-disjoint ideals,** 0-disjoint ideals <of a semigroup> <AL>	nulldisjunkte (0-disjunkte) Ideale *npl*	idéaux *mpl* à intersection 0	идеалы, пересечение которых равно 0
Z 27	**zero-divergence field,** source-free field, solenoidal field, solenoidal vector <VT>	quellenfreies Vektorfeld (Feld) *n*, divergenzfreies Feld (Vektorfeld), solenoidales Feld (Vektorfeld), quellenfreier (solenoidaler) Vektor *m*	champ *m* [à flux] conservatif, champ indivergentiel (sans divergence, à divergence nulle, sans sources, laplacien, solénoïdal), vecteur *m* solénoïdal	поле, не имеющее истоков; соленоидальное (соленоидальное векторное, бездивергентное) поле, поле без источников, трубчатое [векторное] поле, соленоидное поле, соленоидальный вектор
Z 28	**zero[-] divisor,** divisor of zero, zero factor <AL>	Nullteiler *m*, Teiler *m* der Null	diviseur *m* de zéro	делитель нуля
Z 29	**zero element** <of a groupoid> <AL>	Nullelement *n*, absorbierendes Element *n*	élément *m* absorbant, zéro *m*, élément permis <pour une loi de composition>; zéro multiplicatif <dans un ensemble multiplicatif>	поглощающий элемент, нуль
Z 30	**zero element,** origin, zero, null vector, zero vector <of a vector space> <AL>	Nullelement *n*, Nullvektor *m*	zéro *m*, élément *m* neutre, origine *f*, élément (vecteur *m*) zéro	нуль, нулевой элемент (вектор), нуль-вектор, нульвектор
Z 31	**zero element,** zero, null element, least element <LA>	Nullelement *n*, verbandstheoretisches Nullelement	élément *m* nul (minimum), élément-zéro *m*	нуль, нулевой элемент
	zero element <AL>	*s.* 1. Z 14; 2. Z 15; 3. Z 17		
	zero element <SE>	*s.* S 1219		
	zero factor <AL>	*s.* Z 28		
	zero field <AL>	*s.* N 799		
Z 32	**zero-function,** zero function, null function <equal to zero almost everywhere> <AN>	Nullfunktion *f*	fonction *f* zéro	нуль-функция
	zero Gorenstein ring <AL>	*s.* Q 160		
	zero group <GR>	*s.* O 85		
Z 33	**zero homomorphism** <AL>	Nullhomomorphismus *m*, trivialer Homomorphismus *m*	morphisme *m* nul	нулевой (тривиальный) гомоморфизм
Z 34	**zero[-]ideal** <of a Boolean algebra> <AL>	Nullideal *n*	idéal *m* trivial (nul)	нулевой идеал
Z 35	**zero[-] ideal,** null ideal <of a ring *or* semigroup> <AL>	Nullideal *n*	idéal *m* nul, idéal-zéro *m*, idéal zéro	нулевой идеал
Z 36	**zeroid element** <of a semigroup> <AL>	Zeroid *n*, Zeroidelement *n*	élément *m* zéroïde	зероидный элемент, зероид
Z 37	**zero l-ring** <AL>	verbandsgeordneter Zeroring *m*	anneau *m* réticulé de carré nul	структурно упорядоченное кольцо с нулевым умножением
Z 38	**zero manifold** <of a polynomial ideal> <AG>	Nullstellenmannigfaltigkeit *f*, Nullstellengebilde *n*, Lösungsmannigfaltigkeit *f*	variété *f* de zéros	многообразие (множество) нулей
Z 39	**zero map** <AL>	Nullabbildung *f*	application *f* nulle	нуль-отображение, нулевое отображение
	zero map <CA>	*s.* Z 43		
	zero matrix <MD>	*s.* N 783		
	zero measure <ME>	*s.* M 346		
Z 40	**zero-minimality,** 0-minimality <of an ideal> <AL>	0-Minimalität *f*, Null-Minimalität *f*		0-минимальность, нуль-минимальность
Z 41	**zero-minimal two-sided ideal,** 0-minimal two-sided ideal <of a semigroup> <AL>	0-minimales (nullminimales) zweiseitiges Ideal *n*		0-минимальный (нуль-минимальный) двусторонний идеал
Z 42	**zero module** <AL>	Nullmodul *m*	module *m* réduit à zéro	нулевой модуль
Z 43	**zero-morphism,** zero arrow, zero map <CA>	Nullmorphismus *m*, Null-Morphismus *m*, 0-Morphismus *m*, Nullpfeil *m*, Nullabbildung *f*	morphisme *m* nul	нулевой морфизм, нулевое отображение
Z 44	**zero object,** null object <CA>	Nullobjekt *n*	objet *m* nul	нулевой объект, нуль
Z 45	**zero of multiplicity two** <AL, AN>	zweifache Nullstelle *f*, Doppelnullstelle *f*, doppelte Nullstelle	zéro *m* d'ordre 2	нуль кратности два
Z 46	**zero of order *k*,** zero with order of multiplicity *k* <of a regular function> <FT>	Nullstelle *f* der Ordnung *k*, Nullstelle der Multiplizität (Vielfachheit) *k*, *k*-fache Nullstelle	zéro *m* d'ordre *k*	*k*-кратный нуль, корень кратности *k*
Z 47	**zero-one distribution,** 0-1 distribution <ST>	Null-Eins-Verteilung *f*, Null-oder-Eins-Verteilung *f*	distribution *f* de zéro ou un	распределение нуля или единицы

No.	English	German	French	Russian
Z 48	**zero-one law** <ST>	Null-Eins-Gesetz *n*, Null-oder-Eins-Gesetz *n*	loi *f* de zéro ou un	закон нуля или единицы
Z 49	**zero-one method,** truth table method, method of zero-one verification, truth-table decision procedure <LO>	Methode *f* der Wahrheitstafel	méthode *f* des tables de vérité	метод таблиц истинности
Z 50	**zero-one optimization (programming),** 0-1 programming (optimization) <PG>	0-1-Optimierung *f*, Null-Eins-Optimierung *f*	programmation (optimisation) *f* de zéro ou un, 0-1 programmation (optimisation)	программирование (оптимизация) нуля или единицы
Z 51	**zero-one sequence** <ST>	Null-Eins-Folge *f*, Null-oder-Eins-Folge *f*	suite *f* de zéro ou un	последовательность нуля или единицы
Z 52	**zero-polar** <of a null system> <AY>	Nullpolare *f*	antipolaire *f*, polaire *f* nulle	нулевая линия
	zero polynomial <AL>	*s.* N 787		
Z 53	**zero preserving functor** <CA>	nullobjekttreuer Funktor *m*; Funktor, der Nullobjekte erhält	foncteur *m* conservant des objets nuls	функтор, сохраняющий нулевые объекты
Z 54	**zero presheaf** <AL, TO>	Nullgarbendatum *n*	préfaisceau *m* nul	нулевой предпучок
Z 55	**zero quaternion** <AL>	Nullquaternion *f*	quaternion *m* nul	нулевой кватернион
Z 56	**zero ring,** trivial ring <AL>	Zeroring *m*	anneau *m* de carré nul	кольцо с нулевым умножением
Z 57	**zero row** <of a matrix> <MD>	Nullzeile *f*	ligne *f* nulle	нулевая строка
Z 58	**zero section** <of a fibre bundle *or* sheaf> <AL, TO>	Nullschnitt *m*	section *f* nulle	нулевое сечение
Z 59	**zero semigroup,** null semigroup <AL>	Zerohalbgruppe *f*	demi-groupe *m* de carré nul	полугруппа с нулевым умножением, нулевая полугруппа
Z 60	**zero semigroup** <consists of two elements 0, *a*> <AL>	Nullhalbgruppe *f*	demi-groupe *m* nul	нуль-полугруппа
Z 61	**zero-set,** Z-set, exact closed set, functionally closed set <TO>	Nullstellenmenge *f*	ensemble *m* de zéros	множество нулей
	zero sheaf <AL, AT>	*s.* N 794		
	zero solution <AL>	*s.* T 1000/1		
Z 62	**zero square** <as a magic square> <CT>	Nullquadrat *n*	carré *m* [magique] évanouissant	нулевой квадрат
	zero step of the induction <FO, LO>	*s.* B 139		
	zero subgroup <GR>	*s.* U 304		
Z 63	**zero-sum extension** <of a game> <TG>	Nullsummenerweiterung *f*		расширение до игры с нулевой суммой
Z 64	**zero-sum game** <TG>	Nullsummenspiel *n*	jeu *m* de somme nulle (zéro), jeu à somme nulle (zéro)	игра с нулевой суммой, беспроигрышная игра
Z 65	**zero-sum two-person (two-player) game,** two-person zero-sum game <TG>	Zweipersonen-Nullsummenspiel *n*, antagonistisches Spiel *n*	jeu *m* de (à) somme nulle à deux personnes, jeu à deux personnes de (à) somme nulle, duel *m*	антагонистическая игра, игра двух лиц (игроков) с нулевой суммой
Z 66	**zero-tree** <GP>	leerer Baum *m*	arbre *m* vide	пустое дерево
Z 67	**zero-variation,** null variation <RF>	Nullvariation *f*	variation *f* nulle	нулевая вариация
Z 68	**zero variety,** null variety <UA>	Nullmannigfaltigkeit *f*	variété *f* nulle	нулевое многообразие, нуль-многообразие
	zero vector <AL>	*s.* Z 30		
	zero vector <VT>	*s.* N 803		
Z 69	**zero vector space** <AL>	Nullvektorraum *m*	espace *m* vectoriel nul	нулевое векторное пространство
	zero with order of multiplicity *k* <FT>	*s.* Z 46		
Z 70	**zeta-formula, ζ-formula** <NT>	ζ-Formel *f*, Zeta-Formel *f*	formule *f* ζ, formule zêta	ζ-формула, дзета-формула
Z 71	**zetafuchsian (zeta-Fuchsian) function** <FT>	zeta-Fuchssche (zetafuchssche) Vektorform *f*, zeta-Fuchssche (zetafuchssche) Vektorfunktion *f*, zeta-Fuchssche (zetafuchssche) Funktion *f*	fonction *f* zêta-fuchsienne (zêtafuchsienne)	дзета[-]фуксова функция
Z 72	**zeta function** <ζ-function *or* Z-function> <NT>	Zetafunktion *f*	fonction *f* zêta (dzéta)	дзета-функция
	zeta function <FU>	*s.* W 177		
	zeta[-] function <FU, NT>	*s.* R 1046		
	zeta function of Jacobi <FU>	*s.* J 15		
	zeta[-] function of Riemann <FU, NT>	*s.* R 1046		
	zeta function of Weierstrass <FU>	*s.* W 177		
Z 73	**Zeuthen['s] curve** <of an algebraic curve> <AG>	Zeuthensche Kurve *f*	courbe *f* de Zeuthen	кривая Цейтена
Z 74	**Zeuthen['s] formula** <for an algebraic correspondence> <AG>	Zeuthensche Formel *f*	formule *f* de Zeuthen	формула Цейтена
Z 75	**Zeuthen['s] rule** <AG>	Zeuthensche Regel *f*, Regel von H. G. Zeuthen	règle *f* de H. G. Zeuthen	правило Цейтена
Z 76	**Zeuthen-Segre invariant,** invariant of Zeuthen-Segre <AG>	Zeuthen-Segre-Invariante *f*, Zeuthen-Segresche Invariante *f*	invariant *m* de Zeuthen-Segre	инвариант Цейтена-Сегре

No.	English	German	French	Russian
	ZF <SE>	*s.* S 704		
	Z-function of Jacobi <FU>	*s.* J 15		
Z 77	**Z-group** <GR>	*Z*-Gruppe *f*	groupe *m* *Z*	*Z*-группа
Z 78	**$\overline{Z}$-group** <GR>	$\overline{Z}$-Gruppe *f*	groupe *m* $\overline{Z}$	$\overline{Z}$-группа
Z 79	**Z-metacyclic group,** group metacyclic in the sense of Zassenhaus <GR>	metazyklische Gruppe *f* <im Sinne von Zassenhaus>	groupe *m* métacyclique	метациклическая группа
	zn <FU>	*s.* J 15		
	zonal harmonic [function] <FU>	*s.* L 536		
	zonal spherical harmonic <FU>	*s.* L 536		
	zone <EG>	*s.* S 1500		
Z 80	**zone of continued sampling** <ST>	Fortsetzungszone *f*	zone *f* de continuation de l'échantillonnage	зона продолжения выбора
	zone of overlap <ST>	*s.* O 582		
Z 81	**zone of preference,** preference zone <ST>	Entscheidungszone *f*	zone *f* de préférence, zone de décision	зона, в которой принимается окончательное решение
Z 82	**zoposet** <SE>	halbgeordnete Menge *f* mit kleinstem und größtem Element	ensemble *m* ordonné ayant un élément minimum et un élément maximum	частично упорядоченное множество с наименьшим и наибольшим элементами
Z 83	**Zorn['s] lemma (maximal principle, [maximum] principle, theorem),** principle of Zorn <SE>	Zornsches Lemma *n*, Lemma von Kuratowski-Zorn, Kuratowski-Zornsches Lemma	théorème *m* de Zorn, lemme (théorème) *m* de Kuratowski-Zorn, axiome *m* de Zorn	лемма Куратовского-Цорна, лемма (теорема) Цорна
Z 84	**ZPI ring,** Dedekind['s] ring <AL>	ZPI-Ring *m*, Fünf-Axiome-Ring *m* von Noether, Noetherscher Fünf-Axiome-Ring, Dedekindscher Ring *m*, Bereich *m*	anneau *m* de Dedekind	кольцо Дедекинда
Z 85	**z-score,** standard score <ST>	*z*-Note *f*, standardisierte Note *f*	note *f* *z*, cote *f* centrée réduite, note réduite	*z*-метка, стандартная метка
	Z-set <TO>	*s.* Z 61		
Z 86	**Z-statistic,** Fisher['s] *Z*-statistic <ST>	[Fishersche] *Z*-Stichprobenfunktion *f*, [Fishersche] *Z*-Statistik, Fischersche Stichprobenfunktion, Fishersches *Z* *n*, *Z*-Prüfzahl *f*, *Z*-Maßzahl *f*	variable (statistique) *f* *Z*, critère *m* *Z* [de Fisher], *Z* *m* de Fisher	статистика *Z* [Фишера], *Z* Фишера
Z 87	**z-test** <ST>	*z*-Test *m*	test *m* *z*	*z*-критерий
Z 88	**z-transformation,** Fisher['s] [*z*-]transformation, arth transformation <ST>	z-Transformation *f*, Fishersche [*z*-]Transformation *f*, Fisher-Transformation *f*, Areatangenstransformation *f*, arth-Transformation *f*	transformation *f* *z* (*z* de Fisher, de Fisher, argth, arth, de la tangente hyperbolique inverse)	*z*-преобразование, *z*-преобразование Фишера, преобразование Фишера, ареатангенс-преобразование
Z 89	**Zygmund['s] test** <for absolute convergence> <of a Fourier series> <SS>	Konvergenzkriterium *n* von Zygmund, Zygmundsches Konvergenzkriterium	règle *f* (critère *m*) [de convergence] de Zygmund	признак [абсолютной сходимости] Зыгмунда